THE GOOD BEER GUIDE 2021

EST 1972

MANAGING EDITOR
Emma Haines

EDITORS
Ione Brown, Claire-Michelle Taverner-Pearson, Simon Tuite

PROJECT ASSISTANCE
Katie Button, Stewart Campbell

SALES & MARKETING
Toby Langdon

CAMRA BOOKS

Wig & Pen, Norwich, Norfolk (p321)

Special thanks to the nearly 190,000 CAMRA members who carried out research for the pub entries; the Campaign's Regional Directors and Area Organisers, who coordinated the pub entries; the Campaign's Brewery Liaison Coordinators and Brewery Liaison Officers, who carried out research for the brewery entries; Rick Pickup for assistance coordinating the brewery entries; Alex Presland for technical support; Iain Barker, Christine Beatty and Simon Mather at AMA Dataset; Michael Slaughter for advising on heritage pubs; Martyn Cornell, Tom Kerridge, Jessica Mason, Roger Protz and Katie Wiles for supplying articles for the Guide; Alan Murphy for proofreading and picture research assistance; Alexandra Reilly, PA to Tom and Beth Kerridge; all CAMRA's staff and CAMRA's National Executive for their help and support.

Thanks also to the publicans, breweries, CAMRA members and others who have kindly contributed their photographs.

Photo credits: [Key: t = top; b = bottom; c = centre; l = left; r = right] p2 Andrew Michael / Alamy Stock Photo; p8 (br) Irmelamela / Shutterstock; p9 (tl) Kirill Z / Shutterstock; p11 (r) Markus Spiske / Unsplash; p12 (l) MaxyM / Shutterstock; p14 (bl) Alex Segre / Alamy Stock Photo, (tr) Roland Wadden; p15 (tr) JakC / Shutterstock; p18 Martin Pettitt / Flickr CC BY 2.0; p207 Ralph Carpenter; p325 Ian Stamp; p624 (b) Martin Pettitt / Flickr CC BY 2.0; p854 Stewart Campbell; p904 (tl) Mike Tuer, (tr) Steve Murray, (bl) Ewan Munro / Flickr CC-BY-SA 2.0, (br) Phil Emond; p905 (tl) Peter Adams, (tr) Will Drennan, (br) Peter Down; p906 (tl) Odd Wellies / Flickr CC BY 2.0, (tr) Shetland Arts / Flickr CC BY-ND 2.0, (b) alljenji / Flickr CC BY-SA 2.0.

Design: Jack Pemberton.

Production: Database, maps, typesetting of listings and indexes: AMA Dataset Ltd, Preston.

Printing: Printed and bound in the UK by CPI William Clowes, Beccles, Suffolk.

Published by the Campaign for Real Ale Ltd, 230 Hatfield Road, St Albans, Herts, AL1 4LW.

ISBN 978-1-85249-366-0

CONTENTS

PEFC
BMT-PEFC-0826
All of the papers used in this book are recyclable and made from wood grown in managed, sustainable forests. They are manufactured at mills certified to ISO 14001 and/or EMAS.

ABOUT THE GOOD BEER GUIDE

For nearly five decades, the Good Beer Guide has been a comprehensive guide to the UK's breweries, their ales, and the best outlets in which to find them around the country.

There may be other pub guides out there, but this book is different. Where other guides might have a small editorial board pulling together entries, the Good Beer Guide has a huge volunteer team. Based around the country, our volunteers all regularly use the pubs listed and can speak with authority about the beers they have on offer, and the cream of the crop in their region.

We strive hard to ensure that all areas of the country are covered. Each county or region has a listing allocation based on a scientific calculation of its population, number of licensed premises, and levels of tourism. As a result, the Guide's reach is unparalleled.

The Good Beer Guide is also proudly independent. Inclusion in this book is dependent on merit, not on payment. No pubs or breweries paid to be in this book.

PUBS SECTION

CAMRA has more than 180,000 members across more than 200 branches around the UK. It's within these branches that entries are democratically selected. All members are invited to rate beers served to them via the National Beer Scoring System (see p910). These scores are used by branches to identify pubs consistently serving the best real ale. Our volunteers monitor the quality of the cask beer as well as factors that could affect the range on offer and the overall standard of the pub – such as change of ownership or management.

While the core purpose of the Guide is to seek out quality real ale, it also takes into account other things such as history, architecture, food, family and disabled facilities, gardens and special events (such as beer festivals). The pub listings you find in these pages paint a full picture of what you can expect before you embark on a trip to visit them.

The listings are checked many times before publication, to ensure they are accurate and up to date (please see COVID-19 disclaimer below).

COMPREHENSIVE BREWERIES SECTION

The Good Beer Guide includes a comprehensive listing of the more than 1,800 breweries currently operating in the UK – not just those producing real ale – and their core cask-conditioned beers available.

Each one is appointed a local CAMRA volunteer as soon as they come on stream. These volunteer officers will regularly keep in touch with the brewery to stay abreast of what's being brewed, and developments that may be taking place.

COVID-19 - DISCLAIMER

2020 has been an incredibly challenging year for us all, not least the pub and brewing industry. Pubs across the UK were shut from the end of March until early July due to COVID-19 and many did not open their doors immediately after or, in some cases, ever again.

With the help of our dedicated volunteers we have made every effort to ensure that the information in the Guide is as accurate as possible at the time of publication. Because of the nature of the pandemic and reduced footfall due to COVID-19 safety measures, we may lose many more pubs in the future, including those currently listed.

For the most up-to-date information, please check **whatpub.com**, CAMRA's online resource for licensed premises in the UK, or download the **GBG app** (see p910). Regular updates to the Guide are also posted on the main CAMRA website at **www.camra.org.uk/goodbeerguide**.

Descriptions for pubs and breweries have been left as they were prior to lockdown in the hope that we will return to some sort of normality during the currency of this Guide. Please note that food serving times and timing of events such as quiz nights, live music and beer festivals may have changed. Similarly, opening hours for entries are not featured this year, so please check ahead before travelling.

SUPPORTING PUBS

The Great British pub is recognised around the world. It is something that cannot be replicated in any other country. Of course, many places serve beer, wine, spirits and food in different countries, but there is nothing like our pubs. In France they have bistros, brasseries and a coffee culture. In Spain they have tapas and pintxos bars. In Italy you have trattorias and pizzerias, and in Greece you have wonderful tavernas. All of these places have one common goal and that is serving great drinks and simple food with a warm welcome to a community. However, the one thing about the British pub that separates us is real ale. Our brewing heritage varies from region to region. The passion and the heart and soul that goes into brewing is equal to the top wine makers, distillers, cheese makers, bakers, artisan chocolatiers or any other craft-led hospitality producer. It is something we should be very proud of.

We constantly hear stories about the decline of the pub and how many are closing, and it is incredibly sad. There are many reasons, not just one sole focus that is the cause of these shutdowns. Large rents, profit margins being eaten away at, tax, cheaper alcohol being available to drink at home, but perhaps most importantly, the change in people's drinking habits. While pubs close, there are small pockets of thriving activity that lead to encouragement and a brighter future. We see inventive, ingenious and collaborative ideas where pubs are being used as multi-purpose sites, perhaps retail, distilling or some other form of community-led project. The times have changed for the great British pub. 20 years ago, there were only one or two good pubs within your area that would serve good food. Now we expect to be able to have something fantastic, whether it is a simple burger, grilled fish or a lovely salad (perhaps even homegrown in the pub's garden). Although our understanding of what pubs may be, or where they are going to go in the future, leads to perhaps less of them existing, the quality of what the pub brings is at a far higher level. Guest expectation and our delivery is reaching new heights. The pub scene is being recognised the world over as something of a force to be reckoned with.

There are more small-scale individual microbreweries around than ever before. People are driven now on taste, flavour and quality rather than just quantity of imported cold fizz. So, through all of the negativity, and all of the dark few months that the industry has been in with coronavirus, there is, and will be, opportunity for growth. Consumers want great pubs with amazing offerings, served by smiley and friendly people. We need now more than ever to be positive and strong and to drive the word home about how fantastic the Great British pub is, and most importantly, what it brings to each and every community. The one thing that I think we have all missed during lockdown is human connection and social interaction, which above all else, is everything that the Great British pub provides: a warm, happy and friendly place for people to drink and eat. Stay strong and stay supportive.

Tom Kerridge

Tom Kerridge is a Michelin-starred chef, restaurateur, TV personality and publican. He owns the Hand & Flowers, Marlow, which was the first pub to ever receive two Michelin stars, and the Coach, Marlow.

OUR GREATEST CHALLENGE YET

CAMRA has campaigned to support the beer and pubs industry for 50 years, but I think it's safe to say that it has been our most tumultuous year yet.

We fought tooth and nail to save real ale from extinction, and it can now be found in pubs across the country. Our members helped break up the 'big six' brewers, paving the path for nearly 2,000 brewers in operation today.

We have called for guest beer rights, better beer labelling and financial support for the smallest brewers. Our campaigning efforts brought about pubco reform, strengthened planning protection for pubs and reduced their tax burden. We have a lot to be proud of over the last five decades.

Yet none of these events comes close to what happened on the 20th of March 2020. Before that date, the idea that every single pub in the country could be closed overnight was frankly unimaginable.

Pubs – which have long been considered the beating heart of our local communities – were shut for over 100 days. Pubs, clubs, breweries and cider producers scrambled overnight to make sense of the new legislation, which allowed them to continue trading only by delivery or collection services.

CAMRA SPRINGS TO ACTION

I am proud to say that CAMRA was quick to spring to action. Hundreds of our dedicated volunteers helped develop detailed maps of the pubs, breweries and cider producers offering takeaway and delivery services to stay afloat during the closure. Our 'Pulling Together' campaign saw thousands of venues across the country listed, allowing us to encourage beer drinkers to buy locally rather than in supermarkets.

We then developed the Brew2You app, which helped beer and cider drinkers not only find but also order those drinks straight to their door. All revenue generated through the app went straight back to the pubs and breweries that needed it most, generating over £10k in sales every week for the industry.

CAMRA partnered with SIBA and Crowdfunder to launch the Pulling Together Campaign

Our campaign, which received cross-industry support and partnerships with SIBA and Crowdfunder, also collated resources for pubs and breweries – keeping those businesses up to date with the constantly changing advice and information they needed during a critical time.

CAMRA itself was hugely impacted. All beer festivals – including our landmark Great British Beer Festival – were cancelled. Branches and committees could no longer meet face-to-face, and we had to acquaint ourselves with new technology very quickly. Many of our members who rely on their local pub, club, and beer festival for their social life suddenly felt the weight of isolation and loneliness. I don't think I'm alone in remarking on what impact it has had on mental health.

CONNECTING VIRTUALLY

It became increasingly important to connect with our members digitally. We therefore developed the Red (On)Lion, a virtual pub where anyone could pull up a chair to chat with others in the main bar or book a private room with their friends and family. While a virtual pub can never replace the sense of community provided by a true local, the platform allowed us to organise weekly tastings, events and seminars to help people stay connected, socialise with others and stay informed about developments in the industry.

We also sought to help people deepen their understanding and appreciation of their favourite drink, developing educational content as part of our Learn & Discover offering. This ranged from video and audio guides to a dictionary of beer and cider terminology. We also released a new weekly podcast called 'Pubs. Pints. People.' which is freely available to all, and includes exclusive interviews with the likes of Melissa Cole, Roger Protz, Pete Brown and more.

A NEW NORMAL?

Today, it might seem like we are back to some type of a 'new' normal (barring a second wave prior to publication!), but the reality is that the impact of the COVID-19 lockdown will reverberate for a long time – for our pubs and for our nation's psyche.

When pubs across England were encouraged to reopen their doors on 4 July, nearly half were unable to take advantage of 'Super Saturday', having been notified just over a week before. Social distancing measures required significant changes and investment from landlords – moving to full table service, digitised menus and ordering apps, investing in deep cleans and sanitation stations. Many pubs simply did not have the resources to open in time and had to delay their opening date for several weeks to change their business model to what is essentially 'restaurant-style'.

Others remain closed to this day. It may not be too great a leap for the large country pub with ample beer garden space to adapt to the new normal, but the street-corner local and inner-city micropubs are struggling. Many licensees have told us it simply does not make business sense to open their doors on the reduced footfall that is required to ensure their customer's safety.

CAMRA's Great British Beer Festival was cancelled in 2020

Listen to CAMRA's podcast 'Pubs. Pints. People.' on Apple Podcast, Spotify or visit https://shows.acast.com/pubspintspeople

Furthermore, our pub-going experience has been fundamentally altered. What makes our pubs so unique and intrinsic to our local communities is that they provide a casual meeting place where people can chat at the bar, make friends with strangers and join in each other's conversation. Safety measures that require pre-bookings, table service and measured distances are frankly incompatible with the traditional pub atmosphere. Whether we are ever able to recover those essential pub characteristics depends on how long social distancing will need to remain in place.

WHAT'S NEXT?

This is truly a pivotal time that could make or break the industry. Our pubs and breweries are going to need significant and long-term support and funding throughout this transition period and in the months to come to survive. CAMRA will continue to call on the Government and pub companies to support licensees through this period.

Pubs that do survive may change forever – the essential characteristic of a pub rests on that open bar meeting space where you can make friends and socialise. That concept is simply incompatible with a post-COVID-19 world.

If there is one thing that I have learnt from COVID-19 it is that it is impossible to predict the future. That being said, I think it is a safe bet to say that rebuilding our pub culture post-COVID-19 will truly be one of CAMRA's greatest challenges yet.

Nik Antona, National Chairman

BRITISH BEER STYLES

Martyn Cornell and Roger Protz take a look at the history and flavour profiles of some of the beer styles you'll find in the British Isles, recommending some for you to try.

While Britain may have its staple beer styles – such as the enduring bitter style for which it is probably best known – increasingly brewers are looking for inspiration elsewhere.

It's now more common to see British brewers dabbling with wheat beers, lambics and saisons to name a few.

That's not to say the more traditional British styles are dying out. In fact, it's now easier to find beer styles that almost disappeared in the last century, such as mild and porter.

BARLEY WINE

The tradition of super-strong, long-aged, well-hopped ales, filled with flavour, goes back hundreds of years, though such brews have been known as Barley Wines only since the beginning of the 20th century. Older names for strong beers, from 9 to 14 per cent ABV, included Stingo, Old Tom, Huffcap, Crackskull and Audit Ale, this last originally brewed by Oxbridge colleges for the Audit Feast, when the college accounts were signed off. Very strong beers were often celebratory drinks, like the 'coming of age' ales brewed by landowners when an heir was born, laid down in the cellars to be drunk at that heir's 21st birthday. Barley wines were originally dark, with the first golden version made by a Sheffield brewer in 1951. Barley wines deliver rich aromas, often of honey or treacle, with flavours like liquid Christmas cake.

Try: Moor's Old Freddie Walker

BITTER/BEST BITTER/STRONG BITTER

The term 'bitter beer' was first coined in Burton in the 19th century, but it became a recognisable style at the turn of the century as brewers built tied estates of pubs and developed 'running beers' that didn't require long and expensive maturation. To give these beers a mature taste, darker malts such as crystal were added to pale malt: the result was bronze and copper-coloured brews. Today, despite the rise of IPA, bitter remains the most popular cask ale. Currently CAMRA defines bitter as up to 4 per cent, best bitter 4 per cent upwards, and strong or special bitter 5 per cent or more. Expect a beer with a fine balance of nutty malt, peppery hops and ripe fruit, with malt becoming more pronounced in stronger versions, but still with a good hop and fruit balance.

Try: Marble Manchester Bitter; Surrey Hills Shere Drop

FRUIT/SPECIALITY BEERS

Fruit beers are yet a further style inspired by Belgium – in this case fruit lambics. The addition of fruit doesn't mean the beers are sweet as the fruit creates further fermentation, with most of the sugars turned to alcohol. But the beers do receive approval from those drinkers who find hoppy and bitter beers too challenging. As the style has grown in popularity, so too has the range of fruits used: they include mango, lemon, orange and pineapple. Spreading their wings, brewers also add spices, herbs and confectionery to their beers. Such rare plants as bog myrtle have joined hops in the brew kettle while ground coffee beans have become especially popular and chilli adds a distinctive note. Honey, highly fermentable, is another frequent addition and adds a smooth and creamy texture to the finished beer. A newcomer to the sector is beer made with the addition of used bread, to make use of the vast amounts of wasted bread left over from the sandwich industry. Makers include Toast and Crumbs.

Try: Blue Monkey Chocolate Guerilla; Crumbs Sourdough Pale Ale; Titanic Plum Porter.

The British Isles offer a great choice of beer styles to explore

GOLDEN ALE

While gold-coloured beers have been around for many years, golden ales as we now know them were developed in the 1980s by a handful of small brewers determined to wean younger drinkers away from heavily promoted global lager brands. The new style was as pale as lager but had a pronounced hop character. It was such a success that brewers of all sizes rushed to include golden ale in their portfolios. The use of pale and even lager malts means that hops can shine and dominate the palate of the beer with just a touch of honeyed malt. Many brewers use American, European and New Zealand hops to give profound aromas and flavours of citrus fruit, herbal, spicy and resinous notes. Golden ales are often served cooler than other cask beers.

Try: Moor Nor'Hop; Oakham Citra; Salopian Oracle

IPA

India Pale Ale transformed brewing in the 19th century. The new technologies of the Industrial Revolution enabled brewers to use pale rather than brown malt with the result that beers became amber or bronze in colour. IPA was first brewed in London and exported to the Raj in India, but Burton-upon-Trent, with superior brewing water, became the main production centre. IPAs were heavily hopped to withstand long sea journeys lasting between four and six months. The style was ousted from India by the arrival of lager and became a domestic product, its strength much reduced during World War One. It has enjoyed a spirited revival in recent years at the hands of artisan brewers in the US and UK and now has global appeal. Expect a big peppery hop aroma balanced by biscuit malt and tart fruit.

Try: Fyne Superior IPA; Harbour IPA

LAGER

Lager is a German word meaning storage place. For centuries, brewers in central Europe stored their beers in icy caves to avoid spoilage from summer heat and wild yeast infection. With the arrival of ice-making machines and refrigeration in the 19th century, it was possible to produce lager beer on a vast commercial scale. Over time, this style of beer had developed a method of production known

The brewer's art sees raw ingredients transformed into a wide variety of styles of beer

as cold or bottom fermentation, with yeast working more slowly at a lower temperature than ale yeast. Early lager beers were brown in colour, but the style changed dramatically when the first golden lager was brewed in Pilsen in Bohemia, now the Czech Republic, in the mid 19th-century. Lager production today is dominated by a handful of global companies that produce their beers in weeks rather than months. For the true taste of lager, sample such Czech beers as Budweiser Budvar and Pilsner Urquell, aged for 90 days in the case of Budvar. A number of independent British brewers now produce excellent lager beers, including Moor, Geipel, St Austell, Meantime and Signature Brew.

MILD

Mild ale was Britain's favourite beer for many years, the triumphant combination of easy drinking and great flavour making it a hugely popular, cheap refresher after a hard day at the coalface or factory or in the fields. The sharp drop in the numbers engaged in manual work from the 1960s onwards saw sales of the style plummet. However, drinkers are once again appreciating the attractions of a pint of fresh, well-brewed mild, almost always low in strength, at 3 to 3.5 per cent ABV, and bitterness (historically milds could be much stronger, and hoppier, and occasional 19th century-style milds are still brewed). Today's milds are generally dark in colour (though light milds still sell well in, for example, the Midlands), often slightly fruity, possessing touches of caramel, coffee and chocolate.

Try: West Berkshire Magg's Mild

OLD ALE

Once, in the 18th and 19th centuries, there was ale, lightly hopped, though often high in gravity: when it was sold fresh it was called mild ale, and when it had aged, and gained in complexity, it was called old. Gradually the two styles separated, and the Great Gravity Crash that followed the huge tax rises of the First World War, as brewers lowered strengths to keep their beers affordable, meant that old ales fell from 7 per cent or higher to as low as 4.5 per cent. They survive today as cheery, warming, often winter drinks, generally dark, rich and raisiny, with touches of roast grain, toffee and subtle fruity hops offset by just a welcome balancing whisper of aged piquancy.

PALE ALE

Pale ale started life as a lower strength alternative to IPA, which many drinkers found too strong and bitter. Pale ale became a major style in the 19th century, with many brewers opening second plants in Burton-upon-Trent to avail themselves of the mineral-rich waters found there. In the 20th century bitter overtook pale ale in popularity and it became mainly a bottled beer. It has seen a renaissance in recent years, in bottle and draught, with the beer now having noticeable hop flavours, ranging from earthy and spicy to citrus and tropical. It should be a tad darker than golden ale, sometimes with the addition of crystal malt.

Try: Five Points Pale

PORTER & STOUT

Porter began life 300 years ago as a hoppier, more aged version of London brown beer that became popular with the capital's street and river porters, who moved goods around the city and on and off ships. Stout – originally stout porter – was simply the stronger version. Porter declined, and disappeared from Britain in the Second World War, while stout, like other beers, dropped in gravity. Since porter's revival in the late 70s it is now defined as being more hoppy and fruity than stout. Expect deep darkness, mouth-filling roastiness, chocolate, coffee, dark fruit and liquorice. Milk stouts are sweet, thanks to unfermentable lactose sugar, Imperial stouts almost dauntingly powerful.

Try: Enville Old Porter; Acorn Gorlovka Imperial Stout

SAISON

Saison is a beer style from Wallonia, the French-speaking region of Belgium. It started life as a seasonal beer, produced by farmers to refresh their labourers at harvest time. It's now brewed all year round, with the most famous version coming from Dupont on a former farm in the Hainaut district. Many saison brewers – notably Brasserie à Vapeur in Pipaix – add 'botanicals' such as black pepper, ginger, orange peel, curacao and star anise to the base beer. At a time when many beers are heavily hopped, saison has a distinctively rich malt base but with a good balance of spicy hops: Dupont uses East Kent Goldings. A number of British brewers have now taken up the style.

Try: Twisted Barrel Saison From Another Place

SCOTTISH BEER

Historically, Scottish beers tended to be darker and maltier that beers south of the border, though it's an urban myth that Scottish beers are less heavily hopped than English varieties. The rich and fruity beers were prized, with émigrés from the French revolution who settled in Edinburgh calling them 'Scottish Burgundies'. Traditional styles are known as Light, Heavy and Export, not dissimilar to mild, bitter and IPA. They are also called 60, 70 and 80 Shilling ales from a 19th-century system of invoicing. A Wee Heavy or 90 Shilling is a Scottish equivalent of barley wine. Modern Scottish brewers have raised the bar and now produce a broad range of beers, many pale in colour and with greater hop character.

Try: Stewart's 80/- ; Traquair House Ale

SOUR BEER/LAMBIC

Sour beers, sometimes simply called sours, are inspired by the lambic beers from Belgium, which are made by 'spontaneous fermentation', using wild yeasts in the atmosphere. When fermentation is underway, the beer is transferred to oak casks and stored for a year or more, allowing wild yeasts trapped in the wood to add a further fermentation. Belgian brewers often add cherries and raspberries to produce Kriek and Framboise fruit beers while Gueuze is a blend of young and aged lambics. Brewers in Belgium don't like the term 'sour' – they prefer acidic and compare them to Brut Champagne. The beers are challenging, with tart lemon and cider-like notes, while other characteristics are oak, port wine and cognac. The most authentic lambic-style beers produced in Britain are Elgood's Coolship, Kernel, Burning Sky and Wild Beer.

WHEAT BEER

Wheat beer is a style most commonly associated with Bavaria and Belgium – where it's known as Weisse or Weizen – but its popularity has encouraged many British brewers to produce their own interpretations of the style. The term 'wheat beer' is something of a misnomer as they are all a blend of malted barley and wheat. Wheat is a difficult grain to brew with and barley acts as a natural filter during the mashing stage to prevent wheat, which has no husk, from clogging pipes and outlets. Wheat beer, if brewed with special yeast cultures, has distinctive aromas and flavours of cloves, banana and bubblegum. Lightly hopped, it's a splendidly refreshing beer. Belgian versions often have the addition of such herbs, spices and fruit as coriander seeds and orange peel.

Try: Pilgrim Wheat Beer; Windswept Weizen

WOOD-AGED BEER

Metal containers didn't come into widespread use in the brewing industry until the 1920s. Until then beer was stored in casks made from oak. Lager brewers lined their casks with pitch to prevent wood flavours impregnating their delicate brews, but ale, with its more robust character, was able to absorb woody notes. In recent years, many brewers have launched barrel-ageing programmes, either placing regular beers in wood or producing special brews for the programme. Oak casks are happy breeding ground for such wild yeasts as Brettanomyces, which means 'British fungus'. These yeasts add a funky note that brewers call 'horse blanket'. A compound in wood called vanillin adds a noticeable vanilla note to the beers. Brewers also age beers in casks bought from the Scottish whisky, American Bourbon and French wine and cognac industries to age their beers: the result is beers with an unmistakable note of spirit or wine.

Breweries with barrel-ageing programmes include Abbeydale, Burning Sky, Kernel, Weltons and Wiper and True.

Many varieties of hop are grown around the world, with different types used for particular styles of beer

Martyn Cornell is a leading historian of beer, brewing and beer styles and has lectured on beer history at seminars from Denmark to Brazil. His work has been translated into more than half a dozen languages from Swedish to Portuguese and formed the basis for the 'beer styles' modules in courses run by the University of Gastronomic Sciences in Italy. He blogs on beer and beer history at **zythophile.co.uk**

Former editor of the Good Beer Guide, **Roger Protz** is considered one of the leading beer writers in the world, with a long career in journalism and publishing, and having won multiple awards. Roger has authored many books on beer and pubs, including 300 Beers to Try Before You Die. Follow him on Twitter **@RogerProtzBeer** and **protzonbeer.co.uk**

BEER APPRECIATION

A good beer is enjoyable, but a great beer is art in a glass. The breadth of choice of beers in the UK means we have plenty to appreciate. Here's how you can get the most out of your pint.

TEMPERATURE

To enjoy the flavours and aromas of a beer, cask ale should be served at the correct temperature. Too warm and unwanted aromas will be released, too cold and the clean, fresh vibrancy of the beer could be lost. A very low temperature could make the beer cloudy (chill haze).

The ideal serving temperature for most cask-conditioned ale is between 11 and 13°C. Stronger ales can be served slightly warmer: the higher temperature releases fruity aromas and esters, enhancing the flavour. Likewise, a cool, crisp golden ale can be served slightly colder.

CLOUDY OR CLEAR?

For many years, a lot of beer drinkers believed the perfect pint should be crystal clear. But times are changing, and many beers are now being served cloudy. In a lot of beer bars, cloudy is the new normal and quite acceptable.

Supporters of hazy brews say they are packed with tropical fruit and protein flavours, which filtering takes out. Historically, cloudy real ale was a sign that the beer had not been conditioned properly, and that can still be true. A good rule of thumb is, if it doesn't smell right, it is probably off. So, before you send a cloudy beer back check with the bar staff. If they are on top of their game they will know if it's intentional.

GLASSWARE

The choice of glassware can have an effect on appreciation of beer. Brewers in Belgium go to great lengths to design specific glasses to best enhance their beers, and the shape of a glass can affect head creation or allow aromas to be appreciated. Pubs in the UK are increasingly embracing stemmed glasses alongside standard pint glasses, and research shows that beer served in a tankard stays at the best drinking temperature for longer because it isn't warmed by the drinker's hand.

Tutored tastings are a great way to learn more about beer

INSIST ON QUALITY BEER

Real ale, when conditioned with care, should be bright and sparkling, with a lively head, served cool and refreshing at between 11 and 13°C.

Some beers, as mentioned above, may be intentionally cloudy. As a paying consumer, don't be afraid to take your beer back to the bar if it is not in good condition. Bar staff should replace it and might not be aware of an issue unless you tell them.

Take your pint back to the bar if:

- Your beer is served either too warm or too cold (for the style)
- Your beer smells of acetone, vinegar or stale bread
- The pint has no head, is totally flat and out of condition
- It's not only flat but hazy and has yeast particles or protein floating in the liquid

HOW TO TASTE BEER

We can increase our appreciation of beer by sampling and tasting. To taste your beer like an expert, make sure to use all of your senses.

SIGHT

We drink with our eyes, and our first impression is its visual appearance. How does the beer look? What colour is it – is it pale, cloudy, golden, almost black or ruby-hued? Does it have a large head or foam on top? Or is it tight, discrete and somewhat more restrained? Are there bubbles of carbon dioxide rising up the beer? The answers can be an indicator to the beer's style and also of its condition.

AROMA

Gently swirl the liquid in the glass to release the aroma or 'nose' and discover the malt, hop and fruit notes that emerge. Can you discern notes of citrus fruit? If it's a rich, dark stout, do you get a hint of coffee? In a barley wine you might detect some wine, almost sherry-like aromas.

The malts used can give a beer a rich biscuit-like character, while hops also add their own distinctive notes. Traditional English hops give spicy, peppery, woody and resinous notes, while American hops are famous for punchy, pronounced citrus notes, with grapefruit to the fore. Traditional European hops give cedar wood, mint, pine kernels and lemon zest and New Zealand hops have a vinous fruit character. North America, New Zealand and even Eastern Europe produce hops with some very distinct citrus, floral and fruit-like aromas.

SENSATION

What temperature is the beer? Each beer has an optimal serving temperature – has yours been served in the ideal condition for its style? How does the beer feel on your palate (mouthfeel)? Does it feel thick and syrupy, thin and watery, creamy, or smooth? And don't forget to swallow. Ideally there should be a slow, warming feeling, which should linger, but not for too long, in the back of the throat (the 'finish').

TASTE

Anticipate the first sip and then enjoy it. Let it caress your tongue. Our mouths have thousands of taste buds, which can detect salt, sweet, bitter, sour and umami. Take note of the initial flavours, the intermediate flavours, and the aftertaste.

Many people mistakenly believe certain parts of the tongue are exclusively designed to detect a certain taste. Not so, though certain areas may be more susceptible to certain sensations than others. Some beer can play tricks: a hoppy aroma may not always follow through in the taste. Is the beer fruity? Can you detect dark fruit flavours or even a hint of malted biscuit? What about coffee, chocolate or liquorice flavours? Is there a satisfying level of bitterness to your beer, and does the bitterness linger?

For more information on beer styles, see pages 8-11 or **camra.org.uk/learn-discover**

NOT JUST HERE FOR THE BEER

Coronavirus may have challenged the beer and brewing industry, but it has also reminded us why pub culture remains important. Jessica Mason discusses the impact of the virus on us all.

Drinking culture in Britain is rooted in both the casual and the familiar. The importance of that come-as-you-are attitude, found in our nation's pubs, has been archived in our minds as a mode of relaxation for centuries. Add this to the fact that the beer we choose to drink, a much-overlooked element of personal preference and selection, isn't just convenient refreshment. To all of us, that glass holds so much more. It's a small taste of freedom. It's identity. It's liberty.

PUBS ARE IMPORTANT

Beer and pubs are hugely important. Public houses are an intrinsic part of society because we develop our personalities, our social relationships and our moral compasses by actively watching, listening to and talking to others. By doing many things in life that, from the outside appear to be unessential to living and breathing, we forget there is a part of our vitality that is also nourished by doing things. Things that make us smile. Things that make us laugh. Things that make us feel more alive.

"when the pubs closed and the streets fell quiet, we lost some of our sparkle."

We knew lockdown kept our bodies safe. But what we didn't know was how much the pub meant to us. How closely it was connected to our wellbeing. We didn't know, because for so long beer and pubs have been highlighted as all that is wrong in the UK, never what is right. The eye contact. The greeting. The small unspoken geniality of being visible. The taste and the sounds connected to feeling a part of something. All these things happen in the pub. And when the pubs closed and the streets fell quiet, we lost some of our sparkle.

Socialising at the pub with friends and family has been sorely missed

Many pubs and breweries delivered direct to customers during lockdown

SERVING THE COMMUNITY

With a nation already feeling let down and despondent, the absence of the pub came as a heavy blow. But the publicans and brewers who retained their community connections thrived during a time when politicians floundered. North Brew Co delivered beer by bike directly to the homes of those who would ordinarily be propping up the bar, chatting to each person at the end of the journey. Neptune Brewery began supplying five-litre casks to local residents and opened a web store. Cheshire Cat Pubs & Bars began pulling fresh ale into one- and two-litre milk containers, selling them to go. Takeaway beer became the new avocado on toast. And for the first few weeks, we thought it was drinking we missed. By the end of the first month, we all realised that it was human interaction. And every drop off, every chat, every grin or wave - in person - it meant something.

PUBCO SUPPORT

In the background though, those normally running our nation's pubs had their own problems. Caught between lost income and the departure of a lifelong career built up over time. Some pub companies had cancelled rents during closure. But some were unrelenting and while the government had told people to avoid pubs and some had needed to close, none during that time could make a living never mind pay their staff or the rent on a closed premises for months on end. The industry was at a standstill and on its knees.

Harvey's cancelled commercial rent to a 90 per cent discount for four months, then to 40 per cent in September. Lords and Star Pubs & Bars also cancelled rents and stayed in close contact with tenants to support their return. As did the likes of Youngs, Fullers, Wells & Co, Adnams and St Austell. But not all pubcos picked up the phone or responded to their tenant's emails. And some went so far as to demand payments. As in most times of crisis there are heroic displays of warmth and kindness from some amidst the deafening silence of others. While some pubs closed their doors for good, others carefully planned their reopening. And it would be accurate to say we were nervous, all of us, from both sides of the bar.

THE POST-LOCKDOWN PINT

New seating and ordering measures were put in place. We became accustomed to Perspex, scrawling our names and numbers onto paper, temperature checks and the dousing of hand sanitiser. But we had our pubs back. And that was all that mattered.

Remember the first time you revisited the pub after lockdown. Remember that first beer back in a pub. That wasn't just a personal memory, but a part of national history. It was a day our cumulative fugue state ended. It was a victory-cry for our senses. A euphoric "cheers" to that home-from-home.

Going to the pub post-lockdown was a restoration project for the human soul. "This. Is. What. I. Have. Been. Missing." said pretty much everyone's brain as our taste buds did a few joyful somersaults and began strutting around hunting for crisps. For pie. For bowls of chips.

It was a glimpse of what things used to be like. Before breaking news announcements. Before numbered headlines. Before sleeplessness. And before any of our averted gazes and mask-clad faces had witnessed any foreboding distancing tape. So many of us will have closed our eyes during the first few sips of cask ale, happy listening to all the pub sounds - feeling placid for the first time in months.

Pub-going is a little different post-lockdown

PEOPLE POWER

The next phase of developments, whatever they may be, will be our chance to play a part in the future of beer. Our chance to show that we know no business is safeguarded during a pandemic. An opportunity to offer our unwavering support for the pubs and breweries that have, in turn, helped us by making it possible for us to return safely.

We may miss spontaneity. The bustle and camaraderie. But better to miss those things than to lose the sense of togetherness that is gained from sitting across from a friend, glassware on tables, smiles on faces. Better that we inch forwards into 2021 and beyond, united by the unknown. Better that we get to decide the flavour of the day. Exercise our minds. Make conversation. Participate.

We are used to dedicating our time to the preservation of good beer. And the hill this time may be steeper, but we know, beyond certainty, that it's worth the climb. We also know that breweries and pubs - they need us. And we need them.

Jessica Mason, also known as Drinks Maven, is a passionate drinks writer and champion for the hospitality industry. Jessica writes for a range of titles from business digests and trends reports through to tasting notes, reviews and impassioned thought pieces. When she's not writing, she is an events speaker, presenter and awards judge as well as a contributing author to beer and whisky books. She is instrumental in helping excellent drinks reach the best venues and is known for speaking avidly and lyrically about the joys of public houses and the positive impact they can have on our wellbeing. Find out more at **drinksmaven.com**

Visit Pubs & Win Prizes!
CASK FINDER
N
S
W
E
Join ale trails run on behalf of breweries & pub owners
The more pubs you visit the more prizes you win
WIN PRIZES
Discover 9,500 Pubs
10,000 Beers
Beer Festivals & more
CASK MARQUE
THE SIGN OF A GREAT PINT
INDEPENDENTLY INSPECTED
Download NOW!
Download on the App Store
GET IT ON Google Play

GREAT BRITISH STAYS
Explore real Britain from the comfort of a Great British Pub.
A pub feels like home; full of warmth and laughter, character and authenticity. A stay in a pub is where you'll find real places, real people and real stays – Great British Stays.
Discover & book our 1,700 boutique pubs with rooms and traditional country inns at
www.stayinapub.co.uk
STAY IN A PUB
GREAT BRITISH STAYS

The Pubs

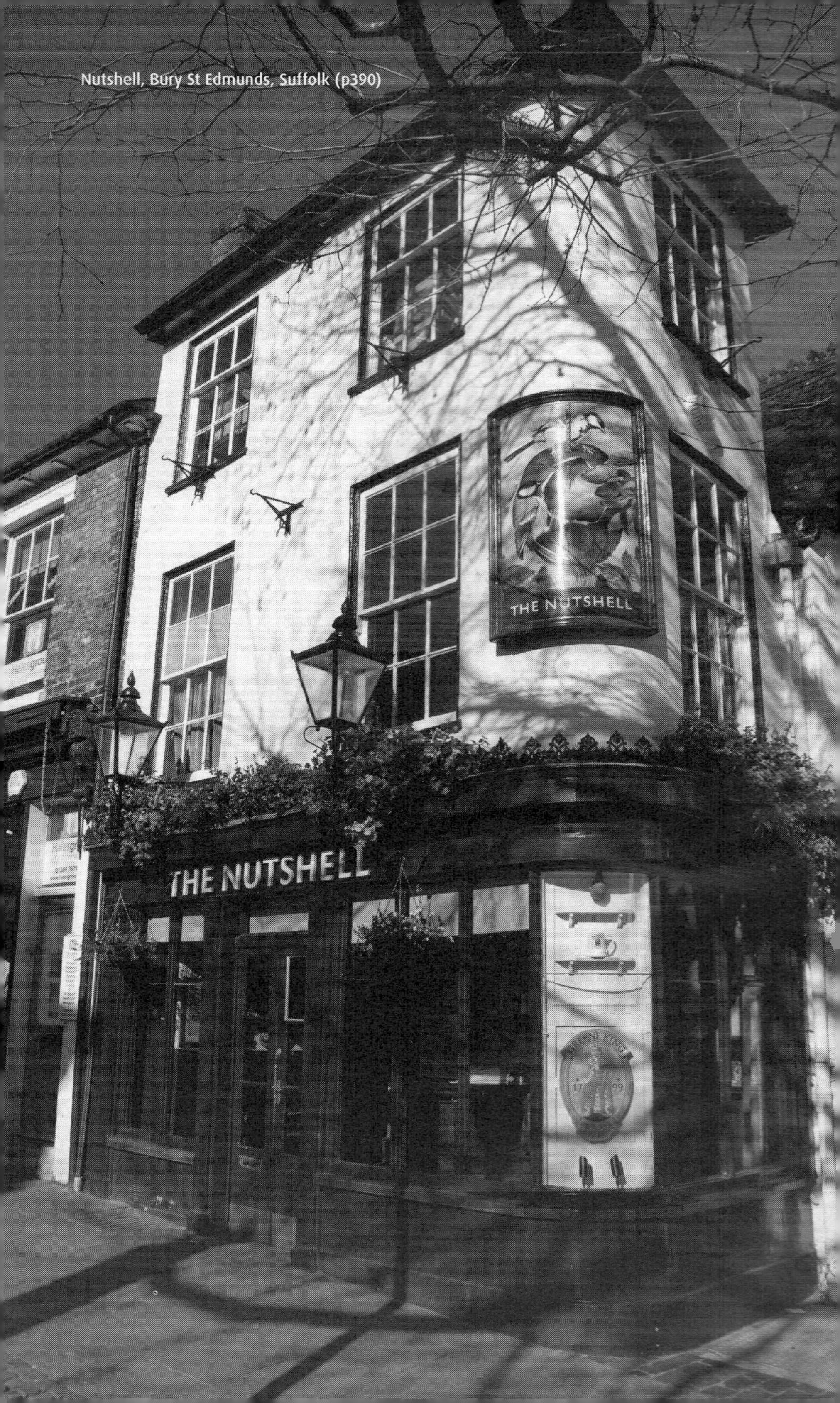

Nutshell, Bury St Edmunds, Suffolk (p390)

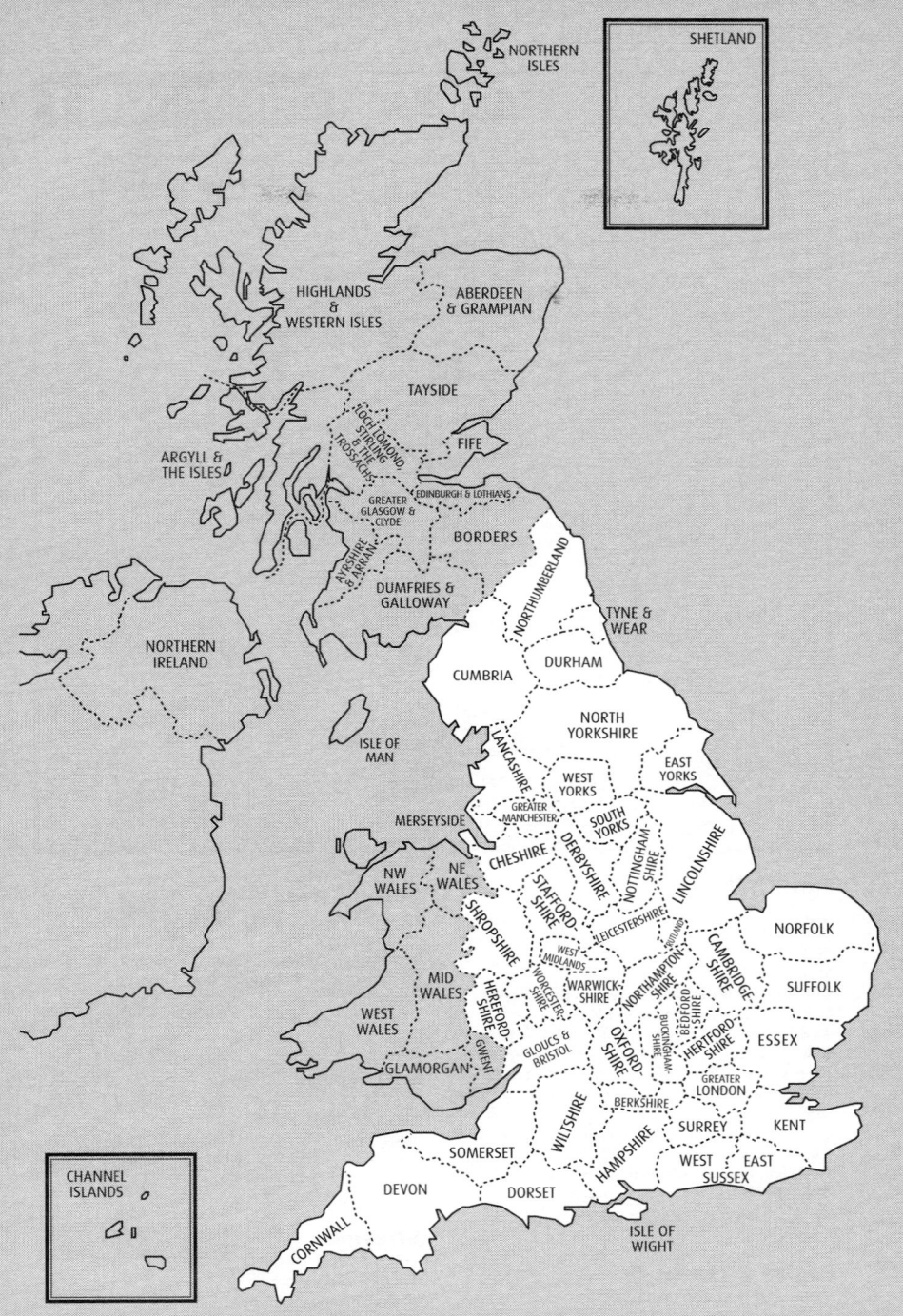

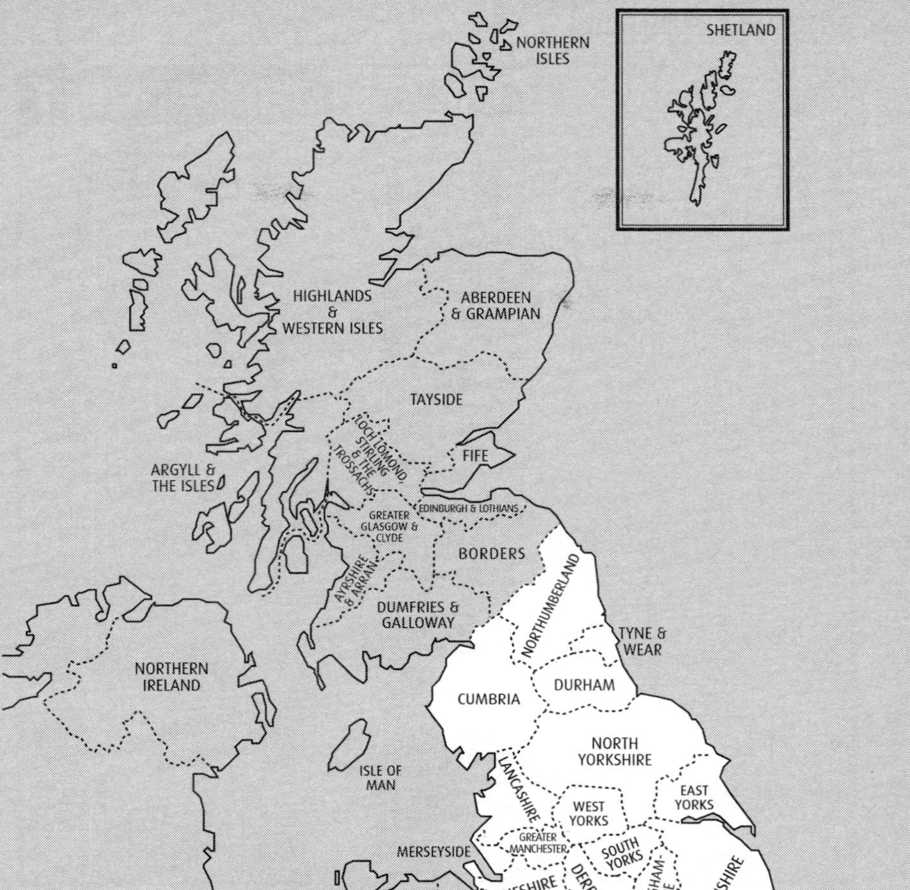
NORTHERN ISLES
SHETLAND
HIGHLANDS & WESTERN ISLES
ABERDEEN & GRAMPIAN
TAYSIDE
LOCH LOMOND, STIRLING & THE TROSSACHS
FIFE
ARGYLL & THE ISLES
EDINBURGH & LOTHIANS
GREATER GLASGOW & CLYDE
BORDERS
AYRSHIRE & ARRAN
DUMFRIES & GALLOWAY
NORTHUMBERLAND
TYNE & WEAR
NORTHERN IRELAND
DURHAM
CUMBRIA
NORTH YORKSHIRE
ISLE OF MAN
LANCASHIRE
WEST YORKS
EAST YORKS
GREATER MANCHESTER
SOUTH YORKS
MERSEYSIDE
CHESHIRE
DERBYSHIRE
NOTTINGHAMSHIRE
LINCOLNSHIRE
NW WALES
NE WALES
STAFFORDSHIRE
SHROPSHIRE
LEICESTERSHIRE
RUTLAND
NORFOLK
WEST MIDLANDS
CAMBRIDGESHIRE
MID WALES
HEREFORDSHIRE
WORCESTERSHIRE
WARWICKSHIRE
NORTHAMPTONSHIRE
SUFFOLK
BEDFORDSHIRE
BUCKINGHAMSHIRE
WEST WALES
OXFORDSHIRE
HERTFORDSHIRE
ESSEX
GLOUCS & BRISTOL
GWENT
GLAMORGAN
GREATER LONDON
BERKSHIRE
WILTSHIRE
SURREY
KENT
SOMERSET
HAMPSHIRE
WEST SUSSEX
EAST SUSSEX
CHANNEL ISLANDS
DEVON
DORSET
CORNWALL
ISLE OF WIGHT

England

BEDFORDSHIRE

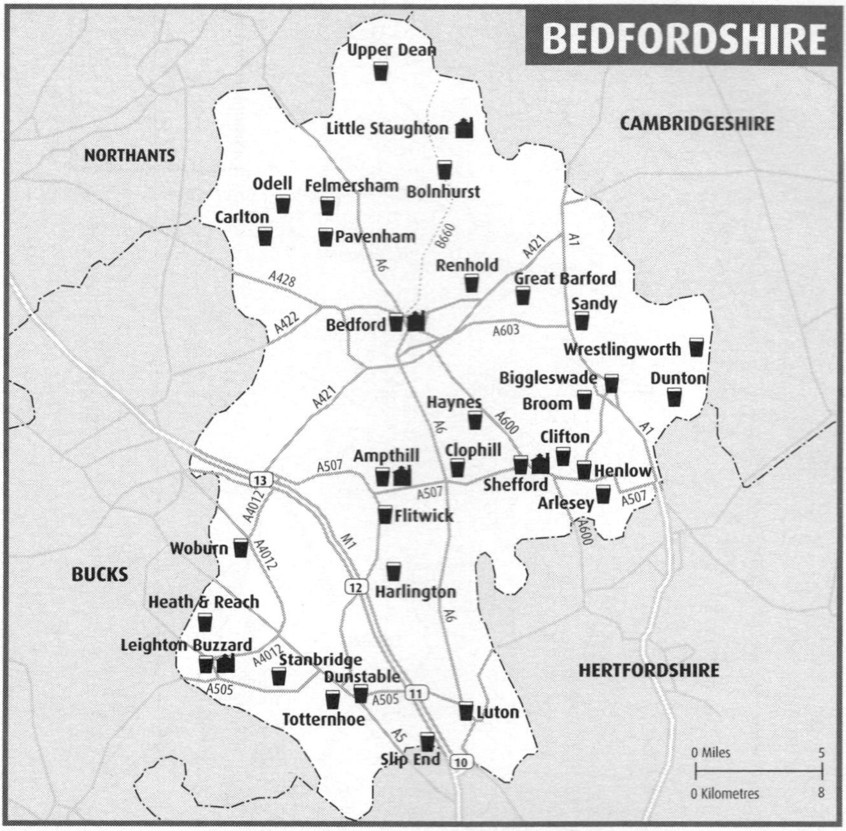

Ampthill

Albion 𝕃

36 Dunstable Street, MK45 2JT

☎ (01525) 634857

B&T Shefford Bitter, Golden Fox, Dragon Slayer; Everards Tiger; 8 changing beers Ⓗ

An award-winning, proper, narrow-fronted Victorian pub with one large bar and 12 handpumps serving Everards Tiger, a range of local B&T beers, eight varied ales mainly from microbreweries plus a changing craft keg beer. Two regular real ciders and a guest are also on offer. There is a meeting room and a secluded patio garden towards the rear. A selection of local clubs and groups is supported. Twice Bedfordshire CAMRA Pub of the Year.

Queen's Head 𝕃

20 Woburn Street, MK45 2HP

☎ (01525) 405016

Bombardier; Courage Directors; Eagle IPA; Young's London Special; 1 changing beer (sourced nationally) Ⓗ

A truly charming and cosy 18th-century tavern in a historic area of Ampthill, close to the park and the Greensand Ridge walk. Beers are mainly from the local Eagle Brewery in Bedford. Inside is a low-beamed saloon bar, a lounge, and another room which is available for private functions. The pub's name refers to Catherine of Aragon, who was imprisoned in Ampthill Castle while Henry VIII dissolved the monasteries and broke from the church of Rome.

Engine & Tender ✔

11 Dunstable Street, MK45 2NJ

☎ (01525) 403319

Greene King IPA; St Austell Tribute; Timothy Taylor Landlord; 1 changing beer (sourced nationally; often Morland, Theakston, Wadworth) Ⓗ

A proper, traditional, single-bar pub with a welcoming atmosphere and a varied clientele. Regular and changing beers come from Greene King and guest brewers. Lunchtime meals are served Wednesday to Friday. Sports are very popular on the multiple TVs. There is seating in front of the pub, a covered archway and a very pleasant patio area to the rear.

Arlesey

Vicars Inn 𝕃

68 Church Lane, SG15 6UX

☎ (01462) 731215

Eagle IPA; 1 changing beer (sourced nationally) Ⓗ

Welcoming pub in view of the church and just a few minutes' walk from the railway station. The large lounge bar is directly opposite the entrance. To the left is a smaller, cosier bar with a fruit machine, decorated with sports memorabilia, historical pictures and a number of vintage water jugs. Darts and dominoes teams are supported and complimentary snacks are often on the bars. The guest ale is usually under 4% ABV.

Q P (9A,96)

Bedford

Brewhouse & Kitchen 𝕃 ✔
115 High Street, MK40 1NU
☎ (01234) 342931
Brewhouse & Kitchen Banker's Draught, Intrepid, Invarsity Ⓗ
A former bank then Wetherspoon pub relaunched by the Brewhouse & Kitchen group in 2016. The microbrewery is located within the main bar area, alongside various seating areas separated by half-height dividers that are features in themselves. Orders can be placed at the table or at the bar – the menu contains an extensive list of drinks as well as food. Seasonal and special ales are available but only in KeyKeg. 🐴❀◐◑♿🍎🚌🐾📶

Castle 𝕃
17 Newnham Street, MK40 3JR
☎ (01234) 353295 🌐 castlebedford.co.uk
Courage Directors; Eagle IPA; Young's London Original, London Special; 2 changing beers (sourced nationally) Ⓗ
Lively town pub with a pleasant walled patio garden, five minutes from the town centre and convenient for the Bedford Blues rugby ground. Lunches are served daily and evening meals weekdays only. Current guest beers with tasting notes are listed on the website and social media. A guesthouse behind the pub provides five en-suite bedrooms. Open mic features on a Monday evening. A former local CAMRA Pub of the Year.
🐴❀🛏◐◑♿🍎P🚌🐾📶

Devonshire Arms 🏆 𝕃 ✔
32 Dudley Street, MK40 3TB (1 mile E of town centre S of A4280)
☎ (01234) 301170 🌐 devonshirearmsbedford.co.uk
Courage Directors; Eagle IPA; 4 changing beers (sourced regionally) Ⓗ
Pleasant late-Victorian pub in a residential area, a Wells house for its whole 120 years. The front bar has bare floorboards and an open fire, while there is a separate rear bar. The garden has a gazebo for smokers and a no-smoking paved area. Beer and cider festivals are held twice a year. A range of wines is sold by the glass or bottle. Local CAMRA Pub of the Year 2020.
Q🐴❀♣🍎🚌(4) 🐾📶

Pilgrim's Progress 𝕃 ✔
42 Midland Road, MK40 1QB
☎ (01234) 363751
Eagle IPA; Greene King Abbot; Ruddles Best Bitter; Sharp's Doom Bar; 6 changing beers (sourced nationally) Ⓗ
Remodelled as a Wetherspoon hotel in 2016, the pub has five internal areas and two outdoor seating areas, one of them no-smoking. The bar is popular with all ages but doesn't usually get overcrowded, even on weekend evenings. There are views into the kitchen, and the varied food menu specifies allergens and calorie content. Wetherspoon Club offers are available. The location is convenient for public transport and offers a good view of the town centre. 🐴❀🛏◐◑♿🚆🍎🚌📶

Wellington Arms 𝕃
40-42 Wellington Street, MK40 2JX (N of town centre)
☎ (01234) 308033
Adnams Southwold Bitter; B&T Shefford Bitter; Draught Bass; 9 changing beers (sourced nationally; often B&T) Ⓗ
A traditional street-corner establishment featuring lots of breweriana. A key part of the Bedford real ale scene for 20 years, it has an interesting selection of 12 ales and two real ciders on handpump. Draught continental beers and a range of bottled Belgian beers are also available. There is a courtyard for drinkers and smokers. The pub attracts a mixed clientele and offers a friendly welcome.
❀🍎🐾

White Horse 𝕃 ✔
84 Newnham Avenue, MK41 9PX
☎ (01234) 409306 🌐 thewhitehorsebedford.co.uk
Courage Directors; Eagle IPA; Marston's 61 Deep; 1 changing beer (sourced regionally) Ⓗ
Three seating areas, all with their own style, are served from a single bar. The smartphone quiz on Sunday and regular Tuesday quiz are popular, as is the Monday evening jazz. Other musical events are advertised on Facebook. Food is freshly cooked to order, with a choice of roasts on Sunday (book ahead on Sun and Tue eve). The beer and wine selection is complemented by a wide choice of gins. Afternoon tea can be ordered for groups.
🐴❀◐◑♿🍎P🚌(4) 🐾📶

Biggleswade

Golden Pheasant 𝕃 ✔
71 High Street, SG18 0JH
☎ (01767) 313653 🌐 goldenpheasantbiggleswade.co.uk
Eagle IPA; 5 changing beers (sourced nationally) Ⓗ
Situated in the centre of town, this pub can trace its roots back to 1876. The low beamed ceiling adds to the traditional feel, while the single-room interior is large enough to accommodate darts teams for matches alongside community groups for meetings. A good range of well-kept beers and ciders is served from the corner bar. The large outside area at the rear is a great space for live music and other charity events. Q❀🚆♣🍎🚌🐾📶

Wheatsheaf ✔
5 Lawrence Road, SG18 0LS
☎ (01767) 222220
Greene King IPA; 2 changing beers (sourced nationally; often Fuller's) Ⓗ
Built in 1873 and tucked away down a back street at the end of a row of terraced cottages, this comfortable and welcoming establishment is community-focused and caters for local darts and dominoes teams. Horse racing and big matches feature on the large TV screens and it can get busy when popular fixtures are shown. The excellent condition of the Greene King IPA and the large family-friendly garden area make the pub worth seeking out. 🐴❀🚆♣🚌(73,188)🐾📶

Bolnhurst

Plough 𝕃
Kimbolton Road, MK44 2EX (on W side of B660 S of turning to Thurleigh) TL088587
☎ (01234) 376274 🌐 bolnhurst.com
Adnams Southwold Bitter; 2 changing beers (sourced regionally) Ⓗ
Award-winning pub restaurant dating in part from the Tudor period, serving excellent food and beer. The bar area is to the left of the entrance, with the restaurant beyond and a second dining/function room to the right. Outside, the large garden has decking and a pond. The

REAL ALE BREWERIES

B&T Shefford
Brewhouse & Kitchen 🛢 Bedford
Crown 🛢 Little Staughton
Eagle Bedford
Kelchner Ampthill
Leighton Buzzard Leighton Buzzard

Plough has no prominent signage, just a modest hanging sign on a post by the road entrance. Closed from Christmas until the second week of January each year. Wheelchair users should contact the pub in advance.
Q🐴❀◐P🐾📶

Broom

Cock ★ ✔

23 High Street, SG18 9NA
☎ (01767) 314411 🌐 thecockatbroom.co.uk
Greene King Abbot; 3 changing beers (sourced nationally; often St Austell, Tring, Wychwood) Ⓖ
Delightful Grade II listed pub on CAMRA's National Inventory of Historic Pub Interiors. At the front are two rooms – a parlour with wood-burning fire and bottle collection and a games room with dartboard and Northamptonshire skittles table. Another room contains a fish tank. Outside is a beer garden and a large area for camping and caravans with access to toilets and water. Drinks are served direct from the cellar steps to customers and food is home-cooked.
Q🐴❀◐⛺♣●P🚌(200) 🐾📶

Carlton

Fox 𝕃

High Street, MK43 7LA (off Turvey Road S of village centre)
☎ (01234) 720235 🌐 thefoxatcarlton.pub
Eagle IPA; Fuller's London Pride; 2 changing beers (sourced regionally) Ⓗ
A charming thatched community pub with a warm welcome and an attractive garden popular with families. Guest beers are often from local microbreweries. Good-value, home-cooked lunches are served daily except Monday and evening meals Tuesday to Saturday. There is a regular quiz on Thursday evening. Spring and summer bank holiday festivals are held using an outbuilding as an additional bar, plus a one-day gin festival in June. A repeat winner of local CAMRA Country Pub of the Year including 2020. Q🐴❀◐♿♣P🚌(25)🐾📶

Clifton

Admiral

1 Broad Street, SG17 5RJ
☎ (01462) 811069
2 changing beers (sourced nationally; often Brains, Harvey's, Robinsons) Ⓗ
Friendly, warm and welcoming pub with a wood-burning stove, serving five real ales, one real cider and bottled craft beers. Nautical themed pictures and model ships adorn the interior, and there are board games and darts available. Monthly pub quizzes and live music events are always popular, as is the annual beer festival. Food offerings are not to be missed, including fish and chips Fridays, weekend breakfasts, Sunday roasts, steak night Mondays plus stone-baked pizzas on summer weekends.
🐴❀◐♣●🚌(9A,9B) 🐾📶

Clophill

Stone Jug

10 Back Street, MK45 4BY (500yds off A6 at N end of village) TL083381
☎ (01525) 860526 🌐 stonejug.co.uk
Otter Amber; Shepherd Neame Spitfire; 3 changing beers (sourced nationally) Ⓗ
Originally three 16th-century cottages, this popular village local has an L-shaped bar serving two drinking areas and a family/function room. Excellent home-made lunches are available Tuesday to Saturday. The guest beers are often from local microbreweries, the cider is Westons. Picnic benches at the front and a rear patio garden offer outdoor drinking space in fine weather. Parking can be difficult at busy times. A good pit stop for the Greensand Ridge Walk and a former CAMRA Pub of the Year. Q🐴❀◐♣●P🚌(44,81)🐾

Dunstable

Gary Cooper 𝕃 ✔

Grove Park, Court Drive, LU5 4GP
☎ (01582) 471452
Greene King Abbot; Ruddles Best Bitter; Sharp's Doom Bar; 7 changing beers Ⓗ
A large, airy, modern Wetherspoon bar serving a selection of up to seven guest ales, often local. The usual range of JDW craft beer is also well stocked. Situated in Grove Park leisure area, the pub has a patio overlooking the Grove House gardens, with many bus routes stopping outside. It gets busy on Friday and Saturday nights. Hollywood star Gary Cooper attended the local grammar school 1910-13. 🐴◐♿●🚌📶

Globe 𝕃

43 Winfield Street, LU6 1LS
☎ (01582) 512300
7 changing beers Ⓗ
Popular beer destination and community local where handpumps boast a good range of seven ever-changing microbrewery beers, a real cider and a perry. More than 20 Belgian beers are also available. Bare boards, bar stools, breweriana and a famous plank at the end of the bar create a traditional town pub atmosphere buzzing with conversation. Regular beer festivals are held. A former county and local CAMRA Pub of the Year.
Q🐴♿♣●🚌(70) 🐾

Victoria 𝕃

69 West Street, LU6 1ST
☎ (01582) 662682
House beer (by Tring); 2 changing beers Ⓗ
The Victoria is a popular town-centre pub near the police station on West Street. It usually offers two varying ales from microbreweries plus a house beer from the local Tring Brewery. Darts, dominoes and crib are popular as well as televised sports in the bar. There is a separate function room next to the rear courtyard. ❀♣🚌

Dunton

March Hare 𝕃

34 High Street, SG18 8RN
☎ (01767) 600258 🌐 themarchharedunton.co.uk
6 changing beers (sourced nationally; often Digfield, Nobby's, Tring) Ⓗ
A much-loved community hub and regular host of live music, this pub dating from the 1840s has an L-shaped, brick-faced bar and oak beam remnants. A wide-ranging selection of both local and national beers of different varieties and gravities is available. Mini beer festivals are held twice a year, plus a gin festival and a cider festival. Games and newspapers are available for drinkers to enjoy. A cosy fire and a sun-drenched beer garden ensure a warm welcome at any time of year.
Q🐴❀♣●🚂🚌(188) 🐾📶

Felmersham

Sun 𝕃

Grange Road, MK43 7EU
☎ (01234) 781355 🌐 thesunfelmersham.com

Eagle IPA; 2 changing beers (sourced regionally) [H]
Pretty, thatched community pub with a family-friendly rear garden, convenient for visits to the historic parish church and a nature reserve just across the river. Guest beers are often from local microbreweries. The creative food menu includes rotisserie-cooked chicken, hand-cut chips and seasonal ingredients from local producers. There is also a monthly food and drink theme night. The refurbished dining room can accommodate up to 40. Local CAMRA Cider Pub of the Year 2020.
🐴❀◑♣🍎P🚌(50)🐾📶

Flitwick

Crown ✔

Station Road, MK45 1LA
☎ (01525) 713737 🌐 crownflitwick.co.uk
4 changing beers (sourced nationally) [H]
This large and tidy, thriving estate pub was successfully rescued by the current tenants who are keen on their real ales, with four changing beers and a craft keg beer usually available. The front bar has TV, jukebox, pool and darts. Saturday music nights are popular. There is a large garden with patio and children's play area. Traditional pub food is served lunchtimes and evenings (lunches only on Sun). 🐴❀◑♿🚆♣P🚌(2)🐾📶

Great Barford

Anchor Inn L ✔

High Street, MK44 3LF (by river 1 mile S of village centre) TL134517
☎ (01234) 870364 🌐 anchoringreatbarford.co.uk
Eagle IPA; Young's London Original; 4 changing beers (sourced nationally) [H]
Busy inn next to the church, looking over a medieval bridge across the River Great Ouse. At least two guest beers are usually available from an extensive range offered by the pub company. Good home-cooked food is served in the bar and restaurant, as well as a fine selection of wines. The place is popular with river users in the summer. Occasional themed food nights are held, mainly during the winter months. Q🐴❀◑P🚌(27)📶

Harlington

Carpenters Arms

Sundon Road, LU5 6LS
☎ (01525) 872384 🌐 thecarpentersarmsharlington.com
Greene King IPA; Woodforde's Wherry; 2 changing beers (sourced nationally; often Shepherd Neame, Wainwright) [H]
Situated in the heart of Harlington, this low-beamed watch-your-head traditional village inn was first licensed in 1790 and has listings of landlords from then until the present. Two regular ales and two changing guests are available. Food is reasonably priced with good helpings and themed food nights. The railway station and bus service along with a range of country walks make this a popular stop-off. Q🐴❀◑♿🚆♣P🚌(42)🐾📶

Haynes

Greyhound ✔

68 Northwood End Road, MK45 3QD (at Northwood End)
☎ (01234) 381239 🌐 thegreyhoundhaynes.co.uk
Greene King IPA, Abbot; 4 changing beers (sourced regionally; often Oakham, Wadworth) [H]
A family-run village pub on the John Bunyan Trail and close to the Greensand Ridge Walk, with a large garden offering play equipment and a pétanque court. Families are welcome in the spacious lounge and dining area until 9pm. The dog-friendly public bar area hosts darts and other village teams. The fortnightly quiz is a popular event. Four changing beers are available in summer. There is no food on Monday or Sunday evening, and Sunday lunch is a carvery. 🐴❀◑♿♣🍎P🚌(9B)🐾📶

Heath & Reach

Axe & Compass

Leighton Road, LU7 0AA
☎ (01525) 237394 🌐 theaxeandcompass.pub
2 changing beers (sourced nationally) [H]
This village community pub has been a free house since 2014. The older front bar, with its low beams, is a lounge and dining area, while the rear public bar has gaming machines, pool table and a TV screen. The large garden includes a children's play area. Regular guest beers often come from local breweries such as Hornes, Tring, Leighton Buzzard, Gun Dog and Vale. Accommodation is available in a separate lodge.
🐴❀🛏◑♣🍎P🚌(150)🐾📶

Henlow

Engineers Arms 🏆 L ✔

68 High Street, SG16 6AA
☎ (01462) 812284 🌐 engineersarms.co.uk
10 changing beers (sourced nationally; often Cotleigh, Hadham, Salcombe) [H]
This multi-award winning pub has enjoyed 25 consecutive years in the Guide under the same landlord. Ten beers and six ciders and perries – typically from Saxby's and Orchard Pig – are sometimes supplemented by two ales served directly from wooden barrels in the cellar. Poker, quiz and board game nights, karaoke, live bands, pub outings, a renowned beer festival, tap takeovers and TV sport ensure there is something for everyone. Local CAMRA Pub and Cider Pub of the Year 2020. Q🐴❀⛺♣🍎🚌(9B,188)🐾📶

Old Transporter Ale House L

300 Hitchin Road, SG16 6DP
☎ (01462) 817410 🌐 theoldtransporter.co.uk
4 changing beers (sourced nationally; often Potbelly, Tring) [G]
Located near RAF Henlow, this single-room beer house has a friendly and welcoming atmosphere, with interesting transport-themed decoration. Real ale is served direct from barrels set up behind the bar. A good selection of ciders is available, mainly from Lilley's, plus a choice of snacks. The pub is home to a darts team and has a widescreen TV for live rugby matches. Events include live music evenings, quizzes, raffles and mini beer festivals – often featuring dark beers.
🐴♣🍎🚌(9B,188)🐾📶

Leighton Buzzard

Bald Buzzard Micropub L

6 Hockliffe Street, LU7 1HJ
☎ 07484 896131 🌐 baldbuzzard.co.uk
5 changing beers (sourced nationally) [G]
This popular micropub opened in 2015, providing the discerning beer enthusiast with a great selection of ales and ciders. Four recently installed KeyKeg dispensers offer an interesting selection of beers not normally found locally. Four ciders are available, served from a chiller room behind the bar, as well as a selection of bottled and canned beers. The bar's seating layout encourages conversation. Phil and Ali run food nights, and generous pork pies are on offer. 🐴❀◑♿♣🍎🥛🚌(70,150)🐾

Black Lion 🏆
20 High Street, LU7 1EA
☎ (01525) 853725 ⊕ blacklionlb.com
Draught Bass; Nethergate Suffolk County Best Bitter; Oakham Bishops Farewell; 5 changing beers (sourced nationally) Ⓗ
This traditional alehouse with 17th-century origins features exposed beams, wooden floors and an open fire. Eight handpumps dispense beers from the likes of Leighton Buzzard, North Cotswold, Slater's and Purity. Eight changing real ciders are also available and an impressive bottled and canned beer menu lists over 100 continental and British beers. There is a large paved garden. Bar snacks are served and bring-your-own cold lunches are welcome. Local CAMRA Pub of the Year 2015-2019. Q❀◐♣●🚌(70,150)🐾

Leighton Buzzard Brewing Company Brewery Tap Ⓛ
Unit 31, Harmill Industrial Estate, Grovebury Road, LU7 4FF (2nd left from Grovebury Rd)
☎ 07538 903753 ⊕ leightonbuzzardbrewing.co.uk
4 changing beers (sourced locally; often Leighton Buzzard) Ⓖ
This place presents a range of four beers dispensed directly from casks in the cool room, plus bottles to drink on the premises and to take home. Real cider and keg beers are also available. Open days are held one Saturday a month between March and December (check the website for dates), with local food offerings and occasional live music. ♿♣●P🚌(D1)🐾

Swan Hotel ✔
50 High Street, LU7 1EA
☎ (01525) 380170
Greene King Abbot; Ruddles Best Bitter; Sharp's Doom Bar; 6 changing beers (sourced nationally) Ⓗ
Dating from the 17th century, this former coaching inn renovated by Wetherspoon is a High Street landmark. With good-value food and 39 guest rooms, the Swan is busy and bustling for much of the week. One long bar provides friendly service to two rooms, a conservatory and a courtyard. Guest beers may come from local microbreweries and real cider is available in the summer months. Families are welcome until 11pm. Events include biannual beer festivals.
Q❀◐♿●🚌(70,150)

White Horse
9 New Road, Linslade, LU7 2LS
☎ (01525) 635739 ⊕ whitehorsebandb.co.uk
Fuller's London Pride; 4 changing beers (sourced nationally) Ⓗ
This is a genuine back-street free house close to the Grand Union Canal and Leighton Buzzard railway station. The L-shaped bar features several sports TV screens. There is a small courtyard to the rear and a small public car park across the road. Guest beers are often from St Austell, Otter and Oakham. An interesting and varied selection of bottled and canned beers is also offered. Accommodation comprises seven rooms in a converted stable block. ♿⇌♣🚌🐾

Luton

Bricklayers Arms
High Town Road, LU2 0DD
☎ (01582) 611017 ⊕ bricklayersarmsluton.co.uk
6 changing beers (sourced nationally; often Oakham) Ⓗ
This quirky High Town pub, run by the same landlady for over 30 years, is busy with Hatters fans on match days. It has TVs in both bars and a popular quiz night every Monday. Six handpumps serve a variety of guest beers from breweries all over the nation, including a choice of light, amber and, usually, a mild ale. Draught Belgian beers and two real ciders are also available.
❀⇌♣●🐾

Globe ✔
26 Union Street, LU1 3AN
☎ (01582) 482259
Greene King IPA; 2 changing beers (sourced nationally) Ⓗ
Popular, homely, street-corner local, just off the town centre. The L-shaped single bar offers Greene King IPA complemented by two constantly changing guests from regional breweries and micros; beer festivals also feature regularly. Sport is shown on TV. Good-value food is served at lunchtime. There is an enclosed patio area to the rear of the small car park. ❀◐♿⇌♣P🐾

Great Northern Ⓛ
63 Bute Street, LU1 2EY
☎ (01582) 729311
St Austell Tribute; Tring Side Pocket for a Toad Ⓗ
This may be the smallest pub in Luton. Its name was changed in the 1860s when the Great Northern Railway was built right on its doorstep. It still retains green Victorian wall tiles and a table featuring quirky brass pint glass holders at each corner. Sports are shown on TV. There is a smoking area at the rear. ⇌♣🐾

White House Ⓛ ✔
1 Bridge Street, LU1 2NB
☎ (01582) 454608
10 changing beers (sourced nationally) Ⓗ
A large two-bar town-centre Wetherspoon with the usual keenly priced food and drinks. It offers 10 different guest ales split across the two separate bars, with local ales often from Vale, Tring or Kelchner breweries. This is a bright and clean pub in the Galaxy Centre, conveniently located for several bus routes. Q❀◐♿⇌●🚌

Odell

Bell
81 High Street, MK43 7AS
☎ (01234) 910850 ⊕ thebellinodell.co.uk
Greene King IPA, Abbot; 4 changing beers (sourced nationally) Ⓗ
Handsome thatched village pub with a large garden near the River Great Ouse. With the Harrold-Odell Country Park just down the lane, this is a popular stop for walkers. Sympathetic refurbishment and a series of linked but distinct seating areas help retain a traditional pub atmosphere. Good-value, quality food includes a Sunday roast, steak and chips night Monday and pie and chips night Tuesday. Brunch is served in the mornings, while tea and cakes are available all day.
Q❀◐P🚌(25,26)🐾

Pavenham

Cock Ⓛ
High Street, MK43 7NJ
☎ (01234) 822834 ⊕ thecockatpavenham.co.uk
Courage Directors; Wainwright; 2 changing beers (sourced nationally; often Eagle, Marston's) Ⓗ
A friendly village pub with a warm welcome and a choice of cask ales. The bar has a late Art Deco look, mirrored in the bright new pub sign outside. Gustav Klimt prints decorate the walls. The large rear garden connects with the Ouse Valley Way and John Bunyan Trail public

footpaths. Pizzas are served on Friday evening and a three-course roast lunch on Sunday. Book meals in advance as dining space is limited.
P (25,29)

Renhold

Polhill Arms

25 Wilden Road, MK41 0JP (at Salph End)
(01234) 771398 polhillarms.co.uk
Hardys & Hansons Bitter; St Austell Tribute; 5 changing beers (sourced nationally; often Greene King)
Family-friendly village local with a welcoming atmosphere and a large garden, play area and restaurant. An interesting collection of pub and brewery artefacts and airship memorabilia is displayed. Traditional pub food is served, including fish and chips (no food Sun or Mon eves). There are regular quiz nights and live music, and skittles is popular. Two real ciders are available in the winter months, four in summer. Local CAMRA Pub of the Year 2018 and 2019.
P (27)

Sandy

Sir William Peel

39 High Street, SG19 1AG
(01767) 680607 sirwilliampeel.wixsite.com/sirwilliampeel
Batemans XB; Oakham JHB; 2 changing beers (sourced nationally)
The pub was created in 1838 when two cottages were combined. A U-shaped bar greets you on entry. Bright patios at the front and rear contrast with the more muted interior, comfortably furnished with tables, chairs and sofas, plus a digital jukebox. A cabinet behind the bar contains several ciders, usually including Westons Old Rosie and Rosie's Pig. The pub is known for its charity fundraising and occasional live music. Separate beer and cider festivals are popular both with locals and beer tourists. P (73,188)

Shefford

Brewery Tap

14 Northbridge Street, SG17 5DH
(01462) 628448
B&T Shefford Bitter; 5 changing beers (sourced nationally; often B&T)
The Tap is primarily a drinkers' pub, offering three B&T beers and three guest ales. Breweriana decorates an open-plan interior divided into two distinct areas, plus a family room at the rear. Lunchtime rolls are available. There is occasional live music or a quiz. The rear patio garden is heated on cool evenings. Car park access is through an archway beside the pub. P

Bridge

50 High Street, SG17 5DG
(01462) 351395
Eagle IPA; 1 changing beer (sourced nationally)
A corner pub next to the site of an old railway bridge, modernised to a high standard. It caters for all ages, with a large rear bar featuring three TV screens and a smaller, quieter front bar. Wednesday is quiz night. New licensees have introduced a choice of changing real ales. Food will be available after a kitchen makeover is completed. Local CAMRA Most Improved Pub 2020.
P

> When you have lost your inns, drown your empty selves, for you will have lost the last of England.
> **Hilaire Belloc, The Four Men, 1912**

Slip End

Rising Sun

1-3 Front Street, LU1 4BP
(01582) 731384 therisingsunslipend.co.uk
3 changing beers (sourced nationally; often Farr Brew)
Comfy two-bar village local, now run by the nearby Wheathampstead brewery Farr Brew following a much-needed complete refurbishment. Two rotating ales from Farr Brew are served plus a range of the brewery's bottles and a changing guest ale. One bar is primarily used as a restaurant where food is served daily. A takeaway pizza service is popular. P

Stanbridge

Five Bells

Station Road, LU7 9JF
(01525) 210224 fivebellsstanbridge.co.uk
Fuller's London Pride; Gale's Seafarers Ale, HSB; 1 changing beer
A Fuller's-owned country pub set in extensive and attractive grounds, with wooden floors, two real fires, a cosy snug and low beams at head height. A separate 80-seater restaurant in the 18th-century wing offers good-quality food and can be used for weddings and other functions. Guest ales are usually from Fuller's/Gale's and may occasionally include one from a local microbrewery. The pub is named after the nearby church which once had five bells – but now has six. P (70)

Totternhoe

Old Farm Inn

16 Church Road, LU6 1RE
(01582) 674053 oldfarminn.co.uk
Fuller's London Pride; Gale's HSB; 2 changing beers
Located in the conservation area of Church End, this charming village pub boasts two inglenooks. The public bar with its low boarded ceiling is where you will find good conversation and traditional pub games. Dogs are welcome in the front bar and there is a child-friendly garden. Quizzes are held on alternate Thursdays. Tasty home-cooked food is served including popular Sunday roasts (no food Mon or Sun eves). Beer festivals are held in May and August. P (61)

Upper Dean

Three Compasses

High Street, PE28 0NE (S of village on road to Melchbourne)
(01234) 708346 thethreecompasses.co.uk
Greene King IPA; St Austell Tribute; Timothy Taylor Landlord
Attractive thatched and partly boarded inn on the southern edge of the village. The main bar is to the left of the entrance with a games area behind. There is a small lounge bar on the right which is used mainly for dining. A large garden is to the rear. Since reopening the pub several years ago, the owners have made great efforts to create a popular rural venue for food and drink. Local CAMRA Most Improved Pub 2019.
P (28)

Woburn

Woburn Ale House 🄻

11 Market Place, MK17 9PZ

☎ (01525) 290142 🌐 woburnalehouse.com

4 changing beers (sourced locally; often Hornes, Leighton Buzzard, Tring) 🄷

Located on Market Place in the historic centre of Woburn, this charming bar, previously a flower shop, has six handpumps for cask ales and two for varying ciders and perries. Local beers feature heavily, in particular from Hornes Brewery and Leighton Buzzard Brewing Company. A wide variety of up to 40 different and interesting artisan keg, canned and bottled beers is also available as well as a broad range of unique wines from around the world. There is comfortable seating towards the rear plus a small courtyard area. ❀♿🍎🚌(49)🐾📶

Wrestlingworth

Chequers 🄻

43 High Street, SG19 2EP

☎ (01767) 631818 🌐 chequersfreehouse.co.uk

Adnams Southwold Bitter; Eagle IPA; 3 changing beers (sourced nationally; often Lacons) 🄷

Popular, friendly, Grade II listed establishment with a spacious interior and several outdoor areas where you can enjoy drinking alfresco when the weather permits. Community groups, a free jukebox, unobtrusive TV sport, live music, cribbage, darts and pétanque teams, well-kept beers and good-value food help make the pub a hub of the village. Ramblers, cyclists, bikers and dogs on leads are all welcome. Outside, there is access to footpaths and bridleways that head westward across east Bedfordshire. 🐎❀◐♣P🚌(188)🐾📶

Castle, Bedford

Public transport information

Leave the car behind and travel to the pub by bus, train, tram or even ferry...

Using public transport is an excellent way to get to the pub, but many people use it irregularly, and systems can be slightly different from place to place. So, below are some useful websites and phone numbers where you can find all the information you might need.

Combined travel information

The national **Traveline** system gives information on all rail and local bus services throughout England, Scotland and Wales. Calls are put through to a local call centre and if necessary your call will be switched through to a more relevant one. There are also services for mobiles, including a next-bus text service and smart-phone app. The website offers other services including timetables and a journey planner with mapping.

- 0871 200 22 33
  www.traveline.info

LONDON

In London use Traveline or **Transport for London (TfL)** travel services. TfL provides information and route planning for all of London's Underground and Overground, Docklands Light Railway, National Rail, buses, River Buses, Tramlink. Detailed ticketing information helps you find the most cost-effective ways to travel.

- 0343 222 1234
  www.tfl.gov.uk

Train travel

National Rail Enquiries covers the whole of Great Britain's rail network and provides service information, ticketing, online journey planning and other information.

- 03457 48 49 50
  www.nationalrail.co.uk

Coach travel

The two main UK coach companies are **National Express** and **Scottish Citylink**. Between them, they serve everywhere from Cornwall to the Highlands. Their websites offer timetables, journey planning, ticketing, route mapping, and other useful information. CAMRA members can benefit from 20% off travel with National Express*. See **camra.org.uk/benefits** for details.

- National Express: 08717 81 81 81
  www.nationalexpress.com
- Scottish Citylink: 0141 352 4444
  www.citylink.co.uk

Megabus

(A Stagecoach Company) operate various long-distance services between major cities and towns in England and Scotland, also Cardiff in Wales.

- 0900 160 0900 (Premium phone line).

Scottish ferries

Caledonian MacBrayne (CalMac) operate throughout Scotland's islands, stretching from Arran in the south to Lewis in the north.

- 0800 066 5000
  www.calmac.co.uk

Northern Ireland & islands

For travel outside mainland Britain but within the area of this Guide, information is available from the following companies:

NORTHERN IRELAND

- Translink: 028 9066 6630
  www.translink.co.uk

ISLE OF MAN

- Isle of Man Transport: 01624 662 525
  www.iombusandrail.info

ISLE OF WIGHT

- Southern Vectus Bus services covering all the Island: 0330 0539 182

JERSEY

- Liberty Bus: 01534 828 555
  www.libertybus.je

GUERNSEY

- Island Coachways: 01481 720 210
  www.buses.gg

Public transport symbols in the Guide

Pub entries in the Guide include helpful symbols to show if there are stations and/or bus routes close to a pub. There are symbols for railway stations (⇌); tram or light rail stations (🚊); London Underground, Overground or DLR stations (⊖); and bus routes (🚌). See the 'Key to symbols' on the inside front cover for more details.

**Membership benefits are subject to change.*

BERKSHIRE

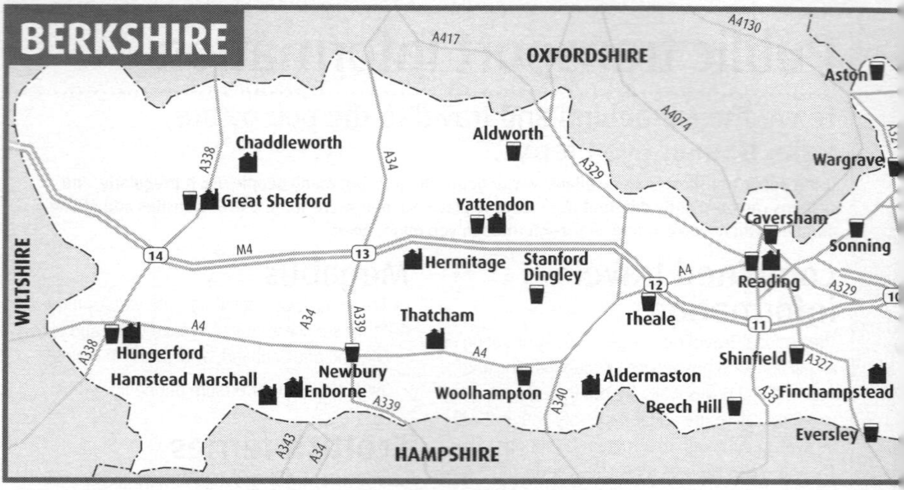

Aldworth

Bell Inn ★ 𝕃

Bell Lane, RG8 9SE (250yds off B4009)
☎ (01635) 578272
Arkell's 3B; Indigenous Baldrick; Rebellion Roasted Nuts; house beer (by West Berkshire); 2 changing beers (sourced locally; often Amwell Springs, Loose Cannon) Ⓗ
A long-standing Guide entry, this traditional inn has been owned by the same family for 250 years, and has been recognised by CAMRA as a having a nationally important historic pub interior. Locals, walkers, cyclists and visitors rub shoulders and share tables to enjoy not only great beer but also an extensive menu of filled rolls, hot soups and proper puddings. Outside is a large, secluded garden. CAMRA National Pub of the Year in 2019.
Q ❀ ◐ ♣ ● P

Aston

Flower Pot

Ferry Lane, RG9 3DG (jct with Renenham Lane)
SU784842
☎ (01491) 574721
Brakspear Gravity; Ringwood Boondoggle; 2 changing beers (sourced nationally) Ⓗ
Charming rural inn set in the heart of the village, close to the River Thames with beautiful views of the countryside. The large, popular garden is a picture in summer, providing a welcoming place to enjoy food and well-kept beers. In the public bar and restaurant you will find an eclectic collection of aquatic taxidermy. Licensees Tony and Pat have been here over 30 years and are Brakspear's longest-serving tenants in a single pub.
Q ❀ ◐ ♿ ♣ ● P

Beech Hill

Elm Tree

Beech Hill Road, RG7 2AZ SU695641
☎ (01189) 883505 🌐 theelmtreebeechhill.co.uk
Ringwood Boondoggle; Timothy Taylor Landlord; 1 changing beer (sourced nationally) Ⓗ
Part pub, part restaurant, the Elm Tree is popular both with locals and visitors from further afield. Diners come to this gastropub to enjoy quality food, but drinkers are equally welcome at the bars. The cosy interior features some lovely murals, a small collection of bells and a real fire. Elaborate decking outside includes palm trees and mood lighting, with spectacular countryside views. The pub may close early on Sunday if quiet. ❀ ◐ ♿ P

Binfield

Binfield Club

Forest Road, RG42 4HP (at mini roundabout jct with Terrace Rd South)
☎ (01344) 420690 🌐 binfieldclub.com
Fuller's London Pride; Sharp's Doom Bar; 2 changing beers (sourced nationally; often Courage, Truman's) Ⓗ
Friendly and welcoming club where CAMRA members are welcome – show your membership card for entry. Its facilities are used by many local organisations and community groups. Four handpumps offer two permanent and two guest beers. Food is served lunchtimes and evenings. Live sport is shown on TV screens and there are pool and snooker tables. The club regularly hosts live music on Friday and Saturday evenings. ❀ ◐ ♣ P (150)

Stag & Hounds 𝕃 ✔

Forest Road, RG42 4HA
☎ (01344) 483553 🌐 thestagandhounds.com
Rebellion IPA; 1 changing beer (sourced locally; often Twickenham) Ⓗ
This Grade II listed, 14th-century building retains many original features and has a real fire in the main bar. It is located at the centre of what was Windsor Forest and, with great walks on the doorstep, is a regular stopping-off point for walkers and cyclists. Two local real ales, one a guest, are on handpump. Food is served all day – diners can eat in the separate restaurant or in the bar area.
❀ ◐ P (150)

Victoria Arms

Terrace Road North, RG42 5JA (100yds S of jct with Tilehurst Lane)
☎ (01344) 483856 🌐 victoriaarmsbinfield.co.uk
Dark Star Hophead; Fuller's London Pride, ESB; 1 changing beer (sourced locally; often Elusive, Rebellion, Stardust) Ⓗ
Welcoming village local at the heart of its community. A real fire keeps it cosy in winter while the terraced garden is popular in summer. The upper walls and beams around

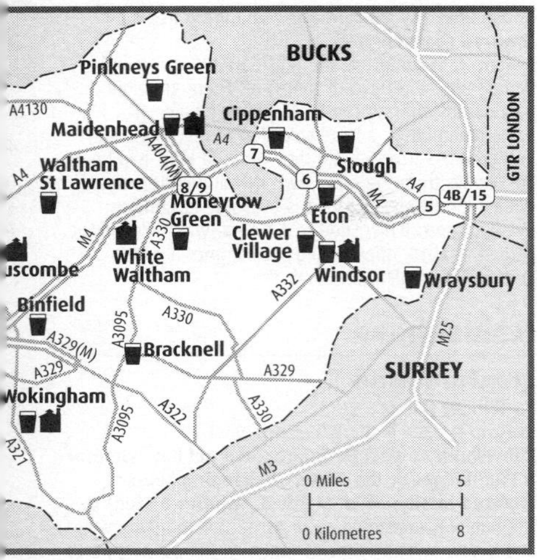

the bar are adorned with hundreds of beer bottles. Quality traditional pub fare is served, with a Sunday roast and children's menu. There is a heated marquee for private functions in the garden and a separate heated smoking area. Fleeces are provided outside on chilly nights. ♘❀◑♣P🚌(150,151)🐾📶

Bracknell

Cannie Man 🄻 ✔

Bywood, RG12 7RF

☎ (01344) 307620 🌐 cannieman.co.uk

Sharp's Doom Bar; 3 changing beers (sourced nationally; often Brains, Dartmoor, West Berkshire) 🄷

A welcoming, friendly estate pub run by a couple who celebrated their 10-year anniversary in 2020. Four handpumps offer a session bitter, a local ale and a selection of guest beers. A true community local, it supports charities and sponsors a local boys' football club. TVs in the large single bar area display a myriad of sporting events and music. Live weekly entertainment features one night over the weekend.
♘❀♣P🚌(171,172) 📶

Old Manor 🄻 ✔

Grenville Place, RG12 1BP (at college roundabout jct with Church Rd)

☎ (01344) 304490

Greene King Abbot; Ruddles Best Bitter; Sharp's Doom Bar; 6 changing beers (sourced nationally; often Binghams, Oakham, Windsor & Eton) 🄷

Featuring in the Guide every year since 2000, this Wetherspoon pub is located in one of the oldest buildings in Bracknell. Tudor origins are obvious, especially the Monk's Room where a priest hole, dating from 1682, can be seen. Two bar areas offer three regular beers and six changing guest ales plus Old Rosie and Black Dragon ciders. With a broad customer mix, the pub gets busy on Friday and Saturday evenings. There are three outside areas to enjoy. Q♘❀◑♿⇌●P🚌(4,53)📶

Caversham

Fox & Hounds 🄻

51 Gosbrook Road, RG4 8BN

☎ (07540) 816293

6 changing beers (sourced nationally; often Oakham, Siren, Wild Weather Ales) 🄷

A regular winner or runner-up local CAMRA Pub of the Year, this place is a popular and lively community hub. It offers eight changing beers, six craft keg lines, six or more ciders and perries, plus a good selection of bottles. A blue plaque commemorates the day in 1960 that John Lennon and Paul McCartney performed a gig here as the Nerk Twins. A quiz night every second Wednesday is always well attended. ♘❀◑♣●P🚌(25,27)🐾📶

Cippenham

Barleycorn 🄻

151 Lower Cippenham Lane, SL1 5DS

☎ (01628) 603115

7 changing beers (sourced nationally) 🄷

Recently refurbished traditional single-bar pub that caters well for a strong local following. Seven guest beers always include one from Rebellion plus a strong ale. The rest are from both national and local breweries, along with a regularly changing real cider plus a choice of fruit ciders. A large collection of bottles and jugs features around the walls. Occasional live music and two sports TVs provide the entertainment. The nearby public car park is free. Q❀♣●P🚌(5)🐾📶

Clewer Village

Swan 🄻

9 Mill Lane, SL4 5JG

☎ 07458 300026 🌐 theswanwindsor.co.uk

Windsor & Eton Guardsman; 2 changing beers (sourced locally; often Windsor & Eton) 🄷

Just 15 minutes' walk from Windsor town centre, this 18th-century village free house has recently been renovated following closure of over three years. Purchased as a community interest company, it has become the hub of the village and now provides board game nights, a knitting circle, quiz nights, occasional music and a book club. Cider offerings include Devon Red from Sandford Orchards and bottles from Crazy Dave's. As renovations are ongoing, at the moment the kitchen can only supply coffee, cakes and the occasional barbecue. Q♘●🚌(71,702) 🐾📶

Eton

George Inn 🄻 ✔

77 High Street, SL4 6AF

☎ (01753) 861797 🌐 georgeinn-eton.co.uk

REAL ALE BREWERIES

Binghams Ruscombe
Bond Brews Wokingham
Butts Great Shefford
Delphic Thatcham (NEW)
Double-Barrelled ◆ Reading
Elusive ◆ Finchampstead
Hermitage Hermitage
Indigenous Chaddleworth
INNformal ▮ Hungerford
New Wharf Maidenhead
Old Windsor Windsor
Saviour ▮ Hamstead Marshall
Siren ◆ Finchampstead
Stardust ◆ White Waltham
Swamp Bog Enborne (NEW)
Two Cocks Enborne
West Berkshire ◆ Yattendon
Wild Weather Aldermaston
Windsor & Eton ◆ Windsor
Zerodegrees ▮ Reading

Windsor & Eton Knight of the Garter, Windsor Knot, Guardsman, Conqueror; 2 changing beers (sourced locally; often Windsor & Eton) Ⓗ
Windsor & Eton's first pub has recently completed a renovation – a new bar hosts six of the brewery's ales, the range subject to change when special or seasonal ales become available. Wooden floors and lighting supplied by carriage lamps and candles help to create a warm, comfortable ambience. Breakfast is served every day. The Hop House, a separate building in the beer garden, is available for private functions. Accommodation is in eight en-suite rooms.
Q🐴❀🛏◐◑⇌●🚌(10) 🐾📶

Eversley

Tally Ho 𝕃
Fleet Hill, RG27 0RR (on A327 jct with B3348)
☎ (01189) 732134 🌐 tallyho-eversley.co.uk
4 changing beers (sourced regionally; often Ascot, Longdog, Red Cat) Ⓗ
Nestling on the Berkshire border with Hampshire, this splendid pub benefits from an extensive riverside garden. Many visitors come to eat in the well-regarded restaurant, but all are free to use the bar area where a good selection of local ales can be found – the house beer is believed to come from St Austell. A changing guest cider is also on handpump. A basket of reading glasses, provided for patrons to borrow, shows the attention to detail here. Q🐴❀◐◑♿P🚌(92)🐾📶

Great Shefford

Great Shefford 𝕃
Newbury Road, RG17 7DS
☎ (01488) 648462 🌐 thegreatshefford.com
West Berkshire Good Old Boy; 5 changing beers (sourced nationally; often Hook Norton, Otter, St Austell) Ⓗ
A recently refurbished 17th-century village inn with several bar and restaurant areas, including a dedicated horse racing lounge with TV. Six cask ales can be found at the bar, complemented by a tempting and eclectic English and European food menu, offering something for everyone. The spacious riverside terrace with an outdoor kitchen is the perfect place to spend a relaxing afternoon. There is a monthly quiz, occasional live music and a beer festival in the summer. A popular stop-off for walkers and cyclists. 🐴❀◐◑♿P🚌(4,4C)🐾📶

Hungerford

Hungerford Club ✔
3 The Croft, RG17 0HY (on foot via Church Lane, by road via Church St and Croft Rd)
☎ (01488) 682357 🌐 hungerford-club.co.uk
Fuller's London Pride; 1 changing beer (sourced nationally) Ⓗ
A warm welcome is assured at this comfortable bowls, tennis and social club, situated in the quiet Croft, just a few yards from the High Street. Games such as billiards and snooker are also played here. A recent refurbishment of the bar area has given the club a fresh look. The changing guest beer, sourced nationally, is often chosen by club members. An annual beer festival is held over the August bank holiday. CAMRA members are welcome. Q🐴❀⇌♣P🚌(3,20)🐾📶

John o' Gaunt 🏆 𝕃 ✔
21 Bridge Street, RG17 0EG (N of canal bridge)
☎ (01488) 683535 🌐 john-o-gaunt-hungerford.co.uk
House beer (by INNformal); 7 changing beers (sourced regionally) Ⓗ
Historic 16th-century Grade II listed town-centre pub named after the Duke of Lancaster. There are eight handpumps offering constantly changing ales, complemented by a large selection of real ciders and bottled beers from around the world. At least two beers are always from the pub's own INNformal Brewery. Quality locally sourced food is available lunchtimes, evenings and all day Sunday. A tiki bar was added in the garden in 2019, open during the summer months.
Q🐴❀◐◑⇌♣●P🚌(3X,20) 🐾📶

Maidenhead

Craufurd Arms 𝕃
15 Gringer Hill, SL6 7LY
☎ (01628) 675410 🌐 craufurdarms.com
Rebellion IPA; West Berkshire Good Old Boy; Windsor & Eton Knight of the Garter; 2 changing beers (sourced locally; often Stardust, Windsor & Eton) Ⓗ
The pub was registered as an Asset of Community Value and is now owned by the community. The building dates back to the late 1800s and was close to Craufurd College, a private school for boys, hence the unusual spelling. The single bar hosts activities including crib on Monday, ladies' darts on Tuesday, gents' darts on Wednesday and a quiz night on Thursday. Two TV screens show Sky and BT sports. Live music features on occasion.
🐴❀⇌♣P🚌(5,8) 🐾📶

Maiden's Head 𝕃
34 High Street, SL6 1QE
☎ (01628) 784786 🌐 themaidenshead.co.uk
4 changing beers (often Rebellion, Stardust) Ⓗ
Large single-room high-street pub offering four constantly rotating guest ales and four keg craft beers (two American), plus Weissbier and Grimbergen Blonde, as well as a range of world bottled beers. Food is served, with a popular roast on Sunday. Outside, there is a large beer garden at the back. Terrestrial TV shows some events. Live music is hosted at the weekend. Dogs are welcome outside. 🐴❀◐◑♿⇌♣🚌📶

Moneyrow Green

White Hart 𝕃 ✔
SL6 2ND
☎ (01628) 621460 🌐 thewhitehartholyport.co.uk
Greene King IPA; 3 changing beers Ⓗ
A welcoming, traditional pub half a mile south of the village. The guest beers include one LocAle and two ales not from Greene King. The wood-panelled lounge features leather sofas and log fires in winter. The larger public bar has wooden flooring, a TV and traditional pub games including bar billiards. There is a quiz night on Monday and open mic on the second Tuesday of the month. Outside is a large fenced beer garden with a pétanque pitch and children's play area.
🐴❀◐◑♣P🚌(53) 🐾📶

Newbury

Catherine Wheel 𝕃
35 Cheap Street, RG14 5DB
☎ (01635) 569897 🌐 thecatherinewheel.com
West Berkshire Good Old Boy; 5 changing beers (sourced nationally; often Binghams, Long Man, Wild Weather Ales) Ⓗ
Refurbished in 2014, this town-centre pub has been growing in popularity. It serves a selection of beers from six handpumps and stocks over 100 UK and international

bottled beers. The covered courtyard is home to the gin yard. Many ciders are available – the pub is a multiple winner of the local CAMRA branch Cider Pub of the Year award. The food menu is based around Pieminister pies, but the skillets are worth a try as well. A children's menu is also available. ➳✿❍▷≉♣●🍺🖵(2,3)❀🦆

Cow & Cask 🅛
1 Inches Yard, Market Street, RG14 5DP (SE of pedestrian crossing at corner of Market St and Bartholomew St)
☎ (07517) 658071 ⊕ cowandcask.co.uk
3 changing beers (sourced regionally; often Loddon, Loose Cannon, XT) 🄶
The small size of Berkshire's first micropub helps to create a friendly atmosphere where conversation flourishes. A large blackboard lists the range of drinks on offer and the number of different beers served since 2014. Three locally sourced real ales are usually available on stillage, along with three or four real ciders from bag-in-box containers. Snacks include pork pies, cheese rolls, crisps and nuts. Crib is often played on Tuesday evening. The pub is near the town's station, cinema and car parks.
Q≉♣●🖵(2) 🦆

Hatchet Inn 🅛 ✪
12 Market Place, RG14 5BD
☎ (01635) 277560
Greene King Abbot; Ruddles Best Bitter; Sharp's Doom Bar; 5 changing beers (sourced nationally; often Loddon, Ramsbury, Two Cocks) 🄷
This Grade II listed Wetherspoon hotel overlooks the pedestrianised Market Place. Since opening in 2011, a dining area extension has added considerable extra space. There is also plenty of seating outside at the front and rear, which is popular all year, especially when the sun shines. Ales are served from two sets of handpumps positioned at each end of the bar, with boxed real cider in the fridge behind. Regular Wetherspoon beer and cider festivals are held. Food is available daily.
Q➳✿⇴◁▷♿≉●P🖵(2,3) 🦆

King Charles Tavern 🅛 ✪
54 Cheap Street, RG14 5BX
☎ (01635) 36695 ⊕ kctavern.com
West Berkshire Good Old Boy; house beer (by Greene King); 6 changing beers (sourced nationally) 🄷
Over 100 years old and a former CAMRA branch Pub of the Year, this tavern is a three-minute walk from Newbury train station. It has a central bar with the cellar directly below. Eight ales are offered, all meticulously kept and available in third-pints for those who want to sample a selection. Fresh home-made food is served, with Sunday lunch a speciality. The front rooms have open fires and a mixture of sofas and chairs. Note the old map of Newbury on the ceiling. ➳✿❍▷≉🖵(2,3)❀🦆

Lock, Stock & Barrel
104 Northbrook Street, RG14 1AA (alley 20m NW of canal bridge)
☎ (01635) 580550 ⊕ lockstockandbarrelnewbury.co.uk
Fuller's London Pride; 4 changing beers (sourced regionally; often Dark Star, Fuller's) 🄷
Centrally located and situated next to the Kennet and Avon canal, this is a popular, traditional pub with a comfortably furnished open-plan interior. There is plenty of outside seating, including a roof terrace. Beers are selected from the Fuller's range including Gales and Dark Star. Traditional pub food is freshly cooked to order by the chef. There is regular live music and families are welcome until 9pm. Dog biscuits and blankets are provided. ➳✿❍▷♿≉🖵(4,4A)❀🦆

Pinkneys Green

Boundary Arms 🅛
112 Pinkneys Road, SL6 5DN
☎ (01628) 629667
Rebellion IPA, Roasted Nuts; 1 changing beer 🄷
This large independent pub opposite the green has recently been refurbished. It has two bars, both with real fires. The public bar is at the front and a pleasant lounge bar at the back, with doors out to the garden where there is a secure children's play area. There are also a couple of tables at the front where you can watch the world go by. Q➳✿♣P🖵(9)❀🦆

Reading

Alehouse 🅛
2 Broad Street, RG1 2BH
☎ (01189) 508119
9 changing beers (sourced nationally; often West Berkshire) 🄷
Popular drinking establishment which always leaves an impression on visitors with its quirky wooden fixtures and reclaimed wooden floor. As a champion of microbreweries, both local and further afield, rare and unusual ales are frequently found on the pumps. A selection of real ciders and perries is also available. Often busy around the bar area, those wishing for a more peaceful drink can take advantage of the secluded snugs at the back of the pub. ➳≉♣●🖵🖵(4,X4)❀

Allied Arms 🅛
57 St Mary's Butts, RG1 2LG
☎ (01189) 583323 ⊕ allied-arms.co.uk
Loddon Hullabaloo; 9 changing beers (sourced regionally) 🄷
A town-centre pub dating from around 1828, with two cosy bars entered through the side passage, not the front door. An enhanced range of up to 10 ales is available each weekend. The large walled garden is a popular refuge from the chaos of the town, with patio heaters for colder nights. A wide and interesting selection of music is available on the jukebox. The pub hosts a regular charity quiz. ➳✿≉●🖵❀🦆

Butler 🅛
85-91 Chatham Street, RG1 7DS
☎ (01189) 595500 ⊕ thebutlerreading.co.uk
St Austell Proper Job; Timothy Taylor Landlord; West Berkshire Mister Chubb's; 2 changing beers (sourced regionally) 🄷
Named after Butler's Wine Merchants, who operated from these premises many years ago, this is very much a local pub in the heart of town. Taken over by a consortium after a long period of Fuller's stewardship, there has been an ongoing process of upgrading both inside and out. Ales are from regional and local breweries, including some unusual choices for the area. Live music is a weekly feature and draws large crowds. ➳✿❍◁≉♣P🖵(15,16) 🦆🦆

Castle Tap 🅛
120 Castle Street, RG1 7RJ
☎ (01189) 580473 ⊕ thecastletap.co.uk
4 changing beers (sourced nationally) 🄷
Alongside its changing selection of real ales and ciders, the Castle Tap boasts an excellent range of bottled and canned beers. While offering a warm welcome to visiting real ale aficionados and craft beer fans, it maintains a friendly local atmosphere. Frequent live music and other events are well worth checking out. And for those feeling peckish, cheeseboards are available. The back room can be booked for functions. ➳✿❍●P🖵(1,2)❀🦆

Fisherman's Cottage 𝕃

224 Kennet Side, RG1 3DW
☎ (01189) 560432 🌐 thefishermanscottagereading.co.uk
4 changing beers (sourced nationally; often Siren, Wild Weather Ales) 🄷
A thriving free house on the towpath of the River Kennet. The ale range includes two national beers, a changing selection on six keg taps, and a large choice of bottled and canned beers. The menu is based around tapas and paella, and includes a good selection of vegetarian and vegan dishes. The garden is a summer delight, including beach hut-style seating. ᘎ❀◐◑♣●P🐾📶

Greyfriar 𝕃

53 Greyfriars Road, RG1 1PA
☎ (01189) 580560 🌐 thegreyfriarreading.co.uk
Hogs Back HBB; 7 changing beers (sourced nationally; often Elusive, Siren, Wild Weather Ales) 🄷
A modern-looking yet traditional pub with eight handpumps and 14 keg lines, offering an impressive choice of beers from independent breweries. Bottled and canned beers also come from country-wide and foreign suppliers. Tap takeovers by various brewers are held on occasion. A small range of paninis is available. A regular quiz night is held every other Monday. Convenient for the railway station and popular with the after-work crowd. ᘎ◐⇌♣🚌(3,8)🐾📶

Nag's Head 𝕃

5 Russell Street, RG1 7XD
☎ (07765) 880137 🌐 thenagsheadreading.co.uk
12 changing beers (sourced nationally) 🄷
With a wide range of real ales, real cider and perry always on offer, visitors are sure to find something to their taste here. There is also a craft beer wall, with vessel and dispense clearly indicated on the adjacent blackboard. A selection of board games is available for those wanting to while away a few sociable hours. The pub gets busy on Reading FC match days. A regular in CAMRA's National Pub of the Year awards.
ᘎ❀◐◑⇌(West) ♣●P🚌(1,2) 🐾📶

Park House (University of Reading) 𝕃

Park House, Whiteknights Campus, RG6 6UR
☎ (01183) 785098
5 changing beers (sourced nationally; often Rebellion, Siren, Titanic) 🄷
The university's old senior common room is open to the public from midday during term time and over the Christmas and Easter vacations. Five ales, mostly local, are usually sold. The bar is popular with the more mature university community and can get busy in the early evening. The large outdoor seating area is perfect for a quiet drink in the evening sun. A regular bus service drops off inside the campus. Note, the bar is cashless.
Qᘎ❀◐◑♿♣●🚌(21,21A) 🐾📶

Retreat

8 St John's Street, RG1 4EH
☎ (01183) 769159 🌐 theretreat.pub
6 changing beers (sourced nationally; often Butcombe, Harvey's, Sharp's) 🄷
A well-loved back-street boozer with a traditional layout and feel. A wide selection of real ales is squeezed into the small bar. The landlord tends to concentrate on well-known regional brands; however, there is a good range of more eclectic choices available in bottles, as well as a number of ciders. The pub is locally renowned for regular live music and hosting community events. A popular quiz night is held every second Wednesday of the month.
Qᘎ♣🚌(4,13) 🐾

Shinfield

Magpie & Parrot

Arborfield Road, RG2 9EA (on A327 E of village)
☎ (01189) 884130
Fuller's London Pride 🄷
A delightful pub in a rural setting, just past the eastern edge of the village. The cosy interior has been expanded – there are now two small, quiet rooms, both festooned with an eclectic selection of memorabilia. A small food menu is available weekday lunchtimes – it is advisable to book for the popular fish and chips on Friday. Opening hours are limited so check ahead to avoid disappointment. Qᘎ❀◐◑●P🚌(3)🐾📶

Slough

Moon & Spoon 𝕃 ✔

86 High Street, SL1 1EL
☎ (01753) 531650
Greene King Abbot; Ruddles Best Bitter; Sharp's Doom Bar; 4 changing beers 🄷
This Wetherspoon establishment has 12 handpumps offering three regulars beers accompanied by up to four constantly changing guest ales, always including one from a local brewery. A couple of ciders are also usually available, often Old Rosie and Black Dragon. At the entrance is an eye-catching sculpture made of 1,148 spoons. The usual Wetherspoon extensive all-day food menu is served. Soft lighting gives the pub a cosy feel, especially at quieter times. ᘎ◐◑♿⇌●🚌(8,2)📶

Sonning

Bull Inn

High Street, RG4 6UP (next to St Andrew's Church)
☎ (01189) 693901 🌐 bullinnsonning.co.uk
Fuller's London Pride; Gale's HSB; 3 changing beers (sourced nationally; often Butcombe, Dark Star, Fuller's) 🄷
Full of character, this delightful 16th-century pub is leased to Fuller's by the adjacent church. Most of the interior is set for dining, but there is a separate Village Bar drinking area, also used as a function room. The regular beers and changing guests are mainly from the Fuller's range. An excellent selection of quality food, from snacks to fine dining, is available seven days a week. A good stop-off for those taking a walk alongside the Thames. Qᘎ❀🛏◐◑P🚌(129)🐾📶

Stanford Dingley

Old Boot Inn 𝕃

RG7 6LT (100yds SW of jct with Cock Lane)
☎ (01189) 745191 🌐 oldbootinnstanforddingley.co.uk
Two Cocks 1643 Cavalier; West Berkshire Mister Chubb's, Good Old Boy; 1 changing beer (sourced locally; often Enbourne, Swamp Bog) 🄷
Welcoming 18th-century inn that is popular with locals and visitors alike. The main bar has exposed beams and is divided into two areas, both with fires during the winter months. There is also a dining room, conservatory and large garden. Seating at the tables includes traditional bar stools and comfortable chairs. The pub runs regular quizzes, games evenings and singalongs, and screens international sporting events. Cask beers are all from local breweries. ᘎ❀🛏◐◑♿P🐾📶

Theale

Bull

41 High Street, RG7 5AH (at jct with Brewery Court)

☎ (01189) 303478 🌐 thebullattheale.co.uk
Wadworth Henry's IPA, 6X; 2 changing beers (sourced nationally) Ⓗ
Originally the brewery tap of Blatch of Theale, many of the brewery buildings have been preserved and can be viewed through the car park or the ivy-clad entrance further up the road. Now a Wadworth tied house, the pub was refurbished a couple of years ago and is a comfortable family-friendly establishment. There is a function room bookable for social occasions. A number of TV screens show sporting events.
P(1)

Waltham St Lawrence

Bell

The Street, RG10 0JJ (at jct with Milley Rd)
☎ (01189) 341788 🌐 thebellwalthamstlawrence.co.uk
Loddon Hoppit; 4 changing beers (sourced locally; often Binghams, Butts, Stardust) Ⓗ
A classic half-timbered 15th-century pub bequeathed to the village in 1608 by Sir Ralph Newbury. It serves as both the village local and a quality restaurant, producing exceptionally good food from fresh, seasonal ingredients and promoting real ales from small, independent breweries. Up to eight ciders and perries are served from the cellar. You will find log fires in the winter and a good-sized beer garden for sunny summer days.
Q(4A)

Wargrave

Wargrave & District Snooker Club

Woodclyffe Hostel, Church Street, RG10 8EP
🌐 wargravesnooker.co.uk
2 changing beers (sourced nationally) Ⓗ
The club opens weekday evenings only and shares the building with the local library. The regularly changing beers reflect members' recommendations, with two on in the winter months and one in the summer. The TV's default is off, though the Six Nations Rugby and World Cup are exceptions. Visitors may show this Guide or CAMRA membership card for entry (£3 fee to use the snooker tables). Winner of CAMRA branch Club of the Year for several years. (850)

Windsor

A Hoppy Place

11 St Leonards Road, SL4 3BN
☎ (01753) 206802 🌐 ahoppyplace.co.uk
2 changing beers (sourced locally; often Binghams) Ⓗ
Windsor's first micropub offers two casks, 10 keg lines and five fridges full of bottled and canned beers, with a focus both on local and international brews. The fridges are arranged by beer style, plus another fridge for cider, including Crazy Dave's. The pub has a canning machine to can cask and keg beer for a takeaway while you wait. The premises can also be used for tutored tasting events or private functions.
(Windsor & Eton Central)

Acre

Donnelly House, Victoria Street, SL4 1EN
☎ (01753) 841083 🌐 theacrewindsor.com
Windsor & Eton Guardsman; 2 changing beers Ⓗ
Formerly the Liberal Club, now a free house open to all. The name refers to the adjacent Bachelors Acre. Three ales are on offer, with Windsor & Eton's Guardsman a permanent feature and two regularly changing guests, often from local breweries. Freshly made rolls, pies and pasties are available daily. Live music is hosted every Saturday night. Two screens show live sporting events and there are excellent facilities for darts. Now with a cellar bar. (2)

Carpenters Arms

4 Market Street, SL4 1PB
☎ (01753) 863739
Fuller's London Pride; St Austell Nicholson's Pale Ale; Sharp's Doom Bar; 5 changing beers (sourced nationally) Ⓗ
Situated on a narrow cobbled street close to the castle, this excellent Nicholson's pub has been voted local CAMRA Pub of the Year several times. The elegantly decorated interior is on three levels, the lowest of which is reputed to house a passageway to the castle. Ashby's Brewery tiles are on the floor by the entrance, harking back to the pub's former owners. The three regular beers are supplemented by five interesting guests, usually including something dark.
(Windsor & Eton Central) (8,702)

Corner House

22 Sheet Street, SL4 1BG
☎ (01753) 862031 🌐 thecornerhousepub.co.uk
Big Smoke Solaris Session Pale Ale; 9 changing beers Ⓗ
This Grade II listed building was completely refurbished in a traditional style by new owners in 2017 and designated as an ale and cider house. Fifteen handpumps serve 10 regularly changing real ales, five ciders and 10 keg lines. A good selection of traditional pub food is available. The pub has a function room upstairs and a small, partly covered roof terrace for those wishing to savour the air. Quiz night is Monday.
(Windsor & Eton Central) (8,702)

Windsor & Eton Brewery Tap Room

1 Vansittart Estate, Duke Street, SL4 1SE
☎ (01753) 854075 🌐 webrew.co.uk
6 changing beers (sourced locally; often Windsor & Eton) Ⓗ
Launched in 2016, the taproom offers seven cask beers and seven keg beers. Uprising keg beers are available and one keg line may be used for cider. Tasting trays are served with three third-pints, for those who wish to try a selection, and the brewery's bottled beers, including some vintage ones, are available to take away. The brewery can be viewed from the bar and there are regular tours – see the website for details.
(Windsor & Eton Central) P(2,8)

Windsor Trooper

97 St Leonards Road, SL4 3BZ
☎ (01753) 670122 🌐 thewindsortrooper.com
Adnams Southwold Bitter; 5 changing beers (sourced nationally) Ⓗ
Large recently refurbished open-plan bar on the edge of the town centre. It offers up to five cask beers plus a number of kegs. The house beer is Windsor Trooper Ale brewed by Caledonian. Pub food is served to accompany the beer. Major sporting events are shown and there is live music on Saturday. The pub has a large conservatory to the rear which is also used as a function room and is available to hire. Accommodation is in nine en-suite rooms. (Windsor & Eton Central)

Wokingham

Crispin

45 Denmark Street, RG40 2AY (opp Denmark St car park)

☎ (01189) 780309 🌐 crispinpub.co.uk
Hogs Back TEA; 4 changing beers (sourced regionally; often Binghams, Rebellion, Siren) Ⓗ
A long-established real ale and cider pub named after St Crispin, the patron saint of cobblers, hence the pub sign. Up to five real ales are available, including many local ones, plus ciders from Tutts Clump and Westons. No food is served but you can bring your own or order in a takeaway. The pleasant garden includes an Aunt Sally pitch and a gazebo. Seasonal beer and cider festivals are held here. Local CAMRA Pub of the Year 2019.
❀⇌♣●⊡🚌(4,X4) 🐾ᯤ

Crooked Billet ✔
Honey Hill, RG40 3BJ
☎ (01189) 780438 🌐 crookedbilletwokingham.co.uk
Brakspear Gravity; Young's London Special; 1 changing beer (sourced nationally; often Wychwood) Ⓗ
Cosy white weatherboard countryside pub situated between Wokingham and Crowthorne. The bar area has a stripped timber floor with comfortable sofas, mismatched furniture and a log fire. A light food menu offers a range of simple bar snacks, while the separate restaurant provides informal dining with options for children. Entertainment includes a weekly quiz night on Wednesday, darts and traditional board games. Dogs are welcome in the bar, with treats available.
Q🐴❀◐◑♣P🐾

Queen's Head Ⓛ ✔
23 The Terrace, RG40 1BP
☎ (01189) 781221 🌐 queensheadwokingham.co.uk
Greene King Yardbird, Abbot; Hogs Back TEA; Loddon Ferryman's Gold; house beer (by Hardys & Hansons); 1 changing beer (sourced locally; often Binghams, Stardust) Ⓗ
Grade II listed 15th-century cruck-framed inn nestling in a terrace close to the station. The characterful single bar has low ceilings, timber floors and a log fire. It is home to a darts team and hosts numerous charity events. As a Greene King Local Hero pub, three local ales are available alongside three from the brewery. Beer paddles with three third-pints are offered to sample a selection. The attractive rear patio and garden are pleasant in summer. Children are welcome until 8pm.
❀⇌♣🚌(4,X4) 🐾ᯤ

Ship Inn 🏆
104 Peach Street, RG40 1XH (jct with London Rd)
☎ (01189) 780389 🌐 shipwokingham.co.uk
Fuller's ESB, London Pride, Oliver's Island; 1 changing beer (sourced regionally) Ⓗ
A large establishment with three bars on the edge of the town centre. A long-established Fuller's pub, it gets busy at weekends and in the summer, particularly when rugby is on TV. Quality food is served lunchtimes, evenings and throughout the day Friday to Sunday. The pub has a strong community focus and runs a loneliness initiative offering free tea, coffee and a chat to senior citizens in the morning. Local CAMRA Community Pub of the Year.
🐴❀◐◑P🚌(4,X4) 🐾ᯤ

Woolhampton

Rowbarge Ⓛ
Station Road, RG7 5SH
☎ (01189) 712213
House beer (by St Austell); 5 changing beers (sourced nationally; often Delphic, Indigenous, Timothy Taylor) Ⓗ
Probably the most accessible country pub in Berkshire, where you can be sure of a warm welcome whether you arrive by foot, car, bike, boat, train or bus. There are six ales on tap and as many separate areas for drinking, dining or just relaxing in front of a real fire. In fine weather enjoy the large garden, adjacent to the River Kennet, where an annual summer ale & cider festival takes place. Q🐴❀◐◑♿⇌(Midgham)♣●P🚌(1)🐾ᯤ

Wraysbury

Perseverance ✔
2 High Street, TW19 5DB
☎ (01784) 482375 🌐 thepercy.co.uk
Otter Ale; 3 changing beers Ⓗ
Comfortable pub with several seating areas. The larger front room has soft sofas, a piano and a large inglenook fireplace, with a real log fire. Another seating area with an open fire leads to the rear dining area, which has well-stocked bookshelves. The rear garden is delightful. Three guest ales are always varied and from some of the more interesting breweries, both LocAle and around the country. Regular beer festivals are held. Quiz night is Thursday and live music features on Sunday afternoon.
Q🐴❀◐◑♣●P🚌(10,305) 🐾ᯤ

Yattendon

Taproom & Kitchen at West Berkshire Brewery Ⓛ
The Old Dairy, RG18 0XT (signed from Chapel Lane)
☎ (01635) 767090 🌐 wbbrew.com
West Berkshire Mister Chubb's, Maggs' Mild, Mister Swift, Good Old Boy, Maharaja IPA; 5 changing beers (sourced locally; often Amwell Springs, Loose Cannon, West Berkshire) Ⓗ
Situated at the side of the brewery, the Taproom & Kitchen occupies a cavernous room which is well patronised and successful. The bar showcases West Berkshire Brewery beers alongside regular guest ales. Many events are held here including brewery tours, quiz nights, films, live music, tap takeovers, live sport and the Tryanuary and OktoberWest beer festivals. There is a large seating area outside, close to a bridleway, and walkers with dogs are welcome. 🐴❀◐◑♿●P🐾ᯤ

Choosing pubs

CAMRA members and branches choose the pubs listed in the Good Beer Guide. There is no payment for entry, and pubs are inspected on a regular basis by personal visits; publicans are not sent a questionnaire once a year, as is the case with some pub guides. CAMRA branches monitor all the pubs in their areas, and the choice of pubs for the guide is often the result of democratic vote at branch meetings. However, recommendations from readers are welcomed and will be passed on to the relevant branch: write to Good Beer Guide, CAMRA, 230 Hatfield Road, St Albans, Hertfordshire, AL1 4LW; or send an email to: **gbgeditor@camra.org.uk**

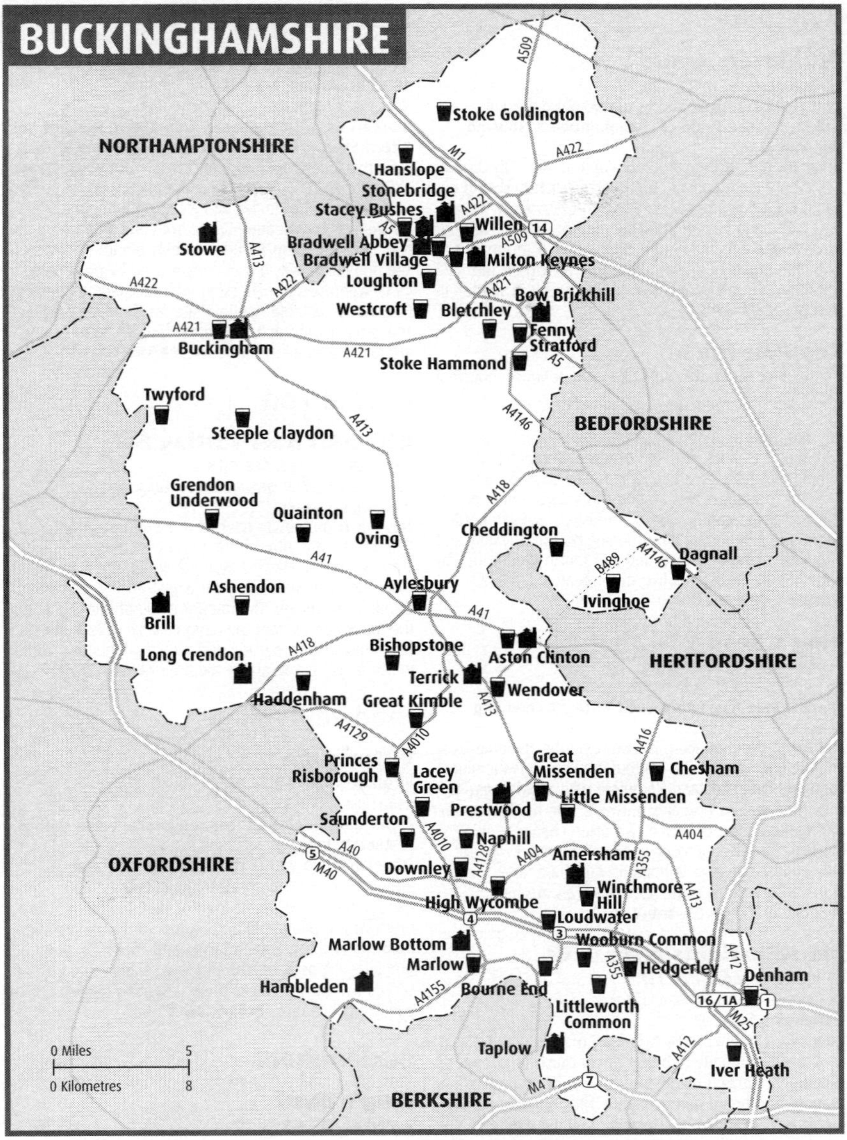

Ashendon

Hundred of Ashendon 🄻

Lower End, HP18 0HE

☎ (01296) 651296 🌐 thehundred.co.uk

2 changing beers (sourced locally; often Tring, Vale) 🄷

Nestling in the countryside, this family-run 17th-century inn is attractively decorated throughout, with an area dedicated to dining. The menu, which changes daily, offers local and seasonal dishes. There are fine views from the beer garden. Dogs, muddy boots and children are all welcome. The pub is close to the National Trust property of Waddesdon Manor and has five beautifully furnished B&B rooms for those wishing to explore the local area. **Q❀🛏◑P🐾ᯤ**

Aston Clinton

Oak ✔

119 Green End Street, HP22 5EU

☎ (01296) 630466 🌐 oakastonclinton.co.uk

Fuller's London Pride; 1 changing beer (often Fuller's) 🄷

Characterful 500-year-old inn with a large, pleasant L-shaped bar with low beams, an inglenook fireplace, wooden floor and plenty of seating. The tiled area to the left has the feel of a public bar, full of local characters and chitchat. Food is freshly prepared using locally sourced ingredients where possible. The family-friendly pub boasts an extensive beer garden with a children's play area and attractive, leafy trees in season.
❀◑♿P🚌(500,61) 🐾ᯤ

Aylesbury

Bricklayers Arms
Walton Terrace, HP21 7QY
☎ (01296) 482930 🌐 bricklayersarmsaylesbury.co.uk
Fuller's London Pride; 2 changing beers (sourced regionally) Ⓗ
Originally part of the hamlet of Walton, this 17th-century inn is on a crossroads around the corner from Walton pond, once a centre for breeding the famous Aylesbury ducks. The pub has an attractive timber-beamed interior on several levels, with a function room at the rear. A large fire provides a warm welcome in winter; the sizeable enclosed beer garden at the back is a suntrap in summer. ❀◑⇌P🚌

Hop Pole Inn Ⓛ
83 Bicester Road, HP19 9AZ (near Gatehouse industrial area)
☎ (01296) 482129
10 changing beers Ⓗ
Well worth a short stroll out of the town centre, this temple of beer regularly sports 10 cask ales including three or four guest ales among the Vale Brewery beers. There is also a good range of – mostly – Belgian bottled beers. The pub hosts a long-running quiz on Tuesday and a ukulele night on the second and fourth Wednesday of each month. Occasional live music features at the weekend. ❀◑●🚌🐾📶

King's Head 🏆 Ⓛ
Market Square, HP20 2RW
☎ (01296) 718812 🌐 farmersbar.co.uk
Chiltern Pale Ale, Beechwood Bitter; 2 changing beers Ⓗ
This magnificent building is owned by the National Trust and the bar is run by the Chiltern Brewery. It is the oldest courtyard inn in England, complete with cobbles, and the converted stables occupies one side. The bar has up to four Chiltern ales, of which two often change, and a guest beer – often a stout or porter in winter. A cider is also usually available. A helpful chalkboard notes current beers and those to come. Beer festivals are held periodically. Q🏇❀◑♿⇌●🚌📶

Old Millwrights Arms Ⓛ ✔
83 Walton Road, HP21 7SN
☎ (01296) 488161 🌐 barrelandstone.co.uk
7 changing beers Ⓗ
Now a firm fixture on the Aylesbury real ale circuit, this is a vibrant community pub that offers much to interest allcomers including open mic, comedy, Dungeons & Dragons and board games nights. The Thursday night quiz is well attended. A selection of up to seven real ales and two ciders plus occasional tap takeovers help make the pub a popular venue. 🏇❀◑♿⇌●P🚌🐾

Bishopstone

Harrow Ⓛ
27 Main Street, HP17 8SF
☎ (01296) 748478 🌐 theharrowbishopstone.co.uk
Chiltern Beechwood Bitter; Vale Gravitas; 1 changing beer (sourced locally; often Chiltern) Ⓗ
Established in 1837, this lovely village pub has been reopened by local owners following a long closure. Now sympathetically renovated and extended, it retains the character of the original building and has a distinct bar area displaying stone flags combined with vintage-style industrial lighting. There is a large area for dining, and a central open fire adds warmth in season. Outside is an attractive garden area. Beers are from local breweries. 🏇❀◑♿P🐾📶

Bletchley

Captain Ridley's Shooting Party ✔
183 Queensway, MK2 2ED
☎ (01908) 621020
Adnams Broadside; Greene King Abbot; Ruddles Best Bitter; Sharp's Doom Bar; 8 changing beers Ⓗ
A Wetherspoon, opened after complete renovation and extension in 2017, with 12 handpumps. The ground floor comprises one large bar with seating throughout. Outside, there is seating at the front and a garden to the rear. Entertainment includes weekly bingo and quizzes. The pub name was a pseudonym used by MI6 agents in 1938 when secretly checking whether nearby Bletchley Park was a suitable wartime site for the code breakers. This provides the pub theme, with many pictures and artefacts celebrating them. 🏇❀◑♿⇌P🚌(1)📶

Bourne End

KEG Craft Beer Tasting Bar
12 Oakfield Road, SL8 5QN
☎ (01628) 529369 🌐 kegcraftbeer.co.uk
2 changing beers
This micropub, newly opened in 2016, goes from strength to strength, offering two cask ales and seven craft keg beers. Named after its owner Kim E Georgiou, the small and welcoming bar is just off the main road through the village. The interior is full of bric-a-brac and the music comes from the patron's vinyl collection. There is limited seating outside and a car park nearby. Well worth a visit if you are in the area. ⇌●🚌(36)🐾📶

Bradwell Village

Victoria Inn
Vicarage Road, MK13 9AQ
☎ (01908) 312769
4 changing beers (sourced regionally; often Hornes, St Austell, Vale) Ⓗ
Stone-built pub with a comfortable and relaxed atmosphere. As you enter, the bar with its four handpumps is directly in front of you. To the right is a room with a pool table and dartboard; to the left is a room on two levels with tables and chairs, an open fireplace, exposed beams and low ceilings. Food is served five days a week. There is seating outside on the paved front terrace. 🏇◑♣🚌🐾📶

Buckingham

King's Head
7 Market Hill, MK18 1JX

REAL ALE BREWERIES

Abington Buckingham
Bad Joke Amersham
Blackened Sun ✎ Milton Keynes: Stacey Bushes
Blackpit ✎ Stowe
Brewhouse & Kitchen ▮ Milton Keynes
Bucks Star ✎ Milton Keynes: Stonebridge
Chiltern ✎ Terrick
Concrete Cow Milton Keynes: Bradwell Abbey
Haresfoot Aston Clinton
Hornes ✎ Milton Keynes: Bow Brickhill
Malt ✎ Prestwood
moogBREW ✎ Taplow
Old Luxters Hambleden
Rebellion Marlow Bottom
Vale Brill
XT ✎ Long Crendon

☎ (01280) 812442 🌐 thekingsheadcoffeebar.com
Purity Pure UBU; 1 changing beer (often Towcester Mill) Ⓗ
The King's Head reopened in 2016 after a second refurbishment in 12 months and is now established as a coffee house that also serves cocktails, gin, beer and draught cider. A pleasant and relaxed venue, seating includes comfortable settees as well as chairs and tables. Breakfast, lunch and evening menus are available, with food ranging from fresh pastries and muffins to pies and burgers. The good-sized and well-appointed patio garden can be a suntrap in summer.

Mitre
2 Mitre Street, MK18 1DW
☎ (01280) 813080 🌐 themitrepub.co.uk
Blackpit Day Tripper; Harvey's Sussex Best Bitter; 3 changing beers (sourced nationally; often Kelham Island, North Cotswold, Thornbridge) Ⓗ
Buckingham's oldest pub is a 15-minute walk from the town centre. The cosy atmosphere is enhanced by an open fire in winter. A free house, it offers changing and interesting beers, often featuring guests from local breweries such as Blackpit. Attractions include darts and board games, plus books that can be borrowed from the shelves. Five large-screen TVs show major events. The pub hosts live music once or twice monthly plus wine and whisky tasting events. Parking is on the street. Local CAMRA Pub of the Year 2020. P

Woolpack
57 Well Street, MK18 1EP
☎ (01280) 817972
St Austell Tribute; Sharp's Doom Bar; 2 changing beers (sourced nationally; often Brains, Otter) Ⓗ
A short walk from the town centre, this busy, nicely modernised pub retains many old features. It has a separate function room and a large riverside garden. Four handpumps serve two regular beers and two guests. Beer festivals add more choice from time to time. Freshly cooked food features local produce where possible. Children are welcome in the large back room and the garden. Parking nearby can be difficult.
Q (X60,X5)

Cheddington

Old Swan
58 High Street, LU7 0RQ
☎ (01296) 662171 🌐 theoldswancheddington.co.uk
Fuller's London Pride; house beer (by XT); 3 changing beers (sourced nationally) Ⓗ
A 16th-century Grade II listed freehouse, it's a 10-minute walk from the Grand Union Canal and a 30-minute walk from the Ridgeway Path and Ashridge Estate. Two wood-burning stoves and low beams contribute to the pub's traditional atmosphere. There are several dining areas – good food featuring locally sourced ingredients is served daily except Sunday evening. Cheddington railway station is a 15-minute walk. P(164)

Chesham

Queen's Head
120 Church Street, HP5 1JD
☎ (01494) 778690 🌐 queensheadchesham.co.uk
Brakspear Gravity; Fuller's London Pride, ESB; 2 changing beers (sourced regionally; often Dark Star, Fuller's) Ⓗ
An atmospheric 18th-century pub in Chesham's oldest neighbourhood, next to the River Chess. It is divided into several areas including a cosy public bar with real fires and an impressive library of beer books. A popular quiz is held on Thursday night and live sporting events are screened. Authentic Thai cuisine is served in the pub and separate restaurant upstairs. Beers are mainly drawn from the extended Fuller's range, with guests often from Dark Star and Gale's. QP

Dagnall

Red Lion
21 Main Road North, HP4 1QZ
☎ (01442) 843020 🌐 theredliondagnall.co.uk
Sharp's Doom Bar; Tring Side Pocket for a Toad; 2 changing beers (sourced nationally; often 3 Brewers, Adnams, Tring) Ⓗ
A warm welcome awaits at this relaxing and friendly free house, with two roaring real fires in winter. The pub offers well-kept beers and freshly prepared home-made food using local produce. The rear dining room, with paintings by local artists, has a cosy atmosphere. In summer, families, cyclists and dogs enjoy the newly planted garden. Quiz night every second Monday, curry night on Tuesday and fish Friday are always popular.
QP

Denham

Falcon Inn
Village Road, UB9 5BE
☎ (01895) 832125 🌐 falcondenham.com
Harviestoun Bitter & Twisted; St Austell Proper Job; Timothy Taylor Landlord; 1 changing beer (sourced regionally; often Adnams, Hop Back, St Austell) Ⓗ
Small one-bar 16th-century pub in Denham Village conservation area, overlooking the village green. The entrance is via interesting old steps straight off the road. There is a lovely sunny garden to the rear. Good food is served lunchtimes and evenings, with bar snacks as well as a restaurant menu. Parking can be difficult, but there is easy access on foot from Denham station close by. High-quality accommodation is offered. Q

Green Man
Village Road, UB9 5BH
☎ (01895) 832760 🌐 greenmandenham.co.uk
Oakham JHB; Rebellion Smuggler; Sharp's Doom Bar; 2 changing beers Ⓗ
This friendly free-of-tie inn has been sympathetically refurbished. The front bar has beams, a real fire and flagged floors, opening out into a large conservatory and well-tended beer garden. With four real ales and tempting food menus, the pub is popular with diners, families and drinkers alike. Historic Denham is a picturesque rural village, a pleasant stroll from the Colne Valley Country Park Visitor Centre.

Downley

De Spencer Arms
The Common, HP13 5YQ (across common from village on flint track beyond the end of Plomer Green Lane)
☎ (01494) 535317 🌐 ledespencersarms.co.uk
Fuller's London Pride, ESB; 2 changing beers (sourced nationally) Ⓗ
A busy pub nestling in the woods on the edge of Downley Common. This friendly traditional local offers a warm welcome to all including walkers and cyclists, dogs and children. A range of home-cooked seasonal food featuring local ingredients is served. The garden is lovely in the summer months. The surrounding area of outstanding natural beauty offers many walks. There is car parking to the rear. P

Fenny Stratford

Chequers 🄻
48 Watling Street, MK2 2BY
☎ (01908) 374527 🌐 thechequersfennystratford.com
Vale Gravitas 🄷; 3 changing beers (sourced nationally; often Box Steam, Titanic, Vale) 🄷/🄶
Reopened in 2017 after extensive refurbishment including an extension to the kitchen. A traditional taproom specialising in ales, beers from Vale are usually available alongside changing guests. Beers are also available to take away. The menu includes pizzas, pastas, pies and fries. There is a courtyard garden at the rear furnished with wooden tables and benches, and a small car park beyond that. Q❀◑⇌P🚌(18,X31)🐾

Great Kimble

Swan 🄻
Lower Icknield Way, HP17 9TR
☎ (01844) 275288
1 changing beer (sourced locally; often Tring) 🄷
In a village at the foot of the Chiltern Hills in excellent hiking, horse riding and cycling country, the Swan is a genuine, family-owned free house. The pub adjoins the village green children's playground. The building dates back to the 18th century and is reputedly haunted. Sunday lunchtimes are popular. Late evening opening hours can be erratic, especially in the winter, as can the selection of ales. ☺❀🛏◑♿⇌♣P🚌(300)🐾📶

Great Missenden

George Ale House
94 High Street, HP16 0BG
☎ (01494) 865185
Harvey's Sussex Best Bitter; 3 changing beers (sourced nationally) 🄷
An old free house that reopened in 2018 following several years of closure. There are three seating areas, some with comfy sofas and real fires, as well as a bottle shop. The pub hosts regular music nights with guitars, banjos and an accordion, all on display on the walls ready to be played. Traditional pub games including dominoes, cribbage, shut the box and board games are popular. Q❀⇌♣●P🐾

Grendon Underwood

Swan
Main Street, HP18 0SW
☎ (01296) 770666
3 changing beers (often Black Sheep, Purity) 🄷
Detached thatched pub situated in a row of houses and easy to miss. It was refurbished and reopened in December 2019 following a village campaign to raise funds to save it. Since then it has become an excellent example of a pub at the heart of the community and hosts many events. The interior is bright and airy with comfortable furnishings. The food offering is impressive. Q☺❀◑P🚌(16,18)🐾

Haddenham

Rising Sun 🄻 ✔
9 Thame Road, HP17 8EN
☎ (01844) 291744 🌐 risingsunhaddenham.co.uk
XT Four; 5 changing beers (sourced locally) 🄷
This bustling village pub boasts six real ales on handpump, with favourites from XT Brewing as well as unusual Animal Brewing Co creations, plus a changing selection of guest ales, craft beers and ciders. With a landscaped garden and treats on tap for canine companions, this family and pooch-friendly pub seamlessly blends the best of old and new. Local CAMRA Pub of the Year 2019. Q☺❀⇌●🚌(280)🐾📶

Hanslope

Club
28 High Street, MK19 7LQ
☎ (01908) 510337
Adnams Ghost Ship; Draught Bass; 1 changing beer (sourced nationally; often Oakham, Shepherd Neame, Timothy Taylor) 🄷
The Club (formerly Hanslope Working Men's Club) welcomes non-members at all times for a nominal fee. Its two rooms, designated the Bar and the Lounge, serve three regular beers and a guest ale that changes weekly. The club offers a wide range of community activities including darts, skittles, pool, cards, quizzes and monthly bingo. It also hosts discos, film nights and children's events. A beer festival is held over the Easter weekend. A former local CAMRA Club of the Year. ☺❀♿♣P🚌📶

Hedgerley

White Horse 🄻
Village Lane, SL2 3UY (in old village, near church)
☎ (01753) 643225 🌐 thewhitehorsehedgerley.co.uk
Rebellion IPA; 7 changing beers (often Mallinsons, Mighty Oak, Oakham) 🄶
Local CAMRA Pub of the Year on numerous occasions, this village local offers an impressive range of real ales. New breweries often feature, as well as favourite beers from Oakham, Mallinsons and Mighty Oak. A draught Belgian beer and three real ciders are also available. This classic pub has a well-tended garden and a heated, covered patio area. Regular beer festivals are held, the largest of which is over the Whitsun weekend and is a must for real ale enthusiasts. Q☺❀◐♣●P🐾📶

High Wycombe

Belle Vue ✔
45 Gordon Road, HP13 6EQ
☎ (01494) 524728 🌐 thebv.pub
Adnams Ghost Ship, Broadside; 4 changing beers 🄷
A friendly pub with an open fire in winter, five real ciders from Westons and frequent music events. It is situated next to the railway line (take the north exit from the station). The name is a mystery as the only view from the pub is of the brick wall enclosing the railway. It was once the corner building of a terrace of workers' houses but they have now all gone. This genuine community venue is a regular in the Guide. ❀⇌♣●🚌🐾📶

Mad Squirrel Brewery Shop Emporium 🄻
4-5 Church Street, HP11 2DE
☎ (01494) 395980 🌐 redsquirrelbrewery.co.uk
Mad Squirrel Mister Squirrel, London Porter 🄷/🄰; 2 changing beers (sourced locally) 🄰
The tasting bar and bottle shop opened in 2016 and has a bar downstairs and another upstairs with more seating. At least two cask ales are offered alongside a range of craft keg beers. There is a walk-in chiller with a selection of real ales in bottles and cans, also available to take away. You can enjoy a pizza with your favourite beer. ❀◑♿⇌●P🗑🚌📶

Rose & Crown ✔
Desborough Road, HP11 2PR
☎ (01494) 571578 🌐 roseandcrownhighwycombe.co.uk

4 changing beers (sourced nationally) 🄷
An L-shaped pub next to the Eden Shopping Centre which has steadily built up its real ale offering and now has an extensive range. It is a comfortable establishment in an area of mainly small businesses. The pub holds quizzes, discos and charity events, and hosts live bands and karaoke once a month. Many sporting events are shown on two large-screen TVs. Snacks are served and Sunday roasts to order. The bus station is close by. ❀♣🚌🐾📶

Iver Heath

Black Horse

95 Slough Road, SL0 0DH
☎ (01753) 652631 🌐 theblackhorseiverheath.co.uk
Hall & Woodhouse Fursty Ferret, Tanglefoot; 1 changing beer (sourced regionally) 🄷
Refurbished by Hall & Woodhouse, this large pub/diner has a country house feel with oak panelling and shelves packed with interesting books. The separate drinking area has comfortable leather armchairs. A green oak conservatory restaurant opens on to the patio and garden. Three Badger ales are available. Meals and snacks, including vegetarian, are served all day. The Uxbridge to Slough bus stops outside.
Q❀◐♿P🚌(3) 🐾📶

Ivinghoe

Rose & Crown 🄻 ✔

Vicarage Lane, LU7 9EQ
☎ (01296) 668472 🌐 roseandcrownivinghoe.co.uk
Sharp's Doom Bar; house beer (by Chiltern); 3 changing beers (sourced nationally; often Butcombe, St Austell, XT) 🄷
The owner's philosophy sums up this lovely country pub: 'We want to run the best pub we can. It means being here for our customers, cooking interesting food made from scratch and serving great tasting drinks. It means looking after our staff and customers fairly and enjoying what we do.' This welcoming free house is well on the way to achieving its aim. It boasts an open fire, slate floors and a clean, bright interior. A quiet area to the rear leads to an outside courtyard patio.
Q❀◐♣●P🚆🚌(61) 🐾📶

Lacey Green

Pink & Lily 🄻

Pink Road, Parslows Hillock, HP27 0RJ
☎ (01494) 489857 🌐 pink-lily.com
Sharp's Doom Bar; 3 changing beers (sourced locally) 🄷
Three-hundred-year-old pub in a timeless hamlet in the heart of the Chilterns. Four cask ales are available, three from various local breweries. The historic Brooke Bar has been preserved as it was when Rupert Brooke, the World War I poet, was a regular. Great food is served. The garden includes a heated outdoor dining space, a play area for children and a barbecue for summer weekends.
Q❀◐♿♣P🐾📶

Little Missenden

Crown Inn

HP7 0RD (off A413, between Amersham and Gt Missenden)
☎ (01494) 862571 🌐 thecrownlittlemissenden.co.uk
St Austell Tribute; 3 changing beers (sourced nationally; often Oakham, Otter, Timothy Taylor) 🄷
This lovely old local has been in the same family for almost a hundred years. Former Watford footballer Trevor How and his wife took over in 1993. The village inn sits in an acre of beautiful countryside, with a patio at the back where children are welcome. Inside you will find a traditional adults-only pub with stone and wood floors, and in winter an open fire. Good pub grub is served at lunchtimes. Three double en-suite rooms are available.
Q❀🛏◐●P🚌(55) 🐾📶

Littleworth Common

Blackwood Arms ✔

Common Lane, SL1 8PP SU937863
☎ (01753) 645672 🌐 theblackwoodarms.net
Brakspear Gravity, Oxford Gold; 4 changing beers (sourced locally) 🄷
A delightful Victorian country pub brought back to life after a long period of closure. Close to Burnham Beeches nature reserve, it is popular with walkers and diners. An attractive garden with plenty of seating is a feature in summer, as is the roaring fire in winter. Four guest ales are offered, two from the Marston's group plus two free of tie. Dogs and horses are welcome – hay can be provided. Cider is available in summer only.
Q❀◐♣●P🐾📶

Loudwater

Derehams Inn

5 Derehams Lane, HP10 9RH
☎ (01494) 530965 🌐 derehamsinn.co.uk
5 changing beers 🄷
A friendly local up a lane off the London Road, with a car park at the rear. Outside is a garden area and a covered smoking area with a pool table. An annual beer festival is held at the beginning of July. This is a traditional pub where families and dogs are welcome. Formerly known as the Bricklayers Arms, it has been run by the same couple for around 20 years. Q❀◐P🚌🐾

Loughton

Talbot ✔

33 London Road, MK5 8AB
☎ (01908) 827296
Fuller's London Pride; Purity Pure UBU; Thornbridge Jaipur IPA; house beer (by Black Sheep); 8 changing beers (sourced nationally; often London Brewing Company, Titanic) 🄷
A large pub with a single bar and the room divided into several seating areas. On Monday and Thursday all real ales are reduced in price. Wednesday is quiz night. Food is served all day, including brunch at the weekend. Check the Ember Inns app for food and drink offers. Under-18s are welcome if dining. The large garden is popular in summer. There is ample free parking.
❀◐♿●P🚌(24,25) 📶

Marlow

Britannia

Little Marlow Road, SL7 1HL
☎ (01628) 483852
McMullen AK Original Mild, Country Bitter; 1 changing beer (sourced regionally) 🄷
The Britannia has been transformed and is now contemporary in style with comfortable sofas and bright decor. There is a strong emphasis on food, with meals served throughout the day. Beers are from the McMullen Brewery, often including its seasonal offering. There is a large area for outdoor drinking. The pub is well connected by buses from Wycombe or Marlow town centre. ❀◐♿P🚌(800,850)📶

Royal British Legion 🄻 ✔
Station Approach, SL7 1NT (next to train station)
☎ (01628) 486659 🌐 rblmarlow.co.uk
6 changing beers (sourced locally) 🄷
A friendly Royal British Legion club that offers a wide range of cask ales and holds two beer festivals a year. Although a private members' club, guests are welcome – show a copy of this Guide or a CAMRA membership card for entry. Various events are held including jazz and music nights. This popular venue is a regular winner of CAMRA Regional Club of the Year. ❀♿⇌♣●P🚌ᯤ

Milton Keynes

Wetherspoons 🄻 ✔
201 Midsummer Boulvard, MK9 1EA
☎ (01908) 606074
Greene King Abbot; Ruddles Best Bitter; Sharp's Doom Bar; 9 changing beers (sourced nationally; often Hornes, Oakham, Tring) 🄷
This Wetherspoon pub is unbeatable for price and range with 12 handpumps offering cask ales including local beers, as well as real ciders. The large open bar is a popular and easily accessible meeting place for many locals including CAMRA members. There are tables and chairs outside. A wide range of canned and bottled craft beers is available for off-sales. The standard Wetherspoon food menu is served from early morning until late evening. A former local CAMRA Pub of the Year. ♘❀◐◑♿⇌●P🚌ᯤ

Naphill

Wheel ✔
100 Main Road, HP14 4QA
☎ (01494) 562210 🌐 thewheelnaphill.com
Greene King Abbot; Ruddles Best Bitter; 2 changing beers 🄷
Popular with regulars and visitors alike, this traditional village local has a cosy atmosphere. There are two bar areas – one small and another that leads to the dining area. The large garden is ideal on summer days. A warm welcome is extended to all, including ramblers in muddy boots enjoying the nearby walks. This pub has been in the Guide for several years and prides itself on serving good cask ale. Q❀🛏◐◑♣P🚌🐾ᯤ

Oving

Black Boy 🄻 ✔
Church Lane, HP22 4HN
☎ (01296) 641258 🌐 theblackboyoving.co.uk
XT Four; 3 changing beers (sourced locally; often Chiltern, Leighton Buzzard, XT) 🄷
Delightful 17th-century inn with a roaring fire in winter. Summer visits are also a treat, with wonderful views across the local countryside from the huge beer garden. The restaurant opposite the bar is separated from the drinking area by an archway. The drinking areas offer flagstone floors and wooden beams. With good food, friendly staff and a great atmosphere, this is a cosy pub and a pleasure to visit. ♘❀◐◑●P🐾ᯤ

Princes Risborough

Bird in Hand 🄻 ✔
47 Station Road, HP27 9DE
☎ (01844) 345602 🌐 birdinhandprincesrisborough.co.uk
Chiltern Beechwood Bitter; Thame Hoppiness; 2 changing beers 🄷
Situated in a residential area near Princes Risborough station, this thriving community local has a compact L-shaped drinking bar supplemented by an outside drinking area and a beer garden. The Thame-based Oak Taverns house offers a good selection of real ales on handpump. Entertainment includes pub quizzes and live music. Parking can be difficult nearby.
❀⇌♣●🚌(300) 🐾ᯤ

Quainton

George & Dragon 🄻
32 The Green, HP22 4AR
☎ (01296) 655436 🌐 georgeanddragonquainton.co.uk
6 changing beers (sourced locally) 🄷
Free house with an adjoining coffee shop, always offering four LocAles plus two guests. It has a friendly public bar with darts, a jukebox and a TV, and a saloon bar dedicated to dining, although home-cooked food is served throughout. Parts of this delightful pub date back to the 1700s, with traditional English features such as inglenook fireplaces, beams and a quarry-tiled floor. Regular beer festivals overlooking the green take place in summer. ♘❀◐◑♿♣●P🚌(16)🐾ᯤ

Saunderton

Golden Cross
Wycombe Road, HP14 4HU
☎ (01494) 565974
Greene King IPA; 2 changing beers (sourced nationally) 🄷
A family-friendly village pub, popular for home-made food as well as real ale, listed as an asset of community value. The large enclosed garden features a marquee, a barbecue area and children's play space. It is set in the Chiltern hills countryside and surrounded by public footpaths. ♘❀◐◑⇌♣P🚌(X30)🐾ᯤ

Stacey Bushes

Blackened Sun Brewery Tap
Unit 3, Heathfield, MK12 6HP
☎ (01908) 990242 🌐 blackenedsunbrewing.co.uk
Blackened Sun Hedone, Luna; 4 changing beers (sourced nationally; often Blackened Sun, Twisted Barrel) 🄿
A tasting area within the Blackened Sun microbrewery, the taproom has six taps serving five house beers and one changing guest, sometimes a collaboration brew. All are real ales, naturally conditioned and served from KeyKegs. Casks are sometimes used during festivals. Bottled house beers and guest beers are also available to take away and growlers can be refilled. Customers may bring their own food or order in from nearby takeaways. Winner of a number of recent local CAMRA awards.
♘♿P🗍🚌🐾

Steeple Claydon

Fountain
10 West Street, MK18 2NT
☎ (01296) 730286
Fuller's London Pride; Sharp's Doom Bar 🄷
A busy free house with two bars – the main bar has a flat-screen TV; the games bar offers darts and pool. Run by the same publican for over 40 years, the pub actively supports charities and the local community. Although no food is sold, a popular fish & chip van visits on Saturday evening. There is car parking at the front, and a garden with a covered smoking area to the side. Winner of a local CAMRA award in 2019. ♘❀♣P🚌(16,18)

Stoke Goldington

Lamb 🅛
16-20 High Street, MK16 8NR
☎ (01908) 551233 ⊕ thelambatstokegoldington.co.uk
Tring Brock Bitter, Death or Glory; 2 changing beers (sourced regionally; often Oakham, Vale) 🅗
In a peaceful village midway between Milton Keynes and Northampton, the Lamb features an intimate bar, a large separate restaurant and a less formal dining room. The bar has a dartboard and a Northamptonshire skittles table. Home-cooked food is served including award-winning pies using local seasonal produce. The large garden has a stage for music events. There is ample parking and walking groups are encouraged to park early and order food before their walk to enjoy on their return. Two en-suite bedrooms are available. Local CAMRA Pub of the Year 2019. Q🌣🕭🕊🕏♣🍴P🚪(37)🐾🛆

Stoke Hammond

Three Locks 🅛
Leighton Road, MK17 9DD
☎ (01525) 270214 ⊕ thethreelocksstokehammond.com
Fuller's London Pride; Tring Side Pocket for a Toad, Ridgeway; 3 changing beers (sourced regionally; often Hornes, Kelchner) 🅗
Canalside pub that supports local breweries and cider makers. Following a major refurbishment in 2020, it has a brighter, fresher look and exposed beams. It offers a good range of food, including vegan and gluten-free options, with a discount for Inland Waterways Association members. There is a beer festival over the May bank holiday weekend and regular live music. The pub is particularly popular in summer, with customers arriving by narrowboat. There is plenty of outdoor seating alongside the canal. 🌣🕭🕊🕏♣🍴P🚪(70)🐾🛆

Twyford

Crown Inn
The Square, MK18 4EG
☎ (01296) 730216 ⊕ thecrowntwyford.co.uk
2 changing beers 🅗
A freehold inn central to the life of the village. The landlady has seen other local pubs decline and close, and has increased opening hours and food provision with the help of her family. The Crown is a deceptively large brick building opposite the village hall. A spacious bar area leads to an even larger lounge/function area on the left. Serving one frequently changing beer from the barrel, it is usual to have seven different beers on during the week. 🌣🕭🕊🕏♣🚪(16)🐾🛆

Wendover

King & Queen ✓
17 South Street, HP22 6EF
☎ (01296) 696872 ⊕ thekingandqueenwendover.co.uk
Timothy Taylor Landlord; Young's London Original; 2 changing beers 🅗
Situated just off the High Street within easy reach of the station, the three-room village pub has a pleasant, homely ambience. Good food is served in the restaurant. There is an impressive wall map of the local countryside in one room. A wood-burning fire helps to provide a warm winter welcome for walkers returning from the nearby Chiltern Hills. Q🌣🕭🕊🕏♣🍴P🚪🐾

Westcroft

Nut & Squirrel ✓
1 Barnsdale Drive, MK4 4DD
☎ (01908) 340031
Adnams Ghost Ship; house beer (by Black Sheep); 4 changing beers (sourced nationally; often Fuller's, Purity, St Austell) 🅗
Popular open-plan pub with nooks and crannies giving a traditional multi-room feel. The restaurant off the bar area offers the extensive Ember Inns menu, catering both for vegetarians and vegans with a dedicated menu. A large rotating selection of Cask Marque-quality ales is offered as well as vegan beer and cider. The pub is located on the edge of Westcroft shopping centre and opposite Howe Park Wood. Local CAMRA Most Improved Pub in 2019. 🌣🕭🕊🕏♣🍴P🚪🐾🛆

Willen

Ship Ashore ✓
Granville Square, MK15 9JL
☎ (01908) 694360
House beer (by Black Sheep); 4 changing beers (sourced nationally; often Brains, Fuller's, St Austell) 🅗
Smart, modern Ember Inns pub on a residential estate close to Willen Lake and its recreational facilities. The large single-room bar has pillars and half walls to give a more intimate feel. There is a constantly changing selection of real ales plus the Black Sheep-brewed house beer. On Monday all real ales are discounted. Food, served all day, includes a dedicated vegetarian and vegan menu. Drinkers and diners are made equally welcome. There is a small garden and ample free parking. 🕭🕊🕏♣🍴P🚪(2)🐾🛆

Winchmore Hill

Potter's Arms ✓
Fagnall Lane, HP7 0PH
☎ (01494) 726222 ⊕ pottersarms.co.uk
Rebellion IPA; 3 changing beers (sourced locally; often Chiltern, Rebellion, Tring) 🅗
Now a free house, this traditional village pub has been extensively refurbished but retains the lovely old original fireplace. There are four beers from local breweries. Good food ranges from snacks to gastro to Thai. A comedy night is held on the last Thursday of the month with a meal included in the price. The garden has wheelchair access, heated umbrellas and seating for alfresco dining. There are four en-suite B&B rooms. 🌣🕭🕊🕏♣P🐾🛆

Wooburn Common

Royal Standard 🅛 ✓
Wooburn Common Lane, HP10 0JS (follow signs to Odds Farm)
☎ (01628) 521121 ⊕ theroyalstandard.biz
Hop Back Summer Lightning 🅗**; St Austell Tribute** 🅖**; 7 changing beers** 🅗
A regular in the Guide, this traditional rural inn is convenient for Odds Farm Park. Its ever-changing guest ales include one dark beer with a higher ABV. Up to eight real ciders are also available. The pub serves good home-made food and families are welcome – it is a popular stopping point for walkers and their dogs. There is ample parking at the side. Well worth seeking out. Q🌣🕭🕊🕏♣P🐾🛆

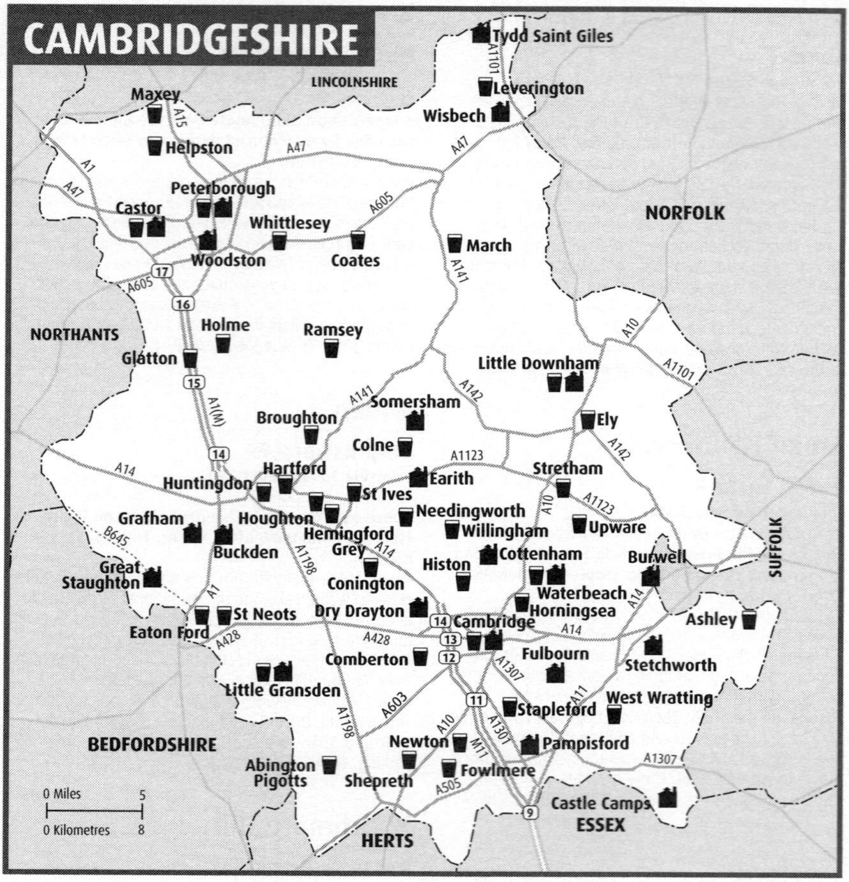

Abington Pigotts

Pig & Abbot

High Street, SG8 0SD (off A505 through Litlington)
☎ (01763) 853515 🌐 pigandabbot.co.uk
Adnams Southwold Bitter; Fuller's London Pride; 2 changing beers (often Mighty Oak, Oakham, Woodforde's) Ⓗ
Located in a surprisingly remote part of the south Cambridgeshire countryside, this Queen Anne-period pub offers a warm welcome. The interior has exposed oak beams and two fireplaces including a large inglenook with a wood-burning stove. A comfortable restaurant serves home-made traditional pub food, specialising in fresh fish & chips, steak and kidney puddings and pies. Two guest beers are stocked, often from Burton Bridge, Humpty Dumpty, Mighty Oak, Timothy Taylor or Woodforde's. A former CAMRA branch Pub of the Year.
Q❀◑♿♣P🐾

Ashley

Crown Inn

24 Newmarket Road, CB8 9DR
☎ (01638) 730117 🌐 thecrowninnashley.co.uk
Mighty Oak Captain Bob; 3 changing beers Ⓗ
This community hub was first recorded as an inn in 1712, though parts of the imposing building are earlier. A former Greene King pub, the Crown became free of tie in 2014. It has a bright bar area with a cosy back room. Real ciders, direct from the box, are stocked. Families and dogs are welcome. Pub games include darts, pool and, in the enclosed rear garden, pétanque.
❀◑♣●P🚌🐾📶

Broughton

Crown Inn

Bridge Road, PE28 3AY
☎ (01487) 824428 🌐 thecrowninnrestaurant.co.uk
2 changing beers (sourced regionally) Ⓗ
An idyllic 19th-century inn opposite the village church. The interior is modern with a small bar area, scrubbed pine tables and a stone floor. Four handpumps serve two real ales – usually from small regional breweries – and two ciders. Excellent seasonally changing food menus attract diners from a wide area. The pub can be busy at weekends – diners should reserve a table. Outside is a large beer garden where a beer festival is held each May.
Q❀◑P🐾📶

Cambridge

Alexandra Arms

22 Gwydir Street, CB1 2LL (300yds from Mill Rd)
☎ (01223) 324441 🌐 thealexcambridge.com
7 changing beers Ⓗ

Refurbished in 2014 in a modern kitchen style, the pub has three distinct areas on two levels, with wooden flooring and plenty of tables. The attractive enclosed garden has a garden room. A Greene King Local Hero pub, it is mainly free of tie, with guest ales frequently from Oakham alongside the regular beers. Food is home made and includes burgers, with bread from a local bakery. 🐎✿◐◑🍎🚌🐾📶

Blue Moon

2 Norfolk Street, CB1 2LF (off East Rd)
☎ (01223) 500238
Adnams Mosaic, Ghost Ship; 2 changing beers 🄷
The Blue Moon became a sister pub to the Cambridge Blue in 2013, hence the name. As well as changing real ciders and real ales, it offers 10 craft keg beers. Tap takeovers are held once a month. The front bar contains old pictures of Cambridge pubs and hand-drawn portraits of the staff. The larger back bar has a pool table and arcade machines. Live music features mainly at the weekend, with other events during the week including a popular quiz on Wednesday. Local CAMRA Young Members and City Community Pub of the Year 2020. 🐎◑♣🍎P🚌🐾

Calverley's Brewery Tap Ⓛ

23A Hooper Street, CB1 2NZ
☎ 07769 537342 🌐 calverleys.com
Calverley's Porter 🄶
Close to Mill Road, the brewery was established in a former stable in 2013. It is open for on-sales on Thursday and Friday evenings and all day Saturday. Up to two beers are served direct from the cask plus a wide – and sometimes unusual – selection of keg beers. A newly constructed taproom provides more seating and frees up space in the brewery, allowing for a wider beer range. Gourmet food vans provide snacks. Q🐎◑🚌🐾

Cambridge Blue

85-87 Gwydir Street, CB1 2LG
☎ (01223) 471680
Changing beers 🄷/🄶
Ever-popular side-street pub close to Mill Road. A large rear extension leads to its garden, which frequently contains a marquee. Breweriana and pumpclips provide much of the decoration. Up to 14 ales from microbreweries nationwide are dispensed by handpump or by gravity from the taproom, often including Animal beers. Up to seven real ciders and perries and a large selection of international bottled beers are also kept. The main beer festival is held in June. 🐎✿◐◑♿♣🍎🚌🐾📶

Champion of the Thames

68 King Street, CB1 1LN
☎ (01223) 351464 🌐 thechampionofthethames.com
Greene King IPA, Abbot; 3 changing beers 🄷
Small, two-room, city-centre establishment with a welcoming atmosphere where the chatter of customers predominates. It is one of four remaining pubs on the King Street Run pub crawl – which at one time involved a pint in each of eight pubs on the street. The oarsman of the name is commemorated in the etched windows. Wood-panelled with fixed benches and a part-glazed partition between the rooms, the pub is identified by CAMRA as having a regionally important historic interior. Pub snacks are available. ✿♣🚌🐾📶

Devonshire Arms Ⓛ

1 Devonshire Road, CB1 2BH
☎ (01223) 316610
8 changing beers (sourced nationally; often Milton) 🄷
Milton Brewery's first Cambridge pub. Just off Mill Road, it attracts a mix of characters for beer, food and a chat. Deceptively large inside, with tall front windows and a high ceiling with fans, outside it has small patio areas front and back. Five Milton cask ales are served, including at least one dark beer, with a further three guests from other micros. There are also bottled and keg beers, including Moravka unpasteurised lager, and two ciders. Food focuses on pizzas, burgers and hot dogs. 🐎✿◐◑🚆♣🍎🚌🐾📶

Flying Pig Ⓛ

106 Hills Road, CB2 1LQ
☎ (01223) 354623 🌐 theflyingpigpub.wordpress.com
Crouch Vale Brewers Gold; Rudgate Ruby Mild; 4 changing beers 🄷
Much-loved, cosy and friendly pub with a local feel that defies its location on a main road. A beer and music venue, its walls and ceiling are adorned with an eclectic collection of old posters and pig paraphernalia. In the evenings the intimate lighting is enhanced by candles. Ales usually include some from local breweries, and craft keg beers are also sold. Basic pub grub is served weekday lunchtimes only. Live music plays on Tuesday, Thursday, some Fridays and Saturday. The pub hosts an annual Pigfest charity music festival. ✿◐🚆🍎🚌📶

Free Press

7 Prospect Row, CB1 1DU
☎ (01223) 368337 🌐 freepresscambridge.com
Greene King XX Mild, IPA, Abbot; 4 changing beers (often Morland) 🄷
This intimate, friendly venue serves high-quality food and great beer. It is Greene King-tied, and the rare XX Mild was its best seller until brewing frequency was reduced. A pub since 1834, it just avoided the 1970s Kite area redevelopment, and is identified by CAMRA as having a regionally important historic pub interior. Only the tiny snug is original – the rest is a loving reconstruction. There is a walled garden at the rear. Named after a Temperance movement newspaper that lasted for just one edition. 🐎✿◐◑♣🍎🚌🐾📶

Geldart ✔

1 Ainsworth Street, CB1 2PF (nr Mill Rd)
☎ (01223) 314264 🌐 the-geldart.co.uk

REAL ALE BREWERIES

Bexar County Peterborough
Burwell Burwell (NEW)
Calverley's ◆ Cambridge
Cambridge ▤ Cambridge
Castor Castor
Crafty Beers Stetchworth
Downham Isle ◆ Little Downham
Draycott Buckden
Elgood's Wisbech
Fellows Cottenham
Grafham Grafham (NEW)
IVO Somersham (NEW)
Lord Conrad's Dry Drayton
Mile Tree Peterborough
Milton Waterbeach
Moonshine Fulbourn
Oakham Peterborough
Papworth ◆ Earith
Rocket Great Staughton
Roughacre Castle Camps
Son of Sid ▤ Little Gransden
Three Blind Mice Little Downham
Turpin's ◆ Pampisford
Tydd Steam Tydd Saint Giles
Xtreme Peterborough: Woodston

Adnams Ghost Ship; Caledonian Deuchars IPA; Oakham Citra; St Austell Tribute; 4 changing beers (sourced nationally) Ⓗ
Large two-bar back-street corner pub with an enclosed patio garden behind. It is decorated throughout with film and music memorabilia, including musical instrument handpumps and menus on 12-inch vinyl. The pub has a good reputation for its home-made food and its beers, with a restaurant area to the right of the entrance and a bar area to the left offering eight ales and a wide selection of malt whiskies and rums. The changing guest beers always include a dark one. Frequent live music is hosted.

Haymakers

54 High Street, CB4 1NG
☎ (01223) 311077
Milton Pegasus; 7 changing beers (often Milton) Ⓗ
Milton Brewery's second of three Cambridge pubs, popular with locals and employees from the nearby science park. There are drinking areas either side of the door and a snug. Dark wood and warm colours abound. A good-sized beer garden is to the rear. The car park contains the largest pub cycle park in Cambridge. Eight real ales, including one dark beer and three guests, are on offer, plus four real ciders or perries, Moravka unpasteurised lager and a rotating Beach Brewery craft beer. Local CAMRA City LocAle Pub of the Year 2019.
P

Live & Let Live

40 Mawson Road, CB1 2EA
☎ (01223) 460261
Nethergate Umbel Ale; Oakham Citra; 3 changing beers Ⓗ
A discreet corner local, just off Mill Road, with roadside cycle parking. It has a simply furnished single bar and a small snug to the rear. Wood panelling plus railway and beer memorabilia add to a yesteryear atmosphere. It is a pub for contemplation, conversation and ale and cider consumption. Five beers cover a range of styles and strengths, alongside three changing ciders or perries. Rum festivals feature twice a year. Local CAMRA Pub of the Year 2020 and Dark Beer Pub of the Year 2019.
Q

Maypole

20A Portugal Place, CB5 8AF
☎ (01223) 352999 maypolefreehouse.co.uk
Changing beers Ⓗ
The Maypole has been in the capable hands of the Castiglione family since 1982, initially as tenants, latterly as owners. Its quality beers won the landlord the CAMRA branch's first Real Ale Champion award. Up to 16 changing ales are kept (more during festivals) including LocAles, with micros predominating. The keg beers include several of interest. It has a busy front bar, a quieter back bar downstairs, a function room upstairs and a large covered patio. Food focuses on home-cooked Italian dishes and English pub classics. Local CAMRA Pub of the Year 2018.

Pint Shop

10 Peas Hill, CB2 3PP (behind Guildhall)
☎ (01223) 352293 pintshop.co.uk/locations/cambridge
Changing beers Ⓗ
This impressive Georgian townhouse, close to the Market Square and behind the Guildhall, was formerly Cambridge University's pensions office. Now refurbished, multiple rooms across three floors provide plenty of drinking and dining areas. The terraced rear patio garden is popular for alfresco eating and drinking. Two real ciders and four cask ales are on offer as well as 24 craft keg beers from the UK and Europe. Dining is upmarket, but home-made bar snacks are available at all times.

Queen Edith

Wulfstan Way, CB1 8QN
☎ (01223) 244536
Milton Pegasus; 7 changing beers (often Milton) Ⓗ
The first new-build pub in Cambridge for around 30 years, after the demolition of a pub of the same name at the rear of the site, and the third Milton Brewery establishment in the city. The style is mock-Georgian inside and out. The larger bar to the left of the entrance has large windows on two sides and a wood-burning stove. The second bar has wooden booths down one side. Regular and changing Milton ales are sold plus guests. Q P

Castor

Prince of Wales Feathers

38 Peterborough Road, PE5 7AL
☎ (01733) 380222 princeofwalesfeathers.co.uk
Adnams Broadside; Castor Ales Hopping Toad; Woodforde's Wherry Ⓗ**; 3 changing beers** Ⓗ/Ⓖ
This village corner pub is about 300 years old, is built of stone and has stained-glass windows, with two patios outside. Originally a boot and shoe shop, it has one main bar area, divided into two by the fireplace. There are two smaller rooms for pool and darts; dominoes and crib are also played. Four real ales are usually served. Entertainment includes Sky Sports, plus live music every Saturday. Away football fans visiting Peterborough are warmly welcomed.

Coates

Vine

4 South Green, PE7 2BJ
☎ (01733) 840343
3 changing beers Ⓗ
Overlooking the village green, this free house was refurbished and extended in 2019. It has three rooms – a lively main sports bar/lounge in the middle, a conservatory at the rear and a conference suite at the front. A varying choice of beers always includes a LocAle. The large outdoor area has space for pétanque terrains and a children's play area. There is a new pool table in the conservatory as well as dartboards. The pub raises money for the Royal British Legion and Coates War Memorial Fund, particularly on Coates Day in late August.
P (33)

Colne

Green Man

1 East Street, PE28 3LZ
☎ (01487) 840368 greenmancolne.co.uk
Adnams Ghost Ship; Milton Justinian; Papworth Half Nelson; 1 changing beer (sourced regionally) Ⓗ
A picturesque, 17th-century village local in an old Fenland fruit-growing area. The corrugated roof covers an original thatch. This busy, friendly pub provides a public bar with pool, darts and TV, plus a warm, sociable lounge with a modern dining extension serving good food. A quiz night is held fortnightly. The garden has a children's play area and hosts barbecues in summer. Camping is available nearby at Earith Lakes. Local CAMRA Pub of the Year 2020. P (21,22)

Comberton

Three Horseshoes

22 South Street, CB23 7DZ

☎ (01223) 262252

Adnams Lighthouse; Greene King IPA; 3 changing beers [H]

Hanging baskets adorn this red-roofed village pub. Popular with local clubs and societies, it sponsors football and cricket teams. Historical photographs of the village and its sports players adorn the walls. The long, low-ceilinged main bar has a cosy alcove at one end and a small raised area at the other, with a games room off to the left. The brick-fronted bar takes up much of the central section. An extensive garden features children's play equipment. ❀♣P (18)

Conington

White Swan

Elsworth Road, CB23 4LN

☎ (01954) 267251 🌐 thewhiteswanconington.co.uk

Adnams Southwold Bitter, Ghost Ship; 1 changing beer [G]

Sturdy 18th-century brick building fronted by an impressive sward for outside drinking. The main bar has a tiled floor and a brick fireplace occupied by a fine cast-iron stove. The former cellar is now in use again, with the real ales served by gravity from behind the low (wheelchair-friendly) bar. The pub was purchased from Greene King in 2013 by the resident of Conington Hall and is run free of tie. Q❀♣P

Eaton Ford

Barley Mow ✔

27 Crosshall Road, PE19 7AB

☎ (01480) 474435

Greene King IPA, Abbot; 2 changing beers [H]

Simple one-bar community pub with a wide variety of activities focused on the regulars, plus live music events and seasonal celebrations. The decor is a mix of plaster, brick and wood panelling, and a long service counter dominates the centre of the bar. Images of past pub social events adorn the walls. There is a covered patio and a large beer garden with an extensive children's play area. The two changing beers are not normally from the Greene King range. ❀♣P (X5)

Ely

Drayman's Son L

29A Forehill, CB7 4AA

☎ (01353) 662920

Three Blind Mice Juice Rocket; house beer (by Three Blind Mice) [H]**; 7 changing beers (sourced nationally; often Three Blind Mice)** [G]

Small, welcoming micropub in former shop premises nostalgically themed with old railway and enamel signs. Drinks are usually delivered to your table. Twelve ales are often available – six on gravity, five KeyKeg and a craft lager on keg. The cask and KeyKeg are mostly from microbreweries both local and further afield. A range of 25 or more ciders is also served, many sourced locally. The cellar is in a temperature-controlled back room. The pub supports local produce including Ely Gin. Local CAMRA Cider Pub of the Year 2020. ♿♣

Prince Albert 🏆 L ✔

62 Silver Street, CB7 4JF (opp cathedral car park)

☎ (01353) 663494

Greene King XX Mild, IPA, Abbot; 5 changing beers (sourced nationally; often Milton, Purity, Timothy Taylor) [H]

The Prince Albert has two distinct characters – the front area is a music-free drinkers' space with a friendly atmosphere where the regulars gather, while the rear area is a restaurant serving meals and snacks (booking advisable for the popular Sunday lunches). The garden at the back is secluded and perfect for alfresco eating and drinking on summer days. The pub is not far from Ely Cathedral and under a mile from the railway station. Local CAMRA Pub of the Year 2020.

Q❀♿

Fowlmere

Chequers

High Street, SG8 7SR

☎ (01763) 209333 🌐 thechequersfowlmere.co.uk

3 changing beers (often Greene King) [H]

Upmarket, food-oriented, 16th-century coaching inn. Drinkers will feel most comfortable in the area to the left of the bar which has a good pub feel, warmed by a roaring fire in winter. Other areas are dedicated to food – Samuel Pepys, who stayed here in 1660, would no doubt approve of the high-quality menu. Four chalet-style rooms overlooking the garden provide accommodation. The sign commemorates the 339th Fighter Group of the USAF who were based nearby. Q❀P (31)

Glatton

Addison Arms L

Sawtry Road, PE28 5RZ

☎ (01487) 830410 🌐 addison-arms.co.uk

Digfield Fools Nook; house beer (by Digfield) [H]**; 2 changing beers (sourced regionally; often Digfield, Nene Valley)** [H]/[G]

Grade II listed pub built at the start of the 18th century and named after playwright and politician Joseph Addison (co-founder of The Spectator), who was a relative of the first landlord. The pub offers at least three real ales – the house beer, Addison Ale, is Digfield Shacklebush. Food prepared from fresh locally sourced supplies is popular. A thriving Sunday night quiz is hosted weekly. The large beer garden is busy in the summer.

Q❀♿♣P (46A)

Hartford

King of the Belgians L

27 Main Street, PE29 1XU (on old village high st)

☎ (01480) 52030 🌐 kingofthebelgians.com

4 changing beers (sourced locally; often Digfield, Elgood's, Nene Valley)

This 16th-century pub at the heart of the community actively supports local charities. It hosts a beer festival in May and another in late August. An ever-changing selection of four real ales, ciders and good-value food is served every day. The public bar is characterised by its low oak beams and a copper-topped bar, and there is a peaceful separate dining area. Entertainment includes regular quizzes, games nights and an open mic night on the first Monday of each month. Local CAMRA Cider Pub of the Year 2020. Q❀♣P

Helpston

Bluebell L

10 Woodgate, PE6 7ED

☎ (01733) 252394 🌐 bluebellhelpston.co.uk

Adnams Ghost Ship; St Austell Trelawny; 1 changing beer (often Black Sheep, Fuller's) H
Quiet 17th-century stone village pub with its main entrance to the side of the building. There are two wood-panelled bars, a number of dining areas, and a snug named after local poet John Clare who worked in the pub as a pot boy and lived next door. Beers come from Adnams and Castor, plus two rotating guests from breweries around the country. Good-value food is served lunchtime and evening. Q ⑤ ❀ ◑ ⓘ ♿ ♣ ♠ P ⊟ ❀ 🛜

Hemingford Grey

Cock L

47 High Street, PE28 9BJ (off A14, SE of Huntingdon)
☎ (01480) 463609 ⊕ thecockhemingford.co.uk
Adnams Southwold Bitter; Brewsters Hophead; 1 changing beer H
A short walk from the River Great Ouse, this village inn and restaurant has won local, regional and national awards. The cosy pub is popular with locals who enjoy the well-kept locally sourced beers. The separate restaurant features an extensive fish board, meat, game and excellent home-made sausages (booking essential at all times). During the summer, occasional beer festivals are held in the beer garden. Q ❀ ◑ ⓘ ♿ ♠ P ❀ 🛜

Histon

Red Lion L ✅

27 High Street, CB24 9JD
☎ (01223) 564437 ⊕ theredlionhiston.co.uk
Adnams Ghost Ship; Tring Side Pocket for a Toad; 6 changing beers (often Batemans, Lacons) H
Two-bar free house adorned with a wonderful collection of breweriana and historical photos. The nine handpumps are in the right-hand bar which is quieter and child-free. Guest beers always include a mild. Belgian and German beers are also on draught plus a range of world bottled beers, two ciders and a perry. Two beer festivals are held each year – the Easter aperitif and the main event in September – with proceeds going to local charities. The left-hand bar welcomes families and dogs. ⑤ ❀ ≠ ◑ ⓘ ♿ ♣ ♠ P ⊟ 🛜

Holme

Admiral Wells L

41 Station Road, PE7 3PH (jct of B660 and Yaxley Rd)
☎ (01487) 831214 ⊕ admiralwells.co.uk
Adnams Southwold Bitter, Ghost Ship, Broadside; 3 changing beers (often Digfield, Oakham, Woodforde's) H
Officially the lowest-level pub in the UK. This Victorian inn was named after one of Nelson's pallbearers, William Wells, by its builder. Following a facelift it now has two bar/lounge areas in a modern contemporary style, a conservatory and a function room at the rear. Outside there is a beer garden at the front, a large car park to the side, a marquee with a bar in summer, and a children's play area. Six ales are usually served, including two sourced locally and one alcohol-free. Quiz night is Tuesday. Q ⑤ ❀ ◑ ⓘ ♣ ♠ P ❀ 🛜

Horningsea

Plough & Fleece ✅

High Street, CB25 9JG
☎ (01223) 860795 ⊕ theploughandfleece.com
4 changing beers H
Since 2012 the Plough & Fleece has been owned by the village following a community buy-out. The low-beamed

front room is set for dining, apart from stools and high tables close to the bar. The main bar is in the back room which has a conservatory extension. The large garden has views over the fields on the Cam. Four changing cask ales come from many small breweries. The menu features locally sourced produce. ⑤ ❀ ◑ ⓘ ♿ ♣ ♠ P ⊟ (196) ❀ 🛜

Houghton

Three Horseshoes

St Ives Road, PE28 2BE (off A1123)
☎ (01480) 462410 ⊕ threehorseshoesinnhoughton.co.uk
Greene King IPA; Oakham JHB; Sharp's Doom Bar; 1 changing beer G
Characterful Grade II listed 17th-century building in a picturesque village, popular with locals as well as walkers and cyclists. The lane opposite leads to the river and the historic Houghton Mill. There are two bar areas and plenty of space for diners. The real ales, usually including one from a local brewery, are served by gravity dispense from a taproom behind the bar. Home-cooked food is available daily (not Mon and Tue in winter months). Q ⑤ ❀ ≠ ◑ ⓘ ♿ ♠ P ❀ 🛜

Huntingdon

Old Bridge Hotel L ✅

1 High Street, PE29 3TQ (at S end of High St on ring road)
☎ (01480) 424300 ⊕ huntsbridge.com
3 changing beers (sourced locally; often Adnams, Lacons, Nene Valley) H
An ivy-clad hotel in what was a private bank in the 18th-century, at the southern end of the High Street with a prominent position beside the River Great Ouse. Enjoy imaginative and high-quality food in the Terrace Restaurant, the covered patio and the garden area or simply relax with a drink in the bar or lounge. The award-winning Old Bridge Wine Shop offers wine tasting. The bus station is a short walk away. Q ⑤ ❀ ◑ ⓘ ♿ ♠ P ⊟ ❀ 🛜

Sandford House L ✅

George Street, PE29 3AD
☎ (01480) 432402
Greene King Abbot; Sharp's Doom Bar; 3 changing beers (sourced nationally; often B&T, Oakham, Titanic) H
A stylish conversion of two Victorian buildings by Wetherspoon which offers several different drinking and dining areas. Sandford House is built on the site of the original Huntingdon Theatre, a chapel dating from 1848, and was the home of the local Victorian industrialist Charles Sandford Windover. More recently, the building was the town's post office and a furniture retailer. Wetherspoon's standard wide range of good-value food and drink is available. A 22-room hotel is at the rear of the pub. ⑤ ❀ ≠ ◑ ⓘ ♿ ≒ ♠ 🛜

Leverington

Rising Sun Inn L

Dowgate Road, PE13 5DH
☎ (01945) 583754
Elgood's Cambridge Bitter; 2 changing beers (often Elgood's) H
Comfortably furnished pub with an enclosed garden. It dates back to at least 1872 and was refurbished a few years ago, but the bar retains the feel of a true village local. It serves Cambridge Bitter and two changing beers including Elgood's seasonals and guest beers. Well known for good-value quality food, the restaurant hosts

regular themed nights – Wednesday is steak night. Dogs and children are welcome. Closing time may be early if there is no trade. A former CAMRA branch Gold Award winner. ❀◑♣P🚌(50)🐾📶

Little Downham

Plough

106 Main Street, CB6 2SX (W end of village)
☎ (01353) 698297
2 changing beers (sourced regionally) Ⓗ
An early-Victorian Grade II listed pub, well preserved in character and charm. At least two changing regional cask ales are usually on handpump. An annual beer festival is held in early September. Excellent Thai cuisine is available to eat in or take away. The pub supports traditional pub games and local customs, and has a good community spirit. Children are welcome until 9pm. ♨❀◑♣P🚌(125)

Little Gransden

Chequers L

71 Main Road, SG19 3DW
☎ (01767) 677348 🌐 chequersgransden.co.uk
4 changing beers (sourced locally) Ⓗ
Village pub owned and run by the same family for over 60 years and in this Guide for more than 25 years. The unspoilt middle bar, with its wooden benches, roaring fire and collection of decoy birds gathering on the beam over the bar, is a favourite spot to pick up on the local gossip. The Chequers' Son of Sid brewhouse supplies the pub and local beer festivals. Friday is fish & chips night (booking essential). A winner of numerous CAMRA awards, and a Pub of the Year finalist in 2018. Q❀◗⛺●P🚍🚌🐾📶

March

Rose & Crown L ✔

41 St Peters Road, PE15 9NA
☎ (01354) 652077
St Austell Cornish Best Bitter; 6 changing beers (often Oakham, Tydd Steam) Ⓗ
Traditional community pub, over 150 years old, with two carpeted rooms and low-beamed ceilings. There is a real fire in the main bar and a pool table in the smaller bar. Six real ales are usually on offer, mainly from microbreweries, including one from Oakham, and up to seven traditional ciders and a perry. A mini beer festival is held at Easter time. A large selection of gins and single malts is also available. Good-quality food is served lunchtime and evening. Quiz night is Thursday. Q❀◑●P🚌📶

Ship Inn L

1 Nene Parade, PE15 8TD
☎ (01354) 607878
Woodforde's Wherry; 4 changing beers (often Church End, Tydd Steam) Ⓗ
Thatched Grade II listed riverside pub, built in 1680, with extensive riverside moorings. Its unusual carved beams are said to have 'fallen off a barge' during the building of Ely Cathedral. A quaint wobbly floor and wall lead to the toilets and a small games room. Reopened as a free house in 2010, following a major refit, the Ship has a friendly and welcoming atmosphere. It features a large collection of pumpclips. Attractions include monthly music from local bands and an annual beer festival in September. Winner of a CAMRA Gold Award in 2019. Q♨❀◖♣🚌🐾📶

Maxey

Blue Bell L

39 High Street, PE6 9EE
☎ (01778) 348182
Abbeydale Absolution; Fuller's London Pride, ESB; Oakham Bishops Farewell; 5 changing beers (sourced regionally; often Grainstore, Oakham, Woodforde's) Ⓗ
Originally a limestone barn, the building was converted many years ago and reflects the rural setting in which it is found. Paraphernalia of country life adorn the stone walls and shelves of the two-roomed interior. Nine handpumps dispense a range of quality ales from large and small breweries far and wide. The pub is a popular meeting place for groups including birdwatchers and golfers. A former Peterborough CAMRA Pub of the Year and Gold Award winner. Q❀♣P🚌(22,413)🐾📶

Needingworth

Pike & Eel

Overcote Lane, PE27 4TW (down a long lane off High St in centre of village)
☎ (01480) 463336 🌐 pikeandeel.com
3 changing beers (sourced regionally; often Adnams, Greene King) Ⓗ
Large riverside hotel and restaurant based around an old building dating from the 1700s with modern extensions. The oak-panelled bar and cosy snug with large inglenook fireplace are at the heart of the original building. A lounge area next to the bar is divided into a number of intimate areas with sofas. The Garden Room restaurant looks out over the river. The hotel offers 13 en-suite rooms. There is a large garden and a popular marina with moorings for up to 180 boats. Q❀🛏◑♿P

Newton

Queen's Head

Fowlmere Road, CB22 7PG
☎ (01223) 870436
Adnams Southwold Bitter, Broadside; 2 changing beers Ⓖ
Change comes gradually to this village local, one of a handful of pubs to have appeared in every edition of this Guide. Beers from brewers other than Adnams are now available from the stillage directly behind the bar. Regular Sunday lunches, a monthly Saturday supper club and Wednesday night food vans have been added to the soup and sandwiches on offer. Otherwise, little has changed since 1974. In fact, a list of landlords displayed in the public bar has only 18 entries since 1729. Q◑♣●P🚌(31)🐾

Peterborough

Bumble Inn

46 Westgate, PE1 1RE
🌐 thebimbleinn.wordpress.com
5 changing beers (sourced nationally) Ⓗ
Local CAMRA Pub of the Year for 2018, this micropub opened in 2016 in what used to be a chemist's shop. Minimalist in style, it has five handpumps dispensing quality ales from far and wide, so expect the unusual. Order a taster paddle of three third-pints if you want to try a selection. Rare bottled and canned beers are also stocked plus two craft keg beers, Korev Cornish keg lager and two ciders. The pub's own Bumbling Brewery beers may also be available. Regular tap takeovers and food nights are hosted. Tea, coffee, soft drinks and home-made pies are also on offer. 🚆●🚌📶

Charters

Town Bridge, PE1 1FP (down steps at Town Bridge)
☎ (01733) 315700 🌐 charters-bar.co.uk
Oakham JHB, Inferno, Citra, Bishops Farewell; 4 changing beers (often Nene Valley) Ⓗ/Ⓖ
The converted Dutch grain barge from circa 1907 sits on the River Nene near the city centre. An oriental restaurant is on the upper deck and food is also served in the bar. Up to 12 beers are on offer plus cider. The large garden with a marquee, bar and landing stage for boats is popular in summer. Live music plays some weekends and in summer outside the pub. It gets busy on football match days. Close to the Nene Valley Railway. Local CAMRA Cider Pub of the Year 2020. 🐎❀◐♣🍎P🚌🐾📶

Draper's Arms

29-31 Cowgate, PE1 1LZ
☎ (01733) 847570
Brewsters Hophead; Grainstore Ten Fifty; Greene King Abbot; Ruddles Best Bitter; Sharp's Doom Bar; 5 changing beers (often Brewsters, Oakham) Ⓗ
A converted former draper's shop, built in 1899 and one of two Wetherspoon pubs in the city. The beer range, with many from local microbreweries, is dispensed through 10 handpumps. The interior is broken up with dividers and wood-panelled intimate spaces. Food is served all day and regular beer and cider festivals are held throughout the year. Quiz night is Wednesday. A regular top 10 real ale pub within the company chain. Close to bus and railway stations. Q🐎◐♿🚆🍎🚌📶

Frothblowers

78 Storrington Way, Werrington, PE4 6QP
☎ 07756 066503 🌐 frothblowers.site
7 changing beers (sourced regionally; often Digfield, Hopshackle, Tydd Steam)
This micropub is easily accessed by bus from the city centre, and is on the No.1 bus Ale Trail. It has five handpumps, and more beers available in the cellar, as well as at least 25 ciders and bottled beers. A hub of the local community, activities include tap takeovers, acoustic music sessions, bus tours, a summer cycling club, knitting club, monthly grub club and cider festivals. Voted Peterborough and Cambridgeshire CAMRA Pub of the Year in 2019, it retained the title for 2020.
🐎❀♿♣🍎P🚏🚌(1)🐾

Hand & Heart ★

12 Highbury Street, PE1 3BE
☎ (01733) 564653 🌐 thehandandheart.com
6 changing beers (sourced regionally; often Brewsters, Rockingham, Tydd Steam) Ⓗ/Ⓖ
Rebuilt in 1938, this Art Deco-style community local is on CAMRA's National Inventory of Historic Pub Interiors. The rear room is connected to the main public bar, with its war memorial and real fire, by a drinking corridor. Traditional pub games are played. Six handpumped ales are available, with more from the cellar. The range is eclectic and forever changing. Beer festivals with live music are held in the large garden on St George's Day and in September, with occasional mini fests through the summer. A Guide regular for over 10 years and a former local CAMRA branch and county Pub of the Year.
Q🐎❀♣🍎🚌(1)🐾📶

Ostrich Inn

17 North Street, PE1 2RA
☎ 07307 195560 🌐 ostrichinnpeterborough.com
Oakham JHB; 4 changing beers (sourced regionally; often King's Cliffe, Nene Valley, St Austell) Ⓗ
Refurbished in 2009, this relaxing side-street pub reopened with its original name restored. The single-room interior has a U-shaped bar and features many pictures for sale by local artists. Up to five regularly changing real ales are on offer, many from local breweries, alongside craft keg and 10 KeyKeg lines. A large gin selection is also stocked. Live music plays most weekends. The small enclosed patio is a suntrap. Popular on football match days. 🐎❀♿🚆♣🍎🚌🐾

Palmerston Arms

82 Oundle Road, PE2 9PA
☎ (01733) 565865
Batemans Gold, XXXB Ⓖ**; Castle Rock Harvest Pale; Oakham Citra** Ⓗ/Ⓖ**; 10 changing beers (sourced regionally; often Lacons, Ossett, St Austell)** Ⓖ
Popular 400-year-old listed stone-built locals' pub. Owned by Batemans, three of its beers are rotated alongside nine or more other real ales, including some from Oakham. Traditional cider, perry and an extensive range of malt whiskies are also available. Most beers are served straight from the cellar, which can be seen through a large glass screen. Rolls and a variety of snacks tempt customers. Live music features most weekends and philosophy nights on occasion. Busy on football match days. ❀♣🍎🚌(1,24)🐾📶

Ploughman

1 Staniland Way, Werrington, PE4 6NA
☎ (01733) 327696
6 changing beers (sourced regionally; often Castor Ales, Hopshackle, Tiny Rebel) Ⓗ
A rejuvenated two-roomed community pub brought to the forefront of the city's real ale outlets by the enthusiastic licensee. Six handpumps serve beers from local breweries and further afield. Many activities and charity events are held regularly as well as live music at weekends. A well-supported annual beer festival is hosted in early July. A former local CAMRA Pub of the Year. 🐎❀♣🍎P🚌(1,22)

Wonky Donkey

102C High Street, Fletton, PE2 8DR
☎ 07835 594104
Phipps NBC India Pale Ale; 7 changing beers (sourced locally; often Digfield, Mile Tree, Tydd Steam) Ⓗ/Ⓖ
Micropub housed in two rooms of a former florist's, situated in a previously pub-free area. Eight beers, many straight from the cask, mostly LocAles and always including a dark ale, are available, alongside a large range of ciders, wines and gins, plus quality bottled lagers. House specials are created by local brewery Mile Tree. Themed evenings include pop-up food nights, cheapskate Tuesday (all ales £3) and a quiz every Thursday. 🐎♿♣🍎🚏🚌(5)🐾

Yard of Ale

72 Oundle Road, PE2 9PA
☎ (01733) 348000 🌐 theyardofalepub.co.uk
Lacons Encore; Rooster's Yankee; Sharp's Doom Bar; house beer (by Digfield); 5 changing beers (often Digfield, Woodforde's) Ⓗ
Built on land that was part of the nearby Palmerston Arms stable yard, this 120-year-old pub was refurbished and reopened in early 2017. Decorated in shades of grey with a warm wooden bar and surround, the large open-plan single room is divided into four distinct areas by the central supporting structure. Entertainment includes live sports TV, darts and pool. Outside is a large beer garden with a pizza oven used in summer. Live music features most weekends. CAMRA branch LocAle Pub of the Year 2019. 🐎❀♣🍎🚌(1)📶

Ramsey

Angel
76 High Street, PE26 1BS
☎ (01487) 711968
Adnams Ghost Ship; Greene King Abbot; 2 changing beers (often Lacons, Tydd Steam) Ⓗ
This traditional brick-built two-room pub was refurbished in 2019. Entry to the main bar area is via the rear car park and beer garden, and it has two dartboards, a jukebox and a pool table. The lounge is accessed from the main road. Friendly staff and locals help provide a great venue to enjoy a drink or two, with a LocAle always available, usually from Tydd Steam. ♣P (31)

St Ives

Nelson's Head
Merryland, PE27 5ED
☎ (01480) 494454 nelsonsheadstives.pub
Greene King IPA, Abbot; Morland Old Speckled Hen; 2 changing beers (sourced regionally; often Grainstore, Nene Valley, Oakham) Ⓗ
Greene King pub in a picturesque narrow street, refitted in the popular alehouse style in the late 1990s. It offers three regular and two changing ales from local breweries, often including a dark beer. Local Cromwell cider is a permanent feature. Meals are served at lunchtime and pizza in the evening. On Sunday afternoon live bands perform and the pub gets extremely busy. A former Hunts CAMRA LocAle Pub of the Year.

Royal Oak
13 Crown Street, PE27 5EB
☎ (01480) 462586
Oakham Inferno; 3 changing beers (often Brewsters, Newby Wyke, Oakham) Ⓗ
One of a number of historic listed pubs in St Ives. Despite the date 1502 over the door, most of the building is from the 18th century. The multi-room layout has been preserved. Changing beers are from local SIBA breweries and often include a porter. Live sporting events are shown on several TV screens, and live music plays on Saturday nights. A locals' pub, but visitors are always made to feel welcome. ♣

St Neots

Ale Taster
25 Russell Street, PE19 1BA
☎ (01480) 581368
6 changing beers (sourced regionally) Ⓖ
A small, traditional, back-street pub operated in the style of a micropub. It features up to three changing ales served from stillage behind the bar, and up to nine real ciders and perries. The owners source beer and cider from local producers as much as possible, and are happy to chat about their beers. Three large fridges display a wide selection of bottled beers from around the world. The pub encourages conversation, with quiet background music and no electronic machines. Traditional bar games are played here. Q♣P (X5)

Olde Sun
11 Huntingdon Street, PE19 1BL
☎ (01480) 216863
Adnams Ghost Ship; Woodforde's Wherry; 2 changing beers (often Adnams, Elgood's, Woodforde's) Ⓗ
Low-beamed and cosy traditional town-centre pub with two large inglenook fireplaces, three bar areas and a secluded patio. The jukebox is zoned, allowing quiet areas for conversation. Shove-ha'penny and bar billiards are played. Five constantly changing guest beers come from various regional breweries including Adnams, Elgood's, Marston's, Thwaites and Woodforde's. A mild and other dark beers are usually among the range. A former local CAMRA Mild/Dark Ales Pub of the Year. ♣ (X5)

Pig 'n' Falcon
9 New Street, PE19 1AE (behind Barretts department store)
☎ 07951 785678 pignfalcon.co.uk
Greene King IPA Ⓗ**, Abbot** Ⓖ**; Potbelly Best** Ⓗ**; 5 changing beers (sourced locally; often Potbelly, Three Blind Mice)** Ⓖ
This busy town-centre free house has up to six real ales and five real ciders, focusing on beers from microbreweries and unusual choices including milds, porters and stouts. A good range of bottled ciders, UK and foreign bottled beers includes Trappist ales. Beer festivals are held throughout the year. Live blues and rock nights are hosted Wednesday to Sunday. Outside is a large, imaginative, covered and heated beer garden. Three Blind Mice beers are real ale served in KeyKegs.
(X5)

Shepreth

Plough
12 High Street, SG8 6PP
☎ (01763) 290348 theploughshepreth.co.uk
4 changing beers (sourced regionally) Ⓗ
Saved from conversion to residential use and reopened in 2014 after extensive renovation, the Plough has a large bar facing the entrance, with a Spitfire-themed drinking area to the right and a larger music-themed seating area to the left. Doors lead to a spacious patio and garden. Cask beers come from small local or regional breweries, and craft keg beers include some from BrewBoard Brewery. A wide range of mostly local real ciders is also available. Frequent live music, comedy and quiz nights are hosted. Local CAMRA Cider Pub of the Year 2018, 2019 and 2020. ♿P

Stapleford

Three Horseshoes
2 Church Street, CB22 5DS
☎ (01223) 503402 threehorseshoes-pub.com
Adnams Southwold Bitter; 6 changing beers Ⓗ
Friendly village local on the southern fringe of Cambridge, attracting the local community and visitors from surrounding villages. It has three areas – the main bar, a small room to the left, and a large room with a TV projector to the right. It stocks a selection of bottled beers. There is a sheltered beer garden at the back. A variety of food is available, with the accent on traditional Cypriot and Greek dishes. Local CAMRA Most Improved Rural Pub of the Year 2020. P

Stretham

Red Lion
47 High Street, CB6 3JQ
☎ (01353) 648132 redlionstretham.com
Marston's Saddle Tank; 2 changing beers (sourced nationally) Ⓗ
A renovated 17th-century pub, set at the heart of the village. It has a traditional public bar and a more relaxed saloon, with extensions to the rear providing extra facilities including a pleasant restaurant in the conservatory. There is seating outside and a heated smoking area in the patio garden. Disabled access is via

the rear of the pub. A bus stop is opposite. B&B accommodation is available in 11 rooms.
⌂☆✉◑●P◳☺☂

Upware

Five Miles Inn
Old School Lane, CB7 5ZR
☎ (01353) 721654 ⊕ fivemilesinn.com
Morland Old Speckled Hen; 3 changing beers (sourced regionally) Ⓗ
The pub's full name is The Five Miles From Anywhere No Hurry Inn. It is located off the beaten track, next to the River Cam, overlooking part of the Fens. Four ales are on handpump with an occasional fifth beer direct from the cask during the summer, along with one real cider. A selection of food is available in the bar and separate restaurant. The pub has visitor moorings and services for narrowboats and motor cruisers, and there is a large car park for those arriving by land. ⌂☆◑&▲♣●P☺☂

Waterbeach

Sun Inn ✅
Chapel Street, CB25 9HR
☎ (01223) 861254
Young's London Original; 3 changing beers Ⓗ
Traditional pub overlooking the village green, offering a changing list of interesting and local ales, often including a dark beer. The small, cosy lounge is dominated by a huge fireplace, while the simply appointed public bar, with its woodblock floor, is always lively. There is a small meeting room and a function room upstairs where regular gigs are hosted. An annual beer and music festival is held over the early May bank holiday weekend. There is no food on Monday or Sunday evening. ⌂☆◑&≈♣●◳(9)☺☂

West Wratting

Chestnut Tree
1 Mill Road, CB21 5LT
☎ (01223) 290384 ⊕ chestnuttreepub.co.uk
Greene King IPA; 3 changing beers Ⓗ
Impressive two-bar Victorian-style pub with modern extensions creating a roomy, comfortable interior. The lounge to the right is mainly set out for dining. To the left is a nicely furnished public bar with a pool table. This friendly pub hosts darts, pool and pétanque teams, and has a small lending library. It has been free of tie since the present owners bought it in 2012. Its three changing beers are mainly from micros, often local. Local CAMRA Pub of the Year 2019 and Rural Community Pub of the Year 2019. Q⌂☆◑♣●P◳(19)☺

Whittlesey

Boat Inn Ⓛ
2 Ramsey Road, PE7 1DR
☎ (01733) 202488 ⊕ quinnboatinn.wordpress.com

Pitchfork Ⓗ; 4 changing beers (sourced regionally; often Grainstore) Ⓗ/Ⓖ
This corner pub has two rooms – a public bar with sports TV and a cosy lounge. Up to 17 traditional ciders and perries supplement the real ales, some of which are served direct from the cask. A whisky club is hosted on the second Friday of the month and there are regular trips to tasting events. Outside is a pétanque terrain which is used by dancers at the Straw Bear Festival in January each year, when there is also an outside bar. ⌂☆✉&●P◳(31)☺☂

George Hotel ✅
10 Market Place, PE7 1AB
☎ (01733) 359970
Adnams Ghost Ship; Greene King Abbot; Oakham Bishops Farewell; Ruddles Best Bitter; Sharp's Doom Bar; 5 changing beers Ⓗ
Built in the town square in the late 1700s, this building was significantly altered in the mid-19th century before getting a Grade II listing in 1974. A busy Wetherspoon pub since 2010, it offers a large selection of real ales and at least two ciders alongside the typical well-priced food menu. There are many pictures around the walls depicting local history, including how the town gained its name, and details about the extensive drainage work that created the East Anglian Fens. ⌂☆◑&●P◳(31,33,701) ☂

Letter B Ⓛ
53-57 Church Street, PE7 1DE
☎ (01733) 206975 ⊕ theletterb.co.uk
Sharp's Doom Bar; 4 changing beers (often Digfield, Tydd Steam) Ⓗ
The Letter B is over 200 years old, with two bars, a small side room with a bar billiards table, and a decked rear patio area. A beer festival is held in January during the Straw Bear Festival weekend, which is popular with locals and visitors. Over recent years the cider range has expanded rapidly to complement the five real ales. A winner of numerous local CAMRA awards including County Pub of the Year and County Cider Pub of the Year. Accommodation is available.
Q⌂☆✉♣●◳(31,33) ☺☂

Willingham

Bank Micropub
9 High Street, CB24 5ES
☎ (01954) 200045 ⊕ thebankmicropub.co.uk
5 changing beers Ⓖ
Formerly a village bank, this single-room micropub opened in 2012. It has a short bar rescued from a closed Cambridge pub. The walls are decorated with photos of local interest. Up to five real ales are available direct from the cask or KeyKeg, with regional and local beers featuring strongly. A large range of craft ales includes three served from kegs. The Bank offers a warm welcome and the casual visitor is certain to be included in local conversation. Q♣●☐◳☺

Noted ales

At one time or another nearly every county town in England of any size has been noted for its beers or ales. Yorkshire claims not only stingo but also Hull and North Allerton ales whilst Nottingham, Lichfield, Derby, Oxford and Burton have almost branded their ales. During the eighteenth century the fame of Dorchester beer almost equalled the popularity of London porter.

Frank A. King, Beer has a History, 1947

LocAle

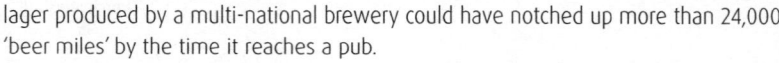

Many entries in the Guide refer to pubs' support for CAMRA's LocAle scheme. The L symbol is used where a pub has LocAle accreditation. The aim of the scheme is to get publicans to stock at least one cask beer that comes from a local brewery, usually no more than 30 miles away.

The aim is a simple one: to cut down on 'beer miles'. Research by CAMRA shows that food and drink transport accounts for 25 per cent of all HGV vehicle miles in Britain. Taking into account the miles that ingredients have travelled on top of distribution journeys, an imported lager produced by a multi-national brewery could have notched up more than 24,000 'beer miles' by the time it reaches a pub.

Supporters of LocAle point out that £10 spent on locally-supplied goods generates £25 for the local economy. Keeping trade local helps enterprises, creates more economic activity and jobs, and makes other services more viable. The scheme also generates consumer support for local breweries.

Support for LocAle has grown at a rapid pace since it was created in 2007. It's been embraced by pubs and CAMRA branches throughout England and has now crossed the borders into Scotland and Wales.

For more information, see camra.org.uk/locale

What is CAMRA LocAle?

- An initiative that promotes pubs which sell locally-brewed real ale
- The scheme builds on a growing consumer demand for quality local produce and an increased awareness of 'green' issues

Everyone benefits from local pubs stocking locally brewed real ale...

- Public houses, as stocking local real ales can increase pub visits
- Consumers, who enjoy greater beer choice and locally brewed beer
- Local brewers, who gain from increased sales and get better feedback from consumers
- The local economy, because more money is spent and retained in the local economy
- The environment, due to fewer 'beer miles' resulting in less road congestion and pollution
- Tourism, due to an increased sense of local identity and pride – let's celebrate what makes our locality different

CHESHIRE

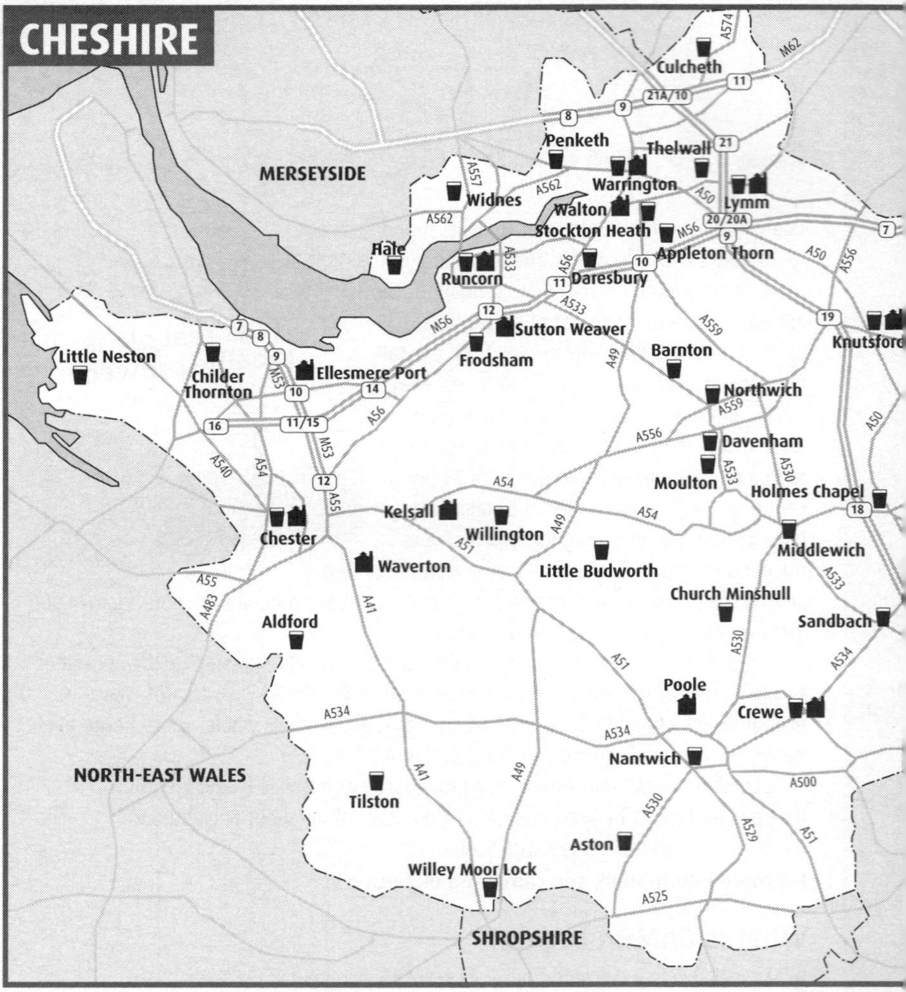

Aldford

Grosvenor Arms 𝕃

Chester Road, CH3 6HJ (on B5130)

☎ (01244) 620228 🌐 grosvenorarms-aldford.co.uk

Timothy Taylor Landlord; Weetwood Eastgate; house beer (by Phoenix); 4 changing beers (sourced nationally) Ⓗ

A spacious, stylish and unashamedly upmarket pub. Full of character, it is multi-roomed with a pleasant garden room leading to an outside terrace and lawn with picnic tables. Inside, the decor is modern-traditional with lots of bare wood, bookcases, pictures and chalkboards. Four changing beers, which occasionally include a mild, complement the house beer brewed by Phoenix, plus beers from Weetwood and Timothy Taylor. High-quality food from an imaginative menu is popular and served all day. Q❀◑♿♣●P🚌(5)🐾📶

Alsager

Lodge 𝕃

88 Crewe Road, ST7 2JA (jct Crewe Rd and Station Rd)

☎ (01270) 873669

House beer (by Marston's); 7 changing beers (sourced nationally; often Dark Star, Oakham) Ⓗ

A variety of pamphlets and flyers greets you on entry, showing you are in a true community pub. Turn left into a well-stocked bar, offering eight different local and national beers. On colder days the open fire is welcome. A pleasing beer garden is accessed from the rear of the room, and there is another bar. A wide selection of ciders, wines, spirits and bottled beers, including low alcohol ones, is also available. Traditional bar snacks are served. Q❀●P🚌🐾

Appleton Thorn

Appleton Thorn Village Hall

Stretton Road, WA4 4RT

☎ (01925) 261187 🌐 appletonthornvillagehall.co.uk

7 changing beers (sourced nationally; often 4Ts, Bingley, Mallinsons) Ⓗ

At the hub of the community and a CAMRA multi-award winner including National Club of the Year, the Village Hall has a central bar serving a function room and smaller, comfortable lounge. A changing choice of seven ales is on offer, from regional and microbreweries, with

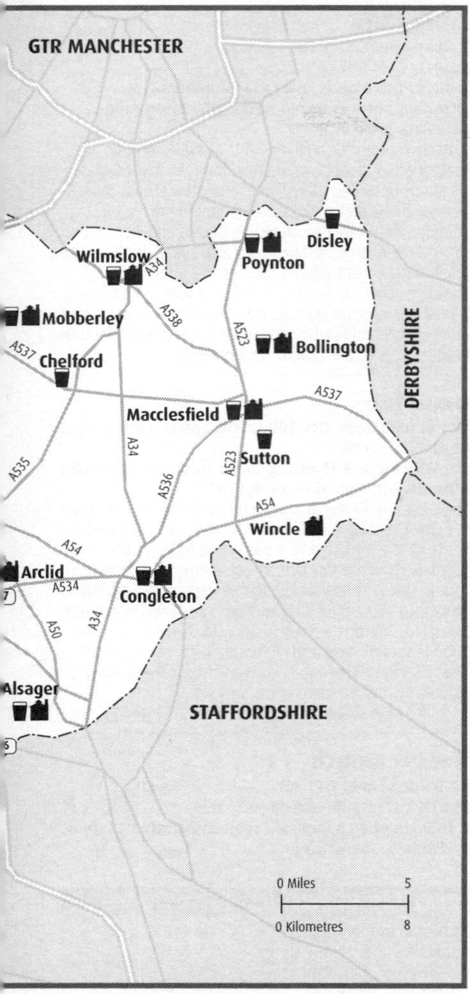

paddles of third-pint tasters available, together with five real ciders. Regular live music and quiz nights are held, and there's an annual beer festival in October. Non-members pay a minimal fee for admission.
Q ♘ ✿ ◐ ♿ ♣ ● P ⊡ 🚌 🐾 📶

Aston

Bhurtpore 🏆 L

Wrenbury Road, CW5 8DQ (just off A530)
☎ (01270) 780917 🌐 bhurtpore.co.uk
11 changing beers (sourced nationally) H
Winner of CAMRA Cheshire Pub of the Year in 2019, this fine country pub boasts 28 consecutive years in the Guide. It has a relaxed, timeless atmosphere in the main bar, with a lovely open fire, where you can enjoy 11 real ales, usually including a dark beer, with many from local breweries, plus a large selection of bottled beers and continental beers on tap. There is a separate restaurant where excellent home-made food is available (curries a speciality), a bar room with a pool table, and the garden to the rear. It is named after Bharatpur, a fortress city in India, shown in colour photos in the side snug.
Q ♘ ✿ ◐ ♿ ⛺ ● P 🚌 (72) 🐾 📶

Barnton

Barnton Cricket Club L

Broomsedge, Townfield Lane, CW8 4QL (down narrow drive to left of Barnton Community Primary School)
☎ (01606) 77702 🌐 barntoncc.co.uk
Sharp's Doom Bar; 3 changing beers (sourced nationally) H
The Pavilion is arranged into two distinct rooms – the large Broomsedge Suite (proudly displaying an extensive range of CAMRA awards above the bar), where Sky and BT sports are shown on a projected screen, and the more intimate Townfield Lounge. The patio overlooks the cricket field. A popular beer festival is held in July. Squash, crown green bowls, darts and dominoes are all played here. Show your CAMRA membership card for admission. A former CAMRA National Club of the Year.
♘ ✿ ◐ ♿ ♣ P 🚌 (4,46)

Bollington

Cotton Tree ✔

3-5 Ingersley Road, SK10 5RE
☎ 07458 302857
Adnams Southwold Bitter; Draught Bass; Sharp's Sea Fury; Wainwright; Weetwood Cheshire Cat; 1 changing beer (sourced nationally) H
The Cotton Tree is a friendly, family-run drinkers' pub. This traditional back-street local is on the corner of a terrace, built of stone, with a stone floor and warmed by a roaring fire in winter. It is opposite the bus terminus and features an array of local transport-themed memorabilia. Six real ales are available including one guest, plus six Westons ciders. There is a secluded beer garden. CAMRA branch Cider Pub of the Year 2020.
♘ ✿ ♣ 🚌 🐾 📶

Poachers Inn L

95 Ingersley Road, SK10 5RE
☎ (01625) 572086 🌐 thepoachers.org
Storm Beauforts Ale; Weetwood Old Dog; 3 changing beers (sourced locally) H
Popular, family-run, community free house near the Gritstone Trail and Peak District National Park. It supports local breweries, with regular ales from Storm and Weetwood, alongside three guests including a dark beer, plus two real ciders and a selection of bottled beers. Good-value home-prepared food features locally sourced ingredients. With a coal fire in winter and a suntrap garden in summer, the pub is welcoming at any time of year. ♘ ✿ ◐ ● P 🚌 (10) 🐾 📶

Vale Inn L ✔

29-31 Adlington Road, SK10 5JT
☎ (01625) 575147 🌐 valeinn.co.uk
Bollington White Nancy, Long Hop, Best, Dinner Ale, Oat Mill Stout, Eastern Nights H
Bollington Brewery and its outlet The Vale are visible from the viaduct of the former railway and handily located for walkers or cyclists near the Middlewood Way. This is a stone mid-terrace pub with a separate beer garden overlooking the recreation ground – a great spot for watching the cricket. Six Bollington beers are available in a range of styles plus two guest ciders. Good home-cooked food is served – booking advisable at busy times. ♘ ✿ ◐ ♣ ● P 🚌 (10) 🐾 📶

Chelford

Egerton Arms L

Knutsford Road, SK11 9BB
☎ (01625) 861366 🌐 chelfordegertonarms.co.uk

5 changing beers (sourced locally; often RedWillow, Tatton) Ⓗ
Large single-roomed pub with a history dating back to the 15th century, when it served as stables. Table candles and a real fire provide a cosy atmosphere in winter, while the garden can be enjoyed in summer. Popular with diners, there is plenty to interest the casual imbiber, with five changing beers, mostly from local brewers. On weekdays, food service may finish early if the pub is quiet. P (88)

Chester

Big Hand Alehouse

85 Watergate Street, CH1 2LF
☎ (01244) 313276 🌐 alehousechester.pub
6 changing beers (sourced nationally; often Big Hand) Ⓗ
Close to the city walls and racecourse, this building has housed various restaurants and bars, and has now been transformed by Big Hand Brewery into a relaxed alehouse. The six cask beers, usually including at least three ales from Big Hand, are complemented by a real cider and a range of keg beers. There is a bar area and a comfortable side room with adjacent cosy areas, one with a bagatelle table. Food is available (Wed-Sun), including popular roasts on Sunday. Q

Cavern of the Curious Gnome

61 Bridge Street Row East, CH1 1NW
☎ 07856 999895 🌐 thecavernofthecuriousgnome.co.uk
4 changing beers (sourced nationally; often Salopian) Ⓗ
Belgian-themed bar located on Chester's famous Rows. Enter via Paysan wine bar, then ascend the steps up to the Cavern of the Curious Gnome, where a large, colourful papier-mache gnome gazes down on proceedings. Red-and-white spotted toadstool seats plus tables with bench seating catch the eye, with more quirkiness to be found in the decor. Four handpumps serve changing cask ales from North-West and Yorkshire breweries. Belgian offerings include lambics, gueuzes, Trappist ales plus Duvel served on draught.

Cellar

19-21 City Road, CH1 3AE
☎ (01244) 318950 🌐 thecellarchester.co.uk
Timothy Taylor Landlord; 5 changing beers (sourced nationally; often Hawkshead, Marble) Ⓗ
Friendly street-level bar – the name relates to the function room in the cellar below. The bar is renowned for its excellent selection of cask ales – the regular Taylor Landlord is complemented by five guest beers and three real ciders. There is also an extensive range of keg and bottled beers. Sport features on three TV screens. Bar snacks are served, plus free bacon sandwiches on Sunday and free food when major sporting events are screened.

Cornerhouse

4-8 City Road, CH1 3AE
☎ (01244) 347518 🌐 cornerhousechester.com
Salopian Oracle; Timothy Taylor Landlord; 2 changing beers (sourced nationally) Ⓗ
Situated in Chester's thriving Canal Quarter, this attractive candlelit mock-Tudor building features lots of bare brick and wood flooring. It offers two regular beers and two changing ales – usually one dark and one pale – plus an extensive bottled beer selection. Live music is hosted Thursday to Saturday and a quiz on Sunday. There is a free-to-hire function room upstairs. Outdoor seating is at the front of the pub. Food is of the platter variety (cheeses and meats) plus snacks.

Cross Keys

2 Duke Street, CH1 1RP
☎ (01244) 344460
Joule's Pure Blonde, Pale Ale, Slumbering Monk; 3 changing beers (sourced nationally; often Arbor, Salopian, Joule's) Ⓗ
Attractive red-brick building with a stylish interior featuring oak floors, wood panelling and stained-glass windows depicting other Joule's hostelries. Four Joule's beers – three regular and one varying – are complemented by two changing guests and one or two real ciders. A large upstairs room is available for hire. The small terrace beer garden catches the afternoon sunshine. There is always a choice of pies, and a traditional roast on Sunday. The pub hosts a popular quiz on Thursday and live Irish music on the second and fourth Wednesdays of the month.

Deva Tap

121 Brook Street, CH1 3DU (at city end of Hoole Bridge)
☎ (01244) 314440
Rat White Rat; 5 changing beers (sourced regionally; often Ossett, Rat, Thornbridge) Ⓗ
The Deva Tap's long, narrow interior is divided into three – a small seating area by the entrance, a larger seating space in the middle and a bar at the far end. The permanent White Rat beer is complemented by four rotating ales, usually including one dark brew. Four ciders and up to 10 KeyKeg, keg and continental beers are also available. There is outside seating in a small courtyard. Food is served Wednesday-Sunday with various meal deal evenings. The pub is convenient for the railway station. Winter opening hours vary.

Goat & Munch

52 Garden Lane, CH1 4EW
☎ 07973 675298 🌐 goatandmunch.com
4 changing beers (sourced regionally; often Chapter, RedWillow, Salopian) Ⓗ

REAL ALE BREWERIES

4Ts Warrington
Beartown Congleton
Blueball ◆ Runcorn
Bollington Bollington
Brewhouse & Kitchen ▮ Chester
Brewhouse & Kitchen ▮ Wilmslow
Chapter Sutton Weaver
Cheshire Brewhouse Congleton
Coach House Warrington
Goodalls ▮ Alsager
Happy Valley Macclesfield
Lymm Lymm
Manning Congleton
Merlin Arclid
Mobberley Mobberley
Modern Day Monks Warrington (NEW)
Norton Runcorn
Oaks Ellesmere Port
Pied Bull ▮ Chester
Poynton ▮ Poynton
RedWillow Macclesfield
Spitting Feathers Waverton
Stag ▮ Walton
Storm Macclesfield
Tantum Poole (NEW)
Tatton Knutsford
Tom's Tap ◆ Crewe
Weetwood Kelsall
Wincle ◆ Wincle

for up to six guest ales, including a selection of bitters, stouts, milds or porters, many from local breweries. Ciders and perries are listed separately and served from the cellar. Food is available all day (booking advised for busy weekend periods). Outside seating is alongside the canal. Q❀◑♿⚌♣●🚌🐾ᯤ

Olde Cottage 🏆 ✔

34-36 Brook Street, CH1 3DZ

☎ (01244) 324065 🌐 oldecottagechester.co.uk

Otter Bitter; 3 changing beers (sourced nationally; often Sharp's) 🄷

Welcoming and traditional community local on the popular eating and drinking Brook Street between the city centre and railway station. To the left is the games room with pool, darts and a bagatelle table (rarely seen outside Chester). The main bar has another dartboard, a small TV and a real fire for the colder weather. The regular Otter Bitter is supplemented by three guests, one free of tie. Various loyalty and discount schemes are offered. ❀⚌♣🚌ᯤ

Telford's Warehouse 🄻

Canal Basin, Tower Wharf, CH1 4EZ (just off city walls)

☎ (01244) 390090 🌐 telfordswarehousechester.com

Salopian Oracle; Weetwood Cheshire Cat; Young's London Original; 3 changing beers (sourced nationally) 🄷

Converted warehouse with a large glass frontage overlooking the Shropshire Union Canal basin. Some walls retain original features and are adorned with interesting industrial artefacts. Three changing beers are usually from microbreweries, including local ones. The pub is a thriving live music venue, charging admission on some evenings after 9pm. Good-quality food is served, and the upstairs restaurant can be hired for private functions. Outside seating is popular in good weather. An annual beer festival is held in October.
❀◑●P🚌(1A) 🐾ᯤ

Childer Thornton

Halfway House

New Chester Road, CH66 1QN (A41 close to M53 jct 5)

☎ (0151) 339 2202

4 changing beers (sourced nationally; often First Chop Brewing, Ringwood, Weetwood) 🄷

Friendly, traditional former coaching inn dating from the 1770s, based at the midpoint between Chester and New Ferry (note the old prints of the pub and surrounds on the walls). The building retains much of its original character, with several drinking areas offering smart, comfortable seating. A community feel is evident, with darts and

Breakfast is served from 10am with the main menus starting from 12pm. Takeaway food is also available. Accommodation is provided in the form of five comfortable bedrooms. ♉❀🛏◑♿♣P🚌(31,31A)🐾ᯤ

Congleton

BarleyHops 🄻

2 Swan Bank, CW12 1AH

☎ (01260) 270164 🌐 barleyhops.co.uk

3 changing beers 🄷

In an impressive street-corner location, this is a micropub and bottled beer specialist. The plain, single-room bar is cosy and friendly, and you will be drawn readily into conversation. There are three handpumps dispensing predominantly local ales. The bottled beer selection focuses on British brews but there is a small, well-chosen selection of foreign beers, too. Occasional attractions include Meet the Brewer events and specialist spirit evenings. Closing time may vary according to demand.
Q♉♣🚌(38,42) 🐾ᯤ

Beartown Tap 🏆 🄻

18 Willow Street, CW12 1RL

☎ (01260) 270775

Beartown Kodiak, Skinful; 4 changing beers (sourced locally; often Beartown, Manning Brewers) 🄷

The tap for Congleton's Beartown Brewery and Manning Brewers has been a leading real ale outlet in Congleton since 1999 and also offers regular brewery tours. At least five real ales are always available. The traditional, opened-out pub layout has several separate areas. There is an upstairs function room that can be booked for meetings, and a secluded outdoor beer terrace. A community pub for conversation, games, a weekly quiz and occasional music, it also hosts pizza and street food nights. ♉❀♣🚌(92)🐾

Wonky Pear

1A Cross Lane, CW12 3JU

☎ (01260) 278555

3 changing beers (often Beartown, Manning Brewers)

A small, modern bar in a converted shop near the station with a large front window and two log-burners. It typically offers three cask beers, often one from Beartown or Manning. A room upstairs can be reserved for meetings. Tuesday is pizza night and board games are played on Wednesday. There is a monthly vinyl night and occasional live music – other events range from tap takeovers to wreath-making. Families are welcome and a loyalty card is available to regular customers.
⚌🚌(91,94)

range of bottled Belgian beers complements the real ale and cider offerings. Q

Raven

Brookhouse Drive, CW2 6NA (jct Brookhouse Drive and Davenport Avenue/Broadleigh Way)

☎ (01270) 482576

Sharp's Doom Bar; 4 changing beers (sourced regionally; often Salopian, Titanic) Ⓗ

Free house with four handpumps in use, increasing to six at weekends. The Doom Bar is complemented by ever-changing local and nationally sourced beers, plus a variety of non-alcoholic beverages. The pub has two seating areas and a large stage for weekend entertainment, including open mic every Wednesday. There is a pool table, darts and dominoes. Outside is a covered patio, while upstairs is a sun terrace and a recently opened separate bar. P (6,12)

Culcheth

Liberty's Gin Bar 𝕃

25 Common Lane, WA3 4EW

☎ (01925) 767029

3 changing beers (sourced locally; often Merlins)

The enthusiastic landlord takes his real ale very seriously, with up to four on offer, often including beers from Merlins Micro Brewery and other LocAle suppliers. Sky Sports and BT Sports are shown on four screens in the

Malt Disley 🏆

22 Market Street, SK12 2AA

☎ (01663) 308020 🌐 maltdisley.co.uk

4 changing beers (sourced locally; often Mobberley, Rock Mill, Torrside) Ⓗ

This vibrant and friendly converted shop is located in the village centre. It is spacious for a micropub and includes a downstairs room. Five cask beers are available, some from local microbreweries, along with a cask cider. Ten KeyKeg beers, including three continental beers plus a further cider, and a range of British and continental bottled beers are also on offer. Live music plays on the last Sunday afternoon of each month. Local CAMRA Pub of the Year 2020. (199)

Frodsham

Helter Skelter 𝕃

31 Church Street, WA6 6PN

☎ (01928) 733361 🌐 thehelterskelter.net

Oakham Bishops Farewell; Salopian Oracle; Weetwood Best Bitter; 7 changing beers (sourced nationally; often Ossett, Thornbridge) Ⓗ

This pub has won local CAMRA Pub of the Year numerous times. It offers three regular cask ales plus a further seven changing guest ales from local and national micros, including dark beers. Two rotating guest ciders and imported bottled beers are also available. The single-room bar has a welcoming, relaxed atmosphere,

attracting both locals and travellers. Excellent food is served in the bar and upstairs restaurant.
◑≠🍎▯🚌(21,48) 🐾📶

Hale

Childe of Hale ✔

6 Church End, L24 4AX
☎ (0151) 425 2954
Greene King IPA; Morland Old Speckled Hen Ⓗ
A pleasant multi-roomed pub which has three handpumps offering beers from the Greene King range. The main lounge is subdivided into separate eating and drinking areas. The bar has several TV screens. Outside, there is a large seating and patio area. Nearby is a statue of the 16th-century giant, John Middleton, known as the Childe of Hale. It is ideal for plane spotters, being only a short distance from Liverpool John Lennon Airport.
Q🛋❀◑♿P🚌(500) 🐾

Holmes Chapel

Bottle Bank

24-26 London Road, CW4 7AL
☎ (01477) 534380
4 changing beers (often Merlins, Mobberley) Ⓗ
The name derives from the bar's previous existence as the NatWest Bank – the strong room at the rear is now used for spirit bottles. A former CAMRA branch Pub of the Year, this modern bar has four regularly changing cask ales and eight keg lines, with third-pints available. Snacks such as pork pies and Scotch eggs are always on offer. 🛋❀♿≠♣🍎🚌(42,316)🐾📶

Knutsford

Folk

76 King Street, WA16 6ED
☎ (01565) 228429 🌐 wineandwallop.co.uk
4 changing beers (sourced locally) Ⓗ
Stylish bar at the heart of Knutsford's busy King Street offering four local and regional cask beers, mainly lower strength and pale varieties. The bar benefits from a garden area on the first floor. At the time of writing, the building is undergoing an expansion into the premises next door which will provide opportunities for a food offering, a wider choice of beers and local live music. Card only, no cash. 🛋❀≠🚌(88,188)🐾📶

Little Budworth

Egerton Arms 🄻

Pinfold Lane, CW6 9BS (on edge of village near Oulton Park and Budworth Common) SJ5942465422
☎ (01829) 760424 🌐 egerton-arms.co.uk
Dunham Massey Big Tree Bitter; 5 changing beers (sourced regionally; often Brimstage, Marble, Pennine) Ⓗ
An unspoilt and friendly pub offering, in addition to its cask ales, a range of continental lagers and other draught beers. Low ceilings, stone-tiled floors, wood panelling, exposed sandstone walls and a wood-burner all add to its traditional ambience. Cricket can be watched from the sunny beer garden in summer. Handy for visiting Budworth Common and Oulton Park racing circuit. Beer festivals, live music and themed events also feature.
🛋❀◑⛺♣P🐾📶

Little Neston

Harp 🄻 ✔

19 Quayside, CH64 0TB (turn left at bottom of Marshlands Rd; pub is 300yds on left overlooking marshes)
☎ (0151) 336 6980
Joseph Holt Bitter; Peerless Triple Blond; Timothy Taylor Landlord; 2 changing beers (sourced nationally) Ⓗ
Former coal miners' inn converted from two cottages. It has a public bar with a real fire in winter and a basic lounge. Set in a glorious location on the Deeside to Neston part of the national cycle network, the pub overlooks the Dee Marshes and North Wales, with a recently enlarged garden and a drinking area abutting the edge of the marshes. A popular curry night features every Tuesday. Q🛋❀◐P🚌(22,487)🐾📶

Lymm

Brewery Tap 🄻

18 Bridgewater Street, WA13 0AB
☎ (01925) 755451 🌐 lymmbrewing.co.uk
Dunham Massey Dunham Dark; Lymm Bitter, Bridgewater Blonde; 4 changing beers (sourced locally; often Dunham Massey, Lymm) Ⓗ
The Brewery Tap, in the red-brick former post office, is a few steps away from the Bridgewater Canal. The bar area is complemented by the front room, with subdued lighting, comfy armchairs and a wood-fired stove. Four changing beers are either from the pub's own microbrewery or nearby Dunham Massey and include at least one dark beer, often the award-winning Porter. An open mic night features twice a month. Local pies are available at all times. 🛋❀♿♣🚌🐾📶

Saddlers 🄻

7 Bridgewater Street, WA13 0AB
☎ (01928) 753139
JW Lees Bitter; Wainwright; 1 changing beer (sourced locally; often Big Bog) Ⓗ
A small, traditional free house, originally owned by the local saddler, in the village centre, a splash away from the Bridgewater Canal, Lymm Dam and heritage walks. There is a cosy snug with a real fire to complement the larger bar area. The pub has a relaxed vibe with an emphasis on conversation and banter or just reading the paper. A popular meeting place for Formula One enthusiasts. Q🛋♿🚌🐾📶

Macclesfield

Park Tavern ✔

158 Park Lane, SK11 6UB
☎ (01625) 667846 🌐 park-tavern.co.uk
Bollington White Nancy, Long Hop, Best, Oat Mill Stout, Eastern Nights Ⓗ
This pub is well worth the 10-minute walk from the town centre. It was reopened by Bollington Brewery in 2011 and features its ales and two real ciders. It has a fresh and modern feel, with an open main bar area and a smaller room to the left of the entrance. Regular events include film nights in a mini cinema, quizzes and science evenings. There is a function room upstairs.
🛋❀◐≠♣🍎🚌(38) 🐾📶

RedWillow 🄻

32A Park Green, SK11 7NA
☎ (01625) 830718 🌐 redwillowbar.com
5 changing beers (often RedWillow) Ⓗ
A double-width former shop, sensitively converted to RedWillow's local tap. The main room has a bar down

most of one side, serving the brewery's cask beers as well as guests from other micros. There is always at least one dark beer, a changing real cider and an impressive range of craft keg beers. Third-pint measures are available. The pub can get busy at weekends. Fresh pizza is served. (38)

Waters Green Tavern

96 Waters Green, SK11 6LH

(01625) 422653

7 changing beers (sourced regionally; often Abbeydale, Acorn, Elland)

Handy for Macclesfield station and a popular stop-off, this pub is a long-standing Guide entry, clocking up over 20 years. With over 30 years' stewardship by the landlord, it offers a good range of up to seven changing ales, often including a dark beer, and a real cider or perry. Good-value home-cooked food is served Monday to Saturday lunchtimes. A real fire warms the L-shaped, open-plan main room. (38)

Wharf

107 Brook Street, SK11 7AW

(01625) 261879 thewharfmacc.co.uk

Oakham JHB; Otter Bitter; 3 changing beers (sourced nationally)

Traditional and popular community free house – with the awards to prove it – in a terrace setting. Refurbished and reopened in 2011, the one-room pub has a separate snug area featuring a real fire, and an open games area with darts and pool. Five handpulls dispense well-chosen ales from local and more nationwide microbrewers, always including a dark beer, plus one cider or perry, and a range of craft keg. Live music often features on a Friday night. (58)

Middlewich

White Bear Hotel

Wheelock Street, CW10 9AG (on lower end of Wheelock St, just off A54 St Michael's Way)

(01606) 837666 thewhitebearmiddlewich.co.uk

4 changing beers (sourced locally)

A successful free house that has now been in the Guide for seven successive years. It dates back to 1625, and was beautifully restored in 2011. There are four separate drinking areas, an alfresco patio, a separate restaurant area and a function room. Four handpumps serve local beers of different styles, and there is usually a real cider too. Dimmed lighting and log-burners help make for a comfortable visit. P (37,42)

Mobberley

Church Inn

Church Lane, WA16 7RD (opp church, signed from local roads)

(01565) 873178 churchinnmobberley.co.uk

House beer (by Tatton); 2 changing beers (sourced regionally)

This Grade II listed 300-year-old dining pub, sister of the nearby Bull's Head, retains vestiges of its former multi-room layout. A house beer is named in honour of Mallory of Everest, who was born in Mobberley and is commemorated in stained glass in the church opposite (his father was a vicar there). There is a fire-lit cricket-themed bar, a characterful boot room and two dining rooms, with a private dining room upstairs and a beer garden to the rear. Information on local walks is available. P (88)

Moulton

Lion

74 Main Road, CW9 8PB

(01606) 606049

Wainwright; Wychwood Hobgoblin Ruby; 4 changing beers (sourced locally; often Cheshire Brewhouse, RedWillow, Tatton)

Featuring in the Guide for six consecutive years, this welcoming community-focused pub is in the centre of the village and dispenses many changing local ales. It hosts a smartphone quiz night each Thursday, and popular themed music events, with regular live music monthly. A complimentary cheeseboard is offered each Friday evening. Outside, there is a beer garden to the side and a sundeck at the front. A function room is available. Local CAMRA Pub of the Year in 2019. P

Nantwich

Black Lion

29 Welsh Row, CW5 5ED (opp Cheshire Cat)

(01270) 628711 blacklion-nantwich.co.uk

Weetwood Best Bitter, Cheshire Cat, Old Dog; 3 changing beers (sourced regionally)

A traditional black-and-white-fronted inn dating from the 17th century, standing among the historic buildings of Welsh Row. Its beautiful plaster and wood-beamed interior retains the expected bowed walls and creaking floorboards. An open fire welcomes you into an open-plan area which, in the past, would have been three separate rooms. The small Hop Room features hop bines on the ceiling and a pot-bellied stove for heating. There is a restaurant upstairs and a covered beer garden to the side. Q (84)

Crown

High Street, CW5 5AS

(01270) 625283 crownhotelnantwich.com

Salopian Shropshire Gold; 4 changing beers (sourced regionally)

A black-and-white-timbered hotel, rebuilt in 1585 after the great Fire of Nantwich. The Grade I listed building is roomy and comfortable inside, with oak beams and wattle and daub walls throughout. Beyond the bar (open to non residents), is the Crown Bar and Grill which offers an extensive menu. Light meals are also available in the bar. The Long Gallery, upstairs, is well worth visiting. The bar serves five real ales – Shropshire Gold and four changing beers. P (84,85)

Vine Inn

42 Hospital Street, CW5 5RP (near St Mary's Church)

(01270) 619055 vineinnnantwich.co.uk

Hydes Old Indie, Original, Lowry; 3 changing beers (sourced regionally)

The Vine is a 17th-century Grade II listed building set on three split levels. A Hydes establishment, it offers six beers and a real cider. With screens showing Sky and BT, it is popular with sports fans, but there is also a quiet room at the back with board games and a real fire. Outside there is a small beer garden. In recent years the pub has become a regular in the Guide due to its well-conditioned beer. (84)

Wickstead Arms

5 Mill Street, CW5 5ST (at jct of Mill St and Barker St)

(01270) 610196 wicksteadpubnantwich.co.uk

5 changing beers (sourced nationally)

This busy traditional pub not far from the town centre reopened in 2014. It has a bar with sports screens and an adjoining lounge also used for dining. Home-cooked classic pub grub is served from an ever-changing menu. Six handpumps offer a wide range of beers including LocAles. ◐◑⇌▯🚌(84,85)🐾ᯤ

Northwich

Baron's Lounge 𝕃

13 Witton Street, CW9 5DE (in pedestrianised town centre)

☎ 07809 209294

4 changing beers (sourced locally; often 4Ts, Beartown, Merlins)

Close to the new Barons Quay development, the Baron's Lounge opened in late 2017 in what used to be a Red Cross shop and converted into a two-storey microbar in 2018. Although a small pub, it packs plenty in, with quiz nights, vinyl music nights, retro games and live music. A suntrap patio is to the rear. Q❀♿♣●▯🚌🐾ᯤ

Salty Dog 𝕃

21-23 High Street, CW9 5BY (in pedestrianised town centre) 🌐 salty-dog.co.uk

4 changing beers (sourced locally; often Bollington, RedWillow, Tatton) 🄷

This former shop, opened in 2017, retains its picturesque black-and-white exterior. The landlord and co-owner played drums in punk band The Business. Live music features along with comedy nights. A room at the rear has a jukebox, table football and retro arcade games. An extensive range of bottled British and European beers is available. The pub was voted one of the best small music venues in the UK by Guardian readers. ᘐ❀♿♣🚌🐾ᯤ

Penketh

Ferry Tavern

Station Road, WA5 2UJ (from car park on Station Rd, cross railway and canal. Pub is alongside bank of River Mersey) SJ5634986649

☎ (01925) 791117 🌐 theferrytavern.com

Bombardier; Jennings Cumberland Ale; Titanic Plum Porter; 5 changing beers (sourced nationally) 🄷

Next to the Marina between the Mersey and St Helens Canal, the Ferry serves three regular beers and five guests, and holds quarterly beer festivals and tap takeovers showcasing favourite breweries. It also offers a wide range of whiskies and gins. Food includes locally made pies at the weekend. The large beer garden is thronged in the summer with walkers and cyclists using the Trans Pennine Trail. Local CAMRA Community Pub of the Year 2019. ᘐ❀◐◑●P🚌(32)🐾ᯤ

Poynton

Flute & Firkin 𝕃

51 Park Lane, SK12 1RD

☎ (01625) 879181

Poynton Vulcan, Dark Side; 4 changing beers (sourced locally; often Poynton, Purple Moose, Titanic) 🄷

This converted shop bar in the centre of town is the tap for the local Poynton Brewery and showcases its beer range. Six handpumps usually dispense four beers from the brewery and a couple of guests, always including a dark beer. As well as the main bar there is an upstairs lounge seating 25 with TV and a heated shed at the rear, available to hire. Special events include pop-up food evenings and acoustic Sunday afternoons. Qᘐ❀●P▯🚌🐾ᯤ

Runcorn

Norton Arms 🏆

125-127 Main Street, WA7 2AD

☎ (01928) 567642 🌐 thenortonarms.co.uk

Greene King IPA; 3 changing beers (sourced nationally) 🄷

A seventh year in the Guide for this Grade II listed, two-roomed, oak-beamed inn in the centre of Halton Village. Although dominated by sports TV, and busy at weekends, this pub is still a nice find. Among the attractions are open mic nights, live music, quiz evenings and a bowling green. Due to the age of the pub, wheelchair access is difficult – the entrance is up a flight of stone steps. Local CAMRA Pub of the Year 2020. ᘐ❀◐◑♿♣P🚌🐾ᯤ

Society Taproom 𝕃

33 Ashridge Street, WA7 1HU (5 mins' walk from station, 10 mins' walk from Old Town)

☎ (01928) 775628 🌐 societyltd.co.uk

2 changing beers (sourced locally; often Blueball, Chapter) 🄷

This brewery and tap was once a Co-operative building. Its beers are from Blueball, attached to the building, plus other breweries including Heavy Industry and Chapter. KeyKeg craft ale is also available. The STR is hidden away in the Dukesfield area of the town, with the entrance under the arches of the railway between Runcorn station and Ethelfleda Bridge. Note that as the bar is closed Monday and Tuesday, the number of cask beers on Sunday may be limited. ◑♿⇌●🚌🐾

Sandbach

Beer Emporium 𝕃

8 Welles Street, CW11 1GT (off Hightown roundabout, down one-way street)

☎ (01270) 760113 🌐 thebeeremporium.com

5 changing beers 🄷

This popular and welcoming micropub converted from a Victorian butcher's shop opened in 2009. The narrow frontage gives way to a long room with a well-stocked L-shaped bar. Five handpumps on the right of the bar are nicely offset by extensive shelving on the left packed with a superb range of bottled beers. The far end of the bar leads to a smaller room with seating. A sister pub to the Bottle Bank in Holmes Chapel. Qᘐ🚌(37,38)🐾ᯤ

Old Hall 𝕃

High Street, CW11 2LJ (opp St Mary's Church on High St)

☎ (01270) 758170

Timothy Taylor Boltmaker; Weetwood Cheshire Cat; house beer (by Brunning & Price); 3 changing beers (sourced regionally) 🄷

One of just a handful of Grade I listed pubs in the UK, the building is a near perfect example of Elizabethan wattle and daub architecture. Guest ales are sourced locally from some of the region's award-winning brewers. In summer, the immaculately kept gardens are one of the most popular spots in the area to while away a lazy afternoon enjoying a drink and a hearty meal. Well worth a visit. ᘐ❀◐◑♿♣P🚌(37,38)🐾ᯤ↺

Stockton Heath

Costello's Bar 𝕃

23 Walton Road, WA4 6NJ

☎ (01925) 600910 🌐 costellosbar.co.uk

Dunham Massey Dunham Dark, Big Tree Bitter; Lymm Bridgewater Blonde; 4 changing beers (sourced locally; often Dunham Massey, Lymm) 🄷

A modern micro-style pub offering seven handpumps, with all beers from either the Dunham Massey or sister

Lymm Brewery stables. This is an excellent venue for the discerning drinker who prefers darker beers. Handily placed in the centre of Stockton Heath, it provides an oasis of calm at the weekend when the area is busy with a young clientele. Q

Sutton

Sutton Hall

Bullocks Lane, SK11 0HE

☎ (01260) 253211

Brunning & Price Original; house beer (by Wincle); 5 changing beers (sourced locally)

Splendid 16th-century manor house set in its own grounds near the Macclesfield Canal. It won a CAMRA national pub design award for its refurbishment in 2008, and retains the appearance of a stately home, with a snug, library and seven dining areas. Once the home of the Lucan family, Wincle's Lord Lucan ale is a regular among the six on offer. While there is a strong emphasis on food, with a wide-ranging menu, drinkers are welcome. Q P (14)

Thelwall

Little Manor

Bell Lane, WA4 2SX

☎ (01925) 212070 littlemanor-thelwall.co.uk

Coach House Cromwell Best Bitter; house beer (by Phoenix); 6 changing beers (sourced nationally)

A large upmarket food-based pub with a changing range of local and regional cask ales. The pub is charmingly furnished and has extensive garden areas for outdoor dining. A regularly changing food menu is served throughout the day. Set in picturesque surroundings, the property was originally the home for the Percival family in the 1600s, with their coat of arms adopted as the pub sign. Details of country walks around the pub are available from the website or bar.

Q P

Tilston

Carden Arms

Mount View, Church Road, SY14 7HB

☎ (01829) 250900 cardenarms.co.uk

Coach House Gunpowder Mild; Salopian Shropshire Gold; Weetwood Eastgate; 2 changing beers (sourced locally; often Peerless, Spitting Feathers, Wincle)

Impressive rural free house at the crossroads in the village. The interior has rug-covered wood and tiled floors, real fires, traditional furniture and attractive framed pictures on the plain white walls. In addition to the three regular beers are two guests, often from local microbreweries. High-quality food is served in the bar area and the stylish dining room. Upstairs, two adjoining Georgian rooms can be booked for groups. Accommodation is available in five bedrooms.

Q P (41)

Warrington

Tavern

25 Church Street, WA1 2SS

☎ 07747 668817

8 changing beers (sourced nationally; often 4Ts, Mallinsons, Oakham)

This pub has been a continuous Guide entry for in excess of 20 years. Its excellent offering of eight beers – two from the local 4Ts Brewery plus six others mainly from small independent brewers in differing styles – ensures that it remains at the forefront of the local real ale scene. Sports TV is popular here with a number of screens allowing different games to be shown simultaneously.

Widnes

Four Topped Oak

2 Hough Green Road, WA8 4PE

☎ (0151) 257 8031 emberinns.co.uk

Wainwright; house beer (by Black Sheep); 2 changing beers

Pleasant, well laid-out pub situated between the comparatively new housing estate of Upton Rocks and the older Hough Green. Several distinct seating areas warmed by gas and coal fires help to create a quiet and relaxed ambience. It has ales on four handpumps and serves a standard Ember Inns food menu. Outside is a large patio area. Q P

Premier

93-99 Albert Road, WA8 6JS

☎ (0151) 422 4920

Greene King Abbot; Ruddles Best Bitter; 3 changing beers

First a cinema, then a bottling plant, this is now a Wetherspoon pub, on the edge of the shopping centre. It has a pleasant atmosphere and a changing clientele depending on the time of day. Sgt Mottershead VC, who died in 1917 while serving on the Western Front with the Royal Flying Corps, used to visit when it was a cinema, and his statue stands in nearby Victoria Park.

Willey Moor Lock

Willey Moor Lock Tavern

Tarporley Road, SY13 4HF (400yds off A49, around 1½ miles N of Whitchurch)

☎ (01948) 663274 willeymoorlock.co.uk

6 changing beers (sourced nationally)

This former lock-keeper's cottage is now a family-run free house. Access from the car park is via a footbridge over the Llangollen Canal. The pub is popular with boaters and also walkers on the Sandstone Trail, especially in the summer. Choose your outside seating either next to the lock or in the attractive garden. Three changing beers, many from local brewers, increase to six in summer. Good-value meals are served.

Q ΔP

Willington

Boot Inn

Boothsdale, Willington Lane, CW6 0NH (signed from Willington Rd) SJ5304667257

☎ (01829) 751375 thebootinnwillington.com

Weetwood Best Bitter, Cheshire Cat; 2 changing beers (sourced locally; often Weetwood)

Hidden in a picturesque location in rolling countryside, this small village pub was originally three cottages. Sandstone walls, tiled floors and low ceilings, along with open fires and a wood-burner, create a cosy atmosphere in winter, while outside patios are popular in summer. It has a good reputation for food, served both in the restaurant and bar area, and also outside in summer. A number of local walks from the pub can be downloaded from the website. Q P

Wilmslow

Brewhouse & Kitchen

6-12 Swan Street, SK9 1HE

☎ (01625) 441850
Brewhouse & Kitchen Bollin Ruby, Fustian Cut, Secret Genius, Lucky Sam Ⓗ
Since opening in 2016, this brewery diner has gone on to establish itself as a key destination pub in the town. The decor is beer-related, with lamps made from beer glasses and bottles. Four cask ales, all brewed on the premises, have locally themed names, and tasting paddles and one-third pints are available. Food focuses on steaks and burgers, but there are also vegetarian and vegan options. The menu gives suggested beer pairings for most dishes. The gleaming copper-coloured brewery is to your left as you enter. Part of the pub can be sectioned off to form a function room.
(88,130)

Old Dancer Ⓛ
16 Grove Street, SK9 1DR
☎ (01625) 530775
5 changing beers Ⓗ
Lively café-bar on the main pedestrian shopping street. Furnished mainly with simple wooden tables on boarded floors, it has walls decorated with striking hand-painted murals on a dance theme. There are also tables outside on the street. Six handpumps serve an interesting range of beers, often local, and a cask cider. Teas, coffees and food are available, including bar snacks, wraps, burgers, locally made pies and salads. The pub hosts live music on Saturdays, film nights and quiz nights.
(88,130)

Harp, Little Neston

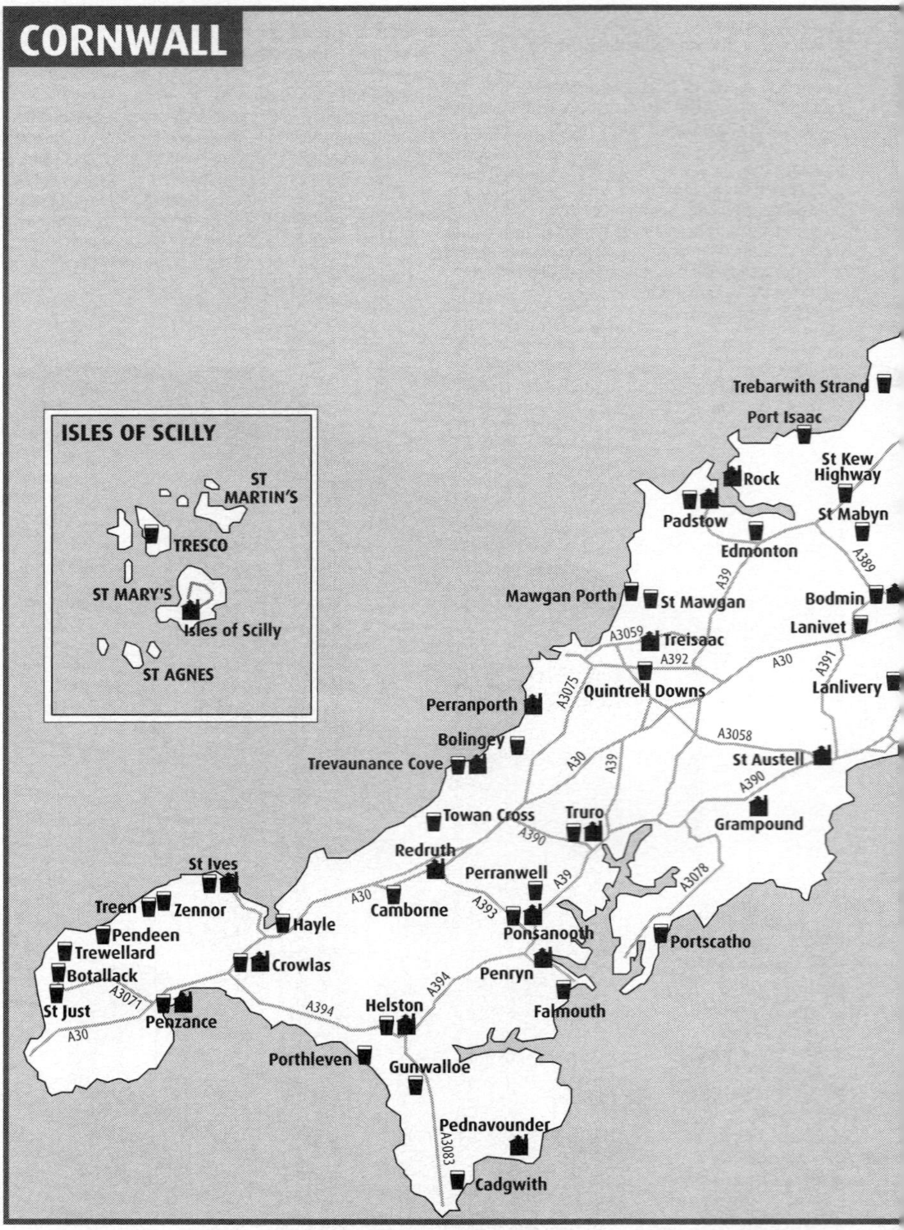

Altarnun

Rising Sun 🄻

PL15 7SN (NW of Altarnun village) SX215825

☎ (01566) 86636 🌐 therisingsuninn.co.uk

Altarnun St Nonna's; Skinner's Lushingtons; 3 changing beers (sourced nationally) Ⓗ

A thriving community pub and tap for nearby Altarnun Brewery on the outskirts of town. The interior of this characterful 150-year-old inn is cosy and warm, with beamed ceilings and an open fireplace, and antique guns and various pictures on the walls. Deceptively spacious, the pub offers ample seating in the bar, two small annexes for pool and drinkers, and a separate restaurant. Outside, there is a large patio and grassed area for games. Food always uses locally sourced ingredients.

Q🐎❀◑♿⛺♣🍎P🐾📶

Blisland

Blisland Inn

The Green, PL30 4JF (off A30 NE of Bodmin) SX100732

☎ (01208) 850739

Dowr Kammel Blisland Gold; house beer (by Sharp's) Ⓗ**; 4 changing beers (sourced nationally)** Ⓗ/Ⓖ

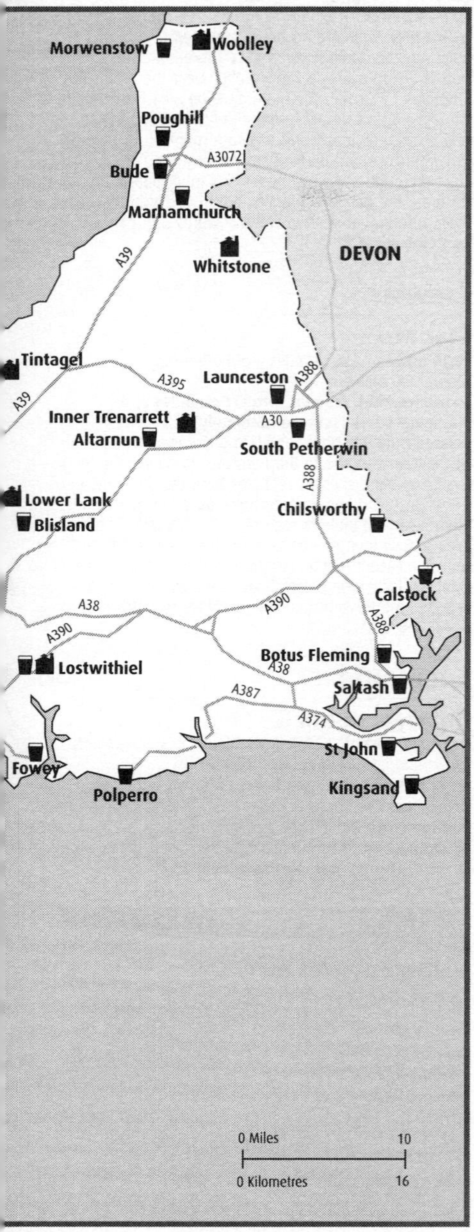

A friendly rural community pub by the village green, the Blisland retains its reputation as a real ale destination on the edge of Bodmin Moor. It has served well over 3,000 different real ales and usually has at least five or six beers on, with several brewed locally, plus frequently changing draught ciders including some unusual varieties. Food is freshly prepared using local produce. The decor is eclectic and includes barometers and Toby jugs as well as an impressive collection of pumpclips and beer mats. Popular with walkers and cyclists, the pub also welcomes well-behaved children and dogs. A winner of many local CAMRA awards and a former National Pub of the Year. **Q✿❀◑♣●⊡🐾**

Bodmin

Hole in the Wall 𝕃 ✔

16 Crockwell Street, PL31 2DS (entrance via public car park)

☎ (01208) 72397 🌐 theholeinthewallbodmin.co.uk

Butcombe Original; Draught Bass; Sharp's Atlantic, Sea Fury; 2 changing beers (sourced nationally; often Skinner's, Young's) Ⓗ

Popular local built in the 18th century as a debtors' prison. The pub can be accessed from the public car park or through a secluded, leafy garden containing its own hop bine and stream, and presided over by a rather bleached stuffed lion. The single bar, which is subdivided by archways, contains a large and eclectic collection of antiques and military memorabilia. Upstairs is a separate function room. The pub has twice won local CAMRA Pub of the Year. **Q✿❀≹♣●🚌**(27,11A)**🐾📶**

Bolingey

Bolingey Inn 𝕃 ✔

Penwartha Road, TR6 0DH (near B3284) SW763531

☎ (01872) 571626

Sharp's Doom Bar; 3 changing beers (sourced nationally; often Dartmoor, St Austell, Wadworth) Ⓗ

Set in a delightful location in a small village about 20 minutes walk from Perranporth. The pub offers two bars – one mainly for drinking with a wooden floor and an open fire (especially popular with sleepy dogs), the other bar with more seating where you can dine if you wish. Four handpumps serve changing local and national ales alongside the ever-present Doom Bar. A beer festival is held twice-yearly in April and October, attracting enthusiasts from near and far. **Q✿❀◑▲♣P🐾📶**

Botallack

Queen's Arms 𝕃

Botallack Road, TR19 7QG (just off Lands End to St Ives road, near St Just)

☎ (01736) 788318 🌐 queensarmscornwall.co.uk

Sharp's Doom Bar; 1 changing beer (sourced locally; often Tintagel) Ⓗ

Tucked away in a hamlet just off the St Ives to St Just coast road, the bar has exposed granite walls and is decorated with pictures by local artists and mining prints. The ceiling beams are adorned with many pumpclips, while the pub's cosy ambience is enhanced by an inglenook fireplace and log-burners. To the rear, a family/pool room leads to an attractive walled beer garden. Snacks and meals are prepared using local produce. **Q✿❀◑▲♣●P🚌🐾📶**

Botus Fleming

Rising Sun Inn

PL12 6NJ (off A388 near Saltash) SX405613

☎ (01752) 842792

Skinner's Betty Stogs; 3 changing beers (sourced nationally; often Dartmoor, Everards, Greene King) Ⓗ

Tastefully refurbished after remaining largely unaltered for years, this rural gem with low ceilings and well-trodden wooden floors is tucked away in a quiet village near Saltash, just off the beaten track. The three real ales are regularly and imaginatively changed; there is, however, no food. Draught cider is generally from Westons. The pub is dog-friendly, supports darts and euchre teams and hosts occasional live music. Regular buses pass on the A388, roughly a 20-minute walk away. **Q❀♣●P🐾📶**

Bude

Barrel at Bude

36 Lansdown Road, EX23 8BN
☎ (01288) 356113 🌐 thebarrelatbude.com
5 changing beers (sourced locally) Ⓗ
This small micropub opened in 2017 in a former fancy dress shop in the centre of town. All the beers and ciders are sourced from within Cornwall and Scilly by the proprietor without recourse to the wholesale trade. The philosophy is that to ensure beers are at their best; all ales available on Thursday should be consumed by Sunday – 'drink the barrel dry' afternoon – ready for a restock the following week. Cornish organic gins and local wines are also sold. ♘🍎P🚌🐾

Cadgwith

Cadgwith Cove Inn

TR12 7JX
☎ (01326) 290513 🌐 cadgwithcoveinn.com
Sharp's Doom Bar, Sea Fury; Skinner's Betty Stogs, Lushingtons Ⓗ
Three-roomed inn tucked away by the harbour and the South-West Coastal Path in a compact fishing village on the Lizard peninsula. Over 300 years old, the inn remains largely unspoilt since its smuggling days. Relics from the local seafaring past and photos of shipwrecks and local scenes adorn the half-panelled walls, while the bar also sports rope handles hanging from the beams for when the pub lists! Expect some lively singing in the evenings, with itinerant musicians often performing.
♘❀🛏◐▲♣🚌(L2)🐾📶

Calstock

Boot Inn

Fore Street, PL18 9RN
☎ (01822) 481589
2 changing beers (sourced nationally; often Exeter) Ⓗ
Split-level 17th-century village inn tucked snugly amid the cottages and narrow cobbled streets of Calstock. With wood beams and wooden floors throughout, the pub's middle level hosts the bar and main drinking area, with dining spaces either side. Up to the left is a space where you can take your dog, while down to the right is a separate main dining room. Largely food-driven, the pub nevertheless welcomes customers who only want a sociable drink. Q♘◐⇌🚌(79)🐾

Camborne

John Francis Basset ✔

21 Commercial Street, TR14 8JZ (pub entrance in Church St)
☎ (01209) 721720
Greene King IPA, Abbot; Sharp's Doom Bar; 5 changing beers Ⓗ
Wetherspoon pub in the former market house built by architect William Bond in 1866. Previous uses of the building have included as a cinema, night club and a pub called the Corn Exchange. Named after a prominent former local mine owner, it is a large, airy, open-plan venue with high ceilings and tall windows. The single long bar offers an impressive selection of varying beers, often locally brewed. A real ale oasis in the town centre, well worth a visit. Q♘❀🛏◐♿⇌♣🍎🚌📶

Chilsworthy

White Hart 🏆 ✔

PL18 9PB (signed from A390) SX416721
☎ (01822) 833876 🌐 whitehartchilsworthy.com
Uley Bitter; 4 changing beers (sourced regionally) Ⓗ
Solid rural community free house tucked into the steep northern slopes of the Tamar Valley near the prominent landmark of Kit Hill. The main drinking area is carpeted throughout and simply furnished with wooden tables and chairs. Previously two separate rooms, it is warmed in winter by wood-burning stoves set in two stone chimney breasts. Horse brasses and other pub artefacts decorate the bar, which opens out at one side to a rear room offering impressive views towards Dartmoor.
♘❀◐♣🍎P🐾📶

Crowlas

Star Inn Ⓛ

TR20 8DX (on A30, 3 miles E of Penzance)
☎ (01736) 740375
Penzance Mild, Crowlas Bitter, Potion No.9; 4 changing beers (sourced nationally) Ⓗ
This roadside free house and former Cornwall CAMRA Pub of the Year is home to the Penzance Brewery. The long U-shaped bar dispenses real ales from the pub's own brewhouse and two or three from other microbreweries. There is a pool table to the right, a comfy raised seating area, a cosy lounge area with leather sofas and chairs, and an adjacent meeting room. This is essentially a beer-drinkers' local where conversation is the main entertainment, with no noisy machines to distract.
❀♣P🚌🐾📶

Edmonton

Quarryman Inn Ⓛ

PL27 7JA (just off A39 nr Royal Cornwall showground)
☎ (01208) 816444 🌐 thequarryman.co.uk
Otter Bitter; 3 changing beers (sourced regionally; often Padstow, Skinner's) Ⓗ
This former schoolhouse and quarrymen's accommodation is now a pub with two distinct areas. The smaller bar area has a flagstone floor and a variety of

REAL ALE BREWERIES

Ales of Scilly St Mary's: Isles of Scilly
Altarnun Inner Trenarrett
Atlantic Treisaac
Black Flag ✎ Perranporth
Blue Anchor ▤ Helston
Castle Lostwithiel
Cornish Crown ✎ Penzance
Dowr Kammel Lower Lank
Driftwood Spars ▤ Trevaunance Cove
Dynamite Valley Ponsanooth
Forge Woolley
Fowey Lostwithiel
Granite Rock Penryn
Harbour Bodmin
Keltek Redruth
Krow Redruth (NEW)
Lizard Pednavounder
Longhill ✎ Whitstone
Padstow Padstow
Penzance ▤ Crowlas
Sharp's Rock
Skinner's ✎ Truro
St Austell St Austell
St Ives St Ives
Tintagel Tintagel
Treen's Ponsanooth
Tremethick Grampound
Woodman's Ponsanooth

sporting memorabilia. The adjacent carpeted lounge is often busy with diners, serving locally sourced home-cooked food. The beers usually vary but with the exception of the Otter Bitter tend to be local, often from the nearby Padstow Brewery. The atmosphere is convivial and conversation flourishes – no mobile phones! Q P (11A,95)

Falmouth

Beerwolf Books

3-4 Bells Court, TR11 3AZ (up side alley off main shopping street)
☎ (01326) 618474 beerwolfbooks.com
6 changing beers (sourced nationally; often Blackjack, Penzance, Shiny) H
Pub or bookshop? Actually, it's both. Popular with all ages, this former maritime storage loft and pleasant outside courtyard is tucked away off Market Street up a side-alley. It is accessed via a steep flight of stairs, at the top of which is the bookshop, while to the right is the bar, dispensing an adventurous selection of constantly changing beers. Four further handpumps ensure that cider lovers are not forgotten. Posters and old photographs decorate the walls. No food is served, but you may bring your own.

Oddfellows Arms

Quay Hill, TR11 3HA
☎ (01326) 218611
Sharp's Atlantic; house beer (by Sharp's) H**; 1 changing beer (sourced locally; often Skinner's)** H/G
Unpretentious single-bar community pub tucked up a hilly side street off the town centre and popular with locals and visitors alike. Decorated with old photographs, it has a convivial atmosphere in which to enjoy the three beers normally on offer, with sometimes a fourth racked up at the back of the bar. A small back room hosts the dartboard, pool table and real fire. The pub organises festivals throughout the year, often involving food made by the locals. Q

Pennycomequick ✓

16 Killigrew Street, The Moor, TR11 3PN
☎ (01326) 311912 pennycomequick.co.uk
St Austell Tribute; 2 changing beers (sourced regionally; often Bath Ales, Tintagel) H
This modernised open-plan bar/restaurant with friendly and knowledgeable staff offers a relaxed and welcoming atmosphere. It has seating at the bar and front snug area for drinkers, and tables for diners. The two changing ales are generally from St Austell Brewery, but other beers from Cornwall or further afield are often available. Food features local seasonal ingredients cooked with flair (booking recommended for evening dining). Pennycomequick is derived from the former Cornish name for Falmouth.

Seaview Inn ✓

Wodehouse Terrace, TR11 3EP
☎ (01326) 311359 seaviewinnfalmouth.co.uk
Sharp's Doom Bar; 2 changing beers (sourced nationally; often Treen's) H
A traditional and comfortable town pub with a large, beamed, open-plan island bar. As the name suggests, it enjoys excellent views over Falmouth harbour and Carrick Roads with all their maritime activity. The locals are a friendly mix of all ages, and the pub welcomes children and dogs. A games area to the rear hosts darts and pool. Accommodation is in three rooms.
Q

Seven Stars ★

The Moor, TR11 3QA
☎ (01326) 312111 thesevenstarsfalmouth.com
Draught Bass; Sharp's Atlantic, Sea Fury; 2 changing beers (sourced locally; often Padstow, Skinner's, Treen's) G
This timeless and unspoilt town-centre local has been in the same family for nearly 170 years and features on CAMRA's National Inventory of Historic Pub Interiors. It has a lively, narrow taproom where beers are served on gravity from a unique, eccentrically designed stillage. There are two quiet rooms at the back. The old bottle-and-jug hatch remains for outdoor drinkers. Bass is ever-present, as are beers from Sharp's Brewery. A real gem that should not be missed. Q

Fowey

Galleon Inn

12 Fore Street, PL23 1AQ
☎ (01726) 833014 galleon-inn.co.uk
Sharp's Cornish Coaster, Doom Bar; 2 changing beers (often Bath Ales) H
Riverside pub in the town centre dating back 400 years, now fully modernised, reached off Fore Street through a glass-covered corridor with a colourful marine life mural. The only free house in Fowey, it features mainly Cornish ales. A wide range of meals is available daily. The main bar and conservatory enjoy delightful harbour views and tables outside overlook the water. There is a heated, sheltered courtyard. Accommodation is en-suite, some rooms with river views. (24,25)

Gunwalloe

Halzephron Inn

TR12 7QB (off A3083 Helston-Lizard road) SW657224
☎ (01326) 240406 halzephron-inn.co.uk
Sharp's Doom Bar; Skinner's Porthleven; 3 changing beers (sourced nationally) H
This quiet, welcoming 500-year-old inn was once the haunt of smugglers, who used a shaft from the pub to a still existing underground tunnel. The two traditional bars remain – the lounge doubling as a restaurant with an adjacent snug. Another restaurant area is in an extension to the rear. Accommodation is in two en-suite rooms. The pub name derives from the old Cornish 'als yffrin' meaning 'cliffs of hell' – timbers from many nearby shipwrecks were incorporated into the pub's structure.
Q P

Hayle

Bird In Hand

Trelissick Road, TR27 4HY
☎ (01736) 753974 birdinhandhayle.co.uk
Treen's Essential; 2 changing beers (sourced regionally; often Dartmoor, Exeter) H
Families are welcome in this spacious pub converted from Victorian stables, adjacent to Paradise Park wildlife sanctuary. The decor in the one-room bar is a mix of local industrial paraphernalia and horse paintings on the walls, painted casks over the bar area, and an end wall decorated with a frieze by Terry English depicting scenes from Cornwall's industrial past. Outside is a large seating area. Parking is shared with the wildlife sanctuary.
P (T1,T2)

Helston

Blue Anchor

50 Coinagehall Street, TR13 8EL

(01326) 562821 spingoales.com

Blue Anchor Jubilee IPA, Middle, Special; 1 changing beer (sourced locally; often Blue Anchor)

A former monks' rest, this 15th-century brewpub is one of the oldest in Britain, changing little over the years and retaining much of its original character. Two separate small bars are found to the right of the central passageway, one with an open fire, and two sitting rooms to the left, all with slate floors. To the rear are a skittle alley and partly covered garden area with its own bar and barbecue. An anchor is visible on the thatched roof. Q

Kingsand

Devonport Inn

The Cleave, PL10 1NF

(01752) 822869 devonportinn.com

Dartmoor Legend; 2 changing beers (sourced locally; often Bays, Otter)

Set between a narrow lane and the sea, this old pub was formerly divided into two bars but is now partly opened out to one, albeit still with distinct drinking areas. The small, wooden-floored bar has snug recesses and is ship-themed. It serves up to two constantly changing real ales, mostly from Devon. Live bands perform monthly in winter and more frequently in summer. The pub provides a welcome halt, both for walkers on the Cornwall coast path and the less energetic. (71)

Lanivet

Lanivet Inn

PL30 5ET (on A389)

(01208) 831212 lanivetinn.co.uk

St Austell Trelawny, Tribute, Hicks; 2 changing beers (sourced nationally; often Bath Ales, Timothy Taylor)

Traditional Cornish pub in the village centre featuring a spacious open-plan bar with a large stone inglenook fireplace, although the layout is generally food-oriented. An extended restaurant hosts weekly theme nights; entertainment is a mix of games, quizzes and music. The beer garden and large car park complete a pub offering something for the whole community. The panda on the pub sign dates from 1937, when London Zoo acquired its first such animal, a Lanivet bamboo grove providing its daily food. P (27)

Lanlivery

Crown Inn

PL30 5BT (in village centre)

(01208) 872707 thecrowninncornwall.co.uk

Sharp's Doom Bar; 2 changing beers (sourced locally; often Harbour, Skinner's)

Picturesque 12th-century listed pub in a long farmhouse style, with the main bar and snug at one end. The rest of the interior comprises a comfortable lounge with an inglenook fireplace containing a huge wood-burning stove, and the restaurant. An old well in the porch can be viewed through its glass cover. Food is available daily, with most of the ingredients sourced locally. Snacks are served all day in summer. Accommodation is in the former piggery and is wheelchair accessible.
Q P

Launceston

Bell Inn

1 Tower Street, PL15 8BQ (next to church tower)

(01566) 779970

House beer (by Holsworthy Ales); 5 changing beers (sourced regionally)

Cosy 14th-century town hostelry originally built to house stonemasons erecting the nearby church. Conversation rules in this locals' pub. The ever-changing beer range features mostly local beers and two ciders, although the selection may be reduced out of season. A separate family room, available for local groups to use, contains ancient frescoes uncovered when previous owners stripped away decades of modernisation. Cribbage and other pub games are played. Food is limited to a pasty or pork pie. Q

Lostwithiel

Globe Inn

3 North Street, PL22 0EG (nr railway station, town side of river bridge)

(01208) 872501

Sharp's Atlantic, Original; Skinner's Betty Stogs

Cosy 13th-century pub in the narrow streets of an old stannary (tin-mining) town, close to the station and medieval stone river bridge. The welcoming, rather rambling interior accommodates a single bar with several drinking and dining spaces, a restaurant and a suntrap patio at the rear. An extensive home-cooked menu features fish and game. The beer range may increase to four in summer. The pub is named after a ship that took part in a sea battle in 1813, when a member of the family who owned it at the time was killed.

Royal Oak

Duke Street, PL22 0AG

(01208) 872552 royaloakcornwall.com

St Austell Tribute, Proper Job; Sharp's Doom Bar; 1 changing beer (sourced regionally; often Cotleigh)

This historic 13th-century inn lies just off the main road through Cornwall's old capital. A traditional, stone-floored public bar contrasts with a comfortable lounge and attached restaurant; there is a patio outside. The pub has a dartboard and pool table, and hosts occasional quiz nights and live entertainment. Accommodation is in six en-suite rooms. There is reputedly a tunnel, once used by smugglers, from the pub cellar to the dungeons of Restormel Castle. Q P

Marhamchurch

Buller's Arms Hotel

Helebridge Road, EX23 0HB (off A39 S of Bude)

(01288) 361277

Sharp's Atlantic; Tintagel Arthur's Ale; house beer (by Tintagel); 1 changing beer (sourced locally; often St Austell)

Large community-oriented village hotel with a spacious beamed and slate-flagged bar room. Decorative bric-a-brac includes buffalo horns, a stuffed fox and a badger at one end of the room, while the other end hosts a dartboard, pool table and an upright piano. The beers may vary occasionally but are generally from local breweries. The pub holds quiz nights and twice-monthly live weekend entertainment. An under-fives soft play area is available most afternoons, and birthday party hosting on Saturday. Q (219)

Mawgan Porth

Merrymoor 🄻 ✔

TR8 4BA (beside B3276 coast road overlooking beach)
☎ (01637) 860258 🌐 merrymoorinn.com
St Austell Tribute; Sharp's Doom Bar, Original; 1 changing beer (sourced locally; often Bath Ales) 🄷
Originally a café whose owner served in the North African Campaign, hence the name. Now an atmospheric pub run by the same family since 1961, it is very much at the heart of the local community and raises huge sums for charity every year. Large picture windows overlook the sandy beach just 50 yards away. It is naturally busy in the season, and has a large beer garden, a spacious main bar and a separate family room.
🐴❀🛏◑⛺P🚌(A5,56) 🐾📶

Morwenstow

Bush Inn

Crosstown, EX23 9SR (off A39 N of Kilkhampton)
SS208150
☎ (01288) 331242 🌐 thebushinnmorwenstow.com
St Austell Tribute, Hicks; 1 changing beer (sourced locally; often Forge, Tintagel) 🄷
Unassuming from the outside, this ancient former chapel dates in parts back to 950AD. Inside it is a little gem – simply furnished, with slate floors, granite walls and exposed beams in two small bar rooms, one of which is subdivided into separate drinking areas. Conversation is the main entertainment, although there is occasional live music. A large garden offers outstanding views over the Tidna Valley and out to sea. Four en-suite rooms and a two-person holiday cottage are available.
Q🐴❀🛏◑♣🍎P🚌(217) 🐾📶

Padstow

Golden Lion Hotel

Lanadwell Street, PL28 8AN
☎ (01841) 532797 🌐 goldenlionpadstow.co.uk
Sharp's Doom Bar, Atlantic; Tintagel Castle Gold 🄷
Padstow's oldest pub, dating back over 400 years, and still used for stabling the famous red 'oss which makes its energetic appearance every May Day during the famous 'obby-'oss celebrations. The busy low-beamed and slate-flagged public bar is partitioned to create a family dining area; the quieter lounge is spacious and comfortable. There is a seated patio outside. The pub is situated a little way from the bustling harbour area but can get crowded during the summer season.
🐴❀🛏◑♿⛺🚌(A5,11A) 🐾📶

Pendeen

North Inn ✔

TR19 7DN (on B3306)
☎ (01736) 788417 🌐 thenorthinnpendeen.co.uk
St Austell Cornish Best Bitter, Tribute, Proper Job; 1 changing beer (sourced locally; often St Austell) 🄷
Welcoming locals' pub serving an old mining village in an area of outstanding natural beauty, close to the coastal path and the famous Geevor and Levant tin mines. The single large room has a beamed ceiling and is carpeted throughout; in the far right corner stands a pool table. A good-value food menu features a comprehensive range of home-cooked curries, the landlord's own speciality. The inn offers accommodation in four double rooms as well as at its own campsite. Q❀🛏◑⛺♣P🚌🐾📶

Penzance

Crown 🄻

Victoria Square, TR18 2EP (on Bread St)
☎ (01736) 351070 🌐 thecrownpenzance.co.uk
Cornish Crown Causeway, Porter; 2 changing beers (sourced locally; often Cornish Crown) 🄷
Close to the railway and bus stations, and brewery tap for Cornish Crown, this back-street gem is tucked away behind the main shopping street. Offering a relaxing atmosphere, it has a tidily furnished bar with upholstered window seats and a huge mirror covering one wall. At the rear is a cosy two-table snug with sofas and board games, while outside is a roadside patio with benches and tables. No food is served but you may bring your own, with plates provided. 🐴❀≠♣🍎🚌🐾📶

Dock Inn

17 Quay Street, TR18 4BD
☎ (01736) 362833 🌐 thedockinnpenzance.co.uk
Blue Anchor Middle; Penzance Potion No.9; Sharp's Doom Bar; 1 changing beer (sourced locally; often Skinner's) 🄷
Old and traditional one-time fishermen's pub near the dockside, close to the Isles of Scilly ferry pier. The pub extends through two old cottages, with the bar in the upper level, while a comfortable lounge next door at the lower level also serves as a dining area. The decor includes a large picture mirror, nautical and mining pictures, and bric-a-brac including a stuffed bird in a cage. A ship's figurehead oversees proceedings in the bar. Q🐴❀🛏◑≠♣P🚌🐾📶

Perranwell

Royal Oak 🄻

TR3 7PX
☎ (01872) 863175 🌐 theroyaloakperranwellstation.co.uk
Padstow Local; Penzance Potion No.9; 2 changing beers (sourced locally; often Exeter, Tintagel) 🄷
This small 18th-century cottage-style village pub prioritises both good beer and food. Most tables are set for dining, but drinkers are equally welcome, as the many sociable regulars at the bar will testify. Booking for meals is advisable however, especially evenings. The beers vary frequently and are mostly from local breweries. The community pub holds monthly quiz nights and fundraising events for local charities.
Q🐴❀◑≠♣🍎P🚌(36,46) 🐾📶

Polperro

Blue Peter Inn 🄻

Quay Road, PL13 2QZ (W side of harbour)
☎ (01503) 272743 🌐 thebluepeterinn.com
St Austell Tribute; Sharp's Original; 4 changing beers (sourced regionally; often Cornish Crown, Dartmoor) 🄷
Named after the naval flag, this friendly inn is reached up a steep flight of steps near the quay, and is the only pub with a sea view in the village. In summer it offers up to six ales from Cornwall and Devon, and a varied menu of home-cooked dishes available all day. Featuring low beams, wooden floors, unusual souvenirs and work by local artists, the pub is popular with locals, fishermen and visitors. 🐴❀◑⛺♣🐾📶

Crumplehorn Inn 🄻

The Old Mill, Crumplehorn, PL13 2RJ (on A387, top of town near coach park)
☎ (01503) 272348 🌐 thecrumplehorninn.co.uk
St Austell Tribute, Proper Job; Tintagel Castle Gold, Harbour Special; 2 changing beers (sourced locally) 🄷

Once a mill and mentioned in the Domesday Book, this 14th-century inn at the entrance to the village still has a working waterwheel outside. The split-level bar has three comfortable areas with low ceilings and flagstone floors. Outside, the spacious patio by the millstream offers large umbrellas as sunshades. A varied menu includes locally sourced food. Accommodation is B&B or self-catering. In summer, catch the milk float tram down to the harbour from the nearby public car park. ❦❀🛏◐▲♣P🚌(72,73) 🐾📶

Ponsanooth

Stag Hunt

20 St Michael's Road, TR3 7EE (on A393)
☎ (01872) 863046
St Austell Tribute; Treen's Classic; 1 changing beer (sourced locally; often Treen's) 🄷
Traditional Cornish granite community pub on the main Falmouth to Redruth road, with convenient bus stops close by. The bar in the lower part of the pub is decorated with photos depicting local scenes. The upper back room has its own small bar and can serve as a function room; it also hosts the Thursday evening jam session and occasional beer festivals. The real ales are mostly locally brewed. Food times may vary; Indian cuisine is the house speciality. Q❦❀◗🍎P🚌(U2)🐾

Port Isaac

Golden Lion ✔

13 Fore Street, PL29 3RB
☎ (01208) 880336 🌐 thegoldenlionportisaac.co.uk
St Austell Trelawny, Tribute, Proper Job, Hicks 🄷
This fine old 18th-century pub in the heart of Port Isaac has several drinking areas and a small balcony overlooking the harbour. Beware the slightly uneven bare-boarded floors which, together with Victorian cast-iron fireplaces, earn it recognition on CAMRA's Regional Inventory of Historic Pub Interiors. The games room downstairs was originally the Bloody Bones locals' bar, and boasts a smugglers' tunnel down to a causeway on the beach. A small flagstoned courtyard at the rear offers alfresco drinking. ❦❀◐♣🚌(10)🐾📶

Porthleven

Ship Inn

Mount Pleasant Road, TR13 9JS
☎ (01326) 564204 🌐 theshipinnporthleven.co.uk
Sharp's Cornish Coaster, Doom Bar; Skinner's Porthleven; Tintagel Harbour Special; 1 changing beer (sourced locally) 🄷
Seventeeth-century fishermen's inn perched on the south-west corner of the harbour, accessed up a steep flight of steps. It enjoys a commanding view over the harbour; here you can sit comfortably and watch the rough seas on stormy days. The rambling split-level interior has wooden and slated floors, beams decorated with an eclectic mix of coins, banknotes, beermats and brass artefacts, and sketches of local characters. A large log fire warms the pub in winter. ❦❀◐🍎🚌(U4)🐾📶

Portscatho

Plume of Feathers ✔

The Square, TR2 5HW
☎ (01872) 580321 🌐 plumeoffeathers-roseland.com
St Austell Tribute, Proper Job; 2 changing beers (often St Austell, Timothy Taylor) 🄷
Built in 1756, the Plume is one of the oldest buildings in the village, and the hub of the local community. Its contemporary exterior hides a traditional wood-beamed, slate-walled interior with cosy nooks, a split-room bar and separate restaurant. The selection of St Austell ales may be supplemented by a changing beer from elsewhere. The pub is focused on home-cooked and locally sourced food, and hosts charity nights and other community events. You will receive a warm welcome here. Q❦🛏◐▲🍎🚌(50)🐾📶

Poughill

Preston Gate Inn

Poughill Road, EX23 9ET (on Sandymouth Bay road)
SS224077
☎ (01288) 354017 🌐 prestongateinn.co.uk
St Austell Hicks; Sharp's Original; Skinner's Lushingtons; 1 changing beer (sourced locally; often Holsworthy Ales, Tintagel) 🄷
This cosy 16th-century building, originally two cottages, has been a village pub since 1983. The spacious U-shaped room hosts a dartboard at one end of the bar; the other end is roomier with more seating and a roaring log fire in winter. Conversation rules here, and the pub is home to darts and quiz teams. Meals include monthly theme nights (booking advised). The beer range may reduce in winter and the cider varies. The name Preston comes from the Cornish word for priest.
Q❦◐▲♣🍎P🚌(128,218)🐾📶

Quintrell Downs

Two Clomes

East Road, TR8 4PD (on A392)
☎ (01637) 879737
Sharp's Doom Bar; 2 changing beers (sourced locally; often Harbour, Padstow) 🄷
Named after the two ovens set either side of the open fireplace – which is now fitted with a wood-burning stove – this 18th-century free house is popular for dining out. Various extensions to the original building have added a large restaurant (booking is advisable, even in winter). Background music plays and there is a TV for sporting occasions. The pub is conveniently situated on a main route into Newquay and close to campsites.
❦❀◐♿▲≹♣🍎P🚌(21,91)🐾

St Ives

Castle Inn

16 Fore Street, TR26 1AB
☎ (01736) 796833
Sharp's Original, Sea Fury; house beer (by Skinner's); 3 changing beers (sourced nationally; often Marston's, Skinner's) 🄷
This pub has had a chequered history, being by turns accommodation for men building Tregenna Castle, a brothel, and a shipping office for the former Union Castle line. Now a thriving town-centre local, popular with locals and visitors alike, its emphasis is on an ever-varying real ale menu, plus a cider or two, or a perry. The single bar sports an eye-catching stained-glass window at the front, and the walls are adorned with various items of nautical bric-a-brac. ❦◐≹♣🍎🚌🐾📶

Pilchard Press Alehouse

Wharf Road, TR26 1LF
☎ (01736) 791665
6 changing beers (sourced locally; often Krow, St Ives, Treen's) 🄷/🄶
Cornwall's first micropub, the Pilchard Press opened in 2016, with space for around 25 people. Situated up an alley off the harbour front, it offers a friendly atmosphere

and up to six real ales from casks racked up on an interesting wooden stillage. There are a few bar stools, plus two tables with chairs and a smaller chessboard/draughts table. Note that the pub may close earlier if the beer runs out. Q🍼⛺⇌🍎🚌🐾

St John

St John Inn

PL11 3AW

☎ (01752) 829299 🌐 stjohninn.co.uk

Draught Bass; 2 changing beers (sourced nationally; often Exmoor, Woodforde's) Ⓗ

Reached down narrow country lanes, this 16th-century village pub is constructed from two former cottages. The pub has a pleasant, cosy ambience, with an L-shaped bar room featuring a beamed ceiling and floor of red tiles, wooden furniture and a warming open fire for winter. A cosy snug opposite the bar, a patio with seating at the front, and an attractive beer garden add to the appeal at this picturesque and welcoming pub. Live events are hosted in a semi-permanent marquee. Q🍼❀◗⛺🍎P🐾

St Just

Star Inn ✓

1 Fore Street, TR19 7LL

☎ (01736) 788767

St Austell Cornish Best Bitter, Tribute, Proper Job; 2 changing beers (sourced regionally; often Bath Ales, St Austell) Ⓗ

How pubs used to be: no food here, just excellent beer and friendly banter. The atmospheric main bar is enhanced by its dark, quirky décor, open fire and mining and rowing artefacts. The wood-beamed ceiling is adorned with flags of the Celtic nations, among others. A separate room opposite doubles as a meeting venue for community groups, while an enclosed beer garden is at the rear of the building. Live music features on Monday and Thursday evenings. 🍼❀♿⛺🚌🐾📶

St Kew Highway

Red Lion Inn Ⓛ

PL30 3DN (just off A39)

☎ (01208) 841271 🌐 redlionstkew.com

St Austell Tribute; 2 changing beers (sourced locally; often Padstow) Ⓗ

Fully community-oriented, this picturesque and friendly family-run 17th-century pub is central to village activities. Its L-shaped single-bar interior divides distinctly in two – the front area mainly for drinking, though it includes an elevated dining space, and the rear a restaurant for more leisurely dining. Comfortable furnishings and open fires contribute to the cosy, relaxed ambience. Up to three ales are offered, mostly from Cornwall or Devon breweries. Interesting freshly cooked meals favour local produce. Q🍼❀◖◗⛺P🚌(95)🐾📶

St Mabyn

St Mabyn Inn

Churchtown, PL30 3BA

☎ (01208) 841266 🌐 stmabyninn.com

Harbour Ellensberg; Sharp's Doom Bar, Sea Fury; Tintagel Cornwall's Pride; 1 changing beer (sourced locally) Ⓗ

Near the church stands this popular, attractive, 17th-century free house, the village local where conversation thrives. It features a single bar with adjoining snug, games room and stylish well-appointed restaurant, and an attractive beer garden outside. Open fires, wood furnishings including settles, stained-glass partitions and windows add character, complemented by an interesting collection of toby jugs, horse brasses and vintage advertising. With four quality ales and a changing choice of food, including Thai nights, this pub is one to seek out. Q🍼❀◖◗♿⛺♣🍎P🚌(55)🐾📶

St Mawgan

Falcon Inn Ⓛ

TR8 4EP (near Newquay airport)

☎ (01637) 860225 🌐 thefalconinnstmawgan.co.uk

Dartmoor Legend; Sharp's Original; 1 changing beer (sourced locally; often Tintagel) Ⓗ

Attractive community pub in the idyllic setting of the Lanherne Valley; a quiet retreat only a few miles from the bustle of Newquay and the airport. The single bar exudes a warm, welcoming atmosphere and offers three real ales, one of which always varies. It is also popular for meals. There is a games room and a large award-winning garden; dogs are welcome here and in the bar. A beer festival with a gin bar is held every July. Q🍼❀🛏◖◗♿♣P🚌(A5)🐾📶

Saltash

Union Inn

Tamar Street, PL12 4EL (on waterfront beneath bridges)

☎ (01752) 844770

Dartmoor Legend, Jail Ale Ⓗ; 2 changing beers (sourced regionally; often Bays, Cornish Crown, Summerskills) Ⓗ/Ⓖ

The frontage of this riverside local, overlooked by the Tamar bridges, is strikingly painted as a union flag. The single bar offers a selection of real ales and a different guest beer, usually on gravity in the cellar. The draught cider is Sam's Devon Dry. Outside drinking is at tables overlooking the river. Live music features on Tuesday or weekend evenings. Tamar Street, the pub's location, used to be known as Pickle Cock Alley as shellfish were sold through open windows. ❀⇌♣🍎P🚌🐾

South Petherwin

Frog & Bucket

PL15 7LP (just off B3254)

☎ (01566) 776988 🌐 frogandbucket.co.uk

5 changing beers (sourced nationally) Ⓗ

Roomy pub, opened in 1989 despite local opposition, but now warmly welcoming all ages and providing a friendly focus for village social life. Up to five varying guest ales are on offer. Off the main bar are a separate lounge, games room and two other rooms, one of which doubles as a restaurant or function room. Offering fine Dartmoor views, the pub is a meeting place for vintage vehicles in summer. Q🍼❀♿♣🍎P🚌(236)🐾📶

Towan Cross

Victory Inn Ⓛ

TR4 8BN

☎ (01209) 890359

St Austell Tribute; Skinner's Betty Stogs, Lushingtons; 1 changing beer (sourced locally) Ⓗ

Built in 1605, this clifftop former coaching inn was originally opened to quench the thirst of local miners. Welcoming and family run, it offers impressive sea views – and breezes – to enjoy alongside Cornish ales and locally sourced quality food. The open-plan single bar separates into drinking and dining areas, extending to the conservatory and spacious beer garden. In former times, funeral corteges would stop outside, rest the coffin on the nearby horizontal Towan Cross, and take refreshment within. Q❀◑Å♣P🚌(304,315)🐾📶

Trebarwith Strand

Mill House Inn

PL34 0HD (off B3263 near Tintagel) SX058865
☎ (01840) 770200 🌐 themillhouseinn.co.uk
Tintagel Castle Gold; house beer (by Tintagel); 1 changing beer (sourced locally; often Sharp's, Tintagel) [H]
Converted 16th-century corn mill and waterwheel set beside a stream in a deep wooded valley. This friendly inn has a stone-flagged bar area accessible up a flight of steps beside the adjacent drinking terrace. The restaurant is in an extension, offering an imaginative menu that changes daily. While the Mill House is primarily a food and accommodation establishment, drinkers are nevertheless welcome in the bar, with a mix of local beers. Q❀🛏◑♣P🐾📶

Treen (Zennor)

Gurnard's Head 𝕃

TR26 3DE (on B3306 Lands End-St Ives coast road)
☎ (01736) 796928 🌐 gurnardshead.co.uk
St Austell Tribute; 3 changing beers (sourced locally; often Cornish Crown, Padstow, Skinner's) [H]
Named after the nearby headland, this imposing and strikingly coloured inn stands near the coastal path on the rugged and beautiful granite moorland of the Penwith peninsula. It has a large bar, cosy snug and stylish restaurant. Wooden furnishings, comfy sofas and open fires add to a relaxed and unhurried ambience, with local art adorning the walls. The varied beer range features Cornish microbreweries, while daily choices in the food menu reflect the availability of local produce.
Q❀🛏◑♣●P🚌(A3,16A)🐾📶

Tresco (Isles of Scilly)

New Inn

Townshill, New Grimsby, TR24 0QG
☎ (01720) 423006
House beer (by Skinner's); 3 changing beers (sourced locally; often Ales of Scilly, Dartmoor, St Austell) [H]
Excellent old pub near New Grimsby harbour, a haven between demanding coastal walks and the boat to St Mary's. Extensions to the garden and a covered pavilion have added to the attractions of this popular real ale outlet. The varying beers are mostly from Cornish breweries, usually Skinner's and St Austell, and local brewer Ales of Scilly is frequently represented. Beer festivals are held over the spring and late summer bank holidays. ❀🛏◑♣🐾📶

Trevaunance Cove

Driftwood Spars ✔

Quay Road, TR5 0RT
☎ (01872) 552428 🌐 driftwoodspars.com
Driftwood Spars; 5 changing beers (sourced locally; often Atlantic, Driftwood Spars, Harbour) [H]
Friendly community-oriented brewpub, well worth a visit. A former 17th-century sail loft and mine warehouse, it features three wood-beamed bars on different levels, with lead-light windows and granite fireplaces. The decor is mainly nautical and shipwreck-themed. Upstairs, the restaurant affords panoramic views across the bay, while over the road the beer garden adjoins the Driftwood Brewery, whose beers are always on the bar alongside favourite regional guests. The pub holds three beer festivals a year, and occasional tutored tastings. Q❀🛏◑♿♣●P🚌(87,315)🐾📶

Trewellard

Trewellard Arms 𝕃

Trewellard Road, TR19 7TA (on B3318/B3306 jct)
☎ (01736) 788634
5 changing beers (sourced regionally; often Cotleigh, Tintagel) [H]
Formerly a mining count house, then a hotel, this is now a family-run free house, where a warm welcome is assured. Its cosy interior accommodates an open-beamed single bar and pleasant restaurant with secluded dining space. Open fires enhance the homely atmosphere. A varying beer menu offers up to five ales and two ciders, and good-value home-cooked food is available. Outside is a paved patio area. A beer festival is held each May. Q❀◑Å♣●P🚌(A3,A17)🐾📶

Truro

Old Ale House ✔

7 Quay Street, TR1 2HD (nr bus station)
☎ (01872) 271122 🌐 old-ale-house.co.uk
Skinner's Betty Stogs, Hops 'n' Honey, Lushingtons, Porthleven [H]**; 4 changing beers (sourced nationally; often Skinner's)** [H]/[G]
This friendly and lively city-centre pub is Skinner's brewery tap. The main bar is atmospheric, with subtle lighting, wooden floors, beamed ceiling and scattered artefacts. Seating is plentiful, while upstairs is a quieter drinking area and function room. Up to 13 real ales and five real ciders are on offer, in addition to an impressive range of up to 40 craft keg and foreign beers. Customers may bring in their own food. Q♿♣●🚌🐾📶

Rising Sun ✔

Mitchell Hill, TR1 1ED
☎ (01872) 240003 🌐 therisingsuntruro.co.uk
Fuller's London Pride; Skinner's Betty Stogs [H]**; 2 changing beers (sourced locally; often Skinner's)** [G]
Near the city centre up a steep hill, this award-winning pub is worth seeking out. Its narrow frontage belies a spacious interior accommodating a small public bar with adjacent dining area, a lounge bar, and a raised restaurant area. Outside is a sheltered patio where periodic beer festivals are held. The pub is comfortably furnished throughout, its decor including old Truro scenes. The changing beer menu offers up to four ales, two dispensed straight from casks. The food menu is popular – booking is advised. Q❀◑♣P🚌🐾📶

Zennor

Tinner's Arms

TR26 3BY (off B3306 St Ives-St Just coast rd)
☎ (01736) 796927 🌐 tinnersarms.com
Skinner's Lushingtons, Porthleven; house beer (by Sharp's) [H]
Popular with walkers and tourists drawn by a local mermaid legend, this ancient granite village pub lies on the north coast of the Penwith peninsula. An atmospheric interior accommodates a single bar and adjacent restaurant, the ambience enhanced by exposed granite walls and wood beams, open fires, wall panels and rustic furnishings. The food menu features local produce, but it's best to phone the pub first if planning to eat here. Folk music features on Thursday evening; Sunday is quiz night.
Q❀🛏◑♣●P🚌(A3,16A,7)🐾📶

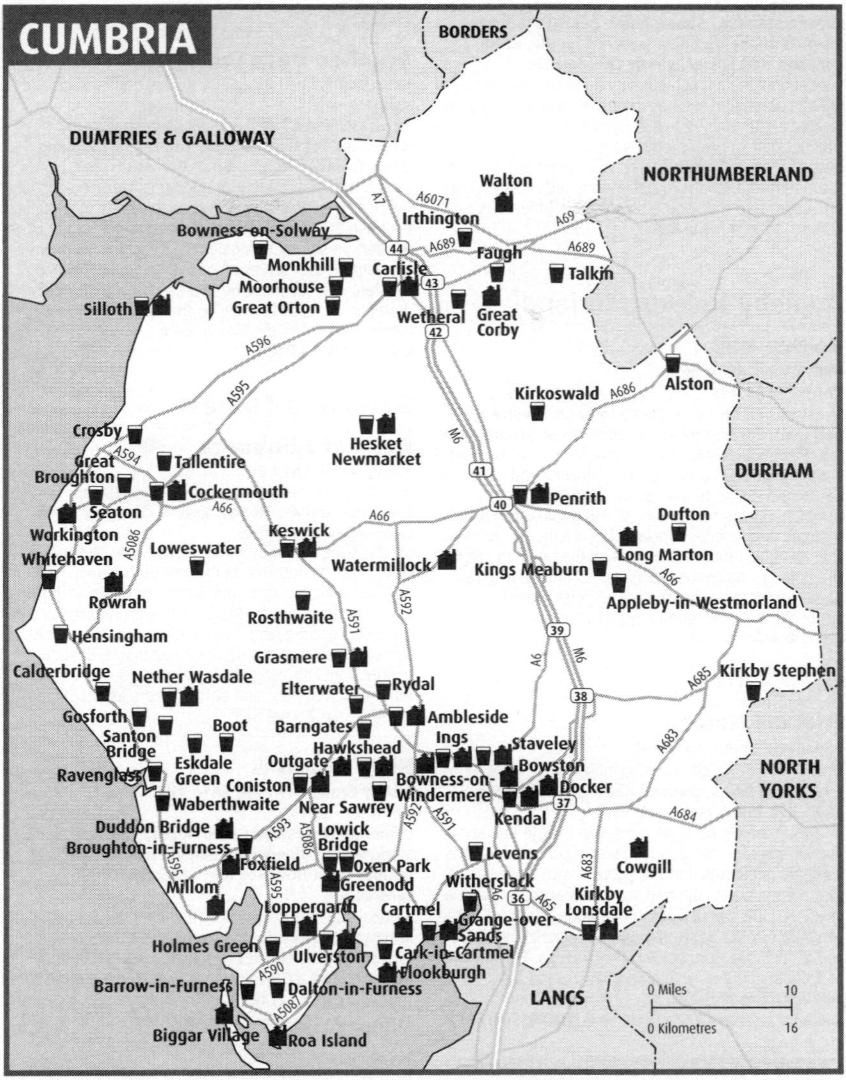

Alston

Cumberland Inn L

Townfoot, CA9 3HX

☎ (01434) 381875 🌐 alstoncumberlandhotel.co.uk

Firebrick Blaydon Brick; 3 changing beers (sourced locally) Ⓗ

A fine 19th-century inn overlooking the South Tyne river. Close to the Coast-to-Coast cycle route and Pennine Way, it is an ideal base to explore the highest market town in England. Changing beers are dispensed from four handpumps. The Cumberland has won many local CAMRA awards, including recognition for its cider, and always has a wide selection of beers, ciders and perries to choose from. Q❀⇌◑●P⊟🐾ᯤ

Ambleside

Golden Rule ✔

Smithy Brow, LA22 9AS

☎ (015394) 32257

Robinsons Cumbria Way, Dizzy Blonde, Cascade IPA, Wizard; 3 changing beers (sourced regionally; often Robinsons) Ⓗ

One of the oldest hostelries in Ambleside, at the bottom of the infamous Struggle leading up to Kirkstone Pass, serving a good range of well-kept Robinsons ales. An exceptional high-quality traditional pub, it has a wonderfully cosy feel, a real fire, bench seating and historical rock-climbing photos decorating the walls. Families with children especially enjoy the attractive snug; generations of visitors continue to visit the pub for its fond memories. It has been a Guide feature since 1977. Q⌂❀♿♣●⊟🐾ᯤ

Royal Oak L ✔

Lake Road, LA22 9BU

☎ (015394) 33382

Greene King IPA, Abbot; house beer (by Greene King); 5 changing beers (sourced locally; often Coniston, Old School, Kirkby Lonsdale)
Typical Greene King pub but with up to six local ales from Kirkby Lonsdale as well as the usual suspects. Centrally located in the Ambleside honeypot, the bar is well run by friendly staff to ensure efficient service. The covered outside seating is always busy, even in winter. Currently the Dog of the Month competition is the most popular attraction. Live music on a Sunday is another new feature.

Appleby-in-Westmorland

Golden Ball

High Wiend, CA16 6RD
(017683) 51493
Marston's Pedigree; 3 changing beers (sourced nationally; often Cross Bay, Eden River, Jennings)
A traditional back-street venue that inhabits its own time warp, the pub has a strong local following and a sociable house lurcher. Up to five lovely changing beers complement the tied pump. An evocative rock jukebox prompts spontaneous dancing, classic films are shown on Thursdays, and there are occasional themed party nights. The pub also has newspapers, books and games. Its partially covered rear patio has an idiosyncratic atmosphere. Closed during Appleby Fair week in June.
Q (563)

Midland Hotel

25 Clifford Street, CA16 6TS
(017683) 51524 themidlandhotelappleby.co.uk
3 changing beers (sourced nationally; often Cross Bay, Eden River, Malvern Hills)
A former railway hotel on the Settle-Carlisle line above the town centre, the pub is modern and light, and has boutique bedrooms that are popular with walkers and steam enthusiasts. The two separate bar rooms have an airy feel, with wooden floors and large windows. Three handpumps offer a mix of local and regional beers; cider and perry in the summer includes Oliver's. The Midland hosts Appleby Beer Fest in September, and has occasional live music. There are lots of outdoor tables and a back garden. Q P (563)

Barngates

Drunken Duck Inn

LA22 0NG (signed off B5286 Hawkshead to Ambleside road)
(015394) 36347 drunkenduckinn.co.uk
Barngates Cat Nap, Cracker, Tag Lag; 3 changing beers (sourced locally; often Barngates)
High above Ambleside, this traditional Lakeland dwelling reflects the simplicity, beauty and longevity of its natural environment. From the fells, it draws water for the beers brewed on-site by Barngates Brewery. The bar has six handpumps and serves all of the Barngates beers on rotation. The outside seating area at the front offers dramatic views of the fells to the north-east. Dogs are allowed except in the dining room.
Q P

Barrow-in-Furness

Duke of Edinburgh

Abbey Road, LA14 5QR
(01229) 821039 dukeofedinburghhotel.co.uk
Lancaster Amber, Blonde, Red; 5 changing beers (sourced regionally)
On the edge of the town centre near the station, the Duke is not as noisy as similar bars in the town. It has an airy feel with modern, comfortable furniture and a fine open fire. Paintings by local artists are displayed around the walls. Good-quality, reasonably priced bar meals are served; there is also a separate restaurant. Beers are mainly from Lancaster Brewery, with guest ales plus three craft keg ales, and bottled beers from around the world. P

King's Arms

Quarry Brow, Hawcoat, LA14 4HY
(01229) 828137
Cumbrian Loweswater Gold; Kirkby Lonsdale Monumental Blonde; 4 changing beers (sourced locally; often Bowness Bay, Cumbrian, Kirkby Lonsdale)
A popular local pub conveniently near the No.1 bus route in Hawcoat Village (between the main town centre and the hospital). It sells ales mainly from Cumbrian micros. A beer menu on a chalkboard lists forthcoming attractions. The pub, which has been on these premises since the 1860s, has been extensively extended and renovated,

REAL ALE BREWERIES

Appleby Kendal
Barngates Ambleside
Beckstones Millom
Biggar Biggar Village (brewing suspended)
Bowness Bay Kendal
Brack'N'Brew Watermillock
Carlisle Carlisle
Coniston Coniston
Cumbrian Hawkshead
Dent Cowgill
Derwent Silloth
Eden River Penrith
Ennerdale Rowrah
Fell Flookburgh
Foxfield Foxfield (brewing suspended)
Grasmere Grasmere
Great Corby Great Corby
Greenodd Greenodd
Handsome Bowston
Hawkshead Flookburgh / Staveley
Healey's Loppergarth
Hesket Newmarket Hesket Newmarket
Jennings Cockermouth
Keswick Keswick
Kirkby Lonsdale Kirkby Lonsdale
Langdale Docker
Logan Beck Duddon Bridge
Old Friends Ulverston
Old Vicarage Walton
Roa Island Roa Island
Shaws of Grange Grange-over-Sands (NEW)
South Lakes Ulverston
Strands Nether Wasdale
Stringers Ulverston
Tarn Hows Outgate
Tirril Long Marton
Tractor Shed Workington
Twisted Magnolia Keswick (NEW)
Ulverston Ulverston
Unsworth's Yard Cartmel
Westmorland Kendal
Wild Boar Bowness-on-Windermere
Windermere Ings

and features an open bar with adjacent separate rooms. Friendly staff give a warm welcome. Well-behaved dogs are allowed in one of the rooms. Q

Boot

Brook House Inn

CA19 1TG (200yds walk from Dalegarth Station – La'al Ratty)

☎ (019467) 23288 brookhouseinn.co.uk

Barngates Goodhew's Dry Stout; Cumbrian Langdale; Hawkshead Bitter; 6 changing beers (sourced nationally)

A family-run tourist inn, at the heart of the western Lake District in beautiful Eskdale, close to the terminus of the La'al Ratty miniature railway. It is renowned for freshly prepared quality food and a changing variety of cask ales. Together with two other close-by Eskdale pubs, it hosts the June beer festival, one of the biggest in the Lake District, usually with entertainment by local morris dancers. A winner of frequent local CAMRA branch awards. Q P

Woolpack Inn

CA19 1TH (¾ mile E of Boot village)

☎ (019467) 23230 woolpack.co.uk

Barngates Brathay Gold; Fell Ghyll; Tirril Borrowdale Bitter, Windermere IPA; 6 changing beers (sourced nationally)

Iconic Lakeland hostelry on the approach to Hardknott Pass. Surrounded by stunning scenery, this popular family-run tourist pub is renowned for good food and excellent cask ales. Separate lounge and walkers' bars offer an attractive mix of traditional and modern styles, with wood-burning stoves in both areas. Together with other nearby pubs in the Eskdale Valley, the Woolpack Inn participates in the annual Eskdale beer festival held in June. It also holds a cider festival in April. Local CAMRA Cider Pub of the Year 2020.
Q (Dalegarth) P

Bowness-on-Solway

King's Arms

CA7 5AF

☎ (016973) 51426 kingsarmsbowness.co.uk

2 changing beers (sourced nationally; often Jennings, Marston's)

In the centre of the village, the King's Arms is a popular stopping-off point for visitors to the area walking the Hadrian's Wall Path. It is a community pub with a library, band practice every other Sunday, and a regular quiz on Thursday night. It also has pool, darts and dominoes teams. Set on the Solway coast in an area of outstanding natural beauty, it is popular with birdwatchers and cyclists as well as walkers. Snacks are available throughout the day in summer. Q P

Broughton-in-Furness

Manor Arms

The Square, LA20 6HY

☎ (01229) 716286 manorarmsthesquare.co.uk

Great Corby Blonde; Hawkshead Windermere Pale; 6 changing beers (sourced regionally)

An outstanding free house owned by the Varty family for more than 30 years. Set in an attractive Georgian square, it has been the recipient of many CAMRA awards. Real ale dominates, always including a dark beer, along with traditional cider and perry. A mini beer festival is held every day. Two fires keep the pub warm and the bar staff are always friendly. Q

Calderbridge

Stanley Arms Hotel

CA20 1DN

☎ (01946) 841235 stanleyarmshotel.com

Wychwood Hobgoblin Gold; 4 changing beers (sourced nationally)

This small family-run village hotel, bordering the Lake District National Park, has a delightful beer garden beside the Calder River, with full fishing rights. Situated on the A595, it gives easy access to western beaches, lakes, fells and valleys. Hearty meals, using locally sourced produce, are served up in the two-room bar and restaurant. It also offers a well-equipped function/conference room. Local attractions include the riverside walk along the Calder past the ruined 12th-century Calder Abbey. Q P

Cark-in-Cartmel

Engine Inn

LA11 7NZ (near station)

☎ (015395) 58341 theengineinncartmel.co.uk

Lancaster Blonde; Timothy Taylor Landlord; 2 changing beers (sourced regionally)

A 17th-century inn, refurbished in 2010, making an excellent end to the walk from Grange described in CAMRA's Lake District Pub Walks book. Beers are selected to provide a range of styles. There is an open bar area with a cosy fire, separate rooms away from the bar and a riverside beer garden. Five en-suite rooms are available. Opening hours and food services times are reduced in winter. P (530)

Carlisle

Beehive

Warwick Road, CA1 1LH

☎ (01228) 549731

Morland Old Golden Hen; 3 changing beers (often Greene King, Marston's)

Large popular pub opposite Carlisle football and rugby grounds on the A69 leading into town (home fans only for some games). It has lots of TV screens for Sky, showing multiple channels at the same time when necessary. Food is served all day, and there is a regular quiz every Thursday night, with live music most Friday evenings. It has a large covered outdoor smoking area. Completely refurbished following devastating flooding in 2015. P

Fat Gadgie

5 Devonshire Street, CA3 8LG

☎ (01228) 812880 thefatgadgie.co.uk

6 changing beers

Opened in 2017 after the closure of a specialist ale bar in the same premises, the space has been refurbished by the new owner to provide a pleasant, quiet drinking environment without the distraction of TV or gaming machines. The bar offers a choice of beers from far and wide, the range changing frequently and targeting the discerning drinker. The Fat Gadgie adds to a series of unusual bar names in this area of the city.

King's Head Inn

Fisher Street, CA3 8RF

kingsheadcarlisle.co.uk

4 changing beers

An excellent city-centre pub, winner of many CAMRA awards, offering a changing range of ales from four handpumps. Pictures of old Carlisle adorn the internal walls and outside is an explanation of why the city isn't in the Domesday Book. Good-value meals are served at lunchtime. The spacious covered outdoor courtyard has a large-screen TV and regularly features live music. Children and dogs are not allowed. ❀◐⇌♣●🚌🐾📶

Spinners Arms Ⓛ

Cummersdale, CA2 6BD

☎ (01228) 532928

Carlisle Spun Gold, Flaxen, Magic Number; 1 changing beer (sourced locally; often Carlisle) 🄷

Cosy family-friendly hostelry, an original Redfern pub with unique and original features. It is the brewery tap for Carlisle Brewing Co, showcasing its beer on five pumps. There is regular live music, with Irish music sessions every first and third Wednesday. Children are welcome until 9pm and well-behaved dogs are permitted. The pub is close to the Cumbrian Way and National Cycle Route 7, which run alongside the picturesque River Caldew. ᘓ❀♿♣P🚌(75)🐾📶

Woodrow Wilson Ⓛ ✔

48 Botchergate, CA1 1QS

☎ (01228) 819942

Great Corby Ale, Blonde; Greene King Abbot; Marston's Old Empire; Ruddles Best Bitter; Sharp's Doom Bar; 6 changing beers (sourced nationally) 🄷

One of two almost adjacent Wetherspoons, this pub is in a refurbished Co-op building and is named after the former US president, whose mother was born in Carlisle. Up to 14 handpumps offer the largest range of real ales to be found in the city. Food is available all day. At the rear there is a spacious outdoor seating area, heated patio and smokers' section. Children are welcome in some parts until 8pm. ᘓ❀◐◑♿⇌●P🚌📶

Cockermouth

Castle Bar Ⓛ ✔

14 Market Place, CA13 9NQ (150yds from Jennings Brewery)

☎ (01900) 829904 🌐 castlebarcockermouth.co.uk

Cumbrian Loweswater Gold; Jennings Night Vision, Cumberland Ale; Titanic Plum Porter; 2 changing beers (sourced nationally) 🄷

The publican here is keen on requests for beers from around the UK, and the chalkboard outside lists current and upcoming real ales and ciders. Parts of the pub date from the 16th century. It was refurbished in the 2000s and commended in the CAMRA Pub Design Awards 2009. Three TVs show sports across the maze-like ground floor. There is a restaurant on the first floor and a relaxing second-floor room with sofas. ᘓ❀◐◑●🚌🐾📶

Cock & Bull

7 South Street, CA13 9RT (opp Sainsbury's)

☎ (01900) 827999 🌐 thenewcockandbull.co.uk

Coniston Bluebird Bitter; Great Corby Blonde, Fox; 2 changing beers (sourced nationally) 🄷

A community pub in the centre of town. It does not serve food apart from bar snacks. There is a constantly changing range of real ales on two of the handpumps, mainly from smaller Cumbrian breweries. The venue is on three levels: below the main bar is a quieter small room; the main area has bar stools plus two seating spaces with a TV showing sports in the front corner; the top level has a pool table and dartboard. ᘓ❀🚌🐾📶

Swan Inn Ⓛ

52-56 Kirkgate, CA13 9PH

☎ (01900) 822425

Jennings Night Vision, Atomic Theory, Cumberland Ale; 2 changing beers (sourced nationally) 🄷

A true community venue well supported by locals, this 17th-century pub has flagged floors, exposed beams, a real fire and quiet nooks and crannies. It hosts a monthly whisky club and folk music sessions. There are six handpumps, with three of the beers coming from the local Jennings Brewery. The large-screen TV at the back shows sport. ᘓ♣🚌🐾📶

Coniston

Black Bull Inn & Hotel Ⓛ

LA21 8DU

☎ (015394) 41335 🌐 blackbullconiston.co.uk

Coniston Bluebird Bitter, Bluebird Premium XB, No.9 Barley Wine, Old Man Ale, Oliver's Light Ale, Special Oatmeal Stout; 3 changing beers (sourced locally; often Coniston) 🄷

A 16th-century coaching inn, this is Coniston Brewing Company's on-site taphouse, also offering good food in traditional comfortable surroundings. A full menu is served from noon. Six regular beers are supplemented by other beers from the brewery on a rotation basis – try a tasting paddle. The spacious bar and lounge are frequented by tourists in this hugely popular, spectacular location near Coniston Old Man. The outside seating area is perfect in summer. Dogs are not allowed in the restaurant. ᘓ❀🛏◐◑♿♣●P🚌(X12,505)🐾📶

Sun Ⓛ

LA21 8HQ

☎ (015394) 41248 🌐 thesunconiston.com

Coniston Bluebird Premium XB; Cumbrian Loweswater Gold; 6 changing beers (sourced locally) 🄷

Take the Walna Scar road up from Coniston village, or down from Coniston Old Man, to visit this 16th-century pub and hotel. The deliberately unmodernised dual-level bar has atmosphere and character, with a slate-topped bar, slate flooring, exposed beams and stone walls, heated by a large open range. Up to eight cask ales are available, mostly from local brewers. The conservatory and terrace enjoy delightful views over the garden. Winter opening hours vary.
Qᘓ❀🛏◐◑♿♣P🚌(505,X12)🐾📶

Yewdale Inn Ⓛ

2 Yewdale Road, LA21 8DU

☎ (015394) 41280 🌐 yewdaleinn.com

Barngates Tag Lag; Cumbrian Legendary Ales Loweswater Gold; Theakston Old Peculier; 1 changing beer (sourced nationally) 🄷

A welcoming village inn in the centre of Coniston, attracting locals and visitors alike. In winter a cosy fire and jovial atmosphere prevail; in summer you can enjoy a drink on the terrace with stunning views of the Old Man of Coniston and surrounding fells, and of Church Beck, a babbling brook running through the village. Opening hours and the availability of food are reduced in winter but details are maintained on the website. Breakfast is served. Accommodation is offered in nine guest rooms. ᘓ❀🛏◐◑♣🚌(505,X12)🐾📶

Crosby

Stag Inn ✔

Lowside, CA15 6SH

☎ (01900) 812549 🌐 staginncrosby.com

Sharp's Doom Bar; Tetley Bitter; 3 changing beers (sourced nationally) 🄷

Welcoming pub, popular with locals and visitors, in a great location with views over the Solway Firth to Scotland. It has a large bar with two serving points and quiet corners. The restaurant area offers an extensive menu to suit all tastes. There is also a function room and a sheltered beer garden. ⑤⊛⊛⊙&&A♣P⊟❏(300)❀ 🛜

Dalton-in-Furness

Brown Cow Inn ⓛ
10 Goose Green, LA15 8AQ
☎ (01229) 462553 🌐 browncowinndalton.co.uk
Black Sheep Best Bitter; 5 changing beers (sourced locally) ⓗ
A warm and friendly atmosphere awaits visitors to this 400-year-old coaching house, which has retained many original features including beams, brasses, local prints and an open fire. A winner of many awards for its six real ales, the pub also serves excellent food from a full and varied menu. Meals can be enjoyed in the large dining room or, on warmer days, on the charming patio with heating and lighting. ⑤⊛⊛⊙P⊟(6,X6)🛜

Dufton

Stag Inn
CA16 6DB
☎ (017683) 51608 🌐 thestagdufton.co.uk
4 changing beers (sourced regionally; often Black Sheep, Bowness Bay, Hawkshead) ⓗ
Attractive old red-sandstone pub overlooking the picture-book village green on the Pennine Way, with relaxing views of the fells from the garden. There is a small bar with an old black range, a snug with wood-burner, and a dining room to the rear facing the North Pennines. Four handpumps serve mostly local ales with guests from the north-east; there is also a keg line for modern craft ales. Hearty meals are available for meat lovers (booking essential). Dufton has holiday cottages, camping and a seasonal YHA. Q⑤⊛⊛⊙A♣P❀ 🛜

Elterwater

Britannia Inn ⓛ ✅
LA22 9HP
☎ (015394) 37210 🌐 britinn.co.uk
Coniston Bluebird Bitter; Langdale Elterwater Gold; house beer (by Langdale); 3 changing beers (sourced locally; often Barngates, Eden River, Langdale) ⓗ
A shining beer beacon in the Langdale valley, especially for walkers on the heights of the stunning surrounding fells. Unsurprisingly popular, the five rooms around the small bar fill quickly and the plentiful outdoor tables are equally busy in summer. It has great atmosphere and excellent beers - featuring Langdale Brewing (the sister business) and other local brewers. Wholesome Lakeland food is served. Residents can recover after their exertions in the nearby spa with its large indoor pool. An autumn beer festival is staged. ⑤⊛⊛⊙&A♣P⊟(516)❀ 🛜

Eskdale Green

Bower House Inn
CA19 1TD (short walk from Irton Road Station - La'al Ratty)
☎ (019467) 23244 🌐 bowerhouseinn.com
Cumbrian Loweswater Gold; Hawkshead Windermere Pale; Timothy Taylor Landlord; 1 changing beer (sourced nationally) ⓗ
This 18th-century Eskdale Valley coaching inn, on the edge of the village and close to the Outward Bound School, is renowned for good food and cask ales, and received a recent local CAMRA branch award. The dining room has oak-panelled seating and beamed ceilings, and there is a real fire in the bar. Outside is an attractive beer garden and a play area for children. The pub has a community focus with cricket and darts teams, and Sunday quizzes for local charities.
Q⑤⊛⊛⊙A⤲♣●P❀ 🛜

Faugh

String of Horses
Head's Nook, CA8 9EG
☎ (01228) 670297 🌐 stringofhorses.com
Allendale Wagtail Best Bitter; 2 changing beers ⓗ
A 17th-century pub altered and extended over the years into a multi-room establishment with traditional atmosphere, good food and accommodation. With a choice of three real ales, often from local breweries and a real cider, this is a pleasant country inn in which to meet for a quiet night out. Q⑤⊛⊙&●P🛜

Gosforth

Gosforth Hall Inn
Wasdale Road, CA20 1AZ (adjacent to St Mary's Church; from A595 follow road signed to Wasdale)
☎ (019467) 25322 🌐 gosforthhall.co.uk
4 changing beers (sourced nationally) ⓗ
On the edge of the village of Gosforth, this popular 16th-century locals' and visitors' pub is renowned for good food and a range of well-kept ales. The former 17th-century farmhouse is Grade II listed and boasts a priest's hole, a spiral staircase to the upper floors, and the widest single-span, sandstone hearth in England. It holds an annual beer festival in August and is a previous local CAMRA Pub of the Year. Q⑤⊛⊛⊙&♣P❀ 🛜

Grange-over-Sands

Keg & Kitchen ⓛ
Main Street, LA11 6AB
☎ (015395) 83003 🌐 kegandkitchen.co.uk
Wychwood Hobgoblin Gold; Wainwright; Unsworth's Yard Sir Edgar Harrington's Last Wolf; 1 changing beer (sourced locally; often Unsworth's Yard) ⓗ
Large pub in the centre of Grange opposite the post office. The main bar and entrance are on the middle floor. The upstairs has been converted to a games area with a pool table. The lower area, called the Gin Pig, can be accessed from the pub or from a separate entrance - it is open Friday and Saturday evenings and has bottled beers from Shaws of Grange. ⑤⊛●&A⤲♣●⊟❀ 🛜

Grasmere

Tweedies Bar & Lodge ⓛ
Red Bank Road, LA22 9SW
☎ (015394) 35300 🌐 tweediesgrasmere.com
Cumbrian Loweswater Gold; Hawkshead Bitter; 12 changing beers (sourced nationally; often Coniston, Hawkshead, Salopian) ⓗ
In the heart of Grasmere, this is an impressive pub that attracts worldwide real ale lovers - an audience it is designed to please. There is always some unusual beer, cider or perry to refresh the weary walker and relieve tired legs. Third-pint bats make sampling the challenging list (with extensive notes on style) an achievable goal. It has plenty of outdoor tables for sunny days. The famous Grasmere Guzzler (and music) festival is held on the first weekend in September.
⑤⊛⊛⊙&●P⊟(555,599)❀ 🛜

Great Broughton

Punch Bowl Inn

19 Main Street, CA13 0YJ

☎ (01900) 267070

3 changing beers (sourced nationally) 🄷

A community pub run by a committee of local volunteers. Although the opening hours are limited, this is more than compensated for by the quality and variation of the two – usually Cumbrian – real ales it sells. It has served 135 different beers in the past year, and holds a guest beer weekend in February. Originally a 17th-century coaching inn, this is definitely a locals' establishment. Q🐎♣P🐾📶

Great Orton

Wellington Inn

CA5 6LZ

☎ (01228) 710775

3 changing beers (sourced locally; often Derwent, Keswick) 🄷

An attractive country inn in a quiet village. Good-value meals are on offer using ingredients sourced locally, including meat from the renowned local butcher. Three handpumps serve ales that come mainly from local breweries like Derwent and Keswick. Live music is being reintroduced here with open mic nights on an occasional basis. There is space for 10 touring caravans on the adjacent campsite. Q🐎❀◐◑♿♣P

Hawkshead

King's Arms Hotel L ✔

The Square, LA22 0NZ

☎ (015394) 36372 🌐 kingsarmshawkshead.co.uk

Cumbrian Loweswater Gold; Hawkshead Bitter; 2 changing beers (sourced locally) 🄷

A characterful 500-year-old village inn sitting on the square of this historic settlement. Its traditional interior features beamed ceilings, an open fire, and a hand-carved king in the bar supporting the floor above. Good food is served in the bar and dining area, and there is frequent live music. The patio on the edge of the square is south-facing. The pub is family friendly and dogs are welcome in the bar. You can park in the central village car park. Winter hours may vary.

Q🐎❀🛏◐◑▲🚌(505)🐾📶

Hensingham

Globe Inn

95 Main Street, CA28 8QX (take A595 from Whitehaven and follow signs for Cleator Moor)

☎ (01946) 590772 🌐 theglobehensingham.co.uk

2 changing beers (sourced nationally) 🄷

An unassuming place from the outside, but as soon as you walk in the friendly character takes hold. There are two separate rooms downstairs with a dining area upstairs, and the food is freshly cooked to order. The beer range changes frequently, with two handpumps on the bar. Sports TV is available, as well as a dartboard. Very much a locals' pub. 🐎❀◐◑🚌🐾📶

Hesket Newmarket

Old Crown L ✔

CA7 8JG

☎ (016974) 78288 🌐 theoldcrownpub.co.uk

Hesket Newmarket Haystacks, Black Sail, Helvellyn Gold, High Pike, Doris' 90th Birthday Ale, Brim Fell IPA; 4 changing beers (sourced locally; often Hesket Newmarket) 🄷

Sitting in the heart of this lovely fellside village, the Old Crown is a showcase for the Hesket Newmarket Brewery, which is immediately behind. It is well known as the first co-operatively owned pub in the country and is popular with locals and visitors alike, and includes Prince Charles and Sir Chris Bonington among its supporters. Opening hours are subject to change so check the website before travelling. Q🐎❀◐◑♣●🐾📶

Holmes Green

Black Dog Inn L

Broughton Road, LA15 8JP (1½miles from Dalton-in-Furness – Tudor Square – on Broughton Rd towards Askam) SD233761

☎ (01229) 462975

Cumbrian Esthwaite Bitter, Loweswater Gold, Langdale; 5 changing beers (sourced nationally; often Abbeydale, Cumbrian, Oakham) 🄷

With five real ales on offer, a warm welcome awaits from the landlord and locals alike. This former coaching inn, with two real fires, quarry-tiled floor and rustic beams, was recently refurbished but retains plenty of character. There is live music monthly, and the Dog Fest music festival is usually held on August bank holiday Sunday. Outside is a decked seating area.

🐎❀🛏◑P🐾📶

Ings

Watermill Inn L

LA8 9PY

☎ (01539) 821309 🌐 watermillinn.co.uk

Windermere Collie Wobbles, A Bit'er Ruff, Blonde; 8 changing beers (sourced locally; often Windermere) 🄷

Multi-roomed former watermill that serves a wide selection of Windermere ales – all brewed on the premises. The beers have doggy names, and dogs have their own website and a special food menu. The family-owned pub has welcomed regular visitors for over 30 years and, as befits the first hostelry in the Lakes, a large car park extension is now accessed via the robust new bridge over the mill race. Q🐎❀🛏◐◑♿▲♣P🚌🐾📶

Irthington

Sally

CA6 4NJ

☎ (016977) 42954 🌐 thesallyirthington.co.uk

Wainwright; 1 changing beer (sourced nationally; often Thwaites) 🄷

Fully refurbished and extended former coaching inn in a village popular as a rest stop for Hadrian's Wall walkers. It is now a gastro-pub and boutique hotel that sells real ale from the Thwaites range. There is a superb slate fireplace in the dining area with a roaring fire in colder weather. Food is served daily and booking is recommended. The unusual name is a diminutive of the original Salutation Inn. 🐎◐◑♿♣P

Kendal

Barrel House L

Unit 16, Castle Mills, LA9 7DE

☎ 07498 203351 🌐 bownessbaybrewing.co.uk

Bowness Bay Swan Blonde, Swan Gold, Swan Black; 7 changing beers (sourced locally; often Appleby, Bowness Bay, Windmill) 🄷

An exciting new venture for Bowness Bay Brewery, housed in an imaginatively redesigned industrial unit beside the brewery and using recycled materials for furniture. The self-referencing use of copper is a visual joy. The bar offers a fantastic opportunity to sample up to 12 beers from the Bowness stable including 0.5% ABV Swan Free. Craft keg lines include two lagers and a local cider. Bookable brewery tours and tastings are available, as well as regular party nights with live music, food and dancing. Upholstered seating is to be found in the outdoor booths.

Factory Tap

5 Aynam Road, LA9 7DE

☎ (015394) 82541 thefactorytap.co.uk

Fyne Ales Jarl; Handsome Lakes Blonde; 9 changing beers (sourced nationally; often Blackjack, Handsome, Tarn Hows) H

Industrial chic conversion of an overseer's cottage in a former mill complex which is a now a hub for art, craft and small commercial units. The Tap showcases a wide range of styles and interesting craft kegs alongside traditional real ales, all served in excellent condition. Popular with local groups, dog walkers and visiting CAMRA branches; regular music and specialist food events are held here. There is an interesting upstairs function room, a sunny terrace in front and a large, partially covered back garden. Regular beer festivals, as advertised, are staged.

Fell Bar

3 Lowther Street, LA9 4DH

☎ 07725 987600 fellbrewery.co.uk

Fell Ghyll H**, Tinderbox IPA, Crag** A**; 11 changing beers (sourced regionally; often Chapter, Flagship, Fyne Ales)** H/A

A tap for artisan Fell Brewery, the town-centre street-side bar on two floors is modern and forward looking. It offers a perfect opportunity to experience craft beers at their best, alongside a solid range of more traditionally styled ales from newer breweries (seven Fell beers, seven guests). Well-informed enthusiastic staff will ensure your conversion to craft – if you need persuading. Another recent boost to Kendal's new youthful focus, this is a vibrant and lively place where everyone is made welcome.

Masons Yard 24

22 Stramongate, LA9 4BN

☎ (01539) 727979 masonsyard24.co.uk

Cumbrian Loweswater Gold; Bowness Bay Swan Blonde; Hawkshead Bitter; Lancaster Blonde; 2 changing beers (sourced regionally; often Cumbrian, Eden River, Fell) H

Originally a traditional market tavern, the pub was reopened as a modern city-style freehouse, with six handpumps serving rapid-turnover regional beers. An extensive brasserie menu is on offer seven days a week, with discounts on food and beer early in the week. The original yard is a suntrap and includes a swish toilet block and two large covered byres (one heated) with ample seating. There is full wheelchair access. Local CAMRA Pub of the Year in 2018, it is convenient for buses, trains and shopping. Q

New Union

159 Stricklandgate, LA9 4RF

☎ (01539) 724004 thenewunion.co.uk

Fyne Jarl H**; 3 changing beers (sourced regionally; often Hawkshead, Kirkby Lonsdale, Thornbridge)** H/A

To say that the landlord is a cider enthusiast would be an understatement – and he has the same passion for all things beer. The Union is not a typical local and this is what makes it special. Up to 30 real ciders and perries plus seven cask and craft keg ales are stocked. Your visit is guaranteed to be memorable whatever your taste. Frequent community events are held alongside tap or cidermaker takeovers, and there are regular beer and cider festivals. CAMRA National Cider Pub 2019.
P (555)

Ring o' Bells

37-39 Kirkland, LA9 5AF

☎ (01539) 720326 ringobellskendal.webs.com

Coniston Bluebird Bitter; 2 changing beers (sourced regionally; often Beckstones, Cross Bay, Eden River) H

A basic old town pub beside the parish church near the River Kent, appreciated for nurturing its beer-loving community of regulars and tourists. It is in something of a time warp, where visitors enjoy the real fire while engaging with local characters and their dogs. Two, sometimes three, well-kept Cumbrian beers are on tap – one changing regularly. Usually, an interesting bag in box cider or perry is also sold. Home-made food is served most days, and sandwiches to order for functions, ladies' darts and meetings. Live music is staged on Sundays and popular bingo sessions monthly. Q P

Keswick

Wainwright

Lake Road, CA12 5BZ

☎ (017687) 44927 thewainwright.pub

Fell Tinderbox IPA; Wainwright; 5 changing beers (sourced nationally) H

The Wainwright has a distinctive black and white frontage and oak flooring within, with two drinking areas served by an L-shaped bar. The interior is mountain-themed with a cosy ambience. The pub has a good reputation for food in terms of quality, quantity and price. The beers and the food mostly come from Cumbria and cider is brewed onsite. A discount is offered to Wainwright Society card-carrying members. A winner of frequent local branch CAMRA awards.
Q

Kings Meaburn

White Horse Inn

CA10 3BU

☎ (01931) 714256

3 changing beers (sourced locally; often Bowness Bay, Eden River, Fell) H

Cosy village local worth seeking out for the warmth of the welcome that is matched by the roaring fire. The pub is famous for the awesome house pies, with a Pie and Pint deal on Friday and Saturday. It also hosts an annual pie-making competition that is open to all. Two or three handpumps serve regularly changing local beers. Frequent charity events with live music are always popular, and an annual beer and music festival features in summer. There is a happy hour on Thursday evening.
Q P

Kirkby Lonsdale

Orange Tree

9 Fairbank, LA6 2BD (turn left past churchyard, hotel is on your right)

☎ (015242) 71716 theorangetreehotel.co.uk

Kirkby Lonsdale Monumental Blonde, Singletrack, Stanley's Pale Ale; 3 changing beers (sourced locally; often Handsome, Kirkby Lonsdale) H

This intimate old pub by the church is effectively a second tap for Kirkby Lonsdale Brewery. The inn has a welcoming, cosy feel, and features up to six handpulled ales on the bar with occasional local guests. The back dining room gets busy on week nights for the special daily meal deals that include a pint; the Friday happy hour is popular with beer drinkers. Accommodation is in six en-suite rooms and offers include golfing or mountain bike breaks. (567)

Royal Barn

New Road, LA6 2AB

(015242) 71918 klbrewery.com/the-royal-barn

Kirkby Lonsdale Jubilee Stout, Monumental Blonde, Ruskin's Bitter, Singletrack, Stanley's Pale Ale, Tiffin Gold; 4 changing beers (sourced locally; often Kirkby Lonsdale)

The Barn is a large quirky conversion showcasing an extensive selection of Kirkby Lonsdale beers in cask, keg, bottle and can. Inside, an atmosphere of fun and warmth pervades the old building, enhanced by the aromas of beer brewing and coffee beans roasting – a wonderful surprise after the plain exterior and unprepossessing entrance. The brewery slogan is: We put the 'ale' in Lonsdale. The tiny market town embraces visitors, with plenty to see and do. P

Kirkby Stephen

Taggy Man

4 Market Street, CA17 4QS

(017683) 72531

4 changing beers (sourced regionally; often Black Sheep, Cross Bay, Keswick)

Old Cumbrian free house below the town centre that is rightly famous near and far for the warmth of its welcome. It is committed to serving a good selection of well-kept local beers with an occasional guest from further afield. It also has a premium spirits and gin bar. Popular with friendly local drinkers rather than diners, the U-shaped bar serves two distinct areas, with hot bar food available throughout the week. Regular live music plus weekly quiz and open mic nights are advertised on social media. Dogs and muddy boots welcome.
P (563,564)

Kirkoswald

Crown Inn

CA10 1DQ

(01768) 870410 crowninnkirkoswald.co.uk

Jennings Night Vision; 2 changing beers

Friendly village pub situated in the main street and well supported by locals. Visitors also travel some distance for the excellent food, which tends to have an Italian flavour and is freshly prepared to order (booking advisable). Two guest real ales are usually available along with Jennings Bitter as the regular. A traditional coal fire helps create a warm atmosphere on cold winter nights. There is a pool table upstairs.

Fetherston Arms

The Square, CA10 1DQ

(01768) 898284 fetherston-arms.co.uk

Theakston Best Bitter; 3 changing beers (often Allendale, Hesket Newmarket)

The Fethers is in the centre of this historic village. Extensive alterations and the friendly enthusiasm of the owners have helped convert this establishment into a truly outstanding pub with a deservedly excellent reputation for its food. Three changing real ales are stocked from breweries such as Allendale and Hesket Newmarket. Check hours in winter. Although the village is not on a bus route it is a 20-minute stroll from Lazonby station on the Carlisle-Settle line. Q

Levens

Hare & Hounds Inn

Church Road, LA8 8PN

(015395) 60004 hareandhoundslevens.co.uk

Bowness Bay Swan Blonde; 4 changing beers (sourced locally; often Barngates, Eden River, Kirkby Lonsdale)

Really cosy and really friendly – a proper Lakeland pub that epitomises natural warmth. A number of small rooms and tiny nooks wrap round the central bar serving five changing Cumbrian beers. A downstairs cellar snug is affectionately known as Duck – for obvious reasons – and the sensitive modern barn conversion offers a classy dining room with a view. Various outdoor terraces give panoramic vistas of Morecambe Bay, Arnside Viaduct and Lyth Valley – famed for its damsons.
Q P (550,552)

Loppergarth

Wellington Inn

Main Street, LA12 0JL (1 mile from A590 between Lindal and Pennington)

(01229) 582388

Healey's Blonde; 4 changing beers (sourced locally; often Healey's)

This superb village local has its own microbrewery, Healey's, a custom-made stainless steel plant which is viewable from the snug. Four handpumps, occasionally five, dispense Healey's beers including an award-winning blonde, a golden bitter, a traditional darker best bitter, a superb mild and occasional specials. Wood-burning stoves make this a cosy pub, with games, books and good conversation. There is a quiz on alternate Saturdays. Well-behaved dogs on leads are welcome.

Loweswater

Kirkstile Inn

CA13 0RU (off B5289, 7 miles S from Cockermouth) NY140210

(01900) 85219 kirkstile.com

Cumbrian Esthwaite Bitter, Langdale, Loweswater Gold; 3 changing beers (sourced regionally; often Cumbrian)

CAMRA award-winning 16th-century coaching inn, scenically located below Melbreak, Crummock Water and Loweswater. Low-beamed ceilings, solid wood tables, chairs and settles feature in three bar areas. There is an open fire for chilly days. Substantial bar meals are served, and it has a well-established restaurant. The building was the original home of Loweswater Brewery and is now the brewery tap for Cumbrian Ales. An annual beer festival features in April. There is an outdoor drinking area in stunning surroundings. Dogs welcome during the day. Q P

Lowick Bridge

Red Lion Inn

LA12 8EF (just off A5084 on Ulverston-Torver road)

(01229) 885366 redlion-lowick.co.uk

Bank Top Flat Cap; Great Corby Corby Ale; 1 changing beer (sourced locally)

This former Hartleys alehouse, worth finding just off the road from Greenodd to Coniston, was purchased by the present owners from Robinsons in 2014. It is now a charming, comfortable country inn, popular with both locals and visitors to the Lakes. Friendly and welcoming, the pub is an ideal base to explore the hidden corners of the Southern Lakes and the Furness and Cartmel Peninsulas. Q 🏨 ❀ 🛏 ◑ ♿ P 🚌 (X12) 🐾 ᯤ

Monkhill

Drovers Rest

CA5 6DB

☎ (01228) 576141

4 changing beers Ⓗ

A traditional country pub close to the popular Hadrian's Wall Path with a strong community focus. Although opened up, the interior still has the feel of three distinct rooms. The bar area is cosy and welcoming, with a roaring fire in winter. Some interesting historical State Management Scheme documents adorn the walls. The Drovers is an oasis for lots of different and sometimes obscure (for the area) real ales. Winner of multiple CAMRA awards including at regional level.

🏨 ❀ ◑ Å ♣ P 🚌 (93) 🐾

Moorhouse

Royal Oak

CA5 6EZ

☎ (01228) 576475

Cumbrian Loweswater Gold; Theakston XB; 1 changing beer Ⓗ

This welcoming, small country pub on the outskirts of Carlisle is over 250 years old, so be prepared to duck as you go through some of the doors. Log-burning stoves add to a rustic atmosphere. Traditional home-cooked food is served – Sunday lunch is a highlight – along with up to three real ales from local breweries plus two real ciders. ❀ ◑ 🍎 🐾 ᯤ

Near Sawrey

Tower Bank Arms 🄻

LA22 0LF (on B5285 2 miles S of Hawkshead)

☎ (015394) 36334 🌐 towerbankarms.co.uk

Barngates Tag Lag; Cumbrian Loweswater Gold; Hawkshead Bitter; 3 changing beers (sourced locally) Ⓗ

A 17th-century Lakeland inn with slate floors, oak beams and a cast-iron range with an open fire, next to the National Trust's Hill Top (Beatrix Potter's home). It delivers great local flavours in food and beer, and has a lovely atmosphere. Booking is essential for evening meals. Five handpumps serve very local beer, with cider and perry dispensed by gravity. Families and dogs are welcomed. There is a seasonal bus service connecting to the Windermere ferry and Hawkshead. Accommodation is available in four en-suite rooms. Note that it is closed Mondays in winter. Q 🏨 ❀ 🛏 ◑ Å ♣ 🍎 P 🚌 🐾 ᯤ

Nether Wasdale

Strands Inn 🄻

CA20 1ET

☎ (019467) 26237 🌐 thestrandsinn.com

Strands Brown Bitter, Errmmm...; 6 changing beers (sourced locally) Ⓗ

In a pretty Lakeland village with superb views across to the Wasdale Screes and up towards Wasdale Head, this is a justifiably popular pub both for tourists and locals. It always offers a range of excellent beers from the adjacent Strands Brewery, with some regular favourites but always including something innovative to sample. All are dispensed by handpump. The pub has a comfortable and welcoming atmosphere, usually with open fires in winter, and excellent bar food. Q 🏨 ❀ 🛏 ◑ Å ♣ P 🐾 ᯤ

Oxen Park

Manor House Hotel 🄻

LA12 8HG

☎ (01229) 861345 🌐 manorhouseoxenpark.co.uk

Cumbrian Loweswater Gold; 2 changing beers (sourced regionally) Ⓗ

In a small village on the outskirts of the Lake District, this former Hartley's pub reopened in 2017 as a free house after an extensive refurbishment to a modern high standard. The beer range varies but includes ales from local breweries. The excellent food menu features a number of vegan dishes (booking is recommended at weekends). Free overnight parking is available for camper vans, with access to toilets and electric hook-up.

🏨 ❀ 🛏 ◑ ♿ Å P 🐾 ᯤ

Penrith

Agricultural Hotel 🄻 ✔

Castlegate, CA11 7JE

☎ (01768) 862622 🌐 the-agricultural-hotel.co.uk

6 changing beers Ⓗ

The hotel is built from local sandstone and the bar and dining room are open plan, with steps from one to the other. There is also a small reception area. The Victorian shuttered sash screen bar has six handpumps. Food is served in the large dining area, as well as in the bar at quiet times. Convenient for the railway station and nearby bus stops. 🏨 ❀ 🛏 ◑ ♿ ⇌ ♣ P 🚌

Fell Bar 🏆 🄻

52 King Street, CA11 7AY

☎ (01768) 866860

6 changing beers Ⓗ

A small and intimate venue in the centre of Penrith, on three floors, which was turned into a pub in 2012. It serves as the tap for Fell Brewery but offers a range of other cask ales and craft beers as listed on the blackboard near the bar. Regular quiz, comedy and music nights are held, details of which are on its Facebook page. 🏨 ⇌ 🚌 🐾 ᯤ

Royal 🄻

Wilson Row, CA11 7PZ

☎ (01768) 862670 🌐 royalpubpenrith.co.uk

3 changing beers Ⓗ

A traditional pub on the edge of the town centre with tiled walls and lots of mellow wood. It has three separate areas served by one bar, where two handpumps offer beers from all over the UK including LocAles. It is home to darts, dominoes and pool teams, and there is full sports TV coverage. Live music sessions with a broad appeal are held on Sunday afternoons outside the football season. Food is served weekday evenings except Friday and weekend afternoons. 🏨 🛏 ◑ Å ⇌ ♣ 🚌 🐾 ᯤ

Ravenglass

Inn at Ravenglass

Main Street, CA18 1SQ (N end of village overlooking Irish Sea)

☎ (01229) 717230 🌐 theinnatravenglass.co.uk

Bowness Bay Swan Blonde; 3 changing beers (sourced nationally) Ⓗ

A 17th-century inn set in a hamlet that was once a Roman port, at the junction of the rivers Esk, Irt and Mite in the Lake District National Park. It offers a good choice of real ales, to be enjoyed after a day in the fells, messing about in boats, or just relaxing round the wood-burning stove in winter – great for sunset views over the estuary. Close to Ravenglass stations for mainline and La'al Ratty. Q❀⇆◑Ʌ⇌♣●P🚌(6)🐾📶

Rosthwaite

Scafell Hotel ✔

Borrowdale, CA12 5XB (on B5289)
☎ (017687) 77208 🌐 scafell.co.uk
Jennings Night Vision; 6 changing beers (sourced nationally) Ⓗ
In the heart of the Lake District and the home of the annual Borrowdale Fell Race, the Riverside Bar welcomes walkers, cyclists and all those who enjoy the outdoor life. The River Derwent rushes past the windows of the bar, where food is served. A selection of malt whiskies is stocked and open fires create a homely feel.
Q❀⇆◑♿Ʌ♣P🚌(78)🐾📶

Rydal

Badger Bar (Glen Rothay Hotel) L

LA22 9LR
☎ (015394) 34500 🌐 theglenrothay.co.uk
Barngates Goodhew's Dry Stout; house beer (by Old School); 4 changing beers (sourced locally; often Great Corby, Hawkshead, Ulverston) Ⓗ
Historic quirky inn, with a lingering feel of Wordsworth and Coleridge, popular with visitors to Rydal. The fires in the panelled bars and dining room are particularly pleasing on wet, windy days, and dogs are welcome. A good range of local ales complements the local dishes. The pub has an informative website, a fascinating live badgercam, unique loos built into the rock face, and two large beer gardens. Just how a quaint old pub should be: good beer, good food, good atmosphere.
Q❀⇆◑Ʌ♣P🚌(555,599)🐾📶

Santon Bridge

Bridge Inn ✔

CA19 1UX (on road from Gosforth to Eskdale)
☎ (019467) 26221 🌐 santonbridgeinn.com
Adnams Mosaic; Jennings Night Vision, Atomic Theory, Cumberland Ale; 6 changing beers (sourced nationally) Ⓗ
Once a modest mail coach halt, this is now a country inn in a lovely location on the banks of the River Irt, at a junction of roads into Wasdale and Eskdale. It is cosy, with low beams, creaking floors and a log fire. Seven beers are from local, regional and national breweries. A recent recipient of a local CAMRA branch award, it holds the World's Biggest Liar competition in November. Food is sourced locally. The inn is licensed for civil marriage ceremonies. Q❀⇆◑♿Ʌ♣P🐾📶

Seaton

Royal Oak

49 Main Road, CA14 1HU
☎ 07393 864592
Butcombe Original; Robinsons Dizzy Blonde; 2 changing beers (sourced nationally) Ⓗ
A lively community pub that is well used by locals. The front bar has a television and seated drinking area and there is a rear room with a pool table and dartboard. A quiz is held on a Wednesday night. The bar has three handpumps offering one changing and two regular beers, with most being sourced nationally.
❀P🚌(47)🐾📶

Silloth

Albion L

Eden Street, CA7 4AS
☎ (016973) 3121
Derwent Parsons Pledge; 1 changing beer (sourced locally; often Derwent) Ⓗ
Traditional one-bar pub with a separate family room containing a pool table and TV, frequented by locals and summer visitors. Pictures of old Silloth decorate the walls along with two models of whaling trawlers. There are numerous photos celebrating the Isle of Man TT races; the local motorcycle club meets here on the first Sunday of each month and welcomes visitors. The nearby Derwent Brewery often tries out new beers at this hostelry. ❀Ʌ♣P🚌🐾📶

Staveley

Beer Hall L ✔

Hawkshead Brewery, Mill Yard, LA8 9LR
☎ (01539) 825260 🌐 hawksheadbrewery.co.uk
Hawkshead Bitter, Brodie's Prime, Cumbrian Five Hop, Lakeland Gold, Red, Windermere Pale; 16 changing beers (sourced locally; often Hawkshead, Fell, Tarn Hows) Ⓗ
The tap for Hawkshead Brewery, set in a picturesque Lakeland village between Kendal and Windermere. The Beer Hall is the brewery's flagship outlet and now reflects the ongoing changes implemented centrally by the new owners, Halewood, who have moved bulk production from Staveley to Flookburgh. The beers have unfortunately lost their award-winning historic names and keg beers have become more prominent at this sprawling venue. Q❀◑♿Ʌ⇌P🚌(555)🐾📶

Eagle & Child Hotel L

Kendal Road, LA8 9LP
☎ (01539) 821320 🌐 eaglechildinn.co.uk
Hawkshead Bitter; 5 changing beers (sourced locally; often Barngates, Cumbrian, Hawkshead) Ⓗ
An astonishing selection of artefacts and pictures, a varied menu and open fires – this eclectic hostelry really is a must-visit. Staveley is a bustling village with much to offer, including the nearby Lakesline railway station. A wide range of interesting beers is served, predominantly Cumbrian. A popular quiz takes place on Thursdays. There is a spacious private function room and upstairs accommodation. A lovely quiet orchard lies behind the pub, and the front garden overlooks the confluence of the rivers Gowan and Kent. The 555 bus stops right outside. Q❀⇆◑⇌♣P🚌(555)🐾📶

Talkin

Blacksmiths Arms L

CA8 1LE
☎ (016977) 3452 🌐 blacksmithstalkin.co.uk
Black Sheep Special Ale; 2 changing beers Ⓗ
Since taking over in 1997, the present owners have made this probably the most popular pub in the vicinity. The winning formula includes four real ales, a superbly stocked bar, friendly, efficient staff, no TV and meticulous attention to detail. With a golf course and country park within two miles and plenty of other outdoor activities locally, it attracts visitors from far outside north Cumbria to this Area of Outstanding Natural Beauty.
Q❀⇆◑♿♣P📶

Tallentire

Bush Inn

Tallentire, CA13 0PT
☎ (01900) 823707
3 changing beers (sourced nationally) Ⓗ
A genuine old-fashioned, Grade II listed pub with exposed beams, stone floors and a wood-burning stove, offering a changing selection of ales, usually including at least one from a Cumbrian brewery. It is home to the local cricket and darts teams, and folk music is hosted on the last Wednesday of the month. Well-behaved dogs are welcome. Food is served in the bar and in the separate dining room Thursday to Saturday, March to December. Q❀◗♣●🐾📶

Ulverston

Beerwolf L

7 Market Street, LA12 7AY
🌐 wearebeerwolf.com
2 changing beers (sourced nationally) Ⓗ
Micropub and bottle shop owned by a CAMRA member. It has two handpumps plus eight KeyKeg beers, with an extensive range of interesting local, national and international bottled and canned beers and ciders, plus growler fills in cans to take away. Tap takeovers (eg Cloudwater, Tiny Rebel) and other events are occasionally held – check the Facebook page. Recently refurbished to give more seating downstairs, with additional seating upstairs making for a pleasant and relaxing atmosphere. ⇌🚌🐾

Devonshire Arms L

Braddyll Terrace, Victoria Road, LA12 0DH (next to railway bridge in town centre)
☎ (01229) 582537
Abbeydale Moonshine; 4 changing beers (sourced regionally; often Abbeydale, Cross Bay, Moorhouse's) Ⓗ
Conveniently situated between the bus and train stations, the Dev is a real locals' pub with a welcoming atmosphere. Four TVs provide comprehensive sports coverage, and there are two dartboards and a pool table. Five constantly changing cask ales and a real cider are all dispensed on handpump. The outside seating area is popular in summer. A meat raffle is held on Sunday evening. The pub has received numerous awards from CAMRA over the years. ❀♿⛺⇌♣●P🚌🐾📶

Mill L ✔

Mill Street, LA12 7EB
☎ (01229) 581384 🌐 mill-at-ulverston.co.uk
Lancaster Amber, Black, Blonde, Red; 6 changing beers (sourced nationally) Ⓗ
The Mill has an interesting characterful layout, centred around a restored original, but now static, waterwheel. The Cask Bar is on the ground floor. On Friday and Saturday both the Loft Bar on the second floor, serving evening cocktails, and the first-floor Terrace Bar with a separate outdoor patio area and largescreen TV, are open. Deservedly popular for quality food; booking is essential for the restaurant. There are picnic tables outside to the front. ❀◖◗♿⇌🚌(6,X6)🐾📶

Old Friends L

49 Soutergate, LA12 7ES
☎ (01229) 208195 🌐 oldfriendsulverston.co.uk
6 changing beers (sourced nationally; often Old Friends) Ⓗ
A 17th-century Grade II listed locals' pub 200 yards uphill from the town centre. It has a cosy snug with an open fire in front of the bar. Another room with a TV is separated by a passageway with a hatch to the bar. Beers are mostly local, with three brewed in the pub's own brewery. A popular quiz night is held every Tuesday. There is a wonderful beer garden with heating in the winter. Open 2-11pm bank holiday Mondays.
❀♣●🚌🐾📶

Rose & Crown

22 King Street, LA12 7DZ
☎ (01229) 583094
Robinsons Dizzy Blonde, Cascade IPA, Trooper, Cumbria Way; 1 changing beer (sourced nationally; often Robinsons) Ⓗ
A warm welcome awaits at this 400-year-old inn which retains many original features, including low beams and real fires. There are five distinct areas (check out Sid's Room, named after a regular who ran the bakery next door). Four handpumps serve Robinson's beers in excellent condition, and high-quality home-cooked food is available at lunchtimes and evenings. Well-behaved dogs are welcomed in the front bar. Enjoy the patio in warmer weather, or sit in the covered area when cooler.
Q❀🛏◖◗⇌🚌🐾

Swan Inn L

Swan Street, LA12 7JX
☎ (01229) 582519
9 changing beers (sourced nationally) Ⓗ
On the edge of the town centre, overlooking the A590, there's an open-plan feel here, yet there are three distinct drinking areas. Premier League football and major sports events are screened, live music features occasionally, and a jukebox allows for all genres of music. A Sunday night quiz rounds off the entertainment. The beer garden is popular, especially in summer. Children are allowed until 8pm. Cash only – no cards.
❀♿♣🚆🚌(6,X6)🐾📶

Waberthwaite

Brown Cow Inn

LA19 5YJ
☎ (01229) 717243 🌐 thebrowncow-inn.simplesite.com
7 changing beers (sourced locally) Ⓗ
A 100-year-old family-run inn, newly refurbished, with a cosy fire in the main bar. The range of ales regularly changes and cider is sold in the summer. The pub is a winner of recent local CAMRA branch awards and holds an annual beer festival. It also has a reputation for good food using local produce. An active centre for the village, the pub hosts live music occasionally at weekends and regular quiz nights. A conference room is available. Situated on the A595 with easy access to the Western fells, beaches and Eskmeals nature reserve.
Q❀🛏◖◗♿⛺♣●P🚌🐾📶

Wetheral

Wheatsheaf Inn L ✔

CA4 8HD
☎ (01228) 560686 🌐 wheatsheafwetheral.co.uk
Great Corby Ale; 2 changing beers Ⓗ
An early 19th-century village pub, just a few minutes' walk from the village green and railway station, deservedly popular with locals and visitors. Along with Corby Ale from the local Great Corby Brewery there are two varying beers from local breweries. Good-value bar meals are served Wednesday to Sunday (booking is advisable at weekends). The regular Tuesday quiz night is popular. A local CAMRA award winner in 2018.
❀◖◗⇌♣P🚌(75)🐾📶

Whitehaven

Candlestick ✓

21-22 Tangier Street, CA28 7UX

☎ (01946) 66288

3 changing beers (sourced nationally) Ⓗ

Town-centre pub, formerly known as The Welsh Arms, close to Whitehaven harbour with a local crowd of regulars. It is in an area with four pubs. The interior divides into a bar area and a comfortable seating section. It gets busy Friday and Saturday nights and hosts live music.

Vagabond

9 Marlborough Street, CA28 7LL (on a continuation of Lowther St, leading to harbour)

☎ (01946) 66653 🌐 thevagabondpub.co.uk

4 changing beers (sourced nationally) Ⓗ

The Vagabond is just off the historic harbourside of this Georgian town. Its name – and its former name American Connection – commemorate the pirate raid of John Paul Jones in 1778. It is a traditional two-storey, wooden-floored pub with a welcoming atmosphere. Food includes stone-baked pizzas. The beers are frequently changing, with choices and styles from Cumbrian, Scottish and national micros.

Witherslack

Derby Arms Hotel L ✓

LA11 6RH

☎ (015395) 52207 🌐 thederbyarms.co.uk

Bowness Bay Swan Blonde; Cumbrian Loweswater Gold; Hawkshead Bitter; 3 changing beers (sourced regionally; often Dent, Fell, Keswick) Ⓗ

A local hub with a community shop next door. Once a busy coaching inn on the old road, this is now a shabby-chic rural retreat for villagers – together with walkers and cyclists. Six pumps feature a great selection of well-kept and mostly local ales that cover all tastes. Hearty local food is served and live music is a regular feature. An air of faded elegance pervades, as befits an estate hostelry once frequented by the local gentry. There are posh bedrooms upstairs, dining rooms downstairs.

P (X6)

Old Crown, Hesket Newmarket (Photo: Mike Tuer)

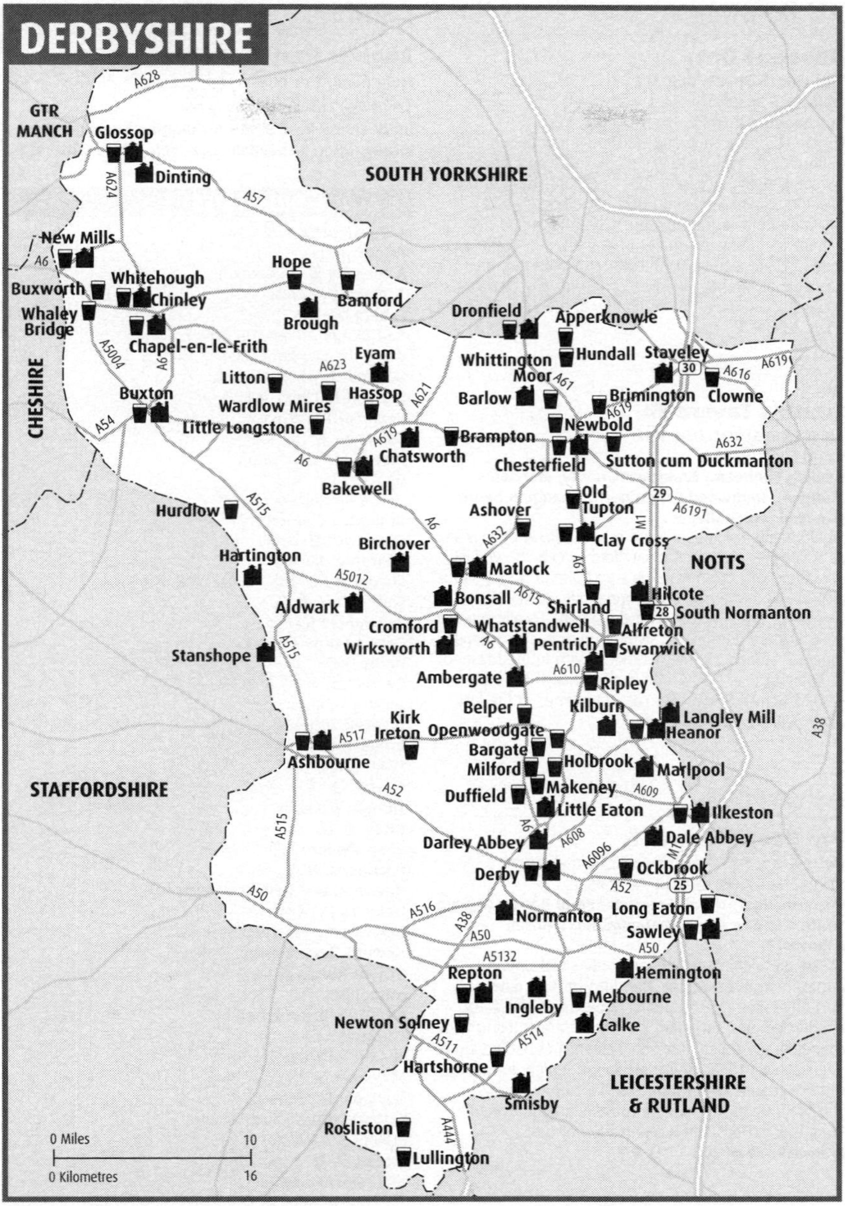

Alfreton

What's Your Poison Ale House

33 High Street, DE55 7DR

6 changing beers (sourced regionally) Ⓗ

A popular micropub situated on the main street in the centre of town. The single room has a central bar and a small drinking area towards the rear, with seating and standing areas throughout. A wide range of changing beers is on offer from its six handpumps, usually including one from Leadmill Brewery. The bar also stocks a good choice of gins. Quiz night is a regular feature. Runner-up in the local CAMRA Winter Ale Trail 2019. Closed on Monday and Tuesday. **Q**♿🍎🚌(9.1,9.3)🐾📶

Apperknowle

Traveller's Rest 🄻

High Street, S18 4BD SK384782

☎ (01246) 460169

Neepsend Blonde; Timothy Taylor Landlord Ⓗ**; 4 changing beers (sourced nationally; often Church End, Coastal, Welbeck Abbey)** Ⓗ/Ⓖ

The Travs is a traditional country pub, serving an excellent range of real ales, ciders and perries. The outdoor drinking area provides sweeping views over the Drone Valley. Good-quality food is on offer alongside the ever-popular cheese and pork pie platters. Jazz is played on Monday night. **Q**🛏❀◐♣🍎**P**🚌(14)🐾📶

Ashbourne

House of Beer
28B Church Street, DE6 1AE
☎ (01335) 343669
10 changing beers
Combined bottle shop and craft ale taproom in a former antique shop, with 10 KeyKeg taps, three permanent and seven changing ales, plus four cider taps. The front area has 400 world beers and ciders, including a good selection from British breweries, both local and nationwide. Many examples of real ale in a bottle and mini-pins are also stocked. Locally sourced pies are available at the bar, and free coffee for any designated driver. Local CAMRA runner-up Pub of the Year 2019 and 2020. ৯●❀❖🛜

Smith's Tavern ✅
36 St John Street, DE6 1GH
☎ (01335) 300809
Banks's Sunbeam; Brakspear Gravity; Marston's Pedigree; Ringwood Fortyniner; 2 changing beers (sourced regionally) H
Small, highly traditional town centre pub, with as many as seven real ales on. The landlord selects the widest possible choice from Marston's portfolio of beers, and is also allowed one free choice guest ale, served at weekends, usually from a local brewery. Locally sourced pork pies are normally available. There is also a good range of around 25 malt whiskies, with tutored tastings throughout the year. A frequent winner of the local CAMRA branch Pub of the Year, five times in the last eight years. Q৯♣❀🛜

Ashover

Old Poets' Corner L
Butts Road, S45 0EW (downhill from church)
☎ (01246) 590888 ⊕ oldpoets.co.uk
Everards Tiger; Titanic Steerage, Plum Porter, Captain Smith's Strong Ale; 6 changing beers (often Ashover) H
An award-winning village pub with a welcoming atmosphere, warmed by open fires on cold days. Recently taken over by Titanic Brewery, it offers 10 handpulled ales, including the Titanic range, along with changing guest ales, traditional ciders and bottled world beers. An excellent choice of food is served, including a carvery at Sunday lunchtime, and a curry night on Thursday. Open mic night is Tuesday and quiz night Wednesday. Dogs and walkers are welcome.
Q❀🛏🍴🕪♿♣●P🚌(63,64)❀🛜

Bakewell

Joiners Arms L
1-2 Rutland Buildings, DE45 1BZ
☎ 07834 950693
6 changing beers (often Peak Ales, Thornbridge) H
A short walk away from the famed Bakewell Pudding Shop, this small, friendly town-centre micropub opened in 2019 in a former newsagents'. Six cask ales and six craft keg ales (often KeyKeg) are sold, mainly sourced locally, as is the selection of wines, gins and whiskies. There are always vegan beers on tap. Open mic takes place on Wednesdays and light, live music on Sunday evenings, from March. Winter opening, until March, is from 3pm. Q৯❀●🚌❀🛜

Bamford

Anglers Rest L
Main Road, S33 0DY
☎ (01433) 659317 ⊕ anglers.rest
Black Sheep Best Bitter; 5 changing beers (sourced locally; often Abbeydale, Bradfield, Little Critters) H

REAL ALE BREWERIES

Aldwark Artisan Aldwark
Alter Ego Heanor (NEW)
Ashleyhay ▊ Wirksworth
Ashover Clay Cross
Aurora Ilkeston
Bad Bunny Ambergate (NEW)
Bang The Elephant Langley Mill
Bentley Brook ✦ Matlock
Big Stone Chinley (NEW)
Birch Cottage Sawley
Birchover ▊ Birchover
Black Hole Little Eaton
Boot Repton
Bottle Brook Kilburn
Brampton Chesterfield
Brunswick ▊ Derby
Buxton ✦ Buxton
Chapel-en-le-Frith Chapel-en-le-Frith
Chickenfoot ▊ Bonsall
Collyfobble ▊ Barlow
Dancing Duck Derby
Derby Derby
Derventio Darley Abbey
Dovedale Stanshope
Draycott Dale Abbey
Drone Valley Dronfield
Eyam Eyam
Falstaff ▊ Derby: Normanton
Furnace ▊ Derby
Globe ▊ Glossop
Grasshopper Langley Mill
Hartshorns Derby
Haywood Bad Ram ✦ Ashbourne
Hemlock Hemington
Hollow Tree Whatstandwell (NEW)
Howard Town Glossop
Instant Karma ▊ Clay Cross
Intrepid Brough
John Thompson ▊ Ingleby
Leadmill Heanor
Leatherbritches ▊ Smisby
Littleover Derby
Marlpool ▊ Marlpool
Matlock Wolds Farm Matlock
Moody Fox Hilcote
Moot Oak ▊ Matlock
Mouselow Farm Dinting
Mr Grundy's ▊ Derby (brewing suspended)
Muirhouse Ilkeston
Old Sawley ▊ Sawley
Peak Chatsworth
Pentrich Pentrich
RBA Derby (NEW)
Rock Mill ✦ New Mills
Shiny ✦ Little Eaton
Silver Staveley
Thorley & Sons Ilkeston
Thornbridge Bakewell
Tollgate ✦ Calke
Torrside New Mills
Townes ▊ Staveley
Urban Chicken Ilkeston
Whim Hartington

At the heart of Bamford and not far from Ladybower Reservoir, this is a community hub in every sense, where the locals have been running the pub (and associated post office and café) since 2013. The main bar is the focal point and is popular with families, walkers and, particularly, cyclists, who have access to dedicated cycle parking and a DIY repair shop. There is also a quieter snug. Good-value, rustic bar food is served Wednesday to Sunday. Q☕❀◐♿⛺♣P🚌(273,274)🐾📶

Bargate

White Hart 🏆

Sandbed Lane, DE56 0JA

☎ (01773) 827397

Draught Bass; Fuller's London Pride; Oakham Citra; 4 changing beers (sourced nationally) [H]

A cosy two-roomed pub in the heart of Bargate above the town of Belper. With a reputation for friendly staff, good beer and a welcoming atmosphere, it is popular with locals and has an excellent selection of changing cask ales. A large beer garden is to the rear and walkers are welcome any time. Bar snacks are usually available. Local CAMRA Pub of the Year 2018 and 2020, and winner of the East Midlands award in 2018. Q☕❀♣P🚌(7.1)🐾

Belper

Angels Micro Pub

Market Place, DE56 1FZ (top right of Market Place)

Oakham Citra; Thornbridge Jaipur IPA; Titanic Plum Porter; 5 changing beers (sourced nationally) [G]

A quirky and friendly bar offering real ales, an excellent choice of real ciders, wines and gin. More like a mini beer festival than a pub, a full selection of ales (up to eight plus eight ciders at times) from Thursday gradually decreases as Sunday approaches and the beer is drunk. Locally sourced pork pies and cheeses are served. Live artists perform most Sunday afternoons. ≋●P🚌🐾

Arkwright's Real Ale Bar

5 Campbell Street, DE56 1AP

☎ (01773) 823117

Marston's Pedigree [G]**; 6 changing beers (sourced nationally)** [H]

Just below the Strutt Club in the centre of town, this is a modern, friendly, one-roomed bar regularly serving six real ales, ciders and perry. Named after Sir Richard Arkwright, an important 18th-century mill owner, it is popular with local drinkers. Some sporting events on terrestrial TV are shown and a no under-14s rule ensures a quiet, relaxing environment. Live acoustic music features and bar snacks are available. ☕♿≋♣●🚌🐾📶

Brampton

Rose & Crown [L] ✔

104 Old Road, S40 2QT

☎ (01246) 563750 🌐 roseandcrownbrampton.co.uk

Brampton Golden Bud, Best; Everards Tiger; 6 changing beers (often Brampton) [H]

Everards' Project William renovation enabled the Brampton Brewery to open its first tied house, and four Brampton beers are always on the bar, including a dark ale. Memorabilia from the original Brampton Brewery festoon the walls. A compact snug provides room for group meetings, while the main room has plenty of quiet corners, and there are outdoor drinking areas to the front and rear, with covered decking. Tuesday is quiz night, Sunday lunch is a highlight, and an annual beer festival is held for St George's Day. Winner of numerous local CAMRA awards. ☕❀◐♣●P🚌(170)🐾📶

Brimington

Brimming with Beer [L]

Patrick Hinds House, Chesterfield Road, S43 1AD (adjacent to Ark Tavern pub)

☎ (01246) 278888

3 changing beers (often Thornbridge) [H]

A beer shop that opened in 2016, with an on-licence. It stocks a vast range of bottled beers from around the world, including British ones. A minimum of three (and up to five) cask ales are served, plus three permanent and two changing keg beers, often KeyKeg, together with ciders. A selection of advertising signs and presentation packs are usually displayed, together with snuff and cigars. Dogs are welcome except on Friday and Saturday evenings. 🚌🐾

Buxton

Ale Stop [L]

Chapel Street, SK17 6HX

☎ 07801 364619

3 changing beers (sourced nationally) [H]

The first micropub in the High Peak, its two rooms converted from a former wine shop off Buxton Market Square. Beer is the thing here, with three changing ales from microbreweries up and down the country, as well as three real ciders. The objective is to bring to Buxton beers which are rarely, if ever, seen in the town. The enthusiastic staff ensure a warm and friendly welcome. An eclectic choice of background music is played on vinyl. ☕♿●🚌🐾📶

Cheshire Cheese [L]

37-39 High Street, SK17 6HA

☎ (01298) 212453

Everards Tiger; Titanic Steerage, Iceberg, White Star, Plum Porter, Captain Smith's Strong Ale; 4 changing beers [H]

A double-fronted building of considerable age, which was refurbished before reopening under the management of Titanic in 2013. The pub is essentially open plan but is split into several distinct areas. Low ceilings with original beams add to the cosy atmosphere and there are two open fires. The bar boasts an array of 10 handpumps serving a range of Titanic beers and guests. Home-made food is available. Entertainment is provided on Saturday evening and there is a quiz on Sunday. Q☕❀◐♿⛺♣●P🚌🐾📶

RedWillow Buxton [L]

1 Cavendish Circus, SK17 6AT

RedWillow Wreckless; 4 changing beers (sourced locally) [H]

Opened in late 2017 and located in a former bank in the centre of town, this is the RedWillow Brewery's second bar. Original features have been retained such as etched windows and the mahogany and glass office, alongside a new bar and a smaller mezzanine area. The five cask ales comprise four RedWillow beers and a guest. Small plates and stone-baked pizzas are served and private beer tastings take place. There is also live music monthly. ☕◐♿≋♣▯🚌🐾📶

Wye Bridge House ✔

Fairfield Road, SK17 7DJ

☎ (01298) 70932

Greene King Abbot; Ruddles Best Bitter; Sharp's Doom Bar; 5 changing beers [H]

A Wetherspoon pub in the former Midland Railway Hotel with a deserved reputation for serving an excellent selection of up to five guest beers in addition to two real ciders on draught. Occasional beer festivals and brewery trips are organised. Information boards describe the history of the spa town. The extensive outdoor patio area is popular in summer and is adjacent to a municipal park. The car park is small but a public car park is just a short walk away. Q❀◑♿⇌●P🚌📶

Buxworth

Buxworth Memorial Club

1 Station Road, High Peak, SK23 7NJ

☎ (01663) 732050

2 changing beers (sourced regionally) Ⓗ

This is a thriving local club, welcoming and straightforward, with a bar area and a larger separate lounge. The two changing cask beers tend to be from local and regional breweries. It is close to the site of the historic refurbished Bugsworth Canal Basin on the Peak Forest Canal, and handy for boaters, cyclists and walkers when visiting this picturesque rural area on the edge of the Peak District. The club is open to non-members. ♣P🚌🐾

Chapel en le Frith

Old Cell Ale Bar ✔

10-12 Market Place, SK23 0EN

☎ 07709 163316 🌐 theoldcell.co.uk

3 changing beers (sourced locally) Ⓗ

A micropub on the historic marketplace in what was originally the local lock-up. The cosy bar area is furnished with rustic tables and chairs. Three changing beers are served, many from local microbreweries. A range of bottled beers is also available, some from the local brewery in the town. Gins also feature. It is well worth a visit, and everyone is welcome. Q♣●🚌🐾📶

Chesterfield

Chesterfield Alehouse 🄻

37 West Bars, S40 1AG

🌐 chesterfieldalehouse.co.uk

6 changing beers Ⓗ

Chesterfield's first micropub is a few minutes' walk from the marketplace. The split-level room has a small seating space leading up a few steps to the serving area, where you'll find six regularly changing beers, always including a stout or a porter. Breweries not often seen locally feature in regular tap takeovers. An extensive keg selection – mainly KeyKeg – is also on offer, and a range of bottled world beers, ciders and wines. Free-to-air sports are often shown in the upstairs room. Q♿♣●🚌🐾📶

Neptune Beer Emporium 🏆 🄻

46 St Helen's Street, S41 7QD

☎ (01246) 220146 🌐 neptunebeeremporium.co.uk

8 changing beers (sourced locally) Ⓗ

This genuine free house and self-styled beer emporium is a compact back-street local with two drinking areas either side of a central bar. The excellent choice of real ales changes all the time, often sourced from various local breweries. They are complemented by an extensive range of continental and craft beers on draught and in bottles, all displayed on a descriptive chalkboard. Live music sessions feature regularly. Local CAMRA Pub of the Year 2020. ◑⇌♣●🚌🐾📶

Pig & Pump 🄻

16 St Mary's Gate, S41 7TJ

☎ (01246) 229570 🌐 pigandpump.co.uk

Brains Rev James; Castle Rock Harvest Pale; Oakham Citra; Titanic Plum Porter; 8 changing beers (often Abbeydale, Peak Ales, Thornbridge) Ⓗ

Formerly the White Swan, this friendly inn is opposite Chesterfield's famous parish church with its crooked spire. It is open plan and split into two areas, one slightly raised. The long bar hosts 12 handpulls serving four regular and up to eight guest ales. An upstairs function room is available for hire. The pub is popular for food (home-made Sunday roast is recommended), and hosts regular live music on Saturday and a quirky quiz on Tuesday. Parking is available in the adjoining public car park. ❀◑♿⇌●P🚌🐾📶

Clay Cross

Rykneld Turnpyke 🄻

4 John Street, S45 9NQ

☎ (01246) 250366

12 changing beers Ⓗ

Formerly Egstow Working Men's Club, this establishment (named after Rykneld Street, the old road between Chesterfield and Derby) is the brewery tap of the on-site Instant Karma Brewing Company. It features a big bar with 12 cask ales, craft keg and a variety of bottles. The large open room is divided into different areas, with comfortable seating and two log-burners. The club has a cosy, welcoming and eclectic feel, and is dog-friendly. ♣●🚌🐾

Three Horseshoes 🄻

49 Market Street, S45 9JE

☎ (01246) 861789

Neepsend Blonde; Thornbridge Jaipur IPA; 2 changing beers Ⓗ

Previously called Corner Pin and Three Bar, this pub returned to its original name when it reopened in 2013. Refurbished in a comfortable, modern style, it serves breakfast, tea and coffee as well as up to four real ales (two regulars and two guests), in a café-bar environment. Open mic night is Tuesday, quiz night is Thursday, there is a singer or bands on Friday, steak night is also Friday and there is karaoke on Sunday. It can cater for weddings and parties. ❀◑🚌📶

Clowne

Centre 🄻 ✔

Recreation Close, S43 4PL

☎ (01246) 819546

4 changing beers (often Timothy Taylor) Ⓗ

A council-run community centre widely used by locals for functions, which can be booked for weddings, parties and special events. There is a popular quiz night with free food on Tuesday, and live music on the last Friday of the month. Regular beers come from the Timothy Taylor range, and there are changing guests. A real ale beer festival is also hosted. The place is well cared for, with a relaxed and friendly atmosphere. Ample car parking is available. ❀♿P🚌

Cromford

Boat Inn 🄻

Scarthin, DE4 3QF (small road behind shops from Greyhound car park)

☎ (01629) 258083 🌐 the-boat-inn.co.uk

Marston's Pedigree; 3 changing beers (sourced locally; often Abbeydale, Dancing Duck, Whim) Ⓗ

Built in 1772, this pub has a cosy atmosphere with beamed ceilings, exposed stone walls and an open fire in the main bar. A small snug, dining area and TV sports bar in the cellar cater for a range of needs. Home-cooked meals are served daily, and there is live music every Friday and Saturday night. The beer garden overlooks the large millpond. Cromford is within the Derwent Mills Valley, which is part of the World Heritage Site along the River Derwent. (6.1)

Derby

Alexandra Hotel

203 Siddals Road, DE1 2QE

(01332) 293993 alexandrahotelderby.co.uk

Castle Rock Harvest Pale; 7 changing beers (sourced nationally)

Named after the Danish princess who married the Prince of Wales (later Edward VII) in 1863, this Castle Rock pub serves its own beers and up to five guest ales including a mild and a stout/porter. It also stocks more than 50 UK and continental bottled beers of varying styles. Themed food nights are held approximately monthly. The lounge is adorned with breweriana and the bar with railway memorabilia; a Class 37 locomotive cab resides in the car park. The Alexandra was the birthplace of Derby CAMRA in 1974. Q P

Babington Arms

11-13 Babington Lane, DE1 1TA

(01332) 383647

Draught Bass; Greene King Abbot; Marston's Pedigree; Ruddles Best Bitter; Small World Thunderbridge Stout, Twin Falls; 11 changing beers (sourced nationally)

Wetherspoon pub in a converted furniture showroom close to the city centre. It boasts a huge range of real ales, many from local microbreweries, and typically has six ciders on handpump or gravity dispense. The back end of the large bar has some half-partitioned banquette seating and caters for family dining. At the front of the pub there is a small fenced-off area where outdoor drinkers can smoke.

Brunswick Inn

1 Railway Terrace, DE1 2RU

(01332) 290677 brunswickderby.co.uk

Brunswick White Feather, Triple Hop, The Usual; Everards Beacon Hill, Tiger; Timothy Taylor Landlord; 10 changing beers (sourced nationally)

Originally part of the railway village, this multi-roomed pub was restored and opened as Derby's first multiple choice real ale house in 1987. A purpose-built brewery was added in 1991 and the pub has since become one of the best known free houses in the country. Owned by Everards, it serves up to 16 real ales including at least six from Brunswick, the in-house brewery. It gets busy on Derby County match days. Local CAMRA Cider Pub of the Year 2020. Q P

Exeter Arms

13 Exeter Place, DE1 2EU

(01332) 605323 exeterarms.co.uk

Dancing Duck Ay up; Marston's Pedigree; 4 changing beers

A joint venture between Dancing Duck Brewery and a local food and drink entrepreneur has resulted in a place with old-world charm, offering a fine range of beers and an excellent dining experience. The small bar has an open fire and leads to several other rooms, including a snug with a wooden settle and an old-fashioned range. The adjoining atmospheric cottage dating from around 1815 has now been incorporated. A popular and quirky quiz is held on Monday evening. P

Falstaff

74 Silverhill Road, Normanton, DE23 6UJ

(01332) 342902 falstaffbrewery.co.uk

Falstaff Fist Full of Hops, Phoenix, Smiling Assassin; 1 changing beer

Tucked away in the back streets, a 20-minute walk from the city centre into the Normanton district rewards you with this atmospheric and reputedly haunted free house. Originally a coaching inn before the neighbourhood was built up, it is now the Falstaff Brewery tap and has long been the best real ale house in the area. The rear lounge is a shrine to Offilers' Brewery, with a display of memorabilia. Other collectables can be viewed throughout the games room and second bar room. Q (4,7)

Five Lamps

25 Duffield Road, DE1 3BH

(01332) 348730 fivelampsderby.co.uk

Draught Bass; Everards Tiger; Peak Ales Chatsworth Gold; St Austell Proper Job; Thornbridge Jaipur IPA; house beer (by Derby); 8 changing beers (sourced regionally)

Since it reopened in 2010, the pub has gone from strength to strength thanks to the dedication of the licensees and staff. Fourteen handpumps showcase many local ales from breweries such as Derby, Peak and Whim. The Lamps is essentially open plan, but has many little nooks and crannies, giving it a homely feel. It has been tastefully refurbished with wood panelling and leather seating in a traditional style. P

Flowerpot

23-25 King Street, DE1 3DZ

(01332) 204955 rawpromo.co.uk

Marston's Pedigree; Oakham Bishops Farewell; Sharp's Doom Bar; Whim Hartington IPA; 9 changing beers (sourced nationally)

Dating from around 1800 but much expanded from its original premises, this vibrant pub reaches back from the roadside frontage and divides into several interlinking rooms. One room provides the stage for regular live bands; another has a glass cellar wall revealing rows of stillaged firkins, which can be seen from the bar and from the road outside. Up to 14 real ales and two ciders are offered. Good en-suite accommodation is available.

Furnace Inn

Duke Street, DE1 3BX

(01332) 385981

Furnace Fun Sponge; Shiny 4 Wood; 6 changing beers (sourced nationally)

A former Hardys & Hansons establishment, reopened in 2012 and transformed into a real ale mecca. It is now the tap for the Furnace Brewery. Up to eight real ales and three ciders/perries are served, complemented by a variety of UK craft beers. There are two distinct open plan rooms with a central bar and, at the rear, a pleasant garden next to the riverside path. Poker and cheese nights feature weekly and regular beer festivals take place throughout the year. P

Last Post

1 Uttoxeter Old Road, DE1 1GA

(01332) 296737 thelastpostderbylt.wixsite.com/thelastpostderbyltd

4 changing beers (sourced nationally)

In the West End area of Derby, this former post office was the city's second micropub. The large single room has the bar towards the back. The small rear yard is a dedicated smoking area. The four changing beers vary continually and one is usually dark. An interesting range of whiskies is also on offer. Live acoustic music features every evening Thursday to Sunday, and beer festivals coincide with those of the local CAMRA branch. (8)

Little Chester Ale House

4A Chester Green Road, Chester Green, DE1 3SF
Hartshorns Ignite; 3 changing beers (sourced nationally) H
On the edge of a tree-lined conservation area, Derby's first micropub is in the historic Little Chester part of the city, the site of Roman Derventio, where two ancient wells can still been seen nearby. This former shop has one small main room with a narrower passageway containing the bar. It has four changing beers, including three from local Hartshorns Brewery, the pub's owner. Q

No.189

189 Blenheim Drive, Allestree, DE22 2GN
Blue Monkey Infinity; Dancing Duck Nice Weather; 3 changing beers H
Opened in 2018, this former launderette, and then beauticians', has proved popular. The single-roomed micropub offers a choice of five real ales, which tend to be from local breweries. Three craft ale taps are also on the bar. Furnishings include a mix of high and low seating, while outside there are benches. The centre of Derby is a 15- minute bus ride. QP

Old Bell Hotel

51 Sadler Gate, DE1 3NQ
(01332) 723090 bellhotelderby.co.uk
Draught Bass; house beer (by Imperial); 6 changing beers (sourced regionally) H
The large Tavern Bar at the front offers a range of real ale and craft kegs, including a house beer. Drinkers after a historic atmosphere should seek out the Tudor Bar to the rear (open Friday and Saturday), which was a men-only bar up until 1975. This 18th-century coaching inn is a welcome oasis in Sadler Gate, a premier shopping street in the Cathedral Quarter. The exterior Tudor-style half-timbering was added in 1929.

Peacock Inn

87 Nottingham Road, DE1 3QS
(01332) 583308
Draught Bass; Whim Arbor Light, Hartington IPA; house beer (by Marston's); 4 changing beers (sourced nationally) H
This attractive 18th-century stone-built roadside pub used to be a staging post on the main coach road out of Derby, which ran alongside the old Derby Canal. Two rooms on different levels are divided by a central bar and feature wooden floors, stove-burners, photos of old Derby and Derby County memorabilia. Up to nine real ales and two ciders and/or perries are on offer; beer festivals are held in the large, covered garden area to the rear. Q

Smithfield Alehouse

Meadow Road, DE1 2BH
(01332) 986601 smithfieldderby.co.uk
Draught Bass; 7 changing beers (sourced nationally) H
The Smithfield rests near the town centre on the banks of the River Derwent opposite Bass's Rec. The large main bar boasts an eclectic range of new and interesting beers, supported by Draught Bass. A separate quiet room with a real fire overlooks the patio next to the river. The pub has regular live music and many beer-related activities. Local CAMRA Pub of the Year 2018-2020 and East Midlands Pub of the Year 2019. P

Standing Order

28-32 Iron Gate, DE1 3GL
(01332) 207591
Draught Bass; Greene King Abbot; Kelham Island Pale Rider; Marston's Pedigree; Ruddles Best Bitter; Sharp's Doom Bar; 12 changing beers H
Named after its former role as a bank, this establishment became the first, grandest and certainly the tallest of the three Wetherspoons in Derby. It features full-size reproductions of paintings of Derby worthies from the time of the Industrial Revolution. There are a few quieter corners but generally this has the feeling of a busy city-centre pub. There is a good changing selection of guest ales. Alcoholic drinks are served from 9am.
Q

Tap

1 Derwent Street, DE1 2ED
(01332) 366283 brewerytap-dbc.co.uk
Derby Business as Usual, Dashingly Dark; 4 changing beers (sourced nationally) H
On the banks of the River Derwent, this flat iron shaped building has a roof terrace that overlooks the river. Two bars sit either side of the main entrance and there is a small courtyard. Exposed brickwork and wooden flooring give a contemporary feel, alongside modern and eclectic food choices. Patrons may choose from six handpumps and a wide range of foreign beers from tap or bottle.

Dronfield

Coach & Horses

Sheffield Road, S18 2GD
(01246) 413269 mycoachandhorses.co.uk
Thornbridge Lord Marples, Jaipur IPA; 4 changing beers (sourced nationally; often Drone Valley, Mallinsons, Thornbridge) H
The pub is next to the ground of Sheffield FC (the world's oldest football club), on the northern edge of Dronfield. It is operated by Thornbridge and showcases a good range of the brewery's beers, with guest ales across a wide range of styles. The large outdoor drinking area is particularly popular. Meals are provided daily from lunchtime onward. The pub hosts a regular quiz night on Thursday and open mic acoustic session on Monday evening. P(43)

Dronfield Arms

Chesterfield Road, S18 2XE
(01246) 414413
Abbeydale Moonshine; 6 changing beers (sourced nationally; often Arbor, Titanic, Vocation) H
The Arms became Dronfield's first brewpub in 2015 when Hopjacker installed a brewery, which is on display through a glass panel in the floor. (Hopjacker has since been disbanded.) The venue features a long bar with up to seven real ales dispensed at the top end, which has a large, comfortable seating area. Also on the bar are several keg fonts including KeyKeg. There is an outside drinking area to the rear above a car park. Quiz night is Monday. P

Duffield

Town Street Tap

17 Town Street, DE56 4EH
07925 461706
6 changing beers (sourced nationally) G
On the main road through Duffield, this micropub for Tollgate Brewery has been converted into a modern, uncluttered drinking space with table service. Of the six

changing real ales, two are from the Tollgate range and at least one is dark. In addition, four ciders are served, and takeouts come in containers or from the bottle shop. There are pork pies and Scotch eggs for the hungry, and free tea and coffee for drivers. Walkers with boots are welcome. Q≥♣●P🚌🐾

Glossop

Bar 2 Ⓛ

9 High Street East, SK13 8DA

☎ 07597 704447

Bradfield Farmers Blonde; Nook Best; 3 changing beers (sourced locally; often Bradfield, Donkeystone, Stockport) Ⓗ

A family-run micropub in a converted shop, opened in 2018 (as Tweed 2, now renamed Bar 2). It is comfortable and a good size for a micropub. In addition to the cask beers on offer, craft keg lagers are also available, together with a good selection of wines and gins. Discreet background music allows drinkers to play traditional pub games or simply to chat. There is also a retro video games table. Children are welcome until 8pm. Glossop train station and regular bus routes are nearby. ≥♣🚌🐾

Crown Inn ★

142 Victoria Street, SK13 8JF (on Hayfield Rd out of town centre)

☎ (01457) 862824

Samuel Smith Old Brewery Bitter Ⓗ

Stone-built end-of-terrace locals' venue, a few minutes from the town centre and railway station, built in 1846 and acquired by the Samuel Smith's Brewery in 1977. It is listed by CAMRA as having a nationally important historic pub interior. Its little-altered four-room interior includes a curved bar serving two side snugs, both with a real fire in winter, and a pool/games room. Pictures of bygone Glossop add to the traditional character. An enclosed outdoor drinking area is provided in the rear yard. Q❀♿≥♣🚌(390)🐾

Star Inn ✔

2 Howard Street, SK13 7DD (next to railway station)

☎ (01457) 761816

4 changing beers (sourced regionally; often Abbeydale, Howard Town, Pictish) Ⓗ

A very popular town centre pub, run by a dedicated CAMRA member. Conversation predominates in the large, comfortable, wood-panelled main room. A smaller room to to the rear displays a large map of part of the Peak District National Park on one wall. Guest beers are mainly from local microbreweries. Close to the railway station, the pub is an ideal starting/finishing point for walking or cycling within the Dark Peak area. Q≥P🚌🐾

Hartshorne

Admiral Rodney Inn ✔

65 Main Street, DE11 7ES (on A514)

☎ (01283) 227771 🌐 theadmiralrodney.uk

Draught Bass; 5 changing beers (sourced nationally) Ⓗ

Traditional village local dating back to the early 19th century, but rebuilt and extended in the late 20th century to provide an open-plan L-shaped drinking area while retaining the original oak beams in the former snug. There is also a secluded raised area tucked away behind the bar. Cheese tasting takes place on the first Monday of the month, open mic night on the third Tuesday, and a quiz night on Sunday. A real cider (choice varies) is available at weekends. The grounds include a cricket pitch, home of Hartshorne Cricket Club. ❀♿♣●P🚌(2)🐾

Hassop

Old Eyre Arms ★ Ⓛ

Hassop Road, DE45 1NS

☎ (01629) 640390 🌐 oldeyrearms.co.uk

Peak Ales Swift Nick; 3 changing beers (sourced locally; often Abbeydale, Bradfield, Kelham Island) Ⓗ

A 300-year-old country pub with two comfortably furnished rooms and a small snug squeezed between, watched over by an imposing grandfather clock. The impressive Eyre family coat of arms is displayed above the fireplace. Excellent, good-value home-cooked food is served lunchtimes and evenings, and in between you can get bar snacks. Up to six real ales are sold during the week but maybe only three at weekends. This is a characterful, unspoilt local with friendly service. Q❀◐♣P🚌🐾

Heanor

Crooked Cask Ⓛ

8 Ray Street, DE75 7GE

☎ (01773) 688140

6 changing beers Ⓗ/Ⓖ

Now an established local, this micropub opened in December 2018. Beers are offered on up to six handpulls and on gravity from a variety of sources, and there are seven ciders and one premium lager. The landlord is enthusiastic about serving up a wide choice of ales, the cellar is in view to the rear of the bar area. The front bar is wood-panelled and on a split level; a smaller room is to the rear. A friendly place to drink. Q❀◐♿♣P🚌🐾

Redemption Ale House Ⓛ

Ray Street, DE75 7GE

☎ 07887 568576

7 changing beers

A large open-plan micropub that opened in 2016 in a former butchers' shop. The original abattoir is still outside and is used as an area for the regular beer festivals. Six varying beers are available and up to 20 real ciders. A large collection of pumpclips adorns the walls, along with old framed photographs showing the building's previous life. There is an upstairs area with a variety of board games. Q❀♿●🚌🐾

Holbrook

Dead Poets Inn Ⓛ

38 Chapel Street, DE56 0TQ

☎ (01332) 780301

Draught Bass Ⓗ/Ⓖ; Greene King Abbot Ⓖ; Oakham Citra; 6 changing beers (often Brunswick, Everards) Ⓗ

Built around 1800 and originally called the Cross Keys, this pub was renamed after an imaginative alteration, and has enjoyed iconic status since then. The Poets is now owned by Everards and leased by the Brunswick Inn in Derby, and is a favourite destination for drinkers near and far. It was the first winner of the local CAMRA branch's Pub of the Year award. Q❀◐●P🚌(71)🐾

Hope

Cheshire Cheese Inn Ⓛ

Edale Road, S33 6ZF

☎ (01433) 620381 🌐 thecheshirecheeseinn.co.uk

Abbeydale Moonshine; Bradfield Farmers Blonde; 4 changing beers (sourced locally; often Abbeydale, Bradfield, Peak Ales) [H]
Cosy country inn dating from 1578 with an open-plan bar and a smaller room at a lower level that probably originally housed animals, but which is now mainly used for dining. Home-cooked meals using local produce are served lunchtimes and evenings. Up to six handpulls offer mainly local ales. The pub is in good walking country, but the parking is limited as the road outside is narrow. Q🐻❀🛏◐P🐾📶

Hundall

Miners Arms [L]
Hundall Lane, S18 4BP
☎ (01246) 414505
Drone Valley Dronny Bottom Bitter; Pictish Alchemists Ale; 3 changing beers (sourced nationally; often Church End, Vocation, Welbeck Abbey) [H]
A traditional village hostelry which has won many local and regional CAMRA branch awards and offers a wide range of beers and real ciders. Regular ales come from Pictish and the local community Drone Valley Brewery, and there are also three changing guests. The pub operates a Monday Club with real ales discounted for all customers, and serves a limited range of pub snacks. A large-screen TV shows sport. There is an excellent beer garden to the rear. Q🐻❀◐♣●P🚋🚌(14)🐾📶

Hurdlow

Royal Oak [L]
SK17 9QJ (just off A515 Buxton-Ashbourne road, Monyash crossroads)
☎ (01298) 83288 🌐 peakpub.co.uk
Sharp's Doom Bar; 2 changing beers (often Abbeydale, Bradfield) [H]
Remote pub with the advantage of being only a few minutes' walk away from the Tissington and High Peak Trail, and ideal for exploring the Peak District National Park. It has open fires and hidden corners, and the emphasis is on food, which also includes breakfast. Accommodation is provided in the Bunk Barn and 20-pitch campsite (no motor homes). Breakfast is served, and main meals from lunchtime. Q🐻❀🛏◐⛺P🐾📶

Ilkeston

Burnt Pig [L]
53 Market Street, DE7 5RB
☎ 07538 723722
5 changing beers [H]/[G]
This micropub has been in the Guide since opening over five years ago. It sells a wide range of top-quality ales which are normally sourced personally by the landlord. Regulars and newcomers are welcomed with equal gusto. The interior is spread over three areas, from the busy bar area to two rooms to the rear. There is a variety of bottled continental ales, and a range of pork pies and cheeses to eat in or take away. Q♣●🚌🐾

Dewdrop [L]
24 Station Road, DE7 5TE
☎ (0115) 932 9684
Oakham Bishops Farewell; house beer (by Oakham); changing beers (often Acorn, Blue Monkey, Castle Rock) [H]
This historic, unchanged, three-roomed pub is a long-standing entrant in the Guide. There is a bar and lounge on either side of the serving area and a separate snug. It serves up to eight real ales, all to an excellent standard. Also on offer are two ciders and a bar menu during the day. There are roaring fires in winter. The reopened Ilkeston railway station is a short walk away.
Q🐻❀◐⚌♣●🚌(27)🐾

Prince of Wales [L]
69 South Street, DE7 5QQ
☎ (0115) 932 5452
3 changing beers [H]
Former Shipstone's pub that is now an established and busy local. The central serving area has a modern public bar to the right with a large TV. The lounge, to the left, provides a quieter and more traditional area to enjoy the beer. Ales are normally from local breweries such as Blue Monkey and Falstaff. There is a rear outdoor smoking area. ❀♣🚌🐾📶

Kirk Ireton

Barley Mow Inn 🏆
Main Street, DE6 3JP (off B5023) SK266501
☎ (01335) 370306
Whim Hartington IPA; 4 changing beers [G]
A firm favourite for generations, this is one of Britain's most venerated pubs, set in a charming village. The gabled Jacobean building houses several interconnecting rooms, and has low beams, mullioned windows and well-worn woodwork, with a welcoming open fire in the main room. It has no bar as such, but a small serving hatch through which the cask ales are fetched from the cellar. Good home-cooked food is served. As of early 2020, brewing has begun on-site. Local CAMRA Pub of the Year 2020. Q❀🛏◐●P🐾

Little Longstone

Packhorse Inn
Main Street, DE45 1NN
☎ (01629) 640471 🌐 packhorselongstone.co.uk
Black Sheep Best Bitter; Thornbridge Wild Swan, Lord Marples, Jaipur IPA; 2 changing beers (often Thornbridge) [H]
Small pub that began life as two miners' cottages and has been welcoming drinkers since 1787. It is just a short walk from stunning views of Monsal Head. Fresh local produce is a passion, an ethos also extended to the beers, with up to six handpulled ales, always including a choice from the nearby Thornbridge Brewery. There is a pleasant beer garden, and food is served all day at weekends. Dogs and walkers are welcome here.
🐻❀◐⛺♣🚌(173)🐾📶

Litton

Red Lion [L] ✔
Church Lane, SK17 8QU
☎ (01298) 871458 🌐 theredlionlitton.co.uk
Abbeydale Absolution; Peak Ales Bakewell Best Bitter; 2 changing beers (sourced locally; often Acorn, Bradfield, Moorhouse's) [H]
Nestling on the green and the only pub in the village, the Red Lion is a welcome refuge for locals and visitors alike. There is a large fireplace warming several rooms off a central passageway. Not to be missed, the annual Wakes Week is at the end of June, when the village hosts events including a well dressing on the green and the pub holds a beer festival. Fresh food is served all day, every day.
🐻❀🛏◐♣P🚌(65,173)🐾📶

Long Eaton

Hole in the Wall

Regent Street, NG10 1JX

Draught Bass; Nottingham Extra Pale Ale; Oakham Citra, Bishops Farewell; 1 changing beer

A traditional and unchanged two-roomed pub. The landlord of over 30 years' service offers five quality real ales. These are normally from the Oakham and Nottingham range, and Draught Bass is always on tap. The smaller public bar has a pool table and is complemented by a quieter lounge, with its own serving hatch. An attractive beer garden is hidden away at the rear. A varied clientele consists of the local trade and real ale enthusiasts. Q

Lullington

Colvile Arms

Main Street, DE12 8EG (centre of village)

07510 870980

Draught Bass; Marston's Pedigree; 2 changing beers (sourced regionally)

Leased from the Lullington Estate, seat of the Colvile family until the early 1900s, this popular 18th-century free house is at the heart of an attractive hamlet at the southern tip of the county. The public bar incorporates an adjoining hallway and features high-backed settles with wood panelling. The bar and a comfortable lounge are on opposite sides of a central serving area. A snug/function room (where dogs are allowed) overlooks the beer garden and lawn. Pop-up food is available Wednesday and Friday evenings. Q P

Makeney

Holly Bush

Holly Bush Lane, DE56 0RX

(01332) 841729 hollybushinnmakeney.co.uk

Fuller's London Pride; Greene King Abbot; Marston's Pedigree; Timothy Taylor Landlord; 4 changing beers (sourced nationally)

An excellent late 17th-century Grade II listed venue with great character. Once a farmhouse and brewery on the Strutt Estate, it stood on the main Derby turnpike before the new road (now the A6) opened in 1818. Dick Turpin reputedly drank here, and it has nationally important, historic interior features throughout its various stone-flagged hideaways, with welcoming fires in winter. A home-cooked lunchtime food menu is available as well as bar snacks. Regular beer festivals feature. Walkers, families and dogs are welcome. Q P

Matlock

Farmacy

76 Smedley Street, DE4 3JJ (jct of Bank Rd/Smedley St)

(01629) 583350 aaabrewery.co.uk

5 changing beers (sourced locally; often Aldwark Artisan Ales)

Up the hill from the town centre and behind the county hall on Smedley Street, this cosy, split-level micropub is the tap for Aldwark Artisan Ales. It has five handpulls – one dispensing real cider – and usually features several beers from its own range, as well as a choice of gins and wines. Pork pies and other snacks are available. Themed nights include music and quizzes.

Newsroom

75-77 Smedley Street East, DE4 3FQ

(01629) 583625

4 changing beers (sourced regionally)

Up the hill from the town centre, this smart conversion from a newsagent to a micropub is an L-shaped room with some exposed brickwork and renovated sash windows. There are four real ales from interesting local and, sometimes, national microbreweries. Six craft ales normally include a stout and a lager, and at least one will be KeyKeg. Upwards of 60 different bottled and canned beers for drinking in or taking away are stocked, as well as a good range of gins and wines.

Red Lion

65 Matlock Green, DE4 3BT

(01629) 584888 theredlionmatlock.co.uk

Moot Ales Best, Blonde, Giddy Edge IPA; 4 changing beers (sourced nationally)

Set back from the A615 behind the bus stop and shops in the Green area of Matlock, this place is just a short walk past the football ground, away from the town centre. It is a large, impressive, open-plan building, with a taproom area to the right, and a comfortable lounge and dining area to the left of the central entrance. Seven handpulls often dispense up to four ales from the on-site Moot Ales Brewery. Dogs are welcome in the taproom only.

Q P

Thorn Tree Inn

48 Jackson Road, DE4 3JQ

(01629) 580295

Draught Bass; Nottingham Extra Pale Ale; Timothy Taylor Landlord; 4 changing beers (sourced nationally)

Sat high above Matlock, this two roomed traditional pub boasts far reaching views of the Derwent Valley and Riber Castle from its heated patio area. Popular with workers from County Hall at lunchtimes and locals at night, children and dogs are welcome, although cat-swinging is not recommended due to the compact nature of the establishment. Three permanent real ales are available with a further selection of four guest ales.

Q

Twenty Ten

16 Dale Road, DE4 3LT

(01629) 259793 twentytenmatlock.co.uk

4 changing beers (sourced locally; often Thornbridge)

A stone's throw from the local train and bus station, the bar nestles among the antique shops of Dale Road. It serves four real ales and focuses on LocAle, with Thornbridge regularly on the handpulls. These are complemented by 16 draught craft beers, of which at least eight are KeyKeg. Food is served at lunchtime followed by light bites menu until early evening. Live music is performed on Friday and Saturday nights.

Melbourne

Chip & Pin

8-10 High Street, DE73 8GJ

07957 806454 chipandpinpub.com

4 changing beers (sourced regionally)

Micropub centrally located in Melbourne's old Midland Bank premises. It is owned by a group of local real ale enthusiasts who serve you at your table. The building has been sympathetically restored and consists of two rooms – a main drinking area and a meeting room for local groups. Real ales are available in third of a pint taster racks. Real cider, wine, soft drinks and snacks are also on sale. Q (2)

Milford

King William
The Bridge, DE56 0RR
☎ (01332) 840842
Draught Bass; Greene King Abbot Ⓖ**; Timothy Taylor Landlord; 3 changing beers (sourced nationally)** Ⓗ
On the A6 between Derby and Belper, this stone-built Georgian inn is dramatically situated at the foot of sandstone cliffs. An open fire at one end of the elongated bar often adds to the ambience of the cosy interior. Original period furniture and quarry-tiled flooring date from the time the place was built. Regular beer festivals and live music are an added attraction at this popular, comfortable pub. ♞🛏♿♣🚌🐾📶

New Mills

Beer Shed
47B Market Street, SK22 4AA
☎ (01663) 742005
3 changing beers (sourced locally; often Rock Mill, Torrside) Ⓗ
New Mills' first micropub, handily situated in the town centre close to Central railway station and bus station. The layout is a bit unusual as the building has a small frontage, but the long narrow bar serves its purpose well. There is also a small downstairs room. The three changing beers feature some from local micros in addition to six KeyKeg fonts and German Flensburger on draught. The cheerful intimate atmosphere makes for a pleasant drinking experience. Q⇌🍎🚌🐾

Masons Arms
High Street, SK22 4BR
☎ (01663) 635466
5 changing beers (sourced regionally; often Robinsons, Storm) Ⓗ
Formerly a Robinsons pub, this is now a free house after a local campaign to save it. It offers a changing range of beers. The pub has recently been refurbished internally, and is very much a community asset. A lively, friendly place with a strong sports orientation, it also hosts regular live music featuring local bands. There is a small drinking area outside. Close to the Sett River Valley and Torrs Millenium Bridge in the centre of town. ⇌P🚌🐾📶

Newbold

Nag's Head Inn 🄻
37 Newbold Village, S41 8RJ
☎ (01246) 297446
Sharp's Doom Bar; 5 changing beers (often Pentrich, Oakham, Pheasantry) Ⓗ
Built in 1760, the venue is Grade II listed. It retains its central bar layout, with six handpulls, surrounded by four separate rooms, one of them with an open fire. Another historic building lies directly behind, the medieval Eyre Chapel, accessed through the pub car park and Grade II* listed. Adjoining this is the Newbold Observatory, which has public open evenings. There is a discount on cask ales on Tuesday, and traditional cider is sold in the summer months. ♞❀♣🍎P🚌🐾

Newton Solney

Brickmakers Arms
9-11 Main Street, DE15 0SJ (on B5008; opp jct with Trent Lane)
☎ 07525 220103 🌐 brickmakersarms.pub
Burton Bridge Sovereign Gold, Bridge Bitter, Burton Porter, Stairway to Heaven; 1 changing beer (sourced regionally) Ⓗ
This cosy local at the end of an 18th-century terrace of cottages was converted into a pub in the early 19th century for workers at a nearby brickworks. It features a narrow central bar leading at one end to a room served through a hatch, and at the other to an impressive oak-panelled room. The street entrance hallway houses a small bring-and-take library, beyond which is a function/meeting room. Monday is quiz night, Tuesday is bingo, and Thursday is poker. Q♞❀♣🍎P🚌(V3)🐾📶

Ockbrook

Cross Keys ✔
Green Lane, DE72 3SE
☎ (01332) 662308 🌐 crosskeys-ockbrook.co.uk
Marston's Pedigree; Sharp's Doom Bar; 2 changing beers Ⓗ
A traditional village pub with a quirky character and a selection of five real ales and one real cider. The bar has a low-beamed ceiling, a darts playing area, several screens for sports TV and a wood-burner for the winter months. Events take place such as karaoke, quizzes and theme nights. Home-made food includes stone-baked pizza. Outside at the front there is a small terrace with seating, and to the side a small enclosed garden and play area. ♞❀◑♣🍎P🚌(9,9A)🐾📶

Royal Oak 🏆 🄻
55 Green Lane, DE72 3SE
☎ (01332) 662378 🌐 royaloakockbrook.com
Draught Bass; 4 changing beers Ⓗ
An attractive 18th-century pub with a number of small rooms. Since 1953 it has been run by the Wilson family, who have brought about many improvements while retaining the original character and features. Excellent home-cooked food is served every day. A large function room allows the venue to host many community and public events including live music and open mic nights. Outside there are two pleasant gardens, one with an enclosed play area for children. Local CAMRA Country Pub of the Year 2020. Q♞❀◑♿♣🍎P🚌(9,9A)🐾📶

Old Tupton

Tupton Tap 🄻
Derby Road, S42 6LA (on A61, main Chesterfield to Derby road)
☎ (01246) 862180
Ashover Tupton Pale, Tupton Tipple; Oakham Citra; 5 changing beers Ⓗ
After a period of closure, this place, originally called the Royal Oak, was reopened following extensive refurbishment by the Old Poets Corner. The pub has a central bar with a large drinking lobby serving both entrances, and there are cosy drinking areas and corners situated around the bar. It now sports eight handpulls, traditional cider and craft beers, with regular beers from Ashover Brewery. Friday is pizza night.
♞❀◗⛺♣🍎P🚌🐾

Openwoodgate

Black Bull's Head
2 Kilburn Lane, DE56 0SF
☎ 07860 757741
Draught Bass; Greene King Abbot; Oakham Bishops Farewell; 6 changing beers (sourced nationally; often Blue Monkey, Castle Rock, Dancing Duck) Ⓗ

A two-roomed former Greene King pub, now a free house serving many real ales and ciders. It offers a warm welcome in comfortable surroundings, with real fires in the winter. The walls are adorned with historic photographs and newspaper clippings of local and national interest, and one wall is dedicated to the RAF. Q❀♣P🚌🐾

Repton

Boot 🄻 ✔

12 Boot Hill, DE65 6FT (from Repton Cross head down Brook End, pub is on right as road is joined by Boot Hill)
☎ (01283) 346047 🌐 thebootatrepton.co.uk
Boot Clod Hopper, Bitter, ESB; 4 changing beers (sourced regionally) 🄷
Close to the Repton Cross at the centre of the village, this inn has been brought back to life by the local Bespoke pub company with a refurbishment and the addition of an on-site microbrewery. Up to six of the real ales on the bar are brewed here. There are two main rooms, one devoted to dining. Food and accommodation are also provided. ❀P🚌(V3)🐾

Ripley

Beehive Inn

151 Peasehill, DE5 3JN
☎ (01773) 749593
9 changing beers (sourced nationally) 🄷
Half a mile from the town centre, this three-roomed free house is a hub for local rugby and pub league teams. There are welcoming fires in winter, Sky TV in the public bar and a large, pleasant beer garden. The Honeypot Bar in a building at the top of the garden has six real ales plus ciders. (Honeypot Bar opening times are 4-10 Thu & Fri; 2-10 Sat; 12-8 Sun.) Q❀♣P🚌🐾

Rosliston

Bull's Head

Burton Road, DE12 8JU (NW edge of village)
☎ 07762 989216 🌐 bullsheadrosliston.co.uk
Draught Bass; Marston's Pedigree; 2 changing beers (sourced regionally) 🄷
Late 19th-century brick-built free house with a comfortable public bar and a smart, cosy lounge, both featuring open fires and beamed ceilings. There is also a large function room in a converted stable block. A collection of china bulls is displayed behind the bar, and interesting models of a Burton Union brewing system can be found in both the public bar and the function room. Filled cobs with chips are served on Sunday lunchtime. The National Forest Rosliston Forestry Centre is about half a mile away. ❀♣P🚌(22)🐾

Sawley

Sawley Junction 🄻

176 Tamworth Road, NG10 3JU
☎ 07966 757407
5 changing beers (sourced regionally) 🄶
This one-roomed family-run pub, already a popular local, has been renovated to a high standard. With the feel of a snug station bar, it is wood-panelled, with railway memorabilia adorning the walls. Four to five gravity-fed cask ales are available, rotating on a regular basis, as well as a variety of real ciders and craft ales. Bar snacks, freshly made sandwiches, savouries and hot drinks are served throughout the day. QP🚌🐾

Shirland

Shoulder of Mutton 🄻

Hallfieldgate Lane, DE55 6AA (on B6013, Wessington-Shirland crossroads)
☎ (01773) 834992
3 changing beers 🄷
Eclectic, traditional, 16th-century drinking den, nestling on the edge of Amber Valley, with a beer garden offering spectacular views and sunsets. This is a true free house serving real ale from small breweries. It has no beer list on the wall because the ales change daily. Regular customers are drawn from far and wide, fuelling the unique, easy atmosphere created by the irrepressible landlord and landlady. Dogs and hikers are welcome. Check out the teacups. Q❀♣P🐾

South Normanton

Devonshire Arms

137 Markey Street, DE55 2AA (at M1 jct 28 take B6019, at mini roundabout turn right into Market St)
☎ (01773) 810748
Sarah Hughes Dark Ruby; Theakstons XB; 4 changing beers 🄷
A genuine free house offering up to six real ales and two real ciders or perries. Customers' suggestions are used to determine guest ales. Home-cooked food is available lunchtimes every day, including a popular Sunday carvery (booking is recommended). A regular winner of local CAMRA Pub of the Year. ♣P🚌(9.1)🐾

Sutton cum Duckmanton

Arkwright Arms 🄻

Chesterfield Road, S44 5JG (on A632 between Chesterfield and Bolsover)
☎ (01246) 232053 🌐 arkwrightarms.co.uk
Greene King Abbot; Whim Arbor Light; 8 changing beers 🄷
Brewers' Tudor-fronted free house. A changing range of 10 guest ales, many from local micros, is complemented by 12 ciders and four perries. Beer festivals are held at Easter and bank holidays, with mini events throughout the year. Quality food is served until early evening Monday to Saturday, and until mid-afternoon on Sunday. The spacious beer garden has play equipment for children. A winner of numerous CAMRA awards, including East Midlands Cider Pub of the Year and local CAMRA Pub of the Year. ❀♣P🚌🐾

Swanwick

Steampacket Inn

Derby Road, DE55 1AB
☎ (01773) 607771
Draught Bass; 5 changing beers (sourced nationally; often Blue Monkey, Derby, Nottingham) 🄷
A friendly and welcoming Pub People Company venue in the centre of Swanwick, the Steampacket boasts an excellent and constantly changing range of well-kept real ales and ciders, many of them from local microbreweries. It regularly serves Nottingham Packet Pale, brewed specially for the Steampacket. The pub is popular and gets lively at weekends, with regular live music. It hosts a beer festival in winter and summer. Quiz night is Tuesday. A welcoming fire greets you in winter, and there are outdoor tables for warmer days.
Q♣P🚌🐾

Wardlow Mires

Three Stags' Heads ★ 𝕃

Mires Lane, SK17 8RW (jct A623/B6465)
☎ (01298) 872268
Abbeydale Deception, Absolution; house beer (by Abbeydale); 1 changing beer (sourced regionally) Ⓗ
A quaint 300-year-old inn with two small rooms, stone-flagged floors and low ceilings. Unspoilt, it is one of the few pubs in the area that has been identified by CAMRA as having a nationally important historic pub interior. An ancient range warms the bar and the house dogs, one of which gave its name to the house beer – Black Lurcher. Traditional cider is only available in summer.
Q❀ẪP🚌(173) 🐾 📶

Whaley Bridge

Whaley Nook

20 Old Road, SK23 7HR (turn up Old Rd opp Co-op; bar is on left)
Abbeydale Deception; 3 changing beers (sourced locally; often Nook) Ⓗ
Following the closure of the Whaley Brewery, the tap has reopened as the Whaley Nook. There is a cosy front bar with a small separate room to the rear. Four handpumps offer three changing ales from local breweries, typically including Eyam Real Ale Company brews, and a regular beer. An interesting selection of gins from far and wide is also stocked. A loyalty card system operates during the week. Works of art by local artists are displayed on the walls and are for sale. **Q⇌🚌**

Whitehough

Old Hall Inn 𝕃

Chinley, SK23 6EJ (in village 750yds off B6062)
☎ (01663) 750529 🌐 old-hall-inn.co.uk
8 changing beers (often Marston's) Ⓗ
The 16th-century Whitehough Hall forms part of this quintessential country inn which has previously won the CAMRA Regional Pub of the Year award, the Great British Regional Pub award for Best Cask Pub for several years, and is a regular entry in this Guide. Eight ales, including seven regularly changing guests from quality local micros, complement those available at the adjacent Paper Mill Inn (under the same ownership). The popular food menu features dishes using local produce. A well-attended beer festival runs in September.
❀🛏◑Ẫ⇌P🚌(189,190) 🐾 📶

Whittington Moor

Beer Parlour 𝕃

1 King Street North, S41 9BA
☎ 07870 693411 🌐 the-beer-parlour.co.uk
8 changing beers (often Double Top, Thornbridge, Timothy Taylor) Ⓗ
Originally a bottle-beer shop with a few handpumps, it moved into larger premises and is now a rustic one-roomed bar. There is a warm, friendly feel and comfy seating, which gives a real micropub feel. A choice of eight changing real ales is offered along with many real ciders and – unique to the area – Belgian and continental beers. You can opt to take a beer home too. **Q♿●🚌** 🐾

Red Lion, Litton (Photo: Dave Pickersgill)

CASK MARQUE—WHO ARE WE?

Cask Marque was founded in 1998 by Paul Nunny, a former Director of Adnams, to improve the quality of cask ale in pubs and raise industry standards.

"We are a not-for-profit organisation set up to ensure that the cask ale you drink in pubs is in perfect condition. Today the Directors are made up of representatives from large and small breweries, pub companies and trade bodies, all engaged in continuing to drive beer quality."

In just over twenty years Cask Marque has:

- Accredited over 10,000 pubs for the quality of their beer
- Visited over 20,000 pubs each year
- Improved standards of cellarmanship through training, qualifications, and star ratings
- Ensured that your beer in the glass is cellar-cool by installing ale python cooling systems
- Communicated what Cask Marque stands for with 77% of consumers recognising the plaque (YouGov 2018)
- Launched the Cask Finder app to find Cask Marque pubs with over 60,000 users per month
- Championed cask ales through the annual Cask Report

Look out for our Marque in the Guide and you are guaranteed to find a great pint of cask ale ✓

Pubs who apply for a Cask Marque accreditation receive two unannounced visits per year from one of 60 assessors who are qualified brewers or senior technical services personnel. On a visit they sample up to six cask ales in the glass and check for temperature, aroma, appearance, and taste. In addition, new pubs must pass an 11-point check list to establish their beer cellar rating.

CASK FINDER

Use the free Cask Finder app and you are guaranteed to receive a great pint of cask ale

To find out more about Cask Marque visit www.cask-marque.co.uk and join us in championing beer quality in the glass

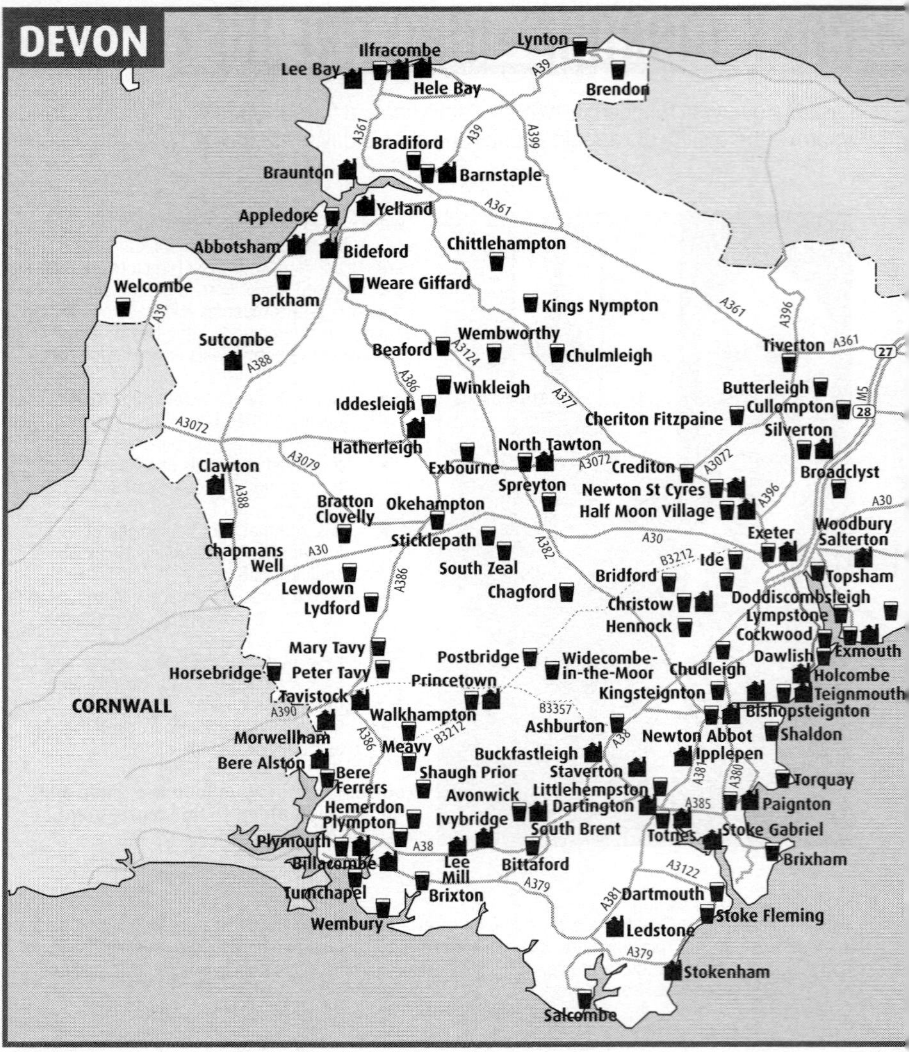

Appledore

Champ 𝕃

Meeting Street, EX39 1RJ (situated just off Appledore Quay)

☎ (01237) 421662 🌐 pubchamp.uk

Clearwater Expedition Ale; 3 changing beers (sourced locally) Ⓗ

Situated in the heart of the charming, picturesque coastal village of Appledore, the Champ is a cosy and quirky evening pub renowned for live music. It has an interesting and eclectic decor. The brewery tap for the nearby Clearwater Brewery, four of its ales are generally on handpump. Real cider is also on offer. Live bands feature regularly on Friday and Saturday, together with popular open mic evenings Tuesday, Wednesday and Thursday, often featuring folk and blues. Soul food is served but customers are also welcome to bring in food to eat on the premises – there is a fish and chip shop next door – while a nearby public car park accommodates camper vans overnight for a modest fee.

Ashburton

Old Exeter Inn 𝕃

26 West Street, TQ13 7DU (on main road through centre of Ashburton, opp church)

☎ (01364) 652013 🌐 oldexeterinn.com

Dartmoor IPA Ⓗ**, Legend; Draught Bass** Ⓖ**; Otter Amber** Ⓗ

The oldest pub in Ashburton was originally built in 1130 to house workers constructing the nearby St Andrews church (opposite the inn), and had additions in the 17th century. Sir Walter Raleigh was arrested here in 1903, for treason against King James I, and taken to the Tower of London. This friendly local has seated drinking areas either side of the entrance, and a wood-panelled L-shaped bar. Behind the bar, in what was the old fireplace, can be seen the large original millstones and this area also houses a granite shelf for serving the gravity-fed ales. There are also two smaller rear seating areas and a flagstone-floored corridor leading to a lovely secluded walled garden at the back. Local real cider and perry are sold. **Q** (88,x38)

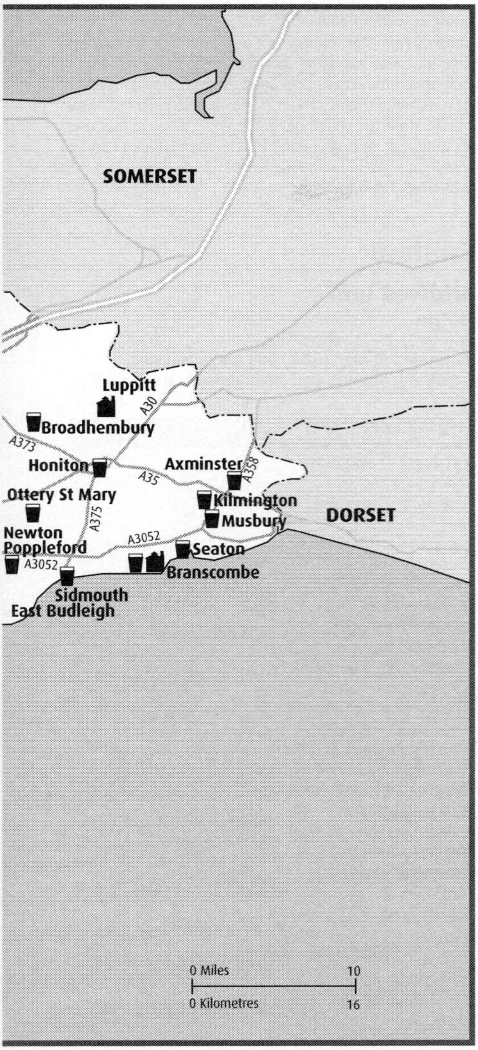

Avonwick

Avon Inn ℄

TQ10 9NB

☎ (01364) 73475 🌐 avon-inn.org.uk

Dartmoor Legend, Jail Ale; Draught Bass; 1 changing beer (sourced regionally) Ⓗ

At the crossroads in the centre of the village, the inn is at the heart of the community, with various events regularly taking place including quiz nights, barbecues and live music. The lounge is now the restaurant. Alongside the ale, up to 10 ciders are available from Ashridge, Countryman, Sandford Orchards and Westons. The village is served by Country Bus 91 between Plymouth and Totnes. Closing time may vary depending on custom. ♉❀◑♿▲♣●P🚌(91)🐾

Axminster

Axminster Inn ℄ ✔

Silver Street, EX13 5AH

☎ (01297) 34947 🌐 axminsterinn.pub

Palmers Copper Ale, IPA, Dorset Gold, Tally Ho!; 1 changing beer (sourced locally) Ⓗ

A friendly, traditional pub, lying just off the town centre, with a real log fire for the winter months and a lovely enclosed beer garden to enjoy in the warmer weather. It is a Palmers house, offering a good range of the brewery's real ales. Live music is featured. Free Wi-Fi is available and there is a skittle alley and dartboard. Children are welcome until early evening.

♉❀⇌♣●P🚌🐾≋

Barnstaple

Panniers ℄ ✔

33-34 Boutport Street, EX31 1RX

☎ (01271) 329720

Greene King Abbot; GT Ales Battleaxe; Ruddles Best Bitter; Sharp's Doom Bar; 4 changing beers (sourced regionally) Ⓗ

Centrally located opposite the Queen's Theatre and close to the historic Pannier Market, this popular JD Wetherspoon pub maintains a changing selection of real ales from local and West Country breweries, as well as from further afield. Framed prints, hung throughout the comfortable premises, depict various items relating to the history of Barnstaple. To the rear, a pleasant courtyard garden drinking area is a suntrap in summer.

♉❀◑♿●🚌≋

Beaford

Globe Inn 🏆 ℄

Exeter Road, EX19 8LR (on main road in centre of village)

☎ (01805) 603920 🌐 globeinnpub.co.uk

3 changing beers (sourced regionally) Ⓗ

Traditional and cosy country inn, with a particular passion for real ale and craft beer to suit all tastes. Three changing and mainly local ales are usually offered, alongside a comprehensive drinks menu that includes more than 40 (often legendary) bottled and bottle-conditioned beers from around the globe. Proud of its environmental credentials, the pub also offers a seasonal and attractively priced food menu, which uses the best of ingredients from local producers. Local CAMRA Pub of the Year 2020. Q♉❀🛏◑♣●🚌🐾≋

Bere Ferrers

Olde Plough Inn ℄

Fore Street, PL20 7JG (close to church and river)

☎ (01822) 840358 🌐 theoldeploughinn.co.uk

Hunters Half Bore; 3 changing beers (sourced locally; often Roam, Salcombe, Summerskills) Ⓗ

A 16th-century village inn with outstanding views over the River Tavy from the beer garden, and only a 15-minute walk from the station on the picturesque Tamar Valley line. Inside, there are flagstone floors, exposed stonework walls, beamed ceilings, real fires and a welcoming atmosphere. Acoustic music, jam sessions, quizzes and themed food nights feature. Up to three guest beers are sourced from local and national breweries, alongside bottled beers from Bere Brewery. Food is served to suit all ages and appetites.

Q♉❀◑⇌♣●🚌(87)🐾≋

Bittaford

Horse & Groom 🏆 ℄

Exeter Road, PL21 0EL

☎ (01752) 892358

Dartmoor Jail Ale; house beer (by Hunters); 3 changing beers (sourced locally; often Exeter, South Hams, Summerskills) Ⓗ
A family-owned pub run by a real ale enthusiast, featuring good home-cooked food and seven pumps, two dedicated to real cider. The other pumps predominantly offer ales from local breweries in south Devon and Cornwall. Third-pint tapas are available. There is a long bar and separate dining area, with pictures of the former Moorhaven Hospital on the wall. A quiz night is held monthly and a beer festival and a cider and sausage festival are hosted during the year, supporting local charities. ♿❀◗▲♣🕪P🚲(X38)🐾

Bradiford

Windsor Arms Ⓛ
55 Bradiford, EX31 4AD (on main road through village, approximately ½ mile N of Pilton)
☎ (01271) 343583
GT Ales Thirst of Many; 1 changing beer (sourced nationally; often Greene King, Timothy Taylor, Wadworth) Ⓗ
A friendly community oriented village local within easy walking distance of Barnstaple. Two changing real ales are kept, one invariably from local GT Ales. Good, freshly cooked and locally sourced food is served Friday to Sunday in the separate lounge bar. A function room with skittle alley, pool table and dartboard lies to the rear of the pub. ♿❀◗♣🕪🐾🛜

Branscombe

Fountain Head Inn Ⓛ
EX12 3BG (on main street 1 mile S of A3052)
☎ (01297) 680359 🌐 fountainheadinn.com
Branscombe Vale Branoc, Golden Fiddle; 1 changing beer (sourced locally) Ⓗ
Set in a beautiful coastal valley, this old walker-friendly pub is at the west end of one of England's longest villages. Ancient features such as an inglenook fireplace, wood panelling and flagstone floors greet customers, while the bar offers Branscombe Vale ales and ciders. Good-value home-cooked food is served – the pub opens early for breakfast Monday to Saturday in summer. A beer festival is held on the closest weekend to the longest day. Q♿❀◗▲♣🕪P🚲(899)🐾

Bratton Clovelly

Clovelly Inn Ⓛ ✓
EX20 4JZ (between A30 and A3079) SX464919
☎ (01837) 871447 🌐 clovellyinn.co.uk
Dartmoor IPA, Jail Ale; Sharp's Doom Bar; 1 changing beer (sourced nationally) Ⓗ
Dating back to the 18th century and with the bar featuring an oak fireplace lintel inscribed 1789, this truly authentic rural Devon pub lies at the heart of the local community. The cosy main bar, with a large wood-burning stove, is complemented by two separate dining areas (it's advisable to book for evening meals) and a games room. Three real ales are kept, with Sam's Medium cider also sold in summer. Good home-cooked food is served seven days a week. ♿❀◗🚻▲♣🕪P🚲(633)🐾

Brendon

Staghunters Inn Ⓛ
EX35 6PS SS767481
☎ (01598) 741222 🌐 staghunters.com
Exmoor Ale; 1 changing beer (sourced regionally) Ⓖ

Nestling on the banks of the River Lyn, within Exmoor National Park, this family owned and run hotel is an ideal base for those exploring the local area. There are 14 well-appointed rooms and dogs can also stay overnight for a nominal charge. The real ales are served on gravity directly from the cellar, generally with two in winter and up to four in summer. Good locally sourced food can be enjoyed in the attractive restaurant.
Q♿❀🛏◗▲♣🕪P🐾🛜

Bridford

Bridford Inn Ⓛ
EX6 7HT
☎ (01647) 252250 🌐 bridfordinn.co.uk
Dartmoor Jail Ale; 3 changing beers (sourced regionally; often Brains, Inveralmond, Morland) Ⓗ

REAL ALE BREWERIES
Art Brew ✦ Sutcombe
Barnaby's Staverton
Barum 🍺 Barnstaple
Bays Paignton
Beer Engine 🍺 Newton St Cyres
Bere Bere Alston
Black Tor Christow
Branscombe Vale Branscombe
Bridgetown Totnes
Buckland Bideford
Checkstone 🍺 Exmouth
Clearwater Bideford
Combe ✦ Ilfracombe (NEW)
Country Life Abbotsham
Crossed Anchors 🍺 Exmouth
Dartmoor Princetown
Devon Earth Buckfastleigh
Exe Valley Silverton
Exeter ✦ Exeter
Fat Belly Ilfracombe
Fat Pig 🍺 Exeter
Grampus 🍺 Lee Bay
GT Braunton
Hanlons Half Moon Village
Holsworthy Clawton
Hunters Ipplepen
Isca Holcombe
Ivybridge Ivybridge (NEW)
Madrigal Hele Bay
Morwell Morwellham
New Devon Exeter (NEW)
New Lion ✦ Dartington
Noss Beer Works Lee Mill
Otter ✦ Luppitt
Platform 5 Newton Abbot
Powderkeg Woodbury Salterton
Red Rock ✦ Bishopsteignton
Riviera Stoke Gabriel
Roam ✦ Plymouth
Salcombe Ledstone
South Hams Stokenham
Stannary ✦ Tavistock
Steel Brew ✦ Plymouth (NEW)
Summerskills Plymouth: Billacombe
Tally Ho! 🍺 Hatherleigh
Taw Valley North Tawton
Teignmouth Teignmouth (NEW)
Teignworthy Newton Abbot
Topsham ✦ Exeter
Totnes 🍺 Totnes
TQ South Brent (NEW)
Yelland Manor Yelland

An idyllic 17th-century Devon longhouse, nestled within the Dartmoor National Park, converted to a pub in 1968, featuring an open-plan space with oak beams, an inglenook fireplace complete with bread oven, and a warming wood-burner. There's a beer garden out front with comfy benches and a view to die for. Freshly cooked and locally sourced food is served daily except Monday. The cellar stocks a number of local ciders.
P (360)

Brixham

Old Coaching Inn

61 Fore Street, TQ5 8AG
(01803) 852000 theoldcoachinginnbrixham.uk
Dartmoor Legend; 2 changing beers (sourced regionally; often Cotleigh, Exmoor, St Austell) [G]
Built in 1790 as a hotel with stables and a courtyard, and now recently refurbished, the inn has a separate bar with a six-cask stillage. This is the only place in Brixham serving two or three real ales direct from the cask. There is a separate restaurant/function room aimed both at diners and for community use by clubs and groups. Note that opening hours are limited in winter – please check the website. (17,12)

Queen's Arms

31 Station Hill, TQ5 8BN (from Brixham Library go up Church Hill East then Station Hill)
(01803) 852074 thequeensarmsbrixham.co.uk
House beer (by Teignworthy); 5 changing beers (sourced nationally; often Branscombe Vale) [H]
This single-bar, end-of-terrace pub has a well-deserved reputation for the quality of its six beers and multiple real ciders. The venue has a friendly atmosphere with a strong community ethos and, on cold winter nights, wood-burning stoves. Good-value Sunday lunches and Monday evening meals feature, plus live music at weekends. A charity beer festival is hosted in early December with over 50 real ales and ciders.
P (17)

Brixton

Foxhound Inn

Kingsbridge Road, PL8 2AH
(01752) 880271 foxhoundinn.co.uk
Courage Directors; house beer (by Summerskills); 3 changing beers (sourced nationally; often Caledonian, Courage, Summerskills) [H]
An 18th-century former coaching house in a rural village just east of Plymouth, with two separate bars and a small restaurant. Traditional English meals are served daily, featuring locally sourced ingredients. Look out for Red Coat, an ale crafted by the landlord, among the four guest ales. A monthly charity quiz night is held. The village is served by a frequent daytime bus service. Local CAMRA branch Country Pub of the Year runner-up 2019.
Q P

Broadclyst

New Inn

Whimple Road, EX5 3BX (½ mile E of village)
(01392) 461312 newinnbroadclyst.co.uk
Dartmoor Jail Ale; Exmoor Gold; Otter Bitter; Sharp's Doom Bar [H]
A large, traditional 17th-century inn set away to the east of the main village, with a recently extended car park to the rear, and a large beer garden and play area. Freshly cooked food is offered lunchtimes and evenings. The skittle alley can double as a function room, and regular events are held (see website for details). Will close earlier if there is no custom in late evening.
Q P

Broadhembury

Drewe Arms

EX14 3NF
(01404) 841267 drewearmsinn.co.uk
Bays Devon Dumpling; Exeter Avocet; Otter Amber, Ale; 1 changing beer (sourced locally) [H]
Grade II listed 16th-century thatched pub with a secluded garden, set in a picturesque estate village of cob and limewashed cottages within the Blackdown Hills. There are low-beamed ceilings and uneven floor levels throughout the many rooms. This is a friendly and welcoming family-run venue, with the emphasis on local real ales and produce. Good-value food is served Tuesday to Saturday (plus Monday in summer) and lunchtime on Sunday – a takeaway menu is also available.
Q P

Butterleigh

Butterleigh Inn

The Green, EX15 1PN (opp church) SS9746108212
(01884) 855433 butterleighinn.co.uk
Cotleigh Tawny Owl; Dartmoor Jail Ale; 1 changing beer (sourced regionally) [H]
In a small, quaint village, hidden down narrow country lanes, this is an excellent country pub with a mixed clientele creating a great atmosphere with diverse conversation. There are two rooms around the bar, with a modern dining room at the back. The patio is covered with grapevines in summer. Good-value home-cooked food is served lunchtimes and evenings Tuesday to Saturday, with a carvery Sunday lunchtime. There is a choice of up to four real ales and three ciders.
Q P

Chagford

Globe Inn

9 High Street, TQ13 8AJ
(01647) 433485 theglobeinnchagford.co.uk
Dartmoor IPA; Otter Bitter [H]; 1 changing beer (sourced locally) [H]/[G]
Overlooking the parish church, the Globe was once a coaching inn and coopery. The pub has become a focal point of this historic Dartmoor stannary town, providing good food, music, a cinema club and many other events. There is a splendid public bar and a separate lounge and dining room, both with large open log fires. A small courtyard garden is at the rear and parking is nearby. The ciders are Sam's and Westons Old Rosie.
(173,178)

Ring o' Bells

44 The Square, TQ13 8AH
(01647) 432466 ringobellschagford.co.uk
Dartmoor IPA, Jail Ale; Otter Bitter [H]
A 16th-century inn in the centre of the town. Archives reveal there had been an inn on this site well before this. Both the bar, which is comfortably furnished with bench and booth seating, and the separate dining room to the rear, have open fireplaces. A passageway leads to a pretty walled garden with plenty of seating and a covered smokers' area. There is parking nearby.
P (173,178)

Chapmans Well

Arscott Arms 𝕃
PL15 9SG
☎ (01409) 211113 🌐 thearscottarms.co.uk
2 changing beers (sourced locally) 🄷
Approximately halfway between Holsworthy and Launceston, this welcoming roadside pub was tastefully renovated and refurbished to a high standard prior to reopening in 2018. Since then it has developed a growing reputation for its well-kept ales and good food. The front bar leads through to an attractive dining area, while outside there is a pleasant beer garden with decking and a good-sized car park. Locally brewed Holsworthy Ales feature regularly. Q❀◐⛺♣P🐾📶

Cheriton Fitzpaine

Ring of Bells 𝕃
EX17 4JG
☎ (01363) 860111 🌐 theringofbells.com
2 changing beers (sourced regionally) 🄷
Thatched Grade II listed pub in the heart of this picturesque village and next to the parish church. Two changing beers are normally on tap at the single bar. Fine food is available lunchtimes and evenings, but those seeking a snack, a quiet pint by the fire or a few drinks with friends in the garden are equally welcome. The landlady has made this a destination for everyone, including their children and the dog. ❀◐♣●P🐾

Chittlehampton

Bell Inn 𝕃
The Square, EX37 9QL (opp St Hieritha's parish church)
SS636254
☎ (01769) 540368 🌐 thebellatchittlehampton.co.uk
Exmoor Ale; 6 changing beers (sourced regionally) 🄷
In the same family since 1975 and popular with locals and visitors alike, this busy village local celebrates 25 continuous years of Guide inclusion in 2021. An impressive selection of real ales is kept, with up to nine regularly available. The bar area is notable for its sporting memorabilia, with good-value home-cooked food being served both here and in the adjoining restaurant. Local CAMRA branch Pub of the Year 2018 and 2019.
❀🛏◐♿⛺♣●P🚌(658,859)🐾📶

Christow

Teign House Inn 𝕃
Teign Valley Road, EX6 7PL
☎ (01647) 252286 🌐 teignhouseinn.co.uk
Otter Bitter; 3 changing beers (sourced regionally; often Black Tor, Hunters, Powderkeg) 🄷
On the edge of Dartmoor in the scenic Teign Valley sits this welcoming, atmospheric country inn with exposed beams and a warming log fire in winter. The pub is supported strongly by the locals, with a large garden attracting families; the adjoining field has space for caravans, camper vans and campers. There is live music every third Tuesday evening and every fourth Sunday afternoon. Excellent food is served, all home cooked, with a special Thai menu which is also available to take away. Q❀◐♿⛺♣●P🚌(360)🐾📶

Chudleigh

Bishop Lacy Inn 𝕃
52-53 Fore Street, TQ13 0HY
☎ (01626) 854585 🌐 thebishoplacy.touchtakeaway.net/menu
3 changing beers (sourced regionally; often Black Tor, Greene King, South Hams) 🄷/🄶
A warm welcome is guaranteed from an ebullient landlady at this Grade II listed building opposite the church and named after the Bishop of Exeter (1420-1455). The left-hand bar is dominated by a magnificent fireplace which was originally used to cure ham and where most of the locals congregate. Witch dolls are suspended around the bar and you are challenged to ask the landlady why! Child and dog friendly throughout, Sambuca the pub dog welcomes fellow well-behaved pooches. Q❀◐♿⛺♣P🚌(39,182)🐾📶

Chulmleigh

Old Court House
South Molton Street, EX18 7BW
☎ (01769) 580045 🌐 oldcourthouseinn.co.uk
Butcombe Original; Dartmoor IPA; 1 changing beer (sourced regionally) 🄷
Charles I stayed here in 1634 when he held court (hence the name) and this is commemorated with an original coat of arms in one of the bedrooms, while a replica hangs above the fireplace in the main bar. Today this friendly, cosy local features two regular real ales, usually joined by a guest beer in summer. Good home-cooked food can be enjoyed in the bar area, in the separate dining room, or in the pretty cobbled courtyard garden.
❀🛏◐♿♣🚌(377)🐾📶

Cockwood

Ship Inn 𝕃 ✔
Church Road, EX6 8NU (just off A379, outside Starcross)
☎ (01626) 890373 🌐 shipinncockwood.co.uk
Dartmoor Jail Ale; St Austell Tribute, Proper Job; 2 changing beers (sourced nationally) 🄷
A busy family-run pub, close to the picturesque harbour at Cockwood, with a large beer garden with views of the estuary, and a log fire in winter. Popular with drinkers and diners alike, it offers a choice of three regular ales and usually two rotating guests, and has an excellent food menu. Meals are prepared with local produce where possible including a varied choice of locally caught fish. The bus stops 100 yards across the bridge.
Q❀◐⛺♣●P🚌(2)🐾📶

Crediton

Crediton Inn 𝕃
28A Mill Street, EX17 1EZ
☎ (01363) 772882 🌐 crediton-inn.co.uk
5 changing beers (sourced nationally) 🄷
The framed deeds date this inn to 1878, with windows etched with the ancient town seal. It is a genuine free house with a welcoming landlady and has been in the Guide for 33 consecutive years. There is normally a Branscombe beer on. The skittle alley doubles as a function room. Good home-cooked food is served at weekends, with snacks and renowned Scotch eggs at other times. A beer festival is held in mid-November.
❀◐⇌♣●P🚌(5)🐾📶

Cullompton

Pony & Trap 𝕃 ✔
10 Exeter Hill, EX15 1DJ (on B3181 S of town)
☎ (01884) 34182
Dartmoor Jail Ale; Draught Bass; Exmoor Ale; Otter Bright; 4 changing beers (sourced regionally) 🄷
A traditional local with a good atmosphere and a mixed clientele. Many local darts and skittles teams are based

here, live music features once a month, and pub games are played. It has a smart interior featuring a log-burner, making it cosy in winter; flowers and ornaments give it a homely feel. Up to eight real ales are on offer including a house beer, plus three real ciders. Outside, the garden has a seating area. Q❀◑♣●🚌(1)🐾

Dartmouth

Seven Stars

8 Smith Street, TQ6 9QR

☎ (01803) 839635 🌐 sevenstars-dartmouth.co.uk

Dartmoor Jail Ale; 3 changing beers (sourced locally; often Exeter, Otter) Ⓗ

Grade II listed and near to the church, the inn reopened after an extensive refurbishment in 2017. The present building was originally two cottages which were merged in the 18th century; the 16th- and 17th-century features enable it to claim to be the oldest ale house in Dartmouth. The ground-floor bar is both atmospheric and contemporary, with two fireplaces. Children and dogs are welcome. Upstairs there is a restaurant and function room, and six en-suite bedrooms.
ఌ⇌◑▲♣●P🚌(3,92)🐾ᯤ

Dawlish

Marine Tavern

2 Marine Parade, EX7 9DJ

☎ (01626) 865245 🌐 marinetaverndawlish.com

Dartmoor Best, Legend; Sharp's Doom Bar; 1 changing beer (sourced regionally) Ⓗ

Traditional seaside pub with a suntrap patio at the front, and a sea-view balcony that also provides a great look-out post for passing steam train specials. Good-value food is served all day in the peak summer season, and lunch and evenings at other times. Accommodation consists of four rooms and children are welcome in an area away from the bar; dogs are also permitted. There are interesting local photos to admire, and occasional live music is hosted. ఌ❀⇌◑⇌●🚌(2)🐾ᯤ

Doddiscombsleigh

NoBody Inn ✔

EX6 7PS (best approached from A38 at top of Haldon Hill)

☎ (01647) 252394 🌐 nobodyinn.co.uk

House beer (by St Austell); 2 changing beers (sourced locally) Ⓗ

A venerable village inn, mainly 17th century with some later additions, full of old beams and antique furniture. Lunch and dinner are served seven days a week. There is a pub garden in the summer and a log fire in the winter. It has an extensive whisky list (240 plus) and wine list (150 plus). Five comfortable bedrooms are available and high-quality food is served every lunchtime and evening. Dogs are welcome in the bar. Only four miles from Exeter Haldon racecourse. Q❀⇌◑P🚌(360)🐾ᯤ

East Budleigh

Sir Walter Raleigh Inn L

22 High Street, EX9 7ED (off B3178 opp Hayes Lane)

☎ (01395) 442510

4 changing beers (sourced regionally) Ⓗ

Set in the middle of a delightful village, the birthplace of Sir Walter Raleigh, this free house is a truly welcoming 16th-century country inn. Good-quality local food is served lunchtimes and evenings, in addition to four varying real ales and up to six real ciders. Originally two cottages, the buildings were converted into a Jacobean-style pub, retaining the original wooden beams throughout. This gem is well worth a visit for good-quality real ale, cider, food and friendly service.
Qఌ❀◑●🚌(157)🐾

Exbourne

Red Lion L ✔

High Street, EX20 3RY (200yds N of jct with A3072)
SS602018

☎ (01837) 851551 🌐 theredlionexbourne.co.uk

Dartmoor IPA, Legend; 1 changing beer (sourced regionally) Ⓖ

A friendly village local with a well-deserved reputation for the quality and consistency of its ales – it has been local CAMRA branch Pub of the Year several times in recent years. Casks are set on stillage at the end of the L-shaped bar, which is notable for the absence of handpumps, as the landlord refuses to serve draught lager. There is always good conversation to be enjoyed here. Live music also features regularly.
Qఌ❀●P🚌🐾ᯤ

Exeter

Bowling Green L ✔

29-30 Blackboy Road, EX4 6ST

☎ (01392) 490300

4 changing beers (sourced locally) Ⓗ

Originally an 18th-century pub called The Ropemakers, this is a cosy local away from the main city centre and close to Exeter City football club at St James Park. It offers an extensive selection of reasonably priced food including pizzas and gluten-free and vegetarian options. Four real ales are stocked; three are rotating and from local breweries. Live music plays every Saturday night and Sunday afternoon, followed by a quiz in the evening.
Qఌ❀◑♿⇌(St James Park)♣●🚌🐾ᯤ

George's Meeting House ✔

38 South Street, EX1 1ED (near bottom of South St)

☎ (01392) 454250

Greene King IPA, Abbot; Sharp's Doom Bar; 6 changing beers Ⓗ

This Wetherspoon opened in 2005 following a sympathetic conversion from a Unitarian Chapel dating from 1760. Many of the original features remain unaltered; these include two upstairs galleries, a pulpit and stained-glass windows. A range of national, regional and local real ales is served, and five real ciders. Food is on offer throughout the day. A newer extension, which is at the rear of the main building, leads to more seating outdoors. Qఌ❀◑♿⇌●🚌ᯤ

Great Western Hotel L

St David's Station, EX4 4NU

☎ (01392) 274039 🌐 greatwesternhotel.co.uk

9 changing beers Ⓗ

The hotel dates from 1840 and is close to St David's railway station. A range of up to nine ales is offered from around the country. The venue has a good community atmosphere, with wheelchair users most welcome thanks to easy access to the bar and toilet. Ideal for stopovers, it offers a variety of 35 en-suite rooms. The Karma restaurant serves traditional bar snacks and has an exclusive Indian cuisine. Two times CAMRA branch Pub of the Year. Qఌ❀⇌◑♿⇌🚌🐾ᯤ

Hour Glass Inn

21 Melbourne Street, EX2 4AU (approx 300yds from Exeter Quayside)

☎ (01392) 258722 🌐 hourglassexeter.co.uk

Exeter Avocet, Ferryman; 2 changing beers (sourced nationally) ℍ
A traditional hostelry in the back streets of Exeter, established in 1848, in the hub of the local area close to the quay and about five minutes' walk from the main city centre. Four handpumps feature regular Exeter beers and interesting guests from around the country. Food is served lunchtimes and evenings in both the bar and the separate restaurant. There is a function room for events such as live music, talks and theatre. Q◑↺&♣●🖫☀🕏

Imperial 𝕃 ✪

New North Road, EX4 4AH
☎ (01392) 434050
Greene King IPA, Abbot; changing beers ℍ
The Imperial features a range of beers from local and national breweries. It was built in 1810 as a private house, converted to a hotel, then opened as a Wetherspoon pub in 1996. It has an orangery and a large beer garden. Regular beer festivals are held, featuring local, national and international breweries. Food is served all day. Located close to the university, there is a bus stop directly outside the premises. St David's railway station is nearby. Q↷🌣◑&≉●P🖫🕏

Ship Inn ✪

1-3 Martins Lane, EX1 1EY
☎ (01392) 272040
Exeter Avocet; Greene King IPA, Abbot; Otter Ale; 2 changing beers (sourced regionally) ℍ
A historic city centre pub situated along a narrow passageway between the High Street and Cathedral Green. It is one of the oldest pubs in Exeter and Sir Francis Drake used to visit. Four regular ales feature along with two guests, mostly local, and up to three ciders. The pub offers good-value food served all day including a children's menu. Live entertainment is hosted on Wednesday, Friday and Saturday. ↷◑&≉●🖫☀🕏

Thatched House Inn ✪

Exwick Road, EX4 2BQ
☎ (01392) 272920 ⊕ thatchedhouse.net
Greene King Abbot; 6 changing beers (sourced locally; often Dartmoor, Hanlons, Salcombe) ℍ
A thatched building dating from the 1600s, this community pub is next to the Exwick playing fields, opposite the Exeter College Sports Hub. It is close to the river, convenient for dog walkers, cyclists and sightseers. Seven real ales and one real cider are usually on sale, along with great-value home-cooked food sourced from local ingredients and producers. There is on-street parking nearby, and it is on the Stagecoach F1 and F2 bus route. Q↷🌣◑&≉●🖫☀🕏

Exmouth

Bicton Inn 🍸 𝕃 ✪

5 Bicton Street, EX8 2RU
☎ (01395) 272589 ⊕ bictoninn.co.uk
Dartmoor Jail Ale; Hanlons Port Stout; 6 changing beers (sourced locally) ℍ
A friendly and popular back-street local, offering good beer and chat. It is a community hub where traditional games are played such as darts, pool and euchre, and regular live music events are featured. Up to eight real ales and two ciders are normally on offer, which usually include several LocAles. The snug is available for small gatherings and meetings, and there is a log-burner in the main bar. Two beer festivals are held throughout the year. Dogs are now allowed when live music is on. ↷≉♣●🖫☀🕏

First & Last Inn 𝕃

10 Church Street, EX8 1PE (off B3178 Rolle St)
☎ (01395) 263275
Dartmoor Jail Ale; Otter Ale; Teignworthy Neap Tide ℍ; 2 changing beers (sourced locally; often Checkstone) 🄶
A Victorian pub near the town centre with a public car park opposite. A genuine free house, it has three distinct areas and a courtyard patio with heated awnings. The Checkstone Brewery started here in 2016 and supplies changing ales from an increasing range. Up to nine ciders are on sale including Westons Old Rosie and Thatchers Traditional. Games include pool and darts, and there is a skittle alley. Televised sport is prominent and live music features regularly. 🌣&≉♣●🖫(57)☀

Grapevine

2 Victoria Road, EX8 1DL
☎ (01395) 222208 ⊕ thegrapevineexmouth.com
Crossed Anchors Bitter Exe, Devon Steam Gold; 4 changing beers ℍ
The Grapevine brewhouse is a stylish Victorian free house in the centre of Exmouth which underwent a minor refurbishment in January 2020. It is home to Crossed Anchors Brewing and Ruby Diner burger specialists. There are 12 craft taps and three bag-in-box ciders that are rotated on a regular basis. There is a discount on food and drink purchased weekday afternoons. Live music features on most Friday and Saturday nights, and an open mic session on Wednesday. ↷🌣◑&≉♣●🖫(57) ☀🕏

Half Moon Village

Hanlons Beer Factory & Kitchen

Hill Farm, EX5 5AE (off food caravan layby on A377)
☎ (01392) 851160 ⊕ hanlonsbrewery.com
3 changing beers (sourced locally) ℍ
The bar and restaurant are on the first floor overlooking the working brewery, which has produced numerous award-winning beers since 2013. The three handpumps serve a range of Hanlons ales including seasonals and varieties. Beers from Prescott Ales of Cheltenham are also frequently available since the brewery was purchased by the business in 2019. The kitchen serves a burger-based menu suited to all ages, and champions local produce; booking is essential as seating is limited. ↷🌣◑&P🖫(5) ☀🕏

Hemerdon

Miners Arms 𝕃

Hemerdon, PL7 5BU
☎ (01752) 336040 ⊕ theminersarmspub.co.uk
Dartmoor Jail Ale; Draught Bass; house beer (by Dartmoor) ℍ; 1 changing beer (sourced locally; often South Hams, Summerskills) ℍ/🄶
Dating from 1783, this pub is rich in history, with its association with the close-by Drakelands Mine. The three regular beers are supplemented by at least one other local ale. A friendly atmosphere and delightful location make it ever popular. There are also a conservatory with a dining area and patio, and a spacious children's play area. Meals can be enjoyed alfresco on a summer's day. Regular beer and cider festivals are held, as are quiz nights and other events. Q↷🌣◑♣●P🖫(59)☀ 🕏

Hennock

Palk Arms 𝕃

Church Road, TQ13 9QB (take B3344 from A38 to Chudleigh Knighton; follow Hennock signs)

☎ (01626) 836584 🌐 theonlypalkarms.co.uk

3 changing beers (often Dartmoor, Otter, Teignworthy) [H]

A 16th-century free house with stunning views over the Teign Valley, well worth seeking out. Popular with cyclists, dog walkers and hikers, it has car parking and camping sites very close to hand. The pub, reputed to be haunted, boasts two log-burning stoves, which add to the warm, welcoming atmosphere. It is close to the unique local library, an ideal starting point to explore Hennock's mining heritage and the outstanding local countryside after a meal and a pint.

Q ♿ ♣ P

Honiton

Holt

178 High Street, EX14 1LA

☎ (01404) 47707 🌐 theholt-honiton.com

Otter Bitter, Amber, Bright, Ale [H]

The Holt has a cosy bar at street level and a fine-dining restaurant upstairs, both smartly decorated. The kitchen is in full view of the clientele. A lunch menu of tapas and home-cooked food is served in the bar. Independently owned by two sons of the Otter Brewery family, the Holt has won Gastro-Pub of the Year and Taste of the West, and currently holds two AA Rosettes. The head chef also runs popular breadmaking and cookery courses.

Q ♣

Horsebridge

Royal Inn

PL19 8PJ (off the A384 Tavistock-Launceston road) SX401748

☎ (01822) 870214 🌐 royalinn.co.uk

Otter Ale; St Austell Proper Job [H]**; 3 changing beers (sourced regionally; often Draught Bass, Exeter, Skinner's)** [G]

Originally built as a nunnery in 1437 by French Benedictine monks and reported to have been visited by Charles I, the pub overlooks an old bridge on the River Tamar, connecting Devon to Cornwall. It features half-panelling, stone floors, log fires and traditional styling in the bar and lounge, with another larger room off the lounge. It has a terraced garden with sheltered seating and free Wi-Fi. Guest beers are usually served on gravity; the locally sourced food is recommended.

Q P (115)

Iddesleigh

Duke of York

EX19 8BG (off B3217 next to church) SS570083

☎ (01837) 810253 🌐 dukeofyorkdevon.co.uk

Adnams Broadside; Bays Topsail; 1 changing beer (sourced nationally) [G]

Dating from the 15th century, this traditional thatched village inn has old beams, inglenook fires and an unfailingly friendly atmosphere. Real ales are dispensed on gravity, while cider comes from nearby Sam's. The pub is renowned for its generous portions of locally sourced, home-cooked food. It is close to the Tarka Trail, River Torridge and Stafford Moor Fishery, and there are seven en-suite rooms for visitors. A popular beer festival is held every August bank holiday weekend.

Q ♿ ♣

Ide

Poachers Inn

55 High Street, EX2 9RW (3 miles from M5 jct 31, via A30)

☎ (01392) 273847 🌐 poachersinn.co.uk

Branscombe Vale Branoc; Exeter Tomahawk; 4 changing beers (sourced locally; often Exeter, Palmers, Sharp's) [H]

Typical busy village pub with a friendly atmosphere, serving a varied menu of home-made locally sourced produce, including excellent-value fish & chips to eat in or take away on Wednesday evening. The comfortably furnished bar has old sofas, chairs and a big log fire in winter – dogs are welcome. There is also a large beer garden overlooking the glorious Devon countryside. Usually five or six ales are on tap, with various guest beers from the West Country.

Q P (360)

Ilfracombe

Admiral Collingwood

Wilder Road, EX34 9AP

☎ (01271) 862373

Greene King Abbot; Ruddles Best Bitter; Sharp's Doom Bar; 3 changing beers (sourced regionally) [H]

Purpose-built JD Wetherspoon pub, on the site of the old Collingwood Hotel, which was voted the best new-build at the National Pub Design Awards in 2015. Situated on Ilfracombe's seafront, there are stunning views from the roof terrace, which is open from March to October. Since opening its doors the pub has earned a well-deserved reputation for its range of well-kept ales, many of which are brewed locally. ♿ P

Hip & Pistol

8 St James Place, EX34 9BH

☎ (01271) 549651

Exmoor Stag; GT Ales North Coast IPA, Thirst of Many; 2 changing beers (sourced nationally) [H]

This extensively modernised Georgian house has a nautical theme. The flooring shows the bay around Ilfracombe in pictorial form, with local landmarks and shipwrecks plotted, together with an impressive pub logo in an image of a compass. Outside, there is a pleasant beer garden at the front. There is always a good selection of real ales, ciders and food here. North Devon CAMRA Cider Pub of the Year 2020.

♿ (21)

Second Stage

Wilder Road, EX34 9AJ

☎ 07967 530936

Exmoor Stag; 1 changing beer (sourced locally) [H]

Opposite the theatre, this old Victorian building is located on the seafront and within easy reach of Ilfracombe's seaside attractions. The pub has a strong commitment to real ale, with the regular Exmoor Stag invariably accompanied by one from the GT Ales range. The bar area has a film-oriented theme, while the raised-level pool room, with its high-quality tables, make the pub something of a mecca for local enthusiasts. Opening hours vary in summer. ♣

Wellington Arms

66-67 High Street, EX34 9QE

☎ (01271) 864720

Fuller's London Pride; Greene King Abbot; Sharp's Doom Bar; 2 changing beers (sourced nationally) [H]

A friendly town local, originally two pubs and now a listed building. There are separate public and lounge bars and a games room, while the cosy lounge retains its original beams and large open fire. TVs and music sound systems enable different channels to be shown in each area, making the pub particularly popular with sports enthusiasts. Up to five competitively priced real ales are usually sold. Regular live music sessions, quiz nights and beer festivals are held. ❀Å♣P🚌🐾📶

Kilmington

New Inn 🄻 ✔

The Hill, EX13 7SF (in village, S of A35)
☎ (01297) 33376 🌐 newinnkilmington.com
Palmers Copper Ale, IPA, 200; 1 changing beer (sourced locally) 🄷
Thatched Devon longhouse that became a pub in the early 1800s. It was rebuilt after a major fire in 2004, retaining a welcoming atmosphere and gaining excellent toilets with wheelchair access. There is a large, safe garden, and a well-used skittle alley. A quiz night is held monthly on the first Sunday, with other events that maintain the pub's position as an important part of village life. Q❀◑♿♣●P🚌🐾📶

Kings Nympton

Grove Inn 🄻

EX37 9ST (in centre of village) SS683194
☎ (01769) 580406 🌐 thegroveinn.co.uk
Exmoor Ale 🄶; 3 changing beers (sourced regionally) 🄷
Thatched, Grade II listed 17th-century inn, with low beams, flagstone floors, an open fire in winter, and a pretty, enclosed terrace to enjoy in summer. A recent local CAMRA Pub and Cider Pub of the Year, it usually has four real ales available, together with a good range of ciders. The pub also has a reputation for its excellent home-cooked food, which can be enjoyed in the dining area adjacent to the bar. Q❀🛏◑♣●P🐾📶

Kingsteignton

Ten Tors Inn ✔

Exeter Road, TQ12 3NP
☎ (01626) 365434
St Austell Tribute, Proper Job; 1 changing beer (sourced locally; often Dartmoor) 🄷
This imposing building set back from the main road was previously the site of a petrol station and a transport café on the old A380. Entrance is through the large car park and up some steps to a porch (with separate wheelchair access). Inside, this friendly St Austell pub has one long bar with spacious separate areas throughout – there is a strong food emphasis, including a restaurant and a carvery, with discounts for the over-55s. There is also an outdoor drinking space (patio and garden areas), a children's play area and a large car park.
Q❀◑♿♣P🚌(2,7)🐾📶

Lewdown

Blue Lion Inn 🄻

EX20 4DL
☎ (01566) 783238
Dartmoor Jail Ale; Otter Amber; Sharp's Doom Bar; 1 changing beer (sourced regionally) 🄷
Roadside inn owned and run by the family, set on the now-bypassed old A30 between Okehampton and Launceston. Originally a 17th-century farmhouse on the Lewtrenchard Estate, the property was extended in the early 1900s. It is home to numerous local groups and several pub teams. Three regular ales and one changing guest is served, often from South West breweries.

Although predominantly wet-sales oriented, good-value food is also served Tuesday-Saturday in the evenings. There are two well-appointed rooms for accommodation. No visiting dogs allowed. ❀🛏◑♿♣●P🚌📶

Littlehempston

Tally Ho 🄻

TQ9 6LY SX813627
☎ (01803) 862316 🌐 tallyhoinn.co.uk
Dartmoor Legend; 1 changing beer (sourced locally; often Teignworthy) 🄷
A 14th-century stone-built inn, community-owned since 2014. The single-roomed bar with timber beams has a cosy feel, complemented by two wood-burners, and is furnished with pews and wooden settles. Guest beers are from local breweries and a real cider is sold. The pub hosts numerous events including an annual beer festival, occasional local live music and a regular Sunday night quiz. The enclosed beer garden is to the rear.
Q❀◑♿●P🚉🚌(7,177)🐾📶

Lydford

Castle Inn ✔

School Road, EX20 4BH
☎ (01822) 820242 🌐 castleinnlydford.co.uk
St Austell Tribute, Proper Job; 3 changing beers (sourced nationally) 🄷
With its low ceilings, slate flooring and exposed beams, this cosy 16th-century inn has bundles of atmosphere. Be sure to check out the rustic main bar area as well as the snug, restaurant, lounge and delightful garden. The four regular beers are supplemented by a varying guest ale in summer. Local attractions include the scenic Lydford Gorge, St Petroc's Church and the castle. The pub is on the National Cycle Network 27 Devon Coast-Coast, Dartmoor Way and West Devon Way cycle/walking routes. ❀🛏◑ÅP🚌(46)🐾📶

Lympstone

Redwing Bar & Dining

Church Road, EX8 5JT
☎ (01395) 222156 🌐 redwingbar-dining.co.uk
Branscombe Vale Branoc; St Austell Proper Job; Sharp's Doom Bar 🄷
Nestled in the beautiful village of Lympstone, on the Exe Estuary, this welcoming, tastefully decorated pub was once known as the Redwing Inn. While the accent is now more on food, there is plenty of seating for drinkers near the bar at small tables and comfortable settees near the entrance. The restaurant area extends into a conservatory, there is a small function room upstairs, and the garden is a suntrap. Excellent fresh food is served, with a set-price menu for weekday lunchtimes. Dogs are welcome in the bar area. Q❀◑♿⇌P🐾📶

Lynton

Cottage Inn 🄻

Lynbridge, EX35 6NR (on B3234 between Barbrook and Lynton)
☎ (01598) 753496 🌐 thecottageinnlynton.co.uk
Fat Belly Carver Doone, Ocean Gold, Guzzler; 2 changing beers (sourced nationally) 🄷
Characterful 17th-century riverside inn with accommodation and an authentic Thai restaurant. Fat Belly ales began here and, although now brewed nearby at Mullacott, they remain a key part of the business. At least three are always on tap, often accompanied by other specials from the brewery. A further selection of

craft beers is served through US-style dispensers. Please check first if visiting in mid-winter as opening hours and mealtimes can vary. ♘❀⇌◐◑⛺●P🚌🐾📶

Mary Tavy

Mary Tavy Inn 🄻

Lane Head, PL19 9PN

☎ (01822) 810326 🌐 marytavyinn.co.uk

Dartmoor IPA, Jail Ale; St Austell Tribute; 2 changing beers (sourced regionally; often Exeter, St Austell) 🄷

A traditional roadside inn where families, visitors and locals are welcome. The popular bar area accommodates pool, darts, TV, a large fire and up to four real ales and a cider. There is also a spacious restaurant and garden with views to Dartmoor. Entertainment includes music nights, charity events, a Sunday carvery and a bank holiday beer festival. Modern B&B accommodation is available in adjacent buildings, camping in the pub grounds, and motorhomes can stay by prior arrangement. Q♘❀⇌◐◑⛺♣●P🚌(46)🐾📶

Meavy

Royal Oak Inn 🄻

PL20 6PJ (on village green)

☎ (01822) 852944 🌐 royaloakinn.org.uk

Dartmoor Jail Ale; Otter Amber; St Austell Tribute; 1 changing beer (sourced regionally; often Dartmoor, Otter) 🄷

People come from miles around to enjoy the food and drink at this tucked-away, civilised but unpretentious 16th-century pub. In the summer, sit outside on one of the benches by the legendary tree and watch children play on the village green. In winter, relax in the public bar and enjoy the conversation, dogs and roaring fire. There is an interesting range of cider, with a festival in August and occasional live music. Local CAMRA Country Pub of the Year 2019. Q♘❀◐◑⛺♣●🚌(56)🐾📶

Musbury

Hind 🄻

The Street, EX13 8AU

☎ (01297) 553553 🌐 thehindmusbury.co.uk

3 changing beers 🄷

Free house on the crossroads of the A358, three miles south of Axminster. There is a public bar and a lounge/restaurant where good-value home-cooked food is served lunchtimes and evenings (no food Sun eve). There are two outside areas: a front courtyard with stunning views over the Axe Valley, and an enclosed rear beer garden with a lawn. Dogs are welcome. Q♘❀◐◑♣P🚌(885)🐾📶

Newton Abbot

Taphouse & Bottle Shop

Tuckers Maltings, Teign Road, TQ12 4AA (500yds from Newton Abbot railway station)

☎ (01626) 334734 🌐 themaltingstaphouse.co.uk

House beer (by Teignworthy); 2 changing beers (sourced nationally; often New Lion) 🄷

A micropub based in the historic but recently closed Tuckers Maltings, also home to the Teignworthy Brewery. The interior reflects the previous use as a maltings, with low ceilings. The walls are covered with historic images of the maltings, the adjacent railway, the local racecourse and the town. A vast range of bottled and canned beers is available, with several craft keg lines. No jukebox, TV or fruit machines here; beer and conversation prevail. Q❀♿⇌●P🚌(12)🐾📶

Teign Cellars 🄻

67 East Street, TQ12 2JR

☎ (01626) 332991 🌐 teigncellars.com

4 changing beers (sourced nationally) 🄷/🄶

This venue has been reincarnated from its previous existence as the Greene Man and, further back, as an annexe of the 1836 workhouse opposite. There are three or four beers on handpumps, with others dispensed on KeyKegs plus a selection of boxed ciders. The single bar room features both hard stools and soft furnishings, and has a periodic beer table. There is a shop to the rear selling 170 bottled beers and cans. Food is excellent and popular, which can make the pub crowded at times. Q♘❀◐◑⇌●P🚌🐾📶

Newton Poppleford

Cannon Inn

High Street, EX10 0DW

☎ (01395) 568266 🌐 pubindevon.com

Exmoor Gold; 1 changing beer (sourced nationally) 🄶

Cheery, welcoming, two-bar venue with tables for dining in the lounge bar and restaurant area. Real ales are served by gravity from stillage behind the bar. This is a friendly locals' haunt with busy passing trade. Good-value home-cooked food, served lunchtimes and evenings, covers most traditional favourites and, locals say, is of a tasty standard. Well-behaved dogs are allowed. There are two large gardens and a skittle alley. The only pub in the village, and a community hub. Q♘❀⇌◐◑♿⛺♣●P🚌(52,157)🐾📶

Newton St Cyres

Beer Engine 🄻

EX5 5AX (beside railway station ½ mile N of A377)

☎ (01392) 851282 🌐 thebeerengine.co.uk

Beer Engine Rail Ale, Piston Bitter; 3 changing beers 🄷

A Victorian hostelry, built in 1850, on the Exeter to Barnstaple Tarka Line. Popular with drinkers and diners alike, it is well frequented by locals, visitors and its own cricket team. Home-cooked food made with locally sourced produce is served lunchtimes and evenings, including the pub's own bread, made with beer yeast. The pub brews its own ales, including four regulars and a seasonal ale which, like the village pictures and old pub signs, reflect a railway theme. Q♘❀◐◑♿⇌P🐾

North Tawton

Railway Inn 🄻

Whiddon Down Road, EX20 2BE (1 mile S of town, just off A3124) SS666000

☎ (01837) 82789 🌐 therailwaynorthtawton.co.uk

Teignworthy Reel Ale; 1 changing beer (sourced regionally) 🄷

Good value and a warm welcome always await you at this friendly Devon local. Adjacent to the former North Tawton railway station, closed in 1971, there are numerous old railway photos on the walls. Reel Ale from Teignworthy is normally joined by a guest ale from one of the other West Country breweries, together with a real cider in summer. The dining room is popular in the evening (no food Thu), with light meals served at lunchtime. Guide dogs only. Q♘❀◐◑♣●P🚌📶

Okehampton

Plume of Feathers Hotel 🄻

38 Fore Street, EX20 1HB

☎ (01837) 53332 🌐 caskhouse.co.uk
Taw Valley Kennard's Steam; 2 changing beers (sourced locally) Ⓖ
Spacious town-centre inn, dating back to the 17th-century, which reopened in 2018 following a 10-year closure. It has since become a particularly favoured haunt of local real ale and live music enthusiasts. The regular Kennard's Steam, brewed specially for the pub by local Taw Valley Brewery, is generally accompanied by guest ales from other nearby breweries and locally made real ciders. Food purchased from surrounding outlets can be consumed on the premises. ❀♿♣●P🚌🐾📶

Ottery St Mary

London Inn

4 Gold Street, EX11 1DG
☎ (01404) 812045
6 changing beers (sourced nationally) Ⓗ
A 17th-century coaching inn, close to the historic 14th-century parish church, and a friendly locals' pub. There are two separate bars offering six changing real ales from breweries near and far, with a good range of styles and strengths all at the same price. Good-value home-cooked food, including a roast on Sunday, is served, and four B&B rooms are available. There is a pool room and function room, and live music is regularly promoted. Q❀◐♿♣🚌🐾📶

Volunteer Inn

Broad Street, EX11 1BZ
☎ (01404) 814060 🌐 volunteerinnottery.co.uk
Otter Bitter; 3 changing beers (sourced regionally) Ⓖ
The building has been part of Ottery St Mary's history since 1810, when it opened as a dwelling, hostelry and recruitment centre for the Napoleonic War. In the centre of the town, it is popular. The front bar remains traditional while the rear bar is more modern. All real ales, mainly from local breweries, are delivered by gravity. Food is served seven days a week, with a roast on Sunday, in the refurbished and extended restaurant. ❀◐♿♣●🚌(4) 🐾📶

Paignton

Henry's Bar Ⓛ ✔

53 Torbay Road, TQ4 6AJ
☎ (01803) 551190 🌐 henrysbarpaignton.co.uk
Sharp's Doom Bar; house beer (by Sharp's); 2 changing beers (sourced nationally; often Dartmoor) Ⓗ
A shining example of a traditional town-centre pub with a focus on offering local and national real ales and ciders. It has close ties with the locals and local events, and is a real hub of the community. The impressive long bar has four handpumps with three regular beers plus one guest; a fifth handpump is dedicated to cider and there are various bottles and polyboxes. Home-cooked food is served daily, with a popular roast on Sunday. Families are welcome. ❀◐⇌●P🚌🐾📶

Paignton Conservative & Unionist Club

34 Palace Avenue, TQ3 3HB
☎ (01803) 551065
Dartmoor Jail Ale; 3 changing beers (often Exmoor, Salcombe, Skinner's) Ⓗ
Resident in an old building which has been a private members' club since 1885, CAMRA members are now welcome here. The Tardis-like entrance brings you into the covered ale bar and leads through to the spacious Palace lounge which hosts cabaret nights, quiz and bingo sessions. Upstairs is a snooker room with two tables and a sports room that is used for the bridge club and euchre games as well as serving as a restaurant.
Q◐⇌♣P🚌📶

Torbay Inn ✔

34 Fisher Street, TQ4 5ER (300yds from local landmark the big tree bus stop)
☎ (01803) 392729
St Austell Tribute; Sharp's Sea Fury; Twickenham Naked Ladies; Wye Valley HPA; 1 changing beer (often St Austell) Ⓗ
Traditional pub with separate lounge and public bars. It dates back to the early 1600s when the sea was on its doorstep and it was opposite a fish market. Time is called via a ship's bell recovered by a local diver from an old wreck. It is documented that Roundhead General Sir Thomas Fairfax stayed here prior to a Civil War battle in Exeter. A warm welcome awaits all visitors.
Q❀♿⇌♣P🚌(12,120) 🐾📶

Parkham

Bell Inn Ⓛ ✔

Rectory Lane, EX39 5PL (½ mile S of A39 at Horns Cross, on opp corner to village primary school) SS387212
☎ (01237) 451201 🌐 thebellinnparkham.co.uk
3 changing beers (sourced regionally) Ⓗ
Sympathetically restored after a serious fire in 2017, this 13th-century thatched inn, with its cob walls, oak beams and wood-burner fires, has retained all of its old-world charm. Three or four changing real ales are on the bar, usually at least one of these from a local brewery. Home-cooked food is served lunchtimes and evenings Wednesday to Saturday, either in the bar or the adjacent raised restaurant area, while the Sunday roast is also popular. Q❀◐♣●P🚌(372)🐾📶

Peter Tavy

Peter Tavy Inn

Lane Head, PL19 9NN
☎ (01822) 810348 🌐 petertavyinn.com
Dartmoor Jail Ale; 4 changing beers (sourced regionally; often Black Tor, Roam, Salcombe) Ⓗ
In a quiet village on the edge of Dartmoor, the inn has a small central bar serving Dartmoor Jail Ale supplemented by a varying range of up to four local guest beers. Traditionally attired throughout, it also has two larger rooms. A patio and hidden garden are added attractions. The pub is renowned for its food but drinkers are made welcome. On the No.27 cycle route and near a caravan and camping site. Q❀◐⛺♣P🚌(46,95)🐾📶

Plymouth

Dolphin Hotel Ⓛ ✔

14 The Barbican, PL1 2LS
☎ (01752) 660876
Dartmoor Jail Ale; Draught Bass; Roam Tavy IPA; St Austell Tribute; Sharp's Doom Bar; Skinner's Betty Stogs; 2 changing beers (sourced regionally; often Roam, St Austell, Sharp's) Ⓖ
A Plymouth institution, this unpretentious hostelry is steeped in history. Up to eight ales are all dispensed by gravity from the cask. Full of character, this charming pub has tiled floors, well-used wooden benches and a traditional open fire, all creating the perfect ambience. The walls are adorned with paintings by local artist, the late Beryl Cook, who painted many of the characters she encountered in the Dolphin. Local CAMRA City Pub of the Year runner-up 2019. ●🚌(25)🐾

Fawn Private Members Club ⬭

39 Prospect Street, Greenbank, PL4 8NY
☎ (01752) 226385
Bays Topsail; 4 changing beers (sourced regionally; often St Austell, Sharp's, Teignworthy) ⊞
This mid 19th-century establishment was originally the Fawn Inn/Hotel, prior to converting to a club. CAMRA members are welcome with a membership card; regular visitors will be required to join. Four guest ales from the local area are generally served, as well as a rotating range of local cider from Countryman. The club is popular for rugby and other televised sports, and supports multiple dart and euchre teams. Local CAMRA branch Club of the Year 2019. ≈♣👜🚆🐾

Ferry House Inn ⬭ ✔

888 Wolseley Road, Saltash Passage, PL5 1LA
☎ (01752) 361063 ⊕ ferryhouseinn.com
Dartmoor Jail Ale; Sharp's Doom Bar, Atlantic ⊞
A warm welcome awaits you and your dog from the landlord and locals at this picturesque riverside pub on the River Tamar. Three regular West Country ales are served, as well as good home-cooked food. A decking area on the edge of the river gives spectacular views of both the road bridge and Brunel's iconic 1859 railway bridge. Photos, some dating back to the turn of the 20th century, adorn the walls. Quiz night is Sunday. ➳🕸🖴🄌🕭🛒🚆(13) 🐾🛜

Fisherman's Arms ⬭

31 Lambhay Street, Barbican, PL1 2NN
☎ (01752) 268243 ⊕ fishermansarms.co.uk
Dartmoor Jail Ale; house beer (by Summerskills); 1 changing beer (often Otter) ⊞
The family owners have returned this former St Austell inn to a traditional free house. The interior is welcoming, with several distinctly decorated areas. The dartboard is back and there is a variety of games and puzzles on offer. Ale and cider festivals are held twice a year. Traditional pub grub at affordable prices is supplemented by specials, with the famous roast available on Sunday. Close to the Royal Citadel and the Barbican. ➳🄌♣🕭🚆(25) 🐾🛜

Fortescue Hotel ⬭ ✔

37 Mutley Plain, PL4 6JQ
☎ (01752) 660673
Bays Devon Dumpling; Dartmoor Legend; Roam Tavy IPA; St Austell Proper Job; Skinner's Betty Stogs; Summerskills Devon Dew; 4 changing beers (sourced nationally; often Cornish Crown, Exeter, South Hams) ⊞
This multi award-winning and lively local is frequented by a broad section of the community, and conversation flourishes. Nine real ales are usually on tap, and up to eight real ciders. A perfect Sunday can be spent here – a good-value home-cooked roast washed down with a pint of Spingo Special, followed by a brain-teasing quiz in the Cellar Bar in the evening. The patio beer garden draws crowds in the summer and is heated in winter. ➳🕸🄌≈♣🕭🚆🐾🛜

Gog & Magog ⬭ ✔

58 Southside Street, Barbican, PL1 2LA
☎ (01752) 264160
Dartmoor Jail Ale; Greene King Abbot; Ruddles Best Bitter; Sharp's Doom Bar; changing beers (sourced nationally; often Dartmoor, Roam, Summerskills) ⊞
Situated in the popular tourist area of the Barbican, this Wetherspoon pub can get busy. It is set back from Southside Street, with an area for smokers and alfresco drinkers and diners. Inside, there is one long bar naturally lit by the high glassed ceiling. One corner of the

bar displays a map with local breweries, real ale and CAMRA information. The usual selection of JDW ales is supplemented by beers from local and national breweries. ➳🕸🄌🄵🕭🚆(25)🛜

Lord High Admiral

33 Stonehouse Street, Stonehouse, PL1 3PE
☎ (01752) 256881
3 changing beers (sourced regionally; often Harbour, Salcombe, Skinner's) ⊞
Facing the popular Rock Salt restaurant, this hidden gem with a nice outdoor area is worth seeking out. The interior, with its exposed stone walls, dried hops adorning the bar area and vintage wooden furniture, has an almost country feel. Unobtrusive laid-back music adds to the chilled vibe, which is unusual for this city. Three interesting regional beers are complemented by a cider from Sandford Orchards, and the craft beers will appeal to many drinkers. Quiz night is popular. ➳🕸🄌♣🚆

Mannamead ⬭ ✔

61 Mutley Plain, PL4 6JH
☎ (01752) 825610
Dartmoor Jail Ale; Greene King Abbot; Ruddles Best Bitter; Sharp's Doom Bar; changing beers (sourced nationally; often Dartmoor, Roam, Summerskills) ⊞
Wetherspoon establishment converted from a former NatWest bank. A wide range of ales from near and far can be found, with at least two local brews usually on the pumps. There is also a good range of real cider and perry. Beer and cider festivals take place several times a year. Brewery showcase events are also held, featuring a large number of local beers, as well as a Devon ale festival. ➳🕸🄌🄵≈🚆🛜

Minerva Inn ⬭

31 Looe Street, Barbican, PL4 0EA
☎ (01752) 223047 ⊕ minervainn.co.uk
St Austell Trelawny, Tribute; 2 changing beers (sourced locally; often Dartmoor, Roam, Summerskills) ⊞
Plymouth's oldest hostelry, dating from around 1540, and within easy walking distance of the city centre and the historic Barbican. It has a long and narrow bar, leading through to a cosy seating area at the rear. Two guest beers are supplemented during spring and autumn beer festivals, where beer could, and does, come from all over the country. Live music takes place Thursday to Sunday evenings and Sunday lunchtime. The pub benefits from a varied clientele. ➳🕸♣🕭🚆🐾🛜

Prince Maurice ⬭ ✔

3 Church Hill, Eggbuckland, PL6 5RJ
☎ (01752) 771515
Dartmoor Jail Ale; St Austell Tribute, Proper Job, Hicks; Sharp's Doom Bar; South Hams Sherman; 2 changing beers (sourced locally; often Hunters, Roam, Summerskills) ⊞
There is very much a village feel to this four-times local CAMRA Pub of the Year, which sits between the church and village green. The six regular ales are supplemented by a changing guest ale. It is named after the Royalist general, the King's nephew, who had his headquarters nearby during the siege of Plymouth in the Civil War. Two log fires keep you warm in winter, adding to the ambience. No food at weekends. ➳🕸🄌♣🕭P🚆(28A)🐾

Pub on the Hoe ⬭ ✔

159 Citadel Road, The Hoe, PL1 2HU
☎ (01752) 202405
House beer (by Hunters); 5 changing beers (sourced locally; often Bays, Roam) ⊞

A busy street-corner pub serving a mixed clientele and near Plymouth Hoe, where Sir Francis Drake famously played bowls. Up to four varying real ales supplement the house beer, Drunken Hoe, and two local real ciders. Good home-cooked food is served all day. The wood-panelled raised and lower deck seating areas add to the nautical theme. Just a short walk from the historic Barbican and well worth a visit.
♞✿🛏◑♣🍎🚌(25)🐾📶

Vessel Beer Shop

184 Exeter Street, St Jude's, PL4 0NQ
☎ 07796 667449 🌐 vesselbeer.co.uk
Changing beers (sourced nationally)
An independent bar and beer shop, located a few minutes' walk from Plymouth city centre and opposite St Jude's retail park. It stocks over 180 different beers from some of the best breweries in Britain and around the world. Bottle and can conditioned beers are sold and there is craft beer on draught. Light snacks may also be available. Regular events include Meet the Brewer or Food Producers, and beer tastings and beer styles. See social media for up-to-date activities. 🚌

Plympton

Union Inn [L]

17 Underwood Road, Underwood, PL7 1SY
☎ (01752) 336756 🌐 unioninnplympton.com
4 changing beers (sourced regionally; often Exeter, Summerskills, Tintagel) [H]
The landlord of this family-run community pub is a beer hunter, sourcing changing brews to charm his regulars' palates and create a year-round beer festival. The four ales on offer are regional, but could be from almost anywhere. The cider selection is also sourced from far and wide but Old Rosie is a regular. A warm welcome is assured at this traditional, cosy, early 19th-century hostelry. A former local CAMRA branch Cider Pub of the Year runner-up. Q♞✿♣🍎P🚌🐾📶

Postbridge

Warren House Inn [L]

Postbridge, PL20 6TA (on B3212 between Postbridge and Bennett's Cross)
☎ (01822) 880208 🌐 warrenhouseinn.co.uk
Otter Ale; 3 changing beers (sourced regionally; often Black Tor, Exeter, Summerskills) [H]
Isolated and exposed at 1,425 feet above sea level, this is one of England's highest pubs. Up to three varying guest beers, mainly from the West Country, are stocked, with Countryman cider also featuring regularly. The characterful main bar boasts two log fires – one never goes out! Excellent-value home-made food includes the famous rabbit pie, local lamb and delicious puddings with clotted cream. There is a large family room, and tables outside give breathtaking views over the moors. Open all day in summer. Q♞✿◑⛺🍎P🐾

Princetown

Plume of Feathers Inn [L] ✔

Plymouth Hill, PL20 6QQ
☎ (01822) 890240 🌐 theplumeoffeathersdartmoor.co.uk
Dartmoor Jail Ale; St Austell Tribute; Sharp's Doom Bar; 3 changing beers (sourced regionally; often Dartmoor, St Austell) [H]
Whatever the season, the Plume is a great destination. Built in 1785, it retains many original features and has a traditional country feel. There are four separate areas – the cosy main bar, the booths, the rear bar and the back room – so you will generally find a seat. In addition there is a function room and plenty of seating in the garden. The pub also offers a children's play area, extensive parking and a wide variety of accommodation including camping. Q♞✿🛏◑♿⛺♣🍎P🚌(98)🐾

Salcombe

Ferry Inn ✔

Fore Street, TQ8 8JE
☎ (01548) 844000 🌐 theferryinnsalcombe.com
Palmers Copper Ale, IPA, Dorset Gold [H]
This Grade II listed building, dating from 1739, is a Palmers Brewery house. The waterside location provides superb views over the estuary, and the patio, close to the water, can be busy during fine weather. A choice of real ales and wholesome pub food at reasonable prices adds to the attraction. Roasts are served on Sunday afternoon, and wine and cheese on Sunday evening.
♞✿◑♣P🚌(606)🐾📶↺

Fortescue Inn ✔

Union Street, TQ8 8BZ
☎ (01548) 842868 🌐 thefortsalcombe.co.uk
Otter Bitter; 2 changing beers (often Salcombe, Sharp's) [H]
Grade II listed 18th-century pub built on reclaimed land; up until 1951 it was called the Union Inn. It is nestled away from prevailing winds on the high street, which is busy with pedestrians. Sometimes the sea advances up Union Street on a high tide. There are three log fires, the menu is varied, and you can eat either in the bar area or in the restaurant. A wide choice of beer is offered from Salcombe Brewery. ♞✿🛏◑⛺♣P🚌(606,164)🐾📶

Seaton

All Hat But No Cattle

34 Queen Street, EX12 2RB
☎ 07912 242385
4 changing beers (sourced locally) [G]
This micropub, known as The Hat, is in an old butcher's shop – the landlord always wears a hat, in a nod to the pub's unusual name. There are four real ales and four real ciders served straight from the casks, which are stored in the old cold room. There is no fizzy beer or lager and no music. The emphasis is on conversation, but not on mobile phones. Snacks such as crisps and biltong are available. Q♞♣🍎🚌🐾

Shaldon

London Inn [L]

The Green, TQ14 0DN
☎ (01626) 872453 🌐 londoninnshaldon.co.uk
Otter Bitter; St Austell Proper Job; 1 changing beer (sourced locally) [H]
Welcoming and attractive white-fronted building in the heart of the village dating from 1790 and located between the estuary beach and the bowling green. Outside at the front is a drinking area while inside is a small locals' public bar, and a larger area more likely to be dominated by diners, while to the rear are photographs depicting Shaldon in a bygone era. Quiz night is Tuesday, with live music on the last Sunday of the month. Q♞✿◑♿🚌(22)🐾📶

Shaldon Conservative Club [L]

Dagmar Street, TQ14 0DU
☎ (01626) 873667
St Austell Tribute; Teignworthy Reel Ale; 1 changing beer (sourced nationally) [H]

Situated in the centre of this picturesque village, tucked away in the side streets, this modern one-roomed club caters for all and welcomes card-carrying CAMRA members. There is a large snooker table, a rear area where live bands perform at the weekend, TV screens, darts, bingo and cards. There is also a weekly meat draw. Three handpumps serve real ale and one cider (Westons Vintage) at reasonable prices, and a mini beer festival is held in August. At the hub of the community it hosts charity events and private parties. ♿♣⬤🚌(22)📶

Shaugh Prior

White Thorn Inn 🄻

PL7 5HA (on Cornwood to Bickleigh road, S of Yelverton)
☎ (01752) 839245
Dartmoor Jail Ale; Fuller's London Pride; St Austell Tribute; 1 changing beer (sourced regionally; often Bays, Dartmoor, St Austell) 🄷
Very much a community village pub, it was completely refurbished by local musician Michael Mathieson, better known as Mad Dog McRea. The three regular beers are supplemented by one other West Country beer. The open-plan bar has a central fireplace, and hosts regular entertainment including folk music on Wednesday, live music on Saturday evening, and a quiz on the last Thursday evening of the month. Situated a mile from the Plym Valley Walking and Cycle Path.
❀◑♣P🚌(59)🐾📶

Sidmouth

Marine

The Esplanade, EX10 8BB
☎ (01395) 513145 🌐 themarinesidmouth.com
Exeter Lighterman; 2 changing beers (sourced regionally) 🄷
A family-run pub with a friendly atmosphere attracting a clientele of all ages. Situated on the seafront, the small outdoor drinking area has tables and chairs for customers to sit and look out to sea while enjoying a pint of one of the three real ales usually on offer, often from local breweries. The food is mainly pizza, hand-made on the premises. Well-behaved dogs are welcome.
❀◑🚌🐾📶

Sidmouth Conservative Club 🄻

Radway Place, EX10 8TL
☎ (01395) 514311 🌐 sidmouthconservativeclub.co.uk
3 changing beers 🄷
Close to the town centre, this warm and friendly club was formed in 1906. It is open to its members and their guests, but card-carrying CAMRA members are welcome at all times. Regular visitors will be asked to join. Otter Brewery and Greene King beers are predominant, but there is also a good variety of ales, rotated regularly. The club has a beer festival during Sidmouth Folk Festival which is open to everyone, all day, every day.
Q◑♣P🚌🐾

Silverton

Lamb Inn 🄻

Fore Street, EX5 4HZ
☎ (01392) 860272 🌐 thelambinnsilverton.co.uk
Otter Ale; 2 changing beers (sourced locally) 🄶
Popular family-run pub in the centre of Silverton, with stone floors, stripped timber, old pine furniture and a large open real fire. Three ales are served by gravity from a temperature-controlled stillage behind the bar at competitive prices. There is a well-used function room and skittle alley, regular quiz nights and occasional live music. Good-value home-cooked food is available lunchtimes and evenings, plus a popular roast on Sunday.
Q❀◑♿♣⬤🚌(55B)🐾📶

South Zeal

King's Arms 🄻

EX20 2JP (centre of village) SX649936
☎ (01837) 840300 🌐 thekingsarmssouthzeal.com
Dartmoor IPA, Legend; 1 changing beer (sourced regionally) 🄷
Thatched 14th-century village local at the hub of the community, which also attracts many visitors exploring the area. Well-behaved dogs are made particularly welcome here. The Dartmoor beers are accompanied by a changing guest ale and locally made cider. Good food is served lunchtimes and evenings every day. Live music sessions are held regularly throughout the year and the pub plays a central role during the Dartmoor Folk Festival in August. Q❀◑♿Å♣⬤P🚌🐾📶

Spreyton

Tom Cobley Tavern 🄻

EX17 5AL (off A3124 in village) SX6986096761
☎ (01647) 231314 🌐 tomcobleytavern.co.uk
10 changing beers (sourced regionally) 🄷/🄶
Named after the local folklore figure, this traditional 16th-century village pub provides a warm welcome to visitors and locals alike. With 10 West Country ales, some served straight from the cask, and 12 ciders and perries usually on offer, it's no wonder the walls are decorated with CAMRA award certificates won over the years. Excellent meals and snacks can be ordered lunchtimes and evenings. Quizzes, darts and other events are supported and there are six en-suite guest rooms.
Q❀🛏◑♣⬤P🐾📶

Sticklepath

Taw River Inn 🄻

Sticklepath, EX20 2NW (on old A30 main road through village) SX642941
☎ (01837) 840377 🌐 tawriver.co.uk
Dartmoor Jail Ale; St Austell Tribute; Sharp's Doom Bar; 1 changing beer (sourced regionally) 🄷
Popular thatched hostelry set in an attractive village on the edge of Dartmoor, close to picturesque walks and numerous places of historic interest. The real ales, together with a real cider made in the village, are all competitively priced, while good-value food is served in both the bar area and dining room. There is a TV in the large single bar, where numerous sports and pub games are played by friendly locals. ❀◑♿♣⬤P🚌🐾📶

Stoke Fleming

Green Dragon ✔

Church Road, TQ6 0PX
☎ (01803) 770238 🌐 thegreendragon-pub.business.site
St Austell Tribute; Salcombe Seahorse; house beer (by Otter); 1 changing beer (sourced regionally) 🄷
Tucked away opposite the village church, on the South West Coast Path, there has been a building on the site since the 12th century. The pub has a cosy bar room – a focus for the village – featuring a large log-burning open fire. The bar, adjacent restaurant and kitchen were refurbished in 2018. Background music is subdued, and there are no gaming machines or TV screens, except for Six Nations rugby. Local legend suggests there is a tunnel underneath the floor to the nearby beach and, some say, a ghost. ❀◑ÅP🚌(3)🐾📶

Teignmouth

Blue Anchor Inn L

Teign Street, TQ14 8EG
☎ (01626) 772741
6 changing beers (sourced regionally; often Exeter, Summerskills, Teignworthy) H
In a conservation area and close to the docks, this is a free house not to be missed. It has a single bar with eight handpumps, some of which are devoted to cider, and the landlord is keen to provide dark beer. The outdoor drinking areas burst with floral colour in summer, and at Christmas feature an impressive display of decorations – but mind the reindeer! Outside is to be found a rare VR letterbox. ❀♿⇌♣●🚌(2,22)🐾

Brass Monkey L ✔

Hollands Road, TQ14 8SR
☎ 07708 910144
St Austell Tribute H
A simple and straightforward one-bar community pub with TV screens and a pool table which is handily situated between the town bus stops and the railway station, and therefore an ideal waiting room for your transport home. It can be a quiet retreat from the nearby town centre for most of the week, in marked contrast to the more boisterous and ever-popular weekend karaokes. Quiz night is Tuesday. Q♿⇌♣🚌(2,22)🐾

Tiverton

White Ball Inn ✔

8 Bridge Street, EX16 5LY
☎ (01884) 251525
Bays Devon Dumpling; Greene King Abbot; Ruddles Best Bitter; Sharp's Doom Bar; 6 changing beers (sourced regionally) H
A former coaching inn, just off the town centre and next to the Exe Bridge. Built around 1823, it became a Wetherspoon in 1998 and was restyled in 2019 to include upstairs toilets, a downstairs extension and sliding and fold-out doors to the large rear seating area and terrace. It features a glass-covered walk-over well. Up to 10 real ales are on tap. ♉❀◐◑♿●🚌📶

Topsham

Bridge Inn ★ L

Bridge Hill, EX3 0QQ
☎ (01392) 873862 🌐 cheffers.co.uk
Branscombe Vale Branoc; changing beers (sourced regionally) G
Historic, cosy, 16th-century inn, beautifully positioned overlooking the River Clyst. It has been run by six generations of the same family since 1897, and was visited by the Queen in 1998. This pub is a delight for real ale fans, with a continually varying range of beers dispensed by gravity direct from the cellar. There are two rooms in the unspoilt interior, plus the malthouse, which is used at busy times and for functions. Traditional lunches such as ploughman's and sandwiches are served. Q❀◐⇌●P🚌(57,T)🐾

Exeter Inn L

68 High Street, EX3 0DY
☎ (01392) 873131

> Beer makes you feel the way you ought to feel without beer.
> **Henry Lawson**

Teignworthy Beachcomber; 3 changing beers (sourced regionally) H
A pub since at least 1860, some of this partially thatched building dates from the 17th century when it was a coaching inn and blacksmith's. It is a friendly local serving four ales and two ciders plus, occasionally, snacks such as rolls. Three TVs show various sports, while the front area is devoted to pool and darts. There is a small, sheltered garden and smoking area at the side.
♉❀♿⇌♣●🚌🐾📶

Torquay

Dolphin

36 Fore Street, St Marychurch, TQ1 4LY
☎ (01803) 323725 🌐 dolphininntorquay.co.uk
Dartmoor Best, Jail Ale; St Austell Tribute; 2 changing beers (sourced regionally; often Otter, Teignworthy) H
This pub is in the heart of St Marychurch precinct and is easily accessible via bus. Dating from 1740, it has recently been refurbished to provide a modern, airy interior, with ample seating, and is under new management. Everyone is welcome here. Three real ales are usually on handpump plus one real cider. Food is served lunch and evening. Live music often features on a Friday evening. There is a garden at the rear.
♉❀◐◑♿●P🚌(22,35C)🐾📶

Totnes

Albert Inn L

32 Bridgetown, TQ9 5AD (from Totnes centre cross river, 100yds on left)
☎ (01803) 863214 🌐 albertinntotnes.com
Bridgetown Albert Ale, Bitter, Cheeky Blonde, Shark Island Stout, West Coast IPA; 2 changing beers (sourced locally) H
A shining example of a traditional pub, this is the only hostelry across the river in the Bridgetown area of Totnes. Celebrating Albert Einstein, this community venue hosts culinary nights, quizzes, regular cider and beer festivals, plus live music and pub teams. Based in a former chapel of ease, it is the brewery tap for the Bridgetown Brewery and is noted for its hideaway beer garden, which affords views of the River Dart.
Q♉❀◐◑♿⛺♣●P🚌🐾📶

Totnes Brewing Company

59A High Street, TQ9 5PB (at top of High Street by Market Square) 🌐 thetotnesbrewingco.co.uk
8 changing beers (sourced nationally; often Totnes) H/P
Modern craft brewpub serving a large and diverse choice of beer. The constantly changing range usually includes at least one ale brewed in-house, together with up to seven guests on handpump. A good range of KeyKeg ales is also available. Takeaway food may be brought in. There is a Saxon castle at the rear of the premises.
Q♉❀♿⛺⇌●🚌🐾📶

Waterman's Arms

Victoria Street, TQ9 5EF
☎ (01803) 863038 🌐 watermansarmspub.co.uk
Dartmoor Jail Ale H**; 2 changing beers (sourced locally; often Hunters)** H/G
Cosy, friendly, single-bar gem of a pub in the back streets of town near the main bus stop. One of its three beers is on gravity from a stillage behind the bar, the other two are on handpump. Comfortably furnished with perimeter banquette seating, wooden tables and chairs, together with stools at the bar, it has a dartboard, gaming/quiz

machines and a jukebox. Outside, to the right, is a small paved patio area with three picnic tables.
Q🍽❀♿⛺⇌♣P🚌🐾📶

Turnchapel

Boringdon Arms 🄻 ✔

13 Boringdon Terrace, PL9 9TQ
☎ (01752) 402053 🌐 boringdon-arms.net
Dartmoor Jail Ale; Fuller's London Pride; Sharp's Atlantic, Sea Fury 🄷
The Bori is a traditional and dog-friendly former CAMRA Regional Pub of the Year, with six letting rooms. It sits in a waterside village on the South West Coastal Footpath, and benefits from a regular bus service from Plymouth or a water taxi service from the Barbican. Four regular ales are available, with more during the four beer festivals held during the year. Good-value, home-cooked food is served daily. There are two secluded gardens to the rear.
Q🍽❀🛏◐◑♣●🚌(2,2A) 🐾📶

Walkhampton

Walkhampton Inn 🄻

PL20 6JY
☎ (01822) 258697 🌐 walkhamptoninn.co.uk
3 changing beers (sourced regionally; often Bays, Dartmoor, Sharp's) 🄷
Set in the centre of the village, this welcoming 17th-century local displays traditional features throughout the bar, dining areas and snug. Up to four different real ales are sold and six real ciders. There are quiz nights, live music and open mic nights throughout the year, and annual real ale and cider festivals. The pleasant courtyard beer garden hosts summer events. This is a good old-fashioned country pub. Q🍽◐◑⛺♣●P🚌(55,56)🐾📶

Weare Giffard

Cyder Presse 🄻

EX39 4QR
☎ (01237) 425517 🌐 cyderpresse.co.uk
Timothy Taylor Landlord; 3 changing beers (sourced regionally) 🄷
Family-run local in a picturesque village on the banks of the River Torridge, with cosy bar and restaurant areas, a beer garden and two en-suite twin rooms. Local CAMRA Cider Pub of the Year in 2018 and 2019, it usually features more than nine real ciders, alongside up to four real ales. Home-cooked food made from local produce is served Wednesday to Saturday and Sunday lunchtime. On Tuesday there is a regular live folk music night.
Q🍽❀🛏◐◑♿⛺♣●P🚌(7A) 🐾📶

Welcombe

Old Smithy Inn 🄻

EX39 6HG (turn off A39 Bideford to Kilkhampton road at Welcombe Cross and follow signs to Welcombe and then to pub)
☎ (01288) 331305 🌐 theoldsmithyinn.co.uk
3 changing beers (sourced regionally) 🄷
A 13th-century thatched inn, nestled at the top of the Welcombe Valley and just a mile from the sea, near the Cornish border. Quality ales from nearby Forge and other local breweries, good ciders and a range of excellent, locally sourced food can all be enjoyed here in a most welcoming atmosphere. Outside there is a pleasant garden and a separate function room. An outstanding beer and music festival is held in July.
🍽❀🛏◐◑⛺♣●P🐾📶

Wembury

Odd Wheel 🄻

Knighton Road, PL9 0JD
☎ (01752) 863052 🌐 theoddwheel.co.uk
Dartmoor Jail Ale; Draught Bass; St Austell Tribute; 3 changing beers (sourced regionally) 🄷
At the northern end of a picturesque village, this friendly country pub was tastefully refurbished several years ago. The three regular beers are supplemented by up to three guest beers, mainly from Devon and Cornwall. Regular beer festivals are held. Food is served daily, with ingredients from locally sourced suppliers. Outside, there is a terraced garden and play area for children. Many walking routes are close by, including the South West Coast Path. 🍽❀◐◑♿♣●P🚌(48)🐾📶

Wembworthy

Lymington Arms

Lama Cross, EX18 7SA (on minor road, midway between Eggesford and Winkleigh)
☎ (01837) 83572 🌐 lymingtonarms.co.uk
Teignworthy Reel Ale; 2 changing beers (sourced regionally) 🄷
Friendly, welcoming pub set in mid-Devon countryside, with a large car park, attractive outdoor seating, a sunny bar/dining area and a characterful restaurant. Although seemingly remote, Eggesford station, where all Tarka Line trains stop, lies only two fairly easily walked or cycled miles away. The regular Teignworthy Reel Ale is usually accompanied by at least two other West Country beers, while good locally sourced and home-cooked food is served. Q🍽❀◐◑♿P🐾

Widecombe-in-the-Moor

Rugglestone Inn 🄻

TQ13 7TF (¼ mile from centre of village)
☎ (01364) 621327 🌐 rugglestoneinn.co.uk
Dartmoor Legend; house beer (by Teignworthy); 2 changing beers (sourced regionally) 🄶
A Grade II listed unspoilt Dartmoor building which was converted to a pub in 1832. Beer can be served through a hatch in the passageway or from a cosy bar with wood-burner. There are two further rooms, one with an open fire. A wide selection of home-cooked food is available. Across the stream is a large grassed seating area with the car park just down the road. Local farm Ashridge real cider is sold plus additional real cider and perry.
Q🍽❀🛏◐◑⛺♣●P🚌(271,672) 🐾

Winkleigh

King's Arms 🄻

The Square, Fore Street, EX19 8HQ (in village square)
☎ (01837) 682681 🌐 kingsarmswinkleigh.co.uk
Hanlons Yellow Hammer; Teignworthy Reel Ale; 3 changing beers (sourced locally) 🄷
Grade II listed 16th-century thatched village pub. The single bar has low-beamed ceilings, a flagstone floor and a welcoming wood-burning fire for colder months. Good food from a varied menu can be enjoyed in a series of intimate dining rooms featuring naval memorabilia, books and an intriguing glass-capped well. To the rear is a cosy private function room. Up to five, mainly Devon-sourced, real ales are usually on the bar, together with two ciders from nearby Sam's.
Q🍽❀◐◑⛺♣●🚌(315) 🐾📶

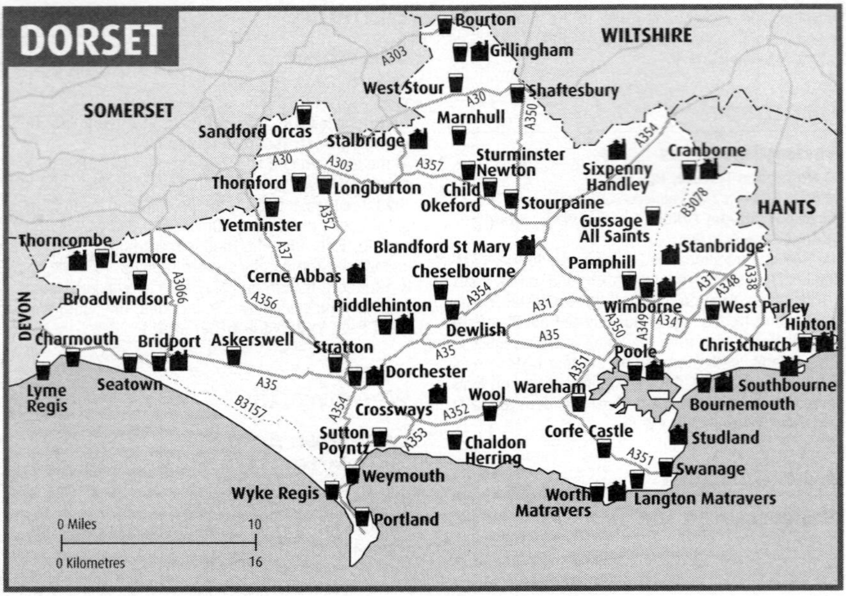

Askerswell

Spyway Inn

DT2 9EP

☎ (01308) 485250 🌐 thespywayinn.com

3 changing beers (sourced locally; often Otter) G

Family-friendly 16th-century smugglers' inn perched on a hill above the village of Askerswell. There is a selection of local ciders as well as a changing selection of beers on gravity. The lounge bar has beams and a wood-burner; a further bar has tables for dining. The south-facing garden is popular with locals, walkers and dog owners and provides stunning views of the surrounding countryside. In winter, the pub is closed Monday lunchtime and from 8pm on Sunday. Q P

Bournemouth

Acorn

1492 Wimborne Road, Kinson, BH11 9AD

☎ (01202) 575062

6 changing beers (sourced regionally; often Sixpenny) H

This imposing 17th-century pub, originally built as a coaching inn, is rich in history and has a connection with local smuggler Isaac Gulliver. It is now in the safe hands of a family who previously ran a multi-award winning pub close by. A large L-shaped bar serves two distinct areas and a well-chosen selection of ales is on offer. The landlord plays music on Sunday afternoon and live music sometimes also features. No children after 6pm.
P

All Hail Ale

10 Queens Road, Westbourne, BH2 6BE

☎ 07786 045996

4 changing beers (sourced nationally) H

A vibrant micropub and bottle shop, this former restaurant has been skilfully converted, with wooden flooring and polished-wood bar and tables. Five handpumps serve a range of ales from independent breweries nationwide, and a real cider. Ten keg pumps offer a varied and well-chosen selection of beers. Popular tap takeovers are held to showcase some of the major new craft ales available. A large blackboard lists the beers available.

Cricketers ✔

41 Windham Road, Springbourne, BH1 4RN

☎ (01202) 551589

Fuller's London Pride; 2 changing beers (sourced nationally) H

Set on two levels, this imposing Victorian local retains many original features including an impressive bar, etched glass and cast-iron pillars. The vaulted upper section was converted from the gym where world champion boxer Freddie Mills once trained. Close to Bournemouth football ground and popular with fans both home and away, sports fixtures are televised. Lunches are served at weekends and the excellent Sunday roasts are popular. Quiz night on Tuesday, pool, darts and other in-house games give this pub an excellent vibe.
P (2)

Firkin Shed

279 Holdenhurst Road, Springbourne, BH8 8BZ

☎ (01202) 302340

6 changing beers (sourced nationally; often Cerne Abbas, Farmageddon, Vibrant Forest) H

A former CAMRA National Cider Pub of the Year, the Shed is a quirky, friendly, family-run micropub. Tables and benches hug the walls of the main bar area and snug, which are decorated with flags, musical instruments, puppets and skulls. A shed is used as the bar, hosting a constantly changing range of cask and keg beers alongside an impressive cider range. The garden area is a great place to relax and enjoy the summer sunshine.
(2,6A)

Micro Moose

326 Wimborne Road, Winton, BH9 2HH

☎ (01202) 538542 🌐 micromoose.co.uk

6 changing beers (sourced nationally) H/G

Established when the Canadian owner decided to convert her coffee shop into a micropub offering 'Great British Ales with Canadian Hospitality'. This friendly and cosy bar serves a selection of local and regional ales on both handpump and gravity. The bottled beer selection is Canadian-themed, as is the decor, complete with fluffy moose head. In common with other micropubs, sharing tables is encouraged. Local cider is also available, and a good selection of bar snacks. Q♠♥🖫😼

Silverback Alehouse
518 Wimborne Road, Winton, BH9 2EX
🌐 silverbackalehouse.co.uk
5 changing beers (sourced regionally) Ⓖ
Set on Winton's bustling high street, this micropub offers a welcome respite from the weekly shop. Carefully chosen real ales are served on gravity, often including beers from the Nottinghamshire area. Six ciders from small independent cider makers are also on offer. Benches and tables line the perimeter, with table service by friendly staff. Light snacks are available and you are welcome to bring in your takeaway. The bar has a relaxed and friendly atmosphere, making it popular with locals and visitors alike. Q♣♥🖫😼🛜

Bourton

White Lion
High Street, SP8 5AT
☎ (01747) 840866 🌐 whitelionbourton.co.uk
Otter Amber; 1 changing beer Ⓗ
The White Lion is a traditional inn dating from 1712. The stone-flagged bar has an open fireplace and many quiet corners for a meal or a drink. A separate restaurant leads off the bar for more formal dining. There is a large beer garden to the rear. The cider is from Rich's or Thatchers. Parking is either opposite the pub or in the car park. Close to Stourhead house and gardens and convenient for local attractions including Stonehenge.
Q🌞🚪◗♥🅿🖫(X4)😼🛜

Bridport

Crown Inn Ⓛ ⦾
56 West Bay Road, DT6 4AX
☎ (01308) 422037
Palmers Copper Ale, IPA, Dorset Gold, 200, Tally Ho!; 1 changing beer (sourced locally; often Palmers) Ⓗ
Welcoming traditional single-bar pub on the A35 roundabout between Bridport and West Bay. It is popular with locals but families, parties and tourists are also made to feel at home. Good food is served daily. The full range of Palmers beers is on offer. Large TV screens show sports and there is a great live music scene at weekends. Outside is a beer garden and a large car park. Closing time may occasionally be later.
🌞🕸◗&♣♥🅿🖫(7,X53)😼🛜

Pursuit of Hoppiness
15 West Street, DT6 3QJ
☎ (01308) 427111 🌐 hoppiness.co.uk
6 changing beers (sourced nationally; often Eight Arch, Tapstone) Ⓗ
Popular town-centre micropub with a single room that accommodates up to 25 people. There are six handpumps serving beers of all styles, changing regularly every few days and sourced from all over the UK. Six ciders are normally available including regulars Dorset Nectar and West Milton. Outdoor seating is at the front. Q🌞♣♥🖫😼🛜

Ropemakers Ⓛ ⦾
36 West Street, DT6 3QP
☎ (01308) 421255 🌐 theropemakers.com

Palmers Copper Ale, IPA, Dorset Gold, 200, Tally Ho!; 1 changing beer (sourced locally; often Palmers) Ⓗ
Deceptively large pub in the centre of town serving the full Palmers range of beers. The interior is divided into lots of separate themed areas decorated with memorabilia and local history. There is a large partially covered courtyard at the rear and wheelchair access via the back door. Music features on Friday and Saturday evenings. The pub closes around 4pm on Sunday in the winter (later on bank holiday weekends or if there is live music). 🌞🕸◗🅰♣♥🖫😼🛜

Woodman Inn
61 South Street, DT6 3NZ
☎ (01308) 456455 🌐 thewoodman.pub
4 changing beers (sourced regionally; often Cerne Abbas, Copper Street, Exmoor) Ⓗ
A friendly pub with a focus on quality beers and ciders. Handy for the twice-weekly markets, it has a cosy one-bar interior with a stone floor and log burner. There are sunny pavement tables at the front, a pleasant garden to the rear and a skittle alley. Real ales change frequently, and up to 12 boxed ciders are available. Regular music events include a folk night, story-telling and DJs. The pub stays open later on Sunday in the summer.
🌞🕸🅰♥🅿🖫😼🛜

Broadwindsor

White Lion Ⓛ ⦾
The Square, DT8 3QD
☎ (01308) 867070 🌐 whitelionbroadwindsor.co.uk
Palmers Copper Ale, Tally Ho!; 1 changing beer (sourced locally; often Palmers) Ⓗ
In a beautiful village, this 17th-century inn, with an inglenook fireplace, serves three ales from nearby Palmers Brewery. You can expect a friendly welcome and good service – children and dogs are welcome. Traditional home-cooked food is available including roasts on Sunday. Look out for the monthly acoustic jam sessions. Q🌞🕸◗♣♥😼🛜

REAL ALE BREWERIES

Barefaced Bournemouth
Brew Shack Sixpenny Handley
Brewers Folly Stanbridge
Brewhouse & Kitchen 🍴 Bournemouth
Brewhouse & Kitchen 🍴 Dorchester
Brewhouse & Kitchen 🍴 Poole
Brewhouse & Kitchen 🍴 Southbourne
Cerne Abbas ◆ Cerne Abbas
Copper Street ◆ Dorchester
Dorset ◆ Crossways
Drop The Anchor Hinton
Eight Arch ◆ Wimborne
Gyle 59 Thorncombe
Hall & Woodhouse (Badger) ◆ Blandford St Mary
Hattie Brown's Worth Matravers
Isle of Purbeck 🍴 Studland
Palmers Bridport
Piddle Piddlehinton
Sandbanks ◆ Poole
Sixpenny ◆ Cranborne
Small Paul's Gillingham
Southbourne Bournemouth
Stripey Cat 🍴 Bridport
Way Outback ◆ Southbourne
Wriggle Valley ◆ Stalbridge

Chaldon Herring

Sailor's Return 𝕃

DT2 8DN

☎ (01305) 854441 🌐 sailorsreturnpub.com

Cerne Abbas Responsibly; Otter Ale; Palmers Copper Ale; 1 changing beer (sourced regionally; often Cerne Abbas, Flack Manor, Palmers) [H]

Historic thatched inn on the edge of a tranquil village, a few miles from the Jurassic Coast. The pub dates from the 1860s but the buildings are much earlier. There are several dining and drinking areas, with flagstone floors throughout. An original inn sign hangs in the main bar. Wednesday is pie night. On Friday night food is only served in the restaurant area (booking advisable). Q🚸✿◑●P🐾📶

Charmouth

Royal Oak Inn 𝕃 ✔

The Street, DT6 6PE

☎ (01297) 560277 🌐 royaloakcharmouth.co.uk

Palmers Copper Ale, IPA, Dorset Gold, 200; 1 changing beer (sourced locally; often Palmers) [H]

A traditional family-run village pub a short walk from the beach on the Jurassic Coast. The friendly staff welcome locals and visitors alike. It serves locally brewed Palmers beers, including the seasonal ales, and a local real cider. Dogs are allowed in the lower bar area. Food is freshly cooked using locally sourced produce (no food all day Tue and Sun eve). Open until 10pm on Sunday evenings in summer. 🚸✿◑▲♣●🚌(X51,X53)🐾📶

Cheselbourne

Rivers Arms

DT2 7NW

☎ (01305) 236586 🌐 theriversarms.co.uk

Hardys & Hansons Olde Trip; Morland Old Golden Hen [H]

Unspoilt inn on the outskirts of the village, believed to have been built to cater for drovers en route to Dorchester. It was threatened with change to residential use but, thanks to a successful local campaign, was saved and has been totally refurbished with a rustic theme. There is an upstairs room, conservatory area, large veranda and a stove in the bar. The pub serves real home-cooked food. Seven en-suite log cabins with valley views provide accommodation. Q🚸✿🛏◑●P🐾

Child Okeford

Saxon Inn

Gold Hill, DT11 8HD

☎ (01258) 860310 🌐 saxoninn.co.uk

Butcombe Original; Otter Bitter; 2 changing beers (sourced regionally; often Butcombe, Dartmoor, Exmoor) [H]

This 300-year-old village inn is hidden behind a row of cottages. The bar and restaurant areas are cosy, boasting a log fire, and are popular with locals and visitors. The large garden is perfect for alfresco dining and hosts a beer and cider festival. Quality home-cooked food is served. The two guest ales are chosen on the recommendation of customers, and there are two real ciders. The pub also does B&B and is an ideal base for exploring the Dorset countryside. 🚸✿🛏◑♣●P🚌(X10) 📶

Christchurch

Saxon Bar

5 The Saxon Centre, Fountain Way, BH23 1QN

☎ (01202) 488931

4 changing beers (sourced nationally; often Downton, Sixpenny, Vibrant Forest) [G]

This friendly, single-room micropub, close to the town centre, has perimeter seating and high tables made from reclaimed wood from Bournemouth Pier. It offers a variety of well-chosen ales, as well as up to 10 real ciders, all served direct to your table. Speciality bar snacks, local and international spirits along with four KeyKeg beers are also available. Please note winter hours vary. Local CAMRA Cider Pub of the Year 2020. Q✿⇌●🚌🐾

Thomas Tripp ✔

10 Wick Lane, BH23 1HX

☎ (01202) 490498 🌐 thomastripp.co.uk

Ringwood Razorback, Fortyniner; 2 changing beers (sourced nationally; often Cerne Abbas, Vibrant Forest) [H]

This lively inn, formerly the Plumbers Arms, was renamed after a legendary local smuggler and is in the historic town centre near the Priory Church and Castle. It features paintings of locals throughout the smuggling era. It is rugby union-oriented and supports East Dorset RFC. Great bar food is available, with speciality fish dishes served in the adjoining shack. The large paved patio area with sheltered alcoves is a must in the summer. Live music plays several nights a week. ✿◑●🚌🐾📶

Corfe Castle

Bankes Arms Hotel 𝕃 ✔

23 East Street, BH20 5ED

☎ (01929) 288188 🌐 bankesarmshotel.co.uk

Palmers IPA, 200; 2 changing beers (sourced regionally) [H]

This historic 16th-century Grade II listed hotel, owned by the National Trust, retains many of its original features including a front drinkers' bar. The restaurant to the rear serves excellent home-cooked food. A large picturesque garden overlooks Swanage Steam Railway and Corfe Castle station and enjoys fantastic views of the Purbeck Hills. Regular beers are from Palmers, and ales recreated by the Dead Brewers Society, brewed by Barnet, are available. Occasional beer festivals are held in the summer. 🚸✿🛏◑⇌●P🚌(40)🐾📶

Corfe Castle Club

70 East Street, BH20 5EQ (off A351)

☎ (01929) 480591

Ringwood Razorback; Timothy Taylor Landlord; 1 changing beer (sourced nationally) [H]

Friendly club in the village centre, formerly a school and built in Purbeck stone. The main bar has upholstered bench seating, TV for major sporting events, darts and Purbeck longboard shove-ha'penny. An upstairs room has a pool table and can be hired for meetings. Filled rolls are available all day. The spectacular garden boasts a boules court and views over the Purbeck hills. Convenient for the castle or steam railway, visitors are welcome with a CAMRA membership card or copy of the Guide. ✿⇌♣P🚌(40)🐾📶

Fox Inn 𝕃 ✔

8 West Street, BH20 5HD

☎ (01929) 480449 🌐 thefoxinncorfecastle.com

Box Steam Soul Train; Butcombe Adam Henson's Rare Breed; Hattie Brown's Moonlite; 1 changing beer [H]

This delightful 16th-century inn is nestled in the heart of historic Corfe Castle and retains many original features. The front door opens into a small traditional snug with steps down to the main bar area, where good pub food is served. Towards the rear is a fabulous garden, complete with barbecue shack, offering fine views over the castle and surrounding Purbeck Hills. Q🐎❀◑⛺⇌🍎🚌(40)🐾

Cranborne

Sixpenny Tap Ⓛ

Holwell Farm, Holwell, BH21 5QP (on B3078)
☎ (01725) 762006 🌐 sixpennybrewery.co.uk
Sixpenny 6d Best Bitter, 6d Gold, 6d IPA; 2 changing beers (often Sixpenny) Ⓗ
Housed in a converted Victorian stables and packed full of quirky miscellaneous items, the Sixpenny Tap has established itself at the heart of the local community. With the brewery located next door, its popular range of ales is served with pride and enthusiasm. The pub hosts many successful and colourful community and charity events in the extensive courtyard, with a warm welcome for all who visit. This is a real countryside gem set within picturesque farmland, and even has its own Tardis.
Q🐎❀♿♣🍎P🐾📶

Dewlish

Oak at Dewlish

DT2 7ND
☎ (01258) 837352 🌐 oakpub.co.uk
3 changing beers (sourced regionally; often Butcombe, Dorset, Fine Tuned) Ⓗ
Unpretentious village inn with three varying ales, mainly from the West Country, and award-winning Rosie's cider. The horseshoe-shaped bar has a dining area and opens onto a patio and large garden. To the rear is a separate room with a pool table. A varied food menu offers good home-cooked dishes made using local produce. Two B&B rooms and self-catering accommodation are available in an adjacent converted coach house. Q🐎❀🛏◑♣🍎🐾

Dorchester

Blue Raddle Ⓛ

9 Church Street, DT1 1JN
☎ (01305) 267762 🌐 blueraddle.co.uk
Dartmoor Jail Ale; Palmers Copper Ale; St Austell Tribute; 2 changing beers (sourced regionally; often Bath Ales, Dark Star) Ⓗ
Town-centre pub with a comfortable and cosy ambience, popular with a wide age range. Well-kept beers include a light and a dark guest ale, alongside real ciders. Locally sourced food is cooked and served to order lunchtimes Wednesday to Saturday and evenings Thursday to Saturday. The walls are covered in interesting and quirky pictures. Folk and Irish music sessions feature regularly. No children are allowed but dogs are welcome.
Q◑⇌🍎🚌🐾📶

Bulls Head

92 High Street, Fordington, DT1 1LD
☎ (01305) 257353
St Austell Tribute; 2 changing beers (sourced nationally; often Bath, Cotleigh, Hanlons) Ⓗ
A spacious local nestled within the heart of Fordington, this free house sports an ever-changing selection of ales from local, regional and national breweries. The pub is often frequented by local skittles, cribbage, darts and pool teams. There is a large car park and garden to the rear. Regular karaoke and quiz nights are held and the pub may stay open later if busy. 🐎❀♣P🚌(2)🐾📶

Convivial Rabbit

1 Trinity House, Trinity Street, DT1 1TT
🌐 convivialrabbit.co.uk
6 changing beers (sourced nationally) Ⓖ
Popular micropub with a changing choice of around six real ales of varying styles and strengths from micro and independent British breweries. Local ciders, gins and wines are also available in addition to cans of craft beer and lager. Rustically decorated and run by friendly and knowledgeable licensees, the pub is tucked away down an alley off Trinity Street, but well worth seeking out when visiting Dorchester town centre. Regular folk, jazz and vinyl nights are hosted. Q❀⇌♣🍎🚌🐾

Royal Oak ✔

20 High West Street, DT1 1UW
☎ (01305) 755910
Greene King Abbot; Ruddles Best Bitter; Sharp's Doom Bar; 5 changing beers (sourced nationally; often Dorset, Otter, Wychwood) Ⓗ
A busy town-centre Wetherspoon establishment offering a wide selection of frequently changing local and national ales on handpump, with regular beer festivals adding to the range. The pub offers a full food menu and is open for breakfast daily, welcoming children and families. It has a number of separate areas for both diners and drinkers. To the rear is a sunny patio area with wheelchair access to the main internal area.
Q🐎❀◑♿⇌🍎🚌📶

Tom Brown's Ⓛ ✔

47 High East Street, DT1 1HU
☎ (01305) 264020 🌐 tombrownspub.co.uk
Dorset Tom Brown's; 2 changing beers (sourced nationally; often Cerne Abbas, Copper Street, Stonehenge) Ⓗ
Formerly home to the Goldfinch Brewery, this town-centre alehouse has an open fire, skittle alley and a function room, and hosts regular live music and other events. In addition to the four real ales, there are up to five real ciders and a selection of more than 20 gins. The large, beautiful riverside garden is ideal for lazy pints in the sun. Food is not served but you are welcome to bring in a takeaway from one of the nearby establishments. Dogs are welcome, except when live music plays.
🐎❀◐♣🍎🚌🐾📶

Gillingham

Buffalo

2 Lydford Lane, SP8 4NJ (100yds S of B3081)
☎ (01747) 823759
Hall & Woodhouse Fursty Ferret, Tanglefoot; 1 changing beer (often Hall & Woodhouse) Ⓗ
This traditional old stone pub, formerly the Drum & Monkey, is tucked away on a side road opposite the old Matthews Brewery which closed in the 1960s. It has been extended and refurbished to capitalise on the large car park, beautiful garden and patio areas, and now caters for up to 60 diners while retaining a well-used public bar. The restaurant trades as Ristorante Da Massimo. 🐎❀◑♿⛺♣P🚌(X2)

Dolphin

Peacemarsh, SP8 4HB
☎ (01747) 824007
4 changing beers (sourced regionally; often Cotleigh, St Austell, Wriggle Valley) Ⓗ
Recently reopened after refurbishment, the pub has two dining rooms and seating for drinkers in the bar. Up to four regularly varying real ales are on offer. The menu changes daily – meals are cooked to order and always

popular (booking is recommended). The beer garden has had a makeover and there is a covered smoking area outside. Q☋❀◐P🚌(X2,25)🐾📶

Phoenix

High Street, SP8 4AY

☎ (01747) 823277

Bath Ales Gem; St Austell Proper Job; Sharp's Doom Bar Ⓗ

Originally a 15th-century coaching inn with its own brewery and stables, following a fire in the 17th century it was rebuilt and renamed the Phoenix. It has an open-plan layout with a dining area to one side and an open fire. Good-value pub grub plus specials are served lunchtimes Monday to Friday, plus a breakfast menu and traditional Sunday lunch. There is a small car park to the rear and two public car parks within walking distance. ◖⇌P🚌(X2)🐾📶

Gussage All Saints

Drovers Inn

Bowerswain Hollow, BH21 5ET

☎ (01258) 840550 🌐 droversinngussage.co.uk

Ringwood Fortyniner; Sixpenny 6d Best Bitter; 2 changing beers (sourced locally; often Ringwood, Sixpenny) Ⓗ

Located in a picturesque village in the heart of rural Dorset and Cranborne Chase, this thriving, award-winning community-owned pub is very much at the centre of local life. With its cosy atmosphere and warm welcome, The Drovers entices you in to sample its changing range of real ales and good-quality food. Although great conversation is the order of the day, the pub hosts many events throughout the year such as festivals and music nights. ☋❀🛏◐⛺●P🐾📶

Langton Matravers

King's Arms

27 High Street, BH19 3HA

☎ (01929) 422979

Ringwood Razorback; 3 changing beers (sourced nationally) Ⓗ

Dating back to 1743, this Purbeck stone-built pub, with original flagstone floors, has many quirky little rooms off a central bar area, and a suntrap rear garden. The seaside town of Swanage with its steam railway is close by, as are many fine walks where you can explore the Purbecks and the South West Coast Path. A welcoming family pub serving good food and well-chosen ales, this is a magnet both for locals and visitors. Q☋❀◐⛺♣●🚌(40)🐾📶

Laymore

Squirrel Inn

TA20 4NT

☎ (01460) 30298 🌐 squirrelinn.co.uk

1 changing beer (sourced nationally; often Fuller's, Otter) Ⓗ

Modernised country pub with a large single-bar area and a separate function room with a double skittle alley and pool table. At least one real ale, three draught ciders and a huge selection of bottled gins are available. Good home-made food is cooked to order, with gluten-free and vegetarian options via prior arrangement. There is a beer garden with a gazebo and camping can be arranged in the field opposite. Families are welcome. Opens late depending on demand. ❀🛏◐♿⛺♣●P🐾📶

Longburton

Rose & Crown

DT9 5PD

☎ (01963) 210202 🌐 roseandcrownlongburton.com

5 changing beers (sourced nationally; often Fine Tuned, Otter, St Austell) Ⓗ

This lovely thatched 17th-century coaching inn is a fascinating blend of traditional beams, stone flags and open fireplaces, set off by contemporary decor. A free house, it offers five constantly rotating national, regional and local beers. Traditional pub food is served in the bar and restaurant (booking essential on Sunday). There is a large beer garden plus a separate self-contained cottage available to hire. Real cider is served in summer. Open all day on bank holidays. Q☋❀🛏◐♣●P🁢🚌(X11)🐾📶

Lyme Regis

Nag's Head 𝕃

32 Silver Street, DT7 3HS

☎ (01297) 442312 🌐 nagsheadlymeregis.com

Otter Bitter, Ale; 2 changing beers (sourced regionally; often Powderkeg, Yeovil Ales) Ⓗ

Friendly community-focused locals' pub away from the seafront. Dating from the Victorian era, the pub is flint and brick built. Up to two guest ales are served. There is regular live music and a big screen shows major sporting events. Four guest rooms are available. The beer terrace enjoys lovely views over Lyme Bay. ☋❀🛏⛺♣🚌🐾📶

Marnhull

Blackmore Vale Inn

Burton Street, DT10 1JJ

☎ (01258) 820701

St Austell Tribute; Wriggle Valley Ryme Rambler; 1 changing beer (sourced regionally; often Bath Ales, Otter, Sharp's) Ⓗ

Refurbished in 2018, this 15th-century building retains some character features and has a spacious bar area with a wood-burner stove and low beams. A separate dining area leads off the bar. An extension is being built, with plans for a bottle store and microbrewery. Music night is Friday, quiz night is Sunday. Q❀◐⛺♣P🚌(X4)🐾

Pamphill

Vine Inn ★

Vine Hill, BH21 4EE (off B3082)

☎ (01202) 882259

2 changing beers (sourced regionally; often Hop Back, Plain) Ⓗ/Ⓖ

Identified by CAMRA as having a nationally important historic pub interior, this multi-award winning country pub, owned by the National Trust, has been managed by the same family for 120 years – the current landlady residing for over 30 of these. The pub has two cosy bars, an upstairs room, and a large suntrap patio and garden providing the perfect place to relax and enjoy a drink. Light snacks including ploughman's and toasties are served at lunchtime. Popular with walkers and cyclists, this is a true rural gem. Q❀◖♣●P🁢🐾

Piddlehinton

Thimble Inn 𝕃 ✔

14 High Street, DT2 7TD

☎ (01300) 348270 🌐 thimbleinn.co.uk

Palmers Copper Ale, IPA, Dorset Gold Ⓗ

Large, partly thatched village pub on the River Piddle, with welcoming staff. The spacious low-beamed bar has a brick fireplace and plenty of nooks and crannies for cosy twosomes and larger groups. The pub offers a well-kept range of Palmers ales, often including Tally Ho! and its seasonal ales. Food is served Monday to Saturday and Sunday lunchtimes. The river runs through the large garden, and there is plenty of parking – motorhomes and camper vans allowed overnight. ♘❀◐♿♣P🐾ᯤ

Poole

Barking Cat Alehouse

182-184 Ashley Road, Upper Parkstone, BH14 9BY

☎ (01202) 258465

🌐 the-barking-cat-alehouse.ueniweb.com

8 changing beers (sourced nationally) Ⓗ

A bustling alehouse serving an interesting choice of ales from local and national microbreweries alongside six ciders, all on handpull. There are also 10 craft keg lines, providing an excellent range for all beer tastes. Customers are welcome to bring in a takeaway – there is a Chinese next door. The large function room has a pool table and dartboards. Entertainment includes a quiz night on alternate Thursdays, Scalextric racing night on the first Friday of the month, and live music on Saturday nights.
♘⇌♣●🚌🐾ᯤ

Bermuda Triangle

10 Parr Street, Lower Parkstone, BH14 0JY

☎ (01202) 748047 🌐 bermudatrianglepub.com

5 changing beers (sourced nationally; often Dark Star, Oakham, Palmers) Ⓗ

Established in 1870, this great local drinkers' pub is at the heart of Ashley Cross. The cosy interior has five distinct bar areas – find your way through the bookcase to discover the hidden sixth room. It is nautically themed and decorated to reflect the Bermuda Triangle story. Five ales on handpump are complemented by two real ciders and speciality keg beers. With a lively and welcoming atmosphere, the pub hosts occasional live music. The outside drinking area with fairy lights is a must in summertime. ❀⇌●🚌🐾ᯤ

Brewhouse ✔

68 High Street, BH15 1DA

☎ (01202) 685288

Frome Same Again, Beer; 3 changing beers (sourced nationally) Ⓗ

This multi-award winning pub is a long-established feature of the town, and a reliable source of interesting ales from Frome Brewery as well as from national microbreweries. Real cider is also available. Entering from the High Street you find tables in the window, and past the busy bar area is a space for pool and darts. Dogs are welcome in this no-frills traditional community pub.
❀⇌♣●🚌🐾ᯤ

Portland

George Inn ✔

133 Reforne, Easton, DT5 2AP

☎ (01305) 820011

Greene King Abbot; 3 changing beers (sourced nationally; often Fuller's, St Austell, Timothy Taylor) Ⓗ

A friendly, family-oriented local dating from the mid-18th century. It has four separate bar and dining areas, and a large enclosed beer garden. Food is available daily Thursday to Sunday – Sunday roasts are popular, as is the Thursday evening curry and quiz. There are usually three constantly rotated guest ales on offer. Live music plays on some Saturday evenings and Sunday afternoons.
♘❀◐●🚌(1,701) 🐾ᯤ

Royal Portland Arms

Fortuneswell, DT5 1LZ

☎ (01305) 862255

2 changing beers (sourced regionally; often Cerne Abbas, Copper Street, Teignworthy) Ⓗ/Ⓖ

Dating back 200 years, this Portland stone pub stands on the main road, with a free public car park opposite. It is a basic one-bar pub offering a varying choice of regional and local ales and a real cider. Live music is hosted on Friday evening and Sunday afternoon. There is a popular cheese club every Wednesday early evening.
Q♣●🂠🚌(1,701) 🐾ᯤ

Sandford Orcas

Mitre Inn

DT9 4RU

☎ (01963) 220271 🌐 mitreinn.co.uk

3 changing beers (sourced nationally; often Church End, Quantock, Yeovil Ales) Ⓗ

Run by the same couple since 1992, the Mitre is a homely, family-friendly pub with a cosy bar and separate restaurant area. There are flagstoned floors throughout, and two open fires, but mind your head on the door lintels. The guest beers are well kept and change regularly. Beer festivals take place twice a year. Booking is recommended for Sunday lunch. The elevated garden at the rear is accessed via steps.
Q♘❀🛏◐♣P🚌(39) 🐾ᯤ

Seatown

Anchor Inn 𝕃 ✔

DT6 6JU

☎ (01297) 489215 🌐 theanchorinnseatown.co.uk

Palmers Copper Ale, IPA, Dorset Gold, 200; 1 changing beer (sourced locally; often Palmers) Ⓗ

A traditional family-friendly country pub on the Jurassic Coast, serving fantastic food. There are plenty of coastal walks to build up an appetite. Warm up by the open fires or enjoy the sea views towards West Bay or Golden Cap from the large terraces. Accommodation is available in three luxury rooms. Q♘❀🛏◐♿⛺♣P🐾ᯤ

Shaftesbury

Ship Inn 🏆 ✔

24 Bleke Street, SP7 8JZ

☎ (01747) 853219

Butcombe Original; Sixpenny 6d IPA; 2 changing beers Ⓗ

Stone-built town pub at the top of the steep Tout Hill. The single bar serves four different areas – the main bar, a games room with pool, darts, fruit machine and jukebox, a snug with an open fire, and a newly refurbished lounge bar. Outside there is a sunny patio and covered smoking area. No hot food is available but you can order from local takeaways or bring your own. ❀●🚌🐾ᯤ

Stourpaine

White Horse Inn ✔

Shaston Road, DT11 8TA

☎ (01258) 453535 🌐 whitehorse-stourpaine.co.uk

Sharp's Doom Bar; house beer (by Flack Manor); 3 changing beers (sourced regionally; often Cerne Abbas, Gritchie, Sixpenny) Ⓗ

Wonderful village free house incorporating the local shop and post office. Originally two adjoining cottages, the pub has multiple cosy spaces with beams and open fireplaces. Five handpumps offer national and regional ales, and cider lovers can enjoy Cranborne Chase direct from the box. Close to the North Dorset Trailway, walkers and cyclists stop here for a well-earned break, and dogs are welcomed with their own firkin of water. The garden areas make this an all-round destination throughout the year. Q੭☆৫▶♣⊕P⊒(X3)⚘☂

Stratton

Saxon Arms
20 The Square, DT2 9WG
☎ (01305) 260020 ⊕ thesaxon-stratton.co.uk
Butcombe Original; St Austell Tribute; Timothy Taylor Landlord; 1 changing beer (sourced nationally; often Cerne Abbas) Ⓗ
Set in the village square, with the church and village hall nearby, this is a thatched inn built of stone and flint in 2001, offering a warm, friendly welcome and a real fire. The pub offers three or four ales, cider and a decent wine list. There is a good menu of locally sourced food – check the website for offers. Dogs are welcome but not in the main restaurant area. Open all day from 11.30am in August. Q੭☆৫▶৬♣⊕P⚘☂

Sturminster Newton

White Hart Alehouse ✅
Market Place, DT10 1AN
☎ (01258) 472558
Fuller's London Pride; 5 changing beers (sourced locally; often Gritchie, Wild Beer, Yeovil Ales) Ⓗ
In the town centre, this thatched Grade II listed pub is now a free house, offering half a dozen real ales and a selection of bottled craft beers. Local breweries are well supported and a range of boxed cider adds to the choice. The open-plan beamed bar has ample seating and a piano. Future plans include updating the kitchen.
੭☆🞵▶♣⊕P⊒(X4)

Sutton Poyntz

Springhead ✅
Sutton Road, DT3 6LW
☎ (01305) 832117 ⊕ thespringhead.co.uk
Greene King Abbot; St Austell Proper Job; Timothy Taylor Landlord; 1 changing beer (sourced nationally) Ⓗ
Set in peaceful surroundings, overlooking the village duck pond, this bar-restaurant dates from the 1900s and is named after the water source nearby that supplies much of the water used in the Weymouth area. Mainly open plan, a fire greets you in winter, when the opening hours are more restrictive. In summer, pizza is served from a wood-fired oven Thursday to Saturday. Three regular ales are complemented by a guest ale from an independent brewery. Children are welcome throughout, with a grassed play area to the rear. Dogs are permitted in the bar area. ੭☆▶Å P⊒(4A)⚘

Swanage

Black Swan Ⓛ ✅
159-161 High Street, BH19 2NE
☎ (01929) 423846 ⊕ blackswanswanage.co.uk
Dorset Knob; 2 changing beers (sourced regionally; often Sharp's, Skinner's, Timothy Taylor) Ⓗ
Traditional Grade II-listed pub on the historic High Street in the heart of Swanage. It has two bars with stone floors and log fires, and serves three well-kept ales – the locally produced Dorset Knob is named after a local biscuit. The pub is renowned for its quality food and booking is recommended. The suntrap garden is the perfect place to

enjoy the last of the evening sunshine. Swanage station is the terminus of the steam railway.
Q੭☆▶⇌⊒(40,50)⚘

Red Lion
63 High Street, BH19 2LY
☎ (01929) 423533 ⊕ redlionswanage.co.uk
Hop Back GFB; Otter Bitter; Sharp's Doom Bar; Timothy Taylor Landlord; 2 changing beers (sourced nationally) Ⓖ
Traditional 17th-century inn serving up to six ales on gravity from the ground-floor cellar behind the bar. A large selection of real ciders and perries is a big draw, with the range displayed on blackboards in both bars. The lounge has a restaurant area where quality food is served, with curry and steak nights always popular. The large, partly covered garden is busy throughout the year. Q੭☆🞵⇌♣⊕P⊒(40,50)⚘☂

Thornford

King's Arms Ⓨ Ⓛ
Pound Road, DT9 6QD
☎ (01935) 872294 ⊕ kingsarmsthornford.com
Sharp's Doom Bar; 3 changing beers (sourced regionally; often Palmers, Plain, Yeovil Ales) Ⓗ
Situated next to an unusual red-brick Victorian clock tower, erected to commemorate Queen Victoria's Diamond Jubilee. Inside, the pub has a traditional bar and a separate restaurant. Outside, there are pleasant seating areas and children's play facilities adjacent to a large skittle alley. The car park is small but on-road parking is available. Guest ale news is posted weekly on Facebook. Local CAMRA Pub of the Year 2020. ੭☆▶♣⊕P⚘☂

Wareham

Horse & Groom Ⓨ Ⓛ ✅
St Johns Hill, BH20 4LZ
☎ (01929) 552222
4 changing beers (sourced regionally; often Copper Street, Hattie Brown's, Palmers) Ⓗ
This free house offers four real ales, with a proud emphasis on those brewed in Dorset, plus real cider. Comfortable, welcoming and spacious, it has a growing reputation for good pub food. Cosy in winter, with two real fires, it also delivers in the summer months, with a pleasant garden tucked away at the rear. The pub hosts quiz nights and occasional curry evenings, offering something for everyone. Local CAMRA Pub of the Year 2020. ੭☆▶⊕⊒(40,X54)⚘☂

King's Arms ✅
41 North Street, BH20 4AD
☎ (01929) 552503 ⊕ kingsarmswareham.co.uk
5 changing beers (sourced nationally; often Exmoor, Otter, St Austell) Ⓗ
This award-winning traditional thatched inn has its roots in the 1500s and survived the Great Fire of 1762. The flagstone-floored public bar is adorned with interesting artefacts including old armament shell casings. There is a dedicated dining area with an excellent range of home-cooked food on offer, a drinking corridor and a large garden to the rear with a covered area for smokers. The five varied guest beers are usually from the West Country. Live music often features at weekends. Q੭☆🞵▶⇌⊕P⊒(40,X54)⚘☂

West Parley

Owls Nest
196 Christchurch Road, BH22 8SS

☎ (01202) 572793 🌐 theowlsnest-westparley.com
4 changing beers (sourced regionally; often Flack Manor, Otter, Sixpenny) H
Charming and welcoming, this Tudor-style building with beamed ceilings and a woodburner has a comfortable vibe. Four handpumps dispense local and regional ales. A beer and home-made pie festival has become an early-in-the-year favourite. There is occasional live music, with an Irish session on the first Thursday of the month. Popular for its home-made food, booking is recommended. Closed Sunday evening January to March. P (13,X6)

West Stour

Ship Inn
A30, SP8 5RP
☎ (01747) 838640 🌐 shipinn-dorset.com
3 changing beers H
Once a coaching inn, this popular roadside pub has views across the Blackmore Vale. The public bar features a flagstone floor while the separate light and airy restaurant area has stripped-oak floorboards. There is a patio and large garden at the rear. This friendly hostelry is renowned for superb home-cooked food (no meals Sun eve) and comfortable accommodation. It usually has six local ciders to choose from and always three ales. Dogs are welcome in the bar. A beer festival is held each July. QP

Weymouth

Globe Inn
24 East Street, DT4 8BN
☎ (01305) 786061
Dartmoor Jail Ale; St Austell Cornish Best Bitter, Proper Job; Sharp's Doom Bar; 2 changing beers (sourced regionally; often Cerne Abbas, Palmers) H
Free house with a friendly welcome, tucked away on a street corner just 30 yards from the iconic harbourside. The Globe is only a short distance from the town centre, the beach and the esplanade, and offers a distinct change from the packed waterside. There is a jukebox and a separate games room with pool table, darts and pub games. A fun quiz is held on Sunday afternoon. Guest ales are not always available in the low season. The cider is Thatchers Cheddar Valley.

William Henry ✔
1 Frederick Place, DT4 8HQ
☎ (01305) 763730
Greene King IPA; Sharp's Doom Bar; Thornbridge Jaipur IPA; 5 changing beers (sourced nationally; often Adnams, Dorset, Titanic) H
A popular Wetherspoon, centrally located close to main transport links. There is an excellent range of ales, with three regulars and at least five guests, plus ciders. The bars are on two levels but wheelchair access is good, including toilets. Family friendly and appealing to all ages, the pub was built in the gardens of the summer residence of Prince William Henry, Duke of Gloucester, brother of George III.

Wimborne

Taphouse
11 West Borough, BH21 1LT
☎ (01202) 911200
9 changing beers (sourced nationally; often Brew Shack, Eight Arch, Sixpenny) H
Close to the historic town centre, the main feature of this narrow wood-panelled pub is the long hardwood bar. The pub offers nine real ales from local, regional and national breweries including popular favourites. Always full of atmosphere, conversation rules in the cosy window seating area and the suntrap patio outside. Live acoustic music features on Sunday.

Wool

Black Bear Inn
High Street, BH20 6BP
☎ (01929) 405541 🌐 blackbear.website
House beer (by Flack Manor); 3 changing beers (sourced nationally) H
Award-winning inn close to the many attractions of the Purbecks. It offers so much more than its four well-kept cask ales. Hearty home-cooked food is served in the front bar and in the restaurant area to the rear. Curry nights, quizzes, walks and a breakfast club all contribute to the pub being a real community asset. The outside seating area is perfect for relaxing in the summer sun. QP (X54)

Worth Matravers

Square & Compass ★ L
Weston Road, BH19 3LF (off B3069)
☎ (01929) 439229 🌐 squareandcompasspub.co.uk
Hattie Brown's HBA, Moonlite; 3 changing beers (sourced regionally) G
A real gem, identified by CAMRA as having a nationally important historic pub interior, which has appeared in every edition of the Guide. It has been in the same family since 1907. Two rooms either side of a serving hatch convey an impression that little has changed over the years. The sea-facing garden offers views across the Purbecks, and fossils are displayed in the adjacent museum. Pasties are available. Beer and cider festivals are held in October and November respectively.
Q

Wyke Regis

Wyke Smugglers ✔
76 Portland Road, DT4 9AB
☎ (01305) 760010 🌐 thewykesmugglers.com
St Austell Proper Job; 3 changing beers (sourced nationally; often Dorset, Fuller's) H
A large, lively local hosting many community events. Regional guest beers often come from the SIBA south-west region. Food is served all week except Monday. In winter, the dining area is set around the wood-burner. There are racks for bicycles at the front and the skittle alley doubles as a function room. Live music plays at weekends, a quiz is held on Sunday nights, and a beer and cider festival features in the summer.
P (1,701)

Yetminster

White Hart Inn L
High Street, DT9 6LF
☎ (01935) 872338 🌐 yetminsterwhitehart.pub
House beer (by Fine Tuned); 2 changing beers (sourced locally; often Piddle, Wriggle Valley, Yeovil Ales) H
A 16th-century, Grade II listed thatched free house. The building is stone-built with mullion windows, and inside, the single-room bar area has low beams and an inglenook fireplace. Four ciders are served along with the beers. The skittle alley is themed after local band The Yetties. Local CAMRA Pub of the Year 2019.
QP

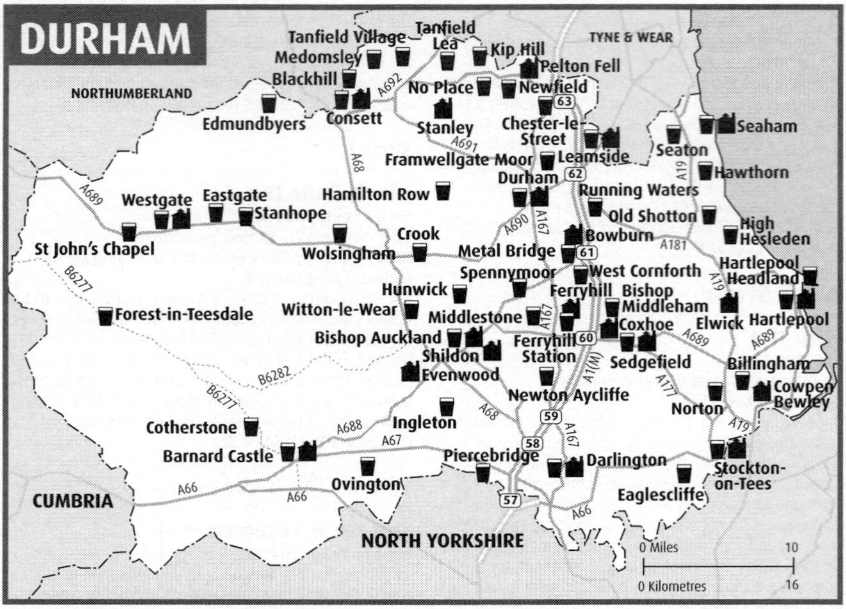

Co Durham incorporates part of the former county of Cleveland

Barnard Castle

Firkin Alley 𝕃

2 Bakery Mews., DL12 8LZ (down alleyway next to YMCA charity shop, behind 20 Horsemarket)

☎ 07825 727660

5 changing beers (sourced nationally) Ⓗ

Hospitable licensees and a friendly local clientele help make this micropub in a former bakery storeroom well worth a visit. It has a bar downstairs and a spacious and comfortable room upstairs, tastefully fitted with warm wood surrounds. The pub offers a good and ever-changing ale selection, mainly from the region, plus a changing choice of cider. Real ale on Thirsty Thursday is £3 a pint. Food on Tasty Tuesday is in aid of local charity the Clique. Q❀🍎🚌(75,76)🐾

Old Well Inn 𝕃 ✔

21 The Bank, DL12 8PH

☎ (01833) 690130 🌐 theoldwellinn.co.uk

Camerons Strongarm; Timothy Taylor Landlord; 3 changing beers (sourced locally) Ⓗ

The boundary of this 17th-century town-centre inn incorporates part of the medieval castle wall. The pub has a cosy front bar and a comfortable lounge, a separate restaurant and an airy conservatory, plus an enclosed beer garden. At least five well-kept beers are available including three guests from local micros, usually including Mithril. Excellent food is served daily, and there is accommodation in 10 rooms. A five-day beer festival is held at Easter. The Castle Players meet here. Q☕❀🛏◑♿🚌(75,76)🐾📶

Billingham

Billingham Catholic Club 𝕃

37 Wolviston Road, TS23 2RU (on E side of old A19, just S of Roseberry Road roundabout, next to bus stop)

☎ (01642) 901143 🌐 billinghamcatholicclub.webs.com

3 changing beers Ⓗ

Now in its 12th year of continuous Guide recognition, this Victorian mansion and former school is a friendly club, where actively supporting the local community comes high on the agenda. Dedicated volunteers ensure that the club's reputation for offering 150 different beers annually continues. Three beers and two ciders are normally served, with eight ales available throughout the popular bank holiday beer and music festivals. Local CAMRA Community Pub of the Year and Club of the Year 2020. ❀♿♣🍎P🚆🚌(35,36)🐾

Crafty Cock 𝕃

113 Station Road, TS23 2RL (at N end of Station Rd, among a row of shops, close to level crossing)

☎ (01642) 881478

3 changing beers Ⓗ

This small, cosy bar is one of several micropub-style outlets in Old Billingham. Friendly and knowledgeable bar staff dispense three beers, including offerings from local breweries, as well as real cider. Third-pint tasting bats are available. This popular micro has become renowned locally for its varied live bands. Tapas is offered Tuesday to Thursday evenings and Sunday lunches are served, with a takeaway and local delivery service also available. ◑♿🍎P🚌(36,X9)

Bishop Auckland

Bay Horse

38-40 Fore Bondgate, DL14 7PE (50yds N of bus station)

☎ (01388) 609765 🌐 dorbiere.co.uk/bay-horse

3 changing beers (sourced nationally; often Camerons) Ⓗ

There has been a pub on this site since 1530, and this lively, open-plan bar is a quiet relief from shopping during the week. With live music on Friday and karaoke on Saturday, it becomes joyfully boisterous at the weekend, and is popular for televised sport. It retains its roots as a long-established, proper pub, with pub games teams and an eclectic choice of ales. ❀♿♣🍎🚌📶

Green Tree

Cockton Hill Road, DL14 6EN
☎ (01388) 663249
2 changing beers (sourced nationally) Ⓗ
A large pub at the south end of the shopping street. It has a bar with pool table area, a spacious lounge, and a big garden patio with a covered smoking area to the rear. Popular for TV sport and the Tuesday quiz, it hosts occasional live music. Interesting football and music memorabilia adorn the walls alongside paintings of the town by local artist Gaz Miller. ❀♿⇌♣🚌🐾

Pollards 🄻

104 Etherley Lane, DL14 6TU (400yds W of railway station)
☎ (01388) 603539
Wainwright; house beer (by Camerons); 3 changing beers (sourced nationally; often Allendale, Consett, Marston's) Ⓗ
This comfortable and busy establishment is a great combination of traditional pub and pleasant diner, a 10-minute stroll from the town centre. Two of the four original areas, including the bar, boast open fires or logburners, and there is a spacious restaurant to the rear where the famous Sunday carvery can be enjoyed. Five well-kept ales, good conversation and a popular quiz on Sunday evening top things off. Q🐎❀◑◗♿⇌♣P🐾

Welcome

Low Waldron Street, DL14 7DS
☎ (01388) 662492
1 changing beer (sourced nationally) Ⓗ
Very much a cosy, local pub, but only a minute's walk from the bus station and main street. There's a single L-shaped room with a dartboard to the rear, and a live singer on Fridays. A great place for a chat that welcomes everybody, and with a great community feel. Closed Tuesdays. Q🐎❀♿⇌♣P🚌🐾📶

Bishop Middleham

Cross Keys 🄻

9 High Street, DL17 9AR (1 mile from A177)
☎ (01740) 651231 🌐 crosskeysbm.com
2 changing beers (sourced nationally) Ⓗ
A busy family-run village inn with a good reputation for food. It has a bar with a real fire, a lounge and a large restaurant at the back. The pub is opposite the remains of Forsters Brewery which closed in 1913 and it may well have been the tap house. The village has a series of walks exploring beautiful countryside and the remains of Bishop Middleham Castle. Q🐎❀◑◗♣🚌🐾

Blackhill

Scotch Arms 🄻 ✔

48 Derwent Street, DH8 8LZ
☎ (01207) 593709
Sharp's Atlantic; 3 changing beers (sourced nationally; often Big Lamp, Caledonian) Ⓗ
A traditional community hostelry off the main street in Blackhill with a large L-shaped bar. The interior was freshened up to celebrate the licensee's 10-year anniversary in 2018. Up to four cask ales are on offer, always including local beers. The welcoming pub is home to pool and darts teams, and a local football team, and popular for sports TV. Charity nights and other live events often feature. Toasted sandwiches are available.
🐎♿♣⚽🐾📶

Chester-le-Street

Butchers Arms ✔

Middle Chare, DH3 3QD (off Front St on left from Market Place)
☎ (0191) 388 3605 🌐 butchersarms.org.uk
Marston's Pedigree; Jennings Cumberland Ale; 3 changing beers (sourced nationally; often Ringwood, Wainwright, Wychwood) Ⓗ
A cosy pub acknowledged for the quality and quantity of its beers, selling at least five cask ales from the Marston's range. The pub is also noted for its food, with home-cooking a speciality; Sunday lunches are popular and good value. Teas and coffees are also served. Dogs are welcome and it is convenient for the railway station and all buses through the town. Quiz night is Tuesday.
Q🐎❀🛏◑♿⇌♣🚌(21) 🐾

Masonic Centre 🄻

Station Road, DH3 3DU
☎ (0191) 388 4905
Roundhill Midnight Slug; 3 changing beers (sourced nationally; often Marston's, Oakham, Roundhill) Ⓗ
Guests are more than welcome at the Masonic Centre just off Front Street in the heart of the town. Press the buzzer on the front door and walk in. As well as four changing real ales, you will also find one of the biggest selections of single malt whisky in the area. Sunday lunches and Friday fish suppers are popular. Local CAMRA Club of the Year 2020. 🐎◑◗♿⇌P🚌(21)🐾📶

Sticky Wicket 🄻

Emirates Durham International Cricket Ground, Riverside, DH3 3QR
☎ (0191) 387 5502 🌐 thestickywicket.co.uk
Timothy Taylor Landlord; 2 changing beers (sourced nationally; often Camerons, Durham, Maxim) Ⓗ
Sports bar within the grounds of the Emirates Riverside cricket venue, home to Durham County Cricket Club. The bar is now open Tuesday to Sunday following a refurbishment in 2019. Food is served daily until 9pm. Quiz night is Tuesday; live music features on Thursday, Friday and Saturday evenings. An admission fee to the ground may apply during a cricket match.
🐎◑◗♿⚽P🚌(71) 🐾

REAL ALE BREWERIES

Barnard Castle Barnard Castle
Black Storm Pelton Fell
Camerons Hartlepool
Caps Off Bishop Auckland (NEW)
Castle Eden Seaham
Consett 🛢 Consett
Crafty Monkey Elwick
Crafty Pint 🛢 Darlington
Durham Bowburn
George Samuel Shildon
Hill Island Durham
Hopburst Darlington
Hopper House Brew Farm ✦ Sedgefield
Mad Scientist 🛢 Darlington
McColl's Evenwood
Roundhill Cowpen Bewley (brewing suspended)
S43 Coxhoe
Saints Row ✦ Darlington
South Causey Stanley (NEW)
Three Brothers Stockton on Tees
Village Brewer: Brew 22 🛢 Darlington
Weard'ALE 🛢 Westgate
Working Hand 🛢 Leamside
Yard of Ale 🛢 Ferryhill

Consett

Company Row L ✓

Victoria Road, DH8 5BQ
☎ (01207) 585600
Greene King Abbot; Ruddles Best Bitter; Sharp's Doom Bar; 3 changing beers (sourced nationally) 🄷
Modern pub named after the rows of houses built by the Derwent Iron Company for its workers, which were mostly demolished in the mid-1920s. This spacious and well-decorated Wetherspoon establishment is a real asset to Consett town centre. An excellent beer selection, including local ales, and good food make this social pub popular with a wide clientele of all ages.
🐎✿◐◑♿♣🍎🚌📶

Grey Horse 🏆 L ✓

115 Sherburn Terrace, DH8 6NE
☎ (01207) 502585
Consett Red Dust, Steel Town Bitter, White Hot, Steelworkers Blonde; 5 changing beers (sourced nationally) 🄷
Traditional pub dating back to 1848. The interior comprises a lounge and L-shaped bar, with a wood-beamed ceiling. Consett Ale Works Brewery is located at the rear. Beer festivals are held twice a year, live entertainment is hosted on Thursday and a quiz on Wednesday. The coast-to-coast cycle route is close by. There is some bench seating outside at the front of the pub. Local CAMRA Town Pub of the Year 2019 and 2020.
✿♿🍎🚌🐾📶

Cotherstone

Red Lion L

Main Street, DL12 9QE
☎ (01833) 650236 🌐 theredlionhotel.blogspot.com
House beer (by Yorkshire Dales) 🄷
An 18th-century Grade II listed coaching inn, built in stone and set in an idyllic village. This homely local, simply furnished and featuring two open fires, has changed little since the 1960s. It has no TV, jukebox or one-armed bandit, just good beer and conversation. Two house ales from Yorkshire Dales are served alongside up to six real ciders. The pub is used by various local clubs, and welcomes children, dogs and clean boots. The small garden is a suntrap. Local CAMRA Community Pub of the Year 2020. 🐎✿♣🍎🚌(95)🐾📶

Crook

Copper Mine L

26 High Jobs Hill, DL15 0UL
☎ (01388) 763333 🌐 copperminecrook.com
3 changing beers (sourced locally; often Allendale, Yard of Ale) 🄷
A comfortable family-run local on the edge of Weardale up the hill from Crook towards Durham. The interior is open plan but with distinct drinking and dining areas. The beers are nearly always from local breweries. Home-cooked quality food is available to cater for all tastes.
🐎✿◐◑P🚌(X46)🐾📶

Horse Shoe L ✓

4 Church Street, DL15 9BG
☎ (01388) 744980
Greene King Abbot; Maxim Double Maxim; Ruddles Best Bitter; 6 changing beers (sourced nationally) 🄷
This busy and tasteful refurbishment has four interlinked drinking areas making up the main part of the pub, with a pleasant sheltered patio to the side. There is the usual Wetherspoon acknowledgement of previous use, in this case a butcher's, in the metal bar top. Local history is reflected in the decor, with a surprise at the top of the stairs in the shape of old mining equipment.
🐎✿◐◑🍎🚌(X1,X46)📶

Darlington

Bondgate Tavern

94 Bondgate, DL3 7JY
☎ (01325) 962114
4 changing beers (sourced nationally) 🄷
One of the newest town-centre bars, handily located on Bondgate where a number of venues serving good beer can be found. Up to four competitively priced real ales are served, with a focus on local breweries. The busy calendar features live music, sport on TV and quizzes during the week. The pub hosts darts and has a pool table and function room. It offers a discount on real ale to CAMRA members. ♿♣🍎🐾

Britannia L ✓

1 Archer Street, DL3 6LR (next to ring road W of town centre)
☎ (01325) 463787
Camerons Strongarm; Draught Bass; John Smith's John Smith's Bitter; 3 changing beers (sourced nationally) 🄷
Warm, friendly, local CAMRA award-winning inn – a bastion of cask beer since 1859. The comfortable, traditional pub retains much of the appearance and layout of the private house it once was – a modestly enlarged bar and small parlour sit either side of a central corridor. Grade II listed for its historic association, it was the birthplace of teetotal 19th-century publisher JM Dent. Three changing guest ales complement the three regular ales. ♣🍎P🐾📶

Darlington Snooker Club L

1 Corporation Road, DL3 6AE (corner of Northgate)
☎ (01325) 241388
4 changing beers (sourced nationally) 🄷
First-floor, family-run and family-oriented private snooker club that was founded over 100 years ago. A cosy, comfortable TV lounge is available for those not playing on one of the 10 top-quality snooker tables. Twice yearly, the club hosts a professional celebrity. Four guest beers from micros countrywide are stocked and two beer festivals are held annually. Frequently voted CAMRA Regional Club of the Year and a former National finalist, it welcomes CAMRA members on production of a membership card or copy of this Guide. 🐎◐⇌🍎

Half Moon L

130 Northgate, DL1 1QS
☎ (01325) 469965
7 changing beers (sourced nationally) 🄷
Old-school pub just across the ring road from the town centre with friendly staff and customers creating a relaxed atmosphere. This local reopened in 2013 as a real ale pub following a long period of closure. It offers seven changing cask ales including brews from micros unusual for the area and occasional beers from the on-site Crafty Pint nano brewery. There is a library area to borrow and exchange books. 🐎♣🍎🐾📶

House of Hop L

4B Houndgate, DL1 5RL
4 changing beers (sourced nationally) 🄷
Smart, contemporary bar in the town centre's Imperial Quarter, with links to the local Three Brothers brewery. The pub serves four changing real ales from across the North-East and beyond. It also offers one of the town's widest ranges of craft keg beers, plus ciders and cocktails. Live music is played regularly. Q🍎🐾📶

Number Twenty 2 Ⓛ ✅

22 Coniscliffe Road, DL3 7RG

☎ (01325) 354590

Village Bull, Old Raby, White Boar; 7 changing beers (sourced nationally) Ⓗ

Town-centre ale house with a passion for cask beer and a winner of many CAMRA awards. Ales are dispensed from up to 16 handpumps, including a stout or porter, plus two real ciders and 10 draught European beers. Huge curved windows, stained-glass panels and a high ceiling give the interior an airy, spacious feel. To the rear is the in-house nano distillery and microbrewery producing gin, vodka and ale. Sandwiches and snacks are available at lunchtime. Home of Village Brewer beers are commissioned from Hambleton by the licensee.
Q꒰ఠ▭ఉ🞄

Old Yard Tapas Bar Ⓛ

98 Bondgate, DL3 7JY

☎ (01325) 467385 ⊕ tapasbar.co.uk

John Smith's Bitter; house beer (by Tyne Bank); 4 changing beers (sourced nationally) Ⓗ

Interesting mixture of a bar and Mediterranean taverna, offering real ales alongside a blend of international wines and spirits in a friendly setting. Five guest beers are stocked, some from local micros, with two more sometimes available in a separate room. Although this is a restaurant it welcomes customers for a pint and tapas. Food is served lunchtime and evening Sunday to Friday and all day Saturday. The pavement café is popular in good weather. A TV shows sport only. Q꒰🏵🕪ఉ🞄🞄🞄

ORB Micropub Ⓛ

28 Coniscliffe Road, DL3 7RG

☎ 07903 237246

6 changing beers (sourced nationally) Ⓗ

Traditional micropub with friendly, knowledgeable staff in a former beauty salon, the first of its kind in Darlington. There is no TV or loud music so this is a place to relax and engage in conversation. It serves six local real ales, with the town's Saints Row a regular supplier, plus 10 craft beers, two real ciders and a large range of single malt whiskies. ORB stands for Orchard Road Brewery. A recent local CAMRA Pub of the Year. Q🞄🞄

Quakerhouse 🏆 Ⓛ

2 Mechanics Yard, DL3 7QF (off High Row)

⊕ quakerhouse.co.uk

9 changing beers (sourced nationally) Ⓗ

Seventeen times local CAMRA Town Pub of the Year, and a former North-East Pub of the Year, this gem is located in one of the town's historic Yards. The lively bar offers nine handpulled guest beers from local and regional breweries plus two changing real ciders. This friendly and welcoming pub is a popular music venue, catering for all tastes from acoustic to rock. It hosts live music every Wednesday and some other nights, with free entry. Home to the Mad Scientist microbrewery.
🏵ఉ♣🞄P▭🞄🞄

Tanners Hall ✅

63-64 Skinnergate, DL3 7LL

☎ (01325) 369939

Greene King Abbot; Ruddles Best Bitter; Sharp's Doom Bar; 7 changing beers (sourced nationally) Ⓗ

A popular Wetherspoon pub named after the local 18th-century leather trade that dominated the town. Its 12 handpumps provide a good selection of real ales including up to nine guests, often from local micros. A spacious interior makes this an ideal venue for the pub's beer festivals and Meet The Brewer nights, and the chain's national events. Reasonably priced food is served until 11pm. Q꒰🏵🕪ఉ🞄🞄

Durham

Bridge Hotel

40 North Road, DH1 4SE (200yds from Durham rail station)

☎ (0191) 386 8090 ⊕ bridgehoteldurham.com

Wainwright; 2 changing beers (sourced nationally) Ⓗ

Friendly pub that attracts a good mix of regulars and visitors to the region. It was built in the 1850s as lodgings for railway workers constructing the viaduct under which it sits, becoming a public house a few years later. The pub has recently been refurbished with a comfortable bar and lower dining area. It serves good quality home-cooked food 11.45am-9pm every day at reasonable prices, and hosts quizzes on Tuesday and Sunday night with a free hot buffet.
꒰🔯🕪ఋ▭(21)🞄🞄

Colpitts Hotel

Colpitts Terrace, DH1 4EG

☎ (0191) 386 9913

Samuel Smith Old Brewery Bitter Ⓗ

A refurbishment has given this late-Victorian pub a smart makeover, but it remains little changed from when it was first built and continues to thrive on its traditional charm. As with all Samuel Smith's pubs, the noise comes from the chatter of conversation rather than from music or TV. The unusual A-shaped building comprises a cosy snug, a pool room and the main bar area partially divided by a fireplace. If you want to take a step back in time, this is the pub for you. Q꒰🞄♣▭🞄

Court Inn Ⓛ

Court Lane, DH1 3AW

☎ (0191) 384 7350 ⊕ courtinn.co.uk

Timothy Taylor Landlord; 5 changing beers (sourced nationally; often Maxim) Ⓗ

A busy venue with decor that reflects the location near the city's Crown Courts. Up to six real ales are on offer at any one time as well as two real ciders. A wide selection of food is served until 10.15pm daily. The pub is popular with locals and students alike, and offers a warm welcome to all visitors. ꒰🏵🕪🞄▭(6)🞄🞄

Dun Cow Ⓛ ✅

37 Old Elvet, DH1 3HN

☎ (0191) 386 9219

Black Sheep Best Bitter; Castle Eden Ale; Moorhouse's White Witch; 1 changing beer (sourced nationally; often Camerons, Daleside) Ⓗ

A Grade II listed pub, parts of which date back to the 15th century. In 995AD, Lindisfarne monks searching for a resting place for the body of St Cuthbert came across a milkmaid looking for her lost cow. She directed them to Dun Holm (Durham), and the pub is named after the historic animal. There is a friendly front snug with a larger lounge to the rear. At least three real ales are usually on offer. Q꒰🕪▭(6,X12)🞄🞄

Half Moon Inn Ⓛ ✅

86 New Elvet, DH1 3AQ

☎ (0191) 374 1918 ⊕ thehalfmooninndurham.co.uk

Draught Bass; Durham White Gold; Sharp's Doom Bar; Timothy Taylor Landlord Ⓗ

Popular city-centre pub, reputedly named after the crescent-shaped bar that runs through it. The decor throughout is traditional, featuring photos of the pub at the beginning of the 20th century, including many from the Miners' Gala. A friendly venue with a relaxed atmosphere, it offers a good selection of ales. The large beer garden overlooks the river. 🏵ఉ▭(6)🞄🞄

Market Tavern

27 Market Place, DH1 3NJ
☎ (0191) 386 2069
Greene King IPA; 4 changing beers (sourced nationally; often Greene King, Maxim)
A busy city-centre pub in Durham's historic marketplace, offering a good selection of five local and national cask ales and one real cider. Despite refurbishments, the pub has managed to keep its traditional wooden alehouse appearance, and pictures of miners' banners take pride of place. Customers are given a warm welcome, and good food based on pub classics is served until 9.30pm. Quiz night is Thursday.

Station House

North Road, DH1 4SE
stationhousedurham.co.uk
4 changing beers (sourced nationally; often Abbeydale, Almasty, North Riding)
A wedge-shaped pub in the shadow of the railway viaduct, opened in 2015 by CAMRA members. It is very friendly, with a back-to-basics approach and an emphasis on conversation. A changing range of real ale and cider is served directly through a hatch from the cold room. Handpumps have recently been installed, with gravity remaining an option. A dark beer is always available, and an extra beer is often added at weekends. Reigning branch City Cider Pub of the Year. Closed Mondays.
Q

Victoria Inn ★

86 Hallgarth Street, DH1 3AS
☎ (0191) 386 5269 victoriainn-durhamcity.co.uk
Big Lamp Bitter; 4 changing beers (sourced nationally; often Durham, Fyne Ales, S43)
This warm and welcoming, family-run, Grade II listed pub has remained almost unchanged since it was built in 1899, and the quaint decor, coal fires, cosy snug and genuine Victorian cash drawer help create an old-world feel. Ales are mainly from local breweries, with a wide selection of single malts also on offer. No meals are served but toasties are available. Voted local CAMRA City Pub of the Year yet again in 2020, the Victoria is popular with locals, students and visitors to the city.
Q (6,PR2)

Waiting Room

Northbound Platform, Durham Railway Station, DH1 4RB
☎ (0191) 386 7773
Hadrian Border Tyneside Blonde; 2 changing beers (sourced locally; often Allendale, Durham, Yard of Ale)
This attractive venue on Durham railway station's northbound platform is an interesting relaunch of the original 1872 Ladies' Waiting Room, out of use for many years other than as a storage facility. In keeping with the building's Grade II listed status the design is traditional, with Chesterfield-style seating, original floorboards and fireplaces, wood panelling and a dark-wood bar. Three handpumps showcase local beers. QP(40)

Water House

65 North Road, DH1 4SQ
☎ (0191) 370 6540
Greene King Abbot; Ruddles Best Bitter; Sharp's Doom Bar; 5 changing beers (sourced nationally)
Situated in former Water Board offices, this popular Wetherspoon pub gets extremely busy at weekends. It offers a good selection of beers from regional and microbrewers, and hosts a beer festival twice a year plus an annual cider festival. The modern decor is complemented by coal-effect open fires. The pub serves good-value food, and hosts a poker night on Monday and a quiz night on Wednesday. Alcoholic drinks are available from 9am.

Eaglescliffe

Cleveland Bay

718 Yarm Road, TS16 0JE (jct of A67 and A135, N of Tees bridge)
☎ (01642) 780275 clevelandbay.co.uk
Timothy Taylor Landlord; Wainwright; 2 changing beers
A large three-roomed locals' pub with an enthusiastic licensee and a reputation for fine premium bitters. Third-pint glasses and tasting notes are available for the four handpumps. The pub's Blues at the Bay live music evenings on Friday feature bands of national and international repute. A free buffet lunch is served on Sunday. A former CAMRA branch Community Pub of the Year. Q♣P(7,17)

Eastgate

Cross Keys

DL13 2HW (on main road)
☎ (01388) 517234 crosskeyseastgate.co.uk
2 changing beers (sourced nationally; often Allendale)
A proper family-run Weardale pub, popular with holidaymakers and locals. The ancient 17th-century building has a pleasant interior with a lively, welcoming bar and a restaurant providing relaxed dining. Allendale Brewery beers feature regularly. There is a beer garden to the rear. Comfortable B&B accommodation is available for those wishing to explore the beautiful surrounding countryside. Q♣P(101)

Edmundbyers

Baa

Low House Haven, DH8 9NL
☎ (01207) 255651 thebaabar.com/thebaa
2 changing beers (sourced nationally; often Cullercoats)
Former Youth Hostel Association building and now an independent hostel close to Derwent Reservoir, dating back to 1600 when it began life as an inn. The cycle sheds have been converted into a welcoming stone-floored micropub-style bar, offering two well-kept ales, invariably from local breweries and often produced especially for the pub. Opening hours may vary, especially out of season, so check before travelling.
Q

Ferryhill Station

Surtees Arms

Chilton Lane, DL17 0DH
☎ (01740) 655724 thesurteesarms.co.uk
Yard of Ale One Foot In The Yard; 4 changing beers (sourced nationally; often Yard of Ale)
Traditional pub serving local and national ales and ciders as well as beers from the on-site Yard of Ale Brewery (est 2008). Annual beer festivals are held in the summer and at Halloween. Live music and charity nights are regular events. Lunches are served on Sunday only. A large function room is available. Local CAMRA Country Pub of the Year 2020 and a former regional Pub of the Year. Q

Forest-in-Teesdale

Langdon Beck Hotel

DL12 0XP (on B6277, 8 miles NW of Middleton-in-Teesdale)

☎ (01833) 622267 🌐 langdonbeckhotel.com

Wainwright; Great North Eastern Rivet Catcher; 1 changing beer (sourced nationally) Ⓗ

Known as the Sportsman's Rest in the early 1800s, this pub is in the North Pennines, three miles from the spectacular High Force and Cauldron Snout waterfalls and close to the Pennine Way. The welcoming inn has long been a destination for walkers, anglers and those seeking hospitality in scenic and peaceful surroundings, whether staying overnight or just long enough to enjoy the excellent food and drink. A beer festival features over the late May bank holiday weekend.
Q♨❀🛏◑♿▲♣P🐾

Framwellgate Moor

Tap & Spile 🄻 ✔

Front Street, DH1 5EE

☎ (0191) 386 5451

6 changing beers (sourced nationally; often Abbeydale, Adnams, Cullercoats) Ⓗ

Welcoming pub with a relaxed atmosphere, popular with beer enthusiasts due to its excellent range of six constantly changing real ales. There are two bars at one side; the other side can be divided into two. Families are welcome in the side room until 9pm. Attractions include quiz night on Wednesday and folk music night on Thursday. ♨●P🚌(21)🐾

Hamilton Row

Black Horse 🄻

DH7 9AU

☎ (0191) 373 4576

2 changing beers (sourced nationally; often Castle Rock, S43) Ⓗ

A friendly local with an open fire at one end and a glass-fronted fire at the other helping to create a warm, cosy atmosphere. Two well-kept real ales always include one from a local brewery. Good-value Sunday lunches are served. There is a pool table. An excellent pub for walkers, handily situated adjacent to the Deerness Valley Way. Q♨◐♣●P🚌(52,725)🐾📶

Hartlepool

Anchor Tap Room & Bottle Shop 🄻

Stockton Street, TS24 7QY (on A689, in front of Camerons Brewery)

☎ (01429) 868686

Camerons Strongarm; 2 changing beers Ⓗ

When Camerons Brewery discovered that it owned an adjacent derelict pub, they converted it into the brewery's tap and visitor centre. Now in its 17th successful year, it operates as a bar and bottle shop. Strongarm and the brewery's monthly specials are always available, together with an array of limited edition and continental bottled beers. Meetings, conferences and social events, as well as superb buffets, can all be arranged. ❀♿⇌P🚌(1,36)🐾

Hops & Cheese 🄻

9-11 Tower Street, TS24 7HH (100 yds S of bus interchange/railway station)

☎ 07704 660417 🌐 hopsandcheese.co.uk

3 changing beers Ⓗ

Run by enthusiastic hosts, fulfilling a vision of bringing home a flavour of the more contemporary tapas-style bars experienced on their continental holidays, this welcoming bar represents something modern, original and different. Three interesting beers, several craft beers and a real cider are available together with artisan cheeses and charcuterie, all served in a relaxed atmosphere. Jazz evenings are organised, while newspapers, a regular book club, off-sales, and low-key background music all enhance the experience.
♨◑♿⇌●🚌(1,36)

Rat Race Ale House

Station Approach, Hartlepool Railway Station, TS24 7ED (on Platform 1)

☎ 07903 479378 🌐 ratracealehouse.co.uk

4 changing beers Ⓗ

The second micropub in the country, now celebrating 11 years of continuous Guide recognition, adheres to the original micropub norms – no fizzy lager or beer, no spirits or alcopops, no TV or jukebox, no one-arm bandit, and even no bar! Since opening in 2009, more than 1,900 beers, sourced from over 550 breweries, have been served direct to the table by the landlord himself. Two real ciders are also on offer, as well as crisps, nuts and scratchings. Local CAMRA Cider Pub of the Year 2020.
Q♿⇌♣●▯🚌(1,36)

Hartlepool Headland

Fishermans Arms 🄻 ✔

Southgate, TS24 0JJ (on headland close to Fish Quay, in Old Hartlepool)

☎ 07847 208599 🌐 thefishhartlepool.co.uk

3 changing beers Ⓗ

The Fish is a friendly, one-room locals' pub. Now free of tie, it serves up to four beers, plus a cider in summer. The pub's theme is Keeping Music Alive: it hosts well-supported open-mic nights, plus live music on Saturday. There is a popular quiz on Sunday, but no jukebox, TV or one-armed-bandit. Two beer festivals, also with live music, are held annually. Winter opening hours may vary. Q●▯🚌(7)🐾📶

Globe 🄻

26 Northgate, TS24 0LJ (on headland, towards Fish Quay)

☎ (01429) 860097

Camerons Strongarm Ⓗ

Opposite the port that was once bustling with shipbuilding, fishing boats, coal staithes and pit props, this typical two-roomed local is under the stewardship of a friendly and experienced licensee with over 25 years of service to the trade. The price of Strongarm (ask for a Hartlepool Head) still represents remarkable value, reflecting the pub's freehold status; savings negotiated with Camerons are passed on to customers. A popular community pub, it is a past winner of local CAMRA Pub of the Year awards. Q♿♣▯🚌(7)

Hawthorn

Stapylton Arms 🄻

Village Green, SR7 8SD

☎ (0191) 527 0778

3 changing beers (sourced regionally; often Maxim, S43, Working Hand) Ⓗ

Delightfully welcoming, locally owned village pub serving excellent food. It has two comfortable well-appointed rooms – one a bar and the other a lounge/restaurant. Three well-kept cask ales showcase the best of North-East breweries. The Monday quiz is well

attended. This hidden-away pub is in an ideal location for walkers exploring the nearby Hawthorn Dene.
Q P

High Hesleden

Ship Inn

Mickle Hill Road, TS27 4QD (between A19 and Blackhall, signed from B1281)
(01429) 836453 theshipinn.net
7 changing beers
Now in its 20th year of family ownership, this rural gem guarantees complete satisfaction. The landlord serves seven beers, most locally sourced, as well as real cider. His wife runs the superb restaurant, offering top-quality food at reasonable prices, including mid-week early-doors two-course specials. There are stupendous coastal views from the well-kept gardens. Six motel-style chalets provide good-value accommodation. The pub closes during the owners' annual holidays, so check before making a long journey. A former CAMRA Regional Pub of the Year. Q P (206)

Hunwick

Joiners Arms

13 South View, DL15 0JW
(01388) 417878 thejoinersarms.webnode.com
3 changing beers (sourced nationally; often Timothy Taylor)
Family-run village local with a welcoming bar, restaurant, tiny snug and covered yard/pool room. The bar is the place for proper conversation, along with three handpumps featuring a changing selection. Quality locally sourced food is served Wednesday to Saturday evenings, and Sunday lunchtime in the restaurant. On Monday evening the pub hosts a cheese night.
P (108,109)

Ingleton

Black Horse

Front Street, DL2 3HS
(01325) 730374
4 changing beers (sourced nationally)
Free house and restaurant set back from the road with a large car park, situated in a picturesque village. The friendly bar runs into the dining area. This is a popular community hostelry with a relaxed atmosphere. Four guest ales come from local micros within a 30-mile radius of the pub. Excellent Italian food is served in the restaurant Wednesday to Sunday. The pub hosts local darts teams and a Sunday night quiz.
Q P (84)

Kip Hill

South Causey Inn

Beamish Burn Road, DH9 0LS
(01207) 235555 southcausey.co.uk
4 changing beers (sourced locally; often Bombardier)
A large and attractive pub with hotel and restaurant facilities. Extensive seating includes soft leather sofas in front of open fires and dining tables. Beers are always available from the on-site South Causey Brewery. The pub opens at 7am for cooked breakfasts, with non-residents welcome. Several rooms can be booked for private functions. Q P

Leamside

Three Horseshoes

Pit House Lane, DH4 6QQ (half a mile N of A690, just outside West Rainton)
(0191) 584 2394 threehorseshoesleamside.co.uk
Timothy Taylor Landlord; 5 changing beers (sourced nationally)
A country pub with an excellent restaurant, the Back Room (booking advisable). The traditional bar has open fires in winter and a large TV for sport. Five real ales and a real cider are served, with Timothy Taylor Landlord always available. The pub is home to a local cycle club and hosts a quiz on Sunday evening. Local CAMRA Country Pub of the Year 2018 and 2019.
Q P

Medomsley

Royal Oak

7 Manor Road, DH8 6QN
(01207) 560336
Hadrian Border Tyneside Blonde; 2 changing beers (sourced nationally; often Consett, Hadrian Border)
Traditional country-style pub with a warm, welcoming feel. It has a large bar with a selection of seating including soft sofas and leather chairs, and plenty of dining space. The pub serves a rotation of quality beers as well as good food. There is a large, attractive rear garden and ample parking to the front. Quiz night is Sunday. Q P

Metal Bridge

Old Mill

Thinford Road, DH6 5NX (off A1M J61, follow signs on A177)
(01740) 652928 oldmilldurham.co.uk
4 changing beers (sourced nationally; often Durham, Bowland, Rudgate)
Originally a paper mill in 1813, the pub offers good-quality food and well-kept ales – four handpumps serve a diverse range, with local breweries supplying at least one of the beers. The food menu is extensive, with daily specials written on a board above the bar. Larger groups are welcome in the conservatory. Accommodation is of a high standard, with all rooms en-suite. Q P

Middlestone

Ship Inn

Low Road, DL14 8AB (between Coundon and Kirk Merrington)
(01388) 810904 theshipinnmiddlestonevillage.co.uk
Timothy Taylor Landlord; 5 changing beers (sourced nationally)
Regular drinkers come from far and wide to the Ship. It has a bar divided into three distinct areas with an open fire, and a large function room upstairs which is the location for occasional beer festivals. The rooftop patio has spectacular views, and there is always an event either taking place or imminent. Various pieces of Vaux memorabilia are on display – one of the many subjects of conversation. Sunday lunches are popular. A former Durham CAMRA Country Pub of the Year.
Q P (56,99)

Newfield

Newfield Inn

Front Street, DH2 2SP
(0191) 370 0565

Maxim Double Maxim
A friendly two-roomed pub in the centre of the village, known locally simply as the Inn. It serves one beer from owner Maxim Brewery from nearby Houghton-le-Spring, plus one guest. The pub hosts a Tuesday night quiz, monthly live music and football on TV, and also offers accommodation. Families are welcome and there is a pleasant beer garden. P (78)

Newton Aycliffe

Turbinia

Parsons Centre, Sid Chaplin Drive, DL5 7PA (off Burnhill Way, next to Methodist church)
(01325) 313034 turbiniapub.co.uk
4 changing beers (sourced nationally; often Mithril, Revolutions, Three Brothers)
Named after the famous Tyneside steamship, this friendly free house comprises a large lounge and function room, with traditional pub decor featuring a pictorial history of the Turbinia – the world's fastest ship on its construction in 1894. The pub serves an ever-changing variety of beers sourced locally and nationally, as well as craft gins. It hosts a beer and cider festival twice yearly. Darts, dominoes and pool are played in the main bar during the week and live music at the weekend. P (7)

No Place

Beamish Mary Inn

DH9 0QH (follow signs to No Place off A693 from Chester-le-Street to Stanley)
(0191) 392 0543 beamish-mary-inn.co.uk
5 changing beers (sourced nationally; often Big Lamp, Consett)
Full of character, this pub is well respected for its warm welcome, generously portioned pub grub and ample selection of well-kept real ale. The location is handy for visitors to the renowned open-air Beamish Museum nearby. Consett Ale Works and Big Lamp beers are usually included among the range of LocAles on offer. Accommodation is available including twin, double and family rooms. Q P

Norton

Hydes Bar

Rowan Yard, Billingham Road, TS20 2RZ (in a former builder's yard, at S end of High St)
(01642) 550662
4 changing beers
Contemporary, friendly bar in the former workshop of John Hyde, a family-run joiner and builder's merchant for more than 50 years. The workshop was refurbished in 2016, highlighting its former use with old items and photographs on display. Large patio doors open on to a south-facing courtyard. Four guest beers and four real ciders are served. Music nights feature throughout the week. (36,37)

Old Shotton

Royal George

The Village, SR8 2ND
(0191) 586 6500 royalgeorgeoldshotton.co.uk
Timothy Taylor Landlord; 2 changing beers (sourced nationally; often Great North Eastern, Harviestoun, Rooster's)
Pub and restaurant on the old village green, now well established following the 2014 refurbishment of its bar plus larger lounge and restaurant area. Handpulled cider is often on offer alongside the cask ale. Traditional pub grub and bar snacks are available. Dogs are welcome, with treats on the bar. Q P

Ovington

Four Alls

The Green, DL11 7BP (2 miles S of Winston & A67)
(01833) 627302 thefouralls-ovington.co.uk
2 changing beers (sourced locally)
Friendly stone-built 18th-century inn opposite the village green in what is known as the 'maypole village'. A Victorian sign denotes the four alls: 'I govern all (queen), I fight for all (soldier), I pray for all (parson), I pay for all (farmer).' The single room interior has an 'upstairs' snug serving excellent, good-value food made with local ingredients. Two real ales are available – a dark and a light from local Mithril Ales. There is seating outside at the front and the rear beer garden is perfect on sunny days. Q P

Piercebridge

Fox Hole

Carlbury, DL2 3SJ (on B6275)
(01325) 374286 the-foxhole.co.uk
Camerons Strongarm; Timothy Taylor Landlord; 1 changing beer (sourced nationally)
In a village built on the site of a Roman fort, The Fox Hole sits almost centrally between the towns of Darlington, Barnard Castle, Bishop Auckland and Richmond. From the welcoming Wellie bar through to the relaxed yet elegant dining room and alfresco dining terrace, the emphasis is on high-quality, carefully locally sourced food and drink, combined with traditional pub values. A warm welcome and friendly service, along with three beers, two regulars and a guest from local micros including Mithril three miles away, combine to make this pub a must-visit. P (75,76)

Running Waters

Three Horse Shoes

Sherburn House, DH1 2SR
(0191) 372 0286 threehorseshoesdurham.co.uk
3 changing beers (sourced nationally)
Country inn nicely situated a few miles from Durham city, offering good food and drink plus comfortable accommodation. Three cask ales are served, usually at least one sourced locally, with alcohol available from noon. The rear beer garden provides excellent views over open countryside. Q P

St John's Chapel

Blue Bell Inn

Hood St, DL13 1QJ
(01388) 537256
2 changing beers (sourced nationally)
Originally a pair of terraced cottages, the Blue Bell is a friendly and cosy pub with a bar across the front of the building leading to a small pool room, and garden to the rear. Situated on the A689, it serves the local community and those who holiday in Upper Weardale. Popular for pub games, it also doubles as a library.
Q (101)

Seaham

Coalhouse

39 Church Street, SR7 7EJ
(0191) 581 6235 seahamcoalhouse.uk

4 changing beers (sourced locally; often Cullercoats, Yard of Ale) Ⓗ
A former bookmakers', now a much valued part of Seaham's licensed trade. The pub was refurbished in 2018 using 100-year-old timbers salvaged from the town's demolished Co-op building. The decor celebrates the area's coal-mining heritage, notably one wall's impressive mural depicting Seaham pits. Four changing cask beers are offered along with up to four real ciders and five keg taps. ❀≈♣●🚌(265,60)🐾

Seaton

Dun Cow L

The Village, SR7 0NA
☎ (0191) 513 1133
4 changing beers (sourced nationally; often Jennings, Maxim, Wainwright) Ⓗ
Friendly and unspoilt inn on the village green, featuring a public bar and lounge areas. This is a pub for good conversation or a game of darts; the TV is only used for special events. The changing guest beer selection usually comprises two light and two dark ales. No meals are served but toasties are always available. The pub hosts regular busker and acoustic music nights. A former local CAMRA Country Pub of the Year. ❀♿♣●P🚌(238)🐾

Sedgefield

Dun Cow L

43 Front Street, TS21 3AT
☎ (01740) 620894 🌐 duncowinn.co.uk
4 changing beers (sourced nationally) Ⓗ
Run by the same landlord for over 40 years, this large and comfortable 18th-century inn has a county-wide reputation for good food using locally sourced produce. Prime minister Tony Blair and US president George W Bush famously had lunch here in 2003. There are three bars including a farmers' bar-cum-snug and restaurant. Four real ales are always available including at least one local beer. Q❀●P🚌(X1)

Spennymoor

Frog & Ferret L

Coulson Street, DL16 7RS
☎ (01388) 815840 🌐 thefrogandferretspennymoor.co.uk
6 changing beers (sourced nationally; often Camerons, Consett, Hadrian Border) Ⓗ
Friendly, traditional family-run free house offering up to six constantly changing real ales, sourced from far and wide, with local and northern microbreweries well represented. The comfortably furnished lounge has a bar with brick, stone and wood cladding and a solid fuel burner. Sports TV is featured and children are welcome until 9pm. Live music is hosted on Saturday night. ♣🚌(6,21)🐾

Grand Electric Hall L ✔

Cheapside, DL16 6DJ
☎ (01388) 825470
Greene King Abbot; Ruddles Best Bitter; Sharp's Doom Bar; 3 changing beers (sourced nationally; often Maxim) Ⓗ
Formerly a cinema and bingo hall in the centre of town, this bright and airy Wetherspoon conversion features film-themed decor and fittings. It has a spacious main area with a high ceiling and a smaller room on a lower level. The large patio drinking area to the front is a suntrap in summer. Alcoholic drinks are served from 9am. ❀♿●🚌(6,21)

Stanhope

Grey Bull

17 West Terrace, DL13 2PB
☎ (01388) 529428
3 changing beers (sourced nationally) Ⓗ
A community-focused hostelry with a warm welcome, at the foot of Crawleyside Bank at the west end of town. It has a busy bar area across the front and a lounge to the rear, served by a central bar that dispenses three cask beers. Tables to the front are popular in fine weather. Convenient for the coast-to-coast cycle route. Q❀♣🚌(101)🐾

Stockton-on-Tees

Golden Smog

1 Hambletonian Yard, TS18 1DS (in ginnel between High St and West Row)
☎ (01642) 385022
4 changing beers Ⓗ
The town's original micropub is named after the environmental conditions that formerly prevailed on Teesside. Four real beers and two real ciders are on handpump alongside an impressive range of Belgian beers – some familiar, most not so familiar, all served in matching glasses in the continental fashion. Third-pints are also available, on bespoke Smog tasting tables. An extensive selection of free bar snacks is offered on Sunday. Winner of many awards including local CAMRA Pub of the Year 2019. Q●🚌🐾

Hope & Union L

9-10 Silver Court, TS18 1SL (just E of High St, through ginnel off Silver St)
☎ (01642) 385022
4 changing beers Ⓗ
A bright, modern pub tucked away in a quiet square in the town's cultural quarter. Hope was Robert Stephenson's second locomotive and Union was a horse-drawn coach, both operated in the 1820s by the world's first passenger railway, the Stockton & Darlington. The pub serves four interesting beers, real cider and a large selection of craft ales, gins and whiskies. The cellar is on open display, as is the kitchen, which offers locally sourced, freshly cooked and good-value dishes all day, every day. ≈●🚌

Lucifers 🏆 L

Calvin House, Green Dragon Yard, TS18 1AE (E of High St, through ginnel off Finkle St)
🌐 lucifers-stockton.business.site
3 changing beers Ⓗ
Friendly staff provide a warm welcome at this micropub within a Grade II listed former warehouse. It is named after local chemist John Walker's 19th-century invention the friction match, known as the lucifer. The pub is billed as the smallest bar in town and can get very busy, its benches, booths and stools making for a cosy atmosphere. Three rotating guest beers, normally including a dark ale, are served alongside two ciders. Third pint glasses are available. Local CAMRA Pub of the Year 2020. ≈●🚌🐾

Thomas Sheraton L ✔

4 Bridge Road, TS18 3BW (at S end of High St)
☎ (01642) 606134
7 changing beers Ⓗ
This pub in a Grade II listed Victorian building, a fine conversion of Stockton's law courts, is named after the great Georgian cabinet maker who was born in the town in 1751. It features a large, airy interior comprising several separate drinking and dining areas, plus a

pleasant balcony and outdoor terrace upstairs. The guest beers, usually locally sourced, are served alongside an extensive and varied range of real ciders. A recent local CAMRA Cider Pub of the Year. **Q**

Wasps Nest

Wasps Nest Yard, 1 Calvert's Square, TS18 1TB (just E of High St, through ginnel off Silver St)

☎ 07789 277364

3 changing beers

This venue, between the Grade II listed Georgian Theatre and the River Tees, is firmly established as a feature of Stockton social life. It is a modern and lively pub serving a selection of local beers, real cider and perry. Third-pint bats are available. The pub's claim to fame is that it has the town's only outdoor courtyard patio drinking area. **Q**

Tanfield Lea

Tanfield Lea Working Men's Club

West Street, DH9 9NA

☎ (01207) 238783

2 changing beers (sourced nationally)

The village has no pub, reflecting its strong Methodist history, but guests are most welcome in this CIU-affiliated club, which has become something of a flagship for real ale in the area after a diet of keg beer for many years. TV sport is shown in the bar and there is a quiet, comfortable lounge. Traditional club activities such as bingo take place and there is usually a live act on Sunday when nibbles are provided on the bar. Local CAMRA Club of the Year 2016-2019. **P** (V7,V8)

Tanfield Village

Peacock

Front Street, DH9 9PX

☎ (01207) 232720

Black Sheep Best Bitter; 1 changing beer (sourced nationally)

A warm welcome is guaranteed in this friendly, traditional, two-bar pub in a pretty village. The Peacock is popular with locals and visitors alike, including bell-ringers from the church opposite. Black Sheep is always available alongside a changing guest beer. Lovely home-cooked meals are served Wednesday to Saturday evenings and Sunday lunchtime – the portions are generous and great value for money. There is a small beer garden and ample parking. **Q P** (V8)

West Cornforth

Square & Compass

7 The Green, DL17 9JQ (off Coxhoe-W Cornforth road)

3 changing beers (sourced nationally)

A proper drinking pub and friendly local on the village green in the old part of Doggy (the village's local nickname). It has sold real ale for more than 40 years and usually offers at least one local beer among its three guests. The pub is home to darts and dominoes clubs and hosts a well-attended Thursday night quiz. There are good views towards the Wear valley and Durham city. **Q P** (56)

Westgate

Hare & Hounds

24 Front Street, DL13 1RX

☎ (01388) 517212

hareandhoundswestgate.blogspot.co.uk

Weard'ALE Chilled Nights, Dark Nights, Gold, Pilsner

On the banks of the Wear, on the A689. The spacious stone-flagged bar is partially fitted out with items salvaged from the former village chapel, and is a great place to catch up on local news. The restaurant's patio overlooks the river; here the beer is being brewed beneath your feet. Food, including the famous Sunday carvery, is locally sourced. **Q P** (101)

Witton-le-Wear

Dun Cow

19 High Street, DL14 0AY

☎ (01388) 488294

3 changing beers (sourced nationally; often Timothy Taylor)

A welcoming local set back from the road through the village, with a single L-shaped room warmed by open fires at both ends. Dating from 1799, the bar is guarded by a sleeping fox who always seems to have just closed his eyes. There are benches to the left of the bar, and seating outside offering pleasant views over the Wear valley. The decor includes some interesting football memorabilia. **Q P**

Wolsingham

Black Lion

21 Meadhope Street, DL13 3EN (50yds N of market place)

☎ (01388) 527772

5 changing beers (sourced nationally)

Nationally recognised for its commitment to real cider, hidden away a minute from the Market Place, this welcoming, comfortable gem is a great place to relax. An open fire features in the single open-plan room, with a pool table to the rear and TV sport to the front. Local charities benefit from the efforts of the pub. Six or more ciders can be on offer. Local CAMRA Country Cider Pub of the Year 2020. **Q** (101)

Publican – a posset, if you please

Anne Boleyn as a Maid of Honour had an allowance of two gallons of ale a day – perhaps to be shared with others? – but to make such ale interesting it was served in possets and caudles, the warmest sweet liquor mixed with honey, spices, roasted crabs or anything else which took the fancy. The weaker ales were relatively baby food. Elizabeth, when queen, issued repeated regulations in defence of weak ale and against strong beer; yet for herself, although she was abstemious, when she wished for a nip drank beer 'so strong that was no man durst touch it'.

Frank Morley, The Great North Road, 1961

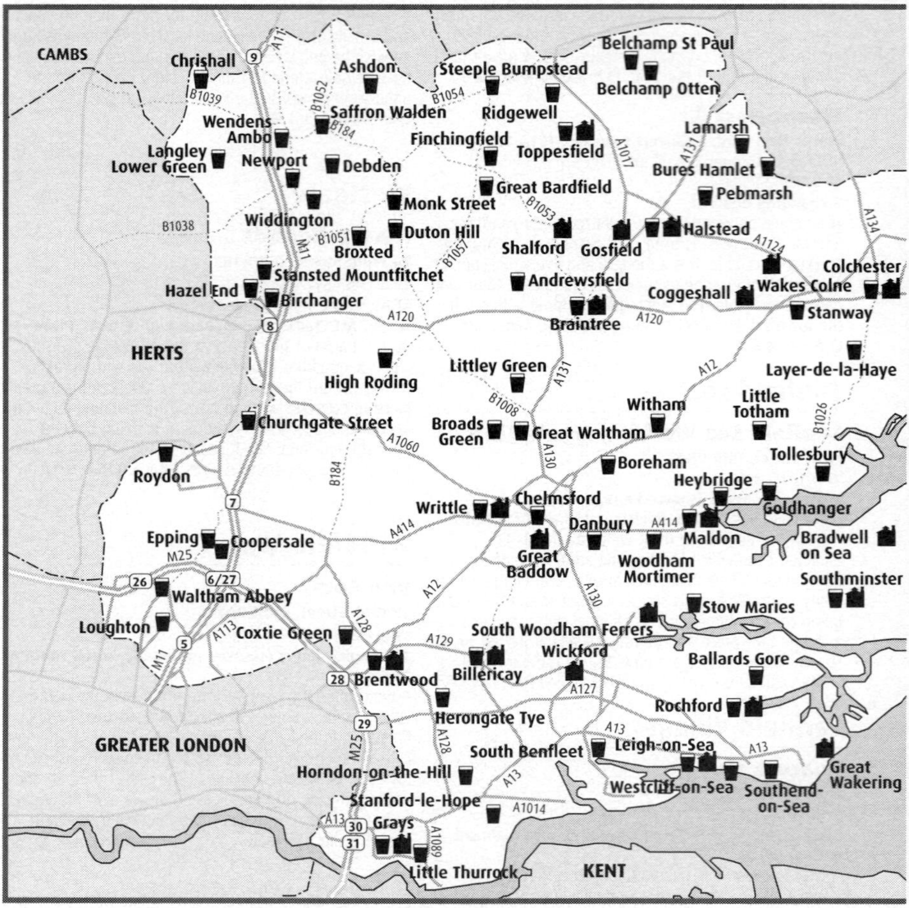

Andrewsfield

Millibar

Stebbing Airfield, New Pasture Lane, CM6 3TH
(accessed by a track beside the runway, near Stebbing Green) TL689248
07923 981900 andrewsfield.com/andrewsfield-millibar
Bishop Nick Ridley's Rite

The manager of the bar at this local flying school is keen on local supply and has installed Ridley's Rite from Bishop Nick Brewery as his sole ale. There is also a range of Bishop Nick bottled beers. The training airfield is a small grass strip dominated by single-engine Cessna aircraft, a Mustang III and B17 Meteor IIIs, and trial flying lessons are available. The public are welcome in the bar and it stays open until 11pm if there are customers.
Q P

Ashdon

Rose & Crown

Crown Hill, CB10 2HA
(01799) 584337
Woodforde's Wherry; 4 changing beers (sourced nationally)

The last remaining pub in this village which once had five more. It has an unusual layout, and a room named after Oliver Cromwell where he is reputed to have kept prisoners, who illustrated the walls with their feelings at the time! This is now hidden behind removable panels. Guest ales often include Nethergate and Essex-brewed beers. This pub is the focus of village social activities. Closed Monday. Q P

Ballards Gore (Stambridge)

Shepherd & Dog

Gore Road, SS4 2DA (between Rochford and Paglesham)
(01702) 258658 theshepherdanddogstambridge.co.uk
6 changing beers (sourced locally; often George's)

A traditional country pub with beams throughout and a real fire, and a regular winner of local CAMRA awards. It is L-shaped, with the bar at the front offering six changing real ales, at least two from local breweries, plus a range of real ciders. Towards the back is the restaurant, serving home-cooked food using local produce. There is seating outside at the front and in the beer garden to the rear, with an outside bar. Regular music events are popular. P (60)

Belchamp Otten

Red Lion

Fowes Lane, CO10 7BQ (on small single track lane, signed by duck pond) TL799415
(01787) 278301

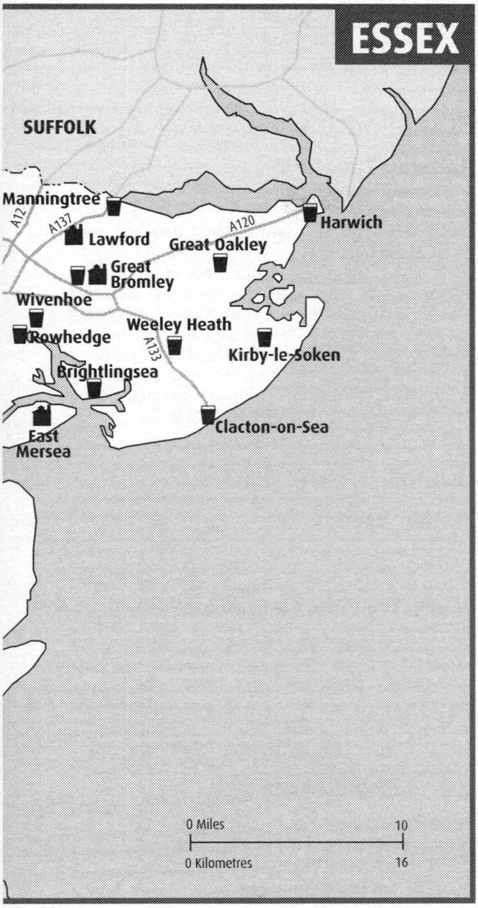

Adnams Southwold Bitter; 2 changing beers (sourced nationally) Ⓗ
Lovely local inn, hidden away in the smallest of the Belchamps. The owner and his friendly labrador provide a warm welcome, with an open fire in winter. The pub does not currently serve food, but has delivery arrangements with local takeaway restaurants. It has darts and a pool table, and occasional events are run. There are excellent views, good walks and cycle rides from here. Closed Tuesday. ❀♣P

Belchamp St Paul

Half Moon ✔

Cole Green, CO10 7DP TL792423
☎ (01787) 277402 🌐 halfmoonbelchamp.co.uk
Greene King IPA; 2 changing beers (sourced nationally) Ⓗ
Beautiful friendly thatched pub dating from about 1685, situated opposite the village green. Three real ales are available and guest beers change regularly. This rural venue is popular with locals and has an excellent choice of freshly made and locally sourced bar and restaurant meals (no food Sun eve or Mon). In the past, it provided one of the locations for the first Lovejoy TV series, and has original wooden beams and low ceilings in places. Q❀♿♣P

Billericay

Billericay Brewing Co Shop & Micropub

52 Chapel Street, CM12 9LS
☎ (01277) 500121 🌐 billericaybrewing.co.uk
Billericay Zeppelin, Blonde, Dickie; 4 changing beers (sourced locally; often Billericay) Ⓖ
Brewery tap micropub next door to the brewery. It serves up to four ales on gravity, mostly from Billericay Brewery, plus two other beers on KeyKeg. It is also a beer shop, with bottles from Billericay plus other breweries, as well as foreign beers. Beer festivals are held each year in March, June, September and December. Seating is on high stools next to solid wooden tables. There is an extra pop-up bar in the brewery at busy times. ❀♣(100,222)

Coach & Horses

36 Chapel Street, CM12 9LU
☎ (01277) 622873
Adnams Broadside; Mighty Oak Captain Bob; Oakham Citra; Wibblers Dengie IPA; 2 changing beers (sourced nationally) Ⓗ
Close to the High Street, this welcoming pub with an inviting atmosphere has appeared in this Guide for over 20 years. Six ales are served, with one always from Oakham. Good quality, home-made food is available lunchtimes and evenings, with a popular Sunday roast, plus themed menus including curry nights. The bar service is efficient and friendly. The walls are adorned with prints and decorative plates, and a collection of tankards hangs from the ceiling. There is a cosy and attractive courtyard garden. ❀♿P(100)

Railway

1 High Street, CM12 9BE
☎ (01277) 652173
Dark Star Hophead; Wibblers Dengie IPA; 3 changing beers (sourced nationally) Ⓗ

REAL ALE BREWERIES

Billericay Billericay
Bishop Nick Braintree
Brentwood Brentwood
Chelmsford Great Baddow
Colchester Wakes Colne
Courtyard Gosfield
Crouch Vale South Woodham Ferrers
Fallen Angel Writtle
George's Great Wakering
JackRabbit Lawford (NEW)
Keppels Rochford
Leigh on Sea Leigh-on-Sea
Maldon Maldon
Mersea Island East Mersea
Mighty Oak Maldon
Moody Goose Braintree
Mr Majolica Grays (brewing suspended)
Neolithic Bradwell on Sea (NEW)
Other Monkey Colchester
Posh Boys Wickford (NEW)
Pumphouse Community Toppesfield
Red Fox Coggeshall
Shalford Shalford
St Botolphs Colchester (NEW)
Sticklegs Great Bromley (brewing suspended)
Watson's Colchester
White Hart Halstead
Wibblers Southminster

Friendly pub with a welcoming atmosphere, which earns the tag line: No.1 in the High Street. It has served over 800 different real ales and won several local CAMRA awards. Guest beers are updated on social media. Regular events include a quiz, live music and charity days. This community-oriented venue has two darts teams and sponsors a local rugby team. Traditional bar games include shove-ha'penny with real ha'pennies. A beer garden is outside, and an open fire indoors during winter. 🛋❀♿⇌♣P🚌🐾ᯤ

Birchanger

Birchanger Sports & Social Club

229 Birchanger Lane, CM23 5QJ
☎ (01279) 813441 🌐 birchangerclub.com
Greene King IPA; 2 changing beers (sourced nationally) [H]
A friendly local social club where CAMRA members are welcome as guests. Many matches and events take place here, so it can get very busy. Beers change frequently as the turnover is high. The club has football, cricket, bowls, darts, crib and snooker teams, and hosts regular quizzes, plus bingo and bottle draws. It has won CAMRA branch Club of the Year on several occasions.
🛋❀◑♿♣●P🚌(7,7A) ᯤ

Boreham

Queen's Head ✔

Church Road, CM3 3EG
☎ (01245) 467298
4 changing beers (sourced nationally) [H]
In the same family for over 20 years, this friendly pub, dating from the 16th century, is tucked away behind houses just past the church. It has two contrasting bars, one with bench seating, where darts, dominoes and crib are played; the other is for dining. In the warmer months the garden is a lovely area to sit at one of the picnic benches and enjoy the tranquil setting, in view of the village church. Home-cooked food is served Wednesday to Sunday. Beer festivals take place over the bank holiday weekends of Easter and August.
🛋❀◑♣●P🚌(40,71A) ᯤ

Braintree

King William IV L

114 London Road, CM77 7PU
☎ (01376) 567755 🌐 kingwilliamiv.co.uk
4 changing beers (sourced nationally) [G]
Friendly free house serving a changing range of real ales, usually featuring Essex microbreweries and at least one from the Moody Goose Brewery, located in the grounds of the pub. An interesting selection of ciders is also on offer. There is a main bar and a small back bar with a dartboard. Outside, a large patio area and extensive gardens host beer festivals and other events. This is a traditional drinking pub and does not offer food other than snacks. Q❀♣●P🚌🐾ᯤ

Brentwood

Victoria Arms

50 Ongar Road, CM15 9AX (on A128)
☎ (01277) 223371
Adnams Ghost Ship; Harvey's IPA, Sussex Best Bitter; 3 changing beers (sourced nationally) [H]
Pleasant and comfortable Gray & Sons pub with a friendly atmosphere. Unusually for the area, there are normally two Harvey's beers on tap, as well as Ghost Ship and three changing ales. There are several TV screens which mostly show sports matches, and an outside smoking area. Cribbage and other card games are played. Local CAMRA Pub of the Year 2018. ❀◑♣P🚌(498,21)

Brightlingsea

Railway Tavern 🏆 L

58 Station Road, CO7 0DT
🌐 alesattherails.co.uk
Crouch Vale Essex Boys Best Bitter; 2 changing beers (sourced nationally) [H]
Guide readers will remember this place as being a regular entry for many years. New owners in 2018 have not only maintained the ales in excellent condition, and continued the real cider festival each May, but are gradually doing some refurbishing, adding a new bar area in late 2019. Not only have they restored the venue to this Guide, but they were also awarded local CAMRA Pub of the Year 2020. Q🛋❀●🚌(7,78)🐾

Broads Green

Walnut Tree L ✔

CM3 1DT
☎ (01245) 360222
Bishop Nick Ridley's Rite; Timothy Taylor Landlord; 1 changing beer (sourced nationally) [G]
Handsome Victorian pub overlooking the green. The front door opens into what was the bottle and jug, but is now a small snug. To the left is the wood-panelled public bar, little-changed since it was built in 1888. To the right is the slightly more modern saloon bar. Outside there is seating at the front, a children's play area and a large garden. There is no food, the landlord preferring to concentrate on his beers and to maintain a traditional atmosphere. Q🛋❀Λ♣●P🐾ᯤ

Broxted

Prince of Wales L ✔

Brick End, CM6 2BJ
☎ (01279) 850256 🌐 princeofwalesbroxted.co.uk
Greene King IPA; 5 changing beers (sourced nationally) [H]
This former Charrington pub has been transformed into a welcoming community venue after the current landlords took over in 2011. It has a comfortable split-level bar, an adjoining room with two wood-burners, and a conservatory seating up to 50. Generous portions of food, mostly locally sourced, will satisfy the most demanding appetite. A small garden is to the rear. Up to five guest beers are sold, with LocAle from Bishop Nick. Closed Monday. 🛋❀◑P🚌(6)🐾ᯤ

Bures Hamlet

Eight Bells L

6 Colchester Road, CO8 5AE (on B1508)
☎ (01787) 227354
Greene King IPA, Abbot; 4 changing beers (sourced nationally) [H]
A real gem, this is a traditional village local with a long-serving landlord in his 40th year here. It has three drinking and dining areas, served by a large bar, and a separate function area. Monthly open mic nights are hosted. Traditional pub food is available daily, with a roast on Sunday. Walkers and cyclists are always welcome. Only five minutes' stroll from Bures station.
Q🛋❀◑♿⇌P🚌🐾ᯤ

Chelmsford

Ale House L

24-26 Viaduct Road, CM1 1TS
☎ (01245) 260535 🌐 the-ale-house-chelmsford.co.uk
12 changing beers (sourced nationally) H
A unique bar in Chelmsford, located under the arches at the railway station, with one of the widest ranges of continuously changing beers in Essex, always including dark and stronger beers, plus eight craft keg beers and 12 real ciders. There are also imported ales on tap and a wide range of bottled beers from around the world. No food is served but customers are welcome to bring their own or order a takeaway. A quiz is held on the last Sunday of the month and there are regular beer festivals.

Endeavour L

351 Springfield Road, CM2 6AW
☎ (01245) 257717
Adnams Ghost Ship; Mighty Oak Maldon Gold, Captain Bob; Wibblers Dengie IPA; 1 changing beer (sourced nationally) H
Busy and friendly pub, comprising three rooms. Four regular ales are available as well as one changing guest beer. Cooked meals are served lunchtimes and evenings, and sandwiches are available all day (Mon-Sat). Booking is recommended for the roast dinner on Sunday. All food is good value, locally sourced and home-cooked. This is a true community local, with darts and crib teams and regular charity events. It shows sport on TV, and has an attractive courtyard garden.

Hop Beer Shop L

173 Moulsham Street, CM2 0LD
☎ (01245) 353570
4 changing beers (sourced nationally) G
Essex's first micropub. Four beers are served by gravity, with local breweries always represented, alongside interesting ales from around the country – usually including a stout or porter and a golden beer. There are also craft keg beers, 100 or so bottled beers from local and international breweries, and bottled cider, which may be drunk here or purchased to take home. Local CAMRA Cider Pub of the Year 2018-2020. Closed Monday.
Q

Oddfellows Arms Smokehouse L

195 Springfield Road, CM2 6JP
☎ (01245) 490514 🌐 theoddfellowsarms.com
Bishop Nick 1555; Dark Star Hophead; St Austell Tribute; Wibblers Dengie IPA; 1 changing beer (sourced nationally) H
The pub has a modern wood interior but maintains the feel of a local. There is a large U-shaped bar area and a back room with a pool table, leading out to the attractive decked garden/smoking area. An extensive menu of home-made food is served weekday lunchtimes and evenings, and all day at weekends, including wood-smoked brisket, ribs and pulled pork. Poker nights are hosted twice a week, live music monthly and a beer festival every year. P

Orange Tree 🏆 L

6 Lower Anchor Street, CM2 0AS
☎ (01245) 262664 🌐 the-ot.com
Mighty Oak Oscar Wilde; 7 changing beers (sourced nationally) H
The Orange Tree is one of the best real ale destinations in Chelmsford and is local CAMRA Pub of the Year 2020. It is a place for conversation and meeting friends, with separate public and saloon bars. A great range of real ales is on tap, always including something dark, plus craft keg beers. Food is served at lunchtime, including a roast on Sunday and a steak and curry night on Thursday evening. Quiz night is Tuesday. QP

Original Plough ✔

28 Duke Street, CM1 1HY
☎ (01245) 250145 🌐 theoriginalploughchelmsford.co.uk
Fuller's London Pride; St Austell Tribute; Sharp's Doom Bar; 3 changing beers (sourced nationally) H
Newly refurbished and conveniently located close to both railway and bus stations, this is now one of Mitchells & Butlers Oak Tree pubs. Six handpulls are available to serve beers. The interior is open plan, with several distinct areas, and with historical local prints throughout. Accessible toilets are on the ground floor. Good-value food is on the menu all day, starting with breakfast. Large screens show news and sporting events. From Monday to Thursday there is a student discount on selected food and drink, and various other meal and drink deals. QP

Queen's Head L

30 Lower Anchor Street, CM2 0AS
☎ (01245) 265181 🌐 queensheadchelmsford.co.uk
Crouch Vale Essex Boys Best Bitter, Brewers Gold; 5 changing beers (sourced nationally) H
Crouch Vale Brewery's first pub, selling three of its beers permanently, with four guests which may include a Crouch Vale seasonal and always include a dark beer. The Victorian L-shaped bar has bare-board flooring and comfortable bench seating. Two fires make it cosy in winter. This popular local can be busy when there is a match at the nearby county cricket ground. The Essex Beard Club meets here once a year in February.
QP

Railway Tavern L

63 Duke Street, CM1 1LW
☎ (01245) 280679
Greene King Abbot; Red Fox IPA; 5 changing beers (sourced nationally) H
A Tardis-like corner pub, right outside Chelmsford station. Not surprisingly, a railway theme dominates. It is long and narrow, with banks of handpumps at opposite ends of the central bar counter. There is a small enclosed garden where you can listen to the station announcements and marvel at the ever-changing mural. It may stay open later on Sundays in the summer. This traditional hostelry also sells craft beers and over 50 different gins. Local CAMRA Pub of the Year 2018.

Woolpack ✔

23 Mildmay Road, CM2 0DN
☎ (01245) 259295
Hardys & Hansons Bitter; 8 changing beers (sourced nationally) H
It is an easy walk from the town centre to this award-winning and friendly Victorian local. There are three rooms, with a lounge area overlooking the large garden. Darts and a pool table are in a smaller room. Pub grub is served, with light snacks until late. There is music on Sunday, a quiz on Tuesday, and beer festivals at Easter and the first weekend in September, with up to 80 beers, ciders and perries. Local CAMRA Pub of the Year 2019.
P

Chrishall

Red Cow

11 High Street, SG8 8RN (N of B1039) TL446393
☎ (01763) 838792 🌐 theredcow.com

Adnams Southwold Bitter; Woodforde's Wherry; 2 changing beers (sourced nationally) 🄷
Thatched 14th-century inn in a small village near the Cambridgeshire/Hertfordshire borders. Guest beers are usually from East Anglia. The pub is frequented by many local groups including the cricket club, the village book group, stallholders from the farmers' market and the WI. Special occasions can be celebrated with meals from the extensive award-winning menu, either in the tiled bar or in the restaurant, separated by original open timbering. There is also a small sweet shop. Situated on the ancient Icknield Way, the pub is a popular stop-off for ramblers. Q🐎❀🛏◑◗P🐾📶

Churchgate Street

Queen's Head

26 Churchgate Street, CM17 0JT (from bypass follow signs to Old Harlow then Churchgate St)
☎ (01279) 427266 🌐 tqhchurchgatest.co.uk
Adnams Southwold Bitter; Hadham Gold, First 🄷**; 2 changing beers (sourced locally)** 🄷/🄶
Originally dating back to Tudor times, with wooden beams spanning a spacious interior, the building is believed to have been an inn since 1750. It is situated in a pleasant village street on the outskirts of Harlow. The smaller side bar has a fire in winter and there is a beach bar and barbecue in the summer. The pub is known for its good food, home-made using fresh ingredients. There are regular quizzes, special events and a Friday burger and beer night. Q❀◑◗♣P🐾📶

Clacton-on-Sea

Moon & Starfish

1 Marine Parade East, CO15 1PT
☎ (01255) 222998
Greene King Abbot; Ruddles Best Bitter; Sharp's Doom Bar; 6 changing beers (sourced nationally) 🄷
This Wetherspoon is conveniently situated opposite Clacton's famous pier and Venetian bridge, and handily placed for the memorial gardens, town centre and railway station, which are a short walk away. There is an outside seating area giving excellent views of the Clacton air show and carnival procession which are staged on different weeks in August. There are always six pumps on with changing guest ales. A quiz is held on three Mondays during the year, raising money for charity.
Q🐎❀◑◗♿⇌●🚌📶

Old Lifeboat House

39 Marine Parade East, CO15 6AD
☎ (01255) 476799
Greene King Abbot; St Austell Proper Job; 3 changing beers (sourced nationally; often Colchester, Greene King, St Austell) 🄷
A regular in this Guide since 2011, this family-run establishment sells five ales, with local brews from Colchester, Mauldons and Mighty Oak featuring regularly, as well as numerous ciders and perries. Food is served on Wednesday evening. Snacks are on offer Tuesday evening and Sunday lunchtime, with a monthly roast instead during the winter months. Darts teams play on Monday or Thursday. 🐎❀◗♿⇌♣●P🚏🚌📶

Colchester

Ale House 🄻

82 Butt Road, CO3 3DA
☎ (01206) 573464 🌐 thealehousecolchester.co.uk
10 changing beers (sourced nationally) 🄷
A free house with a friendly landlady and staff, and relaxing decor. A wide range of ales is sold, dispensed via handpump and also on gravity (including at least one dark beer), as well as real cider. Quiz night is every third Wednesday, with a folk music session on the fourth Tuesday of the month. Darts, bar billiards and TV sport are available. There is a large walled garden at the rear. Currently the CAMRA Town Pub of the Year for Colchester. ❀⇌(Town) ♣●🚌(64) 📶

Bricklayers 🄻 ✔

27 Bergholt Road, CO4 5AA
☎ (01206) 852008
Adnams Broadside; Sharp's Doom Bar, Atlantic; 4 changing beers (sourced nationally) 🄷
Close to Colchester mainline station, the Brick is a lively two-bar hostelry. It has a public bar with darts and pool, a saloon bar with two large TVs showing various sports, plus a snug and a conservatory. There is a car park at the rear, an outside area and a garden. Food is served, with a curry night on Thursday. There are quizzes twice a month and live music on the last weekend of the month.
Q🐎❀◑◗⇌(North) ♣●P🚌🐾📶

British Grenadier 🄻

67 Military Road, CO1 2AP
☎ 07832 215118
4 changing beers (sourced nationally) 🄷
This welcoming local, run by a knowledgeable publican, has featured in the Guide for over 10 years. It is a traditional Victorian two-bar pub with a pool table in the small rear bar and a dartboard in the main bar, which is heated by an open fire in the winter months. This venue is LocAle accredited, and serves a changing range of local, regional and nationally sourced beers and ciders via handpumps. 🐎❀♿⇌(Town)♣●🚏🚌(6,61)🐾📶

Fat Cat

65 Butt Road, CO3 3BZ (near police station)
☎ (01206) 577990 🌐 fatcatcolchester.co.uk
Crouch Vale Brewers Gold; Fat Cat Honey Cat; Hop Back Summer Lightning; Woodforde's Wherry; 8 changing beers (sourced nationally) 🄶
A welcome return to the Guide for this popular single-bar, split-level establishment just outside the town centre. You are always assured of good banter and a pleasing choice of quality ales, all on gravity dispense from a central taproom; there is also a large selection of ciders and Belgian beers. Food is served in the evenings and at lunchtimes from Wednesday to Sunday. It boasts the town's smallest pub garden and has regular crib competitions and a Sunday quiz.
🐎❀◑◗♿⇌(Town) ♣●🚌(64,63) 🐾📶

New Inn 🄻

36 Chapel Street South, CO2 7AX
☎ (01206) 575277 🌐 theoldnewinnpub.co.uk
Bishop Nick Ridley's Rite; 7 changing beers (sourced nationally) 🄷
With a quiet, comfortable and cosy saloon bar, an open fire and a stripped-back public bar featuring music, TV sports and friendly conversation, this is definitely a venue of two halves. There are up to eight real ales and four real ciders, and regular brewery tap takeovers take place throughout the year. Traditional pub food is served Tuesday to Saturday lunchtimes and evenings, with a traditional roast lunch on Sunday. Numerous board games are available in the saloon bar.
Q🐎❀◑◗♿⇌(Town) ♣●P🚌(64) 🐾📶

Odd One Out 🄻

28 Mersea Road, CO2 7ET
☎ (01206) 615102

Colchester Metropolis, No.1; 7 changing beers (sourced nationally) Ⓗ
The multi award-winning Odd One Out features two bars. It offers at least two beers from Colchester Brewery and a range of changing guest ales over seven handpumps, as well as a varied range of ciders. There is a small secluded rear garden allowing for a quiet pint, and a small function room that is well used by a range of community groups. Check Facebook for regular evening quizzes, impromptu music sessions and barbecues.
Q☸❀⇌(Town) ●🚌(8,67) 🐾📶

Purple Dog

42 Eld Lane, CO1 1LS
☎ (01206) 564995 🌐 thepurpledogpub.co.uk
Adnams Ghost Ship; Fuller's London Pride; Sharp's Doom Bar; 3 changing beers (sourced nationally) Ⓗ
This wood-beamed corner pub in the town centre is one of the oldest bars in Colchester, dating back to 1647, and has an outdoor drinking area. Six handpumps provide mainly regional beers, alongside the usual town centre offerings. An extensive menu, complemented by changing special dishes, is available daily. Regular music events including DJs and occasional live bands are hosted and a monthly quiz night. ☸❀◐⇌(Town)🚌📶

Victoria Inn

10 North Station Road, CO1 1RB
☎ (01206) 514510 🌐 victoriainncolchester.co.uk
5 changing beers (sourced nationally) Ⓗ
A multi award-winning hostelry with friendly, knowledgeable staff, on the edge of the town centre. It serves two unique house ales and three guests from microbreweries, both local and further afield, as well as up to nine real ciders, three craft keg taps and an impressive range of cans and bottles. Keg lager, cider and stout are all locally brewed (no mainstream brands). Live music plays on Sunday afternoon. The pub is dog-friendly and child-tolerant, and has a cosy courtyard and a covered area outside. ❀⇌(North)♣●🚌🐾📶

Coopersale

Theydon Oak

9 Coopersale Street, CM16 7QJ
☎ (01992) 572618 🌐 thetheydonoak.co.uk
Adnams Ghost Ship; Fuller's London Pride; St Austell Tribute; Woodforde's Wherry; 2 changing beers (sourced locally) Ⓗ
An ancient inn, parts of which date back 400 years, with log-burners and comfortable seating, lots of exposed beams, horse brasses and antiques. A wide assortment of home-cooked food is served, for which it has a good reputation. A beer festival is held in May and there are events throughout the year. Set in beautiful countryside, not far from Epping – there is a footpath from Epping underground station. Q☸❀◐●P🚌(381)📶

Coxtie Green

White Horse

173 Coxtie Green Road, CM14 5PX (1 mile W of A128, at jct with Mores Lane) TQ564959
☎ (01277) 372410 🌐 whitehorsebrentwood.co.uk
Brentwood Marvellous Maple Mild; Fuller's London Pride; Greene King Abbot; house beer (by Brentwood); 6 changing beers (sourced nationally) Ⓗ
Pleasant country free house with an extended comfortable saloon bar. Badged as the Brentwood Brewery tap, it has 10 handpumps usually dispensing four regular beers and six guests, of which three are usually from Brentwood and the rest from anywhere. There is a large play area in the garden to keep children happy. The local bus service is limited but reliable.
☸❀◐♿♣●P🚌(71,72) 🐾📶

Danbury

Cricketers Arms

Penny Royal Road, CM3 4ED
☎ (01245) 222022 🌐 cricketersarmsdanbury.com
Shepherd Neame Whitstable Bay Pale Ale, Spitfire, Bishops Finger; 1 changing beer (sourced nationally) Ⓗ
The building is 400 years old and has been an inn for about 200 years. This Shepherd Neame pub has been refurbished and has a public bar, main bar, lounge and dining room, plus plenty of outdoor seating. The pub hosts monthly quiz nights, a magic circle on a Tuesday, and an annual beer festival in August. Popular with ramblers and cyclists, the pub also provides towels and snacks for dogs. An arts and crafts centre is attached, and it is close to National Trust properties – Danbury Common, Danbury Park and lakes.
Q☸❀◐♿♣P🚌🐾📶

Debden

Plough

High Street, CB11 3LE
☎ (01799) 541899 🌐 theploughatdebden.co.uk
Greene King IPA; 3 changing beers (sourced nationally) Ⓗ
The sole remaining village pub, with a restaurant and garden, now revitalised by a young, energetic couple. It offers a warm and friendly welcome and runs beer festivals, events and other local celebrations. An interesting and varied range of local beers is available alongside an extensive food menu. The pub is an important social centre for this village and the surrounding area, and a good base for walkers and cyclists. A monthly quiz night is normally held on the third Wednesday. Closed Monday.
Q☸❀◐●P🚌(6,313)

Duton Hill

Three Horseshoes

CM6 2DX (1 mile W of B184) TL606268
☎ (01371) 870681
Mighty Oak Maldon Gold; 2 changing beers (sourced nationally) Ⓗ
Outstanding village local with a garden, wildlife pond and terrace overlooking the Chelmer Valley and farmland. The landlord often hosts a weekend of open-air theatre in July. A millennium beacon in the garden, breweriana and a remarkable collection of Butlins memorabilia are features. A beer festival is held on the late spring bank holiday in the Duton Hill Den. Look for the pub sign depicting a famous painting, Our Blacksmith, by former local resident Sir George Clausen. Local and parish newspapers are available.
☸❀♿♣P🚌(313) 🐾

Epping

Forest Gate Inn

111 Bell Common, CM16 4DZ (off B1393 near Bell Hotel, via Theydon Rd)
☎ (01992) 572312 🌐 forestgateinnepping.co.uk
Adnams Southwold Bitter, Broadside; Bishop Nick Ridley's Rite Ⓗ**; 1 changing beer** Ⓗ/Ⓖ
On the edge of Epping Forest, this is a 17th-century building with low ceilings and flag floors, run by the

same family for 50 years. It is popular with locals, walkers and their dogs. Hot meals and soups are served in the bar, as well as in Haywards Restaurant next door, with a B&B. There is a large grassed seating area. The town centre and London underground station are around a mile away. Q♨❀🛏◐◑●P🚌🐾📶

Finchingfield

Finchingfield Lion 𝕃

6 Church Hill, CM7 4NN (on B1053, opp Guildhall)
☎ (01371) 810400 🌐 thefinchingfieldlion.co.uk
Adnams Southwold Bitter; Greene King IPA; 2 changing beers Ⓗ
A 15th-century coaching inn in a famously picturesque village, just up the hill from the pond. A friendly local with a warm atmosphere, it has a heavily beamed bar area with an open fire, and a separate restaurant and function room. There is also a garden for better weather. Popular with cyclists, walkers and locals; families are also welcome. Good-value home-cooked food is served. Q♨❀◐◑♣●P🚌🐾📶

Goldhanger

Chequers ✔

Church Street, CM9 8AS
☎ (01621) 788203 🌐 thechequersgoldhanger.co.uk
Adnams Ghost Ship; Sharp's Atlantic; Woodforde's Wherry; 3 changing beers (sourced nationally; often Courage, St Austell, Timothy Taylor) Ⓗ
Historic 15th-century village inn with several timbered rooms, including a games room with bar billiards, a snug and a front and back bar with restaurant area. It offers an extensive food menu and takes pride in sourcing local ingredients where possible. There are open fires in two of the bars and the rear courtyard is a suntrap in warmer weather. A small beer festival is held in September. Four ciders are usually available on draught. Excellent footpaths along the River Blackwater are close by, making the pub popular with ramblers and birdwatchers. Q♨❀◐◑♣●P🚌(95)🐾📶

Grays

Theobald Arms

141 Argent Street, RM17 6HR (5-7 mins' walk from Grays rail and bus stations, down Kings Walk)
☎ (01375) 372253 🌐 theosarms.co.uk
4 changing beers (sourced nationally) Ⓗ
Genuine, traditional inn with a public bar that has an unusual hexagonal pool table. The changing selection of four guest beers features local independent breweries, and a range of British bottled beers is also stocked. Regular summer beer festivals are held in the old stables and on the rear enclosed patio. Lunchtime meals are served Monday to Friday. Darts and cards are played. ❀◐♿⇌♣P🚌

White Hart 🏆 𝕃 ✔

Kings Walk, RM17 6HR (5-7 mins' walk from Grays rail and bus stations)
☎ (01375) 373319 🌐 whitehartgrays.co.uk
Dartmoor Best, IPA; 3 changing beers (sourced nationally) Ⓗ
Traditional local just outside the town centre, rejuvenated since it was taken over in 2006. The regular beers are supplemented by three guests (one usually dark) and a selection of over 30 bottled Belgian beers. Good-value meals are served weekday lunchtimes. There is a meeting/function room and a large, secluded beer garden. Live music features on Saturday. An extensive collection of old-fashioned soft toys is displayed on the historic bar-back. The pub supports pool and darts teams, and sport is screened. Local CAMRA Pub of the Year 2019 and 2020. ♨❀🛏◐♿⇌♣P🚌🐾📶

Great Bardfield

Bell Inn 𝕃

Dunmow Road, CM7 4SA
☎ (01371) 239165
Bishop Nick Ridley's Rite, Heresy; 1 changing beer (sourced locally) Ⓗ
A friendly local with a warm welcome, featuring beers mainly from Bishop Nick. It has a beamed bar and restaurant area, with an open fire and a separate public bar with TV and darts. Outside there is a patio area. Good-value, locally sourced food is served. The pub now has a pool table. It is available for private functions and is linked to the Great Bardfield artists. There is a quiz on Sunday afternoon. A refreshment stop on the Dunwich Dynamo cycle trip. ♨❀◐◑♣🚌🐾📶

Great Bromley

Cross Inn

Ardleigh Road, CO7 7TL
☎ (01206) 621772 🌐 greatbromleycross.co.uk
2 changing beers (sourced nationally) Ⓗ
Formerly the home of Frank Goddard, a British heavyweight boxing champion, this is a remote country inn which is an absolute gem, and well worth a visit. It was saved by the community in 2016 after much campaigning, fundraising and a share offer. Since reopening, the interior, including cellar and kitchen, has been refurbished and the toilets extended and twinned, accessible by wheelchair with a radar key 24 hours. The Cross now also hosts a post office, coffee shop and library on Wednesday morning. Closed Monday and Tuesday. ♿●P🚌(105,107)🐾

Great Oakley

Maybush Inn 𝕃

Farm Road, CO12 5AL
☎ (01255) 880123 🌐 maybushinn.co.uk
Courage Directors; house beer (by Eagle); 1 changing beer (sourced nationally) Ⓗ
This community-owned pub, an extremely welcoming and friendly village local, is entirely staffed and managed by volunteers, yet manages to keep its ales in excellent condition, making it a regular entry in this Guide in recent years. It is exceptionally community-focused, with various activities such as quizzes, bingo, crib and music every week. A quiet beer garden has been added. A beer festival to mark the anniversary of the initial opening is held each February. Q♨❀♣●🚌🐾📶

Great Waltham

Rose & Crown 𝕃

Minnows End, Chelmsford Road, CM3 1AG
☎ (01245) 360359 🌐 roseandcrowngreatwaltham.co.uk
Bishop Nick 1555; Greene King IPA; 1 changing beer (sourced nationally) Ⓗ
A rural pub with a traditional bar, a separate snug seating 10 people and a small function room. It also has a restaurant serving home cooking from mainly local produce, with a discount on food for NHS workers. Outside, there is a patio area and decking with themed table tops. An open mic night features on the second Wednesday and a jazz night on the last Wednesday of each month. Q♨◐◑P🚌(10,42)🐾📶

Halstead

Dog Inn 🄻

37 Hedingham Road, CO9 2DB

☎ (01787) 477774

5 changing beers (sourced nationally) 🄷

Welcoming traditional venue with two bars, close to the town centre. The public bar has a TV with sports, and the comfortable saloon has a real fire. Five changing beers are on offer, often from local microbreweries. A large beer garden is at the rear, perfect for sunny days. The pub hosts regular live music including a folk session on the first Sunday afternoon and acoustic sessions on the third Sunday afternoon and one Saturday evening each month. B&B is available with en-suite rooms. **Q🐴❀🛏♣P🚌**(88) **🐾📶**

White Hart Inn 🄻

15 High Street, CO9 2AA

☎ (01787) 475657 🌐 whitehartinnhalstead.co.uk

White Hart Golden Hart, Halstead Bitter; 2 changing beers (sourced nationally) 🄷

The White Hart is one of the oldest coaching inns in Essex. The pub is a medieval hall believed to have been built in the 13th century. It has its own brewery and gin distillery in the old stables; the distillery produces London dry and hop gins. Ales include those from its own brewery as well as local and national beers. Comfortable en-suite bedrooms and traditional home-cooked food are on offer. **❀🛏◐◑P🚌**(88)**🐾📶**

Harwich

Hanover Inn

65 Church Street, CO12 3DR (alongside church in Old Harwich)

☎ (01255) 502927 🌐 hanoverinn.co.uk

4 changing beers (sourced nationally) 🄷/🄶

Local CAMRA Pub of the Year 2019, the Hanover continues to cater both for drinkers and those in need of a hearty meal or snack – the main front bar a friendly home to drinkers and the rear room set up for dining. Up to four changing ales are on handpump, with Green Jack beers regularly featured, alongside two real ciders. **Q🐴◐◑♿⇌♣●🚌🐾📶**

New Bell Inn 🄻

Outpart Eastward, CO12 3EN

☎ (01255) 503545 🌐 thenewbell.co.uk

Greene King IPA; Mighty Oak Oscar Wilde; 2 changing beers (sourced regionally) 🄷

A historic inn that has always been a community favourite, with many local groups meeting within its 18th-century walls. A changing guest real ale and cider line-up is underpinned by that great rarity these days – a regular mild from Mighty Oak, much loved by the locals. Hearty lunchtime food makes this a great refuelling stop for those wanting to explore Old Harwich, and there is a secret walled garden for sunny weekends and summer evenings. **Q🐴❀◐⇌♣●P🚌🐾📶**

Hazel End, Farnham

Three Horseshoes

CM23 1HB

☎ (01279) 813429 🌐 threehorseshoeshazelend.co.uk

Adnams Southwold Bitter; Sharp's Doom Bar; 1 changing beer (sourced nationally) 🄷

A clean and friendly pub opposite the cricket green at Hazel End. It has been completely renovated – a large extension has created more space to both eat and drink here comfortably. Food includes an impressive fish menu. This is a good example of a once run-down premises transformed into a thriving, successful establishment. It has low ceilings, black wooden beams and two wood-burning stoves. **❀◐◑⛺P🐾**

Herongate Tye

Olde Dog Inn 🄻

129 Billericay Road, CM13 3SD (¾ mile E of A128) TQ641909

☎ (01277) 810337 🌐 theoldedoginn.co.uk

Crouch Vale Brewers Gold; Greene King Abbot 🄷**; 2 changing beers (sourced nationally)** 🄶

This 17th-century weatherboarded inn is a privately owned and run free house with traditional decor. It offers a variety of real ales, with one regularly-changing guest beer and a craft beer from countrywide microbreweries, along with more established national brands and its own Olde Dog IPA, brewed locally. Two traditional ciders are also available. Food is served at the bar or in the separate restaurant area, lunchtimes and evenings. Dogs are welcome in the area at the end of the bar known as the Dog House. **🐴❀◐◑♿●P🐾📶**

Heybridge

Maltsters Arms

Hall Road, CM9 4NJ

☎ (01621) 853880

Greene King IPA, Abbot 🄷**; 2 changing beers (sourced regionally)** 🄷/🄶

This friendly Gray's local is a little like someone's comfortable front room converted into a bar. The pleasant atmosphere is enhanced by a collection of mirrors and some breweriana. Three guest beers are usually available, one from a local brewery. Filled rolls are available lunchtimes. The rear patio, with plenty of tables and chairs, can be a suntrap in summer. The pub is popular with ramblers walking the nearby Chelmer and Blackwater Navigation towpath. **Q🐴❀◐♣🚌🐾📶**

High Roding

Black Lion 🄻

3 The Street, CM6 1NT (on B184 Dunmow to Ongar road)

☎ (01371) 872847 🌐 theblacklionhighroding.co.uk

4 changing beers (sourced locally; often Colchester, Hadham, New River) 🄷

A striking half-timbered 14th-century building. It was a coaching inn on the London to Norwich road, and has low ceilings, oak beams and a huge fire in the winter. The restaurant serves good locally sourced food, with a popular roast on Sunday. There is a TV in the end bar, usually showing rugby on Saturday. Tasting evenings feature throughout the year. Outside is a pleasant courtyard garden. **Q🐴❀◐◑♿P🚌**(17,18)**🐾**

Horndon-on-the-Hill

Bell Inn

High Road, SS17 8LD (near centre of village, almost opp Woolmarket and Orsett Rd)

☎ (01375) 642463 🌐 bell-inn.co.uk

Crouch Vale Brewers Gold; Greene King IPA; Sharp's Doom Bar; 2 changing beers (sourced nationally) 🄷

Popular 15th-century coaching inn, where beamed bars feature wood panelling and carvings, run by the same family since 1938. Note the hot cross bun collection; a bun has been added every Good Friday for more than 100 years. Three regular beers are on the bar, plus two guests, including ales from Essex breweries. The award-winning restaurant is open daily, lunchtimes and evenings (booking advisable). Gourmet nights are held – see website for details. Accommodation is available in 27 bedrooms. Q🝕❀🛏◑♿P🚌(11)🐾📶

Kirby-le-Soken

Ship

35 Walton Road, CO13 0DT
☎ (01255) 679149 🌐 theshipkirbylesoken.co.uk
Adnams Southwold Bitter, Ghost Ship, Broadside; 3 changing beers (sourced nationally) Ⓗ
A free house, whose restaurant area offers a wide selection of menus. The Ship has a large beer garden to the rear and an outside seating area to the front. The garden contains a marquee that is used for various events throughout the year, including an annual beer festival. Local CAMRA Cider Pub of the Year in 2017 and 2018, with trays of three thirds of cider available to help you choose a favourite. Well-behaved dogs are welcome. Q🝕❀◑♣🍎P🚌(8,98)🐾📶

Lamarsh

Lamarsh Lion

Bures Road, CO8 5EP (1¼ miles NW of Bures) TL892355
☎ (01787) 227007 🌐 lamarshlion.co.uk
4 changing beers (sourced nationally) Ⓗ
A popular rural 14th-century community venue that boasts Constable and Gainsborough as former customers – their paintings feature outstanding views of the Stour Valley. Formerly an Independent newspaper top 20 new UK pub, its beautifully renovated interior showcases many social events including live music. The varied daily food menu includes specials and all-day breakfasts from 8am. Cyclists and ramblers are welcome, as are dogs. There is parking to the side and rear and outside seating is available in the garden and at the front. Camping is available from spring and a minibus shuttle runs for parties within an eight-mile radius. Q🝕❀🛏◑♿⛺♣P🚌(754)🐾📶

Langley Lower Green

Bull

Park Lane, CB11 4SB TL437345
☎ (01279) 777307 🌐 thebullpub.co.uk
Adnams Mosaic; Greene King IPA; 2 changing beers (sourced regionally) Ⓗ
Classic Victorian village local with original cast-iron lattice windows, in a tiny isolated hamlet close to both Hertfordshire and Cambridgeshire. The pub has a band of local regulars. There is an aquarium in the lounge bar. Occasional quiz nights are held, and open mic nights feature on the last Tuesday of the month. An annual beer festival takes place in September. Parties can pre-book food at times when it is normally unavailable.
🝕❀◑♣P🐾📶

Layer-de-la-Haye

Donkey & Buskins 𝕃

Layer Road, CO2 0HU
☎ (01206) 734774 🌐 donkeyandbuskins.co.uk
Adnams Southwold Bitter; Greene King IPA; 2 changing beers (sourced nationally) Ⓗ
Built circa 1840, this hostelry, run by the same family since 1985, is now an aspiring fresh food gastro-pub supporting local produce suppliers. Up to five ales are available from local and national brewers. It has a bar and three restaurant rooms, a large beer garden off the main road, surrounded by woodland, and a large car park. Q🝕❀🛏◑♿♣P🚌(50)🐾📶

Leigh-on-Sea

Leigh-on-Sea Brewery Tap 𝕃

35 Progress Road, SS9 5PR (near A127, behind an industrial unit and reached by a signposted gravel and concrete path around it)
☎ (01702) 817255 🌐 leighonseabrewery.co.uk
8 changing beers (sourced locally; often Leigh on Sea)
The brewery taproom is on the Progress Road industrial estate. The beer range is a rotation of core beers on either handpump or KeyKeg dispense, with one or two guest beers. The decor features exposed brickwork, tall tables and stools, industrial lighting and a bar top of cockleshells. International rugby and other major sporting events are shown on terrestrial TV. Regular music events take place. Open Thursday to Saturday – hours can vary so check the website or social media.
❀🍎🚌(25,20)🐾📶

Mayflower 𝕃

5-6 High Street, Old Leigh, SS9 2EN (at far end of Old Leigh from railway station, behind chip shop)
☎ (01702) 478535 🌐 mayfloweroldleigh.com
Crouch Vale Brewers Gold; George's Cockleboats; St Austell Proper Job; 3 changing beers (sourced regionally) Ⓗ
Popular pub selling six beers and one cider, including some from local breweries. It has been the local CAMRA Pub of the Year three times in the past. Food is mainly fish and chips from the attached restaurant. One wall lists the names of all who sailed on the Mayflower. Dogs are welcome and there is a pleasant seating area at the back with views of the estuary. 🝕❀◑♿⇌🍎P🚌(26)🐾📶

PeterBoat 𝕃 ✔

27 High Street, Old Leigh, SS9 2EN
☎ (01702) 475666 🌐 the-peterboat.eastangliapubs.com
House beer (by George's); 4 changing beers (sourced regionally) Ⓗ
Welcoming pub on the Old Leigh waterfront, with great views across the estuary, which has been in Old Leigh's records since 1757. The house beer, Hilda B, is brewed locally by George's, and beer from Leigh-on-Sea Brewery is usually on the bar. Excellent beer festivals are held twice a year in the car park and good food is served, with an à la carte menu. Recently award a Highly Commended certificate by the local CAMRA branch.
🝕❀◑♿⇌P🚌(26,17)🐾📶

Little Thurrock (Grays)

Traitors' Gate 𝕃

40-42 Broadway, RM17 6EW (on A126)
☎ (01375) 372628 🌐 traitorsgatepub.wordpress.com
Greene King Abbot; 4 changing beers (sourced regionally) Ⓗ
Taken over by the current operator in 2013, this hostelry has established a reputation for live bands on Fridays and Saturdays and open mic sessions on Thursdays. The quieter, traditional end is to the right of the front bar. It has five handpumps, with four dispensing a rotating selection of guest beers. The small chalkboards above the bar list current and forthcoming beers. Real ales are discounted at various times through the week. The pub is not easy to find due to the lack of external signage.
🝕❀♿♣🚌(66,66A)🐾📶

Little Totham

Swan

School Road, CM9 8LB
☎ (01621) 331713 🌐 theswanlittletotham.com

Crouch Vale Brewers Gold; Mighty Oak Oscar Wilde, Captain Bob; Timothy Taylor Landlord; 3 changing beers (sourced nationally) [G]
Grade II listed, three-roomed, cottage-style inn, which includes a public bar and restaurant. There is a superb range of beers, mostly local, served direct from the cask in a chilled cellar, and a dozen or so ciders including Westons Rosie's Pig and Abrahalls Cracklin' Rosie perry. The walled front garden provides a safe play area and there is a large field to the rear for outdoor activities and events. A two-week beer festival is hosted in June.
Q❀◑♿♣●P▯🐾ᯤ

Littley Green

Compasses [L]

CM3 1BU
☎ (01245) 362308 🌐 compasseslittleygreen.co.uk
Bishop Nick Ridley's Rite; Crouch Vale Essex Boys Best Bitter; 3 changing beers (sourced nationally) [G]
Formerly Ridley's brewery tap, this is a picturesque Victorian country pub in a quiet hamlet. A wood-panelled bar has benches around the walls and a tiled floor. Beers are drawn directly from casks, and it has an interesting range of three ciders and a perry. Renowned filled huffers (giant baps) are available lunchtimes and evenings, plus other traditional dishes. There are seats and tables outside and in the large gardens. Regular beer festivals are held. Accommodation comprises five high-quality rooms. Q❀🛏◑♣●P▯🐾ᯤ

Loughton

Victoria Tavern ✔

165 Smarts Lane, IG10 4BP
☎ (020) 8508 1779 🌐 thevictoriatavern.co.uk
Adnams Southwold Bitter; Greene King IPA; Sharp's Doom Bar; Timothy Taylor Landlord; 2 changing beers [H]
This is an old-fashioned traditional tavern that prides itself on real ale and inclusive conversation. It lies between Loughton and Epping Forest and is a 10-15 minute walk from Loughton tube station. Outside, the pleasant gated garden is popular with locals and walkers; well-behaved dogs are welcome. The pub serves generous portions of fresh seasonal food and has no TV, just good ale, good food and good company.
Q❀◑P🚌ᯤ

Maldon

Mighty Oak Tap Room

10 High Street, CM9 5PJ
☎ (01621) 853892 🌐 micropubmaldon.uk
Mighty Oak Oscar Wilde, Captain Bob, Maldon Gold, Kings; 2 changing beers (sourced locally) [G]
Mighty Oak Brewery's taproom is housed in a 500-year-old beamed building, and showcases its award-winning range of beers, served direct from the cask. The friendly atmosphere in the comfortable downstairs bar, with its bench seating but without piped music, encourages conversation. There is a quiet and relaxing reading room upstairs, furnished with leather sofas and chairs. Cheeseboards and locally produced pork pies are sold. Ciders are from Westons and Celtic Marches. Unplugged acoustic music sessions feature every Sunday afternoon. Closed Monday. Q♿♣●🚌🐾ᯤ

Queen Victoria 🏆

Spital Road, CM9 6ED
☎ (01621) 852923 🌐 queenvictoriamaldon.co.uk
Adnams Southwold Bitter; Greene King Abbot; Maldon Pucks Folly; Mighty Oak Captain Bob; 3 changing beers (sourced nationally; often Dartmoor, Elgood's, Skinner's) [H]
A warm and friendly welcome awaits everyone at this convivial Gray's establishment, with four well-kept ales from local and regional breweries and up to three guest ales and three real ciders. Extensive menus offer locally sourced, home-cooked meals, with vegetarian and vegan options (booking is recommended). Families are welcome throughout, as are dogs, in the beer garden and public bar. Seasonal events are joyfully celebrated, together with beer festivals, darts, dominoes and bar skittles. Local CAMRA Pub of the Year 2020.
❀◑♿♣●P🚌🐾ᯤ

Rose & Crown ✔

109 High Street, CM9 5EP
☎ (01621) 852255
Greene King Abbot; Ruddles Best Bitter; Sharp's Doom Bar; 3 changing beers (sourced nationally) [H]
A 16th-century pub acquired and substantially refurbished by Wetherspoon in 2015. Food is served all day. In common with other Wetherspoons, there are two beer festivals a year, in March/April and October. Children accompanying adults are welcome until 9pm, and are usually found in a room which is apart from the main bar area. Mind your head on the way to the toilets upstairs (the accessible toilet is downstairs).
Q❀◑🚌ᯤ

Manningtree

Red Lion

42 South Street, CO11 1BG
☎ (01206) 391880 🌐 redlionmanningtree.co.uk
Adnams Southwold Bitter; 2 changing beers (sourced regionally; often Colchester, Mighty Oak, Woodforde's) [H]
The Red Lion's history dates back to 1603. Many changes have taken place over the intervening centuries, but recent ones have improved customer space, modernised the toilets and added a small function room, all while maintaining the quality of the ales and the high level of service from the friendly staff. Larger events such as live music and the Oktoberfest take place in a large function room upstairs. The pub doesn't provide food beyond bar snacks but it is takeaway-friendly. ❀♣●🚌🐾ᯤ

Monk Street

Farmhouse Inn [L]

Thaxted, CM6 2NR (off B184, 2 miles S of Thaxted)
TL614288
☎ (01371) 830864 🌐 farmhouseinn.org
Greene King IPA; 2 changing beers (sourced locally) [H]
Built in the 16th century, this former Dunmow Brewery establishment has been enlarged to incorporate a restaurant and accommodation; the bar is in the original part of the building. The quiet hamlet here overlooks the Chelmer Valley, two miles from historic Thaxted. A disused well in the garden supplied Monk Street with water during World War II. There is a rear patio, front garden and a top field. Draught cider from Westons is usually available. ❀🛏◑●P🚌(313)🐾ᯤ

Newport

White Horse Inn

Belmont Hill, CB11 3RF
☎ (01799) 540002

3 changing beers (sourced nationally) [H]
On the main road in the middle of Newport, this is a friendly drinkers' local, serving three changing ales. It is a transformed ex-Greene King house focused on the community, having been purchased by a local business. Extensive repair work has been done to the building, and the change of ownership, with a new enthusiastic licensee, has raised its popularity as a beer drinkers' destination. Food is served on Tuesday evening only.
❀◗⇌♣◘(301) 🐾 ᯤ

Pebmarsh

King's Head

The Street, CO9 2NH
☎ (01787) 267942 🌐 kingsheadpebmarsh.com
Adnams Ghost Ship; 3 changing beers (sourced nationally) [H]
The King's Head, dating back to 1450, was saved by the community and reopened in 2017 after an extensive refurbishment, while maintaining a traditional character. A plaque on the wall displays the names of the many shareholders. There is a single bar serving three areas: one for drinking, one for dining, and another with comfortable seating. The main bar has a real fire. Outside, there are benches in the large garden area. Closed Monday except bank holidays. ❀◐◗P◘🐾 ᯤ

Ridgewell

White Horse Inn 𝕃

Mill Road, CO9 4SG (on A1017) TL735408
☎ (01440) 785532 🌐 ridgewellwhitehorse.com
3 changing beers (sourced nationally) [G]
Set in a pretty village, which was home to the American 381st Heavy Bomb Group during WWII. A dark beer is often on the bar here. Annual beer festivals are held in summer on the patio behind the pub. As well as a choice of excellent real ale and food, the pub offers an interesting selection of good-quality wines to suit a variety of tastes, and 4-star accommodation.
❀◐◗♿♣●P▯◘ ᯤ

Rochford

Golden Lion 𝕃

35 North Street, SS4 1AB
☎ (01702) 545487 🌐 goldenlionrochford.co.uk
Adnams Southwold Bitter; Greene King Abbot; Keppels Golden Crow; 4 changing beers (sourced nationally) [H]
This Grade II listed weatherboarded free house is a long-standing Guide entry and has won many local CAMRA awards. In addition to the three regular ales, four are nationally sourced from Tring, Cotleigh, Irwell Works and Mighty Oak breweries, along with real cider. A beer festival is held in autumn in the attractive patio-style garden. Live sports are occasionally shown on large-screen TV. A wood-burning stove and a comprehensive jukebox add to the atmosphere.
❀♿⇌♣●P◘(7,8) 🐾 ᯤ

Miley

1 Union Lane, SS4 1AP (behind Sainsbury's Local at end of West St, then through pub courtyard)
☎ (01702) 544229
4 changing beers (sourced nationally) [H]
Four ales are served in this friendly, family-owned community local. Some ales are from the wider Greene King range, but others are from smaller breweries such as Billericay, Colchester, Irwell Works and Tombstone. Live music features most weekends, with bands playing on the outdoor stage in the summer. Karaoke and quiz nights are held monthly, along with events such as the annual three-legged charity race. The pub is sports-oriented, with two dartboards and three large-screen TVs showing a variety of events. ❀♿⇌♣●P◘(7,8)🐾 ᯤ

Rowhedge

Olde Albion

High Street, CO5 7ES
☎ (01206) 728972
3 changing beers (sourced nationally) [H]
A free house on the waterfront, playing a substantial role in local village life. The pub serves an interesting range of changing ales from various breweries. There is usually a cheeseboard on Sunday. A fire adds warmth in cold weather, and on fine days there are tables and chairs on the greensward overlooking the River Colne. Beer festivals are held on St George's Day and during the Rowhedge Regatta. ❀♣●◘(66)🐾 ᯤ

Roydon

New Inn ✔

90 High Street, CM19 5EE
☎ (01279) 792225 🌐 thenewinnroydon.co.uk
Adnams Broadside; Greene King IPA; Sharp's Doom Bar; 1 changing beer (sourced nationally) [H]
The New Inn was built in the 18th century in this charming village and retains many period features. It is a short walk from Roydon station and the River Stort Navigation and welcomes many walkers and boaters as well as a local clientele. It has been nominated for 2020 Parliamentary Pub of the Year by the local MP. The large garden has a children's play area. The pub runs a beer festival each September, barbecues on fine Friday evenings and a Wednesday OAP lunch. ❀◐◗⇌P🐾 ᯤ

Saffron Walden

King's Arms 𝕃 ✔

10 Market Hill, CB10 1HQ
☎ (01799) 522768 🌐 thekingsarmssaffronwalden.co.uk
Adnams Southwold Bitter; Oakham JHB; Woodforde's Wherry; 2 changing beers (sourced nationally) [H]
Venerable wooden-beamed, multi-roomed pub, just off the market square (market days are Tuesday and Saturday). It has welcoming log fires in cold weather and a pleasant patio for alfresco dining and drinking. A mild or dark beer is often available in winter. There is live music at weekends, acoustic music on Thursday, and a monthly quiz. Food is served at lunchtimes.
Q❀◐P◘🐾 ᯤ

Old English Gentleman ✔

11 Gold Street, CB10 1EJ (E of B184/B1052 jct)
☎ (01799) 523595 🌐 oldenglishgentleman.com
Adnams Southwold Bitter; Woodforde's Wherry; 2 changing beers (sourced regionally) [H]
An 18th-century town-centre pub with log fires and a welcoming atmosphere. It serves a selection of guest ales and an extensive menu of bar food and sandwiches that changes regularly. Traditional roasts and chef's specials are available on Sunday in the bar or dining area. A variety of works of art is displayed. There is a heated patio at the rear and a wood-burning stove too. Saffron Walden is busy on Tuesday and Saturday market days.
❀◐◘🐾 ᯤ

South Benfleet

South Benfleet Social Club 𝕃

8 Vicarage Hill, SS7 1PB (on B1006)
☎ (01268) 206159
6 changing beers Ⓗ/Ⓖ
A popular social club that is a huge asset to the community. Two beer festivals are held in May and December, and a good range of beers and ciders is always enjoyed. It was CAMRA East Anglia Regional Club 2018 and local CAMRA branch Club of the Year for many years. Games include pool and poker, with quiz nights, sport on TV and live music at weekends all adding to the ambience. CAMRA members and Guide holders are always welcome. ♘❀◖♿⇌♣●P🚌🐾📶

Southend-on-Sea

Last Post 𝕃 ✔

Weston Road, SS1 1AS (opp Southend Central station)
☎ (01702) 431682
Greene King Abbot; Ruddles Best Bitter; Sharp's Doom Bar; 5 changing beers (sourced nationally) Ⓗ
Large Wetherspoon pub with two bars, in an old Victorian post office that was built in 1896. Up to seven cask ales, often including dark beers, and three real ciders are on tap. Accommodation is available and breakfast is served, with main meals available until late. There is a pleasant outside seating area and conservatory. Beer festivals are held twice a year. Close to two railway stations and the bus station. Q♘❀🛏◖◗♿⇌●🚌📶

Mawson's 𝕃

781 Southchurch Road, SS1 2PP (on A13)
☎ (01702) 601781
George's Wallasea Wench, Cockleboats; 4 changing beers (sourced nationally) Ⓗ
This converted shop was Southend's first micropub and has up to six cask ales, with a least two from the local George's Brewery. Six real ciders, three craft keg pumps, two draught German pilsners and two draught ciders, one of which is Rocquette of Guernsey, are exclusively sold in Essex by Mawson's. Set in the Southchurch village area, the bar has a large gallery of Laurel and Hardy pictures. Quiet music adds to happy conversation, with occasional live music and quiz nights.
♘♿⇌(East) ●▯🚌(1,14) 🐾📶

Railway Hotel 𝕃

32 Clifftown Road, SS1 1AJ
☎ (01702) 343194 🌐 railwayhotelsouthend.co.uk
3 changing beers (sourced locally) Ⓗ
An old Victorian railway hotel which retains features from an inter-war Charrington's refit and which has been recognised by CAMRA as having a historic interior of some regional importance. A range of real ales – usually three – is available from Adnams Brewery. Live music plays up to six nights a week. Food is vegan pizza and pasta. There is a large beer garden with decking at the rear. ♘❀◖♿⇌(Central)🚌🐾📶

Southminster

Station Arms

39 Station Road, CM0 7EW
☎ (01621) 772225 🌐 thestationarms.co.uk
Adnams Southwold Bitter; 4 changing beers (sourced regionally; often Bishop Nick, George's, Mighty Oak) Ⓗ
A traditional Essex weatherboarded pub that has featured in this Guide for 30 consecutive years. It is a welcoming and thriving community local. The comfortable bare-boarded bar, with its open log fire, is decorated with railway and brewery memorabilia. An attractive courtyard is popular in fine weather and a barn with a wood-burning stove provides shelter if required. Live blues and folk music is hosted monthly. Annually, a harvest festival charity auction and a conker championship are held. Q❀⇌♣●🚌

Wibblers Brewery Taproom & Kitchen

Goldsands Road, CM0 7JW
☎ (01621) 772044 🌐 wibblers.co.uk/taproomkitchen
Wibblers Dengie IPA Ⓗ**; 6 changing beers (sourced locally; often Wibblers)** Ⓗ/Ⓖ
The taproom is attached to a beautiful, award-winning, restored medieval tithe barn housing Wibblers Brewery. The kitchen offers a wide-ranging menu of excellent home-cooked food, using mostly local produce. The bar is attractively furnished and – weather permitting – you can sit outside in the countryside. The brewery and taproom host open days and various other events throughout the year, including televised rugby and themed food evenings. Southminster railway station is only a five-minute walk away. Closed Monday and Tuesday. Q♘❀◖◗♿⇌●P🚌(31X)🐾📶

Stanford-le-Hope

Rising Sun 𝕃

Church Hill, SS17 0EU (opp church and near A1014)
☎ (01375) 671097
5 changing beers (sourced nationally) Ⓗ
Much-improved two-bar traditional town pub in the shadow of the church. The five guest beers are mainly from independent breweries, including LocAle beers, and up to three ciders or perries are stocked. Regular monthly live music takes place, and beer festivals are held three times a year in spring, summer and winter, with the summer festival in the large rear garden. The back bar is available for private functions. ❀⇌♣●P🚌🐾📶

Stansted Mountfitchet

Rose & Crown 𝕃

31 Bentfield Green, CM24 8HX (1 mile W of B1383)
TL505256
☎ (01279) 812107 🌐 roseandcrownstansted.co.uk
3 changing beers (sourced regionally) Ⓗ
Family-run Victorian pub near a duck pond, on the edge of a small hamlet. This free house has been modernised to provide one large bar but retains the welcoming atmosphere of an active village local. It has been extended to include a fairly large new snug. Food is home-cooked and uses locally sourced produce. A large variety of gins is stocked. There is an old seven-inch singles jukebox on which you can play your own records. Closed Monday. ♘❀◖◗♣P🚌(7,7a)🐾📶

Stanway

Live & Let Live 𝕃

12 Millers Lane, CO3 0PS (in a small lane, 100yds from London Rd)
☎ (01206) 574071 🌐 theliveandletlive.co.uk
4 changing beers (sourced nationally) Ⓗ
A traditional, welcoming local that continues to delight, with a homely saloon bar and public bar, offering sports TV, darts, pool and a comprehensive jukebox. The publicans regularly support local breweries and take great pride in the condition and quality of their real ales. The beers are competitively priced, as is the traditional home-cooked food, served most lunchtimes and Friday and Saturday evenings. Renowned for its beer, sausage

and pie festivals. Runner-up and highly commended local CAMRA Pub of the Year in 2019.
Q🏇❀◑♿♣🍎P🚌(65,70) 🐾📶

Steeple Bumpstead

Fox & Hounds 🄻
3 Chapel Street, CB9 7DQ
☎ (01440) 731810 🌐 foxinsteeple.co.uk
Greene King IPA; 3 changing beers (sourced nationally) ⊞
A 17th-century coaching inn in a picturesque village on the Essex/Suffolk border, featuring an open fire in the main bar, two restaurants, a courtyard rear garden and further seating at the front. Freshly prepared local food from a seasonal and varied menu is served six days a week. On Wednesday evening a complimentary cheese board is offered, with reduced-price real ale and wine all evening. Live bands perform and quiz nights take place throughout the year. Q🏇❀◑♣🚌(18)🐾📶

Stow Maries

Prince of Wales
Woodham Road, CM3 6SA
☎ (01621) 828971 🌐 prince-stowmaries.net
6 changing beers (sourced nationally) ⊞
This classic weatherboarded pub boasts several characterful drinking areas, with open fires and an old bread oven used for baking pizza in the winter months. The extensive garden and courtyards provide plenty of options for outside drinking. Good food is on the menu, made with local produce where possible. Many special events are held including Burns Night, a firework display on the last Saturday in October, and live music. The historic Stow Maries World War I airfield is nearby.
Q🏇❀🛏◑♿P🚭🚌(593) 🐾📶

Tollesbury

King's Head
1 High Street, CM9 8RG
☎ (01621) 869203
Bishop Nick Ridley's Rite; Courage Best Bitter; 3 changing beers (sourced nationally) ⊞
Popular village-centre two-bar local run by a long-serving landlord, offering great-value beer. There is always a cheery welcome for regulars, birdwatchers, walkers and boaters. Good-value pie and pint deals are available all day. The Friday and Sunday lunches are popular and booking is strongly advised. The pub hosts local pool and darts teams, and holds quizzes on a regular basis. Pictures of Tollesbury's yacht racing history feature throughout. Q🏇❀◐♿♣🍎P🚌🐾

Toppesfield

Green Man 🄻
Church Lane, CO9 4DR
☎ (01787) 237418
3 changing beers (sourced nationally; often PumpHouse Community) ⊞
A community-owned local which hosts beer festivals and events throughout the year. It has two pool teams and darts is played in the public bar. There is a brewery next door, PumpHouse Community Brewery. In fact, this village is the only place in the UK to have a pub, brewery and shop all owned by the community. Meals may need booking, and group pre-booking of lunchtime meals is possible on weekday lunchtimes. Sunday lunch is served, fish and chips (including to take away) on Friday, and bacon rolls on Saturday. 🏇❀◑♿♣🍎P🐾📶

Waltham Abbey

Woodbine Inn 🏆 🄻 ✔
Honey Lane, EN9 3QT (close to M25 jct 26)
☎ (01992) 713050 🌐 thewoodbine.co.uk
Adnams Ghost Ship ⊞; Bishop Nick Divine ⊞/Ⓖ; Mighty Oak Oscar Wilde Ⓖ, Captain Bob ⊞; 4 changing beers (sourced locally) ⊞/Ⓖ
Set in Epping Forest, the award-winning pub concentrates on real ales and over 40 small-producer ciders, and makes London Glider cider on site. Food is home-made, with local sausages, ham and steak as specialities. Dogs are welcome in the main bar, where there is bar billiards. The ale sampling society and comedy club meet monthly. National Finalist Cider Pub of the Year 2019, Essex Pub of the Year 2018 and local CAMRA Pub of the Year 2020. 🏇◑♣🍎P🚌(66,66A)🐾

Weeley Heath

White Hart
Clacton Road, CO16 9ED (on B1441, 1 mile from Weeley station) TM153208
☎ (01255) 830384
2 changing beers (sourced nationally; often Greene King, Mauldons, Woodforde's) ⊞
This free house has been run by the same landlords for over 23 years and is a regular in the Guide. It hosts pool and darts teams and has a real ale club. There is a garden with a covered patio for smokers. A great venue for sports enthusiasts, it shows Sky TV and BT Sport. Community focused, it hosts occasional music and quiz evenings. Local CAMRA Pub of the Year 2018 and local CAMRA Cider Pub of the Year in 2020. ❀⛺♣🍎P🚌📶

Wendens Ambo

Bell 🄻
Royston Road, CB11 4JY (on B1039)
☎ (01799) 540382 🌐 thebellinnpub.co.uk
Adnams Ghost Ship; Woodforde's Wherry; 2 changing beers (sourced regionally; often Oakham) ⊞
A lovely country pub in a picturesque village. A chalkboard features forthcoming guest ales here at the bar. Traditional locally-sourced food is available too. A folk open evening is held on the first Wednesday of the month. There is a large garden, a terrace with seating and tables, a pétanque pitch and children's play apparatus. A charity fundraising event is held with a beer festival during the summer bank holiday weekend, known as the Bell Bash. Dogs, walkers and cyclists are welcomed here.
🏇❀◑🚆(Audley End) ♣🍎P🚌(59,301) 🐾📶

Westcliff-on-Sea

Cricketers
228 London Road, SS0 7JG (on A13 London Rd)
☎ (01702) 345053 🌐 thecricketersbarandfood.co.uk
Adnams Ghost Ship; Dark Star Hophead; Greene King Abbot; Mighty Oak Oscar Wilde, Maldon Gold; 1 changing beer (sourced regionally) ⊞
A Gray & Sons establishment with well-kept beer, not far from Southend town centre. A music venue adjoins the pub so it can get busy on music nights. There are also jazz nights featuring Digby Fairweather and guests every second Wednesday of the month, and a quiz on Monday. The five regular beers, one of which is dark, are joined by an extra ale on days when Southend United are playing at home. 🏇❀◑♿🚆🚌🐾📶

Mile and a Third 🏆

67 Hamlet Court Road, SS0 7EU

☎ (01702) 902120 🌐 mileandathird.com

2 changing beers (sourced nationally) Ⓖ

Run by two beer managers from the Rochford beer festival, this is an L-shaped former shop, the front being the bottle shop, while the bar is on the side. There are also four trees inside the venue. Two real ales are served on gravity, and six keg lines plus three real ciders from bag-in-box. The bottle shop's fridge has bottles and cans featuring national and international brewers. All ales and ciders are £3 a pint on Monday. Music is mainly played on vinyl. Local CAMRA Pub of the Year 2020. Closed Tuesday. 🐴♿≢♣●🗑🚌🐾📶

West Road Tap

2 West Road, SS0 9DA

☎ (01702) 330647 🌐 westroadtap.com

3 changing beers (sourced nationally) Ⓖ

Near the Palace Theatre in Westcliff, this is a micropub and bottle shop, serving up to three cask ales on gravity. The cask ale range is sourced nationally. Beer is also served from six KeyKeg taps and there is an extensive fridge selection of craft beer in bottles and cans, which are available to drink on the premises or to take home. Two real ciders in boxes are also sold. Children are welcome until early evening. Local CAMRA Pub of the Year 2019. Closed Monday. Q🐴❀≢●🚌(1,27)🐾

Widdington

Fleur de Lys 🏆 L ✔

High Street, CB11 3SG TL538316

☎ (01799) 543280 🌐 thefleurdelys.co.uk

Adnams Southwold Bitter, Broadside; Woodforde's Wherry; 2 changing beers (sourced nationally) Ⓗ

Rumours of a ghost abound at this welcoming 400-year-old village local, which boasts a large open fireplace and beams. This was the first pub to be saved from closure by the local branch of CAMRA after the branch's formation. Quality meals are offered with fresh local ingredients. A bridge club is held on Monday night. The source of the River Cam, and Prior's Hall Barn, an English heritage site, are both nearby. Local CAMRA Pub of the Year 2020. 🐴❀◐◑♿♣●P🚌(301)🐾

Witham

Battesford Court L ✔

100-102 Newland Street, CM8 1AH

☎ (01376) 504080

Greene King Abbot; Ruddles Best Bitter; Sharp's Doom Bar; 5 changing beers (sourced nationally) Ⓗ

A large Wetherspoon conversion of a former hotel of the same name. The 16th-century building was previously the courthouse of the manor of Battesford. It has distinct areas with wood panelling and oak beams, including a family area. Up to five regional beers are served, including something local, usually from Bishop Nick or Wibblers, plus up to two ciders and perries, usually from Westons and Gwynt y Ddraig. The standard Wetherspoon food offering is available. Q🐴❀◐◑♿●🚌(38,71)📶

Wivenhoe

Black Buoy 🏆 ✔

Black Buoy Hill, CO7 9BS

☎ (01206) 822425 🌐 blackbuoy.co.uk

Colchester No.1; 5 changing beers (sourced nationally) Ⓗ

Local CAMRA Pub of the Year 2020, the Black Buoy is a popular and welcoming community-owned venue. There is a small public bar for drinkers at the front and other areas for drinking and dining, with a range of traditional home-cooked food available every day. The pub hosts beer festivals in May and August in the pleasant outdoor area and garden. Regular quiz and open mic nights take place throughout the year. Q🐴❀🛏◐◑♿≢♣P🚌🐾📶

Horse & Groom ✔

55 The Cross, CO7 9QL

☎ (01206) 824928 🌐 handgwivenhoe.co.uk

Adnams Southwold Bitter, Ghost Ship, Broadside; 3 changing beers (sourced nationally) Ⓗ

A real locals' two-bar pub with a large garden to the rear. Children and dogs are always welcome, and the garden has a small play area. The pub sells Adnams beer as well as a range of guests. Quality home-cooked lunches are served Monday to Saturday, with an ever-popular roast lunch on a Thursday (no food Sun). Regular curry nights take place each month. Q🐴❀◐♿♣P🚌🐾📶

Woodham Mortimer

Hurdlemakers Arms

Post Office Road, CM9 6ST

☎ (01245) 225169 🌐 hurdlemakersarms.co.uk

5 changing beers (sourced locally; often Maldon, Mighty Oak, Wibblers) Ⓗ

A Gray's house, this 400-year-old former farmhouse seamlessly blends restaurant with pub, and good food and beer are both on offer here. One area is dedicated to diners, while drinkers are catered for in a smaller bar. There is a huge beer garden ideal for families, with a play area and shady trees. Barbecues are held on summer weekends, functions are catered for in a marquee or Mortimer's Barn, and a popular beer festival is held in the last week of June. Q🐴❀◐◑♿♣●P🗑🚌🐾📶

Writtle

Wheatsheaf L

70 The Green, CM1 3DU

☎ (01245) 420672 🌐 thewheatsheafwrittle.co.uk

Adnams Southwold Bitter, Broadside; Maldon Drop of Nelson's Blood Ⓗ**; Mighty Oak Oscar Wilde** Ⓖ**, Maldon Gold; Wibblers Dengie IPA** Ⓗ**; 2 changing beers (sourced nationally)** Ⓖ

Traditional village inn built in 1813, with a small public bar, an equally compact lounge, and a covered patio by the road. It is a long-time favourite of the local CAMRA branch. The atmosphere is generally quiet, with the TV switched on only for occasional sporting events. Traditional food is served Tuesday to Saturday lunchtimes. Note the old Gray's sign in the public bar. Q◐♣P🚌

> Good ale is the true and proper drink of Englishmen. He is not deserving of the name of Englishman who speaketh against ale, that is good ale.
> **George Borrow, Lavengro**

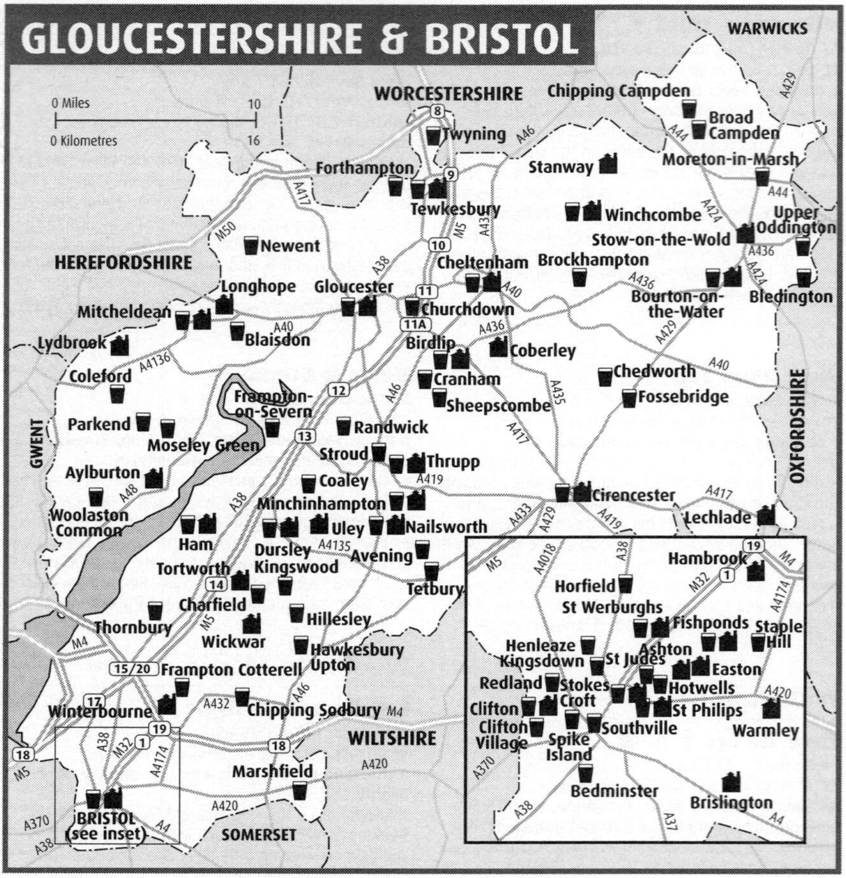

Avening

Bell

29 High Street, GL8 8NF (at bottom of High St on B4014)
(01453) 836422 thebellavening.co.uk
Timothy Taylor Landlord; Wickwar BOB; 2 changing beers (often Butcombe)
This pleasant village local is a friendly, confidently run old inn with exposed stone walls, two bay window seats and a roaring wood-burner. The jovial, amicable regulars are always chatty, enjoying the offerings from the attractive open bar, which features up to four different ales at busy times. The refurbished, comfortable dining area serves a competitively priced menu in collaboration with a local Indian restaurant. This pub can be quietly addictive and quite difficult to leave.

Birdlip

Golden Heart

Nettleton Bottom, GL4 8LA (on A417)
(01242) 870261 thegoldenheart.co.uk
3 changing beers (sourced nationally)
A welcome oasis of tranquillity beside the single carriageway section of the Gloucester to Swindon road, this 400-year-old Cotswold free house retains most of its original features. The small bar, almost hidden beyond a huge open fireplace, looks out on to a stone-paved patio and garden overlooking the valley. The menu uses the finest award-winning meats and local produce. Dogs are welcome, with treats available for them at the bar.

Blaisdon

Red Hart

GL17 0AH (in centre of village, signed from A4136 E of Longhope or N of A48)
(01452) 830477 redhartinn.co.uk
Otter Bitter; 3 changing beers (sourced nationally; often Bespoke, Kingstone, Wye Valley)
Local CAMRA branch Pub of the Year 2020, the Red Hart is a lovely old inn deservedly popular for its excellent food and well-kept ales. A warm welcome is assured. There are designated dining areas, but no separate restaurant, so everyone can enjoy the convivial atmosphere. A well-tended garden is an ideal place for families to enjoy in the summer. The bar area has flagstones, worn through generations of use, and the walls are adorned with memorabilia. Paintings from local artists are displayed for sale.

Bledington

King's Head

The Green, OX7 6XQ (off B4450 on village green)
(01608) 658365 kingsheadinn.net

Hook Norton Hooky; 3 changing beers (sourced regionally) Ⓗ
Delightful, 16th-century stone-built inn overlooking the village green. The pub has original old beams, an open inglenook log fire and high-back settles. This free house, with 12 comfortable letting rooms, is renowned for its wide range of ale and food. Bledington is about four miles from Stow-on-the-Wold, and there are good local walks to nearby villages, with Kingham station close by. The two guest beers are selected from local brewers in Gloucestershire and Oxfordshire. Q🐴❀🛏◐◑♣P🐾📶

Bourton-on-the-Water

Mousetrap Inn Ⓛ

Lansdowne, GL54 2AR (300yds W of village centre)
☎ (01451) 820579 🌐 themousetrapinn.co.uk
3 changing beers (sourced locally) Ⓗ
Traditional Cotswold stone free house, recently refurbished, in the Lansdowne part of Bourton close to the centre, with three changing local beers on offer. A friendly welcome is assured for locals, tourists, children and dogs, with food including breakfast available. A patio area in front with tables and hanging baskets provides a suntrap in the summer. Local CAMRA Pub of the Year runner-up in 2020. Q🐴🛏◐◑♿P🚌(801,855)🐾📶

Bristol

Bank Tavern ✔

8 John Street, BS1 2HR (take lane next to arcade on All Saints St)
☎ (0117) 930 4691 🌐 banktavern.com
4 changing beers (often Cheddar Ales, Plain, Prescott) Ⓗ
Popular and compact one-bar pub, hidden away near the old city wall. The four beers of varying styles are often from microbreweries from the south-west or sometimes further afield, alongside one changing real cider. Quirky humour and many varied events define the place – it is a great alternative to the more predictable establishments all around. Quiz night is Tuesday and live music features every other Thursday. Quality food is served lunchtimes, with booking essential for the award-winning Sunday lunch. 🐴❀◐♣🍎🚌🐾📶

Beer Emporium

13-15 King Street, BS1 4EF
☎ (0117) 379 0333 🌐 thebeeremporium.net
5 changing beers Ⓗ
A two-storey pub on Bristol's historic King Street, with a small ground-level Belgian beer bar (open Wednesday-Sunday late afternoons and early evenings) that belies the huge, subterranean cellar serving a variety of cask, keg, canned and bottled beers. Set inside three tunnels - one for the bar, one for the genuinely authentic Italian pizza and pasta restaurant with additional seating for drinkers, and one for the restaurant kitchen – the underground area is accessible by stairs and lift. 🐴❀◐◑♿🍎🚌📶

Bridge Inn

16 Passage Street, BS2 0JF
☎ (0117) 929 0942
Quantock QPA; 3 changing beers Ⓗ
Conveniently placed near Temple Meads station and Cabot Circus shopping centre, this small, friendly venue is a good place to start a visit to Bristol. An adventurous choice of ales is offered and exceptionally good-value weekday lunches are served from a small menu. Musical memorabilia adorn the walls and board games are available to play. Thirty malt whiskies and selected vodkas, gins and rums are also stocked, together with Belgian bottled beers. Outside tables increase capacity during good weather. ❀◐≹♣🚌🐾📶

Commercial Rooms Ⓛ ✔

43-45 Corn Street, BS1 1HT
☎ (0117) 927 9681
Greene King IPA, Abbot; Sharp's Doom Bar; 9 changing beers (often Bath Ales, Butcombe, Great Western) Ⓗ
This centrally located Grade II listed building, dating from 1810, was Bristol's first Wetherspoon. It offers up to 10 guest beers and food served all day. There is a quieter galleried room at the rear, but the main bar gets busy at peak times. The interior features Greek revival-style decor, a stunning ceiling with dome, and portraits and memorabilia from the venue's days as a businessmen's club. Wheelchair access is via the side entrance in Small Street. Q🐴◐◑♿🍎🚌📶

REAL ALE BREWERIES

Arbor Bristol
Artisan Minchinhampton
Basement Beer Bristol (NEW)
Bath ✐ Bristol: Warmley
Battledown Cheltenham
Bespoke ✐ Mitcheldean
Brewhouse & Kitchen 🛢 Bristol: Clifton
Brewhouse & Kitchen 🛢 Cheltenham
Brewhouse & Kitchen 🛢 Gloucester
Bristol Beer Factory Bristol: Ashton
Brythonic Aylburton
Clavell & Hind ✐ Birdlip
Corinium ✐ Cirencester
Cotswold Bourton-on-the-Water
Cotswold Lion Coberley
Croft ✐ Bristol: Stokes Croft
Dawkins ✐ Bristol: Easton
DEYA ✐ Cheltenham
Donnington Stow-on-the-Wold
Fierce & Noble ✐ Bristol: St Werburgh's
Fishponds 🛢 Bristol: Fishponds
Gloucester ✐ Gloucester
Goff's Winchcombe
Good Chemistry Bristol: St Philips
Great Western Bristol: Hambrook
Hal's Dursley
Halfpenny 🛢 Lechlade
Hillside ✐ Longhope
Incredible Bristol: Brislington
Inferno Tewkesbury
Keep 🛢 Nailsworth
King Street 🛢 Bristol
Left Handed Giant ✐ Bristol: St Philips
Little Giant Bristol: Fishponds
Lydbrook Valley 🛢 Lydbrook
Masquerade Bristol: St Werburgh's
Moor ✐ Bristol
New Bristol ✐ Bristol
Severn Tortworth
Stanway Stanway (brewing suspended)
Stroud ✐ Thrupp
TAP Cirencester
Tapestry ✐ Bristol: St Philips
Three Engineers Winterbourne
Tiley's 🛢 Ham
Uley Uley
Wickwar Wickwar
Wiper and True ✐ Bristol: St Werburghs
Zerodegrees 🛢 Bristol

Cornubia

142 Temple Street, BS1 6EN

☎ 07961 796406 thecornubia.co.uk

8 changing beers [H]

A small, cosy pub adorned with an impressive display of pumpclips and patriotic memorabilia in support of the UK armed forces and associated charities. Up to eight real ales are served with daily changes, and bar snacks including rolls and pork pies are often available. There is a wide range of board games and books, and live music features occasionally. The pub has a real fire and a fish tank with turtles, and the outside area has a boules piste.

Famous Royal Navy Volunteer

17-18 King Street, BS1 4EF

☎ (0117) 316 9237 navyvolunteer.co.uk

6 changing beers [H]

One of several popular pubs on historic King Street. Customers can keep warm in front of the snug fireplace or on fine days enjoy the suntrap roof terrace. Although there are no pumpclips, beer boards on both sides of the bar display what's on offer, with prices shown for third, half and full pints. Sports are often shown on TVs, although the building is big enough to avoid the match if desired. Wheelchair access is at the rear entrance.

Gryphon

41 Colston Street, BS1 5AP

☎ 07894 239567

6 changing beers [H]

A shrine to dark beer and great rock/heavy metal music. Posters, guitars and many pumpclips adorn the walls. Triangular in shape due to its corner plot, and just a few yards uphill from the Colston Hall, the Gryphon has six handpumps dispensing rapidly changing brews, many dark and often strong. Live bands sometimes play upstairs, and beer festivals are held in March and September. It may open earlier on Sundays. Children and dogs are admitted at the licensee's discretion.

LHG Brewpub

Compressor Building, Hawkins Lane, BS1 6EU

lhgbrewpub.com

2 changing beers (often Burning Sky, Left Handed Giant) [H]/[K]

Popular three-floor brewpub which opened in June 2019 in part of the old Courage brewery, and which saw brewing come back on the site in August that year after a number of decades of inactivity. The wide range of beer is served via a variety of dispense methods, including cask handpump, tank-conditioned, KeyKeg and keg. The second floor has its own bar for those who want to use the three dartboards and two pool tables. Card payment only.

Lime Kiln

17 St Georges Road, BS1 5UU (behind City Hall – formerly Council House)

☎ 07903 068256

6 changing beers [H]

Located on College Green, this cosy free house has a small outdoor drinking area at the front. The six handpumps dispense a range of beers in a variety of styles. Many of the breweries featured are seldom seen in Bristol, but local beers are also often stocked, along with one traditional cider. You are welcome to bring your own food. Several beer festivals are hosted throughout the year, some in conjunction with other pubs nearby. P

Old Fish Market

59-63 Baldwin Street, BS1 1QZ (200yds from city centre)

☎ (0117) 921 1515 oldfishmarket.co.uk

Fuller's Oliver's Island, London Pride, ESB; Moor Beer Nor'Hop; 1 changing beer (sourced nationally; often Dark Star, Fuller's, Moor Beer) [H]

There's something for everyone at this Fuller's outlet, which was refurbished in 2014 with decor, seating and lighting in the style of a relaxed lounge. There is a stadium-like atmosphere when major sporting events are shown on the big screen. Live jazz music features every Sunday evening. Between 20 and 30 gins are a great attraction for any fan of the spirit. Food includes a range of chowders, stone-baked pizzas and Sunday roasts. Dog-friendly, with treats and water bowls provided.

Seven Stars

1 Thomas Lane, BS1 6JG (just off Victoria St)

☎ (0117) 927 2845 7stars.co.uk

8 changing beers [H]

Popular free house tucked away in a lane 10 minutes' walk from the city centre and Temple Meads station. For many years one of Bristol's premier ale houses, it serves eight beers of all styles and strengths plus ciders and perries. Sunday afternoons feature quality live acoustic music. No food is served but you may bring in your own. There is an outdoor seating area and an informative plaque detailing how the pub featured in the 18th-century anti-slavery campaign.

Shakespeare Tavern

68 Prince Street, BS1 4QD

☎ (0117) 929 7695

Greene King IPA, Abbot; St Austell Tribute; 4 changing beers (sourced locally; often Bristol Beer Factory, Gloucester, Plain) [H]

By Bristol's historic docks, close to the city centre and Queen's Square, this converted Georgian town house claims to have the longest continuous ale licence in Bristol. Seven handpumps offer three regular ales plus four changing guests of varying styles from breweries near and far. Seasonal beer-related events are held, hosted by local breweries. A large selection of classic meals is on offer. There are benches on the front terrace for watching the world pass by. Q

Volunteer Tavern

9 New Street, BS2 9DX (very close to main Cabot Circus car park across carriageway from shops)

☎ (0117) 955 8498 volunteertavern.co.uk

6 changing beers [H]

Vibrant 17th-century pub tucked away in a quiet side street and convenient for Old Market bus interchange. As well as six changing beers, including a dark one, there are two changing real ciders. The large, fully enclosed, paved and heated garden hosts beer festivals, live music and DJs. Food comes from rotating pop-up kitchens, run by local chefs – check the website for times. Sunday roasts are hugely popular and cannot be booked.

Bristol: Bedminster

Bristol Beer Factory Tap Room

291 North Street, BS3 1JP

☎ (0117) 902 6317 bristolbeerfactory.co.uk/taproom

Bristol Beer Factory Fortitude; 3 changing beers (often Bristol Beer Factory) [H]

A short walk from Ashton Gate Stadium, and busy on match days, this comfortable brewery taproom showcases four rotating real ales from Bristol Beer Factory, along with six keg lines. Visitors are welcome to bring in food from local North Street bakeries and shops; the taproom provides on- and off-sales. Regular beer events are held, both for the Bristol Beer Club and the general public. A large TV screen is used to show Six Nations rugby. There is a small outdoor seating area on the pavement. (24)

Tobacco Factory Café Bar

Raleigh Road, BS3 1TF

(0117) 902 0060 tobaccofactory.com/cafe-bar

Bristol Beer Factory Fortitude; 5 changing beers (often Arbor, Good Chemistry, Siren)

Built in 1912, the Tobacco Factory was part of the vast Imperial Tobacco estate across south Bristol. Saved from demolition in 1993, the café bar opened in 2001 and has been transformed into a vibrant venue offering good-quality, locally produced food and drink, with a number of local breweries' beers served from six cask handpumps and numerous keg fonts. The outside yard is used for special events, such as local brewery tap takeovers and the popular Factoberfest beer festival in mid-September. (24)

Bristol: Clifton

Brewhouse & Kitchen

31-35 Cotham Hill, BS6 6JY

(0117) 973 3793

Brewhouse & Kitchen Crockers, Hornigold, Ameryck, Yankee Cabot; 1 changing beer (often Brewhouse & Kitchen Bristol)

Popular brewpub and dining spot reopened in 2015, on the site of the 18th-century Whiteladies Tavern. The brewery is at one end of the large bar and catches the eye (and nose, on brewing days) upon entry. The in-house brewed beers are all suitable for vegans, except Treason milk stout. Brewery experience days can be booked throughout the year. A function room is available upstairs and a patio area is just across the road.

Bristol: Clifton Village

Portcullis

3 Wellington Terrace, BS8 4LE (close to Clifton side of Suspension Bridge)

(0117) 973 0270

Dawkins Bristol Blonde, Bristol Best; 4 changing beers (sourced nationally)

A pub since 1821, rescued by Dawkins in 2008, featuring a downstairs bar and an upstairs lounge that is also used for functions. It is part of a Georgian terrace close to Clifton Suspension Bridge, and has cosy décor with many photos of film stars. Two to three Dawkins beers and guests from other microbreweries nationwide are served, plus a traditional cider. A large range of Belgian beers is also stocked. The rear garden is accessed from upstairs. (8,505)

Bristol: Fishponds

Snuffy Jack's

800 Fishponds Road, BS16 3TE

8 changing beers

The name of Bristol's third micropub, opened in 2017, relates to a former head miller at the nearby Snuff Mills. Between four and eight real ales are served on gravity from a chilled cabinet, plus two or more changing real ciders. Local beers feature plus some from further afield, with all styles offered. Food is limited to bar snacks. A quiz is held on the first Wednesday of the month. Conveniently close to multiple bus routes with direct links to many areas. Q

Bristol: Henleaze

Westbury Park

Northumbria Drive, BS9 4HP

(0117) 962 4235 westburyparkpub.co.uk

Butcombe Original; Purity Pure UBU; St Austell Tribute; Thornbridge Jaipur IPA; 2 changing beers (often Dark Star, Timothy Taylor)

Featured as the Kebab and Calculator in the BBC series The Young Ones, this circular pub reopened in 2016 after a major refurbishment. The interior is smartly decorated and furnished, with stools at the bar, and dining tables and comfortable seating throughout the open-plan interior. Emphasis is on well-kept, interesting beers, including from local breweries, and quality fresh, locally sourced food, with regularly changing seasonal menus. There is a community focus, newly reintroduced live music, and local clubs and societies are welcomed. P

Bristol: Horfield

Drapers' Arms

447 Gloucester Road, BS7 8TZ

thedrapersarms.co.uk

7 changing beers

Bristol's first micropub, opened in 2015, prides itself on a changing selection of up to eight real ales, on gravity, mostly from Bristol and the surrounding counties. Wine, local gins and bar snacks are also served, but no keg beer, bottled beer, lager or cider. This popular and friendly place follows the micropub tradition of focusing on good beer and conversation, with no music or TV. Two beer festivals are held each year. Q

Bristol: Hotwells

Bag of Nails

141 St Georges Road, BS1 5UW (5 mins walk from cathedral towards Hotwells)

4 changing beers

Close to the floating harbour, this small, partially gas-lit, terraced free house dates from the 1860s and serves up to nine changing cask ales, mainly from microbreweries, as well as a real cider. An eccentric list of rules includes no children, dogs or idiot pub crawls. The interior features terracotta colours, portholes in the floor, many cats roaming free, and eclectic music from a proper record player. There are board games for the customers and toys for the cats.

Grain Barge

Mardyke Wharf, Hotwell Road, BS8 4RU (moored opp Baltic Wharf marina)

(0117) 929 9347 grainbarge.co.uk

Bristol Beer Factory Notorious, Fortitude, Independence; 2 changing beers (sourced locally; often Arbor, Good Chemistry, New Bristol)

This moored barge, built in 1936 and converted into a floating bar by Bristol Beer Factory in 2007, boasts great views of the SS Great Britain, the floating harbour and passing boats. There is seating with wooden tables at either end of the central bar, an extended shelf by the window overlooking the water, and an outdoor drinking area on the top deck. It hosts regular themed food nights, a quiz on Mondays, and live music some evenings.

Merchants Arms

5 Merchants Road, BS8 4PZ
☎ (0117) 907 3047
4 changing beers Ⓗ
A traditional pub free of tie close to the Cumberland Basin selling mainly south-west cask-conditioned ales. It is famous for home-made Scotch eggs, hand-finished pork pies and real Cornish pasties. It has been completely refurbished after a car entered the bar! Both rooms are furnished with dark-wood seating and there is a real log fire in the front room. Sport is sometimes shown on the TV and a wide range of board games is available. Regular poetry nights take place. Q ➘ ♣ P 🖫 🌣 ᚅ

Bristol: Kingsdown

Hare on the Hill

41 Thomas Street North, BS2 8LX
☎ (0117) 987 8462
4 changing beers (sourced locally; often Arbor, Bristol Beer Factory, Moor Beer) Ⓗ
Small street-corner local with an impressive traditional green-tiled frontage. It is simply furnished and has a warm and welcoming feel throughout the stripped-back wood interior. Four handpumps offer a range of locally brewed beers as well as some from further afield. Six craft keg fonts also feature several Bristol-based brewers. The pub hosts an array of events including a weekly quiz, live music, low-key DJs on Saturday nights, and jazz piano evenings twice a month on a Wednesday. ▮ ᚓ 🖫 🌣 ᚅ

Hillgrove Porter Stores

53 Hillgrove Street North, BS2 8LT
☎ (0117) 924 9818
Dawkins Bristol Blonde, Bristol Best; 12 changing beers (sourced regionally) Ⓗ
This traditional community venue has a horseshoe-shaped interior, with a lounge area behind the bar and a pleasant patio. Alongside the two regular Dawkins beers there are up to 12 guests, including dark ales and rare styles, many from south-west breweries, plus a real cider. Japanese meals and bar snacks are served, as well as a popular Sunday afternoon roast. The style is eclectic and relaxed, with a lively atmosphere, a wide range of customers, and occasional DJ sets. 🌣 ▮ ᚓ ● 🖫 🌣 ᚅ

Bristol: Redland

Chums

22 Chandos Road, BS6 6PF
☎ (0117) 973 1498 ⊕ chumsmicropub.co.uk
Wye Valley Bitter; 5 changing beers (often Butcombe, Cheddar Ales, Plain) Ⓗ
A micropub in a converted shop, opened in 2016. Conversation rules and electronic communication devices should be used with discretion. Real ales are dispensed from six handpumps – two from regular breweries – and a dark ale is always available. Six traditional ciders are also available as well as a selection of wines and spirits. Simple bar snacks are served including filled rolls. Two beer festivals are held annually, one of which coincides with the community street party. Q ➘ ᚓ ♣ ● 🖫 🌣

Good Measure Ⓛ

2B Chandos Road, BS6 6PE
☎ (0117) 903 9930
Good Chemistry Time Lapse; 3 changing beers (often Burning Sky, Good Chemistry) Ⓗ
Good Chemistry Brewery's first outlet, opened in 2018, is a boutique bar in the increasingly popular Chandos Road area of Redland. A wide range of drinks from the local area, the rest of the UK and the world, is served. Supplementing the four cask ales, which always include one dark ale and one from Good Chemistry, are eight taps serving seven craft beers, often in KeyKegs. Bottled Belgian beers and organic wines are also sold. There's a quiz every Monday evening. ➘ 🌣 ▮ ᚓ 🖫 🌣 ᚅ

Bristol: St Judes

Swan with Two Necks

12 Little Ann Street, BS2 9EB (off Wade St, near Old Market)
☎ (0117) 955 1837
Good Chemistry Time Lapse; Moor Beer Stout; 3 changing beers (sourced locally; often Arbor, Good Chemistry, Moor Beer) Ⓗ
Under new ownership since September 2019, this small, single-bar venue, tucked away in a side street near Old Market, is rapidly becoming a beer destination as it was back in the 1990s. Two regular ales and three guest beers are served, mainly, but not always, from local breweries, plus a real cider. In addition 14 keg lines dispense a variety of beers, lagers and cider. Food is limited to simple snacks, and music is from the vinyl collection behind the bar. ● 🖫 🌣 ᚅ

Bristol: St Philips

Barley Mow

39 Barton Road, BS2 0LF (400yds from rear exit of Temple Meads station over footbridge)
☎ (0117) 930 4709
Bristol Beer Factory Notorious, Fortitude; 6 changing beers (often Bristol Beer Factory, Siren, Tapestry) Ⓗ
Bristol Beer Factory's flagship outlet has eight handpumps offering up to three beers from the brewery plus constantly changing guests of varying styles from all over the UK, as well as a real cider. There is also an extensive bottled beer selection from around the world. Occasional beer-related events are held and there is a quiz on Tuesdays. A small range of quality dishes changes frequently, with vegan-friendly options. There is a walled rear beer garden and benches at the front. ➘ 🌣 🖟 ▮ ᚓ ● 🖫 (506) 🌣 ᚅ

Bristol: St Werburghs

Duke of York Ⓛ

2 Jubilee Road, BS2 9RS (S side of Mina Rd Park)
☎ (0117) 941 3677
4 changing beers (sourced locally; often Arbor, Electric Bear, Moor Beer) Ⓗ
Tucked away in a side street, this popular local has an eclectic clientele and decor to match. The wooden floors, coloured fairy lights, and intriguing range of memorabilia and artefacts create a welcoming grotto-like atmosphere. Notable features include a rare refurbished skittle alley, carved wooden mirrors and a Grand Old Duke of York exterior mural painted by a local artist. Upstairs is a room with sofas to lounge on. Four changing beers are served, mostly from breweries in Bristol and the surrounding area. ➘ 🌣 ᚓ ♣ ● 🖫 (5) ᚅ

Bristol: Southville

Coronation

18 Dean Lane, BS3 1DD
☎ (0117) 940 9044
Bath Ales Gem; Butcombe Original; Hop Back Summer Lightning; Wickwar Falling Star; 1 changing beer (often Bristol Beer Factory, Twisted) Ⓗ

Popular traditional local in a residential area a short walk from Gaol Ferry Bridge. Five reasonably priced real ales are served as well as a good range of cans and bottles. Straightforward food, with extensive vegan options, is available most evenings, as well as a Sunday roast. Furnishings are simple and cosy and the licensee is the creator of the eclectic artwork that decorates the walls. A small raised seating area at the rear houses a rare circular pool table. (24)

Bristol: Spike Island

Orchard Inn

12 Hanover Place, BS1 6XT (off Cumberland Rd near SS Great Britain)

☎ 07405 360994 orchardinn.co.uk

Otter Bitter; St Austell Tribute; 3 changing beers (sourced regionally; often Box Steam, Gloucester, Otter) G

Nestled on a corner in Spike Island, this friendly, traditional pub is close to the marina and just a short stroll or ferry ride from the city centre. Up to six ales are available, either straight from the barrel behind the bar or fetched from the cellar, where they share space with up to 20 ciders and perries. Sport is occasionally shown on TV in a raised area that doubles up as stage space for live jazz or blues music. (506,M2)

Bristol: Stokes Croft

Canteen L

80 Stokes Croft, BS1 3QY

☎ (0117) 923 2017 canteenbristol.co.uk

Sharp's Atlantic; 4 changing beers (often Bristol Beer Factory, Butcombe) H

Inside a converted 1970s office block, now a cultural community centre, this café-style bar serves five real ales, usually local ones, of varying strengths and styles, and up to three real ciders. Basic furniture of plywood tables and steel-tube chairs sits in an open-plan area, with a stage at the far end which hosts live music every evening. An open kitchen serves a range of good-value locally sourced food and there is an outdoor terrace by the main road.

Broad Campden

Bakers Arms L

GL55 6UR (signed off B4081, at NW end of village)

☎ (01386) 840515 bakersarmscampden.com

Prescott Hill Climb; Wickwar BOB; Wye Valley HPA, Butty Bach; 1 changing beer (sourced locally) H

Fine old village local and genuine free house, first licensed as a public house in 1724. Local guest beers and regular ales are served from the handsome oak bar. A photograph of the building in 1905 shows it as the village bakery and grain store. It boasts Cotswold stone walls, exposed beams and a fine inglenook. Excellent food is available in the bar and dining room extension and there is a large garden and children's play area. QP

Brockhampton

Craven Arms L

Kingsbury Street, GL54 5XQ (off A436 in centre of village in cul-de-sac)

☎ (01242) 820410 thecravenarms.co.uk

3 changing beers (sourced regionally; often XT) H

A 17th-century family-run free house in an attractive hillside village with outstanding views and walks. It has a cosy bar area with an open fire and a dining room separated by church-style stone windows. Three carefully selected beers are well kept by the owner chef. The pub is a regular Guide entry and a true gem, well-managed by a friendly family who organise functions for locals each month and a summer beer festival. Local CAMRA Pub of the Year 2019. QP

Charfield

Pear Tree Micro Pub L

6 Wotton Road, GL12 8TP

☎ (01454) 260663

Great Western Maiden Voyage; 3 changing beers (sourced regionally; often Abbey, Cheddar Ales, St Austell) G

This small one-roomed pub is popular with locals and visitors alike. The restored tiled flooring, the small wooden bar, the way the beers are dispensed through wooden casks mounted in an old fireplace, and the humourous murals covering most of the walls make it a most attractive location for drinkers. It offers up to four beers at busy times, usually from local and regional breweries. There is a large fenced outdoor seating area at the front. QP

Plough Inn

68 Wotton Road, GL12 8SR

☎ (01453) 845297

4 changing beers H

An attractive single-room micropub extensively remodelled in 2019, with two open fireplaces and a large outdoor seating area which also has the original off-sales serving hatch. It offers four real ales plus lagers and ciders. There is a piano in the bar and live music takes place regularly. One of the more unusual features is the large gnu head above the fireplace, which gives its name to the house beer. QP(60,85)

Chedworth

Seven Tuns

Queen Street, GL54 4AE (NE of village and near church)

☎ (01285) 720630 seventuns.co.uk

Hook Norton Hooky; Otter Amber; TAP Old Dairy Gold; house beer (by TAP); 1 changing beer (sourced locally) H

Attractive 17th-century stone-built village free house in the centre of this Cotswold village. Recently reopened after extensive refurbishment, it features exposed stone walls and a fire. There is a main bar and a snug, plus a converted barn restaurant. Five handpumps serve local and regional beers, with the house beer provided by Tap Brewery. There are excellent walks in the area. QP

Cheltenham

Charlton Kings Club

21 Church Street, Charlton Kings, GL53 8AP (opp church)

☎ (01242) 525511 charltonkingsclub.co.uk

4 changing beers (often Butcombe) H

Popular village club in the heart of Charlton Kings. It has a large lounge, a separate sports bar and a skittle alley on the ground floor, plus a large function room and snooker room upstairs. Regular live music takes place upstairs in Vonnies Blues Club and also in the main lounge. Four beers change regularly, generally at least one from Butcombe, with guests sourced nationally. A beer festival is held annually in November. There is a small entry fee for guests but occasional visits by CAMRA members are free. Bar snacks are available. P

Cheltenham Motor Club ⅃

Upper Park Street, GL52 6SA (first right off Hales Rd
from London Rd lights, 100yds on right; pedestrian access
from A40 via Crown Passage opp Sandford Mill Rd jct)
☎ (01242) 522590 ⊕ cheltmc.com
6 changing beers (often Moor Beer, Tiley's) ⊞
Friendly club just off London Road, winner of CAMRA
National Club of the Year 2017 and 2020 plus multiple
other awards. It serves five regularly changing beers
from across the country plus a regular local ale, often
from Tileys at the Salutation, Ham. It also offers at least
one KeyKeg, generally from Deya, and three real ciders,
plus a range of bottled Belgian beers. The club stages an
annual beer festival plus Meet the Brewer/takeover
evenings, and hosts local darts and pool teams. Non-
members are welcome free of charge for occasional
visits. Q ➳ ♣ ♠ P 🖳 (B,51) ♣ 🗢

Jolly Brewmaster ⅃

39 Painswick Road, GL50 2EZ (off A40 Suffolk Rd,
between Suffolks & Tivoli, 200yds S along Painswick Rd)
☎ (01242) 772261
**7 changing beers (often Arbor, Bespoke, Moor
Beer)** ⊞
Frequent local CAMRA Pub of the Year. Thirteen
handpumps feature a changing range of ales sourced
nationally, including up to six ciders. This busy and
friendly community hub features original etched
windows, a horseshoe bar and open fire. It is a traditional
drinking venue and doesn't do meals, but hot bar snacks
such as pasties and pies are generally available later in
the week. The attractive courtyard garden is popular in
the summer, with regular Friday barbecues.
Q ➳ ❀ ● 🖳 (10,94U) ♣ 🗢

Kemble Brewery 🍸 ⅃ ❂

27 Fairview Street, GL52 2JF
☎ (01242) 701053
Wye Valley HPA, Butty Bach; 4 changing beers ⊞
Small, popular, back-street local, current local CAMRA
Pub of the Year, hard to find but well worth the effort.
Originally a butcher's shop in 1845, it became a pub in
1847 and was soon brewing ciders – hence the name –
but no brewing has taken place in recent times. Six ales
are generally available, from near and far. There is a
small attractive walled garden to the rear featuring a
new servery for summer barbecues and pizzas. Fully
refurbished in 2016. Q ➳ ❀ ⏺ ♣ ♠ 🗢

Moon under Water ⅃ ❂

16-28 Bath Road, GL53 7HA
☎ (01242) 583945
**Greene King Abbot; Ruddles Best Bitter; Sharp's
Doom Bar; 5 changing beers** ⊞
Open-plan Lloyds No.1 just off the pedestrianised high
street (Strand). A decked area at the back overlooks the
River Chelt and Sandford Park. Some five changing guest
ales – local to countrywide – supplement the regular
beers, plus a selection of real ciders. The dance floor is
only used in the evening Friday and Saturday, and there
is a generally quiet atmosphere at other times. Food is
served all day. An interactive quiz night is hosted on
Monday. ➳ ❀ ⏺ & ● 🗢

Moran's Eating House

123-129 Bath Road, GL53 7LS (approx ½ mile from
centre at town end of Bath Rd shopping area)
☎ (01242) 581481 ⊕ moranseatinghouse.co.uk
**2 changing beers (often Bespoke, Purity, Wye
Valley)** ⊞
Highly regarded as a restaurant, the Eating House also
has an attractive bar that is popular for beers and wines,
and currently serves two ales. The beer range varies daily

and features interesting brews from near and far. The bar
menu includes tapas and platters. Speciality sandwiches
and home-made cakes are available in the afternoon;
evenings are best for beers. There is a pleasant new
conservatory/private party room to the rear and covered
outdoor seating to the front. Q ➳ ❀ ⏺ 🖳 (F,61) 🗢

Sandford Park Alehouse ⅃

20 High Street, GL50 1DZ (E end of High St, past Strand
on right)
**Wye Valley Butty Bach; 8 changing beers (often
Oakham)** ⊞
CAMRA National Pub of the Year 2015 and a local winner
in recent years, this contemporary alehouse has a U-
shaped main bar area complete with bar billiards, a cosy
front snug with wood-burning stove and a large south-
facing patio/garden. A function room/lounge is on the
first floor. Ten handpumps serve changing ales sourced
from microbreweries both local and national, plus at
least one cider and 16 speciality lagers and craft beers.
Internal screens and the website keep you informed.
Q ➳ ❀ ⏺ ♣ ● 🖳 ♣ 🗢

Whittle Taps ❂

1-3A Regent Street, GL50 1HE
☎ (01242) 222989 ⊕ whittletaps.co.uk
**4 changing beers (sourced nationally; often Purity, St
Austell, Titanic)** ⊞
Modern, open-plan, stylish venue close to the Everyman
Theatre (formerly the Slug & Lettuce), refurbished in
2017 in rustic style. It is named after Frank Whittle, the
inventor of the jet engine, which was originally produced
in Cheltenham where the Regent Arcade now stands. Up
to four real ales plus seven craft keg and three ciders are
sold. Wheelchair access is good, with one small step.
Handy for pre-, post- or interval theatre drinks. May stay
open later on Friday and Saturday if busy.
➳ ❀ ⏺ & ♣ ● ♣ 🗢

Chipping Campden

Eight Bells 🍸 ⅃

Church Street, GL55 6JG
☎ (01386) 840371 ⊕ eightbellsinn.co.uk
**Hook Norton Hooky; North Cotswold Best; Purity Pure
UBU; Wye Valley HPA** ⊞
The Eight Bells was originally built in the 14th century to
house the stonemasons constructing St James' Church
and was later used to store the peal of eight bells. It was
rebuilt using most of the original stone and timbers
during the 17th century. What exists today is an
outstanding example of a traditional Cotswolds inn with
cobbled courtyard. Four handpumps serve local and
regional ales and two real ciders. Local CAMRA Pub of the
Year 2020. Q ➳ ❀ ⇔ ⏺ & ♣ ● (21) 🗢

Chipping Sodbury

Horseshoe

2 High Street, BS37 6AH
☎ (01454) 325658 ⊕ horseshoechippingsodbury.co.uk
7 changing beers (sourced regionally) ⊞
One of the oldest buildings in the town, this was
formerly a stationery shop, then briefly a wine bar, and
was converted into a pub at the start of 2014. It serves
seven beers, often unusual but mostly from the West
Country, including dark or strong choices, as well as real
ciders. There are three linked rooms with assorted
furniture, a gin bar upstairs, a pleasant rear garden and a
cellar. A selection of freshly made rolls is available at
lunchtimes. ➳ ❀ ♣ ● ♣ 🗢

Churchdown

Old Elm

Church Road, GL3 2ER

(01452) 530961 theoldelminn.co.uk

Sharp's Atlantic; 4 changing beers (sourced locally; often Hillside, Stroud)

Set in the heart of this village, the Old Elm has become popular since its refurbishment in 2015. It has gained a deserved reputation for the food – the menu features good vegetarian options – and serves five quality beers, including LocAles. The pub hosts lively quiz and music nights, and food and drink tasting evenings; main sporting events are shown in the sports bar. Families are welcome and the garden hosts a children's play area. There are five letting rooms.

Cirencester

Drillman's Arms

34 Gloucester Road, GL7 2JY (on old A417, 200yds from A435 jct)

(01285) 653892

Sharp's Doom Bar; 3 changing beers (sourced nationally)

A lively Georgian inn, perched beside a busy thoroughfare, featuring a convivial lounge with a wood-burner, a games-dominated public bar and a popular skittle alley. Graced by the same landlady for over 25 years, this cracking free house features low-beamed ceilings, horse brasses, fresh flowers and brewery pictures; it also serves well-priced food (lunchtimes only). An annual beer festival swamps the small front car park on the August bank holiday weekend. Closing time may be earlier on some Sunday evenings.

Marlborough Arms

1 Sheep Street, GL7 1QW

(01285) 651474

Box Steam Piston Broke; North Cotswold Windrush Ale; 6 changing beers (sourced nationally; often Corinium)

A real ale haven, offering eight beers from regionals and microbreweries, plus a plethora of interesting boxed ciders, perries and bottles. This lively, wooden-floored pub lies opposite the old GWR station, and is local CAMRA Pub and Cider Pub of the Year once again. Brewery memorabilia adorn the walls; the ceiling is disappearing behind the encroaching pumpclip collection. Pews and a deep-set fireplace add character. The rear patio is used for barbecues during beer and cider festivals.

Twelve Bells

12 Lewis Lane, GL7 1EA

(01285) 652230 twelvebellscirencester.com

Wye Valley Bitter; 3 changing beers (often Slater's, Three Castles)

A Grade II listed building named after the peal of 12 bells in the parish church. It comprises three areas: the front room with the bar is a popular spot for a beer and a chat, the middle and back rooms are primarily for dining, but not exclusively so. There is a TV but it is only used for major events. Outside is a sunny and colourful garden. Parking is limited but there is a large car park 200 yards away (free after 3pm) and on-street parking after 6.30pm. Q

Coaley

Old Fox

The Street, GL11 5EG

(01453) 890905 oldfoxatcoaley.co.uk

Otter Bitter; Uley Pig's Ear Strong Beer; 4 changing beers

An attractive 300-year-old stone-built village local in the centre of this village on the Cotswold Way. Now a free house, it was refurbished in 2018 and has a single room featuring a large oak bar, with seating on benches and at tables. The bar has six real ale handpumps and three for cider. A wood-burning stove provides a focal point. A traditional menu is served and there are outdoor seating areas to the front and side. Q

Coleford

Dog House Micro Pub

13-15 St John Street, GL16 8AP

07442 787015

4 changing beers (sourced locally)

A friendly welcome is guaranteed at this micropub, with a small front bar extending back into another room. Four changing ales are served, almost invariably including a strong ale or stout. A good selection of cider in boxes is available, alongside a fine gin and rum collection. Social events include charity quiz nights, vinyl nights, Knit and Natter and a fishing club. Acoustic live music and talent showcase evenings take place most weekends. No admittance after 10.30pm. Local CAMRA Cider Pub of the Year 2019 and 2020. Q

Cranham

Black Horse Inn

GL4 8HP (off A46 or B4070)

(01452) 812217

4 changing beers (sourced regionally; often Wye Valley)

A 17th-century, stone-built free house with a proper fire in the main bar, almost hidden up a side lane in the village. A quiet idyll with no jukebox, TV or fruit machines; the lack of a reliable mobile phone signal means patrons here indulge in the traditional pursuit of conversation. The pub is a popular stop-off for walkers exploring the myriad woodland paths nearby. Dogs are welcome. Q

Dursley

New Inn

82-84 Woodmancote, GL11 4AJ (on A4135 Tetbury road)

(01453) 519288

5 changing beers (sourced regionally; often Hal's Ales)

A dog-friendly establishment where the owners' pooches often provide a greeting. The pub is welcoming and comfortable, offering a large L-shaped public bar with a tiled floor and a smaller lounge. The eclectic selection of changing guest beers – usually, but not exclusively, from smaller breweries – is often chosen by regulars. There is a garden at the rear which is popular on sunny days. P(61)

Old Spot Inn

2 Hill Road, GL11 4JQ (by bus station and free car park)

(01453) 542870 oldspotinn.co.uk

Uley Old Ric; 7 changing beers (sourced nationally)

Excellent free house dating from 1776, serving great ales, ciders and perries, named after the Gloucestershire Old Spot pig. A porcine theme blends with the extensive brewery memorabilia, low ceilings, wood-burning stove and welcoming staff to create a convivial atmosphere. There is an attractive garden and a heated outdoor covered area. Freshly prepared food is served at lunchtimes and Sunday afternoon. On the Cotswold Way, the pub is popular with walkers, and hosts regular events in the evenings. Q🐎❀◐♿●🚌🐾📶

Forthampton

Lower Lode Inn Ⓛ

GL19 4RE (follow sign to Forthampton from A438, Tewkesbury to Ledbury road) SO8788231809

☎ (01684) 293224 🌐 lowerlodeinn.co.uk

Sharp's Doom Bar; 4 changing beers (often Bespoke, Brains, Malvern Hills) [H]

Blessed with views across the River Severn to Tewkesbury Abbey, this attractive 15th-century brick-built venue, with its three acres of lawns, is a popular stopover for boats and is a Camping and Caravan Club site. Food, advertised as simple and wholesome, is excellent quality and value for money. A beer festival is held in September. A small ferry operates from the Tewkesbury side from Easter to mid-September. Day fishing is available, plus en-suite accommodation. Opening times are reduced in winter so check ahead. Q🐎❀🛏◐⛺♣●P🐾

Fossebridge

Inn at Fossebridge ✔

GL54 3JS (on A429)

☎ (01285) 720721 🌐 innatfossebridge.co.uk

Butcombe Original; North Cotswold Windrush Ale; Wadworth 6X; 2 changing beers (sourced locally) [H]

An attractive one-bar inn in a pretty hamlet where the Fosse Way drops into the Cotswolds valley of the River Coln, an area of outstanding natural beauty. It has old timbers, and a fine flagstone floor with open fires. It also benefits from an outstanding four-acre garden with a lake and river. A selection of regional ales and guests from local breweries is served in cosy surroundings. Q🐎❀🛏◐●P🐾📶

Frampton Cotterell

Rising Sun

43 Ryecroft Road, BS36 2HN

☎ (01454) 772330 🌐 gwbrewery.co.uk/rising-sun

Great Western HPA, Maiden Voyage, Moose River; 3 changing beers (often Butcombe, Draught Bass, Wadworth) [H]

Village local and brewery tap for the Great Western Brewing Company in nearby Hambrook. There is a room as you enter with a log-burning stove, then three archways past slate pillars to the bar, additional seating up the stairs to the left, and a restaurant in the warm conservatory. Lunchtime snacks and more substantial evening meals are served from an extensive menu, with all food made in-house. The skittle alley can also be used for private functions. Q❀◐♣P🚌(Y4,Y6)🐾📶

Frampton-on-Severn

Three Horseshoes Ⓛ ✔

The Green, GL2 7DY (off B4071)

☎ (01452) 742100 🌐 threehorseshoespub.co.uk

Timothy Taylor Landlord; Uley Bitter; 1 changing beer [H]

There is always a warm welcome in this 19th-century two-bar community pub, originally built by a farrier at the south end of England's longest village green. The food is home-cooked, including the unique 3-Shu pie, which is freshly baked to order. Both bars have coal fires, and dogs are welcome in the flagstoned public bar. Evening jamming sessions are popular (largely biased towards folk music) and there are regular community events. A double boules court hosts annual championships. Q🐎❀◐♿⛺♣●🐾📶

Gloucester

Brewhouse & Kitchen

Unit R1, St Anne Walk, Gloucester Quay, GL1 5SH

☎ (01452) 222965

Brewhouse & Kitchen Stevedore, Shed Head, Down a Pegg, SSB [H]

Based in the bustling Gloucester Quays development, this smart bar and restaurant is part of the growing Brewhouse & Kitchen chain, producing its own range of ales on-site. Customers can sit in comfort and enjoy a quality beer while watching the brewing process. Four cask ales are dispensed, with seasonal specials on keg. On a fine day you can relax by the side of the Gloucester-Sharpness Canal in the outdoor seating area. 🐎◐♿🚌🐾📶

Fountain Inn Ⓛ ✔

53 Westgate Street, GL1 2NW (down an alley between Nos 51 & 55)

☎ (01452) 522562 🌐 thefountaininngloucester.com

Bristol Beer Factory Independence; Dartmoor Jail Ale; St Austell Tribute; 3 changing beers [H]

A stone's throw from Gloucester Cathedral, this interesting 17th-century inn is on the site of an alehouse known to have existed in 1216. A passage leads from Westgate Street into an attractive courtyard where there is a plaque to commemorate King William III riding his horse up the stairs. The Cathedral Bar has a panelled ceiling and carved stone fireplace. The Orange Room serves as a restaurant or as a venue for private functions. ❀◐♿🐾📶

Pelican Inn 🏆 Ⓛ ✔

4 St Marys Street, GL1 2QR (WNW of cathedral)

☎ (01452) 582966

Wye Valley Bitter, The Hopfather, HPA, Butty Bach [H]**, Wholesome Stout** [H]/[G]**; house beer (by Wye Valley); 4 changing beers (sourced regionally; often Wye Valley)** [H]

The Pelican was licensed as an alehouse in the 17th century. It is thought that some of its beams are from Drake's Golden Hind, which began life as the Pelican. After a chequered history the building was refurbished by Wye Valley Brewery in 2012, since when it has steadily grown in popularity. It has a main bar, a side room and an attractive outdoor drinking area. The growing range of cider and perry increases during the summer to complement the 10 ales on offer, including a guest beer. Q❀♿⇌♣●🚌🐾📶

Tank ✔

12-14 Llanthony Road, GL1 2EH

☎ (01452) 690541 🌐 tankgloucester.com

Gloucester Gold, Cascade, New England IPA; 4 changing beers (sourced nationally) [H]

This brewery tap is a welcoming, urban warehouse-style bar with a contemporary feel, located in the heart of the Gloucester Docks redevelopment. The decor utilises the building's strengths, and is well worth a look. Though primarily selling Gloucester beers, there is a wide range of guest beers, craft and bottled beers, and ciders. Food on offer is in the shape of local meats and cheeses served on platters, along with a selection of hand-made pizzas. ◐♿●🚌(10)🐾📶

Ham

Salutation Inn Ⓛ
Ham Green, GL13 9QH (from Berkeley take road signposted to Jenner Museum)
☎ (01453) 810284 ⊕ the-sally-at-ham.com
Tiley's Ordinary Bitter; 5 changing beers (sourced nationally; often Arbor, Bristol Beer Factory, Moor Beer) Ⓗ
Multi award-winning rural free house, popular with locals and visitors alike, offering up to seven real ales and nine real ciders and perries, plus an extensive bottled beer and cider menu. The on-site microbrewery, Tiley's Ales, produces a range of traditional ales. There are three bars – two cosy ones share a central wood-burner – and a skittles alley/function room. Food is served at lunchtimes and on occasional evenings only; there are also folk nights and singalongs. Q ➥ ⊛ ◑ ⚘ ♣ ● P ⚙ 🕏

Hawkesbury Upton

Beaufort Arms Ⓛ
High Street, GL9 1AU (off A46, 6 miles N of M4 jct 18)
☎ (01454) 238217 ⊕ beaufortarms.com
Bristol Beer Factory Independence; Butcombe Original; 3 changing beers (sourced regionally) Ⓗ
A wonderful Grade II listed Cotswold stone free house, built in 1602, close to the historic Somerset Monument. It features separate public and lounge bars, a dining room and a skittle alley/function room, which are required to house a veritable plethora of ancient brewery and local memorabilia. Up to five ales and a traditional cider are served on handpump. Outside is an attractive garden with a barbecue used for local community activities. A great bunch of regulars assure a warm welcome.
Q ➥ ⊛ ◑ ⚘ ♣ ● P ⚙ 🕏

Hillesley

Fleece Inn Ⓛ
Chapel Lane, GL12 7RD (between Wotton-under-Edge and Hawkesbury Upton)
☎ (01453) 520003 ⊕ thefleeceinnhillesley.com
Sharp's Atlantic; Wye Valley Butty Bach; 4 changing beers (often Arbor, Church End, Oakham) Ⓗ
An attractive 17th-century local set in the heart of the village. It has a single bar with a wood-burning stove, a separate lounge/dining room and a snug area. The bar offers up to six real ales as well as guest craft keg and draught cider. Food is available at lunchtime and in the early evening. There is a large attractive lawned garden with a safe play area for children, and a private car park.
Q ➥ ⊛ ◑ ● P ⚙ 🕏

Kingswood

Lyons Den
121 Regent Street, BS15 8LJ
6 changing beers (often Bristol Beer Factory, New Bristol, Tiny Rebel) Ⓖ
Micropub opened in May 2019 in a former charity shop at the eastern end of the main shopping street. The bar area as you enter is simply furnished and there is a small snug space at the rear. The beers and ciders for sale are displayed on a retro-style computer screen on the wall. Board games are available to play and there is low-volume background music. Look out for regular tap takeovers from local breweries and some from further afield. Q ➥ ⊛ ● 🟥 ⚙

Marshfield

Catherine Wheel
39 High Street, SN14 8LR
☎ (01225) 892220 ⊕ thecatherinewheel.co.uk
Butcombe Original; Stroud Organic Pale Ale; 1 changing beer (sourced locally; often Bath Ales) Ⓗ
An impressive building in a historic conservation village on the edge of the Cotswolds Area of Outstanding Natural Beauty and eight miles from Bath. Much of the pub dates back to the 17th century. Simple, sympathetic décor complements the exposed stone walls and large open fireplaces. It has good ale, good food, a warm interior and a large cosy bar area, with several rooms off including a panelled dining room.
Q ➥ ⊛ ⇆ ◑ ♣ P 🟥 ⚙ 🕏

Minchinhampton

Crown Inn
High Street, GL6 9BN
☎ (01453) 488160 ⊕ thecrown-minchinhampton.com
Butcombe Adam Henson's Rare Breed; 6 changing beers (sourced nationally; often Elland, Froth Blowers, RAW) Ⓗ
Late 17th-century Cotswold stone coaching inn triumphantly resurrected by Julian Dunkerton's Lucky Onion Group in 2019. Light streams in through two bay windows and six tall sashes on a spectacular carved bar front salvaged from France, topped with a copper counter and eight handpumps. The bay windows areas are occupied by high circular tables and stools, with low tables and chairs, benches and banquettes filling the rest of the space. Towards the rear, tables are laid out for dining and it becomes dark and alluring, with subdued lighting and candles. ➥ ⊛ ◑ ⚙ 👤 ● 🟥 (69) ⚙ 🕏

Mitcheldean

Brewery Tap
Unit 4B, Building 6, The Mews, GL17 0SL
☎ (01594) 546426 ⊕ bespokebrewery.co.uk/the-brewery-tap
Bespoke Saved by the Bell, Beware the Bear, Money for Old Rope, Over a Barrel; 1 changing beer (sourced locally) Ⓗ
The Tap is on the ground floor of the imposing Francis Wintle's Forest Brewery which closed in 1930 and now forms part of the Mitcheldean Enterprise Workshops on Vantage Point Business Village. The Bespoke Brewery operates in the former yeast cellar, in the shadow of the old malthouse. The bar has flagstones on the floor and is divided into two parts. There is an external covered smoking area. Social events include three beer and cider festivals a year and occasional live music. Convivial conversation is encouraged. Q ➥ ⚘ ● ⚙

Moreton-in-Marsh

Bell Inn Ⓛ ⚠
High Street, GL56 0AF (on A429)
☎ (01608) 651688 ⊕ thebellinnmoreton.co.uk
Prescott Hill Climb; Purity Pure UBU; Timothy Taylor Landlord; 2 changing beers (sourced locally; often Hook Norton, North Cotswold) Ⓗ
An old High Street coaching inn dating from the 18th century, now pleasantly refurbished. The interior consists of a mainly open-plan area which has been sympathetically divided into more intimate snug sections, with a real fire and good food. A large courtyard is found through the old arched entrance with an enclosed garden at the rear. The Bell is famed for its links

with JRR Tolkien, Lord of the Rings author – a map of Middle Earth adorns the walls. Local and national ales are stocked. Q⚭❀🛏◑♿⛺⇌P🚌(801)🐾📶

Moseley Green

Rising Sun L ✔

GL15 4HN (off A48 at Blakeney toward Parkend and first left)

☎ (01594) 562008 🌐 risingsunmoseleygreen.co.uk

Wickwar BOB; 3 changing beers (sourced nationally) Ⓗ

In splendid isolation deep in the woodlands of the Forest of Dean, this pub is popular with walkers, cyclists and locals. It originally served miners working at the nearby collieries. When enjoying the panoramic views, it is difficult to imagine that this was once a scene of industrial activity. There are extensive grounds with patios for alfresco dining, ideal for families. Brass bands play in the garden on Sunday evenings in summer. ⚭❀🛏◑♣●P▯🐾

Nailsworth

George Inn L

Newmarket Road, GL6 0RF

☎ (01453) 833228

Goff's Jouster; Uley Bitter; 1 changing beer (sourced regionally; often Prescott, Severn, Wye Valley) Ⓗ

Traditional Cotswold stone village inn overlooking the Newmarket valley. It lies to the west of Nailsworth and is a gentle 15-minute uphill walk from the town centre. The centrally located front door opens on to a single large room that divides into three distinct spaces. The walls are of stripped stone, now mostly whitewashed. The building is south-facing, so the popular outdoor seating areas to the front and side are both suntraps. Footpaths radiate in all directions, including one up the hill behind the pub to the Forest Green Rovers FC ground (a 20-minute walk). Q⚭❀◑⛺♣●P🐾📶

Newent

Black Dog

47 Church Street, GL18 1AA

☎ (01531) 248260 🌐 blackdognewent.co.uk

Sharp's Doom Bar; 3 changing beers (often Bespoke, Cotswold Lion, Prescott) Ⓗ

A recently refurbished 18th-century half-timbered pub in the heart of Newent. It is family-friendly, welcoming both children and dogs. There is an open lounge and separate dining room serving daytime and evening meals. Entertainment includes evenings of live music, traditional games and a large sports TV. There is a sheltered outdoor smoking area and on-site parking. ⚭❀🛏◑♣P🚌🐾📶

King's Arms 🏆

Ross Road, GL18 1BD (on B4221)

☎ (01531) 820035

3 changing beers (often Bespoke, Shepherd Neame, Titanic) Ⓗ

Following major improvements, the pub has a comfortable refitted bar area with open fires, a large function room and skittle alley, and a big lower bar and dining room. There is also a spacious outdoor decked courtyard. With a good reputation for home-cooked food, the pub offers a wide menu including speciality pizzas, midweek offers and popular Sunday lunches. Q⚭◑♣P

Parkend

Fountain Inn

Fountain Way, GL15 4JD

☎ (01594) 562189 🌐 thefountaininn.info

Wye Valley HPA, Butty Bach; 2 changing beers (often Hillside) Ⓗ

Popular village inn, situated close to cycle trails, a preservation railway, RSPB reserve and other major attractions. Built over 200 years ago, it was extended when the Severn and Wye Railway reached the village in 1875. Many items of local historic interest are on display in the pub. A wide selection of local beers and ciders and an extensive menu of good quality food are on offer, including a popular Sunday carvery. Accommodation is available in the inn itself, while an adjoining bunkhouse caters for groups. There are also two spaces for motorhome stop-overs. Q⚭❀🛏◑♿⛺♣P🐾📶

Woodman

Folly Road, GL15 4JF

☎ (01594) 563273 🌐 thewoodmanparkend.co.uk

5 changing beers Ⓗ

Affectionately known as the Woody, this was originally the New Inn – Whitbread changed the name in the 1970s. Now a popular inn opposite the village cricket ground, it offers an excellent and varied food menu. Live music features at weekends and a well-patronised Woodystock festival in August. The pub is near Whitemead Forest Park, backs on to a family cycle trail, and is convenient for the Dean Forest Railway. It can get busy in the summer. ⚭❀🛏◑♿⛺♣●P🚌(727)

Randwick

Vine Tree Inn L

The Stocks, GL6 6JA

☎ (01453) 763748 🌐 thevinetreerandwick.co.uk

3 changing beers (sourced regionally; often Purity, Tiley's, Tiny Rebel) Ⓗ

A secluded gem nestling in the flank of a steep hill with spectacular views. It comprises three interconnected spaces, the walls a mixture of grey-painted matchboard wainscots, rustic stone and artex, the furniture scrubbed tables and wheel-backed chairs. Outside, the beer garden has plenty of seating and glorious views across the valley. The landlord has thrown his heart and soul into the pub and community – the Vine Tree is a centre for village football, cricket, table tennis and darts teams, and a mecca for walkers. Q⚭❀◑⛺♣●P🐾📶

Sheepscombe

Butchers Arms L ✔

GL6 7RH (signed off A46 N of Painswick and B4070 N of Slad) SO8911610434

☎ (01452) 812113 🌐 butchers-arms.co.uk

Battledown Pale Ale; 2 changing beers (sourced nationally; often Backyard, Bristol Beer Factory, Vocation) Ⓗ

Handsome 17th-century Cotswold stone building overlooking a wooded valley. Its inn sign, a painted three-dimensional carving of a butcher quaffing ale while tethered to a pig, is world famous. An adventurous range of ales from across the country is featured on the guest pump. In 2014 the lean-to outdoor toilets metamorphosed into a new bar, seamlessly executed in reclaimed stone and Welsh oak. This complements a quality inter-war refurbishment that added the generous bay windows and porch. A wood-burning stove offers warmth in winter; the forecourt tables and sloping side garden are suntraps in summer. Q⚭❀◑♿♣●P▯🐾📶

Staple Hill

Wooden Walls Micropub

30 Broad Street, BS16 5NU
5 changing beers Ⓗ
Micropub opened in May 2018 in a former carpet shop on the main shopping street. The single room is pleasantly furnished and lined with wooden walls. Drinks for sale are displayed on a large blackboard that surrounds the serving hatch. Between five and 10 real ales are on offer alongside several real ciders, in addition to gin and wine, but no lager. There are a few steps up to the toilets and paved rear garden. Q❀♣●🚌🐾

Stroud

Ale House 🄻

9 John Street, GL5 2HA (opp Cornhill farmers' market)
☎ (01453) 755447 🌐 thealehousestroud.com
Burning Sky Plateau; Tiley's Special Pale; 6 changing beers (sourced nationally; often Electric Bear, Grey Trees, Siren) Ⓗ
Built in 1837 for the Poor Law Guardians, this Grade II listed building is a mecca for ale lovers. The bar occupies the double-height top-lit former boardroom, where an all-year-round beer festival showcases ales from Elusive, Red Cat and many others – plus a cider and perry. Two smaller rooms are adjoining. Live music plays on Friday or Saturday, and world-class jazz once a month on Thursday. A fiendishly difficult quiz on Sunday is set by the landlord – who also prepares the speciality home-made curries, chilli and other dishes. A restored bar billiards table is a welcome recent addition.
Q❀◐♿⇌♣●🚌🐾📶

Bowbridge Arms 🄻

London Road, Bowbridge, GL5 2AY (on A419)
☎ (01453) 298914 🌐 thebowbridgearms.co.uk
Bath Ales Gem; St Austell Proper Job; 1 changing beer (often Bath Ales, Butcombe, Stroud) Ⓗ
Friendly, traditional, Cotswold-stone pub at eastern edge of Stroud. Close to the Bowbridge Lock on the Thames and Severn Canal, it is a 15-minute walk from the town centre and railway station. Its comfortable, modern interior is dominated by a stonking Clearview stove. A separate pool room leads to a small VIP lounge available for private hire or to watch sports on a large flat-screen television. Large, south-facing, suntrap outdoor seating area, including children's play area. Views across the valley to Rodborough Common. Good value home-cooked food including typical pub grub (lasagne, burgers). Pizzas are a speciality. Q👶❀◐♿P🚌🐾📶

Crown & Sceptre 🄻

98 Horns Road, GL5 1EG
☎ (01453) 762588 🌐 crownandsceptrestroud.com
Stroud Budding; Uley Bitter, Pig's Ear Strong Beer; 1 changing beer (sourced regionally; often Blue Anchor) Ⓗ
Lively back-street local at the heart of its community. The walls display an eclectic mix of framed prints, posters and clocks. Local groups meet round a large oak table in a side room, including Knit and Natter on Tuesday. The pub also has its own motorcycle society. Food includes the famed Up The Workers good-value set meal on Wednesday, plus Sunday roasts. Sport is screened in the back bar. A terrace to the rear offers panoramic views across the valley to Rodborough Common.
👶❀◐♣●P🚌(8,227)🐾📶

Prince Albert 🄻 ✔

Rodborough Hill, GL5 3SS (corner of Walkley Hill)
☎ (01453) 755600 🌐 theprincealbertstroud.co.uk
Otter Bitter; Stroud Budding; Timothy Taylor Landlord; 4 changing beers (sourced nationally; often Battledown, Bristol Beer Factory, Sharp's) Ⓗ
This lively, cosmopolitan, Cotswold-stone pub below Rodborough Common is simultaneously bohemian, homely and welcoming, with a big reputation for live music. The L-shaped bar boasts an eclectic mix of furniture, fittings and memorabilia – the walls are covered with film and music posters – and a log fire. The pub hosts a May beer festival, exhibitions and open mic nights (some events are ticketed). Pop-up street food is available Thursday to Sunday. At other times, bring your own or phone for a takeaway. Stroud CAMRA Pub of the Year 2020. 👶❀◐⛺♣●🚌(40)🐾📶

Tetbury

Royal Oak 🄻 ✔

1 Cirencester Road, GL8 8EY (on B4067)
☎ (01666) 500021 🌐 theroyaloaktetbury.co.uk
Butcombe Haka; Moor Beer So'Hop; Stroud Tom Long; 2 changing beers (sourced regionally) Ⓗ
This wonderful, award-winning local utilises clever design to marry a traditional feel to a modern layout. The swathe of wooden surfaces provides a welcoming feel, with a small fireplace adding warmth. Offerings from the six handpumps include a cider from Severn and a vegan ale from Moor – chosen to match the vegan dish on the seasonal menu. The one-pot meal goes down well, especially on quiz nights. Upstairs dining rooms and six letting rooms are popular, as are the lively music and beer festivals. 👶❀🛏◐♿♣●P🐾📶

Tewkesbury

Berkeley Arms

8 Church Street, GL20 5PA (between Tewkesbury Cross and abbey on old A38)
☎ (01684) 290555 🌐 berkeleyarms.pub
Wadworth Henry's IPA, 6X, Swordfish; 1 changing beer (often Wadworth) Ⓗ
A 15th-century half-timbered Grade II pub, just off Tewkesbury Cross. At the rear of this two-bar venue, a barn, believed to be the oldest non-ecclesiastical building in this historic town, is used as a meeting room year round and as a rehearsal space for the famous Tewkesbury Pub Singers. Live music is performed on Friday and Saturday evenings. Buses to Cheltenham and Gloucester stop close by. Voted best Wadworth outlet in 2018. 👶❀♿⛺♣●🚌(41)🐾📶

Cross House Tavern 🄻 ✔

108 Church Street, GL20 5AB
☎ 07931 692227 🌐 thecrosshousetavern.pub
5 changing beers (often Inferno, Ledbury, Malvern Hills) Ⓖ
Tewkesbury's first micropub was originally two houses in the early 16th century. It was extended in the 17th century, and extensively renovated throughout circa 1865. The Cross House Tavern's heritage has been restored with a great deal of dedication. It has again become a Victorian-style establishment serving real local ales (including vegan beer), ciders, perries, wines and snacks – all sourced within 20 miles. The beer is served from tapped casks, much as it was when the building was known as the Tolsey Inn & Coach House in the early 20th century. Q⛺●🚌🐾

Royal Hop Pole 🄻 ✔

94 Church Street, GL20 5RS (centre of town between abbey and cross)
☎ (01684) 278670

Great Western Old Higby; Greene King IPA; Hook Norton Old Hooky; Ruddles County; 4 changing beers (sourced locally; often Battledown, Exmoor, Prescott) ⊞
This well-known landmark is an amalgamation of historic buildings from the 15th and 18th centuries. It has been known as the Royal Hop Pole since being visited in 1891 by Princess Mary of Teck (Queen Mary, Royal Consort of George V). The Hop Pole is mentioned in Dickens' Pickwick Papers. Purchased by JD Wetherspoon, it reopened in 2008. There is wood panelling on almost every wall of this spacious, multi-roomed drinking establishment, with a large patio and garden area at the rear. Q🍼❀🛏◑♿⛺P🚌📶

Thornbury

Anchor Inn 🄻 ✔
Gloucester Road, BS35 1JY
☎ (01454) 281375 🌐 theanchorthornbury.co.uk
Draught Bass; 7 changing beers (often Exmoor, Fuller's, St Austell) ⊞
Licensed since 1695, this friendly, traditional inn serves one regular beer and between five and seven changing guests, plus a real cider. Good home-cooked food is available daily. There are two large rooms, one of which has been split to provide a function/meeting area and is also used by local artists. The pub has its own darts, cribbage, dominoes and cricket teams, and angling syndicate. The garden includes a boules piste and children's play area. 🍼❀◑♣🍎P🚌🐾📶

Butcher's Hook 🄻
8 High Street, BS35 2AQ
☎ (01454) 501800
6 changing beers (often Hop Back, Moor Beer, Tiley's)
A Grade II listed building that was for 200 years a butcher's shop. It has some superb period features such as fireplaces, alcoves and ceiling beams in its three rooms, and a huge, ancient front door. Up to eight cask beers are on handpump, including at least two from Tiley's, brewed at the Salutation at Ham, as well as six real ciders. The food offering consists of cheese platters and pork pies from local producers. Q🍎🚌🐾📶

Thrupp

Stroud Brewery Tap 🄻
Kingfisher Business Park, London Road, GL5 2BY
☎ (01453) 887122 🌐 stroudbrewery.co.uk
Stroud Tom Long, Organic Pale Ale, Budding; 2 changing beers (often Stroud) ⊞
Stroud Brewery occupies a purpose-built new building beside the Thames & Severn Canal. The taproom opens directly on to a terrace beside the towpath. To one side is an open kitchen with an authentic Italian wood-fired pizza oven. Seating consists mostly of wooden benches beside long tables – it is somewhere between a diminutive Bavarian beer hall and Wagamama. There are also squishy leather sofas and large oak casks for vertical drinking. At the far end – and with small windows allowing glimpses of the brewery – is a small stage with an upright piano. 🍼❀◑♿🍎P🚌🐾📶

Twyning

Village Inn 🄻 ✔
The Green, GL20 6DF
☎ (01684) 293500 🌐 thevi.co.uk
Wye Valley HPA; 4 changing beers (often Butcombe, Sharp's, Wye Valley) ⊞
Busy village inn with a rambling bar area and low ceilings, circa 1457, popular with the locals. Watch out for the low entrance doorway. The front patio overlooks the village green and the attractive gardens enhance the beautiful village setting. There are pleasant walks to the river where the ferry runs daily to Tewkesbury and Bredon. The pub is used by local skittles and darts teams and as a meeting place for many local societies and clubs. 🍼❀◑⛺♣

Upper Oddington

Horse & Groom 🄻 ✔
GL56 0XH (top of village signed of A436 E of Stow)
☎ (01451) 830584 🌐 horseandgroom.uk.com
Prescott Hill Climb; Wye Valley Butty Bach; 1 changing beer (sourced locally) ⊞
You are assured of a warm welcome at this privately owned, 16th-century inn run by friendly licensees. The extended bar area for locals with its own sitting room is linked by a real open log fire in an inglenook setting. Wye Valley beers are stocked, with a weekly changing guest usually from a Gloucestershire brewer. There is a large car park and an attractive garden and patio area. Situated in good walking country close to Stow, the pub has eight letting bedrooms. Q🍼❀🛏◑P🚏🐾📶

Winchcombe

Lion Inn ✔
37 North Street, GL54 5PS
☎ (01242) 603300 🌐 thelionwinchcombe.co.uk
Marston's EPA; North Cotswold Best; Prescott Grand Prix; Wye Valley Butty Bach ⊞
A comfortable 15th-century coaching inn in the centre of the town, renovated in 2011. It retains its traditional appearance, with exposed oak timbers and stone fireplaces. A popular venue with locals and visitors, the bar offers changing local real ales on four handpumps. The pub also has an attractive restaurant and accommodation, and a secluded lawn and patio at the rear. 🍼❀🛏◑🍎P🚌🐾📶

Woolaston Common

Rising Sun
The Common, GL15 6NU (1 mile off A48 at Woolaston) SO5901500924
☎ (01594) 529282
Butcombe Adam Henson's Rare Breed; Wye Valley Bitter; 1 changing beer (sourced regionally) ⊞
Accessed through narrow lanes, this pub comes as a surprise in its isolated location. Yet the place is positively thriving and enjoys loyal custom from locals and visitors alike. A good selection of local ales, an excellent reputation for home-cooked food, a small snug and an open fire all contribute towards making this a classic destination. The pub is in fine walking country and affords great views. Q❀◑♣P

> Not all chemicals are bad. Without chemicals such as hydrogen and oxygen, for example, there would be no way to make water, a vital ingredient in beer.
> **Dave Barry**

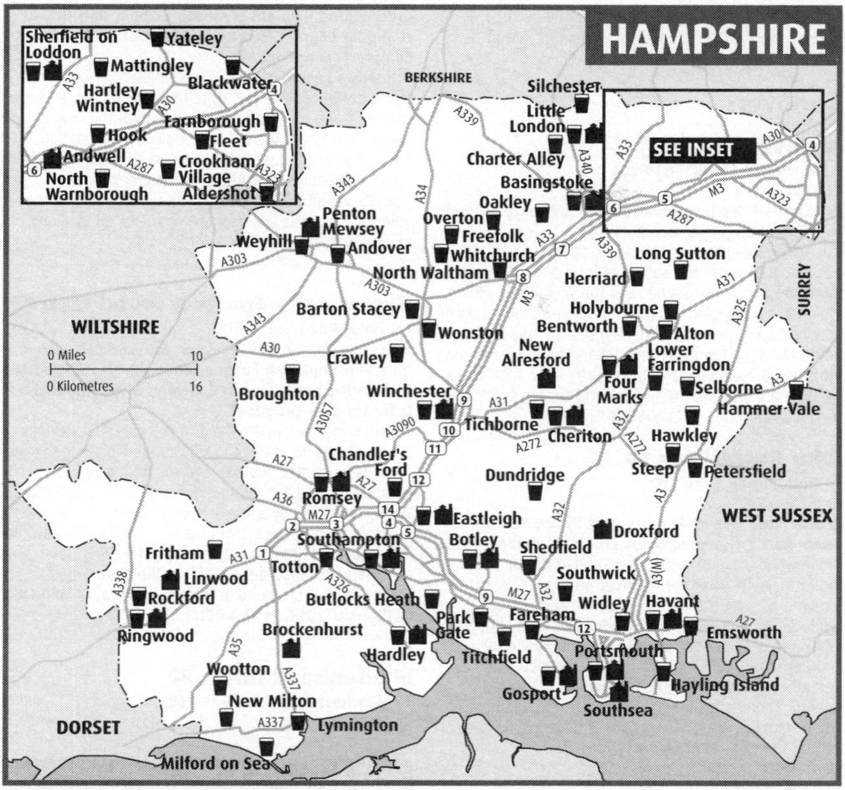

Please note: Ringwood Brewery renamed Best Bitter to Razorback but it is still available in some outlets as Best Bitter

Aldershot

Garden Gate L ✔

2 Church Lane East, GU11 3BT

☎ (01252) 219717

Surrey Hills Ranmore; Twickenham Grandstand Bitter; West Berkshire Good Old Boy; 1 changing beer (sourced regionally; often Ascot Brewing Company, Banks's, Surrey Hills) H

Close to Aldershot's bus and railway station, the Garden Gate, at the heart of its local community, repays a visit. Conversation reigns, with background music. Three or four handpumps are on the bar, with the licensee preferring to source predominantly from local breweries. Thursday night quizzes are well attended and a music quiz is held on the first Sunday of the month. Popular with dogs and their owners. ❀≠P🚌🐾📶

West End Centre

48 Queens Road, GU11 3JD

☎ (01252) 330040

1 changing beer (sourced nationally) H

A flourishing community arts centre, housed in an ex-junior school. The bar is open to all in the evening unless a ticketed event or private booking is being held. If an evening event has sufficient support, there will be one real ale available. The bar always offers a good selection of regional bottled and canned beers, as well as keg beers – ring ahead to enquire about real ale availability. A vibrant beer festival is held in early January.
Q♿P🚌(4,5) 📶

Alton

Eight Bells L

33 Church Street, GU34 2DA

☎ (01420) 82417

Flack Manor Flack's Double Drop; Flower Pots Perridge Pale, Bitter; 1 changing beer (sourced nationally; often Skinner's, Stonehenge) H

This genuine free house, a pub since at least the 1840s, is a regular outlet for Flower Pots ales, and the guest beer turnover can be rapid. The main bar is a haven for good beer and conversation, while the rear drinking area has a TV for major sporting events. An open fire is welcoming in the winter months, and outside the pleasant paved patio, with floral shrub borders in summer, has a covered smoking refuge and an old well.
Q❀≠🚌(13) 🐾📶

Railway Arms L

26 Anstey Road, GU34 2RB

☎ (01420) 82218

Triple fff Alton's Pride, Moondance; 5 changing beers (sourced nationally; often Fuller's, Red Cat, Triple fff) H

Friendly pub close to the Watercress Line and mainline station. A striking sculpture of a steam locomotive emerges from the front over outside seating. Owned by Triple fff Brewery, its beers are supplemented by guest ales, often from local micros. Real cider is from Seacider and a selection of continental bottled beers is available. The rear bar can be hired. The patio area out the back, designed with a traditional railway theme, incorporates a covered smoking area. Local CAMRA Cider Pub of the Year 2020. ❀≈♣●🛏(64,65)❀≋

Andover

Andover Tap
2 Winchester Street, SP10 2EA
☎ 07866 555243
Penton Park Hastings; house beer (by Unity Brewing Co) Ⓗ; 6 changing beers Ⓗ/Ⓖ
This small, independent micropub, opened in August 2019, specialises in the supply of local beers in a simply furnished former patisserie near the High Street. There are up to 12 available – four on handpump, four casks on gravity dispense and four KeyKeg beers – and three or four real ciders. The pub is owned and run by the brewer from Test Brewing which has recently been mothballed. Families are welcome until 8pm and simple snacks are served at all times. Q❀&●🛏❀

John Russell Fox ✅
10 High Street, SP10 1NY
☎ (01264) 320920
Greene King Abbot; Ruddles Best Bitter; Sharp's Doom Bar; 7 changing beers (sourced regionally) Ⓗ
Refurbished, modernised and extended Wetherspoon in the former offices of the Andover Advertiser, which was founded by John Russell Fox; the first edition was produced here in 1858. A large entrance area with many tables leads to the bar with 10 handpumps. A 30-bedroom hotel and roof garden were added in 2018. References to printing and newspapers adorn the interior. There is a separate raised seating/dining area where families are welcome and a large public pay car park at the rear. ❀🚪◑&●🛏≋

Town Mills
20 Bridge Street, SP10 1BL
☎ (01264) 332540 ⊕ thetownmills.co.uk
Wadworth Henry's IPA, 6X; 2 changing beers (sourced regionally; often Wadworth) Ⓗ
Just off the town centre, this establishment is a historic mill with a working water wheel, with the River Anton passing through. There are several separate areas for dining and drinking including a comfy lounge upstairs. Pub games are also played upstairs and a well-supported quiz is held on Wednesday evening. The riverside garden is popular in summer months. Usually three to four beers are stocked from the Wadworth's guest list. ❀❀◑&♣P🛏❀≋

Barton Stacey

Swan Inn
The Street, SO21 3RL
☎ (01962) 760470 ⊕ theswanbartonstacey.co.uk
Alfred's Saxon Bronze; Exmoor Fox; 1 changing beer Ⓗ
A 300-year-old restored village inn serving well-kept ales and good food. Bar staff are welcoming to visitors and their dogs. A large restaurant is behind the bar area. The pub has low beams and a large inglenook fireplace; outside is a large car park and garden. Sunday evening opening hours are seasonal; check times on the website or call ahead if making a special visit. ❀◑&P≋

Basingstoke

Angel ✅
Unit R6, Lower Ground, Festival Place, RG21 7BB
☎ (01256) 854800

Greene King IPA, Abbot; Sharp's Doom Bar; 4 changing beers (often Andwell, Ascot Brewing Company, Longdog) Ⓗ
Formerly a Lloyds No.1 Bar, this spacious one-bar modern pub is at the edge of the restaurant quarter in the town's Festival Place shopping centre, handy for the nearby bus station and five minutes' walk from the rail station. Popular with younger people, it can get busy and often noisy in the evenings, especially at weekends. Lunchtimes attract a wider age range and tend to be quieter. The walls are adorned with TVs, all in silent mode. ❀❀◑&≈●🛏≋

Basingstoke Sports & Social Club ✅
Fairfields Road, RG21 3DR
☎ (01256) 473646 ⊕ basingstokesportsandsocialclub.com
Dark Star Hophead; Fuller's London Pride; Gale's HSB; 2 changing beers (sourced locally; often Andwell, Little London, Longdog) Ⓗ
This thriving sports-based members' club has a drinks licence so the bar is open to all. Founded in 1865, the site is home to cricket, football and rugby. It has five handpumps and the rotating guest ales are usually local. Widescreen TVs cover major sports events. An annual programme of social activities is held and facilities can be hired (it has a small function room). Opening hours and meal times change depending on the season and sporting fixtures, so phone for details. Local CAMRA Club of the Year 2018. ❀◑♣P🛏(1,3)❀≋

Maidenhead Inn Ⓛ ✅
17 Winchester Street, RG21 7ED
☎ (01256) 316030

REAL ALE BREWERIES

Alfred's Winchester
Andwell ◆ Andwell
Botley Botley
Bowman Droxford
Brewhouse & Kitchen ▤ Portsmouth
Brewhouse & Kitchen ▤ Southampton
Brewhouse & Kitchen Southsea
CrackleRock Botley
Dancing Man ▤ Southampton
Emsworth ◆ Havant
Fallen Acorn Gosport
Flack Manor Romsey
Flower Pots Cheriton
Irving Portsmouth
Itchen Valley New Alresford
Little London Little London
London Road Brew House ▤ ◆ Southampton
Longdog Basingstoke
Newtown Gosport
Penton Park Penton Mewsey
Pig Beer Brockenhurst (NEW)
Queen Inn ▤ Winchester
Red Cat ◆ Winchester
Red Shoot ▤ Linwood
Ringwood Ringwood
Sherfield Village Sherfield on Loddon
Southsea Portsmouth
Staggeringly Good ◆ Southsea
Steam Town Eastleigh
Stratton Lane ◆ Winchester (NEW)
Tap It ◆ Southampton
Triple fff ◆ Four Marks
Unity ◆ Southampton
Urban Island ◆ Portsmouth
Vibrant Forest ◆ Hardley

Greene King Abbot; Ruddles Best Bitter; Sharp's Doom Bar; 3 changing beers (sourced nationally; often Loddon, Longdog, Windsor & Eton) [H]
On the site of an old inn of the same name, this relatively small Wetherspoon is in the Top of Town pedestrian area. The long, narrow, split-level layout has a single bar and an additional downstairs area. There is a small garden/smoking area at the rear. The guest ales vary but are usually local. The bar gets exceptionally busy on weekend evenings with nearby nightclub visitors. Children are welcome until 8.30pm and a public pay car park is at the rear. 🪑❀◑♿🚆●🚌📶

Wheatsheaf

Winton Square, RG21 8EU
☎ (01256) 479601
Butcombe Original; Otter Ale; Sharp's Doom Bar, Atlantic [H]
This is a lively wet-led local with the atmosphere you would expect from a popular town-centre pub. It is basically a traditional boozer with no frills but a warm welcome. A good choice of well-kept cask beers is served at good prices for the area. Large screens show sports fixtures at weekends and some evenings. 🚆🚌

Bentworth

Sun 𝕃

Well Lane, GU34 5JT
☎ (01420) 562338 🌐 suninnbentworth.com
Palmers Copper Ale; 4 changing beers (sourced regionally; often Andwell, Bowman, Itchen Valley) [H]
Up to six good-quality beers, mostly from Hampshire and other local breweries, are available in this (at times) very busy pub. Excellent food is served and it is advisable to book in advance for evening and weekend meals. The pleasant garden is set at a higher level than the pub and is noted for its display of sunflowers in summer. Parking can get interesting at busy times. Q🪑❀◑P🐾

Blackwater

Mr Bumble 𝕃

19 London Road, GU17 9AP
☎ (01276) 32691
Fuller's London Pride; 3 changing beers (sourced regionally; often Dark Star, Triple fff, Windsor & Eton) [H]
Very much a community local, Mr Bumble is near the station and bus stops. There is a large L-shaped bar with comfortable seating, tables and chairs. The regular London Pride is accompanied by a wide range of real ales and four still ciders. A few steps around the corner from the main bar takes you to the Sports Bar with darts and three pool tables. There are widescreen TVs for major sporting events, and live music is staged on Thursday and Saturday. 🪑🚆♣●P🚌(3)🐾📶

Botley

CrackleRock Tap Room 𝕃

30A High Street, SO30 2EA (down alley between Clarke Mews and Max Plumbing) SU5130213037
☎ 07733 232806 🌐 cracklerock.co.uk
CrackleRock Crackerjack, Fire Cracker, Gold Rush, Crafty Shag, Dark Destroyer, Crackatoa IPA; 3 changing beers (sourced locally; often Bowman, Steam Town) [H]
A cosy and friendly brewery tap seating up to 60, down an alley in this small town. It mainly dispenses its own beers from the brewery opposite via nine handpumps, usually including one or two local guest beers. There are seven keg beers (normally guests from local breweries). It occasionally hosts a cider festival and various other events, and has gone from strength to strength since moving from its original location across the road. ⛺●🚌(3,X9) 🐾

Broughton

Tally Ho!

High Street, SO20 8AA
☎ (01794) 301280 🌐 thetallyhobroughton.co.uk
Ringwood Best Bitter; 3 changing beers (sourced nationally) [H]
One of two pubs in this village near the Clarendon Way and midway between Winchester and Salisbury. The chef patron has won several culinary awards including Michelin nominations in previously run restaurants and pubs, and the menu reflects this; sandwiches are also available. In summer a cider is also usually on offer. August bank holiday has a beer and cider festival. 🪑❀◑⛺♣●🐾📶

Butlocks Heath

Roll Call 𝕃 ✔

Woolston Road, SO31 5FJ
☎ (023) 8045 2358 🌐 therollcall.co.uk
Courage Best Bitter; Flower Pots Bitter; Ringwood Fortyniner [H]**; 1 changing beer (sourced locally; often Bowman)** [G]
Welcoming, comfortable and attractive pub, popular with locals and visitors alike. It was rebuilt after being bombed in WWII, and has a large car park and garden. Inside it has two comfortable bars and features a real fire, a wood-burner, and tankards hanging from the ceiling. The public bar has three handpumps, two of which serve local real ales. Another supplementary local beer is often served direct from the cask. Good-quality food is available Thursday to Sunday. 🪑❀◑♿⛺♣P🚌(6,X15) 🐾📶

Chandler's Ford

Steel Tank Alehouse 🏆 𝕃

1 The Central Precinct, Winchester Road, SO53 2GA
☎ 07379 553025
6 changing beers (sourced nationally; often Eight Arch, Flower Pots, Vibrant Forest) [H]
A former bank in a shopping precinct four minutes' walk from the rail station, and a minute's walk from bus stops. Its beer quality, knowledgeable staff and friendly atmosphere attract customers from a wide area. Handpumps serve six beers and two ciders. There are eight keg taps and a selection of canned and bottled beers. Furniture, mainly wooden, includes beer-cask stools and cable-reel tables; walls celebrate beer and football. Snacks include pork pies, sausage rolls and samosas. Q♿🚆●▯🚌(1,X7)🐾📶

Charter Alley

White Hart 𝕃

White Hart Lane, RG26 5QA
☎ (01256) 850048 🌐 whitehartcharteralley.com
3 changing beers (sourced locally; often Harvey's, Hop Back, Loddon) [H]
Cosy inn, built in 1819, the epicentre of this rural village, with a friendly greeting for all. With log fires, oak beams and a capacious dining area, it has a breweriana-decorated bar where a frequently changing array of ales features. A variety of quality food and home-made pies is served. A stalwart Guide entry for 27 years, it recently

started brewing a diverse range of ales on a small scale as the Secret Brewing Company. The website shows which beers are on and coming next in the cellar.
Q❀⇌◑P🐾ᯤ

Cheriton

Flower Pots Inn Ⓛ

Brandy Mount, SO24 0QQ (¼ mile N of A272 Cheriton/Beauworth crossroads) SU5812928293
☎ (01962) 771318 🌐 flowerpotscheriton.co.uk
Flower Pots Perridge Pale, Bitter, Goodens Gold; 1 changing beer (sourced locally; often Flower Pots) Ⓖ
A 19th-century building with a cosy lounge and public bars, set in a pretty village with a 13th-century church and Civil War battlefield. Flower Pots Brewery, provider of the many ales, is across the car park. Westons Old Rosie and Rosie's Pig ciders are also sold. There is no food Sunday and Monday evenings, Wednesday is curry night, and pies are available between sessions. Motorhomes may use the field, subject to approval, but there are no facilities. Supervised children are welcome inside until 6pm. Open all day on bank holiday Mondays.
Q❀◑●P🚌(67) 🐾ᯤ

Crawley

Fox Ⓛ

Main Road, SO21 2PR
☎ (01962) 461302 🌐 the-fox.pub
Alfred's Saxon Bronze; Bowman Swift One; Timothy Taylor Landlord; 1 changing beer (sourced locally; often Alfred's, Flower Pots) Ⓗ
An upmarket country pub in a picturesque village in the hills to the north-west of Winchester. The real ales are from top breweries and mostly local. The bar area is complemented by a contemporary restaurant and the dining room has viewing windows into the kitchen. The food is excellent quality, Hampshire-sourced and cooked fresh on-site. Afternoon teas are served Monday to Saturday. Accommodation is offered in five luxury en-suite rooms. ♉❀⇌◑♿⛺♣P🚌(16)🐾ᯤ

Crookham Village

Spice Merchant ✔

The Street, GU51 5SJ
☎ (01252) 621126
Timothy Taylor Boltmaker; 1 changing beer (sourced nationally; often Hogs Back, Otter, Twickenham) Ⓗ
A village establishment, formerly the Black Horse, reopened as the Spice Merchant in 2018. Decorated in a light, airy style, it specialises in Thai and other South-East Asian food. The front area is laid out more as a pub and welcomes drinkers, especially by the bar. There are two real ales available, with a rotating beer from a choice of four from the Enterprise Inns list. The pub was successfully registered as an Asset of Community Value in April 2017. ♉❀◑♿P🚌(10)🐾ᯤ

Dundridge

Hampshire Bowman Ⓛ

Dundridge Lane, SO32 1GD (turn E off B3035 ½ mile N of Bishops Waltham then 1½ miles) SU5778218424
☎ (01489) 892940 🌐 hampshirebowman.com
Bowman Swift One; West Berkshire Good Old Boy; 4 changing beers (sourced nationally; often Flack Manor, Andwell, Palmers) Ⓖ
Not the easiest pub to access, but well worth the drive, cycle or walk. The 18th-century two-bar coaching inn has many interesting features including an ancient tricycle, bows, pub signs and beer bottles. It typically serves five (mostly local) beers direct from the cask, and 10 ciders, plus a wide variety of home-cooked locally-sourced food, including numerous specials. Outside is a large garden with a patio and children's play area, which is very popular during summer weekends.
Q♉❀◑♿♣●P🐾ᯤ

Eastleigh

Steam Town Brew Co Ⓛ

1 Bishopstoke Road, SO50 6AD
☎ (023) 8235 9139 🌐 steamtownbrewco.co.uk
7 changing beers (sourced locally; often Steam Town) Ⓗ
This lively venue opened in 2017, incorporating a fine six-barrel brewery (visible from the dining area) and dispensing four or five of its own beers plus real cider, sometimes a perry, and several other local breweries' ales. The decor is industrial shabby-chic, reflecting Eastleigh's former railway works nearby. This extends to much of the dining area, which is furnished with repurposed first-class carriage seating. Live music sessions feature several times a week and brewery-tutored beer tasting sessions are held monthly.
♉❀◑⇄●🚌🐾ᯤ

Emsworth

Coal Exchange ✔

21 South Street, PO10 7EG
☎ (01243) 375866 🌐 thecoalexchange.co.uk
Dark Star Hophead; Fuller's London Pride; Gale's Seafarers Ale, HSB; 2 changing beers (sourced nationally; often Butcombe, Fuller's) Ⓗ
A traditional establishment near Emsworth harbour. The green-tiled frontage shows that for many years this was a Gale's house. The single L-shaped bar has open fireplaces, and on the walls are maps and photographs of the town in days gone by. To the rear is a small walled garden, a real suntrap on warmer days. The name derives from when the pub was used by local farmers to trade produce for coal delivered to the nearby harbour.
♉❀◑⇄🚌(700) 🐾

Fareham

Crown Ⓛ ✔

40 West Street, PO16 0JW
☎ (01329) 241750
Greene King IPA, Abbot; Sharp's Doom Bar; 2 changing beers (sourced nationally; often Fallen Acorn, Itchen Valley) Ⓗ
This town-centre Wetherspoon is in a pedestrianised street on the site of the Crown Brewery, which existed in Victorian times. It has two areas, one of which is primarily intended for diners. Wall-mounted portraits with brief histories of famous local figures add to the cosy atmosphere. The two guest beers normally include one from a local brewery. Convenient for the bus station and shops. Alcoholic drinks are served from 9am.
Q♉❀◑♿●🚌ᯤ

West Street Alehouse Ⓛ

164A West Street, PO16 0EH
☎ 07927 004735
3 changing beers (sourced regionally) Ⓗ
Fareham's first micropub is ideally situated close to rail and bus stations. Opened in June 2019, the bar serves three ales on handpump, five craft beers from the tap wall and up to four ciders, all of which are listed on a TV screen. With plenty of seating and no loud music, it is

easy to converse while drinking. There is a bottle shop with local and foreign cans and bottles available to take away. A gem to be recommended. Q❀⇌●🚌🐾

Farnborough

Prince of Wales 🄻 ✔

184 Rectory Road, GU14 8AL

☎ (01252) 545578 🌐 theprincepub.uk

Dark Star Hophead; Fuller's London Pride; Hop Back Summer Lightning; West Berkshire Maggs' Mild; 6 changing beers (sourced nationally) 🄷

This cosy free house has featured in the Guide for over 30 years, offering four regular beers, six guests, five kegs and a real cider. A popular beer festival is held every October. Good lunches are served throughout the week, with evening meals Monday and Friday only. Quiz night is on the first Sunday and live music on the third Sunday of each month. Various charity events are held during the year. ❀◑⇌●P🚌(41)🐾

Swan

91 Farnborough Road, GU14 6TL

☎ (01252) 510920 🌐 swanfarnborough.com

4 changing beers (sourced regionally; often Ascot Brewing Company, Dorset, Itchen Valley) 🄷

A large, imposing building half-a-mile south of the town centre on the A325 overlooking the Farnborough Airport runway. Inside it is one large open-plan space, with clever use of partitions creating three distinct areas. It caters equally for drinkers and diners, with excellent food and a changing selection of four ales from small independents across southern England, usually with one local. There are monthly live music and quiz nights and quarterly open mic nights. ❀◑♿P🚌(1)🐾

Tilly Shilling ✔

Unit 2-5 Victoria Road, GU14 7PG

☎ (01252) 893560

Greene King Abbot; Ruddles Best Bitter; Sharp's Doom Bar; 4 changing beers (sourced nationally; often Ascot, Binghams, Hogs Back) 🄷

Modern town-centre Wetherspoon named after Beatrice Shilling, a celebrated engineer at the nearby former Royal Aircraft Establishment. Its aviation theme includes a row of airline seats and various Spitfire memorabilia. The large rectangular open-plan lounge features a glass frontage that opens in good weather, extending the pub onto the pavement. Ten handpumps serve three regular and four changing guest beers. Real cider is dispensed from boxes in fridges at the end of the bar. Alcoholic drinks are on sale from 9am. ◑♿⇌●🚌

Fleet

Prince Arthur 🄻 ✔

238 Fleet Road, GU51 4BX

☎ (01252) 622660

Greene King Abbot; Ruddles Best Bitter; Sharp's Doom Bar; 4 changing beers (sourced nationally; often Langham, Twickenham, Windsor & Eton) 🄷

A traditionally designed pub in a former grocery shop building over 100 years old, with alcoves, wood surrounds and a rustic feel. It is named by Wetherspoon after Prince Arthur, son of Queen Victoria, who lived in Fleet in the 1890s while he was British Army Commander at Aldershot. In July 2019 the pub celebrated 22 years since it first opened. Seven different casks ales are on tap, including local ales supplied direct from 12 breweries across Hampshire, Berkshire and Surrey. Q❀◑♿●🚌(7,10)

Four Marks

Offf the Rails 🄻

Unit 3, Magpie Works, Station Approach, GU34 5HN

☎ (01420) 561422 🌐 triplefff.com

Triple fff Alton's Pride, Moondance; 3 changing beers (sourced locally; often Triple fff) 🄶

Offf the Rails was extended in October/November 2019 to create two distinct drinking areas centred on a bar serving two regular and up to three seasonal or more obscure ales from the adjoining Triple fff Brewery. Bag-in-the-box and bottled ciders are also sold. The pub adjoins the Triple fff off-licence featuring bottled ales from microbreweries far and wide. The brewery holds an open day in August. ♿⇌●P🚌(64)🐾

Freefolk

Watership Down Inn 🄻

Freefolk Priors, RG28 7NJ

☎ (01256) 892254 🌐 watershipdowninn.com

5 changing beers (sourced locally) 🄷

Built in 1840 in the Upper Test Valley and still affectionately known locally as the Jerry, the inn has been named in honour of local author Richard Adams' book Watership Down, set in the downland just to the north of the pub. Outside there is an extensive garden, patio and family area. Occasional live music evenings are arranged and each May a beer festival is held. The pub is popular with walkers and cyclists in the Test Valley and close to the Laverstoke Gin Distillery. Q❀🛏◑P🚌(76)🐾

Fritham

Royal Oak 🄻 ✔

SO43 7HJ (W end of village) SU2321614135

☎ (023) 8081 2606

Flack Manor Flack's Double Drop; Hop Back Crop Circle, Summer Lightning; house beer (by Bowman); 4 changing beers (sourced locally; often Hattie Brown's, Stonehenge, Three Daggers) 🄶

A gem towards the end of the no-through-road. The inside comes up to expectation – low beams, log fires and farmhouse-cottage decor. Behind the single bar, three regular and four guest beers, under black cooling covers, are directly dispensed. The extensive garden has seating and houses three shepherd's bothy accommodation units, an ice-cream kiosk in summer and a local produce farm shop (open weekends). Lunch is served daily (from mid-afternoon Sat & Sun), plus home-cooked winter suppers or summer barbecues on Thursday evenings. Q❀🛏◐♿🐾

Gosport

Four-Ale Taproom 🄻

45 Stoke Road, PO12 1LS

☎ (023) 9258 4455 🌐 fouraletaproom.co.uk

4 changing beers (sourced regionally; often Fallen Acorn, Urban Island) 🄶

Gosport's first micropub opened in 2018 in previously unlicensed premises. There is no bar and the four cask beers from small and independent breweries are on a gravity stillage along one wall. Four ciders are on the go plus keg real ale and an interesting range of bottled and canned beers. On the walls there is a map of the breweries supplying beer, and pumpclips of beers and ciders recently served. A free cheeseboard is put out on Sunday lunchtime. Q♣●P🚌🐾

Junction Tavern

1 Leesland Road, Camden Town, PO12 3ND
☎ (023) 9258 5140
3 changing beers (sourced regionally; often Cotleigh, XT) Ⓗ
This venue is on the now disused railway line between Gosport and Fareham, which closed in 1953 and is now a cycle track and footpath. The three real ales usually include a dark beer, and there are four ciders and a perry. The canopy over the bar is decorated with pumpclips of the beers sold. A beer festival takes place over the Easter weekend. 🐎❀♣🍎🚌(E1)🐾📶

Queen's Hotel 🏆 Ⓛ

143 Queens Road, Forton, PO12 1LG
☎ 07974 031671 🌐 cliveluff.wixsite.com/queenshotel
Fallen Acorn Expedition IPA; Ringwood Fortyniner; Young's London Original; 2 changing beers (sourced nationally; often Newtown, Titanic) Ⓗ
No trip to Gosport is complete without a visit to this street-corner local, a regular entry in the Guide for over 35 years. The guest beer range always includes a dark beer, and up to two ciders are stocked. The main feature of the bar is a large fireplace with a carved wood surround. Snacks are served Friday lunchtimes and a regular beer festival takes place in October. Local CAMRA Pub of the Year 2020. ❀♣🍎🚌

Hammer Vale

Prince of Wales

Hammer Lane, GU27 1QH
☎ (01428) 652600 🌐 princeofwaleshaslemere.co.uk
Dark Star Hophead; Fuller's London Pride; Gale's HSB; 2 changing beers (sourced nationally; often Fuller's) Ⓗ
An interesting hostelry dating from 1924, with many original features such as stained-glass windows, including one for Amey's of Petersfield, who built the pub. It is well worth visiting in order to sample the Pride, HSB and Fuller's and Dark Star guests. Outside is a large seating area and car park, well sited for walkers and campers. Excellent meals and bar snacks are served (no food Mon). Stories abound as to how a large roadhouse was sited away from the main road.
Q🐎❀◐♿⛺♣P🐾📶

Hardley

Vibrant Forest Brewery Taproom Ⓛ

Unit 3, The Purlieu Centre, Hardley Industrial Estate, SO45 3AE
☎ (023) 8200 2200 🌐 vibrantforest.co.uk
7 changing beers (sourced locally) Ⓖ
The Taproom is warm, welcoming and well equipped with tables and benches. Beers come from the Vibrant Forest range in all formats, with occasional guests. Ciders, perries, wines and soft drinks are also available. Snacks are served and a street food truck is on-site most weekends, with food ranging from Thai to curry, burger or pizza. There is a large outside seating area (mostly covered), plus a smaller smoking area. Well-behaved children and dogs welcomed. Q◖♿P🚌(8,9)🐾📶

Hartley Wintney

Waggon & Horses

High Street, RG27 8NY
☎ (01252) 842119 🌐 thewagg.co.uk
Butcombe Original; Gale's HSB; 4 changing beers (sourced nationally; often Castle Rock, Flower Pots, Sharp's) Ⓗ
The current landlord served several years behind the bar of this award-winning local before taking over. Changing guest beers often include Courage Best and others from microbreweries. The lively public bar contrasts with a quieter lounge. Tables outside on the pavement enable guests to enjoy the atmosphere of the village, renowned for its unique shops. At the rear is a large, pleasant courtyard garden and a heated, covered smokers' area. Food is served lunchtimes only Monday to Saturday.
Q❀◖🍎🚌(7) 🐾📶

Havant

Wheelwright's Arms Ⓛ ✔

27 Emsworth Road, PO9 2SN
☎ (023) 9247 6502 🌐 wheelwrightshavant.co.uk
Fallen Acorn Pompey Royal; 3 changing beers (sourced locally; often Crafty, Irving, Langham) Ⓗ
This imposing Edwardian hostelry serves up to four cask beers, mainly from local microbreweries, with handpulled ciders also offered. A range of bottled beers from the UK and abroad is also stocked, plus a selection of quality wines and spirits. The south-facing front terrace and secluded courtyard garden are popular in warm weather. The pub hosts a number of local organisations and offers private hire space. Major sporting fixtures are shown on TV.
Q🐎❀◐♿⇌♣🍎P🚌(27,700) 🐾📶

Hawkley

Hawkley Inn ✔

Pococks Lane, GU33 6NE
☎ (01730) 827205 🌐 hawkleyinn.co.uk
Flower Pots Perridge Pale, Goodens Gold; house beer (by Greyhound); 4 changing beers (sourced regionally; often Flower Pots, Red Cat, Triple fff) Ⓗ
A genuine free house set in the South Downs National Park. Popular with locals and passers-by alike, it has a good selection of guest beers, showcasing 164 ales from 42 breweries in the last year. The annual beer festival takes place in May/June (see the website for details). The inn serves great food and has five rooms available for B&B. 🐎❀🛏◐♿🍎🐾📶

Hayling Island

Maypole

9 Havant Road, PO11 0PS
☎ (023) 9246 3670 🌐 maypoleonhayling.co.uk
Fuller's London Pride; Gale's Seafarers Ale, HSB; 1 changing beer (sourced nationally; often Fuller's, Gale's) Ⓗ
A pleasant roadside house with friendly and welcoming staff. It has a single quiet bar and a separate restaurant. There are plenty of tables and seating space in the bar area. The large beer garden at the back looks over fields. The Maypole has a good local reputation for its food as well as for keeping its draught beers in fine condition, and typifies what a good traditional pub should be.
🐎❀◐♿P🚌(30,31) 🐾📶

Herriard

Fur & Feathers Ⓛ

Back Lane, RG25 2PN
☎ (01256) 510510 🌐 thefurandfeathers.co.uk
Hogs Back TEA; 3 changing beers (sourced locally; often Fallen Acorn, Itchen Valley, Red Cat) Ⓗ
Family owned and run free house built in 1855 to service farm workers, now open plan with a central bar area. Beers are mainly from Hampshire breweries such as

Flack Manor, Longdog and others. Two dining areas provide a pleasant atmosphere to enjoy the mouthwatering locally sourced menu that changes on a daily basis. Reservations are recommended, but a quiet pint can be enjoyed at any time. A well-appointed secluded garden features partly paved and grassed areas. Seasonal hours may vary so phone ahead. Q🍺❀◑♿P🚌(13X)📶

Holybourne

Queen's Head 🅻

20 London Road, GU34 4EG

☎ (01420) 768213 🌐 queensheadalton.co.uk

3 changing beers (sourced nationally; often Otter, Skinner's, Triple fff) 🄷

A traditional pub serving three regularly changing ales in a convivial atmosphere. There is usually a local Triple fff offering, with others coming from the Greene King list. The separate restaurant area serves home-made food in generous portions. There is a games room with darts and pool. The extensive garden is popular in the summer months, when licensing hours may be extended. Live music events are held throughout the year. Happy hour is 4.30-6pm Monday to Friday. Q🍺❀◑♣P🚌(65)🐾📶

Hook

Crooked Billet ✔

London Road, RG27 9EH

☎ (01256) 762118 🌐 thecrookedbilletpub.co.uk

Courage Best Bitter; Sharp's Doom Bar; 2 changing beers (often Timothy Taylor) 🄷

A free house just outside Hook which has been under the same safe ownership for 32 years. Enjoy the pleasant riverside garden in fine weather and the air-conditioned bars, restaurant and snug at any time. In winter, warm up by a traditional log fire. Good food and real ales are always on offer here; food is served up to 8pm on Sunday. A beer and music festival is held over the August bank holiday weekend. Quiz night is on the first Monday of the month. Q🍺❀◑♿P🐾📶

Little London

Plough Inn

Silchester Road, RG26 5EP

☎ (01256) 850628

Little London Hoppy Hilda; Otter Amber; Ringwood Razorback 🄷**; 2 changing beers (sourced regionally; often Butts, Church End, Dark Star)** 🄶

Excellent traditional village inn and recent CAMRA Regional Pub of the Year. Enjoy beer or a real cider gravity fed from casks behind the bar and sit in front of a log fire or out in the peaceful garden. A good range of baguettes is available (no food Sun eve). The pub is popular with locals and also visitors to Pamper Forest and the nearby Roman remains in Silchester. Q🍺❀♣🍎P🚌(14)🐾

Long Sutton

Four Horseshoes

The Street, RG29 1TA (signed from B3349) SU748470

☎ (01256) 862488

2 changing beers (sourced nationally; often Andwell, Palmers, Slater's) 🄷

A truly rural pub, simply decorated and situated to the east of Long Sutton in a popular walking area. Formerly a Gale's tied house, it is now a free house normally offering two low-strength guest beers. There are twice-monthly quiz and jazz nights in the spacious but cosy bar which has two real fires. Simple English dishes are served, with a popular roast on Sunday. Midweek lunchtime opening is only by prior arrangement. Q🍺❀◑P🐾📶

Lower Farringdon

Golden Pheasant 🏆 🅻 ✔

Gosport Road, GU34 3DJ

☎ (01420) 588255

Crafty One; Sharp's Doom Bar, Atlantic; 3 changing beers (sourced regionally; often Andwell, Dark Star, Otter) 🄷

The owners have run pubs in the area for many years, and nine years ago brought their expertise to this delightful privately owned free house. The beers are well kept, with seven handpumps serving three permanent and four guest beers. The food is freshly cooked, with vegetarian options – the fish and chips warrants special mention due to the secret recipe batter. As the local CAMRA Pub of the Year 2020, this inn is not to be missed. Opens early for tea and coffee. Q🍺❀◑♣P🐾📶

Lymington

Monkey House 🅻

167 Southampton Road, SO41 9HA

☎ (01590) 676754 🌐 themonkeyhouse.co.uk

Sixpenny Best; 2 changing beers (sourced locally; often Hop Back, Red Cat, Sixpenny) 🄷

A genuine, traditional 18th-century free house and B&B with a good reputation for delicious fresh food (be sure to book). The friendly staff make ordering a pint or two easy, with the choice of the regular Sixpenny Best Bitter and two changing beers, mainly local. Plans are afoot for the additions of a microbrewery and an extension. This family friendly pub is a must-visit. Q🍺❀🛏◑♿P🚌(6)🐾📶

Mattingley

Leather Bottle 🅻

Reading Road, RG27 8JU

☎ (0118) 932 6371

Brunning & Price Original; 4 changing beers (sourced locally) 🄷

A classic old village inn with a beautiful tiled roof sheltering mellow Hampshire brick, and a pleasant garden area in summer. Here you'll find comfortable, relaxed surroundings and a warm, friendly atmosphere. Enjoy a quick lunchtime bite to eat, or a long lingering dinner with friends and family. The cask ale list shows the mileage to the brewery. Dog walkers meet here every third Saturday morning and there is live acoustic music monthly. Early booking is advised for the popular Sunday lunch. Q🍺❀◑♿P🐾📶

Milford on Sea

Wash House

27 High Street, SO41 0QF

☎ (01590) 644665 🌐 thewashhousebar.co.uk

4 changing beers (sourced locally; often Andwell, Hop Back, Piddle) 🄷

A welcoming and friendly micropub in an idyllic village, a short stroll from the sea and the historic Hurst Castle, just the place in which to refuel, relax and enjoy a pint after a scenic walk. Four varied beers, local and national, are on tap, and up to 10 ciders. So why the Wash House? The venue used to be a place where you washed your smalls. Today it serves stunning beer. Q🍺♿🍎🚌(X1)🐾

New Milton

Hourglass

8 Station Road, BH25 6JU
☎ (01425) 616074 🌐 hourglassmicropub.co.uk
4 changing beers (sourced nationally) G
Friendly, welcoming micropub serving four continuously changing cask ales on gravity, usually including one dark beer, plus several bag-in-box ciders and six KeyKeg beers. An April beer festival, in its second year, is held at the Memorial Hall just across the road. A popular weekly Tuesday curry evening, a quiz night every other Thursday, and a music jam on the first Sunday each month, give this place a strong community feel. Takeaway food may be brought in and dogs are welcome. Q≹♣●🚌🐾📶

North Waltham

Fox L ✔

Popham Lane, RG25 2BE (between village and A30)
☎ (01256) 397288 🌐 thefox.org
Courage Best Bitter; Sharp's Doom Bar; West Berkshire Good Old Boy; 1 changing beer (sourced locally; often Andwell, Little London, Test) H
Lovely traditional country pub on the edge of the village and overlooking extensive farmland. It is divided into two – a popular restaurant and a public bar where food is also served (booking advisable). Local seasonal produce is featured where possible. Outside there is an extensive beer garden and a children's adventure play area. The Ushers signage remains on the rear of the building.
Q❀◑♿P🚌🐾📶

North Warnborough

Mill House L

Hook Road, RG29 1ET (from M3 jct 5 head towards Odiham and pub is on right)
☎ (01256) 702953
Hogs Back TEA; house beer (by St Austell); 4 changing beers (sourced regionally; often Andwell, Longdog, Triple fff) H
Listed as one of eight mills of Odiham in the Domesday Book, current sections are 17th-century additions, and the building was last used as a corn mill in 1895. It has a pleasant central bar space, separate dining areas and a lower-level view of the waterwheel and restaurant. The area surrounding the millpond fed from the Whitewater provides pleasant outdoor seating linking the function barn and parking. Part of the Brunning & Price group since 2018. Q❀◑♿P🚌(13)🐾📶

Oakley

Barley Mow L

19 Oakley Lane, RG23 7JZ
☎ (01256) 782591 🌐 barleymowatoakley.com
Red Cat Scratch; Sharp's Doom Bar; 1 changing beer (sourced locally; often Flower Pots, Red Cat) H
A traditional, non-chain local in the heart of a picturesque village, serving well-kept and traditional ales. It is not tied, allowing a far greater variety among changing beers. There is also a wide selection of gins. Warm, family-oriented and dog-friendly, it is often used as a refreshment and meeting point for ramblers. On Monday evening a fish and chips van visits and you can eat in the pub or have a beer while waiting.
Q❀◑♣P🚌(11)🐾📶

Overton

Old House at Home

Station Road, RG25 3DU
☎ (01256) 770335 🌐 theoldhouseathome.com
Black Sheep Best Bitter; Dark Star Hophead; St Austell Tribute; 2 changing beers (often Brains, Exmoor, Penton Park) H
A hostelry with a traditional feel and an excellent Thai restaurant and takeaway, also serving pub food and great-value dinners on a Sunday. It has five ale pumps dispensing three regular and two changing beers. There is a large garden with a play area and decking. A fun quiz is hosted on a Sunday and there are teams in local crib, pool and quiz leagues. Q❀🛏◑♣P🚌(76)🐾📶

Park Gate

Village Inn ✔

67 Botley Road, SO31 1AZ
☎ (01489) 573223
Ember Pale Ale; 4 changing beers (sourced nationally) H
A large, sprawling, single-storey Ember Inn, modern in style, with plenty of tables and an emphasis on meals. Beer drinkers aren't ignored either, with at least four rotating ales on handpump at any time. In keeping with current trends, there are some alcohol-free beers and wines too. It is a comfortable pub with a large car park, close to Swanwick station; parking is thus free only for customers. ❀◑♿≹(Swanwick)P🚌(28,28A)🐾📶

Petersfield

Townhouse L

28 High Street, GU32 3JL
☎ (01730) 265630 🌐 petersfieldtownhouse.com
3 changing beers (sourced regionally; often Downlands Brewery, Langham, Red Cat) H
In the heart of Petersfield, this is a bistro-style establishment offering food (breakfast, lunch and dinner), with a variety of keg beers and a good selection both of local ales and those from further afield. It has a family environment where children and dogs are welcome. A separate function room, upstairs, is available for hire. ❀◑≹♣P🚌(67)🐾📶

Portsmouth

Admiral Drake L

8 Kingston Crescent, Rudmore, PO2 8DH
☎ (023) 9265 1599
Greene King Abbot; 3 changing beers (sourced nationally; often Irving, Urban Island, Yeovil Ales) H
Dating from 1936, this pub now stands isolated – dwarfed by the Rudmore flyover. The U-shaped bar room is bare boarded and furnished with a mix of traditional tables and chairs as well as high tables and bar stools. There is a performance area for live bands to the right as you enter. In winter a real log fire is a welcome sight opposite the bar counter. Outside events are held during the summer in the large car park. ❀◑♿♣●P🚌🐾📶

Apsley House

Auckland Road West, Southsea, PO5 3NY
☎ (023) 9282 1294
Hop Back Summer Lightning; Sharp's Doom Bar; Timothy Taylor Landlord H
A small traditional back-street pub tucked away between Southsea Common and the bars of Palmerston Road. It gets busy when events are held locally, and the benches on the front patio are at a premium. It is home to both

darts and pool teams and hosts occasional live music. There is a raised section with seating that is usually a lot quieter than the main bar.

Artillery Arms

Hester Road, Milton, PO4 8HB

(023) 9273 3610

Triple fff Alton's Pride, Moondance; 4 changing beers (sourced locally; often Fallen Acorn, Triple fff, Urban Island)

Superb split-level community venue serving six well-kept ales from Hampshire and Sussex, all clearly displayed and described on a large blackboard, complete with tasting notes. There is a large enclosed garden, used for events throughout the summer. The pub supports both darts and pool teams, and other traditional games are played. Slightly out of the way, but only five minutes' walk from Fratton Park, it can get busy on match days but is welcoming to away supporters. P (1,2)

Barley Mow

39 Castle Road, Southsea, PO5 3DE

(023) 9282 3492 barleymowsouthsea.com

Fuller's London Pride; Gale's HSB; 6 changing beers (sourced nationally)

Although designed by AE Cogswell, this building is not typical of his work. The lounge bar is wood-panelled and for many years the ceiling had a painting of the Battle of Southsea, now residing in the City Museum. This is a true community pub, hosting many events including live music, quizzes and raffles. The patio garden is a hidden gem which has won awards in its own right. The bar also has bar billiards and shove-ha'penny tables.
(3)

Brewhouse & Kitchen

26 Guildhall Walk, Landport, PO1 2DD

(023) 9289 1340

Brewhouse & Kitchen Sexton, Mucky Duck, Black Swan, Mary Rose; 1 changing beer (sourced locally; often Brewhouse & Kitchen Portsmouth)

Known locally as the Mucky Duck, this pub is distinctive from the outside with its Brewers' Tudor timber-clad Grade II listed façade. It brews its own beer in a 2.5-barrel plant. Next door is the newly refurbished New Theatre Royal and 30 seconds away is the Portsmouth Guildhall venue. On one of the brew days there's a chance to become a brewer for the day. Food is served all day. (7,700)

Bridge Tavern

54 East Street, Old Portsmouth, PO1 2JJ

(023) 9275 2992 bridge-tavern-portsmouth.co.uk

Fuller's London Pride; Gale's Seafarers Ale, HSB; 2 changing beers (sourced nationally; often Fuller's)

In the heart of the Camber Docks, this pub has a traditional feel. The single bar is divided into a number of areas, probably hinting at a previous multi-roomed layout. The name refers to the movable bridge that used to span the dock nearby. The dock is home to Portsmouth's fishing fleet, and the patio provides a superb place to sit on a summer's day and watch the comings and goings of a small port. (16)

Eastney Tavern

100 Cromwell Road, Eastney, PO4 9PN

(023) 9282 6246 eastneytavern.co.uk

Sharp's Doom Bar, Atlantic; 3 changing beers (sourced locally; often Fallen Acorn, Goddards)

A large wooden bar greets you as you walk in. Floor space is cleverly split into three: to the right, seating and space to watch Sky and BT Sport, to the left a cosy restaurant area, and an open seating area. This Victorian pub occupies a prominent corner plot and is a two-minute walk to the seafront. LocAle is supported with Fallen Acorn and Goddards Brewery, and two handpulls are for Sharp's Brewery. (16)

Fawcett Inn

176 Fawcett Road, Southsea, PO4 0DP

(023) 9229 8656

Ringwood Razorback; Titanic Plum Porter; 1 changing beer (sourced locally; often Banks's, Irving, Marston's)

Designed by AH Bone and built in 1886 for the Brickwoods Brewery, the Fawcett Inn occupies a prominent position on a busy street corner. With its half-timbered Brewers' Tudor style and witch's hat tower, it has an imposing presence. It now sports one large, curved bar room, having been knocked through in the days of Whitbread. A popular venue for Pompey football fans on match days, the pub is boarded throughout and furnishings are mostly traditional.
(18)

Hole in the Wall

36 Great Southsea Street, Southsea, PO5 3BY

(023) 9229 8085 theholeinthewallpub.co.uk

Flower Pots Goodens Gold; 5 changing beers (sourced nationally)

The Hole is a wood-panelled gem that may be one of the smaller pubs in Portsmouth but, being a genuine free house, it offers a good range of beers from a wide selection of local and national breweries. Check the website for the current beer range. Real ciders are usually stocked as well. It opens on Saturdays from noon for Pompey home games, but there is no admittance after 11pm. Dogs must be on leads. (3)

Lawrence Arms

63 Lawrence Road, Southsea, PO5 1NU

(023) 9282 1280 lawrence-arms-portsmouth.co.uk

Harvey's Sussex Best Bitter; 5 changing beers (sourced nationally; often Irving, Langham, Urban Island)

Traditional local a short walk from Fratton station. Five ales are from near and far and always include a dark one. There is a range of cans and bottles for consumption on the premises or to take away. The pub is current local CAMRA Cider Pub of the Year, with six available in winter and up to 12 at other times. Toasted sandwiches are on offer at all times. The L-shaped bar is complemented by an enclosed patio that is popular in summer.
(18)

Merchant House

9-11 Highland Road, Eastney, PO4 9DA

4 changing beers (sourced nationally)

A modern-style pub featuring a range of cask, KeyKeg, canned and bottled beers from different parts of the country. A large screen on the wall displays the current offerings. The main bar is divided into two, one part being on a slightly higher level. The floor and walls are bare wood and brick. To the rear is a staircase leading down to a third drinking area. (1,2)

Northcote Hotel

35 Francis Avenue, Southsea, PO4 0HL

(023) 9278 9888

Irving Invincible; Long Man American Pale Ale; Timothy Taylor Landlord; house beer (by Wadworth); 1 changing beer (sourced locally; often Langham, Irving)

A large traditional pub just off Albert Road which still retains its two bars. The public bar has a pool table and dartboard. The smaller lounge has comfortable seating that forms several booth-type areas and is decorated with memorabilia of the cinema, including Laurel & Hardy, the Marx Brothers and the most famous of fictional detectives, Sherlock Holmes. There is also a large partly covered patio drinking area. ❀♣●🚌(2)

Old Customs House

Vernon Building, Gunwharf Quays, PO1 3TY

☎ (023) 9283 2333 🌐 theoldcustomshouse.com

Fuller's London Pride, ESB; Gale's Seafarers Ale, HSB; 2 changing beers (sourced nationally; often Dark Star) Ⓗ

Proclaiming itself the only traditional pub in the Gunwharf Quays retail complex and marina, this Grade II listed building retains the layout of the former naval offices of HMS Vernon. A stone's throw from the Spinnaker Tower, there is a heated rear patio area and seating at the front which is ideal for people-watching during the summer. It is open all day for food, including breakfast, and a number of the food dishes include Fuller's ales in their recipes. ❀◑♿⇌🚌🐾📶

Pembroke

20 Pembroke Road, Old Portsmouth, PO1 2NR

☎ (023) 9282 3961

Draught Bass; Fuller's London Pride; Greene King Abbot Ⓗ

A solidly traditional street-corner pub close to the Anglican cathedral. Originally called the Little Blue Line, it featured in novels by Captain Marryat. The interior is decorated with naval memorabilia, and photographs and paintings of Portsmouth in days gone by. The single bar has a piano and features two tiled fireplaces. It is believed that Lord Nelson walked past here on his way to HMS Victory to sail to Trafalgar. ♣🚌🐾📶

Phoenix

13 Duncan Road, Southsea, PO5 2QU

☎ (023) 9278 1055

Ringwood Fortyniner; 2 changing beers (sourced nationally; often Irving, Red Cat, Urban Island) Ⓗ

A street-corner local a short distance from Albert Road and a real community pub. The public bar is basically decorated and has memorabilia related to Portsmouth FC. The smaller comfortable lounge has many photos of people who have appeared at the nearby King's Theatre (see how many you recognise) as well as some of the theatre's interior. A quirky patio garden separates the main buildings from the games room, which was once part of the Dock End Brewery. ❀♣●🚌(2)🐾

Rose in June 𝕃 ✔

102 Milton Road, Milton, PO3 6AR

☎ (023) 9282 4191 🌐 theroseinjune.co.uk

Fallen Acorn Twisted Oak; Hop Back Summer Lightning; Irving Frigate; Purity Pure Gold, Pure UBU; West Berkshire Good Old Boy; 2 changing beers Ⓗ

Four of the listed beers are always on the bar, plus weekend specials. Situated about 10 minutes' walk from Fratton Park, this two-bar (three for football) pub is popular with football fans. Events include quizzes and pool and darts matches. The extensive garden has a play area and is used for barbecues and a summer beer festival. A February winter beer festival is also held. Seven real ciders are stocked (see board) and roast dinners are served on the third Sunday of the month. Q❀●P🚌🐾📶

Winchester Arms

99 Winchester Road, Buckland, PO2 7PS

☎ (023) 9266 2443

Wychwood Hobgoblin Gold; 3 changing beers (sourced regionally) Ⓗ

The Winch is a proper back-street local, offering one regular beer and two or three varying guests; ciders are served during the summer. Every third Sunday evening of the month is open mic night with music and comedy, and there is live music on other weekends. The garden has a covered smoking shelter. A beer festival is held over the spring bank holiday weekend. Closing time may be later on Friday and Saturday if busy. ❀●🚌🐾📶

Ringwood

Railway 𝕃

35 Hightown Road, BH24 1NQ

☎ (01425) 473701 🌐 therailway.co

Ringwood Best Bitter; 4 changing beers (sourced nationally) Ⓗ

Unspoilt traditional two-bar community pub with a small rear snug. Four changing beers are served, with Ringwood Best Bitter as a regular, and bag-in-box ciders. Reasonably priced, home-cooked food is available – the pub is gaining a reputation for the best burgers in the New Forest – and there is a separate vegan menu and a popular Sunday roast. Dogs and children are welcome, with a large secure garden area, but if eating outside watch out for the hungry chickens!
Q❀◑▲♣●P🚌(Ringo)🐾📶

Rockford

Alice Lisle

Rockford Green, BH24 3NA (¼ mile E of A338 at Blashford along Ivy Lane, then left) SU1592808081

☎ (01425) 474700 🌐 thealicelisle.co.uk

Fuller's Oliver's Island, London Pride; Gale's HSB; 1 changing beer (sourced nationally; often Dark Star, Flack Manor, Fuller's) Ⓗ

Nestled in the heart of the New Forest, this historic, 18th-century, Grade II listed Fuller's house is a must when visiting the area. Laid back from the road on a large green, often the home for New Forest ponies, this pub offers three regular cask ales and one that changes. The award-winning kitchen always sources locally produced goods – for the Sunday roast you need to book or be disappointed. Popular with families and ramblers all year round. ❀◑♿♣●P🐾📶

Romsey

Old House at Home

62 Love Lane, SO51 8DE

☎ (01794) 513175 🌐 theoldhouseathomeromsey.co.uk

Fuller's London Pride; Gale's Seafarers Ale, HSB; 2 changing beers (often Fuller's) Ⓗ

A popular Fuller's pub close to the town centre, between the railway station and the bus station, and adjacent to a large public car park. The main bar has a low-beamed ceiling with some seating booths. It extends up through another bar area, where acoustic/folk music is played on Monday evening, to an attractive walled garden and heated patio. There is a separate restaurant area just off the bar serving good-quality, mainly locally sourced, meals. ❀◑⇌P🚌🐾📶

Selborne

Selborne Arms 𝕃

High Street, GU34 3JR

☎ (01420) 511247 🌐 selbornearms.co.uk

Bowman Swift One; Ringwood Fortyniner; 3 changing beers (sourced regionally; often Itchen Valley, Parkway, Triple fff) Ⓗ

A traditional but greatly extended village pub with real fires and a friendly atmosphere in the two separate bars. Up to three guest beers, many from local microbreweries, are sold. Beer bats offering three thirds of cask beers for the price of a pint are a welcome feature. Extensive menus showcase local and home-made produce, with vegetarian and gluten-free options. The safe play area in the garden is popular with children. Opening times may vary - check website. Q☺☼ⒹP☐(38) ❀❦

Shedfield

Wheatsheaf Inn L
Botley Road, SO32 2JG
☎ (01329) 833024
Flower Pots Bitter, Goodens Gold; 4 changing beers (sourced locally; often Reunion, Steam Town, Stonehenge) Ⓖ
Popular two-bar roadside pub dispensing mainly Flower Pots beer directly from casks behind the bar. Two or three other beers, usually local, are also sold plus a choice of Westons real ciders. Good home-cooked food is served lunchtimes and Tuesday and Wednesday evenings. Live blues, jazz or folk music features on most Saturday evenings and a meat draw every Sunday. A beer festival is held over the spring bank holiday weekend. The garden's flowers are delightful in summer. Q☺Ⓓ♿♣♠P☐(69) ❀❦

Sherfield on Loddon

Four Horseshoes L ♥
Reading Road, RG27 0EX
☎ (01256) 882296 ⊕ the4horseshoes.co.uk
Sharp's Doom Bar; 2 changing beers (often Sherfield Village) Ⓗ
This family-run village inn is Grade II listed and dates back to the 16th century, with traditional low beams, some bench seating and wood-burners. The single bar with three handpumps serves four areas, one with a sports TV. At the front is a pleasant patio and at the rear a summer beer garden with play equipment. Families and dogs are welcome. Sherfield Village beers are on one handpump, with another LocAle as guest. Q☺☼Ⓓ♣P☐(14) ❀

Silchester

Calleva Arms
The Common, RG7 2PH
☎ (0118) 970 0305 ⊕ callevaarms.co.uk
Dark Star Hophead; Fuller's London Pride; Gale's Seafarers Ale, HSB; 1 changing beer Ⓗ
An attractive village pub opposite the common, named after the local Roman settlement of Calleva Atrebatum. A Fuller's house, its five handpumps serve four regular Fuller's ales plus one guest, which is often a Fuller's seasonal or a local ale. There is a welcoming bar with a separate comfortable dining area; an excellent choice of bar and restaurant food is also served in the conservatory and the large garden in the summer months. ☼☼Ⓓ♣P☐(14) ❀❦

Southampton

Beards & Boards
33 Bedford Place, SO15 2DG
3 changing beers (sourced nationally) Ⓗ
A friendly and welcoming micropub dispensing a changing selection of real ales on three handpumps. There are also 10 keg taps and four draught ciders. It has

a stripped-back industrial decor with displays of skateboarding activities, and features music turntables with the option to bring and play your own vinyl. The place is popular with all ages and holds dedicated music evenings. It has a range of board games, a Sega games console, and lets you bring your own food or have it delivered. ☼♿♠☐❀❦

Bitter Virtue L
70 Cambridge Road, SO14 6US
☎ (023) 8055 4881 ⊕ bittervirtue.co.uk
2 changing beers (sourced regionally; often Siren, Steam Town, Vibrant Forest) Ⓖ
Opened in 1997, and in every edition of the Guide since 1999, Bitter Virtue is a mecca for beer enthusiasts. Customers come from near and (often very) far, drawn by its range of about 1,000 bottled and canned beers (from the UK, Belgium, Germany, Netherlands, Scandinavia, the US, and a few other countries), two cask ales, and bottled ciders and meads. The selection may overwhelm the unprepared, but the knowledgeable staff will happily assist in your decision making. Q♠☐❀

Bookshop Alehouse
21 Portswood Road, SO17 2ES
4 changing beers (sourced locally; often Eight Arch, Elusive, Vibrant Forest) Ⓗ
Formerly an antiquarian bookshop, shelves full of books remain, some for sale. A single bar serves a varying beer range from four cask handpumps and four keg taps, all listed on a blackboard. There is also a good variety of bottled and canned beers plus real ciders. The basement room accessed by stairs opened in February 2020, providing additional seating. The atmosphere is friendly and relaxed, and dogs are welcome. Food can be brought in from the myriad of local takeaways. Q♿⇌♣♠☐❀❦

Butcher's Hook
7 Manor Farm Road, SO18 1NN
☎ (023) 8178 2280 ⊕ butchershookpub.com
4 changing beers (sourced nationally) Ⓖ
Southampton's first imaginative and inspirational micropub. The four different local or national cask ales normally include a dark one. With six craft KeyKeg lines, it prides itself on having the freshest and highest-rated craft beers from the UK and beyond. Regular beer-themed events bring locals and beer fans from around the city; these include the Butchers Brew Club, which frequently collaborates with local breweries. Always busy, with a great conversational drinking atmosphere, it is not to be missed. Q♿⇌♣♠☐(7)❀❦

Crammed Inn
48 High Street, SO14 2NS
☎ (023) 8057 6252
3 changing beers (sourced regionally; often Longdog, Steam Town, Urban Island) Ⓗ
Nestled among restaurants and a sports bar, this is an oasis of quality real ale. It has a relatively small footprint and visitors will have to be careful not to miss its narrow frontage. The bar is at the rear, offering a continually changing range of beers, mainly from local breweries. Old pictures, maps of Southampton and modern artwork cover the walls. Wednesday is quiz night and Friday features live music. ♿♣☐❀❦

Dancing Man L
Wool House, Town Quay, SO14 2AR
☎ (023) 8083 6666 ⊕ dancingmanbrewery.co.uk
6 changing beers (sourced nationally; often Dancing Man) Ⓗ
The iconic Grade I listed Wool House hosts this attractive pub. The interior decoration doesn't disappoint, and the

place is lauded for its sympathetic conversion into modern-day use. Most beers are from the on-site brewery, which promotes unfined beers and has been a frequent award-winner at local and regional CAMRA beer festivals. One-off and rare brews are regularly available. The upstairs restaurant and bar are in a beautiful, airy space and can be hired for private functions.

Fox & Hounds

106 Pound Street, SO18 6BP (off West End road to N of A3024 Bitterne bypass) SU4532611386

☎ 07701 385258

Flower Pots Goodens Gold G

Excellent two-bar community local which sells Flower Pots Goodens Gold from the cask. It boasts a billiards table, an excellent jukebox (free on Sunday) and runs various themed nights including poker, crib, dominoes, quiz and a meat draw. Families and dogs are welcome. The large, enclosed garden has plenty of seating – and this is possibly the only pub in Southampton that has a humane moth trap to help identify passing specimens.

Freemantle Arms

31 Albany Road, SO15 3EF

☎ (023) 8077 2536 thefreemantlearms.co.uk

House beer (by Ringwood); 4 changing beers (sourced regionally; often Fallen Acorn, Goddards, Otter) H

A warm welcome from friendly staff and customers awaits in this well-established and popular local in a quiet residential cul-de-sac not far from busy Shirley Road. Five real ales, mainly from regional breweries, are on the bar. Darts and cribbage are played and a TV shows BT Sport channels. Children are welcome in the pub and attractive garden until 8.30pm. No food is served but there are occasional barbecues in the garden.

(Millbrook)

Guide Dog

38 Earl's Road, SO14 6SF

☎ (023) 8063 8947

Dark Star Hophead, American Pale Ale; Flower Pots Bitter, Goodens Gold; Steam Town Stoke; 6 changing beers (sourced nationally; often Arbor, Red Cat, Steam Town) H

The Guide Dog is in the residential area of Bevois Valley. The single-bar front room serves a wide range of real ales from its 11 handpumps. The Dog House back room provides more seating and is occasionally used for acoustic music evenings and private functions. A Thai curry evening is held on Thursday (booking advised). The pub can be busy on football days and sometimes opens early depending on kick-off time. Q (7,U6)

Hop Inn

199 Woodmill Lane, SO18 2PH

☎ (023) 8055 7723

Bowman Swift One; Gale's HSB; Sharp's Doom Bar; 2 changing beers (sourced nationally) H

A popular traditional 1930s corner house divided into two bars with separate entrances. It has an unusual interior, with walls at different angles and bar fronts that are curved. The cosy lounge bar has a central fireplace and is decorated with chinaware. The public bar offers darts, pool, table football and a jukebox, and behind it is a covered patio leading to a hidden garden. Home-cooked traditional pub food is served Tuesday to Saturday lunchtimes and Tuesday to Friday evenings.

P (16,7)

London Road Brew House

67-75 London Road, SO15 2AB

☎ (023) 8098 9401 londonroadbrewhouse.com

London Road Brew House Bantam, Kodiak; 2 changing beers (sourced locally; often Flack Manor, Red Cat) H

A popular brewpub with the on-site six-barrel brew-plant supplying most of its beers; tours can be booked. The rustic, industrial-inspired pub boasts seven handpumps and seven craft beer fonts on the main bar. The split-level ground floor has a gas-fired pizza oven. A large mezzanine provides additional seating. Live sports are screened throughout. Features include video game machines, a pool and football table, and there are live bands.

Olaf's Tun

8 Portsmouth Road, SO19 9AA

☎ (023) 8044 7887 olafstun.co.uk

4 changing beers (sourced nationally) G

A great traditional micropub near the original chain-link ferry crossing the River Itchen, as depicted famously by Lowry. With a warm community feel, it offers four gravity-dispensed cask ales plus four KeyKegs and two ciders. No food is served but freshly-baked pizzas can be ordered at the bar for delivery. Seating is a mixture of tables, chairs and benches over the cask storage. Dogs are welcome, with treats available. Easily accessed by public transport. Q

Paddle & Peel

Unit 7A, Kemps Quay, Quayside Road, SO18 1AD (S of Quayside Rd, behind Kinley's Garage) SU4380213115

3 changing beers (sourced locally) G

A small one-roomed bar hidden away in a modern quayside industrial unit. An enormous old picture of the Queen Mary dominates the wall next to the bar. Real ale is served on gravity, with two or three beers typically coming from local breweries. The bar opened in Summer 2019 and is well-known for its wood-fired oven pizzas served from a hatch in the pub. Q P

Park Inn

37 Carlisle Road, SO16 4FN

☎ (023) 8078 7835 theparkinn.co.uk

Wadworth Henry's IPA, 6X, Swordfish; 3 changing beers (sourced nationally) H

This classic Victorian era street-corner local is a most welcoming one-bar venue, with the two halves of the U-shaped room still retaining distinctly separate public and saloon atmospheres. Although a Wadworth tied house, the licensee is at liberty to stock up to three beers from other breweries, and many interesting choices make an appearance. There is often a real cider in summertime. No food is served, but on Friday and Saturday lunchtimes substantial cooked snacks are available. On Sunday lunchtime the bar snacks are free.

Platform Tavern

Town Quay, SO14 2NY

☎ (023) 8033 7232 platformtavern.com

Fuller's London Pride; Gale's Seafarers Ale; 3 changing beers (sourced locally) H

Built into the remnants of the city's ancient walls (a small portion is visible behind glass), there is one bar here with a dining area beyond. The decor has an eclectic African art theme. Two beers from Fuller's and three locals are usually offered, plus a bag-in-box cider. One of the city's noted music venues, live music features virtually every weekend and consequently the bar may be extremely busy. There is a beer festival over the August bank holiday weekend.

South Western Arms

38-40 Adelaide Road, SO17 2HW

☎ (023) 8122 0817

Hop Back Summer Lightning; 8 changing beers (sourced nationally; often Exmoor, Long Man, Truman's) H

Dating from the Victorian times, this pub retains some original features. It is split over two floors, with some quirky wall pictures and bric-a-brac displayed on bare brickwork. The upper floor, a games room, has pool, darts and table football. Up to eight changing ales from national breweries are featured. A pleasant, spacious courtyard includes a partially covered smoking area. Regular live music on Saturday evening is hosted and there is a popular jukebox. Adjoining St Denys railway station (east side). ❀⇌♣●P🚌(7)🐾

Witch's Brew L

220 Shirley Road, SO15 3FL

☎ 07403 871757 🌐 thewitchsbrewsouthampton.com

5 changing beers (sourced regionally; often Bedlam, Flower Pots, Padstow) G

Formerly a mystic and new age shop, this place lives up to its name with its witch-themed decor and bespoke furniture. A friendly welcome from staff and customers is assured. The bar is at the back and all beers (typically five) are served on gravity straight from the casks into oversized glasses. The beer quality is recognised through it being a local CAMRA Pub of the Year finalist in recent years. Dogs are permitted on leads. Q❀♣●🚌🐾

Southwick

Golden Lion L

High Street, PO17 6EB

☎ (023) 9221 0437 🌐 goldenlionsouthwick.co.uk

Suthwyk Old Dick, Skew Sunshine Ale; 4 changing beers (sourced regionally; often Langham, Palmers, Urban Island) H

Famous historic free house in a privately owned village. It has many military artefacts, and Montgomery and Eisenhower were visitors, partly planning D-Day in the snug. A number of vintage vehicle societies visit during the warmer months. The Old Dick beer is named after the last brewer at the historic brewhouse behind the pub. The award-winning food can be enjoyed in the main bar or the quieter dining area. Jazz night is every Tuesday. Members of the Britstop Motorhome Club are also welcome. Q☎❀ⒹⒹ♿Ⓐ♣●P🐾📶

Steep

Harrow ★ L

Harrow Lane, GU32 2DA

☎ (01730) 262685 🌐 theharrowinnsteep.co.uk

2 changing beers (sourced locally; often Flack Manor, Hop Back, Langham) G

Genuinely unspoilt, the pub has two cosy rooms with serving hatches; beer is always 4% ABV or less, coming from a range of local breweries. Ciders are from Cheddar Valley and Meon Valley. There are several benches at the front, and a lovely well-kept garden. The toilets are across the road. The Harrow has been identified by CAMRA as having a nationally important historic pub interior. Q❀ⒹⒹ●P🐾

Tichborne

Tichborne Arms L

SO24 0NA (1¼ miles S from B3047 Alresford Rd jct) SU5719930412

☎ (01962) 733760 🌐 tichbornearms.co.uk

Bowman Swift One; Flower Pots Bitter; Langham Arapaho; Palmers Copper Ale; 2 changing beers (sourced locally; often Bowman, Langham) G

A traditional thatched inn built in 1939 and in Tichborne's historical heart; there has been a pub here since 1487. The main bar is a cosy, partially candlelit room with a wood-burner and grandfather clock. The second bar is similarly snug, with its open fire, and is home to a dartboard and slate shove-ha'penny board. Good-quality beers are poured straight from the cask, and excellent food is all fresh and uses locally sourced produce. Q☎❀ⒹⒹⒶ♣●P🐾📶

Titchfield

Wheatsheaf L

1 East Street, PO14 4AD

☎ (01329) 842965 🌐 wheatsheaftitchfield.co.uk

Fallen Acorn Hole Hearted; Flower Pots Bitter; 4 changing beers (sourced regionally; often Fallen Acorn) H

A 17th-century free house, owned by the licensee since 2017, which has established a reputation for top-quality real ale. The premises comprise a main bar with a real fire, a cosy snug and a bistro restaurant. Separate bar and restaurant menus are available. Regular beer and cider festivals are held at the end of January and July each year. No food is available Sunday evening. Q☎❀ⒹⒹ♿●P🚌(X4)🐾

Totton

6 Barrels

31 Salisbury Road, SO40 3HX

☎ (023) 8178 3030 🌐 6barrels.co.uk

Steam Town Stoke, Barton; 4 changing beers (sourced locally; often Vibrant Forest) H

Formerly a Thai takeaway, now a micropub, furnished with wood-panelled walls and benched tables. Four handpumps supply locally brewed ales, and a good selection of KeyKeg beers, ciders and perries is also offered. Customers can buy pizza from next door to eat in the bar, should they choose. A selection of board games is also available for customers if they run out of conversation. Outside are more tables and benches in a roped-off, uncovered seating area. ♿⇌●🚌🐾📶

Weyhill

Weyhill Fair

Weyhill Road, SP11 0PP

☎ (01264) 773722 🌐 weyhillfairandover.co.uk

Fuller's London Pride; Gale's Seafarers Ale, HSB; 2 changing beers (often Butcombe, Castle Rock, Wychwood) H

Country-style pub three miles west of Andover, standing on the site of the historic Weyhill fairground. The three regular Fuller's beers are usually supplemented by both a seasonal and a guest beer from the Fuller's portfolio. Good food uses locally sourced ingredients where possible and is available to eat in or take away, including the popular Fish Friday. An outdoor music and beer festival is usually held in July, featuring local bands and musicians. Closed on Monday in winter. ☎❀ⒹⒹⒶP🚌🐾📶

Whitchurch

King's Arms

10 Church Street, RG28 7AB

☎ (01256) 896333 🌐 thekingsarmswhitchurch.co.uk

6 changing beers H

A two-bar traditional community-style pub in the town centre. Beers often include local and regional offerings, with three usually on tap. One bar has a large screen and pool table with a cosy snug off, while the other bar is comfortable for socialising or for a good-value meal. Built in 1575, the building became an inn in 1675, and a sympathetic refurbishment in 2013 has retained the original period character and features. The pub holds numerous events and themed evenings with special menus. ❀◑≠♣P⊟(76,86)✿ᯤ

White Hart Hotel ✔

The Square, RG28 7DN

☎ (01256) 892900 ⊕ whitehartthotelwhitchurch.co.uk

Arkell's Wiltshire Gold, Hoperation IPA; 1 changing beer Ⓗ

An impressive former coaching inn dating from 1461 and now a centre of community life, with a lively public bar, pleasant dining area and a quiet restaurant to the rear. It is a hotel but is open to visitors. At the rear is a courtyard with seating. Regular events are held, from discos and bands to charity challenges, and private functions are catered for. Note the stained-glass features and the unusual decorated bollards outside the front door. Q❀◑♿≠P⊟(76,86)✿ᯤ

Widley

George Inn

Portsdown Hill Road, PO6 1BE

☎ (023) 9222 1079 ⊕ the-george-inn.co.uk

Flower Pots Goodens Gold; Fuller's London Pride; Greene King Abbot; Sharp's Doom Bar; Timothy Taylor Boltmaker; 2 changing beers (sourced nationally; often Irving, Langham, Goddards) Ⓗ

An 18th-century Grade II listed building on top of Portsdown Hill and offering views across Portsmouth to Langstone Harbour, the Solent and the Isle of Wight. It was a coaching inn on the old London to Portsmouth road and then a tram stop on the Portsdown and Horndean Light Railway. It has a single bar decorated with photos of the pub in days gone by and brewing memorabilia, much related to the former Brickwoods brewery. ❀◑P⊟(7,8)✿ᯤ

Winchester

Albion 𝕃

2 Stockbridge Road, SO23 7BZ

☎ (01962) 867991

Flower Pots Perridge Pale, Bitter, Goodens Gold; 1 changing beer (sourced locally) Ⓗ

A comfortable, unpretentious free house, where conversation remains in fashion, attracting an enthusiastic clientele. Although no longer run by Flower Pots, it remains faithful to that brewery's beers; the guest may occasionally be another LocAle. The pub doesn't do meals, but the pork pies (made near Petersfield), and Scotch eggs and chutneys (made by a member of staff) are recommended. Most of Winchester's bus services call at nearby City Road or the railway station. Q≠⊟✿ᯤ

Black Boy 𝕃

1 Wharf Hill, SO23 9NQ (just off Chesil St, B3404)

☎ (01962) 861754 ⊕ theblackboypub.com

Alfred's Saxon Bronze; Flower Pots Bitter; 3 changing beers (sourced locally; often Bowman, Hop Back, Itchen Valley) Ⓗ

An ancient building, a warren of interconnected rooms, spaces and corridors on many levels surrounding an island bar, where three of the five beers vary but are usually locally brewed. The decor defies description; there are collections of every imaginable sort in every possible area – fire buckets on one wall, electrical test meters on another, briar pipes snaking across a ceiling, and taxidermy everywhere. Part of the building, co-owned (the Black Hole), houses 10 en-suite double B&B rooms. Q❀◑♣⊟(4)✿ᯤ

Fulflood Arms 𝕃

28 Cheriton Road, SO22 5EF

☎ (01962) 842996 ⊕ thefulfloodarms.co.uk

Greene King IPA; Morland Old Speckled Hen; Red Cat Art of T; Steam Town Stoke; 6 changing beers (sourced locally; often Flower Pots, Red Cat, Steam Town) Ⓗ

Classic back-street local. The original dark-green tiled façade and etched windows are evidence of its 19th-century former Winchester Brewery ownership. Inside is a smart and comfy, capacious single bar with a wood-burning stove, and a library which includes newspapers (note the city map on the ceiling). Patios, both front and rear, are available for alfresco drinkers. Sports events shown on TV attract an enthusiastic local following. No food is served, but takeaways may be ordered. ❀≠♣⊟(4)✿ᯤ

Hyde Tavern 𝕃

57 Hyde Street, SO23 7DY

☎ (01962) 862592 ⊕ hydetavern.co.uk

Flower Pots Bitter; Harvey's Sussex Best Bitter Ⓗ**; 4 changing beers (sourced locally; often Flower Pots, Red Cat, West Berkshire)** Ⓖ

Time has stayed still for this small medieval timber-framed tavern. The two-roomed interior is below street level, with low ceilings and undulating floors. Standing by the big old log fire in winter with a pewter tankard of porter you could be back in Dickens' England. The cellar room hosts folk music and touring live artists, and encourages new singer/songwriters. Four changing and two regular ales, one of which is Harvey's, make this a pub not to be missed. Q❀≠♣⊟✿ᯤ

Old Vine 𝕃 ✔

8 Great Minster Street, SO23 9HA

☎ (01962) 854616 ⊕ oldvinewinchester.com

Alfred's Saxon Bronze; Timothy Taylor Landlord; 2 changing beers (sourced locally) Ⓗ

An entrance board outside this Grade II* listed Georgian hotel proudly states 'Free of tie', while inside a bar display proclaims membership of the Timothy Taylor Champions' Club. Cask ale clearly counts here; the four offered include at least one locally brewed. The large dining area serves high-quality food, using much local produce. Accommodation is in five double rooms and a top-floor suite. A small, 16-seat, function room is bookable. The pub directly overlooks the museum and is in turn overlooked by the cathedral. Q❀◑♣⊟(1,69)✿ᯤ

Westgate 𝕃 ✔

2 Romsey Road, SO23 8TP

☎ (01962) 820222 ⊕ westgatewinchester.com

House beer (by London Road Brew House); 4 changing beers (sourced locally; often Flower Pots, Itchen Valley, Red Cat) Ⓗ

In a prominent corner position at the top of the High Street and opposite the Great Hall, the Westgate is one of a chain of pubs and hotels owned by the City Pub Group. Five real ales are usually on the bar and two KeyKeg beers. Westgate Bitter is from Southampton's co-owned London Road Brew House. There is a separate dining room just off the main bar, a courtyard garden and 10 en-suite bedrooms. ❀◑≠♣⊟✿ᯤ

Wykeham Arms

75 Kingsgate Street, SO23 9PE

☎ (01962) 853834 🌐 wykehamarmswinchester.co.uk

Flower Pots Goodens Gold; Fuller's London Pride; Gale's Seafarers Ale, HSB; 1 changing beer (sourced regionally) 🄷

A fine Georgian building dating from 1755, immediately outside the city's ancient southern Kingsgate, close to Winchester College. Although a Fuller's establishment, beers include a local Flower Pots ale. Over two dozen wines are available by the glass. A most civilised, conversational pub, it has a number of interconnected rooms served from one central bar area, with an enormously varied bric-a-brac collection and much Nelsoniana featuring throughout. High-quality accommodation and meals (including early opening for breakfast) ensure the Wykeham appears in many guides. Q❀🛏◑🚌(1,69)🐾📶

Wonston

Wonston Arms 🏆 🄻

Stoke Charity Road, SO21 3LS

☎ 07909 993388 🌐 thewonston.co.uk

4 changing beers (sourced locally; often Bowman, Oakham, Red Cat) 🄷

This is a gem of a pub in the heart of the village and around a 15-minute walk from Sutton Scotney and the nearest bus stop. It is a true community local catering for everyone. Although it doesn't serve food, there are pop-up street food vendors most nights. Folk music is on the second and fourth Wednesdays of the month, and jazz sessions, a pop-up café, quizzes and a photography club also feature. Local CAMRA Pub of the Year 2017-2019, and CAMRA National Pub of the Year 2018. Q❀♣●P🐾📶

Wootton

Rising Sun 🄻 ✔

Bashley Common Road, BH25 5SF

☎ (01425) 610360 🌐 therisingsunbashley.co.uk

Flack Manor Flack's Double Drop; Morland Old Speckled Hen; 2 changing beers (sourced regionally; often Fine Tuned, Hop Back, Andwell) 🄷

Prominent and extensive 1900s roadside pub with stained glass windows and old print collections. On the edge of open forest and close to Hoburne Bashley holiday park and local riding stables, it welcomes walkers, dogs and horses – there is a tethering post next to the car park. There is a large, separate family room and secure adventure playground. Changing guest ales are mainly from local breweries, and occasionally a real cider is available. An extensive menu, served all day, offers many daily specials, catering for all tastes and appetites. 🐴❀◑♿P🚌(C32,C33)🐾📶

Yateley

Dog & Partridge

105 Reading Road, GU46 7LR

☎ (01252) 870648 🌐 dogandpartridgeyateley.co.uk

Sharp's Doom Bar; 3 changing beers (sourced nationally; often Greene King, St Austell, Theakston) 🄷

Customers are assured of a friendly welcome in this village pub at the heart of the local community next to the village green. It has built up an excellent reputation for quality cask beer and home-made food. Sharp's Doom Bar is the main ale, while there are three changing guests. Sunday lunch is popular and booking is essential. Quiz night is on Monday and live music on Saturday. TV sport is shown at the far end. 🐴❀◑♿P🚌(3)🐾📶

Wonston Arms, Wonston (Photo: Simon Urry)

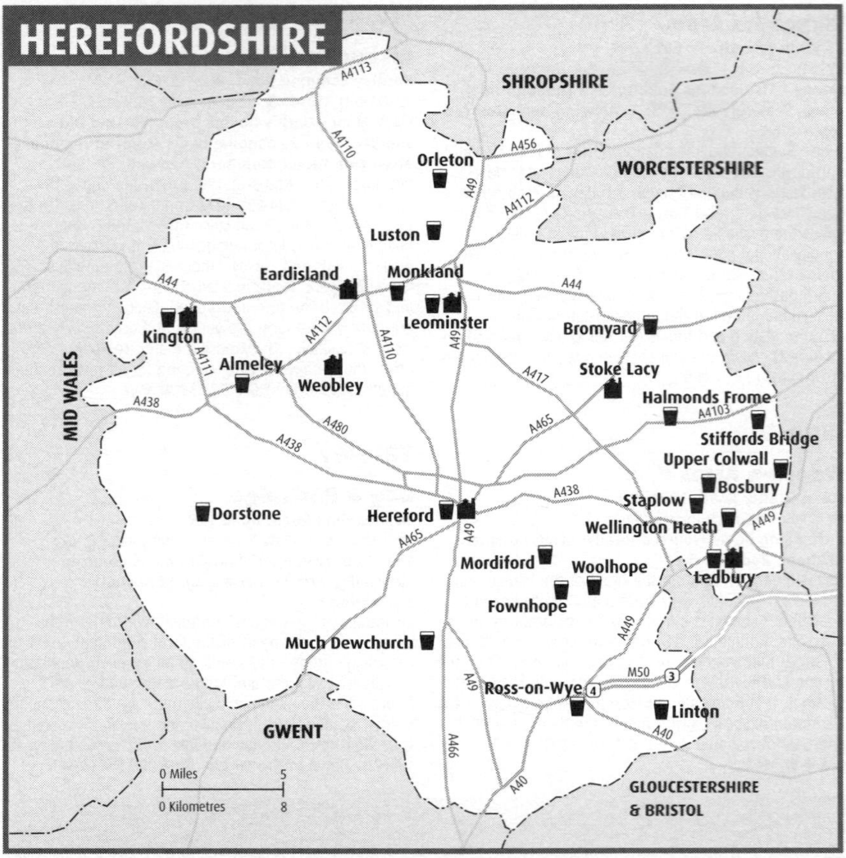

Almeley

Bells Inn 𝕃

HR3 6LF (in village)

☎ (01544) 327216 🌐 thebellsinnalmeley.com

Goff's Lancer; 2 changing beers (sourced locally; often Hobsons, Swan, Wood) Ⓗ

A genuine welcome is guaranteed at this enthusiastically run, traditional country inn set in the heart of its rural community, which incorporates an award-winning farm shop and delicatessen. The bar has a low ceiling and an alcove housing the dartboard. Home-prepared lunches are served plus fish & chips every Friday evening (booking required). A food van visits every first Saturday evening of the month. The guest beers are typically from local breweries. ☎❀◐♣●P🚌🐾 ᯤ

Bosbury

Bell Inn 𝕃 ✔

HR8 1PX (on B4220, in village)

☎ (01531) 640285 🌐 bosburyandcoddington.co.uk/the-bell-inn-bosbury

Otter Bitter; Wye Valley Butty Bach; 1 changing beer Ⓗ

A two-bar black and white half-timbered inn in a terrace opposite the imposing village church, the bells of which lend the place its name. A restaurant area serving food (not Mondays or Sunday evenings) contrasts with a basic yet comfortable public bar, replete with grand fireplace, alcoves, books and newspapers. Friendly and welcoming, this pub lies at the heart of its community. A large garden features at the rear. Plenty of on-street parking is available. Q☎❀◐◑♣●🚌(417)🐾 ᯤ

Bromyard

Rose & Lion 𝕃 ✔

5 New Road, HR7 4AJ

☎ (01885) 482381

Wye Valley Bitter, HPA, Butty Bach Ⓗ

A longstanding member of the expanding Wye Valley pub estate, the Rosie is very much a town pub from the old school, with a loyal following by locals. Two small, largely unaltered rooms are complemented by a further bar area to the rear, plus a more contemporary annexe and a pleasant garden. Furnished throughout in a modern but appropriate style, there is always a buzz

REAL ALE BREWERIES

Arrow ▮ Kington
Hereford ▮ Hereford
Ledbury Ledbury
Little Dewchurch Hereford (NEW)
Simpsons ▮ Eardisland
Swan Leominster
Weobley ▮ Weobley
Wobbly ◆ Hereford
Wye Valley Stoke Lacy

about the place. No food is served. The car park is small, but there is free on-street parking nearby.
Q☞✿&♣P🍴🚪(420) ☻

Dorstone

Pandy Inn 🅛
HR3 6AN (signed off B4348)
☎ (01981) 550273 ⊕ thepandyinn.co.uk
Sharp's Atlantic; Wye Valley Butty Bach; house beer (by Grey Trees); 1 changing beer 🅗
Opposite the small village green, the Pandy has a history dating back to the 12th century. Although opened out inside, discrete areas give an intimate feel, alongside timber framing, exposed stone walls and a huge fireplace. The pub caters equally for drinkers and diners, with an interesting range of dishes, including vegetarian ones. It will open on weekday lunchtimes for groups by prior arrangement. Gwatkins cider is on handpump. A monthly quiz and curry night is hosted (booking advisable). Winter hours apply early October to early April. Q☞✿◑♣●P🚪☻🎵

Fownhope

New Inn 🅛
HR1 4PE (on B4224, in village)
☎ (01432) 860350 ⊕ thenewinnfownhope.co.uk
Hobsons Best; house beer (by Wye Valley); 1 changing beer (often Hobsons, Swan, Wye Valley) 🅗
A genuine locals' pub at the heart of a thriving village community. The single room with exposed beams and light decor is divided into more discrete spaces by a central, bare-brick fireplace. Outside is a large, lawned garden. Typical pub food is served lunchtimes plus Friday and Saturday evenings, with a roast on Sunday. A quiz is held on the last Thursday of the month. Fownhope football team use the pub as a base.
☞✿◑&Å♣P🚪(454) ☻🎵

Halmonds Frome

Major's Arms 🅛
WR6 5AX (¾ mile N of A4103 at Bishops Frome)
SO675481
☎ (01531) 640261
Otter Bitter; Purity Pure Gold; Wye Valley HPA 🅗
An isolated hillside inn, a former cider mill which achieved national fame in 1991 when it temporarily became the Miners Arms as the coalmines were being closed wholesale. The no-frills, high-ceilinged main room has stone walls and a large wood-burner. An archway leads through to another drinking area and a patio, from which there are superb views, particularly sunsets, over west Herefordshire and into Wales. Complimentary bar snacks are often provided, and live music occasionally.
☞✿Å♣P☻🎵

Hereford

Barrels 🅛 ✅
69 St Owen Street, HR1 2JQ
☎ (01432) 274968
Wye Valley Bitter, The Hopfather, HPA, Butty Bach, Wholesome Stout; 1 changing beer (sourced locally; often Wye Valley) 🅗
Local CAMRA Pub of the Year seven times, The Barrels is a must-visit Hereford institution with a warm welcome for all. With no food, no gimmicks, but oodles of character across five rooms, this is a community inn of the highest order. It has a fantastic covered courtyard to the rear which hosts a charity beer and music festival

each August bank holiday weekend. Events include jazz on the first Monday of the month and comedy on some Wednesday evenings. There are TVs throughout turned on for major events. ☞✿♣●🚪☻🎵

Beer in Hand
136 Eign Street, HR4 0AP
☎ 07543 327548 ⊕ beerinhand.co.uk
5 changing beers 🅖
Herefordshire's first micropub, this minimalist, single-bar establishment was converted from a launderette in 2013. In recent years it has won CAMRA Herefordshire Pub of the Year and Cider Pub of the Year. With an impressive chilled racking system, it typically sells up to five ales on cask, six keg beers (including one from Odyssey Brew Co), and eight mainly local ciders and perries. Snacks are always available and artisan pizzas are made on-site Thursday and Friday evenings. Quiz night is the first Wednesday and folk night the third Thursday of the month. Q☞✿◑&♣●🚪☻

Britannia 🅛 ✅
7 Cotterell Street, HR4 0HH
☎ (01432) 341780
Wye Valley Bitter, HPA, Butty Bach 🅗
Reopened by Wye Valley Brewery following an impressive refurbishment which included a new extension with an oak-vaulted ceiling and a landscaped rear garden/patio, this is a back-street venue with real pedigree. The large central bar-servery is bookended by two distinct seating areas with modern decor. Snacks such as sandwiches are always available, and pork pies and barbecues in summer. A quiz is held monthly on a Thursday. A popular pub for an area of the city otherwise devoid of quality choices. ☞✿&♣🚪☻🎵

Kington

Olde Tavern ★ 🅛
22 Victoria Road, HR5 3BX
☎ (01544) 231417
Hobsons Mild; 4 changing beers (often Ludlow, Salopian, Swan) 🅗
A living and breathing Victorian time warp – once called the Railway Tavern (the railway closed in the 1950s) and before that the Tavern in the Fields – the pub is a microcosm of the town's development. On entering the lobby, with original serving hatch intact, to the left is a small bar with original timberwork, bench and alcove seating, and multifarious curios. To the right is the old smoke room with its fine flagstone floor and bench seating. The pub has a strong local following.
Q☞✿Å♣🚪☻

Ledbury

Feathers Hotel
25 High Street, HR8 1DS
☎ (01531) 635266 ⊕ feathersledbury.co.uk
Ledbury Bitter; house beer (by Wadworth); 2 changing beers (often Malvern Hills, St Austell) 🅗
This elegant black and white Elizabethan coaching inn, one of the flagship hotels for the county, has recently benefited from a major refurbishment. The fine Grade II* listed building includes a function room that was once the town theatre, and hand-painted murals in the upstairs corridors. The smart, plush, quiet bar is complemented by a restaurant and separate coffee shop and eatery. The toilets are accessible to wheelchairs.
Q☞✿🛏◑&P🚪☻🎵

Prince of Wales

Church Lane, HR8 1DL

(01531) 632250 powledbury.com

Eagle IPA; Hobsons Town Crier; Ledbury Dark; Otter Amber; Wainwright; 2 changing beers

Tucked away down a picturesque cobbled alley leading to the church, this 16th-century timber-framed pub has two bars plus an alcove where folk jam sessions are held on Wednesday evenings. A multi-award winner, it is a genuine community pub – always bustling with locals and visitors. Rosie's Pig and Snails Bank draught ciders are available as well as one rotating craft beer and an extensive range of foreign beers in bottles and cans. The bar meals are good value (booking advisable for Sunday roasts).

Leominster

Chequers

63 Etnam Street, HR6 8AE

(01568) 612473

Wye Valley Bitter, The Hopfather, HPA, Butty Bach, Wholesome Stout; 1 changing beer (often Wye Valley)

Probably the oldest pub in the town, with a fine timber-framed façade and interesting protruding gables. A wonderful front bar was at one time two bars, but still has much charm, with a fine tiled floor, original fireplace, timbers and cosy window alcoves. To the rear is a more conventional lounge bar and dining area serving good-value meals Monday to Thursday and a games room. Outside is a patio with a feature oak-timbered shelter. A quiz is held monthly on Wednesdays, and jazz on the first Fridays in summer. Q P

Linton

Alma Inn

HR9 7RY (off B4221, W of M50 jct 3) SO659255

(01989) 720355 almainnlinton.co.uk

Butcombe Original; Ludlow Gold; Malvern Hills Black Pear; Oakham JHB; 1 changing beer (often Bristol Beer Factory, Hop Shed, Swan)

Hidden behind a plain façade is an understated but multi-award winning pub of outstanding calibre. The convivial front bar with wood-burner and original timber furniture contrasts with the rear pool room and a separate wood-panelled dining room. Hearty, freshly prepared pub classics are offered, with seasonal specials, light bites and bar snacks. Events include the nationally renowned Linton Music Festival in July, hosted in the extensive gardens along with a beer festival. A quiz is held every last Sunday of the month. CAMRA Herefordshire Pub of the Year 2018. Q P

Luston

Balance Inn

HR6 0EB (on B4361 in village)

(01568) 616801 thebalanceinnluston.business.site

Hobsons Best; Wye Valley HPA, Butty Bach; 1 changing beer (often Swan)

Located on the site of an old wool weighing station – hence the name – in a small village, the Balance has an unspoilt interior with exposed beams and open fires. The main bar is complemented by a snug with chesterfield sofa, a games room with pool table and dartboard, and a large conservatory. Locally sourced meals are served daily, including in-house stone-baked pizzas, and takeaways are available. (490)

Monkland

Monkland Arms

HR6 9DE (on A44 W end of village)

(01568) 720510 themonklandarms.co.uk

Hobsons Best; Wye Valley Butty Bach; 2 changing beers (sourced locally; often Ludlow, Swan, Wood)

A single bar serves the drinking area, with dining areas to the side and rear. The beer garden has seating under cover, with views across open country. Home-cooked, locally sourced food is served, including traditional Sunday lunches. Up to seven local draught ciders are available and a range of four real ales. Quiz night is the last Wednesday of the month and live music is hosted on some Saturdays and Sundays. P (502)

Mordiford

Moon Inn

HR1 4LW (on B4224 in village)

(01432) 873067 mooninnmordiford.co.uk

Otter Bitter; St Austell Proper Job; Timothy Taylor Landlord; Wychwood Hobgoblin Ruby

This comfortable half-timbered two-bar village inn started life as a farmhouse over 400 years ago. Popular with locals and with families tripping out from Hereford, it benefits from its proximity to the Mordiford Loop – a well-known local walk – as well as the Rivers Lugg and Wye. Traditional, locally sourced pub food is served, with a pie & pud night on Wednesday. There is a children's play area in the garden, plus a camping and caravan site to the rear. P (453)

Much Dewchurch

Black Swan

HR2 8DJ (on B4348 in village)

(01981) 540295

Timothy Taylor Landlord; 2 changing beers (often Butcombe, Slater's, Swan)

One of the oldest pubs in Herefordshire, this delightful 15th-century beamed village inn comes complete with its own priest hole. A small lounge leads to the dining room with open fire. A separate public bar with flagstone floors leads to a pool and darts room. Home-prepared, mainly locally sourced food is available every session. The guest beers are typically from regional breweries. Draught Gwatkins perry is available plus ciders from Cockyard, Colcombe House and other local makers. Thursday is folk night. Herefordshire CAMRA Cider Pub of the Year 2019. P

Orleton

Boot Inn

SY8 4HN (off B4361 in village)

(01568) 780228 bootinnorleton.co.uk

Hobsons Twisted Spire, Best; Ludlow Ludlow Blonde; 1 changing beer

The Boot reopened under community ownership in 2019, following a period of closure. A major refurbishment of this distinguished Grade II listed, 16th-century, half-timbered masterpiece has been achieved to good effect – it has been sympathetically opened out while maintaining a separate dining room, snug and original inglenook fireplace. Good seasonal food is served and booking is advised (and essential at weekends). P (490)

Ross-on-Wye

Mail Rooms ✔

Gloucester Road, HR9 5BS

☎ (01989) 760920

Greene King Abbot; Ruddles Best Bitter; Sharp's Doom Bar; 4 changing beers 🄷

Behind the fine red-brick and stone façade of what was once the main post office is this single-bar Wetherspoon conversion, complete with vaulted ceiling, exposed air-conditioning ducts and an airy conservatory to the rear. Good-value food is served all day, including a children's menu. Three regular beers are complemented by up to four guests from a diverse range of breweries, plus two ciders. Alcoholic drinks are served from 9am. **Q** (32,33)

Tap House

1 Millpond Street, HR9 7BZ

☎ 07510 156708

6 changing beers (sourced nationally; often Hop Shed) 🄷

Opened in 2018, this micropub occupies what was, until 1965, the tap for Alton Court Brewery. It has a simply furnished main room and a snug. Serving six real ales from smaller breweries far and wide, plus a local cider, it has transformed the choice of real ale in Ross. No meals are available, but cobs are served Friday to Sunday. A new brewery, Motley Hog, is set to open. Herefordshire CAMRA Pub of the Year 2019. **Q**

Staplow

Oak Inn

HR8 1NP (on B4214)

☎ (01531) 640954 oakinnstaplow.co.uk

Bathams Best Bitter; Ledbury Gold; Wye Valley Bitter; 1 changing beer 🄷

A stylishly renovated and well-run roadside country inn offering exceptional food, good beer and quality accommodation. A contemporary public area neatly divides into three – a reception bar area with modern sofas and low tables, a snug, and a main dining area featuring an open kitchen. At the rear is a further room with scrubbed tables. Such is the reputation of the Oak that booking is essential for food and accommodation. **Q** **P** (417)

Stiffords Bridge

Red Lion Inn

WR13 5NN (on A4103)

☎ (01886) 880318 redlioncradley.com

Pitchfork Golden Ale; Wye Valley Butty Bach; 4 changing beers (often Malvern Hills, Purity, Salopian) 🄷

This multi-roomed roadside pub is as popular with out-of-town diners as it is with locals and drinkers. A survivor of multiple floods, it is characterised by modern flagstone floors, wood panelling, bare brick walls, cosy window alcoves and a large fireplace with a wood-burner. There are pleasant and extensive gardens to the rear where events are hosted. Traditional locally sourced food dominates the menu. The guest beers are from breweries far and near, many unusual for the area, supplemented by a craft keg beer and two real ciders. **P**

Upper Colwall

Chase Inn

Chase Road, WR13 6DJ (off B4218, turning at upper hairpin bend signed British Camp) SO766431

☎ (01684) 540276 thechaseinnmalvern.co.uk

Bathams Best Bitter; Courage Directors; 2 changing beers (often Enville, Exmoor, Malvern Hills) 🄷

Small and cosy two-bar free house hidden away in a quiet wooded backwater on the western slopes of the Malvern Hills. With a genteel atmosphere, it is popular with walkers and locals alike. It comprises a small lounge for dining (booking advisable at weekends) and a long, narrow public bar, both adorned with many artefacts and curios. A delightful manicured rear beer garden commands panoramic views across Herefordshire to the Welsh Hills. A quiz is held on the first Monday of the month. **Q** **P** (675)

Wellington Heath

Farmers Arms

Horse Road, HR8 1LS (in village E of B4214)

☎ (01531) 634776 farmersarmswellingtonheath.co.uk

Wye Valley HPA, Butty Bach; 2 changing beers (often Ledbury, Purple Moose, Salopian) 🄷

Follow the signs carefully to find this pub in its dispersed rural community. The bar and main dining area are in the original mid-19th century building, and on either side are more modern extensions housing a games room with pool table and a restaurant. The food ranges from burgers and pub classics to steaks and speciality dishes. Eight local draught ciders are available. A popular Beer & Beast festival is held in July. Open on bank holiday Mondays. **P** (675)

Woolhope

Crown Inn

HR1 4QP (in village) SO611357

☎ (01432) 860468 crowninnwoolhope.co.uk

Ledbury Bitter; Wye Valley HPA; 1 changing beer 🄷

Situated next to the church, the Crown has a large bar, complemented by a restaurant and a public bar area in the conservatory by the front door. Sandwiches and meals are all locally sourced and home-prepared. Curries feature on Monday evenings and a gourmet night is held on the third Thursday of the month. A wide range of local cider and perry is stocked, in bottle and on draught, the latter including the pub's own produce under the brand name Kings. **P** (453)

Recipe for buttered beer

Take a quart of more of Double Beere and put to it a good piece of fresh butter, sugar candie an ounce, or liquerise in powder, or ginger grated, of each a dramme, and if you would have it strong, put in as much long pepper and Greynes, let it boyle in the quart in the maner as you burne wine, and who so will drink it, let him drinke it hot as he may suffer. Some put in the yolke of an egge or two towards the latter end, and so they make it more strength-full. **Thomas Cogan, The Haven of Health, 1584**

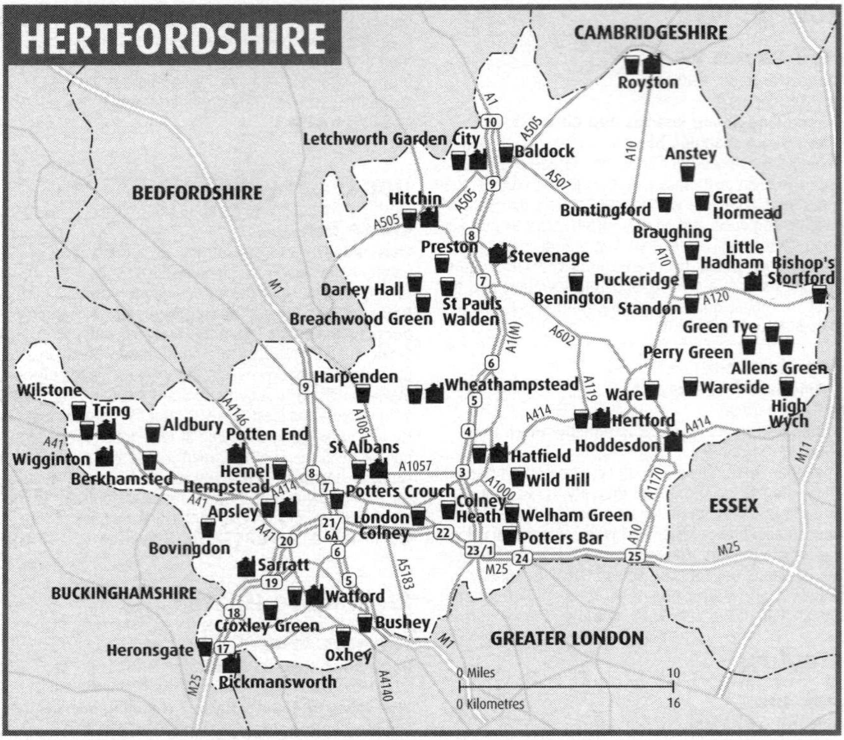

Aldbury

Valiant Trooper 🄻

Trooper Road, HP23 5RW

☎ (01442) 851203 🌐 valianttrooper.co.uk

Chiltern Beechwood Bitter; Tring Side Pocket for a Toad; 3 changing beers (sourced locally; often Chiltern, Tring, XT) 🄷

Situated in the heart of the Chiltern Hills, the Valiant Trooper is a traditional 17th-century inn. It retains a lovely classic style and charm, with a beer garden for summer and roaring log fires for winter. The venue offers an outstanding selection of beers in excellent condition, from local breweries and further afield, and has a separate restaurant serving an array of good British pub fare. Q❀◑♿♣●P🚌(387,389)🐾📶

Allens Green

Queen's Head 🄻

East Herts, CM21 0LS TL455170

☎ (01279) 723393

Fuller's London Pride; Mighty Oak Maldon Gold 🄷; 2 changing beers (sourced locally) 🄷/🄶

This village inn serves a changing range of beers. Hot snacks are available except in especially busy periods. The pub boasts a large garden and is popular with walkers and cyclists as well as regulars. A frequent winner of local CAMRA Pub of the Year over the past decade and current Hertfordshire Cider Pub of the Year. Q❀♿●P🐾📶

Anstey

Blind Fiddler

Anstey Village, SG9 0BW

☎ (01763) 848000

Buntingford Twitchell; Fuller's London Pride; 1 changing beer (sourced nationally) 🄷

Named after the local legend of Fiddler George, the Blind Fiddler has been opened out into one large bar area with a separate restaurant. Regular beers come from Buntingford and Fuller's and entertainment includes monthly quiz nights and live music. Pétanque, played in the garden, is popular, and there is a rare bar billiards table. ❀◑♣P🐾📶

Apsley

White Lion 🄻

44 London Road, HP3 9SB

☎ (01442) 211808 🌐 whitelionhemelhempstead.co.uk

Fuller's London Pride; 3 changing beers (sourced locally; often Mad Squirrel, Paradigm, Pope's Yard) 🄷

A popular neighborhood local that takes pride in dispensing frequently changing, well-kept local ales and some from further afield. It is comfortably furnished with a cosy feel, although basically open plan with four distinct areas and a rear patio. A darts team is supported and dominoes frequently appear. There is regular karaoke for the tolerant and demonstrative. ❀♿≠♣P🚌(500,H19)🐾📶

Baldock

Cock

43 High Street, SG7 6BG

☎ (01462) 896594

Greene King IPA; Morland Old Speckled Hen; Greene King Abbot; 2 changing beers (sourced nationally) 🄷

The Cock dates from the 17th century, and features a cosy beamed interior and a welcoming open log fire. It is a traditional pub in a historic Roman market town. The split-level layout enhances this popular, friendly local's character. An enclosed outside drinking area is available in good weather. Regular live music events take place. 🐎❀♿⇌🚌(635,98) 🐾📶

Orange Tree Ⓛ ✔

Norton Road, SG7 5AW

☎ (01462) 892341 🌐 theorangetreebaldock.com

Greene King XX Mild, IPA, Abbot; 9 changing beers Ⓗ

Three hundred year old multi-roomed pub home to more than ten local clubs and societies. Nine guest ales are from small breweries always including two from the local Buntingford Brewery, plus five local real ciders. Huge malt whisky collection and large vintage bottled beer collection on display. Good home cooked food is available with meats and sausages from local, award winning Chapman's Butchers. Quiz night is Tuesday. Rugby Internationals shown in all rooms, can get crowded. 🐎❀◐◑♿⇌♣🍎P🐾📶

Benington

Lordship Arms 🏆

42 Whempstead Road, SG2 7BX

☎ (01438) 869665 🌐 lordshiparms.com

Black Sheep Best Bitter; Crouch Vale Brewers Gold; Timothy Taylor Landlord; 6 changing beers (sourced nationally) Ⓗ

Under the same ownership for 25 years, this pub is a repeat winner of local and county CAMRA awards, and is local CAMRA Pub of the Year 2020. The single bar is decorated with telephone memorabilia. The garden features floral displays to be enjoyed in the summer. Wednesday evening curries are popular and lunchtime snacks are served. There is a classic car gathering on the third Tuesday of each month April to September. Winter Sunday hours can vary – call to check. Q❀◐🍎P🚌📶

Berkhamsted

Bull

10 High Street, HP4 2BS

☎ (01442) 767440 🌐 thebullberkhamsted.co.uk

Timothy Taylor Landlord; Tring Side Pocket for a Toad; 2 changing beers (sourced locally; often Tring) Ⓗ

This stunning high-street establishment is the oldest surviving pub in Berkhamsted, dating back to at least 1535. It has a large red-brick fireplace, wood panelling and an extensive canalside beer garden. Beers are well-kept and mostly local. The pub holds regular quizzes, frequently shows sport on TV and serves breakfast, lunch and dinner. 🐎❀◐◑⇌♣P🚌(500,501)🐾

Rising Sun Ⓛ

1 Canal Side, George Street, HP4 2EG (at lock 55 on Grand Union Canal)

☎ (01442) 864913

Tring Drop Bar Pale Ale; house beer (by Tring); 3 changing beers (sourced nationally; often Chiltern, Froth Blowers Brewing Co, Milestone) Ⓗ

The Riser is a thriving canalside pub with plenty of outdoor space – a firm favourite of local hikers, dog walkers and cyclists. The recipient of many well-deserved CAMRA awards, it serves five well-kept real ales and up to 15 real ciders. The pub hosts many popular events including quiz nights, folk music afternoons, a cheese club and quarterly beer and cider festivals. A range of bar snacks is offered such as pork pies and nachos, as well as the renowned ploughman's. 🐎❀◐◑⇌♣🍎🚌(500,501) 🐾📶

Bishop's Stortford

Bishop's Stortford Sports Trust Ⓛ

Cricketfield Lane, CM23 2TD

☎ (01279) 654463 🌐 bssportstrust.co.uk

6 changing beers (sourced locally; often New River, Hadham, Mauldons)

Everyone is welcome at this pub within a club – no membership required. Conversation flourishes in the comfortable seating area as the satellite sports screens usually have the sound off. Outside drinking in summer comes with an attractive view. The venue is easily reached from town via Chantry Road; turn left at the end to see the grounds on the right. Local CAMRA Club of Year 2020 and a recent National finalist. 🐎❀♿P

Star Ⓛ ✔

7 Bridge Street, CM23 2JU

☎ (01279) 654211

5 changing beers (sourced regionally) Ⓗ

A 17th-century town-centre pub catering for all ages. It is busy on Friday and Saturday evenings with a young crowd, but normally attracts a mixed clientele. Tuesday is quiz night. A quiet pint can be enjoyed on other evenings and at lunchtimes. Beers from regional and local breweries are offered on a changing basis. Reasonably priced traditional pub food is freshly prepared throughout the day. ❀◐◑⇌🍎🚌📶

Bovingdon

Bell Ⓛ ✔

79 High Street, HP3 0HP

☎ (01442) 832800 🌐 bellbovingdon.co.uk

Tring Side Pocket for a Toad; 3 changing beers (sourced nationally; often Timothy Taylor, Tring, Young's) Ⓗ

Welcoming 18th-century beamed village pub. The main bar is split level with a smaller adjoining snug and a restaurant to the rear. It has gained an excellent reputation for its food, complemented by fine ales, one of which is brewed locally. Log fires ensure a cosy atmosphere in winter; the garden terrace is an ideal place to relax in summer. Events include themed food evenings, quiz nights and occasional live music. 🐎❀◐◑🚌(105) 🐾📶

REAL ALE BREWERIES

- **3 Brewers of St Albans** Hatfield
- **Belgian Brewer** ✎ Bishop's Stortford
- **Bog Brew** ▤ Stevenage
- **Bowtie** Watford (NEW)
- **Buntingford** Royston
- **Creative Juices** ✎ Rickmansworth (NEW)
- **Farr Brew** Wheathampstead
- **Garden City** ▤ Letchworth Garden City
- **Hadham** Little Hadham
- **Hitchin** Hitchin
- **Lock 81** Watford (NEW)
- **Mad Squirrel** ✎ Potten End
- **McMullen** Hertford
- **New River** Hoddesdon
- **Oxhey Village** Watford (NEW)
- **Paradigm** Sarratt
- **Pope's Yard** Apsley
- **Summershed** Wigginton (NEW)
- **Tring** Tring
- **White Hart Tap** ▤ St Albans (brewing suspended)

Braughing

Brown Bear

14 The Street, SG11 2QF
☎ (01920) 822157 🌐 brownbearbraughing.co.uk
3 changing beers (sourced nationally) Ⓗ
A pub since at least 1740, the Brown Bear has a public bar and a restaurant, both with impressive fireplaces – have a go at identifying the implements. A widely varying choice of three real ales is usually available. This place offers something for everyone, including a Thursday quiz, darts and pétanque teams, a large garden with a pizza oven, occasional outside bars and monthly live music. P (331)

Breachwood Green

Red Lion

16 Chapel Road, SG4 8NU
☎ (01438) 833123 🌐 redlionbreachwoodgreen.co.uk
Greene King Abbot; St Austell Tribute; Woodforde's Wherry; 1 changing beer (sourced nationally) Ⓗ
As the only pub in the village, the Red Lion attracts many locals and some from further afield. It features a quiet drinking area and a TV showing main sporting events. It serves good home-made food, plus guest beers that are unusual for this area. Darts, dominoes, association football and cricket teams are hosted. The garden provides great views of the countryside and is a good vantage point from which to view aircraft approaching Luton Airport. P

Buntingford

Crown

17 High Street, SG9 9AB
☎ (01763) 271422
Draught Bass; St Austell Trelawny; 1 changing beer (sourced nationally) Ⓗ
This town-centre pub has a large front bar with dartboard, plus a cosy back bar and function room. Outside is a covered patio and a secluded garden with pétanque piste. Although the emphasis is on drinking, traditional fish & chips is served on Friday evenings and an acoustic music night takes place on the third Monday of the month. On CAMRA's Regional Inventory of Historic Pub Interiors. Q (386,331)

Bushey

Swan

25 Park Road, WD23 3EE
☎ (020) 8950 2256 🌐 swanpubbushey.co.uk
Black Sheep Best Bitter; Greene King Abbot; Timothy Taylor Landlord; Young's Bitter Ⓗ
Traditional Victorian pub just off the main high street with a single bar and two coal fires. A real gem, it has old photos and sporting mementos adorning the walls. The original jug-and-bottle window has been retained. Hot snacks are available at all times including toasties and pies. It hosts a book club, and offers entertainment including darts, board games and shut the box. The Ladies is accessed via the garden. (142,258)

Colney Heath

Crooked Billet

88 High Street, AL4 0NP
☎ (01727) 822128 🌐 thecrookedbilletpub.com
Sharp's Doom Bar; Tring Side Pocket for a Toad; Young's London Special Ⓗ
Popular and friendly cottage-style village pub dating back over 200 years. A genuine free house, it stocks three beers from national and regional breweries and micros. A wide selection of good-value, home-made food is served lunchtimes and Friday and Saturday evenings. Summer barbecues and Saturday events are held occasionally. This is a favourite stop-off for walkers on the many local footpaths. Families are welcome in the bar until 9pm and in the large garden, where there is play equipment. P (304)

Croxley Green

Sportsman

2 Scots Hill, WD3 3AD (at A412 jct with the Green)
☎ (01923) 443360
Oakham JHB; Sharp's Doom Bar; 5 changing beers (sourced nationally; often New River, Paradigm, Vale) Ⓗ
A family-run community pub with friendly, welcoming service, providing a traditional pub atmosphere in a modern context. It serves two regular real ales plus five varying guest beers from near and far. Craft keg versions of the prize-winning Paradigm Black Friday and Oakham Green Dragon are regularly available. The pool table and dartboard continue to be well used. Comfortable outdoor seating is provided. Quiz night is Wednesday; live music features every other Sunday afternoon. Croxley tube station is a 12-minute walk. P

Darley Hall

Fox

Darley Road, LU2 8PP
☎ (01582) 731366 🌐 thefoxdarleyhall.co.uk
4 changing beers (sourced locally) Ⓗ
Late 19th-century double-fronted pub in a hamlet close to Luton Airport. It is first recorded as having a landlord in the 1891 census. The interior comprises a single bar with adjoining dining area, offering a warm welcome to all. Outside is a walled family-friendly garden, plus a large mezzanine decking area linked to the excellent restaurant overlooking the Hertfordshire countryside. P

Great Hormead

Three Tuns

Pelham Road, SG9 0NT
☎ (01763) 289405
Adnams Southwold Bitter; 2 changing beers Ⓗ
A 16th-century thatched pub with a restaurant area that was added at the rear after a fire in 1996. The main bar has a lovely fireplace. Monthly quiz nights are popular. The food has a good reputation and Thursday night fish & chips often sells out. Adnams Bitter is a regular, with guest beers from local breweries Buntingford and New River. P

Green Tye

Prince of Wales

Green Tye, Much Hadham, SG10 6JP TL444184
☎ (01279) 842139 🌐 thepow.co.uk
Abbeydale Moonshine; Wadworth Henry's IPA; 2 changing beers (sourced regionally) Ⓗ
A traditional and friendly village local, whether you are a walker, cyclist, dog owner or just plain thirsty. Food includes sandwiches and great-value good pub grub. There is a small garden for fine weather. Well-established beer festivals in May and September feature a barbecue and entertainment. Q P

Harpenden

Carpenter's Arms

14 Cravells Road, AL5 1BD

☎ (01582) 460311

Adnams Southwold Bitter; Courage Best Bitter; Greene King Abbot; 2 changing beers (sourced nationally) Ⓗ

Landlord Tony has been running Harpenden's smallest pub since 2006, offering five real ales including two changing guest beers. It is popular with all sections of the community – and their dogs. The cosy interior is comfortably furnished, with an open fire warming the bar in cold weather. The spacious, secluded patio is a suntrap in summer. BT Sport and terrestrial sport are shown on TV, with rugby union internationals especially popular. Meals are available Tuesday to Saturday lunchtimes. Q❀◖P🚌🐾📶

Cross Keys 𝕃 ✔

39 High Street, AL5 2SD (opp War Memorial)

☎ (01582) 763989

Rebellion IPA; Timothy Taylor Landlord; Tring Side Pocket for a Toad Ⓗ

A regular entry in the Guide, located on the lower High Street, this two-bar pub has retained its traditional charm with a rare fine pewter bar top and flagstone floors. The original oak-beamed ceiling has tankards from past and present customers. In spring and summer, enjoy your pint in the secluded, attractive rear garden, and in autumn or winter savour your beer in front of the saloon bar's fire. Traditional home-cooked lunches are served Monday to Saturday. Q🐎❀◖≹♣🚌🐾📶

Hatfield

Horse & Groom

21 Park Street, AL9 5AT

☎ (01707) 264765

Greene King Abbot; Otter Bitter; 4 changing beers (sourced nationally) Ⓗ

In the heart of Old Hatfield, this allegedly haunted, 16th-century, Grade II listed building is thought to house a priest hole. The pub serves up to six real ales, and hosts beer festivals during the year. Tuesday is bangers and mash night and Saturday is chilli and rice night – purchase an ale for a free portion. Enjoy Thai food on Friday evenings. Hatfield railway and bus stations are nearby using 'blood and guts alley'.
Q🐎❀◖◗♿≹♣🍎🚌🐾📶

Hemel Hempstead

Monk's Inn 🏆 𝕃

31-32 The Square, HP1 1EP

☎ 07554 661877

Titanic Plum Porter Ⓖ**; 9 changing beers** Ⓗ/Ⓖ

A new and exciting addition to the Hemel Hempstead beer scene. The town's first micropub boasts a fantastic array of well-kept changing beers in an impressive range of styles on both gravity and handpump. Converted from an old betting shop, the small interior has furniture from the much-missed Bree Louise pub at Euston. Comedy nights, pub quizzes and music nights are held regularly. Local CAMRA Pub of the Year 2020. Q🐎❀♣🍎▯🚌🐾📶

Heronsgate

Land of Liberty, Peace & Plenty 🏆 𝕃

Long Lane, WD3 5BS TQ023949

☎ (01923) 282226 🌐 landoflibertypub.com

8 changing beers (sourced nationally; often Downton, Tring, XT) Ⓗ

Welcoming, award-winning pub just off the motorway, popular with walkers, cyclists, locals and real ale enthusiasts. Up to eight microbrewery beers are offered in a range of styles and strengths. Real cider, perry and a wide choice of whiskies are also available, as are gins and bottled beers. Beer festivals, tastings and a monthly charity quiz are held throughout the year. Bar snacks are served all day. There is a large outside pavilion and garden for families. ❀♣🍎P▯🚌(R2)🐾📶

Hertford

Black Horse 𝕃 ✔

29-31 West Street, SG13 8EZ

☎ (01992) 583630 🌐 theblackhorse.biz

6 changing beers (sourced nationally) Ⓗ

A community-focused, timbered free house, dating from 1642 and situated in one of Hertford's most attractive streets, near the start of the Cole Green Way. Six real ales from around Britain are on offer, including one from Hertfordshire. An interesting menu features curries, game and daily specials, and the pub has its own bakery producing pastries. The well-kept garden includes a separate and safe children's area. Handy for Hertford Town FC supporters, the pub also has its own Black Horse Rugby Club which plays home games at nearby Hertford RFC. 🐎❀◖◗≹♣🍎🚌🐾📶

Great Eastern Tavern

29 Railway Place, SG13 7BS

☎ (01992) 582048

McMullen AK Original Mild, Cask Ale; 1 changing beer (sourced nationally) Ⓗ

Popular, buoyant and traditional back-street McMullen local with two contrasting bars bedecked with pictures and artefacts. There is live TV sport and interesting rock and blues piped music. A folk club is hosted on the first Thursday of the month and a quiz on the first Sunday. Sandwiches are available at lunchtimes. A chilli challenge is held every February. Outside are two small gardens – the larger, to the rear, is paved and adorned with a stunning array of plants.
🐎❀≹♣P🚌(395,310)🐾📶

Hertford Club

Lombard House, Bull Plain, SG14 1DT

☎ (01992) 421422 🌐 hertford.club

4 changing beers (sourced nationally) Ⓗ

Dating from the 15th century with later additions, Lombard House, on the River Lea, was built as an English hall house and is one of the oldest buildings in Hertford. It has been the home of this private members' club since 1897. CAMRA members are welcome and may be signed in on production of a membership card. You will find three or four changing beers and real cider, which in summer can be enjoyed in the delightful walled garden and riverside terrace. Home-cooked food is served at lunchtimes and on Friday evening. Local CAMRA Club of the Year 2020. 🐎❀◖◗≹♣🍎▯🚌📶

Old Barge ✔

2 The Folly, SG14 1QD

☎ (01992) 581871 🌐 theoldbarge.com

Marston's 61 Deep; 3 changing beers (sourced nationally) Ⓗ

A free house on Folly Island, pleasantly situated canalside on the River Lea, offering a good selection of ales – often including a dark brew – and a range of ciders and perries. Locally sourced home-cooked food is served all day, with roasts on Sunday. There is a popular Sunday night quiz and a music quiz on the last Thursday of the month. The Spring Fling music festival takes place on the second May bank holiday Monday. Look out for the annual duck race. ⛓❀◑⇌♣●🚌📶

Old Cross Tavern 🏆 L

8 St Andrew Street, SG14 1JA

☎ (01992) 583133 🌐 oldcrosstavern.com

Timothy Taylor Landlord; 5 changing beers Ⓗ

Superb town free house offering a friendly welcome. Up to six real ales, usually including a dark beer of some distinction, come from brewers large and small, and there is a fine choice of Belgian bottle-conditioned beers. Two beer festivals are held each year – one over a spring bank holiday weekend, the other in October. No TV or music here, just good old-fashioned conversation. Home-made pork pies and Scotch eggs are available. Local CAMRA Pub of the Year 2020. Q⇌♣🚌(395)🐾

White Horse

33 Castle Street, SG14 1HH

☎ (01992) 500557 🌐 white-horse-hertford.co.uk

Dark Star Hophead; Fuller's London Pride, ESB; Gale's Seafarers Ale; 2 changing beers (sourced nationally) Ⓗ

A charming old timber-framed building with two downstairs bars and additional rooms upstairs, one featuring bar billiards, others where children are welcome. Guest beers are from Fuller's and different breweries around Britain. Home-cooked Thai food and pub favourites are available all day. The White Horse welcomes dogs and has no gaming machines to interrupt its atmosphere of engaging conversation.
Q⛓❀◑⇌♣●🚌🐾📶

High Wych

Rising Sun

High Wych Road, CM21 0HZ

☎ (01279) 724099

4 changing beers (often Oakham, Woodforde's) Ⓖ

This friendly village local has never used handpumps – a range of four or five beers is served on gravity, often featuring East Anglian breweries. Although refurbished, the original character has been preserved by the stone floor, attractive fireplace and wood panelling. The pub is popular with locals and walkers, and has a separate restaurant upstairs. It holds an annual vegetable competition. Parking is in the village hall car park opposite. Q❀♣P🚌(347)🐾

Hitchin

BB's Bar

Bridge Street, SG5 2DE

☎ (01462) 656084

Fuller's London Pride; Oakham Citra; 2 changing beers (sourced nationally) Ⓗ

A sports and music bar with a friendly pub atmosphere, named after blues legend BB King. The cask taps bar counter is at the rear of the front room, separate from the main bar counter. A second room at the rear opens at busy periods and is also available for private functions. The beer range usually includes two Oakham ales plus two others. ⛓❀🐾

Half Moon L

57 Queen Street, SG4 9TZ

☎ (01462) 453010

Adnams Southwold Bitter; Young's Bitter; 10 changing beers (sourced nationally) Ⓗ

This welcoming one-bar pub dates from the 18th century. The two house ales and eight different guest ales ensure a variety of beer styles is always on offer from a range of breweries near and far, alongside a choice of traditional ciders. Home-cooked food is served every day except Monday, with bar snacks always available. Twice-yearly beer festivals, regular quizzes and music nights are popular in this friendly community pub. ⛓❀◑⇌♣●P▯🐾📶

Victoria ✔

1 Ickleford Road, SG5 1TJ

☎ (01462) 432682 🌐 thevictoriahitchin.com

Greene King IPA, Abbot; 4 changing beers (sourced nationally) Ⓗ

This popular and busy community pub dating from 1865 hosts a range of events from quiz nights and live music to comedy and cabaret, as well as an annual beer and cider festival and the Vic Fest music festival. Two regular Greene King beers are complemented by two guests. Good-value home-made modern British food is served every day, plus roasts on Sunday. Pie nights feature regularly. The historic barn is available for community use and live events. ⛓❀◑♿⇌♣🚌📶

Letchworth Garden City

Garden City Brewery & Bar L

22 The Wynd, SG6 3EN

☎ 07932 739558 🌐 gardencitybrewery.co.uk

8 changing beers Ⓖ

Award-winning family-run brew-bar opened in 2016 in a converted café on a charming pedestrianised street. All ales are on gravity: usually four of the brewery's own, only available here, and four guests. A large selection of local and UK-wide ciders is also on offer, alongside locally produced bar snacks. The paved beer garden has hay bale seating and an awning. There is a regular events programme and the TV shows tennis and rugby. The bar is five minutes' walk from the station, with parking adjacent and a playground opposite. Local CAMRA Cider & Perry Pub of the Year 2020. Q⛓❀♿⇌●P🚌🐾📶

London Colney

Bull L

Barnet Road, AL2 1QU

☎ (01727) 823160

St Austell Tribute; Timothy Taylor Landlord; 2 changing beers Ⓗ

A lovely 17th-century timbered building near the River Colne, offering a range of real ales. It has a cosy lounge featuring an original fireplace, and a large public bar with a dartboard and TV. Evening events include live music sessions. Good-value home-made meals are served Monday to Saturday lunchtimes and evenings, with breakfast on Saturday and a roast on Sunday. Outside is a children's play area. ❀◑♣P🚌🐾📶

Oxhey

Railway Arms ✔

1 Aldenham Road, WD19 4AB

☎ 07976 647569

Greene King IPA, Abbot; 2 changing beers (sourced nationally; often Purity, St Austell, Timothy Taylor) Ⓗ

Friendly and welcoming two-bar pub opposite Bushey station. Railway memorabilia adorn the pub, as befitting its name. Historically it was used as a masons' meeting house, as indicated by the coat of arms on the side of the pub. Now it is a multi-screen TV sports venue with a wide variety shown, including Gaelic football. The public bar features a pool table and signed Watford FC shirts.
⛓❀⇌⊖(Bushey) ♣P🚌(142,258,602) 🐾📶

Villiers Arms
108 Villers Road, WD19 4AJ
☎ (01923) 448848
Timothy Taylor Landlord; 2 changing beers (sourced nationally; often Rebellion, Tring) Ⓗ
Traditional family-run village pub, popular with the locals. Its layout dates from the 1950s, with a single semicircular bar. Numerous drink-related items are among the memorabilia in the lounge bar. Up to three real ales are served, together with a selection of other drinks. The pub has a cosy feeling in winter and a bright, airy feel in summer, making it a year-round favourite. Q⇌(Bushey)

Perry Green

Hoops
SG10 6EF
☎ (01279) 843568 thehoopsatperrygreen.com
Hadham Gold, Oddy, First Ⓗ
A traditional country pub on the edge of the Henry Moore estate, the Hoops is a rural gem. Food is served and drinkers are always welcome in the bar area. The superb large gardens are ideal for fine-weather drinking. The winter opening hours are extended in summer. Closing time can depend on how busy the pub is, so phone to check if you're planning a late visit. QP

Potters Bar

Admiral Byng
186-192 Darkes Lane, EN6 1AF
☎ (01707) 645484
Greene King Abbot; Ruddles Best Bitter; Sharp's Doom Bar; 8 changing beers (sourced nationally) Ⓗ
A friendly community Wetherspoon pub with a display of two model sailing ships and other memorabilia celebrating the exploits and death of Admiral Byng, who was executed for 'failing to do his utmost' to save Minorca from falling to the French in 1756 (the family estate is nearby). In summer the frontage of the pub is opened onto the street, with additional seating provided. There is a good choice of real cider.
♿⇌(84,610)

Potters Crouch

Holly Bush
Bedmond Lane, AL2 3NN (off B5183 at jct of Potters Crouch Lane and Ragged Hall Lane) TL116052
☎ (01727) 851792 thehollybushpub.co.uk
Fuller's London Pride, ESB; Gale's Seafarers Ale Ⓗ
This charming wisteria-covered early 17th-century pub sits in rural surroundings. It is attractively furnished throughout, containing large oak tables and period chairs. The atmosphere in the three pleasant bar areas is convivial and conversational, with no jukeboxes, slot machines or TVs to disturb guests. The food menu is not extensive but is of high quality. Children are welcome. The garden is ideal in summer. Q♿P

Preston

Red Lion
The Green, SG4 7UD (on village green at crossroads)
☎ (01462) 459585 theredlionpreston.co.uk
Fuller's London Pride; Young's Bitter; 3 changing beers Ⓗ
This attractive free house was the first community-owned pub in Britain. It offers a variety of beers, many from small breweries. Fresh home-made food is served, often featuring locally sourced ingredients (no food Sun eve and Mon). The pub hosts the village cricket teams and raises funds for charity. Winner of numerous local CAMRA Pub of the Year awards in recent years, and national finalist for the 2019 Pub of the Year.
QP

Puckeridge

White Hart
Braughing Road, SG11 1RR
☎ (01920) 821309
McMullen AK Original Mild, Country Bitter; 1 changing beer (sourced nationally) Ⓗ
This 14th-century pub was named after the emblem of Richard II. Its many interior rooms include a dining room with a huge fireplace; ask about the story of the beam above it. The large garden has a children's play area, and there is a thatched gazebo built around a tree in the car park. Breakfast is served on Saturdays.
P(386,331)

Royston

Manor House
14 Melbourn Street, SG8 7BZ
☎ (01763) 250160
Greene King Abbot; Ruddles Best Bitter; Sharp's Doom Bar; 3 changing beers (sourced nationally) Ⓗ
Much of this Grade II listed former town house dates from the early 18th century, though one block was added much later. Royston Manor House was the name adopted in 1948 for what later became known as the Manor House Club. This Wetherspoon pub is bursting with character, its ambience enhanced by local art pieces. The decorative iron railings at the front were removed during World War II. ♿(331)

St Albans

Farmer's Boy
134 London Road, AL1 1PQ
☎ (01727) 860535 farmersboycalendar.co.uk
Bath Ales Gem; Dark Star Hophead; 3 changing beers (sourced nationally) Ⓗ
Cosy pub close to St Albans City station offering a friendly welcome to locals and visitors alike. Two regular real ales and three guests are served alongside craft keg and an extensive selection of canned and bottled beers. Entertainment includes live music on Thursday and Sunday night, a jukebox that is free on Monday, and BT Sport on TV. The enclosed outdoor drinking area hosts summer music events and regular beer festivals.
♿⇌

Garibaldi
61 Albert Street, AL1 1RT
☎ (01727) 894745 garibaldistalbans.co.uk
Fuller's Oliver's Island, London Pride, ESB; Gale's HSB; 1 changing beer (sourced nationally) Ⓗ
A fine example of a back-street local, described as a Tardis with ale, bigger inside than outside. Its beers are kept in superb condition by licensees who are past winners of the Fuller's Master Cellarman award. The friendly staff serve tasty home-cooked food at weekend lunchtimes and afternoons, with a roast on Sunday (make sure you book). This genuine community pub hosts regular live music on Saturday nights, plus occasional quiz nights, food nights and charity events throughout the year. ♿⇌

Great Northern ✔
172 London Road, AL1 1PQ
☎ (01727) 730867 🌐 greatnorthernpub.co.uk
Black Sheep Best Bitter; 3 changing beers (sourced nationally) 🄷
A lively free house, this independent Grade II listed pub has been modernised and features a pumpclip wall. It serves four regularly changing cask beers and a wide selection of UK and international craft keg beers, bottles and cans. The menu of locally sourced modern European food is available Wednesday to Sunday lunchtimes and Tuesday to Saturday evenings. The pub hosts a quiz every Tuesday and beer festivals in summer, plus tap takeovers throughout the year. 🎠❀◑♿🚆🍎🚌🐾📶

Lower Red Lion 🄻
34-36 Fishpool Street, AL3 4RX
☎ (01727) 855669 🌐 thelowerredlion.co.uk
Tring Side Pocket for a Toad; 4 changing beers (sourced nationally) 🄷
Classic Grade II listed pub in a conservation area in one of St Albans' most picturesque streets. The Lower Red was an early champion of CAMRA's values in the real ale revival movement and continues to stock quality real ales, ciders and perries. Home-cooked food is served lunchtimes and weekday evenings. A recently added function room serves as an additional dining area on Sunday. B&B is available. Q❀🛏◑🍎P🚌🐾📶

Mermaid
98 Hatfield Road, AL1 3RL
☎ (01727) 845700
Oakham Citra; 5 changing beers (sourced nationally) 🄷
Welcoming community venue catering for regulars and the after-work crowd, a short walk from the city centre and St Albans City railway station. It serves a good choice of ales, usually including a stout or porter, plus ciders and bottled foreign beers, and has won several local CAMRA awards for both beer and cider, including Cider & Perry Pub of the Year 2020. Beer festivals are held on the May Day and August bank holiday weekends, and a cider festival over the spring bank holiday. Wednesday is live music night. Q🎠❀◑♿🚆♣🍎P▯🚌🐾📶

Robin Hood ✔
126 Victoria Street, AL1 3TG
☎ (01727) 856459 🌐 robin-hood-st-albans.co.uk
Harvey's Sussex Best Bitter; 2 changing beers (sourced nationally) 🄷
Friendly single-bar pub that is handy for St Albans City station and football ground. Real cider or perry is always available to complement the rotating beer range. A secluded garden to the rear offers summer enjoyment. The traditional jukebox and table skittles provide entertainment all year round, and folk music is performed on Wednesday evenings. Toasted sandwiches are available lunchtimes on weekdays.
🎠❀🚆♣🍎🚌🐾📶

Six Bells 🄻 ✔
16-18 St Michael's Street, AL3 4SH
☎ (01727) 856945 🌐 the-six-bells.com
Oakham JHB; Timothy Taylor Landlord; Tring Ridgeway; 3 changing beers 🄷
Characterful 16th-century pub in the attractive St Michael's village, a short walk from the city centre and Abbey, and close to Verulamium Park and Museum. It offers three regular beers and three changing guests – one always from a Hertfordshire brewer – plus real cider in summer. Good-quality home-cooked food is served lunchtimes and evenings (no food Sun eve). Outside is a pleasant patio area. 🎠❀◑♣🍎P🚌(300,301,302)🐾📶

Waterend Barn
Civic Close, St Peters Street, AL1 3LE
☎ (01727) 814100
Greene King Abbot; Ruddles Best Bitter; Sharp's Doom Bar; 6 changing beers (sourced nationally) 🄷
This large Wetherspoon originated as two characterful 16th and 17th-century timber barns transported from elsewhere in Hertfordshire in the early and middle 20th century. The timber construction of its several drinking areas is largely exposed. A wide range of real ales is served and food is available all day, including early morning breakfasts. 🎠◑♿🍎🚌📶

White Hart Tap 🄻
4 Keyfield Terrace, AL1 1QJ
☎ (01727) 860974 🌐 whiteharttap.co.uk
Timothy Taylor Boltmaker, Landlord; Tring Side Pocket for a Toad; 4 changing beers (sourced nationally) 🄷
One-bar back-street local featuring three beers free of tie, mostly from microbreweries. The pub also brews occasional ales on the premises in various styles. Good-value, home-cooked food is served lunchtimes and Monday to Saturday evenings, with roasts on Sunday and monthly themed food nights. Quiz night is Wednesday; other attractions include summer barbecues and an annual beer festival. There is a heated, covered smoking area outside and a public car park opposite the pub.
🎠❀◑♿🚆♣🍎▯🚌🐾📶

St Pauls Walden

Strathmore Arms 🄻
London Road, SG4 8BT TL193222
☎ (01438) 871654 🌐 thestrathmorearms.co.uk
Tring Side Pocket for a Toad; 4 changing beers (sourced nationally) 🄷
This pub on the Bowes-Lyon estate has been serving drinkers since 1882. It offers a constantly changing list of guest beers, featuring obscure breweries. Unusual bottled beers are also sold along with real ciders and perries. A regular in the Guide since 1981, the pub displays a full collection of the Guides going back to 1976. It has a separate snug. Pizza and pasta evening is Wednesday and gourmet food nights are held on occasion (booking essential). Well known for fundraising locally. Q🎠❀◑⛺♣🍎P🚌🐾📶

Standon

Star ✔
62 High Street, SG11 1LB
☎ (01920) 823725 🌐 starstandon.co.uk
Greene King IPA, Abbot; 2 changing beers 🄷
Traditional 17th-century pub with exposed wooden beams. It has a separate sports-themed public bar and a quiet and comfortable saloon/restaurant. Food is classic pub grub with roasts on Sunday. Two guest beers are offered, at least one not from Greene King – usually from a small independent local brewer.
🎠❀◑♣P🚌(331,386)🐾📶

Tring

King's Arms 🄻
King Street, HP23 6BE (corner of Queen St and King St in middle of Tring Triangle) SP921111
☎ (01442) 823318 🌐 kingsarmstring.co.uk
Tring Moongazing; 4 changing beers (sourced nationally; often Leighton Buzzard, Oakham, Vale) 🄷
Light and airy free house in the centre of Tring, popular with all ages and known as the pink pub due to its

fuchsia exterior. It offers a changing range of five real ales and one real cider. Pub snacks and home-cooked food are served daily. Inside are two real fires. Outside in winter there is a heated patio with canopies; in summer this becomes a beer garden and venue for live music and a beer festival. Children and dogs are welcome. Q

Ware

Crooked Billet

140 Musley Hill, SG12 7NL

☎ (01920) 462516

4 changing beers (sourced nationally)

Friendly gem of a traditional community pub, well worth the half-mile walk up New Road and Musley Hill from the town centre. Its two small bars feature TV sport, pool and darts. It serves a varying range of four or five real ales, including a mild, porter or stout. Filled rolls are available on Saturday evenings. There are tables outside. (395)

Wareside

Chequers

Ware Road, SG12 7QY (b1004)

☎ (01920) 467010

Timothy Taylor Landlord; house beer (by Hadham); 1 changing beer (sourced regionally)

A rural free house dating from the 15th century, the Chequers was originally a coaching inn and has three distinct bars plus a restaurant. All the food is home made and reasonably priced, with plenty of vegetarian options. Walkers and cyclists are welcome, making this a good base for a ramble. No games machines, no music, and a ban on swearing! Q P (M3,M4)

Watford

Wellington Arms

2 Woodford Road, WD17 1PA

☎ (01923) 220739

Fuller's London Pride; 2 changing beers (sourced locally; often Tring)

Modernised street-corner free house close to Watford Junction station and a short walk from the town centre. Run by the same family for 30 years, the pub serves good-quality cask ales. Traditional British food is available weekdays, and occasionally at weekends before Watford FC home games. Sporting events are shown on TV screens around the pub. There are 12 letting rooms available. (Junction) P

West Herts Sports Club

8 Park Avenue, WD18 7HP (S of A412 nr town hall)

☎ (01923) 229239 westhertssportsclub.co.uk

Tring Side Pocket for a Toad; Young's Bitter; 3 changing beers (sourced nationally; often Farr Brew, Paradigm, Vale)

The bar is decorated with sporting memorabilia and shows events on two large TV screens. Its separate function room, home of the Watford Beer Festival, is available to hire. The club fields were the site of Watford FC's first ground and there is a pleasant view over them from the patio. Show a CAMRA membership card or copy of this Guide to gain entry up to four times a year. P

Welham Green

North Mymms Social Club

38 Station Road, AL9 7PG

☎ (01707) 263275

2 changing beers (sourced nationally)

A friendly village social club that admits card-carrying CAMRA members for a nominal fee – knock on the door and wait for admittance. Pool and darts are popular in the main bar area, with teams competing in local leagues, and there are two full-sized snooker tables upstairs. The club hosts a monthly Saturday night quiz plus various themed days throughout the year. Filled rolls are usually available Monday to Saturday. P (610)

Wheathampstead

Reading Rooms

36 The High Street, AL4 8AA

☎ (01582) 833000

3 changing beers (sourced locally; often Farr Brew)

The first brewery-owned micropub and bottle shop in south Hertfordshire, opened in 2018. It is run by Farr Brew who are based two miles away at Samuels Farm, where there has been a taproom open on Saturday for several years. This former florists' consists of three distinct rooms including the whole upper floor. Two beers from Farr Brew feature, along with one guest and a real cider. Spirits from the local Black Bridge Distillery are also stocked. Q

Wild Hill

Woodman

45 Wildhill Road, AL9 6EA (between A1000 and B158) TL264068

☎ (01707) 642618

Greene King IPA, Abbot; 4 changing beers (sourced nationally)

A friendly and unpretentious rural pub that is very community-oriented. It thrives on and is a staunch supporter of real ale, serving up to six beers including four guests. Lined oversized glasses are available on request. The large garden is ideal in summer. Good pub grub is served lunchtimes (no food Sun). Look for God's Waiting Room. A multiple winner of local and Hertfordshire CAMRA Pub of the Year. P

Wilstone

Half Moon

60 Tring Road, HP23 4PD

☎ (01442) 826410

Sharp's Doom Bar; Tring Side Pocket for a Toad; 1 changing beer (sourced locally; often Malt, Tring, XT)

An unspoilt two-room village pub, close to the Aylesbury arm of the Grand Union Canal. The interior features exposed wooden beams and an inglenook fireplace; outside are gardens to front and back. Three beers are available on handpump, including one changing guest from a local brewery. Good-value home-cooked food is served. The pub is popular with locals and dog walkers, and offers a range of traditional games to keep visitors amused. Q P (164)

For we could not now take time for further search (to land our ship) our victuals being much spent especially our beer. **Log of the Mayflower**

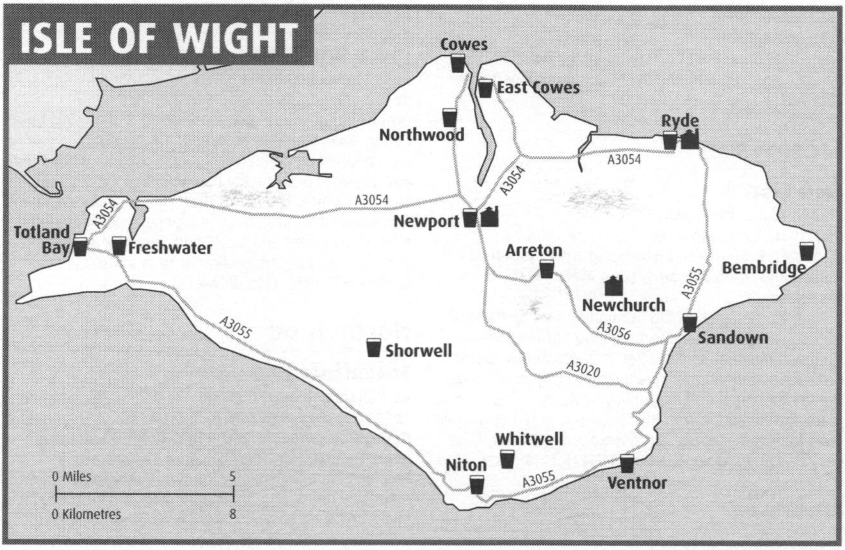

Arreton

Dairyman's Daughter Ⓛ

Main Road, PO30 3AA (main road from Newport)
SZ53258680
☎ (01983) 539361 🌐 dairymansdaughter.co.uk
Ringwood Fortyniner; 5 changing beers (sourced nationally; often Lancaster Bomber, Ringwood) Ⓗ
Arreton Barns Craft Village includes the Dairyman's, Shipwreck Centre and Maritime Museum and IW Studio Glass, all worth visiting, plus the 11th-century church of St George and the grave of the original Dairyman's Daughter. The pub provides up to six beers including local ales, as well as a large selection of Island bottled beers in the old brewery. Lunchtime and evening meals can be enjoyed indoors or in the garden. Tuesday is folk night and live music plays Friday to Sunday.
❀◑♿P🚌(8)🐾📶

Bembridge

Old Village Inn ✔

61 High Street, PO35 5SF
☎ (01983) 872616 🌐 yeoldevillageinn.co.uk
4 changing beers (sourced nationally; often Brains, Joseph Holt, Marston's) Ⓗ
The Old Village is reputed to have been serving pints since 1787, and now offers a fine choice of real ales and wines in a refined and relaxed atmosphere. The menu specialises in local meat and fish dishes. Live music plays on Friday and Saturday, and a popular quiz is held on Monday. There is a patio area and covered space to the rear and a pétanque terrain. Q❀◑♣P🚌(8)🐾📶

Cowes

Anchor Inn Ⓛ

1 High Street, PO31 7SA (opp Sainsburys)
☎ (01983) 292823 🌐 theanchorcowes.co.uk
Fuller's London Pride; Goddards Fuggle-Dee-Dum; 3 changing beers (sourced nationally; often Fuller's) Ⓗ
Originally the Three Trumpeters back in 1704, this place is close to the marina, tempting visiting yachtsmen for their first pint ashore. A recent conversion has integrated the stables and added a pleasant beer garden. A good selection of beer is on offer, with one Island ale and three or more guests always available. The varied menu is served in prodigious quantities. Live entertainment features regularly. Accommodation is in seven comfortable rooms. ❀🛏◑🚌(1)🐾📶

Cowes Ale House

5A Shooters Hill, PO31 7BE (up hill from Sainsbury's)
☎ (01983) 294027
4 changing beers (sourced nationally) Ⓖ
Like its sister pub, Newport Ale House, this venue, conveniently situated in the main street, is small, friendly and sometimes crowded. Four real ales are usually on stillage in a range that rotates regularly - expect to find the occasional mild or porter. Bar snacks are available. Events feature throughout the week including a well-supported Irish night on Monday, the ever popular quiz on Wednesday and music Friday and Sunday. Q♿🚌(1)🐾📶

East Cowes

Lifeboat Ⓛ

Britannia Way, PO32 6UB
☎ (01983) 292711 🌐 thelifeboatcowes.co.uk
Fuller's London Pride; Goddards Fuggle-Dee-Dum; 1 changing beer (sourced nationally; often St Austell) Ⓗ
Large, comfortable, waterfront pub in the heart of East Cowes marina. The modern interior is tastefully decorated with much wood and bare brick. The decked patio has a superb view over the river and marina activities, and is surrounded by stylish contemporary buildings. The focus here is on food, but a good range of well-kept beers is available. In winter food service times are reduced and the bar closes at 10.30pm.
Q❀◑♿⛺P🚌(4,5)🐾📶

Ship & Castle Ⓛ

21 Castle Street, PO32 6RB
☎ (01983) 716230
Fuller's London Pride; 2 changing beers (sourced regionally; often Adnams, Goddards, Island) Ⓗ
Handy for the ferry terminal and near the floating bridge to Cowes, this town-centre drinking establishment is

now a free house, offering three well-kept real ales throughout the year. Not overly large, you are assured a warm welcome. Prices are reasonable, especially during happy hour. Frequent and lively music sessions are held. Q♿🅰️🚃(4,5) 🐶🛜

Freshwater

Red Lion 🄻

Church Place, PO40 9BP SZ34508738
☎ (01983) 754925 ⏛ redlion-freshwater.co.uk
St Austell Proper Job; 3 changing beers (sourced nationally; often Adnams, Long Man, West Berkshire) 🅷
Former three-bar coaching inn dating back to the 11th century, now converted to one large bar but still retaining much of its character. It is situated in the most picture-postcard area of Freshwater in the church square and by the Causeway, and enjoys splendid views of the River Yar towards Yarmouth. The pub is noted for its fine food (diners are advised to book ahead). Closing time may be earlier in winter. Q❀🕦P🚃(7,12)🐶 🛜

Newport

Bargeman's Rest 🄻

Little London Quay, PO30 5BS
☎ (01983) 525828 ⏛ bargemansrest.com
Goddards Fuggle-Dee-Dum; Ringwood Razorback, Fortyniner; 4 changing beers (often Andwell, Marston's, Wychwood) 🅷
This massive, locally owned pub has previously been an animal feed store and a sail and rigging loft for the barge fleet that once used the river. The huge bar room provides intimate drinking areas, and the nautical memorabilia, decor and ambience are what you would expect from a traditional, well-seasoned pub. The outdoor drinking area is only a few feet from the bustling River Medina. Beer and food are consistently good and the range is varied. Live entertainment features most nights. 🐕❀🕦&P🚃🐶🛜

Man in the Moon 🄻 ✅

16-17 St James Street, PO30 5HB
☎ (01983) 530126
Greene King Abbot; Sharp's Doom Bar; 7 changing beers (often Goddards, Island) 🅷
Opened in 2014, this impressive Wetherspoon conversion of the former Congregational Church maintains the character of the original while adding sympathetic extensions. The drinking and dining areas include an upstairs gallery and an outdoor area where dogs and children are welcome. Although a food-led pub, the beers are well kept, with a good selection of local brews among the large rotating selection of ales. You may find the excellent Island Brewery RDA here and often a cider on handpump. 🐕❀🕦&🚃🛜

Newport Ale House 🍸 🄻

24A Holyrood Street, PO30 5AZ
☎ (01983) 559376
3 changing beers (sourced nationally) 🄶
This listed building has previously traded as a hairdresser's, undertakers and posting house and stables. It is the Island's smallest pub, recalling the days when there were many such establishments in Newport. This is a hugely popular venue with all generations, where conversation comes easy – it can get crowded and noisy. Live music is often hosted, including on a Sunday afternoon. The beer choice is always interesting and varied. No meals, but snacks are high quality. Local CAMRA Pub of the Year 2019. Q♿🚃🐶🛜

Niton

Joe's Bar 🄻 ✅

High Street, PO38 2AZ
☎ (01983) 730280
Greene King Abbot; Yates' Islander; 2 changing beers (often Blue Monkey, Salopian, Titanic) 🅷
Joe's opened when the village inn closed for a short time and has since become the hub of village life, also serving as a post office, tea room, confectioner and newsagent. The wood-fired pizza oven is a popular addition. Ruby Mild, Plum Porter and local specialities are regular visitors. A unique establishment with an excellent garden and patio. Q♿❀🕦🚃(6)

Northwood

Travellers Joy 🄻 ✅

85 Pallance Road, PO31 8LS SZ48009360
☎ (01983) 298024 ⏛ travellersjoycowes.co.uk
Brains Rev James; Island Wight Gold; 3 changing beers (sourced nationally; often Theakston) 🅷
This long-standing country inn was the Island's first beer exhibition house and offers up to five ales including local favourite Island Brewery Wight Gold. Real cider is usually available. A good range of home-cooked food is served. With a garden and play area that is well cared for, and camping nearby, the pub is a good base for visitors as well as a thriving local community centre. Popular events are Derek's Sunday quiz and bingo night on Monday. Q♿❀🕦🅰️♣P🚃(1) 🐶🛜

Ryde

Railway 🄻

68 St Johns Road, PO33 2RT (by St Johns Station)
☎ (01983) 611500
6 changing beers (often Heritage, Island) 🅷
Refurbished to a high standard by the previous owner, the pub has retained the flagstone floors, beams and plenty of wood. For the horticulturally minded, note the ginkgo biloba tree in the garden, a species whose ancestry can be traced back over 200 million years. The handy train station is close by, bringing visitors from Portsmouth to enjoy the competitively priced, quality real ales. Six handpumps feature one regular and many changing beers – fewer in winter. Live music is hosted on Friday. 🐕❀&🚆♣🚃🐶

S Fowler & Co 🄻 ✅

41-43 Union Street, PO33 2LF (top of Union St)
☎ (01983) 812112
10 changing beers (sourced nationally) 🅷
Although not the most charismatic pub in the Wetherspoon chain, this converted drapery store offers a constantly changing range of well-kept beers. Its name was at the suggestion of the local CAMRA branch – not only is Fowler the name of the former store, but also that of the first local CAMRA chairman and revered early campaigner. The family-friendly food area is upstairs. Situated in the centre of town, there is a bus stop conveniently outside. Q♿🕦&🚆🚃🛜

Solent Inn

7 Monkton Street, PO33 1JW
☎ (01983) 613761

REAL ALE BREWERIES	
Goddards	Ryde
Island	Newport
Yates'	Newchurch

Timothy Taylor Landlord; Wychwood Hobgoblin Gold; 1 changing beer (sourced nationally; often Morland, St Austell) 🄷
Excellent street-corner local with a warm, welcoming atmosphere. Parts of this handsome pub are ancient, going back to medieval times. It originally fronted the sea before reclamation of land, hence the name. Meal times can change depending on the season. There is live music at the weekend. Beware – the public bar slopes alarmingly! Q🛋❀◐♿⇌♣🚌🐾

Sandown

Castle Inn 🄻
12-14 Fitzroy Street, PO36 8HY (off High St)
☎ (01983) 403169 🌐 sandowncastle.co.uk
Gale's HSB; Goddards Fuggle-Dee-Dum; Shepherd Neame Spitfire; Wychwood Hobgoblin Gold; 2 changing beers (sourced regionally; often Andwell, Hop Back, St Austell) 🄷
The Castle is an excellent town free house and locals' pub, home to crib and darts teams. Six real ales are on offer including the best from local breweries. There is a children's room at the back and a patio for warm weather. The TV is only turned on for special events. Happy hour (5-7pm nightly) is popular, as is the Sunday quiz. Beer festivals are held twice a year, usually featuring local ales and cider. Q🛋❀♿⇌♣🚌(3,8)🐾📶

Shorwell

Crown Inn 🄻 ✔
Walkers Lane, PO30 3JZ
☎ (01983) 740293 🌐 thecrowninnshorwell.co.uk
Gale's HSB; Timothy Taylor Landlord; house beer (by Yates'); 1 changing beer (sourced locally; often Goddards, Sharp's, Timothy Taylor) 🄷
This 300-year-old hostelry in a picturesque village offers a range of four ales and good home-cooked pub food. It has a trout stream running through the garden, ducks in abundance, and plenty of car parking. The perfect stop-off point for walkers, cyclists and nature lovers, on a hot summer's day the garden is a delight. In winter it is closed on Monday and no food is served on Tuesday. Q🛋❀◐♿♣P🚌(12)🐾📶

Totland Bay

Highdown Inn 🄻
Highdown Lane, PO39 0HY (W of Alum Bay) SZ32348596
☎ (01983) 752450 🌐 highdowninn.com
3 changing beers (sourced regionally; often Adnams, Andwell, Island) 🄷
Situated close to Farringford House, once home to Alfred Lord Tennyson, this hospitable pub is an ideal base for walkers and cyclists alike. An interesting range of home-cooked food includes a seasonal variety of fresh local game, fish and vegetables, served in generous portions, and a children's menu. B&B accommodation is in three comfortable rooms, and there is a campsite close by. Unfortunately, no buses serve the pub in winter. Q🛋🛏◐⛺P🚌📶

Waterfront 🄻
The Beach, PO39 0BQ
☎ (01983) 756969 🌐 thewaterfront-iow.co.uk
Sharp's Doom Bar; 3 changing beers (sourced regionally; often Andwell, Dorset, Island) 🄷
Pleasant and popular pub-restaurant beside the sea, enjoying excellent Solent views to Portland and beyond. Beers are reasonably priced and the constantly changing range has increased in recent years, with up to 12 ales in the cellar including stouts and milds. During the summer months there is a tented area outside, and the pub is accessible from the cliff path. Food includes a Sunday roast. Q🛋❀◐P🚌🐾📶

Ventnor

Spyglass Inn 🄻
The Esplanade, PO38 1JX
☎ (01983) 855338 🌐 thespyglass.co.uk
Ringwood Razorback, Fortyniner; 3 changing beers (sourced locally; often Andwell, Goddards, Yates') 🄷
Nineteenth-century ex-guesthouse at the western end of Ventnor Esplanade in a superb position overlooking the English Channel. The temptation has been avoided to knock all the rooms into one; instead they have been incorporated into the overall layout. The inn has considerable character and boasts a large collection of seafaring memorabilia. Local seafood is a speciality. Entertainment features most evenings and Sunday lunchtime, and families are welcome. The beer range may reduce to four in winter. 🛋❀🛏◐P🐾📶

Volunteer 🄻
30 Victoria Street, PO38 1ES
☎ (01983) 852537
5 changing beers (sourced regionally; often Adnams, Goddards, Wychwood) 🄷
Built in 1866, the Volunteer is one of the smallest pubs on the island and a former local CAMRA Pub of the Year. Up to five beers are available including a local brew. No chips, no children, no fruit machines, no video games – just a pure adult drinking house and one of the few places where you can still play rings and enjoy a traditional games night. A wonderful, traditional pub. Q♣🚌(3,6)🐾

Whitwell

White Horse Inn 🄻
High Street, PO38 2PY SZ52007800
☎ (01983) 730375 🌐 whitehorseiow.co.uk
4 changing beers (sourced nationally; often Bombardier, Rudgate, Young's) 🄷
Built in 1454, this ancient stone building is considered to be the oldest established inn on the Isle of Wight. An extension to the side adds a family area and additional dining space. The remainder of the building is traditional, with intimate areas to the rear. Four handpumps serve a changing range of beers and the excellent menu is extensive; it also does breakfast. A large garden is fine for children on warmer days. Q🛋❀◐♿P🚌(6)🐾📶

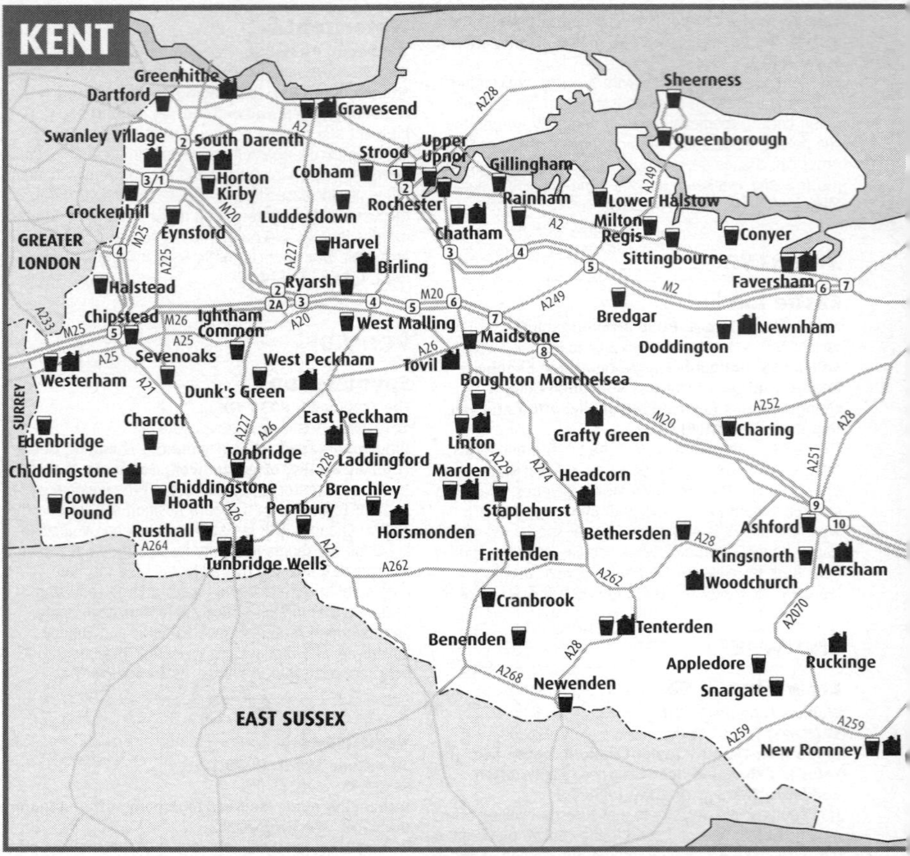

Appledore

Black Lion

15 The Street, TN26 2BU (in centre of village)

☎ (01233) 758206 blacklion-pub.com

Greene King IPA; 4 changing beers (sourced locally)

A traditional English pub and restaurant, set in a historic village which can trace its history back to Viking times, when it was a busy port. The bar is decorated with an interesting collection of ancient pumpclips and blowlamps. Locally sourced food is available every day but reservations are not accepted on Sunday. Handy for ramblers on the Saxon Shore Way and the Royal Military Canal. Q (11B)

Ash

Chequer Inn

4 Chequer Lane, CT3 2ET

☎ (01304) 273680 thechequerinnash.co.uk

Fuller's London Pride; Harvey's Sussex Best Bitter; Ramsgate Gadds' No.5 Best Bitter Ale; 1 changing beer (sourced locally)

A 14th-century timber-framed community-owned pub purchased in 2019. Sympathetically refurbished, the wooden floors, panelling and furniture give warmth to the main bar and restaurant. Three real ales, including one from a local brewery, feature alongside local wines and gins. Home-made food, from local ingredients, ranges from vegan dishes to Sunday roasts, with seafood a speciality. Events, many community-oriented, include Meet up Monday and Wednesday Family Night. There is a large garden with a bat and trap pitch. A free public car park is nearby. P (43)

Ashford

County Hotel

10 High Street, TN24 8TD (at lower end of High St)

☎ (01233) 646891

Greene King Abbot; Ruddles Best Bitter; Sharp's Doom Bar; 4 changing beers (sourced nationally)

A spacious Wetherspoon in an 18th-century building in the centre of Ashford, with one bar and three separate seating areas. Originally displaying red brick, the top floor and the parapet are now tile-hung. Up to two real ciders are dispensed from polypins in the fridge. Food is served every day, and children are allowed in the dining area until 9pm. Summer and autumn national and international beer festivals are held.

Q P

Beltinge

Copper Pottle

84 Reculver Road, CT6 6ND

☎ 07710 001261 copperpottle.co.uk

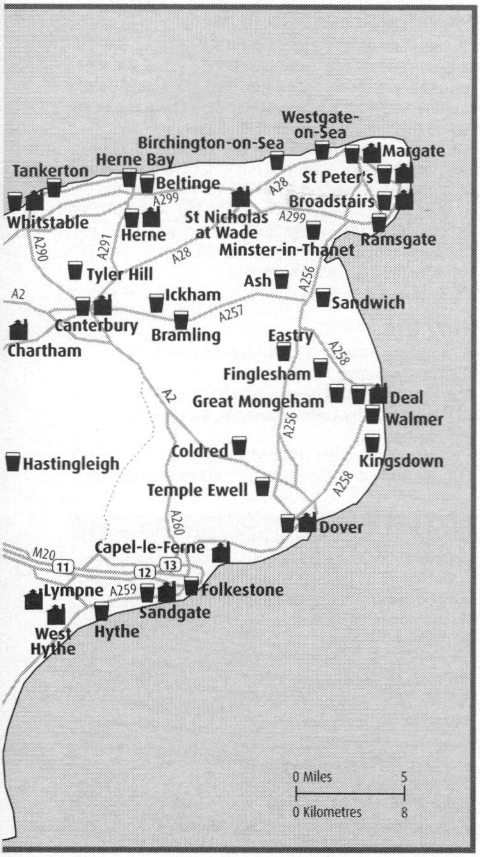

Ramsgate Gadds' No.5 Best Bitter Ale; 3 changing beers (sourced regionally) G

Originally a pet food shop, this friendly micropub has an attractive blue-tiled frontage. Drinks are dispensed via a small bar counter. Conversation is encouraged with a layout of high and low narrow tables, and the walls are decorated with amusing posters and postcards. Every six weeks there is a charity fundraising event, which might be a quiz evening, food evening or a barbecue. The south-facing garden is a good place to enjoy a beer, cider or wine. Open on bank holiday Mondays. Q

Benenden

Bull L

The Street, TN17 4DE

☎ (01580) 240054 thebullatbenenden.co.uk

Dark Star Hophead; Harvey's Sussex Best Bitter; Larkins Traditional Ale; 1 changing beer (sourced locally; often Long Man) H

A genuine free house dating back to 1608 and overlooking the picturesque village green. The public bar features a large inglenook fireplace and the interior has wooden floors and exposed oak beams throughout. A separate restaurant/function room offers meals using locally grown produce, and food is also served in the public bar (booking is advisable for Friday fish and chips and the Sunday lunchtime carvery). A monthly acoustic music session is held on one Sunday.
Q P (297)

Bethersden

George L

The Street, TN26 3AG (off A28 between Ashford and Tenterden in centre of village)

☎ (01233) 820235

Greene King Yardbird; Harvey's Sussex Best Bitter, Old Ale; St Austell Cornish Best Bitter; 1 changing beer (sourced nationally) H

A two-bar free house in a picturesque Kentish village, decorated with pictures of local life. The public bar is a survivor of what village inns used to be like, with wood panelling, hops over the bar, a wood-burning stove, pub games, a jukebox and good conversation. Food is served daily except Monday lunchtime and Sunday evening, with a carvery on Wednesday evening and Sunday lunchtime. A beer festival is held around St George's Day. Buses from Ashford and Tenterden stop outside.
P (2)

Birchington-on-Sea

Old Bay Alehouse

137 Minnis Road, CT7 9NS

oldbayalehouse.co.uk

3 changing beers G

This is a fine micropub an easy five minutes' stroll from the beach at Minnis Bay. The bar counter on the right serves real ales and ciders on gravity dispense from a temperature-controlled cool room behind. Seating is at wall-mounted benches with high tables, plus some low tables and chairs. There are comfy armchairs in the front window. The real ale selection always includes at least one local beer. Bar snacks are always available and there are occasional pop-up food events. Q (34)

Boughton Monchelsea

Cock Inn L

Heath Road, ME17 4JD TQ776512

☎ (01622) 743166 cockinnmaidstone.co.uk

Shepherd Neame Master Brew, Spitfire Gold; 2 changing beers (sourced regionally; often Shepherd Neame) H

A 16th-century coaching inn built to provide lodgings for Canterbury pilgrims, full of character, with oak beams and an inglenook fireplace. A large and varied menu, complemented by real ales, is served in both the bar and restaurant; Sunday roasts are popular (no food Sun eve). There is a large patio area. Various board games are available. Situated near the Greensand Way, dogs and walkers are welcome. Q P (59)

Bramling

Haywain L

Canterbury Road, CT3 1NB

☎ (01227) 720676 thehaywainbramling.co.uk

Fuller's London Pride; 3 changing beers (sourced regionally; often Goacher's, Ramsgate, Whitstable) H

Classic friendly country pub featuring hop bines, a cosy snug and a charity library where books are sold for 50p each. Traditional games include darts and bat and trap. There is a Monday quiz night and a Wednesday crib night. Guest beers are usually from Kent breweries, and an annual beer festival is hosted over the late spring bank holiday weekend in a marquee in the attractive garden. Excellent home-cooked food is served, using local produce. P

Bredgar

Sun Inn
The Street, ME9 8EY
☎ (01622) 884221 ⊕ thesuninn.co.uk
Sharp's Sea Fury; Shepherd Neame Master Brew; 1
changing beer (often Adnams, Musket) ⊞
A village inn since the early 1700s, this place has a
sizeable front room with a long bar separating it from the
large Old Barn restaurant to the rear. The clientele is a
mixture of locals plus passing trade. Tastefully in keeping
with its surroundings, with a real fire in the front bar, the
pub is food-led but does offer a fair choice of cask beers.
There is a quiz on the first Wednesday of the month and
music nights are planned monthly. ゝ✿◑&P✿

Brenchley

Halfway House Ⓛ ✔
Horsmonden Road, TN12 7AX (½ mile SE of village)
☎ (01892) 722526 ⊕ halfwayhousebrenchley.co.uk
Goacher's Fine Light Ale; Kent Session Pale; Skinner's
Betty Stogs; Tonbridge Rustic; Young's London
Special; house beer (by Goacher's); 3 changing beers
(sourced locally; often Canterbury Ales, Cellar Head,
Musket) Ⓖ
In an attractive rural setting, this award-winning free
house and Guide entry of 15 years' standing offers up to
10 beers direct from cooled casks, along with
Chiddingstone and Turners ciders. Substantial home-
made dishes using local produce are served, including
traditional Sunday roasts. Choose between the cosy,
rustic interior complete with hanging hops, farming
instruments and an open fire, or the spacious garden
incorporating an outside bar and a separate family area.
Beer festivals are held on Whitsun and August bank
holidays. Qゝ✿◑♣●P呈(297)✿令

Broadstairs

Pub Micropub
9 The Broadway, CT10 2AD
☎ (01843) 868356 ⊕ thepubmicropub.com
3 changing beers Ⓖ
A micropub which opened in the former Offy off-licence
in 2018 serving real ales, ciders, craft KeyKeg beers,
wines and a range of gins. It is run by enthusiastic and
friendly young family relatives. Real ales and ciders are
sold on gravity dispense from a chilled cellar room, and
there are also three wall-mounted keg taps selling
KeyKeg beers. Seating is at a mix of high and low tables,
and you can also sit outside on the pavement.
ゝ⇌●呈✿令

Canterbury

Eight Bells ✔
34 London Road, CT2 8LN
☎ (01227) 454794
Young's London Original, London Special ⊞
A small, traditional local dating from 1708 and rebuilt in
1902, retaining original embossed windows and outside
toilets, and decorated with memorabilia. There is live
music monthly on a Friday, and a quiz, usually on the first
Wednesday of the month. Five darts teams play every
week and their trophies are on display. The only food is a
Sunday lunchtime roast, for which booking is advisable.
There is an attractive small walled garden and a
comfortable heated smoking area. ゝ✿◑⇌♣●✿令

Foundry Brew Pub Ⓛ
77 Stour Street, CT1 2NR (just off High St)
☎ (01227) 455899 ⊕ thefoundrycanterbury.co.uk
Canterbury Brewers & Distillers Foundryman's Gold,
Foundry Torpedo, Streetlight Porter; 3 changing beers
(often Canterbury Brewers & Distillers) ⊞
The home of Canterbury Brewers & Distillers. Double
doors from the bar open into the attractive brewery and
restaurant area, which is available for functions and
brewery tours. Six ales are usually on tap, all brewed on
the premises. Cider, vodka, rum and gin are also made
here. Food is served till daily. Winner of Kent Tourism Pub
of the Year 2019. ゝ✿◑&⇌●呈令

New Inn
19 Havelock Street, CT1 1NP (off ring road nr St
Augustine's Abbey)
☎ (01227) 464584 ⊕ newinncanterbury.co.uk
7 changing beers (often Oakham, Ramsgate,
Thornbridge) ⊞
A Victorian back-street terraced pub a few minutes' walk
from the cathedral, St Augustine's Abbey and the bus

REAL ALE BREWERIES

Alpha State Horsmonden
Amazing ≣ Sandgate
Angels & Demons Capel-le-Ferne
Boutilliers Faversham
Breakwater Dover
Brew Buddies ✦ Swanley Village
Brumaison Marden
By The Mile Broadstairs (brewing suspended)
Canterbury Ales Chartham
Canterbury Brewers ≣ Canterbury
Dartford Wobbler South Darenth
Farriers Arms ≣ Mersham
Fonthill ≣ Tunbridge Wells
Four Candles ≣ St Peters
Goacher's Tovil
Goody Herne
Headcorn Hop Headcorn
Hinks Ruckinge (NEW)
Hop Fuzz West Hythe
Hopdaemon Newnham
Iron Pier ✦ Gravesend
Isla Vale Margate
Kent Birling
Larkins Chiddingstone
Mad Cat Faversham
Musket Linton
NauticAles Broadstairs
Nelson Chatham
No Frills Joe ✦ Greenhithe
Northdown Margate
Old Dairy Tenterden
Pig & Porter Tunbridge Wells
Ramsgate Broadstairs
Range Lympne
Romney Marsh New Romney
Running Man Chatham
Shepherd Neame Faversham
Stag Woodchurch
Swan on the Green ≣ West Peckham
Time & Tide Deal
Tír Dhá Ghlas ≣ Dover
Tonbridge East Peckham
Turnstone Whitstable
Wantsum St Nicholas at Wade
Westerham ✦ Westerham
Whitstable Grafty Green
XYLO ✦ Margate (NEW)

station. The welcoming main bar has a cosy wood-burner, a jukebox and a changing range of seven cask beers. The floor is hand-stencilled by the landlady, and there are other creative features. At the back is a long, bright conservatory with newspapers and a range of board games. Beer festivals are held on the Whitsun and August bank holiday weekends in the pub and the attractive garden. Q

Thomas Tallis Alehouse

48 Northgate, CT1 1BE
thethomastallisalehouse.co.uk
3 changing beers (sourced locally; often Kent, Old Dairy, Ramsgate) [G]
Canterbury's first micropub ale house, located in a lovely 15th-century half-timbered building, part of the historic Hospital of St John. Three different Kent cask beers and many national and international beers are stocked – in KeyKeg, bottles and cans – as well as five to six Kentish ciders. One of the two front rooms has a log-burning stove, the rear snug has armchairs and a sofa. Generally a seat/table service applies. Outside seating is available on the street. Q

Unicorn

61 St Dunstan's Street, CT2 8BS
(01227) 463187 unicorninn.com
4 changing beers (often Hopdaemon, Long Man, Shepherd Neame) [H]
Comfortable pub, near the historic Westgate, that dates from 1604 and has an attractive suntrap garden. Bar billiards is played and a quiz, set by regular customers, is held every Sunday evening. One guest beer is often from one of several Kent microbreweries, and beer updates are posted on Facebook and Twitter. There is a good range of bottled beers. Food is good value, with a meal deal on selected dishes. Sporting events (not Sky) are televised unobtrusively. Q

Charcott

Greyhound

off Camp Hill, TN11 8LG (½ mile N of B2027 at Chiddingstone Causeway)
(01892) 870275 thegreyhoundcharcott.co.uk
4 changing beers (sourced locally; often Brumaison, Kent, Old Dairy) [H]
Reopened with new owners in 2017, this small hamlet pub has become a firm favourite with locals and those from surrounding villages, making it the very heart of the community. The beers and ciders are from within a 30-mile radius and much attention is given to supporting local producers when creating the menus. Although seemingly remote, the Greyhound is easily accessible from Penshurst railway station via a surfaced footpath across fields. Check the website for news of live music evenings and special events.
Q (210)

Charing

Bowl Inn

Egg Hill Road, TN27 0HG (signposted from A20 and A251)
(01233) 712256 bowlinncharing.com
4 changing beers (sourced locally; often Old Dairy, Ramsgate, Tonbridge) [H]
A 16th-century free house on the top of the North Downs in an Area of Outstanding Natural Beauty. An inglenook fire warms the bar, and there is a large garden with a heated patio area. The pub is a popular stop-off point for walkers and cyclists and offers five rooms. Camping is also available. It is open for longer in summertime, and has a large, popular restaurant. Q P

Chatham

Thomas Waghorn

14 Railway Street, ME4 4JL
(01634) 405422
Greene King IPA, Abbot; Sharp's Doom Bar; 3 changing beers (sourced nationally; often Wantsum) [H]
An establishment ideally situated in the heart of Chatham, with both the railway and bus stations within easy walking distance. A former post office, this Wetherspoon outlet is named after a 19th-century Chatham-born naval officer. It is on two levels, both having outside drinking areas, with various seating arrangements including some booths. A quiz is held every Wednesday. Some interesting and unusual guest ales are served alongside the usual fare offered by Wetherspoon.

Chiddingstone Hoath

Rock

Hoath Corner, Rywell Road, TN8 7BS (1½ miles S of Chiddingstone)
(01892) 870296 therockpub.co.uk
Larkins Traditional Ale; 2 changing beers (sourced locally; often Dark Star, Long Man) [H]
Featuring brick flooring, an inviting inglenook fireplace, extensive wooden beams and the ancient game of ring the bull, the Rock oozes character. Despite its rural location, it attracts visitors in cars, on foot and even on horseback. Cosy and informal, the desire is to remain a proper pub with proper grub, catering for a community dedicated to rural pursuits. The staple Larkins Traditional is brewed just a couple of miles down the road. Best wishes for another half a millennium of history!
Q P (232)

Chipstead

Bricklayers Arms

39-41 Chevening Road, TN13 2RZ (opp entrance to sailing club)
(01732) 743424 the-bricklayers-arms.co.uk
Harvey's Sussex Best Bitter [G]; 2 changing beers (sourced locally; often Harvey's) [H]
Located opposite Chipstead sailing lake, this vibrant Harvey's brewery-owned community pub features Winston Churchill, who once lived nearby, on its sign, laying bricks. Sussex Best is served direct from casks behind the bar, while the brewery's monthly seasonal brews are dispensed by handpump. An excellent choice of home-cooked meals, supplemented by many themed food nights, can be enjoyed either in the side cottage restaurant, the flagstone-floored bar complete with log fire, or the adjacent dining space. Walkers and their dogs are welcome. Q P (401,402)

Cobham

Darnley Arms

40 The Street, DA12 3BZ
(01474) 814218 thedarnleyarms.com
Dark Star Hophead; Greene King IPA; 2 changing beers (sourced locally; often Iron Pier, Pig & Porter) [H]

This friendly local is in the centre of a small, charming village. It has a large horseshoe-shaped bar with a small separate side room for meetings. The décor features local memorabilia including the coat of arms of the Darnley family, who lived at nearby Cobham Hall. It serves two regular real ales, and changing beers mainly from local breweries in Kent. The wide menu features traditional English food with fish specialities.
Q ⏁ ❀ ⇦ ◑ ♣ ♠ P ➠ (416) ♨ 🛜

Coldred

Carpenters Arms Ⓛ
The Green, CT15 5AJ
☎ (01304) 830190
2 changing beers (often Ramsgate, Romney Marsh) Ⓗ/Ⓖ
Overlooking the village green and duck pond, this 18th-century two-roomed inn is a real gem and well worth seeking out. It has been in the Fagg family for over a century, and largely unchanged for the last 50 years. The pub is the centre of the community and conversation is king. At least two real ales are served, alongside three real ciders from Kentish Pip. Regular community events are hosted including quizzes and vegetable competitions, and a beer festival is held in June.
Q ⏁ ❀ ♣ ♠ P ♨ 🛜

Conyer

Ship ✅
Conyer Quay, ME9 9HR
☎ (01795) 520881 ⊕ shipinnconyer.co.uk
3 changing beers (sourced regionally; often Adnams, Old Dairy) Ⓗ
An 18th-century creekside pub with a nautically themed interior. Bare floorboards and scrubbed pine tables add rustic charm, and a real fire adds character. Popular with the boating fraternity, walkers and cyclists, it is located on the Saxon Shore Way, and is a 20-minute walk from Teynham train station. Food, with an emphasis on local produce, is served from noon daily. A small courtyard garden overlooks the creek. ⏁ ❀ ◑ ♣ ♠ P ➠ ♨ 🛜

Cowden Pound

Queen's Arms ★ Ⓛ
Hartfield Road, TN8 5NP (on B2026 halfway between Edenbridge and A264)
Larkins Traditional Ale, Best; 1 changing beer (sourced locally; often High Weald, Pig & Porter) Ⓗ
An unspoilt inn of historic interest, the public bar almost untouched since the end of the 19th century. A small bowl for coins, with notes placed underneath, is used in lieu of a till. The saloon retains its original curved Victorian panelled counter with decorative brackets. Beer from the nearby Larkins Brewery is served, alongside occasional guests from Kent or Sussex and the local Chiddingstone cider. A pub where conversation with friendly, chatty locals accompanied by their dogs is the norm. Q ❀ ♣ ♠ P ♨

Cranbrook

Larkins' Alehouse 🍷 Ⓛ
7 High Street, TN17 3EB
☎ 07786 707476 ⊕ larkins-alehouse.co.uk
4 changing beers (sourced locally; often Cellar Head, Goacher's, Larkins) Ⓖ

Opened in 2017, this community focused micropub has put the heart back into the town. The single room is simply furnished with a small bar, and there is a courtyard beer garden. Welcoming staff will guide you to the chalkboard displaying current beers and Kentish ciders (Biddenden, Turners), and wines, spirits and soft drinks are also served. Home-made pork pies, rolls and chutneys are for sale, although you're welcome to bring in your own food or order in a takeaway. On Sunday lunchtimes home-made food is provided by the pub and customers. Q ⏁ ❀ ♣ ♠ ➠ (5,297) ♨ 🛜

Crockenhill

Chequers ✅
Cray Road, BR8 8LP
☎ (01322) 662132 ⊕ chequerscrockenhill.co.uk
Courage Best Bitter; 3 changing beers (sourced regionally; often Fuller's, Woodforde's, Wychwood) Ⓗ
Friendly village local offering one permanent beer and three changing guest ales from a wide selection of breweries. Lunches and evening meals are served, with discounts for over-55s at the beginning of the week. There is a quiz on Monday evenings and various other events on regular occasions. Several pictures of old Crockenhill indicate that the pub has been a hub of village life for many years. ⏁ ❀ ◑ ♣ P ➠ (477) ♨ 🛜

Dartford

Dartford Jug Ⓛ
8 Market Street, DA1 1ET
☎ (01322) 276600 ⊕ thedartfordjug.co.uk
Kent Session Pale; 6 changing beers (sourced regionally; often No Frills Joe, Thornbridge) Ⓖ
Dartford's only micropub, with seating made from modified beer casks at the front, leading to a space with fixed tables and stools, and a serving counter at the rear. The bar is decorated with a map and pictures of old Dartford. Real ales and ciders from Turners are dispensed from a cold room – the current offerings are listed on a screen at the bar. Snacks such as crisps, peanuts, Scotch eggs and a cheeseboard are available. Newspapers are in a rack for customers' use. Q ⏁ ⇌ ♠ 🛜 ➠

Dartford Working Men's Club Ⓛ ✅
Essex Road, DA1 2AU
☎ (01322) 223646 ⊕ dartfordwm.club
Courage Best Bitter Ⓗ**; 14 changing beers (sourced regionally; often Dark Star, Leatherbritches, Oakham)** Ⓗ/Ⓖ
A finalist in 2017 for CAMRA National Club of the Year, this modern venue serves 15 ales on handpump plus ciders on gravity. It hosts the BBC award-winning Dartford Folk Club every Tuesday night, and has free live music every Thursday and Saturday night as well as on the last Sunday afternoon of the month. Tribute acts perform every other Friday night and a quiz takes place on the first Wednesday of the month. CAMRA members are welcome as guests. ❀ ◑ ➠ ♣ ♠ 🛜 🛜

Foresters ✅
15/16 Great Queen Street, DA1 1TJ
☎ (01322) 223087
Adnams Ghost Ship; Harvey's Sussex Best Bitter; 1 changing beer (sourced nationally) Ⓗ
A pleasant Victorian side-street local, just off East Hill, five minutes' walk from the town centre. It is quiet at lunchtimes but busy in the evenings with live sports on TV and darts, pool and crib teams. The U-shaped bar has a

log-burning fire at one end. The graveyard opposite contains the unmarked pauper's grave of famed steam pioneer Richard Trevithick – its approximate location indicated by a plaque on the north wall.

Malt Shovel

3 Darenth Road, DA1 1LP
(01322) 224381 maltshovelda1.co.uk
St Austell Tribute; Young's London Original, London Special; 2 changing beers (sourced nationally) H
A traditional pub in the country style, dating from 1673, five minutes' walk from the town centre. It has two separate bars. The first is a small taproom with a low ceiling featuring an 1880s Dartford Brewery mirror. The second is a larger saloon bar leading to a conservatory, where meals are served Wednesday to Sunday lunchtimes and Wednesday to Saturday and Monday evenings. A large beer garden is accessed from the conservatory. A popular open quiz is staged on Monday evenings and crib on Tuesdays. There is a small car park next to it. QP

Deal

Farrier

90 Manor Road, CT14 9DB
(01304) 360080
Fuller's London Pride; St Austell Proper Job; 4 changing beers H
This traditional black and white beamed pub is at least 16th century, possibly older, and is reputedly the oldest pub in Deal. It is a friendly environment with a real community feel to it, and a relaxing place to chat and enjoy the four ales on offer. Inside are two open fires and plenty of seating. The background music is kept deliberately quiet. The events diary includes pool and darts matches, monthly quiz nights and a Sunday meat raffle. P

Just Reproach

14 King Street, CT14 6HX
4 changing beers G
This town-centre micropub has a welcoming ambience. Its high benches and table service make for a friendly, convivial atmosphere. Up to five real ales are served, with at least one from a Kent brewery, and at least one Kentish cider. Also sold are wines from the local Barnsole vineyard and Australia, gins and soft drinks. Snacks include pork pies, Scotch eggs and local cheese. The pub has no keg, fruit machines or music, and do not let your mobile phone ring! Q

Ship Inn

141 Middle Street, CT14 6JZ
(01304) 372222
Dark Star Hophead; Ramsgate Gadds' No.7 Bitter Ale, Gadds' No.5 Best Bitter Ale; Timothy Taylor Landlord; 1 changing beer (often Ramsgate) H
Only 10 minutes' walk from the town centre, this unspoilt, traditional inn is in Deal's historic conservation area. Dark wooden floors and subdued lighting create a warm and comfortable atmosphere, complemented by the nautical theme. A wide variety of drinkers enjoys the good range of beers dispensed from five handpumps, including beers from Ramsgate and Dark Star. The small cosy rear bar overlooks a large patio garden, accessed by a staircase, with a covered smoking area.

Doddington

Chequers

The Street, ME9 0BG (6 miles W of Faversham)
(01795) 886366 chequersinndoddington.co.uk
Shepherd Neame Master Brew; 1 changing beer (sourced regionally; often Shepherd Neame) H
A listed coaching inn with oak timbers, mullioned windows and an inglenook fireplace, serving up to three ales during the summer. It is reported to have two resident ghosts – a Cavalier from the English Civil War and a ghoul with a passion for the piano. This centre of village life provides a full post office service every Tuesday between 1-3pm. It also hosts regular live music as well as other events. P(345)

Dover

Breakwater Brewery Taproom

St Martin's Yard, Lorne Road, CT16 2AA
07866 198075
Breakwater Dover Pale Ale; 6 changing beers (sourced locally; often Breakwater) G
Opened in 2016, the brewery tap is on the site of the Harding's Wellington Brewery, which closed in 1890. The bar is modern, well lit and furnished with chunky, wooden furniture, and the bar counter resembles a stone breakwater. Cask ales from the brewery are served on gravity along with the pub's own house ciders. Stone-baked pizzas are available from the in-house pizzeria (Thu-Sat). Regular live music events are held and tours of the brewery are possible by prior arrangement.

Eight Bells

19 Cannon Street, CT16 1BZ
(01304) 205030
Greene King Abbot; Ruddles Best Bitter; Sharp's Doom Bar; 9 changing beers (often Old Dairy, Wantsum, Weltons) H
The name of this popular and bustling Wetherspoon pub, situated on the precinct, is linked to the church opposite. Inside, it has a large open-plan room with a long bar and a raised restaurant area. At the front an enclosed seating area looks out on to the precinct. Twelve handpumps dispense a range of regular and guest beers, including at least two from a Kent microbrewery. There are real ale offers on Monday. The pub is close to public transport services. Q(Priory)

Louis Armstrong

58 Maison Dieu Road, CT16 1RA
(01304) 204759
4 changing beers (sourced locally; often Old Dairy, Ramsgate, Westerham) H
Down-to-earth pub and music venue that has featured live music for over 50 years. The large L-shaped bar and stage is surrounded by music posters, a large mirror and long bench seating. Up to four real ales are sold, principally from Kent microbreweries, with an occasional real cider from a Kent cider maker. On Wednesday evenings good-value food is served. The pub has a pleasant beer garden, is easily accessible by bus, and has car parking nearby.

White Horse

St James Street, CT16 1QF
(01304) 213066 thewhitehorsedover.co.uk
Harvey's Sussex Best Bitter; Timothy Taylor Landlord; 3 changing beers (sourced nationally; often St Austell) H

The inn's history can be traced back to 1574, making this probably the oldest pub in Dover. The furniture is simple but comfortable. In 2002, the venue was adopted by Channel swimmers and the walls are covered with their signatures. Up to three real ales are served from national breweries, and real cider is available in summer. The pub is a short walk from the bus station and there is public car parking nearby. ⛧❀◐●🚆❀

Dunk's Green

Kentish Rifleman 🅛
Roughway Lane, TN11 9RU (jct with Dunks Green Rd, 4 miles N of Tonbridge, off A227)
☎ (01732) 810727 ⊕ thekentishrifleman.co.uk
Harvey's Sussex Best Bitter; 3 changing beers (sourced locally; often Tonbridge, Westerham, Whitstable) 🅗
A charming old-English pub complete with low oak-beamed ceilings and open fireplaces, the Rifleman serves up quality beer and food in an informal atmosphere that is welcoming to villagers and visitors alike. Local suppliers feature throughout a food menu that emphasises seasonal produce, while the beer selection will please those eager to sample well-maintained Kent and Sussex ales. Full of bonhomie since the 16th century, this place is well worth seeking out. Q⛧❀◐P🚆(222) ❀

Eastry

Five Bells ●
The Cross, CT13 0HX
☎ (01304) 611188 ⊕ thefivebellseastry.com
Greene King IPA; 2 changing beers 🅗
A traditional community pub in the heart of the village with a comfortable lounge bar and dining room. Two ales are served, with an occasional mild from the Wantsum Brewery. The old fire station, with historic memorabilia, serves as a sports bar and function room. The busy calendar features live music, quiz nights and an Easter beer festival. Home-made food is served all day, including a good-value two-course lunchtime menu Monday-Saturday. The suntrap patio has a children's play area and pétanque pitch. ⛧❀◐▲♣P🚆(81)🗟

Edenbridge

Secret Cask
91 High Street, TN8 5AU (at S end of High St near bridge)
☎ 07595 262247
5 changing beers (sourced locally; often Gun, Kent, Pig & Porter) 🅖
Housed in a former florist's shop, this micropub was opened in the summer of 2018 and consists of two simply furnished cosy rooms with a small bar. A changing selection of five real ales, mainly from Kent and Sussex, is served direct from the cask and displayed on the wall alongside the ciders from Biddenden. Four craft beers on keg are also available, as well as wines and local gins. The walls are decorated with beer pumpclips, which are a testament to the variety served. Q≋●🚆❀🗟

Eynsford

Five Bells
High Street, DA4 0AB
☎ (01322) 863135

Harvey's Sussex Best Bitter; 1 changing beer (sourced nationally; often Adnams, Fuller's, St Austell) 🅗
Traditional community venue in the heart of an attractive village. The public bar retains a homely atmosphere, with wooden tables and a wood-burning fire in winter. There is a comfortable separate saloon bar with a dartboard. Dogs are welcome in the public bar. To the rear is a pleasant garden and a small car park. Food is not served here but try the larger sister pub, the Malt Shovel, nearby. Q❀♣P🚆(421)❀🗟

Faversham

Bear Inn
3 Market Place, ME13 7AG
☎ (01795) 532668 ⊕ bearinnfaversham.co.uk
Shepherd Neame Master Brew; 1 changing beer (sourced locally; often Shepherd Neame) 🅗
A 16th-century inn in the historic market square, with a couple of tables out the front where people like to sit in summer. It has a regionally important historic pub interior with wood panelling, and three separate bar areas off a corridor running the length of the building. A general knowledge quiz is held on the last Monday of the month. The Bear is a good place to try Shepherd Neame beers, and it often serves a seasonal or guest beer. Popular both with locals and visitors to Faversham. Q◐≋♣🚆🗟

Corner Tap
37 Preston Street, ME13 8PE
☎ 07718 649995
Whitstable Native Bitter, East India Pale Ale, Kentish Reserve; 3 changing beers (sourced nationally; often Oakham, Rudgate, Titanic) 🅖
A popular, comfortable micropub that is now an established feature of the local drinking scene, and has links to Whitstable Brewery. Converted from what was once a shop, it has two rooms, with some solid and comfortable furniture. Cask beers and a range of keg products are dispensed from taps on the wall behind the bar in the front room, and the room at the rear is a lounge area with a Chesterfield and armchairs. There is air-conditioning throughout. The pub also sells a selection of ciders, wines and gins. Q⛧≋●🚆❀🗟

Elephant 🅛 ●
31 The Mall, ME13 8JN
☎ (01795) 590157
5 changing beers (sourced regionally; often Hopdaemon, Mighty Oak, Rother Valley) 🅗
A two-roomed traditional free house with a refurbished and extended function room at the back and much nautical memorabilia on the walls. The landlord takes pride in serving good real ale, occasionally including a beer matured in the cellar, and has won numerous CAMRA awards over many years. The place is host to local clubs and puts on regular live music. The well-tended walled garden at the back and a log fire within means this continues to be an appealing pub to visit at any time of the year. ⛧❀♣●🚆❀

Furlongs Ale House
6A Preston Street, ME13 8NS
☎ 07747 776200
5 changing beers (sourced locally; often Canterbury Ales, Kent, Ramsgate) 🅗
Faversham's first micropub, opened in 2014 and popular ever since. Furnished with wooden benches and solid tables, it has been extended recently by adding an outside seating area and rear walled garden. Beers are drawn by handpump from the cellar to the small bar,

many coming from Kent microbreweries, although others from across the UK also feature. The emphasis is on the hop. Kentish gins, wines and ciders are also served. Q❀⇌●🚌🐾

Shipwright's Arms L

Hollowshore, ME13 7TU (over 1 mile N of Faversham at confluence of Faversham and Oare creeks) TR017636

☎ (01795) 590088 🌐 theshipwrightsathollowshore.co.uk

Goacher's Real Mild Ale; Kent Prohibition; house beer (by Goacher's); 3 changing beers (sourced locally; often Harvey's) [G]

A 300-year-old family-run free house with a welcoming host. A visit here is well worth the 45-minute walk across countryside from Faversham, or via the slightly longer sea wall path. The wooden-clad building's cosy interior reflects a nautical heritage. There is comfortable seating around the fireplaces. The large garden at the rear is open from spring to autumn, with outside seating at the front in all seasons. Opening hours are seasonal, telephone ahead. Q❀◑♣P🐾

Finglesham

Crown Inn L

The Street, CT14 0NA

☎ (01304) 612555 🌐 thecrowninnfinglesham.co.uk

Dark Star Hophead; 2 changing beers [H]

Traditional village pub with a warm welcome and a friendly atmosphere. Three to four real ales are served, one usually from a local microbrewery, and you can get quality home-made food lunchtimes and evenings, including a roast on Sunday. Eat in the bar or the restaurant, which opens onto the pleasant garden. Occasional live music events take place, bat and trap is played in summer, and there is a children's play area. The magnificent Kentish barn is available for functions and weddings. Opening hours may be extended in summer. ❀◑♣P🚌(81)🐾

Folkestone

Bouverie Tap L

45 Bouverie Road West, CT20 2SZ

☎ (01303) 255977 🌐 thebouverietap.co.uk

3 changing beers (sourced locally) [H]

A small pub, decorated with interesting old posters, at the west end of Folkestone, offering three changing local ales and a cider. Food is prepared using locally sourced ingredients, including roasts on Sundays, which can be enjoyed in the basement restaurant or bar area. Breakfasts are available on Saturday and Sunday, and alcoholic drinks are served early for those who like a hair of the dog with their breakfast! Dogs are welcome, and children up to 7pm. ◑♿⇌●🚌🐾

Chambers L

Radnor Chambers, Cheriton Place, CT20 2BB (off Hythe end of Sandgate Rd)

☎ (01303) 223333 🌐 thechamberspub.co.uk

Adnams Lighthouse; 3 changing beers (sourced regionally) [H]

A spacious cellar bar with six handpumps, beneath a licensed coffee shop. Beers can come from local breweries, alongside at least two real ciders. Food includes Mexican, European and daily specials (no food Mon and Fri eves). There is a disco on a Friday and a quiz on the first Sunday of the month (see Facebook for details), and live music on a Thursday, usually with free admission. A beer festival is held over the Easter weekend. ◑⇌●🚌

East Cliff Tavern

13-15 East Cliff, CT19 6BU

☎ (01303) 251132

2 changing beers (sourced regionally) [H]

Friendly terraced back-street pub dating from 1862, and in the same family since 1967. It is near a footpath across the disused railway line, a short walk from the harbour. The main bar is to the right and there are usually two beers on, often from local breweries, with Biddenden or Kingswood cider on gravity behind the bar. Old photographs of Folkestone decorate the walls. Community events include weekly raffles. Opening hours may vary; check if making a special visit. Q❀♣●🚌🐾

Firkin Alehouse

20 Cheriton Place, CT20 2AZ

☎ 07894 068432 🌐 firkinalehouse.co.uk

4 changing beers (sourced regionally) [G]

Folkestone's first micropub. Up to four cask beers, often including one from a Kent microbrewery, and up to six ciders, are all served on gravity from a temperature-controlled cellar room. The display fridge offers a selection of bottled and canned foreign and British beers, and a limited wine selection is stocked. Bar snacks include pickled eggs and onions and other basic fare. You won't find music or pub games, just good company and conversation, making this a place to enjoy a good drink and relax. Q⇌●🚌🐾

Kipps' Alehouse

11-15 Old High Street, CT20 1RL

☎ (01303) 246766

3 changing beers (sourced regionally; often Mad Cat) [G]

This alehouse follows the general principle of a micropub, serving real ale directly from the cask. The choice usually includes one Kentish ale, one award winner, and then another unusual beer from around the country from a small independent microbrewery. Several ciders are on sale from boxes, alongside a variety of bottled craft beers and draught international lagers. A range of international vegetarian food is available. Music is played some Sunday afternoons. ❀◑♿♣●🚌🐾

Frittenden

Bell & Jorrocks ✓

Biddenden Road, TN17 2EJ TQ815412

☎ (01580) 852415 🌐 thebellandjorrocks.co.uk

Black Sheep Best Bitter; Harvey's Sussex Best Bitter; 2 changing beers (sourced nationally; often Dark Star, Fuller's, Tonbridge) [H]

An archetypal village pub that is the social centre of the local community. Previously called the Bell, it gained its current name when the pub opposite, the John Jorrocks, closed in 1969. Excellent food is available. Originally a coaching inn dating from the early 18th century, its stables are used for a mid-April beer festival with about 25 different beers. The pub is a good base for walks in the picturesque Low Weald countryside surrounding the village, and for nearby Sissinghurst Castle. ❀◑Å♣🐾

Knoxbridge L

Cranbrook Road, TN17 2BT TQ788406

☎ (01580) 895374 🌐 theknoxbridge.co.uk

3 changing beers (sourced regionally; often Brumaison, Harvey's, Musket) [H]

A relaxed family-friendly pub serving great food cooked by a French chef, complemented by up to three changing ales from local and distant breweries. Some beers may be unfamiliar, so may be purchased as three third-pint glasses in a wooden tray. A selection of gins is stocked and a gin festival is staged in September. A beer festival is held on the weekend of St George's Day, with a large number of military vehicles in attendance. An hourly bus stops outside the door. (5)

Gillingham

Frog & Toad

38 Burnt Oak Terrace, ME7 1DR

(01634) 852231

4 changing beers (sourced nationally; often Cotleigh, Parkway, Wadworth) H

A three-times winner of local CAMRA Pub of the Year, this traditional, back-street corner one-bar establishment is just 10 minutes' walk from the town centre. In keeping with the frog theme, there is a treat to be found on the glass rack over the bar for the musically minded, and a collection of vintage photos of the area adorns the walls. A large patio garden at the rear has covered wooden tables and seating. A permanent outdoor stillage is in place to serve real ale and ciders during regular beer festivals. Occasional entertainment is hosted at weekends and Sunday lunch is available (booking required).

Past & Present Ale House

15 Canterbury Street, ME7 5TP

07725 072293

3 changing beers (sourced nationally; often Dartmoor, Nelson, Titanic) G

Medway's first micropub and the local CAMRA's Pub and Cider Pub of the Year once again. It moved to larger premises in spring 2020 but with the same ethos of selling three to five cask ales and up to 12 ciders. There is high seating in the front area in micropub style, while the rear area has low seating and a bar serving rum, whisky, gin and KeyKeg beer. A good assortment of bar snacks is available. Regular cider and ale festivals are held throughout the year. There is a smoking area.

Q

Will Adams

73 Saxton Street, ME7 5EG

(01634) 575902

3 changing beers (sourced nationally; often Adnams, Oakham, St Austell) H

A traditional back-street venue close to the town centre that has had 26 consecutive entries in this Guide. Offering up to three ales and five ciders, it has been run by the owners for 27 years. Some sporting events are shown on TV. On Gillingham FC match days the pub opens earlier and offers food for fans – the chilli is a speciality, but beware, it is not for the faint hearted! The pub is a member of the Oakademy of Excellence, which grants access to limited and special brews from Oakham brewery.

Gravesend

Compass Alehouse

7 Manor Road, DA12 1AA

07951 550949 thecompassalehouse.co.uk

4 changing beers (sourced nationally) G

A genuine micropub opened in 2014. It has a small front room with high bench seats, and a smaller snug off a little courtyard to the rear. Four changing real ales and five ciders are stocked, often from Kent producers. Convivial atmosphere and conversation are paramount – talking on mobile phones is discouraged and incurs a fine for charity. Regular events include a games night on Tuesday, bi-monthly Belgian beer tastings and two beer festivals. A water bowl is provided for dogs.

Q

Jolly Drayman

1 Love Lane, Wellington Street, DA12 1JA (off Milton Rd)

(01474) 352355 jollydrayman.com

Dark Star Hophead; St Austell Proper Job; Skinner's Betty Stogs; 2 changing beers (sourced nationally; often Iron Pier) H

This cosy pub on the eastern edge of the town, also known as the Coke Oven, is part of the former Walker's Brewery. It features quirky low ceilings and a relaxed atmosphere. Daddlums (Kentish skittles) is played most Sunday evenings, and men's and women's darts teams are hosted. Lunches are served daily, all afternoon on Sunday. Live music takes place on the first Saturday of the month, there are monthly open mic sessions, and a quiz on alternate Tuesdays.

Three Daws

7 Town Pier, DA11 0BJ

(01474) 566869 threedaws.co.uk

6 changing beers (sourced locally; often Canterbury Ales, Dartford Wobbler, Iron Pier) H

A historic riverside inn with stories of ghosts, press gangs, smugglers, secret tunnels and more, offering views of the Thames and passing river traffic. The bar is upstairs, with a large function room below. The interior is divided into small rooms with photos and pictures of local or marine interest, and has very few right angles. Meals are served every day using local ingredients. Live music features on Friday, a quiz on Sunday and beer festivals in August and October.

Three Pillars

25 Wrotham Road, DA11 0PA (on A227 opp civic centre)

07794 348529

5 changing beers (sourced nationally; often Kent, Mighty Oak, Wantsum) G

A small cellar bar underneath the Masonic Hall, reached by steep steps to the right of the hall. Two carpeted front rooms lead to the brick-floored bar area. The ceilings are low throughout and there are photos of Gravesend pubs past and present. There is a quiz on the third Thursday of each month and live music on some Sundays, featuring solo acts or small groups. Patrons must not use the Masonic Hall car park.

Great Mongeham

Leather Bottle

103 Mongeham Road, CT14 9PE

2 changing beers (sourced locally; often Canterbury Ales, Romney Marsh) H

This street-corner free house is on the outskirts of Deal. The large bar room has a relaxed, smart, modern feel. A locals' pub with no frills, it offers top-quality ales and good company. While largescreen sports TVs and great beer do not always agree, they do here. There are darts and pool teams, and occasional karaoke, quiz nights and charitable events. Euchre night is Friday. Outside, there is a large garden and a small covered patio for smokers.

P(82)

Halstead

Rose & Crown

Otford Lane, TN14 7EA

☎ (01959) 533120

Larkins Traditional Ale; 5 changing beers (sourced nationally; often Mighty Oak, Rudgate, Tonbridge) ⊞
Accessible from junction 4 of the M25 and bordering Greater London, this is still unmistakably a village pub. Two equally sized rooms are differentiated solely by the dartboard in the public bar and a roaring fire in the lounge. The owner's passion for cask beer is reflected in the choice of six ales, with half from local breweries and the remainder sourced nationally. Good-value lunchtime food includes an over-50s menu. The place has a timeless quality that modern establishments cannot match. ✿❁◗♣P🖥(3,R5)✿ 🖙

Harvel

Amazon & Tiger 🅛
Harvel Street, DA13 0DE

☎ (01474) 814705

3 changing beers (sourced locally; often Kent, Tonbridge, Westerham) ⊞
Situated in a remote village near the North Downs Way and Pilgrims Way, this place is popular with walkers. Built in 1914 opposite the original pub, it was designed to blend in with the surrounding properties. There are two distinct bar areas where modern furnishings combine with flagstones and wood floors. A good range of ales is served, mainly from West Kent and East Sussex. Fresh fish night is Thursday. The village cricket team can be watched from the garden. One newly furnished holiday let is available. Q✿❁⇦◗♣P✿🖙

Hastingleigh

Bowl Inn 🅛
The Street, TN25 5HU TR095449

☎ (01233) 750354 🌐 thebowlonline.co.uk

3 changing beers (sourced locally) ⊞
This lovingly restored listed village inn with vintage advertising material retains many period features. The main bar welcomes families but the snug room is child-free and used for village meetings. A beer festival is held on the August bank holiday Monday. Excellent sandwiches and baguettes are available weekends. Opening hours may vary if custom warrants it. CAMRA branch Pub of the Year in 2018 and 2019. Q✿❁◗♣✿🖙

Herne

Butcher's Arms 🅛
29A Herne Street, CT6 7HL (opp church)

☎ 07908 370685 🌐 micropub.co.uk

Fuller's ESB; Oakham Citra; Old Dairy Copper Top; 2 changing beers (sourced locally; often Adnams, Old Dairy) 🅖
Britain's first micropub, opened in 2005, is a real ale gem and the inspiration for others since. Once a butcher's shop, it still has the original chopping tables. There is seating for 12 customers and standing room for 20 – the compact drinking area ensuring lively banter. The range of ales changes frequently and customers can also buy beer to drink at home. The Butcher's Arms has won many CAMRA awards and the landlord was voted one of CAMRA's top 40 campaigners. Q▲✿🖥✿

Herne Bay

Bouncing Barrel 🅛
20 Bank Street, CT6 5EA

☎ 07777 630685

4 changing beers (sourced regionally; often Goody Ales, Old Dairy, Ramsgate) 🅖
A welcoming micropub with bench seating for 20 customers around old workshop tables. The beer range changes regularly and comes mainly from microbreweries, with generally at least one from a Kent brewery. Local snacks are available. The venue is named after the bombs used in the Dam Buster raids, which were tested off the coast nearby. The pub has a mural of a bomber flying past the Reculver Towers. Regular small beer festivals are held throughout the year.
Q✿♿♣●🖥✿

Parkerville
219 High Street, CT6 5AD

☎ 07939 106172

4 changing beers (sourced locally) 🅖
Lively micropub in a former music store. The spacious front seating area has a corner bar, and a small stage with a piano in the front window. The back bar has a TV screen for big events only. Beers are often from local microbreweries and there is a good selection of ciders, whiskies, rums, artisan gins and wines. Occasional live music is staged, and the pub celebrates its birthday every 24 July with music and food. Q✿♿●🖥✿

Horton Kirby

Bull 🅛
Lombard Street, DA4 9DF

☎ (01322) 860341 🌐 thebullhortonkirby.com

Dark Star Hophead; 4 changing beers (sourced locally; often Kent, Oakham, Whitstable) ⊞
A friendly, comfortable one-bar village local with a large garden affording views across the Darent Valley, within walking distance of Farningham Road railway station. It has five handpumps, with one regular and four rotating guest ales. There is an open mic night on the first Friday of each month and a quiz on the last Monday. Regular beer festivals are hosted, normally over the Whitsun and August bank holidays, supported by Ron's garden bar.
✿❁◗♣🖥(414) ✿🖙

Hythe

Three Mariners 🅛
37 Windmill Street, CT21 6BH

☎ (01303) 260406

Young's London Original; 4 changing beers (sourced regionally) ⊞
Hidden away in a side street not far from the Royal Military Canal, this traditional corner two-bar pub is well worth a visit when in Hythe for the excellent quality and selection of real ales and cider. Friendly staff and local customers are happy to chat while you enjoy a pint of local or regional beers. No food is served. There is a partly heated drinking area outside. ❁≈♣●🖥✿

Ickham

Duke William
The Street, CT3 1QP

☎ (01227) 721308 🌐 thedukewilliamickham.com

3 changing beers (sourced locally; often Angels and Demons, Wantsum, Whitstable) [H]
An attractive, busy establishment in a quintessentially English village, welcoming towards locals, diners and drinkers, with a roaring log fire in winter and a conservatory dining area at the rear. There is also a large patio. Guest ales are mostly from local microbreweries. The venue is a welcome addition to Michelin-starred chef Mark Sargeant's portfolio: his aim is to 'mirror simplistic but perfect pub meals'. There is also a bar menu served Monday to Saturday. (11)

Ightham Common

Old House [L]
Redwell Lane, Redwell, TN15 9EE (½ mile SW of Ightham village, between A25 and A227) TQ590558
(01732) 886077 oldhouse.pub
6 changing beers (sourced locally; often Goacher's, Hopdaemon, Long Man) [G]
A Kentish red-brick, tile-hung cottage located in a narrow, isolated country lane. It has a nationally important historic pub interior, the main bar featuring a Victorian wood-panelled counter, parquet flooring and an imposing inglenook fireplace. Up to six changing beers are dispensed by gravity, often from wooden casks, including at least one bitter, a golden ale and a dark beer. Kentish ciders are always stocked. Local CAMRA Pub of the Year 2018-2020. May close earlier in the evening if not busy. Q P

Kingsdown

King's Head [L]
Upper Street, CT14 8BJ
(01304) 373915 kingsheadkingsdown.co.uk
3 changing beers (often Goacher's, Ramsgate) [H]
A traditional 18th-century village pub with three beamed rooms surrounding the central bar. It has a dining/family room, a rear courtyard, a skittle alley and a heated smoking area. Local historical photos adorn the walls, and in winter a log fire warms the public bar. Three to four real ales feature, including beers from Goacher's and Ramsgate. Cider is on sale in the summer. Home-made food is served lunchtimes and evenings on Saturday and Sunday. Events include quiz nights and a guitar club. (82)

Kingsnorth

Queen's Head
Ashford Road, TN23 3ED
(01233) 620769 queenshead-kingsnorth.co.uk
Harvey's Sussex Best Bitter; 2 changing beers (sourced regionally) [H]
A warm and inviting 18th-century Grade II listed pub in a village to the south of Ashford, serving great food and a range of quality ales (two of which change at least weekly), wines, spirits and soft drinks. All are welcome including families, children and dogs. A community venue, it runs a range of events including live music and quiz nights (details on the website). Closed on Monday during the winter months. P

Laddingford

Chequers
The Street, ME18 6BP TQ689481
(01622) 871266 chequerssladdingford.co.uk
Adnams Southwold Bitter; 3 changing beers (sourced nationally) [H]
An attractive oak-beamed building dating from the 15th century, and the heart of village life. A variety of events is held throughout the year, including a beer festival at the end of April. A log fire burns in winter, and the pub frontage is a sea of flowers in summer. Good food is served and, on Thursdays, a wide selection of sausage dishes is a feature. The large garden has children's play equipment, and accommodation is available. Buses stop outside. Q P (23,25)

Linton

Armoury [L]
Loddington Farm, Loddington Lane, ME17 4AG
(01622) 749931 musketbrewery.co.uk
6 changing beers (sourced locally; often Musket) [G]
The Musket Brewery tap overlooks the new brewhouse that is visible through the windows. There are up to eight casks on the stillage. Comfortable seating is provided in a good-sized area, and beer may also be ordered for collection. Pizzas are usually available, and monthly bookable themed dining events like Burns Night or St George's Night are held. A large grassed area opposite offers tables and cushioned casks on sunny days, with shade under the trees. Q P (59)

Lower Halstow

Three Tuns [L]
The Street, ME9 7DY
(01795) 842840 thethreetunsrestaurant.co.uk
Goacher's Real Mild Ale; 3 changing beers (sourced locally; often Hop Fuzz, Romney Marsh, Wantsum) [H]
True family village inn with a cheerful atmosphere and lively chatter. Real ale is actively supported, with a range of mainly Kentish beers – third-pint flights are available for the indecisive – and several local ciders are sold, including Dudda's Tun. The pub has a good reputation for high-quality locally sourced food and has won many awards. A beer festival is held during the August bank holiday and a quiz is hosted monthly. Beams and brick walls, sofa seating and a log fire add character. The owners celebrated their 10th year here in 2020. P

Luddesdown

Cock Inn [L]
Henley Street, DA13 0XB (1 mile SE of Sole Street station) TQ664672
(01474) 814208 cockluddesdowne.com
Adnams Lighthouse, Southwold Bitter, Broadside; Goacher's Real Mild Ale; Harvey's Sussex Best Bitter; St Austell Trelawny [H]
A proudly traditional rural free house dating from 1713, under the same ownership since 1984. Eight real ales are on handpump. It has two distinct bars, a large conservatory, a comfortable heated smoking area and a separate function room where many local clubs and societies meet. Traditional pub games are played, including pétanque and bar billiards, and there is a free quiz on Tuesday evenings devised and hosted by the landlord. Doorstep sandwiches are available at all times. Children are not permitted. Q P

Maidstone

Cellars Alehouse 𝕃

The Old Brewery, Buckland Road, ME16 0DZ (if front gates are closed use rear via alley alongside railway)
☎ (01622) 761045 🌐 thecellarsalehouse.co.uk
6 changing beers (sourced nationally; often Bristol Beer Factory, Cellar Head, Gun) Ⓖ
In a former barley wine cellar of the old Style & Winch Brewery with access down a flight of steps, this establishment has a surprisingly spacious interior, with wooden pews, seats and tables. The barrel-vaulted ceiling is adorned with pumpclips and hops. Real ales are served by gravity from the capacious cool room, and at least 10 real ciders, a few craft keg beers and gins are also stocked. Evening entertainment may include quizzes, folk music, comedy and Meet the Brewer events. Q≉♣●🚌🐾

Flower Pot 𝕃

96 Sandling Road, ME14 2RJ
☎ (01622) 757705 🌐 flowerpotpub.com
Goacher's Gold Star Strong Ale; 8 changing beers (sourced nationally; often Fyne Ales, Thornbridge) Ⓗ
A street-corner alehouse and a must-visit when in Maidstone. The upper bar has nine handpumps, with the ales mainly from microbreweries. Up to four ciders and perries are served directly from the container, and there is a small selection of KeyKeg beers. Beers and ciders are displayed on video screens. There are music nights on some Saturdays, jam nights on Tuesdays, monthly vinyl nights on Fridays, and an annual beer festival. Maidstone United football ground is nearby.
❀◑≉♣●▯🚌(101,155)🐾📶

Olde Thirsty Pig 𝕃 ✔

4a Knightrider Street, ME15 6LP
☎ (01622) 299283 🌐 thethirstypig.co.uk
4 changing beers (sourced locally; often Musket, Range Ales, Tonbridge) Ⓗ
Reputedly the third oldest building in the town, dating from around 1430, with a wealth of massive timber beams, sloping floors and curious nooks and crannies on two storeys. It was originally a farmhouse within the estate of the Archbishop's Palace. The beer is mainly from Kent microbreweries, draught cider is stocked, and many bottled beers are available including from overseas. There are two small meeting rooms and a heated and covered courtyard area. ❀●🚌🐾📶

Rifle Volunteers 𝕃

28 Wyatt Street, ME14 1EU
☎ (01622) 758891 🌐 theriflevolunteers.co.uk
Goacher's Real Mild Ale, Fine Light Ale, Crown Imperial Stout, Gold Star Strong Ale; 1 changing beer (sourced locally; often Goacher's) Ⓗ
One of only two Goacher's tied houses, the Rifle is just a short walk away from Maidstone town centre. This Victorian stone-built single-bar venue is on CAMRA's Regional Inventory of Historic Pub Interiors. The absence of a jukebox or gaming machines emphasises that it is a place for conversation or a quiet drink. A popular fun quiz open to all is held on alternate Tuesdays, with a local winter quiz league operating on other weeks. Snacks are not advertised but can be made to order.
Q❀≉♣●🚌🐾📶

Stag

11 Middle Row, ME14 1TG
☎ (01622) 296420
Rockin' Robin Reliant Robin; 2 changing beers (sourced nationally; often Kent, Old Dairy) Ⓗ
Run by Rockin' Robin since August 2019, the Stag is a historic pub in the town centre that has had several names in recent years. It has been redecorated externally and internally in a mid-grey, and the beams have been stripped back to their original colour. You can enter it from either the High Street or via Bank Street to the room at the rear. Three steps lead down to the toilets. Three handpumps are usually active, and there may be a couple of fires going in winter. ❀≉🚌🐾📶

Marden

Marden Village Club 𝕃

Albion Road, TN12 9DT
☎ (01622) 831427 🌐 mardenvillageclub.co.uk
Shepherd Neame Master Brew; 5 changing beers (sourced regionally; often Goacher's, Kent, Ramsgate) Ⓗ
Six real ales are now offered at this Grade II listed club, five changing regularly and coming generally from local Kent microbreweries. Many members are followers of football and rugby on the TV and are also involved in the club's snooker and darts teams; others simply enjoy the friendly ambience. It has frequently been voted CAMRA branch Club of the Year. Card-carrying CAMRA members are welcome but regular visitors will be required to join.
♿≉♣●🚌(23)🐾📶

Margate

Fez

40 High Street, CT9 1DS
4 changing beers Ⓖ
This eclectically furnished micropub, opened in 2015, has a mixture of high and low tables along with some raised bench seating. Brewery and fairground memorabilia adorn the walls while musical instruments are fixed on the ceiling. The small bar counter at the rear has a temperature-controlled cellar room from which cask ales and ciders are served on gravity dispense. A limited wine range is also offered, along with a selection of soft drinks. ≉♣●🚌🐾📶

Two Halves

2 Marine Drive, CT9 1DH
☎ 07538 771904
3 changing beers Ⓖ
A friendly and welcoming micropub with an incredible location on Margate's seafront. The beers are from all regions of the country and are regularly changed – the landlord knows his ale. Beer and cider are kept in immaculate condition in a large stillage room. No matter what the weather, this venue has a great aspect, where you can see the sun set out of the window or just watch the world go by. Look for the old-fashioned postcards in the loo. Local CAMRA Pub of the Year 2018. Q≉●🚌🐾

Milton Regis

Three Hats

93 High Street, ME10 2AR
☎ (01795) 427645
4 changing beers (sourced nationally) Ⓗ
In the medieval High Street, the Three Hats is the focal point for many social activities. An open-plan interior with low beams to the front rises just enough at the rear to accommodate a dartboard, beyond which is a large patio area and garden. Occasional live music and karaoke take place, with a meat raffle on Sunday. Food is served.
❀◑●🚌(347)🐾📶

Minster-in-Thanet

Hair of the Dog

73 High Street, CT12 4AB
☎ 07885 362326 🌐 hairofthedogpub.co.uk
3 changing beers [G]
This micropub, previously a dog groomers, offers a warm welcome on the village high street. Usually offering three real ales and at least three ciders, all are served from the cask in a cool room directly off the bar. The furniture is rustic with a mix of high and low seating and tables, where one can play a mix of old games such as shove ha'penny or try and crack some of the puzzles left out. Dogs still welcome. Q🐎≠♣●🚌🐾

New Romney

Smugglers' Alehouse 𝕃

10 St Lawrence Court, High Street, TN28 8BU
☎ 07919 156336 🌐 smugglersalehouse.co.uk
3 changing beers (sourced regionally) [H]
A micropub at the south end of the High Street where you can relax, read the newspapers or join in with the conversations between customers and staff. In addition to the changing real ales and ciders on offer, there is a good selection of wines and spirits. You can also usually get tea, coffee and various snacks (including pickled eggs). Well-behaved dogs on leads are welcome.
Q⛺●P🚌🐾

Newenden

White Hart 𝕃

Rye Road, TN18 5PN (on A28 in centre of village)
TQ834273
☎ (01797) 252166 🌐 thewhitehartnewenden.co.uk
Harvey's Sussex Best Bitter; Rother Valley Level Best; 2 changing beers [H]
This historic 16th-century weatherboarded building includes old oak-beamed bars and an inglenook fireplace. The pub provides good-quality home-cooked food and has six en-suite rooms. Conveniently situated for the Kent & East Sussex Railway and several National Trust properties, it is an ideal location for exploring the Rother Valley. A quiz is held on the first Monday of the month. 🐎❀🛏◑♿⛺≠♣●P🚌(2)🐾📶

Pembury

King William IV

87 Hastings Road, TN2 4JS
☎ (01892) 458241 🌐 kingwilliampembury.com
Greene King Abbot; St Austell Proper Job; 4 changing beers (sourced regionally; often Cellar Head, Fuller's, Long Man) [H]
A refurbished free house under family ownership, the King Will has been given a new lease of life as a thriving community pub. Local breweries are well supported and it also sells a real cider from Biddenden or Seacider. Spacious, with ample seating, large front and rear gardens, room for darts and bar billiards games, and regular live music evenings, it has something for everyone. The menu includes home-made Cornish pasties which complement the regular appearance of a Cornish beer, reflecting the landlord's origins.
🐎❀◑♣●P🚌(6,297)🐾📶

Queenborough

Admiral's Arm 🏆 𝕃

West Street, ME11 5AD (in Trafalgar Court, 30yds left from crossroads of High St and Park Rd)
☎ (01795) 668598 🌐 admiralsarm.co.uk
4 changing beers (sourced nationally; often Ilkley, Oakham, Ramsgate) [H]/[G]
This micropub, frequented by locals and visitors alike, is in the historic heart of Queenborough, and has a nautical theme including local shipping maps. The welcoming owners happily serve a good range of ales direct from the cask or via handpump, plus eight KeyKeg beers, ciders and many gins. The pub hosts regular quiz nights, cheese Sundays, and serves excellent pizzas at weekends from its pizza oven. Local CAMRA Pub and Cider Pub of the Year 2018-2020, and Kent Pub of the Year 2019. Q🐎❀◑≠♣●🚌(334)🐾📶

Rainham

Mackland Arms

213 Station Road, ME8 7PS (a 5-minute walk N of railway station)
☎ (01634) 232178 🌐 macklandarms.co.uk
Shepherd Neame Master Brew, Spitfire; 1 changing beer (sourced nationally) [H]
A popular, traditional local, this Shepherd Neame tied house has three linked areas with plush red seating and a pleasant decor. The island bar displays three ales on handpump as well as an Orchard View 4.5% ABV cider. Darts teams play twice a week, there is a pool table at the rear, and sport is shown on two screens. No food is served. There is a large rear garden. A bus stop opposite the pub will connect with the main routes of the A2.
🐎❀≠♣🚌(327)🐾

Prince of Ales 𝕃

121 High Street, ME8 8AN (near centre of Rainham)
☎ 07982 756412 🌐 princeofales.co.uk
4 changing beers (sourced nationally; often Kent, Oakham, Tonbridge) [G]
Situated on the main A2, next to the post office, opposite the Citroen dealer and two minutes from bus stops, this attractive micropub is run by a dedicated team. Four changing beers, mostly Kent-based local ales, are served direct from casks in the chiller room, as are three ciders of the bag-in-box type. Wooden tables and benches predominate inside and in the small outside area. An annual beer festival is held. Wine, prosecco and soft drinks are served, but no food. Children and animals are not permitted. Q❀≠♣●▯🚌(132)

Ramsgate

Artillery Arms

36 Westcliff Road, CT11 9JS
☎ (01843) 853202
Oakham Citra; Ramsgate Gadds' No.5 Best Bitter Ale; 4 changing beers (often Mallinsons, Ramsgate, Thornbridge) [H]
A celebrated alehouse a short walk from the town attracting a diverse clientele. The lower bar area with stairs leads to an upper area with more seating. The landlord maintains a long tradition of stocking a carefully considered range of real ales. Handpumps serve a selection of beers from Kent and around the country. Interesting old painted windows depict battle scenes, and the theme is continued with displays of other militaria. ♣●🚌🐾

A popular micropub close to Sittingbourne town centre and railway station. It has just one room, with bench seating around four large wooden tables. Local beers feature alongside ales from national breweries such as Blue Monkey and Cloudwater. A range of real ciders is also available. Blackboards with beer lists include a number of KeyKeg offerings. Occasional events such as Meet the Brewer and quizzes take place. Opening hours can be flexible with advance notice.
Q♿≠♣●🚌(334,347)🐾

Yellow Stocks

22A High Street, ME10 4PD
☎ 07572 180627
2 changing beers (sourced locally; often Canterbury Ales, Iron Pier, Ramsgate) G
A micropub which opened in September 2018 in what used to be a clothes shop. It is named after a type of hand-made building brick once manufactured in large quantities in the surrounding countryside. Real ales, ciders and perries are dispensed from a temperature-controlled cellar room behind the small bar counter. Most of the real ales and ciders have a Kentish provenance, but some unusual regional beers are offered. Occasional comfort food is available on the bar. There is a spotlessly kept unisex toilet, and a garden and outside smoking area at the rear. ❀≠♣●🚌🐾

Snargate

Red Lion ★ L

TN29 9UQ (on B2080, 1 mile NW of Brenzett) TQ990285
☎ (01797) 344648
Goacher's Real Mild Ale; 3 changing beers (often Goacher's) G
An unspoilt, multi-room 16th-century smugglers' inn which has been in the same family for over 100 years. It passed to the next generation in 2016 but is still universally known as Doris's. Decorated with posters from the 1940s and the Women's Land Army, it has a nationally important historic pub interior and is well worth a visit. A beer festival is held in June near to the summer solstice, with a mini festival in October.
Q❀♣●P🚌(11B)🐾

South Darenth

Queen L

58-62 New Road, DA4 9AR
☎ (01322) 862430
Fuller's London Pride; Greene King Abbot; Kent Session Pale, Brewers Reserve H
Originally three separate cottages in a back-street terrace, this community local lies within walking distance of Farningham Road railway station. It has two separate bars, one with a sports theme and adorned with memorabilia of London football teams, the other a quieter saloon bar. A genuine free house, it promotes beers from Kent Brewery. The pub has a garden and patio area, and free bar food is available Sunday lunchtimes. Children are welcome until 8.30pm.
❀◖≠♣●🚌(414)🐾

Staplehurst

Lord Raglan L

Chart Hill Road, TN12 0DE (½ mile N of A229 at Cross at Hand) TQ786472
☎ (01622) 843747
Goacher's Fine Light Ale; Harvey's Sussex Best Bitter; 1 changing beer (sourced locally) H
Owned by the same family for many years, this is an unspoilt free house retaining the atmosphere of a country pub from bygone days. The bar is hung with hops and warmed by two log fires and a stove. The large orchard garden catches the evening sun. It serves excellent food from a popular menu, and perry and local Double Vision cider are stocked. Well-behaved children and dogs are welcome. A short walk from the Cross-at-Hand (No.5) bus stop on the A229. Q❀◖◗●P🐾

Strood

10:50 from Victoria L

Rear of 37 North Street, ME2 4SJ (in railway arch opp Asda car park)
☎ 07941 449137
Grainstore Ten Fifty; Kent Session Pale G**; 3 changing beers (sourced locally)** H/G
An oasis in a beer desert, this micropub, local CAMRA Pub of the Year in 2019, is hugely popular both with locals and real ale fans. Wood-panelled throughout, the walls are adorned with railway and other memorabilia. Five ales are served including regulars Grainstore 1050 and Kent Session Pale, the remainder being a mix from Kentish and regional micros, alongside six ciders. A log-burner keeps customers cosy in the colder months and there is an outside patio and garden area for warmer times. Q❀♿≠♣●P🚌(191)🐾

Tankerton

Tankerton Arms L

135 Tankerton Road, CT5 2AW
☎ 07897 741811 🌐 thetankertonarms.co.uk
Northdown Merry Margate; 3 changing beers (sourced locally; often Mad Cat, Old Dairy, Turnstone) G
This friendly micropub, with a firm policy of supporting Kent microbreweries, is situated among Tankerton's small shops. There are occasional beer swaps with regional breweries. The pleasant, airy room is lined with high wooden tables and stools, encouraging good conversation among customers, and is adorned with bunting and pictures of Thames sailing barges and the sea forts. Italian antipasti evenings are held every few weeks. There is a patio in front for outdoor drinking.
Q❀♿♣●🚌🐾

Temple Ewell

Fox

14 High Street, CT16 3DU
☎ (01304) 823598
Exmoor Fox; 2 changing beers (often Breakwater) H
A traditional village pub with a warm welcome for locals and visitors. Enjoy real ales in a good range of styles and strengths in the main bar or in one of the smaller rooms. A variety of events, quiz nights, curry nights and occasional music evenings keep the place busy. In June a charity beer festival is organised by the local Rotary Club. There is an attractive streamside garden with a skittle alley. Close to Kearnsey Abbey gardens and public transport. ❀◖◗≠♣P🚌(15,68)🐾

Tenterden

This Ancient Boro' 🏆

3 East Cross, TN30 6AD

☎ (01580) 388815 ⊕ thisancientboro.com

9 changing beers (sourced nationally) [G]

This was a Whitbread venue until 1968; it then became a Chinese restaurant, finally reverting to its original name in 2018 to become an alehouse and tapas bar. It is now a hybrid of the original pub and a micropub, with no live music or gaming machines. A variety of ales is sold by gravity dispense from cooled casks on stillage in the bar area, and a selection of ciders is served from a fridge. Local CAMRA Pub of the Year 2020. Q◑⇌♣●🚌🐾📶

Tonbridge

Beer Seller ✔

64 High Street, TN9 1EH

☎ (01732) 666336 ⊕ thebeerseller.co.uk

Cellar Head Session Pale Ale; Goacher's Gold Star Strong Ale; Long Man Best Bitter; Pig & Porter Blackbird; Tonbridge Traditional Ale; 4 changing beers (sourced locally) [G]

Reminiscent of its sister pub, the Halfway House at Brenchley, this former shop has been uniquely styled as a Kentish barn, with farmyard implements and rustic paraphernalia to give a relaxed countryside feel in the centre of town. Up to 10 cask beers are served by gravity from a cold room behind the bar, along with eight real ciders. Snack food is available until half an hour before closing. A function room and a separate off-licence are to be found upstairs. Q♿⇌●🚌🐾📶

Humphrey Bean ✔

94 High Street, TN9 1AP (near castle and river)

☎ (01732) 773850

Greene King Abbot; Ruddles Best Bitter; Sharp's Doom Bar; 6 changing beers (sourced nationally; often Oakham, Old Dairy, Tonbridge) [H]

A regular Guide entry, the Bean continues to provide a comprehensive selection of six guest ales and to stage occasional Meet the Brewer evenings. Westons Old Rosie, together with an additional cider such as Marcle Hill or Black Dragon, is kept in the chiller. There are various seating areas, and an attractive and spacious garden overlooking the River Medway and Tonbridge Castle. Inside, a flame-effect gas fire keeps customers warm in winter. Community events are hosted, including a Wednesday quiz. Q❀◑♿⇌●P🚌📶

Nelson Arms 🏆

19 Cromer Street, TN9 1UP

☎ (01732) 358284 ⊕ thenelsonarms.com

Young's London Original; 5 changing beers (sourced nationally; often Arbor, Kent, Tonbridge) [H]

Saved from extinction by multi award-winning owners, this place was revitalised in 2018 to become a destination of choice close to the station. The Nelson commemorates the naval hero with a nautical theme of pictures, artefacts and bar names, and is smartly furnished with tiling, hop decoration and plenty of seating and tables. Ten handpumps dispense a well-chosen range of beer styles, along with Biddenden and Chiddingstone cider. Food service is until late, TV sports fans are well catered for, and live music is performed on Friday evenings. ❀◑⇌♣●🚌🐾📶

Tunbridge Wells

Fuggles Beer Café L ✔

28 Grosvenor Road, TN1 2AP (opp Tesco bus stop)

☎ (01892) 457739 ⊕ fugglesbeercafe.co.uk

Burning Sky Plateau; Tonbridge Coppernob; 3 changing beers (sourced nationally; often 360 Degree, Bristol Beer Factory, Downlands) [H]

A respected town-centre drinking establishment catering for a wide range of tastes. It offers cask ales, ciders, wines, spirits and a huge range of bottled beers reflecting quality throughout, often served in a bustling atmosphere. The distinct European feel runs through to the cured meat and cheeseboards, open sandwiches and salads. Informed, friendly staff contribute to the impression of a well-run and welcoming destination. Frequent events, including brewery tap takeovers, are organised, advertised on the website and within the café. ◑⇌♣●🚌🐾📶

George ✔

29 Mount Ephraim, TN4 8AA

☎ (01892) 539492 ⊕ thegeorgepubtunbridgewells.co.uk

Long Man Best Bitter; house beer (by Fonthill); 4 changing beers (sourced locally; often Cellar Head, Gun, Pig & Porter) [H]

After several appearances in other guises, this Georgian coaching inn has rediscovered itself as a smart and friendly pub. A free house, it is home to the Fonthill nanobrewery, whose beers often appear on the bar, alongside a selection of ales from Kent and Sussex, and a local cider such as Turners or Seacider. It has front terrace seating and a rear staircase leading down to the haven of a secluded courtyard garden. Light bites are served every day beyond lunchtimes. ❀◑⇌●🚌🐾📶

Grove Tavern L ✔

19 Berkeley Road, TN1 1YR

☎ (01892) 526549 ⊕ grovetavern.co.uk

Harvey's Sussex Best Bitter; Timothy Taylor Landlord; 2 changing beers (sourced nationally; often Black Sheep, Otter, Salcombe) [H]

Ascending cobbled Warwick Road from the High Street leads you to the old village area and an integral part of it, the Grove – a long-term Guide fixture. Any newcomer here will find themselves readily included in friendly conversation while selecting between firm favourites, Harvey's Best and Landlord, or two interesting guest beers. The social nature of the pub is emphasised with a display of images of fondly remembered former patrons, friends and their dogs on the far wall. Q⇌♣🚌🐾📶

Mount Edgcumbe

The Common, TN4 8BX (signposted lane off Mt Ephraim)

☎ (01892) 618854 ⊕ themountedgcumbe.com

Harvey's Sussex Best Bitter; 3 changing beers (sourced locally; often Cellar Head, Old Dairy, Pig & Porter) [H]

Tunbridge Wells's country pub in the middle of town; a Georgian gem situated a short walk from the railway station and High Street yet surrounded by woodland. Set in isolation, the Grade II listed building enjoys a countryside feel and has a large terrace overlooking the common and sandstone rock formations, as well as its own sixth-century sandstone cave. There is an extensive food menu featuring locally sourced produce, with light meals served through the afternoon on Friday and Saturday. ❀◑⇌♣P🚌🐾📶

Opera House ✔

88 Mount Pleasant Road, TN1 1RT

☎ (01892) 511770

Greene King IPA, Abbot; Sharp's Doom Bar; 7 changing beers (sourced nationally; often Brewsters, Dark Star, Oakham) [H]
Following an impressive project to restore the building to its original use, the Opera House is a jewel in the crown for Wetherspoon. A large range of guest ales from near and far can now be enjoyed in opulent surroundings, with fine views of the theatre circle, private boxes and stage. It is conveniently situated in the centre of town close to the Victoria shopping centre, Assembly Halls, Trinity theatre and numerous bus routes.
Q ♨ ◐ ♿ ≋ 🚌 📶

Royal Oak L

92 Prospect Road, TN2 4SY
☎ (01892) 542546
Harvey's Sussex Best Bitter; 5 changing beers (sourced locally; often Cellar Head, Five Points, Iron Pier) [H]
Deservedly popular community venue a short walk from the town centre. The large open-plan panelled room has a central bar serving an eclectic range of real ales and ciders. A Hoppy Monday discount is available on some beers and third-pint taster racks are offered. Pub classics and snacks are served every day (except Mon), and roasts on Sunday. The atmosphere varies from a gentle buzz at quieter times to a more lively vibe when sports are screened on TV or when live music plays on Saturday evening. ♨ ❀ ◐ ≋ ♣ ● P 🚌 (6,285) 🐾 📶

Sussex Arms ✔

Sussex Mews, TN2 5TE
☎ (01892) 549579 🌐 thesussextw.co.uk
Long Man Long Blonde; Timothy Taylor Landlord; 4 changing beers (sourced regionally; often Adnams, Downlands, Musket) [H]
Tucked away behind the Corn Exchange just off the Pantiles, the Sussex offers a retreat away from the crowds, with a sunny patio on one side and a covered, traffic-free terrace on the other. The interior is cosily lit, homely and comfortable, with wooden furnishings, sofas and a log fire. Ascension cider is served alongside ales that come mostly from south-east breweries. A programme of regular live music and comedy entertainment in the pub's Forum basement is displayed on the walls. ♨ ❀ ≋ ♣ ● 🚌 🐾 📶

Tyler Hill

Tyler's Kiln

27 Hackington Road, CT2 9NE
☎ (01227) 471912 🌐 tylerskiln.co.uk
Harvey's Sussex Best Bitter; Shepherd Neame Master Brew; 2 changing beers (sourced regionally; often Harvey's) [H]
A community-focused village pub, refurbished to a high standard with innovative touches, cosy armchairs and an open fire. Tiles from the ancient nearby kiln are on display. The separate snug with its soft furnishings is a good place for families. The well-designed garden has a fountain and high-tech heating. Events include coffee mornings, live music and quizzes. A loyalty scheme is offered and a small range of groceries is stocked. Local CAMRA branch Pub of the Year 2019.
Q ♨ ❀ ◐ ♿ P 🚌 (5) 🐾 📶

> Charles Collins liveth here;
> Sells rum, brandy, gin and beer;
> I make this board a little wider
> To let you know I sell good cyder.
>
> **17th-century notice at the Arrow, Knockholt, Kent.**

Upper Upnor

King's Arms

2 High Street, ME2 4XG
☎ (01634) 717490 🌐 kingsarmsupnor.co.uk
5 changing beers (sourced nationally) [H]
You will find a good choice of five guest real ales here, including a mild, and a selection of ciders, perries and European bottled beers. The large garden often hosts beer festivals. The pub has a reputation for quality food, and offers restaurant and bar menus. Upnor Castle sits at the far end of the High Street – the pub is close to the free village car park. Q ♨ ❀ ◐ ♣ ● P 🚌 (197) 🐾 📶

Tudor Rose ✔

29 High Street, ME2 4XG
☎ (01634) 714175 🌐 tudorroseupnor.co.uk
Shepherd Neame Master Brew, Whitstable Bay Pale Ale; 2 changing beers (sourced nationally) [H]
A pub with character in this quaint village overlooking the River Medway and next to Upnor Castle. The narrow cobbled street dates from the 17th century. There is a large walled garden at the rear, and numerous rooms linked to its L-shaped bar. It has a good reputation for quality food. Customers may use the free car park at the far end of the High Street. Q ♨ ❀ ◐ ♣ ● P 🚌 (197) 🐾 📶

Walmer

Berry 🏆 L

23 Canada Road, CT14 7EQ
☎ (01304) 362411 🌐 theberrywalmer.co.uk
Harvey's Sussex Best Bitter; Oakham Citra [H]; 12 changing beers (often Ramsgate, Time & Tide) [H]/[A]
A multi award-winning alehouse with a warm welcome and friendly service located off Walmer seafront. The bar has a light and airy feel and at the back there is a pleasant patio. There is plenty of choice of quality ales and ciders, with up to 11 cask beers, seven KeyKeg ales (many from Time & Tide), and more than 12 ciders. Three beer festivals are hosted annually. Events include monthly quizzes, live music and pop-up food nights.
♨ ❀ ♣ ● 🚌 🐾

West Malling

Bull Inn L

1 High Street, ME19 6QH
☎ (01732) 842753 🌐 thebullinnwestmalling.com
Goacher's Gold Star Strong Ale; Timothy Taylor Landlord; Young's London Original; 4 changing beers (sourced nationally; often Goacher's, Musket, Ramsgate) [H]
At the north end of the town, near the railway bridge, you will find this friendly free house, with wood panelling and a real fire, and a terrace at the rear. There is a focus on local beers, as well as one local cider on handpump. A quiz is held on Monday evening and live music on some Saturdays. Good food using locally sourced ingredients is offered daily except Monday. A lower-priced beer labelled Bull's Malling Special is normally from Musket. Q ♨ ❀ ◐ ♣ ● 🚌 (72,151) 🐾 📶

Malling Jug

52 High Street, ME19 6LU (in narrow alley opp Swan St between funeral directors' and hospice shop)
☎ (01732) 667832 🌐 themallingjug.co.uk
Kent Session Pale; 7 changing beers (sourced nationally; often Goacher's, Kent, Tiny Rebel) G
A small, stylish pub down an alleyway off the High Street. Current and forthcoming beers are shown on a board near the bar and on clipboards dotted around. Various bottled and canned beers, mainly from the UK and Belgium, are listed at sensible prices. A periodic table of styles helps you to choose your beer. Newspapers are supplied but there is no music or electronic machines. There are snacks to accompany the drinks, and table service is available at busy times. (72,151)

Westerham

Westerham Brewery Tap Room

Beggars Lane, TN16 1QP
☎ (01732) 864427 🌐 westerhambrewery.co.uk
Westerham Spirit of Kent, British Bulldog; 2 changing beers (sourced locally; often Westerham) H
Brewing was proudly restored to Westerham town after an absence of half a century with this modern development, comprising brewery, taproom and shop. The stylish bar offers four core or seasonal cask ales along with a range of keg beers, and is surrounded by merchandise, bottles and mini-casks to take home. Further seating extends among the brewing vessels. Street food operators provide pizzas, burgers and moules Friday through Sunday. Brewery tours are bookable every Friday and Saturday, and many other events are listed on the website. P (1,246)

Westgate-on-Sea

Bake & Alehouse

21 St Mildred's Road, CT8 8RE
☎ 07913 368787 🌐 bakeandalehouse.com
5 changing beers G
A welcoming micropub down the alleyway between the Carlton cinema and a bookmakers', an oasis for the local real ale drinker. Around five changing beers, mainly from Kentish breweries, are served straight from barrels kept in a temperature-controlled room, alongside a selection of Kentish ciders. With seating for around 20 people, the small interior has been managed well, creating a welcoming atmosphere. Locally produced cheese and pork pies are available. Local CAMRA Pub of the Year 2019 and 2020. Q

Whitstable

Black Dog

66 High Street, CT5 1BB
Kent Session Pale; 4 changing beers (sourced regionally; often Angels & Demons, Four Candles, Kent) G
An attractive town-centre micropub, named after a Led Zeppelin song, enjoying lush Victorian decor with a twist. The long, narrow room is lined with high bench seating and quirky artwork. Five changing real ales, displayed on handpumps, are actually dispensed by gravity from the cooled cellar room. Up to 25 ciders and perries, mostly from Kent, are also stocked. The simple menu includes hot and cold food. A quiz is held on the first Wednesday of each month.

Handsome Sam

3 Canterbury Road, CT5 4HJ
☎ 07931 662081
House beer (by Four Candles); 3 changing beers (sourced regionally; often Dark Star, Mighty Oak) G
Popular micropub just outside the town centre and 10 minutes from the railway station. Named after the owner's late cat, the high-ceilinged pub has original exposed beams. The walls are adorned with modern art and guitars, the bay windows with hops. The three or more beers always include a pale ale, a copper ale and a stronger one. The house beer, Old Hector, is brewed by Four Candles. There are 10 ciders, 12 malt whiskies, wines, tea, coffee and snacks. Q

Ship Centurion

111 High Street, CT5 1AY
☎ (01227) 264740
Adnams Southwold Bitter; 4 changing beers (sourced regionally; often Canterbury Ales, Goacher's, Ramsgate) H
A friendly and traditional town-centre pub. Colourful hanging baskets add to its charm in summer, and pictures of Whitstable are displayed in the bar. A Kentish beer is always served. Home-cooked bar food often includes authentic German dishes, and there is a schnitzel on Saturday (no food Sun). Live music plays on Thursday evenings (except in January). A good place to watch sport on Sky.

What is real ale?

Real ale is also known as cask-conditioned beer or simply cask beer. In the brewery, the beer is neither filtered nor pasteurised. It still contains sufficient yeast and sugar for it to continue to ferment and mature in the cask. Once it has reached the pub cellar, it has to be laid down for maturation to continue, and for yeast and protein to settle at the bottom of the cask. Some real ale also has extra hops added as the cask is filled, a process known as 'dry hopping' for increased flavour and aroma. Cask beer is best served at a cellar temperature of 11-13 degrees C, although some stronger ales can benefit from being served a little warmer. Each cask has two holes, in one of which a tap is inserted and is connected to tubes or 'lines' that enable the beer to be drawn to the bar. The other hole, on top of the cask, enables some carbon dioxide produced during secondary fermentation to escape. It is vital that some gas, which gives the beer its natural sparkle or condition, is kept within the cask: the escape of gas is controlled by inserting porous wooden pegs called spiles into the spile hole. Real ale is a living product and must be consumed within three or four days of a cask being tapped as oxidation develops.

George, Bethersden, Kent (p189)

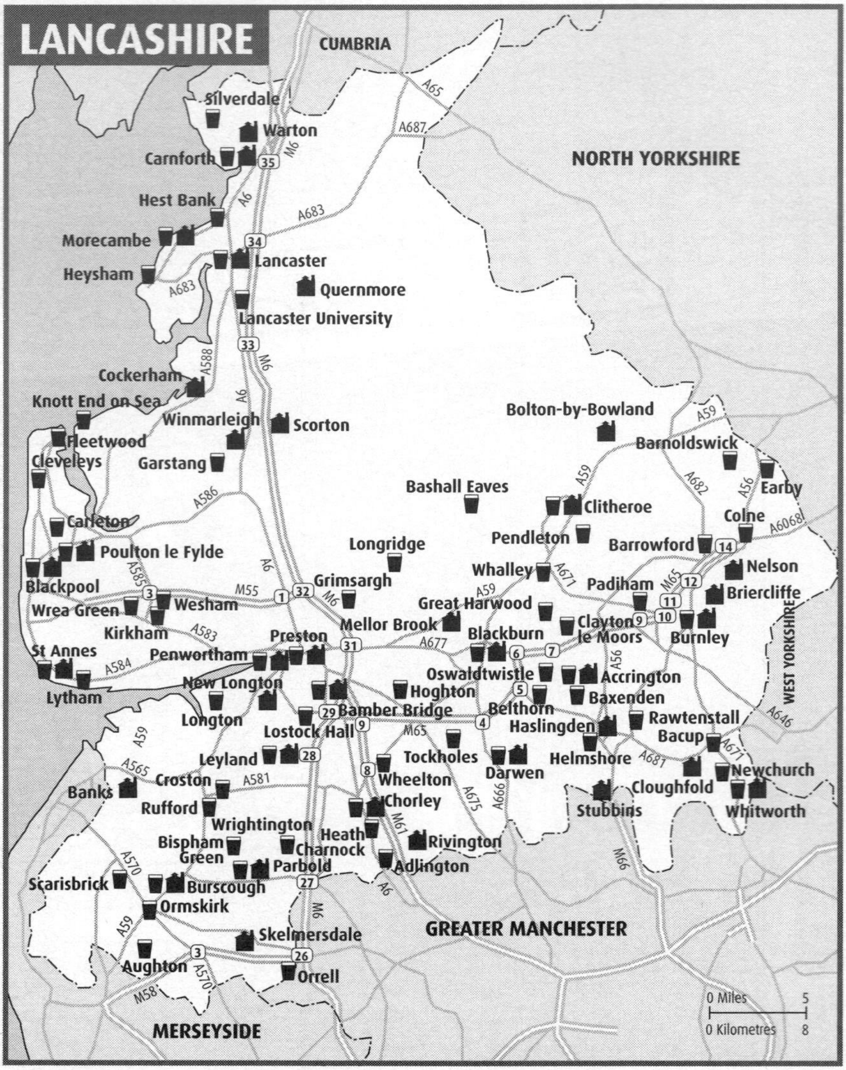

Accrington

Canine Club 𝕃

45-47 Abbey Street, BB5 1EN

☎ (01254) 233999

Tetley Bitter; 3 changing beers (sourced nationally; often Old School, Reedley Hallows, Worsthorne) 🄷

An award-winning social club in an area of the town centre known for its many independent retailers. The central bar serves a comfortable lounge to the front, and a games room to the rear where snooker, pool and darts are played. There is a large upstairs function room. This traditional club is always busy but is welcoming to all. Alongside the Tetley Bitter there is a changing range usually featuring local breweries, plus a visitor from further afield, often Old School microbrewery. The Canine was a recent local and regional CAMRA Club of the Year.

⇌♣🚌(464,X41) 📶

Adlington

Spinners Arms 𝕃

23 Church Street, PR7 4EX

☎ (01257) 483331

Moorhouse's Pride of Pendle; Rudgate Ruby Mild; 5 changing beers (sourced regionally; often Abbeydale, Oakham) 🄷

The pub is known as the Bottom Spinners to differentiate it from the other Spinners Arms in the village. Built in 1838, it is welcoming and friendly; a single bar serves three seating areas. There is no pool table or gaming machine, just an open log fire. The bar menu offers home-cooked food with Sunday specials. Two regular cask ales and five alternating guest ales are served, often from local breweries. Small functions are catered for. There is a pleasant drinking space outside at the front.

🐴❀◐⇌P🚌(8A) 🐾📶

Aughton

Derby Arms

Prescot Road, L39 6TA (on B3197 at Bowkers Green between Ormskirk and Kirby)
(01695) 422237
Tetley Bitter; 4 changing beers (often Lytham, Rudgate)
Friendly country pub with a long CAMRA award-winning heritage. The interior is intimate, with many small nooks and crannies, and there is a changing choice of beers on three guest handpumps from a wide range of local or national breweries. Quiz nights are held on Tuesdays and Thursdays and regular charity events are hosted. Excellent-value food is served, including breakfast on Saturdays. Q P

Bacup

Crown Inn

19 Greave Road, OL13 9HQ
(01706) 873982
Pictish Brewers Gold; 3 changing beers (sourced regionally)
Cosy traditional country pub with a large L-shaped bar and stone-flagged floors throughout. Built in 1865, it was once owned by Baxter's of Glentop Brewery. A welcoming coal fire adds warmth in the cooler months. There are always three beers on, usually sourced locally, and food is available most evenings. Quiz nights are hosted on Wednesday and Sunday, and on the second floor is a function room accommodating up to 35 guests. There is a patio beer garden to the front. Beer festivals feature in July and October. P (465)

Bamber Bridge

Beer Box

Unit 3, 143 Station Road, PR5 6LA
(01772) 339619
5 changing beers (sourced locally)
This is Bamber Bridge's second micropub. It opened in 2018 and is on the main road running through the northern end of the town, in premises previously occupied by North West Domestic Services. There is one relatively large room with plenty of seating and some standing room as well. Up to five real ales are dispensed, including one dark beer, mainly from local breweries. Q (125)

Brig 'n' Barrel

188 Station Road, PR5 6TP
07728 794755 brig-n-barrel.business.site
6 changing beers (sourced locally)
Bamber Bridge's first micropub opened in 2018 in a former electrical shop. It specialises in quality cask and craft beers and gins. There are six handpumps serving a changing selection of mostly locally brewed beers from smaller breweries, and two real ciders are also available. There is just one room in this dog-friendly, cosy, rustic establishment, with a small amount of outside seating. Q (125)

Barnoldswick

Barlick Tap Ale House

8 Newtown, BB18 5UQ
07739 088846
5 changing beers (sourced nationally)
This friendly one-room micropub was the first to be established in the town. It is just off the town square, two minutes from the main bus stop. A choice of five changing cask ales is offered, one of which is a dark beer and one a LocAle. There is also a large selection of continental bottled beers and always two ciders. The pub hosts occasional events and tastings, and is free of music. Q (X43,280)

Barrowford

Bankers Draft

143 Gisburn Road, BB9 6HQ
07739 870880
5 changing beers (sourced nationally)
This imposing detached former bank is now a small and friendly micropub, specialising in real ale and conversation, with no loud music or TVs. The five handpumps dispense continually rotating cask ales from national small brewers, offering a great variety of beer styles, from hoppy blondes and traditional bitters to dark beers. There is also a good selection of wines and bottled craft lagers and wheat beers, with at least one real cider normally on draught. Q P (2)

Bashall Eaves

Red Pump Inn

BB7 3DA
(01254) 826227 theredpumpinn.co.uk

REAL ALE BREWERIES

3 Piers Poulton-le-Fylde
4 Mice Bolton-by-Bowland
Accidental Lancaster
Avid Quernmore
Beer Brothers Bamber Bridge
Big Clock Accrington
Bishop's Crook Penwortham
Bowland Clitheroe
Brewsmith Stubbins
Chain House New Longton
Chapel Street Poulton-le-Fylde
Clay Brow Skelmersdale
Crankshaft Leyland
Cross Bay Morecambe
Farm Yard Cockerham
Fuzzy Duck Poulton-le-Fylde
Hop Vine Burscough
Hopstar Darwen
Lancaster Lancaster
Lytham St Annes (brewing suspended)
Mighty Medicine Whitworth
Moorhouse's Burnley
Northern Whisper Cloughfold
Old School Warton
Oscars Nelson
Parker Banks
Patten Winmarleigh (NEW)
Priest Town Preston
Problem Child Parbold
Providence Bamber Bridge
Q Brew Carnforth
Reedley Hallows Burnley
Rivington Rivington
Rock Solid Blackpool
Rossendale Haslingden
Snowhill Scorton
Three B's Blackburn
Thwaites Mellor Brook
West Coast Rock Blackpool
Withnell's Chorley
Worsthorne Briercliffe

Copper Dragon Scotts 1816; 2 changing beers (sourced locally; often Hopstar, Reedley Hallows, Three B's) H
Large, mainly dining country pub near Clitheroe. There is a central bar with three handpumps, and a casual drinking area opposite. A chalkboard behind the bar provides tasting notes for current beers. Meals are served Friday and Saturday evenings and Sunday lunchtimes only. Real fires add warmth in winter, and hunting and sporting memorabilia adorn the walls. There are spectacular views across to Pendle Hill and Longridge Fell, and this is ideal country for walking and cycling. Opening hours may be reduced in winter. ❀⇌◑P🐾

Baxenden

Dog & Partridge ✔
41 Back Lane, BB5 2RE
☎ (01254) 239992
Theakston Best Bitter; 4 changing beers (sourced nationally) H
A popular village pub which sits on the original road from Accrington to Manchester. Behind it is Baxenden Cricket Club, who play in the Ribblesdale League. The Dog has been partially opened up but retains separate areas for drinking. A weekly quiz is hosted and there is usually entertainment on Saturday night. Note the etched Lion Ales on the glass of the entrance door. Buses from Accrington to Manchester and the Rossendale Valley pass close by. ❀♣P🚌

Belthorn

Dog Inn L
61 Belthorn Road, BB1 2NN
☎ (01254) 433188 🌐 thedoginnatbelthorn.net
3 changing beers (sourced locally) H
This is the first community-owned pub in East Lancashire and is run as a community benefit society. It has flagged floors on several levels and a real fire. Situated in hill country, with great views across the moors and out to the coast, it is popular with walkers and their dogs. Full meals are served lunchtimes and evenings, with a coffee shop menu in between. Beers are mainly from the local Three B's and Blackedge breweries. ❀◑♣●P🚌🐾📶

Bispham Green

Eagle & Child
Malt Kiln Lane, L40 3SG
☎ (01257) 462297 🌐 eagleandchildbispham.co.uk
Southport Golden Sands; Thwaites Original; Wainwright; 5 changing beers (sourced regionally) H
An 18th-century inn with eight handpumps showcasing local ales. Southport Golden Sands is always served and a variety of guests include Prospect, Wigan Brewhouse and Moorhouse's. This busy country venue has been Lancashire Dining Pub of the Year and is noted for its food. The huge beer garden, with its wildlife area and fine views, hosts a beer festival on the first May bank holiday. Quiz night is every Monday. ♉❀◑●P🐾📶

Blackburn

Black Bull L
Brokenstone Road, BB3 0LL (corner of Brokenstone Rd and Heys Lane) SD666247
☎ (01254) 581381 🌐 threebsbrewery.co.uk
Three B's Stoker's Slake, Bobbin's Bitter, Oatmeal Stout, Black Bull, Weavers Brew, Knocker Up; 2 changing beers (sourced locally; often Three B's) H
In the heart of rural Lancashire, this is an independent award-winning family-run inn with brewery attached. There are eight handpumps serving a fine selection of Three B's ales, including the exclusive Black Bull Bitter. The three-beer wedges are popular. It was built on a farmhouse in the 18th century, purchased by Robert Bell from Thwaites, and transformed to a pub for those who appreciate fine beer and friendly conversation. You won't find a jukebox, fruit machines or food, just a friendly, relaxing atmosphere. Q♉❀♿♣P🐾

Drummers Arms L
65 King William Street, BB1 7DT
☎ 07341 565657
Three B's Stoker's Slake; 4 changing beers (sourced locally; often Big Clock, Cross Bay, Hopstar) H
Single-roomed bar on the pedestrianised area opposite the town hall. It is handy for the library and King George's Hall and provides a refuge from the hordes of shoppers in the nearby mall. The walls are adorned with breweriana and old pub signs. The bar hosts occasional live music sessions; at other times expect a range of classic tracks from the eclectic jukebox. Most beers are from nearby breweries, though a visitor from afar sometimes puts in an appearance. The large front windows make this a great place for watching the world go by. ⇌●🚌🐾

Hare & Hounds L
78 Lammack Road, BB1 8LA
☎ (01254) 676724
4 changing beers (sourced regionally; often Bowland, Reedley Hallows, Worsthorne) H
Former Whitbread estate pub rescued by the current landlord and backed by a passionate local community. It is adjacent to Old Blackburnians FC, and to Pleckgate and Lammack playing fields. Local breweries such as Three B's, Bowland, Reedley Hallows, Moorhouse's and Worsthorne feature regularly. The large, comfortable open-plan lounge is served from a bar with five handpumps. There is a variety of quality live entertainment at weekends, when it can get busy. ♉❀♿♣P🚌(25,10) 🐾

Blackpool

1887 The Brew Room L
139-141 Church Street, FY1 3NU
☎ (01253) 319165 🌐 thebrewroom1887.co.uk
West Coast Rock Blackpool Blonde, Golden Mile, Oyston Stout, Tangerine Dream, Wonky Donkey; 5 changing beers (sourced nationally; often Anarchy, Cross Bay, Tiny Rebel) H
Blackpool's first brewpub of recent times, home to the West Coast Rock Brewery, reopened in December 2018 approximately 150 yards from the Winter Gardens. A viewing platform overlooks the brewery and visitors are encouraged to watch the process. The pub offers a selection of 10 real ales, ciders and craft beers as well as authentic German lagers. A simple menu of sizeable snacks is served all day. Live music features on most Friday and Saturday nights and a popular quiz is held on Monday. ♉⇌🚊♣●🚌🐾📶

Albert's Ale Micropub L
117 Albert Road, FY1 4PW
☎ (01253) 292827 🌐 blackpoolmicrobar.co.uk
4 changing beers (sourced locally) H/G
Quirky hotel cellar bar close to the Winter Gardens complex in the heart of Blackpool's hotel quarter. It is just 10 minutes' walk from the Promenade and Tower. At least four changing ales are served, mostly from local brewers and normally including a dark beer. A wide

range of ciders, perries and predominantly Belgian bottled beers is also available. The hotel has 11 comfortable bedrooms. Level access is available on request. Closed Monday to Wednesday.

Blackpool Cricket Club

Barlow Crescent, West Park Drive, FY3 9EQ (follow signs to Stanley Park)

☎ (01253) 393347 blackpoolcricket.co.uk

Wainwright; 4 changing beers (sourced regionally; often Cumbrian Legendary Ales, Moorhouse's, Reedley Hallows)

On the western edge of Stanley Park, this club hosts many sports teams. Several TVs show various sports fixtures. Upstairs function rooms are available for social events. The venue has its own squash courts and holds quiz and entertainment nights, as well as an annual beer festival. There is free entry to the club and all cricket games except Lancashire's. A many-times local CAMRA Club of the Year. P (18)

Layton Rakes

17-25 Market Street, FY1 1ET

☎ (01253) 743710

Greene King Abbot; Ruddles Best Bitter; Sharp's Doom Bar; 7 changing beers (sourced regionally; often Acorn, Bank Top, Phoenix)

Built on the site of two former shops in 2011, this warm and friendly pub welcomes locals and visitors. With its town-centre location it is ideal for meeting up for drinks after shopping and can get busy at weekends and during the holiday season. If you prefer a quiet drink or meal, the first floor is ideal, and there is a rooftop terrace for good weather. Bars are on all three floors, which are accessible by lift.

No.10 Ale House

258 Whitegate Drive, FY3 9JW

☎ (01253) 694913

5 changing beers (sourced regionally; often Acorn, Bradfield, Titanic)

Sister pub to No.10 in St Annes on Sea, this micropub opened in 2018. The bright front room and bar area leads to a comfortable rear room. On the bar are five ales sourced from all over, plus two ciders. There is also an upstairs room where diners can partake of a popular Thai menu. The walls indicate the owners' support for Blackpool Football Club, and display many fine prints of bygone Blackpool. A bus stop is outside.

Burnley

Boot Inn

18 St James' Street, BB11 1NG

☎ (01282) 463720

Reedley Hallows Nook of Pendle; Ruddles Best Bitter; Sharp's Doom Bar; house beer (by Worsthorne); 8 changing beers (sourced nationally)

A Wetherspoon close to the bus station on the main shopping street. There is a long rounded bar, pictures of old Burnley, seating at differing levels and all of the usual Wetherspoon amenities. The current building replaced an old inn which was once a farmhouse. It was designed by Blackpool architect H Thomson and built in 1911 in the Edwardian baroque style, as was the White Lion on the opposite corner. Q

Bridge Bier Huis

2 Bank Parade, BB11 1UH

☎ (01282) 411304 thebridgebierhuis.co.uk

Moorhouse's Premier Bitter; 4 changing beers (sourced regionally)

An award-winning true free house with a large open-plan bar that has a log-burner and a small snug to one side. It offers mainly microbrewery beers alongside a changing real cider. More than 60 foreign bottled beers are sold, plus seven foreign beers on tap including rare German brews. Wednesday is quiz night and live music is hosted on occasional weekends. This welcoming pub opens Monday or Tuesday evening if Burnley FC are at home. P

New Brew-m

11 St James Row, BB11 1DR

☎ 07902 961426

Reedley Hallows Pendleside; 5 changing beers (sourced nationally)

A smart micropub in the centre of town which is run as the Reedley Hallows Brewery tap. There is always at least one of its own beers on the bar, alongside five others sourced nationwide using the head brewer's contacts from years in the trade. A good range of foreign bottled beers and bottled ciders is available. The fully glazed frontage makes the bar feel light and airy. There is a small room upstairs for extra seating. Open on a Tuesday evening if Burnley FC are at home. Q

Talbot

65 Church Street, BB11 2RS

☎ (01282) 412074 talbotburnley.co.uk

Moorhouse's Premier Bitter; Timothy Taylor Boltmaker; 6 changing beers

A warm welcome awaits you at this large free house just off the town centre and dating back to the 1800s. The licensee is a real ale enthusiast and keen supporter of local breweries. Live music features every weekend. There are two pool tables plus a large-screen TV for sports fans. Four well-appointed en-suite rooms are available for guests, who also have use of the private car park. P (M2,M3)

Burscough

Hop Vine

Liverpool Road North, L40 4BY (in village centre on A59)

☎ (01704) 893799 thehopvinepub.co.uk

Timothy Taylor Landlord; 4 changing beers (sourced regionally; often Hop Vine, Salopian)

This spacious former coaching house is now a thriving community brewpub renowned for its friendly atmosphere and popular for its exceptional ale and food. The classic country-pub interior has wood panelling and characterful wood flooring throughout and is decorated with historic local maps, photographs and vintage bottled ales. The Hop Vine Brewery operates from the attractive floral courtyard at the rear. Catering for all ages, the pub offers great-value meals, live music, and twice-yearly beer festivals. P

Old Packet House

29 Liverpool Road North, L40 5TN

☎ (01704) 807330

Coach House Blonde; 3 changing beers (often Bank Top, Prospect)

A typical village canalside venue in the centre of Burscough. The licensee says he is concentrating on real ale although he also serves food afternoons and evenings (except Mon & Tue). You can watch the canal boats go past from the garden or the canalside, and the pub is just over the road from Burscough Wharf, so is ideal for a ramble along the canal with its many pubs offering real ale. There is a series of old prints of Burscough on the walls inside.

Carleton

Castle Gardens ✓

Poulton Road, FY6 7NH

☎ (01253) 890015

Moorhouse's White Witch; Purity Pure UBU; Wainwright; house beer (by Black Sheep); 5 changing beers (sourced nationally) Ⓗ

There has been a pub on this site since about 1750. This popular establishment is both a food-led destination and a local community venue. A range of nine ales is normally available including five changing guests. A weekly quiz takes place every Tuesday and live music plays regularly at weekends. There is a large outdoor drinking area to the side. ♨❀◑♿⛺●P🚌(14)🐾📶

Carnforth

Royal Station

Market Street, LA5 9BT

☎ (01524) 733636 🌐 royalstation.co.uk

6 changing beers Ⓗ

Traditional Victorian station hotel which is slowly getting a facelift. A grand entrance and a foyer lead to a tapas bar, while round the back is the larger and more basic Junction Bar (revamped in 2016), where the games, real ale and live music on Friday and Saturday nights are to be found. In 1900 it became the Royal Station Hotel in recognition of the fact that the Duke of York, later to become George V, availed himself of the hotel's hospitality during a shooting trip. A microbrewery is planned. ❀◑≹♣🚌🐾📶

Snug

Unit 6, Carnforth Gateway Building, LA5 9TR (at N end of former mainline up platform)

☎ 07927 396861 🌐 thesnugmicropub.blogspot.co.uk

5 changing beers Ⓗ

The area's first micropub, where the only drinks are ale, cider, wine, a few soft drinks and at least 10 good-quality gins; the only food a few light snacks; and the only sounds conversation and the roar of passing trains. The decor is similarly stripped back to painted walls, bare floorboards and tall, chunky tables. The eye is naturally drawn to a beautiful glazed wooden cabinet, where all the drinks are stored. Parking is in the station car park (a charge applies). Q❀♿≹♣●▯🚌🐾

Chorley

Ale Station 🄻 ✓

60 Chapel Street, PR7 1BS

☎ (01257) 368003

6 changing beers (sourced locally; often Hawkshead, Rock the Boat) Ⓗ

Family-run micropub conveniently near to both the bus and train stations. A modern-looking venue with a wine-bar feel, this inviting pub offers a full range of drinks. Nine changing real ales are served, mainly from north-western microbreweries, although expect to find others from far and wide. There are also two changing real ciders, craft lager and fine wines. A state of the art digital display board provides full price information and real ale details, in addition to updated train times for the railway traveller. Pictures of old Chorley adorn the walls. Q♿≹●🚌🐾📶

Bob Inn

24 Market Place, PR7 1DA

☎ 07767 238410

3 changing beers (sourced nationally) Ⓗ

A tiny bar housed in a market stall with an adjacent unit now used as a lounge area; this multi award-winning pub is the smallest outlet in the local CAMRA branch area. Outside seating is available and drinkers often spread out into the market. With three changing cask beers from smaller breweries nationally, and at least two real ciders, there is something for every taste. Conversation and banter are an important part of the experience. No food is served but you are welcome to bring your own. Q♨♿≹●🚌🐾

Malt 'n' Hops 🄻

50-52 Friday Street, PR6 0AA

☎ (01257) 260074

Bank Top Dark Mild; 8 changing beers (sourced nationally; often Fernandes, Moorhouse's, Rat) Ⓗ

Converted from an old shop in 1989, the pub is handily situated for both the railway and bus stations. It has a single L-shaped bar on two levels with a bright yet traditional feel, and a pleasant beer garden. A genuine free house, it offers two regular dark beers and up to seven changing ales usually from Lancashire and Yorkshire micros, including Rat, Wily Fox, Ossett, Elland, Lancaster, Fernandes, Goose Eye and Blackedge. Good-value filled rolls and pork pies are usually available. ♨❀≹●🚌🐾📶

Masons Arms 🄻

98 Harpers Lane, PR6 0HU

☎ 07464 841589

6 changing beers (sourced locally; often Blackedge, Pictish) Ⓗ

Tastefully modernised multi-room pub a mile from the town centre. The taproom has six changing ales on at any one time, usually including a dark beer, mainly from north-west micros, although beers from further afield are also offered. The taproom and two lounges complete with wood-burning stoves give distinctly different drinking areas. Light and airy, this is a cosy place with a growing reputation for good beer. Pizzas are served daily. Awarded local CAMRA Most Improved Pub of the Year in 2018. ♨❀🚌(24,125)🐾📶

Prince of Wales ✓

9-11 Cowling Brow, PR6 0QE

☎ (01257) 260815

Banks's Sunbeam; Jennings Cumberland Ale; Marston's 61 Deep; Wainwright; 4 changing beers (sourced nationally) Ⓗ

Friendly multi-roomed local with a central bar that serves a taproom, large lounge and pool room, with a further room off the entrance hall. There are real fires in both lounges and a beer garden to the rear. Close to the Leeds-Liverpool canal and with access nearby, this is a great walkers' pub; dogs are welcome and treats are provided. Live music plays at the weekends but the place is quiet at other times. Eight beers from the Marston's stable are usually on offer, with the guest beers changing regularly. Sandwiches and pies may be available. ♨❀≹♣🚌🐾📶

Shepherds' Hall Ale House 🄻

67 Chapel Street, PR7 1BS

5 changing beers (sourced nationally) Ⓗ

A friendly and welcoming bar next door to the bus station. This first micropub in Chorley opened in 2014 and was refurbished in 2020. Up to five beers are served from microbreweries all over the country. You should find a wide range of beer styles, always including a dark ale. Third-of-a-pint beer paddles are available alongside two real ciders, two craft keg lines often featuring Rivington brews, and a wide variety of other drinks to suit all tastes. Q≹♣●▯🚌🐾📶

Clayton le Moors

Old England Forever ✔
13 Church Street, BB5 5HT
☎ (01254) 383332
Bank Top Dark Mild, Flat Cap; 4 changing beers (sourced nationally; often Bank Top, Prospect) Ⓗ
Acquired by the Bank Top Brewery in 2018, this Edwardian terraced pub was completely refurbished prior to reopening in a style reminiscent of the brewery's establishments in and around Bolton. It sits just off Barnes Square and is easily reached from the towpath of the Leeds-Liverpool canal. The single room has long bar with a section of glass flooring in front offering views of the cellar. The building is wheelchair-friendly and has fully accessible toilets. Q❀♿♣●🚌(6,7)

Cleveleys

Jolly Tars ✔
154–158 Victoria Road West, FY5 3NE
☎ (01253) 856042
Greene King Abbot; Ruddles Best Bitter; Sharp's Doom Bar; 7 changing beers (sourced nationally; often Bank Top, Moorhouse's, Phoenix) Ⓗ
The Jolly Tars is named after a popular nine-strong family troupe who entertained the locals and visiting crowds during the 1940s. It has a great reputation for food and drinks and friendly staff, and is a welcoming environment in which to enjoy a quiet drink, with several secluded booths. The popular front drinking area can get busy. Several bespoke pieces of John Ditchfield Glasform glass decorate the pub. ❀◐♿●🚌

Clitheroe

Bowland Beer Hall ✔
Greenacre Street, BB7 1EB
☎ (01200) 401035 🌐 holmesmill.co.uk/beer-hall
Bowland Pheasant Plucker, Gold, AONB, Boxer Blonde, Hen Harrier, Buster IPA; changing beers (sourced nationally) Ⓗ
The enormously popular beer hall is now a major part of Clitheroe's thriving beer scene. Up to 24 guest ales are on offer alongside a large number from the on-site Bowland Brewery, visible from the main bar area. There are many beery events such as Meet the Brewer evenings. A completely new selection of ales is offered every Thursday, with weekly drink-up sessions. The complex hosts a hotel, cinema, coffee shop and delicatessen and is a short walk from Clitheroe Castle and the town centre. Many buses stop close by. ❀◐♿≉●P🚌🐾

New Inn 🄻
20 Parson Lane, BB7 2JN
☎ (01200) 423312
Coach House Gunpowder Mild, Farrier's Best Bitter, Blueberry Classic Bitter; Moorhouse's Premier Bitter, Pride of Pendle, Blonde Witch; 5 changing beers (sourced regionally; often Prospect, Saltaire, Worsthorne) Ⓗ
The bar at the New Inn is a welcome sight, with at least 10 beers on offer. The bar itself is central, with a number of smaller rooms clustered around it. In addition to the regular beers from Coach House and Moorehouse's you may also find the likes of Saltaire, Ilkley, Prospect or Wharfedale breweries represented. The pub dates from the early 1800s and faces Clitheroe Castle. It's just a short walk from the bus and railway stations. Q❀▲≉🚌🐾

Colne

Admiral Lord Rodney 🄻
Mill Green, BB8 0TA
☎ (01282) 219759 🌐 thelordrodney.co.uk
9 changing beers (sourced regionally; often Goose Eye, Ilkley, Reedley Hallows) Ⓗ
A much-loved community pub in Colne's South Valley area, the old industrial heart of the town. The stone-flagged floor includes mosaics, and there are beautiful tiles up the inner staircase. Set out in three rooms, the venue has become the meeting place for a number of clubs. There is regular live entertainment during the evenings, plus local history and art displays. There has been a recent refurbishment, with open fires and flagged floors, plus a much-improved outdoor seating area and a separate smokers' area. All are made welcome.
Q❀◐♣🐾

Boyce's Barrel
7 New Market Street, BB8 9BJ
☎ 07736 900111
5 changing beers (sourced nationally) Ⓗ
The first micropub in Colne, a member of the Micropub Association, offering five high-quality real ales, with no music or lager, just a great atmosphere and plenty of banter. Tastefully styled with tall polished wooden sleeper tables, it is reminiscent of a rail staging post. Ales are rotated often, with new beers put on the bar almost as soon as a barrel runs dry. All ales are from non-local breweries, and one mild and one porter or stout are always among the range. A place that's sure to suit any real ale fan's tastes. Q♿≉●🚌🐾

Croston

Wheatsheaf ✔
Town Road, PR26 9RA
☎ (01772) 600370 🌐 wheatsheaf-croston.com
Goose Eye Chinook Blonde; Hawkshead Windermere Pale; Hop Back Summer Lightning; 2 changing beers (sourced nationally) Ⓗ
On the main road and overlooking the village green, this recently refurbished venue has a contemporary feel. It has a distinct area for dining as well as a comfortable drinking space with sofas and chairs. There is a large patio to the front, which is used to hold an annual beer festival during October. Three regular and two changing ales are served. Children are welcome. Food is available lunchtimes and evenings during the week and all day at weekends, with the pub opening for breakfast on Saturday and Sunday. ❀◐♿≉P🚌🐾

Darwen

Bird in th' hand 🄻
225 Duckworth Street, BB3 1AU
☎ 07926 115292
4 changing beers (sourced regionally; often Blackedge, Hopstar, Three B's) Ⓗ
A bar-cum-bottle shop with four handpumps and one boxed cider. There are 10 craft lines, and three for ciders. One wall has shelves with a wide range of Belgian, international and UK bottled beers, some of which are bottle conditioned, and craft ciders, which can be consumed on or off the premises. One room has benches with a log-burner, another has relaxing sofas. Toilets are upstairs. The bar may close earlier at the start of the week if it's quiet. Named after the inn which stood here over 100 years ago. ≉●🚌(1)🐾

Earby

Red Lion 𝕃

72 Red Lion Street, BB18 6RD

☎ (01282) 843395

Naylor's Gold, Pinnacle Blonde; 4 changing beers (sourced locally; often Settle) 🄷

A warm and friendly welcome awaits you from both host and regulars. This is a truly traditional country pub, owned by local people. Both rooms have been renovated with taste, including a wood-burner in the lounge. An extensive food menu is served in the lounge lunchtimes and evenings. The pub is close to a holiday hostel and is a drinkers' delight. Q

Fleetwood

Royal Oak Hotel 𝕃

171 Lord Street, FY7 6SR

☎ (01253) 873486

Banks's Sunbeam; house beer (by Reedley Hallows); 5 changing beers (sourced locally; often Blackedge, Moorhouse's, Worsthorne) 🄷

Known locally as Dead 'Uns, this pub was rescued from closure in 2013, and still retains many original features. Up to five beers are dispensed along with cider, the beers usually coming from within a 50-mile radius. There is a small outside drinking area at the rear and dogs are permitted in the vaults. Away fans are welcome when playing Fleetwood Town FC. Live music features occasionally on Friday and Saturday nights.

Steamer

Queens Terrace, FY7 6BT

☎ (01253) 681001

Lancaster Red; Reedley Hallows Pendleside; 3 changing beers (sourced nationally; often Bowness Bay, Cross Bay, Kirkby Lonsdale) 🄷

One of Fleetwood's oldest pubs, this former coaching inn is close to the town's museum and Fleetwood Market, and convenient for buses, trams and the Knott End ferry. Up to five beers are served. Live music features on Friday and Saturday nights, with a singer on Tuesday afternoon and karaoke on Friday afternoon. Pool, darts, dominoes and snooker can be played. If you are lucky, you might be served by TV legend Syd Little. Food is available Tuesday to Sunday.

Garstang

Th' Owd Tithe Barn ✔

Church Street, PR3 1PA

☎ (01995) 604486 🌐 tithebarngarstang.com

Wainwright; 3 changing beers 🄷

This pub was built in 1701 as a tithe barn. The canal company later dug a large basin next to it, enabling perfect patio drinking in the summer. It was converted to a pub-restaurant in 1973. Most of the interior is a large dining area heated by a substantial wood-burning stove, but there are two smaller rooms which are comfortably pubby and well used by locals. The building is open to the rafters and the space aloft houses a display of obsolete agricultural implements. Quiz night is Tuesday.

P

Great Harwood

1B Tap

1B Glebe Street, BB6 7AA

4 changing beers (sourced nationally)

Welcoming two-roomed bar opened in former office premises by three real ale enthusiasts. It is close to Towngate square and preservation area, on a side street opposite the post office. The main room, featuring plenty of brewery-related items, sells a changing and skilfully selected range of cask beers, which usually includes a stout or porter. Local breweries such as Snaggletooth are predominant. A side room housing a separate bar serving gin and world beers offers additional seating. Note the collection of beer festival glasses on display in the bar.

P(6,7)

Grimsargh

Plough 𝕃 ✔

187 Preston Road, PR2 5JR

☎ (01772) 700666 🌐 ploughgrimsargh.co.uk

Timothy Taylor Landlord; house beer (by Theakston); 3 changing beers (sourced nationally; often Blackedge, Lancaster, Titanic) 🄷

Large traditional village pub with separate bar and dining areas. On the main Preston to Longridge road in the centre of the village, it has a friendly and welcoming atmosphere. Good home-cooked food is served. Popular with the locals, this place is family-friendly, with a large garden at the rear. Dogs are welcome in the bar area. There are five handpumps with two regular beers, Timothy Taylor Landlord and Grimsargh Wetlands (Theakston's Lightfoot) plus three guests ales, one of which is a LocAle from the SIBA list.

P(1)

Heath Charnock

Yew Tree 𝕃

Dill Hall Brow, PR6 9HA

☎ (01257) 480344 🌐 yewtreeinnanglezarke.co.uk

4 changing beers (sourced locally; often Blackedge, Northern Monkey) 🄷

Attractive, isolated, stone-built inn with great views over open countryside. With flagged floors on two levels, the interior is essentially open plan, but walls and partitions divide it into cosy areas. The bar showcases ales from the nearby Blackedge and Northern Monkey breweries, as well as a guest from another independent local brewery. The Yew Tree has long had a reputation for quality food, with a full range of meals made from locally sourced produce wherever possible. Dogs are welcome in the bar area but not the restaurant. Closing time can vary.

Q P

Helmshore

Robin Hood Inn 𝕃 ✔

280 Holcombe Road, BB4 4NP

☎ (01706) 404200

Hydes Original; 4 changing beers (sourced locally) 🄷

Traditional stone-built village pub which, although opened up, still retains the impression of having three separate rooms, with two open fires. The original Glen Top Brewery windows are a feature. Beers from the seasonal ranges of Hydes and Beer Studio dominate the changing range. A quiz night is held on Thursday. A small beer garden overlooking Helmshore Textile Museum and lodge can be reached by steps to the side.

Q (11)

Hest Bank

Crossing

6 Coastal Road, LA2 6HN

☎ 07584 660075

5 changing beers (sourced nationally) Ⓗ
Former café that opened as a micropub in 2018. A stone-built, possibly Victorian, building with a timber extension and a plate-glass window from café days, it has a U-shaped layout, with the bar counter near the entrance on one side. There is a wood-burning stove in the middle and a back room offering games, copies of Railway magazine and photos of Hest Bank station (closed 1969). The name refers to the fact that the pub is close to both one of the last level crossings on the West Coast Main Line and the ancient route over the sands.
Q♣🚌(5,55)🐾📶

Heysham

Bookmakers ✔
364 Heysham Road, LA3 2BJ
☎ 07785 257648
5 changing beers Ⓗ
A new micropub in a former betting shop, set among other shops in a suburban neighbourhood; a most welcome addition to the micropub scene in this area. The single wedge-shaped room is done out in industrial chic, with a few comfy chairs and bar stools and an arrangement of standing and seating areas. It attracts large numbers of locals. ♿♣🍎🚌🐾

Hoghton

Royal Oak Ⓛ
Blackburn Old Road, Riley Green, PR5 0SL
☎ (01254) 201445 🌐 royaloak-rileygreen.co.uk/index.htm
Thwaites Mild, Original, Gold; 2 changing beers (sourced regionally) Ⓗ
An attractive stone-built pub on the old road between Preston and Blackburn, near Riley Green basin on the Leeds-Liverpool canal. Popular with diners and drinkers alike, it has four distinct rooms including the dining area served from the long bar. Low-beamed ceilings, bare walls and traditional decor give the rooms a rustic feel. A pleasant beer garden has views of nearby Hoghton Tower. There are three regular Thwaites cask ales and two changing guest beers, normally from Thwaites or from the Marston's range. Q🔥❀◐◑🍎P🚌(152)🐾📶

Kirkham

Tap & Vent Brewhouse Ⓛ
26 Poulton Street, PR4 2AB
8 changing beers (sourced regionally; often Lytham) Ⓗ
A traditional-looking shop from the outside, a modern pub on the inside, this is the new home to Lytham Brewery right in the centre of Kirkham, just up from the Market Square and bus stops. Its beers feature but do not dominate the bar, which has a good range of guest ales, continental lagers and bottled beers in two large fridges. A quieter snug is hidden behind the bar.
Q🔥❀♿♣🍎🚌🐾📶

Knott End on Sea

Knott End Working Mens Club
Salisbury Avenue, FY6 0BP
☎ (01253) 812226 🌐 knottendwmc.co.uk
3 changing beers (often Bank Top) Ⓗ
Friendly private club which allows CAMRA members free entry on production of a membership card or a copy of the Guide; otherwise it's £1 entry. It has three main rooms, with one central bar serving three cask beers, mostly from fairly local breweries. There is a comfortable lounge to the right on entry. A large games room including snooker and pool tables is to the rear, and a function room is available for private parties, live music and other club events. 🔥❀◐♿♣P🚌(2C,89)📶

Lancaster

Bobbin ✔
36 Cable Street, LA1 1HH
☎ (01524) 32606
5 changing beers (often Anarchy, Dark Star, Tiny Rebel) Ⓗ
Large mainly Victorian and part 18th-century pub, entirely open plan but with raised areas and pillars creating separate spaces. It has 70s-style flock wallpaper and laminate flooring throughout. There is an extremely eclectic jukebox, plus live music Friday and Saturday and pool night on Wednesday. The Bobbin is frequented by a goth/metal crowd but they are by no means the only customers. Handy for the bus station. ❀♿⇌♣🍎🚌🐾📶

Cornerhouse
34 New Street, LA1 1HU
☎ (01524) 845939 🌐 cornerhouselancaster.co.uk
8 changing beers (sourced locally; often Cumbrian Legendary Ales, Farm Yard) Ⓗ
A conversion of one end of an old department store, comprehensively refitted in 2018 in a modern interpretation of gin palace style. Most of the space is for dining, but there is a large bar offering the choice of communal drinking at a long marble-topped table or at more discreet areas around the walls. There is also plenty of standing room. A couple of Farm Yard ales are usually among the range, and cocktails are a speciality, with a huge selection of spirits and mixers. Live music plays most week nights. Outside tables are sheltered from the worst of the weather. ❀♿⇌♣🚌🐾📶

Merchants ✔
29 Castle Hill, LA1 1YN
☎ (01524) 66466 🌐 merchants1688.co.uk
House beer (by Old School); 7 changing beers (sourced regionally; often Allendale, Kirkby Lonsdale, Tirril) Ⓗ
A converted wine merchants' cellars built in 1688, with an extensive outdoor drinking space, creating a peaceful haven from the hubbub of the city centre. The main drinking areas are in three separate tunnels, with a fourth forming the entrance and bar. One tunnel is now a restaurant; another is used for functions. Look for the stoneware bottles used in the construction of the cellar walls. A house beer, Castle Blonde, is brewed by Old School. Quiz night is on Sunday. Many board games are available, and there is live music late every Saturday evening. ❀◐◑⇌🚌🐾📶

Olde John o' Gaunt ✔
53 Market Street, LA1 1JG
☎ (01524) 65356
6 changing beers (often Titanic, Wainwright, Wychwood) Ⓗ
Dating from 1871, a handsome Victorian frontage hides a narrow pub in which the walls are crammed with a variety of objects collected by the former licensee – including beer mats, jazz posters and photos of musicians. At lunchtime most of the customers are from nearby banks and offices, in the evening mostly regulars. The pub usually features music in the evenings. Sunday lunches are served. There is a quiz on Thursday.
❀⇌🍎🚌🐾📶

Robert Gillow ✔
64 Market Street, LA1 1HP
☎ (01524) 840316 🌐 robertgillow.co.uk

Hydes Original, Lowry; 4 changing beers (sourced nationally; often Hydes) Ⓗ
This establishment was converted from retail premises in 2007, retaining the façade with its huge curved windows. Refurbished in 2016, the interior is standard 21st-century pub design with wooden dividing screens and furniture of varying height. An upstairs room is also open to the public and available to book. A continually changing range of real ale is available alongside a collection of world-wide bottled beer including some quite rare, strong and expensive brews. Food is served daily. Q◐◑≠♣🚌🐾📶

Three Mariners ✔
Bridge Lane, LA1 1EE (near Parksafe car park entrance)
☎ (01524) 388957 🌐 thethreemarinerslancaster.co.uk
Oakham Citra; Robinsons Wizard, Dizzy Blonde; 7 changing beers Ⓗ
Commonly claimed to be the oldest pub in Lancaster, it certainly looks ancient, inside as well as out, but it has suffered some rebuilding, and had a comprehensive revamp in 2004. The cellar is excavated at first-floor level. The pub is now a popular watering hole with a thriving local clientele. Home-cooked, reasonably priced food is served. Irish folk features on Tuesday, folk on the first Friday of the month, and bluegrass on the third Friday of the month. There is limited parking.
Q❀◐◑♿≠♣●🚌🐾📶

Lancaster University

Graduate College Bar
Bailrigg, LA2 0PF (on Graduate Square in Alexandra Park, Graduate College is signposted)
☎ (01524) 592824 🌐 lancaster.ac.uk/eat
4 changing beers (sourced nationally) Ⓗ
The bar is much pubbier and attracts a wider age range than the usual student hangout. The choice of beer is good, with eight handpumps. There is a beer fest in June. Curry night is Friday, while open mic night alternates with live bands on Thursdays. The university bars all have alternative names: this one, for some reason, is Herdwick. Pork pies and pickled eggs are for sale, and the beer list is on Untappd. Reduced hours operate in vacations. ❀♿♣●🚌(2,4)🐾📶

Leyland

Golden Tap Ale House Ⓛ
1 Chapel Brow, PR25 3NH
☎ (01772) 431859
6 changing beers (sourced nationally) Ⓗ
Located in what was a shop, the Golden Tap opened its doors in 2016 and is a cosy one-roomed micropub – one of two in Leyland. Six changing cask ales are on the bar, usually including two dark beers, from microbreweries far and wide, but usually at least one from the local region. No food is served other than a few snacks, but it is right in the heart of the town's fast food and takeaway area. ⛽≠♣●🚌(109,111)🐾📶

Market Ale House Ⓛ
33 Hough Lane, PR25 2SB
☎ (01772) 623363
6 changing beers (sourced nationally) Ⓗ
Opened in 2013 in former shop premises, this was the area's first micropub and is located at the entrance to the old Leyland Motors North Works, which now serves as the town's market hall. Six changing real ales come from local and national breweries. Varying ciders, wines and a few spirits are also served. Food is limited to Lancashire cheeses. There is no TV but there is live acoustic music on Sunday afternoon. In summer, tables are put on the wide pavement to create an outside drinking area.
≠♣●🚌🐾📶

Longridge

Hoppy Days Ⓛ
36A Derby Road, PR3 3JT
☎ 07772 901515
5 changing beers Ⓗ
A warm and friendly welcome awaits you at this pleasant single-room real ale house. There are five handpumps showcasing a variety of quality beers, in a range of strengths and styles, many from small local microbreweries, including a dark beer. The ales are kept in a temperature-controlled chiller room. Bottled beers, wines and real cider are also served here, in a relaxed, convivial atmosphere. The pub is considered by CAMRA branch members to have done the most for real ale locally and was an award winner in 2017/18.
Q⛺●🚌(1)🐾📶

Longton

Dolphin
Marsh Lane, PR4 5JY
☎ (01772) 612032
4 changing beers (sourced locally) Ⓗ
An isolated country pub (also known locally as the Flying Fish) at the end of a lane on Longton Marsh, close to the Ribble Way. The cask ales can be found in the wood-floored public bar to the right of the main entrance. There is a restaurant in the rear conservatory and a large and varied menu covers everything from sandwiches to man vs food challenges. Up to four handpulled real ales and a cider are on offer – a changing selection with an emphasis on local microbreweries. Evening closing time is flexible dependent on trade. ⛽❀◐◑♿⛺●P🐾

Lostock Hall

Anchor ✔
Croston Road, PR5 5LA (300yds from B5254 alongside Preston-Blackburn railway line)
☎ (01772) 335637
5 changing beers (sourced nationally) Ⓗ
Just a short distance from the Tardy Gate shopping area, this friendly community pub offers five changing cask ales from across the country, with LocAle beers often on the bar. Now a Guide entry for more than 10 years, this was one of the first pubs in the area to host regular beer festivals, with marquees erected on a large grassy area next to it. A traditional roast is served on Sunday afternoons; Thursday is pie night. Q⛽❀♿≠♣P🚌📶

Lytham

Craft House Beer Café 🏆
5 Clifton Street, FY8 5EP
☎ (01253) 730512
4 changing beers (sourced regionally; often Cumbrian, Rat) Ⓗ
A microbar, now in its fourth year, where a warm and friendly welcome is guaranteed. It has fast developed into a popular destination for real ale drinkers. Four varying ales are served, always including a dark beer, sourced from far and wide, and supplemented by a wide selection of world and British bottled beers. The bar is dog-friendly and has pavement seating, weather permitting. A small food menu is on offer daily. Local CAMRA Pub of the Year 2020. Q❀◐≠●🚌🐾📶

Taps ✓

12 Henry Street, FY8 5LE

☎ (01253) 736226

Greene King IPA; Moorhouse's Pendle Witches Brew; Morland Old Speckled Hen; Robinsons Dizzy Blonde; 6 changing beers (sourced nationally) H

For the 27th consecutive year, this multi award-winning pub features in this Guide. The Taps continues to provide a wide range of well-kept ales from near and far, always including a mild and normally a stout or porter. At least two ciders are usually available. Regular charity events are staged including an annual 30-mile bike ride, and a popular quiz is held on Monday evening. Food is home-cooked, mostly from locally sourced ingredients.

Morecambe

Eric Bartholomew ✓

10-18 Euston Road, LA4 5DD

☎ (01524) 405860

Greene King Abbot; Ruddles Best Bitter; Sharp's Doom Bar; 3 changing beers (often Cross Bay) H

Opened in 2004, this Wetherspoon pub is dedicated to Eric Morecambe (ne Bartholomew). The pub near the sea front functions on two levels with an upstairs lounge and dinner area. The long bar services an open-plan pub with pictures of nineteenth-century Morecambe and some artwork with a Morecambe and Wise theme. There is some outside seating at the front for smokers but no drinking is allowed. Close to shops and a public car park.

Q

Little Bare

23 Princes Crescent, LA4 6BY

☎ 07817 892370

5 changing beers H

A micropub that opened in 2017 in a former off-licence, retaining the shop window. With grey paint, bare floorboards and candles after dark, it follows the standard formula for this kind of venue: no food, no music, no machines. There is a second room down a corridor with extra seating, and a small beer garden to the rear of the premises, accessed through the back room. (Bare Lane)

Morecambe Hotel

25 Lord Street, LA4 5HX

☎ (01524) 415239

Cross Bay Halo; 4 changing beers H

The place to come if you want a choice of Cross Bay beers, this hotel reopened in 2015 after renovation in contemporary style, and is now light and airy, with flagged floors and a variety of seating and tables. The bar, faced with unplaned wood, has four rooms around it, and a surprisingly spacious garden. Screens show videos of 20th-century Morecambe. For most of the day, food dominates. This was a coaching inn built long before there was a town called Morecambe.

Royal L

257 Marine Road Central, LA4 4BJ

☎ (01524) 416668 theroyalmorecambe.co.uk

House beer (by Cross Bay); 5 changing beers (sourced regionally) H

A survivor from Edwardian Morecambe, originally built around 1850 and far from intact, although the 2012 renovation respected the remaining features and blends with them. The single bar room stretches from the handsome bay window overlooking Morecambe Bay and the Eric Morecambe statue to the rear windows, and is complemented by an upstairs room variously used for dining or functions. Steak night is Thursday, and there is live music Thursday, Saturday and Sunday. The house beer from Cross Bay is offered at reduced price.

(4,6)

Newchurch

Boar's Head L

69 Church Street, BB4 9EH

☎ (01706) 224751

4 changing beers (sourced nationally) H

A large three-storey building on the corner of Church Street and Newchurch Road and close to St Nicholas Church. The stone above the door indicates that the building was constructed in 1674, and it was once owned by Kenyons Brewery. The central bar, with its four handpumps, serves three drinking areas. It is said that somewhere in the cellar was a sealed-up door to an underground passage leading to the church.

(10)

Ormskirk

Cricketers L

24 Chapel Street, L39 4QF

☎ (01695) 571123 thecricketers-ormskirk.co.uk

4 changing beers (sourced regionally; often Old School, Reedley Hallows) H

Close to Ormskirk town centre, the pub prides itself on both quality food and cask ales, featuring six from local and regional breweries. The extensive food menu is served all day in its restaurant or bar area. Cricket memorabilia around the walls reflect the pub's close relationship with Ormskirk Cricket Club.

P(375,385)

Tap Room No. 12 L

12 Burscough Street, L39 2ER

☎ (01695) 581928

4 changing beers (sourced regionally) H

This former shop has been custom-converted into a Belgian-style single-room bar. It features four changing cask ales sourced regionally and an extensive range of foreign bottled beers and authentic foreign lagers on draught. There is a quiz every Wednesday and live music Friday and Saturday, with background music during the rest of the week.

Orrell

Delph Tavern

Tontine Road, WN5 8UJ

☎ (01695) 622239

5 changing beers H

Free house popular with locals and visitors, dispensing five changing ales with an emphasis on local breweries. Food is served every day and offers a balance of traditional pub classics alongside innovative street food. Live sports are shown on a number of unobtrusive screens while a vault area offers pool and darts. The outside space has a small play area as well as tables to enjoy food and drinks. Weekly quiz nights are well attended. P

Oswaldtwistle

Black Dog L ✓

384 Union Road, BB5 3NW

☎ (01254) 390084

House beer (by Thwaites); 4 changing beers (sourced nationally) H

A well-known venue for miles around, this used to be the last stop on a famous pub crawl from the now-demolished Church Commercial. The Dog has been opened up but retains distinct drinking areas. Usually there are three beers from the Thwaites range plus a guest. The urinals in the gents have miniature goalposts with an attached ball for target practice. There is a cobbled area with bench seating to the front and a car park to the side. Frequent buses between Blackburn and Accrington stop outside. ♿❀Ⓟ🚌(6,7)🍽🐕🛜

Vault 🅛

343 Union Road, BB5 3HS
☎ (01254) 872279
Moorhouse's White Witch; 4 changing beers (sourced regionally) 🅗
A single-roomed bar with separate seating areas on the busy main road through Oswaldtwistle. It is easy to reach by public transport as buses from Accrington and Blackburn pass the door every few minutes. There is high bench seating around the walls and a standing area at the bar. The six handpumps dispense four changing beers and two ciders. Q🐕🚌(6,7)🍽

Padiham

Boyce's Barrel

9 Burnley Road, BB12 8NA
☎ 07736 900111
5 changing beers (sourced nationally; often Hambleton, Hop Back, Rudgate) 🅗
A single-roomed micropub on the main road through town with a collection of advertising signs adorning the walls. It is the sister pub of Boyce's in Colne and run by the same management team. Seven handpumps dispense two pale, two dark and one bitter ale, and two ciders. Two further boxed fruit ciders are available and there is a small selection of wine and gins. Food is limited to crisps and nuts. Frequent buses to and from Burnley stop nearby. Q♿🐕🚌(M2,152)🍽

Hare & Hounds 🅛 ✅

58 West Street, BB12 8JD
☎ (01282) 545308
5 changing beers (sourced regionally; often Big Clock, Reedley Hallows, Worsthorne) 🅗
A true free house with five varying beers. There are two rooms off the bar and a large separate room to the side, all with real fires. The pub is at the entrance to both Padiham cricket club and Padiham FC football ground. There is a large beer garden to the rear. BT and Sky Sports are shown and there is occasional live music at weekends. ♿❀🐕♣🚌(M2,152)🍽🛜

Molly Rigby's 🅛 ✅

17-19 Mill Street, BB12 8EX
☎ (01282) 778997 ⊕ mollyrigbys.co.uk
House beer (by Worsthorne); 3 changing beers (sourced locally; often Reedley Hallows, Worsthorne) 🅗
This is a private members' club where guests are welcome but should be signed in. The building was formerly the headquarters of Padiham Urban District Council before the town hall was built in the 1930s, and latterly served as the Royal British Legion office before closing and becoming semi-derelict. It was successfully revived in 2004. The house beer, Thickneck, is rebadged Worsthorne Pack Horse. Big-screen sports are shown and there is Sunday afternoon bingo and occasional Friday curry nights. ♿❀🍴♣🚌(152,M2)

Parbold

Railway Hotel 🅛 ✅

1 Station Road, WN8 7NU
☎ (01257) 462917
Tetley Bitter; 6 changing beers (sourced locally; often Hophurst, Problem Child, Prospect) 🅗
A former Marston's inn now privately owned, this non-food pub, frequented by locals, has its emphasis on excellent beer and hospitality. There is a central drinking area and two small rooms to either side. A coal fire adds to the ambience in winter together with comfy seats and sofas. There is a large-screen TV and pool table set back. A quiz is held on Tuesday. One regular beer, Tetley Bitter, is complemented by six changing local ales.
Q♿🐕🍴⇄♣Ⓟ🚌🍽🛜

Wayfarer 🅛

1-3 Alder Lane, WN8 7NL
☎ (01257) 464600 ⊕ wayfarerparbold.co.uk
Problem Child Good Spankin'; 5 changing beers 🅗
A country inn with a focus on dining. There are six handpulls including one for cider, and a range of craft keg beers. Landlord and brewer Jonny Birkett is happy to show you around his on-site microbrewery, Problem Child Brewing. The pub has low-beam ceilings with cosy nooks and crannies. It is popular with walkers, with the Leeds-Liverpool canal and Parbold Hill nearby, and local walks are shown on the website. The countryside beer garden enjoys pleasant views.
Q♿❀⊙🍴⇄♣Ⓟ🚌🍽🛜

Windmill Hotel

3 Mill Lane, WN8 7NW
☎ (01257) 462935 ⊕ thewindmillparbold.co.uk
Wainwright; 4 changing beers (sourced nationally) 🅗
A former grainstore to the adjacent windmill, parts of the building dating back to 1794. Two open fires add to the warm welcome for drinkers, diners, bargees and walkers – it is often busy with diners during the early evening. Up to five real ales are on the bar including some from the Windmill Brewery. A separate snug to the right of the doorway features delightful carved animals in the wooden panels. Unfortunately there is no wheelchair access due to the steep stone steps. Q♿❀⇄Ⓟ🚌🍽

Pendleton

Swan with Two Necks 🏆 🅛

Main Street, BB7 1PT
☎ (01200) 423112 ⊕ swanwithtwonecks.co.uk
5 changing beers (sourced regionally; often Goose Eye, Phoenix, Tiny Rebel) 🅗
A plethora of awards acknowledge that this has been one of the best pubs in north-west England for the past decade. It has been run by the same owners for over 30 years. There is a rumour that the beer is so good because the landlord talks to it. Five handpulls offer a wide range that may feature beers from Blackedge, Fernandes, Rat and Goose Eye. Real cider is also available. Food is high quality yet reasonably priced. There are real fires during the winter months and a large beer garden with amazing views. Q❀⊙🍴♣🍴Ⓟ🍽

Penwortham

Black Bull Inn 🅛 ✅

83 Pope Lane, PR1 9BA
☎ (01772) 752953 ⊕ blackbull-penwortham.co.uk
Robinsons Dizzy Blonde; Theakston Best Bitter; 3 changing beers (sourced nationally) 🅗
Attractive cottage-style inn dating back to the early 1800s, with a village atmosphere despite its location in a

well-populated area. On entering, a narrow passageway leads through to a central bar serving several drinking areas including a separate public bar. The pub actively supports local charities and was the local CAMRA branch's first ever Community Pub of the Year in 2018. Up to five cask ales are served, one of the guests usually coming from a LocAle brewery. Q❀♣P🚌🐾📶

Tap & Vine

69 Liverpool Road, PR1 9XD

☎ (01772) 751116 🌐 tapandvine.co.uk

4 changing beers (sourced locally)

Penwortham's first micropub, this is an upmarket wine bar-style establishment housed in a former arts and crafts shop. It has limited seating and can get quite busy at times, although to the rear there is a small secluded room with a wood-burning stove, and there is also outside seating in the summer months. Four changing beers are always on offer, often including some from lesser-known microbreweries. Snack foods and platters are served. Q🐎♣🍎🚌🐾📶

Poulton le Fylde

Old Town Hall ✔

5 Church Street, FY6 7AP

☎ (01253) 892257

6 changing beers (sourced locally; often Bank Top, Moorhouse's, Reedley Hallows) 🄷

Located in the heart of Poulton facing the old churchyard, this building, as its name suggests, was once the town hall. The pub's open-plan layout retains some of its heritage features. It is a popular venue with local real ale enthusiasts. Live bands play at weekends, an upstairs function room is available, live sports are shown on many TVs, and a dedicated area is provided for horseracing enthusiasts. 🐎♿⇌♣🚌🐾📶

Poulton Elk ✔

22 Hardhorn Road, FY6 7SR

☎ (01253) 895265

Greene King Abbot; Ruddles Best Bitter; Sharp's Doom Bar; 7 changing beers (sourced nationally; often Bowland, Cross Bay, Saltaire) 🄷

A thriving, well-run establishment – the 900th Wetherspoon pub to be opened by its owners – formerly a night club and before that the area telephone exchange. Popular for its food, it can get busy at weekends. There are two outdoor drinking spaces – a front terrace and a pleasant suntrap area to the rear. The name refers to a 13,000-year-old elk skeleton that was discovered nearby – a sharpened flint found with it is the earliest evidence of man in the area. 🐎❀◑♿⇌🍎🚌📶

Preston

Black Horse ★ ✔

166 Friargate, PR1 2EJ

☎ (01772) 204855

Robinsons Dizzy Blonde, Unicorn, Trooper, Old Tom; 4 changing beers (sourced nationally) 🄷

A Victorian Grade II listed building close to the historic open market. With its tiled bar and walls and mosaic floor, it has been identified by CAMRA as having a nationally important historic pub interior. Two front rooms are adorned with Robinsons memorabilia and photos of old Preston; the famous hall of mirrors seating area is to the rear. Real cider and a selection of pork pies is always available. Four Robinsons beers are sold, plus four changing guest ales from far and wide. Awarded the 2019/20 George Lee Memorial Trophy, the local branch's premier accolade. 🐎⇌♣🍎🚌🐾📶

Continental

South Meadow Lane, PR1 8JP

☎ (01772) 499425

House beer (by Marble); 6 changing beers (sourced nationally) 🄷

Beside the River Ribble, the railway line and Miller Park, the Continental has a main bar area plus a lounge with a real fire in winter and a conservatory overlooking the garden. Live music and theatre regularly feature in a separate events space which is also used to host beer festivals. There are eight handpumps dispensing a cider and up to seven microbrewery beers, including the house ale from Marble and a dark beer. Freshly cooked meals are served daily except Monday. A two-time winner of local CAMRA Pub of the Year.
Q🐎❀◑♿⇌🍎P🐾📶

Ferret

55 Fylde Road, PR1 2XQ

☎ (01772) 200017 🌐 theferret.info

5 changing beers (sourced nationally) 🄷

The Ferret is predominantly a live music venue, situated opposite the university student union, but is not strictly a student hangout. There are five handpumps featuring a changing array of beers, with LocAles often represented. One changing cask cider is also sold. Background rock music plays most of the time and there may be a cover charge on the door when live bands play, although Friday and Saturday nights are usually free. Live music includes rock, heavy metal, jazz and many other styles.
❀🍎🚌🐾📶

Guild Ale House 🏆

56 Lancaster Road, PR1 1DD

☎ 07932 517444

7 changing beers (sourced regionally; often Bank Top, Elland, Pomona Island) 🄷

Preston's first micropub, which opened in 2016 just a few doors away from Preston's Guild Hall complex. The main room has high- and low-level seating and the high ceilings give a light and airy feel. A small lounge is tucked away to the rear and there is a comfortable lounge upstairs. Seven changing beers are on sale, mainly local or from Yorkshire, and at least one dark ale. A range of continental beers is offered in keg and bottle. There is no jukebox, music, TV or food, but a live acoustic session is hosted on Sunday afternoon. Local CAMRA Pub of the Year. Q🐎❀♿⇌♣🍎🚌🐾📶

Moorbrook

370 North Road, PR1 1RU

☎ (01772) 823302 🌐 themoorbrook.co.uk

8 changing beers (sourced nationally) 🄷

This traditional pub is where the local CAMRA branch was formed in 1973. It has a wood-panelled bar with two rooms off the main bar area. The beer garden to the rear is a suntrap. Eight guest ales are sourced from all over the country, providing a wide choice of regional beers and beer types, while retaining a strong emphasis on local microbreweries. Food includes authentic wood-fired pizzas and home-made shortcrust pies. The pub gets busy on Preston North End match days. Local CAMRA Pub of the Year 2019. 🐎❀◑♿🚌🐾📶

Old Vic 🄻 ✔

79 Fishergate, PR1 2UH

☎ (01772) 828519

Bombardier; 6 changing beers (sourced nationally) 🄷

Opposite the railway station and on bus routes into the city, this popular pub helpfully provides travellers with a TV screen showing live updates of train departures. It can get busy, particularly at weekends. The rear of the building has recently been extended, with a separate area for pool players and darts enthusiasts. Seven handpumps offer a good range of beers, with Yorkshire breweries Ossett and Rat being particularly popular. The car park is only available on a Sunday and in the evenings.

Orchard

Earl Street, PR1 2JA

☎ 07756 583621

2 changing beers (often Farm Yard, Nightjar, Wily Fox) Ⓗ

The Orchard was opened in 2018, a sister pub to the Guild Ale House. Located within the Grade II listed covered market, the decor and framework is of wood recycled from old market trestle boards plus lots of modern glass. No food is served but there is plenty available from the neighbouring market, which can be brought in. Two cask beers and 10 craft ales are always on tap alongside real cider. Q

Plau

115 Friargate, PR1 2EE

☎ (01772) 561404 plau.co.uk

House beer (by Kirkstall); 3 changing beers (sourced nationally) Ⓗ

Recently restored and reopened on the site of a former pub, The Plough, which originally closed in 1913. The building dates back to the 18th century and the main bar is spread over three levels. Further bars in the vault, where there is a restored and exposed 40ft deep stone well. Four cask ales are on tap, with three always changing, typically coming from a wide range of local microbreweries, alongside the house beer, 1668, produced by Kirkstall Brewery. Up to eight craft keg beers are also served as well as an extensive range of gins.

Plug & Taps

32 Lune Street, PR1 2NN

4 changing beers Ⓗ

Craft beer and real ale bar with 10 keg lines and four handpumps, a large can and bottle fridge and occasional real cider boxes. Changing beers come from anywhere in the country and internationally, with three house beers from Outstanding Brewery and a permanent Rivington Brewery line. There are also occasional tap takeovers from various breweries. The main bar has air con, there is a large function room upstairs with a jukebox, and an outside seating area for use in warm weather.

Plungington Hotel

67 Lytham Road, Fulwood, PR2 3AR

☎ (01772) 712000 theplungingtonhotel.com

Castle Rock Harvest Pale; Timothy Taylor Golden Best; 4 changing beers Ⓗ

Traditional family-friendly community inn with a restaurant area to one side and a friendly, welcoming atmosphere. It has six handpumps with three house beers (by Timothy Taylor, Castle Rock and its own Plungington Bitter) and three changing guest beers, often including unusual beers from microbreweries. This pub has possibly the largest beer garden in Preston, with some sheltered seating and a grassed area where the annual gin festival has been held for the past two years, offering over 100 gins as well as guest real ales and ciders. P (23)

Princess Alice

29-31 Cambridge Walk, PR1 7SL

☎ (01772) 823737

4 changing beers (sourced regionally; often Lancaster, Worsthorne) Ⓗ

A friendly Victorian street-corner local in a redeveloped residential area. The ornate tilework reflects the former Matthew Brown Brewery ownership. The interior has been modernised and opened out. A large number of TV screens show multiple (often sports) channels. The regular beer is Lancaster Blonde and changing beers are normally from small Lancashire breweries, often Lancaster and Worsthorne. It is only 15 minutes' walk from Deepdale Stadium and is popular on match days. P (23)

Vinyl Tap

28 Adelphi Street, PR1 7BE

☎ (01772) 561871

6 changing beers (sourced nationally) Ⓗ

This single-room bar adjacent to the university opened in 2018. There are six real ale pumps serving a wide range of microbrewery beers, often from breweries unusual for the area. Vinyl-themed events and a jukebox are attractions Sunday to Thursday; customers can pick and choose from an ever-growing collection or bring their own to play while enjoying a drink and a bite to eat. Friday and Saturday vary between live music and guest vinyl DJ slots with music spanning most genres. Local CAMRA Most Improved Pub of the Year 2019.

Rawtenstall

Casked Ale House & Ginporium

14-16 Bury Road, BB4 6AA

☎ 07764 695261

House beer (by Reedley Hallows); 5 changing beers (sourced regionally; often Brewsmith, Irwell Works, Nightjar) Ⓗ

Now expanded into next door with varied seating and imaginative lighting, the pub is on the edge of Rawtenstall town centre. Up to six, mainly local, cask beers are dispensed on handpump plus six modern keg beers. Many of the beers are from breweries around the Rossendale Valley. It lies a short walk away from the East Lancashire heritage railway station and just along from Fitzpatrick's famous temperance bar. Local CAMRA Pub of the Year 2019. (464,X43)

Hop Micro Pub

70 Bank Street, BB4 8EG

☎ 07753 775150 hopmicropubs.com

Deeply Vale Hop; 5 changing beers (sourced regionally) Ⓗ

A micropub with a big heart. Situated on a cobbled street, Hop conjures up a pleasant and congenial venue more reminiscent of the traditional local. It is spread across three levels, with a heated outside drinking area. Six handpulled cask ales are on offer, including the permanent Hop from Deeply Vale, as well as keg craft beers and ciders, so there is always a fantastic choice. Close to the terminus of the East Lancashire heritage railway.

Rufford

Hesketh Arms

81 Liverpool Road, L40 1SB (on A59 at jct with B5246)

☎ (01704) 821002

Moorhouse's White Witch, Pride of Pendle; 7 changing beers (sourced regionally; often Cross Bay, Phoenix, Reedley Hallows) Ⓗ

A spacious former Greenall's inn, the Hesketh is now a free house serving up to six ales, mostly from local microbreweries. Set in a charming village, it is near to the National Trust property of Rufford Old Hall, the delightful St Mary's Marina, and the popular Mere Sands nature reserve. A large split-level venue with several dining areas, it serves good-quality food throughout the day. Monthly live entertainment and a Tuesday quiz attract a mixed clientele. Q🐎❀◐◑♿⇌P🚌(2A,347)

St Annes

Fifteens at St Annes ✔

42 St Annes Road West, FY8 1RF

☎(01253) 725852

House beer (by Coach House); 5 changing beers (sourced regionally; often Acorn, Bradfield, Titanic) Ⓗ

This multi award-winning Guide regular attracts a varied and loyal clientele. A former Lloyds bank, it has many original features including glorious stained-glass windows, and probably the world's most comfortable (and tranquil) bank vault. There is regular entertainment, with live bands at weekends, an open mic night fortnightly on a Wednesday, and a popular quiz on Sunday evening. A happy hour discount is offered every day. ⇌♣●🚌🐾

No.10 Ale House Ⓛ ✔

10 Park Road, FY8 1QX

☎(01253) 423240 🌐 no10alehouse.com

5 changing beers (sourced regionally; often Bradfield, Moorhouse's, Phoenix) Ⓗ

This popular one-room micro has already won several CAMRA awards in its first four years including Pub of the Season. Quirky and original in style, it is on the larger side of micro. There is occasional live music and a monthly quiz, but the usual background music is muted and the TV shows major sporting events only – conversation is king here. Quality bar snacks, including pie and mash, are served, as well as coffee.
❀♿⇌●🚌🐾

Victoria ✔

Church Road, FY8 3NE

☎(01253) 721041

Draught Bass; Greene King IPA; 3 changing beers (sourced nationally) Ⓗ

A magnificent late-Victorian pub, saved from demolition by local activists a few years ago. It was once multi-roomed but, following a tasteful refurbishment, is now mostly open plan. An original vault with a separate entrance and a snooker room still exists. A range of five beers welcomes the thirsty drinker, and the big-screen TV is not too intrusive. Food is served all day. Dogs are only allowed in the vault. 🐎❀◐◑♿⇌♣P🚌(11,68)🐾📶

Scarisbrick

Heatons Bridge Inn ✔

2 Heatons Bridge Road, L40 8JG (on B5242 by Leeds-Liverpool Canal)

☎(01704) 840549

Moorhouse's Black Cat; 2 changing beers (sourced regionally; often Wily Fox) Ⓗ

Fine canalside inn dating from 1837, when it served as offices for the Leeds and Liverpool freight services. It is a traditional hostelry, with separate areas and home-cooked food. Pillbox beer is often served as a memorial to WWII, and there is a lookout post outside. Twice-yearly military displays and annual classic bus services prevail, with themed beers for the occasion. This pub is popular with families, walkers and cyclists, is in an excellent rural setting, and has a garden with a dining area.
🐎❀◐◑♿⛺♣🚌(375)🐾📶

Silverdale

Woodlands

Woodlands Drive, LA5 0RU

☎(01524) 701655

4 changing beers Ⓗ

A large country house on an elevated site from circa 1878, converted to a pub with only minimal alterations. Most of the trade is provided by locals. The bar has a large fireplace as big as the counter and enjoys fine views across Morecambe Bay. Beer pumps are in another room, with a list of available ales on the wall facing the bar. Home-made sandwiches are served at weekends. The smoking area is covered and sheltered. A beer festival of 30 ales is held in October, and a quiz on the last Sunday of the month. To contact the pub you need to ring twice. Q🐎❀♣●P🚌🐾

Tockholes

Royal Arms Ⓛ

Tockholes Road, Rydal Fold, BB3 0PA (3 miles W of Darwen)

☎(01254) 705373

3 changing beers (sourced nationally; often Hopstar, Moorhouse's, Three B's) Ⓗ

Traditional free house formed from two cottages knocked together. It is in the West Pennine Moors, close to Darwen Tower and adjacent to Roddlesworth Visitor Centre, and looks over moors, woods and reservoirs. The pub is small but has a great atmosphere within its four back-to-back rooms, where the original stone walls, real fires and flagged or wooden floors have been retained. Most beers are from local microbreweries and good food is served. Friendly staff welcome walkers, cyclists, ramblers and dogs alike. Opening hours and food times are liable to change so check before travelling.
Q🐎❀◐◑♣P🐾📶

Wesham

Stanley Arms

8 Garstang Road South, PR4 3BL

☎(01772) 469495

Butcombe Original; 2 changing beers (sourced nationally) Ⓗ

Originally formed from three terraced houses, this welcoming community local is on a side street just three minutes' walk from Kirkham railway station and bus stops, and is approximately a half-mile walk from AFC Fylde's football ground. The comfortable open-plan interior contains many photos of old Preston and Blackpool landmarks. The landlord is the longest serving in the area and provides good food, often cooked by himself, including breakfasts at weekends.
🐎❀◐◑♿⇌♣●🚌(61,78)🐾📶

Whalley

Dog Inn Ⓛ

55 King Street, BB7 9SP

☎(01254) 823009

6 changing beers (sourced regionally) Ⓗ

Deservedly popular and often busy, especially at weekends, the Dog has been run by the same family since the early 1990s. Six handpumps serve a range of beers, changed continually, from breweries such as Acorn, Hetton, Moorhouse's, Peerless and Wishbone. Food is served only at lunchtimes and is always excellent. This traditional, historic inn is very close to the ruins of Whalley Abbey and is handy for exploring the picturesque Ribble Valley. 🐎❀◐⇌🚌🐾📶

Wheelton

Dressers Arms 🄻 ✔

9 Briers Brow, PR6 8HD (near jct with A674)
☎ (01254) 830041 🌐 dressersarms.co.uk
Black Sheep Best Bitter; Copper Dragon Golden Pippin; Hawkshead Windermere Pale; 4 changing beers (sourced nationally; often Prospect, Reedley Hallows) Ⓗ
A stone-built country pub with a surprisingly modern interior. A mixture of flagged and wooden floors, painted walls and open stonework gives it a bright and airy feel. Popular for food, with an extensive menu, it also offers up to seven cask ales, often including a dark brew and usually featuring beers from local microbreweries. The pleasant west-facing beer garden has views over the local countryside. Q🚼❀🛏◑P🚌(24)🐾📶

Red Lion

Blackburn Road, PR6 8EU (in centre of village opp clock tower)
☎ (01254) 659890 🌐 theredlionatwheelton.co.uk/#top
Hawkshead Iti, Lakeland Gold; Oakham JHB; Timothy Taylor Landlord; 4 changing beers (sourced nationally; often Rudgate, Salopian, Saltaire) Ⓗ
Built around 1826, this former Matthew Brown house retains the Lion Ales windows and a large stone lion at roof level above the door. The pub is close to the West Pennine Moors; many local walks pass by. Food is served seven days a week. There is a comfortable lounge with an open fire and a second room up a few steps. Eight handpumps showcase four regular beers and four changing real ales from larger independents, usually featuring a stout and a strong ale (over 5.5% ABV). Q🚼❀◑P🚉🚌(24)📶

Whitworth

Whitworth Vale & Healey Band Club 🄻 ✔

498 Market Street, OL12 8DP
☎ (01706) 852484
Thwaites Original; 3 changing beers (sourced nationally) Ⓗ
Popular local club, noticeable for being the home of the local brass band of the same name. The club is part of a terrace by the main road through the town, with a regular bus service passing by the door. Quite spacious, despite the low ceiling, it also has an outside seating area. Up to four beers are on offer, with Thwaites Original as a regular. CAMRA branch Club of the Year and regional finalist in 2019. ❀🚉🚌(464)🐾📶

Wrea Green

Wrea Green Institute

Station Road, PR4 2PH
☎ (01772) 682118 🌐 wreagreentute.co.uk
Coniston Bluebird Bitter; Wainwright; 3 changing beers (sourced nationally) Ⓗ
The Tute has been a community club near the centre of this picturesque village for over a century. Nicely renovated, it provides a main bar with pool tables and a comfortable lounge with old village pictures. There is also a function room downstairs. A beer festival is held in September and there are regular music, folk and poker nights. Snacks are available. Visitors should present a copy of this Guide or a membership card to be signed in. 🚼❀♿♣P🚌(61,76)🐾📶

Wrightington

White Lion ✔

117 Mossy Lea Road, WN6 9RE
☎ (01257) 425977 🌐 thewhitelionlancs.co.uk
Banks's Amber Ale; Jennings Cumberland Ale; 6 changing beers (sourced nationally) Ⓗ
This popular country pub has a good range of food and beers on eight handpumps. It hosts a Monday Club with drinks offers, a quiz on Tuesday, a poker league on Thursday, a monthly cocktail night and live music every Saturday. It is community-oriented, running the village scarecrow festival and themed evenings throughout the year. Families are welcome, with board games inside and a large beach hut themed garden area.
Q🚼❀◑♿P🚌(113)

Three Mariners, Lancaster (Photo: Reading Tom/Flickr CC BY 2.0)

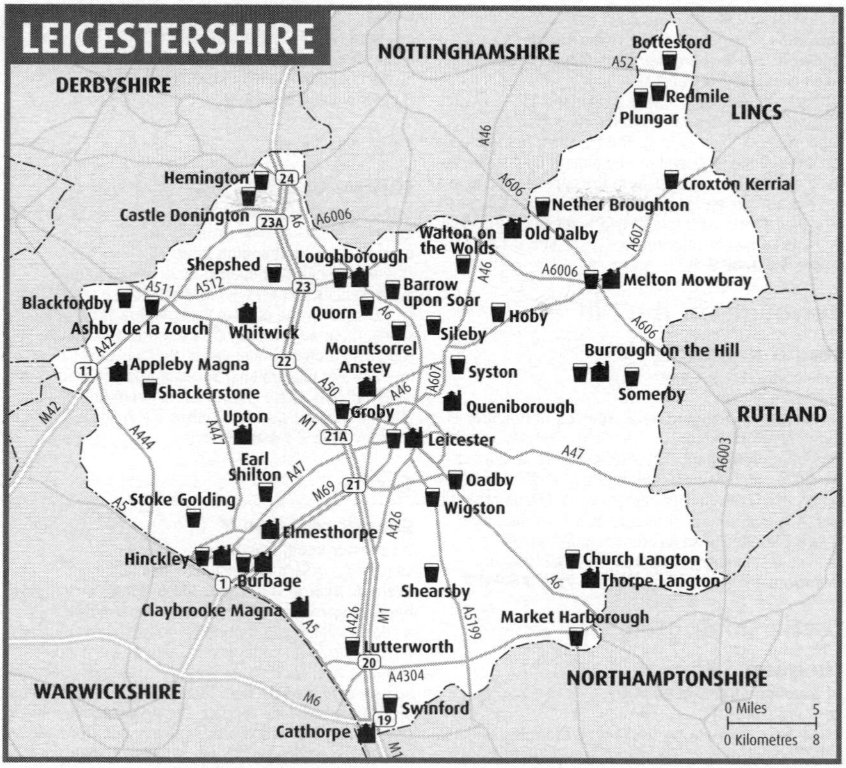

Ashby De La Zouch

Tap at No.76

76 Market Street, LE65 1AP

Tollgate Ashby Pale; 6 changing beers 🄷

This Ashby micropub, on the high street, is a relatively recent addition to the Ashby scene. A Tollgate Brewery pub, it offers seven real ales, with four on handpump and three on gravity. Third-pint tasting trays are available for those wishing to try the full range of beers. Pork pies are served. 🚌

Barrow upon Soar

Soar Bridge Inn

29 Bridge Street, LE12 8PN

☎ (01509) 412686

Everards Tiger, Old Original; 4 changing beers (often Everards) 🄷

Situated next to the bridge that gave it its name, this pub is popular with walkers, boaters and drinkers. The large single-room interior divides into distinct areas, with a separate restaurant, function room and skittle alley. Outside there is a floodlit pétanque court, beer terrace and garden. Children and well-behaved dogs are welcome. Home-made food is available Tuesday to Sunday, with a different theme each evening. Q🍺❀◑♿⛺≠♣●P🚊🚌(K2,CB27) 🐾

Blackfordby

Black Lion

3 Main Street, DE11 8AB

☎ (01283) 337551 🌐 theblacklionblackfordby.com

Draught Bass; 5 changing beers (sourced locally; often Blue Monkey, Derby) 🄷

Popular local in a quiet village in north-west Leicestershire, bought from Enterprise Inns and reopened in 2013 as a free house following a substantial refurbishment. Grade II listed, with old beams and open fires, it has a lovely courtyard and a covered smoking area. Guest beers are often sourced from small local breweries, and up to four ciders are on draught. Cheeseboards and ham and cheese cobs are available. Quiz night is the first Sunday of each month, jam night the last Wednesday. Q🍺❀♿♣●P🚌🐾📶

Bottesford

Bull 🄻

Market Street, NG13 0BW

☎ (01949) 842288

Castle Rock Harvest Pale; Fuller's London Pride; Theakston Best Bitter 🄷

Set on the main road through this busy village, well served by train and bus, the Bull has a large bar area with a real fire, pool table and plenty of seating. There is also a separate lounge for quieter drinking, plus a function room and outdoor seating area. Three cask ales are served, including one LocAle. Memorabilia in the lounge and a plaque outside commemorate Stan Laurel and Oliver Hardy's visits in the 1950s, when Laurel's sister was the landlady. ❀♿≠♣P🚌📶

Burbage

Lime Kilns Brew Pub 🄻 ✔

Watling Street, LE10 3ED

(01455) 631158 limekilnsinn.co.uk
Butcombe Original; Timothy Taylor Landlord; Wadworth 6X; 3 changing beers (sourced locally; often Buswells Brewery) [H]
A former 18th-century coaching inn alongside the Ashby Canal and A5, featuring free gardenside moorings and a large canalside beer garden. The first-floor lounge has canal views and an open fire. The ground-floor stable bar has a wood-burner and opens to the beer garden, where there is a marquee for functions. Traditional food is served all week, with special deals Monday to Thursday evenings. Buswells microbrewery is on site.
Q P

Burrough on the Hill

Stag & Hounds

4 Main Street, LE14 2JQ
(01664) 454250
Parish PSB; 1 changing beer (sourced nationally) [H]
Formerly a 16th-century inn, the Stag & Hounds operated more recently as Grant's Free House before reclaiming its original name following refurbishment in 2019. It has a bar on two levels, a cosy lounge and a restaurant to the rear. A central servery dispenses PSB from the Parish Brewery, located in an adjacent outbuilding, plus a guest ale. The restaurant serves locally sourced food and champions the area's best suppliers. P

Castle Donington

Chequered Flag

32 Borough Street, DE74 2LA
07841 374441
House beer (by Dancing Duck) [G]**; 6 changing beers** [H]
A thriving micropub in the heart of a busy street. It serves real ale straight from the cask, visible from a temperature-controlled cool-room cellar. A range of eight ciders and quality wines is also kept. Award-winning local pork pies and pickles can be enjoyed with your beer, subject to availability. Skylink bus services make the pub accessible from Derby, Nottingham, Loughborough and Leicester. Q

Church Langton

Langton Arms

Main Street, LE16 7SY
(01858) 545396 thelangtonarms.com
4 changing beers (sourced nationally; often Charnwood, Langton)
Country pub that was closed for two years before being reopened by Little Britain Pub Company in 2018, having been extended and refurbished. It feels like both a village local and a high-quality restaurant, serving excellent local beers alongside fine seasonal food cooked on-site. The garden is pleasant in summer or winter, adding to the appeal of a pub that is worth visiting at any time of year. P (44)

Croxton Kerrial

Geese & Fountain

1 School Lane, NG32 1QR
(01476) 870350 thegeeseandfountain.co.uk
5 changing beers [H]
Traditional village inn with a quiet and relaxed atmosphere, featuring wood fires, a flagstone floor and rustic seating. Dogs, children, cyclists and walkers are all welcome. Local ales always feature on the five handpumps, with guest beers from nearby microbreweries, plus lagers and three real ciders. Food is served every day, and B&B rooms are available. Regular live music nights and occasional mini beer and cider festivals are held throughout the year. A regular winner of the local CAMRA Pub of the Year award.
Q P

Earl Shilton

Shilton Vaults

3 The Hollow, LE9 7NA
07715 106876 shiltonvaults.co.uk
Draught Bass; 4 changing beers [H]
Three-room pub that opened in 2018 in a former NatWest bank premises. It has a main bar, a central room and another in the original vault, with a small outdoor space. There are 12 cask spaces on racks in the air-conditioned ground-floor cellar. The pub serves three or four real ales plus craft lagers, eight traditional ciders and speciality gins. There is direct access from the street; the toilets are upstairs. A sister pub to the Pestle & Mortar in Hinckley. Q

Groby

Stamford Arms

2 Leicester Road, LE6 0DJ
(0116) 287 5616 stamfordarms.co.uk
Everards Beacon Hill, Tiger, Old Original; 4 changing beers (sourced nationally; often Everards) [H]
A superb village pub that serves food, modernised in 2020 and continuing to develop into an outstanding venue. It offers seven cask ales plus craft beer, cider and an extensive gin selection. The food is traditional, with a pizza oven and daily specials. The neighbouring 17th-century thatched Blacksmith's Cottage is let for holidays and nightly bookings. The pub is ideally located for Bradgate Park and the National Space Centre.
P

Hemington

Jolly Sailor

21 Main Street, DE74 2RB
(01332) 812665
Black Iris Snake Eyes; Marston's Pedigree; Oakham Bishops Farewell; 3 changing beers [H]
This 17th-century building is thought to have once been a weaver's cottage. A pub since the 19th century, it retains many original features including old timbers, open fires and a beamed ceiling – convenient for

REAL ALE BREWERIES

Anstey Anstey
Belvoir Old Dalby
Buswells Burbage
Charnwood Loughborough
Dow Bridge Catthorpe
Elmesthorpe Elmesthorpe
Framework Leicester
Golden Duck Appleby Magna
Great Central Leicester
Langton Thorpe Langton
Market Bosworth Upton
Moonface Loughborough (NEW)
Mount St Bernard Whitwick
New Buildings Hinckley
Parish Burrough on the Hill
Pig Pub Claybrooke Magna
Q Brewery Queniborough
Round Corner Melton Mowbray
West End Leicester

hanging a collection of blowlamps and beer mugs. Well-filled rolls are available and there is a free cheeseboard on the bar. ❀◑P🐾≋

Hinckley

Elbow Room Ale & Cider House Ⓛ

26 Station Road, LE10 1AW (below Cineworld at The Crescent)

☎ 07900 191388

House beer (by Furnace); 6 changing beers Ⓖ

Family-run micropub decorated in an industrial style, offering a warm welcome and a great atmosphere. The ales and ciders are served by gravity directly from the cellar behind sliding glass doors. More than 40 gins are available, along with high-quality wines, whiskies, vodkas, world craft beers and lagers plus a range of soft drinks. Pork pies and Scotch eggs complement the drinks. There is no TV, jukebox or gaming machine as conversation is king. Children are welcome until 8pm. Q❀◑♿≠♣●🚌(3&7)🐾≋

New Plough Inn ✔

Leicester Road, LE10 1LS

☎ (01455) 615037 🌐 thenewploughinn.co.uk

Marston's Saddle Tank, Pedigree; 3 changing beers (often Jennings, Ringwood, Wychwood) Ⓗ

Award-winning Victorian pub offering old settles, more than 50 gins and a comfortable ambience. Rugby and cricket memorabilia reflect sponsorship of local teams. Darts, dominoes, skittles, crib and shooting teams attract the local community, as does the Stables function room. Popular quizzes have raised large sums for charity. The owners are CAMRA members who also run the historic Greyhound nearby. ❀♿♣🚌(1,159)🐾≋

Pestle & Mortar 🏆 Ⓛ

81 Castle Street, LE10 1DA

☎ 07715 106876 🌐 thepestlehinckley.co.uk

Draught Bass; 8 changing beers (sourced locally) Ⓗ

Comfortable and pleasantly quirky micropub with a friendly atmosphere, catering for a wide range of drinking tastes. Its handpumps dispense up to eight changing real ales from casks behind the bar. As many as 22 changing real ciders are also served, including Westons Old Rosie Rhubarb. Cobs and pork pies are available. Local CAMRA Pub of the Year and Cider Pub of the Year 2019. Q≠♣●🚌(8,X55)🐾≋

Queen's Head

Upper Bond Street, LE10 1RJ

☎ 07748 100212

4 changing beers Ⓗ

A warm welcome awaits at this multi award-winning Victorian free house serving four varying real ales. It has been sympathetically refurbished and features open fires and a Victorian range, helping to enhance a cosy atmosphere. A local CAMRA Pub of the Year on several occasions, it has featured in the Guide since 2013. Sorry, no children and no pets. ❀♣🚌

Hoby

Blue Bell Ⓛ

36 Main Street, LE14 3DT

☎ (01664) 434247 🌐 bluebell-hoby.co.uk

Everards Beacon Hill, Sunchaser, Tiger, Old Original; 2 changing beers (sourced nationally) Ⓗ

A picturesque thatched village pub with a beer garden providing fine views across the Wreake Valley. Exposed wooden beams and tiled floors with rug coverings give it a cosy and pleasant feel. There is always a good range of Everards beers available, and usually a guest ale or two. The pub is frequently busy – it is an ideal stop-off point for those seeking refreshment while walking the Leicestershire Round footpath. ❀◑♣●P🚌🐾≋

Leicester

Ale Stone

660 Aylestone Road, LE2 8PR

☎ (0116) 319 2320

House beer (by Leatherbritches); 4 changing beers Ⓗ

Micropub in a converted shop unit, featuring a nicely furnished interior with wooden benches and dados all round. Up to five real ales, plus four ciders and perries, are stillaged in a temperature-controlled glass-fronted cellar. Ham and cheese cobs and coffee are available. This and sister pub the Blue Boar are unique in the city in using oversize glasses to guarantee a full pint. The two pubs arrange regular tap takeovers and beer bus trips. Q●▯🚌🐾≋

Ale Wagon

27 Rutland Street, LE1 1RE

☎ (0116) 262 3330 🌐 alewagon.co.uk

Hoskins Hob Bitter, IPA Ⓗ**; house beer (by Hoskins)** Ⓟ**; 4 changing beers (sourced regionally; often Hoskins)** Ⓗ

Run by the Hoskins family, this city-centre pub with a 1930s interior, including an original oak staircase, has two rooms with tiled and parquet floors and a central bar. The interior features photos of the former Queens Hotel which was across the road from the pub in the 1930s, and the former Hoskins Brewery. A function room is available to hire. The pub is handy for the nearby Curve Theatre. ≠♣●🚌

Black Horse

65 Narrow Lane, Aylestone, LE2 8NA

☎ (0116) 283 7225

Everards Beacon Hill, Tiger; 4 changing beers (sourced nationally; often Brunswick, Everards, Titanic) Ⓗ

Welcoming, traditional Victorian pub with a distinctive bar servery, set in a village conservation area on the city's edge. It was sympathetically refurbished in 2018. Up to eight real ales are offered alongside home-cooked food. Quiz night is Sunday and comedy features regularly. There is a large beer garden, and a skittle alley and function room available to hire. Beer festivals and community events are regularly hosted. Coaches are welcome by prior arrangement. The pub has a customer loyalty scheme. Q❀◑♣●🚌🐾≋

Black Horse Ⓛ

1 Foxon Street, LE3 5LT

☎ (0116) 254 0446

Everards Beacon Hill, Sunchaser, Tiger, Old Original; 2 changing beers (sourced nationally) Ⓗ

The only remaining traditional community pub in a street of youth-oriented bars. It has two rooms separated by a central bar, with wood-panelled walls and practical furniture providing a comfortable setting. Guest beers are sourced through Everards; the cider is Westons Old Rosie. The pub hosts live music four nights a week and a quiz on the first Sunday of the month. A roof terrace is popular for open-air drinking. ❀♣●🚌🐾≋

Blue Boar 🏆 Ⓛ

16 Millstone Lane, LE1 5JN

☎ (0116) 319 6230 🌐 blueboarleicester.co.uk

Beowulf Finn's Hall Porter; house beer (by Shiny); 11 changing beers Ⓗ

Light, airy single-room micropub, named after the Blue Boar Inn where Richard III stayed before the Battle of

Bosworth Field. The cellar is visible through a glass partition behind the bar. The house beer is brewed by Bang the Elephant, and guest ales come from microbreweries around the country. This and sister pub the Ale Stone are the only pubs in the city using lined glasses to ensure customers get a full pint.
Q♞◑≠♣●▯⊟🐾ᯤ

Globe

43 Silver Street, LE1 5EU
☎ (0116) 253 9492 🌐 theglobeleicester.com
Everards Beacon Hill, Sunchaser, Tiger, Old Original; 3 changing beers (often Everards) Ⓗ
Dating back to 1720 and sympathetically remodelled in 2001, the pub features an island servery surrounded by small rooms, and offers a range of beers and ciders alongside good food. Some original features remain, notably the snug near the entrance. Upstairs is a function room with its own servery. There is a pleasing collection of local photos and bric-a-brac throughout. Restored gas lights are used on special occasions. ♞◑♿●⊟🐾ᯤ

King's Head

36 King Street, LE1 6RL
☎ (0116) 254 8240
Black Country Bradley's Finest Golden, Pig on the Wall, Fireside; 7 changing beers Ⓗ
A traditional one-room city-centre local owned by Black Country Ales. Its 12 handpulls dispense seven regularly changing guest beers and two varying ciders. Two changing keg ales and a range of bottles are also stocked. Meals are not served but filled cobs are often available. The pub shows sport on TV and hosts seasonal beer festivals. Its open fire and roof terrace help make it popular throughout the year with real ale and cider enthusiasts. ❀≠●⊟🐾ᯤ

Marquis Wellington

139 London Road, LE2 1EF
☎ (0116) 254 0542 🌐 themarquiswellington.com
Everards Beacon Hill, Sunchaser, Tiger, Old Original; 3 changing beers Ⓗ
This historic pub with a richly decorated façade stands out on the London Road thoroughfare. It is popular with local workers, shoppers and students. A good range of real ales, ciders and quality food, including a vegan menu, is available. The pub hosts live music nights and a weekly quiz night on a Monday, raising money for charity. The garden has beach huts to shelter from the sun and which can be heated for cooler nights.
♞❀◑♿≠●⊟🐾ᯤ

Old Horse ✔

198 London Road, LE2 1NE
☎ (0116) 254 8384 🌐 oldhorseleicester.co.uk
Everards Beacon Hill, Tiger; 4 changing beers (sourced nationally; often Everards) Ⓗ
Traditional 19th-century coaching inn, handy for dog walkers, students and sports fans. It sells four guest beers which change monthly. The addition of a cider bar serving eight handpulled ciders earned the pub recent local CAMRA Cider Pub of the Year awards. Tasty, good-value food is served, including a Sunday carvery. Behind the building is the largest pub garden in Leicester, complete with children's play equipment. Regular quiz nights, karaoke and special events take place.
♞❀◑♿♣●P⊟🐾ᯤ

Queens Road Tap

109 Queens Road, LE2 1TT
6 changing beers (often Tollgate) Ⓗ
Micropub that was opened in a former shop in 2017 by the Tollgate Brewery, based at the Calke Estate in south-east Derbyshire. The modern single-room interior has rustic furniture. The pub serves a constantly varying range of six real ales, including three or four from Tollgate, plus several guests and two ciders. There is no music or TV. The bus to Leicester stops right outside but evening services are limited. Q●⊟

Real Ale Classroom Ⓛ

22 Allandale Road, LE2 2DA
☎ (0116) 319 6998 🌐 therealaleclassroom.com
5 changing beers (sourced regionally; often Grainstore, Oakham) Ⓖ
A classroom-themed micropub run by career-change teachers in a converted shop. The furniture includes reclaimed desks with original graffiti; the beers are written up on a blackboard. Cask ales and ciders are served from a home-made chiller cabinet behind the high bar. A log-burner warms the rear room. In both rooms seating around large tables encourages conversation between regulars and visitors. Crisps, nuts, scratchings and take-away cans are available.
Q❀♣●⊟🐾ᯤ

Salmon

19 Butt Close Lane, LE1 4QA (from clock tower walk down Churchgate; Butt Close Lane is second left)
☎ (0116) 253 2301
Black Country Bradley's Finest Golden, Pig on the Wall, Fireside; 7 changing beers (sourced nationally) Ⓗ
A small corner local with a U-shaped single room and a bright, traditional interior. A Black Country Ales pub since 2016, the Salmon has a friendly, welcoming atmosphere and a strong sports following. Its 12 handpumps dispense the brewery's ales alongside guest beers and two real ciders. Cobs, pork pies and Scotch eggs are offered throughout the day and there is a Sunday carvery. Bus stations are nearby. Q♞❀♿♣●⊟🐾ᯤ

Sir Robert Peel

50 Jarrom Street, LE2 7DD
☎ (0116) 255 9419 🌐 sirrobertpeel.net
Everards Beacon Hill, Sunchaser, Tiger; 3 changing beers Ⓗ
Run by a friendly, knowledgeable couple, this is one of the few original pubs left in the city. It was given a refurbishment in traditional style by Everards in 2013. The brewery's well-kept beers are served alongside a range of guests and a real cider. The traditional pub food is popular. A large beer garden provides a relaxing space for dining and drinking. The pub gets busy on football and rugby match days. ❀◑♿●⊟🐾

Two-Tailed Lion

22 Millstone Lane, LE1 5JN
☎ (0116) 224 4769 🌐 thetwotailedlion.com
3 changing beers (sourced nationally) Ⓗ
Cosy two-storey free house and bottle shop that opened in 2018. It specialises in a changing selection of six keg lines and three cask lines, local and national, with a range of bottles and cans alongside, as well as real cider. Locally sourced bar snacks are served every day. The pub is beautifully furnished, with plenty of seating downstairs. Two extra rooms upstairs can be hired free of charge. ♞●⊟🐾

West End Brewery

68-70 Braunstone Gate, LE3 5LG
☎ 07875 745302 🌐 thewestendbrewery.co.uk
West End Project Pale, Stout, West Coast IPA; 3 changing beers (sourced nationally; often West End) Ⓗ

Leicester's original brewpub, opened in 2016. The owner/brewer aims to produce innovative beers, and plans to extend the range over time – capacity increased to a five-barrel plant in 2019. He likes to experiment with his recipes and takes on board customers' feedback. The brewery is behind the pub and is open to visitors. Four house beers are available plus at least two guests or farmhouse ciders from quality local microbreweries or from further afield. Live music is hosted once a month.

Wygston's House

12 Applegate, LE1 5LD

(0116) 296 4301 wygstonshouse.co.uk

Charnwood Vixen; 3 changing beers (sourced locally)

The best-preserved medieval house in Leicester, Wygston's opened as a bar and restaurant in 2017. Its central entrance leads into a stone-flagged passage, with small, elegant rooms on either side. The corridor opens out at the back into the medieval part of the house, a bar area with a wood-beamed ceiling. Upstairs is a light, airy room also with an old beamed ceiling and views over historic Leicester. There is an extensive and attractive patio outside.

Loughborough

Moon & Bell

6 Wards End, LE11 3HA

(01509) 241504

Greene King IPA, Abbot; Kelham Island Pale Rider; Ruddles Best Bitter; Sharp's Doom Bar; 4 changing beers

A large venue in the Grade II listed Atherstone House. The pub serves a fine selection of house and guest ales, usually including a mild, plus an extensive food menu. Beer and cider festivals are held frequently, including twice-yearly Wetherspoon real ale festivals. A marquee is erected in the spacious rear garden, serving many beers on handpull in addition to those available inside. Q P

Moonface Brewery & Tap

13 Moira Street, LE11 1AU

(01509) 700171

5 changing beers

A small, neat bar that opened in 2018 in a former warehouse building and art studio. Three to five real ales are served direct from casks stillaged behind the counter, with a constantly changing range. There are no keg beers. The in-house Moonface microbrewery, visible in a room directly behind the bar, is now in full production. Local CAMRA Pub of the Year 2020.

Needle & Pin

The Rushes, LE11 5BE

07973 754236

4 changing beers

A micropub in what was the old H&R Electronics shop. Beer is served downstairs in a continental-style bar with high stools. The upstairs room has a record player, board games and music. More than 50 continental and craft beers are stocked.

Organ Grinder

4 WoodGate, LE11 2TY

(01509) 264008

Blue Monkey BG Sips, Infinity, Guerrilla, Ape Ale; 4 changing beers (sourced locally; often Blue Monkey)

Previously known as the Pack Horse, and bought by Blue Monkey in 2012, the building has received a top-to-bottom renovation, uncovering lots of interesting original features. The stable bar at the back reflects the pub's past life as a coaching inn. Eight cask ales are always available alongside a choice of four real ciders, sometimes a perry, and Belgian bottled beers. Bar snacks include an interesting range of pork pies.

Swan in the Rushes

21 The Rushes, LE11 5BE

(01509) 217014

Castle Rock Sheriff's Tipple, Harvest Pale, Elsie Mo; 6 changing beers (often Castle Rock, Charnwood)

Traditional three-room Castle Rock pub comprising a quiet, traditionally styled lounge, a contemporary dining room and a lively bar with a jukebox. A constantly changing range of up to seven guest beers always includes a mild. Real cider, perry, a wide variety of continental bottled and draught beers and a good choice of malt whiskies and country wines are also available. Upstairs is the Hop Loft function room and a first-floor outside terrace. Q P

White Hart

27 Churchgate, LE11 1UD

(01509) 236976

Charnwood Salvation, Vixen; Draught Bass; Timothy Taylor Landlord; 2 changing beers (sourced locally; often Leatherbritches, Sarah Hughes)

Free house that combines quality ales with attractions including a secluded patio and beer garden to the rear. It serves changing guest beers sourced from local breweries such as Leatherbritches and Charnwood. Sarah Hughes Dark Ruby is also a regular. Bar snacks and tapas are available until early evening. Live music plays on Friday evening and Sunday afternoon.

Lutterworth

Fox

34 Rugby Road, LE17 4BN (400yds from Whittle roundabout)

(01455) 550935 fox-lutterworth.co.uk

Draught Bass; Sharp's Doom Bar; 2 changing beers (sourced nationally; often Timothy Taylor, Wadworth)

Welcoming 18th-century establishment at the southern end of Lutterworth, described as the town's village pub. An L-shaped, open-plan interior with a wooden-floored bar and carpeted dining area is warmed by two open fires. Meals are served lunchtimes and evenings, including excellent Sunday roasts. Thai food is available in the evenings in the adjacent Sawasdee restaurant. Outside is a large garden and drinking area. Quiz night is Tuesday. P (58,X44)

Greyhound

9 Market Street, LE17 4EJ (on main road)

(01455) 553307 greyhoundinn.co.uk

4 changing beers

A Grade II listed coach house on the main thoroughfare, dating from 1758 and offering a warm welcome. The lounge contains original features and period style furnishings, with nautical pictures and old clocks. The bar includes a wood-block floor. A variety of food including light meals is available all day, with an evening menu served in the plush restaurant. The pub is a popular venue for private parties and weddings. It has a paved courtyard outside for summer drinks. Q

Real Ale Classroom

4 Station Road, LE17 4AP

(0116) 319 6998 therealaleclassroom.com

4 changing beers (sourced nationally)

A spacious micropub with a schoolroom theme, owned by former teachers. It offers a constantly changing line-up of four cask and four craft keg ales plus a wide range of bottled and canned beers and five ciders from nationally renowned brewers. The bar has a log-burner for winter and a fantastic beer garden to enjoy in summer. Friendly staff are knowledgeable about the drinks on offer, including excellent gins and spirits from local distillers. Snacks are from local suppliers.
Q♣●(X84,58)

Unicorn

29 Church Street, LE17 4AE (nr church)
☎ (01455) 552486 unicornlutterworth.co.uk
Adnams Southwold Bitter; Draught Bass; Greene King IPA; 2 changing beers (sourced nationally; often Sharp's) H
Traditional street-corner local with a black and white frontage, built in 1919 on the site of an 18th-century coach house in the town centre. The large public bar, with its open fire, shows TV sport and hosts teams playing darts, dominoes and skittles. The small, comfortable lounge, divided by a central fireplace, displays photographs of old Lutterworth. Alongside the adjacent dining room it forms a family-friendly area where the pub's good, inexpensive, lunchtime food, including vegetarian and children's options, is served.
♣P(8,X44)

Market Harborough

Beerhouse

76 St Mary's Road, LE16 7DX
☎ (01858) 465317
8 changing beers (sourced nationally) P
Market Harborough's first micropub, set in a converted furniture shop directly behind the chip shop on St Mary's Road. The focus is very much on beer – no food, gaming machines or loud music. There are 20 taps for draught products – eight for cask ales, the rest for KeyKegs and ciders. Monday is quiz night, and the pub hosts occasional comedy nights, vinyl nights and live music. Other attractions include a book club and cider festival.
●P

Melton Mowbray

BeerHeadZ

7 King Street, LE13 1XA
☎ (01664) 561958 beerheadz.biz
6 changing beers (sourced nationally) H
Opened in 2018, this is one of the newest micropubs from the BeerHeadZ company, offering a wide range of beer styles, many from innovative and new breweries. Real cider and a good range of craft beers are also available. The pub is in a manor house that dates from the 14th century and is one of Melton Mowbray's oldest buildings, with a timber frame going back to 1301. In the 1500s it was the manor of John Mowbray. More recently it was a dressmaker's; the signage remains on the front of the pub. Q●(5,19)

Melton Mowbray & District Indoor Bowls Club

Leicester Road, LE13 0LR
☎ (01664) 410159 meltonindoorbowls.co.uk
Parish PSB; 1 changing beer (sourced nationally; often Belvoir) H
A modern indoor bowls club, founded in 1985. The bar is within sight of the greens, with tables and chairs from which play can be viewed. At least one real ale is always available, usually Parish PSB and sometimes also a local Belvoir Brewery beer. Card-carrying CAMRA members can purchase a pint at the bar. Beer can also be enjoyed with a meal in the Clubhouse restaurant, which is open to the public (booking recommended). Q≠P

Round Corner Brewing

Melton Mowbray Market, Scalford Road, LE13 1JY
roundcornerbrewing.com
1 changing beer (sourced locally; often Round Corner)
Round Corner Brewing opened in 2018 in what had been a sheep shed in the heart of Melton's cattle market. It has a taproom at the front in which the brewery's beers can be enjoyed – a handpull on the bar offers a regularly changing ale. Round Corner brews on the principle of 'bringing beer back to its agricultural roots', hence the brewery's location. The taproom has quickly established itself as a popular venue with local CAMRA members and earned a place in the Guide. Q≠P(5,19)

Mountsorrel

Sorrel Fox

75 Leicester Road, LE12 7AJ
☎ (0116) 230 3777
Charnwood Salvation, Vixen; 2 changing beers (sourced locally; often Charnwood) H
The Sorrel Fox is Charnwood Brewery's first micropub in the village. It is cosy with a lovely log-burner, and welcomes dogs. Charnwood's popular cask ales and craft beers are served alongside an imported Austrian lager, complemented by quality wines, a selection of gins and a couple of rums. The pub is close to the A6, with a bus stop for routes to Leicester, Loughborough and Shepshed.

Swan

10 Loughborough Road, LE12 7AT
☎ (0116) 230 2340
Black Sheep Best Bitter; Castle Rock Harvest Pale; 2 changing beers (often Dancing Duck, Greene King) H
Seventeenth-century, Grade II listed coaching inn on the banks of the River Soar, entered via a narrow arch into a courtyard. The split-level interior has open fires, stone floors and low ceilings, and includes a small dining area with a polished wood floor. Good-quality, interesting food is cooked to order, the menu changing weekly and featuring regular themes. Outside is a long secluded riverside garden with moorings. A beer festival is held annually. QP

Nether Broughton

Anchor

Main Road, LE14 3HB
☎ (01664) 822461
House beer (by Ringwood); 1 changing beer H
A cosy village pub on the A606 which reopened in 2015. The main bar has a real fire and a dartboard, and there is a separate dining area offering a quieter space. Traditional fare is served regularly, with occasional themed nights. It hosts regular charity events, and welcomes families and dogs. The house beer is Ringwood Razorback but served under its old name of Best Bitter. ♣P

Oadby

Cow & Plough

Gartree Road, LE2 2FB
☎ (0116) 272 0852

Fuller's London Pride; Steamin' Billy Bitter, Skydiver; 4 changing beers (sourced regionally; often Abbeydale, Belvoir, Charnwood) 🄷
Situated in a former farm building with a conservatory, the pub is decked out with breweriana. It is home to Steamin' Billy beers, named after the owner's now departed Jack Russell who features on the logo and pumpclips. A mild is always available and a real cider in the summer months. An annual beer festival is held. The renowned restaurant is in former dairy buildings.
Q⚭❀◐♿♣●P🐾ᯤ

Lord Keeper of the Great Seal ✔

96-100 The Parade, LE2 5BF
☎ (0116) 272 0957
Greene King Abbot; Ruddles Best Bitter; Sharp's Doom Bar; 6 changing beers (sourced regionally) 🄷
Named after Sir Nathan Wright, a judge and local landowner who was Keeper of the Seal in the early 18th century, this typical Wetherspoon conversion of a row of shops stands on the site of a former infants school. The pub displays pictures of historic local buildings and industries, and has a varied library of books. It holds regular beer festivals and charity events. Families are welcome until 9pm. ⚭❀◐♿●🚌(31,31A)ᯤ

Oadby Royal British Legion Club Ltd

4a Wigston Road, LE2 5QA
☎ (0116) 271 4415
3 changing beers 🄷
The club is open to CAMRA members, their guests and members of RBL/CIU. It was founded in a former 19th-century private dwelling in the shadow of St Peter's Church. There is a lounge bar and a chapel of remembrance to the front, and a large concert room to the rear. The first-floor games room hosts darts and a skittles table. A small lawn with garden furniture is alongside the car park to the side of the club.
⚭❀♿♣●P🚌ᯤ

Plungar

Anchor 🄻

Granby Lane, NG13 0JJ
☎ (01949) 860589
3 changing beers 🄷
This brick-built pub in the heart of the village dates from 1774 and previously served as the local courtroom. It has a large bar, lounge area and separate restaurant, plus an annexe housing the pool table, and an attractive beer garden. Up to three beers, at least one local, are available in a range of styles. The pub is popular with locals and visitors, cycling groups, horse riders and anglers using the nearby fishing lakes.
Q⚭❀◐♿♣P🚌(24)🐾ᯤ

Quorn

Manor House

Woodhouse Road, LE12 8AL
☎ (01509) 413416 🌐 themanorhouseatquorn.co.uk
Charnwood Salvation; Draught Bass; Timothy Taylor Landlord; 2 changing beers (often Leatherbritches) 🄷
Built in 1899 by the Great Central Railway, the Manor House was designed to serve passengers arriving at Quorn and Woodhouse station, which it still does today – the heritage railway's steam and diesel trains pass by 150 yards from the door. It is a free house serving two guest beers during the week and three at weekends. The interior features an open-plan bar and award-winning restaurant, plus a function and meeting room that can be hired. Q❀◐♿⛺⇌♣P🚏🚌🐾

Redmile

Windmill Inn 🄻 ✔

4 Main Street, NG13 0GA
☎ (01949) 842281
2 changing beers (sourced locally) 🄷
The Windmill is a privately owned freehold restaurant and bar, owner operated, one mile down the hill from Belvoir Castle. It has two rooms, a stone-floored bar complete with log fire, and a lounge, plus a generous terrace. It enjoys a cult status among fans of the TV show Auf Wiedersehen, Pet, in which it appeared as the Barley Mow, and photos taken during filming are on display.
Q⚭❀◐⛺P🚌🐾ᯤ

Shackerstone

Rising Sun

Church Road, CV13 6NN
☎ (01827) 880215 🌐 risingsunpub.com
Draught Bass; Marston's Pedigree; Timothy Taylor Landlord; 1 changing beer 🄷
A traditional family-owned free house in the heart of Shackerstone, near the Ashby Canal and preserved Battlefield Railway. It has a wood-panelled bar serving traditional ales, a restaurant, pool room with Sky Sports, family-friendly conservatory and an attractive garden. The pub, popular with locals and visitors alike, is renowned for the quality and variety of its ales and serves good food – the ideal hub for visiting this rural part of Leicestershire. ⚭❀◐⛺⇌♣●P🚌(7)🐾ᯤ

Shearsby

Chandlers Arms 🄻

Fenny Lane, LE17 6PL
☎ (0116) 247 8384 🌐 thechandlersinshearsby.co.uk
Belvoir Beaver Bitter; Dow Bridge Acris; 4 changing beers (sourced regionally) 🄷
Quintessential local inn with a big reputation – the pub is a community hub for the village and welcoming to visitors. Its name derives from the building's original use as a tallow candlemaker's premises. The beer garden overlooks the village green from a high vantage point. Microbrewery beers are always on the bar, often locally sourced, including a stout or porter. Good food is available, but the owners see it as primarily a drinkers' pub. ⚭❀◐♣●🐾ᯤ

Shepshed

Black Swan ✔

21 Loughborough Road, LE12 9DL
☎ (01509) 506222 🌐 blackswanshepshed.co.uk
Charnwood Vixen; Draught Bass; Greene King Abbot; Timothy Taylor Landlord 🄷
Multi-roomed pub in a prominent position close to the town centre, offering two guest beers alongside the regulars. An extremely good range of whiskies is also kept. The main room has two drinking areas, both with comfortable seating. A further small room can be used by families and is available to hire for functions. Wednesday is quiz night. Local events include music by the ukulele orchestra. Shepshed Dynamo football ground is nearby.
⚭◗P🚏🚌

Horse

196 Ashby Road West, LE12 9EF
☎ (01509) 507006 🌐 thehorseshepshed.co.uk
Charnwood Vixen; Greene King Abbot; Marston's Pedigree; 1 changing beer 🄷

The Horse, one of the oldest free houses in the town, is traditionally built, with a restaurant and bar. In 2015 major extension work almost doubled the size of the premises, enabling a much greater emphasis on food. It has a feature fireplace with wood-burning stove, and outside an alfresco dining area with wood-fired pizza oven. A good range of beers is available and the pub takes pride in serving freshly prepared food made on the premises, where possible using produce sourced within a five-mile radius of Shepshed. ❀◐P

Sileby

Horse & Trumpet

4 Barrow Road, LE12 7LP

☎ (01509) 812549

Belvoir Dark Horse; Charnwood Vixen; Steamin' Billy Tipsy Fisherman, Bitter, Skydiver; 2 changing beers Ⓗ

This multi-room inn with open fires has undergone a huge transformation since becoming part of the Steamin' Billy chain. Two guest beers plus a real cider and perry are on offer. No hot food is served but cobs are available. There is a monthly curry club. The pub hosts weekly open mic nights and monthly jazz nights, and has a function room. Well-behaved dogs are welcome in the bar and outside seating area. Q❀♣P (KB2)

Somerby

Stilton Cheese 🏆 L

High Street, LE14 2QB

☎ (01664) 454394 🌐 stiltoncheeseinn.co.uk

Marston's Pedigree; Grainstore Ten Fifty; 3 changing beers (sourced nationally) Ⓗ

Welcoming family-run pub, built in local ironstone in the late 16th century. Inside is a cosy bar and an adjoining room displaying an eclectic collection of copper pots and pans, horse brasses, pictures of hunting scenes and a stuffed pike and badger. At least four real ales are always available, often from local breweries. Local CAMRA Pub of the Year 2019 and 2020. Q❀◐♣P

Stoke Golding

George & Dragon L

Station Road, CV13 6EZ

☎ (01455) 213268

Church End Goat's Milk, Gravediggers Ale, What the Fox's Hat, Stout Coffin, Fallen Angel; 3 changing beers (sourced locally; often Church End) Ⓗ

Renowned village local serving eight real ales from the Church End range and a real cider. Good home-cooked lunches feature local produce, and bar snacks, made on the premises, are always available. The second Tuesday of each month is steak night, and lunch is served on the last Sunday. Close to the historic Bosworth battlefield, the pub supports a number of clubs and societies, and is popular with walkers, cyclists and boaters from the nearby Ashby Canal. Q❀◐⛺♣P (66)

Swinford

Chequers ✔

High Street, LE17 6BL (near church)

☎ (01788) 860318 🌐 chequersswinford.co.uk

Adnams Southwold Bitter; 2 changing beers (sourced nationally; often St Austell, Timothy Taylor) Ⓗ

In January 2020, the landlord celebrated 33 years at this family-run community local, where a warm welcome is assured. The menu caters for all and includes vegetarian and children's options. The large garden and play area are popular with families in good weather. A marquee provides the venue for the annual beer festival and is available for private hire. Pub games include table skittles. Within a mile is the 18th-century Stanford Hall, with a caravan park and museum. ❀◐⛺♣P

Syston

Beer Pharmacie L

3 High Street, LE7 1GP

☎ (0116) 269 6933 🌐 beerpharmacie.co.uk

Shipstones Mild, Original; 3 changing beers (often Oakham) Ⓗ

Syston's first micropub opened in 2018 with a 1950s pharmacy theme, displaying medical artefacts, equipment, advertisements and a friendly skeleton sitting on a dentist's chair. Upstairs is a vinyl lounge with a 1950s movie theme and seating for about 70 people. Another room is available for private hire. The pub serves a varying selection of real ales plus up to six craft kegs. It doesn't do meals, but cheese cobs and other snacks are available. Q♿♣

Queen Victoria L

76 High Street, LE7 1GQ

☎ (0116) 260 5750

Everards Beacon Hill, Sunchaser, Tiger, Old Original; 4 changing beers (sourced nationally) Ⓗ

A former coach house, the building is 200 years old. Everards has traded here since 1922. Three rooms have been knocked together to form the bar at the front, and there is a small room to the rear. At the back is a carvery restaurant, a courtyard drinking area and a large garden with a pétanque court. There is regular entertainment. Beer and cider festivals are held throughout the year. Guest beers are sourced through Everards and can include regional and microbrewery beers.
❀◐♿♣P

Walton on the Wolds

Anchor

2 Loughborough Road, LE12 8HT

☎ (01509) 880018

Adnams Southwold Bitter; Fuller's London Pride; Timothy Taylor Landlord; 1 changing beer (often Charnwood) Ⓗ

The Anchor is in the centre of a small village within easy reach of Leicester and Nottingham via the A46. It is a popular venue for walkers who stop for a well-earned home-cooked lunch in front of the log fire. There is a menu to suit all tastes plus an extensive specials board. Outside is an elevated seating area to the front and a garden and large car park to the rear.
Q❀◐P

Wigston

Tap & Barrel

58 Leicester Road, LE18 1DR

☎ (0116) 319 0123 🌐 tapandbarrelwigston.co.uk

5 changing beers Ⓖ

This micropub has an unpretentious ambience enhanced by a rustic timber bar, bare wooden floorboards, exposed ceiling joists braced with traditional herringbone strutting, a free-standing log-burning stove, and a wooden staircase that leads to an extra seating area. Behind the bar, beers are dispensed straight from casks kept in a cooler cabinet. ♿♣P

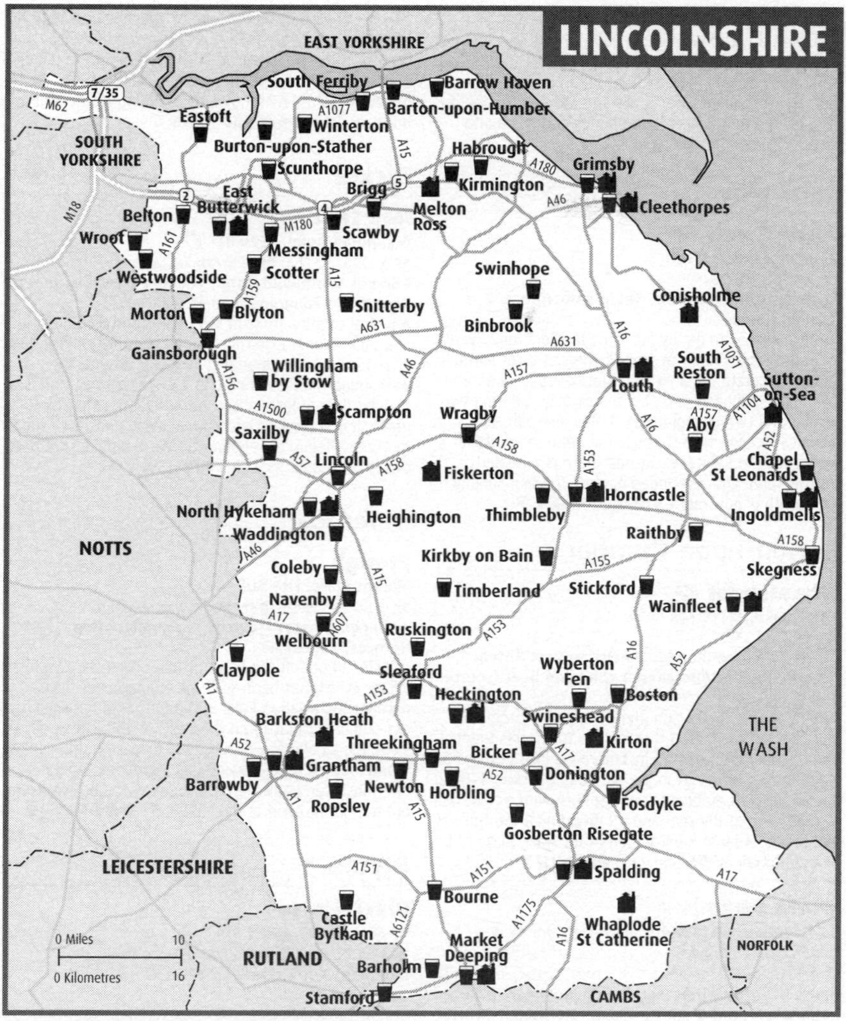

Aby

Railway Tavern

Main Road, LN13 0DR (off A16 via South Thoresby)
☎ (01507) 480676 🌐 railwaytavern-aby.co.uk

Bombardier Burning Gold; Sharp's Doom Bar; house beer (by Black Sheep); 2 changing beers (sourced nationally; often Adnams, Oakham, St Austell) Ⓗ

A rural inn that was closed when the licensees took it on over 15 years ago; since then it has grown to the successful pub it is now, serving the community and raising money for charity. The pub has won numerous awards including local CAMRA Country Pub of the Year four times. It offers a wide range of real ales and a menu based on local produce. Two holiday cottages are available for short breaks or week-long bookings.
Q≿❀⇌◑♿⛺♣P🐾

Barholm

Five Horseshoes 𝕃

PE9 4RA
☎ (01778) 560238

Adnams Southwold Bitter; Draught Bass; Oakham JHB; 3 changing beers (often Grainstore, Hopshackle) Ⓗ

A classic 18th-century stone-built country pub, well known for supporting many charities. It comprises two bars, two cosy side rooms and a pool room. A wood fire burns throughout the winter. A real cider is served along with three permanent and three changing ales. Pizzas are available on Friday and Saturday evenings, while barbecues and live music events in the large garden are a feature of the summer months. **Q≿❀◗♿●P🐾📶**

Barrow Haven

Haven Inn 𝕃

Ferry Road, DN19 7EX (approx 1½ miles E of Barrow-upon-Humber)
☎ (01469) 530247 🌐 thehaveninn.co.uk

Theakston Old Peculier; Timothy Taylor Landlord; 1 changing beer (sourced nationally) Ⓗ

Built in 1730 as a coaching inn in the quiet north Lincolnshire countryside for travellers using the ferry, the Haven has been renowned for hospitality, good food and drink, and comfortable lodgings ever since. Full of character, a warm welcome awaits, with a bar, lounge and large comfortable conservatory, perfect for walkers from along the Humber Bank to call in for a well-kept pint. The restaurant offers daily specials and a generous carvery. The pub hosts regular bands and has a late licence. ⚘❀⛟◐♿⇋P🐾

Barrowby

White Swan ✔

Main Street, NG32 1BH

☎ (01476) 562375

Castle Rock Harvest Pale; Sharp's Doom Bar; 2 changing beers Ⓗ

Popular village inn run by the same landlord for 27 years, an enthusiastic CAMRA member. There is a comfortable lounge, separate bar area and a further space where the local darts, cribbage and pool teams play. Offering two regular and two changing guest ales, the pub also provides locally sourced traditional home-made food Wednesday to Saturday. Outside there is a heated smoking area and a secluded garden. The first Sunday of the month is quiz night. Q⚘❀◐♣P🚌🐾📶

Barton-upon-Humber

Wheatsheaf ✔

3 Holydyke, DN18 5PS

☎ (01652) 633292

Ossett Yorkshire Blonde; Theakston Best Bitter; Timothy Taylor Boltmaker; 1 changing beer (sourced nationally) Ⓗ

Serving four real ales and and occupying a prominent place on the main road through the town, this friendly 18th-century local owned by Enterprise Inns displays a list of former licensees in the bar dating back to 1791. It has an unspoilt, traditional atmosphere with a front bar, a small snug at the rear and a seating area for drinkers and diners. A large beer garden at the back makes for pleasant outdoor drinking. Q⚘❀◐●P🚌📶

White Swan 𝕃

66 Fleetgate, DN18 5QD (follow signs for railway station)

☎ (01652) 661222

House beer (by Westgate); 3 changing beers (sourced nationally; often Great Newsome, Horncastle Ales) Ⓗ

Multi award-winning, this renovated 17th-century coaching inn, directly opposite the bus/train interchange, offers all a warm welcome, with diverse community groups meeting here regularly. One house beer plus three different cask ales from near and far are complemented by a rotating craft keg beer, and changing ciders and perries in summer. Food is served Wednesday-Sunday. A deceptively spacious rear courtyard is ideal for outdoor drinking. Quiz night is Sunday, a vinyl night monthly. Check out the attached curiosity shop. Q⚘❀⛟◐♿⇋♣●P🚌📶

Belton

Crown Inn 𝕃

Church Lane, DN9 1PA (turn off A161 at All Saints Church and follow road behind)

☎ (01427) 872834

Bradfield Farmers Blonde; Brakspear Gravity; Jennings Cocker Hoop; Oakham Citra; 2 changing beers (sourced regionally; often Abbeydale, Ringwood) Ⓗ

Difficult to find but well worth the effort, this inn has long been a haven for the discerning drinker. Six cask ales are always available, one of which is usually from the Cuckoo Brewery, which is part-owned by the licensees. The pub is active in the community, and hosts quizzes, beer festivals and live entertainment. A winner of several local CAMRA awards including District Pub of the Year. ⚘❀⛺♣●P▯🚌(399)🐾📶

Bicker

Red Lion

Donington Road, PE20 3EF

☎ (01775) 821200 🌐 redlionbicker.co.uk

Adnams Southwold Bitter; Courage Directors; Greene King IPA; 1 changing beer Ⓗ

A typical country inn with low beams and tiled floor, in a pleasant setting. Extensively and tastefully redecorated in 2015, it reopened after two years' closure. The welcoming multi-roomed pub has a small bar, and is a popular dining destination with a varied, extensive menu. It is known to date from at least 1665, the time of the Great Plague of London. The Wash would have been closer years ago. ⚘❀◐♿♣P🚌(59)📶

Binbrook

Plough

Market Place, LN8 6DE

☎ (01472) 398808 🌐 theploughbinbrook.com

4 changing beers (sourced regionally; often Horncastle Ales) Ⓗ

A Victorian pub in the heart of this Lincolnshire Wolds village which has been well maintained over the decades. Its aviation links to the former airbase nearby are proudly displayed on the walls, with pictures of Lightning jet planes which used to fly past. Home-cooked food is served regularly and has a growing reputation. Live music can be heard most weekends. Dogs welcome but not during food service times. ⚘❀◐♣P🚌(3)🐾

Blyton

Black Horse

93 High Street, DN21 3JX

☎ (01427) 628277 🌐 blackhorseblyton.co.uk

Batemans XB; 2 changing beers Ⓗ

REAL ALE BREWERIES

8 Sail ◆ Heckington
Austendyke Spalding
Bacchus ▮ Sutton-on-Sea
Batemans ◆ Wainfleet
Blue Bell ▮ Whaplode St Catherine
Brewsters Grantham
Consortium ▮ ◆ Louth
Dark Tribe ▮ East Butterwick
Docks ◆ Grimsby
Ferry Fiskerton
Firehouse ◆ Louth
Fuddy Duck Kirton
Greg's ▮ Scampton
Hopshackle Market Deeping
Horncastle ▮ Horncastle
Leila Cottage ▮ Ingoldmells
Lincolnshire Craft Melton Ross
Newby Wyke Grantham
Poachers ◆ North Hykeham
Welland Spalding
Wickham House Conisholme (NEW)
Willy's ▮ Cleethorpes
Zest Barkston Heath

One of two pubs in the village, sited at the northern end. The interior is divided into five distinct areas: two for dining, two for drinking and one for the pool table and darts. There is also an outside drinking space. One beer is often from Batemans, alongside two changing choices, sometimes from local brewers. Self-contained accommodation is available and there is generous parking.

Boston

Coach & Horses

86 Main Ridge, PE21 6SY
(01205) 612649
Batemans XB, XXXB; 1 changing beer (sourced locally; often Batemans)
Close to the Boston United football ground, the pub has an open-plan lounge with a polished wooden bar and wood-panelled ceiling. Wooden cabinets showcase a large collection of miniature bottles. Other items such as a deer's antlers, a large clock and photographs of musicians adorn the walls. The pub hosts pool, darts, poker and quiz teams, and is popular with football supporters. There is regular entertainment at weekends.

Eagle

144 West Street, PE21 8RE
(01205) 361116
Castle Rock Black Gold, Harvest Pale, Preservation, Screech Owl; 7 changing beers
Part of the Castle Rock chain, the Eagle is known as the real ale pub of Boston. This friendly two-roomed hostelry has an L-shaped bar with a large TV screen for big sports events. The small, cosy lounge has an open fire. A wide range of guest ales is stocked, and at least one cider. The function room upstairs is home to Boston Folk Club. Friday is quiz night – allegedly the hardest in town.
Q

Goodbarns Yard

8 Wormgate, PE21 6NP
(01205) 355717
Morland Old Speckled Hen; Timothy Taylor Landlord; 1 changing beer (sourced nationally)
This pub is in a cobbled medieval street which runs northwards away from the Boston Stump, parallel to the River Witham. The 700-year-old inn is popular for meals, with a busy restaurant. Old signs and pictures of Boston adorn the walls. A large garden with tables and covered patio areas overlooks the river. In winter, an open fire welcomes you.

Bourne

Anchor

44 Eastgate, PE10 9JY
(01778) 422347
House beer (by Dancing Duck); 4 changing beers (sourced regionally; often Nene Valley, St Austell, Thornbridge)
A traditional two-roomed local with a patio by the banks of a tributary of the River Glen, strong on sports, with pool and darts played, Sky Sports on TV and several sporting trophies on display. It raises funds for the local Air Ambulance service. The house beer, Bourne Particular, is supplied by Dancing Duck, as is Roundheart, brewed for sister pub the Hand & Heart in Nottingham. There is a small car park. P

Brigg

Yarborough Hunt

49 Bridge Street, DN20 8NS (across bridge from marketplace)
(01652) 658333
Lincolnshire Craft Beers Best Bitter, Lincoln Gold, Bomber County; 4 changing beers (sourced nationally; often Skinner's, Timothy Taylor, Wychwood)
Traditional pub in the town centre, with a main bar and a number of interconnecting rooms, some with real fires. Many vintage photographs and old brewery signs and notices are displayed. There are three real ales from Lincolnshire Craft Beers plus four rotating guests and a real cider. Fourteen keg taps also offer a choice of continental and craft beers. An enclosed beer garden is at the rear. No food is served but customers can bring their own sandwiches. Q (4,X4)

Burton-upon-Stather

Ferry House Inn

Stather Road, DN15 9DJ (follow campsite signs through village and go down hill at church)
(01724) 721783
2 changing beers (sourced locally; often Lincolnshire Craft Beers, Wold Top)
Friendly village pub on the banks of the River Trent, in the same family for over 60 years. It has its own microbrewery offering occasional brews and real cider is also sold. A heritage group beer festival is held on the last weekend in August. Good-value home-cooked food is served Friday night, all day Saturday, and Sunday lunchtime. The pub has a large outdoor play area, hosts live music events, and is a popular meeting place for local heritage groups. Opening hours are reduced in January so check ahead. Cask Marque approved.
Q P (60)

Castle Bytham

Castle Inn

High Sreet, NG33 4RZ
(01780) 411223
Hop Back Summer Lightning; Oakham Citra; 2 changing beers
One of the original public houses in a historic village, the decor consisting of old oak beams, period furnishings and walls hung with antique prints. This 17th-century gem has Summer Lightning permanently on offer, with regularly changing guest ales sourced regionally and nationally. An excellent food menu is available, with home-made food cooked on a wood-fired stove served lunchtime and evening. Q

Fox & Hounds

6 High Street, NG33 4RZ
(01780) 410336
Marston's Pedigree; 3 changing beers (often Oakham, Timothy Taylor)
A welcoming, friendly village local which has been in the same family for 16 years. Marston's Pedigree and ales from Oakham are always available plus two changing guest beers. A regular quiz night is held on the first Sunday of the month. There is excellent home-cooked food to be enjoyed, including at a curry night on the first Thursday of the month, with food from the award-winning Bengal Clipper in Stamford. P

Chapel St Leonards

Admiral Benbow

The Promenade, PE24 5BQ
☎ (01754) 871847 🌐 admiralbenbowbeachbar.co.uk
Black Sheep Best Bitter; 2 changing beers Ⓗ
A beach bar on the promenade, with an outside seating area on the Hispaniola boat deck. Opening times and facilities are dependent on the weather and are limited in winter (see the website for current times). Bar snacks and hot food are sold, with picnic trays and plastic glasses to take your favourite food and ale on to the beach. Dogs are welcome on leads, with blankets and dog treats available. If the flag is flying the bar is open.
❀◐🚌🐾📶

Claypole

Five Bells 𝕃

95 Main Street, NG23 5BJ
☎ (01636) 626261 🌐 thefivebellsclaypole.co.uk
4 changing beers (sourced nationally; often Tetley) Ⓗ
Traditional village pub that always has four beers and two ciders on the bar. The guest ales are predominantly from local microbreweries. There is a large public bar, a small lounge and a restaurant serving home-cooked food. An annual beer festival is held in June. Outside there is a spacious beer garden and children's play area. Four en-suite rooms are available.
Q❀🛏◐◑♿♣●P🚌🐾📶

Cleethorpes

Crow's Nest

Balmoral Road, DN35 9ND
☎ (01472) 698867 🌐 crowsnestcleethorpes.co.uk
Samuel Smith Old Brewery Bitter Ⓗ
A short drive away from Cleethorpes seafront, this is a lovely example of a traditional estate pub. Built in the 1950s, it offers a warm and friendly welcome to the local community and any new visitors. A Samuel Smith's establishment, it also provides accommodation (book in advance). Recently refurbished to a good standard, and with a garden, this is worth a visit. Q🛏♣P🚌(7,4)

No. 2 Refreshment Room

Station Approach, DN35 8AX
☎ 07905 375587
Hancocks HB; Rudgate Ruby Mild; Sharp's Atlantic, Sea Fury; 2 changing beers (sourced nationally) Ⓗ
A local CAMRA award-winning pub, set on the railway station forecourt itself so handy for train travellers. An excellent choice of quality real ales is always available, served in a convivial atmosphere. There is also a range of ciders. Known locally as Under the Clock, this small one-roomed bar is a regular in this Guide. ❀⇌●🚌📶

No.1 Pub

Railway Station, DN35 8AX
☎ (01472) 696221
Batemans XXXB; Draught Bass; 6 changing beers (sourced regionally; often Axholme, Horncastle Ales) Ⓗ
Large railway bar on Cleethorpes station. This popular local has a main bar with a smaller real ale-themed back room overlooking the station platform. The walls are adorned with local railway memorabilia. There is outside seating at the front for the warmer weather. The pub is known for its home-cooked meals. On most weekends live music is a feature, and it also has a yearly music festival. ◐◑⇌♣●P🚌🐾📶

Willy's

17 High Cliff, DN35 8RQ
☎ (01472) 602145
Draught Bass; Willy's Original; 2 changing beers (sourced nationally) Ⓗ
A seafront bar with views over the Humber Estuary to the Yorkshire coast. It mainly operates from the downstairs bar; an upstairs bar is used for functions. There is some outdoor seating. Willy's Original Bitter is brewed in the on-site microbrewery. Good-quality locally sourced home-made food is served. A mix of ages sees a gentler, quieter crowd of an afternoon, with DJs at weekends.
❀◐◑⇌●🚌🐾

Coleby

Tempest Arms

Hill Rise, LN5 0AG
☎ (01522) 810258 🌐 thetempestcoleby.co.uk
Brains Rev James; Castle Rock Harvest Pale; St Austell Cornish Best Bitter; Timothy Taylor Landlord; 2 changing beers (sourced nationally; often Black Sheep, Oakham, Robinsons) Ⓗ
Despite its recently enlarged dining area, and sturdy dining tables throughout, this warm and friendly local is still very much a drinkers' pub. Two stove-heated seating areas surround the well-stocked central bar. Immaculately kept, and now locally owned, the pub attracts Viking Way trekkers, regional bus users and villagers alike. Meals and snacks are served all day (except Mon). Diners enjoy views over the terraced beer gardens and the panoramic Witham-Trent valley.
Q❀◐◑●P🚌(1)🐾📶

Donington

Black Bull

7 Market Place, PE11 4ST
☎ (01775) 822228 🌐 theblackbulldonington.co.uk
Batemans XB; Sharp's Doom Bar; 3 changing beers (often Batemans) Ⓗ
Busy local just off the A52. Five handpumps feature three regular beers and occasionally two varying guest beers from small brewers as well as large regionals. The comfortable bar has low, beamed ceilings, wooden settles and a cosy fire in winter. Due to the return in 2020 of the remains of Captain Matthew Flinders, navigator and cartographer, born 1774, to this town which was his birthplace, the pub has an exclusive beer named in his honour, brewed by Batemans.
❀◐◑♣●P🚌🐾📶

East Butterwick

Dog & Gun 𝕃

High Street, DN17 3AJ (off A18 at Keadby Bridge, on E bank)
☎ (01724) 782324 🌐 doggunpub.com
3 changing beers (sourced locally; often Dark Tribe) Ⓗ
Village inn on the main road next to the banks of the River Trent. There are outside seating areas at the front and side of the building and across the road on the river bank. Inside are three rooms, two with open fires lit in winter. Rustic decor includes wooden tables and chairs, padded bench seats and flagstone and wooden floors. The Dark Tribe Microbrewery is at the back of the pub. Food is popular and reservations advised.
❀◐◑♿♣P🚌(12)📶

Eastoft

River Don Tavern

Sampson Street, DN17 4PQ (on A161 Goole-Gainsborough road)

☎ (01724) 798040 🌐 theriverdoneastoft.co.uk

2 changing beers (sourced regionally; often Bradfield, Rooster's) 🄷

Traditionally styled pub on the main road through the village, with dark-wood ceiling beams, rustic furniture and vintage photos adorning the walls. An L-shaped bar serves two open-plan areas, one of which is for dining. A separate restaurant is used for the renowned Sunday carvery. Two changing real ales are featured (three in summer), plus a real cider. An orchard at the rear is a pleasant place for summer drinking. Accommodation is in four outdoor lodges and three rooms. 🐎❀🛏◑♿♣●P🚌(361)🐾ᯤ

Fosdyke

Ship Inn

Moulton Washway, PE12 6LH

☎ (01205) 260764 🌐 shipinnfosdyke.com

Adnams Southwold Bitter, Broadside; Batemans XB 🄷

Just outside Fosdyke when travelling from Boston on the A17 next to the bridge, as its name suggests this former Batemans pub is dedicated to things maritime – maps, photographs, charts, model ships and artefacts of many descriptions are plentiful. The week's tidetable is also detailed on a blackboard. The inn is near the busy Fosdyke Marina – boaters and landlubbers are all well catered for, with excellent home-cooked food, good beer and a warm welcome. Q🐎◐◑P🐾ᯤ

Gainsborough

Blues Club

Northolme, North Street, DN21 2QW

☎ (01427) 613688

3 changing beers (often Horncastle Ales) 🄷

The club has a bar area with several TVs showing sport, a quieter lounge and a large function room that hosts regular live entertainment (admission charges may apply). Two or three changing real ales are usually on offer and details of forthcoming beers are available on request. CAMRA guests are always welcome on production of a membership card. 🐎≉♣🚌ᯤ

Eight Jolly Brewers 🄻

Ship Court, DN21 2DW

Changing beers 🄷

The branch's flagship real ale haven, in this Guide since 1995, based in a 300-year-old Grade II listed building. Six or more changing beers are always on sale, many from northern microbreweries, but new breweries from all areas feature. Real cider and continental bottled beers are also on tap. The pub holds a fortnightly Wednesday quiz night, and customers bring in food to share on Sunday lunchtime. Q♿≉●P🚌(200)

Sweyn Forkbeard 🏆 ✔

22-24 Silver Street, DN21 2DP

☎ (01427) 675000

Greene King Abbot; Ruddles Best Bitter; Sharp's Doom Bar; 3 changing beers 🄷

This town-centre Wetherspoon, local CAMRA Pub of the Year 2019 and 2020, is one of the must-visit pubs in town. The three rotating guest ales often include some oddities for this part of the country. Customers can ask for their favourite beer and it often appears. The pub is named after the Danish King of England in 1013, whose son Canute is rumoured to have attempted to stop the aegir (the tidal bore on the River Trent). Typical good value Wetherspoon food menu is available all day. 🐎◐◑♿≉(Central) ●🚌ᯤ

Gosberton Risegate

Duke of York 🄻

106 Risegate Road, PE11 4EY

☎ (01775) 840193

Batemans XB; St Austell Tribute; 1 changing beer (sourced locally) 🄷

A friendly pub and a long-standing entry in this Guide, with a deserved reputation for value-for-money beer and food. The guest beers come from a range of independent brewers. A wide choice of food is available, with portions to suit the largest appetite. Local community life is supported through charities, sports teams and other social events. Q🐎❀◐◑♣P🐾

Grantham

Chequers 🄻

25 Market Place, NG31 6LR

☎ (01476) 570149

3 changing beers (sourced nationally; often Brewsters) 🄷

This cosmopolitan and contemporary bar features local breweries Brewsters and Zest; other breweries may include Bakers Dozen, Kelham Island and Framework. The regular beers are supplemented with changing guests. Located on a paved side street between the High Street and the Market Square, known locally as Butchers Row, the bar has a relaxing atmosphere during the day and comes alive and vibrant in the evenings and weekends. Q❀≉●🚌🐾ᯤ

Grantham Railway Club 🄻

Huntingtower Road, NG31 7AU

☎ (01476) 564860

2 changing beers 🄷

A community-run club voted local CAMRA Club of the Year for 2020, which offers ales from Grantham's three local brewers. Formerly the British Rail Staff Association, it plays host to numerous cribbage, darts and dominoes teams as well as supporting various social and community organisations. There is live music every Saturday night, with a spacious back room available to hire. CAMRA members are welcome. 🐎❀♿≉♣P🐾ᯤ

Lord Harrowby 🄻

65 Dudley Road, NG31 9AB

☎ (01476) 563515

4 changing beers 🄷

A friendly back-street community local, one of the few in Grantham. Reminiscent of how pubs used to be, it comprises a bar, snug and lounge with a real fire. It has a dartboard and crib is played in leagues. There is an enclosed area at the back where at least two beer festivals with live music are held. The landlord, a CAMRA member and real ale enthusiast, offers a permanent LocAle and four changing guest beers. Q❀≉♣●🐾ᯤ

Nobody Inn 🄻

9 North Street, NG31 6NU (opp Asda car park)

☎ (01476) 562206 🌐 nobody-inn.business.site

6 changing beers (often Black Sheep, Newby Wyke, Sharp's) 🄷

The Nobody is famous for its hidden toilet door behind the bookcase. The pub sells beer from the award-winning Newby Wyke brewery in Grantham. It gets lively at the weekends and when a big sporting event is taking place, but it is also a nice place for a quiet drink with

good bar staff. Popular live music is staged most Saturday nights. Watch out for the giant spider!
♣●⊟✻ᯤ

Grimsby

Docks Beers
The Church, King Edward Street, DN31 3JD
☎ (01472) 289795 ⊕ docksbeers.com
Axholme Cleethorpes Pale Ale; 2 changing beers Ⓗ
Docks Beers Brewery taproom is set in an old church, selling three cask ales and a craft beer selection. Axholme beers are often available as well. Docks Beers has recently increased capacity and you can sit and watch the brewery at work. A space upstairs offers different events, and food stalls are set up outside most weekends. ♞⊟✻

Rutland Arms
26 Rutland Street, DN31 3AF
☎ (01472) 268732
Old Mill Traditional Bitter; 2 changing beers Ⓗ
Close both to bus routes and train station, this pub is easy to find and tends to be a favourite with local football supporters. It has four handpumps and sells a selection of Old Mill beers. A TV shows live sporting events. The interior is one single long room with a pool table and dartboard at the end. It is currently being refurbished.
Q♞✿⇌(New Clee) ♣P⊟✻ᯤ

Spider's Web
180 Carr Lane, DN32 8LN
☎ (01472) 692065
John Smith's Bitter; 3 changing beers (sourced nationally; often Leeds, Wainwright) Ⓗ
This friendly family-run community pub has a lively bar, quiet lounge and a function room that holds frequent live music events from artists of many genres. In the bar, games such as poker, darts and pool are played. There is also a weekly quiz night. Outside is a large suntrap garden with space for children to play and a smoking area. Q♞✿♣P⊟(4)✻ᯤ

Yarborough Hotel ✔
Bethlehem Street, DN31 1JN
☎ (01472) 268283
Greene King Abbot; Kelham Island Easy Rider; Ruddles Best Bitter; 12 changing beers (sourced regionally) Ⓗ
A large open-plan Wetherspoon serving 15 real ales from national brands through to more local ales from the Lincolnshire area. Like many in the chain, it can be popular on Tuesday steak night and again on Thursday curry night. It has been restored as a grand hotel next door to Grimsby Town railway station after a troubled past where it was under threat of demolition, and is now a thriving pub again. A frequent winner of local CAMRA Pub of the Year. Q♞✿⊨◐♿⇌●⊟

Habrough

Station Inn
Station Road, DN40 3AP
☎ (01469) 572896
3 changing beers (sourced regionally; often Bradfield, Theakston, Timothy Taylor) Ⓗ
Originally a hotel built in 1848 for the Great Grimsby & Sheffield Junction Railway, this inn has one large room with access to the bar and a smaller area for pool and bar games. It has a good community spirit – live bands play once a month on Saturday, and with karaoke, theme nights and traditional pub games, this is a lively environment. Three handpumps feature changing beers from regional brewers. Dogs are welcome.
♞✿⇌♣●P✻

Heckington

8 Sail Brewery Bar
Heckington Mill, Hale Road, NG34 9JW
☎ (01529) 469308 ⊕ 8sailbrewery.co.uk
8 Sail Windmill Bitter, Blonde, Rolling Stone, King John's Jewels, Oat Malt Stout; 3 changing beers (sourced locally; often 8 Sail) Ⓗ
In part of the Heckington Windmill complex, this is a single-room brewery bar featuring a restored Victorian counter with church pew and Britannia bar seating. Three changing 8 Sail Brewery beers of varying styles are usually sold, with occasional guests. A selection of German bottled beer and local cider is also available. Beer festivals are held mid-July over the Heckington Show weekend and in September. On winter Saturdays and Sundays closing time may be earlier – check the Facebook page. Q♞✿♿⇌●P⊟✻ᯤ

Heighington

Butcher & Beast
High Street, LN4 1JS
☎ (01522) 790386 ⊕ butcherandbeast.co.uk
Batemans XB, XXXB; Timothy Taylor Landlord; 3 changing beers (sourced nationally; often Castle Rock, Oakham) Ⓗ
Welcoming old stone Batemans pub with a splendid array of exterior floral decor. It has distinctive drinking areas, a real fire and old photographs adorning the walls. Along with a fine selection of gins there is at least one real cider. The restaurant at the rear offers quality food and has a steak night Monday, fish night Tuesday, and serves a roast on Sunday. Quizzes and charity nights are popular. The garden boasts a beautiful patio area. Local buses run until early evening.
Q♞✿◐♣●P⊟(2,10)✻ᯤ

Horbling

Plough Inn
4 Spring Lane, NG34 0PF
☎ (01529) 240263 ⊕ ploughinnhorbling.co.uk
Grainstore Ten Fifty; 2 changing beers Ⓗ
A community pub owned by the parish of Horbling, built in 1832 and set just off the main road. In addition to the lounge/bar, its snug is surely one of the smallest and most intimate of its kind. Guest beers come from a wide range of breweries, often micros, and change frequently. Quality meals are served throughout the pub and in a separate restaurant. The Spring Wells, a feature worth seeing, are just a few yards down the lane.
♞◐♿♣●P✻ᯤ

Horncastle

King's Head
16 Bull Ring, LN9 5HU
☎ (01507) 523360
Batemans XB, Gold, XXXB; 1 changing beer (sourced regionally) Ⓗ
A comfortable, cosy and friendly establishment. Unusually for this locality, the building has a thatched roof, hence its local name, The Thatch. Three beers from Batemans are generally on the bar plus a guest. Reputedly the place inspired an 00-gauge Hornby model, an example of which is displayed behind the bar. Summertime sees the pub resplendent with hanging

baskets and it has been a winner of Batemans' Floral Display competition. Try spotting the cat, Rufus.
&❀◑●🖥😺🗢

Old Nick's Tavern
8 North Street, LN9 5DX
☎ (01507) 526862
4 changing beers (sourced locally; often Horncastle Ales) ⊞
Built in 1752 as a coaching inn, this original building is now a town-centre pub with its own microbrewery, the home of Horncastle Ales – the head brewster is the landlord's daughter. It has been refurbished and incorporates the original hanging sign and old photos of the pub. Regular live bands are featured. There are five handpumps, four of which usually offer Horncastle ales. Currently no food. &❀♣●🖥😺🗢

Ingoldmells
Countryman 🅛
Chapel Road, PE25 1ND
☎ (01754) 872268
Leila Cottage Leila's Lazy Days, Ace Ale, Leila's One Off ⊞
The privately owned Countryman appears to be a modern building but it incorporates the early 19th-century Leila Cottage, which gives its name to the brewery behind the pub. A notorious smuggler, James Waite, used to reside here when Ingoldmells was a wild and lonely place, but he certainly wouldn't recognise the current holiday coast, with Skegness, Butlin's and Fantasy Island nearby. Information boards give brewery, pub and beer information for visitors. The pub is on northern bus routes from Skegness. &❀◑&▲♣P🖥🖥

Kirkby on Bain
Ebrington Arms
Main Street, LN10 6YT
☎ (01526) 354560 ⊕ ebringtonarms.com
Batemans XB; Sharp's Doom Bar; Timothy Taylor Landlord; 1 changing beer (often Adnams) ⊞
Attractive country pub close to the River Bain and dating from 1610. World War II airmen used to slot coins into the ceiling beams to pay for beer when they returned from missions over Germany. Sadly, many of these coins are still in situ and make a unique memorial to the dead. The popular restaurant offers good food made with local produce (booking advised). There is one guest beer in winter, often two in summer.
Q&❀◑&▲♣P🖥(65)😺🗢

Kirmington
Marrowbone & Cleaver
High Street, DN39 6YZ
☎ (01652) 688335 ⊕ marrowboneandcleaver.com
Sharp's Doom Bar; house beer (by Batemans); 1 changing beer ⊞
After a period of closure, this village pub was refurbished and reopened by motorbike racer Guy Martin. It is adorned with racing memorabilia and also items from the 166 Squadron inside. It is a family-run pub, with Guy's sister Sally managing it. Although it is mainly food-oriented it has three handpumps. Drinkers are given a warm welcome as well as diners. The house beer was developed through a collaboration between Guy Martin and Batemans Brewery. Q&❀◑&♣P😺

Lincoln
Adam & Eve Tavern
25 Lindum Road, LN2 1NT
☎ (01522) 537108 ⊕ adamandevelincoln.co.uk
Castle Rock Harvest Pale; Morland Old Speckled Hen; 2 changing beers (sourced nationally) ⊞
A short walk from the cathedral or a hill climb from downtown Lincoln, this multi-room tavern is ideal for small to mid-sized gatherings. Helping to keep music live with weekly music nights, it is also home to popular Sunday quiz nights and a monthly music quiz. The pub is great for watching sporting events, and if games are your thing, darts and pool feature, along with gaming machines as well as a selection of board games.
&❀◑♣P🖥😺🗢

BeerHeadZ
4 Eastgate, LN2 1QA
☎ (01522) 255430 ⊕ beerheadz.biz
4 changing beers (sourced nationally) ⊞
Situated in the uphill city area, this bright, colourful pub has an industrial feel. It is part of a small chain of new generation indie pubs. It serves up to six cask ales, craft keg beers, two ciders and a range of bottled and canned beers, and uses oversized glasses. Customers are welcome to bring in their own food. Regular events take place include quizzes, live music and tap takeovers.
●🖥😺🗢

Cardinal's Hat
268 High Street, LN2 1HW
☎ (01522) 527084
Adnams Mosaic; Lincolnshire Craft Beers Lincoln Gold; Rat White Rat; house beer (by Lincolnshire Craft Beers); 4 changing beers (sourced nationally) ⊞
A Grade II* listed building at the foot of Lincoln's Steep Hill, this three-storey, half-timbered building was an inn between the 16th and 18th centuries. More recently it was the HQ for St John Ambulance Brigade. A sensitive conversion back to a public house in 2015 revealed a number of historical features. Reputedly named after Cardinal Wolsey, Bishop of Lincoln (1514-1515), it has a large, ground-floor bar area plus smaller atmospheric snugs and rooms. Eight ales and four ciders can be enjoyed alongside a food menu of charcuterie and cheese. &❀◑&⇌●🗢

Golden Eagle
21 High Street, LN5 8BD
☎ (01522) 521058
Castle Rock Harvest Pale; Sharp's Doom Bar; 7 changing beers (sourced nationally; often Pheasantry, Saltaire, Welbeck Abbey) ⊞
Popular, thriving and traditional two-roomed pub on the lower High Street, close to the LNER Stadium and therefore busy on match days. It sells up to nine real ales, and over 50 craft ales from the fridge in the bar area. Outside is a large garden with cosy sheltered seating. Two annual beer festivals are the highlight of the social calendar. Harvey the dog is always happy to greet customers. A small function room is available to hire. Q&❀♣●P🖥😺🗢

Joiners Arms
4 Victoria Street, LN1 1HU
☎ (01522) 244470
5 changing beers (sourced nationally) ⊞
A short walk from the High Street, this traditional back-street boozer features five changing ales, and has an increasing selection of gins. It is a popular venue for live entertainment and beer festivals. Traditional pub games include Lincoln's only bar billiards table. A quiz takes

place every Tuesday and open mic every Friday. Enjoy a drink by the open fires. Football fans (home and away) will find a warm welcome. A characterful beer garden is to the rear. ❀♣🐾📶

Ritz L ✔
143-147 High Street, LN5 7PJ
☎ (01522) 512103
Greene King Abbot; Ruddles Best Bitter; Sharp's Doom Bar; 6 changing beers (sourced nationally) Ⓗ
Part of the Wetherspoon chain, the Ritz was originally a cinema and entertainments centre. The venue is a split-level building with a family area on the ground and the bar with seating above; it has a lift for access if required. Its past use is reflected in both the interior and exterior décor. Food is served all day, with speciality nights. A Meet the Brewer event is held on the last Thursday of each month. Close to the city's transport hub.
Q♘❀◐♿≠🍎🚌📶

Strait & Narrow
29-31 Strait, LN2 1JD
☎ (01522) 589598 🌐 thestraitandnarrow.co.uk
Timothy Taylor Landlord; 3 changing beers (sourced nationally; often Tiny Rebel) Ⓗ
At the foot of Lincoln's famous Steep Hill, this former retail outlet was converted in 2012 into a continental-style beer bar. It retains its impressive windowed frontage overlooking The Strait. The interior, on different levels, has comfortable seating and quirky lighting. Around 130 bottled and canned beers from around the world are stocked and many are displayed in wall cabinets. DJs provide music on Wednesday to Saturday evenings. ♘♿≠📶

Strugglers Inn L ✔
83 Westgate, LN1 3BG
☎ (01522) 535023 🌐 strugglers-lincoln.co.uk
Greene King Abbot; Ossett Yorkshire Blonde; Timothy Taylor Landlord; 7 changing beers (sourced nationally; often Dukeries, Pheasantry, Welbeck Abbey) Ⓗ
A traditional two-roomed inn next to Lincoln Castle, this small pub is big on character. It is a great location for locals and tourists alike. The walls and ceilings in both the main bar and the snug are adorned with pumpclips of beers that have previously featured. Two real fires make for a warm winter welcome, while outside is a hidden beer garden, great for summer drinking. There is no sound system but regular live music plays on Sunday.
Q❀♣🚌🐾📶

Victoria
6 Union Road, LN1 3BJ
☎ (01522) 541000
Batemans XB; Castle Rock Harvest Pale; Timothy Taylor Landlord; 3 changing beers (sourced nationally) Ⓗ
Thirty seven continuous years in this Guide are a tribute to the long-time manager, and testament to the consistent provision of good ale in the city. The Victoria is in the most historic part of Lincoln and has a sunny outdoor area for drinkers to enjoy a pint. A refurbishment is on the horizon but we are assured that the character and simplicity of this traditional two-room pub will be preserved. Q❀◐🍎🚌🐾📶

Louth

Boar's Head
12 Newmarket, LN11 9HH
☎ (01507) 654127
Caledonian Deuchars IPA; Theakston Best Bitter; Timothy Taylor Landlord; 1 changing beer Ⓗ
A traditional three-roomed pub just outside the centre of this market town. It is well known locally for its real ales. Games include darts, dominoes and pool. On Thursday, cattle market day, it may open early.
Q♘❀◐♿♣🍎🚌🐾📶

Brown Cow ✔
133 Newmarket, LN11 9EG (top of Newmarket on jct with Church St)
☎ (01507) 605146
Black Sheep Best Bitter; Castle Rock Harvest Pale; Fuller's London Pride; 1 changing beer Ⓗ
The owners are celebrating 10 years behind the bar of this friendly free house. With a great atmosphere and excellent beer, it is a must when visiting Louth. A free quiz is held every first Sunday of the month. The kitchen serves traditional, home-cooked food, made with locally sourced products. The pub is a popular community meeting place. ♘❀◐♿▲🚌🐾📶

Cobbles Bar
New Street, LN11 9PU (off Cornmarket)
Black Sheep Best Bitter; 1 changing beer Ⓗ
Traditional pub-style bar based in the centre of town, with friendly staff. This small but accommodating venue has multiple personalities, from a bustling coffee shop serving light lunches to a busy pre-club local with DJ and live music at weekends. It has a good beer trade, with two contrasting cask ales, as well as a huge selection of exotic spirits. Wheelchair access is right through the front doors. ◐♿🚌

Consortium Micropub L
13C & D Cornmarket, LN11 9PY
☎ (01507) 600754 🌐 theconsortiumlouth.co.uk
5 changing beers (often Consortium)
Micropub in a small courtyard 100 yards from the Market Place. Six real ales and two real ciders are always on, changing every week. It has its own microbrewery upstairs that usually provides three of the six ales on the bar. This bar was opened in 2017 to give people a chance to taste various ales from around the UK.
Q♘♿▲🍎P🗑🚌(51)🐾📶

Olde Whyte Swanne ✔
45 Eastgate, LN11 9NP
☎ (01507) 824141 🌐 whyteswannelouth.co.uk
Rudgate Ruby Mild; 3 changing beers Ⓗ
The oldest pub in this pretty market town, established in the early 1600s. Upon entering this Grade II listed building you are met by traditional low-beamed ceilings and a real fire. Beyond this is a modern room used for dining and meetings. The bar offers a good variety of beers and cider on handpump. Q♘❀◐♿🗑🚌🐾📶

White Horse
Kenwick Road, LN11 8EG
☎ (01507) 603331
Black Sheep Best Bitter; Courage Best Bitter; Draught Bass; 1 changing beer Ⓗ
A friendly pub with a great atmosphere, where all the family are welcome. Popular with locals, it serves excellent hearty meals and real ales. It has a TV and all major sporting events are covered, and an outdoor seating area with a large car park. Open daily, but hours change in the winter months – please call for details.
Q♘❀◐♿▲♣P🚌🐾📶

Woolpack L
Riverhead Road, LN11 0DA (next to canal)
☎ (01507) 606568 🌐 woolpacklouth.com

Batemans XB, Gold, XXXB; 1 changing beer Ⓗ
The Woolpack is close to the theatre and is popular with drinkers and diners alike. It usually offers four or five real ales on handpump. The Grade II listed building is dog-friendly, and has wheelchair access and baby-changing facilities. There is a beer garden and ample parking. ♞❀◑♿P🚌🐾📶

Market Deeping

Bull

19 Market Square, PE6 8EA
☎ (01778) 343320
Everards Tiger, Old Original; 2 changing beers (sourced regionally) Ⓗ
A friendly and family-oriented 16th-century coaching inn that is now an Everards house. The old-world, split-level layout features oak beams, flagstones and exposed stone walls. There is a lounge, a small dining room and the famous Dug-out bar. Four handpumps serve real ales from Everards and occasional guest breweries. Real cider is always available, along with a large selection of gins and fine wines. The local CAMRA branch was formed here in 1974. Q♞❀◑♿🍎P🚌📶

Vine Inn L

19 Church Street, PE6 8AN
☎ (01778) 348741
Sharp's Doom Bar; house beer (by Worthington's); 3 changing beers (often Abbeydale, Courage, Skinner's) Ⓗ
Formerly a Charles Wells pub, now a free house, this small, friendly venue features oak beams and stone floors, with many 20th-century prints on the walls. There is a large patio at the rear. Five handpumps dispense Sharp's Doom Bar and Vine Ale (Hancock's HB) plus a changing range of guests. Boxed real cider is available, and free nibbles are provided Sunday lunchtime and early evenings during the week. The TV is only used for major sporting events. ❀🍎P🚌(101)🐾📶

Messingham

Horn Inn

61 High Street, DN17 3NU
☎ (01724) 761190
Timothy Taylor Landlord; 3 changing beers (sourced regionally; often Black Sheep, Courage, Purity) Ⓗ
Attractive village local furnished in country-style decor. A central bar serves three distinct areas used for drinking and dining, one of which is decorated with brewery memorabilia. A varied menu is available in the evening Wednesday and Thursday, and all day Friday to Sunday. Four real ales are usually featured. A sheltered patio is at the rear for outdoor drinking. Quiz night is Monday. Dogs are welcome, with biscuits available at the bar.
♞❀◑♿P🚌(100,103)🐾📶

Pooley's 🏆

46 High Street, DN17 3NT
☎ 07860 799178
5 changing beers (sourced regionally; often Batemans, Ossett, Rat) Ⓗ
Comfortable, traditional village local, which is only open in the evenings. A bar at one end serves three distinct drinking areas with bare-brick walls, rustic furniture, wooden and flagstone floors and real fires. The walls display attractive vintage posters and signs. Five changing real ales are on tap, often from Adnams, Batemans, Fernandes, Oakham, Ossett and Rat, plus a large selection of malt whiskies, gins and wines. Winner of several local CAMRA awards. Q♿🚌(100,103)🐾📶

Morton

Ship Inn ✔

34 Front Street, DN21 3AE
☎ (01427) 613298
Sharp's Atlantic; Timothy Taylor Landlord; 1 changing beer Ⓗ
To the north of Gainsborough, this is a quaint typical village pub. There are weekly darts, dominoes and pool matches and regular quiz evenings. It has two rotating cask ales and food is available six days a week, with Sunday lunches proving to be popular. ♞◗♣🚌

Navenby

Lion & Royal

57 High Street, LN5 0DZ
☎ (01522) 810368
Greene King IPA, Abbot; 3 changing beers (sourced nationally; often Parkway, Welbeck Abbey) Ⓗ
An imposing stone building in the centre of the village. Cosy real fires are lit when needed and there is a large beer garden for the warmer weather. 'Royal' was added to the name following a visit by the Prince of Wales in 1870. Guy Gibson of RAF 617 Squadron fame spent his wedding night here. The pub is on the Lincoln to Grantham bus route and is popular with walkers on the nearby Viking Way. ♞❀◑♿♣P🚌(1)🐾📶

Newton

Red Lion

NG34 0EE
☎ (01529) 497256 🌐 theredlionnewton.com
2 changing beers (sourced locally) Ⓗ
This popular village pub has been a part of this beautiful country village for over 300 years. It has friendly and helpful staff, and dispenses well-kept changing local beers and good traditional home-made food. The bare-boards bar with light-wood counter, black-beamed ceiling and roaring fire, and carpeted restaurant area, make this a warm and welcoming venue. There is a back terrace by the car park and a delightful new function room with accommodation. Q♞❀🛏◑♿P🐾📶

North Hykeham

Centurion ✔

Newark Road, LN6 8LB
☎ (01522) 509814
Bombardier Gold; Sharp's Doom Bar; house beer (by Black Sheep); 2 changing beers (sourced nationally; often Adnams, Oakham, St Austell) Ⓗ
The pub's name reflects the Roman history of the area, as it is near the route of the ancient Fosse Way linking Lincoln to Exeter. Built in 1969, the Centurion is a hive of activity and a great meeting point for the local community and beyond. A warm welcome awaits for diners and drinkers alike. Food and ale offers feature throughout the week, and there are twice-weekly quizzes. Regular bus services from the city mean you can leave the car at home and properly enjoy the range of ales. ♞❀◑♿🍎P🚌📶

Raithby

Red Lion

Raithby Road, PE23 4DS
☎ (01790) 753727 🌐 redlioninn.pub
Batemans XB; 2 changing beers (often Batemans, Ferry Ales) Ⓗ

A cosy village inn built around 1650, with beamed low ceilings in its many small rooms that surround the bar. Pictures of outdoor pursuits and old photographs adorn the walls. It sits in an attractive quiet village on the edge of the Lincolnshire Wolds, in an excellent location for walking and cycling. The pub changed hands in December 2018 and is popular for its fresh locally sourced food. Q❀◑♿♣P🚌🐾📶

Ropsley

Green Man 🏆

24 High Street, NG33 4BE

☎ (01476) 585897 🌐 the-green-man-ropsley.com

Wainwright; 3 changing beers (sourced nationally; often Caledonian, Grainstore, Theakston) 🄷

Newly crowned local CAMRA Pub of the Year 2020 and Country Pub of the Year 2019, this 17th-century village local has a growing reputation for innovative food, including exotic meats, locally sourced game and seafood. Its relaxed tea room area is frequented by walkers and cyclists, and it also has a pleasant, tranquil beer garden. Themed food and drink matching evenings are held regularly, and it is renowned for an extensive bottled range. ❀◑♣P🐾📶

Ruskington

Shoulder of Mutton

11 Church Street, NG34 9DU

☎ (01526) 832220

Bombardier; John Smith's Bitter; 2 changing beers (sourced regionally; often Sharp's) 🄷

A popular and thriving pub in the heart of the village attracting customers of all ages. It is one of the oldest buildings in Ruskington and was once a butcher's shop, hence the name. A few old meat hooks can still be seen in the wooden ceiling in the bar. Changes have been made in recent years but have not spoilt the essential character. Standing guard outside is Knight and Day, a sculpture from Lincoln's 2017 Knight's Trail.
❀⇌♣P🚌(31)🐾📶

Saxilby

Anglers ✔

65 High Street, LN1 2HA

☎ (01522) 702200 🌐 anglerspublichouse.com

Theakston Best Bitter; 3 changing beers (sourced nationally; often Beermats, Pheasantry) 🄷

A family-run village local with a strong community and pub-sport focus. Regular charity fundraising events are held, along with darts, dominoes, pool and cribbage matches. The quieter lounge has old village photos. Pop-up food stalls visit on some Friday and Saturday evenings. An outside drinking area has a boules court. Close to the railway station, bus stops and visitor moorings on the Fossdyke, the country's oldest canal.
Q❀⇌♣P🚌🐾📶

Scampton

Dambusters Inn 🄻

23 High Street, LN1 2SD

☎ (01522) 731333 🌐 dambustersinn.co.uk

Greg's Dambusters Ale, Scampton Ale; 5 changing beers (sourced nationally; often Oakham, Pheasantry, Shepherd Neame) 🄷

Some pubs are special places of pilgrimage, and 10 visitors' books are testament to the international reputation of this multi award-winning village local. The Dambusters is a living testament to the eponymous WWII squadron, with memorabilia displays worthy of a national museum and an annual commemorative beer festival drawing drinkers from near and far to toast the 617 Squadron heroes. This is a proper pub, a flourishing microbrewery – two beers brewed by the landlord are usually available – and a popular food destination. Situated at the end of RAF Scampton's runway, it is a perfect venue for plane spotting. Q❀◑🍎P🚌(103)🐾📶

Scawby

Sutton Arms

10 West Street, DN20 9AN (on main road through village)

☎ (01652) 652430 🌐 suttonarmsscawby.co.uk

Black Sheep Best Bitter; Sharp's Doom Bar; 2 changing beers (sourced nationally; often Great Newsome, Hawkshead, Milestone) 🄷

A village inn with a strong emphasis on food; the extensive menu includes daily specials. A two-sided central bar serves a large dining area and separate restaurant, plus a narrow snug bar used mainly for drinking. The interior is attractively styled in country pub decor, including ceiling beams and dark wood fittings. Two regular real ales are always on the bar plus two rotating guests from all over the country. Quiz night is on Sunday evening. ❀◑♿P🐾📶

Scotter

Sun & Anchor

54 High Street, DN21 3RX

☎ (01724) 763444

Bradfield Farmers Blonde; Butcombe Original; Ossett Yorkshire Blonde; 1 changing beer 🄷

A traditional village inn with a bar and lounge serving good pub food and one regular and two guest ales in a friendly and welcoming atmosphere. All the latest sporting matches and events are shown. There is a darts and pool area, dominoes is played regularly, and there is a spacious private beer garden with a children's play area, and a large car park. ❀◑♿♣P🚌(101)🐾📶

Scunthorpe

Blue Bell ✔

1-7 Oswald Road, DN15 7PU (at town centre crossroads)

☎ (01724) 863921

Greene King Abbot; Ruddles Best Bitter; 6 changing beers (sourced regionally; often Bradfield, Kelham Island, Ossett) 🄷

Popular town-centre Wetherspoon, recently refurbished and enlarged, taking over three neighbouring properties to double its size. It also boasts a spacious ground-floor beer garden and smoking area, plus a large open terrace on the first floor accessed by stairs and a lift. The usual Wetherspoon food menu is served daily, and occasional themed events and beer, cider and gin festivals are hosted. ❀◑♿🍎🚌📶

Honest Lawyer

70 Oswald Road, DN15 7PG

☎ (01724) 276652

Sharp's Sea Fury; 3 changing beers (sourced locally; often Kelham Island, Milestone) 🄷

A compact town-centre pub with an upstairs restaurant now used for occasional events such as comedy or themed food nights. The downstairs bar area is narrow, with high shelves and tables and stools along one side, opening out at the back with tables, chairs and sofas. TVs, mostly showing sports, are in each area. There is a pavement drinking space out front with more tables and chairs. One regular real ale is supplemented by up to three rotating guest ales. ❀♿🚌📶

Malt Shovel

219 Ashby High Street, DN16 2JP (in Ashby Broadway shopping area)
☎ (01724) 843318
Exmoor Gold; 5 changing beers (sourced regionally; often Abbeydale, Bradfield, Rat) 🄷
Recently refurbished, popular high-street pub, with a front beer garden overlooking the shopping area. It has a single, comfortably furnished, carpeted lounge, with more seating in a conservatory leading off to the beer garden. Usually busy at meal times, booking for food is recommended, and children are allowed only if dining. Quiz night is usually on Thursday with live music on Friday, although days may vary. Five permanently rotating guest beers plus real ciders and perries are served from the cellar. The attached social and snooker club is members only. ❀◑♿🍎🚌

Skegness

Seathorne Arms

Seathorne Crescent, PE25 1RP
☎ (01754) 767797
2 changing beers (often Greene King, Morland) 🄷
Set back from Roman Bank and 15 minutes' walk from Butlin's, the pub has a large outside seating area and a spacious single-room interior with partitioned spaces for eating, pub games, drinking and TV watching. The landlord operates a constantly rotating two-beer selection, and there is an extensive food menu featuring locally sourced meat. The pub has a seasonal trade dependent on local caravan sites; it is closed in January and hours may vary February-March. ❀◑♿♣🚌🐾📶

Vine Hotel

Vine Road, PE25 3DB (off Drummond Rd)
☎ (01754) 763018
Batemans XB, XXXB; 1 changing beer (often Batemans) 🄷
A delightful building, one of the oldest in Skegness, dating from the 18th century and set in two acres of pleasant grounds. Inside are comfortable wood-panelled bars in which to enjoy a quiet pint or two after experiencing some of the noisier attractions and bustle of Skegness. Within striking distance of the Gibraltar Point National Nature Reserve, walking trails, beach and golf links, the inn has reputed Tennysonian connections. ❀🛏◑♿P🚌🐾📶

Sleaford

Carre Arms Hotel

Mareham Lane, NG34 7JP
☎ (01529) 303156 🌐 carrearmshotel.co.uk
3 changing beers (often Draught Bass, Marston's, Springhead) 🄷
A family-owned and run hotel previously owned by Bass, adjacent to the Bass Sleaford Maltings complex which is now awaiting a regeneration scheme. It has a comfortable bar area with two rooms, offering three regularly changing real ales from both larger regional breweries and local breweries. A cider is also often available on handpump. An extensive food menu is offered, featuring fresh, locally sourced ingredients, served in the bar area and restaurant. There is a pleasant covered courtyard, ideal on inclement days. ❀🛏◑♿🚆🍎P🚌

White Horse

Boston Road, NG34 7HD
☎ (01529) 968003
Bombardier; 2 changing beers (often Batemans, Horncastle Ales) 🄷
On the junction of Carre Street and Boston Road, the pub serves the housing area along the Boston Road. It is one of the few remaining traditional locals in Sleaford, with wet sales only. The interior has been opened out into a single L-shaped room but retains a cosy feel. Sports predominate, with both darts and pool teams. ❀🚆♣P🐾📶

Snitterby

Royal Oak

High Street, DN21 4TP (1½ miles from A15)
☎ (01673) 818273 🌐 royaloaksnitterby.co.uk
JW Lees Bitter; Rooster's Buckeye 🄷; 4 changing beers (sourced nationally; often Dancing Duck, Timothy Taylor) 🄷/🄶
Traditional village community local with wooden floors and open fires. It has a bustling bar while several interconnecting areas provide quiet corners and there is Sky/BT Sports in the snug. Outside is a newly landscaped streamside garden in the shade of a weeping ash tree. Popular food nights are limited to alternate Fridays (see website for details), so the pub remains focused on company, conversation and good beer. Up to eight real ales are served in the main bar, with low-alcohol draught beer also available. Q❀◑♿♣🍎P🐾

South Ferriby

Hope & Anchor 🄻

Sluice Road, DN18 6JQ
☎ (01652) 635334 🌐 thehopeandanchorpub.co.uk
House beer (by Theakston); 2 changing beers (sourced nationally; often Lincolnshire Craft Beers, Theakston) 🄷
A 19th-century Michelin Bib Gourmand-listed inn standing at the confluence of the rivers Humber and Ancholme, next to the 150-year-old lock. Extensive estuary views are enjoyed from the dining room and outside seating area. The pub is popular with diners, while others just drop in for a pint after a walk or birdwatching. The front bar has three handpumps serving the permanent house beer, one changing national beer, and one changing local beer from one of five nearby breweries. Q❀◑♿P🚌(350)🐾📶

South Reston

Waggon & Horses

Main Road, LN11 8JQ
☎ (01507) 450364 🌐 waggonandhorsesreston.co.uk
Batemans XB; Draught Bass; 1 changing beer (often Marston's) 🄷
A warm and inviting traditional country pub in a small village not far from a hedgehog sanctuary. Great ales and high-quality meals using locally sourced ingredients are served every day. Open fires warm the bar and there is a lovely 50-seater dining room to the rear (booking is advisable). A shop on the far left offers newspapers and convenience store items. Q◑♿♣🚌(9)

Spalding

Ivy Wall ✔

18-19 New Road, PE11 1DQ
☎ (01775) 719770

Greene King Abbot; Morland Old Speckled Hen; Ruddles Best Bitter; Sharp's Doom Bar; Wychwood Hobgoblin Ruby; 2 changing beers (sourced nationally) Ⓗ
The town-centre site on which this spacious modern pub now stands has had a variety of uses over the years, and used to be on the bank of the Westlode River. Excavations during the rebuild in 2005 discovered an undercroft and cellar from the late medieval period, on view beneath toughened glass at the front of the bar. Guest ciders are sold and food is served all day. Photographs and archaeological finds are displayed on the walls. ✿◑♿≠●🚌

Priors Oven 𝕃
1 Sheep Market, PE11 1BH
6 changing beers (sourced locally) Ⓖ
The first micropub to be opened in Lincolnshire. The building was part of the Priory of Spalding and is believed to be almost 800 years old. Because of its shape it has always been known as The Oven or The Prior's Oven, and was at one time used as Spalding's monastic prison. Its more recent use was as a bakery, and it became a pub in 2013. As well as the ground floor bar with its vaulted ceiling, a stone spiral staircase leads up to a gin bar. Beer can be bought in a third-pint measure. Q≠●🚌

Red Lion Hotel ✔
Market Place, PE11 1SU
☎ (01775) 722869 🌐 redlionhotel-spalding.co.uk
Bombardier; Draught Bass; Greene King Abbot Ⓗ
A carefully refurbished 18th-century family-run hotel with a cosy, comfortable and welcoming bar overlooking the marketplace. The bar is popular owing to its consistently well-kept range of cask ales, which the staff take great pride in serving in top condition. It is a rare outlet for Bass in the locality. For fine sunny days there are outside tables and chairs beneath attractive floral displays. 🛏♿≠P🚌🐾

Stamford

Jolly Brewer 𝕃
1 Foundry Road, PE9 2PP
☎ (01780) 755141 🌐 thejollybrewer.com
Brewsters Marquis; Oakham JHB; 4 changing beers (sourced locally; often Bakers Dozen) Ⓗ
A locals' pub dating back to 1830 and twice local CAMRA Pub of the Year, the Brewer boasts a roomy split-level drinking area with open fires in the winter and a separate dining room. Six handpumps dispense LocAles, national ales and its own Bakers Dozen beers. The real cider is usually Old Rosie. The car park and large patio host a beer festival in the autumn, while games, including the World Pushpenny Championships, are a feature. Q✿◑≠♣●P🚌(9,202)🐾

King's Head
19 Maiden Lane, PE9 2AZ
☎ (01780) 753510 🌐 kingsheadstamford.co.uk
5 changing beers Ⓗ
Compact 19th-century inn just off the High Street. It has a single-room split-level interior featuring a wood-burning stove and wooden-beamed ceiling, and there is a pleasant patio area to the rear. The pub operates a one-barrel policy, with five constantly changing ales from the length and breadth of the country – over 400 were promoted in the first two years of the scheme. The popular food menu features locally sourced produce. Q✿◐≠🚌

Tobie Norris
12 Saint Pauls Street, PE9 2BE
☎ (01780) 753800
Fuller's London Pride; Oakham JHB Ⓗ**; 6 changing beers (sourced regionally; often Adnams)** Ⓗ/Ⓖ
The building, parts of which date back to 1280, was bought by Tobie Norris in 1617 and used as a bell foundry. Formerly a RAFA club, a major refurbishment gave it many small rooms with real fires, stone floors and low beams. Three handpumps serve beers from local and countrywide breweries, with more available directly from the cask. A former local CAMRA Pub of the Year. Q✿◑≠♣🚌(202,203)🐾

Stickford

Red Lion 𝕃
Church Road, PE22 8EP
☎ (01205) 480395
Black Hole Lincoln Imperial Ale; 2 changing beers (often Settle, Sharp's) Ⓗ
Red Lion is one of the most common pub names in England, and frequently found hereabouts because it was a heraldic emblem of the 14th-century John of Gaunt, Earl of Lancaster and Lord of the Manor at nearby Bolingbroke Castle. This traditional pub has one larger open-plan room, with a small separate dining and function room. The owners are keen on live music and host regular events (see Facebook for details). ✿◑⛺●P🚌(113)🐾

Swineshead

Green Dragon
Market Place, PE20 3LJ
☎ (01205) 821381
Batemans XB; Theakston Traditional Mild; 3 changing beers (sourced regionally) Ⓗ
Originally called the Green Dragon, the pub's fortunes gradually declined until new owners brought it back to life with a new name. A change of ownership has now seen it revert to its original name, and it is a vibrant and thriving village local, successfully blending old and new to recreate a genuine community venue with an emphasis on beer and traditional pub games. Pizza and bar snacks to eat in or take away are available Thursday to Saturday. ✿◗♣P🚌(K59)🐾

Swinhope

Clickem Inn
Binbrook Road, LN8 6BS (2 miles N of Binbrook on B1203)
☎ (01472) 398253
Batemans XXXB; Timothy Taylor Landlord; house beer (by Pheasantry); 3 changing beers (sourced regionally; often Horncastle Ales, Rudgate, Springhead) Ⓗ
The name originates from the counting of sheep passing through a nearby clicking gate. Set in the picturesque Lincolnshire Wolds and a popular stopping place for walkers and cyclists, the pub is renowned for its home-cooked food served in the bar and conservatory. It offers six real ales including the house beer, Terry's Tipple, and a traditional cider. There is pool, darts and a jukebox. Monday is quiz night. A covered area is provided for smokers. Q✿◑♣●P🐾

Thimbleby

Durham Ox

Main Road, LN9 5RB

☎ (01507) 527152 🌐 durhamoxpubthimbleby.co.uk

Adnams Ghost Ship; Batemans XB; 1 changing beer (sourced regionally) Ⓗ

Fine country inn over 200 years old and reopened in 2013. This welcoming establishment, with its beamed ceilings, cowshed bar and RAF corner, also has a large field at the rear for caravans and camper vans. There is an extensive menu serving local produce. The pub is named after a huge 18th-century ox which toured the country; at its largest it weighed 270 stone. ❀◑◗⛺●P🚌🐾

Threekingham

Three Kings Inn

Saltersway, NG34 0AU

☎ (01529) 240249 🌐 thethreekingsinn.com

Draught Bass; Morland Old Speckled Hen; Timothy Taylor Landlord; 1 changing beer (sourced regionally) Ⓗ

A classic country inn with charm and character. Its bright and comfortable lounge bar, with attractive rural prints, and panelled dining room serving locally sourced food, are deservedly popular with locals and visitors. Guest beers are usually from independent brewers. There's a pleasant beer terrace and garden for summer months and a large function room. The pub's name refers to the slaying, by the Saxons, of three Danish chieftains in battle in 870 at nearby Stow; look for the effigies above the entrance. Q❀◑◗P🐾

Timberland

Penny Farthing

4 Station Road, LN4 3SA

☎ (01526) 378881 🌐 thepennyfarthinginn.co.uk

2 changing beers (sourced nationally; often Pheasantry, Milestone) Ⓗ

A country pub in the heart of the village serving at least two changing beers, often from local breweries. It has a large open-plan layout with various spaces for dining and a comfortable seating area. Families and dogs are welcome. Food is locally sourced and specials are on offer Tuesday to Friday, and there is a popular Sunday lunch. A regular quiz is held on Tuesday plus occasional comedy and music evenings. Five en-suite bedrooms are available. Q❀🛏◑◗♿♣P🐾📶

Waddington

Three Horseshoes

High Street, LN5 9RF

☎ (01522) 720448

John Smith's Bitter; 5 changing beers (sourced nationally; often Great Newsome, Newby Wyke, Parkway) Ⓗ

At the heart of Waddington, next to the church and with easy access to the bus route, this is a real community local providing social gatherings on most nights. Darts, quizzes, poker and live entertainment feature regularly. Two bars with real fires provide a cosy environment in which to play traditional pub games and enjoy real ale from five handpumps. Large screens show sports events. ❀♣🚌(1,13)🐾📶

Wainfleet

Batemans Brewery Visitor Centre Ⓛ

Salem Bridge Brewery, Mill Lane, PE24 4JE

☎ (01754) 880317 🌐 bateman.co.uk

Batemans XB, Gold, Salem Porter, XXXB; 1 changing beer (sourced locally; often Batemans) Ⓗ

Visiting this brewery provides the chance to experience the blend of Batemans' proud 140-plus years of craft brewing tradition with its forward-looking outlook. Mr George's Bar, within the attractive windmill, is the ideal venue to sample a range of its beers. Further entertainment is to be found with brewery tours, featuring the Theatre of Beers, and in the pleasant beer garden with its games. Opening days and times vary throughout the year (see the website for details). Usually closed in January. ❀◑♿⛺⇌♣P🚌(7)🐾📶

Welbourn

Joiners Arms

21 High Street, LN5 0NH

☎ (01400) 279356

Sharp's Doom Bar; Joseph Holt Bitter; 1 changing beer (sourced nationally) Ⓗ

This brick-built free house is the sole pub in the village. Inside is a single long bar area with a small alcove at one end, and it has a cosy and welcoming atmosphere. Good homely food is on offer Friday to Sunday, with special feature nights. Two en-suite letting rooms are available. There are occasional quiz and music nights, plus other social events. ❀🛏◑◗♣P🚌(1)🐾📶

Westwoodside

Carpenter's Arms

Newbigg, DN9 2AT (follow B1396 to centre of village)

☎ (01427) 752416

Black Sheep Best Bitter; Bradfield Farmers Blonde; Brains Rev James; 2 changing beers (sourced nationally; often Marston's, Welbeck Abbey, Wychwood) Ⓗ

A regular in the Guide for many years, this friendly village local takes an active part in community events, and has raised significant sums for local charities. A recent change of ownership has not altered the pub's long-held reputation for beer quality. Four cask ales are sold, two of which change regularly. It is a past winner of several CAMRA awards and previous holder of the local Haxey Hood trophy. ❀◑♣P🚌(399)🐾📶

Willingham by Stow

Half Moon Ⓛ

23 High Street, DN21 5JZ

☎ (01427) 788340

Sharp's Doom Bar; 3 changing beers (often Batemans) Ⓗ

Traditional village pub in a building dating back to 1850, with a public bar, a lounge bar, an open fire and a beer garden. There are four beers on the bar, one regular and three changing. Food is served from Thursday to Sunday and the fish & chips are popular with locals and visitors alike. Entertainment nights feature on a relatively regular basis and there are themed charity nights. Q❀◑◗♿♣●🚌🐾

Winterton

George Hogg Ⓛ ✔

26 Market Street, DN15 9PT

☎ (01724) 732270 🌐 thegeorgehogg.co.uk

Draught Bass; 4 changing beers (sourced regionally; often Batemans, Lincolnshire Craft Beers)

A popular Grade II listed building in the marketplace, this is a friendly local CAMRA award-winning pub with a large lounge and public bar, both with real fires. Guest beers change on a regular basis, often from local breweries. Offering a good old-fashioned pub atmosphere, the George is a meeting place for local football teams and supporters' clubs, and hosts occasional live music. There is an outdoor seating area, and the Fastcat bus stops outside. The pub is Cask Marque accredited. Q P (350)

Wragby

Ivy

Market Place, LN8 5QU

(01673) 858768 theivywragby.co.uk

Batemans XB; Draught Bass; Timothy Taylor Boltmaker; 2 changing beers (sourced nationally; often Batemans)

At the heart of the small market town of Wragby lies this Seventeenth-century pub with three separate areas including a restaurant. The wood-burning stove gives a homely feeling in winter. A varied selection of real ales is available, and tasty home-cooked food is served, including vegan and gluten-free menus. There is a popular quiz on Sunday evening and sport is screened in the main bar. The pub's crib team plays in the local league. Six en-suite letting rooms are available and there is free parking opposite. Q (50,56)

Wroot

Cross Keys

High Street, DN9 2BT

(01302) 770231

Theakston Best Bitter; 3 changing beers (sourced regionally; often Acorn, Pheasantry, Welbeck Abbey)

A highly successful community pub serving a remote village of fewer than 500 inhabitants. It takes part in a whole range of local events and always has a friendly, welcoming atmosphere. This multi-roomed venue sells four cask ales – the three guest beers are usually from nearby breweries. Evening meals are available on Thursday and also at the weekend. Q P

Wyberton Fen

Hammer & Pincers

Swineshead Road, PE21 7JE

(01205) 361323 hammerandpincers-boston.co.uk

Adnams Ghost Ship; Fuller's London Pride; Sharp's Doom Bar; Woodforde's Wherry

A family-run and lively community establishment on the outskirts of Boston, close to the Downtown shopping centre and supermarket. It has two rooms and a conservatory area, with a 1970s feel to the main public bar. Reasonably priced meals are served, including breakfast, and a typical pub food menu is offered later in the day. An outside seating area to the front is decorated with flower baskets in the summer. P

Victoria, Lincoln (Photo: John McLinden/Flickr CC BY-ND 2.0)

London index

*Shown on Inner London map

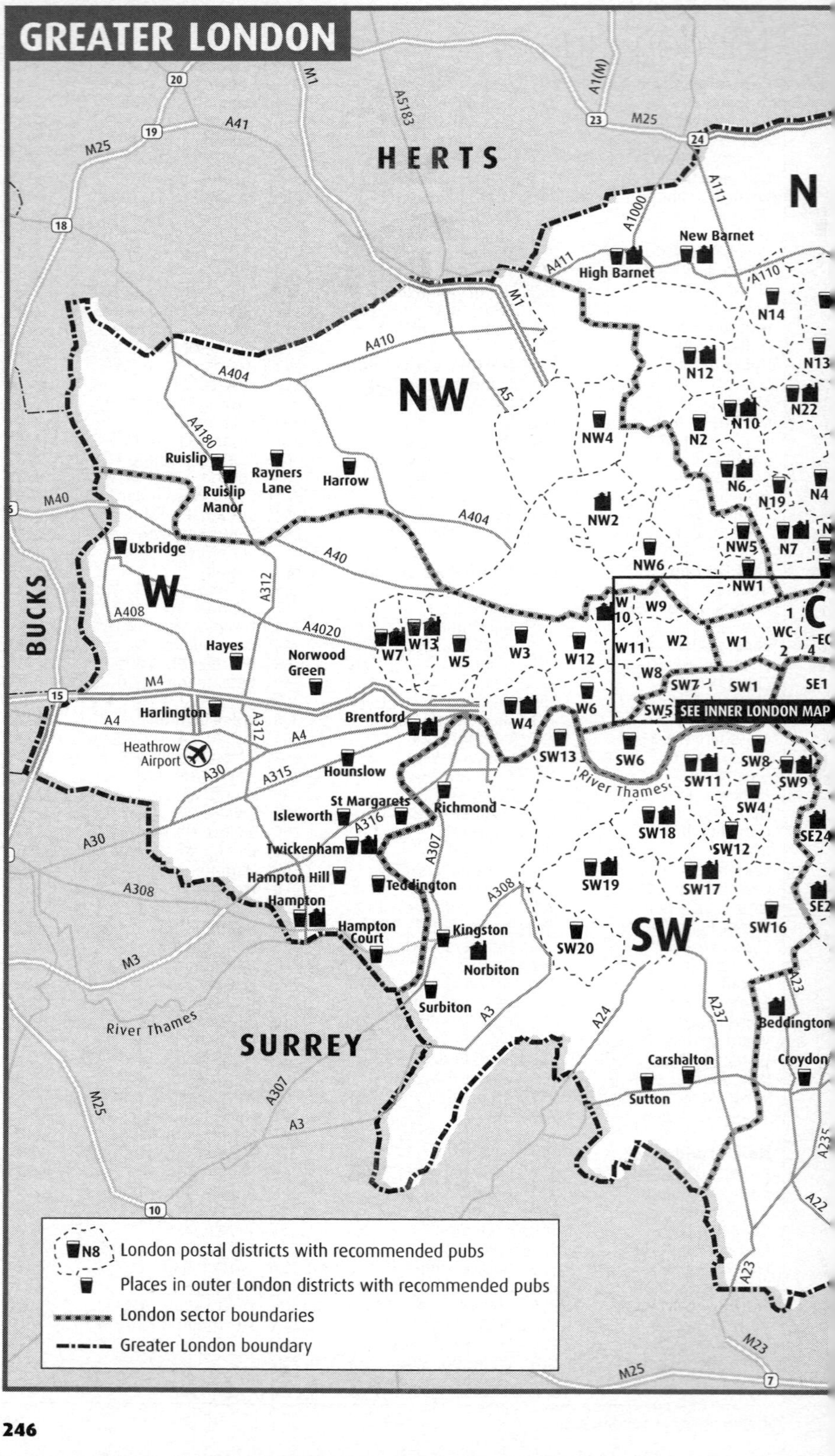
GREATER LONDON
HERTS
BUCKS
SURREY
NW
W
SW
N
C
M25
M1
A5183
A1(M)
A41
A1000
A111
A411
A110
A410
A404
A5
A4180
M40
A40
A312
A408
A4020
M4
A4
A30
A315
A316
A307
A308
M3
A3
A24
A237
A23
A235
A22
M23
River Thames
High Barnet
New Barnet
N14
N13
N12
N22
N10
N2
N6
N19
N4
N7
NW4
NW2
NW5
NW6
NW1
Ruislip
Ruislip Manor
Rayners Lane
Harrow
Uxbridge
Hayes
Norwood Green
Harlington
Heathrow Airport
Hounslow
Brentford
Isleworth
St Margarets
Richmond
Twickenham
Hampton Hill
Teddington
Hampton
Hampton Court
Kingston
Norbiton
Surbiton
W7
W13
W5
W3
W12
W4
W6
W9
W10
W11
W2
W1
W8
WC1
WC2
EC4
SW7
SW1
SE1
SW5
SEE INNER LONDON MAP
SW13
SW6
SW8
SW9
SW11
SW4
SW18
SW12
SE24
SW19
SW17
SW16
SW20
Beddington
Carshalton
Croydon
Sutton
N8 London postal districts with recommended pubs
Places in outer London districts with recommended pubs
London sector boundaries
Greater London boundary

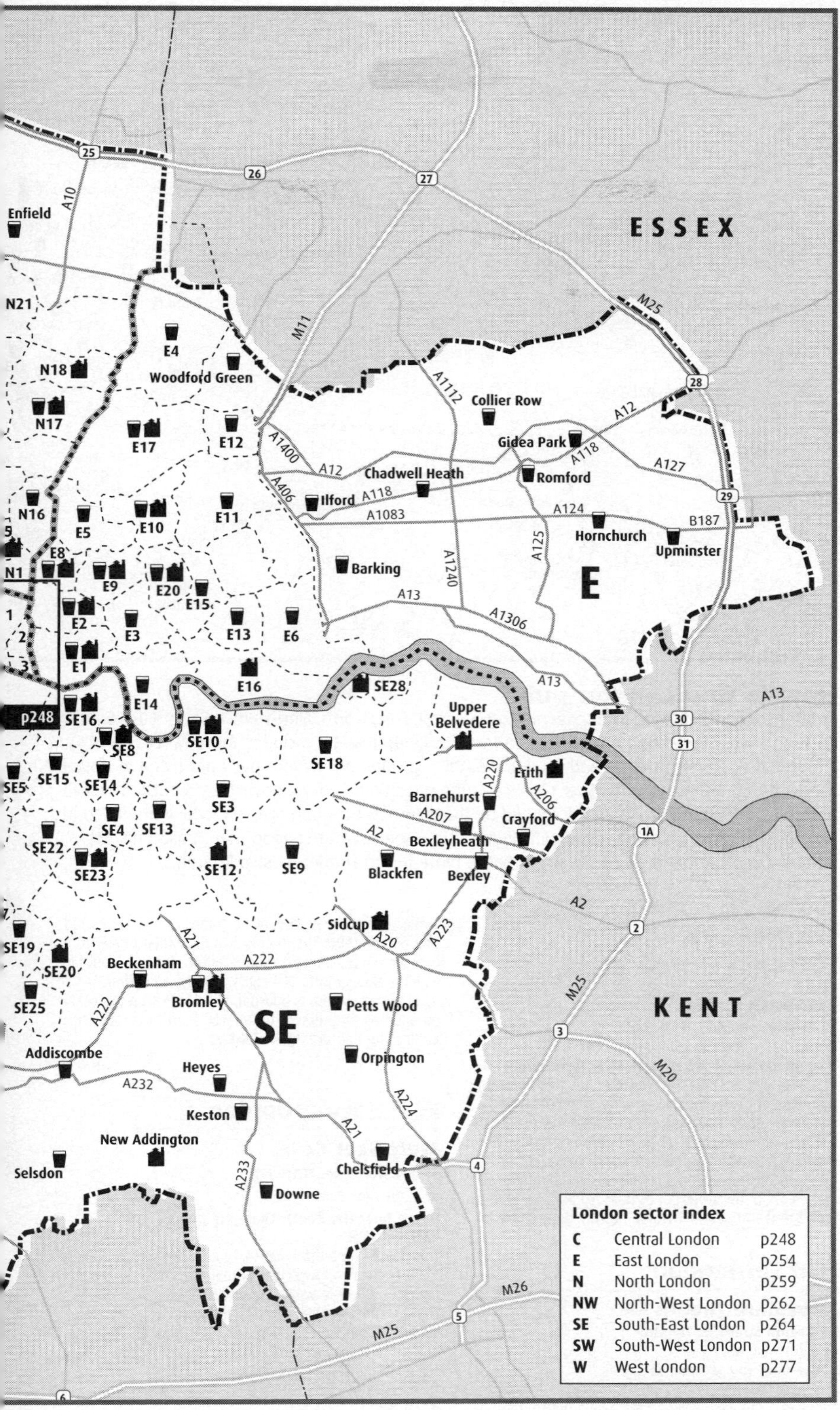
ESSEX
KENT
E
SE
Enfield
N21
N18
N17
N16
N1
E4
Woodford Green
E17
E12
E5
E10
E11
E8
E9
E20
E15
E2
E3
E13
E6
E1
E16
E14
SE28
SE16
SE8
SE10
SE18
Upper Belvedere
SE5
SE15
SE14
SE3
SE4
SE13
SE22
SE23
SE12
SE9
SE19
SE20
SE25
Collier Row
Gidea Park
Romford
Chadwell Heath
Ilford
Hornchurch
Upminster
Barking
Erith
Barnehurst
Crayford
Bexleyheath
Blackfen
Bexley
Sidcup
Beckenham
Bromley
Petts Wood
Orpington
Addiscombe
Heyes
Keston
New Addington
Selsdon
Chelsfield
Downe
p248
M25
M11
M20
M26
A10
A12
A13
A118
A127
A124
A125
A1083
A1112
A1400
A406
A1240
A1306
A2
A20
A21
A206
A207
A220
A222
A223
A224
A232
A233
B187
London sector index
C Central London p248
E East London p254
N North London p259
NW North-West London p262
SE South-East London p264
SW South-West London p271
W West London p277

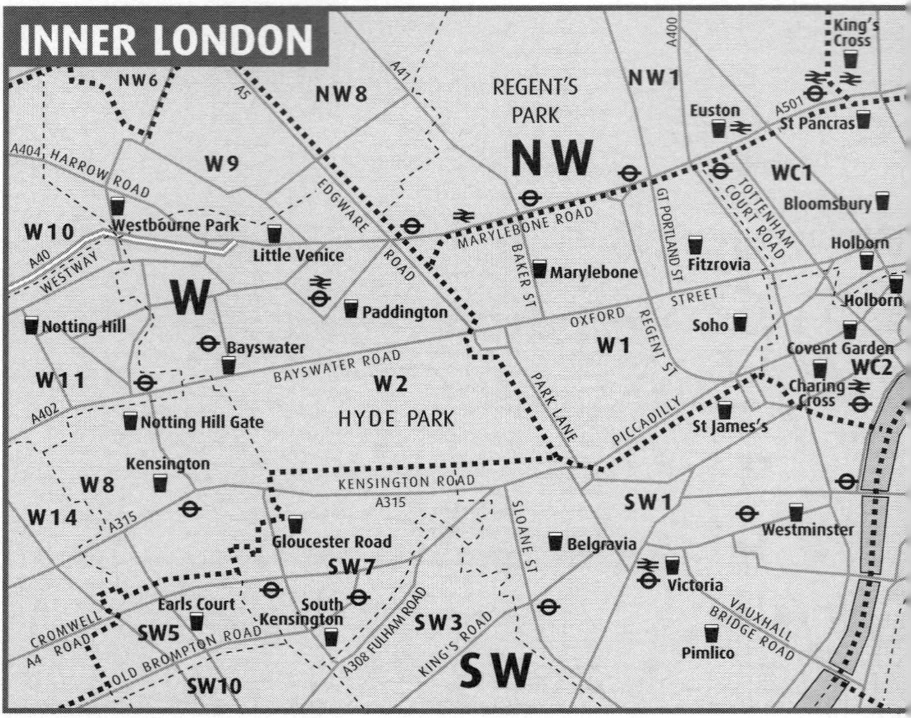

How to find London pubs

Greater London is divided into seven sectors: Central, East, North, North-West, South-East, South-West and West, reflecting postal boundaries. The Central sector includes the City (EC1 to EC4) and Holborn, Covent Garden and the Strand (WC1/2) plus W1, where pubs are listed in postal district order. In each of the other six sectors the pubs with London postcodes are listed first in postal district order (E1, E2 etc), followed by those in outer London districts, which are listed in alphabetical order (Barking, Chadwell Heath, etc) – see Greater London map. Postal district numbers can be found on every street name plate in the London postcode area.

CENTRAL LONDON

EC1: Clerkenwell

Exmouth Arms 🄻

23 Exmouth Market, EC1R 4QL

☎ (020) 3551 4772 🌐 exmoutharms.com

4 changing beers (often Dark Star, Revolutions) 🄷

Operated by Barworks, this hostelry has four constantly changing real ales alongside a wide range of bottled and keg beers. Bar snacks and main meals are available. The last rebuilding was in 1915 (see date stone); the exterior shows former Courage ownership. The interior has been totally reconstructed in minimalist fashion but it feels like a proper pub. The small bar upstairs is now a cocktail bar. ❀◑♿⇌(Farringdon) ⊖(Angel/Farringdon) ●🚌🐾📶

EC1: Farringdon

Jerusalem Tavern ✔

55 Britton Street, EC1M 5UQ

☎ (020) 7490 4281

House beer (by St Peter's) 🄰

The premises date from 1719/20, with the frontage added in 1810. Originally a merchant's house, then a workshop for the clock-making trades, it was converted to a pub in 1996. The interior is a recreation of an 18th-century tavern, complete with real fire. The only outlet in London belonging to St Peter's brewery in Suffolk, its dispense system is unusual, with beer from the cellar pumped by air pressure to emerge from fake cask ends behind the bar. Q☕◑⇌⊖●🚌🐾

EC1: Hatton Garden

Craft Beer Co 🄻

82 Leather Lane, EC1N 7TR

☎ (020) 7404 7049

House beer (by Kent); changing beers (sourced nationally) 🄷

This popular pub offers up to 14 cask ales, 20 keg lines, many bottles and two ciders. Downstairs it has stools and tables around the walls and plenty of standing room. There is more seating upstairs and a small standing area outside. Food is pies and Scotch eggs, though you can order in a takeaway. Interesting features include a glass ceiling and a large Bass mirror.
☕❀⇌(Farringdon) ⊖(Chancery Lane/Farringdon) ●🚌🐾📶

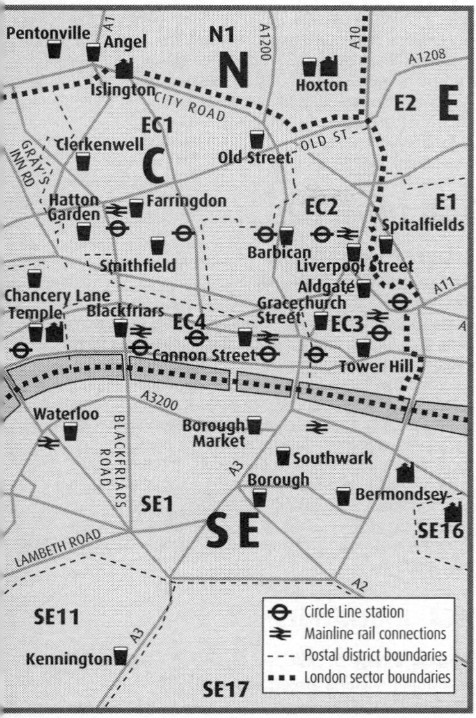

Olde Mitre ★ 🄻 ✔

1 Ely Court, Ely Place, EC1N 6SJ

☎ (020) 7405 4751 🌐 yeoldemitreholborn.co.uk

Fuller's Oliver's Island, London Pride; Gale's Seafarers Ale; 4 changing beers (often East London, Sambrook's, Windsor & Eton) 🄷

Hidden in an alley between Hatton Garden and Ely Place, there has been a pub on this site since 1546. Mainly dating from the 18th century, the current building has two bars and an upstairs function room, reached by a narrow staircase. All are wood panelled, giving a traditional feel, and the pub has been identified by CAMRA as having a nationally important historic interior. Bar snacks include a range of toasties.

Q✿◑⇄(City Thameslink) ⊖(Chancery Lane/ Farringdon) 🍎🚌📶

EC1: Old Street

Craft Beer Co

233 Old Street, EC1V 9HE

☎ (020) 7250 0388

House beer (by Kent); 5 changing beers (sourced nationally) 🄷

This large, single-room bar is 50 yards from Old Street tube, Exit 1. Twenty-five keg taps complement the cask ales on offer. Two quiet TVs display the beer list and occasional free-to-air sporting events. The walls are covered with old beer mirrors and signs. Live jazz is played on Thursday evenings. Food is limited to toasties, but there is an arrangement with a local pizza house that will deliver. ♿⇄⊖🚌🐾📶

Old Fountain 🄻

3 Baldwin Street, EC1V 9NU

☎ (020) 7253 2970 🌐 oldfountain.co.uk

Fuller's London Pride; Oakham Citra; Signature Roadie; 6 changing beers (often Five Points) 🄷

A privately owned free house with a single bar on two levels, a fish tank gracing the upper area. It is popular with workers from nearby Silicon Roundabout. You can relax upstairs on the roof garden with its two large parasols and heating. The extensive beer range comes mainly from local breweries, featuring new brews and providing many local bottled beers.

♉✿◑⇄⊖♣🍎🚌🐾📶

EC1: Smithfield

Hand & Shears ★ ✔

1 Middle Street, EC1A 7JA

☎ (020) 7600 0257

St Austell Tribute; Timothy Taylor Landlord; 3 changing beers (often Black Sheep, Sharp's) 🄷

Close to the site of St Bartholomew's Fair, this Grade II listed pub has long associations with the cloth trades. In various forms it has served Smithfield since 1123 and was given a Justice's Licence in 1552. The current building dates from 1843 and has a wealth of Victorian features. A central island bar serves a number of separate areas. The wooden floors and panelling contribute to the atmospheric character.

◑⇄(Farringdon) ⊖(Barbican) ♣🍎🚌🐾📶

EC2: Barbican

Wood Street

53 Fore Street, EC2Y 5EJ

☎ (020) 7256 6990 🌐 woodstreetbar.co.uk

Dark Star Hophead; Harvey's Sussex Best Bitter, Old Ale; Purity Mad Goose; 1 changing beer (sourced nationally) 🄷

This independent hidden gem, open on weekdays, is tucked away at the south edge of the Barbican complex at the north end of Wood Street. The modern interior is light and airy. A downstairs bar has two pool tables, two dartboards and a separate poker room. The wood-panelled main bar has plentiful varied seating. Observe the Barbican water feature ponds from the rear windows. Burgers and bites are served lunchtimes and evenings. Dark beers feature on rotation.

♉◑⇄⊖(Moorgate) ♣🍎🚌🐾📶

EC2: Liverpool Street

Hamilton Hall ✔

Unit 32, Street-level Concourse, Liverpool Street Station, EC2M 7PY

☎ (020) 7247 3579

Greene King IPA, Abbot; Sharp's Doom Bar; 7 changing beers (sourced nationally) 🄷

Once a ballroom, now a Wetherspoon that has retained a lavish interior. Real ale is dispensed from 10 handpumps on the entrance level bar and five on the upstairs bar. There is an outside seating area and children are welcome during the day. Breakfasts are served on weekdays. The pub can be busy at times. TV screens show train departure and arrival times.

Q♉✿◑♿⇄⊖🍎🚌📶

Magpie ✔

12 New Street, EC2M 4TP

☎ (020) 7929 3889

Fuller's London Pride; St Austell Nicholson's Pale Ale; Sharp's Doom Bar; 5 changing beers (sourced nationally) 🄷

This ornate Nicholson's pub, down the road opposite Liverpool Street station, was the location of London's first

electric ambulance station in 1920. Many pictures of old Bishopsgate adorn the walls. Choose between bar stools, chairs and leather sofas or watch the world go by through the large, clear front window. The upstairs restaurant can double as a function room. The Ladies' toilet is also upstairs. Two quiet TVs show rolling news and occasional free-to-air sporting events.
♞◑⇌⊖🚌📶

EC3: Aldgate

Hoop & Grapes ✔

47 Aldgate High Street, EC3N 1AL
☎ (020) 7481 4583
Fuller's London Pride; St Austell Nicholson's Pale Ale; Sharp's Doom Bar; 5 changing beers (sourced nationally) Ⓗ
On the eastern edge of the City, this Grade II* listed pub survived the Great Fire of London by 50 yards and is a rare example of a timbered building in London. Although only called the Hoop & Grapes since 1920, the inn on this site goes back to the 13th century and had a licence in 1580. It was renovated in 1983, preserving the sense of antiquity. Now an M&B Nicholson's outlet, it boasts an extensive food menu.
♞◑⇌(Fenchurch St) ⊖(Aldgate/Aldgate E) 🍎🚌🐾📶

EC3: Gracechurch Street

Crosse Keys ✔

7-12 Gracechurch Street, EC3V 0DR
☎ (020) 7623 4824
Fuller's London Pride; Greene King IPA, Abbot; Sharp's Doom Bar; changing beers (sourced nationally) Ⓗ
Housed in a grandiose building that used to be the headquarters of a banking corporation, this pub is named after a coaching inn that was once nearby. Twenty four handpumps dispense the four regular beers, up to 18 rotating guest ales and two ciders. The ales are listed on TV screens above the bar and are ordered by pump number. There are function rooms to the rear. A spiral staircase leads down to the toilets.
Q♞◑♿⇌(Cannon St/Fenchuch St) ⊖(Bank/Monument) 🍎🚌📶

EC3: Tower Hill

Liberty Bounds ✔

15 Trinity Square, EC3N 4AA
☎ (020) 7481 0513
Adnams Broadside; Fuller's London Pride; Greene King IPA, Abbot; Sharp's Doom Bar; 5 changing beers (sourced nationally) Ⓗ
Opposite the Tower of London, and surrounded by handsome buildings, this Wetherspoon is in a converted bank. Recently refurbished, it has two levels connected by a grand staircase. Displays reflect the unusually rich local history, with a bias to the Tudors. The food and drink are good value for the area and, unusually for a city pub, it is open at weekends. Wheelchair access is through the rear entrance in Muscovy Street.
Q♞◑♿⇌(Fenchurch St) ⊖(Tower Gateway/Tower Hill) 🍎🚌📶

EC4: Blackfriars

Black Friar ★ ✔

174 Queen Victoria Street, EC4V 4EG
☎ (020) 7236 5474
Fuller's London Pride; St Austell Nicholson's Pale Ale; Sharp's Doom Bar; 7 changing beers Ⓗ
The Black Friar has been identified by CAMRA as having a nationally important historic pub interior and is a

REAL ALE BREWERIES

Anspach & Hobday ✐ SE1: Bermondsey
Barnet ▤ High Barnet
Battersea ✐ SW11: Nine Elms
Beerblefish ✐ N18: Upper Edmonton
Bexley Erith
Block ▤ N1: Hoxton
Brewhouse & Kitchen ▤ E2: Hoxton
Brewhouse & Kitchen ▤ EC1: Islington
Brewhouse & Kitchen ▤ N5: Highbury
Brick SE8: Deptford
Brixton ✐ SW9: Brixton
Brockley ✐ SE12: Hither Green
Broken Drum Upper Belvedere
Bullfinch ✐ SE24: Herne Hill
By The Horns ✐ SW17: Summerstown
Canopy ✐ SE24: Herne Hill
Clarkshaws ✐ SW9: Loughborough Junction
Cronx New Addington
Ealing ✐ Brentford (NEW)
East London E10: Leyton
Enfield N18: Upper Edmonton
Essex Street ▤ WC2: Temple
Five Points E8: Hackney Downs
Fuller's W4: Chiswick
Goodness ✐ N22: Wood Green (NEW)
Gorgeous ▤ N6: Highgate
Greenwich ▤ SE10: Greenwich
Greywood N22: Wood Green (NEW)
Hammerton ✐ N7: Barnsbury
Hop Stuff SE28: Thamesmead
Howling Hops ▤ ✐ E9: Hackney Wick
Husk ✐ E16: West Silvertown
London Beer Factory ✐ SE27: West Norwood
London Beer Lab ✐ SW9: Brixton
London Brewing ▤ N12: North Finchley
Marko Paulo ▤ W13: Northfields
Mechanic ✐ E1: Bethnal Green
Moncada ✐ NW2: Dollis Hill
Muswell Hillbilly ✐ N10: Muswell Hill
Mutineers Bromley
One Mile End ✐ N17: Tottenham
Park ✐ Norbiton
Portobello W10: North Kensington
Redemption ✐ N17: Tottenham
Sambrook's ✐ SW11: Battersea
Signal Beddington
Signature ✐ E17: Walthamstow
SlyBeast ▤ SW18: Wandsworth (NEW)
Southey ✐ SE20: Penge
Southwark ✐ SE1: Bermondsey
Spartan ✐ SE16: South Bermondsey
Tankleys Sidcup
Tap East ▤ E20: Stratford
Three Sods ✐ E8: London Fields
Tiny Vessel Hampton
Truman's ✐ E9: Hackney Wick
Twickenham ✐ Twickenham
Urban Alchemy New Barnet (NEW)
Villages ✐ SE8: Deptford
Volden SE23: Forest Hill
Watling Street ✐ N17: Tottenham
Weird Beard W7: Hanwell
Wild Card ✐ E17: Walthamstow
Wimbledon ✐ SW19: Colliers Wood

stunning example of the rare Art Nouveau style. It was famously saved from demolition by Sir John Betjeman in the 1960s. Just opposite Blackfriars station, it is lively, frequented both by office workers and tourists. Look out for the friars in marble and brass who line the walls under the coving. 🐎❀◑⇌⊖🚌🐾📶

EC4: Cannon Street

Bell ✔

29 Bush Lane, EC4R 0AN

☎ (020) 7283 0029 🌐 bellbushlane.co.uk

Courage Best Bitter; Harvey's Sussex Best Bitter; Sharp's Doom Bar; Timothy Taylor Landlord; 1 changing beer (sourced locally) 🄷

Copper pots and pans hang from the ceiling of this no-nonsense, ex-Courage, one-bar drinking house near Cannon Street station. A list of previous licensees going back centuries hangs on the back wall next to the photo of Sid James. Televised sports are quietly shown, with tasteful background music gently playing. Food is mainly pie and mash, with the small upstairs dining area doubling as a function room. ◑⇌⊖🚌📶

Pelt Trader

Arch 3, Dowgate Hill, EC4N 6AP

☎ (020) 7160 0253 🌐 pelttrader.com

6 changing beers (sourced nationally) 🄰

Nestled under an archway beneath Cannon Street station, this independent venue offers six cask taps behind the bar along with 14 keg taps showcasing a variety of modern craft beer and cider. Owned by the Bloomsbury Leisure Group, the archway opened as a bar in 2013. Decorative mirrors portray pelt traders, with Skinners' Hall directly opposite the front door. Pizzas can be ordered from the bar. Available for private hire at weekends. 🐎❀◑⇌⊖🍎🚌🐾📶

EC4: Temple

Old Bank of England

194 Fleet Street, EC4A 2LT

☎ (020) 7430 2255 🌐 oldbankofengland.com

Fuller's London Pride; McMullen AK Original Mild, Country Bitter, IPA 🄷

A Grade II listed building, Bank of England premises until 1975, sensitively refurbished as a Fuller's Ale & Pie house in 1994. It has an island bar, a gallery and various murals depicting the rich history of the area. Note the ornate high ceiling and chandeliers. New owner McMullen has been in charge since early 2019. There are two dining/function rooms. At the back is a beer garden. Occasionally the whole pub may be hired out, so check before visiting. ❀◑⇌(City Thameslink)⊖🚌🐾📶

WC1: Bloomsbury

Calthorpe Arms

252 Grays Inn Road, WC1X 8JR

☎ (020) 7278 4732 🌐 calthorpearmswc1.co.uk

Young's London Original, London Special; 3 changing beers (often Sambrook's, Twickenham, Young's) 🄷

Unusual double doors lead into this single-bar corner local. With no music it is easy to strike up a conversation at the bar, or take one of the tables along the sides for more privacy. The upstairs dining room opens lunchtime and can be booked at other times. Evening meals are served Monday to Saturday. Young's bottle-conditioned beers are stocked, plus a Young's seasonal and/or two guest beers (often from London). There is pavement seating outside. ❀◑⊖(Russell Sq)🍎🚌🐾

Marlborough Arms ✔

36 Torrington Place, WC1E 7LY

☎ (020) 7636 0120

Greene King IPA, Abbot; 4 changing beers (often Greene King) 🄷

Traditional, welcoming inn, named after the coat of arms first worn by the third Duke of Marlborough, John Churchill. The pub attracts students, business people, tourists and locals from a surprisingly residential neighbourhood. A large open area is surrounded by oak panelling and some fine features, with the bar to one side. There are plenty of tables and seating, with a nod to informality and comfort in the small area beyond the bar. The staff are friendly and knowledgeable. 🐎❀◑♿⇌⊖(Goodge St) 🚌🐾📶

Swan 🄻 ✔

7 Cosmo Place, WC1N 3AP

☎ (020) 7837 6223

Greene King IPA, Abbot; Hammerton N1; 4 changing beers (often Five Points, Greene King) 🄷

Popular family-oriented venue among the tourist hotels on Southampton Row, close to Great Ormond Street Children's Hospital. There is a single long room and tables in front on a pedestrian passage. Eight handpumps offer three regular real ales and four guests, mainly from London breweries, together with a real cider. Pub grub and snacks are served all day. A large-screen TV shows live sports events. Q🐎❀◑♿⊖(Russell Sq)🍎🚌🐾📶

WC1: Holborn

Craft Beer Co

168 High Holborn, WC1V 7AA

☎ (020) 7240 0431

Kent Pale; 14 changing beers (sourced nationally) 🄷

Though in the ancient parish of St Giles, whose church featured in several of Hogarth's etchings, including Gin Lane, the location of this pub on the north-eastern edge of Covent Garden will probably have a more modern resonance. On two levels, the sixth Craft Beer Co outlet would be more at home in Beer Street, with its 15 pumps dispensing a changing range of ales from across the UK. There are frequent tap takeovers and Meet the Brewer events. ◑⊖(Covent Garden/Holborn)🚌

Holborn Whippet

25-29 Sicilian Avenue, WC1A 2QH

☎ (020) 3137 9937 🌐 holbornwhippet.com

5 changing beers (often Five Points, Redemption) 🄿

A flow-jet is used to pump the beer to the taps here; a blackboard above shows what is on sale. Real ales come from the likes of Adnams, Five Points, Mighty Oak, Moor, Oakham, Redemption and other London breweries; many other draught beers are sold. The food menu is simple but changing, so check the website. The decor is basic, with wooden floors, brown tiles and cream-painted walls. Outside there is seating on the delightful Sicilian Avenue. ❀◑⊖🍎🚌

WC1: St Pancras

Queen's Head 🄻

66 Acton Street, WC1X 9NB

☎ (020) 7713 5772 🌐 queensheadlondon.com

Redemption Trinity; 2 changing beers (sourced regionally) 🄷

Narrow, late-Georgian premises off Gray's Inn Road, with a single bar, a smoking patio at the rear and benches in front. The piano is used for jazz and blues on Thursdays and late Sunday afternoons. Microbrewery guest beers usually include a dark one. One handpump serves cider,

with three more real ciders and a range of other draught and bottled beers in stock. Sharing snack platters are on offer at this comfortable pub frequented by locals and the occasional tourist.
❀◐⇌⊖(King's Cross St Pancras) ●▣ᯤ

Skinners Arms
114 Judd Street, WC1H 9NT
☎ (020) 7837 6521 ⊕ skinnersarmslondon.com
Greene King IPA, Abbot; 4 changing beers (often Siren) Ⓗ
Named after the City livery company and standing on a street named after a past master of the company, this traditional, quiet, corner pub has in effect been converted to one bar, despite the signs on the doors and in the stained glass. A raised seating area is on the left as you enter and the previously separate room at the back is now a large alcove with more seating.
❀◐⇌⊖(King's Cross St Pancras) ▣

WC2: Chancery Lane

Knights Templar ✔
95 Chancery Lane, WC2A 1DT
☎ (020) 7831 2660
Fuller's London Pride; Greene King IPA; Sharp's Doom Bar; 8 changing beers (sourced nationally) Ⓗ
Named after its original landowners, this imposing conversion of a Grade II listed bank retains magnificent slender scroll-topped columns and a high ochre-painted ceiling with illustrated panels and large chandeliers. The long curved wooden bar counter is overseen by a sculpted knight as the centrepiece of the ornate bar-back. Three mezzanine rooms may be reserved, two of them panelled libraries with balconies overlooking the bar, and the whole place can be hired at the weekend, so check before visiting on a Saturday.
Q⛾◐♿⊖(Chancery Lane/Temple) ▣ᯤ

WC2: Charing Cross

Harp 🏆 L ✔
47 Chandos Place, WC2N 4HS
☎ (020) 7836 0291
Dark Star Hophead, American Pale Ale; Fuller's London Pride; Harvey's Sussex Best Bitter; 5 changing beers (sourced nationally) Ⓗ
Small, friendly, Fuller's premises that became a haven for beer choice as a free house run by the late, legendary, Binnie Walsh. Ciders and perries complement the fine beer range. The narrow bar is adorned with mirrors and portraits, and a cosy upstairs room provides a refuge from the throng. Numerous awards include the CAMRA National Pub of the Year accolade for 2010. Since 2019 it has occasionally served beers from the wood, usually on a Wednesday. Q◐⇌⊖●▣ᯤ

Lemon Tree ✔
4 Bedfordbury, WC2N 4BP
☎ (020) 7831 1391 ⊕ lemontreecoventgarden.com
Harvey's Sussex Best Bitter; St Austell Tribute; 3 changing beers (often Adnams, Portobello, Truman's) Ⓗ
This one-bar pub next to the stage door of the Coliseum is a favourite among locals, musicians and theatregoers. The Thai restaurant upstairs doubles as a function room. Look out for the entrance, slightly set back. There is an emphasis on London brews among the guest beers by popular demand. The pub is operated by All Our Bars, a small chain based in Edenbridge. ◐⇌⊖▣ᯤ

Princess of Wales ✔
27 Villiers Street, WC2N 6ND
☎ (020) 7484 0748
St Austell Nicholson's Pale Ale; 4 changing beers (sourced nationally) Ⓗ
A new Guide entry, this welcome retreat has portraits and biographies of famous local residents on the walls of the ground-floor bar, including Alexandra, wife of Edward VII, after whom the pub was named (despite contrary information on its website). The upstairs Rudyard Kipling Dining Lounge has its own bar and street entrance. There are occasional Meet the Brewer evenings and Nicholson's beer festivals. Be aware that in the evening beer is only served in plastic containers.
◐⇌⊖▣ᯤ

WC2: Covent Garden

Cross Keys
31 Endell Street, WC2H 9BA
☎ (020) 7836 5185 ⊕ crosskeyscoventgarden.com
Brodie's Bethnal Green Bitter, Piccadilly Pale Ale; Greene King IPA; Hardys & Hansons Olde Trip; 1 changing beer (often Windsor & Eton) Ⓗ
The ornate 1840s façade reveals a long, welcoming bar, subdued lighting, comfortable banquette seating and tables and chairs. Copper kettles, pans, street signs, stuffed fish, framed pictures and photos, Beatles memorabilia and a fine Truman, Hanbury, Buxton & Co mirror cover the walls. Families are welcome (over-12s only) during the day unless it is busy, but no dogs. Brodie's beers are brewed at Rhymney Brewery in Wales. ⛾◐⊖▣

Lamb & Flag
33 Rose Street, WC2E 9EB
☎ (020) 7497 9504 ⊕ lambandflagcoventgarden.co.uk
Dark Star Hophead; Fuller's Oliver's Island, London Pride, ESB; Gale's Seafarers Ale; 2 changing beers (sourced nationally) Ⓗ
This Grade II listed building, owned by Fuller's since 2013, remains a pleasant traditional local without muzak or games machines, tucked away up Rose Street from Garrick Street. It has two dark wood-panelled rooms, the rear one with an attractive fireplace and a connecting passage from the main bar on the ground floor. Note that the upstairs bar and restaurant has table service only. Charles Dickens and Karl Marx were both regulars.
⛾❀◐⇌(Charing Cross) ⊖(Covent Garden/Leicester Sq) ▣🐾ᯤ

White Swan ✔
14 New Row, WC2N 4LF
☎ (020) 3077 1129
Fuller's London Pride; St Austell Nicholson's Pale Ale; Sharp's Doom Bar; 5 changing beers (sourced nationally) Ⓗ
Grade II listed, once owned by the London banking firm of Hoare & Co, this M&B Nicholson's premises is popular with Covent Garden tourists and is a rare WC2 outlet for real cider. It may appear crowded at first glance, but it is longer than it looks and there are more seats at the back. The first-floor dining room can be booked for functions. Note its contrasting fireplaces. The place had a spruce up in February 2020.
⛾◐⇌(Charing Cross) ⊖(Leicester Sq) ●▣ᯤ

WC2: Holborn

Shakespeare's Head
Africa House, 64-68 Kingsway, WC2B 6BG
☎ (020) 7404 8846

Fuller's London Pride; Greene King IPA, Abbot; Sharp's Doom Bar; house beer (by Windsor & Eton); 5 changing beers (sourced nationally) H
Large Wetherspoon bank conversion from 1998, named after a famous pub in the locality until the demolition of Wych Street over 100 years ago. It is usually busy with shoppers, tourists, local office workers and, during term time, students from the nearby London School of Economics. Here is a convenient place for a couple of pints after your cultural sojourn at the British Museum.
Q

WC2: Temple

Edgar Wallace

40 Essex Street, WC2R 3JF
☎ (020) 7353 3120 theedgarwallace.co.uk
Crouch Vale Brewers Gold; 7 changing beers (often Dark Star, East London, Timothy Taylor) H
Just off Fleet Street near the Royal Courts of Justice, this is a real gem of a one-room local, with additional seating upstairs. The comfortable downstairs room, its walls and ceiling covered with beer mats and old advertising signs, has a fine wooden bar offering a wide range of rotating ales. This quiet pub allows no music, laptops, mobiles and so on. Good-value food is served all day.
Q

George L ✔

213 Strand, WC2R 1AP
☎ (020) 7353 9638 georgeinthestrand.com
Greene King IPA, Abbot; house beer (by Greene King); 4 changing beers H
Opposite the Royal Courts of Justice, the George has a splendid exterior dating from an 1898 rebuild. It is believed to be named after a previous landlord; former reference to royalty has been removed from the current signs. Inside, the bar is long, with some partitioned seating areas opposite, leading to a room at the back and the upstairs Pig & Goose restaurant. For details of theatre ticket food offers and pre-theatre special deals, see the website. (City Thameslink)

Temple Brew House ✔

46 Essex Street, WC2R 3JF
☎ (020) 7936 2536 templebrewhouse.com
House beer (by Essex Street); 5 changing beers (sourced nationally; often Essex Street) H
Just off the Strand and Fleet Street, this basement bar is run by the City Pub Group and continues its development of microbrewpubs. The Essex Street Brewery five-barrel plant is visible from the bar, a single room with minimal decor, novel lighting and schoolroom-style furnishings, with some tables set aside for dining. The bar is generally quiet during the day though it does get noisy of an evening. Q

W1: Fitzrovia

Queen Charlotte

43 Goodge Street, W1T 1TA
☎ (020) 7323 9361
3 changing beers (often Siren) H
A big welcome awaits you in this small, single-bar corner pub with bare wooden floors and simple furnishings. Changing offerings from Siren and other smaller breweries are sold in one-third and two-third pint measures as well as the usual halves and pints. Plenty of other interesting draught and bottled beers are also stocked. Meals, including speciality burgers, are served all day, as well as brunch on Saturday.
(Goodge St)

Stag's Head L

102 New Cavendish Street, W1W 6XW
☎ (020) 7580 8313
Fuller's London Pride; 1 changing beer (often Tring) H
A smart, oak-panelled building with a historic interior of regional importance, offering a friendly welcome to regulars and visitors alike. Rebuilt in the late 1930s by brewers William Younger, it has a marvellous Art Deco exterior, sporting a curved corner profile. Vertical drinking is assisted by unusual peninsular shelf projections to the bar and elsewhere. Sun lovers and smokers can relax on shaded benches outside. Traditional pub food is available lunchtimes only except Sunday, when service continues through the afternoon.
(Great Portland St)

W1: Marylebone

Barley Mow ★

8 Dorset Street, W1U 6QW
☎ (020) 7487 4773 barleymowlondon.co.uk
Fuller's London Pride; Sharp's Doom Bar; 4 changing beers (sourced nationally) H
Dating from 1791, the pub is Grade II listed and identified by CAMRA as having a nationally important historic interior, with a main bar and a small snug at the rear. It retains both its original matchboard panelling, now displaying prints of 18th-century Marylebone and, most notably, two small drinking compartments fronting the main bar counter. Both bars are furnished with upholstered pews, benches and stools. Food from a short menu of home-made items is served weekday lunchtimes only. (Baker St)

Golden Eagle

59 Marylebone Lane, W1U 2NY
☎ (020) 7935 3228
Fuller's London Pride; St Austell Tribute; 2 changing beers (often North Cotswold, Twickenham) H
First licensed in 1842 and rebuilt in 1890, this single-bar pub is traditional in every way: small and cosy, with smart decor, a fine etched bar-back mirror and leaded windows. The historic interior is of regional importance. The landlady and her family celebrated 25 years here in 2016. Piano singalongs on Tuesday, Thursday and Friday evenings maintain the timeless atmosphere. Real ales are quality, not quantity. Q(Bond St)

Jackalope

43 Weymouth Mews, W1G 7EQ
☎ (020) 3455 2871 jackalopelondon.com
4 changing beers (often Adnams, Five Points, Redemption) H
One of Marylebone's two remaining mews pubs, formerly the Dover Castle, built in 1777 and Grade II listed. The mirrors underneath the dividing beam allowed coachmen to observe when their passengers wanted to depart. Now owned by Bloomsbury Leisure, operators of the Euston Tap, it has downstairs London's first Liu Xiaomian noodle kitchen, specialising in ramen dishes. A jackalope is a cross between a jack rabbit and an antelope, a mythical creature of North American folklore.
(Great Portland St/Regent's Park)

Thornbury Castle L

29A Enford Street, W1H 1DN
☎ (020) 7723 8540 thornbury-castle.business.site
6 changing beers (often Park, Tring, Vale) H
A small, family-run place in a side street near Marylebone station, with wood panelling throughout and

a raised seating area at the back. There is a strong Rugby Union connection (Wasps) and it may open at weekends for big games on TV. Discerning drinkers will find it a worthwhile alternative to the more mainstream pubs in the area. Thai food is served. Q☺❍☷✿☺♨🚪♥ ⚛ 🛜

W1: Soho

Dog & Duck ★ ✔
18 Bateman Street, W1D 3AJ
☎ (020) 7494 0697
St Austell Nicholson's Pale Ale; Sharp's Doom Bar; 5 changing beers (often St Austell, Sharp's) ⊞
In the heart of Soho, this Grade II listed Nicholson's outlet, built in 1897, has a nationally important historic pub interior. An elaborate mosaic depicts dogs and ducks, and wonderful advertising mirrors adorn the walls. The upstairs Orwell Bar can be hired for functions. The pub is small and so popular, especially with media people, that it is not just smokers who have to drink outside. The bar extends towards the Frith Street door. ❍❾(Tottenham Court Rd) 🚪⚛

Lyric ⓛ
37 Great Windmill Street, W1D 7LT
☎ (020) 7434 0604 ⊕ lyricsoho.co.uk
Harvey's Sussex Best Bitter; 8 changing beers (often Siren, Southwark) ⊞
A small, independently owned bar just off Shaftesbury Avenue, bay-fronted with a tiled, panelled interior and popular with local trade. Once two adjacent taverns, the Windmill and the Ham, it merged in the mid-18th century to form the Windmill & Ham, renamed in 1890 and rebuilt 16 years later. Alongside the draught beers, including London specialities, cask ales may come from Big Smoke, Brodie's, Dark Star, Magic Rock, Marble, RedWillow, Redemption, Tiny Rebel or Thornbridge. ☎❍❾(Piccadilly Circus) ●🚪⚛ ⚛

Old Coffee House
49 Beak Street, W1F 9SF
☎ (020) 7437 2197
3 changing beers (often Brodie's, Redemption, Windsor & Eton) ⊞
A large but cosy venue, close to the buzz of Carnaby Street. First licensed as the Silver Street Coffee House, it was rebuilt in 1894 and is now Grade II listed. The long bar and dark panelling are adorned with Watney's Red Barrel signage, brewery mirrors and sundry prints, posters, pictures and brassware. At lunchtimes you will find good-sized portions of pub grub, very reasonably priced. ☎☺❾(Piccadilly Circus)🚪♥

Queen's Head ⓛ ✔
15 Denman Street, W1D 7HN
☎ (020) 7437 1540 ⊕ queensheadpiccadilly.com
Fuller's London Pride; Sambrook's Wandle Ale; 3 changing beers (often Dark Star, Gun, Sambrook's) ⊞
A rare West End free house with plenty of vertical drinking space below and a restaurant upstairs. The traditional feel is enhanced by an attractive bar-back and wall mirroring downstairs, and an unusual leather-fronted bar in the restaurant. With its real ales and quality food including good-value pies, snacks and cheeseboards at the bar, this pub is popular both before and after theatre visits. ☎❍❾(Piccadilly Circus)🚪♥ ⚛

Star & Garter
62 Poland Street, W1F 7NX
☎ (020) 7437 9278
Fuller's London Pride; Greene King IPA; 1 changing beer (often St Austell) ⊞

A few minutes' walk from Oxford Circus, here is a proper unreconstructed beer house to gladden the hearts of aficionados, with no fripperies like meals or Wi-Fi. Formerly a Courage house, as the painted windows attest, it has a small, cosy, wood-panelled bar with a matchboard ceiling. An additional bar upstairs is usually open on Thursday and Friday nights to cope with the throng. ❾(Oxford Circus/Piccadilly Circus)🚪♥

EAST LONDON
E1: Spitalfields

Commercial Tavern
142 Commercial Street, E1 6NU
☎ (020) 3137 9563 ⊕ commercial-tavern.com
4 changing beers (often Burning Sky, Thornbridge, Tiny Rebel) ⊞
Built in 1865, this Grade II listed pub has an unusual curved frontage and interesting features. The warm, vibrant atmosphere welcomes you as you walk through the tabled area to the bar at the rear. Alongside the four cask beers are 10 keg fonts. The larger of the two upstairs rooms has its own bar; the smaller is more intimate. The selection of freshly cooked sourdough pizzas includes cheese-free options. ☎❍♿(Liverpool St) ❾(Liverpool St/Shoreditch High St) 🚪♥ ⚛

King's Stores ✔
14 Widegate Street, E1 7HP
☎ (020) 7247 4089 ⊕ kingsstores.co.uk
Greene King IPA; 4 changing beers (sourced nationally; often Hop Stuff, London Beer Factory, Sharp's) ⊞
A Greene King Metropolitan outlet, this is a corner house in the narrow streets near Old Spitalfields Market. The decor is minimal, with bare floorboards and brick walls. The front is the main drinking area while the rear is more for eating, and there is also a restaurant upstairs. Five real ales always include at least one London brew. TVs show sporting events. ☎❍♿☷❾(Liverpool St)🚪♥ ⚛

Pride of Spitalfields
3 Heneage Street, E1 5LJ
☎ (020) 7247 8933
Crouch Vale Brewers Gold; Fuller's London Pride, ESB; Sharp's Doom Bar; 1 changing beer (often Truman's) ⊞
Just off Brick Lane, this single-bar free house has been run by the same landlady for the past 30 years and with most of the same staff. A real ale enthusiast, she has all the ales delivered direct from the brewery. Food at lunchtime is simple fare. Originally tied to the Star Brewery in Romford, the pub had changed its name from the Romford Arms by the early 1980s. Many local pictures adorn the walls. ☎❾(Aldgate East/Shoreditch High St) 🚪♥

Williams Ale & Cider House ⓛ ✔
22-24 Artillery Lane, E1 7LS
☎ (020) 7247 5163 ⊕ williamsspitalfields.com
Greene King IPA, Yardbird; 5 changing beers (often Southwark, Truman's, Twickenham) ⊞
In a narrow street near Old Spitalfields Market, here is a large, comfortably furnished venue with bare floorboards and brick walls. The beer range always features London breweries. Seven ciders are also on handpump. TVs are switched on for major sporting events only. This is one of the few pubs in the area with dartboards. Food from a varied menu is served all day. Children are not admitted. ❍☷❾(Liverpool St) ♣●🚪♥ ⚛

E1: Wapping

Prospect of Whitby

57 Wapping Wall, E1W 3SH

(020) 7481 1095

Greene King IPA, Abbot; 4 changing beers (often East London, Redemption, Sambrook's)

A traditional establishment, popular with tourists and locals alike for its historical relevance and tales. On the ground floor the ancient pewter bar is supported by old beer barrels and has six handpumps. There are several seating areas including an atmospheric riverside terrace with the shade of a tree. Additional seating can be found upstairs on the balcony. Food is served all day from an extensive menu. Three function rooms are available for hire. Occasional sporting events are shown. (100,D3)

E2: Bethnal Green

Camel

277 Globe Road, E2 0JD

(020) 3620 2333

Adnams Mosaic; Sambrook's Wandle Ale; 3 changing beers (often Five Points, St Austell, Three Sods)

A small refurbished Victorian pub with a single bar and a traditional feel. One of the guest beers is usually from Five Points Brewery in Hackney. There is food throughout the day, with a range of pies and mash, toasties and puddings. The distinctive exterior tiling gives a clue to the original brewery; the last one with a tie was Ind Coope. Convenient for the Museum of Childhood and York Hall.

King's Arms

11A Buckfast Street, E2 6EY

(020) 7729 2627 thekingsarmspub.com

3 changing beers (often Five Points, Howling Hops, Siren)

A single-bar back-street local run by Barworks since refurbishment seven years ago. Three cask ales are offered along with over a dozen keg beers and a large range of bottles. Two ciders are available. There are no pumpclips; the beer menu is on the tables and the wall, and can also be found on the website. The only food offerings are Scotch eggs and tortas with cheese or meat. There is seating outside.
(Bethnal Green/Shoreditch High St)

E3: Bow

Eleanor Arms

460 Old Ford Road, E3 5JP

(020) 8980 6992 eleanorarms.co.uk

Shepherd Neame Master Brew, Whitstable Bay Pale Ale; 2 changing beers (sourced nationally; often Shepherd Neame)

This multi award-winning pub, slightly off the beaten track but convenient for Victoria Park, is well worth visiting. Quiz night is the first Thursday of the month. On Sunday evening the pub becomes the Old Ford Jazz Club and usually hosts a jam session. It retains 1930s wood panelling and has a beer garden to the rear. The management team is in its second decade and enjoys occasional help from its customers. (8)

E4: Chingford

King's Head

2B Kings Head Hill, E4 7EA

(020) 8529 6283

Fuller's London Pride; Morland Old Speckled Hen; St Austell Tribute; Sharp's Doom Bar; 6 changing beers (sourced regionally)

This roomy Stonegate pub is in an old building with a contemporary interior. The six changing beers are often from London, Essex and Hertfordshire brewers. Popular with diners, it has seating outside and, unusually for London, there is a car park. Six Nations rugby is shown. Quiz nights are on Sunday and Wednesday; music on Friday nights alternates each week between live bands and a DJ. P

E5: Clapton

Anchor & Hope

15 High Hill Ferry, E5 9HG (800yds N of Lea Bridge Rd, along river path)

(020) 8806 1730 anchor-and-hope-clapton.co.uk

Fuller's London Pride, ESB; 1 changing beer (often Fuller's)

One of Fuller's smallest pubs, on the bank of the River Lea and dating from about 1850. Refurbished a couple of years ago, it has one room with wood panelling and a dartboard at the rear, a wood fire and the bar at the front. Drinkers include wildlife enthusiasts and birdwatchers, boaters and locals. Food is served at weekends and there are barbecues in summer. You can moor outside if you arrive by boat. (393)

E6: East Ham

Miller's Well

419-421 Barking Road, E6 2JX

(020) 8471 8404

Greene King Abbot; Ruddles Best Bitter; Sharp's Doom Bar; 3 changing beers (sourced nationally)

A popular Wetherspoon outlet, across the road from East Ham town hall, converted from three shops in 1993. The walls are decorated with the usual mix of local historic photographs and pictures. In the back bar there is a memorial to John Travers (Jack) Cornwall VC and Edgar Kingborne Myles VC, and the British Legion poppy appeal. The pub now has a darts team. Q

E8: Hackney

Pembury Tavern

90 Amhurst Road, E8 1JH

(020) 8986 8597 pemburytavern.co.uk

Five Points Pale, Railway Porter; house beer (by Five Points); 2 changing beers (often Harvey's, Milton)

A large corner pub now run by the Five Points Brewery, located under nearby railway arches. On occasion instead of the regular beers there may be tap takeovers by other breweries. There is always a friendly vibe. Pizzas are available Monday to Saturday, and roasts (including vegan options) on Sunday. Monday quizzes and occasional comedy nights are held; check the website for upcoming events. Local CAMRA Community Pub of the Year 2020.
(Downs) (Central/Downs)

E9: Homerton

Chesham Arms

15 Mehetabel Road, E9 6DU

(020) 8986 6717 cheshamarms.com

4 changing beers (sourced nationally)

This lovely traditional back-street local was saved from closure following a high profile campaign a few years ago. There are two real fires inside and an attractive garden down at the back. Very much part of the community, it has a book swap shop and occasional singalongs on the piano. Four changing ales and one cider are served in winter, three and two respectively in summer. Pizzas are available from the local Yard Sale Pizza eatery. ⛆❄🌀➡️⊖(Hackney Central)🚶♿🚪🐾🛜

E10: Leyton

Coach & Horses
391 High Road, E10 5NA
☎ (020) 8281 3398 ⊕ thecoachleyton.com
Mighty Oak Captain Bob; 4 changing beers (often East London, Purity, Sharp's) 🅷
A recently refurbished pub with a horseshoe bar. Some beers from London breweries are among those on the handpumps and 20 keg fonts. There is ample seating in the two rooms and rear beer garden. Monday is quiz night; Dungeon and Dragon games and Escape Room adventures are also played here (book ahead). The menu includes speciality burgers, steak & Guinness and vegetarian pies, and Sunday roasts. The pub gets busy on Leyton Orient match days. ⛆❄🌀⊖🚶🚪🐾🛜

Drum 🅻 ✅
557-559 Lea Bridge Road, E10 7EQ
☎ (020) 8539 9845
Greene King Abbot; Ruddles Best Bitter; Sharp's Doom Bar; 7 changing beers 🅷
A Wetherspoon for 38 years, this is one of the oldest in the chain, as well as the second smallest. Imaginatively converted from an auction house, it is a friendly pub with a strong local following and a major focus on cask ales. Inside is a long bar, a main seating area and an additional seating and family section. Outside at the back is a garden. Q⛆❄🌀⊖(Midland Rd)🚶P🚪🛜

Leyton Orient Supporters Club 🅻
Breyer Group Stadium, Oliver Road, E10 5NF
☎ (020) 8988 8288 ⊕ orientsupporters.org
Mighty Oak Oscar Wilde 🅶**; 10 changing beers** 🅷
Multi award-winning club, once a CAMRA national finalist and now local CAMRA Club of the Year for 2020. Open only on home match days (but not during the matches) and for England soccer fixtures, it hosts four brewery tap takeovers every year. The bar can get extremely busy but the volunteer staff are efficient. On match days CAMRA members may need to show their membership card but other events are open to all. Q⛆❄⊖🚶🚪

Leyton Technical
265B High Road, E10 5QN
☎ (020) 8558 4759 ⊕ leytontechnical.com
Volden Session Ale; house beer (by Volden); 2 changing beers (sourced nationally) 🅷
Formerly the Town Hall, this multi-roomed pub has a complex pattern on the mosaic floor and ornate plasterwork on the ceiling. Beers from London brewers and further afield are served from any of eight handpumps and 12 keg fonts. A warm welcome and friendly service are guaranteed. Wednesday is quiz night. A varied menu includes plant burger, macaroni cheese, sausage and mash and Sunday roasts. Busy on Leyton Orient match days. ⛆🌀♿⊖🚶🚪🐾🛜

E11: Leytonstone

North Star
24 Browning Road, E11 3AR
☎ 07747 010013
East London Foundation Bitter; Oakham JHB; 4 changing beers (sourced nationally) 🅷

A recent local CAMRA Pub of the Year, named after a steamship, this community-oriented side-street venue has a long-serving landlord. Separate rooms either side are served from a central bar. Pizzas and Thai dishes are served from late afternoon (not Mon). There is a garden to the rear and pavement tables at the front. England sports matches are shown on terrestrial channels. A jukebox supplies music. ⛆❄🌀⊖♿🚪🐾

Northcote Arms ♟
110 Grove Green Road, E11 4EL
☎ (020) 8518 7516 ⊕ thenorthcotee11.com
4 changing beers (sourced locally; often Crate, East London, Signature) 🅷
A local community pub between Leyton and Leytonstone. The interior is divided into different areas including a small snug, and is comfortably furnished. Entertainment includes quizzes, vinyl record nights, live music and drag cabaret on Sunday evenings. There are two gardens to the rear, with a whisky bar, and pavement tables at the front. Highly regarded pizzas are served. The TV shows only major sporting events. Local CAMRA Pub of the Year 2020. ⛆❄🌀⊖(Leyton)🚶🚪🐾🛜

Red Lion 🅻 ✅
640 High Road, E11 3AA
☎ (020) 8988 2929 ⊕ theredlionleytonstone.com
Sharp's Atlantic; Volden Session Ale, Pale Ale; 7 changing beers (sourced nationally; often Volden) 🅷
Popular with young families, this pub has a decor with retro touches from Antic such as stylus record players and vinyl records on the shelves. There is a large semi-covered garden to the rear and also a restaurant. As well as the real ale and cider, a good selection of bottles is available. The ballroom upstairs hosts live music every Sunday, usually jazz/funk, with a DJ on Friday and Saturday nights and a quiz night on Monday. ⛆❄🌀🍴🌀♿🐾🚪🚪🛜

E11: Wanstead

George 🅻 ✅
159 High Street, E11 2RL
☎ (020) 8989 2921
Fuller's London Pride; Greene King IPA, Abbot; Sharp's Doom Bar; 8 changing beers (sourced nationally) 🅷
Interior decorations reflect the name of the original tavern on this site, from about 1716, which was the George & Dragon. A large dragon hangs from the ceiling above the main bar and there is a carved wooden dragon chair for the solo drinker. The walls are adorned with pictures of famous Georges. Cask beers are served at the downstairs bar only. The smoking area and car park are at the rear. Q⛆❄🌀♿⊖🚪🛜

E12: Manor Park

Golden Fleece ✅
166 Capel Road, E12 5DB
☎ (020) 8478 0024
Greene King IPA, Abbot; Timothy Taylor Landlord; 3 changing beers (often Castle Rock, Greene King) 🅷
With its large family-friendly garden, this pub is busy in the summer. Recently refurbished, it has a comfortable atmosphere. Food is available all day all week. There is regular entertainment including a quiz night on Wednesday and a jam session for local musicians most Friday evenings. TV screens show sporting events. ⛆❄🌀♿⊖🚶P🚪🐾🛜

E13: Plaistow

Black Lion ✔

59-61 High Street, E13 0AD

☎ (020) 8472 2351 🌐 blacklionplaistow.co.uk

Mighty Oak Captain Bob; 3 changing beers (sourced nationally) Ⓗ

A rare freehold pub for East London, run by the same landlord for 34 years. Rebuilt in the 18th century, it has two bars, an original cobbled courtyard, a function room in a converted outbuilding, and a garden. The narrow main bar is where four ales are on offer. There is a smaller back bar accessible by a separate door or through the main bar. Sports TVs can be viewed from all points. 🐴❀◑⊖♣P🚌📶

E14: Canary Wharf

Ledger Building ✔

4 Hertsmere Road, E14 4AL

☎ (020) 7536 7770

Fuller's London Pride; Greene King IPA, Abbot; Sharp's Doom Bar; 5 changing beers (often Truman's, Twickenham) Ⓗ

In a building dating from 1800, this pub stands on the north-west corner of the former Import Dock and takes its name from the original use, which was to hold the ledgers of the West India Docks. The rotating guest ales on the large single bar often come from London breweries. Pictures of the area adorn the walls. Three further rooms provide plenty of space. A smoking area is out front. Q🐴❀◑♿⊖(West India Quay)🚌📶

E14: Crossharbour

Pepper Saint Ontiod ✔

21 Pepper Street, E14 9RP

☎ (020) 7987 5205 🌐 peppersaintontiod.com

3 changing beers (often East London, Five Points, Truman's) Ⓗ

A stylish 1990s pub, run by Antic since 2009, with outside seating and lovely views across the Inner Millwall Dock. Ontiod is the estate agents' contraction of On the Isle of Dogs. Expect a friendly welcome; children are allowed until the evening every day and dogs too. The downstairs bar usually has at least one guest ale. The upstairs area offers pool, table football and sports TV.
🐴❀◑♿⊖♣🚌📶

E14: Limehouse

Craft Beer Co

576 Commercial Road, E14 7JD

☎ (020) 7790 2726

House beer (by Kent); 5 changing beers (sourced nationally) Ⓗ

Very close to Limehouse station, this Craft Beer Co pub since 2016 gives a nod to its origins, with memorabilia from Charrington, Bass and Worthington. Children are welcome during the day and dogs too. Cask beers include either a stout or a porter, and a wide range of keg beers is available. On Sunday late afternoon there is live music in the downstairs bar area. There is extra room upstairs and also a secret garden. 🐴❀◑≠⊖🚌🐾📶

E15: Stratford

Goldengrove ✔

146-148 The Grove, E15 1NS

☎ (020) 8519 0750

Adnams Broadside Ⓗ/Ⓖ; Fuller's London Pride; Greene King IPA, Abbot; Sharp's Doom Bar; 5 changing beers (often Hackney) Ⓗ

An early Wetherspoon pub, converted from a clothes shop in 1993. It takes its name from a poem by the Victorian poet Gerard Manley Hopkins, who was born nearby. Generous seating extends to a large beer garden with a covered area. Situated close to Stratford station, Shopping Centre, Westfield and the Olympic Park, the bar can get busy on event days.
Q🐴❀◑♿≠⊖(Maryland/Stratford) 🍎🚌📶

E17: Walthamstow

Bell Ⓛ ✔

617 Forest Road, E17 4NE

☎ (020) 8523 2277 🌐 belle17.com

Sharp's Doom Bar; Timothy Taylor Landlord; 8 changing beers (sourced nationally) Ⓗ

An imposing pub at a busy junction. The spacious interior has two distinct areas, while a sizeable garden at the rear has sheltered seating. There is a quiz on Tuesday evening, live music every second Saturday and a DJ on Fridays and remaining Saturdays. On the second Sunday of the month there is live jazz. A TV screen is used only for major sporting events. Accompanied children are welcome until the evening. 🐴❀◑♿♣▯🚌🐾📶

Olde Rose & Crown Ⓛ ✔

53-55 Hoe Street, E17 4SA

☎ (020) 8509 3880 🌐 yeolderoseandcrowntheatrepub.co.uk

6 changing beers (sourced nationally; often East London) Ⓗ

A spacious Victorian community pub with a welcoming atmosphere. There is a theatre upstairs and a function room downstairs. Various events are held including a folk club on Sunday evening, open mic on the first Wednesday and a 78rpm record night on the second Wednesday of each month. Live music often features in the bar on other nights. Though on an Ei (Stonegate) lease, the pub is now free of tie. Alcoholic drinks are served from noon. 🐴❀◑⊖(Central)♣🍎🚌🐾📶

E20: Westfield Stratford City

Tap East Ⓛ

7 International Square, Montfichet Road, E20 1EE

☎ (020) 8555 4467 🌐 tapeast.co.uk

6 changing beers (sourced nationally; often Tap East) Ⓗ

A brewpub oasis with comfortable seating in the Great Eastern Market, down at the end by the international station. You can see the brewery through a glass door and windows. Behind the bar a screen shows the current three house beers, three guests and real cider. A good range of international bottled beers is also stocked with occasional tasting sessions (book in advance). Snacks and pies are served all day. The bar can be busy on West Ham match days.
🐴❀♿≠⊖(Stratford/Stratford Intl) ♣🍎P🚌📶

Barking

Barking Dog ✔

61 Station Parade, IG11 8TU

☎ (020) 8507 9109

Adnams Broadside; Greene King Abbot; Ruddles Best Bitter; Sharp's Doom Bar; 6 changing beers (sourced nationally) Ⓗ

A busy town-centre Wetherspoon, close to Barking station and many bus routes, and popular with locals and passing commuters alike. There can be up to five regular and seven changing beers. Bag-in-box real ciders include Westons Old Rosie and Gwynt y Ddraig Black Dragon. Food is served all day, alcoholic drinks from 9am. Muted TV screens show rolling news and occasional sport. ❧◑⌂♿≈⊖●🚌🔊

Chadwell Heath

Eva Hart ✅
1128 High Road, RM6 4AH (on A118)
☎ (020) 8597 1069
Greene King Abbot; Ruddles Best Bitter; Sharp's Doom Bar; 8 changing beers (often Adnams, Fuller's, Truman's) 🅗
Large and comfortable split-level Wetherspoon pub divided into several distinct drinking areas. The building dates from 1892 and used to be the local police station. It is named after a local musical personality who was one of the longest-living survivors of the 1912 Titanic disaster; photographs and memorabilia are on display around the pub. Alcoholic drinks are served from 9am, food all day. Toilets (except accessible) are upstairs. Muted TVs show subtitles. Q❧❀◑⌂♿⊖P🚌🔊

Collier Row

Colley Rowe Inn ✅
54-56 Collier Row Road, RM5 3PA (on B174)
☎ (01708) 760633
Greene King Abbot; Ruddles Best Bitter; Sharp's Doom Bar; 4 changing beers (sourced nationally) 🅗
Converted by Wetherspoon from two shops, the pub is close to six bus routes, giving easy access to and from Romford. Alongside the ales, it has two ciders on gravity dispense (usually Westons Old Rosie and Gwynt y Ddraig Black Dragon). It is often lively around the bar, but there are quieter alcoves at the rear. Alcoholic drinks are served from 9am. Food is served all day, every day and steak night is particularly popular. ◑♿●🚌🔊

Gidea Park

Gidea Park Micropub ♟
236 Main Road, RM2 5HA (on A118)
☎ (01708) 397290
6 changing beers (sourced nationally) 🄶
Havering Borough and East London's second micropub opened in 2017 after winning a planning appeal for the change of use. Four to eight real ales from microbreweries are served (in all legal measures) from casks in the ground-floor cellar, also real ciders, wines and gins. There are high and low tables and chairs, unusual spider lighting and an ever-growing display of pumpclips from beers sold here. Mobile phones should be silent. Local CAMRA Pub of the Year 2020.
Q❧◑♿⊖♣●🚌🚌(174,498) ♨🔊

Ship ✅
93 Main Road, RM2 5EL (on A118)
☎ (01708) 741571 ● theshipgideapark.co.uk
Greene King IPA; Sharp's Doom Bar; Timothy Taylor Landlord; 1 changing beer (sourced nationally) 🅗
More than 250 years old, this Grade II listed split-level pub has extensive dark-wood panelling, timber beams and huge fireplaces. The building is largely unchanged and has low ceilings in places – so duck or grouse! It is a family-run business. A quiz night is held on Thursday and live music hosted on Saturday.
Q❧❀◑⊖P🚌(174,498) ♨🔊

Hornchurch

J.J. Moon's
48-52 High Street, RM12 4UN (on A124)
☎ (01708) 478410
Greene King Abbot; Ruddles Best Bitter; Sharp's Doom Bar; 8 changing beers (sourced nationally) 🅗
A busy Wetherspoon, opened in 1993 and popular with all age groups, featuring a good variety of ales with an emphasis on breweries from London and the South-East. Watercolour paintings of local scenes provide the main decoration, with the usual local interest panels to the rear. Families are welcome until the evening, and alcoholic drinks are served from 9am. Silent TVs show subtitles. Q❧◑♿⊖(Emerson Park/Hornchurch)🚌🔊

Ilford

Great Spoon of Ilford ✅
114/116 Cranbrook Road, IG1 4LZ (on A123)
☎ (020) 8518 0535
Greene King Abbot; Ruddles Best Bitter; Sharp's Doom Bar; 4 changing beers (sourced nationally) 🅗
A large, lively Wetherspoon in a former video shop, popular with all ages, friendly, relaxing and good value. Many yards of books line the shelves in the seating alcoves along the left-hand side of the pub. Photographs and descriptions of local scenes adorn the walls. Alcoholic drinks are sold from 9am. Meals include daily specials. There is no music, just silent TV news with subtitles. The toilets (except accessible) are upstairs.
Q❧❀◑♿⊖●🚌🔊

Jono's ✅
37 Cranbrook Road, IG1 4PA (on A123)
☎ (020) 8514 6676
Castle Rock Harvest Pale; St Austell Tribute 🅗
Just one minute's walk from the station, Jono's is a converted shop with an unusual style. The front of the bar is in dark wood and the rear is half-timbered, with a patch of thatch over the seating. Large-screen TVs show sports fixtures; it can be noisy at times. Friendly and efficient bar staff serve well-kept ales; Castle Rock beer is rare in East London. The pub hosts a Thursday quiz and live music on Friday and Saturday evenings. ⊖🚌🔊

Romford

Moon & Stars ✅
99-103 South Street, RM1 1NX
☎ (01708) 730117
Greene King Abbot; Ruddles Best Bitter; Sharp's Doom Bar; 6 changing beers (sourced nationally) 🅗
Reopened with a new roof terrace and lift after a £1.1 million refurbishment, this Wetherspoon pub has a raised rear area where children are welcome. Food is served all day. The real ciders are now dispensed from handpumps. Wall panels display local history and an assortment of books fills the shelves. Close to Romford station and buses, the pub is busy on Thursday and Friday evenings. Toilets (except accessible) are upstairs.
Q❧❀◑♿≈⊖●🚌🔊

Upminster

Upminster TapRoom 🄻
1B Sunnyside Gardens, RM14 3DT (off St Mary's Lane)
☎ 07841 676225
Dark Star Hophead; 6 changing beers (sourced locally) 🄶
Upminster and East London's first micropub, opened in a converted office in 2015 as a snack bar selling real ale

before obtaining change of use on appeal. Garlands of hops adorn the walls. The ales are served straight from casks in the cool cellar visible from the bar. Walk or use public transport to get here, and silence mobile phones or pay a fee for charity. Local CAMRA Pub of the Year 2018. Q≿❀◗♿⇌⊖●▯🚌🐾

Woodford Green

Travellers Friend ✔

496-498 High Road, IG8 0PN (on slip road off A104)
☎ (020) 8504 2435 🌐 thetravellersfriendwoodford.co.uk
Bombardier; St Austell Tribute; Timothy Taylor Landlord; Young's London Original; 4 changing beers (sourced nationally) Ⓗ
After five years under the ownership of two local families, this friendly, comfortable pub was completely refurbished in 2017 and extended above and behind, and the rare snob screens from the bar counter relocated above the bar-back. The original oak panelling was removed, part was restored and some was replaced. There are picnic tables at the front and in the side beer garden. To the rear is a small car park. Up to eight real ales may be on the bar. ≿❀◖◗♿●P🚌(20,179)🐾

NORTH LONDON

N1: Angel

Angel 𝕃 ✔

3-5 Islington High Street, N1 9LQ
☎ (020) 7837 2218
Greene King IPA; Sharp's Doom Bar; 6 changing beers (often Truman's, Twickenham, Windsor & Eton) Ⓗ
A large, modern, open-plan Wetherspoon conversion with some booths towards the back giving slightly more privacy. The adjacent tower was a part of the Angel, one of the first talkie cinemas, which was sadly mostly demolished. With the long-gone Philharmonic Hall (subsequently Grand Theatre), this was always a centre of popular entertainment. Its classic columns and caryatids can apparently be seen in the Museum of London. ≿❀◖◗♿⊖●🚌ᯤ

N1: Hoxton

Wenlock Arms 𝕃

26 Wenlock Road, N1 7TA
☎ (020) 7608 3406 🌐 wenlockarms.com
Mighty Oak Oscar Wilde; 7 changing beers (sourced nationally) Ⓗ
Free house saved from closure by a vigorous local campaign. It features beers from small and medium-sized breweries across the UK, usually including a mild and subject to regular change. With up to seven ciders and perries, and a small snacks menu of toasties, Scotch eggs, sausage rolls and pickled eggs, this is a truly welcoming street-corner local with an international reputation. ≿◖◗♿⇌⊖(Old St)♣●🚌🐾ᯤ

N1: King's Cross

Parcel Yard

West Side, King's Cross Station, N1C 4AP
☎ (020) 7713 7258
Dark Star Hophead; Fuller's Oliver's Island, London Pride, ESB; Gale's Seafarers Ale, HSB; 4 changing beers (often Adnams, Dark Star, Fuller's) Ⓗ
A large pub, upstairs at the rear of the concourse, converted from the former station parcel office. It is used by local workers and commuters, and for meetings. As well as bars on two levels, there are semi-private rooms converted from offices (available to book) and an indoor balcony. No music plays; the decor is minimal and features rescued furniture. Food, starting with breakfast, is served throughout the day. Wheelchair access is by lift. Smoking is not permitted.
≿❀◖◗♿⇌⊖(King's Cross St Pancras) ♣🚌ᯤ

N1: Pentonville

Craft Beer Co

55 White Lion Street, N1 9PP
☎ (020) 7278 0318
Kent Pale; 9 changing beers (sourced nationally) Ⓗ
Multi-room pub with a wooden bar displaying 10 handpumps, all serving beers from independent brewers. Green curtains and red carpet give some warmth to the main bar, which has two Victorian pillars, a wooden floor and raised tables and stools, all overseen by Winston Churchill. A cosy room with settees and subtle lighting is to the right as you enter, and there is a smaller room at the back. To the side is a small garden.
❀◖◗⊖(Angel) ▯🚌

King Charles I

55-57 Northdown Street, N1 9BL
☎ (020) 7837 7758
4 changing beers (sourced nationally) Ⓗ
The historic 1930s interior of this Georgian building is small and cosy, containing knick-knacks and homely artefacts, warmed by real fires in the winter. Food can be ordered at the bar or from the Blue River café opposite during daytime. Live blues, folk and indie music can be impromptu or planned. Since 2015 the pub has been community-owned, with a 20-year lease shared by local residents and regulars.
❀⇌⊖(King's Cross St Pancras) 🚌🐾ᯤ

N2: East Finchley

Bald Faced Stag ✔

69 High Road, N2 8AB
☎ (020) 8442 1201 🌐 thebaldfacedstagn2.co.uk
Greene King IPA, Yardbird; 2 changing beers (often Old Dairy, Sambrook's, Triple fff) Ⓗ
A short walk from the underground station, the pub's four handpumps in prime position are a great welcome as you enter; two guest ales are often from south-eastern breweries. There is a separate dining room to the left, with comfy seating in the front and to the right of the bar. A decked garden for outside drinking surrounds a historic sycamore tree. Note that wheelchair access is through the rear car park. Children are admitted until mid-evening. ≿❀◖◗♿⊖P🚌🐾ᯤ

N4: Stroud Green

Brave Sir Robin

29 Crouch Hill, N4 4AP
☎ (020) 7018 3830 🌐 bravesirrobin.co.uk
4 changing beers (often Hammerton, Moor Beer) Ⓗ
Occupying a street-corner site, with what might best be described as modern decor, this pub has been through various guises but now seems to have hit on a winning formula, with a regularly changing range of cask beers and ciders updated on its website. These are supported by fresh, seasonal, modern European-style food. For those who like to try the non-cask side there is a range of over 10 such beers, many from London. Local CAMRA Cider Pub of the Year 2020. ◖◗⊖(Crouch Hill)●🚌🐾ᯤ

N5: Canonbury

Snooty Fox

75 Grosvenor Avenue, N5 2NN

☎ (020) 7354 9532 snootyfoxlondon.co.uk

Otter Ale; 3 changing beers (sourced nationally)

A vibrant community pub with 1960s icons depicted throughout, serving up to four real ales and a real cider. The airy bar features a 45rpm jukebox. Outside there is a pleasant patio with seating. A function room accommodates local groups and private dining. The pub is well known for its ale and cider festivals, which attract people from far and wide. The kitchen serves quality modern British food and an excellent Sunday roast. Local CAMRA Pub of the Year 2019.

N7: Holloway

Coronet

338-346 Holloway Road, N7 6NJ

☎ (020) 7609 5014

Fuller's London Pride; Greene King IPA, Abbot; Ruddles Best Bitter; Sharp's Doom Bar; 6 changing beers (sourced nationally)

Impressive Wetherspoon conversion of a cinema, the Savoy, designed by William Glen, which showed its last film in 1983. The pub displays large prints of movie stars and former local entertainers, with an old projector the centrepiece of a raised dais towards the rear. Sometimes there are single-brewery festivals. Expect plastic glasses and higher prices when Arsenal are playing at home. Tables (some under cover) are on the pavement.
Q

N10: Muswell Hill

Mossy Well

258 Muswell Hill Broadway, N10 3SH

☎ (020) 8444 2914

Fuller's London Pride; Greene King IPA, Abbot; Sharp's Doom Bar; 8 changing beers (often Redemption, Truman's)

A former Express Dairies tearoom and milk depot but a pub since 1984, reopened by Wetherspoon in 2015. Its name derives from the etymology of Muswell. Many internal features reflect its milky history. It is spacious inside, with a mezzanine floor and outdoor drinking areas at both front and back. Despite the size it can be packed. A Westons cider is served from the fridge.
Q

N12: North Finchley

Bohemia

762-764 High Road, N12 9QH

☎ (020) 8446 0294 thebohemia.co.uk

London Brewing Beer Street, 100 Oysters Stout; 2 changing beers (often London Brewing)

A lively brewpub, home to the London Brewing Company. Four or five real ales are sold, mainly from the on-site brewery, as well as a wide range of craft keg and bottled beers. Five more handpumps dispense cider. Table tennis, table football and a selection of board games can be played. There are also monthly jazz and comedy nights, together with a weekly Tuesday night quiz. Good food is served all day.
(Woodside Park)

Elephant Inn

283 Ballards Lane, N12 8NR

☎ (020) 8343 6110 elephantinnfinchley.co.uk

Fuller's London Pride, ESB; 2 changing beers (often Adnams, Dark Star, Fuller's)

Formerly the Moss Hall Tavern, this corner pub has a U-shaped bar with televised sports to the right, a relaxing TV-free area to the left, and raised tables and stools in the middle. Newspapers are usually provided. In front, there is a large patio with wooden seating below a wooden pagoda. Dark Star or Fuller's seasonal ales are often complemented by a true guest ale. Food from the Thai restaurant upstairs can be served in any of the drinking areas. (West Finchley)

N13: Palmers Green

Alfred Herring

316-322 Green Lanes, N13 5TT

☎ (020) 3232 1083

Greene King Abbot; Ruddles Best Bitter; Sharp's Doom Bar; 7 changing beers (often East London, Redemption, Sambrook's)

A busy Wetherspoon shop conversion opened in 2006 in the heart of the Green Lanes retail area, comprising a large open drinking and dining space with side booths. Seven of the 10 handpumps offer a varying range, with the manager regularly obtaining beers from the wide choice of London breweries. Alfred Herring was a local First World War soldier awarded the Victoria Cross for his heroic action in France in 1918. Photos and information on local history adorn the walls. Q

N14: Southgate

New Crown

80-84 Chase Side, N14 5PH

☎ (020) 8882 8758

Greene King Abbot; Ruddles Best Bitter; Sharp's Doom Bar; 6 changing beers (often Redemption, Sambrook's, Wimbledon)

There was an Old Crown on Chase Side until its demolition in the 1960s, hence the name. This large, well-established Wetherspoon's is convenient for the tube, and four bus routes stop outside. Converted from a Sainsbury's store more than 20 years ago, it is has a single open-plan seating area. Up to six guest ales come from small and large breweries across the country, but with emphasis on London brews whenever possible.
Q

N16: Stoke Newington

Rochester Castle

143-145 Stoke Newington High Street, N16 0NY

☎ (020) 7249 6016

Greene King IPA, Abbot; Sharp's Doom Bar; 4 changing beers (sourced nationally)

A Grade II listed building, with an impressive frontage featuring some fine tiling and a large skylight at the back, this is a welcome outlet for cask beer and is now Wetherspoon's longest-trading venue. The pub here dates from 1702 as the Green Dragon, subsequently demolished and rebuilt by Richard Payne from Rochester (hence the name) although it was briefly the Tanners Hall in the 1980s. The cider is stored in polypins in a fridge behind the bar.

N17: Tottenham

Antwerp Arms

168-170 Church Road, N17 8AS

☎ (020) 8216 9289 antwerparms.co.uk

Redemption Pale Ale, Hopspur; 2 changing beers (sourced locally; often Redemption)

Tucked away in the historic and atmospheric Bruce Castle Park area, this Georgian building with beer garden is Tottenham's longest-established working pub, serving local people since 1822. Facing demolition in 2013, it was saved by the local community and CAMRA campaigners and is now owned as a community collective, and is in effect a permanent outlet for Redemption Brewery beers. Food is served at limited times so do check their website. Local CAMRA Pub of the Year 2020. ❀(White Hart Lane)♣P

N19: Upper Holloway

Landseer Arms

37 Landseer Road, N19 4JU

☎ (020) 7281 2569 landseerarms.com

Hammerton N1; 4 changing beers (often One Mile End, Reunion, Twickenham) H

A Victorian pub, very different from most of the places on nearby Holloway Road, and one that has been through many incarnations, eventually renamed after the artist whose works included the Trafalgar Square lions and the painting Monarch of the Glen. The spacious interior includes a conservatory-style area (sometimes used for dining) on the other side of the bar. There is plenty of pavement seating, with retractable awnings and heaters. Food is served in one form or another all day.

❀♿♣

Shaftesbury Tavern

534 Hornsey Road, N19 3QN

☎ (020) 7272 7950 theshaftesburytavern.co.uk

Hammerton N1; 3 changing beers (often Fuller's, Sambrook's) H

A nice old venue, now operated by Remarkable Pubs and comprehensively restored following a 2014 refurbishment, with the former pool room turned into the restaurant area under a fine skylight. The historic interior is identified by CAMRA as of regional importance. Outside at the front there is seating on the terrace. Food comes from a predominantly Thai menu, with some classics such as fish and chips or sausage and mash. Quiz night is Tuesday. ❀♿(Crouch Hill)

St John's Tavern

91 Junction Road, N19 5QU

☎ (020) 7272 1587 stjohnstavern.com

Fuller's London Pride; 4 changing beers (often Crate, Hammerton, Howling Hops) H

Another piece of the real ale renaissance taking place in this part of London. Although the emphasis here is undeniably on food (hams hanging in the food preparation area are visible from the bar), this gastro-pub has up to five real ales on at any one time and is big enough for those who just want a drink to enjoy one without feeling uncomfortable. The whole impression is one of space, helped by a large bar area and high ceilings. ❀(Archway)♣

N21: Winchmore Hill

Little Green Dragon

928 Green Lanes, N21 2AD

☎ (020) 8351 3530 littlegreendragonenfield.com

5 changing beers (often Hammerton, Thornbridge, Vibrant Forest) G

This micropub was Greater London Pub of the Year in 2018 and the local CAMRA winner in 2019 and 2020. The cask ales and real ciders from the taproom delight regulars and newcomers alike. Meet the Brewer events are often held, as well as regular music nights. The variety of seating, including a church pew, bus seats and padded kegs, contributes to the friendly community atmosphere. No excuses for missing your bus – electronic live times are displayed.

Q❀≠♣(125,329)

Orange Tree

18 Highfield Road, N21 3HA

☎ (020) 8360 4853

Greene King IPA; 2 changing beers (often New River, Redemption, St Austell) H

A traditional back-street local with a large garden and play area for children. The garden also hosts summer barbecues. The landlord is proud to have been in this Guide continuously since 1995 and there is a strong sense of the pub being a well-used community local. Major sports events are shown and there is a pool table and dartboard. Quiz night is every Wednesday. The New River Walk is close by. ❀≠♣P(329)

N22: Wood Green

Prince

1 Finsbury Road, N22 8PA

☎ (020) 8888 6698 theprincen22.co.uk

4 changing beers (often Hammerton) H

A handsome two-roomed venue occupying a prominent corner site, brought back to life in 2016 with up to four regularly changing cask ales, nine keg beers and a range of ciders. The beers come from small breweries across the UK and are listed on the website as they change. Snacks are served weekday lunchtimes, Japanese dishes in the evenings and all day at weekends.

❀≠(Alexandra Palace)

Enfield

Moon under Water

115/117 Chase Side, EN2 6NN

☎ (020) 8366 9855

Greene King Abbot; Ruddles Best Bitter; Sharp's Doom Bar; 5 changing beers (often New River, Redemption, Twickenham) H

An early Wetherspoon that used to be the British School, opened in 1838 and closed in 1901. It has since been a dairy, then a restaurant. The building has a church-like appearance with light flooding in on three sides. Popular with all age groups, it has a dedicated area for families. The beers often include local and London brews. Sparklers may be used; if you are concerned, ask for them to be removed.

❀♿≠(Chase) P(191,W9)

Wonder

1 Batley Road, EN2 0JG

☎ (020) 8363 0202

McMullen AK Original Mild, Cask Ale; 1 changing beer (sourced locally; often McMullen) H

An old-fashioned two-bar back-street local offering two regular ales plus a seasonal offer from McMullen or its own Rivertown beers. The large public bar has a real fire and a dartboard, and is where honky tonk piano and spoons are played on Saturday evening and Sunday afternoon. Some tables feature tabletop playing boards, such as backgammon and snakes and ladders. There is also a quiet lounge area. Outside are traditional pub tables on the pavement.

Q❀♿≠(Gordon Hill) ♣P(191,W8)

High Barnet

Lord Nelson

14 West End Lane, EN5 2SA

☎ (020) 8449 7249
Young's London Original, London Special; 1 changing beer (often Ringwood, Young's) [H]
A friendly one-bar pub hidden away off Wood Street. There is often a guest beer alongside the Young's regulars. Interesting features include a fabulous collection of novelty salt and pepper pots, various nautical objects including a display of model ships above the bar, and an example of a snob screen by the side door. The pub hosts regular events including Tuesday night bingo and a Thursday night quiz. Lunch is served Wednesday and Friday. ❀◖♣🚌🐾📶

Olde Mitre Inne ✔
58 High Street, EN5 5SJ
☎ (020) 8449 5701
Adnams Southwold Bitter; Greene King Abbot; Timothy Taylor Landlord; Tring Side Pocket for a Toad; 4 changing beers (often Five Points, Redemption, Tiny Rebel) [H]
The oldest coaching inn in Barnet, this Grade II listed building oozes character and charm. A traditional pub, it has beams, exposed brickwork, wood panelling, open fires and friendly, efficient and well-trained staff. Family-friendly (customers are requested to refrain from bad language), it has a large courtyard that can be heated and covered in winter months. There is live music every Sunday evening, a quiz every Thursday and monthly bingo nights. 🐴❀◖◗⊖♣🍎🚌🐾📶

Olde Monken Holt ✔
193 High Street, EN5 5SU
☎ (020) 3674 3145 🌐 ye-olde-monken-holt.business.site
Greene King IPA, Abbot; St Austell Tribute; Timothy Taylor Landlord [H]
This historic pub, close to the site of the 1471 Battle of Barnet, can be found at the northern end of the High Street. Dating from 1863, the premises are welcoming and popular, with attentive staff serving four regular beers. Recognised as a music venue, it hosts a Wednesday open mic night, a Friday DJ, Saturday live music and a Sunday Irish music night. Popular sports events are shown on many TVs towards the rear.
🐴❀♿♣🚌(84,399) 🐾📶

New Barnet

Railway Bell ✔
13 East Barnet Road, EN4 8RR
☎ (020) 8449 1369
Courage Directors; Greene King IPA, Abbot; Sharp's Doom Bar; 6 changing beers (often Adnams, East London, Enfield) [H]
There has been a pub on this site since the late 19th century. Photographs and information about railways and the local area adorn the walls. With a large conservatory giving it a bright and spacious feel, it also has a generous patio and garden with a no-smoking area where you can watch the trains go by. One of the earliest Wetherspoon pubs, it has featured in over 20 editions of this Guide since 1977. Q🐴❀◖◗♿🚆🍎🚌📶

NORTH-WEST LONDON

NW1: Camden Town

Camden Road Draft House
102-104 Camden Road, NW1 9EA
☎ (020) 7485 4530
3 changing beers (often Sambrook's, Siren) [H]
Previously the Eagle, Rosie O'Grady's, Mac Bar and Grand Union, this huge pub was massively improved by Draft House group in 2017 and in turn by BrewDog in 2018. It has a horseshoe-shaped bar, eclectic lighting and music memorabilia; a large mural reflects Camden's musical history. A board lists the various beers available. Food includes Sunday roasts. A function area to the side can be reserved. There is a quiz on Tuesday and a DJ on Friday.
🐴❀◖◗♿⊖(Camden Rd/Town) 🍎🚌🐾📶

Colonel Fawcett Ⓛ
1 Randolph Street, NW1 0SS
☎ (020) 7267 9829 🌐 thecolonelfawcett.co.uk
3 changing beers (sourced nationally; often Hammerton) [H]
Dating from 1843 and originally known as the Camden Arms, this was the site of one of the last fatal duels in England in 1873, and the pub is now named after its victim. He died upstairs and his ghost is reputed to still drink here. Hidden down the back streets of Camden, this pub has gone from strength to strength under its new independent operators, with regular events including quiz nights and Friday/Saturday DJ nights.
❀◖◗⊖(Camden Rd) 🚌📶

Golden Lion Ⓛ
88 Royal College Street, NW1 0TH
☎ (020) 7097 4760 🌐 goldenlioncamden.com
Dark Star Hophead; Fuller's London Pride; Sambrook's Junction Ale [H]
A lovely and popular community pub, saved from closure in 2013; the licensee and the local community, supported by Camden Council, waged a long campaign to prevent its conversion into flats. This came to its final and excellent conclusion with the sitting tenant buying the building, which he now leases out. Tasteful decor complements the pub's historic features, mainly the mirrored bar-back. A real back-street community boozer.
🐴❀◖◗♿⊖(Camden Rd) ♣🍎🚌🐾📶

Tapping the Admiral Ⓛ
77 Castle Road, NW1 8SU
☎ (020) 7267 6118 🌐 tappingtheadmiral.co.uk
House beer (by Brakspear); 7 changing beers (sourced regionally) [H]
Local CAMRA Pub of the Year 2018, this is a lively and enjoyable community venue where friendly, knowledgeable staff offer a warm welcome. Guest ales come mainly from local breweries. Great British food includes speciality home-made pies. Outside at the back is a well-designed, heated and covered beer garden. There is a popular Wednesday quiz and live traditional music on Thursday evening. Look out for monthly tap takeovers, pop-up events, and also the pub's cat, Nelson.
Q🐴❀◖◗♿⊖(Kentish Town West) 🍎🚌🐾📶

NW1: Euston

Doric Arch Ⓛ
Euston Station Colonnade, 1 Eversholt Street, NW1 2DN
☎ (020) 7383 3359 🌐 doric-arch.co.uk
Dark Star Hophead, American Pale Ale; Fuller's Oliver's Island, London Pride, ESB; 3 changing beers (often Adnams, Dark Star, Fuller's) [H]
Up a flight of stairs, the large picture windows afford a bird's eye view of the busy urban world below. Right next to Euston station, the bar is used extensively by commuters, aided by the train times screen. Excellent staff are helpful and informative about the ales, including guest beers, increasingly from Dark Star. Brewery and railway memorabilia adorn the walls. Alcoholic drinks are served from 10am, food all day. Toilets are at basement level. 🐴◖◗🚆⊖(Euston/Euston Sq)🍎🚌📶

Euston Tap

West & East Lodges, 190 Euston Road, NW1 2EF
☎ (020) 3137 8837 🌐 eustontap.com
10 changing beers (sourced nationally) 🄿
Fronting the main station building, these impressive Grade II listed Portland stone lodges, separated by a bus lane, are relics from the original 1830s station. Up to 10 changing beers, mostly from smaller breweries, are pumped up to taps behind the bar. Small ground-floor spaces are augmented by seating (and toilets) up the wrought iron spiral staircases and large heated drinking areas outside. The East Lodge opens later in the afternoon. Both sides offer traditional cider.
❀≠⊖(Euston/Euston Sq) ●🚌🐾📶

Exmouth Arms ✔

1 Starcross Street, NW1 2HR
☎ (020) 7387 5440
Titanic Plum Porter; 4 changing beers (often Sambrook's, Signature, Southwark) 🄷
Adjacent to the HS2 works, this is a lively venue with a boutique hostel on the upper floors and an open-plan kitchen offering burgers and tapas from Burger Craft. The interior has large picture windows and comfortable seating – booths by the windows, high tables and benches – around a large L-shaped bar fronted by mosaic tiles. Local cask beers appear regularly; bottled and canned beers are displayed on the wall of beer. Breakfasts are served. Outside there is plentiful bench seating. ❀🛏◐◑≠⊖(Euston/Euston Sq)●📶

NW4: Hendon

Midland Hotel

29 Station Road, NW4 4PN
☎ (020) 3602 1320
Oakham Citra; 2 changing beers (often 3 Brewers of St Albans, New River) 🄷
A surviving and characterful Victorian local, a stone's throw from the railway station. The main bar area is at the front. A larger room with snooker table at the rear occasionally hosts live music. Two cask beers are usually on tap, three at busier times. Known locally as the Mids, this is very much a community pub; it offers a warm welcome to all. A large outside area houses a small collection of classic cars, including a Trabant.
♘❀◐◑≠♣P🚌(83,183) 📶

NW5: Kentish Town

Grafton 𝕃 ✔

20 Prince of Wales Road, NW5 3LG
☎ (020) 7482 4466 🌐 thegraftonnw5.co.uk
3 changing beers (sourced nationally) 🄷
Popular award-winning pub with beautiful Victorian features, combining a traditional feel with many contemporary touches and specialising in local cask beers. The spacious ground-floor horseshoe bar is partly tiled, with ample seating. There is also an upstairs bar/function room (no real ale) and an elegant covered roof garden. Knowledgeable and friendly bar staff are happy to advise you. Quiz night is Tuesday and there is comedy on Wednesday, as well as the piano and board games.
♘❀◐◑♿≠⊖(Kentish Town/Kentish Town West)
●🚌🐾📶

Lion & Unicorn 𝕃

42 Gaisford Street, NW5 2ED
☎ (020) 7267 2304 🌐 thelionandunicornnw5.co.uk
Young's London Original; 3 changing beers (often Redemption, Southwark, Twickenham) 🄷
This popular community venue is a great favourite, with its genuine homely feel, open fire and comfortable seating. Run by friendly management and staff as a Geronimo-branded gastro-pub, it offers a good-quality cask ale range featuring several local breweries. Both front and back gardens have won local and regional awards. A quiz is held on Sunday. Comedy nights are hosted on occasion. Upstairs is the Proforca theatre – details of productions are available on the Proforca website. ♘❀◐◑♿≠⊖●🚌🐾📶

Pineapple 𝕃

51 Leverton Street, NW5 2NX
☎ (020) 7284 4631 🌐 thepineapplepubnw5.com
House beer (by Marston's); 4 changing beers (sourced nationally) 🄷
An authentic and friendly community venue, saved from closure by the locals, Grade II listed and with a regionally important historic interior, notable for its mirrors and splendid bar-back. The front bar, with comfortable seating around tables, leads through to an informal conservatory overlooking the patio garden. The menu is Thai kitchen cuisine. Local beers can come from across London and, the pub being free of tie, the range changes regularly. Q♘❀◐◑≠⊖●🚌🐾📶

Southampton Arms

139 Highgate Road, NW5 1LE
🌐 thesouthamptonarms.co.uk
8 changing beers (sourced nationally) 🄷
The pub does what it says on the sign outside: Ale, Cider, Meat. This multiple CAMRA award-winning venue has 14 handpumps on and behind the bar, serving almost equal amounts of cider and different beers from microbreweries across the UK. Snacks include pork pies, roast pork in baps, cheese and meat baps, plus veggie options. Music is played on vinyl only and the piano is in regular use. Down at the back is a secluded patio.
❀◐◑≠⊖(Gospel Oak/Kentish Town) ●🚌

NW6: Kilburn

Sir Colin Campbell 𝕃

264-266 Kilburn High Road, NW6 2BY
☎ (020) 7693 5443 🌐 thesircolincampbell.co.uk
Timothy Taylor Landlord; 2 changing beers (sourced nationally) 🄷
This pub was acquired and restored to its original beauty in early 2017 by three local people. Cask beer returned, plus a good selection of bottled and canned beers, and there is live traditional Irish music every Friday, Saturday and Sunday night. Two separate rooms around a central bar give a real feel of how traditional pubs used to be. Rotating pop-up kitchen opening times vary with the supplier; check the website for information.
♘❀◐◑♿≠⊖(Brondesbury) 🚌🐾📶

Harrow

Castle ★

30 West Street, HA1 3EF
☎ (020) 8422 3155
Fuller's London Pride, ESB; Gale's HSB; 1 changing beer (often Dark Star, Ossett, Wimbledon) 🄷
A lively and friendly Fuller's house in the heart of Harrow-on-the-Hill. Built in 1901 and Grade II listed, it has a nationally important historic interior. Food is served throughout the day; reservations are recommended for Sunday lunchtimes. Three real coal fires help to keep the pub warm and cosy in the colder months, and a secluded beer garden is popular during the summer. Local CAMRA Pub of the Year 2019. ♘❀◐◑♣🚌(258,H17)🐾📶

Moon on the Hill ✔

373-375 Station Road, HA1 2AW

☎ (020) 8863 3670

Greene King Abbot; Sharp's Doom Bar; 4 changing beers (often Redemption, Sambrook's, Truman's) Ⓗ

Small, busy Wetherspoon close to Harrow-on-the-Hill station and served by numerous bus routes. Guest beers come mostly from London brewers. Serving food all day, it is popular with price-conscious regulars, office workers and students from the nearby University of Westminster. It gets extremely busy when there are sporting events on at nearby Wembley Stadium. Q (Harrow-on-the-Hill)

Rayners Lane

Village Inn ✔

402-408 Rayners Lane, HA5 5DY

☎ (020) 8868 8551

Greene King IPA, Abbot; Sharp's Doom Bar; Twickenham Naked Ladies; 4 changing beers Ⓗ

A split-level, double-fronted shop conversion. The rear of the pub, accessed down a few steps, sports the traditional Wetherspoon booths with a row of tables down the centre. A terraced area behind has a variety of large potted plants among the picnic tables. The front pavement has a few tables and chairs for that alfresco moment. There is a good cross-section of customers who mingle quite happily together. Alcoholic drinks are served from 9am. Q

Ruislip

Hop & Vine

18 High Street, HA4 7AN

5 changing beers (sourced nationally) Ⓖ

A conversion from a former café, with seating at low tables plus chairs and benches. The small bar counter in the right-hand corner dispenses real ales, keg beers and ciders from a temperature-controlled cellar room behind it. Bottled and canned beers, wines and spirits are also sold. Snacks are enhanced by cheeseboard and charcuterie board options. There may be six or seven cask beers at weekends, often with table service.
Q

Ruislip Manor

J.J. Moon's ✔

12 Victoria Road, HA4 0AA

☎ (01895) 622373

Courage Directors; Greene King Abbot; Ruddles Best Bitter; Sharp's Doom Bar; 7 changing beers (often Twickenham) Ⓗ

A large Wetherspoon conversion conveniently opposite the tube station. It is popular and often busy in the evening and at weekends. Food and beer alike are of good value, with the usual promotions. At the rear is an elevated section for dining, leading outside to a small garden patio, while the front has a partitioned-off smoking area on the street. Q

SOUTH-EAST LONDON

SE1: Bermondsey

Simon the Tanner

231 Long Lane, SE1 4PR

☎ (020) 7357 8740 🌐 simonthetanner.co.uk

4 changing beers (often Anspach & Hobday, Firehouse, Henry Smith) Ⓗ

In a quiet road just off busy Bermondsey Street, the Simon is a mid-terrace, modestly-sized Grade II listed pub. A former Shepherd Neame outlet, it is now a free house. The regularly changing real ales are from small breweries, and there is also real cider. Food includes Scotch eggs, vegetarian bar snacks, burgers, and cheese and meat sharing platters or a three-course dinner, with roast on Sunday. A quiz is held on a Tuesday. Children are welcome until early evening.

SE1: Borough

King's Arms

65 Newcomen Street, SE1 1YT

☎ (020) 7407 1132 🌐 kingsarmsborough.co.uk

Harvey's Sussex Best Bitter; Purity Mad Goose; Timothy Taylor Landlord; Truman's Swift; 1 changing beer (often Five Points, Theakston) Ⓗ

A Grade II listed single-bar pub just off the busy Borough High Street, with a traditional and comfortable historic interior. The striking plaque above the entrance originally adorned the old London Bridge. Five cask beers are usually on tap and traditional, mainly British, meals are served lunchtimes and evenings. Closed on Sunday. (London Bridge)

Libertine ✔

125 Great Suffolk Street, SE1 1PQ

☎ (020) 7378 7877 🌐 thelibertine.co.uk

Sharp's Doom Bar; 2 changing beers (often Signature, Twickenham) Ⓗ

Originally a Whitbread house, this lively and spacious pub is popular with a mix of workers, locals and students. The food offering specialises in pizzas and there is a discount for students on Monday and Wednesday. The pub hosts live music or a DJ Thursday to Sunday evenings and a quiz on Tuesday. Major sporting events are also shown and there is a dartboard.

Royal Oak ✔

44 Tabard Street, SE1 4JU

☎ (020) 7357 7173 🌐 royaloaklondon.co.uk

Harvey's Dark Mild, IPA, Sussex Best Bitter, Armada Ale; 3 changing beers (often Harvey's) Ⓗ

A charming back-to-basics drinkers' pub separated into two sections by the bar counter and an off-sales hatch. This is Sussex-based Harvey's Brewery's first London tied house and is renowned for friendly and attentive service. A wide range of beers includes seasonal brews and, unusually for London, a mild. The pub is something of a local institution, with regulars coming from miles around to spend time here. (London Bridge)

SE1: Borough Market

Barrowboy & Banker

6-8 Borough High Street, SE1 9QQ

☎ (020) 7403 5415

Dark Star Hophead; Fuller's Oliver's Island, London Pride, ESB; 2 changing beers (often Fuller's, Wimbledon) Ⓗ

The interior of this busy Fuller's Ale & Pie establishment retains much of the opulence from its time as the first branch of the National Westminster Bank. The double-height ceiling and enormous windows provide a sense of spaciousness. A sweeping staircase leads up to one of two dining areas, with an extensive menu, including chef's specials, available daily. Major non-football sporting events are shown. The pub is handily located for Southwark Cathedral, Borough Market and the many Bankside tourist attractions.
(London Bridge)

Globe
8 Bedale Street, SE1 9AL
☎ (020) 7407 0043 🌐 theglobeboroughmarket.com
5 changing beers (often Sambrook's) [H]
In the heart of Borough Market, this venue dates from 1872, built in a Gothic revival style by Henry Jarvis. It is featured in two films – Blue Ice and Bridget Jones's Diary. The cask beers are often from local breweries and there is a wide choice of bottles and cans. The upstairs restaurant offers a high-quality menu, with options for vegetarians. (London Bridge)

Old King's Head
King's Head Yard, 45-49 Borough High Street, SE1 1NA
☎ (020) 7407 1550 🌐 theoldkingshead.uk.com
Harvey's Sussex Best Bitter; St Austell Tribute, Proper Job; Sharp's Doom Bar; 2 changing beers (often Harvey's) [H]
A traditional hostelry down a narrow, cobbled lane off Borough High Street. Stained-glass windows hint at a bygone era and the pictures adorning the walls tell the story of a pub, and an area, that has a rich history. The layout inside is simple, with an L-shaped bar in one corner usually offering six real ales on handpump. The clientele is a mix of tourists, office workers and visitors to the nearby Borough Market.
(London Bridge)

Rake
14 Winchester Walk, SE1 9AG
☎ (020) 7407 0557
4 changing beers (sourced nationally) [H]
On the edge of Borough Market, this small bar prides itself on offering a high-quality, varied beer selection, and over the years has become a real global destination for beer aficionados and brewers. Four handpumps are complemented by a comprehensive range of bottled beers, mainly from North America and Europe, plus a small range of wines and spirits. Beer festivals, brewery tap takeovers and other themed beer selections all feature. Q (London Bridge)

SE1: Southwark

Ring
72 Blackfriars Road, SE1 8HA
☎ (020) 7620 0811 🌐 theringbarlondon.co.uk
Sharp's Doom Bar; 4 changing beers (often East London, Sharp's) [H]
A pleasant bar named after the boxing arena that stood opposite the pub during the early part of the 20th century, with boxers calling in for a drink before and after bouts. It has a gym and a ring upstairs, and pictures of the rich local boxing history adorn the walls. Additional outdoor seating is located on the pavement. Major sporting events on terrestrial TV are shown.
(Waterloo/Waterloo East)

SE1: Waterloo

King's Arms [L]
25 Roupell Street, SE1 8TB
☎ (020) 7207 0784 🌐 thekingsarmslondon.co.uk
Adnams Southwold Bitter; house beer (by Sharp's); 7 changing beers (sourced nationally) [H]
Tucked away in a back street, this popular pub is worth seeking out, and it gets busy in the early evenings. It has been identified by CAMRA as having a regionally important historic pub interior. Two small rooms are separated by a central bar and there is also space for drinking outside at the front. Nine real ales usually include two or more from London breweries and at least one dark beer. To the rear is a Thai restaurant.
(Waterloo/Waterloo East)

Waterloo Tap
Arch 147, Sutton Walk, SE1 7ES
☎ (020) 3455 7436 🌐 waterlootap.com
5 changing beers (often East London, Siren) [A]
This fairly compact, modern sister pub to the Euston Tap is in a railway arch close to Waterloo station and a short stroll from the South Bank, making it handy for visitors to the BFI IMAX and Royal Festival Hall complex. The cask ales are all dispensed from taps mounted on the copper bar-back. Details of the current beers are listed on a blackboard above the bar.

SE3: Blackheath

Hare & Billet ✓
1A Eliot Cottages, Hare & Billet Road, SE3 0QJ
☎ (020) 8852 2352 🌐 hareandbillet.com
Greene King IPA; house beer (by Greene King); 6 changing beers (often Old Dairy, Sambrook's, Twickenham) [H]
An inn of this name has existed on the site since at least 1732, though the current building dates from the 19th century. The decor is faux-Victorian in a contemporary style, with stripped natural finish wood cladding and bare floorboards. Up to eight real ales may be on offer. Plastic glasses are used in summer for outdoor drinking overlooking the heath's open expanse. The pub part-sponsors the cleaning and maintenance of the pond opposite. (380)

SE4: Brockley

Brockley Barge ✓
184 Brockley Road, SE4 2RR
☎ (020) 8694 7690
Greene King IPA, Abbot; Sharp's Doom Bar; 5 changing beers (often Portobello, Sambrook's, Twickenham) [H]
A former Courage public house, now part of the Wetherspoon chain, a stone's throw from the railway station. It is a popular, thriving hub whose clientele reflects the vibrant local area. The premises are laid out in a semi-horseshoe shape with a variety of seating spaces. A small courtyard to the south side is well used in the summer. The name comes thanks to the former Croydon Canal, which was where the railway line now runs. Q

SE4: Crofton Park

London Beer Dispensary
389 Brockley Road, SE4 2PH
☎ (020) 8694 6962
House beer (by Southey); 2 changing beers (often Siren, Southey) [H]
This former wine bar is one of the handful of Beer Dispensary premises run by Penge-based Southey Brewery. A bar counter was added in 2019 and now sports a set of handpumps, one of which serves a real cider. The changing guest beer is usually from a microbrewery. The bar is popular with families; children are welcome until the evening. Various burgers on the menu include vegetarian and vegan options. Meal deals are available most evenings.

SE5: Camberwell

Hermits Cave

28 Camberwell Church Street, SE5 8QU
☎ (020) 7703 3188
Dark Star Hophead; 4 changing beers (often Five Points) Ⓗ
An imposing corner pub run by the same family for 25 years and popular with a cross-section of local residents and art college students. The premises have remained essentially unchanged, with etched windows and wooden floors adding to the traditional feel. A corner TV provides the only distraction to convivial conversation. Guest beers come from independent breweries. Three real ciders on handpump increase to five during summer months. An impressive range of whiskies includes examples from Wales and Japan.
♿⇌⊖(Denmark Hill) ●P🚌🐾

SE5: Denmark Hill

Fox on the Hill ✔

149 Denmark Hill, SE5 8EH
☎ (020) 7738 4756
Fuller's London Pride; Greene King Abbot; Ruddles Best Bitter; Sharp's Doom Bar; 5 changing beers (often By the Horns, Sambrook's) Ⓗ
An attractive, brick-built Wetherspoon opposite Ruskin Park. A series of rooms, with quiet alcoves and screened booths, surrounds a central bar area. Framed prints celebrate the numerous historic figures and notable thinkers who lived nearby, often lending their names to the streets. A lawned area to the front affords views across to central London and there are spacious gardens at the rear. The pub is popular when Dulwich Hamlet FC are playing at home. ✿◑♿⇌⊖●P🚌📶

SE8: Deptford

Brookmill

65 Cranbrook Road, SE8 4EJ
☎ (020) 8333 0899 🌐 thebrookmill.co.uk
3 changing beers (often Brixton, Brockley, Wimbledon) Ⓗ
Spacious Victorian corner pub, reopened under new management in 2016. Much of the original exterior survives but the interior has been modernised and now has a more contemporary feel, with bare-board flooring and partly exposed brickwork. There is an outdoor area and also an upstairs function room. Good-quality food is served daily. The changing selection of real ales tends to favour local south London brews.
Q✿◑⇌(St Johns) ⊖(Elverson Rd) ♣🚌(47,225) 🐾📶

Dog & Bell 🏆 L ✔

116 Prince Street, SE8 3JD
☎ (020) 8692 5664
Fuller's London Pride; 5 changing beers (often Clarkshaws, Dent, Old Dairy) Ⓗ
A Guide stalwart for over 30 years, this is a traditional and welcoming pub down a side street a short stroll from the centre of Deptford. Complementing six real ales is a selection of Belgian bottled beers, malt whiskies and simple, tasty meals. A lively bar and a real fire in winter greet a good mixed clientele including locals, cyclists and those strolling along the nearby Thames Path. Regular beer festivals are often themed around the UK patron saints' days. Q✿◑⇌♣🚌🐾

Job Centre ✔

120 Deptford High Street, SE8 4NS
☎ (020) 8692 6859 🌐 jobcentredeptford.com
Volden Session Ale; 2 changing beers (often Brixton, Brockley, Thornbridge) Ⓗ
Opened by Antic in 2014 and named after a former occupier of the premises. The surprisingly spacious rectangular bar area has minimalist decor that could best be described as industrial shabby-chic, featuring bare concrete flooring and exposed ducts and pipework. Take note that the toilets are up a fairly steep flight of stairs. Music is often playing from a twin-deck turntable. The beer range has a mainly regional focus. Food is varied and includes light bites and burgers.
✿◑⇌⊖(Deptford Bridge) 🚌🐾📶

SE9: Eltham

Long Pond L

110 Westmount Road, SE9 1UT
☎ (020) 8331 6767
House beer (by Tonbridge); 5 changing beers (often Hop Fuzz, Pig & Porter, Tonbridge) Ⓖ
A micropub in a former plumbers' merchants and named after the pond in nearby Eltham Park North. Mainly Kentish ales are served from a rear, chilled stillage room. Wine, several gins, a malt whisky and Dudda's Tun real cider or perry are also sold, with limited bar snacks. Seating is mainly at high benches and tables, though the rear snug features low tables and chairs. Winner of several local CAMRA awards. Children and dogs are not admitted. Q♿⇌●🚌(B16)

Park Tavern ✔

45 Passey Place, SE9 5DA
☎ (020) 8850 3216 🌐 parktaverneltham.co.uk
8 changing beers (often Crafty Brewing, Stonehenge, Whitstable) Ⓗ
Traditional Victorian pub with an original Truman's Brewery tiled frontage and signage. The compact interior has an L-shaped bar with stylish lamps and chandeliers. Etched windows feature elegant drapes, and decorative plates and pictures line the walls. Light background music is played. There is a well-kept, heated rear garden and further seating to the front and side. Alongside the range of real ales is an impressive selection of craft kegs and lagers, whiskies and wine. ✿◑⇌🚌🐾

Rusty Bucket

11 Court Yard, SE9 5PR
☎ 07776 145990 🌐 therustybucket.pub
3 changing beers (often Kent, Oakham, Siren) Ⓖ
This venue reopened in 2018 after the redevelopment of the former Crown pub, retaining the original frontage. Inside, the walls are half-panelled and brightly painted. The place is run along micropub lines by a couple of friends who are enthusiastic and knowledgeable about beers. The cask ales and some real ciders are dispensed from a walk-in chilled cellar cupboard. A host of other draught, bottled and canned beers is on offer. Live music sessions are held on Sundays. ♿⇌♣●🚌🐾📶

SE10: East Greenwich

River Ale House

131 Woolwich Road, SE10 0RJ
☎ 07963 127595
7 changing beers (often East London, Kent, Siren) Ⓗ/Ⓖ
A converted shop unit opened in 2017 in the micropub style, comprising two rooms with a rustic feel and a small step between them. Real ales and ciders are dispensed from a temperature-controlled cellar room behind the bar counter. Wines and spirits are available too. This friendly, family-run house, where conversations

with strangers are inevitable, has quickly become a part of the local community and has developed a wider following too. Local CAMRA branch Pub of the Year 2019. Q♿⇌(Westcombe Park) ♣●▯▯🐾≋

SE10: Greenwich

Morden Arms

1 Brand Street, SE10 8SP

☎ (020) 8858 2189

Truman's Runner; house beer (by Banks's); 3 changing beers (often Truman's) Ⓗ

Unpretentious, without an external pub sign or even name, this ex-Courage corner house is now an independent venue with a strong orientation to live music. One of a dying breed of back-street boozers in the area, it has a clientele of locals and music lovers. A free cheeseboard is available on Sunday and cribbage night is on Monday. The beer range is mainly from Truman's, with other local guest beers appearing occasionally.
❀⇌⊖♣▯🐾≋

Plume of Feathers ✔

19 Park Vista, SE10 9LZ

☎ (020) 8858 1661 🌐 plumeoffeathers-greenwich.co.uk

Adnams Southwold Bitter; Harvey's Sussex Best Bitter; 2 changing beers (often Pig & Porter, West Berkshire) Ⓗ

With parts dating from 1691, this cosy and quiet historic tavern sits opposite the northern wall of Greenwich Park, close to the National Maritime Museum. The maritime association is reflected inside the bar with much memorabilia on display and interesting historical paintings. Bar meals are served and there is a separate restaurant to the rear. Afternoon tea can be booked in advance for a minimum of eight people. Outside is a pleasant garden area. The pub has a football team, the Plume Rockets, and a golf society.
❀◐⇌(Maze Hill) ⊖(Cutty Sark) ▯🐾≋

SE11: Kennington

Mansion House ✔

48 Kennington Park Road, SE11 4RS

☎ (020) 7582 5599 🌐 oakalondon.com

Oakham JHB, Inferno, Citra, Bishops Farewell; 1 changing beer (often Gale's, Oakham) Ⓗ

Oakham Ales' flagship pub in London was previously a cocktail lounge and piano bar. A modern interior with an oriental flavour is styled 'Oaka at the Mansion House', a setting for enjoying pan-Asian meals served by attentive staff. During the summer, the front glass doors open out on to the outside seating area. One guest or seasonal Oakham beer complements the permanent range. Discounted cask beers are on the bar in the early evening. ◐♿⇌(Elephant & Castle)⊖▯🐾≋

Old Red Lion ✔

42 Kennington Park Road, SE11 4RS

☎ (020) 7735 4312 🌐 theoldredlion.com

4 changing beers (often Volden) Ⓗ

A Grade II listed twin-bar Antic venue with plenty of character and a fine example of the Brewers' Tudor style, having been rebuilt by Charrington in around 1929. Identified by CAMRA as having a regionally important historic interior, it has many original features including exposed wooden beams, fireplaces and low doors connecting the bars. There are usually two varying real ciders. Monthly quiz and folk music nights are held; often there is background music.
❀◐⇌(Elephant & Castle) ⊖●▯🐾≋

SE13: Lewisham

Suttons Radio

139-141 Lewisham High Street, SE13 6AA

☎ (020) 8463 0725 🌐 suttonsradio.com

Volden Session Ale; 2 changing beers (often Bristol Beer Factory, East London, Volden) Ⓗ

The name of this Antic pub, in the heart of the Lewisham street-market area, was taken from an old shop sign belonging to a previous business and discovered during renovation works. Hence the various quirky displays of period radiograms, music centres and radios. Also note the large illuminated map extracted from Charles Booth's London poverty map series. Real ales and the cider are well kept. The bar counter is constructed from old snooker table slate. ◗♿⇌⊖♣●▯🐾≋

SE14: New Cross

Royal Albert ✔

460 New Cross Road, SE14 6TJ

☎ (020) 8692 3737 🌐 royalalbertpub.com

Volden Session Ale; 7 changing beers (often Bristol Beer Factory, Five Points, Moor Beer) Ⓗ

This Grade II listed Victorian inn, retaining the original etched-glass windows and bar-back, has a convivial atmosphere and offers one real cider on handpump as well as a cask beer range that always includes one of Antic's Volden brews. Furnishings and decor are an eclectic mix, and the food is distinctive and enticing. There is a quiz on Monday evening, a DJ on Friday and live music on Sunday. The pub is popular with local academia. ❀◐⇌⊖♣●▯🐾≋

SE15: Nunhead

Beer Shop London

40 Nunhead Green, SE15 3QF

☎ (020) 7732 5555 🌐 thebeershoplondon.co.uk

3 changing beers (often Anspach & Hobday, Moor Beer, Squawk) Ⓖ

A former corner shop, haberdashery, and latterly a recording studio. The knowledgeable staff serve a varied selection of three real ales direct from the cask, along with an extensive range of bottled beers, plus wine, spirits and soft drinks. Boxed cider, from various producers, is also on offer, as are snacks. Events such as Meet the Brewer evenings are hosted on occasion.
❀♿⇌●▯(78,P12) 🐾≋

SE16: Rotherhithe

Mayflower

117 Rotherhithe Street, SE16 4NF

☎ (020) 7237 4088 🌐 mayflowerpub.co.uk

House beer (by Greene King); 5 changing beers (often Bexley, St Austell) Ⓗ

This nautical-themed pub celebrates the Mayflower's historic journey taking the Pilgrim Fathers to New England. Those with a family connection may sign the Mayflower Descendants Book. The interior is in the style of a 17th-century tavern and at the rear is a wooden jetty over the River Thames. This is a popular place for tourists and the only pub licensed to sell UK and US postage stamps. The house beer is the appropriately named Scurvy Ale. Q❀◐⊖●▯(381,C10)

SE18: Shooters Hill

Bull

151 Shooters Hill, SE18 3HP

☎ (020) 8856 0691

3 changing beers (often Exmoor, Greene King, Long Man) [H]
On the brow of a hill, this reputedly haunted Grade II listed premises was rebuilt in 1881. It retains separate public and saloon bars with individual street entrance doors, and a central circular bar counter serving both rooms. The saloon bar is well appointed, whereas the public bar has a more basic appearance. There is a pool table and occasional live music events are held. The licensee makes good use of his pub company's beer range. 🐴❀♣🚌🐾📶

SE19: Crystal Palace

Westow House ✔
79 Westow Hill, SE19 1TX
☎ (020) 8670 0654 🌐 westowhouse.com
Adnams Ghost Ship; Volden Session Ale; 5 changing beers (often Arbor, Marble, Volden) [H]
Large Victorian corner hostelry bordering the edge of the Crystal Palace triangle, with a varied clientele. Antic's style of vintage shabby-chic provides a warm ambience and there is a spacious, partly covered outdoor seating area at the front. Up to seven cask ales are complemented by changing ciders. The pub hosts regular live music, particularly on Friday, and a quiz on Tuesday evening. The pinball machine and table football are both enthusiastically used. 🐴❀◐⇌⊖♣●🚌🐾📶

SE22: East Dulwich

East Dulwich Tavern ✔
1 Lordship Lane, SE22 8EW
☎ (020) 8693 1316 🌐 eastdulwichtavern.com
Dark Star Hophead; Volden Session Ale; 4 changing beers (often Brick, Truman's, Twickenham) [H]
An imposing building in a prominent corner position and the home of the Antic pub company. The interior is classic boozer, but in tune with the times and alive with customers. Previously a hotel, the upper storeys are now offices, although the first-floor masonic hall with its own bar opens occasionally for music and events, including a monthly film club. There is usually real cider during summer months, and good-quality food is on offer.
🐴❀◐♿⇌♣●🚌🐾📶

SE23: Forest Hill

Blythe Hill Tavern ★
319 Stanstead Road, SE23 1JB
☎ (020) 8690 5176 🌐 blythehilltavern.org.uk
Dark Star Hophead; Harvey's Sussex Best Bitter; Sharp's Doom Bar; 2 changing beers (often Brockley, St Austell) [H]
A multiple award-winning house, this friendly Victorian local has an unusual three-bar layout, identified by CAMRA as a nationally important historic pub interior. Usually five cask beers and up to 13 real ciders are on sale. In two of the bars TV screens show sporting events, especially horse racing. Live traditional Irish music is performed on Thursday evening and there are regular poetry nights. The pretty rear garden includes a children's play area.
Q🐴❀⇌(Catford/Catford Bridge) ●🚌🐾📶

SE25: South Norwood

Shelverdine Goathouse 𝕃 ✔
7-9 High Street, SE25 6EP
☎ (020) 8916 1001 🌐 shelverdinegoathouse.com
Volden Session Ale; 5 changing beers (sourced nationally) [H]
Modern Antic pub with three distinct areas, all with large windows overlooking the High Street. These are decorated in different styles: kitchen equipment, clocks and pictures. Guest beers are selected from around the country but often come from London breweries. A home fan-only policy operates when Crystal Palace are playing. Check social media for regular real ale club events, quiz nights and live music. ◐♿⇌⊖(Norwood Jct)♣🚌🐾📶

Addiscombe

Claret & Ale
5 Bingham Corner, Lower Addiscombe Road, CR0 7AA
☎ (020) 8656 7452
Palmers IPA; 5 changing beers (sourced nationally) [H]
Small, privately owned and friendly free house around the corner from Addiscombe tram stop, making its 33rd appearance in this Guide. The Claret is a community pub where conversation is king. The changing beers come from all over the UK, and mainly from microbreweries. A board opposite the bar indicates beers that are on and coming up. Up to four draught ciders are also stocked, served from the cellar. Events are held regularly to raise money for charity. ♿🚊●▯🚌🐾📶

Barnehurst

Bird & Barrel 𝕃
100 Barnehurst Road, DA7 6HG
Bexley Own Beer, Redhouse Premium; house beer (by Bexley); 2 changing beers (sourced nationally; often Bexley) [H]
A micropub opened in 2018 in a former tropical fish emporium close to Barnehurst Station. In effect this is a Bexley Brewery tap – one guest beer complements two of the brewery's ales. House beer Hills & Holes is named after the old name of the lane serving the station. Seating is at a handful of standard-height tables and there is a decent-sized beer garden. Three keg beers and wines and spirits are also sold here. Last orders are 20 minutes before closing time. Q🐴❀⇌●🚌🐾📶

Beckenham

Bricklayers Arms ✔
237 High Street, BR3 1BN
☎ (020) 8402 0007 🌐 bricklayersarms.co
St Austell Tribute, Proper Job; Young's London Special; 1 changing beer (sourced nationally) [H]
Traditional local high-street pub providing a friendly welcome to a clientele of all ages. There is an open log fire in winter and a covered outdoor seating area with heaters and even a TV screen. The changing guest ales often reflect customers' recommendations, and occasional beer festivals are held. Sunday hours apply on most bank holidays. Sit under the super-lifesize Spider Man if you dare!
🐴❀⇌(Junction/Clock House) 🚊(Junction) ♣●🚌🐾📶

Bexley

Black Horse ✔
63 Albert Road, DA5 1NT
☎ (01322) 523371
Harvey's Sussex Best Bitter; Whitstable East India Pale Ale; 2 changing beers (often Courage, Harvey's) [H]
A friendly back-street local, convenient for buses. The front bar extends on both sides from the main door. Through a rear door at the right, the smaller Posh Bar service area, decorated with Italian Job artist's prints, looks out on to a garden with a small goldfish pond. Activities include monthly live music, an open mic night

the first Tuesday of every month, darts on Tuesday, poker on Wednesday, and a quiz on the first and third Thursdays. Mind the step down to the Gents.
Q❀◐⇌♣🚌🐾

Bexleyheath

Furze Wren ✔

6 Market Place, Broadway Square, DA6 7DY
☎ (020) 8298 2590
Greene King Abbot; Ruddles Best Bitter; Sharp's Doom Bar; 7 changing beers (often Brains, Courage, Ringwood) Ⓗ
Spacious Wetherspoon establishment named after a local bird, better known as the Dartford Warbler. The pub is at the heart of the shopping area, with buses serving every route through town. Plenty of seating and large windows make it a great place to eat, drink and people-watch; it attracts a full mix of clientele. Local history panels are displayed around the pub. Alcoholic drinks are served from 9am. Q🐎❀◐◑♿♣🍎🚌📶

Kentish Belle

8 Pickford Lane, DA7 4QW
☎ (020) 3417 2050 🌐 thekentishbelle.co.uk
7 changing beers (often Arbor, No Frills Joe, Thornbridge) Ⓖ
The sole micropub in Bexleyheath for now, next to the station, with solid walnut furniture and an Art Deco feel. William Morris wallpaper is a nod to the artist, whose home is just under a mile away at the Red House. Regular events include tap takeovers, quiz nights and mini festivals. Beers from near and far, and ciders and perries, are poured in a chilled cellar room with festival-size capacity. CAMRA Greater London Regional Cider Pub of the Year 2019. Q🐎⇌♣🍎P📺🚌🐾📶

Robin Hood & Little John 🏆 Ⓛ

78 Lion Road, DA6 8PF
☎ (020) 8303 1128 🌐 robinhoodbexleyheath.co.uk
Adnams Southwold Bitter; Bexley Own Beer; Fuller's London Pride; Harvey's Sussex Best Bitter; Shepherd Neame Whitstable Bay Pale Ale; 3 changing beers (often Bexley, Shepherd Neame, Westerham) Ⓗ
A back-street local dating from the 1830s when it was surrounded by fields. The real ales come mostly from independent breweries including Bexley. The pub has a good reputation for its home-cooked lunchtime meals (no food Sun) with Italian specials, which can be eaten at tables made from old Singer sewing machines. A frequent local CAMRA branch Pub of the Year and regional winner three times. The year 2020 marks 40 years of Ray and Katerina running this pub. Over-21s only. Q❀◐🚌(B13)🐾

Blackfen

Broken Drum Ⓛ

308 Westwood Lane, DA15 9PT
☎ 07803 131678 🌐 thebrokendrum.co.uk
3 changing beers (sourced nationally) Ⓖ
A micropub named after an inn in a Terry Pratchett novel. Seating comprises a settle in each of the bay windows and a variety of tables and chairs, plus pavement tables and chairs for fair-weather drinking. Cheesy Thursday is the first Thursday of each month. With occasional quizzes and excursions, this is a real community pub. Society for the Preservation of Beers from the Wood London Pub of the Year 2018 and local CAMRA Pub of the Year 2018.
Q🐎♣🍎P📺🚌(51,132)🐾📶

George Staples ✔

273 Blackfen Road, DA15 8PR
☎ (020) 8850 3181
Fuller's London Pride; Sharp's Doom Bar; 4 changing beers (sourced nationally) Ⓗ
The Woodman, originally dating from 1845 and one of the first buildings in Blackfen, was demolished and rebuilt in 1931 by Reffells Brewery. Renamed after the original landlord in 2007 and refurbished again in 2018, this is a large, comfortable, single-roomed pub/sports bar with sports TV screens in all parts. It has a buy five, get one free loyalty scheme. There is plenty of outdoor seating, mainly on artificial grass, with pleasant lighting and plants on the walls. 🐎❀◐◑♿🍎P🚌(51,132)🐾📶

Bromley

Partridge

194 High Street, BR1 1HE
☎ (020) 8464 7656 🌐 partridgebromley.co.uk
Dark Star Hophead; Fuller's London Pride, ESB; Gale's HSB; 2 changing beers (often Butcombe, Fuller's) Ⓗ
Grade II listed former National Provincial Bank, now a Fuller's Ale & Pie House, retaining many original features including the high ceilings and chandeliers. There are two small snug rooms off the main bar. An upmarket menu includes vegetarian choices. Located by the Market Square, the pub is popular with shoppers and for live music on Saturday nights. A refurbishment is planned, with the real ale range increasing from six to eight choices. Q🐎❀◐◑♿⇌(North/South)🚌🐾📶

Red Lion ✔

10 North Road, BR1 3LG
☎ (020) 8460 2691 🌐 redlionbromley.co.uk
Greene King IPA, Abbot; Harvey's Sussex Best Bitter; 2 changing beers (often Black Sheep, Jennings, Oakham) Ⓗ
A traditional, well-kept venue in the quiet back streets just north of Bromley town centre. The only pub in the borough to have featured in every edition of this Guide since the local branch was formed in 2011, the Red Lion is well worth seeking out. It retains many original features, including tiling. An extensive library of books dominates one wall. A range of good-value meals is served and a real fire keeps you warm in winter.
Q❀◐◑⇌(North)♣🚌

Star & Garter 🏆

227 High Street, BR1 1NZ
☎ (020) 3730 9458
7 changing beers (often Bristol Beer Factory, Fyne Ales, Siren) Ⓗ
A late 19th-century Grade II listed pub, reopened in 2016 after more than two years' closure and offering real ale for the first time. Completely refurbished, it now boasts eight handpumps, one of which frequently dispenses real cider. Real ales are usually non-mainstream, with local and regional microbreweries strongly represented. Customers are welcome to order in food from local takeaways. Local CAMRA Pub of the Year 2018-2020.
Q🐎♿⇌(North/South)🍎🚌🐾📶

Chelsfield

Five Bells ✔

Church Road, BR6 7RE TQ482682
☎ (01689) 821044 🌐 thefivebells-chelsfieldvillage.co.uk
Courage Best Bitter; 3 changing beers (often Otter, Timothy Taylor, Young's) Ⓗ
At the centre of an unspoilt 17th-century village, this inn is at the heart of the local community and retains a rural

feel despite being just inside the M25 (use the nearby junction 4). It retains a traditional public bar, with separate entrances providing access to the saloon and dining areas. Guest beers sometimes come from small local breweries and at least one beer festival is held every year. The large garden has a children's play area.
Q❀◑♣P🚌(R7) 🐾📶

Crayford

Penny Farthing

3 Waterside, DA1 4JJ
☎ 07772 866645 🌐 pennyfarthingcrayford.co.uk
4 changing beers (often Old Dairy, Wantsum, Whitstable) G
Bexley's second micropub, opened in 2014. Ale and cider are served from a cold room with a viewing window. A charity fine is levied should your mobile phone ring. Kentish brewers feature mostly, with an increasing cider range supplementing Dudda's Tun and Westons. Pavement seating during summer overlooks a small riverside park. Usually open bank holidays, this is a good venue from which to watch local public events. Local CAMRA Pub of the Year and London regional runner-up in 2018. Q❀≉♣🍎🚌🐾

Croydon

Cronx

Units 3 & 4, Boxpark Croydon, 99 George Street, CR0 1LD
☎ (020) 8688 4912 🌐 thecronx.com
House beer (by Cronx); 6 changing beers (often Cronx) H
A modern micropub-sized bar, part of Croydon's Boxpark development beside East Croydon station, accessed from Dingwall Road. Six handpumps serve a range of mainly Cronx beers, and a real cider, while 10 keg taps dispense a varying selection of Cronx and non-mainstream brewery beers. The decor is simple but stylish, employing scaffolding and adapted beer casks. Beer is served in plastic glasses to customers taking their drinks out into the Boxpark complex, where food can be bought.
♿≉(East) 🍎🚌📶

Dog & Bull ✔

24 Surrey Street, CR0 1RG
☎ (020) 8667 9718 🌐 dogandbullcroydon.co.uk
Young's London Original, London Special; 2 changing beers (sourced nationally) H
This historic Grade II listed pub with an island bar and stained-glass windows is a favourite with local traders as well as visitors to the Surrey Street market. The large garden is unexpected, and has been brought up to date with booths equipped with TV, large awnings and a bar and barbecue in the summer. A small upstairs function room is available for hire.
❀◑≉(East/West) (George St/Reeves Corner) ⊖(West) 🚌🐾📶

George ✔

17-21 George Street, CR0 1LA
☎ (020) 8649 9077
Burning Sky Plateau, Aurora; Greene King IPA, Abbot; Sharp's Doom Bar; Thornbridge Jaipur IPA; 9 changing beers (often Surrey Hills, Tillingbourne) H
A converted shop, this town-centre pub is named after a former Croydon coaching inn, the George & Dragon. It has two bars – the rear one is raised (with a ramp for access) and lined with booths, and has six handpumps often showcasing beers from breweries such as Dark Star, Oakham, Saltaire and Thornbridge. The front bar offers a wider mix of beers, including real ales from local breweries and the Wetherspoon national range.
◑♿≉(East/West) (George St/Reeves Corner) ⊖(West) 🍎🚌📶

Green Dragon ✔

58 High Street, CR0 1NA
☎ (020) 8667 0684
8 changing beers H
A converted bank with a modern twist, the pub boasts a vast range of ales and other draught beers from local and national breweries, as well as ciders. Located between the historic Surrey Street market and the south Croydon restaurant quarter, it attracts a wide clientele. The upstairs function room hosts weekly events such as quizzes, poker and open mic nights.
◑♿≉(East/West) (George St/Reeves Corner) ⊖(West) ♣🍎🚌📶

Skylark ✔

34-36 South End, CR0 1DP
☎ (020) 8649 9909
Greene King Abbot; Ruddles Best Bitter; Sharp's Doom Bar; 6 changing beers H
A spacious Wetherspoon in the restaurant quarter south of the town centre. The main bar is wood-panelled, with a raised library area to the rear. The decor includes pictures of nearby former Croydon airport, London's first civil airport. A grand staircase at the rear leads to an upstairs bar, not always in use and offering a reduced range of beers. Changing ales are mainly from microbreweries, often local ones.
❀◑♿≉(South) 🍎🚌📶

Spreadeagle

39-41 Katharine Street, CR0 1NX
☎ (020) 8781 1134 🌐 spreadeaglecroydon.co.uk
Fuller's Oliver's Island, London Pride, ESB; Gale's HSB; 2 changing beers H
Large street-corner pub built in 1893 as a bank. The spacious interior boasts wood panelling, high ceilings, glass mirrors and an imposing staircase leading up to two function rooms, one occasionally used as a 50-seater theatre/cinema. As well as real ale from six handpumps, a good range of other draught and bottled beers is on offer. The pub has Fuller's Master Cellarman accreditation. Quiz night is Sunday. Occasional events are held in the upstairs theatre.
❀◑♿≉(East/West) (George St/Reeves Corner) ⊖(West) 🚌📶

Downe

Queen's Head ✔

25 High Street, BR6 7US TQ432616
☎ (01689) 852145 🌐 queensheaddowne.com
Fuller's London Pride; 3 changing beers (often Adnams, Westerham) H
Attractive and traditional venue with open fireplaces, dating from 1565 and named following a visit by Queen Elizabeth I. Though situated in the centre of this historic country village, it is less than 20 minutes by bus from Bromley or Orpington. It may have enjoyed the patronage of Charles Darwin, who lived locally at Down House. There are several dining areas benefiting from a daily menu including home-made pies. The pub is popular with walkers all year round.
❀◑♣🍎P🚌(146,R8) 🐾📶

Hayes

Real Ale Way L

55 Station Approach, BR2 7EB

☎ 07446 897885 🌐 therealaleway.com

House beer (by Tonbridge); 9 changing beers (often Larkins, Mad Cat, Whitstable) G

Opened in July 2018, this family-owned micropub offers a welcome new choice for local drinkers and rail commuters alike. It overlooks the entrance to Hayes station, and numerous local bus routes stop outside. Up to nine Kentish real ales are served from a cold room. The Kent theme extends to the wines and spirits, as well as to the bar snacks. The premises, once a bank and more recently an accountancy office, are quite large by micropub standards. Q≋●🚌🐾

Keston

Greyhound ✔

Commonside, BR2 6BP TQ413646

☎ (01689) 856338 🌐 greyhoundkeston.co.uk

Sharp's Doom Bar; Timothy Taylor Landlord; 4 changing beers (sourced nationally) H

A popular local with an enthusiastic and welcoming landlord. It overlooks the common and is on walking routes including the London Outer Orbital Path, but is also easily accessed by bus from Bromley. The pub is at the heart of village life, with a crowded calendar of local events, detailed in the newsletter. A beer festival is held during the Easter weekend, when up to 15 non-mainstream beers can be enjoyed.

Q🍴❀◑♣●P🚌(146,246) 🐾📶

Orpington

Orpington Liberal Club L

7 Station Road, BR6 0RZ

☎ (01689) 820882 🌐 orpingtonliberalclub.co.uk

4 changing beers (sourced nationally) H

Friendly club serving a changing selection of beers (over 200 different real ales every year) mainly from smaller breweries. Real cider and bottled lower-alcohol and gluten-free beers are also available. Two real ale festivals are held each year. The club is a hub of the local community, hosting many events in its spacious hall and supporting local charities. It reached the last four in the CAMRA 2020 National Club of the Year competition. A CAMRA/NULC card is required for entry.

Q🍴❀≋♣●P▯🚌🐾📶

Petts Wood

One Inn the Wood L

209 Petts Wood Road, BR5 1LA

☎ 07799 535982 🌐 oneinnthewood.co.uk

House beer (by Tonbridge); 4 changing beers (often Kent, Ramsgate, Tonbridge) G

The first micropub in the local area, opened in a former wine bar near the station in 2014 and winner of several CAMRA awards. Seating is on benches, with a large woodland backdrop dominating the left-hand wall. Beer is served from a glass-fronted cool room. Wine, gin and soft drinks are also sold, together with a range of mainly locally produced snacks. Families and dogs are welcome.

Q🍴≋●🚌🐾

Selsdon

Golden Ark

186 Addington Road, CR2 8LB

☎ (020) 8651 0700

4 changing beers (sourced locally) H

A newish micropub in the main street, offering a full range of alcoholic drinks. Bottled and canned beers and cider are also available for off-sales. Boards detailing current beers are hung on the ceiling beam above the corner bar. The bar and some of the wooden tabletops have been artistically finished, and artworks adorn the walls. The pub has strong links with the local community.

Q🍴♿♣●🚌🐾

SOUTH-WEST LONDON

SW1: Belgravia

Antelope

22-24 Eaton Terrace, SW1W 8EZ

☎ (020) 7824 8512

Fuller's Oliver's Island, London Pride, ESB; Gale's Seafarers Ale; 1 changing beer (sourced nationally) H

Dating back to 1827, this Fuller's venue spent several years as a Nicholson's pub until 2005. Original preserved features include etched-glass windows, a side room used as a snug, and the central bar. This is an upmarket house and the clientele consists mainly of local professionals. The pub plays cricket matches against the Churchill Arms (Notting Hill). The upstairs bar and side room can be hired for functions. Q🍴◑⊖(Sloane Sq)🚌📶

Star Tavern

6 Belgrave Mews West, SW1X 8HT

☎ (020) 7235 3019

Fuller's London Pride, ESB; 3 changing beers (often Butcombe, Dark Star, Wimbledon) H

Down a mews, near embassies and rich in the history of the powerful and famous, this is rumoured to be the place where the Great Train Robbery was planned. A popular Fuller's pub where local residents, business people and embassy staff rub shoulders with casual visitors, it has featured in all 48 editions of this Guide. A Fuller's special brew or, now, a beer from the wood, may occasionally be served. Upstairs is a function room.

🍴◑⊖(Hyde Park Corner/Knightsbridge) ♣🚌🐾📶

SW1: Pimlico

Cask Pub & Kitchen

6 Charlwood Street, SW1V 2EE

☎ (020) 7630 7225 🌐 caskpubandkitchen.com

10 changing beers H

Formerly the Pimlico Tram, it was converted 10 years ago to a beer destination by new owners, who have since rescued several more pubs. Ten handpumps serve a changing choice of beers from selected microbreweries. A vast range of bottled beers from the UK and around the world complements some unusual keg offerings. Burgers feature on the weekday menu, with roasts on Sundays until late afternoon. Local CAMRA Pub of the Year 2019 and a runner-up several times.

❀◑≋(Victoria) ⊖🚌🐾📶

SW1: St James's

Red Lion ★

2 Duke of York Street, SW1Y 6JP

☎ (020) 7321 0782

Fuller's Oliver's Island, London Pride, ESB; Gale's Seafarers Ale; 2 changing beers (often Fuller's) H

Close to the upmarket shops in Jermyn Street, this is a deservedly celebrated little gem, worth visiting just for its nationally important historic pub interior and, in particular, its spectacular Victorian etched and cut mirrors and glass. The Grade II listed building dates from 1821 and was given a new frontage in 1871. With little space

inside, visitors often spill out on to the pavement. Beware of the precipitous steps down to the toilets. Food is served until late afternoon.
Q⊖◑⊕(Green Park/Piccadilly Circus)🚆🐾🕏

SW1: Victoria

Willow Walk 🗓 ✅
25 Wilton Road, SW1V 1LW
☎ (020) 7828 2953
Fuller's London Pride; Greene King IPA, Abbot; Sharp's Doom Bar; 6 changing beers ⊞
Ground-floor Wetherspoon conversion from a Woolworth's in 1999, extending from opposite the eastern side entrance to Victoria station back to Vauxhall Bridge Road, with entrances on both streets. Some wood panelling, a fairly low ceiling and subdued lighting create a warm atmosphere. Friendly and attentive staff look after a mixed clientele including families. There are usually some London-brewed guest beers. Alcoholic drinks are served from 9am. Q⊖◑◐&⇌⊖🍴🚆🕏

SW1: Westminster

Buckingham Arms
62 Petty France, SW1H 9EU
☎ (020) 7222 3386 ⊕ buckinghamarms.com
Young's London Original, London Gold, London Special; 3 changing beers (often Young's) ⊞
Said to have once been a hat shop, the Bell opened here in the 1720s. Renamed the Black Horse soon after, rebuilt in 1898, renamed again in 1901 and substantially renovated in recent years, this is another pub that has appeared in all 48 editions of the Guide. A mix of modern and traditional seats and tables draws civil servants, visitors and the occasional MP. Open during the day on Sunday from the end of March through the summer.
⊖◑⊖(St James's Park) 🚆

Speaker ✅
46 Great Peter Street, SW1P 2HA
☎ (020) 7222 4589 ⊕ speakervictoria.co.uk
Timothy Taylor Landlord; 4 changing beers (often London Brewing, Mad Squirrel, Reunion) ⊞
A friendly pine-panelled one-bar local decorated with parliamentary caricatures. Dating from 1729 or earlier, the Castle, renamed the Elephant & Castle around 1800 and the Speaker from 1999, was part of the Devil's Acre, a notorious slum next to the world's first public gasworks. Local estate residents and office workers are welcome, not to mention an occasional MP or two, all to enjoy the attractive range of beers and the hot bagels. No music, TV or children. Closed at weekends.
⊖(St James's Park) 🚆🕏

SW4: Clapham

Abbeville ✅
67-69 Abbeville Road, SW4 9JW
☎ (020) 8675 2201 ⊕ theabbeville.co.uk
Sharp's Doom Bar; 2 changing beers (often By the Horns) ⊞
A Three Cheers gastro-pub, halfway down a bus-free residential road running behind Clapham Common South Side. The interior is mostly half-panelled, with cream walls decorated with old prints. Separate drinking areas are on different levels in front of and around two small side bars, and there are 10 tables outside. Deservedly popular, the pub attracts a mixed, mainly 30s-40s clientele – families and pets are welcome. Food is served all day on Saturday. Small functions can be hosted and big-screen sports may be requested. ⊖◑◐⊖(South)

King & Co
100 Clapham Park Road, SW4 7BZ
☎ (020) 7498 1971 ⊕ thekingandco.uk
3 changing beers (sourced nationally; often XT) ⊞
An innovative pub offering an enterprising and changing range of beers from microbreweries throughout the UK, plus real ciders from smaller producers. On Tuesdays there is a £1 discount on each pint of real ale. The single bar is basically furnished, with current beer offerings displayed on a large board. The kitchen is periodically taken over by street-food specialists, and the Sunday roast lunches are popular. There are tables outside at the front. ⊖❀◑⊖(Common)♣🍴🚆🐾🕏

SW5: Earls Court

King's Head
17 Hogarth Place, SW5 0QT
☎ (020) 7373 5239
Fuller's Oliver's Island, London Pride; 2 changing beers (often Fuller's) ⊞
A comfortable, friendly corner venue with a modernised interior, hidden away off the busy Earls Court Road; it is a 1937 rebuild of the oldest (circa 17th century) licensed premises in the area. Seating is a mixture of high stools around tall tables, dining tables and settees with low tables. Three Fuller's cask ales are supplemented by a guest, usually from another local brewery. Alcoholic drinks are served from 11am. A quiz is hosted on Monday evening. ⊖◑&⇌(West Brompton)⊖🚆🐾🕏

SW6: Fulham

King's Arms
425 New Kings Road, SW6 4RN
☎ (020) 7371 9585 ⊕ kingsarms-fulham.co.uk
Wadworth Henry's IPA, Horizon, 6X, Bishops Tipple, Swordfish; 1 changing beer (often Wadworth) ⊞
After a £300,000 refurbishment, the King's Arms reopened in 2016 as Wadworth's first pub in the capital. The large corner building at the north end of Putney Bridge has been divided into separate areas and comfortably and tastefully furnished with fabric-upholstered banquettes and chairs. Food includes stone-baked pizzas and Match Day menus; there is a restaurant upstairs. A patio smoking area is to one side. ⊖❀◑&⊖(Putney Bridge)🚆🐾🕏

Lillie Langtry ✅
19 Lillie Road, SW6 1UE
☎ (020) 3637 6690 ⊕ thelillielangtry.co.uk
3 changing beers (often Hogs Back, Timothy Taylor) ⊞
Fulham's oldest surviving 19th-century pub, built in 1835 as the Lillie Arms, named after its freeholder owner, Sir John Scott Lillie. Enlarged in 1875 with a new ground-floor addition and revamped frontage, it was given its present name in 1979 in tribute to the famous actress and courtesan. It served no real ale until 2016 when Hippo took over and carried out an extensive refurbishment. ❀◑&⇌⊖(West Brompton)🚆🐾🕏

SW6: Parsons Green

White Horse 🗓 ✅
1-3 Parsons Green, SW6 4UL
☎ (020) 7736 2115 ⊕ whitehorsesw6.com
Harvey's Sussex Best Bitter; Oakham JHB; 6 changing beers (often Hogs Back, Saltaire) ⊞
A large, light and airy Mitchells & Butlers pub that normally boasts five guest beers on handpump and an international selection of bottled beers. Regular beer and

food-matching events take place as well as beer festivals. The Old Ale Festival in late November has run for 36 years, with a stillage in the Coach House, normally reserved for dining. It can get busy when Chelsea FC are playing at home, but upstairs there is room to escape the crowds. The covered patio area in front accommodates outdoor drinkers. Q❀◑♿⊖🚌(22,424)🐾📶

SW7: Gloucester Road

Queen's Arms

30 Queen's Gate Mews, SW7 5QL

☎ (020) 7823 9293 🌐 thequeensarmskensington.co.uk

St Austell Proper Job; Sharp's Doom Bar; Timothy Taylor Landlord; 5 changing beers (sourced nationally) Ⓗ

Lovely corner mews pub, discreetly tucked away off Queen's Gate, well worth seeking out for its real ales and its large range of interesting draught and bottled beers, malt whiskies and other spirits. Note the unusual curved doors. The L-shaped room has wooden floors and panelling. The clientele reflects the location: glamorous locals, students from Imperial College and musicians from, and visitors to, the nearby Royal Albert Hall – all of whom, if wise, reserve tables. ◑♿⊖🚌🐾📶

SW7: South Kensington

Anglesea Arms ✔

15 Selwood Terrace, SW7 3QG

☎ (020) 7373 7960 🌐 angleseaarms.com

Greene King IPA, Abbot; 4 changing beers (often Sambrook's, Timothy Taylor, Vale) Ⓗ

A real ale stalwart from CAMRA's early years. Built in 1827, it was a Meux tied house for more than a century. Now a Grade II listed Greene King Metropolitan house, it has the air of a country inn, with outside seating and an interior featuring a diverse collection of mirrors, prints, photographs and paintings. As well as the range of real ales, it offers a variety of food at reasonable prices for the area. Q❀◑⊖🚌🐾📶

SW8: South Lambeth

Fentiman Arms

64 Fentiman Road, SW8 1LA

☎ (020) 7793 9796 🌐 thefentimanarms.co.uk

St Austell Proper Job; Young's London Original; 3 changing beers (often Sambrook's, Twickenham, Wimbledon) Ⓗ

On the border of South Lambeth and Kennington, and within easy reach of the Oval cricket ground, this elegant, 19th-century end-of-terrace building has been impressively refurbished as a comfortable, popular dining pub where drinkers are also welcome. There is a front terrace and, at the back, an enclosed, split-level garden patio with a Burger Shack and views over the adjacent post-war estate. The decor includes Penguin paperback covers in the rear ante-room. ❀◑⊖(Oval)🚌🐾📶

Surprise

16 Southville, SW8 2PP

☎ (020) 7622 4623

Young's London Original, London Special; 1 changing beer (often Sambrook's, Young's) Ⓗ

Tucked away next to Larkhall Park, this small, down-to-earth, L-shaped local was refurbished in 2018 and now includes a conservatory extension. It is the only building remaining from streets that were replaced by the park after WWII bomb damage. The back room walls display caricatures of regular customers, while the middle section has black and white photographs of Battersea Power Station. A third real ale is very occasionally available. ❀⊖(Stockwell/Wandsworth Rd)♣🚌🐾

SW9: Brixton

Craft Beer Co

11-13 Brixton Station Road, SW9 8PA

☎ (020) 7274 8383

House beer (by Kent); 8 changing beers (often Northern Monk) Ⓗ

Close to Brixton market, this modern pub has a retro feel with hints of an American diner. Downstairs there is an industrial vibe, with red high stools, while upstairs there are bright blue bench seats, a tumbling blocks parquet floor, neon signs and enamel brewery advertisements from Belgium and France. London microbreweries are represented among the draught and bottled beers, as are Belgian Trappists and Lambic. The pub gets busy when concerts are on at the nearby O2 Academy. ❀⇌⊖●🚌🐾📶

SW11: Battersea

Asparagus ✔

1-13 Falcon Road, SW11 2PL

☎ (020) 7801 0046

Greene King Abbot; Ruddles Best Bitter; Sharp's Doom Bar; 5 changing beers (sourced nationally; often Sambrook's) Ⓗ

A lively Wetherspoon serving an interesting variety of guest ales including dark beers and lower-gravity session styles, as the growing collection of pumpclips on display demonstrates. The light and airy interior is complemented by the outside patio, which is a suntrap in the warmer months. The pub attracts a wide cross-section of local residents and workers as well as visitors from further away. ❀◑♿⇌⊖(Clapham Jct)●🚌📶

Battersea Brewery Tap Room

12-14 Arches Lane, SW11 8AB

☎ (020) 8161 2366 🌐 batterseabrew.co.uk

4 changing beers (sourced regionally; often Battersea) Ⓗ

Opened in November 2018 as the tap to the adjacent Battersea Brewery, both housed in railway arches alongside the Power Station development. Although the brewery mainly produces keg beers, up to four cask-conditioned ales are on handpump, sometimes including a guest beer. Snacks include cheese and charcuterie. Terrestrial TV sport is on screen for major events. A Home Brew Club is based here. Close to the planned Battersea Power Station Northern Line underground due to open in autumn 2021. ❀♿⇌(Park)♣🚌🐾📶

SW11: Clapham Junction

Beehive ✔

197 St Johns Hill, SW11 1TH

☎ (020) 7450 1756

Dark Star Hophead; Fuller's London Pride Ⓗ

Tasteful and elegant refurbishment and enthusiastic management have revitalised this classic Fuller's local. A roll-up TV screen shows major sporting events. The rear area is available for functions and there is now a sheltered garden. Food, although limited, is excellent. Blankets are thoughtfully supplied for guests wishing to sit outside. Look out for the wonderful 1898 housing survey map of SW London; since then the Luftwaffe and town planners have altered things somewhat! ❀◑⇌⊖🚌🐾📶

Eagle Ale House 𝕃

104 Chatham Road, SW11 6HG

☎ (020) 7228 2328

Surrey Hills Shere Drop; changing beers (often Downton, Hackney, Pilgrim) Ⓗ

A short uphill walk from Northcote Road, this traditional pub has a warm, friendly welcome for everyone and their dog. Guest beers are from microbreweries, including local choices. Major sporting events are shown on four TV screens including one in the heated marquee in the garden, which can be hired for private events. Live music sessions are also popular. Local CAMRA Pub of the Year more than once and usually among the top three. ❀🚌(319,G1)🐾📶

SW12: Balham

Balham Bowls Club ✔

7-9 Ramsden Road, SW12 8QX

☎ (020) 8673 4700 🌐 balhambowlsclub.com

Volden Session Ale Ⓖ; 3 changing beers (often By the Horns, Sambrook's, Twickenham) Ⓗ

Converted by Antic in 2006, this former club just off Balham High Road retains a traditional feel but is now more popular with young people. The multi-roomed historic interior, which is of regional importance, features wood panelling, decorated with emblematic military shields and sporting paraphernalia. Guest beers may be from Volden but are typically from other London microbreweries. Live music entertains on Friday evenings. ❀◑≋⊖🚌🐾📶

Bedford ✔

77 Bedford Hill, SW12 9HD

☎ (020) 3976 8007 🌐 thebedford.com

Sambrook's Wandle Ale; Timothy Taylor Landlord; 2 changing beers (often Brixton, Gipsy Hill) Ⓗ

A thriving landmark Grade II listed building with several Art Deco features dating from its construction in 1931. In addition to the busy front bar and restaurant area in the former saloon there is an impressive circular galleried theatre space at the rear, regularly used for comedy and live music. Other events run from bridge and dance classes to yoga and zumba. Accompanied children are welcome until the evening. Outside seating is provided in a small partly covered yard.
❀🛏◑♿≋⊖♣🚌🐾📶

Nightingale 𝕃

97 Nightingale Lane, SW12 8NX

☎ (020) 8673 1637 🌐 thenightingalebalham.co.uk

Young's London Original, London Special; 3 changing beers (often By the Horns, St Austell, Sambrook's) Ⓗ

Recent renovation has not altered the basic layout of this country pub in town, dating from the mid-19th century and featuring some fine etched-glass windows. It has two distinct areas: a public bar at the front and a saloon area at the rear. It raises a lot of money for charity with its summer walk, which has been held annually for over 40 years. There is a warm welcome for everyone, both regulars and occasional visitors.
❀◑♿≋(Wandsworth Common) ⊖(Clapham South) ♣🚌(G1) 🐾📶

SW13: Barnes

Red Lion

2 Castelnau, SW13 9RU

☎ (020) 8748 2984 🌐 red-lion-barnes.co.uk

Fuller's London Pride, ESB; 3 changing beers (often Dark Star) Ⓗ

Large Victorian landmark establishment at the entrance to the Wetland Centre, comprising a front bar area and spacious rear dining room with a mosaic domed ceiling light, leaded stained-glass windows and an impressive fireplace. Outside is a covered patio and a large artificial grass garden with a children's play area. A garden bar is open on busy summer days. There is seating around the front and side, including two four-seater heated cabins. The pub has a Master Cellarman award.
Q❀◑♿P🚌🐾📶

SW16: Streatham

Earl Ferrers 𝕃

22 Ellora Road, SW16 6JF

☎ (020) 8835 8333

Sambrook's Wandle Ale; 3 changing beers (often By the Horns, Timothy Taylor, Twickenham) Ⓗ

This Victorian single-room corner pub is behind Streatham Leisure Centre. The main bar is to the left as you enter. To the right is a smaller area containing an impressive painting of the fourth Earl Ferrers who was hanged for murder in 1760. Beers are from local breweries plus one from Timothy Taylor. Draught cider is normally served. Outside tables and an enclosed patio accommodate smokers. Sunday lunches are popular. Tuesday is cheese day. There is regular live music.
❀◑♿≋(Streatham/Common) ♣●🚌🐾📶

Railway 🏆 𝕃 ✔

2 Greyhound Lane, SW16 5SD

☎ (020) 8769 9448 🌐 therailwaysw16.co.uk

Sambrook's Wandle Ale; 4 changing beers (often By the Horns, Portobello, Southwark) Ⓗ

Showcasing beers exclusively from London microbreweries, both cask and bottled, this is a busy two-bar community venue close to Streatham Common station. The back bar, which is available for hire, opens in the afternoon as a popular tearoom. There is seating outside and in the back yard. It hosts a quiz on Tuesday, music nights and a popular comedy night on the last Sunday of the month. Local CAMRA Pub of the Year winner for 2019. ❀◑♿≋(Common)🚌(60,118)🐾📶

SW17: Summerstown

By the Horns Brewery Tap

25 Summerstown, SW17 0BQ

☎ (020) 3417 7338 🌐 bythehorns.co.uk

3 changing beers (sourced locally) Ⓗ

A friendly brewery taproom open Tuesday to Sunday, close to AFC Wimbledon's new stadium. Three cask beers are usually on, with other draught and canned choices and occasional guests from small breweries. There is plenty of room in the two bar areas and the enclosed space outside. Major sporting events are shown on two large projection TVs, and board games and the like are available. Pizzas are on offer every session. Brewery tours can be arranged. ❀P🚌🐾

SW17: Tooting

Antelope ✔

76 Mitcham Road, SW17 9NG

☎ (020) 8672 3888 🌐 theantelopepub.com

Sambrook's Wandle Ale; Thornbridge Jaipur IPA; Volden Session Ale; 3 changing beers (often By the Horns, Sambrook's, Twickenham) Ⓗ

A lively pub in Tooting's bustling town centre, the Antelope has an historic interior of regional importance, decorated in the shabby-chic style typical of its operators, Antic. The main bar area, retaining some Barclays

signage, leads into a dining space at the rear which adjoins the large Rankin Room used to show big-screen sports, and a back yard with seating. Regular events include a quiz on Monday and live music. Children are welcome until mid-evening.
♞❀◑♿⇌⊖(Broadway) ●🚌🐾📶

SW18: Wandsworth

Cat's Back ✔

86-88 Point Pleasant, SW18 1NN

☎ (020) 8617 3448 🌐 thecatsback.com

Harvey's IPA, Sussex Best Bitter, Old Ale; 1 changing beer Ⓗ

As befits premises owned by one of Britain's most traditional breweries, the Cat's Back has the feel of a back-street local in an area dominated by new riverside residential developments. Regular events include life drawing (Monday), poker night (Wednesday) and live music or theatre (most Thursdays). In winter a real fire adds to the cosy atmosphere. Outside, there is a single bench on the pavement at the front and a rear patio with tables and chairs. ♞❀◑♿♣🚌🐾📶

Old Sergeant Ⓛ

104 Garratt Lane, SW18 4DJ

☎ (020) 8874 4099 🌐 theoldsergeant.co.uk

Sambrook's Wandle Ale; Young's London Original, London Special Ⓗ

This small public house, now decorated in Young's contemporary style, is a long-standing local favourite and deservedly popular with drinkers and diners alike. The John Young Room upstairs has a remarkable collection of brewery memorabilia on display and is available for hire. Outside seating is provided on the pavement at the front and in the enclosed beer garden. Cask beer from the nearby SlyBeast microbrewery is sometimes served here.
♞❀◑♿🚌(44,270) 🐾📶

Royal Standard

1 Ballantine Street, SW18 1AL

☎ (020) 8874 0470 🌐 royalstandardwandsworth.co.uk

Fuller's London Pride; St Austell Tribute; 1 changing beer (often St Austell) Ⓗ

A small and welcoming back-street corner pub at the heart of the local community, redecorated in recent years to give a light and airy feel. The attractive exterior features pretty stained-glass top lights. Quiz night is every other Thursday and board games and glossy magazines are available. Takeaway menus, plates and cutlery are provided for customers to order food to eat in.
❀♿⇌(Town) ♣🚌🐾📶

SW19: South Wimbledon

Sultan

78 Norman Road, SW19 1BT

☎ (020) 8544 9323

Hop Back GFB, Summer Lightning; 4 changing beers (often Downton, Hop Back) Ⓗ

Hop Back's only London tied house, an attractive two-bar 1950s brick building, identified by CAMRA as having a regionally important historic interior. Mostly carpeted, it has dark wood walls, large tables with chairs, some fixed seating, and settees in the conservatory. Four guest ciders are on handpump in the small saloon bar. The beer club on Monday and Wednesday evenings gives 50p a pint discount. Bottled Crop Circle and Typhoon are gluten-free real ales.
♞❀♿⇌(Haydons Rd) ⊖(Colliers Wood/South Wimbledon) ♣●P🚌🐾📶

Trafalgar Ⓛ

23 High Path, SW19 2JY

☎ (020) 8542 5342 🌐 trafalgarfreehouse.co.uk

Downton Quadhop; Surrey Hills Shere Drop; 4 changing beers (often Binghams, Lincoln Green, XT) Ⓗ

A small, street-corner house conversion dating from the 1860s with a 1906 extension. This narrow, one-bar establishment was refurbished in 2014 and is furnished with farmhouse chairs and tables and Nelson memorabilia, reflecting local history. Alongside the excellent cask choice is an interesting range of bottled, canned and KeyKeg varieties, and Lilley's and other ciders. The pub frequently features live music, which is especially enjoyable in the cosy atmosphere.
❀🚊(Morden Rd) ⊖●🚌🐾📶

SW19: Wimbledon

Crooked Billet

14-15 Crooked Billet, SW19 4RQ

☎ (020) 8946 4942 🌐 thecrookedbilletwimbledon.com

Sharp's Doom Bar; Young's London Original, London Special; 3 changing beers (often Young's) Ⓗ

A homely late 18th-century building, extended in 1969 into an adjacent cottage and again more recently to increase dining space. The wood-panelled walls are adorned with old prints, photographs and local painters' works. There are flagstone and wooden floors, a variety of seating and a real fire in winter. Good food is served throughout, including in the intimate restaurant room at the back. Quiz night is Monday. Plastic glasses are used outside in the summer. ♞❀◑🚌(200)🐾📶

Hand in Hand Ⓛ

7 Crooked Billet, SW19 4RQ

☎ (020) 8946 5720 🌐 thehandinhandwimbledon.co.uk

Courage Directors; Young's London Original, London Special Ⓗ**; 5 changing beers (often Adnams, Young's)** Ⓗ/Ⓖ

Newly refurbished dog-friendly ale house on the edge of Wimbledon Common with separate drinking areas and a variety of seating. At least three guest beers are usually sold, increasingly from local breweries. Children are welcome in the family room. This is an excellent place to eat, inside or on the front patio, with beer included in several recipes. There is poker on Monday, a quiz on Tuesday and occasional beer tastings and cellar tours.
Q♞❀◑♿♣🚌(200) 🐾📶

SW20: Raynes Park

Edward Rayne Ⓛ ✔

8-12 Coombe Lane, SW20 8ND

☎ (020) 8971 0420

Greene King IPA, Abbot; Sharp's Doom Bar; 6 changing beers (often Oakham, Thornbridge, Wimbledon) Ⓗ

A popular, comfortable and spacious Wetherspoon pub built in 2006, displacing a supermarket. The name commemorates the 19th-century landowner whose estate was sold for the railway and surrounding suburban development. The half-panelled interior features mirrored pillars. A separate area at the rear serves as a restaurant, where children are welcome. Smokers can use the front veranda seating. Ciders are kept in a fridge behind the bar. Alcoholic drinks are served from 9am.
Q♞◑♿⇌●🚌📶

Carshalton

Hope

48 West Street, SM5 2PR

(020) 8240 1255 hopecarshalton.co.uk

Downton New Forest Ale; Windsor & Eton Knight of the Garter; 5 changing beers

Traditional multi award-winning free house owned by several of its regulars. Seven handpumps dispense a range of the country's finest beers, served in measures from a third-pint upwards. A good range of craft keg and bottled ale is also sold, and knowledgeable staff are always ready to advise you about your choices. A marquee with its permanent bar is used for events and private hire. Good-value pub grub is served until mid-afternoon, and pot meals during the evening. Over-14s only. Q P

Railway Tavern

47 North Street, SM5 2HG

07710 476437 railwaytaverncarshalton.co.uk

Fuller's London Pride; Gale's Seafarers Ale, HSB

Street-corner community local in Carshalton Village, with hanging baskets, and window boxes beneath the fine etched windows. Inside is a small U-shaped drinking area around a central bar. As well as various items of railwayana, the walls display certificates and awards to mark achievements and qualifications of the pub and its staff. The landlord is a Fuller's Master Cellarman.

Sun

4 North Street, SM5 2HU

(020) 8773 4549 thesuncarshalton.com

6 changing beers (sourced nationally)

This handsome and imposing Victorian pub was given a tasteful makeover several years ago and has not looked back since. Several distinct areas accommodate diners, with excellent food, and discerning drinkers, with a wide beer choice on six handpumps. In summer the large courtyard garden with its continental-style veranda is popular. A huge upstairs function room is available for hire. Q

Kingston

Canbury Arms

49 Canbury Park Road, KT2 6LQ

(020) 8255 9129 canburyarmskingston.co.uk

Harvey's Sussex Best Bitter; Surrey Hills Shere Drop; 2 changing beers (often Oakham, Park)

A delightful Art Deco-style pub with a separate restaurant area and first floor function room. Party bookings are welcome, with special menus by arrangement. The extensive home-cooked menu and snacks are available all day in the bar and restaurant, with children welcome until the evening. Wine makers', gourmet and brewer's evenings are hosted. There is a patio area to the side and a paved garden at the rear. See the website for details of local parking arrangements.

Druid's Head

3 Market Place, KT1 1JT

(020) 8546 0723

Greene King IPA, Abbot; 5 changing beers (often Timothy Taylor, Twickenham)

Kingston's oldest pub, Grade II listed, was originally a 17th-century coaching house. The old snug bar has been knocked through to become part of the split-level main bar, but the fireplace has been retained. Note the mews and interesting glasswork. There is a large, enclosed beer garden. Food is served all day and includes traditional roasts on Sunday. Upstairs rooms are available for hire. The internal staircase and high rose ceiling can be viewed on request. Q

Willoughby Arms

47 Willoughby Road, KT2 6LN

(020) 8546 4236 thewilloughbyarms.com

7 changing beers (sourced nationally; often Twickenham, Weltons)

Friendly Victorian back-street local, with a games and TV sports bar and a quieter lounge area. Upstairs is a soundproofed function room. Free of tie, it sources beers from smaller breweries. Pizzas and pies are cooked to order. The spacious garden includes a covered, heated and lit smoking area with a large TV screen. Quiz night is Sunday. A loyalty card operates Sunday to Thursday evenings. Beer festivals are held around St George's Day and Halloween. Local CAMRA Pub of the Year 2020. Q (371,K5)

Wych Elm

93 Elm Road, KT2 6HT

(020) 8546 3271 thewychelmkingston.com

Dark Star Hophead; Fuller's London Pride, ESB; Gale's Seafarers Ale; 2 changing beers (often Dark Star)

This traditional hostelry nestles in the heart of north Kingston. With independent owner-operators, it is a proper local offering great food and friendly service. The guest ale is supplied by Fuller's but is often from another brewery – a Master Cellarman takes care of the beers. There is a secluded garden, log-burners in winter, a dartboard and board games. Some major sporting events are shown and parties and celebrations can be hosted. Charity quizzes, piano and wine evenings are also held. Q (K5)

Richmond

Mitre

20 St Mary's Grove, TW9 1UY

(020) 8940 1336 themitretw9.co.uk

Timothy Taylor Landlord; 6 changing beers (often Oakham, Siren, Thornbridge)

A traditional simply furnished pub tucked away off Sheen Road with a decked area at the front and a patio garden at the back. Leaded stained-glass windows feature different colourful church mitres. Cask beers are on constant rotation from independent brewers outside the M25, with three handpumps dispensing cider or perry. A bar billiards table is available. Food can be delivered from Basilico Pizza. Rudi lives here, officially the cutest pub dog in Britain. P

Roebuck

130 Richmond Hill, TW10 6RN

(020) 8948 2329

Greene King IPA, Abbot; 5 changing beers (often Purity, Surrey Hills, Thames Side)

Close to Richmond Park, this 200-year-old pub, rebuilt in 1741, commands the famous view over the Thames painted by Turner – the only view protected by an Act of Parliament. Inside are a number of comfortable secluded areas, and upstairs is a function room and bar for hire. Guest beers are on constant rotation and Old Rosie is now a regular cider. Patrons can also use the outside terrace across the road. (371)

Surbiton

Antelope

87 Maple Road, KT6 4AW

(020) 8399 5565 theantelope.co.uk

Big Smoke Solaris Session Pale Ale; 9 changing beers (sourced nationally; often Big Smoke) H
The original home of the Big Smoke Brewery, with two or three of its beers usually available. The spacious split-level interior has a real fire in winter and a covered, heated and lit courtyard behind, beyond which the old brewhouse now acts as dining or function room. Five changing ciders are usually sold. Home-cooked food includes roasts on Sunday. Popular with locals and commuters, it can be particularly busy evenings and weekends. A former local CAMRA Pub of the Year.

Black Lion ✔
58 Brighton Road, KT6 5PL
☎ (020) 8399 8856 🌐 blacklionsurbiton.co.uk
Surrey Hills Ranmore; Timothy Taylor Landlord; Young's London Original, London Special; 1 changing beer (often Harvey's, Twickenham) H
Traditional, lively corner pub owned by Young's since 1840, when the coach to Brighton stopped outside. A dark wood bar serves two areas, as well as some raised seating to the side. The lounge space is carpeted, and has upholstered benches around the leaded windows, while the public area has a slate floor. Live sport is shown on TV. Quiz night is Tuesday, and bands play most Saturday evenings. Seven letting rooms are available.

Lamb L
73 Brighton Road, KT6 5NF
☎ (020) 8390 9229 🌐 lambsurbiton.co.uk
Black Sheep Best Bitter; Hop Back Summer Lightning; Surrey Hills Shere Drop; 1 changing beer (sourced nationally) H
Small, family-run free house, very involved with the local community, especially in encouraging creative activities. Built in 1850 and formerly four separate rooms, it retains the original horseshoe-shaped bar. It had a small brewery in Victorian times. The changing beer is usually from a microbrewery, sometimes local. Specialist cheeses are always available, with cheeseboards on offer all day. Live music and other events are held regularly, including pop-up street-food stalls in the garden.

Sutton

Cock & Bull
26-30 High Street, SM1 1HF
☎ (020) 8652 9910 🌐 thecockandbulluk.co.uk
Fuller's Oliver's Island, London Pride, ESB; 2 changing beers H
A warm and friendly Fuller's house at the top of the High Street, a short distance from the station and bus stops. The building is a former bank branch, now a spacious one-bar pub with three separate drinking areas and an outdoor heated smoking area. Five plasma screens show major sporting events. There is a quiz on Thursday and live music on Saturday. An extensive menu caters for all tastes, and children are welcome during food service hours.

Shinner & Sudtone L
67 High Street, SM1 1DT
☎ (020) 8643 8395 🌐 shinnerandsudtone.com
Volden Session Ale; 2 changing beers (sourced nationally) H
In the shopping area of Sutton, this pub is decorated in Antic's familiar shabby-chic style. Its name combines that of a former department store nearby and an old name for Sutton. The long bar has tables and chairs either side of a central walkway, leading to a small raised area at the rear. A Volden beer is usually on tap, and a board indicates guest beers waiting in the cellar. Acoustic and open mic nights are held regularly.

WEST LONDON

W2: Bayswater

Champion ✔
1 Wellington Terrace, W2 4LW
☎ (020) 7792 4527 🌐 thechampionpub.co.uk
Adnams Ghost Ship; 4 changing beers (often By the Horns, Dark Star, Oakham) H
The nearest pub to Kensington Palace, opposite the security-protected road on the northern side of Kensington Gardens. Built in 1838 and Grade II listed, it was refurbished in 2004 and spruced up more recently by owners Mitchells & Butlers. In warm weather the front windows are often opened into the bar. A plush basement area leads on to a sunken beer garden, with patio heaters for cold weather.
⊖(Notting Hill Gate/Queensway)

W2: Little Venice

Bridge House ✔
13 Westbourne Terrace Road, W2 6NG
☎ (020) 7266 4326 🌐 thebridgehouselittlevenice.co.uk
Sharp's Doom Bar; Timothy Taylor Landlord; 2 changing beers (often St Austell, Thornbridge) H
Dating from 1848, this pub beside the canal is now a lounge-style bar, ideal for a quiet afternoon drink. There is a good solid bar counter, wooden floor and panelling, with old mirrors (Bass and H D Rawlings' High Class Mineral Waters) above the fireplace. A chandelier, pastel-painted walls, high and standard tables and chairs, and low easy chairs complete the setting. There is an extensive menu for lunch and dinner.
Q ≠(Paddington) ⊖(Warwick Ave)

W2: Paddington

Mad Bishop & Bear
Upper Level, The Lawn, Paddington Station Concourse, W2 1HB
☎ (020) 7402 2441
Dark Star Hophead; Fuller's London Pride, ESB; 5 changing beers (often Tiny Rebel, Wild Beer, Wimbledon) H
Above the shopping complex just behind the station concourse, the modern pub interior features one long bar, railway memorabilia and train information screens. The raised areas can be hired for events and there are café-style seats outside. It may not be crowded even in the rush hour, but the bar could close early if football crowds are passing through.

Victoria ★
10A Strathearn Place, W2 2NH
☎ (020) 7724 1191 🌐 victoriapaddington.co.uk
Fuller's Oliver's Island H/P, London Pride, ESB; 3 changing beers (often Dark Star, Thornbridge, Tiny Rebel) H
There is plenty to admire in this Grade II listed mid-Victorian inn, popular with tourists and locals alike. The nationally important historic interior includes ornately gilded mirrors above a crescent-shaped bar, painted tiles in wall niches and numerous portraits of Queen Victoria. The walls display cartoons, paperweights and a Silver Jubilee plate. Upstairs, via a spiral staircase, the Library and Theatre Bar provide extra space. Tuesday is quiz night. Paddington station is a few minutes away.
Q ≠⊖(Lancaster Gate/Paddington)

W3: Acton

Red Lion & Pineapple ✔
281 High Street, W3 9BP
☎ (020) 8896 2248
Greene King IPA, Abbot; Sharp's Doom Bar; 6 changing beers (sourced nationally) Ⓗ
A Wetherspoon at the top of Acton Hill formerly owned by Fuller's, originally two pubs which then combined in 1906 – hence the unique name. The larger room is home to the circular bar, surrounded by red and black tiles. The windows are large, with etched and stained tops, and the walls are decorated with historical photographs of Acton. The smaller room is mainly used by diners and families. Alcoholic drinks are served from 9am.
🐴❀◐♿⊖(Town) 🚌📶

West London Trades Union Club
33-35 High Street, W3 6ND
☎ (020) 8992 4557 🌐 wltuc.com
2 changing beers (often Nelson) Ⓗ
Small, friendly club, run as a co-operative, which combines excellent beer with a busy cultural and social life. Two real ales are served from a variety of independent breweries, and particularly from the wide Nelson range. The Acton Community Theatre is upstairs, and film shows are also held. The local CAMRA branch is an associate member; show a CAMRA membership card or this Guide for entry. Closed on most Saturdays (check the website for exceptions). Q🐴❀⊖(Central)🚌🐾📶

W3: North Acton

Castle
140 Victoria Road, W3 6UL
☎ (020) 8992 2027 🌐 castlenorthacton.co.uk
Fuller's London Pride; 2 changing beers (sourced locally; often Fuller's) Ⓗ
A 1920s Fuller's premises built for industrial North Acton and Park Royal, but now among new housing, hotels and student accommodation. The BBC rehearsal rooms were next door and the pub features in many memoirs of the TV industry. Usually busy with local workers on weekday evenings, it is quieter during the day and at weekends. Seating areas surround the island bar, and there is a family room and a paved garden. 🐴❀◐♿⊖P🚌🐾📶

W4: Turnham Green

George IV
185 Chiswick High Road, W4 2DR
☎ (020) 8994 4624
Dark Star Hophead; Fuller's London Pride, ESB; Gale's Seafarers Ale; 4 changing beers (often Anspach & Hobday, Fuller's, Windsor & Eton) Ⓗ
There has been an inn here in the heart of Chiswick since 1777, and the present inter-war pub is reputed to have its own ghost, George. Inside, the different areas include the board game-themed mezzanine, while the Boston Room across the rear courtyard hosts events including a comedy club and is available for private hire. Fuller's small-batch brews are among the beers on offer. Up to two staff here are Fuller's Master Cellarmen.
🐴❀◐♿⊖🍎🚌🐾📶

Tabard 𝕃 ✔
2 Bath Road, W4 1LW
☎ (020) 8994 3492
Greene King IPA, Abbot; 6 changing beers (often Black Sheep, Truman's, Twickenham) Ⓗ
Built in 1880 as part of the Bedford Park estate, the first London garden suburb, this Grade II* listed pub has a regionally important historic interior. Features include the replica swing sign (the original was painted by TM Rooke), interior tiling by William de Morgan and Walter Crane, and Arts & Crafts mirrors and pictures. The dining area usually has live music on Saturday evening and a quiz on Wednesday. An intimate fringe theatre is upstairs. 🐴❀◐♿⊖♣🚌🐾📶

W5: Ealing

Plough
297 Northfield Avenue, W5 4XB
☎ (020) 8567 1416
Fuller's London Pride; Gale's Seafarers Ale; 2 changing beers (often Dark Star, Fuller's, Tiny Rebel) Ⓗ
Popular with all ages and a real hub for the Little Ealing community, the pub has a children's playground and extensive garden, a restaurant area serving a quality menu, and an L-shaped front of house for adults only. A centre for the Ealing jazz scene, it features regular Sunday evening performances as well as fringe sessions for the summer Ealing Jazz Festival. Quiz night is every Tuesday. Charles Blondin, the Victorian tightrope walker, lived opposite. 🐴❀◐♿⊖(Northfields)P🚌(E2,E3)🐾📶

Questors Grapevine Bar 𝕃 ✔
12 Mattock Lane, W5 5BQ
☎ (020) 8567 0011 🌐 questors.org.uk/grapevine
Fuller's London Pride; 2 changing beers Ⓗ
A friendly theatre club bar near the centre of Ealing and Walpole Park, run by enthusiastic volunteers. CAMRA members and Questors theatre ticket holders are welcome. Guest beers include some from local breweries. Beer festivals are held twice-yearly and there are malt whisky tastings. Some books and the odd board game are available. Local CAMRA Club of the Year 2019 and winner of the CAMRA national award in 2012.
Q🐴❀♿⇌⊖(Broadway) ♣P🚌🐾📶

Sir Michael Balcon ✔
46-47 The Mall, W5 3TJ
☎ (020) 8799 2850
Greene King IPA, Abbot; Sharp's Doom Bar; 4 changing beers (often Hadrian Border, Purple Moose, Sambrook's) Ⓗ
On the busy Uxbridge Road east of Ealing town centre, this became a Wetherspoon in 2008, named after the legendary film producer whose life and films form the basis of many of the wall displays. The interior is split-level, with a raised area at the rear and a glass-covered area at the front for smokers.
Q🐴❀◐♿⇌⊖(Broadway) 🍎🚌📶

W5: North Ealing

Greystoke 𝕃 ✔
7 Queens Parade, Hanger Lane, W5 3HU
☎ (020) 8997 6388
Greene King IPA, Abbot; 5 changing beers (often Wimbledon) Ⓗ
A spacious family dining pub opposite North Ealing station, built in typical 1930s style, with affordable hot food and a changing selection of Greene King beers. The single open-plan bar is comfortably furnished. All major sporting events from around the world including NFL are shown. A weekly quiz is hosted on Thursday as well as regular live music events.
🐴❀◐♿⊖♣P🚌(112,483) 🐾📶

W6: Hammersmith

Craft Beer Co

17-18 Broadway Shopping Centre, W6 9YD
☎ (020) 8748 7033
Kent Pale; 5 changing beers (sourced nationally) [H]
Opened in May 2019 as a welcome addition to the local scene, the transformed pub has an unusually stylish room, L-shaped round the bar counter, and an outside terrace with heater. Up to six real ales are on handpump plus 20 craft keg lines, while more than 50 bottles and cans include some rarities at appropriate prices. Bar snacks, burgers and salads are the food offering. Convenient for the Apollo music venue, it may be busy before concerts there.

Dove

19 Upper Mall, W6 9TA
☎ (020) 8748 9474
Fuller's Oliver's Island, London Pride, ESB; 1 changing beer (often Fuller's, Gale's) [H]
A Grade II listed pub dating from the 1740s, with a regionally important historic interior, overlooking the Thames and hence often crowded in summer. The likes of Dylan Thomas, Ernest Hemingway and Alec Guinness have enjoyed a pint or two here. Down from the main room, a tiny public bar holds the Guinness world record for the smallest bar area. The food service can be slow at busy times but is worth the wait.
(Ravenscourt Park)

Plough & Harrow L ✓

120-124 King Street, W6 0QU
☎ (020) 8735 6020
Fuller's London Pride; Greene King IPA, Abbot; Sharp's Doom Bar; 6 changing beers [H]
On the site of an inn established in 1419, and more recently a Rolls-Royce showroom, this light and airy Wetherspoon pub opened in 2002. It has a mixture of stone and carpeted floors and a long metal-topped bar. It offers 10 handpumps, with more than half of them devoted to an ever-changing range of guest beers, many from microbreweries. There are several no-smoking tables outside. Alcoholic drinks are served from 9am.
Q (Hammersmith/Ravenscourt Park)

W7: Hanwell

Dodo Micropub 🏆 L

52 Boston Road, W7 3TR
☎ (020) 8567 5959 🌐 thedodomicropub.com
5 changing beers (sourced locally) [G]
A classic micropub shop conversion that landed in Hanwell in 2017. Up to five cask beers are served from a temperature-controlled cellar room at the rear, along with cider and wine. The beer range almost always includes some from local breweries. There is a small bar counter by the front door but table service is the order of the day here. Q

Fox

Green Lane, W7 2PJ
☎ (020) 8567 4021 🌐 thefoxpub.co.uk
Fuller's London Pride; St Austell Proper Job; Timothy Taylor Landlord; 3 changing beers (sourced nationally) [H]
Wonderful back-street free house in the welcoming multicultural town of Hanwell, as popular with walkers, cyclists and other nearby canal users as with locals. A good range of beers, with changing guest ales from independent breweries, is complemented by excellent, inexpensive food, including a popular Sunday lunch (booking recommended). Two annual beer festivals are hosted and occasional jazz sessions. Local CAMRA branch Pub of the Year on many occasions.
P (195,E8)

Green W7 L

13 Lower Boston Road, W7 3TX
☎ (020) 8840 6789 🌐 thegreenw7.com
Fuller's London Pride; 2 changing beers (often Portobello, Twickenham, Windsor & Eton) [H]
Previously the White Hart, the Dolphin and the Inn on the Green, this pub dates from at least 1860 and retains a lot of wood panelling and tiling. A pizza oven was installed in 2017 and burgers are also served. There may be up to four changing beers on tap, with the Monday club offering draught beer at £3 per pint.
P

Viaduct ✓

221 Uxbridge Road, W7 3TD
☎ (020) 8567 5866 🌐 viaduct-hanwell.co.uk
Fuller's London Pride, ESB; Gale's Seafarers Ale; 3 changing beers (sourced locally; often Dark Star, Fuller's, Gale's) [H]
A friendly Fuller's house much larger on the inside than it looks from outside. The separate function room used for Friday comedy nights is available for hire. The pub was renamed circa 1838 after the Wharncliffe Viaduct located behind it – the first viaduct to carry a commercial electric telegraph. Ealing Hospital is close by.
Q P

W8: Kensington

Elephant & Castle ✓

40 Holland Street, W8 4LT
☎ (020) 7937 6382
Fuller's London Pride; St Austell Nicholson's Pale Ale; Sharp's Doom Bar; 3 changing beers (sourced nationally) [H]
First licensed in 1865 as a beer house in what were two adjacent houses, and tucked away north-east of Kensington Town Hall, this busy cosy, wood-panelled Nicholson's pub with its rural feel is a welcome refuge from the hurly-burly of Kensington High Street. Guest beers come from a wide range of breweries. Hearty food, especially pies and sausages, is available throughout the day. Note the fine Charrington's bar-back.
(High St Kensington)

W8: Notting Hill Gate

Churchill Arms

119 Kensington Church Street, W8 7LN
☎ (020) 7727 4242 🌐 churchillarmskensington.co.uk
Fuller's Oliver's Island, London Pride, ESB; 2 changing beers (often Fuller's) [H]
A multi award-winning, deservedly popular establishment with a regionally important historic interior including snob screens, now rare. Churchillian and Irish memorabilia are among the bric-a-brac suspended from the panelled ceiling. The Thai restaurant in the conservatory was one of the first in a London pub. Outside, at busy times, drinkers stand on the pavement below the numerous hanging flower baskets. At Christmas the tree decorations are quite something to behold. Q

Windsor Castle ★ ✓

114 Campden Hill Road, W8 7AR
☎ (020) 7243 8797 🌐 thewindsorcastlekensington.co.uk
Marston's Pedigree; Timothy Taylor Landlord; 4 changing beers [H]

A back-street, Grade II listed inn dating from 1830. Sited on a corner, it contrasts an old-world rural feel with a modern upmarket service and menu style. The bar room is divided into four drinking areas but, surprisingly, the partitions and other wood panelling of the nationally important historic interior are not original – they date from a 1933 refurbishment. The four changing real ales rotate through some interesting brews. A beer garden to the rear boasts its own bar. Q♨❀◑⊖🚌🐾ᯤ

W9: Westbourne Park

Union Tavern 🄻

45 Woodfield Road, W9 2BA

☎ (020) 7286 1886

Five Points Pale; Fuller's London Pride; 3 changing beers (often Windsor & Eton) 🄷

Following a takeover by Fuller's, this is now a part-tied beer house offering five cask ales and 12 craft keg beers produced within 30 miles and, with just one brewery exception, in London. The mainly young crowd enjoys reduced beer prices on Monday, various music nights and a Meet the Brewer event on the first Tuesday of the month. Good-value food is another attraction, with traditional Sunday lunches. The canalside terrace is a delight all year round but comes into its own on a warm, sunny day. ♨❀◑⊖🚌🐾ᯤ

W11: Notting Hill

Walmer Castle ✔

58 Ledbury Road, W11 2AJ

☎ (020) 7229 4620 🌐 walmercastlenottinghill.co.uk

St Austell Tribute; Sharp's Doom Bar; 2 changing beers 🄷

Mitchells & Butlers took over the Walmer Castle in 2015; it is new to this Guide. The friendly, homely pub has a small snug at the back and a restaurant-cum-function room upstairs. An excellent food menu includes brunch, sandwiches and Sunday roasts. Board games are available. Portobello Market is close by.
Q♨❀◑⊖(Notting Hill Gate) ♣🚌🐾ᯤ

W12: Shepherds Bush

Central Bar ✔

Unit 1, West 12 Shopping Centre, Shepherds Bush Green, W12 8PH

☎ (020) 8746 4290

Greene King IPA, Abbot; changing beers 🄷

A Wetherspoon opened in 2002 on the upper floor of a new shopping centre, with commendable beer quality since 2019. Access from the ground floor is via escalator or lift. A wide entrance leads into a long bar with large windows overlooking the Green. The pub is named after the Central London Railway or 'tuppenny tube', now the Central Line, which reached Shepherds Bush with a station opposite the pub opened by the Prince of Wales (later Edward VII) in 1900.
Q♨◑⇌⊖(Shepherds Bush/Market) 🍎🚌ᯤ

Defector's Weld 🄻

170 Uxbridge Road, W12 8AA

☎ (020) 8749 0008 🌐 defectors-weld.co.uk

Young's London Original, London Special; 3 changing beers (often Redemption, Truman's, Twickenham) 🄷

Since Young's took over this pub it has continued to rotate local guest beers. The large horseshoe-shaped main bar has a welcoming mix of sofas, tables and chairs. An upstairs bar is available for hire. DJs play music Thursday to Sunday evenings. Home fans only are allowed here on Queen's Park Rangers match days, but card-carrying CAMRA members not wearing team colours are welcome.
Q❀◑♿⇌⊖(Shepherd's Bush/Market) 🚆🚌🐾ᯤ

W13: West Ealing

Forester ★ ✔

2 Leighton Road, W13 9EP

☎ (020) 8567 1654

Dark Star Hophead; Fuller's London Pride, ESB; 3 changing beers (often Adnams, Butcombe, Fuller's) 🄷

Built in 1909 from designs by Nowell Parr for the Royal Brewery of Brentford and bought by Fuller's in 2012, this pub has a nationally important historic interior. Thai and English food are served daily, except on Sunday when there is a traditional carvery. Wednesday is quiz night and on Thursday there are poker tournaments. Two guest beers are supplemented by two extra beers from Fuller's (often Gale's HSB), and two beer festivals are held annually.
♨❀🛏◑♿⊖(Northfields/West Ealing) ♣🍎🚌(E2,E3) 🐾ᯤ

Owl & The Pussycat 🄻

106 Northfield Avenue, W13 9RT

🌐 markopaulo.co.uk

Marko Paulo range; Ealing range 🄷

Unique to West London, this combination of microbrewery and bar has retained the atmosphere of the former bookshop. Drinkers can view the brewing process while avid readers can browse through the beer-related books and magazines. The ciders are often from Oliver's if not home-produced. Conversation is all important in this small, friendly environment. Local CAMRA Pub of the Year 2019 and Cider Pub of the Year 2019 and 2020. Q⊖(Northfields)♣🍎🚌(E2,E3)ᯤ

Brentford

Black Dog Beer House

17 Albany Road, TW8 0NF

☎ (020) 8568 5688 🌐 blackdogbeerhouse.co.uk

7 changing beers (often East London, Manchester, Tiny Rebel) 🄷

This landmark building, a former Royal Brewery (Brentford) pub dating back to at least 1861, has now become a local favourite after reopening in 2018. The light and open L-shaped room has plenty of seating, no TVs, music from classic vinyl LPs and an eclectic food menu. As well as seven real ales and five ciders, 14 more beers and ciders on keg taps are listed on two chalkboards. Dogs are welcome though, sadly, the eponymous hound lives elsewhere. ❀◑⇌♣🍎🚌🐾ᯤ

Express Tavern

56 Kew Bridge Road, TW8 0EW

☎ (020) 8560 8484 🌐 expresstavern.co.uk

Big Smoke Solaris Session Pale Ale; Draught Bass; Harvey's Sussex Best Bitter; 7 changing beers (sourced nationally) 🄷

A local landmark since the 1800s, still featuring its illuminated external Bass signage, with Draught Bass remaining a fixture on the bar. It has a regionally important historic pub interior. The Chiswick Bar has 10 ale handpumps and an upright piano, with music also on vinyl LPs. The Saloon and Lounge Bar handpumps serve five ciders and perries. To the rear is a glazed conservatory and a beer garden with a covered and heated terrace. ❀◑♿⇌(Kew Bridge)♣🍎🚌🐾ᯤ

Hampton

Jolly Coopers

16 High Street, TW12 2SJ

☎ (020) 8979 3384

Courage Best Bitter; Hop Back Summer Lightning; 3 changing beers (often Ascot, Park, Reunion) Ⓗ

A popular, traditional community pub, proud of its heritage; a wooden wall panel lists landlords from 1727 to the present owners who took over in 1986. The small horseshoe bar features guest beers mainly from local breweries. Walls are adorned with water jugs and local memorabilia, including some coopers' tools. Extensive tapas and traditional food, including Sunday lunches (booking essential), are served in Squiffy's restaurant and, weather permitting, on the sun patio outside.
🐎❀◑♿⇌♣🚌🐾📶

Hampton Court

Mute Swan

3 Palace Gate, KT8 9BN

☎ (020) 8941 5959

House beer (by St Austell); 5 changing beers (often Crafty Beers, Red Cat, Wimbledon) Ⓗ

A friendly Brunning & Price pub and dining room opposite the palace gates. A good selection of food is served both upstairs and in the main bar. Bar bites are also listed on a chalkboard. The cask beers change frequently, with a cider on handpump often also on the go. Seating and tables are provided outside. There are no TV screens to spoil the atmosphere, which draws locals and tourists alike. No prams are allowed inside.
◑⇌♣🍎🚌🐾📶

Hampton Hill

Roebuck

72 Hampton Road, TW12 1JN

☎ (020) 8255 8133 🌐 roebuck-hamptonhill.co.uk

St Austell Tribute; Sambrook's Junction Ale; Young's London Original; 2 changing beers (often Park, Triple fff, Windsor & Eton) Ⓗ

Comfortable Victorian street-corner pub with screens dividing the single bar into various seating areas. An amazing array of bric-a-brac and other displays (framed banknotes, military memorabilia, model seaplanes, a wickerwork Harley-Davidson) keeps growing but does not detract from the comfort of the place. The small garden has a gazebo for smokers and there is a garden room (available for hire) for cooler evenings. The real fire never goes out in winter. ❀🛏◐⇌(Fulwell)🚌📶

Harlington

White Hart

158 High Street, UB3 5DP

☎ (020) 8759 9608

Fuller's London Pride, ESB; 1 changing beer (often Dark Star, Fuller's, Gale's) Ⓗ

Large, Grade II listed Fuller's pub standing proud at the north end of the village. The bar provides access to an open-plan area with soft seating, leading to seating favoured by diners. It was refurbished in 2009 to improve facilities and create the open feel it has now. Local history is the theme of the wall displays, enjoyed by regulars and visitors from the nearby Heathrow airport. Quiz night is Thursday. Fuller's or Gale's seasonal ales are sometimes on the bar. 🐎❀◑♿P🚌🐾📶

Hayes

Botwell Inn ✔

25-29 Coldharbour Lane, UB3 3EB

☎ (020) 8848 3112

Greene King Abbot; Ruddles Best Bitter; Sharp's Doom Bar; 3 changing beers (often Adnams, Hogs Back, Windsor & Eton) Ⓗ

A spacious Wetherspoon pub opened in 2000 following a shop conversion from furnishers S Moore and Son, with several areas for dining and drinking. There is a fenced paved area to the front and a patio at the rear with large parasols with heaters. At least one Westons cider is stocked. Several beer festivals are held annually.
Q🐎❀◑♿⇌⊖(Hayes & Harlington) 🍎🚌📶

Hounslow

Moon under Water ✔

84-88 Staines Road, TW3 3LF

☎ (020) 8572 7506

Greene King Abbot; Ruddles Best Bitter; Sharp's Doom Bar; 5 changing beers (sourced nationally) Ⓗ

Licensed from 9am, this is a 1991 Wetherspoon shop conversion still in original style, displaying many local history panels and photographs. It is a regular venue for the town's beer lovers, also attracting others from surrounding areas. Up to five guest ales are offered, both national and local, with more at festival times, when 10 handpumps are put to work. The cider is usually Westons Old Rosie. Families are welcome during the day.
Q🐎❀◑♿⊖(Central) 🍎🚌📶

Isleworth

London Apprentice ✔

62 Church Street, TW7 6BG

☎ (020) 8560 1915

Greene King IPA, Abbot; 3 changing beers (often Exeter, Sambrook's, Timothy Taylor) Ⓗ

Famous Grade II listed former Isleworth Brewery pub on the river in old Isleworth. Rebuilt in the early 1700s, the interior is classic traditional, although opened out, with an upstairs function room with superb views. The large patio has many tables, with more on the riverbank. A real cider is served in summer. Food is popular. There is usually music on Friday evening, a poker night on Thursday and a quiz on Sunday. 🐎❀◑♿🍎P🚌

Norwood Green

Plough

Tentelow Lane, UB2 4LG

☎ (020) 8574 7473

Fuller's London Pride, ESB; Gale's Seafarers Ale; 1 changing beer (often Fuller's, Harvey's, St Austell) Ⓗ

Dating back to around 1650, this Grade II listed building with low exposed beams and two real fires is Fuller's oldest tied house. The landlord takes pride in friendly service, a well-kept range of real ales and ciders, and good food served every day of the week. Musicians entertain from time to time inside the pub as well as in the garden during the summer. There is now patio seating at the front. 🐎❀◑♿♣🍎🚌(120)🐾📶

St Margarets

Crown

174 Richmond Road, TW1 2NH

☎ (020) 8892 5896 🌐 crowntwickenham.co.uk

Harvey's Sussex Best Bitter; Oakham Citra; Surrey Hills Shere Drop; 1 changing beer (often Big Smoke, Park, Twickenham) Ⓗ
A large pub dating from about 1730 and Grade II listed, with a substantial refurbishment enhancing the Georgian heritage of the original building. The Victorian hall at the back has been opened up for dining and the courtyard garden attractively remodelled. Inside are various seating areas and three fireplaces, one in the bar area with a real fire. Several windows and doors are original. Food is served throughout the day.

Teddington

Masons Arms

41 Walpole Road, TW11 8PJ
☎ (020) 8977 6521 🌐 the-masons-arms.co.uk
Sambrook's Junction Ale; Vale Best IPA; 2 changing beers (often Andwell, Coastal, Kissingate) Ⓗ
A small, friendly back-street community free house built in 1860. It is a beer drinkers' haven, with bottles, pictures and pub memorabilia on display. Carpeting and comfortable seating create a cosy atmosphere. There is a log-burning stove, dartboard and a small secluded rear patio. Music evenings include a bring-your-own-vinyl night on the third Tuesday of the month. Guest beers come from a wide range of UK independent brewers. Local CAMRA Pub of the Year 2019.

Twickenham

Prince Albert

30 Hampton Road, TW2 5QB
☎ (020) 8894 3963
Fuller's Oliver's Island, London Pride, ESB; 1 changing beer (often Big Smoke) Ⓗ
Opened by the Star Brewery in 1840, this convivial pub was unofficially known later as Wiffen's – run by three generations of the family whose name is still displayed behind the bar. It has an attractive garden, a Thai restaurant and live music on Saturday evening. Two annual beer festivals feature small brewers. The smoking patio has a sports screen. A finalist in the Fuller's Master Cellarman competition for three years running.
(Strawberry Hill)

Rifleman

7 Fourth Cross Road, TW2 5EL
☎ (020) 8255 0205
Butcombe Original; Twickenham Naked Ladies; Young's London Original; 3 changing beers (often Harvey's, Twickenham) Ⓗ
A gem of a traditional late-Victorian pub, originally a 19th-century beer house whose name commemorates riflemen billeted nearby in Napoleonic times. It benefits from a small beer garden, front patio and close proximity to several bus routes. Very much a community hub, it has board games, TV sport and events on Thursdays. Twickenham Stadium and Harlequins rugby clubs are a 15-minute walk. A Twickenham Fine Ales house since July 2019. (Strawberry Hill)P

White Swan

Riverside, TW1 3DN
☎ (020) 8744 2951 🌐 whiteswantwickenham.co.uk
Otter Bitter; Twickenham Naked Ladies; 3 changing beers (often Gale's, Reunion, West Berkshire) Ⓗ
A Grade II listed building and award-winning traditional pub, built around 1690. Entry is via steps up to the first floor, with real fires and walls covered with rugby and other memorabilia. A small veranda/balcony and a triclinium (a three-sided room with window seats) afford views of the river and Eel Pie Island. Directly opposite is a larger beer garden (tides permitting), right on the water's edge. A summer beer festival and an annual raft race are held. Q

William Webb Ellis

24 London Road, TW1 3RR
☎ (020) 8744 4300
Greene King IPA, Abbot; Sharp's Doom Bar; Twickenham Naked Ladies; 8 changing beers (often Oakham, Twickenham, Windsor & Eton) Ⓗ
What was Twickenham's post office is now a spacious Wetherspoon venue in the centre of the home of English rugby, named after the schoolboy said to have invented the game. Twelve handpumps are in constant use. Food is served all day. Silent screens show live news and sport. There is a patio outside to the rear. Licensing restrictions stipulate there is no new admittance an hour before last orders.

Uxbridge

Queen's Head

54 Windsor Street, UB8 1AB
☎ (01895) 258750
Greene King IPA, Abbot; 3 changing beers (often Cotleigh, Rebellion, Twickenham) Ⓗ
A Grade II listed, mid 16th-century inn that still retains its old feel, opposite the church and a few yards down from the tube station. The decorations and furnishings are in keeping with its age. It has bay windows, wooden floorboards, low ceilings, walls largely of exposed brick, and an irregularly shaped bar. Local CAMRA Pub of the Year 2019.

A short history of the Good Beer Guide

The Good Beer Guide was first published in 1972 and was just 18 pages long. Rather than a printed and bound edition, it was just a collection of sheets of paper stapled together and posted out to CAMRA members. The first printed edition was published in 1974 and contained a comment on Watney's brewery that was considered libellous, causing the first print run to be pulped and the description for the brewery to be revised. There are a few copies of the first print run out there but they change hands for a fair amount of money.
There has been a bound edition of the Guide printed annually since 1974, meaning it is now in its 48th year. The longest serving editor was Roger Protz, who edited the Guide from 1978-1983 and 2000-2018.

GREATER MANCHESTER

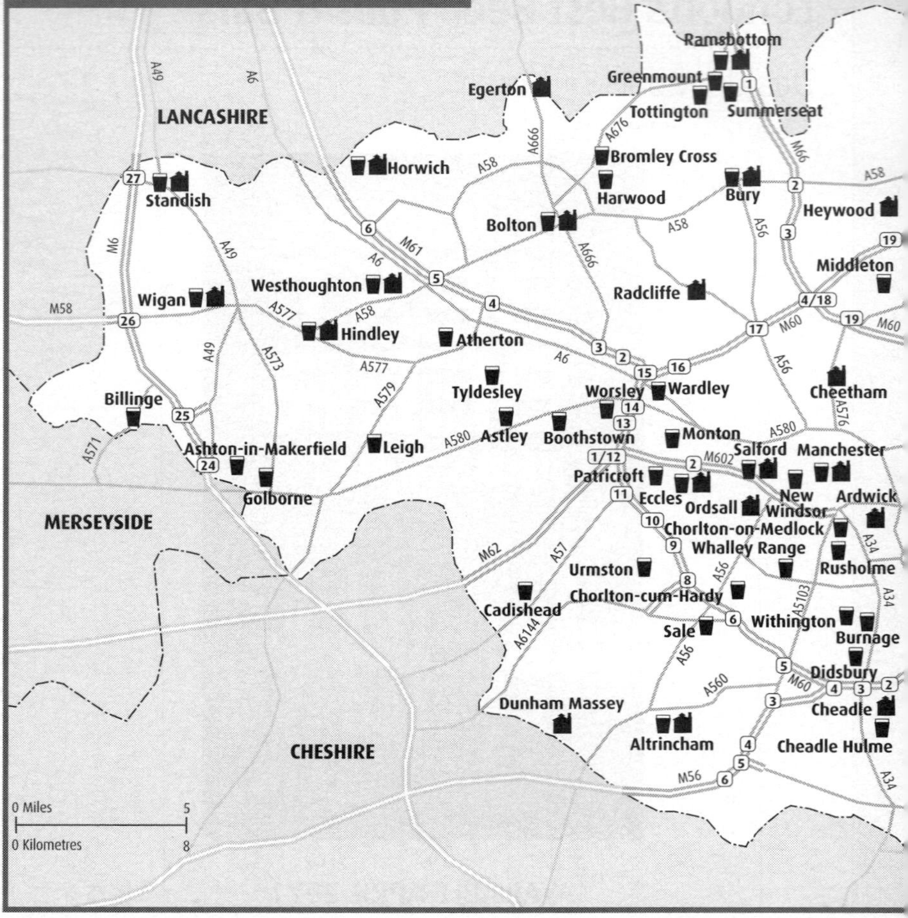

Altrincham

Costello's Bar

18 Goose Green, WA14 1DW (alleyway from Stamford New Rd/opp Regent Rd, adjacent to new hospital)
(0161) 929 0903 costellosbar.co.uk
Dunham Massey Dunham Dark, Big Tree Bitter; 5 changing beers (sourced locally; often Dunham Massey)
Small bar in Altrincham's attractive and popular Goose Green, behind the new hospital. The taphouse for Dunham Massey Brewery, it has a modern feel and is a favourite both with locals and visitors. On the bar there are seven handpumps that feature a continually changing selection of beers from the brewery's 25 recipes. Numerous award certificates adorn the walls, reflecting the bar's fine reputation.

Jack in the Box

Altrincham Market Hall, Market Street, WA14 1SA
07917 792060
House beer (by Blackjack); 4 changing beers (sourced nationally)
A Blackjack Brewery bar in the popular Altrincham Market House, part of the town's historic market. The small bar houses six handpumps, two dispensing beers from Blackjack and the others mostly ales from elsewhere including local breweries such as Track, Squawk and Stubborn Mule. Eight keg taps are on the back wall. The casks and kegs are housed in a chilled cellar behind the bar. Food is available throughout the Market House.

Old Packet House

1 Navigation Road, WA14 1LW
(0161) 929 1331
Tatton Blonde; Timothy Taylor Golden Best, Landlord
Dating back to the 18th century, this was once the second inn on the journey from Manchester along the Bridgewater Canal, which runs just behind the pub. Leaded and stained glass feature in the back bar and partitions around the pub. The main bar area is divided by an impressive central chimney, warmed by a real fire in winter. Home-cooked food is popular with local office workers at lunchtime. Attractions include quiz night on Monday, karaoke on Friday and regular football on TV.

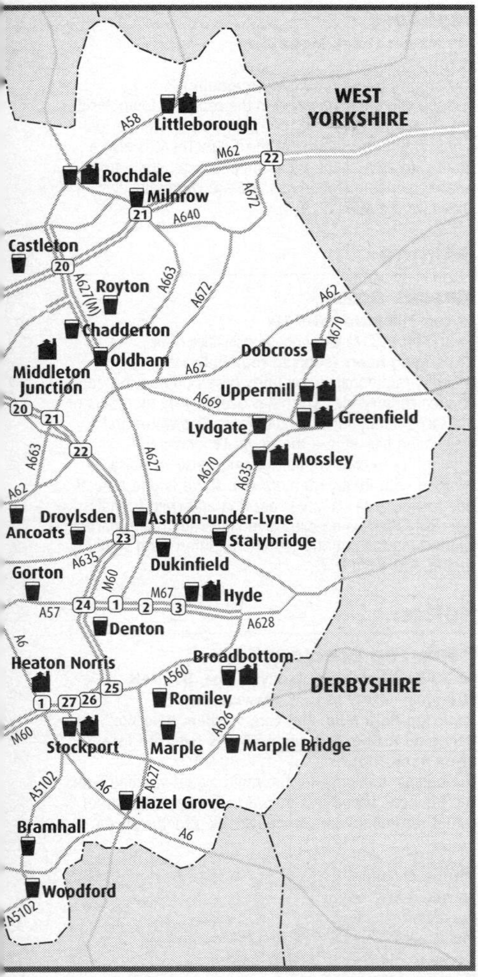

Pi 𝕃

18 Shaws Road, WA14 1QU

☎ (0161) 929 9098 🌐 abarcalledpi.com

Tatton Blonde; 2 changing beers (sourced nationally; often RedWillow, Saltaire, Stubborn Mule) Ⓗ

Next door to the bustling Market Hall eatery, the smaller Pi is quieter but still popular. Its three handpumps serve one regular beer from Tatton and two guests. There are also guest keg beers from breweries such as Cloudwater and Lervig, plus a wide selection of bottles and cans in the large fridges. More seating is available upstairs. Outside at the front are pavement tables with blankets for cooler weather. Pieminister pies and mash are served daily. ☺❀◐♿⇌🚉♣●🚌🐾📶

Ancoats

Cask

2 New Union Street, Cotton Field Wharf, M4 6FQ (over bridge from Redhill St)

☎ (0161) 392 0809

6 changing beers (sourced regionally; often Squawk) Ⓗ

This sister pub to Cask Liverpool Road is on the ground floor of a newly built complex, adjacent to the Rochdale canal and within the marina area at New Islington. It serves a changing range of six handpulled ales from local and regional breweries, plus a cider on handpump and 20 keg beers, some from Spain and other European countries. A courtyard overlooking the marina is open to 9pm every day. ♿🚉(New Islington)♣●🐾

Ashton-in-Makerfield

Caledonian Hotel

154 Bolton Road, WN4 8AE

☎ (01942) 727875

2 changing beers (sourced regionally) Ⓗ

Large former Walkers free house, built in 1897, featuring an open-plan lounge, games room with TV and an upstairs function room. Two guest beers are served. Prints of old Ashton are on display. The pub hosts an open mic night on Tuesday, a popular quiz on Thursday evening and live music in the lounge most Saturday nights. It also holds occasional mini beer festivals. ☺❀♣P🚌📶

Twisted Vine Ale House 🏆 𝕃

15 Wigan Road, WN4 9AR

7 changing beers (sourced regionally) Ⓗ

A microbar from Hophurst Brewery, it opened in 2018 offering seven cask handpumps, six keg taps, three real ciders and a selection of gins, spirits and wines. The pub has a quiz night and beer club, and hosts live music on Sundays and the first Thursday of the month. It is open to over-18s only and welcomes dogs. Local CAMRA Pub of the Year 2020. ●🚌🐾

Ashton-under-Lyne

Ash Tree ✔

9-11 Wellington Road, OL6 6DA

☎ (0161) 339 9670

Greene King Abbot; Moorhouse's Blond Witch; Ruddles Best Bitter; Sharp's Doom Bar; 4 changing beers (sourced regionally) Ⓗ

Directly facing the Victorian Market Hall, this pub was extended into the former snooker hall next door in 2019. Its upper-floor veranda overlooks a beer garden that stretches the depth of the building, creating a space that is particularly attractive in fine weather. The pub's 11 handpumps serve Wetherspoon's regular beers plus others sourced locally and nationwide. ☺❀◐♿⇌🚉●P🚌📶

Dog & Pheasant ✔

528 Oldham Road, OL7 9PQ

☎ (0161) 330 4894

Marston's Saddle Tank, Pedigree Ⓗ**; 3 changing beers** Ⓗ/Ⓖ

Popular local near the Medlock Valley Country Park, a regular in this Guide since 1992. Its large U-shaped bar serves three areas, plus another room at the front. The beer range is supplemented by three guest ales from the Marston's portfolio. A menu of good-value food includes vegetarian options. Quiz night is Thursday and open mic evening takes place on Monday. ❀◐♿P🚌(409,419)

Tapsters 𝕃

31 Old Street, OL6 6LA (100yds from SE corner of Market Hall)

☎ (0161) 465 0205

3 changing beers (sourced nationally; often Jennings, Robinsons, Theakston) Ⓗ

Previously a high-street shop in the town centre close to the indoor market and both the bus and rail stations. Opened in 2018, it has been fitted out to a high standard resulting in a welcoming, quiet, comfortable and spacious place to enjoy a pint or two. There is a small courtyard-style beer garden to the rear. Food is served. Three cask ales are on offer mainly supplied by national and regional brewers. Q❀◐♿⇌🚉🚌📶

Astley

Cart & Horses Hotel

221 Manchester Road, M29 7SD

☎ (01942) 886530

Joseph Holt Bitter Ⓗ

Friendly traditional roadside community pub with darts and dominoes teams. The lounge has two seating areas plus a third that is used for dining. There are benches at the front and a large beer garden and patio at the rear. Good-value food is served every day and there are regular live music nights. Q♘❀◐◑♣P🚌(34)🐾

Atherton

Pendle Witch

2-4 Warburton Place, M46 0EQ

☎ (01942) 884537

Moorhouse's Black Cat, Premier Bitter, Pride of Pendle, Blond Witch, Pendle Witches Brew; 2 changing beers Ⓗ

A real gem hidden down a narrow alley near the church and marketplace. The entrance leads to an open-plan bar that serves the full range of Moorhouse's beers plus guests. A large selection of Belgian bottled beers is also kept. There is a conservatory at the front and a games area and bar to the rear. The well-kept patio is popular in summer. ♘❀◐♿♣P🚌(V2)

Taphouse

119 Market Street, M46 0DF

☎ (01942) 367519

4 changing beers (sourced regionally) Ⓗ

Micropub on the main street in the centre of town. Inside this comfortable, friendly one-room bar there are four tables with extra seating at the sides. There is also a small yard area at the back. Beers are generally from small regional microbrewers and are competitively priced. ♘❀♿●🚌(V2)📶

Billinge

Masons Arms

99 Carr Mill Road, WN5 7TY

☎ (01744) 603572 🌐 masonsarmsbillinge.co.uk

5 changing beers (sourced regionally) Ⓗ

Friendly, traditional, community-based pub on the edge of open countryside, which has been run by members of the same family for over 200 years. The warm and welcoming bar, where the single TV allows the opportunity to chat without glaring music or noise, is adorned with Rugby memorabilia. There is also a quiet side lounge area. All areas are dog and child friendly. Externally there is an extensive landscaped beer garden overlooking the countryside and an interesting smoking shelter. ❀♿●P🚏🐾📶

Bolton

Bank Top Brewery Tap

68-70 Belmont Road, Astley Bridge, BL1 7AN

☎ (01204) 302837 🌐 banktopbrewery.com

Bank Top Dark Mild, Flat Cap, Pavilion Pale Ale, Palomino Rising; 5 changing beers (sourced locally; often Bank Top) Ⓗ

The original taphouse for the multi-award winning Bank Top Brewery, based less than a mile away. This street-corner community local comprises two rooms plus a

REAL ALE BREWERIES

Alphabet ✎ Manchester
Bank Top Bolton
Beatnikz Republic Manchester
Beer Nouveau ✎ Manchester: Ardwick
Blackedge ✎ Horwich
Blackjack Manchester
Brightside Radcliffe
Cheadle 🛢 Cheadle
Cloudwater Manchester
Deeply Vale Bury
Donkeystone ✎ Greenfield
Dunham Massey Dunham Massey
Escape Bolton (NEW)
Federation 🛢 Altrincham (brewing suspended)
First Chop Eccles
Fool Hardy 🛢 Stockport: Heaton Norris
Four Kings ✎ Hyde
Gasworks 🛢 Manchester
Green Mill 🛢 Broadbottom
Hay Rake 🛢 Littleborough
Holy Well Egerton
Hophurst Hindley
Howfen Westhoughton
Hydes Salford
Irwell Works ✎ Ramsbottom
Joseph Holt Cheetham
JW Lees Middleton Junction
Made of Stone 🛢 Stockport
Manchester Manchester
Manchester Union Manchester
Marble ✎ Salford
Martland Mill Wigan
Mayflower Hindley
Millstone Mossley
Northern Monkey ✎ Bolton
Origami Manchester
Outstanding Manchester: Ordsall
Phoenix Heywood
Pictish Rochdale
Pomona Island Salford
Prospect Wigan
Red Rose Ramsbottom (NEW)
Remedy 🛢 Stockport
Rising Sun 🛢 Mossley
Robinsons Stockport
Runaway Manchester
Saddleworth 🛢 Uppermill
Serious ✎ Rochdale
Seven Bro7hers Salford
Silver Street Bury
Squawk Manchester: Ardwick
Stockport Stockport
Stubborn Mule Altrincham
Thirst Class Stockport
To The Moon Stockport (NEW)
Track Manchester
Twisted Wheel ✎ Standish (NEW)
Wander Beyond Manchester
Watts Brewing? 🛢 Stockport
Wigan Wigan
Wily Fox Wigan

large outdoor area with smoking shelter. There are nine handpumps showcasing the brewery's ales – including regulars Flat Cap, Pavilion Pale and Dark Mild plus the current seasonal – and a guest beer. Up to six cellar-cool bag-in-box real ciders are also on offer.
🐎❀♿♣🍎🚌(1,534,535) 🐾📶

Great Ale at the Vaults 𝕃

Vaults Below Market Place, BL1 2AL
☎ (01204) 773458
4 changing beers (sourced locally) 🄷
Atmospheric bar situated in the centre of the refurbished vaults of the former Market Hall, whose upper floors contain shops and a cinema. Four handpumps dispense Vaults Bitter, specially brewed by Outstanding Brewery, and guest beers from near and far. Tasting paddles of cask ale are available, plus usually one real cider. Cold bar food is offered. Adjoining the bar are numerous food outlets. **Q**🐎◑♿⇌🍎**P**🚌📶

Hen & Chickens ✔

143 Deansgate, BL1 1EX
☎ 07850 026681
5 changing beers (sourced locally; often Lancaster, Northern Monkey, Three B's) 🄷
The Hen & Chickens has long been one of the most pleasant and popular of town-centre pubs. Its smart exterior and colourful floral displays brighten up this end of Deansgate. Inside there is a central horseshoe bar serving both sides of the pub. Although now open plan, the entrance doors lead on the left to the smaller vault with a comfortable raised seating area, and on the right to the lounge where food is available. ❀◑⇌♣🚌📶

Northern Monkey 🏆 𝕃

Nelson Square, BL1 1AQ
☎ 07737 125629 🌐 northernmonkeybrew.co.uk
4 changing beers (sourced locally; often Hophurst, Northern Monkey) 🄷
This brewpub was set up and renovated from what was previously a restaurant, though originally it was the dining room of the Pack Horse Hotel which dominated this side of Nelson Square. The four real ales include Northern Monkey beers, brewed on the premises, and sometimes a couple of guests. At least one dark ale is normally available. Eight fonts serve modern keg beers from Northern Monkey and elsewhere. 🐎⇌🚌🐾📶

One for the Road

F14-F15 Ashburner Street Lifestyle Hall, BL1 1TJ
☎ 07725 338773
3 changing beers (sourced locally) 🄷
This microbar is in Bolton's award-winning indoor market. It serves three beers from a wide range of smaller breweries, plus a selection of bottled and canned beers. A large seating area at the front of the bar is home to take-away food vendors, with dishes from Malaysia and Cameroon alongside more standard sandwiches and pasties. Opening days and hours are restricted to those of the main market. **Q**🐎♿⇌🍎**P**🚌📶

Swan & Barristers Bar

7 Bradshawgate, BL1 1EL (entrance to both bars is in passageway between them)
☎ (01204) 365174
Bank Top Flat Cap; Moorhouse's Blond Witch; 5 changing beers (sourced locally; often Abbeydale, Blackedge, Wainwright) 🄷
Swan & Barristers is a prominent Grade II listed building comprising two separate bars with a shared courtyard and toilet area between them. The Swan is a comfortable, spacious bar which converts to a nightclub at weekend evenings. Barristers has a wood-panelled interior with a traditional pub atmosphere. Cask beers from local breweries such as Bank Top, Moorhouse's and Blackedge are supplemented by ales from further afield such as Fyne, Coniston and St Austell. ❀◑♿⇌🍎🚌🐾📶

Boothstown

Royal British Legion

Victoria Street, M28 1HQ (close to jct with Vicars Hall Lane)
☎ (0161) 790 2928
Joseph Holt Bitter; Wainwright 🄷
A large, friendly club, welcoming to non-members. A lounge to the right of the entrance leads to a games and television room, while a function room is found at the rear. The garden is ideal for summer drinking. Live entertainment features and a beer festival is held in November. The steward and stewardess have been awarded the Queen's medal for voluntary service. A regular winner in the Club Mirror awards and local CAMRA Club of the Year. **Q**🐎❀♿♣**P**🚌📶

Bramhall

Mounting Stone

8 Woodford Road, SK7 1JJ (jct Bramhall Lane S)
☎ (0161) 439 7563 🌐 themountingstone.co.uk
Bollington Long Hop, Bollington Best; 4 changing beers (sourced locally) 🄷
The sister pub to Cheadle Hulme's Chiverton Tap, this is a cosy, friendly micropub right in the village centre. The former blacksmith's operates over two floors – ground and basement – with a small beer garden to the rear. The name derives from a local large stone that allowed riders to mount their horses. Alongside the Bollington ales are four from microbrewers, one usually a dark beer. The pub opened an on-site, one-barrel brewery named Made of Stone in 2018. **Q**🐎❀♿⇌🍎🚌🐾📶

Broadbottom

Harewood Arms 𝕃 ✔

2 Market Street, SK14 6AX
☎ (01457) 762500 🌐 greenmillbrewery.com/harewood-arms
Green Mill Chief, Old Git; 4 changing beers (sourced locally; often Green Mill) 🄷
A large pub for all the community in this quiet village on the edge of the Peak District. Home to the Green Mill Brewery, it serves five regular Green Mill ales plus seasonals, guests and a rotating real cider. Partially open plan, with various seating areas and two real fires, the pub also has a beer garden to the rear. Approximately five minutes' walk from Broadbottom railway station and on local bus routes. 🐎❀◑♿⛺⇌♣🍎▯🚌🐾📶

Bromley Cross

Nook & Cranny

211/213 Darwen Road, BL7 9BS
☎ 07403 030394
3 changing beers (sourced locally; often Northern Monkey, Northern Whisper) 🄷
Friendly micropub that opened in 2018 in what was once a shop, extended into the adjacent premises a year later to provide additional seating. Large bench tables help spark a convivial atmosphere that attracts locals and visitors alike. Three handpumps dispense ales, most from local breweries. There is also a good range of real ciders and modern keg beers. ⇌🍎**P**🚌🐾📶

Burnage

Reasons to be Cheerful

228 Fog Lane, M20 6EL (jct of Elmsmere Rd, near Burnage BR and Parrs Wood Rd)

☎ (0161) 425 9678 ⊕ reasonsbeercafe.co.uk

3 changing beers (sourced locally) Ⓗ

Modern beer café in former shop premises on a shopping parade near Burnage railway station. The small, inconspicuous frontage hides a long but welcoming interior, including an alcove providing seating and a view of the street. The L-shaped bar is fitted with three handpulls. Eight craft beer taps are mounted on the back bar, and there is also a display rack for off-sales. A secluded rear room can accommodate up to 20 people. Outside at the front is a small drinking area. Card payment only. Q✿✿≉ℛ(Didsbury Village)●➡✿ ≈

Bury

Art Picture House Ⓛ ✅

36 Haymarket Street, BL9 0AY

☎ (0161) 705 4040

Brightside Odin Blonde; Greene King Abbot; Moorhouse's Blond Witch; Ruddles Best Bitter; changing beers Ⓗ

Town-centre pub in a beautifully restored former 1920s cinema opposite the bus and tram interchange. Its large seating area is on two levels with several private booths facing the back bar. Eight handpumps dispense regular and changing beers from near and far, served by a team of experienced bar staff who can help with your selection. Food is available every day. ➷◗◗&≉(Bolton St ELR) ℛ●➡ ≈

Elton Liberal Club

New George Street, BL8 1NW

☎ (0161) 764 1776 ⊕ eltonliberalclub.co.uk

2 changing beers (often Brewsmith, Brightside, Moorhouse's) Ⓗ

Private members' club whose facilities include three bars, three snooker tables and a TV showing sport, plus two function rooms available to hire for members. Outside is a bowling green with seating around it. Live music plays every Saturday and Sunday, with a band on the last Sunday of the month. Guests must be signed in by members. Q➷✿✿&♣P➡✿ ≈

Lamb Ⓛ

533 Tottington Road, Woolfold, BL8 1UB (on B6213 from Bury)

☎ (0161) 764 2714

3 changing beers (sourced locally; often Bingley, Brewsmith, Moorhouse's) Ⓗ

A well-run local with a reputation for being a friendly pub where all are welcome and beers are in tip-top condition. The warm atmosphere is enhanced by an open fire in winter. The Lamb, originally a coaching house, was built in 1831. Two handpumps are always in use, one serving Doom Bar and the other a changing ale. Local microbreweries are promoted, predominantly Brewsmith although others feature. ➷✿♣P➡(469)✿ ≈

Robert Peel Ⓛ ✅

10 Market Place, BL9 0LD

☎ (0161) 764 7287

Greene King Abbot; Ruddles County; Sharp's Doom Bar; changing beers (often Brightside, Moorhouse's, Phoenix) Ⓗ

Well-established and popular Wetherspoon pub in Bury's cultural quarter, named after the local mill owner and MP whose son became Prime Minister and founded the modern police force. The pub has the largest open public

area in Bury. Its decor celebrates other local worthies such as Richmal Crompton, author of the Just William books. Ten handpumps include six dedicated to the regular brews, the others dispensing varying ales. Four real ciders are always available. ➷◗◗&≉(Bolton St ELR) ℛ●➡✿ ≈

Thirsty Fish Ⓛ

Unit 1A Princess Parade, Millgate Shopping Centre, BL9 0QL

Beartown Creme Bearlee; Deeply Vale Citra Storm; house beer (by Beartown); 8 changing beers (often Brewsmith, Moorhouse's) Ⓗ

A true microbar that opened in 2018 in a former unit in the shopping centre. The Thirsty Fish is adjacent to the famous Bury Market and the Bury Interchange transport hub, handy for the bus and Metrolink. The bar sells eight constantly changing real ales. It also has a good selection of continental lagers and up to six real ciders. Children are not permitted. &≉(Bolton St ELR)ℛ●➡✿ ≈

Trackside Bar Ⓛ ✅

Bolton Street Station, BL9 0EY (platform 2 East Lancs Railway)

☎ (0161) 764 6461 ⊕ eastlancsrailway.org.uk/plan-your-day-out/food-drink/the-trackside.aspx

House beer (by Northern Whisper); changing beers Ⓗ

The Trackside combines some excellent ales and cider with the nostalgia of the East Lancashire Railway. At the bar, the house beer from Northern Whisper is joined by 11 varying guest ales alongside craft keg and foreign bottled beers. This former local CAMRA branch Cider Pub of the Year sells up to 10 real ciders or perries. The station platform just outside has seating under a roof canopy, creating a lovely suntrap, with wall heaters for cooler weather. ➷✿✿&Å≉(Bolton St ELR)ℛ●P➡✿ ≈

Cadishead

Grocer's ♆

152A Liverpool Road, M44 5DD (close to Moss Lane next door to Plough)

☎ 07950 522468

3 changing beers (sourced regionally; often Blackedge, Brewsmith, Dunham Massey) Ⓗ/Ⓖ

This micropub in what was a grocer's shop has thrived since opening in 2015. It has one room and no bar; beers are brought to your table by the proprietor from a separate air-chilled room. One beer is on handpull and two on gravity, alongside three ciders or perries. The lack of TV, jukebox or other electronic entertainment means conversation is king. The pub is cash only and may close early if quiet. It has a yard to the rear for outside drinking. Local CAMRA Pub and Cider Pub of the Year 2020. Q➷✿✿&●➡(67,100)✿

Castleton

Blue Pits Inn

842 Manchester Road, OL11 2SP

☎ (01706) 632151

JW Lees Manchester Pale Ale, Bitter; 1 changing beer (sourced locally; often JW Lees) Ⓗ

Friendly pub in the heart of Castleton, popular with locals and easily accessible by bus or train. The former railway building has a tiled mosaic of 19th-century brewery owner and local mayor John Willie Lees on an outside wall. Three quality JW Lees beers are always served. Entertainment includes karaoke and quiz nights plus pub games in the taproom. ➷✿✿≉♣P➡(17)✿ ≈

Old Post Office Ale House

858 Manchester Road, OL11 2SP
☎ (01706) 645464
House beer (by Pictish); 4 changing beers (sourced locally; often Beartown, Outstanding)
Opened in 2016, this microbar is well served by public transport – the railway station is across the road and the bus to Rochdale stops outside the door. Five handpulled beers are served alongside a good selection of real ciders and other drinks. There is no food but you can bring your own. The bar welcomes dogs and has a well laid-out beer garden at the rear. Q❀⇌🍏🚌(17)🐾📶

Chadderton

Crown Inn

72 Walsh Street, OL9 9LR (off Middleton Rd via Peel St)
☎ (0161) 915 1557
JW Lees Bitter; 2 changing beers (sourced locally; often Leatherbritches, Millstone, Naylor's)
Large and open family-run free house in the industrial heart of Chadderton, close to Freehold Metrolink and bus services. The pub hosts the Hollinwood rugby league club plus football and darts teams, and can suddenly be enlivened when players return to discuss victory or defeat. Live music plays on Saturday night and sport is screened on three TVs, with a big screen for major events. ❀♿(Freehold)♣🚌(415)🐾📶

Rose of Lancaster

7 Haigh Lane, OL1 2TQ
☎ (0161) 624 3031 🌐 roseoflancaster.co.uk
JW Lees Manchester Pale Ale, Bitter; 3 changing beers (sourced locally; often JW Lees)
A lounge bar, conservatory restaurant and separate vault where sporting events are screened provide plenty of choice for the Rose of Lancaster's varied clientele. Beers from JW Lees' seasonal and Boilerhouse ranges are always available. A covered patio with views of the Rochdale Canal is popular in fine weather. Nearby bus and train links facilitate travel to this well-run and popular pub. ❀◐♿⇌(Mills Hill)♣P🚌(59,412)📶

Cheadle Hulme

Archive Bar & Bottle

2 Mellor Road, SK8 5AU (jct Station Rd)
4 changing beers (sourced regionally)
Opened in 2019, this homely, modern micropub occupies former restaurant premises opposite the station. The bar operates over two floors with upstairs accessed by a spiral staircase, divided into a lounge area and snug (toilets are here too). Four changing ales are served, one usually a dark beer. The bar also offers 12 eclectic keg lines and two keg ciders. A well-stocked fridge holds over 300 beers. Note the archive display of beer bottles on shelves throughout every room. ❀◐⇌🚌🐾📶

Chiverton Tap

8 Mellor Road, SK8 5AU (off Station Rd)
☎ (0161) 485 4149 🌐 chivertontap.co.uk
Bollington Long Hop, Bollington Best; 4 changing beers (sourced locally)
Friendly micropub in what was once Arthur Chiverton's draper's shop. Note the mosaic in the doorway and framed displays of photographs and drapery tools on the walls and bar. Alongside its cask and keg beers, the pub serves a wide variety of gins and a changing bag-in-box real cider. In 2019 it expanded with a first-floor function room and outside area at the rear with tables.
Q♿⇌🍏🚌🐾📶

Chorlton-cum-Hardy

Beer House

57 Manchester Road, M21 9PW
☎ (0161) 881 9206
Marble Manchester Bitter, Pint; 4 changing beers (sourced locally; often Ilkley, Pomona Island, Squawk)
Ever-popular micropub whose knowledgeable staff provide a warm welcome. The focus is on quality beer, with regulars Marble Bitter and Pint plus a changing selection of guests. Top-quality craft beers are served from the keg, along with excellent canned and bottled brews. Real cider, often Hallets, is dispensed by handpump. Traditional games supplement games console favourites from the 1980s. No food is served but bar snacks are available. ❀♣🍏🚌(86)🐾📶

Chorlton Tap

533 Wilbraham Road, M21 0UE
☎ (0161) 861 7576 🌐 chorltontap.wixsite.com/chorltontap
Wander Beyond Peak; 5 changing beers (sourced regionally; often Howard Town, Marble, Pictish)
This taproom for the Wander Beyond brewery was previously a beer specialist for 25 years as the Bar. What was once two distinct properties is now a small bar area and spacious adjacent room. Two handpumps and several keg lines dispense the brewery's beers, alongside four guests on handpump. Monday is quiz night. Food is available Friday to Sunday.
❀◐♣🍏🚌🐾📶

Font

115-117 Manchester Road, M21 9PG
☎ (0161) 871 2022 🌐 thefontbar.wordpress.com
8 changing beers (sourced nationally; often RedWillow, Mallinsons, Track)
Notable beer and cider haven that has been voted local CAMRA Cider Pub of the Year six times in the last seven years. It features eight varying real ales on the bar, one usually from RedWillow. There are also 16 keg lines of which roughly half are regularly changing guests. A small font wall dispenses up to six ciders. The open kitchen serves breakfast as well as a full menu daily. A quiz is held on Tuesday. ❀◐🍏🚌(86)🐾📶

Chorlton-on-Medlock

Sandbar

120-122 Grosvenor Street, M1 7HL (off Oxford Rd A34/B5117 jct) 🌐 sandbarmanchester.co.uk
Facer's Clwyd Gold; Phoenix Arizona; Silver Street Brewing Co Porter; 4 changing beers (sourced regionally)
Originally two 18th-century town houses, this is now one of the longest-established bars on the university area beer scene. Quirky and bohemian, it is popular with students and university staff alike. There are regular exhibitions of photographs and paintings, and displays of old curios. The cask beers are usually local and are accompanied by modern British and European bottled, canned and kegged beers, plus a changing guest cider. Home-made vegetarian and vegan pizzas are available most days. Payment by card only.
❀◐⇌(Manchester Oxford Rd)(St Peters Sq)🍏🚌📶

Denton

Carters Arms

Stockport Road, M34 6AQ
☎ (0161) 320 3752
Black Sheep Best Bitter; Wainwright; 2 changing beers (sourced locally)

Friendly local with two large open-plan rooms. The lounge-style space to the left is regularly hired out for functions for up to 70 people; the traditional bar/games room on the right features wood panelling and dark leather seating. The pool team plays on Wednesday, live music features on Friday, karaoke and disco night is Saturday. Accompanied children are welcome until 8pm. There is wheelchair access to the rear. The pub is accessible by bus from Manchester and Stockport.
Q♿♣P🚌🐾

Crown Point Tavern

16 Market Street, M34 2XW (in Denton Civic Sq)
☎ (0161) 337 9615 🌐 thecrownpointtavern.co.uk
5 changing beers (sourced locally)
A micropub on the pedestrianised Denton Civic Square, popular for watching televised sporting events. Six real ales are served, typically sourced from Greater Manchester, with information including style and taste shown on a blackboard. They are complemented by an extensive selection of bottled local craft beers, two real ciders and a range of gins. Offers include 10 per cent discount for OAPs on weekdays and a cask club card giving every 10th pint free. Entertainment includes a DJ on Sunday. Q♿♣🚌🐾

Lowes Arms

301 Hyde Road, M34 3FF
☎ (0161) 336 3064 🌐 lowesarms.co.uk
4 changing beers (sourced regionally; often Conwy, Cross Bay)
Built in 1824 to serve the new Manchester Road, this thriving local has a reputation for quality beers and good-value food. Ales from Cross Bay and Conwy breweries feature regularly on the frequently changing list of guest beers. The comfortable lounge is also the main food area. The vault has a pool table and can be used as a function room. The pub hosts local league darts and dominoes teams, and holds occasional beer festivals.
Q♿♣P🚌(150,201)🐾

Didsbury

Fletcher Moss ✓

1 William Street, M20 6RQ (off Wilmslow Rd, A5145 via Albert Hill St)
☎ (0161) 438 0073 🌐 thefletchermoss.co.uk
Hydes Original, Lowry; 5 changing beers (sourced nationally; often Hydes)
Named after the alderman who donated the nearby botanical gardens, this thriving community local provides a haven for lively conversation. Three traditional front snugs contain a collection of pretty porcelain teapots. The rear opens into a conservatory leading to outdoor covered terraces and a beer garden. A quiz is held on Tuesday and acoustic music plays on alternate Mondays. The TVs are silent except for major sporting events.
Q♿(Village)🚌

Gateway ✓

882 Wilmslow Road, M20 5PG (jct Kingsway and Manchester Rd)
☎ (0161) 438 1700
Greene King Abbot; Ruddles Best Bitter; house beer (by Brightside); 5 changing beers (sourced nationally)
This comfortable and popular 1930s roadhouse, conveniently located opposite the Parrs Wood leisure complex and public transport interchange, stands out due to its welcoming atmosphere, enthusiastic staff and excellent beer. The large Wetherspoon pub's central island bar is surrounded by distinct seating areas, ensuring that you can always have a quiet drink somewhere. An upstairs function room plays host to local social activities and groups.
Q♿(East)(East)P🚌

Dobcross

Dobcross Band Social Club

Platt Lane, OL3 5AD
☎ (01457) 873741 🌐 dobcross.club
Bradfield Farmers Blonde; JW Lees Bitter; 2 changing beers (sourced locally; often Greene King, Joseph Holt)
This club, near Oldham, is over 100 years old and provides beautiful views of Saddleworth Moor. The function room hosts three brass bands, including the famous Dobcross Silver Band. The games room has a dartboard and full-sized snooker table; a TV shows BT Sport. Crown green bowls takes place in summer. Local CAMRA branch Club of the Year 2019 and 2020.
♿♣P🚌(356)🐾

Navigation Inn

21-23 Wool Road, OL3 5NS
☎ (01457) 872418 🌐 thenavigationdobcross.com
Greene King Abbot; Millstone Tiger Rut; Timothy Taylor Landlord; 1 changing beer (often Millstone)
Traditional family-run pub, built in 1806 and nestling in the rolling countryside of Saddleworth close to the Huddersfield Narrow Canal. It serves several handpulled beers alongside wines and a varied choice of freshly prepared food. A venue for the popular Saddleworth Rushcart Festival in August.
Q♿P🚌(184,354)🐾

Droylsden

Silly Country Bar & Bottle Shop

121 Market Street, M43 7AR
4 changing beers (sourced locally)
Modern open-plan bar and bottle shop on the corner of Droylsden Shopping Centre. Opened in 2018 by a group of local real ale enthusiasts, it has provided a much-needed boost to the real ale scene in the area. Five handpumps dispense four mostly local ales and a cider, complemented by an extensive range of bottled beers and ciders. Droylsden tram stop is across the road from the bar. Q♿♣🚌🐾

Dukinfield

Angel

197 King Street, SK16 4TH
☎ (0161) 830 0223 🌐 theangeldukinfield.co.uk
4 changing beers (sourced nationally)
Popular and well-furnished community pub near the centre of Dukinfield, featuring a traditional snug to the left and lounge to the right. It serves four constantly changing beers from national and local breweries. The pub hosts a quiz on Sunday and has local league teams in pool, darts, dominoes and crib. Children are welcome until 8pm. The sizeable upstairs function room has its own bar and is available to hire. ♿♣P🚌(330)🐾

Eccles

Lamb Hotel ★

33 Regent Street, M30 0BP (opp Metrolink station)
☎ 07827 850252
Joseph Holt Mild, Bitter; 1 changing beer (sourced nationally)
Classic red-brick and terracotta Grade II listed Joseph Holt pub that has starred in several television dramas. Its

interior features Jacobean-style door surrounds, terrazzo floors and a dado of green tiles leading to a screened, curved mahogany bar with polished brass and exquisite etched glass. To the right of the bar is a vault; to the left a lobby leading to lounges and a billiard room with full-sized table and raised seating. Q≠♣P🚌🐾ᯤ

Golborne

Queen Anne

14 Bridge Street, WA3 3PZ

☎ (01942) 726922 🌐 queenanne-golborne.co.uk

2 changing beers (sourced regionally) Ⓗ

Tucked away on Bridge Street just off the East Lancs Road, the Queen Anne is handy for Haydock Park racecourse and caters for pre-race parties. Home-cooked food is served in the bar and separate dining area, with early-bird specials on weekdays plus Sunday roasts. The beer garden is a suntrap in summer. Q❀P🚌(10)ᯤ

Gorton

Vale Cottage

Kirk Street, M18 8UE (off Hyde Rd A57, E of jct Chapman St)

☎ (0161) 223 4568 🌐 thevalecottage.co.uk

Timothy Taylor Landlord; 2 changing beers (sourced nationally) Ⓗ

Well hidden in the Gore Brook conservation area, the Vale Cottage has the feel of a country pub. Parts date from the 17th century, hence the low-beamed ceilings, multiple drinking areas and reputed ghost. A relaxed, friendly atmosphere, where conversation predominates, is disturbed on Tuesday by a lively and popular general knowledge quiz. Indulge in an excellent home-cooked meal in the garden, or even join in the music quiz and steak night on the last Thursday of the month.
Q❀♿≠(Ryder Brow/Belle Vue/Gorton) P🚌ᯤ

Greenfield

Donkeystone Brewery Tap

Units 17-18 Boarshurst Business Park, OL3 7ER

☎ (01457) 238710 🌐 donkeystonebrewing.co.uk

Donkeystone APA, Bad Ass Blonde, Bray, DPA, Neddy; house beer (by Donkeystone); 4 changing beers (sourced locally; often Donkeystone) Ⓗ

The Tap adjoins the Donkeystone Brewery, a steep stroll from Greenfield village and surrounded by good walks around the popular Dovestone reservoir and wider Saddleworth area. It serves 10 beers via six handpulls and four keg fonts. Bench seating and sofas are arranged in front of an efficient wood-burning stove. Dog walkers, children and mountain bikers are welcome.
♿P🚌(180,350) 🐾

Wellington Inn 🄻

29 Chew Valley Road, OL3 7AF

☎ (01457) 873450

Coach House Gunpowder Mild; Mansfield Cask Ale; Millstone Tiger Rut; Phoenix Arizona; Salopian Lemon Dream; Wainwright; 2 changing beers (sourced locally; often Donkeystone, Phoenix) Ⓗ

Family-owned village end-of-terrace free house with a welcoming feel. The building comprises a small bar area offering seven handpulled beers, a main room popular with diners, and a side room with a dartboard, cribbage and dominoes. There is outdoor seating. The pub serves good-value home-cooked food including daily specials on Wednesday, Friday and Sunday. Pies, puddings and real chips are particularly popular, and fish on Friday.
▲≠♣🚌(180,350) 🐾ᯤ

Greenmount

Greenmount Cricket Club

Brandlesholme Road, BL8 4DX

☎ (01204) 883667 🌐 greenmountcc.leaguerepublic.com/index.html

Brewsmith Bitter; 1 changing beer (often Eagle, Strata) Ⓗ

Friendly club that welcomes visitors, card-carrying CAMRA members and well-behaved dogs, and is popular with walkers due to its proximity to the Kirklees Trail. It has two pool tables, with one kept for league matches. Sitting outside on a warm summer weekend watching cricket and supping fine ales is many people's idea of heaven. During the cricket season the club is open midday-10.30pm at weekends. ❀♣P🚌🐾ᯤ

Harwood

House without a Name 🄻

75 Lea Gate, BL2 3ET

☎ (01204) 433568 🌐 housewithoutaname.co.uk

Joseph Holt Bitter; Sharp's Doom Bar; 4 changing beers (sourced locally; often Moorhouse's, Northern Monkey, Titanic) Ⓗ

Locally known as the No Name, this cosy terraced venue was two 1830s cottages before being refurbished and sensitively modernised, retaining the flag floors and wooden beams. Its main lounge has a bar servery and features a blackboard beer listing, real fire and TV showing sport. There is also a small bar to the left. Simple bar food is served during opening hours.
❀🚌(480,507) 🐾ᯤ

Hazel Grove

Grove Alehouse

145 London Road, SK7 4HH (opp Hope St)

☎ 07594 123174

5 changing beers (sourced regionally) Ⓗ

Micropub with an airy feel, set in former butcher's premises. Its bar is made from reclaimed wood and sits in an L-shaped drinking area with a good mix of bench seating, bar stools, tables and chairs. The five handpumped beers include a dark ale and are mostly from local producers. Three real ciders are served from the fridge. Bring-your-own cheese tastings are held on the first Sunday of the month. Q❀≠♣🚌🐾ᯤ

Hindley

Hare & Hounds 🄻

31 Ladies Lane, WN2 2QA

☎ (01942) 200370

5 changing beers Ⓗ

In this Guide several times, this small but traditional venue is between Hindley railway station and the town centre. There is a large cosy lounge and a distinct bar/vault area. The lounge displays pictures from bygone Hindley and has a large-screen TV for sports. It has a team playing in the local darts league. ❀≠♣🐾ᯤ

Horwich

Bank Top Brewery Ale House 🄻 ✔

36 Church Street, BL6 6AD

☎ (01204) 693793 🌐 banktopbrewery.com

Bank Top Bad to the Bone, Dark Mild, Flat Cap, Pavilion Pale Ale, Palomino Rising, Port o' Call; 3 changing beers (sourced locally; often Bank Top) Ⓗ

Award-winning Bank Top Brewery pub, in a conservation area opposite Horwich parish church and alongside 18th

and 19th-century cottages associated with the area's history of textiles and bleaching. The pub serves eight beers from Bank Top, including Dark Mild, a former Champion Mild of Britain, plus one changing guest. Alongside are up to six real ciders and perries, most kept cellar cool. Walkers and their dogs are welcome.
Q🔥❀♣🍎🚌(125) 🐾

Brewery Bar Ⓛ

Moreton Mill, Hampson Street, BL6 7JH (just behind the Old Original Bay Horse)
☎ (01204) 692976 🌐 thebrewerybar.co.uk
Blackedge Hop, Black, Pike; 4 changing beers (sourced locally; often Blackedge) Ⓗ
This bar above the award-winning Blackedge Brewery has seven handpumps serving its beers, plus a range of real ciders. Converted from a former industrial premises and retaining some original features, it has comfortable settees and barrel tables with stools spread throughout a large drinking area. Locally made pork and Blackedge Ale pies are usually available. The brewery is visible through large glass windows as you enter. Note there is no lift.
🔥❀♣🍎🚌📶

Crown Ⓛ

1 Chorley New Road, BL6 7QJ
☎ 07827 850221
Joseph Holt Mild, IPA, Bitter, Two Hoots; 4 changing beers (sourced locally; often Bank Top, Blackedge, Bootleg) Ⓗ
A spacious, comfortable and popular landmark pub whose multi-room layout provides a home to many community activities. The separate pool and games room with its own bar hosts darts, dominoes and pool teams. Elsewhere are quiet drinking areas and a large sports TV. There is live entertainment on Saturday and Sunday evening and home-cooked food is served every day. The Crown's location attracts outdoor enthusiasts stopping for a pint after enjoying the beautiful countryside of the neighbouring West Pennine Moors.
🔥❀◐♿♣P🚌(125,575) 🐾📶

Tap & Cork Ⓛ

179 Lee Lane, BL6 7JD
☎ (01204) 695506
3 changing beers (sourced locally; often Escape) Ⓗ
Small, comfortable bar with a stripped-back modern style of bare brick and wood. Its size encourages friendly chat between a mixed crowd of drinkers enjoying some adventurous beers from local brewers, including up to three real ales. An unusual multi-keg font serves modern keg beers. British and foreign beers and ciders are available from a wall of fridges for consumption on or off the premises. The toilets have an adapted cask washbasin. 🔥🚌(125)🐾📶

Hyde

Cheshire Ring Hotel Ⓛ

72-74 Manchester Road, SK14 2BJ
☎ 07917 055629
6 changing beers Ⓗ
One of the oldest pubs in Hyde. Seven handpumps offer a range of ales from Beartown plus microbreweries from near and far, in addition to ciders, perries and continental beers. A selection of bottled beers is also stocked. Home-made curries are available on Thursday evening, Sunday is quiz night and Laurel and Hardy films are shown once a month. Opening hours vary with the season and closing time may be earlier than usual on Mondays and Tuesdays. 🔥❀⇌🍎P🚌(201)🐾

Sportsman Inn Ⓛ

57 Mottram Road, SK14 2NN
☎ (0161) 368 5000
Rossendale Floral Dance, Glen Top Bitter, Ale, Halo Pale, Pitch Porter, Sunshine Ⓗ
This former regional CAMRA Pub of the Year is popular with locals and retains its character while serving a full range of Rossendale Brewery ales. Upstairs is a restaurant offering Cuban tapas and vegetarian options. Choice of food in the pub varies but Wednesday is curry night and on Sunday there is a traditional roast for from noon until it's gone. The pub hosts pool and chess teams. Its rear patio includes a covered and heated smoking area. 🔥❀◐⇌♣P🚌🐾📶

Tweed Tap Ⓛ

3 Hamnett Street, SK14 2EX
☎ 07889 750492
4 changing beers (sourced locally; often Prospect, Purity) Ⓗ
Micropub in former shop premises that opened in 2017 selling beers from the now closed Tweed Brewery. The surprisingly spacious dark-wood interior gives a rustic feel. A dark beer and trio tasters (three third-pints) are always available. Wednesday is games night although, with cards and dominoes on every table, regulars tend to play every night, also enjoying games including Scrabble and Trivial Pursuit. Two minutes from Hyde Bus Station, 10 minutes from Hyde Central Railway Station.
Q🔥⇌(Central) ♣🍎🚌🐾📶

Leigh

Bobbin 🏆

38A Leigh Road, WN7 1QR
☎ (01942) 581242 🌐 thebobbinleigh.co.uk
4 changing beers (sourced locally) Ⓗ
One-room micropub on the edge of the town centre, offering a warm welcome and comfortable seating. Beers are from regional microbreweries, with current and future selections shown on the website. A dark beer and real cider are always available, and prices are competitive. Open from 1pm on Sundays when Leigh RLFC are at home. Q♿🍎🚌🐾📶

Weavers Arms ✔

9-13 Lord Street, WN7 1DP
☎ (01942) 267510
3 changing beers (sourced nationally) Ⓗ
The atmosphere in this town-centre pub just off the main shopping street changes depending on the time. During the day it is relaxed, with shoppers and families dining. In the evening it is a popular meeting place that shows football and rugby on TV and provides entertainment at weekends. Cask beers are on special offer on Tuesday and Wednesday. 🔥❀◐♿♣🚌📶

Littleborough

Hare on the Hill

132 Hare Hill Road, OL15 9HL
☎ (01706) 538523 🌐 hare-on-the-hill.co.uk
Vocation Bread & Butter; 4 changing beers (often Pictish, Saltaire, Tiny Rebel) Ⓗ
Small, busy pub just outside the centre of the village. It serves four cask ales from a mini-tap beer wall, and also has four craft keg, two lager and two cider taps, plus a wide selection of cans and bottles. Good food is served at lunchtime and evenings (booking advisable). There is a large beer garden to the rear. ❀◐⇌🍎P🚌(588)🐾📶

White House ⎣

Blackstone Edge, Halifax Road, OL15 0LG
☎ (01706) 378456 ⊕ thewhitehousepub.co.uk
Theakston Best Bitter; 3 changing beers (often Abbeydale, Newby Wyke) Ⓗ
Classic moorland pub on the A58 between Rochdale and Halifax. Built in 1691 as the Coach & Horses, it enjoys commanding views over the Lancashire plain. The pub has a bar area and four separate rooms. The bar stretches into the rear room, with two handpumps on that side. Theakston Best is a regular, alongside three changing beers on handpump. Good food is served daily from an extensive menu. A family-run pub for over 30 years.
Q ⑤ ❀ ◑ ⅍ ▲ P ❚ (X58) ❖

Lydgate

White Hart Inn ⎣ ✪

51 Stockport Road, OL4 4JJ
☎ (01457) 872566 ⊕ thewhitehart.co.uk
JW Lees Bitter; Timothy Taylor Golden Best, Boltmaker; 3 changing beers (often Donkeystone, Ossett, Salt) Ⓗ
Hilltop gastro-pub with impressive views over the surrounding countryside and Greater Manchester. A free house, it serves three regular beers from JW Lees and Timothy Taylor plus guest ales usually sourced from local breweries. The building dates from 1788 and was once a police station. The multi-room layout has log-burning stoves in the bar area and brasserie, behind which are a restaurant, function rooms and guest accommodation. Quality food is served daily from an award-winning kitchen. Q ⑤ ❀ ➼ ◑ ⅍ P ❚ (84) ❖ ❖

Manchester

Angel

6 Angel Street, M4 4BQ (off Rochdale Rd)
☎ (0161) 833 4786
10 changing beers (sourced nationally) Ⓗ
The Angel's location on a busy junction on the outskirts of the Northern Quarter makes it a hard place to reach at times but the effort is worthwhile. The fine selection of beers on offer from its dozen handpumps ensures there is something to suit most palates. The house beer is a light pale ale from Howard Town, often balanced by a powerful dark beer from Blackedge.
⑤ ❀ ➼ (Victoria) ☒ (Shudehill) ● P ❖ ❖

Beatnikz Republic Bar

35 Dale Street, M1 2HF (corner of Dale St and Tariff St)
☎ 07761 800828 ⊕ beatnikzrepublic.com/bar
3 changing beers (often Beatnikz Republic)
Open since 2018 in a Grade II listed former office block, the bar is less than a mile from the Beatnikz Republic brewery. Entering up a number of steps reveals a long, narrow room with high tables to the left and table and bench seating on the right, and the bar at the far end. There are four handpumps for the brewery's cask ales and a cider, plus 14 keg fonts on the back wall, as well as gin from local producers, Three Rivers.
➼ (Piccadilly) ☒ (Piccadilly Gardens) ● ❖

Brink

65 Bridge Street, M3 3BQ
☎ (0161) 834 6346 ⊕ brinkmcr.co.uk
5 changing beers (sourced locally) Ⓗ
Cosy single-room basement bar that is a much-valued part of the Manchester craft beer scene, providing a place to enjoy a quiet drink away from the bustle of the city centre. It serves several changing cask and keg beers plus ciders, all brewed within a 25-mile radius of nearby

St Ann's Church. The bar is also a local gin specialist. A spectacular panoramic photo of the Manchester skyline occupies most of one wall.
⑤ ➼ (Salford Central) ☒ (St Peters Sq) ♣ ● ❚ ❖ ❖

Cafe Beermoth

40A Spring Gardens, M2 1EN (entrance on Brown St)
☎ (0161) 835 2049 ⊕ beermoth.co.uk/cafe
7 changing beers (sourced nationally) Ⓗ
Welcoming modern bar near Market Street, with a Belgian flavour and a relaxed and fun city-centre atmosphere. It serves an excellent range of beers from seven cask handpumps, plus 10 keg lines and a wide range of bottled ales. Attractions include regular tap takeover and Meet the Brewer events, plus food pop-ups and occasional live music at weekends. The outdoor seating area is great for watching the world go by.
⑤ ⅍ ☒ (Market St) ❖ ❖

Cask

29 Liverpool Road, M3 4NQ
☎ (0161) 832 2633
4 changing beers (sourced regionally; often Mallinsons, Pictish, Track) Ⓗ
Deceptively deep pub in the heart of Castlefield that consistently sells excellent cask ale. With beer on four handpumps, it usually offers a good range of flavours, including a dark. The selection of international beers is particularly impressive, both on fonts and in bottles. Although no food is provided, customers are permitted to bring their own, including takeouts from the excellent chippy next door. ❀ ➼ (Deansgate) ☒ (Deansgate-Castlefield) ● ❚ ❖ ❖

City Arms ✪

46-48 Kennedy Street, M2 4BQ (to rear of Waterhouse pub)
☎ (0161) 236 4610
8 changing beers (sourced regionally; often Manchester, Titanic) Ⓗ
A compact pub with two traditional rooms and many original features. The room facing the street contains the bar and a few tables and is fairly basic. To the rear is a smarter, cosier room to hang out in good company. Eight handpulls offer a full range of beer styles in excellent condition, including a mild. The pub is often full and filled with groups of people conversing.
❀ ◑ ➼ (Oxford Rd) ☒ (St Peters Sq) ♣ ● ❚ ❖

Crown & Kettle

2 Oldham Road, M4 5FE (corner Great Ancoats St)
☎ (0161) 236 2923
8 changing beers (sourced nationally) Ⓗ
This Grade II listed street-corner building has a large drinking area in front of the bar along with a small vault and a snug at the rear. The high ornate ceiling in the main bar is well worth seeing. Eight cask handpumps are supplemented by seven craft keg ales and up to eight ciders. Tap takeovers and occasional beer festivals are held, along with regular music events and comedy nights. Hot pies are available.
❀ ⅍ ➼ (Victoria) ☒ (Shudehill) ● ❚ ❖ ❖

Gas Lamp

50A Bridge Street, M3 3BW
☎ (0161) 478 1224 ⊕ thegaslamp.co.uk
4 changing beers (sourced nationally; often Pomona Island, Squawk) Ⓗ
An interesting pub housed in the former Manchester and Salford Children's Mission. It has an impressive frontage but the small doorway that leads down to the subterranean bar can easily be missed. The main bar area has Victorian glazed-brick walls and wooden flooring. A

narrow passageway leads to a cosy back room with photos of the building's history. One of the beers is usually from the pub's own brewery in Salford, Pomona Island. ⇆≢(Salford Central)ℚ(St Peters Sq)●🖵🏵️🛜

Hare & Hounds ★
46 Shudehill, M4 4AA (opp Shudehill bus station)
☎ (0161) 832 4737
Joseph Holt Mild, Bitter; Robinsons Dizzy Blonde Ⓗ
Fine beers and friendly staff help make the Hare & Hounds popular, especially with older customers. This Grade II listed pub on CAMRA's National Inventory of Historic Pub Interiors dates back to about 1800 and was remodelled in 1925. The building's mottled tile frontage and an interior featuring lots of attractive tiling make it a rare survivor of the period, particularly given its city-centre location. The entrance corridor leads to a lobby in front of the bar. There is a vault at the front and a comfortable lounge at the rear.
≢(Victoria) ℚ(Shudehill) 🖵🏵️🛜

Jack in the Box
1 Eagle Street, M4 5BU
Blackjack Carousel Blonde; 7 changing beers (sourced nationally) Ⓗ
A lively bar in a modern market hall-style venue. Run by the team behind Blackjack and its sister bar in Altrincham market, the bar serves a good selection of quality cask and keg beers. With eight handpumps and 10 keg lines, it offers a changing range of local beers plus some from further afield in a relaxed atmosphere. Food can be obtained from vendors within the market, and bar customers can sit anywhere in the hall. Welcomes families and dogs. ⇆&≢(Victoria)ℚ(Shudehill)●🗖🏵️🛜

Lass o' Gowrie ✅
36 Charles Street, M1 7DB (just off Princess St)
☎ (0161) 273 5822 ⊕ thelassogowrie.com
7 changing beers (sourced locally; often Greene King) Ⓗ
A Victorian tiled frontage is a highlight of this pub, whose interior is also traditionally decorated. It attracts a varied clientele, especially students in term time. Seven beers are served on handpump - a mixture of Greene King and local ales. There is a compact snug at the back and a small decked area over the River Medlock for outside drinking. Locally produced snacks and pub grub are offered, with many vegetarian and vegan options.
⇆🍴≢(Oxford Rd) ℚ(St Peters Sq) 🚲●🖵(50,147) 🏵️🛜

Marble Arch Inn 🍴 ★
73 Rochdale Road, Collyhurst, M4 4HY (corner Gould St)
☎ (0161) 832 5914 ⊕ marblebeers.com
Marble Pint, Manchester Bitter, Earl Grey IPA; 4 changing beers (sourced nationally; often Marble) Ⓗ
Marble Brewery's flagship establishment, this famous real ale pub is a 10-minute walk from the city centre. It serves five local Marble beers, three real ciders and a selection of craft keg ales. The interior's many interesting features include a sloping mosaic floor leading you to the bar. The impressive vaulted ceiling, frieze and walls are covered with Victorian tiles. There is also a plainer back room where food is served, and a beer yard at the rear.
Q⇆🏵️🍴≢(Victoria) ℚ(Shudehill) ●🖵🏵️🛜

Northern Monk Refectory
10 Tariff Street, M1 2FF (between Dale St and Hilton St)
☎ (0161) 236 9876
Timothy Taylor Landlord; 3 changing beers (often Northern Monk) Ⓗ
Leeds brewer Northern Monk's first north-west outlet opened in 2018. The bar is in the room to the left as you

enter. Four handpumps serve cask ales alongside 18 keg lines. The interior includes bare wooden floorboards and a mixture of booth seating and high tables. Downstairs is a function room. Breakfast is available.
🍴≢(Piccadilly) ℚ(Piccadilly Gardens) ●🗖🖵🏵️

Peveril of the Peak ★
127 Great Bridgewater Street, M1 5JQ (jct Great Bridgewater St and Chepstow St)
☎ (0161) 236 6364
Brightside Odin Blonde; Millstone Tiger Rut; Timothy Taylor Landlord; Titanic Plum Porter Ⓗ
The Pev's warm welcome for locals and visitors alike has long made it a favourite of Manchester ale lovers. The splendour of its exterior's green tiles is matched by the interior's wood and stained-glass panels. Four handpumps serve beer in the front room, with a blackboard displaying the choice. The snug is a cosy alternative to the liveliness often found on the other side. Q🏵️≢(Oxford Rd)ℚ(St Peters Sq)🚲🖵🏵️🛜

Port Street Beer House
39-41 Port Street, M1 2EQ (opp Brewer St)
☎ (0161) 237 9949 ⊕ portstreetbeerhouse.co.uk
7 changing beers (sourced nationally) Ⓗ
Vibrant pub split over two floors of a former shop in the Northern Quarter, its walls adorned with pictures of beer and beer festivals. It serves seven cask beers from a variety of breweries, alongside cider and a range of contrasting worldwide keg beers, bottles and cans. The pub hosts tap takeovers and beer festival fringe events. There is outside seating at the front and a courtyard at the rear.
⇆🏵️≢(Piccadilly) ℚ(Piccadilly Gardens) 🚲●🖵🏵️🛜

Smithfield Market Tavern
37 Swan Street, M4 5JZ (corner Coop St)
☎ (0161) 839 1514
6 changing beers (sourced nationally; often Blackjack) Ⓗ
One of the premier cask pubs in the Northern Quarter, the lively Smithfield is the flagship for Blackjack Brewery. It serves six cask ales, usually including two from Blackjack, plus 10 keg beers and an interesting selection of bottled brews. A traditional bar billiards table and other pub games provide entertainment.
≢(Victoria) ℚ(Shudehill) 🚲●🗖🖵🏵️🛜

Marple

Samuel Oldknow
22 Market Street, SK6 7AD
☎ 07766 301627
6 changing beers (sourced locally) Ⓗ
Named after a local mill owner who was responsible for much of the development of Marple and Mellor some 200 years ago, this is a somewhat quirky two-level bar in a converted shop. Six vintage-style handpulls dispense five changing real ales plus a real cider. The regular beers are from Brightside and Outstanding, complemented by guests from local micros. A range of bottled beers is also available to take away or to drink on the premises. Opening hours are subject to change. Q⇆🏵️●🖵🏵️🛜

Traders
111-113 Stockport Road, SK6 6AF
☎ (0161) 427 0667
3 changing beers (sourced regionally) Ⓗ
An interesting combined micropub and bottle shop, based in converted shop premises, which was called Beer Traders before its expansion in 2019. Three handpulls serve changing beers, normally from local micros. The aim is to have one traditional bitter, one

darker beer and something hoppy. Three bag-in-box ciders are also available. Live music often features on Tuesday evening. Opening times can vary – it may be worth checking prior to a visit. ❀≠●⊟❀

Marple Bridge

Norfolk Arms

2 Town Street, SK6 5DS

☎ (0161) 427 8090 🌐 thenorfolkarms.co.uk

5 changing beers (sourced regionally; often Seven Bro7hers, Storm) Ⓗ

A recently refurbished stone-built pub in an attractive setting next to the River Goyt bridge. Comfortably furnished, it attracts a wide-ranging clientele by catering for all tastes. Five locally and regionally sourced real ales are usually on offer, providing a welcome addition to the choice in the area. The atmosphere is warm and friendly, with good-value food available. Live music plays on Thursday and occasional beer festivals are held in summer. Well served by public transport. Q❀◑♿≠⊟❀

Northumberland Arms

64 Compstall Road, SK6 5HD

☎ (0161) 285 3755 🌐 thenorthumberlandarms.com

Robinsons Unicorn; Saltaire Blonde; Track Sonoma; Wainwright; 2 changing beers (sourced locally; often Bank Top) Ⓗ

Former Robinsons house that reopened in 2017 as a pub owned and operated by the local community. Used by numerous groups for meetings and activities, the place fulfils its role as a true local and a well-used hub of the district. Its small bar area serves three rooms, one of which is used for pub games. The traditional exterior is enhanced by a pleasant beer garden. Frequent buses pass the door. ❀♣P⊟(383,384)❀

Middleton

Ring o' Bells

St Leonards Square, M24 6DJ

☎ (0161) 654 9245

JW Lees Manchester Pale Ale, Bitter; 2 changing beers (sourced locally; often JW Lees) Ⓗ

A pub since 1831, the Ringers enjoys a fine elevated location opposite the medieval parish church within a conservation area. Visitors can enjoy stunning views across to Oldham and beyond, especially at night. Lees' seasonal and Boilerhouse beers are served. Very much community focused, the pub hosts a unique Pace Egg play on Easter Monday and a Maypole event on the May bank holiday Monday. Quizzes and monthly live music add to its appeal. There is an attractive beer garden to the rear. ❀♣P⊟(17)❀

Tandle Hill Tavern

14 Thornham Lane, M24 2SD (1 mile on unmetalled road from either A664 or A627)

☎ (0161) 376 4492

JW Lees Bitter, Stout; house beer (by JW Lees); 1 changing beer (sourced locally; often JW Lees) Ⓗ

A one-mile walk from either end of an unmade, potholed lane rewards the drinker with the pub nestling among a number of farms. It has a main bar area and a separate quiet side room, with a walled rear beer garden plus benches to the front and side for outdoor seating. The house beer is dry-hopped Lees Bitter; guest ales are from Lees and Boilerhouse. No food is served. Closed Mondays & Tuesdays. In adverse weather, or in winter, phone ahead to check opening times. Q❀P❀

Milnrow

Waggon Inn

35 Butterworth Hall, OL16 3PE

☎ (01706) 648313 🌐 waggoninnmilnrow.co.uk

Banks's Amber Ale; 2 changing beers (often Jennings, Marston's) Ⓗ

Built in 1782, this pub, locally known as the Back Waggon, has a traditional ambience. The building has been sympathetically refurbished, retaining many original features including mullioned windows. An excellent food menu features tapas and a Sunday roast. Within easy walking distance of Milnrow's Metrolink stop and local bus services. ❀◑♿P⊟

Monton

Malt Dog 𝕃

169 Monton Road, M30 9GS (opp Hawthorne Avenue)

☎ 07541 553646 🌐 maltdog.com

3 changing beers (sourced locally; often Brightside, Saltaire, Seven Bro7hers) Ⓗ

Popular pub in what was a jewellery shop, converted in 2013 and now a thriving part of the Monton village scene. It serves up to three changing guest ales plus a large selection of bottled and canned beers from around the world. There is a small bar at the rear, plus an upstairs room that often hosts music events. The toilet is accessible via steep stairs. Q❀⊟❀

Mossley

Church Inn 𝕃

82 Stockport Road, OL5 0RF

☎ 07739 396818 🌐 meliaschurchinnmossley.simplesite.com

4 changing beers (often Cross Bay, Donkeystone) Ⓗ

End-of-terrace free house that takes its name from the nearby St John's Church. Three of its six handpumps dispense local beers, chosen with the regulars in mind. The bar in the comfortable lounge also serves the games room, where the pool table is popular. Saturday is karaoke night; Tuesday is more sedate, with live bluegrass often enjoyed. ♣P⊟(353)

Fleece Inn 𝕃

53 Stamford Street, OL5 0LN

☎ (01457) 835487

House beer (by Irwell Works); 6 changing beers (sourced locally; often Parkway, Titanic, Weetwood) Ⓗ

The Fleece is less than half a mile from the station but up a steep hill, so you will deserve a pint after the climb (or you could catch the bus). In 1890 the inn could accommodate three travellers, feed up to 50 and stable one horse. Today the visitor will find a locals' pub with a horseshoe bar. Beer festivals and other events are held in the separate front lounge. Dogs are welcome but horses perhaps less so. ❀≠♣●⊟❀

Rising Sun 𝕃

235 Stockport Road, OL5 0RQ

☎ (01457) 238236 🌐 risingsunmossley.co.uk

Millstone Tiger Rut, Stout; 6 changing beers (sourced locally; often Rising Sun, Saltaire, Thornbridge) Ⓗ

Free house that was once a Wilsons pub and now has a small brewery attached. Open plan with log-burning stoves, it has 10 handpumps serving a selection of regular and guest beers plus cider. The pub and its patio provide a fine view over the Tame Valley to the Pennines. A boisterous atmosphere is guaranteed when live music is being performed, or Manchester City or United are in action on the numerous TVs. ❀◑●P⊟(353)

New Windsor

Union Tavern

105 Liverpool Street, M5 4LG (corner Wilna Terrace opp West Charles St)

☎ (0161) 737 6831

Joseph Holt Bitter Ⓗ

A fine example of a traditional tiled Victorian street-corner local, this pub is among the last survivors of its kind and remains little changed amid extensive development. Its central bar serves a lounge and vault plus a pool room at the rear. The walls are adorned with Manchester United photographs and memorabilia, and pictures of former local pubs that have been closed and demolished. ❀≠♣P🚌(79)🐾📶

Oldham

Ashton Arms 𝕃

28-30 Clegg Street, OL1 1PL (opp Odeon cinema complex)

☎ (0161) 630 9709

Millstone Tiger Rut; Phoenix Arizona; Pictish Porter; 6 changing beers (often Elland, Riverhead, Stockport) Ⓗ

Popular town-centre free house that has recently been refurbished. It features an open-plan interior with the bar on a raised area to the rear. An excellent range of four to six real ales is offered, many from local microbreweries such as Donkeystone and Pictish. The pub also has a wide variety of Belgian and German bottled beer, plus traditional cider or perry. Good-value home-cooked food is served weekdays, with sandwiches at the weekend. Q❀(Central) ♣🍎🚌📶

Cob & Coal Tap 𝕃

Units 12-14 Tommyfield Market, Albion Street, OL1 3BG

☎ (0161) 624 0446

6 changing beers (often Millstone, Salopian, Saltaire) Ⓗ

Popular pub that has provided a warm welcome, good service and excellent ale since opening in Oldham Market Hall in 2019. Its handpumps serve up to six changing beers that are always in top condition. The pub also offers many foreign beers on tap and in bottles, plus a good selection of real ciders. Well worth a visit. 🍎🚌

Patricroft

Queen's Arms

Green Lane, M30 0SH (up ramp opp James Nasmyth Way)

☎ (0161) 789 2019

Wadworth 6X Ⓗ

Traditional pub that dates from 1828 and was renamed after Queen Victoria visited Salford in 1851. It was built as a refreshment stop in readiness for the Liverpool and Manchester Railway, and is claimed to be the world's first railway pub. The bar serves a comfortable lounge to the rear, a vault and, across a lobby, a homely parlour. Known locally as the Top House, the pub was Grade II listed at the instigation of the local CAMRA branch. Q❀≠♣P🚌(67,100)🐾📶

Ramsbottom

Irwell Works Brewery Tap 𝕃

Irwell Street, BL0 9YQ

☎ (01706) 825019 🌐 irwellworksbrewery.co.uk

Irwell Works Lightweights & Gentlemen, Breadcrumbs, Copper Plate, Costa Del Salford, Marshmallow Unicorn, Mad Dogs & Englishmen; 8 changing beers (often Irwell Works) Ⓗ

Small local on the first floor above the Irwell Works Brewery, decorated with old photographs of the Ramsbottom area. The brewery focuses on traditional beers made with predominantly English hops and barley. The pub's eight handpumps usually offer the full range of Irwell's beers alongside two handpumped ciders. Snack food is served Friday to Sunday. The pub is a short walk from the East Lancashire Railway, the local preserved railway, and features on its ale trail. ❀≠(ELR) ♣🍎🚌(472,474)🐾📶

Ramsbottom Royal British Legion

Central Street, BL0 9AF

☎ (01706) 822483 🌐 branches.britishlegion.org.uk/branches/ramsbottom/club-news

Fyne Ales Jarl; 1 changing beer (sourced locally) Ⓗ

A one-room establishment in a back street in the centre of Ramsbottom. The members and steward are more than welcoming; membership is not required unless you become a regular. Two handpumps are in use all the time with different beers including many from local microbreweries. The club is a short walk from the East Lancs Railway. On-street parking is close by. There is a smoking area outside the entrance. ≠(ELR) ♣🚌(472,474)🐾📶

Rochdale

Baum 𝕃

35 Toad Lane, OL12 0NU

☎ (01706) 352186 🌐 thebaum.co.uk

6 changing beers (sourced nationally; often Pictish, Vocation) Ⓗ

A former CAMRA National Pub of the Year and regular winner of local CAMRA Pub of the Year, the Baum has an old-fashioned frontage and interior, complemented by a beer garden and conservatory to the rear. It serves six changing cask ales, mostly from microbreweries, plus two guest ciders. Its good-quality bar food is reasonably priced and mostly sourced locally. The pub is in the Toad Lane conservation area, next to the Rochdale Pioneers Museum and within easy reach of the tram and bus interchange. ❀🍎🚌🐾📶

Cask & Feather

1 Oldham Road, OL16 1UA

☎ (01706) 667826

3 changing beers Ⓗ

Lively and popular sports bar, previously called the Junction, that was home to two microbreweries before being transformed by its current owners around five years ago. Its three handpumps dispense changing cask ales, with two or three real ciders also served on gravity. Bar snacks are available at weekends. Entertainment includes pool and darts, plus poker night on Wednesday, karaoke on Saturday and alternate rock or karaoke on Friday. Local CAMRA Most Improved Pub 2019. ❀≠♣🍎🚌

Flying Horse Hotel 🏆 𝕃

37 Packer Street, OL16 1NJ

☎ (01706) 646412

10 changing beers (sourced locally; often Phoenix, Pictish, Serious) Ⓗ

An impressive Edwardian stone free house situated in the Town Hall Square. Built in 1691 and rebuilt in 1926, it retains many original features including log fires. Ten cask ales are sold alongside four real ciders. The menu features meat from the local butcher and pies made on the premises. Live music plays on Thursday, Friday and Saturday and live sport is screened. There is also accommodation and a function room for hire. Local CAMRA Pub of the Year in 2018 and 2019.

Oxford

662 Whitworth Road, OL12 0TB
(01706) 345709 theoxfordpub.com
Wainwright; 2 changing beers (sourced regionally; often Hawkshead, Timothy Taylor)
Busy pub on the A671 Rochdale to Burnley road, known locally for its friendly reception, well-kept beer and good food. Its interior comprises a central bar and servery surrounded by tables, with a large separate dining area. Outside is a substantial beer garden. Three real ales are on handpump; Wainwright is a permanent beer, with the other changing ales usually coming from small local or regional breweries. Q P (486)

Regal Moon

The Butts, OL16 1HB
(01706) 657434
Elland 1872 Porter; Greene King Abbot; Hawkshead Windermere Pale; Moorhouse's Blond Witch; Ossett Silver King; Ruddles Best Bitter; changing beers (often Brains, Phoenix, Pictish)
Large, open Wetherspoon pub serving a varied range of real ales alongside keg and bottled beers. Its cask ale and cider are dispensed from no fewer than 18 handpulls. The food includes pizzas and is reasonably priced. The pub's popularity makes it noisy at times but there is no loud TV. Local CAMRA Cider Pub of the Year in 2019.

Romiley

Jake's Ale House

27 Compstall Road, SK6 4BT
07927 076941
5 changing beers (sourced locally; often Poynton)
In just a few years this micropub in a former shop has established itself as a popular part of the Romiley pub scene. It has a small front bar with a relaxed atmosphere, and a smaller room at the rear. Many of the beers are from local microbreweries. It is close to the railway station and good bus routes, and the Peak Forest Canal is a short walk away. Opening hours may vary.
Q

Royton

Puckersley Inn

22 Narrowgate Brow, OL2 6YD (off A671 via Dogford Rd & Fir Lane)
(0161) 652 2834
JW Lees Supernova, Manchester Pale Ale, Bitter; 1 changing beer (sourced locally; often JW Lees)
This welcoming JW Lees local is a detached, stone-fronted pub on the edge of the green belt, with panoramic views over Royton, Shaw and Oldham. The building has a small vault, a comfortable lounge and a dining extension where children are welcome. Cosy corners provide plenty of space to chat and enjoy the four Lees beers on offer. An excellent range of meals is served lunchtimes and evenings.
P (408)

Rusholme

Ford Madox Brown

Unit 1, Wilmslow Park, Wilmslow Road, M14 5FT (jct Hathersage Rd)
(0161) 256 6660
Greene King Abbot; Ruddles Best Bitter; Sharp's Doom Bar; house beer (by Brightside); 4 changing beers (sourced nationally)
Modern Wetherspoon pub paradoxically named after the eminent Victorian Pre-Raphaelite painter (he lived nearby in Victoria Park), and built near the site of the old Rusholme Hall. Handy for the curry mile, universities and the Whitworth Art Gallery, it is popular not just with students but with a real cross-section of people. Although an open-plan pub it has a warm feel, the community atmosphere enhanced by brewery visits and local events. Q

Sale

JP Joule

2A Northenden Road, M33 3BR
(0161) 962 9889
Greene King Abbot; Ruddles Best Bitter; Sharp's Doom Bar; Wychwood Hobgoblin Gold; 5 changing beers (sourced nationally; often Hawkshead, Peerless, Titanic)
Named after the famous physicist who lived in Sale (and also worked in a brewery), this popular Wetherspoon is near the tram station and on several bus routes. It is set on two levels with a grand staircase leading to the upper floor. A total of 14 handpumps dispense nine real ales, with four duplicated upstairs. Five beers are constantly changing and sourced regionally. Real ale and cider and perry festivals are held twice a year. Q

Salford

Eagle Inn

18-19 Collier Street, M3 7DW (opp Rolla St)
(0161) 819 5002 eagleinn.info
Bootleg Fools Gold, Chorlton Pale Ale; Joseph Holt Bitter, Two Hoots
Hidden gem of a traditional back-street boozer, known to locals as the Lamp Oil. A Grade II listed building dating from 1902, it features a fine terracotta plaque of an eagle above the door – for years this was the only pub sign. A central bar and corridor lead to three small rooms. Old Rosie cider is served on handpull alongside the ales. The attached cottage next door has been converted into a live music venue. The pub itself is handily located for Manchester Arena.
Q (Central) (Victoria)

New Oxford

11 Bexley Square, M3 6DB (corner of Browning St)
(0161) 832 7082 thenewoxford.com
House beer (by Phoenix); 16 changing beers (sourced regionally; often Empire, Moorhouse's, Phoenix)
Multiple award-winning corner house dating from the 1830s, containing two main rooms. It features 20 handpumps and a 24-font central bar. The 17 cask ales are sourced regionally, and usually include at least two dark beers. The other three handpumps are for cider or perry – one from Thatchers plus two guests. An extensive range of bottled Belgian beers adds further variety. Good-value lunches are served Monday to Friday.
(Central)

Salford Arms Hotel

146 Chapel Street, M3 6AF (corner Bloom St)
(0161) 288 8883
6 changing beers (sourced regionally; often Beartown, Northern Monkey)
A welcoming establishment that is also an eight-bedroom hotel, handy for Salford Central station. The tiled entrance from Bloom Street leads to the partially

open-plan bar, with a function room to the right. The walls are hung with prints, newspaper cuttings and 78rpm records; both areas have TV screens for sport. The pub serves up to six changing guest beers, usually including light and dark ales. Events include a quiz on Tuesday and language exchange on Wednesday. ⛯❀⇌≹(Central) ♣🚌🐾📶

Stalybridge

Bridge Beers 𝕃

55 Melbourne Street, SK15 2JJ
☎ 07948 617145 🌐 bridgebeers.co.uk
4 changing beers (sourced locally) Ⓖ
A combined micropub and bottle shop on the main pedestrianised shopping street in Stalybridge. Originally a hairdressers, the interior has been restyled to suit its new function. A small entrance area leads to the bar which sits in front of a row of stillaged casks, of which four are generally in use. The bottle display is opposite. Upstairs is a comfortable lounge. Beers are constantly changing and all locally sourced. Last entry is one hour before closing. Q⛯≹♣●🚌🐾

Crafty Pint

41 Melbourne Street, SK15 2JJ
☎ 07512 753554
4 changing beers Ⓗ
Microbar next to the canal, serving four changing real ales, mainly from local breweries but some from further afield. It also offers a good selection of bottled beers, mostly from Germany. This a bar where conversation dominates rather than piped music and TV screens. Board games are available. Children and dogs are welcome. Q⛯≹🚌🐾📶

Society Rooms ✔

49-51 Grosvenor Street, SK15 2JN
☎ (0161) 338 9740
Greene King Abbot; Ruddles Best Bitter; Sharp's Doom Bar; 5 changing beers (sourced nationally) Ⓗ
Split-level pub near the town-centre bus terminus, named after the former Co-op store premises it occupies. A large beer garden helps make this one of the country's largest Wetherspoon outlets. It is popular with local drinkers due to its enthusiastic management and focus on cask beers. The pub serves eight real ales and two real ciders, and hosts two beer festivals each year, one including cider. ⛯❀◑♿≹●🚌📶

Station Buffet Bar ★

Stalybridge Railway Station, Platform 4, Rassbottom Street, SK15 1RF (access from station Platform 4)
☎ (0161) 303 0007 🌐 beerhouses.co.uk/pub/stalybridge-buffet-bar
Changing beers (sourced regionally) Ⓗ
One of the few Victorian station buffet bars remaining and well worth missing a train for. A sympathetic refurbishment has allowed expansion of the food menu which includes home-cooked meals. Nine handpumps dispense a variety of beers, most of which are locally sourced, plus at least one real cider or perry. A good range of bottled beers is also available. Events include live music and Meet the Brewer nights. Monday is quiz night. On the Transpennine Real Ale Trail. Q◑♿≹●P🚌

Standish

Albion Ale House 𝕃 ✔

12 High Street, WN6 0HL
☎ (01257) 367897 🌐 albionalehouse.co.uk
8 changing beers Ⓗ
The first micropub in Standish, located in a former shop on the High Street. Now well established, it has a loyal clientele and is a recent local CAMRA Community Pub of the Year. It normally serves at least five cask ales, including one dark beer. Snacks are also usually available. Attractions include occasional live music and beer festivals. Q⛯❀♿🚌(362,113)🐾

Foresters Arms 𝕃

41 Shevington Moor, WN6 0SQ
☎ (01257) 472733 🌐 foresters.pub
8 changing beers (sourced regionally) Ⓗ
Vibrant country pub with a long history, having opened in the mid-1850s as the Rose & Crown, and then the Silver Tally, until a recent refurbishment and name change. Despite modern furnishings, the pub retains a traditional atmosphere, with three distinct areas for drinking, dining and games. Alongside the cask ales, a variety of locally sourced food is served. Q⛯❀◑♿P🚌(113)🐾📶

Standish Unity Club 𝕃

Cross Street, WN6 0HQ
☎ (01257) 424007 🌐 standishunityclub.com
Sharp's Doom Bar; 4 changing beers Ⓗ
In the centre of Standish but tucked away so a little tricky to find, this popular club offers five real ales including one dark beer, often Titanic Plum Porter. The club is divided in two – a large function room and a bar area including the games room, plus a quieter drinking area. A frequent winner of local CAMRA Club of the Year. Q⛯♿♣P🚌(362,113) 📶

Stockport

Angel Inn

20 Market Place, SK1 1EY (opp Market Hall)
☎ (0161) 429 0251
House beer (by Beartown); 4 changing beers (sourced regionally) Ⓗ
After 67 years' closure, the Angel was reopened in 2018 by a consortium of locals. It is a vibrant combination of the traditional and new – stand-up drinking near the bar gives way to two seating areas behind, with a mix of wainscoted and rustic brick walls. The bar is dominated by an impressive array of German lager fonts, without detracting from its commitment to serving real ales and cider on handpump. A large selection of gins is also kept. A popular drop-in for the town's market customers. ⛯❀♿≹●🚌🐾📶

Arden Arms ★ ✔

23 Millgate, SK1 2LX (jct Corporation St)
☎ (0161) 480 2185
Robinsons Wizard, Dizzy Blonde, Unicorn, Trooper Ⓗ, Old Tom; 1 changing beer (often Robinsons) Ⓖ
Grade II listed and on CAMRA's National Inventory of Historic Pub Interiors, this multi-room pub is just down the hill from Stockport's Market Place. Note the superb curved, glazed bar, the grandfather clock, and particularly the snug, which can only be accessed through the bar area itself (one of only four such in the UK). The building alone warrants a visit, and the food is also recommended. The large, attractive courtyard hosts live music on Saturday nights. A true gem. ⛯❀◑♿♣🚌(384,383) 🐾📶

Armoury ✔

31 Shaw Heath, Edgeley, SK3 8BD (on B5465, jct Greek St)
☎ 07931 621220
Robinsons Dizzy Blonde, Unicorn, Cascade IPA, Trooper; 1 changing beer (often Robinsons) Ⓗ

Comfortable, multi-roomed local with a military history and a strong community following. The pub caters for so many functions and groups that it is almost always busy, welcoming darts players, sports watchers, the White Ensign Association, the Army Reserve and many others. Much memorabilia is on display in the bar room. The pleasant, secluded beer garden is a suntrap in fine weather. Q❀♿≠♣🚌🐾📶

Bakers Vaults ✔

Market Place, SK1 1ES (jct Vernon St)
☎ (0161) 480 9448
Robinsons Dizzy Blonde, Unicorn, Cascade IPA, Trooper, Old Tom; Titanic Plum Porter; 3 changing beers (sourced nationally) [H]
Excellent market pub with a unique atmosphere, being both cosy and relaxed as well as lively and vibrant. The Grade II listed building was refurbished in 2014. Its gin palace-style interior's high ceilings and tall windows create a light and airy feel. This is one of the few Robinsons Brewery houses to serve guest beers from other brewers. Local CAMRA Pub of the Year 2019.
❀◐≠♣●🚌🐾📶

Blossoms

2 Buxton Road, Heaviley, SK2 6NU (at A6/A5102 jct)
☎ (0161) 222 4150
Robinsons Dizzy Blonde, Unicorn, Trooper [H], **Old Tom; 1 changing beer (often Robinsons)** [G]
Landmark street-corner local whose three rooms radiate off a traditional drinking lobby, served by the central bar. Many old features remain, particularly in the rear Smoke Room. The full Robinsons range is served, including a seasonal beer. Popular quizzes are held on Wednesday night; the upstairs function room hosts live music on Friday night and at the weekend. Outside drinking is catered for in the cobbled alleyway. Q❀◐≠♣P🚌🐾📶

Hope Inn

118 Wellington Road North, Heaton Norris, SK4 2LL (N of Belmont Way)
☎ (0161) 637 6191 🌐 thehopestockport.co.uk
Outstanding 3.9; 9 changing beers (sourced nationally; often Fool Hardy Ales) [H]
An imposing brick-built Victorian pub that dominates the northern approach to Stockport and is home to Fool Hardy Ales. The 11 handpumps in one comfortably furnished room serve cask ales: five from Fool Hardy and the others changing guests. The second, more traditional room dispenses real ciders and draught foreign beers. A large decking area to the rear is an attraction on sunny days. Q❀♣●P🚌🐾📶

Magnet 🏆

51 Wellington Road North, Heaton Norris, SK4 1HJ (jct Duke St)
☎ (0161) 429 6287 🌐 themagnetfreehouse.co.uk
Salopian Oracle; 13 changing beers (sourced nationally) [H]
Popular, family-run pub that recently celebrated ten years as a free house. It offers 14 cask ales alongside 12 craft keg beers, with digital boards displaying the available selection. On the left is a bustling vault leading to a lower pool room and a series of other rooms. Outside is a twin-storey beer terrace. A pizza vendor operates on Friday evening. Local CAMRA Pub of the Year 2020. Q❀≠♣P🚌🐾📶

Olde Vic

1 Chatham Street, Edgeley, SK3 9ED (jct Shaw Heath)
🌐 yeoldevic.pub/en
5 changing beers (sourced nationally) [H]
Now owned by its regulars, Ye Olde Vic continues to benefit from a programme of improvements although inside it remains enjoyably shambolic. Bric-a-brac abounds, with something to catch your eye at every turn. The five changing guest beers come from small breweries around the UK and the pumpclips on the ceiling are a potted history of lost beers and brewers. Look for the sign over the bar describing the various forms of sparkler used in dispensing your beer.
Q❀≠♣●🚌🐾📶

Petersgate Tap

19A St Petersgate, SK1 1EB (jct Etchells St)
☎ 07925 078426 🌐 petersgatetap.com
Hawkshead Windermere Pale; 5 changing beers (sourced regionally) [H]
This family-run bar on two floors of a former betting shop is a dark-beer specialist and serial award winner, especially for cider. Downstairs its style is fairly modern with a continental feel to the bar area. Recycled oak-topped tables and a mix of seating sit under interesting posters and breweriana on the walls. Monthly events in the upstairs room range from tutored beer or cider tastings to live music and poetry and prose evenings.
Q❀♿≠●🚌🐾📶

Railway

1 Avenue Street, Portwood, SK1 2BZ (jct Gt Portwood St)
☎ (0161) 429 6062
Dunham Massey Dunham Porter; Outstanding UltraPale; Phoenix Arizona; Pictish Brewers Gold; Salopian Oracle; Thornbridge Jaipur IPA; 3 changing beers (sourced nationally) [H]
Street-corner local popular with its loyal crowd of regulars as well as shoppers from the Peel Centre across the road. Its 11 handpumps showcase a range of beer styles, including three changing guests, one of which is a rotating mild. These are supplemented by a changing guest cider and a range of Belgian, German and other bottled beers. The bar billiards table is well used and the outside drinking area is a summer suntrap.
Q❀♣●🚌🐾📶

Summerseat

Footballers Inn

28 Higher Summerseat, BL0 9UG
☎ (01204) 880008
Bowland Hen Harrier; Theakston Best Bitter; Wainwright; 3 changing beers (often Moorhouse's, Timothy Taylor) [H]
Once the regular haunt of some of the stars of Coronation Street in the 1960s and 70s, this is a stone-built two-roomed pub. It has a central bar with TV and a main lounge featuring a log-burner. Its handpumps serve three regular and three guest real ales. The pub, frequently in this Guide, is a 15-minute walk from the East Lancashire heritage railway line station.
❀≠(ELR) ♣P🚌(477) 🐾📶

Tottington

Dungeon Inn

9 Turton Road, BL8 4AW
☎ 07706 737753
Wainwright; house beer (by Thwaites); 4 changing beers [H]
A traditional, family-friendly Thwaites pub. It has a quiet front lounge featuring an open fire in cold weather, and a separate pool room off the main bar. To the rear at a lower level is a suntrap beer garden. Six handpumps

serve regular and guest ales. Live music is performed on Saturday. The pub is recognised by CAMRA as having a historic interior of regional importance. Dogs are welcome until 7.30pm. 🚸❀◐♣🚌(480,469)🐾📶

Tyldesley

Mort Arms

235-237 Elliott Street, M29 8DG
☎ 07584 341099
Joseph Holt Bitter; 1 changing beer (sourced locally; often Bootleg) 🄷
From the façade to the interior, this 1930s pub is recognisable as a Holt's hostelry. The entrance has two etched doors directing you into either the taproom or the lounge, with a central bar serving both. This is a community-based venue that supports and participates in the local darts and dominoes leagues. As well as the Bitter, there is often a guest beer from Joseph Holt or Bootleg. ❀♣🚌(V2)📶

Union Arms

83 Castle Street, M29 8EW
☎ (01942) 870645
3 changing beers (sourced locally; often Wainwright) 🄷
This family-friendly pub is part of the local community with regular charity events and occasional theme nights including live music. The interior is divided into a number of separate connected areas. The left side is the vault and the right is a lounge used for dining. There are usually three real ales including Wainwright, with fresh home-cooked food served during the week and lunch on Sunday. Most sporting events are shown on TV. 🚸❀◐◑♣🚌(V2) 🐾

Uppermill

Albion Tap 🄻

72 High Street, OL3 6AW
☎ (01457) 870770
Donkeystone DPA, Kaihe; 1 changing beer (often Marble, Millstone, Thornbridge) 🄷
This stylish bar was once a book shop and a bottle shop. It has a stainless-steel bar, high wooden tables, exposed stonework and a mural of a Saddleworth snow scene. Bees adorn the ceiling, with a tribute to the Manchester Arena victims. In addition to the four cask ales are eight keg fonts, with Track, Cloudwater and Tiny Rebel often featured. A carefully curated choice of UK and foreign bottles and cans is also available, along with a good selection of gins and vodkas. 🚸♿🚌(84,350)🐾

Cross Keys Inn ✔

Running Hill Gate, OL3 6LW (off A670 up Church Rd)
☎ (01457) 874626 🌐 crosskeysinn.net
JW Lees Dark, Manchester Pale Ale, Bitter, Founder's; 1 changing beer (sourced locally) 🄷
Overlooking St Chad church and Saddleworth, this attractive 18th-century stone building is Grade II listed. It has exposed beams throughout and was sympathetically refurbished in 2017. The public bar has a stone-flagged floor and a Yorkshire range. Home-cooked food features daily specials. Outside is a small garden with children's play area to the rear, and an extended patio with smoking area to the front. The pub hosts folk music on Wednesday night and the Rushcart festival in August. Walkers and dogs are welcome. Q🚸❀◐◑♿P🐾📶

Urmston

Assembly

31 Station Road, M41 9JG
☎ (0161) 989 0845 🌐 theassemblymcr.co.uk
2 changing beers (sourced regionally; often Hawkshead, Kirkstall, Pomona Island) 🄷
This recent arrival on Urmston's bar scene has added two real ale handpumps since opening in 2018. The style of its long, narrow ground-floor room and smaller upstairs lounge is stripped back, with plenty of bare wood on display. Some unusual beers from near and far are served from a well-stocked fridge. The pub hosts regular Meet the Industry evenings featuring brewers and distillers. A Cloudwater beer is sometimes on the bar. 🚸❀♿≢♣🚌🐾

Barking Dog

9A Higher Road, M41 9AB
☎ (0161) 215 0858 🌐 the-barking-dog.co.uk
House beer (by Marston's); 2 changing beers (sourced nationally) 🄷
This conversion of an old post office has been a welcome addition to the burgeoning Urmston scene. Its main room features high and low tables plus several settees, and a bar whose five handpumps include one serving cider. To the right is a snug where the building's post office past is most visible. A glass-fronted display cabinet in the corridor marks the former strongroom. Fresh meals are available using locally sourced ingredients where possible and include home-cooked pies and platters. 🚸❀◐◑♿≢♣🍎🚌🐾📶

Flixton Conservative Club ✔

Abbotsfield, 193 Flixton Road, M41 5DF
☎ (0161) 748 2846 🌐 flixtonconservativeclub.co.uk
6 changing beers (sourced nationally; often Dunham Massey, Elland, Pictish) 🄷
Former CAMRA Club of the Year set in its own grounds with an adjacent bowling green. The new stewards have maintained the high standards of their predecessors, with six handpumps on the main bar. More handpumps in the large upstairs function room cater for a brewery tap takeover on the last Friday of each month. Attractions include four snooker tables, Saturday bingo and quizzes on Friday and the last Sunday of the month. 🚸❀≢(Chassen Road) ♣P🚌(255) 📶

Lord Nelson

49 Stretford Road, M41 9LG
☎ 07827 850255
Joseph Holt Mild, Bitter; 1 changing beer (often Joseph Holt) 🄷
Big, classic community pub in a remarkable French-style building, with a 'best room' and a rather spartan vault. Draught beers remain the best sellers. The pub is quiet and relaxing by day, becoming vibrant when football is shown on TV. Tuesday is quiz night. The pub hosts the infamous Disco Erotica on Saturday night, and does not admit children at any time. It is known for charity fundraising and was voted local CAMRA Community Pub of the Year 2020. ❀≢♣P🚌🐾📶

Prairie Schooner Taphouse 🄻

33 Flixton Road, M41 5AW
🌐 prairie-schooner-taphouse.co.uk
4 changing beers (sourced locally; often Brightside, Dunham Massey, Outstanding) 🄷
The Schooner has been a valued part of the Urmston pub scene since opening in 2014. Its four handpumps serve mostly local ales, alongside eight keg fonts and a wide variety of bottled and canned beers from around the world. There is also real cider on draught, plus a selection

of gins and whiskies. Food is usually limited to nibbles such as nuts and crisps but the pub hosts bimonthly street food events. Q♉❀♿⇌♣🚌(255)🐾📶

Wardley

Morning Star

520 Manchester Road, M27 9QW (opp Bagot St)
☎ (0161) 727 8373

Joseph Holt Mild, Bitter, Two Hoots; 1 changing beer (sourced locally) Ⓗ

Built in 1890, this red-brick pub is a popular community local with a modernised interior. A vault with dartboard and TV is on the left as you enter. Opposite is a small front room leading to the larger lounge. All three rooms are served from the central bar, one of the few still dispensing Holt's Mild. An extensive food menu is offered. The front terrace beer garden is popular in summer. Wednesday is quiz night and live entertainment features at the weekend. ♉❀◐◑♿⇌♣P🚌📶

Westhoughton

Beer School 𝕃

88 Market Street, BL5 3AZ
☎ (01942) 396280 🌐 thebeerschool.co.uk

4 changing beers (sourced locally) Ⓗ

This micropub, decked out like a school, has developed into a lively and popular part of the Westhoughton community. Its 'cellar', on view behind the bar, supplies four handpumps serving beers of varied style and strength, some from local suppliers. Up to four bag-in-box real ciders are available, many from leading producers. Drinks can be sampled before ordering. Note that the toilets are upstairs. ❀⇌●🚌🐾📶

Whalley Range

Hillary Step 𝕃 ✔

199 Upper Chorlton Road, M16 0BH
☎ (0161) 881 1978 🌐 thehillarystep.co.uk

5 changing beers (sourced regionally; often RedWillow, Squawk, Track) Ⓗ

Modern bar in a small strip of shops and bars a short walk north of Chorlton. Five handpumps serve beers mostly from local and regional breweries, usually including a dark ale in winter. The eight keg fonts include a regular sour. Light snacks are offered including pork pies, Scotch eggs, olives and nuts. Attractions include backgammon on Monday night and live jazz on Sunday night, plus a quiz on the first Tuesday of the month and Step Sessions on the first Thursday. Children are welcome until 7pm. ♉❀♣🚌(86)🐾📶

Wigan

Anvil 𝕃 ✔

Dorning Street, WN1 1ND
☎ (01942) 239444

Banks's Mild; Brakspear Oxford Gold; Wainwright; 4 changing beers (sourced nationally) Ⓗ

Popular town-centre pub close to the bus station with seven handpumps dispensing various guest beers, two real ciders, six draught continental ales and a range of bottled beers. Several TV screens show sports action and the small snug contains the Wall of Fame displaying numerous award certificates. There is a garden at the rear. Over-18s only. ❀⇌(Wallgate/N Western)●🚌

Crooke Hall Inn 𝕃

Crooke Road, WN6 8LR
☎ (01942) 236088 🌐 crookepub.com

6 changing beers Ⓗ

Multi-roomed canalside inn in a picturesque location in Crooke, three miles from the centre of Wigan. Very much the hub of the village, it welcomes children and dogs until 9pm and is popular with locals and visitors alike. Home-made food features locally sourced ingredients where possible. The pub has a large beer garden and a separate cellar bar that is ideal for functions. Local CAMRA Community Pub of the Year 2020. ♉❀◐◑●P🚌(635,635)🐾📶

John Bull Chophouse

2 Coopers Row, Market Place, WN1 1PQ
☎ (01942) 242862 🌐 johnbullchophousewigan.co.uk

House beer (by Thwaites); 10 changing beers Ⓗ

A vibrant and lively inn in a town-centre building over 300 years old which has been cottages, stables and a slaughterhouse in the past. Run by the same family for over 40 years, it is reputed to have the best pub jukebox in the North-West. Six handpumps serve Thwaites beers. This quirky pub is set over two floors, with toilets upstairs and public seating outside. Closed Monday and Tuesday in winter. ❀⇌(Wallgate/N Western)●🚌🐾

Raven Hotel 𝕃 ✔

5 Wallgate, WN1 1LD
☎ (01942) 239764 🌐 theravenwigan.com

Tetley Bitter; 4 changing beers Ⓗ

An early 1900s commercial hotel, virtually derelict before a tasteful renovation in 2012 that retained and restored many original features including tiles, panelling and windows. The retro decor is typical of this small local pub chain, with cosy coal fires in winter and two unobtrusive TVs. The pub serves a varying range of real ales and cider on handpump, alongside good home-made food at reasonable prices. Loyalty cards are offered and a Wednesday cask critics night gives discounts on real ale. ♉❀◐◑♿⇌(Wallgate/N Western) ●🚌🐾📶

Sherrington's 𝕃

57 Kenyon Road, WN1 2DU
☎ 07500 171114 🌐 sherringtonsbar.com

6 changing beers (sourced locally; often Wily Fox) Ⓗ

Industrial-themed bar with six real ales on handpump, three from Wily Fox plus three varying guests. The 10 taps serve craft, lager and continental beers alongside a selection of UK and continental bottled ales. There is also an upper-floor gin bar, and tea, coffee and hot chocolate are available. Local CAMRA Best New Cask Outlet 2020. Q♉❀♿●🚌🐾📶

Swan & Railway 𝕃 ✔

80 Wallgate, WN1 1BA
☎ 07957 876053 🌐 swanandrailwayhotelwigan.co.uk

Banks's Sunbeam; Courage Directors; Draught Bass; 4 changing beers (sourced locally) Ⓗ

Built in 1898, this classic Victorian pub features an impressive stained-glass window, and an interior adorned with historical photos of old Wigan, the local railway and rugby league. Its seven handpumps serve ales including Draught Bass, Banks's Sunbeam and Courage Directors. The pub also supports local breweries by regularly offering beers from Hophurst, Prospect, Wily Fox and Wigan Brewhouse. ❀◐⇌♣🚌🐾📶

Tap 'n' Barrel 𝕃 ✔

16 Jaxon's Court, WN1 1LR
☎ (01942) 386966 🌐 tapnbarrelwigan.co.uk

Martland Mill Lancashire Loom; 6 changing beers (sourced regionally) Ⓗ

Next to the bus station in a narrow shopping mews, this microbar is the brewery tap for Martland Mill. The main bar area is long and narrow, leading to a covered and

heated, smoke-free garden, which hosts live music on Sunday afternoon. There is additional seating upstairs. Four real ciders are served from the fridge. Beer and cider are available in paddles of three third-pints. Occasional beer and sausage festivals are held.
Q⇌(Wallgate/N Western) 🍎🚌🐾📶

Wigan Central 𝕃

Arch No.1 & 2, Queen Street, WN3 4DY
☎ (01942) 246425 🌐 wigancentral.bar
House beer (by Prospect); 6 changing beers (sourced nationally) 🄷
This award-winning two-roomed pub has a railway-themed interior with a live feed displaying arrival and departure times from both nearby railway stations. The pub serves real ales from all over, alongside continental bottled beers displayed in the 'library'. Bar snacks are available. Live music plays on Sunday. Local CAMRA Cider Pub of the Year 2020 and a recent National Pub of the Year runner-up. Q♿⇌🍎🚌🐾📶

Withington

Victoria ✔

438 Wilmslow Road, M20 3BW (on B5093, jct Davenport Av)
☎ (0161) 434 2600
Hydes 1863, Original, Lowry; 5 changing beers (sourced nationally; often Hydes) 🄷
This friendly Hydes community pub attracts a convivial cross-section of Withington life, from seasoned locals to fresh-faced students. Its late 19th-century exterior features etched windows. The refurbished interior has been opened out to create distinct drinking areas, each with its own atmosphere. Attractions include a pool table at the rear, an occasional quiz, sport on TV and live entertainment at the weekend. 🐴❀♣🍎🚌🐾📶

Woodford

Davenport Arms (Thief's Neck)

550 Chester Road, SK7 1PS (on A5102, jct Church Lane)
☎ (0161) 439 2435 🌐 davenportarms.co.uk
Robinsons Wizard, Dizzy Blonde, Cumbria Way, Unicorn, Old Tom; 1 changing beer (often Robinsons) 🄷
Characterful red-brick farmhouse-style pub which received a smart refurbishment several years ago but which retains a multi-roomed feel with real fires in winter. This is its 34rd consecutive year in the Guide, and the licence has now been in the same family for a mammoth 88 years. Excellent food is mostly home made, with some adventurous specials. Outside, the spacious forecourt and attractive garden, set well away from the road, are popular in summer, boasting impressive floral displays. 🐴❀◐◑♣P🚌(42B)🐾📶

Worsley

Worsley Old Hall

Worsley Park, off Walkden Road, M28 2QT (next to Worsley Park Marriott Hotel)
☎ (0161) 703 8706
Brunning & Price Original; house beer (by Facer's); 4 changing beers (sourced regionally; often Howard Town, Moorhouse's) 🄷
Attractive 17th-century pub in extensive parkland. The Grade II listed building, refurbished in 2013, has spacious drinking and dining rooms that are comfortably furnished, the walls sporting interesting historical pictures. The pub dispenses a good range of beers including at least six cask ales plus an array of KeyKeg taps. Excellent food is served and there is an extensive beer garden at the rear. Q🐴❀◐◑♿♣P🚌(33,34)🐾📶

Arden Arms, Stockport (Photo: Lawrence Devaney)

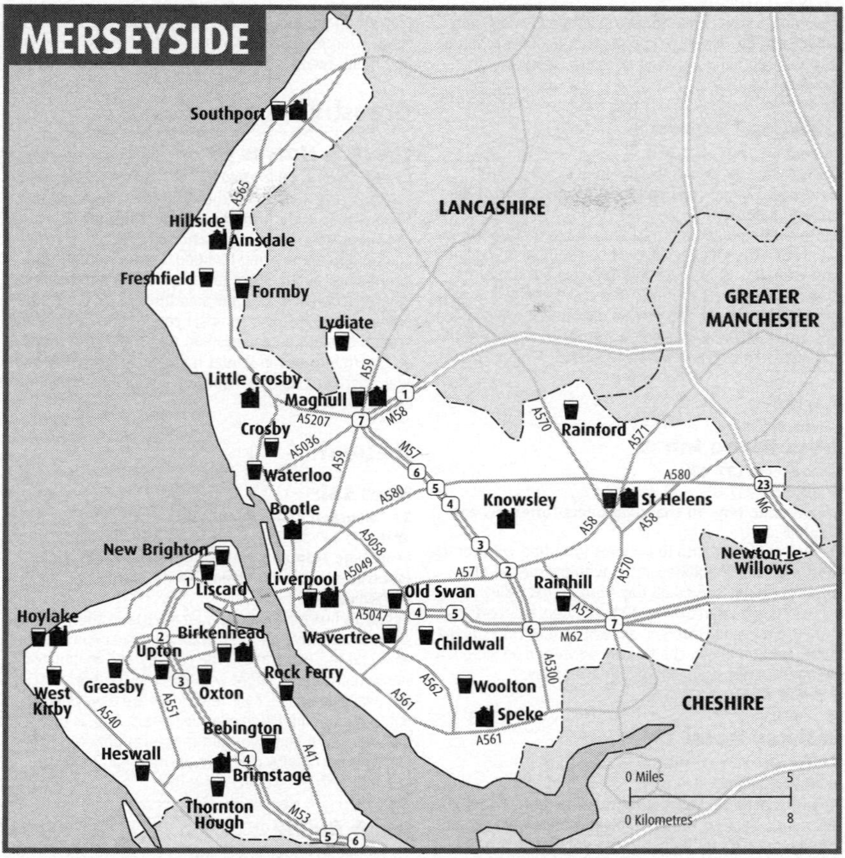

Bebington

Rose & Crown ✓

57 The Village, CH63 7PL

☎ (0151) 644 5829 🌐 roseandcrownbebington.co.uk

Thwaites Original, IPA, Gold, Amber; house beer (by Thwaites); 2 changing beers (sourced nationally) Ⓗ

This old coaching inn, built in 1732, is a thriving, vibrant and friendly community pub. It has a lounge, small bar and games room, with traditional decor and old photos of the area adorning the walls. Thwaites brews the house beer, Rose Gold, and some of the changing beers, with frequent guests from other breweries. Nearby Port Sunlight Village was founded by William Hesketh Lever in 1888 to house his soap factory workers and is the home of the Lady Lever Art Gallery. Q⚇≈♣🚌🐾📶

Travellers Rest ✓

169 Mount Road, CH63 8PJ

☎ (0151) 608 2988 🌐 thetravsbebington.co.uk

Sharp's Doom Bar; Wainwright; 4 changing beers (sourced nationally; often Brimstage, Fuller's) Ⓗ

Reputedly over 300 years old, this former coaching inn is close to Storeton Woods. It has a cosy country-pub feel and is decorated throughout with brasses and bric-a-brac. The main bar area and two side rooms are served from a central bar. Guest ales are often from local microbreweries. At lunchtime the emphasis is on food, but in the evening this is very much a traditional pub. No evening meals Monday and Tuesday.

Q⚇◐♿🍎🚌(464,487) 🐾

Birkenhead

Gallaghers Traditional Pub 🄻

20 Chester Street, CH41 5DQ

☎ (0151) 649 9095

6 changing beers (sourced nationally; often Brimstage, Rat, Salopian) Ⓗ

Multiple-award winning free house close to the Mersey ferries, rescued after closure and refurbished in 2010. It is decorated with a fascinating range of military memorabilia and a collection of shipping images. Several ciders are always on offer. Meals are served daily (no food Mon). Live music plays every Sunday, and cheese night is the last Sunday – bring your own cheese. The outside area at the rear has a retractable roof.

❀◐≈(Hamilton Sq) ♣🍎🚌🐾

Crosby

Corner Post 🄻

25 Bridge Road, L23 6SA

☎ 07587 177453

4 changing beers (sourced locally; often Peerless, Rock the Boat) Ⓗ

Crosby's second micropub, located in a former post office – hence the name – is easily spotted by the postbox outside. Interesting pictures depicting the history of the building and local area adorn the walls. Bottled continental beers, wine and soft drinks are available to complement the real ales and cider. Close to the 53 bus

route and a short walk from Blundellsands and Crosby railway station, it is also near the Iron Men attraction on Crosby beach. Well-behaved dogs are welcome.
Q≠♣●▭(53) 🐾

Liverpool Pigeon 𝕃
14 Endbutt Lane, L23 0TR
☎ 07766 480329 🌐 liverpoolpigeon.co.uk
5 changing beers (sourced locally; often Bristol Beer Factory, Salopian) 🄷
Merseyside's pioneering micropub, named after a now extinct bird from Polynesia, is a fine example of the type, with real ales, ciders and bottled beers but no spirits, alcopops, keg beers or music. The cask beers will usually include a local brew and often a dark beer. Locally made pies are available at the bar. A former Liverpool CAMRA Pub of the Year. Q♿♣●▭▭(47,54)🐾

Formby

Cross House Inn ✔
Cross Green, L37 4BH
☎ (01704) 873775
Greene King IPA; 10 changing beers (often Greene King) 🄷
The pub is divided into four rooms furnished with comfy sofas and chairs, and decorated with pictures of old Formby. Food is served all day from an extensive menu and a specials board. Up to 10 cask beers can be found, many from local breweries, as well as four ciders and a good selection of gin. Children are permitted up to 9pm if dining. Cask ale is discounted on a Monday.
Q❀◐♿P▭(47,X2) 🐾 ᯤ

Railway Hotel ✔
2 Duke Street, L37 4AS
☎ (01704) 831072
Thwaites Original; Wainwright; 2 changing beers 🄷
This pub is close to Formby railway station and also on the main bus route to Southport. On Monday it offers a cask ale club with beers at £2.49 all day. Two guest ales are available from a range of 20 seasonal ales – customers can vote for their favourites.
◐♿≠♣●P▭(44) 🐾 ᯤ

Freshfield

Beer Station
3 Victoria Buildings, L37 7DB (opp railway station)
☎ (01704) 807450
3 changing beers (sourced locally; often Neptune, Red Star, Rock the Boat) 🄷
Freshfield's first micropub, with a focus on all things local. Beers are chosen to showcase the area's brewers, with the exception of one 'foreign' beer a month from out of the region. A fridge with bottled beers adds to the variety. Local pies are available. The walls are decorated with work by local artists. Dogs are welcome on a lead.
Q♿≠♣●▭🐾 ᯤ

Freshfield 𝕃 ✔
1 Massams Lane, L37 7BD (from station turn inland into Victoria Rd then left into Gores Lane)
☎ (01704) 874871
Greene King IPA, Abbot; Oakham Citra; 11 changing beers (sourced regionally) 🄷
A community pub at its heart with three distinct areas – a dining room serving quality food, an area dominated by a bar full of handpumps, and 'the flags' where well-behaved dogs are welcome. Sport is shown on three large TVs and a real fire adds warmth in winter. Real cider is available on occasion during festivals. This is a place to meet, talk and spend time with friends old and new. A former CAMRA National Pub of the Year finalist and multi award-winner. ❀◐♿≠♣P▭🐾 ᯤ

Greasby

Coach & Horses ✔
Greasby Road, CH49 3NG
☎ (0151) 677 4509 🌐 coachandhorsesgreasby.co.uk
Black Sheep Holy Grail; Butcombe Original; 2 changing beers (sourced nationally) 🄷
Charming whitewashed traditional street-corner local, dating back nearly 300 years. Formerly a farmhouse where ale was brewed and sold from 1725, it became a pub in the 1820s. The compact central bar space serves several discrete areas including two small cosy rooms, and warming fires in winter help create a country-pub feel. There is a folk/acoustic jam session every Monday.
Q❀♣P▭ ᯤ

Heswall

Beer Lab
53 Telegraph Road, CH60 0AD
☎ (0151) 342 5475
Brimstage Trapper's Hat Bitter; 3 changing beers (sourced regionally; often Lister's, Purple Moose, RedWillow) 🄷
Heswell's first micropub opened in 2018 in a former cycle shop, an easy five minutes' walk from the main shopping area and the bus station. The relaxed and minimalist single-room bar is bright and airy, making the most of the available space. Four real ciders are always on the bar together with Belgian bottled beers. Beer is served in pint, one-third and two-third measures only (no half-pints). Local CAMRA Cider Pub of the Year 2020.
Q♣●▭🐾 ᯤ

Jug & Bottle 𝕃
13 Mount Avenue, CH60 4RH
☎ (0151) 342 5535 🌐 the-jugandbottle.co.uk
Brains Rev James; Brimstage Trapper's Hat Bitter; 6 changing beers (sourced nationally; often Big Bog, Castle Rock, Peerless) 🄷
Originally a private house built in the 1870s, later becoming offices, then opening as the Mill House Hotel in 1986, then the Jug & Bottle in 1993. The building is hidden behind the village hall and library a short distance from the main shopping street. Inside, different cosy

REAL ALE BREWERIES
Ad Hop Liverpool
Big Bog ◆ Speke
Black Lodge ◆ Liverpool
Brimstage Brimstage
Brooks Hoylake
Carnival ◆ Liverpool (NEW)
Connoisseur St Helens (brewing suspended)
Craft, The Southport
Gibberish ▮ Liverpool
Handyman ▮ Liverpool
Howzat ▮ St Helens (NEW)
Liverpool Liverpool
Love Lane ▮ Liverpool
Melwood Knowsley
Neptune ◆ Maghull
Peerless Birkenhead
Rock the Boat Little Crosby
Southport Southport
Stamps Liverpool: Bootle
Tyton Ainsdale (NEW)

areas and open fires create a warm and friendly atmosphere, while the decking outside gives views towards the River Dee and North Wales.
Q

Hillside

Grasshopper

70 Sandon Road, PR8 4QD
(01704) 569794
8 changing beers (sourced regionally; often Bank Top, Cross Bay, Salopian)
This micropub opened in 2016 in what was a Martins Bank branch until 1978 – the logo of Martins was a grasshopper – situated in a row of shops close to Hillside train station. There is outdoor seating at the front and a secluded beer garden to the rear. Eight changing real ales and six real ciders are served. Local CAMRA Pub of the Year 2018 and Cider Pub of the Year 2019 and 2020.
QP(47)

Pines

3 Hillside Road, PR8 4QB
07454 453090
2 changing beers (sourced regionally; often Salopian)
An attractively decorated bar in what was once a hairdresser's in an area that previously had no pubs or bars but now has two award-winning outlets. Two handpumps offer a varied choice of beers, and a selection of bottled beers is also kept. An outside seating area at the front is popular in the warmer months. Sometimes the bar can be noisy and at others it can be quiet and relaxing depending on the time of day.
P(47)

Hoylake

Black Toad

32 Market Street, CH47 2AF
07835 360691 theblacktoad.co.uk
3 changing beers (sourced regionally; often Chapter, Neptune, Peerless)
Micropub opened in July 2019 in an abandoned shop unit on the main shopping street in the centre of Hoylake. The narrow main room and bar is attractively decorated with simple furniture and there is a smaller cosy room behind. Outside at the rear is a pleasant beer garden. The owners ensure a balanced selection of cask beers at all times. Q(38,407)

Plasterers Arms

35 Back Seaview, CH47 2DJ
(0151) 345 0249
Purple Moose Cwrw Glaslyn/Glaslyn Ale; Rat White Rat; 4 changing beers (sourced nationally; often Black Sheep, Timothy Taylor)
Friendly, traditional two-room pub in an old fishing community, sadly long gone. A pub for over 150 years, it has fascinating decor – note the mirrored ceiling – with information about the pub and local history. Close to the beach, it is popular with walkers and birdwatchers, and a short walk to Market Street for shops, buses and the railway station. There is seating outside and a children's playground opposite. Regular entertainment features at weekends. Parking is on the street nearby.
Q(38,407)

Liscard

Lazy Landlord Ale House

56 Mill Lane, CH44 5UG
07583 135616
Joseph Holt Bitter; Oakham Citra; 4 changing beers (sourced nationally; often Brimstage, Peerless, Rat)
Wirral's first micropub, opened in converted shop premises in 2014. It is run by cask ale enthusiasts the Henry brothers. Two small cosy rooms, decorated with breweriana, artworks and a small library, are served from the front bar. Mostly frequented by a more mature, discerning clientele of regulars, the pub is a venue for meetings of local societies. There are two ciders, usually from SeaCider and Snail Bank. Local CAMRA Pub of the Year 2017-19. Q(410,432)

Liverpool: Childwall

Childwall Fiveways L

179 Queens Drive, L15 6XS
(0151) 738 2100
Greene King Abbot; Ruddles Best Bitter; 6 changing beers (sourced nationally; often Robinsons)
A former Higson's tied house, this large single-roomed pub opened as a Wetherspoon in 2010. Located in a leafy suburb, it has good motorway and public transport links. The refurbished interior is decorated with wood panelling, and outside there is a beer garden. A popular establishment, it can get busy, especially at weekends. The site was used for a water tank during WWII.
P(79,81)

Liverpool: City Centre

Augustus John L

Peach Street, L3 5TX (off Brownlow Hill)
(0151) 794 5507 the-augustus-john.business.site
5 changing beers (sourced nationally; often Peerless, Rock the Boat)
Opened in 1968 and run by the University of Liverpool, the Augustus John is an open-plan pub popular with students, lecturers and locals. Cask ales always come in a range of styles – light and dark – and there are two ciders on handpump and many more in the cellar. Pizza is served at all times, sport is shown and there is a jukebox. Closed over Christmas and New Year. A local and regional CAMRA Cider Pub of the Year. (79)

Baltic Fleet L

33A Wapping, L1 8DQ
(0151) 709 3116
Brimstage Trapper's Hat Bitter; Melwood Derby Stout; Robinsons Trooper; 3 changing beers (sourced locally; often Big Bog, Rock the Boat)
Grade II listed building near the Albert Dock. It has a distinctive flat-iron shape and the interior is decorated on a nautical theme. The existence of tunnels in the cellar has led to speculation that the pub's history may involve smuggling. It also originally had many doors to allow customers to escape the press gangs. It can get busy when events are on at the nearby M&S Bank Arena.

Belvedere L

8 Sugnall Street, L7 7EB (off Falkner St)
(0151) 709 0303
4 changing beers (sourced regionally; often Higson's, Liverpool Brewing, Rat)
Tucked away in the Georgian area of the city, close to the famous Philharmonic Hall and frequented by its orchestra members, this small two-roomed pub is a free house

serving four rotating beers from mainly local microbreweries. Redeemed in 2006 from closure for housing development, the Grade II listed building retains original fixtures and interesting etched-glass features. It has a mixed local clientele, and various small cultural groups meet and good conversation thrives.
Q❀●▯🚌🐾📶

Bridewell 𝕃

1 Campbell Square, L1 5FB
☎ (0151) 707 2372
Kirkstall Pale Ale; 4 changing beers (sourced nationally; often Melwood) 🄷
Grade II listed building dating from the mid-19th century when it was a police bridewell. The former cells are used as seating areas and provide an unusual focus in the downstairs bar. Five cask beers, including one local, and a range of craft keg and continental beers are on sale. There is an outdoor patio area at the front. The pub is situated close to the Liverpool One shopping area, the Albert Dock and the riverfront. ❀≹📶

Crown Hotel ★ 𝕃

43 Lime Street, L1 1JQ
☎ (0151) 707 6027 🌐 thecrownliverpool.co.uk
Greene King IPA; Timothy Taylor Landlord; 6 changing beers (sourced nationally; often Peerless) 🄷
Grade II listed pub with a nationally important historic interior and ornate plasterwork ceilings. Close to Lime Street Station and public transport links, the building is noticeable for its walkers Ales Warrington stucco frieze. Many of the original features are retained in the two downstairs rooms, including some impressive wood panelling and original push bells. There is also an ornate glass dome above the staircase. Breakfast is served until 12pm after which food is served until 10pm.
☕◑≹(Lime St) 🚌📶

Dickens & King 𝕃

2B Maryland Street, L1 9DE
☎ 07595 588426
3 changing beers (sourced locally; often Ad Hop, Neptune, Red Star) 🄷/🄶
Cosy bar next door to Shisha downhill from the Hope & Anchor. Three or four - often local - cask ales are on gravity dispense in pins, alongside a selection of bottle beers and craft keg. The bar also specialises in artisanal gins and vodkas. There is a small room upstairs with more seating. Opening times may vary. ≹●🚌(86)📶

Dispensary

87 Renshaw Street, L1 2SP
☎ (0151) 709 2160
Fernandes Malt Shovel Mild; Rat White Rat; Titanic Plum Porter; 4 changing beers (often Oakham, Ossett, Titanic) 🄷
This lively city pub is a haven for real ale drinkers of all ages. It was formerly a Cains tied pub but is now leased out as a free house. The attractive bar area has Victorian features, and there is a raised wood-panelled area to the rear. Originally The Grapes, the old sign is behind the bar. It can be busy when matches are shown on the big screens. ◖≹🚌

Doctor Duncan's

St Johns Lane, L1 1HF
☎ (0151) 709 5100 🌐 queensquare.co.uk/doctor-duncans
House beer (by Red Star); 4 changing beers (sourced nationally; often Red Star, Salopian) 🄷
This former Cains Brewery flagship pub has an impressive Victorian interior with four distinctively different drinking areas – the green tiled room is particularly handsome. The pub's name commemorates the first chief medical officer of Liverpool and a ruthless campaigner against poor living conditions in Victorian Liverpool – medical memorabilia can be found throughout. The house beer is from Red Star. ◑≹♣🚌🐾📶

Excelsior 𝕃 ✔

121-123 Dale Street, L2 2JH (close to Birkenhead Tunnel entrance)
☎ (0151) 352 9544
Salopian Oracle; Sharp's Doom Bar; Timothy Taylor Landlord; 3 changing beers (sourced regionally; often Big Bog, Salopian) 🄷
Large, comfortable corner pub on the edge of the business district. The main room has a three-sided bar and a series of distinct seating areas. There is a large room off the main space with a raised seating area – this can be hired for meetings and functions. Three screens show sports events, particularly football, but are generally silent otherwise. ◑≹P🚌📶

Fly in the Loaf ✔

13 Hardman Street, L1 9AS
☎ (0151) 708 0817
Okell's Bitter; 5 changing beers (sourced nationally; often Kirkstall, Okell's) 🄷
A former bakery, the name comes from the slogan 'no flies in the loaf'. Owned by Isle of Man brewer Okell's, it serves its beers alongside a changing range of guests from around the country, many from microbreweries, and a good selection of foreign beers. The spacious interior has a light, airy frontage with contrasting wood-panelled areas towards the rear. There is an attractive small on-street drinking area at the front and a function room upstairs. ◑♿≹🚌(86)📶

Grapes 𝕃

60 Roscoe Street, L1 9DW
☎ (0151) 709 3977
8 changing beers (often Ad Hop, Chapter) 🄷
This corner local dates back to 1804 and has the original Mellors signage outside. It is known as the Little Grapes but, after a major refurbishment in 2016, the pub is now larger. Stairs lead to a partly sheltered patio area atop the new extension. Most of the nine handpumps serve beers from local and regional smaller breweries, and one pump now regularly serves a real cider. An extensive selection of rums is also kept. Live jazz features every Sunday night. ❀≹♫🚌(82)📶

Head of Steam

85-89 Hanover Street, L1 3DZ
☎ (0151) 708 6096
Camerons Strongarm; 6 changing beers (sourced locally; often Camerons, Neptune, Tiny Rebel) 🄷
Opened in 2017, with no connection to the Head of Steam previously on Lime Street, this is a large venue with plenty of seating in various arrangements. Most major sporting events are shown live so it can get very busy, especially in the evening. Many foreign bottled and keg beers are on offer alongside the real ales. A private function area is available to hire. Handy for Liverpool One shops. ◑≹●🚌📶

Lime Kiln 𝕃 ✔

Fleet Street, L1 4NR
☎ (0151) 702 6810
Greene King Abbot; Ruddles Best Bitter; 9 changing beers (sourced nationally; often Peerless) 🄷
On first impression, the decor and layout may appear not to offer much for the real ale drinker, but looks can be deceiving. Thanks to continued commitment, real ale is well catered for, with at least one local beer usually available. Handpulls are in the downstairs bar only.

Situated in the Concert Square area, the pub is a peaceful haven during the day. A Victorian warehouse occupied the site, which was home to manufacturing chemists, from the early 1900s to the 1950s.

Lion Tavern ★ 🅛 ✅
67 Moorfields, L2 2BP
🌐 theliontavernliverpool.co.uk
Wily Fox Crafty Fox; house beer (by Rock the Boat); 4 changing beers (sourced nationally; often Liverpool Brewing, Red Star, Rock the Boat) 🅗
Named after the locomotive that worked the Liverpool and Manchester Railway (and is on display at the Liverpool museum), the Lion features mosaic floors, a tiled corridor plus intricately etched and stained glass. Refurbished in 2017, the pub retains Grade II listed status and is on CAMRA's National Inventory of Historic Pub Interiors. Up to eight beers are from the SIBA list, usually including ales from local micros. Westons cider is regularly available and local gins are kept.

Pen Factory
13 Hope Street, L1 9BQ
☎ (0151) 709 7887 🌐 pen-factory.co.uk
5 changing beers (sourced nationally; often Brimstage, Hawkshead, Titanic) 🅗
The Pen Factory opened in 2015, brought to you by the innovator of the original Everyman Bistro, entrepreneur Paddy Byrne. This large open-plan bistro-style establishment with a wood-burning stove and a small garden is a convivial place to drink and eat. At least five handpumps include beers from smaller breweries such as Brimstage. The food is excellent, not your average pub grub. The venue can be busy before or after productions at the nearby Everyman Theatre or Philharmonic Hall. (86)

Peter Kavanagh's ★ ✅
2-6 Egerton Street, L8 7LY (off Catharine St)
☎ (0151) 709 3443
Greene King Abbot; 4 changing beers (sourced nationally; often Castle Rock) 🅗
On CAMRA's National Inventory of Historic Pub Interiors and situated in the Georgian area. The snugs feature murals by Eric Robinson and there are fine stained-glass windows with wooden shutters. The benches have carved armrests thought to be caricatures of Peter Kavanagh, the licensee for 53 years until 1950. These features were not adversely affected when the pub was expanded, firstly in 1964 into next door, then in 1977 into next door but one. Liverpool CAMRA Pub of the Year 2019. (80,86)

Roscoe Head
24 Roscoe Street, L1 2SX
☎ (0151) 709 4365 🌐 roscoehead.co.uk
Tetley Bitter; Timothy Taylor Landlord; 4 changing beers (sourced regionally; often Rock the Boat) 🅗
One of the Magnificent Five pubs to feature in every edition of the Guide. Conversation and the appreciation of real ale rule in this cosy four-roomed hostelry. Run by members of the same family for over 30 years, the name commemorates William Roscoe, a leading campaigner against the slave trade. Six handpumps feature ales from national and local breweries. Hot pies are available. There has been concern over the future of the pub in recent years, with an active Save the Roscoe Head campaign.

Ship & Mitre 🅛 ✅
133 Dale Street, L2 2JH (by Birkenhead Tunnel)
☎ (0151) 236 0859 🌐 theshipandmitre.com

Flagship Sublime, Lupa, Silhouette; 5 changing beers (sourced nationally; often Big Bog, Flagship) 🅗
The name derives from two previous incarnations, the Flagship and the Mitre. The 1930s Art Deco pub is partly hidden by the Queensway Tunnel entrance. Fifteen handpulls offer an ever-changing array of beers and real ciders – friendly and knowledgeable staff are always willing to make a recommendation. There is also an impressive range of world beers. The pub now brews its own Flagship beers using the plant at Stamps Brewery in Crosby.

Thomas Rigby's ✅
23-25 Dale Street, L2 2EZ
☎ (0151) 236 3269
Okell's Bitter, Dr Okell's IPA; 4 changing beers (often Kirkstall) 🅗
This multi-roomed, Grade II listed building, bearing the name of a wine and spirit dealer, now supplies an extensive world beer range on draught and in bottles. The regular beers on handpump come from the pub's owner, Okell's. Good-value food including specials is served until early evening, with one room offering a friendly and efficient table service. The old coaching inn courtyard for outdoor drinking is shared with sister pub Lady of Mann.

Vernon Arms 🅛
69 Dale Street, L2 2HJ
☎ (0151) 236 6132
Brains Rev James; house beer (by Stamps); 3 changing beers 🅗
Situated close to the business district, the Vernon retains the feel of a street-corner local. The single long-roomed bar serves three drinking areas including a back room with frosted-glass windows advertising the Liverpool Brewing Company, which used to serve the pub. The main bar has wood panelling, several large columns and a small snug area. Real cider on handpull is unusual for the city centre.

Liverpool: Old Swan

Ale House
674/676 Prescot Road, L13 5XG
☎ 07944 565323 🌐 thealehouse.pub
5 changing beers (sourced nationally) 🅗
Bigger than other micropubs in the area, this new bar opened in 2016 in a building that was previously a job centre. It currently has six handpumps, one dispensing cider. Another cider or perry is served from the cool room. Beers are a mixture of better or lesser known brands supplied by agents, and local ales supplied directly, usually including a porter or stout.

Liverpool: Wavertree

Handyman Supermarket 🅛
461 Smithdown Road, L15 3JL
☎ (0151) 733 3048 🌐 handymansupermarket.co.uk
Handyman Pale; 3 changing beers (sourced locally; often Handyman, Melwood, Red Star) 🅗
A brewpub opened in 2017 in a former hardware shop, hence the name. It has a large open-plan bar plus an events/function room at the rear. The brew plant is on the mezzanine above the bar. Handpumps serve the brewery's own cask beers and there is a selection of bottled beers and craft keg on taps. Beers are often brewed collaboratively at other breweries. The Handyman beers are unfined. The pub hosts many events from live music to craft fairs.

Willow Bank 🄻 ✔

329 Smithdown Road, L15 3JA

☎ (0151) 733 5782

Greene King IPA, Abbot; Tetley Bitter; house beer (by Greene King); 4 changing beers (sourced nationally; often Big Bog, Ossett) ⊞

Vibrant, traditional, multi-room pub with the original public bar dating from the time it was a Walkers house. It attracts a mixed clientele including shoppers, locals and students. Up to eight changing guest beers are on offer – real ale night is Tuesday – and there are occasional beer festivals. Westons Rosie is available. Good-value food is served including Sunday lunches. The attractive roadside patio is popular. Live sport is shown on large screens and a well-attended quiz night is hosted.

P (86)

Liverpool: Woolton

Gardeners Arms ✔

101 Vale Road, L25 7RW

☎ (0151) 428 0775

Adnams Ghost Ship; Greene King IPA; Sharp's Doom Bar; 3 changing beers (sourced regionally; often Big Bog, Taylors) ⊞

Friendly community village pub situated over the hill from Woolton village and separated from Menlove Avenue by blocks of flats. Guest beers regularly include a local Big Bog beer. A quiz is held on Tuesday evening. Woolton is famous as the home of the Beatles – their original name was The Quarrymen after Woolton quarry and they first met at the local St Peter's Church.

(76)

Lydiate

Scotch Piper ★ ✔

Southport Road, L31 4HD (800yds N from A5147/Moss Lane jct)

☎ (0151) 526 2207

3 changing beers (sourced nationally; often Titanic) ⊞

The Scotch Piper is a whitewashed, thatched, medieval, cruck-framed Grade II* listed building just north of Lydiate. The doorway opens into a traditional bar with a servery on the left. A passage to the right leads to a further two rooms, the middle one with simple old woodwork. The end room, added later, is less rustic but retains some upholstered bench seating. The toilets are outside. Piper 1320 house beer is from Marston's.

Q P (300)

Maghull

Frank Hornby 🄻 ✔

38 Eastway, L31 6BR

☎ (0151) 520 4010

5 changing beers (often Brightside, Elland, Saltaire) ⊞

A Wetherspoon establishment named after local man and famous inventor of the Hornby train set. Samples of his work are on display in the pub including Meccano and Dinky Toys. Situated in a surburban street, the bar is spacious and light inside with a decked area outside at the front. A varied selection of guest ales includes some from local microbreweries. Alcoholic drinks are served from 10am. No children after 10pm. Q P

Maghull Cask Café

43 Liverpool Road South, L31 7BN

☎ (0151) 526 3877

5 changing beers (sourced locally; often Neptune, Oakham) ⊞

This micropub is a hidden gem. Opened in 2018, it serves a good range of changing cask ales, continental bottles and gins. Beers are from regional brewers such as Oakham, Titanic and Salopian. Friendly, knowledgeable staff help to create a welcoming atmosphere where conversation prevails. The Liverpool to Leeds canal runs through Maghull and the pub makes a good base for a nice walk towards Burscough. Q (300,310)

New Brighton

Bow-Legged Beagle 🄻

88 Victoria Road, CH45 2JF

☎ 07597 900114 🌐 thebowleggedbeagle.co.uk

5 changing beers (sourced regionally; often Beartown, Neptune) ⊞

Wirral's second micropub opened in 2017 in a former street-corner shop with a basic no-frills format and immediately proved popular with locals and visitors. It offers a friendly ambience and a regularly changing range of new and unusual local beers. There is seating outside on the pavement in summer. Close to the seafront and other local attractions. Q

Magazine Hotel 🏆 🄻 ✔

7 Magazine Brow, CH45 1HP (above Egremont Promenade)

☎ (0151) 630 3169 🌐 the-magazine-hotel.co.uk

Brimstage Trapper's Hat Bitter; Draught Bass; 3 changing beers (sourced regionally; often Big Bog, Brimstage) ⊞

This unspoilt multi-roomed, low-beamed pub with an attractive black and white frontage, dating from 1759, suffered a fire in 2010 but has been restored without losing its unique character. Three rooms lead off the main central bar area with an open fireplace. Traditionally renowned for its Draught Bass, other beers are often from local microbreweries. One changing real cider is kept. Overlooking Egremont Promenade, the pub has fine views over the River Mersey to Liverpool. Local CAMRA Pub of the Year 2020.

Q P (106,107)

Newton-le-Willows

Kirkfield Hotel ✔

2-4 Church Street, WA12 9SU

☎ (01925) 222058 🌐 thekirkfield.co.uk

4 changing beers (sourced locally) ⊞

Extensively renovated in late 2018, the Kirkfield hotel offers quality food and a good choice of real ales in the separate bar. Breakfast is served. Situated across the road from St Peter's Church and the Willow Park, this is a popular establishment. P (34)

Oxton

Oxton Bar & Kitchen 🄻

2 Claughton Firs, CH43 5TQ

☎ (0151) 651 2535 🌐 oxtonbar.co.uk

Brimstage Trapper's Hat Bitter; 2 changing beers (sourced locally) ⊞

In the centre of the attractive Oxton village among shops, bars and restaurants, this former John Smith's pub built in 1969 has been tastefully converted into a smart, comfortable, single-room lounge bar with an attractive outside seating area. There is a strong emphasis on quality food, ranging from sandwiches and snacks to full meals. Beers are often from local microbreweries.

P (492,495)

Rainford

Junction 🄻

News Lane, WA11 7JU

☎ (01744) 882868 🌐 junctionpubrainford.co.uk

5 changing beers 🄷

A community free house with a strong emphasis on showcasing local produce and local music. Beer festivals feature regularly, including one around the May Day bank holiday. A popular venue for local musicians, it hosts the Wooden Horse Folk Club on Sunday evening. Vintage car and motorcycle events also feature in the large space to the rear of the premises. ❀◐♿▲≈♣●P🚌(38,157)🐾📶

Rainhill

Skew Bridge Alehouse 🄻

5 Dane Court, L35 4LU

☎ (0151) 792 7906 🌐 skewbridge.co.uk

Lister's Best Bitter; Outstanding 3.9; 5 changing beers (sourced locally; often Big Bog, Melwood, North Riding) 🄷

This venue offers a selection of up to six cask ales, four real ciders and three craft lagers. Locally sourced ales are complemented by beers from across the UK. A range of wines, gins and single malt whiskies is also stocked. With no TV or music to distract customers, conversation is very much encouraged. During the summer months, outdoor seating is available. A folk, roots and acoustic night takes place on the first Tuesday of every month. Q❀♿≈♣●P🚌📶

Rock Ferry

Refreshment Rooms 🄻

2 Bedford Road East, CH42 1LS

☎ (0151) 644 5893 🌐 refreshmentrooms.com

House beer (by JW Lees); 1 changing beer (sourced locally) 🄷

Refurbished and reopened in 2012 under its original name, the pub was built in the 1880s for ferry passengers to Liverpool. The ferry terminal is long gone but there are excellent views over the Mersey. One central bar services two rooms. The focus is on food, with excellent reasonably priced meals served daily until 9pm. The house beer, HMS Conway, is from Lees, and the real cider is from Rosie's. Off the beaten track but well worth seeking out. ❀◐≈●🚌📶

St Helens

Cowley Vaults 🄻 ✔

50 Cooper Street, WA10 2BH

☎ (01744) 750849

6 changing beers 🄷

A short distance from the town centre, the pub has six handpulls serving cask ales on rotation, two real ciders and a large range of whiskies and gins. A friendly local community venue, it hosts pool teams and live music entertainment on the last Saturday of every month. Quiz night on Thursday evening includes free half-time refreshments. The beer garden is to the rear. Award-winning sister pub The Turk's Head is next door. ❀♿♣●🚌🐾📶

Cricketers Arms 🄻 ✔

64 Peter Street, WA10 2EB

☎ (01744) 361846

House beer (by Howzat); 11 changing beers (sourced nationally) 🄷

A former CAMRA National Pub of the Year, this family-run establishment has 13 handpulls always offering at least one dark beer, plus 10 ciders and a range of spirits including over 100 gins. The traditional community pub has beer gardens, darts and pool leagues, quiz nights and fundraising events. An outside bar is used for beer festivals and private events. In 2019 the on-site Howzat brewery began production of house beers for this pub and others within the local area. ❀♣●P🚌(10)🐾📶

News Room

89 Duke Street, WA10 2JG

☎ (01744) 322129

2 changing beers (sourced nationally) 🄷

The music-themed News Room offers three handpulls, craft beers and a range of foreign bottled beers as well as gins, rums and malt whiskies. Set in stylish surroundings where conversation is encouraged, it has a warm, friendly, laid-back atmosphere, with music from the 60s, 70s and 80s playing on large screens. Themed music nights are hosted every six to eight weeks. ♿🚌

Sefton ✔

1 Baldwin Street, WA10 1QA

☎ (01744) 22065

5 changing beers (sourced nationally) 🄷

A recently refurbished, modern and comfortable, town-centre pub that caters for everyone, whether you are looking for good pub food, live sport or just drinks with friends. The large room has a long bar down one side offering five regularly changing cask conditioned ales. There is a function room upstairs and live bands often play. ❀◐♿≈🚌📶

Talbot Ale House 🄻

97 Duke Street, WA10 2JG

☎ (01744) 322185

11 changing beers (sourced nationally) 🄷

A true community pub with a traditional bar, multi-function lounge and quiet room. The well-appointed beer garden adds extra drinking space. There are ales on 10 handpumps plus nine ciders, as well as a wide range of gins and malt whiskies. The pub hosts many games and quiz leagues, and karaoke on a Saturday night. A loyalty card is available for regular customers. Q❀♣●P🚌🐾📶

Turk's Head 🏆 🄻

49 Morley Street, WA10 2DQ

☎ (01744) 751289

14 changing beers 🄷

Current local CAMRA Pub of the Year, near the town centre. An attractive Tudor-style 1870s pub, it offers a rotating range of real ales on 14 handpulls, 15 draught ciders and a large whisky and gin bar. The upstairs tower lounge serves cocktails, craft and continental beers, and hosts live music on Saturday evening. Home-made high-quality food is available Wednesday to Sunday. Tuesday evening is smart phone quiz night with free half-time refreshments. There is a large beer garden to the rear. ❀◐♿♣●🚌🐾📶

Southport

Beer Den 🄻

65-67 Duke Street, PR8 5BT

☎ (01704) 329007

2 changing beers (sourced nationally; often Parker) 🄷

Southport's newest micropub was set up by the Parker Brewery and serves two of its own beers on rotation plus two guests. Two German lagers and an American IPA complement the range, alongside a carefully chosen spirit and wine selection. The pub is just around the corner from the famous British Lawnmower Museum. QP🚌(46)

Guest House 🏆

16 Union Street, PR9 0QE

☎ (01704) 537660 🌐 guesthouse-southport.blogspot.com

Butcombe Adam Henson's Rare Breed; Ruddles Best Bitter; Theakston Best Bitter; house beer (by Caledonian); 2 changing beers (often Phoenix, Salopian, Southport) Ⓗ

Close to the station and Lord Street, this listed building has an impressive frontage and interior with three separate wood-panelled drinking areas. The bar has 11 handpumps, one serving a local microbrewery beer, and a wide range of malt whiskies. A quiet, traditional pub, it attracts a mixed clientele, with a quiz night on Thursday and acoustic folk club on the first and third Mondays of the month. There is seating outside at the front and a courtyard area to the rear. Q❀◐⇌●🚌ᯤ

Phoenix ✔

4-6 Coronation Walk, PR8 1RF

☎ (01704) 513233

Sharp's Doom Bar; 2 changing beers Ⓗ

Popular sports pub at the south end of Lord Street, serving good food at reasonable prices. Family-run and free of tie, it is a favourite with real ale drinkers. The pub has plenty of traditional games and hosts a poker night on Monday and Wednesday, darts on Tuesday, and live music on Friday. Football is shown on plasma TV screens scattered about the pub, with major fixtures shown on a large screen. A great family-friendly establishment. ♿⇌♣🐾ᯤ

Sir Henry Segrave Ⓛ ✔

93-97 Lord Street, PR8 1RH (on A565, S end of Lord St)

☎ (01704) 530217

Greene King Abbot; Moorhouse's Pendle Witches Brew; Phoenix Wobbly Bob; Ruddles Best Bitter; Sharp's Doom Bar; Wainwright; 6 changing beers (sourced regionally; often Lytham, Robinsons, Saltaire) Ⓗ

Named after the former land speed world record holder who used to race on Southport flats, this is a spacious Wetherspoon pub with an attractive 19th-century exterior. The manager is a strong supporter of real ale and runs regular beer festival trips and occasional Meet the Brewer evenings. Twelve handpumps offer the best all-round choice of microbrewery beers in Southport – regular orders are placed with Phoenix, Saltaire, Titanic and Hawkshead. There is outside seating on Lord Street. Q❀◐♿⇌●🚌ᯤ

Tap & Bottles

19A Cambridge Walk, PR8 1EN

☎ (01704) 544322

4 changing beers Ⓗ

A micropub in the arcade between Chapel Street and Lord Street next to the Atkinson Centre. Four real ales may come from virtually anywhere, with a preference for North-West breweries. A huge range of bottles is also offered, but not all are real ale in a bottle. A small selection of pies is served all day. There is an old working pinball machine at the back of the pub. Q❀♿⇌♣●🚌🐾ᯤ

Thornton Hough

Red Fox Ⓛ

Neston Road, CH64 7TL

☎ (0151) 353 2920

Brightside Odin Blonde; house beer (by Phoenix); 8 changing beers (sourced locally) Ⓗ

An impressive sandstone building dating from the 1860s, set in extensive grounds. Refurbished in 2014, it is now a smart gastro-pub. The front bar area retains a pub feel, with the restaurant areas to either side. A smaller bar area at the back serves the terrace and large garden. Changing beers are usually from local microbreweries and the house beer by Phoenix is Brunning & Price Original Bitter. Up to 10 ciders are available. Q❀◐♿●P🚌(487) 🐾ᯤ

Upton

Bow-Legged Beagle Ⓛ

19 Arrowe Park Road, CH49 0UB

☎ 07989 392757

4 changing beers (sourced regionally; often Beartown, Neptune, Salopian) Ⓗ

This micropub opened in 2018 in a former bank on a busy row of shops near the centre of the village. The light, airy room has basic furnishings and a friendly ambience. Some of the old bank safes have been retained. This is the second Bow-Legged Beagle following the success of the New Brighton micropub of the same name. Q🚌🐾ᯤ

Waterloo

Four Ashes Ⓛ

23 Crosby Road North, L22 0LD

6 changing beers (often Neptune, Rock the Boat, Wily Fox) Ⓗ

A family-run micropub owned by the Ashe family – hence the name. On the site of a former restaurant, it is a great addition to the vibrant real ale scene in and around Waterloo station. Beers are ordered direct from local microbreweries or through a wholesaler, resulting in a varied and interesting selection, always including at least one dark beer. Beers conditioning in the cellar are displayed on the wall. Q♿⇌♣●🚌🐾

Trap & Hatch

135 South Road, L22 0LT

☎ (0151) 928 5837

3 changing beers (sourced regionally) Ⓗ

Situated on a busy suburban street, this micropub has a modern and stylish interior featuring low lighting and long tables. Unobtrusive music plays but does not detract from good conversation. Live music features on Saturday evening. The bar has three handpulls offering a choice of interesting beers not often seen in this area. There is also a good range of bottle beers and real cider. ❀♿⇌●🚌🐾ᯤ

Volunteer Canteen ★ Ⓛ

45 East Street, L22 8QR

☎ 07891 407464

4 changing beers (sourced nationally) Ⓗ

A cosy, traditional pub in a Grade II listed terraced building, the Volly, as it is locally known, still provides table service. Nestling in the back streets of Waterloo, the pub dates from 1871 and, until the 1980s, was owned by Higsons, evidence of which can be seen etched into its windows. Small breweries around Merseyside and north Wales often supply guest ales. Pies, pâté, olives and nuts are served at all times. Q❀⇌♣🚌(53) 🐾ᯤ

Waterpudlian Ⓛ

99 South Road, L22 0LR

☎ (0151) 280 0035

5 changing beers (sourced locally; often Brimstage, Oakham, Salopian) Ⓗ
Previously Stamps Too, this is a former local CAMRA branch Pub of the Year and its original accredited LocAle pub. The friendly open-plan bar, where lively banter often prevails, is the haunt both of real ale enthusiasts and live music fans. Five handpumps serve mainly local beers, from Liverpool, Brimstage and Southport in particular, with occasional ales from further afield. A sixth handpump dispenses real cider. Bands and local musicians feature Thursday to Sunday.
♿⇌🍎🚌(53,133) 🐾📶

West Kirby

West Kirby Tap Ⓛ ✔

Grange Road, CH48 4DY
☎ (0151) 625 0350 🌐 westkirbytap.co.uk
Spitting Feathers Session Beer, Thirstquencher; 7 changing beers (sourced nationally; often Black Lodge, Oakham, Spitting Feathers) Ⓗ
A smart, modern, open-plan bar with plain wooden panelling, bare brick walls and a log-burning stove. Owned by Spitting Feathers brewery, it serves a wide range of beers, mainly from microbreweries, and one real cider. Food includes impressive platters of cheese, fish, cold meats and vegan snacks. Live music plays on Saturday night and the pub can get busy. Close to the shops and a short walk to the beach for those trekking to Hilbre Island, tides permitting. 🐴◑♿⇌🍎🚌🐾📶

White Lion Ⓛ

51 Grange Road, CH48 4EE
☎ (0151) 625 9037
Black Sheep Best Bitter; Brains Rev James; 3 changing beers (sourced nationally) Ⓗ
A 200-year-old sandstone building close to the centre of West Kirby. This traditional pub is a little quirky and laid out on several different levels, with lots of cosy nooks to sit in, along with a real fire to keep you warm in winter. In summer months you can enjoy the lovely beer garden at the rear. Quiz night is Monday. ❀⇌🚌🐾

Magazine Hotel, New Brighton

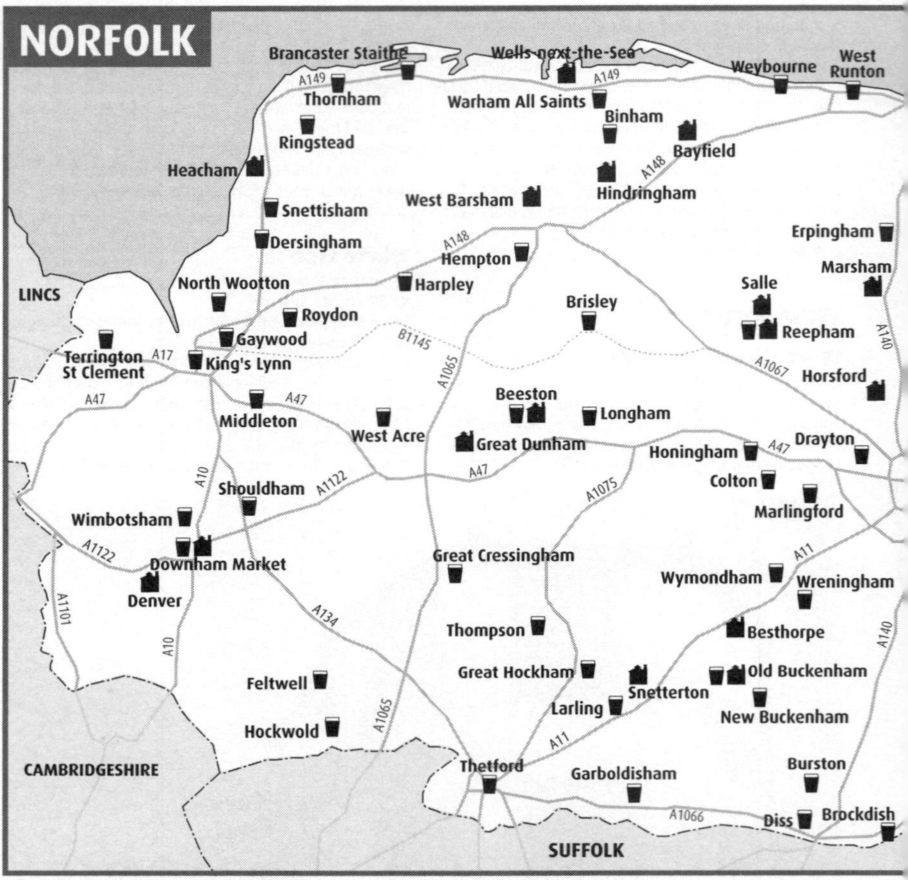

Banningham

Crown Inn ✔

Colby Road, NR11 7DY (N of B1145 1 mile E of A140)
☎ (01263) 733534 🌐 banninghamcrown.co.uk
Greene King IPA, Abbot; 4 changing beers Ⓗ
Traditional 17th-century free house overlooking the village green. The original beamed bar interior has a warm atmosphere enhanced by a log fire in winter. Seven handpumps feature up to four guest beers from regional and microbreweries, with an artisan cider from local producers. Popular for fine cuisine using local produce, the restaurant is open to the kitchen and chefs. The patio, garden and barbecue areas are ideal for summer alfresco dining. The website has details of regular events, the annual music festival and winter opening times. Q❀◐♿⛺♣P🚌🐾📶

Beeston

Ploughshare

The Street, PE32 2NF
☎ (01328) 598995 🌐 beestonploughshare.com
Beeston Worth the Wait; 3 changing beers (sourced nationally; often Beeston) Ⓗ
This popular community-owned pub reopened in 2019 after extensive refurbishment. It has a comfortable bar with an inglenook fireplace and a log-burner, and a separate dining room with a small area off the bar that doubles as a café during the day. Additionally, there is another room off the end of the bar that houses a small shop providing day-to-day essentials. One Beeston beer is always available, and traditional English meals are served in the bar and dining room. Outside is a large patio and car park. Q🐎❀◐♿⛺P🚌🐾📶

Binham

Chequers Inn

Front Street, NR21 0AL
☎ (01328) 830297 🌐 binhamchequers.co.uk
Adnams Southwold Bitter; 4 changing beers (sourced nationally; often Moon Gazer) Ⓗ
A traditional brick-and-flint village pub, the Chequers is a tremendously popular place both with locals and visitors – a friendly establishment with strong support from the surrounding community. The food menu comprises a range of good wholesome fare at reasonable prices. There is an additional specials menu and regular themed evenings. One of the guests beers is from Moon Gazer, others are regional but often from Norfolk. In addition to the bar area, there are benches and tables inside and out, and a large garden to the rear. 🐎❀◐♣P🚌🐾📶

Brancaster Staithe

Jolly Sailors

Main Road, PE31 8BJ

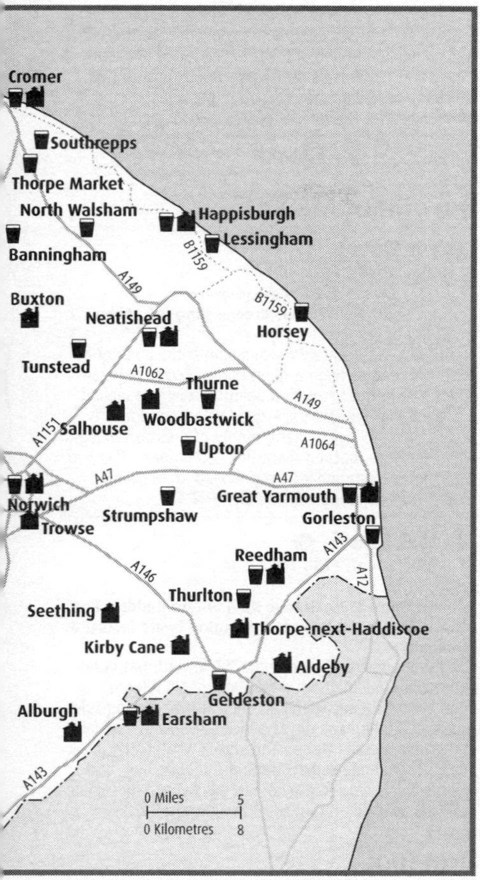

☎ (01485) 210314 🌐 jollysailorsbrancaster.co.uk
Brancaster Best; Woodforde's Wherry; 2 changing beers (sourced nationally) Ⓗ
A cosy inn with several small drinking areas and two dining rooms, convenient for the Norfolk coast path and Brancaster Staithe harbour. It has a garden and play area, an ice cream hut, and welcomes families and dogs. Brancaster beers are produced by a local brewery to the pub's recipes and at least one is always on the bar. Food offerings include local seafood and stone-baked pizza. A beer and music festival is held every June and a cider festival in September. Coasthopper buses stop outside. Q❀◑♿⛺♣P🚌🐾

Brisley

Brisley Bell 𝕃

The Green, NR20 5DW
☎ (01362) 705204 🌐 thebrisleybell.co.uk
Adnams Ghost Ship; Woodforde's Wherry; 4 changing beers (sourced nationally) Ⓗ
A country pub with excellent views across a large open common. Remodelled in 2016, it retained its beams and brick interiors, and two large inglenook fireplaces. The pub has been much expanded, particularly at the rear, with a large patio and garden. The impression is one of space with a warm welcome for diners, casual drinkers and dogs. An award-winning menu is locally sourced, as are most of the cask beers. Q❀◑♿P🚌🐾

Brockdish

Old King's Head

50 The Street, IP21 4JY
☎ (01379) 668843 🌐 kingsheadbrockdish.co.uk
Adnams Southwold Bitter; Humpty Dumpty Little Sharpie, Big Sharpie; 2 changing beers (often Shortts, Wolf) Ⓗ
A 16th-century beamed community inn with a friendly atmosphere. The pub reopened in 2015 with the addition of a coffee shop serving delicious home-made cakes (and bread at weekends). It has a family-friendly bar, and a standing bar with a wood-burner, both serving imaginative Italian food. Locally sourced meats and ingredients are used where possible. Gluten-free meals and cakes are also available. Regular music events take place, usually on a Thursday. A gin club adds to the mix, with 150 gins available. Local artists display work in the bars and gallery. Local CAMRA branch Pub of the Year 2018. ❀◑♿♣P🚌(581)🐾

Burston

Crown Inn

Mill Road, IP22 5TW (by crossroads in middle of village, on green)
☎ (01379) 741257 🌐 burstoncrown.com
Adnams Southwold Bitter Ⓗ/Ⓖ**; Greene King Abbot; 4 changing beers (often Adnams)** Ⓗ

REAL ALE BREWERIES

All Day ◆ Salle
Ampersand Earsham
Barsham West Barsham
Beeston Beeston
Birdhouse Downham Market (NEW)
Blimey! Norwich
Bull of the Woods Kirby Cane
Chalk Hill ▮ Norwich
Dancing Men ▮ Happisburgh
Elmtree Snetterton
Fat Cat ▮ Norwich
Fengate Marsham
Fox ▮ Heacham
Golden Triangle Norwich
Grain Alburgh
Humpty Dumpty Reedham
Lacons Great Yarmouth
Malt Coast Wells-next-the-Sea
Moon Gazer Hindringham
Mr Winter's Norwich
Neatishead ▮ Neatishead
Oakwood Wells-next-the-Sea
Opa Hay's Aldeby
Panther Reepham
People's Thorpe-next-Haddiscoe
Poppyland Cromer
Redwell Norwich: Trowse
S&P Horsford
St Andrews Brewhouse ▮ Norwich
Stumptail Great Dunham
Tindall Seething
Tipples Salhouse
Tombstone ▮ Great Yarmouth
Two Rivers Denver
Wagtail Old Buckenham
Waveney ▮ Earsham
Why Not Norwich
Wildcraft Buxton
Wolf Besthorpe
Woodforde's Woodbastwick
Yetman's Bayfield

An attractive 16th-century Grade II listed pub featuring exposed beams, deep sofas, newspapers and a log fire blazing in the inglenook fireplace. There are two bars, one with a pool table and darts. Boules is played in the garden in summer. A small restaurant serves a mixed cuisine of locally sourced freshly cooked food – booking advisable (no food Sun eve or Mon). There is live music on Thursday evening and music and other entertainment regularly throughout the year, including a beer festival. The village is famous for the Burston School Strike that ran from 1914 to 1939. Q✿⚫🍴♣P🐱❄

Colton

Norfolk Lurcher 🅛
High House Farm Lane, NR9 5DG (2 miles from S of A47 Norwich southern bypass)
☎ (01603) 880794 🌐 the-norfolklurcher.com
Beeston Worth the Wait; 3 changing beers 🅗
Welcoming country pub in the heart of the Norfolk countryside yet only a short drive from Norwich. Family-owned and run, it always has four handpumps serving the best of local breweries, or try one of the 60 single malts. Large comfortable bar areas are complemented by the excellent Ugly Bug restaurant serving locally produced food. The extensive beer garden is popular on warmer days. Monthly jazz and regular food and music evenings take place. There are eight en-suite bedrooms.
Q✿⚫🍴♿🅰♣P🐱❄

Cromer

Red Lion Hotel 🅛
Brook Street, NR27 9HD (S of church on clifftop)
☎ (01263) 514964 🌐 redlion-cromer.co.uk
6 changing beers 🅗
Splendidly situated with views of Cromer pier and the sea, the 19th-century Red Lion has retained many original features including panelling, a Victorian tiled floor and open wood fires. The work of local artists decorates the walls of the two bar areas. Up to six guest ales are usually served, often from local breweries such as Winter's and Green Jack. Beer festivals are held in the summer. The restaurant offers an extensive menu including breakfast. Accommodation is also available.
Q✿🍴⚫♿❄●🐱❄

Dersingham

Coach & Horses ✅
77 Manor Road, PE31 6LN
☎ (01485) 540391 🌐 thecoachpub.com
Woodforde's Wherry; 3 changing beers (sourced nationally) 🅗
Although the good-value home-cooked food is popular, this is at heart a village local rather than a gastro-pub. A former winner of the Norfolk CAMRA Pub of the Year, it offers cider alongside the beers on the bar. There is a pool table in the games room and a large garden with a play area. Live music and quiz nights are regular features. There are three letting rooms for those wishing to visit nearby attractions such as Sandringham or wanting to stay for the annual beer festival.
Q✿⚫🍴🅰●P🐱❄

Diss

Saracen's Head Hotel ✅
75 Mount Street, IP22 4QQ (at N end of town next to church)
☎ (01379) 652853 🌐 saracensheaddiss.co.uk
Adnams Ghost Ship; Woodforde's Wherry 🅗

Fine old hotel in the centre of this market town serving well-kept beers and good home-cooked food. The pub was originally the hall of the Weavers Guild and is a legacy that reminds us of the prosperous past of Diss, which in medieval times was an important commercial woollen centre. The interior of this two-roomed hostelry features numerous original beams and mullioned windows. Q✿⚫🍴⚫♣●P🐱

Downham Market

Crown Hotel
12 Bridge Street, PE38 9DH
☎ (01366) 382322 🌐 crowncoachinginn.com
Adnams Southwold Bitter; Greene King IPA, Abbot; 2 changing beers 🅗
An unspoilt 16th-century coaching inn at the heart of the town. Entering through a room with a lovely staircase brings you to the bar with a beamed ceiling, panelled walls and large fireplaces. A good selection of ales is served. There is a restaurant, plenty of outside seating, and a separate function room that caters for parties and weddings. Accommodation is provided in 18 rooms, including family suites. Q✿🍴⚫❄P🐱❄

Whalebone 🅛 ✅
58 Bridge Street, PE38 9DJ
☎ (01366) 381600
Adnams Ghost Ship; Greene King Abbot; Ruddles Best Bitter; Sharp's Doom Bar; 3 changing beers (sourced nationally) 🅗
This listed building, formerly the White Hart, has been extensively modified but retains the original façade. A large bar area leads to the gardens at the rear and side. On the walls, heritage displays include whaling, drainage of the Fens, Horatio Nelson and replica whalebones. Look out for the unique carpet. There are regular beer and cider festivals plus occasional tap takeovers. Wheelchair access is available throughout. 🐱⚫❄●P🐱❄

Drayton

Bob Carter Centre 🅛
School Road, NR8 6DW
☎ (01603) 867102
6 changing beers 🅗
A sports and social club near the centre of Drayton. The large single bar has plenty of comfortable seating. Up to five real ales are available at all times, including two from Greene King and three from smaller local breweries. Home-cooked food is served in the restaurant. The club was local CAMRA Club of the Year 2019 and is very supportive of CAMRA aims. ⚫P🐱❄

Earsham

Queen's Head 🅛
Station Road, NR35 2TS (just W of Bungay)
☎ (01986) 892623
Waveney East Coast Mild, Lightweight; 2 changing beers 🅗
On the Norfolk-Suffolk border, near Bungay, this busy 17th-century locals' brewpub has a large front garden overlooking the village green. The main bar has a flagstone floor, wooden beams and a large fireplace with a roaring fire in winter. It is home to the Waveney Brewing Company, and four ales and at least one real cider are usually on the go. There is a separate dining area serving food at lunchtimes (not Mon and Tue). The landlord has owned the premises since 1998, and it is a previous local CAMRA Pub of the Year.
Q✿⚫♿♣●P🐱(580) 🐱❄

ENGLAND

Erpingham

Spread Eagle L

The Street, NR11 7QA
☎ (01263) 761938
Adnams Ghost Ship; Grain ThreeOneSix; Woodforde's Wherry; 3 changing beers Ⓗ
Reopened in late 2019 after a period of closure, and once more with its original name, the pub traces its history back to the 1720s. It features a cosy main bar with wood-burning stoves, a function room, plus a large garden. The changing beer range will always include ales from both Adnams and Lacons, and there may be a real cider. There are plans for food service, but the emphasis is on real ale and a warm welcome. ❀♿Ã♣P🚌🐾 ᯤ

Feltwell

Wellington L

27-29 High Street, IP26 4AF
☎ (01842) 828224 🌐 feltwellington.co.uk
3 changing beers Ⓗ
The Wellington reopened after extensive refurbishment in 2014. Landlords Chris and Chris run a 70/30 wet-led pub serving award-winning food. There is a cosy lounge bar with a separate games room featuring pool and darts, and a 36-seat restaurant to the rear. One real cider is always on handpump. There is plenty of interesting memorabilia relating to the pub's namesake bomber.
❀◐♿♣●P ᯤ

Garboldisham

Fox Inn L

The Street, IP22 2RZ
☎ (01953) 688538 🌐 garboldishamfox.co.uk
6 changing beers (sourced locally; often Boudicca, Cliff Quay, Elmtree) Ⓗ
A 17th-century coaching inn with a welcoming feel near Bressingham Gardens and Banham Zoo. It was bought by the locals to serve as a community pub and reopened in 2016, although renovation continues. It offers ales from breweries such as Walls, Blimey, Norfolk Brewhouse, Wolf, and Adnams from the keg. Rumour has it that one of the pub ghosts is a black labrador. Food such as pizza and souvlaki is available on Saturday evenings from street-food vendors, Sunday roasts are served and local ice cream is sold in tubs. Q❀♣●P🐾 ᯤ

Gaywood

White Horse

9 Wootton Road, PE30 4EZ
☎ (01553) 763258
🌐 whitehorse-kingslynn.craftunionpubs.com
2 changing beers
This local pub can be found near the Gaywood clock. Since refurbishment in 2017 it has an open-plan one-roomed bar, with a number of TVs showing various sporting events. There is also a sheltered seating and smoking area at the rear. Two beers are available, generally from breweries from around the country.
❀♣P🚌 ᯤ

Geldeston

Locks Inn L

Locks Lane, NR34 0HS (around 800yds along a marsh-lined track off Station Rd)
☎ (01508) 518414 🌐 geldestonlocks.co.uk
Grain Best Bitter, Oak, Redwood, ThreeOneSix; 1 changing beer (sourced nationally) Ⓗ
The Locks Inn has large gardens and overnight moorings for boats. Six cask Grain Brewery beers are served along with a selection of craft keg offerings. The original small main bar has low ceiling beams and a clay tile floor, and is lit by candles at night. There is a large function room and restaurant either side on the main bar.
Q❀◐♿Ã♣P🚌🐾 ᯤ

Wherry L

7 The Street, NR34 0LB (200yds from the moorings at Geldeston Dyke)
☎ (01508) 518371 🌐 wherryinn.co.uk
Adnams Southwold Bitter, Ghost Ship; 1 changing beer Ⓗ
A typical Norfolk country pub a short walk from the river and in a beautiful setting. The classic public bar boasts a clay tile floor, with a larger main bar/conservatory at the rear, a lovely open fire, and a pleasant west and south facing garden. Two or three well-kept Adnams ales are regularly on offer. Food is also featured, making the Wherry an essential stop.
Q❀◐♿Ã♣P🚌🐾 ᯤ

Gorleston

Oddfellows Arms L

43 Cliff Hill, NR31 6DG
☎ 07876 545982 🌐 oddiesgy.co.uk
Lacons Encore, Legacy; 2 changing beers (often Lacons) Ⓗ
A cosy local with two bars, a short distance from the harbour. Music and jam sessions are held on many Fridays, especially in summer. There are always four beers on offer, sometimes more, mainly from the multi award-winning Lacons Brewery in Great Yarmouth – the pub could almost be considered its brewery tap. Various bottled and canned craft ales from around the world are also stocked. There is a west-facing outdoor seating area and limited parking at the rear. ❀♿♣P🐾 ᯤ

William Adams ✔

176-177 High Street, NR31 6RG
☎ (01493) 600295
Greene King Abbot; Ruddles Best Bitter; Sharp's Doom Bar; 6 changing beers (sourced nationally) Ⓗ
New-build Wetherspoon pub, named after a well-known local swimming instructor and lifesaver. It has one large open room with all the usual JDW facilities, plus a pleasant enclosed seating area outside with a designated smoking section. The decor depicts the renowned local fishing industry and seaside themes. Six real ales are served, with the chance of some real bag-in-box ciders.
❀◐♿●🚌 ᯤ

Great Cressingham

Olde Windmill Inn

Water End, IP25 6NN (off A1065 south of Swaffham)
☎ (01760) 756232 🌐 oldewindmillinn.co.uk
Adnams Southwold Bitter, Broadside; Greene King IPA; 2 changing beers (sourced nationally) Ⓗ
Family run for three generations, the Windmill is a large rural pub and hotel, with a cosy feel despite its size. It offers a rolling range of beers including house beer Windy Miller – most ales are supplied by Purity. Real cider is also available. A popular food menu has something for everyone. The dining areas vary in size from a large conservatory to smaller, intimate rooms. Modern hotel accommodation is in separate buildings behind the pub.
Q❀◐♿Ã♣●P🐾

Great Hockham

Eagle

Harling Road, IP24 1NP
(01953) 498893 hockhameagle.com
Black Sheep Best Bitter; Fuller's ESB; Greene King IPA; Morland Old Speckled Hen; Timothy Taylor Landlord; 2 changing beers
In 2019 the landlord celebrated 10 years at this large family-friendly pub, set in a picturesque village close to Thetford Forest. Two bars divided by an open fire serve five real ales on handpump. Outdoor seating is provided at the front and in an enclosed brick-weave courtyard at the rear. The pub is home to three pool teams and a darts team and holds quiz and bingo nights on alternate Wednesdays, both preceded by fish and chips. There are also other regular events. P

Great Yarmouth

Barking Smack

16 Marine Parade, NR30 3AH
(01493) 859752 barkingsmack.com
Grain ThreeOneSix, Redwood, Oak; 1 changing beer (often Lacons)
Named after the famous Short Blue fishing fleet that moved from Barking to Gorleston in the 19th century, this is an ex-Lacons pub. It has a smart modern interior with an elegant carved wooden bar, and a large patio opening on to Marine Parade and the seafront. A range of Grain beers is served. The Hippodrome Circus is nearby. Closed January to mid-March – check opening times out of season.

King's Arms

229 Northgate Street, NR30 1BG (close to marketplace)
(01493) 843736 thekingsarmsgreatyarmouth.co.uk
Adnams Broadside; Woodforde's Wherry; 1 changing beer
Close to the market place, this pub consists of one large room divided into drinking areas, with a comfortable seating space with a real fire at one end. Outside is a large, well-kept garden, ideal for summer drinking and dining. An annual August bank holiday beer festival is staged. Adnams Broadside and Woodforde's Wherry are complemented by a more local offering. Friendly bar staff and the landlord and landlady give the pub a welcoming atmosphere. P

Lichfield Arms

116-117 Lichfield Road, NR31 0AB
(01493) 302959
2 changing beers
A traditional community pub, full of character and characters, with various entrances from the street into a large single U-shaped bar room. At either end of the bar there is a dartboard and a pool table, with different board games also available. There is a patio and covered smoking area outside. The landlord, who has been at the pub for 30 years, offers two rotating guest ales. Well-behaved dogs are welcome.

Mariners

69 Howard Street South, NR30 1LN (between Palmers and Star Hotel)
(01493) 331164
Greene King Abbot; 10 changing beers
Traditional two-bar flint-walled pub in the town centre which stocks up to 10 ales and several ciders or perries from all over the country. It has a maritime theme and displays photos of numerous ships on the walls. In the winter customers can enjoy their drinks next to a lovely open fire. Knowledgeable staff and a great choice of varying real ales make the Mariners well worth a visit. Local CAMRA Cider Pub of the Year 2019.
P

Red Herring

24-25 Havelock Road, NR30 3HQ (off St Peters St and at back of Time & Tide museum)
07876 644742
4 changing beers
The Red Herring gets its name from the fish that were cured in the nearby but now closed smokehouses. It offers four changing beers alongside two ciders on the handpumps. The Herring has a dartboard and pool table, and hosts a darts and pool team. It is close to the impressive medieval walls and the award-winning Time and Tide museum. There is always a relaxed and friendly atmosphere here along with a good regular following.
Q

Tombstone Saloon

6 George Street, NR30 1HR (on NE corner of Hall Quay)
07584 504444 tombstonebrewery.co.uk
10 changing beers
Western-style bar specialising in real ale and cider, operated by the local Tombstone Brewery, which is sited at the rear of the premises. Staff are friendly and knowledgeable about beer, and there are usually up to six Tombstone real ales plus four others from various breweries. The bar also has a stock of rare spirits from around the world as well as wines and a European bottled beer selection. Local CAMRA Pub of the Year 2018. Q

Happisburgh

Hill House

The Hill, NR12 0PW (off B1159, behind church)
(01692) 650004 hillhouseinn.co.uk
6 changing beers (often Lacons)
A Grade II listed, 16th-century former coaching inn in an attractive coastal village. Sir Arthur Conan Doyle stayed at the pub in 1903, and the on-site brewery is named after a Sherlock Holmes story, the Dancing Men. Six real ales are served, with at least two brewed on-site, and usually one real cider or perry. A noteworthy beer festival is hosted each June offering over 120 real ales and ciders.
P (34)

Harpley

Rose & Crown

Nethergate Street, PE31 6TW
(01485) 521807
Woodforde's Wherry; 4 changing beers
Just off the A148 King's Lynn to Fakenham Road, this attractive 17th-century pub offers guest ales from local breweries. It features open bar areas with a stylish and comfortable feel and has log fires in winter. Outside is an enclosed beer garden for summer drinking. There is an extensive menu serving excellent food, including one of the best Sunday roasts around. The unspoilt village provides pleasant walks and is close to Houghton Hall. Local CAMRA Pub of the Year 2019.
Q P (X29)

Hempton

Bell

24 The Green, NR21 7LG
(01328) 864579 hemptonbell.co.uk
Woodforde's Wherry; 3 changing beers

A popular family-run village pub with a relaxed, friendly atmosphere. It retains a two-bar layout little altered since the early 1970s. Pub games, including dominoes, cribbage and poker dice, are popular – you will be welcome to get involved. Changing guest beers are from micros or independent breweries. Open mic folk sessions take place on the second Tuesday of the month and regular quizzes are held. ❀⛺♣P🚌🐾ᯤ

Hockwold

Red Lion

114 Main Street, IP26 4NB

☎ (01842) 829728 🌐 redlionhockwold.com

3 changing beers Ⓗ

Traditional, friendly village pub set on a green. The Red Lion was refurbished and reopened as a free house in 2012; it has a smart, but comfortable interior – see how many toby jugs you can spot. A good selection of home-made food is served all week, with a carvery on Sunday and Tuesday lunchtime; Thursday evening is steak night. There are regular, well-supported quizzes and darts matches. Outside is a spacious garden with plenty of seating, a smoking shelter and a children's play area. ☕❀◑◐♣P🐾

Honingham

Buck 🄻

29 The Street, NR9 5BL (centre of village)

☎ (01603) 880393 🌐 thehoninghambuck.co.uk

Lacons Encore, Charter, Legacy; 1 changing beer Ⓗ

Dating back to 1789, this traditional one-bar village pub has a separate restaurant area with an emphasis on home-cooked food. An excellent menu of unusual dishes is freshly cooked to order, making this a great venue for eating. The Buck has served Lacons real ales since the brewery bought it in 2015. Slate floors, oak beams, a large fireplace and period furniture enhance the image of a country pub. There is a large garden with plenty of seating. Accommodation is in 8 en-suite rooms. Q☕❀🛏◑◐♿P🚌🐾ᯤ

Horsey

Nelson Head 🄻

The Street, NR29 4AD (just off B1159, 300yds down lane N of Horsey Mill)

☎ (01493) 393378 🌐 thenelsonhead.com

Woodforde's Wherry, Nelson's Revenge Ⓗ**; 8 changing beers** Ⓖ

This traditional National Trust-owned country pub has a bar area with open fire and a separate dining area, and is decorated with Nelson-related memorabilia and paintings. Quality food is served, prepared using locally sourced ingredients. The extensive beer garden is host to festivals and events all year round. Staff are friendly, knowledgeable and eager to help if required. The pub is on the popular walk to access the beach and seal population. Q☕❀◑◐♿♣●P🐾ᯤ

King's Lynn

Live & Let Live 🄻

18 Windsor Road, PE30 5PL (off London Rd near Catholic church)

☎ (01553) 764990

5 changing beers Ⓗ

Popular back-street local with two bars, a small cosy lounge and a larger public bar with a TV. Five beers are served including a mild (rare for the area). Cider drinkers have a wide choice, normally including something from Westons – the pub is the local CAMRA branch's Cider Pub of the Year for 2020. Live music is sometimes played in the public bar. ●🐾

Marriott's Warehouse

South Quay, PE30 5DT

☎ (01553) 818500 🌐 marriottswarehouse.co.uk

Sharp's Doom Bar; 2 changing beers Ⓗ

This 16th-century riverside building, originally a warehouse for corn, salt and wine, has been converted into a café/restaurant. There is a drinking area on the first floor with table service, with views across the river towards the Minster, and outdoor tables on the quayside. One of the guest ales is usually Moon Gazer. Pay parking is available on the quayside and behind the building. ☕◑◐Pᯤ

Stuart House Hotel

35 Goodwins Road, PE30 5QX (up gravel drive off Goodwins Rd)

☎ (01553) 772169 🌐 stuart-house-hotel.co.uk

3 changing beers (sourced nationally) Ⓗ

The public bar of this hotel tucked away close to The Walks has featured in the Guide for around 25 years. Visitors will find a garden for summer and a real fire in the bar in winter. The annual beer festival coincides with the King's Lynn music festival. Beers are usually from larger regional producers. Note that the pub is open evenings only, unless by arrangement. ❀🛏◐⇌P🐾ᯤ

Larling

Angel

NR16 2QU (1 mile SW from Snetterton racetrack, just off A11)

☎ (01953) 717963 🌐 angel-larling.co.uk

Adnams Southwold Bitter; 4 changing beers Ⓗ

Five real ales plus a real cider are on handpump here, always including a mild. Over 100 whiskies are stocked, as well as 50 gins. The lounge and bar have real open fires, and there is a dining room which serves home-made fare in generous portions. A friendly atmosphere is enjoyed by locals, visitors, campers and rallyists who use the Angel's campsite. A popular long-running beer festival in August showcases over 80 real ales with live music. Q☕❀🛏◑◐♿⛺●P▯

Lessingham

Star Inn 🄻

Star Hill, NR12 0DN (just off main B1159, corner of High Rd and Star Hill)

☎ (01692) 580510 🌐 thestarlessingham.co.uk

Fat Cat Norwich Bitter; Lacons Encore; 2 changing beers (sourced nationally) Ⓖ

A traditional pub with a friendly atmosphere, and a log fire in winter. Four ales, including one guest, are served from the cask, as are three ciders. The Star is popular for quality meals with carefully sourced ingredients served in decent portions. Food may be enjoyed in the bar, a separate restaurant or the spacious beer garden. Two en-suite double B&B rooms make this the perfect base to explore the nearby coast and the Broads. Closing time may be early on Sunday winter evenings. A rural gem. Q❀🛏◑◐♣●P▯🚌(34)🐾ᯤ

Longham

White Horse

Wendling Road, NR19 2RD

☎ (01362) 687464 🌐 longhamwhitehorse.co.uk

Greene King Yardbird; 3 changing beers (sourced regionally) H
An attractive and traditional village local with a cosy feel and a high standard of decor. It has a main bar area with separate dining rooms off to the left and right, plus a large conservatory also used for dining at the rear, overlooking the garden. The real ale is generally from a local regional brewery, with one traditional cider also usually available. The extensive menu caters for all tastes and requirements, with ingredients sourced locally. B&B is available. Q

Marlingford

Marlingford Bell

Bawburgh Road, NR9 5HX
☎ (01603) 880263 thebellatmarlingford.co.uk
4 changing beers H
This extended country village pub has a refurbished front bar with a wood-burning stove making it nice and cosy in winter. There are no regular beers – the changing ales come from Lacons, Winter's and Woodforde's, and occasionally other small Norfolk breweries, one dispensed on gravity. The large function and restaurant room with a separate bar at the rear opens on to a large garden. Quality, locally sourced food is made on the premises, and excellent bar menu dishes are served on biodegradable trays. Sunday roasts are popular (booking advised). Q

Middleton

Gate

Hill Road, Fair Green, PE32 1RW (N of A47, follow Fair Green signs)
☎ (01553) 840518 thegatefairgreen.co.uk
Greene King Abbot; Woodforde's Wherry, Norfolk Nog; 1 changing beer (sourced nationally) H
Although there is a pleasant dining room, this friendly family-run pub just off the A47 is still at heart a village local. The bar and semi-separate area with a jukebox and TV screen are used mainly by those who just want a drink. Food features seasonal produce and ingredients sourced from local suppliers. The pretty garden is popular in summer. Note that the pub is closed on Monday and there is no food on Tuesday. Q

Neatishead

White Horse

The Street, NR12 8AD
☎ (01692) 630828 thewhitehorseinnneatishead.com
Woodforde's Wherry; 6 changing beers (sourced nationally) H
Traditional Broadland village centre pub, sympathetically modernised while retaining many original features including three separate drinking areas and a log fireplace in the bar. Six of the seven real ales are mainly from microbreweries across the UK, including from the in-house brewery, and change frequently. Up to seven craft keg beers are available. Beer festivals are held in spring and autumn. Meals are home-prepared with local produce and are reasonably priced, served in a comfortable split-level restaurant. Moorings are a short walk away. Q

New Buckenham

King's Head

Market Place, NR16 2AN (opp village green)
☎ (01953) 861247
Adnams Southwold Bitter; Oakham Inferno; 1 changing beer (often Fuller's, Shepherd Neame) H
A free house facing the green in what was, in the 12th century, a new town. The pub served as a coaching inn between London and Norwich in the early part of the 16th century. It has a contemporary feel but retains the inglenook fireplace and exposed beams in the original part of the building. There is a large restaurant extension at the rear. Q

North Walsham

Hop In

2 Market Street, NR28 9BZ
☎ 07426 139417 thehopin.co.uk
6 changing beers G
Owned and run by keen CAMRA members, this was Norfolk's first micropub, situated in a former taxi office just around the corner from the marketplace. Six changing ales are served on gravity dispense plus real cider, and there is usually one dark beer available. In keeping with the micropub philosophy, there is no Wi-Fi, music or machines, just good conversation. There is a small seating area downstairs and more upstairs, plus a small patio area outside. Q

North Wootton

Red Cat Hotel

Station Road, PE30 3QH (opp Church of All Saints, at N end of Nursery Rd and W end of Manor Rd)
☎ (01553) 631244 redcathotel.co.uk
Adnams Southwold Bitter; 1 changing beer H
This traditional village local offers two real ales. Nicely decorated and in a quiet location, it has attractive gardens for summer drinks. Ask about the history of the namesake red cat – if you can believe it. The pub is near National Cycle Route 1, the Sandringham Estate and the west Norfolk coast. Q P (3)

Norwich

Alexandra Tavern

16 Stafford Street, NR2 3BB (on corner of Stafford St and Gladstone St, off Dereham Rd)
☎ (01603) 627772 alexandratavern.co.uk
5 changing beers (sourced locally) H
Popular, bustling and friendly, this pub is a real gem sited just outside the city centre. The interior is brightly decorated, with the walls featuring pictures and articles of a nautical nature. The bar serves up to five changing beers from local breweries, and two real ciders. Food is served daily, with a good variety, including a soup menu. There is a dartboard and plenty of board games to choose from, with children also welcome until early evening. Q

Artichoke

1 Magdalen Road, NR3 4LW
☎ (01603) 662807
8 changing beers (often Golden Triangle) H
A 1930s flint building, originally decorated in the Brewers' Tudor style, with two circular bars with cone-shaped roofs (giving the pub its name), original Young's, Crawshay & Young's windows, parquet flooring and a long solid wood bar. Bought and significantly but sensitively refurbished by the owner of Golden Triangle Brewery in 2018, the bar now has eight handpumps offering two or three Golden Triangle beers, a great selection of craft beers, and real cider. Live music features occasionally, and pop-up caterers provide food at weekends. P

Beehive L
30 Leopold Road, NR4 7PJ (between Unthank and Newmarket roads)
☎ (01603) 451628 🌐 beehivepubnorwich.co.uk
5 changing beers [H]
A friendly two-bar local with knowledgeable staff, featuring a comfortable lounge bar with sofas. The popular beer garden is used all year round and for charity barbecues during the summer months. A beer festival is held in late June with around 25 ales and ciders. There is a function room upstairs with a pool table (available to hire). The pub has hockey, korfball, golf, darts and pool teams, plus a regular quiz on Wednesdays, folk music nights and themed food evenings. Q❀♣P

Coach & Horses
82 Thorpe Road, NR1 1BA
☎ (01603) 477077 🌐 thecoachthorperoad.co.uk
Chalk Hill Tap Bitter, CHB, Gold, Dreadnought; 3 changing beers [H]
Close to the station, this coaching inn, with its iconic balcony, is the home of the Chalk Hill Brewery, and serves its full range of beers. A tour of the brewery is available by appointment. Excellent-value food is served along with Burnards cider. Sport, especially rugby, is shown on big screens, and the large fire is welcome in winter. Not far from the football ground and busy before matches. ❀♿P

Coach & Horses
51 Bethel Street, NR2 1NR
☎ (01603) 618522 🌐 thecoachandhorsesbethelstreet.co.uk
6 changing beers (sourced locally) [H]
Historic city-centre local near the Theatre Royal, the Forum and City Hall. It has a bright, welcoming bar with several separate seating areas including in cosy alcoves. A Greene King house, it offers a good selection of beer styles from local breweries in a range that changes regularly. Food is based on an English tapas theme, which works well. Try some celeb spotting too, or a game of bar billiards. Q❀♣

Coachmakers Arms L
9 St Stephens Road, NR1 3SP
☎ (01603) 662080 🌐 coachmakers-arms-norwich.co.uk
Greene King Abbot; Wolf Golden Jackal; Woodforde's Mardler's, Nelson's, Reedlighter, Wherry; 4 changing beers (sourced locally) [G]
A popular city-centre venue, this free house offers a range of 10 permanent gravity-dispensed ales. Dating from the 17th century, the reputedly haunted former coaching inn stands on the site of an old asylum. It has a single large L-shaped beamed bar room with unobtrusive Sky TV and a dartboard. Outside, a spacious courtyard converted into a large sports bar/function room complements the garden patio. ❀♣

Duke of Wellington L
91-93 Waterloo Road, NR3 1EG
☎ (01603) 441182 🌐 dukeofwellingtonnorwich.co.uk
Fuller's London Pride [H]**; Oakham JHB, Bishops Farewell** [G]**; Wolf Golden Jackal** [H]**, Wolf in Sheep's Clothing; 20 changing beers** [G]
Friendly pub with a changing range of guest ales to complement the permanent beers, the majority of which are served on gravity from a taproom behind the bar. A beer of the month from Wolf Brewery is available at a discount. The attractive award-winning enclosed rear garden/patio area accommodates a beer festival in late August plus regular barbecues at weekends in summer. Events include monthly quiz evenings. Customers can bring their own food or sample the filling and inexpensive pies and sausage rolls. ❀♿♣P

Fat Cat L
49 West End Street, NR2 4NA
☎ (01603) 624364 🌐 fatcatpub.co.uk
Crouch Vale Yakima Gold; Fat Cat Norwich Bitter [H]**, Marmalade Cat; Greene King Abbot; Oakham Bishops Farewell, Green Devil** [G]**; 20 changing beers** [H]/[G]
An amazing range of brewery memorabilia is displayed around the walls and alcoves of this traditional pub, refurbished in 2018. Ales from the Fat Cat range are served, plus about 10 regular and 20 guest beers from all over the UK, real ciders, and several quality keg beers. Food is limited to good-value rolls and pies. A gem of a pub – exactly what a real ale outlet should be, with excellent, friendly service. Two-times CAMRA National Pub of the Year. Q❀

Fat Cat & Canary L
101 Thorpe Road, NR1 1TR
☎ (01603) 432393
Fat Cat Norwich Bitter, Hell Cat, Honey Cat, Marmalade Cat, Wild Cat; 7 changing beers (sourced nationally) [H]
The third member of the Norwich-based Fat Cat mini-chain, about a mile and a half from the centre of the city, serving most of the Fat Cat Brewery's ales, and various guests from around the UK, together with continental beers and real ciders. There is a small TV to the rear of the main bar, a large car park and terraces to the front and rear, the latter being heated. Home-made rolls are available. Busy on Norwich City match days.
❀♿P

Fat Cat Brewery Tap L
98-100 Lawson Road, NR3 4LF
☎ (01603) 413153 🌐 fatcattap.co.uk
Fat Cat Norwich Bitter, Honey Cat, Marmalade Cat [H]**, IPA; Oakham Bishops Farewell; 20 changing beers (sourced nationally)** [G]
Home of the Fat Cat Brewery, serving the Fat Cat range plus a huge range of real ales, ciders and quality keg beers from across the country. Live music on Fridays and Sundays complements a variety of events including tap takeovers, themed beer evenings, a monthly cycling club, and a fortnightly quiz. Loaded chips and cheeseboards are available. A distinctive selection of breweriana adorns the ceiling beams and walls. Norfolk CAMRA Pub of the Year 2018.
Q❀♿♣P(11,11A)

Golden Star
57 Colegate, NR3 1DD
☎ (01603) 632447 🌐 goldenstarnorwich.co.uk
Greene King IPA, Abbot; 3 changing beers (sourced nationally) [H]
A welcoming and relaxing pub with a main bar area and a second room to the left of the bar, hosting bar billiards and live music sessions. A quiz is held on Sunday evening. An excellent specials menu is served daily, including locally sourced meat. A wide selection of music is played, but unobtrusively. Handy for Norwich Playhouse and Norwich University of the Arts. There is a small patio at the rear, and tables outside the front in summer. ❀♣

Jubilee L ✔
26 St Leonards Road, NR1 4BL
☎ (01603) 618734
Hop Back Summer Lightning; Woodforde's Wherry; 4 changing beers (sourced regionally) [H]
Attractive Victorian corner pub with a warm welcome. There are two bars, a comfortable conservatory and an enclosed patio garden. Many of the well-kept ales and craft beers are local. This popular venue, within easy

reach of the city centre, is at the heart of the community and caters for all tastes, from sports fans to those who enjoy local history talks. Customers are welcome to bring in takeaway food, but there are regular Sunday roasts and occasional pop-up street-food fairs.
Q🔥❀≠♣⚽🚌🐾📶

King's Arms

22 Hall Road, NR1 3HQ
☎ (01603) 477888
Batemans Gold; 10 changing beers (sourced nationally) Ⓗ
A friendly Batemans house just south of the city, serving a wide range of guest ales to complement the Batemans beers, usually including a stout or porter and a mild. Between three (in winter) and six (in summer) real ciders are also stocked. Customers can bring their own food from various nearby takeaways, with plates and condiments provided. Monthly quiz nights, poker evenings and live music take place. The pub is a recipient of many Batemans cellar-keeping and floral display awards. It gets busy on football match days.
🔥❀♿♣⚽🚌(39,40) 🐾📶

King's Head 🄻

42 Magdalen Street, NR3 1JE
☎ (01603) 620468 🌐 kingsheadnorwich.com
House beer (by Winter's); 10 changing beers Ⓗ
Friendly and welcoming traditional-style two-bar pub which offers no keg beer, but up to 10 quality real ales, mostly local but with a few from around the country, plus two ciders. The house beer, KHB, is brewed by Winter's. Local fresh eggs and honey are often available. No food is served except snacks, pork pies and pickled eggs, but customers can bring or order in their own, with plates and cutlery supplied. Bar billiards is well supported, with two teams in the local league. Q❀♣⚽🍺🚌🐾📶

Leopard 🄻

98-100 Bull Close Road, NR3 1NQ
☎ (01603) 631111
6 changing beers (sourced regionally; often Lacons, S&P, Tombstone) Ⓗ
Welcoming, traditional single-bar corner local with a variety of changing ales, many from smaller breweries. The pub has a clean and bright bar area which gives a spacious feel, plus a pleasant and quiet enclosed courtyard garden at the rear. Customers can bring in food and cutlery will be provided. There is a quiz night usually on the third Tuesday of the month, and a live music night once a month on a Friday. ❀♿♣⚽🍺🚌🐾📶

Lollards Pit 🄻

69-71 Riverside Road, NR1 1SR
☎ (01603) 624675 🌐 lollards-pit-pub.ueniweb.com
Woodforde's Wherry, Nelson's Revenge; 4 changing beers Ⓗ
An attractive 17th-century inn, one of the first built outside the city walls, on the site of Lollards Pit – a place of execution for heretics for over 200 years. The pub is close to the river and yacht station moorings. Guest ales are from local breweries, and there are also interesting offerings from further afield. Snacks include local pork pies and sausage rolls, with a more extensive food offering planned. The pub hosts local community groups, weekly quiz and bingo nights, and weekend parties.
🔥❀♿≠♣⚽🚌🐾📶

Lord Rosebery

94 Rosebery Road, NR3 3AB
☎ (01603) 414284 🌐 theroseberynorwich.co.uk
4 changing beers (sourced nationally) Ⓗ
A popular Victorian corner pub which has been stylishly refurbished. Four real ales are available on a rotational basis, mostly sourced from local brewers. Additionally, several real ciders are on sale. Food is served daily except Monday, including an excellent burger menu. The Sunday roasts are popular. Regular live bands and reggae record nights makes this a popular destination for music lovers. B&B accommodation is available.
❀🛏◑♿♣⚽P🐾📶

Murderers

2-8 Timber Hill, NR1 3LB
☎ (01603) 621447 🌐 themurderers.co.uk
Wolf Edith Cavell; house beer (by Wolf); 9 changing beers Ⓗ
A busy city-centre pub that appeals to all sections of the public, with 10-12 real ales, including two permanent beers, one of which is the house Murderer's Ale (brewed by Wolf). Beer festivals feature in summer and autumn, with over 40 beers available, including many from local brewers. The upper area has a large-screen TV, making it a popular venue for viewing sporting events. A traditional British menu is served in generous portions.
❀◑⚽🚌🐾📶

Plasterers Arms 🄻

43 Cowgate, NR3 1SZ
☎ (01603) 387525 🌐 theplasterersarms.co.uk
Adnams Mosaic; Moon Gazer Pintail; 8 changing beers (sourced nationally) Ⓗ
This is a friendly corner local with a wide range of beers from around the country, specialising in new and exciting breweries. A variety of craft keg beers is also available, alongside a great range of bottled and canned beers. The pub offers tap takeovers, sport (with a big screen for more important events), music from DJs on Sundays, excellent pizzas, and breakfast at weekends. It also hosts a Fem.ale Festival celebrating great women in the brewing industry. Q◑⚽🚌🐾📶

Playhouse Bar

42-58 St George Street, NR3 1AB
☎ (01603) 612580
4 changing beers (sourced nationally) Ⓗ
A bar serving the Norwich Playhouse theatre – it can be crowded before performances and at the interval – with a good-sized lounge across the foyer and a large tree-shaded patio by the river. It stocks three or four beers, often including an Adnams ale, and an eclectic and interesting selection of guests. The bar features a 3D cityscape on the ceiling and an unusual collection of objets d'art. There are regular DJ sessions at weekends.
❀♿🚌📶

Plough

58 St Benedict Street, NR2 4AR
☎ (01603) 661384
6 changing beers Ⓗ
A popular pub in one of the city's oldest areas, near the Norwich Arts Centre. One of four Grain Brewery-owned outlets, it sells six ales, usually all from the brewery. The two-bar interior is fairly small, with wooden chairs and tables, and has an open fire in winter. The large Mediterranean-style courtyard garden is a fine place to spend a summer's evening. Grain lager and craft beers are also served, along with Vic's special sausage pie, and there are barbecues in the summer. ❀♣🚌🐾📶

Ribs of Beef 🄻 ✔

24 Wensum Street, NR3 1HY
☎ (01603) 619517 🌐 ribsofbeef.co.uk

Adnams Ghost Ship; Oakham JHB; Wolf Golden Jackal; Woodforde's Wherry; 5 changing beers (sourced nationally) 🄷
Traditional and well-decorated pub overlooking the River Wensum. A welcoming row of nine handpumps dispenses four regular ales and a selection from quality non-local microbreweries. Foreign beers and real cider are also available. Good food is made with locally sourced ingredients. The atmosphere is relaxed and friendly, with a room downstairs, a small riverside terrace and several tables outside at the rear. There is a quiz every Thursday night and live music on Sunday evening. Sporting fixtures are shown live on TV.
❀◑♣●🚌🐾ᯤ

Rose
235 Queens Road, NR1 3AE
☎ (01603) 623942 🌐 theroseinnnorwich.co.uk
5 changing beers (sourced nationally) 🄷
Popular pub close to Carrow Road, the home of Norwich City FC. The owner's passion for beer shows in the selection of five regularly changing real ales and six craft ales from some of the most exciting breweries around the country, plus several real ciders. Regular beer, cider and gin festivals and frequent tap takeovers are held. There is an excellent food offering, with in-house burgers and curries from a local Indian restaurant delivered to your table Tuesday to Saturday, plus sausages and mash on Sunday. A bar billiards table has recently been installed. ❀🛏◑♿⛺●🚌🐾ᯤ

St Andrews Brewhouse ✔
41 St Andrews Street, NR2 4TP
☎ (01603) 305995 🌐 standrewsbrewhouse.com
6 changing beers 🄷
Grade II* listed building refurbished during 2015 in distressed industrial style, now a brewhouse and restaurant with an eclectic food menu. The bar and microbrewery face St Andrews Street, while the restaurant has views of the ancient St Andrews Hall, home of the Norwich Beer Festival. Six handpumps dispense mostly house beers. Wensum Ale (gluten-free) is served, with a couple of local guests or seasonal specials and sometimes a cider/perry, supplemented by a good range of craft beers. Upstairs rooms feature board games and views of the brewery fermentation tanks.
Q🐴❀◑♿♣🚌🐾ᯤ

Trafford Arms 🄻 ✔
61 Grove Road, NR1 3RL
☎ (01603) 628466 🌐 traffordarms.co.uk
Adnams Southwold Bitter, Ghost Ship; 8 changing beers (sourced nationally) 🄷
Close to the city centre, this friendly local has a strong community feel and is open all day every day. It is a flagship for real ale in Norwich, offering regular and ever-changing guest beers, often including a dark ale. High-quality pub food is sold and there are special themed food evenings, weekend breakfasts, and home-cooked Sunday roasts. The February Valentine's beer festival is a major attraction, as is the regular quiz on the last Sunday of the month. 🐴❀◑P🚌ᯤ

Vine 🄻
7 Dove Street, NR2 1DE
☎ (01603) 627362 🌐 vinethai.co.uk
Fat Cat Tom Cat; Oakham JHB; 2 changing beers 🄷
Norwich's smallest pub, just off the marketplace, serving up to four quality ales, mostly from local breweries, plus traditional Thai cuisine in an award-winning combination. It has been in the same hands for over 10 years. The restaurant is upstairs, although customers often eat downstairs in the bar area, and functions are catered for outside normal opening hours on demand. Beer festivals are held in City of Ale week. Extra tables and chairs are set outside in the pedestrianised street. Occasionally open on a Sunday. Q❀◑♣●🚌

White Lion
73 Oak Street, NR3 3AQ
☎ (01603) 632333
7 changing beers 🄷
A good changing range of real ales from local breweries and others is on sale here – often from Winter's, Bull of the Woods and Wildcraft. Eight to 10 ciders are also available plus, usually, at least one perry. Helpful and knowledgeable bar staff are on hand. Food is varied and excellent value, using traditional local produce, with daily specials. Bar billiards, board games and darts are played. The traditional interior is split into three rooms, with a front and back bar and a games room to the side.
Q❀◑♣●▯🚌🐾ᯤ

Wig & Pen 🄻
6 St Martin at Palace Plain, NR3 1RN
☎ (01603) 625891 🌐 thewigandpen.com
Adnams Southwold Bitter; 5 changing beers 🄷
Pretty, beamed 17th-century free house with a spacious patio, immediately opposite the Bishop's Palace, and with an impressive view of Norwich Cathedral spire. Six ales are always available, usually including two local beers. The small back room can be used for meetings. Good-quality food is served lunchtimes and evenings. The pub is a short walk from Tombland, where there are bus stands for several bus routes, and is an ideal starting or stopping place for a walk along the river.
Q❀🛏◑♿🚌ᯤ

Old Buckenham

Ox & Plough
The Green, NR17 1RN (in centre of village overlooking green)
☎ 07887 691722
Adnams Southwold Bitter; Sharp's Doom Bar; 3 changing beers (often Hop Back, Oakham) 🄷
Family-friendly community pub on one of the largest village greens in England and at the centre of local life. It has two open-plan drinking areas, one of which is quiet, without TV or electronic game machines. The garden at the front overlooks the green. Real ale is dispensed from three to five handpumps. As a member of the Oakham Oakademy of Excellence it serves various changing Oakham ales; Green Devil is a regular keg. Bar snacks are the only food. 🐴❀♿♣P🐾ᯤ

Reedham

Ship 🄻 ✔
19 Riverside, NR13 3TQ
☎ (01493) 700287 🌐 theshipreedham.com
Adnams Southwold Bitter, Broadside; 1 changing beer (sourced nationally) 🄷
This riverside pub, situated along the Wherrymans Way, has two bars – one small with a pool table and fruit/gaming machines, and one larger. There are also two separate dining areas at the end of the pub. Outside is a covered area and a grassed riverside garden with extra seating and garden benches for alfresco eating and drinking. Free moorings are available on a first come first served basis. Q🐴❀◑♿P🐾ᯤ

Reepham

King's Arms 𝕃
Market Place, NR10 4JJ
☎ (01603) 870345 🌐 kingsarmsreepham.com
Adnams Southwold Bitter, Ghost Ship; Greene King Abbot; Panther Golden Panther; Woodforde's Wherry; 1 changing beer (sourced nationally) [H]
An old coaching inn dating back to 1667, in the picturesque square of this small market town, with original beams, Norfolk brickwork and open fires. There are several comfortable drinking and dining areas, and tables in front with views across the square. Five permanent real ales are on sale, including at least one from the local Panther Brewery, plus a guest. The comprehensive menu is mostly sourced from nearby suppliers. Jazz bands play in the rear courtyard on summer Sundays. Q❀◑🚌🐾

Ringstead

Gin Trap Inn ✔
6 High Street, PE36 5JU
☎ (01485) 525264 🌐 thegintrapinn.co.uk
Adnams Southwold Bitter, Ghost Ship; Greene King IPA; Woodforde's Wherry; 1 changing beer (sourced nationally) [H]
This attractive, whitewashed 17th-century coaching inn has been a pub since 1668. There is outside seating at the front and an enclosed garden to the rear. It has a split-level bar and a separate restaurant, although food is served throughout. Regular themed food evenings are hosted as well as live music nights. The main bar has a log-burning stove. The drinks menu also features a range of some 100 different gins including the pub's own Gin Trap gin. ❀🛏◑♿P🐾📶

Roydon

Union Jack
30 Station Road, PE32 1AW (off A148)
☎ 07771 660439
Adnams Broadside; 3 changing beers (sourced nationally) [H]
Popular with locals, this traditional village pub has twice been local CAMRA Pub of the Year. Four handpumps dispense one regular and three changing ales, and beer festivals are held over the Easter and August bank holidays, usually featuring local breweries. There are occasional food nights, live music each month, regular bingo and quizzes, and weekly support for darts, crib and dominoes. Outdoor seating is at the front.
Q❀🛏Ʌ♣●P🚌(48)🐾📶

Shouldham

King's Arms 🏆 𝕃
The Green, PE33 0BY
☎ (01366) 347410 🌐 kingsarmsshouldham.co.uk
2 changing beers [G]
Named the local CAMRA Pub of the Year for 2020, the King's Arms has now received this accolade four times in the last five years. This is a community-owned business and also includes a café. The beer is served in lined glasses straight from the cask and two or three choices are usually available. Cider is also often on offer. Many community activities take place, from poetry evenings and live music to quiz nights. Details are chalked up on a noticeboard. ❀◑●P🚆🐾📶

Snettisham

Rose & Crown
Old Church Road, PE31 7LX (off B1440)
☎ (01485) 541382 🌐 roseandcrownsnettisham.co.uk
Adnams Broadside; Marston's Pedigree; Woodforde's Wherry; 2 changing beers (sourced nationally) [H]
The old front bar has been progressively added to, creating a more modern area mainly used by those enjoying the highly regarded food. Breakfast is served every day before the bar opens. There is a garden and play area for children, and accommodation is offered. This multi award-winning pub features in many guides and is popular, so you may need to book a table.
Q❀🛏◑♿♣P🚌🐾📶

Southrepps

Vernon Arms ✔
2 Church Street, NR11 8NP (NE of Thorpe Market, off A149 Cromer-North Walsham road)
☎ (01263) 833355 🌐 vernonarms.com
Adnams Southwold Bitter; Fat Cat Norwich Bitter; Greene King Abbot; 1 changing beer (sourced nationally) [H]
A brick and flint village-centre local with a lively and welcoming atmosphere. The three regular ales are augmented by a variety of guest beers. The pub is popular for its fine food, prepared with locally sourced ingredients where possible. Takeaway fish and chips is available Tuesday to Saturday early evening. The front terrace includes a heated and covered smoking area and there is a garden at the rear. Various acoustic music sessions are held. Gunton station just under 1½ miles.
❀◑♿Ʌ≉♣P🚌(33,33A)🐾📶

Strumpshaw

Shoulder of Mutton 𝕃
9 Norwich Road, NR13 4NT (on Brundall-Lingwood rd)
☎ (01603) 926530
Adnams Ghost Ship; Sharp's Doom Bar; Timothy Taylor Landlord; 3 changing beers [H]
A traditional village pub with a friendly welcome. There are two main bar areas sharing the log-burner, and a separate dining room. Beers are from a variety of regional and microbreweries, complemented by three local ciders. Meals are freshly prepared from local produce, with seafood and home-made pies prominent. The rear patio overlooks the courtyard where pétanque is played. Live music and events take place. Close to the Broads and a nationally important RSPB site.
❀◑♿Ʌ♣●P🚌(15A)🐾📶

Terrington St Clement

Wildfowler
28 Sutton Road, PE34 4PQ
☎ (01553) 829107 🌐 the-wildfowler.com
Greene King IPA, Abbot; 2 changing beers (sourced regionally) [H]
Stylish and friendly, this popular pub is at the heart of the village. It has a spacious, modern restaurant serving imaginative food from a changing menu. There is plenty of seating for drinkers in the bar area, where you can sample one of a variety of guest ales. Live music often features at weekends. ❀◑♿P🚌(505)

Thetford

Albion 𝕃 ✔
93-95 Castle Street, IP24 2DN (opp Castle Park and Hill)

☎ (01842) 338208
Greene King IPA; Woodforde's Wherry; 1 changing beer (sourced nationally) Ⓖ
A classic flint Norfolk town pub, revitalised by the management team a few years ago. Its Greene King-refurbished interior has been adapted with wherry-themed tables, creating a comfortable space to drink. The six handpumps offer a range of standard and more interesting choices. There is seating outside with a view of the Norman castle mound and its surrounding Iceni hill fort. Food is not available but you are welcome to order in from one of the food outlets in the town. ❀♿♣P🐾

Black Horse 𝕃
64 Magdalen Street, IP24 2BP
☎ (01842) 762717
Adnams Southwold Bitter; Greene King IPA; Woodforde's Wherry; 2 changing beers Ⓗ
A good no-nonsense town pub offering a varying range of ales on five handpumps. It stages a popular annual St George's Day beer festival. The food is home-made and good both in quality and value – desserts are a feature – served in a small but pleasant eating area. Look for the changing murals on the end wall. ❀◐◑♿P

Red Lion 𝕃 ✔
Market Place, IP24 2AL
☎ (01842) 757210
Adnams Broadside; Greene King IPA, Abbot; 3 changing beers (sourced nationally) Ⓗ
On the market square, the Red Lion has had a varied history. It was opened by Lacons and the wall outside still retains its plaque, then it became a Portuguese restaurant, before becoming a Wetherspoon establishment. The decor features information about local history and attractions. There is often a dark ale on the bar. The pub has a variety of eating and drinking areas plus an outdoor space. ♨❀◐◑⇄●📶

Thompson

Chequers Inn
Griston Road, IP24 1PX
☎ (01953) 483360 🌐 thompsonchequers.co.uk
Greene King IPA; Woodforde's Wherry; 1 changing beer Ⓗ
A 16th-century gem in this pretty village, featuring a steep thatched roof and timber-framed construction. Stooping to Tudor height will keep your head from the beams. There are two rooms for dining, and a small area and another small room for drinking. The pub has an excellent reputation for food. In fine weather the garden is popular, with plenty of picnic tables. Guest beers are mostly from Woodforde's. ♨❀🛏◐◑♿P

Thornham

Lifeboat Inn ✔
Ship Lane, PE36 6LT (signed from A149 Coast Road)
☎ (01485) 512236 🌐 lifeboatinnthornham.com
Greene King Abbot; Woodforde's Wherry; 2 changing beers (sourced nationally) Ⓗ
A busy pub just off the North Norfolk Coastal Path on the edge of the salt marshes, with a wide range of drinking areas, from the dark and cosy bar to the light and airy conservatory. There is an enclosed garden at the rear. The interior has been tastefully renovated while retaining the atmosphere of the smugglers' inn it undoubtedly once was. Food is served throughout and there is also a large separate restaurant. Accommodation is available in 13 rooms. Q♨❀🛏◐◑P🐾📶

Thorpe Market

Gunton Arms 𝕃 ✔
Cromer Road, NR11 8TZ (on W of A149 Cromer to North Walsham road, SE of Thorpe Market; look for hanging sign, lit at night)
☎ (01263) 832010 🌐 theguntonarms.co.uk
Adnams Broadside; Lacons Legacy; Woodforde's Wherry; 1 changing beer (sourced nationally) Ⓗ
A fine country inn with magical vistas of Gunton Park and its deer herd. It boasts tasteful decor with comfortable furnishings and a log fire in winter. East Anglian ales predominate, with regular guests. First-class cuisine is served in three restaurants; several dishes are cooked on an open range in the vaulted Elk Room. There is a beer garden for alfresco dining, and a food and music festival is held in summer. Sixteen rooms and suites are available. ❀🛏◐◑♿♣P🚌(4)🐾📶

Thurlton

Queen's Head 𝕃
Beccles Road, NR14 6RJ
☎ (01508) 548667 🌐 queensheadthurlton.co.uk
3 changing beers (often People's) Ⓗ
A bustling community-owned pub with three real ales, including exclusive beers from the nearby People's Brewery. Other local and national ales are regularly available. The comfortable bar is on three levels, with a pool table at one end and a cosy log fire in the winter. Excellent locally sourced food is served, with themed menus and breakfast on Wednesdays. There is live music every weekend. Families, dogs and children are welcome. Q♨❀◐◑♿♣●P🚌(86)🐾📶

Thurne

Lion Inn
The Street, NR29 3AP
☎ (01692) 671806 🌐 thelionatthurne.com
6 changing beers (sourced nationally) Ⓗ
A large country pub in a remote village near the River Ant, at the end of Thurne Dyke. There are plenty of moorings nearby for passing Broads cruisers, and a big garden. Meals made from locally sourced produce are served in the restaurant or bar. Six changing real ales are on handpump, plus a choice of up to six real ciders, and there are 16 keg taps for craft offerings. Local CAMRA Pub of the Year 2019. Q♨❀◐◑♿▲♣●P🐾

Tunstead

Horse & Groom
Market Street, NR12 8AH
☎ (01603) 737555 🌐 tunsteadhorseandgroom.co.uk
Adnams Ghost Ship; Lacons Encore; 1 changing beer (sourced nationally) Ⓗ
Traditional village local with three drinking areas surrounding the central bar and a separate games room. Of the three cask ales, one changes regularly. The restaurant is at one end, away from the bar. Meals are freshly cooked using locally sourced ingredients where possible. There is a front terrace and a small rear courtyard. Quiz night is every fourth Tuesday and an acoustic music session is held on the second Wednesday of the month. Q❀◐◑♿▲♣P🚌🐾📶

Upton

White Horse 𝕃
17 Chapel Road, NR13 6BT (about 10 mins' walk from moorings at Upton Dyke)

☎ (01493) 750696 🌐 whitehorseupton.com
Woodforde's Wherry; 3 changing beers (sourced locally) [H]
Traditional broadland pub dating from 1798, a 10-minute walk from Upton Dyke Staithe and moorings. It was renovated in 2012, and is now owned by the local community. A community shop caters for locals and holidaymakers alike. Beers are usually from local breweries. Genuine pub food features strongly, with noted Sunday roasts, while fish & chip night is Friday. An annual beer, cider and perry festival takes place over the first full weekend in July. P

Warham All Saints

Three Horseshoes

The Street, NR23 1NL (2 miles SE of Wells)
☎ (01328) 710547 🌐 warhamhorseshoes.co.uk
Woodforde's Wherry [G]**; 3 changing beers (sourced nationally)** [H]
A traditional brick and flint village pub with a warm atmosphere, log fires in winter and a unique serving hatch. Four cask beers include three from micros, and one cider is usually on sale. Food, including the famous pies, uses local ingredients. There is a separate dining room and a games room in the barn. The secluded garden is perfect for alfresco dining and has its own bar in summer. Q P

West Acre

Stag L

Low Road, PE32 1TR
☎ (01760) 755395 🌐 westacrestag.co.uk
3 changing beers [H]
This cosy pub is well worth finding at the east end of picturesque West Acre, and is popular with locals, walkers, cyclists and riders. It is a strong supporter of local ales, maintaining a high standard of three varying beers and hosting excellent beer festivals. There is a popular monthly quiz on Sunday nights. The restaurant serves a variety of great-value freshly prepared meals using locally sourced ingredients. Q P

West Runton

Village Inn

Water Lane, NR27 9QP
☎ (01263) 838000 🌐 villageinnwestrunton.co.uk
4 changing beers (sourced locally; often Adnams, Moon Gazer) [H]
A large inn a short distance from the station and the beach, set in pleasant gardens in the centre of this quiet coastal village. Up to five well-kept and mostly local ales are stocked and rotated. Excellent home-cooked meals can be enjoyed in the dining areas or outside, where there is plenty of seating in the flint-walled garden. In the 1970s major rock bands such as Deep Purple played secret gigs at the Pavilion which was at the rear of the pub (sadly now demolished). Q P

Weybourne

Ship Inn L ✔

The Street, NR25 7SZ
☎ (01263) 588721 🌐 theshipinnweybourne.com
Woodforde's Wherry; 3 changing beers (sourced locally; often Moon Gazer) [H]
In the heart of this attractive north Norfolk coastal village, the Ship has up to four cask ales and only sells local beers, including Woodforde's, Humpty Dumpty, Beeston, Moon Gazer, Wolf, Grain and Panther, plus a range of bottled craft beers. Home-cooked food is served lunchtimes and evenings. A monthly quiz night is hosted. There is a pleasant enclosed garden for the summer, and the North Norfolk Railway and Muckleburgh Collection of military vehicles are close by. The Coasthopper bus stops outside. Q P

Wimbotsham

Chequers Inn ✔

7 Church Road, PE34 3QG
☎ (01366) 386768 🌐 thechequerswimbotsham.co.uk
Greene King IPA, Abbot; Woodforde's Wherry; 2 changing beers [H]
A traditional English pub dating back to the mid-17th century overlooking the village green. There is a large bar and dining area with pub activities for the locals. An extensive food and drink menu is offered every day with the exception of Sunday evening. The pub has a separate function room, and a car park to the rear. P

Wreningham

Bird in Hand ✔

Church Road, NR16 1BJ
☎ (01508) 489438 🌐 birdinhandwreningham.com
Adnams Ghost Ship; Ruddles Best Bitter; Woodforde's Wherry; 1 changing beer (sourced nationally) [H]
A friendly family-run Grade II listed free house with conference and restaurant facilities, and Casque Mark cellar standards. Close to Lotus Cars, the bar displays Lotus racing memorabilia among rural items and old photos of the village. Occasional quiz nights are held, and regular acoustic music nights. It has a large car park, a lovely garden and a courtyard.
Q P (37A,805)

Wymondham

Feathers

13 Town Green, NR18 0PN
☎ (01953) 605675
Adnams Southwold Bitter, Ghost Ship; Fuller's London Pride; St Austell Tribute Extra; 2 changing beers (sourced nationally) [H]
The Feathers dates from the 18th century. The interior has two main drinking areas and alcoves, served by one bar. Alcoves and walls are adorned with postcard collections, enamel signs and farming and rural memorabilia, including an old bike. There is a large well-furnished patio garden at the rear, and good-value food is available lunchtime and evening.

Green Dragon L ✔

6 Church Street, NR18 0PH (between Market St and Wymondham Abbey)
☎ (01953) 607907 🌐 greendragonnorfolk.co.uk
Green Dragon Bridge Street Bitter; 4 changing beers (sourced regionally) [H]
A haunted half-timbered inn recognised by CAMRA as having a historic interior of regional importance with an attractive beer garden. On the road to Wymondham's beautiful abbey, this inn dates back to 1371. One bar serves the downstairs area, a snug and the restaurant. The interior has beamed timbers and carved stone, and shows evidence of medieval construction methods. The rotating real ales are mostly from local or East Anglian breweries. Beer festivals are held in May and August, with live music. Excellent home-made food features locally sourced ingredients where possible.
Q

Ribs of Beef, Norwich, Norfolk (p320)

NORTHAMPTONSHIRE

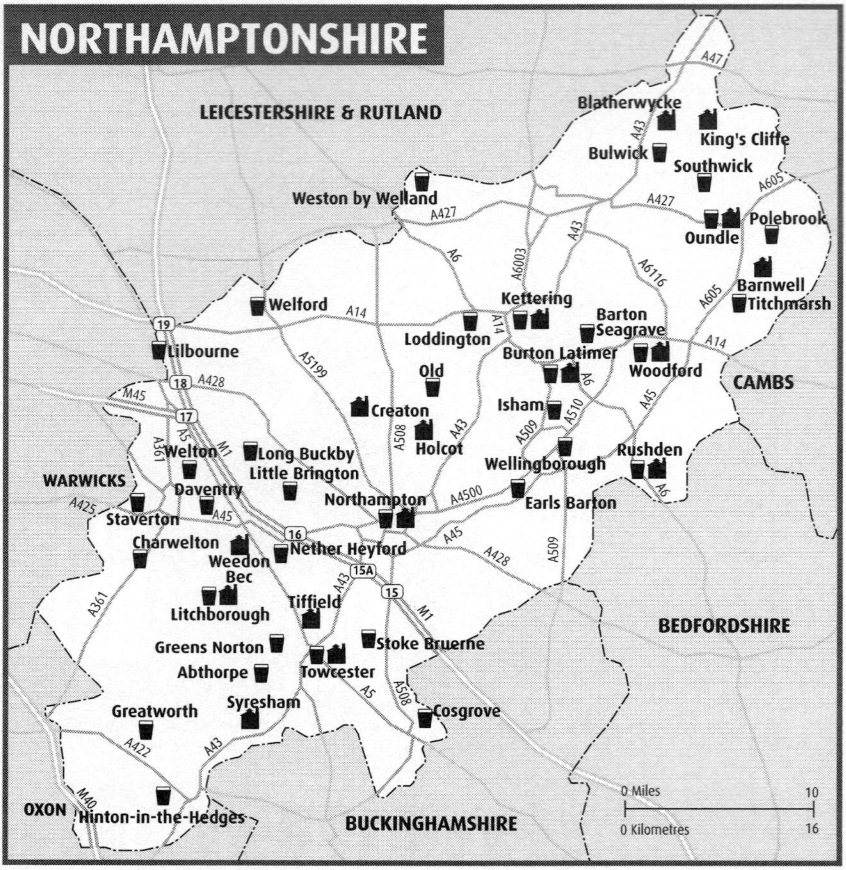

Abthorpe

New Inn 𝕃

Silver Street, NN12 8QR (off Main St, left at church)
☎ (01327) 857306 🌐 newinnabthorpe.co.uk

Hook Norton Hooky, Hooky Gold, Old Hooky; 1 changing beer (often Hook Norton) Ⓗ

A tranquil country hostelry tucked away close to the village green and church, welcoming to visitors and locals alike. It is a quintessentially English village pub built of local mellow sandstone, complete with low ceilings and an inglenook fireplace with seating. The pub serves good food including meats from the owner's farm, plus ales that are still brewed in the traditional way by Hook Norton – its seasonal beers feature as guests. Traditional pub games including darts and Northamptonshire skittles are played. ❀◑♿♣P🐾

Barton Seagrave

Stirrup Cup 𝕃 ✔

Woodland Avenue, NN15 6QR (off A14 jct 10)
☎ (01536) 722841 🌐 thestirrupcupbartonseagrave.co.uk

Ruddles Best Bitter; 3 changing beers (sourced regionally; often Black Sheep, Potbelly) Ⓗ

New to the Guide, this community-focused estate pub is about to celebrate its half century. The traditional sports bar features darts, pool and skittles, while the lounge offers breakfast, lunch and afternoon tea, Monday to Friday. Under new management since 2017, there is a greater emphasis on beer choice, with a local from Potbelly usually on the bar plus two guests. Evening entertainment includes a quiz on Wednesday, jazz on Thursday and open mic on Sunday.
Q❀◑♿♣P🚌🐾

Bulwick

Queen's Head 𝕃

Main Street, NN17 3DY
☎ (01780) 450272 🌐 queensheadbulwick.com

Digfield Shacklebush; Grainstore Red Kite; 2 changing beers Ⓗ

Seventeenth-century stone pub with a Collyweston slate roof on the main street opposite the church. Access is through a small back door via the patio and outside dining area at the rear. Inside, there is a single bar with four handpumps offering a range of changing beers, often from local micros. High-quality locally sourced food is served in a number of interconnecting dining areas and is thoroughly recommended (booking advisable). A former local CAMRA branch Pub of the Year. Open on some Mondays in summer. Q❀◑♣P🐾

Burton Latimer

Duke's Arms 𝕃 ✔

123 High Street, NN15 5RL (off A14 jct 10)
☎ (01536) 390874

3 changing beers (sourced nationally)
For many years keg only, this revitalised pub now features three handpumps for real ale and is the local outlet for Three Hills Brewing. A central U-shaped bar serves the opened-out rooms, with comfortable leather seating and more traditional seating in the small bay windows. The walls are adorned with vinyl LPs and a collection of books is available for customers to read. Ukulele night is Tuesday. There is no parking but a free car park is just across the road. ☺❀♣●🚌🐾📶

Charwelton

Fox & Hounds
Banbury Road, NN11 3YY (on A421)
☎ (01327) 260611 🌐 foxandhoundscharwelton.co.uk
3 changing beers (sourced regionally; often North Cotswold) Ⓗ
An attractive stone-built pub, with parts dating from the 15th century. It was purchased by the local community following its closure in 2012, thus safeguarding its future. Comfortably furnished, it is a cosy place to enjoy the three beers on offer from local microbreweries. Food is available all week in the bar and restaurant. Note the Hunt Edmunds ceramic plaque by the entrance – the former Banbury brewery once owned the pub.
☺❀◑P🚌🐾📶

Cosgrove

Barley Mow ✔
7 The Stocks, MK19 7JD
☎ (01908) 562957 🌐 thebarleymowcosgrove.co.uk
Everards Sunchaser, Tiger, Old Original; 1 changing beer (sourced regionally; often Titanic) Ⓗ
A beautiful countryside pub backing on to the Grand Union Canal by Bridge 65. The 17th-century building's main bar and adjoining areas provide a charming environment, especially when the log fire is ablaze. Outside is a patio leading onto a lovely garden. The home-cooked food caters for all dietary requirements. Events are staged throughout the year, and may include a murder mystery evening as well as the monthly quiz.
Q☺❀◑♿ΔP🚌🐾📶

Daventry

Early Doors 🄻
3 Prince William Walk, NN11 4AB
☎ 07944 649426 🌐 earlydoorsdaventry.co.uk
Phipps NBC India Pale Ale; 5 changing beers (sourced locally; often Towcester Mill, Vale, XT) Ⓖ
A welcome return to the Guide for Early Doors – a father and son team has now taken over from the founders of the very first Northamptonshire micropub. Tucked away down a narrow alley, this is a warm and welcoming oasis in the heart of Daventry, with a real community feel. The bar is simply decorated and is made from reclaimed doors and weathered scaffolding planks. Ales, including a dark beer, are all on gravity, and locally produced cider is made within one mile of Welton. Q♿●P🚌🐾

Earls Barton

Saxon Tavern 🄻 ✔
25B The Square, NN6 0NA
☎ 07956 462352
6 changing beers (often Nene Valley, Potbelly, Towcester Mill)
A large, comfortable and relaxed single-room micropub with welcoming hosts. It has a central village location between the famous Barker Shoes and the historic Saxon tower – the premises was previously the local headquarters of the Magic Circle. Six casks with cooling jackets are stillaged behind the bar. A wide selection of 130 gins is offered, along with bottled beers and box ciders from the fridge. A former CAMRA Rural Pub of the Season. Q❀♣●P🚌🐾

Greatworth

Greatworth Inn 🄻
Chapel Road, OX17 2DT (off B4525)
☎ (01295) 521426 🌐 thegreatworthinn.co.uk
4 changing beers (sourced regionally)
A stone-built free house dating from the 16th century, located in the centre of this attractive village. It was restored to its former glory by the owners on their return to the village, with numerous improvements undertaken while retaining a cosy and traditional pub atmosphere. The bar area features an inglenook fireplace with a log-burning stove; there is also a dining area. An annual soap box derby is held in June and a beer festival in August.
Q☺❀◑♿♣P🐾📶

Greens Norton

Butchers Arms 🄻
10 High Street, NN12 8BA
☎ (01327) 358848 🌐 thebutchersarms.pub
Great Oakley Wot's Occurring; St Austell Tribute; Silverstone Pitstop; 2 changing beers (sourced regionally; often Great Oakley) Ⓗ
A large pub at the centre of the village with a modern rustic bar and relaxed dining area, featuring wooden flooring and panelling throughout, complemented by bay window seating and a real wood-burning fire. Outside is a landscaped, tiered garden. Listed as an asset of community value by the parish council, the freehold was bought by a group of local investors keen to see the pub remain at the heart of the village.
Q☺❀◑♿♣●P🚌(86,87)🐾📶

Hinton-in-the-Hedges

Crewe Arms 🄻
Sparrow Corner, NN13 5NF
☎ (01280) 705801 🌐 crewearmshinton.co.uk
Hook Norton Hooky; Timothy Taylor Boltmaker; 1 changing beer (sourced nationally; often Vale) Ⓗ

REAL ALE BREWERIES

Avalanche Burton Latimer (NEW)
Boot Town Burton Latimer
Cotton End 🛢 Northampton
Creaton Grange Creaton
Digfield Barnwell
Great Oakley Tiffield
Holcot Hop-Craft Holcot
Hoppy Family Kettering
King's Cliffe King's Cliffe
Litchborough Artisan Litchborough
Maule Northampton
Nene Valley (NVB) ◆ Oundle
Phipps Northampton
Potbelly Kettering
Purple Cow 🛢 Kettering
Rockingham Blatherwycke
Roman Way ◆ Weedon Bec (NEW)
Silverstone Syresham
Three Hills Woodford
Towcester Mill ◆ Towcester
Weldon Rushden

Stone-built and situated in a gully in the village, the Crewe Arms can be hard to find – the entrance is through the rear gravel car park. Four comfortably furnished rooms provide a relaxed environment. The pub's cellar, located in the main dining area, may have been part of a tunnel between the village manor and the local church. Two real ales are served during the week and three at weekends. Happy hour is 6-8pm Friday-Sunday. B&B is available in two rooms. Q🐴❀🛏◐♿P🚌📶

Isham

Lilacs

39 Church Street, NN14 1HD (off A509 at church)
☎ (01536) 722348 🌐 thelilacsisham.co.uk
Greene King IPA; 3 changing beers (sourced regionally; often Oakham, Potbelly)
Following closure in 2018, the freehold of this building was purchased by locals in order to preserve a pub in Isham, and it has since reopened. In the heart of the village and named after a local breed of rabbit, the traditional inn is popular with regulars, diners and drinkers alike. It has a small lounge, the former snug with a dartboard, and a large room to the rear. Quiz and live music nights are held regularly. Two of the guests beers are from Oakham and Potbelly.
Q🐴❀◐♿♣P🚌(X4) 🐾📶

Kettering

Alexandra Arms

39 Victoria Street, NN16 0BU
☎ (01536) 522730
Hop Back Summer Lightning; Marston's Pedigree; Wychwood Hobgoblin Gold; 11 changing beers (sourced nationally)
Traditional town-centre street-corner local where you will always find a beer from an unknown brewery. The landlord continues to search out new and interesting ales, served through 14 handpumps. Two opened-out rooms contain a piano and settee, with the walls covered in breweriana and pumpclips. The rear bar has a TV and Northants skittles. Q❀♣●🚌🐾

Piper

Windmill Avenue, NN15 6PS (near Wicksteed Park)
☎ (01536) 513870 🌐 thepiper.net
Castle Rock Harvest Pale; Fuller's London Pride; 4 changing beers (sourced nationally; often Nobby's, Potbelly)
Popular 1950s two-roomed pub which has been run by an enthusiastic CAMRA member for 30 years. It has a quiet lounge to the left, while to the right is a more lively bar/games room where a quiz is held on Sunday night. A beer festival is held on the third weekend of August. There is an outdoor seating area across the road. Nearby Wicksteed Park was one of Britain's first theme parks, and Tresham College is opposite.
Q🐴❀◐♿⛺♣●P🚌🐾📶

Three Cocks

48 Lower Street, NN16 8DJ (opp Morrisons)
☎ 07909 698798
Full Mash Séance; Grainstore Ten Fifty; Oakham Inferno; 4 changing beers (sourced regionally; often Church End, Froth Blowers)
A popular locals' town-centre pub comprising an L-shaped servery at the centre looking after the two main bar areas, furnished with comfortable armchairs and high-backed stools. Guest ales are on the main bar, the regulars to the side, always including a dark, a strong, a light and a citrus beer. On an upper level is a games area featuring Northants skittles and darts. Home to three skittles teams, also of interest are board games and monthly quiz evenings. Q🐴♿♣●🚌🐾

Lilbourne

Head of Steam

10 Station Road, CV23 0SX (just off Rugby Rd)
☎ (01788) 860166
5 changing beers (sourced nationally; often Church End, Phipps NBC, Wye Valley)
Converted from a house in 2013, this thriving, railway-themed free house is the local CAMRA Country Pub of the Year. Friendly conversation dominates in this community pub, creating a welcoming atmosphere. Locally sourced pork pies, cheeseboards and freshly made rolls are available. Sunday lunches are served, and there is a steak and cheese night every other Thursday. Beers often come from Wye Valley. The large garden, with an outside bar throughout the summer, makes this a popular destination in warm weather. Q🐴❀◐♿♣●P🐾📶

Litchborough

Old Red Lion

4 Banbury Road, NN12 8JF (opp church)
☎ (01327) 830064
Great Oakley Wagtail; 2 changing beers (sourced regionally)
A traditional four-roomed stone-built village pub that is well worth seeking out, popular with walkers and cyclists on the Knightly Way. The bar has flagstone flooring and seats inside the large inviting inglenook. The rear snug is a comfy casual room with double doors leading to a courtyard. The extension houses a restaurant and shop with local farm produce. Q🐴❀◐♿P🚌🐾📶

Little Brington

Saracen's Head

Main Street, NN7 4HS
☎ (01604) 770640 🌐 thesaracensatbrington.co.uk
Timothy Taylor Landlord; 3 changing beers (sourced regionally; often Black Sheep, Grainstore)
Delightful ironstone building with old etched windows at the front, set in a pretty village. The bar is open plan but serves distinctly different areas of the pub. The floors are a mixture of flagstones and old wooden planking, and there is a large, attractive inglenook with wood-burner. The three rotating guest ales are usually from local breweries. On a sunny day the extensive outside area is an ideal spot to enjoy a drink. 🐴❀🛏◐♿P🐾📶

Loddington

Hare at Loddington

5 Main Street, NN14 1LA (on village loop)
☎ (01536) 710337 🌐 thehareatloddington.com
Greene King Abbot; Sharp's Doom Bar; 2 changing beers (sourced regionally; often Church End, Phipps NBC)
The Hare is a listed building set in a conservation area in a picturesque village built from local ironstone. It stands back in the middle of Main Street, surrounded by listed houses, and has a pleasant front garden. Inside, it comprises four areas – two are spread around the central bar and two are for dining, serving good home-cooked food from local producers. The guest beers are from established breweries or local microbreweries.
Q🐴❀◐♿●P🚌(35) 🐾

Long Buckby

Badgers Arms 🄻
2 High Street, NN6 7RD
☎ (01327) 843003
4 changing beers (sourced regionally; often North Cotswold, Potbelly, XT) 🄶
Opened in 2017, this micropub rapidly gained a reputation for quality local beers and ciders, plus an ambience and welcome that are second to none. Unusually, the bar is upstairs and has two distinct drinking areas, while downstairs there is another small room, with table service for those unable to manage the stairs. Winner of CAMRA Regional Cider Pub of the Year in 2019 and a finalist in the National awards. Q

Nether Heyford

Foresters Arms 🄻
22 The Green, NN7 3LE
☎ (01327) 340729
2 changing beers (sourced locally) 🄷
The owners have made many improvements since buying this attractive, double bay-fronted ironstone pub in 2012, not least the introduction of their enlightened choice of two rotating beers, one always sourced locally. Real cider is available on gravity dispense behind the bar. The pub remains the hub of village life and while predominantly for drinkers, it also offers simple bar meals and snacks. On Thursday and Friday evenings a mobile pizza van sets up shop in the pub forecourt. P(D3)

Northampton

Albion Brewery Bar 🄻
54 Kingswell Street, NN1 1PR
☎ (01604) 946606
Phipps NBC Red Star, Steam Roller, Cobbler's Ale, India Pale Ale, Ratliffe's Celebrated Stout, Bison Brown; 1 changing beer (sourced nationally) 🄷
Phipps NBC returned to its roots in a Victorian brewery in the heart of Northampton in 2014, 40 years after Phipps' Bridge Street premises closed. The brewery bar subsequently opened, with an oak and glass partition between the bar and brewery enabling the equipment to be viewed. Almost all of the bar fittings are reclaimed, with many coming from closed Phipps NBC pubs. Much memorabilia is on display. Eight handpumps serve six in-house ales plus a rotating guest, with the final pump reserved for a Northamptonshire cider.
Q(7,X6)

Cordwainer 🄻 ✔
The Ridings, NN1 2AQ (nr jct with Fish St)
☎ (01604) 609000
Greene King Abbot; Phipps NBC Gold Star; Ruddles Best Bitter; Sharp's Doom Bar; 8 changing beers (often Phipps NBC) 🄷
Large, popular town-centre Wetherspoon, which has recently been refurbished and now has a first-floor terrace and a ground-floor garden area. There is a large bar on both floors with two sets of handpumps. A wide choice of 12 real ales and an occasional real cider is available, and up to four beer festivals are held each year. Food is served throughout the day, including specials, from the extensive Wetherspoon menu.

Kingsley Park Working Men's Club 🄻
120 Kingsley Park Terrace, NN2 7HJ
☎ (01604) 715514 🌐 kpwmc.co.uk
Fuller's London Pride, ESB; Greene King IPA; Shepherd Neame Spitfire; Tetley Bitter; 3 changing beers (sourced nationally; often Elgood's, Nobby's, Phipps NBC) 🄷
Long-established and thriving working men's club on the main road in a residential area, which was founded in 1892 in a nearby street. There are eight handpumps serving five regular and three changing beers, overseen by an award-winning steward. Live music is hosted two nights a week and trips out are organised for members. A former local CAMRA Club of the Year. Q

Lamplighter 🄻
66 Overstone Road, NN1 3JS
☎ (01604) 631125 🌐 thelamplighter.co.uk
5 changing beers (sourced locally) 🄷
A deservedly popular, traditional, street-corner pub just off the town centre, attracting young and old alike. There is an open fire in the bar and a heated courtyard. Five rotating beers come from established micros, including LocAles. Home-cooked food is served and children are welcome during mealtimes. The pub aims to support local industry by using nearby suppliers. It hosts weekly DJ nights, live music and quiz nights, and beer festivals throughout the year.

Malt Shovel Tavern 🄻
121 Bridge Street, NN1 1QF
☎ (01604) 234212 🌐 maltshoveltavern.com
Hook Norton Old Hooky; Oakham JHB, Bishops Farewell; Phipps NBC India Pale Ale; 10 changing beers (sourced nationally) 🄷
Close to the town centre and opposite the Carlsberg brewery, this popular pub has won many awards over the past 20 or more years, including local CAMRA Pub of the Year on numerous occasions. Breweriana features everywhere, with real cider, LocAle, Belgian draught and bottled beers available. Two beer festivals with live bands are held each year on bank holidays. Blues bands play on Wednesday nights. Home-made lunches are served all week. The pub has a strong rugby following and is well worth a visit.

Olde England 🄻
199 Kettering Road, NN1 4BP (near racecourse)
☎ (01604) 603799
Digfield Chiffchaff; Jennings Cumberland Ale; Marston's Old Empire; Potbelly Beijing Black; Ringwood Fortyniner; Vale Gravitas 🄷**; changing beers (sourced regionally; often Nobby's, Phipps NBC)** 🄷/🄶
Converted end-of-terrace Victorian building on three floors with bars on two floors. The ground and first floors have a medieval theme, with solid fuel burners, while the cellar has a contemporary style and is more intimate. Around 10 beers from local micros and regional breweries are served by handpump alongside 15 ciders. Various board games, cards and dominoes are provided. Live folk music plays on Thursday. A former local CAMRA Cider Pub of the Year and Northants Town Community Pub. Q

Pomfret Arms 🄻
10 Cotton End, NN4 8BS
☎ (01604) 555119 🌐 pomfretarms.co.uk
Cotton End Coffee Porter; Great Oakley Wot's Occurring, Tiffield Thunderbolt; 3 changing beers (sourced locally) 🄷
With its own microbrewery, this town pub is situated on the south-west side of the River Nene in Cotton End. Its small central bar has six handpumps serving both the front opened-out room and rear bar. The brewery and a function room are in a separate building in the lovely

beer garden. One Cotton End beer is usually available, alongside ales from Great Oakley. Check Facebook for seasonal opening hours. ➋❀♿●🚻🐾❄🛜

Road to Morocco
Bridgwater Drive, NN3 3AG
☎ (01604) 632899
Greene King IPA; St Austell Tribute; Theakston Old Peculier; 3 changing beers (sourced nationally) Ⓗ
Run by a CAMRA member, this popular 1960s brick-built estate pub has a slight Moorish theme in some of the decor. There are two connected but distinctly different rooms. The bar area is quite lively, particularly when sporting events are shown on TV. This is also where darts and pool are played. The homely lounge is generally the quieter area of the pub, except during rugby matches featuring the Northampton Saints. There is a jukebox in the bar. Quiz night is Tuesday. ➋❀♿🐾●🚻(5)❄🛜

St Giles Ale House Ⓛ
45 St Giles Street, NN1 1JF
☎ (01604) 636332
6 changing beers (sourced nationally; often Framework, Grainstore) Ⓗ
Northampton's first and only micropub, opened in 2016 following conversion from retail premises. It specialises in real ale and real cider, with ales from around the country which tend to be new releases or from more obscure breweries. Beer club runs from Tuesday to Thursday teatime, with a discount on ale and cider. With no music or fruit machines, this is an ideal place for drinking and conversation. A former local CAMRA Pub of the Year. Q❀♿🐾●🚻(5)❄🛜

Old

White Horse Ⓛ
Walgrave Road, NN6 9QX
☎ (01604) 781297
Grainstore Cooking, Red Kite, Triple B; 2 changing beers (sourced locally) Ⓗ
A rustic country pub comprising two opened-out rooms with polished wooden floors and a real fire, and a small snug towards the rear. Upstairs is the Millstone room which can be used for functions and leads to the south-facing garden overlooking the church. The menu is relatively small, offering interesting home-cooked seasonal lunches and evening meals including pub classics and specials. Attractions include monthly live music and quiz nights and a weekly Tuesday pie night. Q➋❀♿🚻❄🛜

Oundle

Ship Inn Ⓛ
18 West Street, PE8 4EF
☎ (01832) 273918 ⊕ theshipinnoundle.co.uk
Brewsters Hophead; Fuller's London Pride; 2 changing beers Ⓗ
This Grade II listed pub is full of character with original beamed ceilings and the ghost of a former landlord. It has three bars with many small rooms adjoining, and a large function room available to hire for birthday celebrations and small weddings. Good food is served in all rooms. Accommodation is in two stone annexes and a small cottage to the rear. The rear car park is accessed through an archway off West Street.
Q❀🛏🐾◑♿🅿️🚻(X4)❄🛜

Polebrook

King's Arms Ⓛ
Kings Arms Lane, PE8 5LW
☎ (01832) 272363 ⊕ kingsarmspolebrook.co.uk
Digfield Fools Nook; 3 changing beers Ⓗ
Traditional stone-built thatched inn, accessible from doors at the front and rear off the car park. The pub is open plan with a main bar, three areas for diners, and an enclosed garden with a play area. Four beers are dispensed via handpump, always including at least one from the nearby Digfield Ales. Food is offered from an extensive menu and specials board. Third-pint glasses are available, giving the opportunity to taste a wider variety of beer. Happy hour is 6-7pm Monday.
Q❀◑♿🐾●🅿️🚻❄🛜

Rushden

Rushden Historical Transport Society Ⓛ
Station Approach, NN10 0AW (on ring road)
☎ (01933) 318988 ⊕ rhts.co.uk
Phipps NBC India Pale Ale; 6 changing beers (sourced regionally; often Marston's, Woodforde's) Ⓗ
This award-winning club occupies the former Midland Railway station. The ladies' waiting room is now the bar, with gas lighting and walls adorned with enamel advertising panels, railway photos and many CAMRA awards. On the platform, carriages provide a meeting room, Northants skittles, and a buffet for the numerous open days held during the year when steam and diesel train rides are provided. A beer festival is held in September. Show a copy of the Guide to sign in.
Q➋❀♿🐾●🚻

Southwick

Shuckburgh Arms Ⓛ
Main Street, PE8 5BL
☎ (01832) 272044 ⊕ shuckburghpub.co.uk
Brewsters Hophead; Digfield Barnwell Bitter; 3 changing beers (sourced locally; often Fuller's, Grainstore) Ⓗ
Thatched stone-built pub in the village centre, serving five real ales. The bar area doubles as a restaurant and there is a small side room. To the rear is a covered outdoor area, car park, large garden and the village cricket pitch. The pub is run by the local community with shareholders and a small committee. It hosts the annual World Conker Championship in October. Popular well-priced food is available, including breakfast by arrangement. Q❀◑🏕🐾♣🅿️🚻❄🛜

Staverton

Countryman Ⓛ ✔
Daventry Road, NN11 6JH (on A425)
☎ (01327) 311815 ⊕ thecountrymanstaverton.co.uk
Bombardier; 2 changing beers (sourced locally; often Church End, Hook Norton) Ⓗ
A delightful 17th-century ironstone coaching inn that is the sole survivor of the three pubs that once served this lovely village close to Daventry. The long wooden-beamed bar serves four areas, and an open hearth fire between the rooms provides some seclusion. The landlord offers a good choice of ales, always including one local brew. There is also a wide choice of reasonably priced food, sourced locally whenever possible.
Q➋❀◑♿🅿️🚻(66)❄🛜

Stoke Bruerne

Boat Inn ✔

Shutlanger Road, NN12 7SB

☎ (01604) 862428 🌐 boatinn.co.uk

Banks's Amber Ale; Jennings Cumberland Ale; Marston's EPA, Old Empire; Ringwood Boondoggle; Wychwood Hobgoblin Ruby; 1 changing beer (sourced nationally) 🄷

Situated on the banks of the Grand Union Canal, the Boat Inn has been owned and run by the Woodward family since 1877. The delightful tap bar's interconnecting rooms have canal views, open fires, original stone floors and window seats, while an adjoining room has Northants skittles. Popular with diners, a large extension houses the lounge, restaurant and bistro. Additional beers are sold in summer. A canal boat is available to hire. Breakfast is served. Q🚼❀◑◗♿⛺♣P🐾📶

Titchmarsh

Wheatsheaf

1 North Street, NN14 3DH

☎ (01832) 732203 🌐 the-wheatsheaf.pub

Butcombe Gold; Nene Valley Blonde Session Ale; 1 changing beer (often Nene Valley) 🄷

Closed for four months, the pub was reopened in 2017 by new owners following a small refurbishment. Nestled among the stone buildings of Titchmarsh's conservation area, the Wheatsheaf has a cosy bar area with beamed ceiling, comfy leather sofas, tub chairs, high tables, a fireplace and books. There is a separate restaurant area and, outside, a patio and beer garden. Three cask ales are on offer, always including a couple from Nene Valley, and traditional cider. Northamptonshire skittles is played, with league matches on some Mondays. An array of freshly cooked food caters for most dietary requirements.
🚼❀◑◗🍎P🐾

Towcester

Towcester Mill Brewery Tap 𝕃

Chantry Lane, NN12 6AD

☎ (01327) 437060 🌐 towcestermillbrewery.co.uk

Towcester Mill Old Mill Bitter, Crooked Hooker, Mill Race, Bell Ringer, Black Fire, Roman Road; 2 changing beers (sourced locally) 🄷

Popular and welcoming brewery tap in a historic Grade II listed mill dating from 1794, straddling the old mill race and adjacent to Bury Mount on which the town's fort once stood. The bar retains many original features including beams, stonework and a wooden floor, with a second room to cope with demand. A large garden runs alongside the mill. Two guest ales are from other local breweries and six ciders are available.
Q🚼❀♿🍎P🚌🐾📶

Welford

Wharf Inn 𝕃

NN6 6JQ (on A5199 by canal basin)

☎ (01858) 575075 🌐 wharfinnwelford.co.uk

Grainstore Ten Fifty; Marston's Pedigree; Oakham Bishops Farewell; 3 changing beers (sourced locally) 🄷

This original ironstone building dates from 1814 and is situated at the end of the Welford cut on the Grand Union Canal, a few yards from the border with Leicestershire. Inside, the main room is segregated by an open fireplace between the two rooms. A smaller snug and back bar is occasionally used. Good-value food is served. Guest beers are often sourced locally or regionally. The pub is popular with walkers – ask for the leaflet with suggested routes. A former local CAMRA Rural Pub of the Year.
Q🚼❀🛏◑◗♿🍎P🚌(60)🐾📶

Wellingborough

Coach & Horses 𝕃 ✔

17 Oxford Street, NN8 4HY (800yds from Market Sq)

☎ (01933) 441848

🌐 thecoachandhorseswellingborough.co.uk

12 changing beers (sourced nationally; often Castle Rock, Elland, Salopian) 🄷

A regular CAMRA award winner and long-standing Guide entry, this popular town-centre local is a former CAMRA East Midlands Leicestershire and Northamptonshire Pub of the Year. A constantly changing choice of 12 real ales and 15 ciders is always on offer. The central bar serves three drinking areas which are adorned with breweriana. Traditional home-cooked food is available including a wide choice of pies (no food Sun eve, Mon & Tue). A quiz is held on alternate Wednesdays, and a beer festival in August. Q🚼❀◑◗♿♣🍎🚌🐾📶

Little Ale House 𝕃

14A High Street, NN8 4JU

☎ 07870 392011

5 changing beers (sourced locally; often Castle Rock, Digfield, Oakham) 🄷/🄶

A wonderfully friendly one-roomed micropub whose small size encourages interaction between guests and the landlady. Up to five rotating real ales are served on handpump and gravity, including a porter or stout. In addition, up to seven draught ciders and a good selection of gins, single malt whiskies, wines and soft drinks are also stocked. A quiz is held on the first Tuesday of the month. Close to Jackson's Lane car park.
Q🚼♣🍎P🚌🐾📶

Little R'Ale House 𝕃

Midland Road, NN8 1NA

☎ 07711 928330 🌐 thelittleralehouse-bar.business.site

4 changing beers (sourced locally; often Nene Valley, Potbelly) 🄶

Charming micropub on the station platform, occupying the former munitions building and filled with memorabilia. Up to four ales are served straight from the barrel, as well as two ciders and an interesting range of bottled beers and craft tins. Occasional music events and comedy nights are held. The patio area allows outdoor summer drinking. The pub is dog-friendly and popular with locals and commuters alike. Q🚼❀≋🍎P🚌🐾📶

Queen's Head

49 Broad Green, NN8 4LH

☎ (01933) 224098 🌐 queensheadwellingborough.co.uk

Timothy Taylor Boltmaker; 3 changing beers (sourced regionally) 🄷

A new entry to the Guide, this multi-roomed pub was extended into the adjacent property many years ago. It has five drinking areas including the main L-shaped bar with a small brick-built servery and seating around the windows. To the left through an interconnecting room is a small snug complete with bookshelves and a Singer sewing machine. The rear bar serves the games rooms where bar billiards and darts are played. BT and Sky sports are screened. 🚼❀◑♣🚌(X4)🐾

Welton

White Horse

High Street, NN11 2JP (off A361 betwen Rugby and Daventry)

☎ (01327) 702820 🌐 thewhitehorsewelton.co.uk
Banks's Amber Ale; Oakham Bishops Farewell; Purity Pure Gold; Sharp's Atlantic; 1 changing beer (sourced nationally) 🄷
This charming 17th-century country pub is heated with wood-burners. There are two bars split over two levels – a traditional bar where darts and skittles are played, and a comfortable beamed lounge leading to the restaurant which serves a wide variety of food. A large canopied patio overlooks the lawned garden. Regular live bands play during the summer. Local Vale of Welton cider is stocked. Visit the recently opened Little Shop of Ale for bottles to take away. Children and dogs are welcome. ❀◐♣●P🐾

Weston by Welland

Wheel & Compass

Valley Road, LE16 8HZ (off B664)
☎ (01858) 565864 🌐 thewheelandcompass.co.uk
Banks's Amber Ale; Greene King Abbot; Marston's Pedigree; 2 changing beers (sourced nationally) 🄷
A rural pub in the picturesque Welland Valley, which has been refurbished to open up the entrance lobby and incorporate part of the former dining area, featuring flagstone floors, a wood-burner and sofas. Good-value food includes lunchtime specials. The outside drinking area offers good views across the valley and is an ideal playground for children. This is a popular stopping-off place for walkers on the Jurassic Way which runs close by. ❀◐♿●P🐾

Woodford

Dukes 🄻

83 High Street, NN14 4HE (off A510)
☎ (01832) 732224
Black Sheep Baa Baa; Fuller's London Pride; Greene King Abbot; 3 changing beers (sourced nationally; often Digfield, Oakham, Phipps NBC) 🄷
Overlooking the village green, this community-focused inn was renamed in honour of the Duke of Wellington, who was a frequent visitor to Woodford. The interior includes a split main bar, lounge restaurant, rear room and an upstairs games room. The pub holds a May bank holiday beer festival and an August bank holiday music festival, plus regular open mic, disco, karaoke and acoustic music nights. Every village should have a pub like this. **Q**❀◐♣●P🚌(16X)🐾

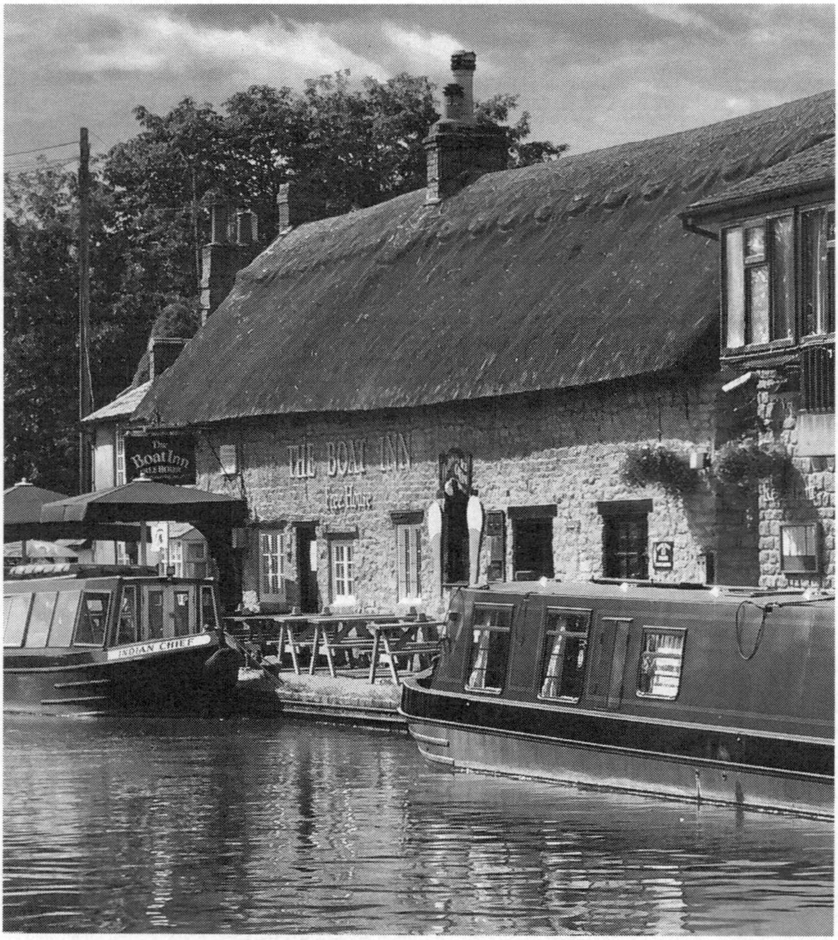

Boat Inn, Stoke Bruerne (Photo: David Merrett/Flickr CC BY 2.0)

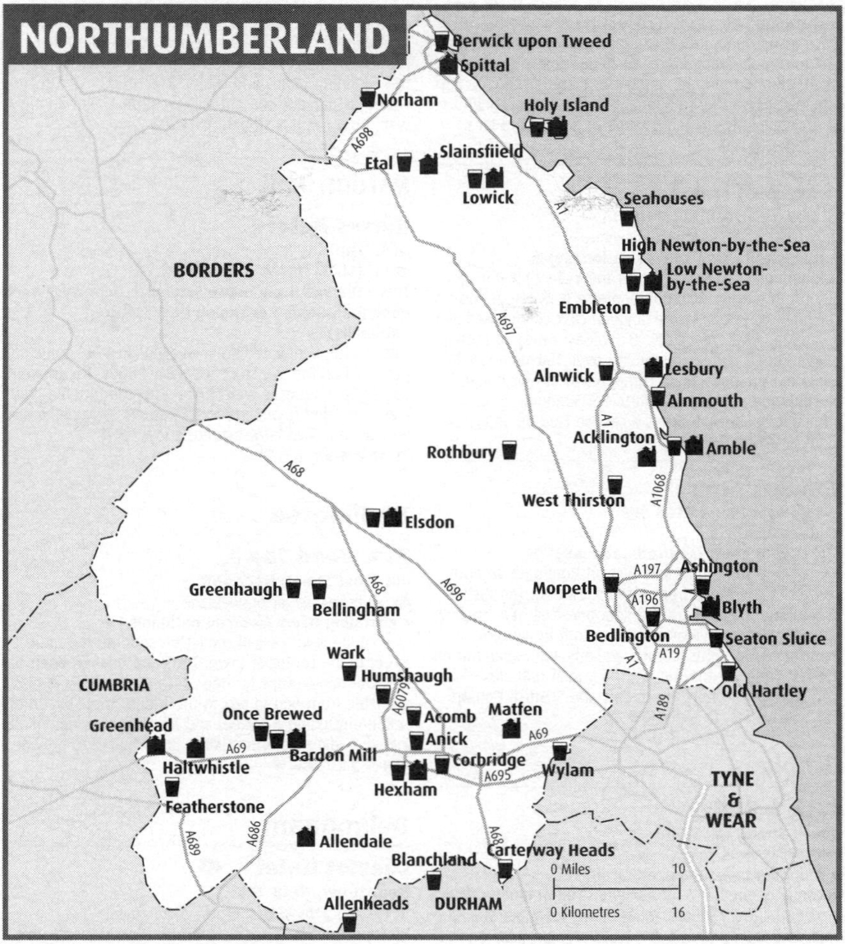

Acomb

Miners Arms

Main Street, NE46 4PW

☎ (01434) 603909 🌐 theminersacomb.com

Hadrian Border Tyneside Blonde; 2 changing beers (sourced nationally) Ⓗ

Superb, traditional, family-run 1746 inn with an emphasis on real ale, which is served in oversized lined glasses. The bar is divided by a central staircase and has a cosy feel. Music and folk nights feature regularly. A traditional pub food menu offers home-made meals using locally sourced ingredients. ♘❀◑♿♣▯🚌 (680)🐾

Allenheads

Allenheads Inn 𝕃

NE47 9HJ

☎ (01434) 685200 🌐 allenheadsinn.co.uk

Anarchy Blonde Star; Hadrian Border Northern Pale; 3 changing beers (sourced nationally) Ⓗ

Superb 18th-century multi-room rural inn with a public bar with a log fire, games room and dining room. On the Coast-to-Coast cycle route, it is popular with cyclists, ramblers and tourists. Good bar meals are available at a decent price. The multi-roomed premises is bedecked with memorabilia and knick-knacks from a bygone age. The pub will open early on request for coach parties and other groups. ♘❀⇌◑♣P🚌 (688)🐾

Alnmouth

Red Lion Inn 𝕃 ✔

22 Northumberland Street, NE66 2RJ

☎ (01665) 830584 🌐 redlionalnmouth.com

4 changing beers (sourced regionally) Ⓗ

Charming, family-run, 18th-century coaching inn with a cosy lounge bar with attractive woodwork. The decked area at the bottom of the garden enjoys panoramic views across the Aln Estuary. Occasional live music plays – in the open air in summer. Guest beers usually include one local and two interesting brews from further afield. An annual beer festival is held in October. It opens early for breakfast, and excellent en-suite B&B accommodation is available.
Q♘❀⇌◑●P🚌 (X18) 🐾📶

Alnwick

Ale Gate 𝕃

25 Bondgate Without, NE66 1PR

☎ 07979 101332

6 changing beers (sourced locally) H
Once a shop unit, latterly an insurance office, Alnwick's first micropub opened in early 2019. It has a single open main room to the right, and a raised area to the rear. Six handpumps on the traditionally styled dark-wooden bar offer a regularly changing range of beers from local breweries. ●♠🖥♣

John Bull Inn L
12 Howick Street, NE66 1UY
☎ (01665) 602055 ⊕ john-bull-inn.co.uk
4 changing beers (sourced nationally) H
Frequently local CAMRA Pub of the Year, this 180-year-old inn thrives on its reputation as a back-street boozer. The landlord offers a wide range of cask-conditioned ales at varying ABVs, real cider, the widest range of bottled Belgian beers in the county and over 150 single malt whiskies. The darts team competes in the local league and the pub upholds the North-East tradition of an annual leek show. There is a cheese club on Saturday night. Q❀♣●🖥♣

Tanners Arms L
2-4 Hotspur Place, NE66 1QF
☎ (01665) 602553
5 changing beers (sourced nationally) H
Ivy-covered stone-built pub just off Bondgate Without and a short distance from Alnwick Garden. The rustic single room has a flagstone floor and tree beer shelf. A large fireplace provides added warmth in winter. Acoustic music nights feature regularly, with open mic on the last Friday of the month. The varied real ales frequently come from North-East and Scottish Borders microbreweries. 🚲♣♣●🖥♣🛜

Amble

Cock & Bull L
Queen Street, NE65 0DQ
⊕ cockandbullpub.co.uk
4 changing beers (sourced locally) H
Recently opened in a former tourist information office next to the town square, it has bench seating around the walls and trestle tables. The walls are dark blue and there is an orange skylight in the ceiling. The pub features a local artist of the month with works on display and for sale. There is some seating outside. Four handpumps serve locally brewed ales.
❀♣🖥(X18,X20) ♣🛜

Anick

Rat Inn
NE46 4LN (follow signpost at Hexham A69 roundabout)
☎ (01434) 602814 ⊕ theratinn.com
Timothy Taylor Landlord; 4 changing beers (sourced locally) H
Superb 1750 country inn with spectacular views across the Tyne Valley. It has an excellent local reputation for good food prepared with locally sourced ingredients and appears in several food guides. Half portions are available for children. Bottled beers are stocked. The first Thursday of the month is singers/poetry night. Well worth the short taxi ride from Hexham rail station.
Q🚲❀🕙♣●P🖥(74)

Ashington

Hop 77
77 Station Road, NE63 8RS
3 changing beers (sourced nationally) H

Ashington's first micropub opened in a former shop unit in September 2019. It has a single room with a bar counter in one corner. Furnishings are a mix of sofas and free-standing tables and chairs. It is sited on the main street just beyond the old railway station, and an easy walk from the bus station. 🚲♦🖥♣

Bardon Mill

Bowes Hotel L
NE47 7HU
☎ (01434) 344237 ⊕ theboweshotel.uk
Twice Brewed Brew House Sycamore Gap; Wychwood Hobgoblin Gold; 1 changing beer (sourced nationally) H
This recently renovated hotel was built in 1906, but a pub has been on the site since the early 1800s. The modern, open-plan interior is welcoming with comfortable grey walls, wooden floors and check carpets. Quiz night is Wednesday. Two large screens show sport.
🚲🛏🕙🚆🖥(685) 🛜

Bedlington

Box Wood Tap L
40C Front Street, NE22 5UB
⊕ the-box-wood-tap.business.site
4 changing beers (sourced nationally) H
This venue is in a small converted shop on the main street in the centre of town. The hand-built wooden bar has four handpumps for beer. A range of ciders is also available from bag-in-box in the fridge. There is some seating including a settee, and an extension was made into the adjoining former shop unit in 2019 to provide more space. ●🖥♣

Bellingham

Cheviot Hotel L ⊘
Main Street, NE48 2AU
☎ (01434) 220696 ⊕ thecheviothotel.co.uk
Hadrian Border Tyneside Blonde; High House Farm Nel's Best; Wylam Jakehead IPA; house beer (by Hadrian Border) H
Friendly hotel opposite the bus stop. A log-burning stove warms the bar area. Cask beer is available all year round including one varying ale from Hadrian Border Brewery. There is plenty of outside seating at the front. Regular theme nights are hosted. 🚲❀🛏🕙♣♣P🖥(680)♣🛜

REAL ALE BREWERIES
Allendale Allendale
Alnwick Lesbury
Beacon Brauhaus Holy Island (brewing suspended)
Bear Claw Spittal
Brewis ♠ Amble (NEW)
Chasing Everest Blyth
Cheviot Slainsfield
Credence Amble
First & Last 🍺 Elsdon
Grounding Angels Hexham
Hetton Law Lowick
Hexhamshire Hexham
High House Farm Matfen
Muckle Haltwhistle
Rigg & Furrow ♠ Acklington
Ship Inn 🍺 Low Newton-by-the-Sea
Twice Brewed 🍺 Bardon Mill
Wrytree Greenhead

Berwick upon Tweed

Barrels Ale House

59-61 Bridge Street, TD15 1ES

(01289) 308013

5 changing beers (sourced nationally)

There is an Old Curiosity Shop-ambience to this pub, located in the old part of Berwick next to the original road bridge over the Tweed. A downstairs bar is used by DJs and bands at weekends. Outside is a unique open drinking area surrounded by high walls. A former CAMRA award winner.

Curfew

46A Bridge Street, TD15 1AQ

07842 912268

4 changing beers (sourced nationally)

Established for five years, Berwick's first micropub is located up a small lane which opens out into a large courtyard off Bridge Street. It has a small bar area with a bottle fridge to one side, offering interesting local keg beers and foreign bottles. The courtyard makes a pleasant outdoor drinking area in summer. Excellent pork pies are available. CAMRA Northumberland Pub of the Year in 2018. Q

Pilot

31 Low Greens, TD15 1LZ (from station take road opp Castle Hotel towards coast)

(01289) 304214

3 changing beers (sourced nationally)

Popular with locals and sought out by train trippers who have heard about this gem. The friendly bar staff provide a warm welcome to all. The stone-built end-of-terrace pub dates from the 19th century and has a regionally important historic interior. It retains the original small room layout and boasts several nautical artefacts over 100 years old. It is home to a darts team and hosts music nights.

Blanchland

Lord Crewe Arms

The Square, DH8 9SP

(01434) 677100 lordcrewearmsblanchland.co.uk

4 changing beers (sourced nationally; often Twice Brewed Brew House)

In the centre of the village, this ancient building is now a multi-roomed pub with the bar in a medieval vaulted room. Downstairs has flagstone floors and dogs are welcome. The restaurant upstairs has fine moorland views. Real fires give the stone rooms a welcoming warmth. P

Carterway Heads

Manor House Inn

DH8 9LX (on A68 S of Corbridge)

(01207) 255268 themanorhouseinn.com

Timothy Taylor Landlord; 3 changing beers (sourced nationally)

A warm and hospitable country inn with three open fires. A double-glazed window in the bar wall allows customers to view the well-maintained cellar. Good home-cooked food is on offer and popular both with tourists and locals. There are superb views over the valley from the rear beer garden. Derwent Reservoir is nearby. Excellent accommodation is available.

P

Corbridge

Angel of Corbridge

Main Street, NE45 5LA

(01434) 632119 theangelofcorbridge.com

Great Corby Corby Ale; Hadrian Border Tyneside Blonde; house beer (by Wylam); 3 changing beers (sourced locally)

Superb old coaching inn dating from 1726 on the main road with good transport links. Seven handpulls are on the bar and a wonderful selection of malt whiskies is also kept. Family-friendly and with a reputation for good food, the pub is popular with tourists, ramblers and locals. The lounge area has comfy leather seating and outside is a relaxed seating area. Q P

Elsdon

Bird in Bush

Village Green, NE19 1AA

(01830) 520804

4 changing beers (sourced locally)

This inn, in the north-west corner of the green in this quiet village, reopened two years ago. Now fully restored, it offers beers from a wide range of sources including from the on-site brewery, so look out for First and Last ales at the bar. Food is served Friday to Sunday and accommodation is available. P

Embleton

Greys Inn

Stanley Terrace, NE66 3UZ

(01665) 576983

5 changing beers (sourced locally)

Pleasant, traditional inn in a lovely seaside hamlet, just a short walk to a wonderful beach. It has three open fires, and is home to a ladies' darts team, clay pigeon club and golf club. Winter hours may vary.

(418,X18)

Etal

Black Bull

TD12 4TL

(01890) 820200 theblackbulletal.co.uk

House beer (by Cheviot); 2 changing beers (sourced locally; often Cheviot)

Northumberland's only thatched pub was fully renovated and reopened in 2018 in an attractive modern style, following a prolonged closure. An exposed roof structure adds to the charm. Comfortable modern pale-wood furniture features throughout the spacious, open-plan interior. Three handpumps serve real ales exclusively from Cheviot Brewery, with a special dark bitter made for the pub. There is a function room and large outdoor seating area. P (267)

Featherstone

Wallace Arms

Rowfoot, NE49 0JF

(01434) 298921

Allendale Pennine Pale; Great North Eastern Rivet Catcher; 2 changing beers (sourced nationally)

Cosy country pub warmed by real fires, with no jukebox or fruit machines. Split over two levels and three rooms, it has a traditional bar area and various spaces. The welcoming landlady is always prepared to open early for groups of walkers, preferably if arranged in advance. Opening hours are reduced in winter – check ahead.

Q P

Greenhaugh

Holly Bush Inn

NE48 1PW

☎ (01434) 240391 hollybushinn.net

High House Farm Nel's Best; 1 changing beer (sourced nationally) Ⓗ

Independently owned pub, over 300 years old and set in the heart of the Northumberland National Park and the Dark Sky Park, making it ideal for those with an interest in real ale and real stars. No TV and no mobile reception make for a peaceful drinking experience. The pub hosts informal jam sessions – bring your instrument if you like. **Q** **P**

Hexham

Dipton Mill Inn

Dipton Mill Road, NE46 1YA

☎ (01434) 606577 diptonmill.co.uk

Hexhamshire Blackhall English Stout, Devil's Elbow, Devil's Water, Old Humbug, Shire Bitter, Whapweasel Ⓗ

The tap for Hexhamshire Brewery, now located in the beer garden, this small inn is run by real ale enthusiasts who brew their own excellent beers. Blackhall English Stout has proved so popular with drinkers that it has ousted Guinness. To complement the ales there is great home-cooked food – Saturday is curry night. A cosy atmosphere and warm welcome make this pub well worth seeking out. Local CAMRA Pub of the Year 2020. **Q** **P**

Heart of Northumberland

5 Market Street, NE46 3NS

☎ (01434) 608013 thehearthexham.com

Timothy Taylor Landlord; 4 changing beers (sourced locally) Ⓗ

Five handpumps, four selling local ales, adorn the bar in this food-led pub. The single large room is divided almost in two near the end of the bar, with wooden floors throughout. A blazing fire in the six-foot open fireplace warms things nicely in the back room. Excellent food is served.

High Newton-by-the-Sea

Joiners Arms

Town Square, NE66 3EA

☎ (01665) 576112 Joiners-arms.com

House beer (by Anarchy); 3 changing beers (sourced locally; often Alnwick) Ⓗ

Eighteenth-century former manor house, tastefully restored and refurbished following closure for two years. Set in a pleasant hamlet on the B1340, the pub portrays a typical Northumbrian scene with outdoor seating overlooking the small picturesque green. The house ale, St Mary's, reflects the name of the local church and for every pint sold a donation is made towards the church upkeep. The Joiners describes itself as a gastro-pub, but offers a takeaway menu as well. Five en-suite bedrooms are fitted out to a high standard. **P** (418)

Holy Island

Crown & Anchor Hotel

Market Place, TD15 2RX (check tidetable for causeway crossing times)

☎ (01289) 389215 holyislandcrown.co.uk

Hadrian Border Secret Kingdom, Tyneside Blonde; 1 changing beer (sourced locally) Ⓗ

Exposed floorboards and wooden tables and benches provide comfortable seating in the cosy bar – note the Gothic carving of a local monk in the corner. There is a comfortable sitting room to the rear. The large beer garden provides scenic views to Lindisfarne Castle and the ruined priory to the rear of the pub. (477)

Humshaugh

Crown Inn

NE46 4AG

☎ (01434) 681231 crowninnhumshaugh.co.uk

Hadrian Border Tyneside Blonde; 3 changing beers (sourced nationally) Ⓗ

A traditional village pub in the centre of the beautiful village of Humshaugh, five miles north of the market town of Hexham. The Crown has a homely charm, with a wood-burning stove, cask ales and traditional home-cooked food. Simple guest accommodation is offered in comfortable rooms, ideal for those wishing to explore Hadrian's Wall. (680)

Low Newton-by-the-Sea

Ship Inn

Newton Square, NE66 3EL

☎ (01665) 576262 shipinnnewton.co.uk

Ship Inn Sea Coal, Sea Wheat; 4 changing beers (sourced nationally) Ⓗ

This small pub nestles in the corner of three sides of a square of former fishermen's cottages, a few yards from the beach. It attracts drinkers seeking ales from the in-house microbrewery, diners enjoying an excellent menu featuring fresh local ingredients, and walkers exploring the local scenery. A public car park is close by at the top of the hill. Opening times may vary in winter; phone ahead if travelling. **Q**

Lowick

Black Bull

Main Street, TD15 2UA

☎ (01289) 388375 blackbulllowick.co.uk

4 changing beers (sourced locally) Ⓗ

The pub closed in 2014 after several years of brewery ownership and was declared an asset of community value in 2015 after much campaigning by the local people. In the same year a family business created to support rural and community development in Northumberland acquired the freehold. Through the efforts of family, friends, volunteers and local contractors, the pub was totally refurbished and reopened as a premium country inn in 2017. **P** (464)

Morpeth

Office

The Toll House, Castle Square, NE61 1YL

☎ 07957 721066

8 changing beers (sourced locally) Ⓗ

A micropub with no music or games machines. It features eight handpulls and three craft keg beers, all of local origin, and three real ciders served on gravity from the glass-fronted fridge opposite the bar. No food is available. Local CAMRA Pub of the Year 2020. **Q**

Norham

Masons Arms

17 West Street, TD15 2LB

☎ (01289) 382326 ⊕ themasonsarmsnorham.co.uk
Allendale Wagtail Best Bitter; 3 changing beers (sourced nationally) Ⓗ
The cosy wood-panelled public bar, with a real fire at its heart, is the hub of this pub. Photos of bygone Norham adorn the walls, along with collections of fishing gear and joinery tools, and an old Younger's brewery mirror. The area is popular with tourists – nearby are a ruined castle and the railway station museum. Close to the Tweed Cycle Way and bus stop. ⚙🍴♣🚌(67)

Old Hartley

Delaval Arms 🅛
NE26 4RL
☎ (0191) 237 0489 ⊕ thedelavalarms.wordpress.com
4 changing beers (sourced nationally) Ⓗ
Multi-roomed Grade II listed building dating from 1748, with a listed WWI water storage tower (part of Roberts Battery) behind the beer garden. It is the first pub in Northumberland for those following the coastal route. Good-quality, affordable meals complement the beer, with guest ales coming from local micros. To the left as you enter is a room served through a hatch from the bar and to the right a room where children are welcome. Q🐕⚙🍴P🚌(308,309) ♿

Once Brewed

Twice Brewed Inn 🅛 ✅
Miltary Road, Bardon Mill, NE47 7AN (on B6318 Military Rd)
☎ (01434) 344534 ⊕ twicebrewedinn.co.uk
6 changing beers (sourced nationally; often Twice Brewed Brew House) Ⓗ
A excellent remote inn on the Military Road, with Hadrian's Wall, Steel Rigg and Vindolanda nearby, attracting walkers and tourists. It has a fully refurbished bar area and offers a wide range of bottled beers from around the world. It has full wheelchair access and welcomes dogs. B&B is offered in 18 en-suite bedrooms. The Twice Brewed Brew House started producing its own beers in 2017, using water from its own well. Q🐕⚙🍴◑♿ÅP🚌♿🎵📶

Rothbury

Narrow Nick 🅛
High Street, NE65 7TB
☎ 07707 703182
6 changing beers (sourced locally) Ⓗ
The micropub in this market town opened in 2016 in what was previously a clothes shop. The front windows feature Art Deco-style stained glass. The single room has the bar at one side sporting six handpumps offering a range of local brewery beers. A large range of gins is also kept. Wooden bar-back fittings have recently been added. Winter opening times may vary. Q♿🚌♿

Seahouses

Olde Ship Inn 🅛
7-9 Main Street, NE68 7RD
☎ (01665) 720200 ⊕ seahouses.co.uk
Black Sheep Best Bitter; Courage Directors; Hadrian Border Farne Island Pale Ale; Morland Old Speckled Hen; Ruddles County; Theakston Best Bitter; 4 changing beers (sourced nationally) Ⓗ
This farmhouse, built in 1745, was converted to the licensed trade in 1812 and has a regionally important historic pub interior. Family owned since 1910, the pub has three quality bars adorned with a veritable treasure

trove of 19th and 20th century maritime memorabilia. Fully residential, it offers an interesting menu of fish, fresh crab meals and snacks. Q🐕⚙🍴◑♿♣♿P🚌(418,X18)

Seaton Sluice

Melton Constable ✅
Beresford Road, NE26 4QL
☎ (0191) 237 7741 ⊕ themeltonconstable.co.uk
Adnams Southwold Bitter, Broadside; Ossett Yorkshire Blonde; 2 changing beers (sourced nationally) Ⓗ
Large roadside pub a few minutes' walk from the beach and local history sights. It is named after the southern seat of Lord Hastings, a member of the Delaval family – Delaval Hall is close by. Tuesday is steak night, Wednesday is quiz night, Sunday evening features live music. A fishing club meets here late at night and the BSA owners' club gets together on the first and third Thursdays of the month. 🐕⚙◑♿P🚌♿📶

Wark on Tyne

Battlesteads Hotel 🅛 ✅
NE48 3LS
☎ (01434) 230209 ⊕ battlesteads.com
4 changing beers Ⓗ
Well-appointed 1747 converted farmhouse near Hexham with a superb rear walled garden, restaurant, large conservatory and accommodation. The five handpulls provide an excellent choice of beers, all in tiptop condition. Ingredients for the quality menu come from within a 25-mile radius, including home-grown fruit and vegetables. Accommodation includes ground-floor rooms with wheelchair access. Handy for PlusBus via Hexham rail station. 🐕⚙🍴◑♿Å♿P🚌(680)♿📶

West Thirston

Northumberland Arms 🅛 ✅
The Peth, NE65 9EE
☎ (01670) 787370 ⊕ northumberlandarms-felton.co.uk
3 changing beers (sourced nationally; often Allendale) Ⓗ
This fine stone pub was originally a coaching inn in the 1820s for Hugh Percy, 3rd Duke of Northumberland. The building has been lovingly restored in an eclectic style while remaining warm, comfortable and welcoming. Bare stone walls and real fires add to the ambience. A large function room caters for groups of up to 30. The beer range is predominantly from local breweries. 🐕⚙🍴◑P🚌(X15)

Wylam

Boathouse 🅛
Station Road, NE41 8HR
☎ (01661) 853431
12 changing beers (sourced nationally) Ⓗ
Superb two-roomed pub with 15 handpulls, three dedicated to cider, with more ciders in the cellar. Beers are sourced locally and nationwide, and on bank holidays themed beer festivals are held. Toasties and sandwiches are available during the day. The pub is a popular stopping-off point for Whistle Stops II travellers. Fifteen CAMRA awards cover one wall including North-East Regional Pub of the Year. Alternate Tuesdays are buskers' nights. Q🐕⚙🌾♣♿P♿📶

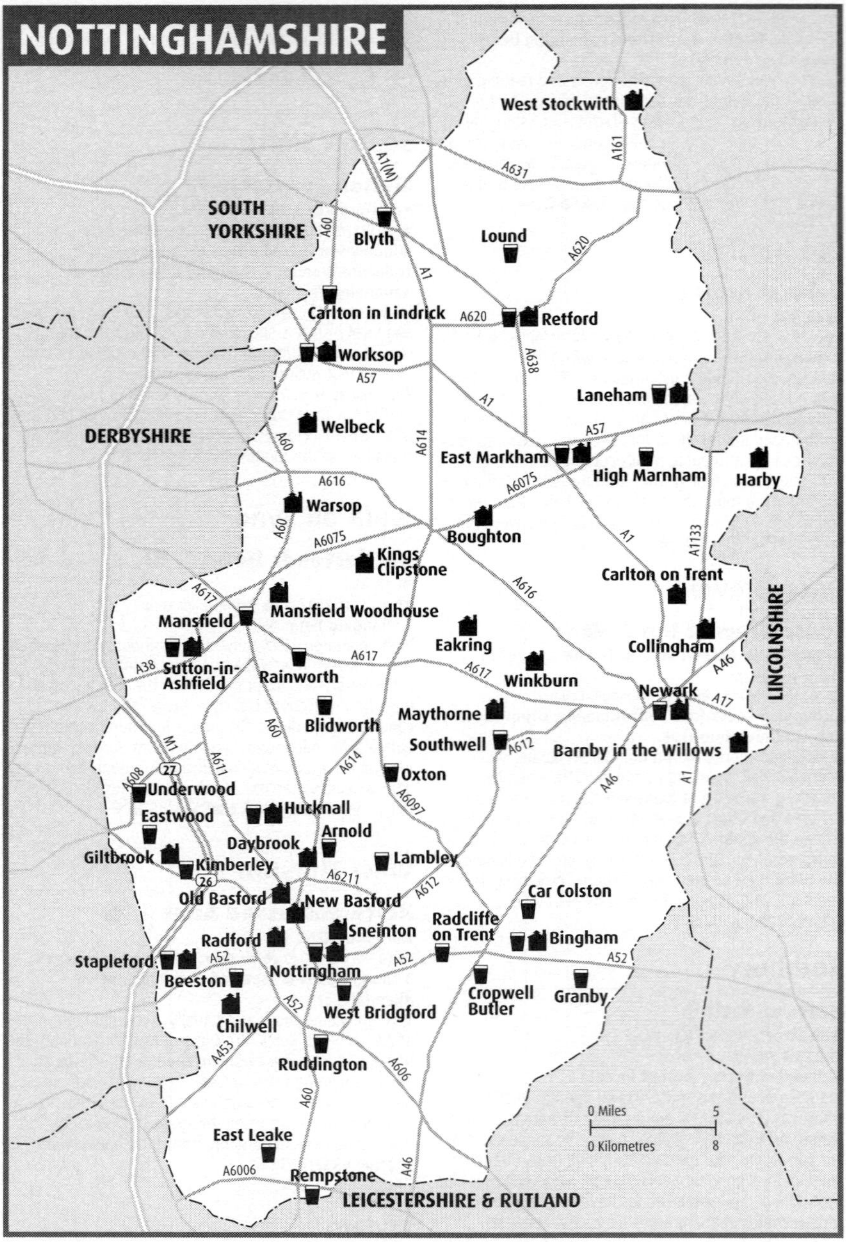

Arnold

Abdication

89 Mansfield Road, Daybrook, NG5 6BH

theabdication.co.uk

4 changing beers H

Originally built in 1936/37, this modern, independent micropub, opened in 2014, is part of the Home Brewery Coronation Buildings, opposite the gates of the former brewery, and was for many years a shop. The four changing cask ales, four craft beers and three ciders are from microbreweries, small producers or the on-site Good Stuff nanobrewery, and come in a mix of styles. An archway divides the single room, giving an appearance of a much larger area. **Q**

Robin Hood & Little John

1 Church Street, NG5 8FD (on corner of Cross St)

(0115) 920 1054 therobinhoodandlittlejohn.co.uk

Everards Tiger; Lincoln Green Marion, Archer, Tuck; 10 changing beers H

Former Home Brewery pub now operated by Lincoln Green and Everards breweries. The bar features Home Ales memorabilia, while the lounge has details of the pub's history and the local area. The rear courtyard has outdoor seating and a covered skittles alley. Along with 10 real ale pumps in each bar offering microbrewery beers, the real cider wall has four taps dispensing real ciders from small local producers and further afield.

Beeston

Crown Inn ★ L

Church Street, NG9 1FY

☎ (0115) 967 8623

Blue Monkey Infinity; Brewsters Hophead; Dancing Duck Nice Weather; Everards Sunchaser, Tiger; Nottingham Rock Ale Mild Beer; 8 changing beers H

Nineteenth-century, Grade II listed alehouse, acquired and sympathetically refurbished by Everards. Up to 14 ales and several real ciders and perries are served at this former East Midlands CAMRA Pub of the Year. An outside bar opens during the summer, extending the range to 22 beers. Inside, there are five distinct drinking areas including a snug and three-seat 'confessional', once used as a hideaway by the local vicar. Although busy, the pub retains a community feel, with a cosy atmosphere throughout. Substantial snacks are available.

Q P

Star Inn L

22 Middle Street, NG9 1FX

☎ (0115) 854 5320 starbeeston.co.uk

10 changing beers H

Former Shipstone's pub still with branded windows, restored beyond its former glory. The decor is tasteful and minimal with three separate rooms, complemented by a permanent marquee, sports/games room, spacious garden and patio outside. The bar featured in Boon and Auf Wiedersehen, Pet. Ten cask ales are on offer as well as a wide selection of whiskies, gins, rums and wines. Pizzas are served along with a range of traditional bar snacks. Families are welcome during the day. Local CAMRA LocAle Pub of the Year 2019.

P

Victoria Hotel L

85 Dovecote Lane, NG9 1JG

☎ (0115) 925 4049 victoriabeeston.co.uk

Castle Rock Harvest Pale; Fuller's London Pride; 11 changing beers H

A genuine free house located alongside the platform of Beeston railway station, this restored Victorian masterpiece has mass appeal. Thirteen real ales are joined by real ciders and perries, an extensive whisky and wine list, and a renowned food menu. Taster trays of three third-pints are offered. Two distinct bars are complemented by a dining room and a covered, smoke-free seating area outside. VicFest is hosted in July in addition to beer festivals throughout the year.

Q P

Bingham

Horse & Plough L

Long Acre, NG13 8AF

☎ (01949) 839313

Castle Rock Harvest Pale, Preservation; 7 changing beers H

In the heart of a busy market town, this small pub was once a Methodist chapel, with a traditional interior and flagstone floor. A terrace was added in 2019. Up to nine cask ales and four ciders are available in a wide range of styles and strengths, showcasing smaller producers alongside established favourites. Pub meals are served in the bar and the restaurant upstairs offers a varied seasonal menu. Four times local CAMRA Pub of the Year.

Wheatsheaf

Long Acre, NG13 8BG

☎ (01949) 837430 thewheatsheafbingham.co.uk

Shipstones Original; 6 changing beers H

The Wheatsheaf reverted to its traditional name when it reopened in 2016 under new ownership. Ten handpumps offer a changing range of cask ales and ciders. Food is served lunchtimes and evenings both in the bar and the separate restaurant. The pub has a real fire in the bar, a fantastic outdoor terrace and hosts live music every week. A former regional CAMRA Cider Pub of the Year. P

Blidworth

Black Bull

Main Street, NG21 0QH

☎ (01623) 490222 blackbullblidworth.co.uk

5 changing beers H

REAL ALE BREWERIES

Angel Nottingham
Beermats Winkburn
Beeston Hop Nottingham: Sneinton
Black Iris Nottingham: New Basford
Black Market Warsop
Blue Monkey Nottingham: Giltbrook
Brewhouse & Kitchen Nottingham
Castle Rock Nottingham
Cat Asylum Collingham
Dukeries Worksop
FireRock Sutton in Ashfield
Fish Key Nottingham (NEW)
Full Mash Stapleford
Good Stuff Nottingham: Daybrook
Grafton Worksop
Handley's Barnby in the Willows
Harby Harby
Harrison's Retford
Idle West Stockwith
Kings Clipstone Kings Clipstone
Lazy Bay Nottingham
Lenton Lane Nottingham
Lincoln Green Nottingham: Hucknall
Linear Bingham
Liquid Light Nottingham
Lord Randalls Newark
Magpie Nottingham
Mallard Maythorne
Maypole Eakring
Milestone Newark
Navigation Nottingham
Neon Raptor Nottingham
Newark Newark
Nottingham Nottingham: Radford
Pheasantry East Markham
Prior's Well Mansfield Woodhouse
Reality Nottingham: Chilwell
Rufford Abbey Boughton
Scribblers Stapleford
Scruffy Dog Sutton-In-Ashfield
Shipstone's Nottingham: Old Basford
Springhead Laneham
Tom Herrick's Carlton on Trent
Vaguely Bingham (NEW)
Welbeck Abbey Welbeck

Refurbished, family-owned pub offering a warm welcome to locals and visitors. The large bar room serves up to five rotating guest beers, some of which are brewed in Nottinghamshire. The restaurant offers good English food and more adventurous meals including vegetarian options, plus traditional roasts on Sundays. The menu changes reflecting seasonal availability, using ingredients freshly sourced from local suppliers. Dogs are allowed in the bar only. The pub opens early for breakfast, and B&B is available in four rooms.
❀♿P🚌(141) 🐾 📶

Blyth

Red Hart [L]

Bawtry Road, S81 8HG (opp church)
☎ (01909) 591221 🌐 redhart.co.uk
3 changing beers (sourced regionally) [H]
An attractive village pub in the centre of Blyth with a lounge, a traditional taproom – with a pool table, darts and sports TV – a dining room, and a spacious seating area outside. The walls in the lounge are decorated with photographs and paintings of nearby locations. Three changing beers are available and food is served daily.
Q❀♿♣P🚌(25,29) 🐾 📶

Car Colston

Royal Oak 🏆 ✔

The Green, NG13 8JE
☎ (01949) 20247 🌐 royaloakcarcolston.co.uk
Bombardier; Wainwright; 2 changing beers [H]
This country inn – a former hosiery factory – is on one of England's largest village greens. The pub has a cosy bar with comfortable seating and a real fire, a separate, generously sized restaurant and a function room. Four beers, all from the Marston's range but often less-heralded brews, are available in the bar. Food is served lunchtimes and evenings. There is a skittle alley to the rear, a beer garden and camping facilities.
❀♿Ă♣P🐾 📶

Carlton in Lindrick

Grey Horses Inn [L]

The Cross, S81 9EW (in centre of old village)
☎ (01909) 730252
Welbeck Abbey Henrietta, Portland Black; house beer (by Welbeck Abbey); 3 changing beers (sourced regionally) [H]
The Grey Horses is situated at the heart of the village within the conservation area, and has a front bar accessible from the street, a spacious lounge bar where excellent food is served and a large beer garden. The pub is the tap for Welbeck Abbey Brewery, serving three or four of its beers plus two or three guests. It hosts an annual beer festival, usually in June. A warm welcome is assured at this recent local CAMRA award-winning hostelry. Q❀♿♣P🚌(21,22)🐾 📶

Cropwell Butler

Plough [L] ✔

Main Street, NG12 3AB
☎ (0115) 933 3124 🌐 theplough-cropwellbutler.co.uk
Adnams Ghost Ship; Bradfield Farmers Blonde; Sharp's Doom Bar; 1 changing beer [H]
Set in the centre of the village, this pub has a welcoming interior with real fires in both the bar and larger restaurant. The spacious beer garden provides a picturesque setting in summer. Four cask ales are available including one LocAle. A full lunchtime and evening food service is provided. Regular quiz nights take place, often combined with themed food menus.
❀♿♣P🚌(100) 📶

East Leake

Nag's Head [L]

14 Main Street, LE12 6PG
☎ (01509) 854016
Charnwood Salvation, Vixen; Sharp's Doom Bar; 3 changing beers (sourced regionally) [H]
Refurbished fairly recently, this cosy village pub offers two rooms – one split-level, the other small. Both rooms are furnished in a contemporary manner yet retain a rustic feel with real fires. To the rear is an attractive garden. A good range of local and guest beers is served, along with simple bar snacks. Music nights are a regular feature here. A pool table is available.
Q❀♣P🚌🐾 📶

Round RobINN [L]

54 Main Street, LE12 6PG
☎ (0115) 778 8168
6 changing beers (sourced locally) [G]
Micropub opened in 2015, serving six local beers on gravity, cooled on racks behind the bar. A range of ciders and continental bottled beers are also available. The single room accommodates up to 45 patrons – seating is a mixture of chairs, cushioned benches and high stools. A small outdoor area to the front offers alfresco drinking. Light bar snacks are served. Q♿♣🚌(1)🐾

East Markham

Queen's Hotel

High Street, NG22 0RE
☎ (01777) 870288
Adnams Southwold Bitter; Everards Beacon Hill, Tiger; 2 changing beers (sourced regionally) [H]
This cosy pub has a warm, friendly atmosphere enhanced by an open fire in winter. A single bar with five handpumps serves the lounge and dining areas. Food ranges from hot and cold snacks to full home-cooked meals. There is a large garden area at the rear of the car park. The Queen's has received several local CAMRA awards. Q❀♿P🚌(136,37)🐾

Eastwood

Gamekeeper's [L]

136 Nottingham Road, NG16 3GD
5 changing beers [H]
This micropub in the centre of Eastwood opened in 2017. It serves up to five ales, mainly local ones. The bar is at the back to the right; a seating area is at the front, along with an alcove area to the left. There is also a small garden/patio area outside at the rear. Pub snacks are normally available. Q❀♿🚌🐾 📶

Tap & Growler

209 Nottingham Road, Hill Top, NG16 3GS
🌐 tapandgrowler.co.uk
8 changing beers (sourced locally) [H]/[G]
Situated in a row of shops, this welcoming micropub sells a range of mostly local real ales, five on handpump and up to five more on gravity. The pub gets its name not just from the growler beer jug – when the building was renovated a ceramic lion was found and it is now proudly on display as The Growler. A pub quiz is held on Monday. There is a fine hidden garden at the rear. A former winner of Nottingham CAMRA LocAle Pub of the Year.
Q❀♿♣🚌🐾 📶

Granby

Marquis of Granby

Dragon Street, NG13 9PN
☎ (01949) 859517
Brewsters Hophead, Marquis; 4 changing beers 🄷
Believed to be the original Marquis of Granby, dating back to 1760 or earlier, this small two-roomed pub is the brewery tap for Brewsters – usually serving four, but up to six, cask ales. Guest beers mostly come from microbreweries, and include a mild, stout or porter. York stone floors complement the yew bar tops and wood-beamed rooms, period wallpaper features throughout and the lounge has a welcoming open fire in the winter months. Q❀♿♣P🚌🐾📶

High Marnham

Brownlow Arms

NG23 6SG (on edge of village)
☎ (01636) 822505 🌐 thebrownlowarms.co.uk
Everards Tiger; Greene King Abbot; 1 changing beer (sourced locally) 🄷
A friendly rural pub beside the River Trent dating back hundreds of years and fully restored in 1996 following a fire. The traditional free house offers two regular and one changing ale. The extensive menu features good and reasonably priced meals. The pub is within easy access of Retford, Lincoln and Newark and has its own caravan park adjacent and fishing. Q❀◑♿▲♣P🐾

Hucknall

Byron's Rest 🄻

8 Baker Street, NG15 7AS
Titanic Plum Porter; 7 changing beers (often Magpie) 🄷
A sewing shop that was turned into a micropub in 2018. Typical of a medieval burgage plot, it is narrow in width but extends considerably to a newly repositioned bar and comfortable bench seating at the rear, creating the illusion of separate drinking areas. A snug just off the entrance provides further seating. At the rear, a secret garden has been created – a tranquil oasis in the heart of the town. Up to eight real ales are served.
Q❀≠♣●🚌🐾📶

Kimberley

Roots Emporium

17 Nottingham Road, NG16 2NB
☎ 07864 572037
6 changing beers 🄷
Converted from a furniture and gift shop, much of this micropub's fixtures and fittings are made from the stock of the former business. The open-plan interior is small but reasonably spacious, with a patio at the front extending the drinking area further. Walls are adorned with interesting memorabilia including items relating to the former Kimberley Brewery. Beers are generally from microbreweries, always including at least one local brew.
Q❀♿♣●🚌🐾

Lambley

Woodlark Inn 🄻

Church Street, NG4 4QB
☎ (0115) 931 2535 🌐 woodlarkinn.co.uk
Theakston Best Bitter; Timothy Taylor Landlord; 4 changing beers (often Fish Key) 🄷
Located in the quaint-sounding Dumbles area of the village, this traditional pub dating back to the 19th century is the home of the Fish Key microbrewery. It is popular both with locals and visitors from afar. There are two rooms – a bare red-brick bar with exposed beams and a lounge/restaurant serving excellent home-cooked food. A music-free environment enables customers and staff to enjoy the art of conversation.
Q❀◑♣●P🚌(46,47) 🐾📶

Laneham

Bees Knees 🄻

Springhead Brewery, Robin Hood Site, Main Street, DN22 0NA (centre of village)
☎ (01777) 228090 🌐 springhead.co.uk
Abbeydale Daily Bread, Moonshine, Absolution; Oakham Citra; Pheasantry Dancing Dragonfly; 5 changing beers 🄷
A popular country pub with three small rooms converted from a shop on the Springhead Fine Ales brewery site and well supported by locals. It serves five regular ales and up to five rotating guests. Over 100 gins are also available. Excellent food is served (booking recommended). Quiz night is Wednesday and live jazz plays on the first Sunday of the month. There is an adequate outside seating area. A former local CAMRA award winner. Q◑♿▲●P🚌🐾📶

Lound

Bluebell Inn

Town Street, DN22 8RN (on main road through village)
☎ (01777) 818457 🌐 bluebellinnretford.co.uk
3 changing beers (sourced locally)
A traditional village inn with a lounge bar where food is served and a taproom with a pool table. The pub has a good reputation for the quality of its food and beers which rotate on demand. There is a large car park and a fenced seating area outside. French boules is played in the summer on Wednesday and Sunday. Wednesday is quiz night. Q❀🛏◑♿♣P🚌🐾📶

Mansfield

Bold Forester ✔

Botany Avenue, NG18 5NF
☎ (01623) 623970
Greene King IPA, Abbot; Hardys & Hansons Olde Trip; Morland Old Speckled Hen; 8 changing beers 🄷
Hungry Horse-branded pub and restaurant offering up to 12 real ales. Food is served daily. The open-plan interior has large-screen TVs showing most major sports. The beer garden is popular with families in the summer. Situated on the main road into Mansfield, it has a large car park and regular bus services passing the door.
❀◑♿≠♣●P🚌📶

Brown Cow

31 Radcliffe Gate, NG18 2JA
☎ (01623) 645854
Everards Tiger; 9 changing beers (often Silver) 🄷
Owned by Everards brewery and run by Silver Brewhouse as a Project William business. A range of up to 12 real ales is offered alongside ciders and international bottled beers. There are two separate bar areas and a function room upstairs. The pub is a short walk from the town centre. Q❀🛏◑≠♣●P🚌🐾📶

Garrison

Leeming Street, NG18 1NA
☎ (07702) 253235
Moody Fox Cub, Pale Tale; 4 changing beers 🄷

This is the brewery tap for the Moody Fox brewery based nearby in Hilcote. It is inspired by TV show Peaky Blinders, with some beer names reflecting the theme. Six real ales and a range of ciders are available. Located in the pedestrianised area of the town centre, it is a five-minute walk from public car parks. Q

Railway Inn

9 Station Street, NG18 1EF

(01623) 623086

4 changing beers

Close to the town centre bus and train stations, this community pub serves popular home-cooked meals. As well as the main bar area there are two separate rooms for diners or those looking for a quieter space. Up to four real ales and one or two real ciders are offered. The walled garden is popular in the summer.

Q

Redgate

189 Westfield Lane, NG19 6EH

(01623) 624406

3 changing beers

A community-focused pub with a spacious lounge, a separate restaurant area serving popular home-cooked food and a skittles alley. Darts and dominoes are also played. Sports memorabilia is on display in the main bar/lounge. Three regularly changing real ales are offered from local and national breweries. Dogs are allowed in the bar area only. Q (6,23B)

Newark

Flying Circus

53 Castle Gate, NG24 1BE

(01636) 302444 flyingcircuspub.co.uk

4 changing beers (sourced nationally)

Reopened in its present incarnation in 2014, the pub walls are decorated with Monty Python quotes and brewery logos, and old aircraft are suspended from the ceiling. The four changing cask ales are complemented by a wide range of keg, bottled and canned craft beers, plus real ciders and perries. More beers may be available when the pub holds one of its many special musical events, including some served by gravity from the Barrel House to the rear of the building.

Fox & Crown

4-6 Appletongate, NG24 1JY

(01636) 605820

Castle Rock Harvest Pale, Preservation, Elsie Mo; 7 changing beers (sourced nationally)

Town centre local offering up to 10 real ales on handpump, mostly from the Castle Rock portfolio, as well as two draught craft beers and around 50 artisan beers in bottles and cans. Up to 20 traditional ciders and perries are served by gravity from a cool room. The interior is open-plan with a central bar and three side rooms. Entertainment includes an open mic night on Wednesday and occasional bands. Traditional pub food and light bites are served daily. A former CAMRA Pub and Cider Pub of the Year. Q (1,2)

Just Beer Micropub

32A Castle Gate, NG24 1BG (in Swan & Salmon Yard off Castle Gate)

(01636) 312047 justbeermicropub.biz

4 changing beers (sourced nationally)

Micropub offering a varied range of cask ale, craft beer, cider and perry, including world and unusual UK craft ales from the fridge. Several beer festivals are held throughout the year. Snacks include local pork pies, cheeseboards and pork scratchings. Traditional pub games are played, with an annual cribbage tournament. Two times regional CAMRA Pub of the Year and seven times Newark Pub of the Year. Q

Organ Grinder

21 Portland Street, NG24 4XF

(01636) 671768

Blue Monkey BG Sips, Funky Gibbon, Infinity, Chocolate Guerilla, Ape Ale; 1 changing beer (sourced regionally)

Opened as the Organ Grinder in 2014, this no-nonsense beer-drinking pub offers six or seven real ales from Blue Monkey and an occasional guest ale. A range of bottled beers is also stocked. Bar snacks are served to accompany the ales. The Monkey Room is adorned with film and music posters with monkey and ape references. Books, games and a piano are available for customer use. A covered smoking area is to the rear.

Prince Rupert

46 Stodman Street, NG24 1AW

(01636) 918121 kneadpubs.co.uk

Brains Rev James; Oakham JHB; 4 changing beers (sourced nationally)

Reopened in 2010, this historic pub dates back to around 1452. Multi-roomed on two separate levels, exposed beams are evident in several rooms and various interesting artefacts and brewery memorabilia decorate the walls and ceilings. The Nelson Room has an open fire. An extensive lunchtime and evening menu featuring fresh local produce is available, with stone-baked pizzas a speciality. A former local CAMRA Pub of the Year, it has featured in the Guide for 10 consecutive years.

Q

Nottingham: Central

Barrel Drop

7 Hurts Yard, NG1 6JD (in passageway off Upper Parliament St)

(0115) 924 3018

5 changing beers (often Magpie)

City-centre micropub opened in 2014 but taken over by the local Magpie Brewery in 2018. Five beers are available from Magpie and other microbreweries around the country. There are also several taps dispensing keg beers and real ciders. Tucked away in Hurts Yard, it has steps leading down to the bar and a side room to the right. A further room leads off from the bar.

Q

BeerHeadZ

Cabman's Shelter, 1A Queens Road, NG2 3AS (adjoining Nottingham Station)

07914 136055

5 changing beers

Small but sympathetically restored Edwardian cabman's shelter, adjacent to the main railway station entrance. It is run by BeerHeadZ, who operate similar outlets across the east Midlands. The single room has a central bar and retains period features including bench chests, wooden panelling, windows and coat hooks. Beer barrels with wooden tops serve as seats. The four real ales change regularly, and are seldom repeated. A large choice of bottles and cans is also available to enjoy in or take out.

Q

Fox & Grapes

21 Southwell Road, NG1 1DL

(0115) 841 8970

Castle Rock Harvest Pale, Preservation, Elsie Mo; 5 changing beers

An impressive renovation of an Edwardian-fronted Victorian inn by Castle Rock Brewery in 2017. The former two-room layout has been opened up into a single L-shaped room with raised areas on either side of the front door. A high ceiling and large windows give a light, airy feel. Sadly the fancy Edwardian window frames were lost in an earlier refit. The pub serves eight real ales, eight keg beers and ciders plus locally produced coffee, gin and artisan food. ☋❀◑♿⚐●🚌🐾📶

King William IV 𝕃

6 Eyre Street, Sneinton, NG2 4PB

☎ (0115) 958 9864 🌐 thekingbilly.co.uk

Oakham Citra, Bishops Farewell; house beer (by Black Iris); 6 changing beers ⊞

Known widely as the King Billy, this Victorian gem on the edge of the city centre is close to the Motorpoint Arena. A family-run free house that oozes charm and character, it is a haven for real ale drinkers, with a choice of up to eight microbrewery ales from near and far, as well as real cider. Folk music is popular on Thursday night. Take a look at the award-winning pub sign.
Q☋❀♣●🚌(43,44) 🐾📶

Lincolnshire Poacher 𝕃

161-163 Mansfield Road, NG1 3FR

☎ (0115) 941 1584

Castle Rock Harvest Pale, Preservation, Sherwood Reserve, Elsie Mo, Screech Owl; 8 changing beers ⊞

Thirteen handpumps offer a wide selection of guest ales, mainly from microbreweries. A mild, stout or porter is always available alongside real ciders and perries, continental bottled beers and a fine selection of whiskies. The food menu features locally sourced ingredients. The pub displays artwork celebrating its long-standing twinning with In de Wildeman bar in Amsterdam, and various memorabilia of local and international interest. Live music plays on Sunday and Wednesday. Q❀◑♿⚐♣●🚌🐾📶

Newshouse 𝕃

123 Canal Street, NG1 7HB

☎ (0115) 952 3061

Burton Bridge XL Bitter; Castle Rock Harvest Pale; Totally Brewed Slap in the Face; 2 changing beers (sourced locally) ⊞

In times past, newspapers would be read out here to inform the illiterate of elections at home and military victories overseas, hence the name. The walls are covered with framed front pages of local newspapers showing headlines going back over many years. The public bar has a large TV screen, dartboard, bar billiards and table skittles. The lounge has more comfortable seating. Light lunches are served and snacks at all times.
☋❀◐♿⇌⚐♣▯🚌🐾📶

Organ Grinder 𝕃

21 Alfreton Road, Canning Circus, NG7 3JE

☎ (0115) 970 0630

Blue Monkey Marmoset, BG Sips, Primate Best Bitter, Infinity, Guerrilla; 3 changing beers (sourced regionally; often Blue Monkey) ⊞

Single-roomed, multi-level pub boasting a piano and a wood-burning fire. To the rear is a small courtyard leading to a raised decked area. Major sporting events, especially rugby, are shown on TV in the first floor function room. The full Blue Monkey range of beers is offered, as well as two guest ales and three real ciders or perries. It doesn't offer meals, but bar snacks such as Scotch eggs and Stilton-topped pork pies are available.
☋❀⚐♣●🚌🐾📶

Vat & Fiddle 𝕃

Queens Bridge Road, NG2 1NB

☎ (0115) 985 0611

Castle Rock Black Gold, Harvest Pale, Session, Preservation, Elsie Mo, Screech Owl; 7 changing beers ⊞

The tap for the adjoining Castle Rock Brewery, this 1937 Art Deco gem is two minutes from Nottingham rail station. At least eight of the 13 handpumps serve cask beers from the Castle Rock range, with guest beers including LocAles and others from further afield. There are also over 10 real ciders. Hot food is served all week. The outside area to the rear overlooking the brewery yard features an impressive mural depicting Nottingham events. ☋❀◑♿⇌⚐♣●🚌🐾📶

Nottingham: East

Bread & Bitter 𝕃

153-155 Woodthorpe Drive, Mapperley, NG3 5JL

☎ (0115) 960 7541

Castle Rock Black Gold, Harvest Pale, Preservation, Elsie Mo, Screech Owl; Fuller's London Pride; 5 changing beers ⊞

Castle Rock pub converted in 2007 from the premises of an old bakery on Mapperley Top. The original baker's oven fronts are still embedded in an inside wall, giving the place a warm and welcoming feel. The pub started a revival of real ale outlets in Mapperley. Twelve handpumps serve Castle Rock beers, a mild, rotating guest ales and cider alongside an extensive foreign bottled beer list. Food is all home cooked and varies frequently – look for the specials board.
Q☋❀◑♿●🚌🐾📶

Old Volunteer 𝕃

35 Burton Road, Carlton, NG4 3DQ

☎ (0115) 987 2299

10 changing beers (often Flipside) ⊞

Refurbished by Flipside Brewing in 2014, the pub showcases five of the brewery's beers alongside five guests and a real cider. The interior is separated into distinct areas using wooden dividing beams, raised levels and different types of flooring. Outside is a patio area with parasols. Food choices include speciality burgers, and snacks are always available. Beer festivals are held in a marquee in the car park. ❀◑♿⇌●P🚌🐾📶

Nottingham: North

Doctor's Orders 𝕃

351 Mansfield Road, Carrington, NG5 2DA

☎ (0115) 960 7985 🌐 doctorsordersmicropub.co.uk

5 changing beers (sourced locally) ⊞

Compact beer emporium with two distinct areas. A small square lounge leads to a corridor flanked on one side by a narrow raised seating area with benches, with a small bar and serving area at the rear. Beer and cider are served at your table from handpumps at the rear. While now owned by Magpie Brewery, the pub continues with its original ethos of providing a range of microbrewery beers in an intimate atmosphere. Q☋❀♿♣●🚌🐾📶

Lion Inn 𝕃

44 Mosley Street, New Basford, NG7 7FQ

☎ (0115) 970 3506 🌐 thelionatbasford.co.uk

Castle Rock Harvest Pale; Draught Bass; 9 changing beers ⊞

A large, traditional free house with a central horseshoe bar and a rustic bare-brick decor. The focus is on a changing range of cask ales and traditional ciders from near and far. Outside there is a covered smoking area and a large garden with seating for the summer months. Live music features every weekend, in a wide variety of styles. The pub welcomes dogs and was a regional winner in the Rover Dog-Friendly Pub Awards in 2019. ♘❀◐◗♿🚌♣●P🚌🐾📶

Nottingham: South

Trent Navigation Ⓛ

Meadow Lane, NG2 3HS
☎ (0115) 986 5658 🌐 trentnavigation.com
Navigation Patriot, New Dawn Pale, Rebel, Saviour; 3 changing beers (often Navigation) [H]
This popular former Victorian canalside inn is a stone's throw from the Notts County football ground. The Navigation Brewery is housed in the former stables of the canal horses at the back of the building, separated by a large-screened patio area. Navigation beers occupy most of the pumps with the remainder given over to cider. A large and varied menu is served every day. Live sport and sports news is shown on the various TVs. ❀◐◗♿♣●P🚌🐾📶

Nottingham: West

Plough Inn Ⓛ

17 St Peter's Street, Radford, NG7 3EN
☎ 07972 094425
Nottingham Rock Ale Bitter Beer, Rock Ale Mild Beer, Legend, Extra Pale Ale; 2 changing beers [H]
The tap for the adjoining Nottingham Brewery, the Plough offers a number of the brewery's ales and some changing guests. A traditional two-roomed public house with a cosy interior and two wood-burning stoves, it has a wide clientele including students living nearby. It hosts a popular quiz night once a week and several live music evenings during the month. The garden area features a skittles alley. Q♘❀◐♣●P🚌🐾📶

Oxton

Old Green Dragon Ⓛ ✔

Blind Lane, NG25 0SS
☎ (0115) 965 2243
6 changing beers [H]
Restored to its former glory by the current owners in 2013, this is both a classic, traditional village pub and a lively, contemporary eating venue. It offers a varied selection of six real ales from both local and national breweries and at least two real ciders. Outside is a patio area and an enclosed garden at the rear. The pub has three electric car charging points. Local CAMRA Pub of the Year in 2019. ♘❀◐◗♿●P🐾📶

Radcliffe on Trent

Chestnut Ⓛ ✔

Main Road, NG12 2BE
☎ (0115) 933 1994 🌐 chestnutradcliffe.com
Adnams Mosaic; Bombardier; Woodforde's Wherry; 4 changing beers [H]
Well-regarded, cask beer-led village pub. Originally the Cliffe Inn, following a major refurbishment in 2006 it became The Horse Chestnut and in 2015 simply The Chestnut. Seven reasonably priced real ales are served including different guests, one always a local brew. Quality home-made food, ranging from stone-baked pizzas to classic British dishes, is served in a relaxed, casual atmosphere. ♘❀◐◗♿≢●P🚌🐾📶

Yard of Ale

1 Walkers Yard, NG12 2FF (between Costa and public car park)
☎ (0115) 933 4888 🌐 yard-of-ale.business.site
6 changing beers [H]/[G]
This small, friendly micropub opened in 2016 in a former café and chocolate shop in the centre of the village. The single-room premises are narrow, with access from the side. Up to seven guest ales are on offer, always including at least one local brew and a dark ale. There is a separate gin bar known as Gin Within. Q≢●P🚌🐾

Rainworth

Inkpot

Kirklington Road, NG21 0JY
☎ (01623) 230500
4 changing beers [H]
This micropub usually serves a range of up to four real ales and 11 real ciders. Based in what was once a betting shop, it is named after the octagonal building that used to stand nearby, now demolished, which was the toll house for the road to Mansfield. Local CAMRA Cider Pub of the Year 2019. Q♘●🚌(28,141)🐾

Rempstone

White Lion Ⓛ

Main Street, LE12 6RH
☎ (01509) 889111
Belvoir Dark Horse; Charnwood Vixen; Draught Bass; 1 changing beer [H]
This small, welcoming village pub with a friendly clientele was saved from closure some years ago by four locals. It has just one room, warmed by a cosy fire in winter, and offers a choice of local and guest beers. Occasional themed events are held. Bar snacks are available. Q♘❀◗♣🚌🐾📶

Retford

BeerHeadZ

3 Town Hall Yard, DN22 6DU (off Market Square, through arch to rear of 10 Green Bottles)
☎ (01777) 949631
5 changing beers (sourced regionally) [H]
A small, friendly pub serving five rotating guest beers, three ciders and a range of over 100 bottled beers. The ales, often one-offs from near and far, are kept in excellent condition and served in oversized glasses so you can be sure of a full pint. BeerHeadZ has won several CAMRA awards and is a former Nottinghamshire Pub of the Year. Q♿●▯🚌🐾📶

Brew Shed

104-106 Carolgate, DN22 6AS (on Carolgate bridge opp Masonic Hall)
Harrison's Vacant Gesture, Best Bitter, Pale Ale, Stout, Proof of Concept; 2 changing beers (sourced regionally) [H]
The tap for Harrison's Brewery. The open-plan main room is at street level, with a smaller room downstairs leading to a large patio beside the canal. Five Harrison's Brewery beers, two rotating guests and a variety of kegs are on offer, alongside real cider and a good selection of gins, spirits and wines. Nottinghamshire CAMRA Pub of the Year 2019. Q♘❀♿♣●P🚌🐾📶

Idle Valley Tap Ⓛ

Carolgate, DN22 6EF (at S end of main shopping area)
☎ (01777) 948586

7 changing beers (sourced regionally; often Welbeck Abbey) H
Originally the tap for Idle Valley, since the brewery closure beers are now from elsewhere. Four (more when busy) rotating guest beers are on offer, along with gins, wines and spirits. The one-room pub has a pool table and dartboard away from the bar. The outside space has been put to good use, with plenty of seating attracting large numbers in fine weather.

Ship Inn

Wharf Road, DN22 6EN (oppsite Little Theatre nr Asda)
☎ (01777) 704412 🌐 theshipinnretford.com
Batemans XB, Gold, Salem Porter, XXXB; 3 changing beers (sourced nationally) H
The pub has undergone an extensive upgrade and has reverted to its original name. There are two rooms – the main one is on different levels and has space for drinking and playing pool, the other is the dining area, serving good home-cooked food. A large covered seating area outside has TVs and a stage for bands. Four Batemans beers and three guests are available. Q

Ruddington

Frame Breakers L

High Street, NG11 6DT
☎ (0115) 859 0060 🌐 theframebreakers.co.uk
Nottingham Legend, Extra Pale Ale; house beer (by Nottingham); 3 changing beers (often Nottingham) H
A large open-plan hostelry on a corner plot, with an L-shaped bar and seating on three sides. Run by Nottingham Brewery, it showcases the brewery's beers alongside a couple of changing guests – always including a dark beer – and four ciders on the cider wall. There is a large outdoor seating area. Live music features every Sunday. A yearly beer festival is held to coincide with the local annual Ruddfest. P (3,10)

Southwell

Final Whistle

Station Road, NG25 0ET
☎ (01636) 814953
Brewsters Hophead; Draught Bass; Everards Tiger; Salopian Oracle; 6 changing beers (sourced nationally; often Oakham) H
Located at the end of the Southwell Trail, a disused railway line, this comfortable multi-roomed pub has a railway theme and is teeming with memorabilia. The courtyard garden is laid out like a mock station and has a separate bar and function room called The Locomotion. The main bar has 10 handpumps which always offer Bass and a stout or porter. Quiz nights are Sunday and Tuesday, folk club is on a Thursday. Various quality bar snacks are available. QP (28,100)

Old Coach House L

69 Easthorpe, NG25 0HY
☎ (01636) 819526 🌐 pubpeople.com
Sharp's Doom Bar; 6 changing beers (sourced nationally) H
Traditional open-plan pub with five different drinking areas, oak beams and a large range fire. Six regularly changing real ales are on handpump from both local and national breweries, often including Oakham JHB and Timothy Taylor Landlord. Live music features regularly on Saturday night, an open mic session is held on the last Sunday of the month, and a New Orleans pianist plays on the first Sunday. Outside to the rear is a well-kept patio garden. Q

Stapleford

Horse & Jockey L

20 Nottingham Road, NG9 8AA
☎ (0115) 875 9655 🌐 horseandjockeystapleford.co.uk
Full Mash Horse & Jockey; 12 changing beers H
An open-plan bar with seating throughout and further seating up a couple of steps in an area that can also be used for functions. An array of 13 ales includes a house beer from the local Full Mash brewery, the rest always changing. Bar snacks are served – filled rolls, pork pies and sausage rolls. Popular with walkers and cyclists, the pub is close to the Erewash Valley trail, and also offers some accommodation. QP

Sutton-in-Ashfield

FireRock

24 Outram Street, NG17 4FS
☎ (07875) 331898
2 changing beers H
Opened in 2018, this large open-plan bar is the tap for FireRock Brewing. Up to two real ales are on offer alongside a wide range of KeyKeg beers, bottles and cans. A good range of (often rare) spirits is also available. Regular live music is hosted on the stage and there is a smaller snug space with a nautical decor.

Scruffy Dog

Station Road, NG17 5HF
☎ (01623) 550826
5 changing beers (often Abbeydale, Thornbridge)
Comfy sofas and a real fire on colder days welcome visitors to this dog-friendly pub. Refurbished by the current owners, it has its own on-site Scruffy Dog microbrewery – the brew plant is visible from the end of the main seating area. Eight changing real ales are usually available from the brewery, plus up to five guest ales. QP

Underwood

Ginger Giraffe Micropub & Gin Bar

14 Alfreton Road, NG16 5GB
☎ (01773) 533090
5 changing beers (often Castle Rock, Thornbridge, Titanic) H
This large micropub located within an old factory unit has expanded several times to cope with demand. It offers five real ales, a range of real ciders and a wide choice of spirits, especially gin. There is a main bar area and a separate games room with a pool table and sports TV.
QP

West Bridgford

Poppy & Pint L

Pierrepont Road, NG2 5DX
☎ (0115) 981 9995
Castle Rock Sheriff's Tipple, Harvest Pale, Preservation, Screech Owl; 8 changing beers H
Former British Legion Club converted in 2011 to become a Castle Rock pub. It has a large main bar with a raised area and a family space with a café bar (children are welcome until 9pm). A large upstairs function room features a folk club and the beer garden overlooks a bowling green. Twelve handpumps dispense Castle Rock beers plus guests, often from new breweries. There are usually two real ciders, and excellent food is served. The car park has an electric car charging point.
P

Stratford Haven

2 Stratford Road, NG2 6BA

(0115) 982 5981

Adnams Broadside; Batemans XB; Castle Rock Harvest Pale, Elsie Mo, Screech Owl; Everards Tiger; 6 changing beers

A former pet shop, The Strat has a single central bar with extended seating at the back and a secluded snug to the right. Up to 12 cask ales plus a cider are available on handpump at any one time, including at least six from owner Castle Rock's portfolio. Guest ales are predominantly from microbreweries near and far. Themed food nights feature Monday to Thursday. Sunday is silent quiz night. Q

Worksop

Dukeries Brewery Tap

18 Newcastle Avenue, S80 1ET

07584 305027

5 changing beers (sourced locally; often Dukeries)

A true real ale outlet close to the Worksop's pedestrian area and an asset to the town. The pub and brewery are in the same building. At least five rotating beers, usually from Dukeries, are on offer. Various events are held including occasional beer festivals, poker nights and live music nights.

Liquorice Gardens

1A Newcastle Street, S80 2AS (just off town centre)

(01909) 512220

Greene King Abbot; Ruddles Best Bitter; 5 changing beers (sourced nationally; often Little Critters, Milestone, Pheasantry)

The pub serves an excellent range of ales, wines and spirits. Most of the real ale is from the local area and the selection changes weekly. A good choice of food is available and there are ample seating areas as well as a covered garden and smoking area. Beer and cider festivals are held occasionally.

Mallard

Station Approach, S81 7AG (on station platform, entrance from main car park)

07973 521824

4 changing beers

Formerly the station buffet, this small pub offers a warm welcome. Four changing real ales are available, usually including a dark beer, plus two ciders, a selection of foreign bottled beers, country fruit wines and specialist gins. As well as the cosy main room there is a room downstairs used for special occasions. Four beer festivals are held each year. The recipient of many local CAMRA awards. Q P

Station Hotel

Carlton Road, S80 1PS (opp station car park entrance)

(01909) 474108 thestationhotelworksop.co.uk

5 changing beers (sourced regionally)

Situated opposite Worksop railway station on the edge of the town centre, there is always a welcome at this pub. Four or five regularly changing real ales are available. The long bar serves a lounge drinking area with a separate dining room attached, and there is a further small room suitable for meetings. A spacious and well-maintained garden with seating is to the rear. Food is served lunchtimes and evenings and accommodation is offered. Q P (5)

King William IV, Nottingham: Central (Photo: Andrew Ludlow)

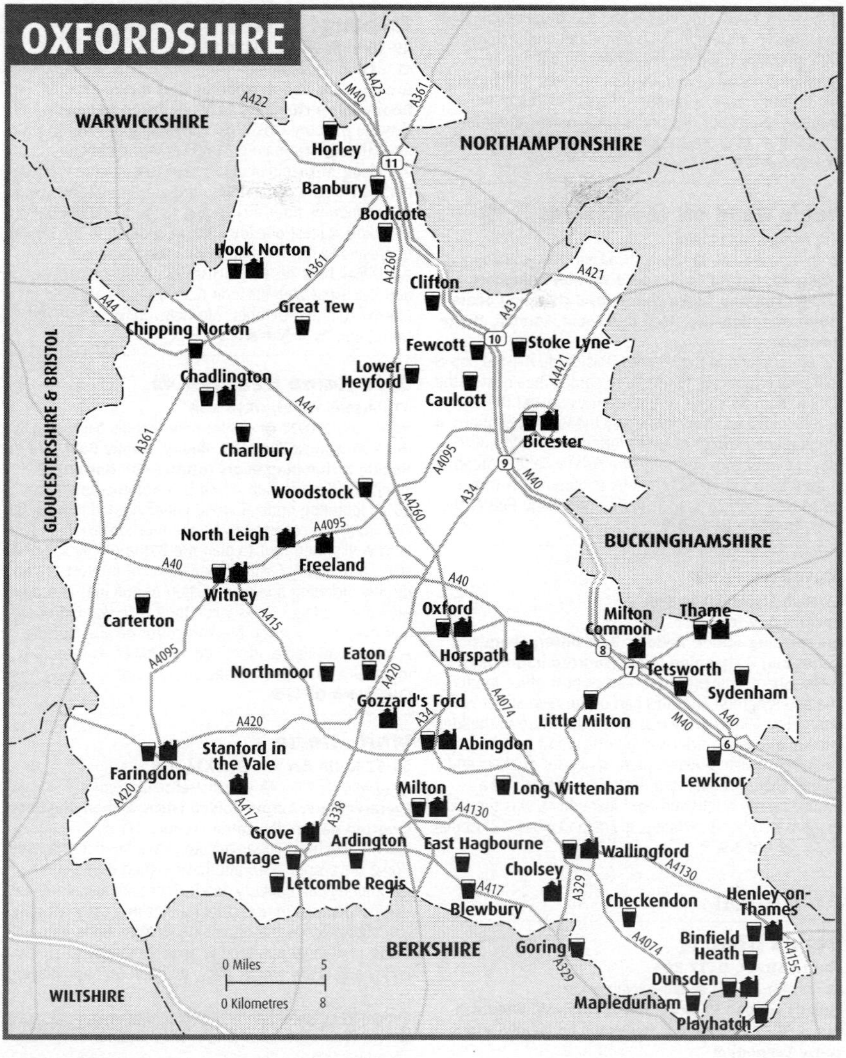

Abingdon

Brewery Tap 🄻

40-42 Ock Street, OX14 5BZ

☎ (01235) 521655 🌐 thebrewerytap.net

Loose Cannon Abingdon Bridge; 5 changing beers (sourced locally; often West Berkshire, White Horse, XT) 🄷

Morland created a tap for its brewery in 1993 from three Grade II listed town houses. The brewery is no more but the pub, run by the same family since it opened, has thrived. It offers a diverse range of beers, all sourced locally, and hosts three beer festivals each year featuring ales from further afield. The pub has three rooms, two of them away from the bar, and a courtyard outside. Local CAMRA Town and Village Pub of the Year 2019 and 2020.
Q ♿ ♣ P

Broad Face 🄻 ✔

30-32 Bridge Street, OX14 3HR

☎ (01235) 538612 🌐 broadfaceabingdon.co.uk

House beer (by Greene King); 7 changing beers (sourced nationally; often Dark Star, Loose Cannon, Morland) 🄷

Deceptively large, two-roomed, Grade II listed pub near the river with a small outside seating area on Thames Street. The building was erected in 1840 but there are records of a pub on the site as far back as 1734, and possibly before that as the Saracen's Head. Traditional theories behind the pub's unique name are written on the outside wall. Welcoming to locals and visitors alike, the pub serves quality home-cooked food and a range of ales, aiming to showcase the best of local produce.
Q ♿

King's Head & Bell 🄻

10 East St Helen Street, OX14 5EA

☎ (01235) 525362 🌐 kingsheadandbell-abingdon.com

Loose Cannon Abingdon Bridge; 2 changing beers (sourced nationally; often Hook Norton, Loose Cannon, Sharp's) 🄷

In existence before 1554 as the Bell and for some time a coaching inn, in the 19th century it claimed to have stabling for nearly 100 horses and supplied the volunteer fire brigade. Although much renovated and restored – with alterations and refurbishment carried out in summer 2019 by new management – the building still has historic traces. A number of rooms include two meeting rooms upstairs and a large conservatory for diners. The old courtyard is now a pleasant beer garden. 🐴❀◐◑♿♣🚌🐾📶

Nag's Head on the Thames 🄻 ✔

The Bridge, OX14 3HX

☎ (01235) 524516 🌐 thenagsheadonthethames.co.uk

Brakspear Oxford Gold; Loose Cannon Abingdon Bridge; Timothy Taylor Landlord; 4 changing beers (sourced nationally; often Brakspear, Loddon, White Horse) 🄷

Set on an island in the Thames, this Grade II listed pub is split over two levels, with a large garden area next to the river and lovely views of the countryside and the town's historic buildings. Now owned by the Brakspear pubco, it offers a good choice of beers, often local. Live music plays at weekends and some weekdays. Salter's Steamer cruises from Oxford stop nearby in summer. A three-times local CAMRA branch Town and Village Pub of the Year. 🐴❀◐◑♿🍎P🚌🐾📶

Narrows 🄻 ✔

25 High Street, OX14 5AA

☎ (01235) 467680

Greene King Abbot; Ruddles Best Bitter; Sharp's Doom Bar; 4 changing beers (sourced nationally) 🄷

Wetherspoon converted the former post office in 2013. The pub is named after this part of the High Street which during the 19th century was called the Narrow. The long bar leads to the former sorting office and telephone exchange which provides more space for drinkers and diners. There are plenty of historical photos and a traditional red telephone box. Abingdon's was the last manual telephone exchange in England when it closed in 1975. 🐴❀◐◑♿🚌📶

Ardington

Boar's Head 🄻

Church Street, OX12 8QA

☎ (01235) 835466 🌐 tbhardington.co.uk

Fuller's London Pride 🄷**; North Cotswold Windrush Ale** 🄷/🄶**; 2 changing beers (sourced locally; often Loose Cannon)** 🄷

The Boar's Head is an attractive timbered building in a side road between Ardington House and the church. The traditional country inn has one bar, subdivided for diners, and warmed by log fires in winter. In summer there is a garden terrace for eating and drinking alfresco. This cosy and friendly pub is an ideal place to try home-cooked seasonal food or sample the excellent beer range. Q🐴❀◐◑♿♣P🚌(X32,X33) 🐾📶

Banbury

Bailiff's Tap

4 Southam Road, OX16 2ED

4 changing beers (sourced locally) 🄶

Banbury's first micropub opened in 2017. It is based in what was a bailiff's office and serves a variety of beers, mostly from independent breweries, with three ciders usually also available. In its first year it offered 232 different beers, all served direct from barrels on stillages in the bar. A traditional snack selection includes pork pies and crisps. The lively front bar buzzes with conversation. Q♣🍎🚌🐾

Exchange 🄻 ✔

49-50 High Street, OX16 5LA

☎ (01295) 259035

Greene King Abbot; Ruddles Best Bitter; Sharp's Doom Bar; 9 changing beers (sourced nationally) 🄷

Close to Banbury Cross, this imposing split-level site was once the town's main post office and telephone exchange. Many old photos and pictures on the walls pay homage to Banbury and the surrounding area. Two banks of handpumps offer a changing range of ales, usually including at least one local ale, in addition to the regular beers and real cider. Good-value food is served. The April/May beer festival focuses on international beers, and the usual Wetherspoon beer festivals are held in March/April and October. Alcoholic drinks are served from 9am. 🐴◐◑♿≠🍎🚌📶

Olde Reine Deer Inn ✔

47 Parsons Street, OX16 5NA

☎ (01295) 270972 🌐 ye-olde-reinedeer-inn-banbury.co.uk

Hook Norton Hooky Mild, Hooky, Hooky Gold, Old Hooky; 3 changing beers (often Hook Norton) 🄷

Traditional English pub which first became an inn in 1570, featuring original wood panelling dating from the Civil War. It is reported to be the location where Cromwell's men met to plan the Battle of Edgehill and siege of Banbury Castle. Many items of interest are on display including a large selection of pub jugs and other brewery artefacts. Good-value food is served lunchtimes and evenings; see the blackboard for details. Outside seating is available. Identified by CAMRA as having a regionally important historic pub interior. Q❀◐◑≠♣🍎P🚌🐾

White Horse 🄻

50-52 North Bar Street, OX16 0TH

☎ (01295) 277484 🌐 whitehorsebanbury.com

Everards Tiger; Turpin Golden Citrus; 8 changing beers (sourced nationally; often Titanic, XT) 🄷

The friendly hosts Eileen and Ken have been at the White Horse since April 2015 and have turned it into the community pub Banbury needs. There are always at least five handpumps in use, offering ales in a range of styles and strengths for the discerning drinker. Good home-made traditional pub food is served Tuesday to Sunday. Friday nights are always busy, with a local band playing,

REAL ALE BREWERIES

- **Amwell Springs** Cholsey
- **Barn Owl** Gozzard's Ford
- **Bell Street** ▤ Henley-on-Thames (brewing suspended)
- **Bellinger's** Grove
- **Bicester** ▤ Bicester
- **Brakspear** ✎ Witney
- **Brewery58** Wallingford
- **Chadlington** Chadlington
- **Church Hanbrewery** ✎ North Leigh
- **Faringdon** ▤ Faringdon
- **Hook Norton** Hook Norton
- **Little Ox** Freeland
- **Loddon** ✎ Dunsden
- **Loose Cannon** ✎ Abingdon
- **LoveBeer** Milton
- **Philsters** Milton Common
- **Shotover** Horspath
- **Tap Social Movement** ✎ Oxford
- **Thame** ▤ Thame
- **Turpin** Hook Norton
- **White Horse** Stanford in the Vale
- **Wriggly Monkey** ✎ Bicester
- **Wychwood** ✎ Witney

the rest of the week the noise comes from the buzz of conversation. The pub hosts a regular Sunday quiz and a beer festival at Easter. Q🐴❀◑♿⇌♣●🚌🐾📶

Bicester

Angel ✓

102 Sheep Street, OX26 6LP

☎ (01869) 360410 🌐 theangelbicester.co.uk

Bicester Angelic Upstart; 5 changing beers (sourced regionally; often Chiltern, Rebellion, Vale) 🄷

A traditional pub close to the centre of town. A log fire on cold days adds to the welcoming atmosphere. The bar area is a good place to sample six real ales, including beers brewed in the microbrewery behind the pub. Bar snacks are limited, but street food is available on summer weekends. There is a large seating area outside and a permanent marquee. The microbrewery operates to seasonal demand. Q🐴❀♿⇌(North)♣P🚌🐾📶

Binfield Heath

Bottle & Glass 🄻

Harpsden Road, RG9 4JT

☎ (01491) 412625 🌐 bottleandglassinn.com

Loddon Hoppit; Rebellion IPA; 1 changing beer (sourced locally; often Loddon) 🄷

Classic thatched Grade II listed country pub with original stone floors and a wood-burner in the left hand bar and modern wooden flooring throughout the rest of the building. The handpumps are in the smaller right hand bar. The restaurant is in a modern extension to the rear, serving traditional British food with a modern twist. Coffees, teas and soft drinks are available, and they do breakfast Friday to Sunday. Alcoholic drinks are served from noon. 🐴❀◑♿♣P🐾📶

Blewbury

Blueberry 🄻

London Road, OX11 9NU (on A417)

☎ (01235) 850296 🌐 the-blueberry.co.uk

Loose Cannon Abingdon Bridge; St Austell Tribute; West Berkshire Good Old Boy; 1 changing beer (sourced locally) 🄷

Formerly a 1930s roadhouse, The Blueberry has been a village pub since the current owner, a small local pubco, purchased it in 2014. Extensively refurbished, it has a single bar that extends to the restaurant area at the rear. Four real ales are served including a guest. The menu offers good value including the pub speciality – pizza cooked in the wood-fired oven – plus a take-away option. 🐴❀◑♿♣P🚌(94,94S)🐾📶

Bodicote

Plough Inn

9 High Street, OX15 4BZ

☎ (01295) 258909 🌐 ploughbodicote.co.uk

Wadworth Henry's IPA, 6X; 1 changing beer (sourced nationally) 🄷

A prominent corner building on the main street, the front entrance lobby has a traditional jug and bottle off-sales hatch, sadly no longer in use. There is a comfortable bar to the right and a separate seating area to the left. On the bar can be found two regular ales and occasional seasonals from Wadworth, although guest ales may also make an appearance. There is regular live music and a fortnightly quiz on Tuesday. Outside is a pleasant seating area for warmer days. Q🐴❀◑♿⛺●🚌(B3)🐾📶

Carterton

Siege of Orleans

5 The Giles Centre, Alvescot Road, OX18 3DH (down passage next to cycle shop)

☎ (01993) 845663

4 changing beers (sourced regionally) 🄷

Not so much a pub as a self-styled micro-alehouse, set in a former record shop so on the small side. It has four handpumps dispensing mainly local ales from relatively unknown breweries alongside a selection of bottled and keg beers from around the world and two real ciders. A gin bar opens upstairs Thursday to Saturday evenings. Regular retro games nights and competitions are hosted. Q♿♣●P🚌📶

Caulcott

Horse & Groom

Lower Heyford Road, OX25 4ND

☎ (01869) 343257 🌐 horseandgroomcaulcott.co.uk

Black Sheep Best Bitter; Church End Goat's Milk; 3 changing beers (sourced nationally; often Church End, Goff's, Vale) 🄷

Lovely 16th-century coaching house with a warm welcome and a cosy fire in winter. Three guest ales are served along with the two regulars. The French landlord/chef offers seasonal and locally sourced food, including Thursday steak night and Sunday lunch (booking advised), along with themed French evenings. A Bastille Day beer festival is held annually. Dogs are allowed in the beer garden (but not in the bar). A Guide regular and three times local CAMRA Pub of the Year. Q🐴❀◑P📶

Chadlington

Tite Inn

Mill End, OX7 3NY

☎ (01608) 676910 🌐 thetiteinn.co.uk

Sharp's Doom Bar; 2 changing beers (sourced nationally; often Chadlington, Cotswold Lion, Sharp's) 🄷

A friendly welcome awaits in this cosy country pub in the Evenlode Valley. One regular and two guest ales are served along with a Westons cider on handpump. In winter there is a roaring fire, and for summer a beautiful hillside beer garden where a peaceful pint can be enjoyed, along with good reasonably priced food. Tite is old local dialect for spring – water runs under the pub and down the hill. Walkers are welcome.
Q🐴❀◑⛺●P🚌🐾📶

Charlbury

Rose & Crown ✓

Market Street, OX7 3PL

☎ (01608) 810103 🌐 roseandcrown.charlbury.com

Ramsbury Farmer's Best; Wye Valley HPA; 6 changing beers (sourced nationally; often Dark Star, Oakham, XT) 🄷

A popular and welcoming traditional pub, the Rose & Crown has deservedly been in the Guide for a consecutive 34 years. Real ales include Ramsbury Farmer's Best, a Wye Valley beer and six changing beers, along with six traditional ciders and perries, giving a fantastic choice at the bar. There is fortnightly live music and an annual beer festival each January. A former local and county CAMRA Pub of the Year.
🐴❀⛺⇌♣●🚌(S3,X9)🐾📶

Checkendon

Highwayman L
Exlade Street, RG8 0UA
☎ (01491) 682020 🌐 thehighwaymaninn-checkendon.co.uk
Fuller's London Pride; Loddon Hoppit; West Berkshire Good Old Boy H
The original building dates from 1625 but the inn now has a contemporary ambience while retaining the feel of a traditional pub, with two rooms for dining and a separate attractive bar and drinking area with wood-burner, beams, settles and exposed brickwork. There may be occasional seasonal ales from Loddon and West Berkshire breweries as alternatives to the beers listed. Excellent home-cooked and reasonably priced food is served. A large enclosed garden with children's play-area is popular with families. Q♨❀◑♿P🐾📶

Chipping Norton

Chequers
Goddards Lane, OX7 5NP (next to theatre on corner of Spring St)
☎ (01608) 644717
Fuller's London Pride, ESB, 1845; Gale's HSB; 3 changing beers (sourced nationally; often Dark Star, Fuller's, Gale's) H
Traditional English pub with an emphasis on real ale and home-cooked food. Up to six ales from the Fuller's, Gale's and Dark Star ranges are available and a cider served on gravity. The bar has four separate areas, with an airy restaurant and function space to the rear (the back rooms can be booked for private parties). A feature fireplace warms the small main bar area in winter, providing an excellent place to relax. The pub is popular with discerning drinkers and visitors to the adjacent theatre. Q♨◑♿♣●🚌🐾📶

Clifton

Duke at Clifton L
Main Street, OX15 0PE
☎ (01869) 226334 🌐 thecliftonduke.co.uk
Hook Norton Hooky; Turpin Golden Citrus; 2 changing beers (often North Cotswold, Tring, XT) H
This 17th-century Grade II listed thatched country inn has been rejuvenated by new owners since it reopened in 2017. A roaring fire in the inglenook fireplace – and in good weather the superb garden – make it a delightful setting in which to sample the award-winning ales, whatever the season. Fabulous food is served from an à la carte menu using locally sourced ingredients. Four well-appointed rooms and a fully serviced campsite with glamping hut provide excellent accommodation. Walkers, dogs and wellies are all welcome.
Q♨❀🛏◑♿⛺♣P🐾📶

Dunsden

Loddon Taproom
Dunsden Green Farm, Church Lane, RG4 9QD
☎ (0118) 948 1111 🌐 loddonbrewery.com
Loddon Hullabaloo H**; 6 changing beers (sourced locally; often Loddon)** H/G
Opened in 2018 and adjoining the main brewhouse, this increasingly popular taproom features three Loddon ales on handpump and a further four direct from the cask in the brewhouse. With both indoor and outdoor seating, it is the perfect place to enjoy a pint in the beautiful countryside. A small range of home-made snacks is available. The shop offers a wide range of produce from within 40 miles of the brewery, including local wines, spirits, liqueurs and cider. The taproom will stay open beyond the core hours if there is custom, and groups can visit at other times by arrangement.
♨❀♿♣P🚌(800) 🐾📶

East Hagbourne

Fleur de Lys
30 Main Road, OX11 9LN
☎ (01235) 813247 🌐 thefleurdelyspub.co.uk
Morland Original Bitter; house beer (by LoveBeer); 4 changing beers (sourced nationally) H
The Fleur de Lys is a family-friendly 17th-century pub in a rural village. It offers two regular beers – one a house beer (Wibbly Wobbly Whippet 4.1% ABV) from nearby microbrewery LoveBeer – and up to four nationally sourced guests. The spacious bar and dining area are comfortable and cosy, warmed by an open fire. Live music evenings are hosted regularly, including two weekend music festivals in the summer. Aunt Sally is played in fine weather. Local CAMRA and runner-up Regional CAMRA Pub of the Year 2019.
♨❀◑♿♣●P🚌(94,94S) 🐾📶

Eaton

Eight Bells L
OX13 5PR
☎ (01865) 862261 🌐 8bells.co.uk
Loose Cannon Abingdon Bridge; 2 changing beers (sourced regionally) H
A cream-painted cottage-style brick building in the centre of the hamlet, to which extensions have been added over the years. Inside is a no-frills public bar with wooden benches and tables and a larger, simply furnished lounge bar, which leads on to the restaurant/function room. Three beers from local breweries and further afield are sold. Q♨❀◑♿P🚌🐾📶

Faringdon

Swan L ✔
1 Park Road, SN7 7BP
☎ (01367) 241480 🌐 swanfaringdon.co.uk
4 changing beers (sourced nationally; often White Horse) H
An attractive free house with its own Faringdon microbrewery. The large, friendly, multi-level single bar has cosy nooks and a log fire, and a small roadside patio for sunny afternoons. The focus is on beer, wine and a large selection of gins – four constantly changing guest beers and two ciders are on handpump. Third-pint glasses are available for the unsure. There is a regular quiz night on Tuesday. Q♨♣●🚌(66)🐾📶

Fewcott

White Lion L ✔
Fritwell Road, OX27 7NZ
☎ (01869) 346676
3 changing beers (sourced nationally; often Black Sheep, Wadworth) H
A welcoming family-friendly free house with two large-screen TVs for sport lovers. Three constantly changing real ales are served, and a real cider in summer, plus a large selection of gins and whiskies. The beer garden is popular in warmer weather, featuring a large children's pirate ship, and Aunt Sally is played here. A regular in the Guide, the pub is a former local CAMRA Pub of the Year and Cider Pub of the Year. ♨❀♿♣●P🐾📶

Goring

Goring Social Club

1 High Street, RG8 9BA

☎ (01491) 873105 🌐 goringsocialclub.co.uk

Hook Norton Hooky; 2 changing beers (sourced nationally) Ⓗ

This popular and friendly club is a haven for beer lovers with its middle pump serving a constantly changing ale sourced from all over Britain. The other pumps dispense a regular session ale and a seasonally changing guest. The club hosts numerous and popular community events including quizzes, meat raffles and the occasional live band. TV and function rooms are available. Entry is £1 with a CAMRA membership card. Local CAMRA Club of the Year multiple times including 2020.

🐴⇌(Goring & Streatley) ♣P🚌📶

Great Tew

Falkland Arms

19-21 The Green, OX7 4DB

☎ (01608) 683653 🌐 falklandarms.co.uk

Wadworth Henry's IPA, Horizon, 6X, Bishops Tipple, Swordfish; 2 changing beers (sourced nationally; often Hook Norton, Yates') Ⓗ

A traditional 16th-century English country pub, with simple wooden furniture on flagstone and bare-board floors, and an array of jugs hanging from the ancient beams. The walls are adorned with brewing memorabilia; in winter a fire in the large inglenook adds warmth. Handpumps dispense a choice of five regular ales, two guests and a cider. Accommodation and good locally sourced food are available. A beer garden overlooking the picturesque thatched Great Tew Estate is ideal for a summer pint. Q🐴❀🛏◖◗●P🐾📶

Henley-on-Thames

Bird in Hand 🏆

61 Greys Road, RG9 1SB

☎ (01491) 575775

Brakspear Gravity; Fuller's London Pride; 3 changing beers (sourced nationally; often Loddon, Rebellion, Tring) Ⓗ

Celebrating 26 consecutive years in the Guide, the Bird has flourished under the stewardship of the same family throughout. Three guest beers complement the two regulars. TVs show sporting events, and the pub is home to darts and cribbage teams and hosts regular quiz nights. The family room leads to a delightful garden boasting a pond and aviary, and dogs on leads are welcome. Hot and cold snacks are available all day. A frequent winner of local CAMRA Pub of the Year including 2020. Q🐴❀Å⇌♣🚌🐾📶

Hook Norton

Malthouse Kitchen

Brewery Lane, OX15 5NY (follow brown tourist signs to Hook Norton Brewery)

☎ (01608) 730384

Hook Norton Hooky Mild, Hooky, Hooky Gold, Old Hooky; 3 changing beers (sourced nationally; often Hook Norton) Ⓗ

Redesigned in 2017, this establishment is popular with tourists and local residents. The licensed restaurant is open daily for breakfast and lunch. Brewery tours are held every day of the week, plus themed evening events and open tap beer nights (5-8pm on the second Wednesday of the month). The well-stocked shop dispenses more than brewery merchandise. Various meeting and event rooms are available to hire, as is the microbrewery itself to brew your own beer.

🐴◖Å●P🚌(488) 🐾📶

Pear Tree Inn Ⓛ ✔

Scotland End, OX15 5NU (follow brown tourist signs to Hook Norton Brewery)

☎ (01608) 737482 🌐 peartreeinnhooknorton.co.uk

Hook Norton Hooky Mild, Hooky, Hooky Gold, Old Hooky; 2 changing beers (sourced locally; often Hook Norton) Ⓗ

Nestling at the bottom of the lane, a few hundred yards from the Hook Norton Brewery, this managed house dispenses a full range of the brewery's beers. The single bar is cosy in winter and the large child-friendly garden, where Aunt Sally is played, is popular for summer drinking. With its three bedrooms it is a great base for a stopover before/after the popular brewery tours, which operate seven days a week, or for discovering this interesting local area.

Q🐴❀🛏◖◗♿Å♣●P🚌(488) 🐾📶

Horley

Red Lion 🏆 Ⓛ

Hornton Lane, OX15 6BQ

☎ (01295) 730427

Hook Norton Hooky; Purity Pure UBU; Sharp's Doom Bar; Turpin Golden Citrus Ⓗ

A focal point for the community, this village pub offers a friendly welcome to visitors, including walkers and well-behaved dogs. The tranquil garden is ideal for a summer evening's tipple. Three handpumped ales are served – four on special occasions. The annual beer festival on St George's Day is a must for all. Aunt Sally, darts and dominoes are played, and a TV shows live sporting events. Local CAMRA Pub of the Year 2020. ❀♣P🐾📶

Letcombe Regis

Greyhound Inn Ⓛ

Main Street, OX12 9JL

☎ (01235) 771969 🌐 thegreyhoundletcombe.co.uk

4 changing beers (sourced nationally; often North Cotswold, Ramsbury, Thornbridge) Ⓗ

Large, welcoming pub in the centre of the village, refurbished to a high standard. Inside is a single bar with dining areas and a formerly hidden inglenook fireplace. Locally sourced home-cooked food and four constantly changing handpumped beers are served. The garden has been re-landscaped for outdoor dining during the summer months. There is parking at the side of the building, as well as provision for secure bicycle storage. Within a couple of miles of the Ridgeway, the pub is a welcome place of refreshment for wayfarers. Accommodation is offered in eight boutique en-suite bedrooms. Q🐴❀🛏◖◗♿ÅP🐾📶

Lewknor

Leathern Bottle

1 High Street, OX49 5TW (N off B4009 near M40 jct 6)

☎ (01844) 351482 🌐 theleathernbottle.co.uk

Brakspear Gravity; Marston's Pedigree; 1 changing beer (sourced nationally) Ⓗ

This traditional Grade II listed country pub, run by two generations of the same family for nearly 50 years, has featured in all but one edition of the Guide. It serves good home-cooked pub food, and has a family-friendly garden. The guest beer comes from the Brakspear pubco-approved list. The venue offers a warm welcome to all, including walkers from the nearby Ridgeway, with some of the best trails starting and finishing here. It is also a short walk from the Oxford Tube and the airline coach stop. Q

Little Milton

Lamb

High Street, OX44 7PU (on A329)
☎ (01844) 279527 lambinnlittlemilton.co.uk
Brakspear Gravity; Courage Directors; 1 changing beer (sourced nationally)
Thatched 16th-century stone pub on the main road through the village. The attractive, welcoming split-level bar in this Grade II listed inn features original beams and has seating areas for those who just want a drink, as well as for diners enjoying the high-quality pub food. To the rear is a patio and a walled flower garden where a beer festival is held in July. Brakspear Gravity and Courage Directors are the regular ales, along with a changing guest. Quiz night is the first Thursday of the month. P

Long Wittenham

Plough

24 High Street, OX14 4QH
☎ (01865) 407738 theploughinnlw.co.uk
Butcombe Original; 2 changing beers (sourced nationally; often Amwell Springs, Loose Cannon, West Berkshire)
A traditional Grade II listed family-friendly pub built in the 17th century in this rural south Oxfordshire village. Its large garden stretches down to the River Thames and has ample outdoor seating and a children's play space. There are two bar areas and a separate restaurant. One regular and two changing beers are served, from breweries and microbreweries mainly in the South-East. The pub hosts many community events, notably Wittfest, a music festival each June that raises money for charities. P(D1)

Lower Heyford

Bell Inn

21 Market Square, OX25 5NY
☎ (01869) 347176
2 changing beers (sourced nationally; often Butcombe, Skinner's, Vale)
Historic stone-built pub at the heart of the village with a spacious multi-room layout. Four handpumps dispense regularly changing ales, often from Vale and Butcombe, and regularly changing ciders, often Westons and Farmer Jims. A music evening is held monthly on a Thursday. A short walk from Heyford station and Oxford Canal, the pub can get busy in the summer months – its large garden adding to the attraction.
(Heyford) P(250)

Mapledurham

Packhorse

Woodcote Road, RG4 7UG (on A4074)
☎ (0118) 972 2140 packhorsepub.co.uk
West Berkshire Good Old Boy; house beer (by St Austell); 3 changing beers (sourced nationally)
Originally a farm on the Mapledurham House estate dating from the 1600s, this Grade II listed Brunning & Price establishment is now a cosy pub and restaurant. The low-beamed bar has ample seating for drinkers and invariably features local microbrewery beers. The house beer is Traditional Bitter (3.5% ABV) brewed by St Austell. The larger restaurant area offers a wide-ranging good-value menu. A large, secluded garden at the rear has a shaded seating area overlooking fields. A beer and cider festival is held in July. QP

Milton

Plum Pudding

44 High Street, OX14 4EJ
☎ (01235) 834443 theplumpuddingmilton.co.uk
Loose Cannon Abingdon Bridge; LoveBeer OG; 1 changing beer (sourced nationally)
Plum Pudding refers to the Oxford Sandy and Black pig, one of the older and rarer British breeds. The pub serves three real ales plus up to four real ciders. Regular live music is hosted, and beer festivals in April and October. Sitting in the pleasant walled garden, you wouldn't know it, but you are only a couple of minutes from the busy A34. En-suite accommodation is available. The pub is a former local CAMRA Pub of the Year, repeat local Cider Pub of the Year, and was regional Cider Pub of the Year in 2019. P

Northmoor

Red Lion

Standlake Road, OX29 5SX
☎ (01865) 300301 theredlionnorthmoor.com
Brakspear Gravity; Loose Cannon Abingdon Bridge; 2 changing beers (sourced locally; often Cotswold Lion, North Cotswold, Vale)
Traditional village inn with whitewashed stone walls, heavy oak beams, real fires and a large garden. Purchased by the local community from Greene King in 2014, the pub has gone from strength to strength. The focus is on local produce, with a changing menu of home-cooked food, some of which is grown in the pub's kitchen garden. A selection of three or four local beers is available in the small bar alongside locally made soft drinks from Samuelsons of Witney. QP

Oxford

Bear Inn

6 Alfred Street, OX1 4EH
☎ (01865) 728164 bearoxford.co.uk
Fuller's London Pride, ESB; Gale's HSB; Shotover Scholar; 2 changing beers (sourced regionally; often Fuller's, Gale's)
The Bear's precise age is open to debate but it's definitely old; the present building dates back to 1606 and is listed by CAMRA as having a regionally important historic pub interior. Tucked away behind the town hall, it is a tied house in more ways than one, renowned for its collection of tie remnants taken from customers. A small pub popular with students and visitors, it gets crowded at times but offers extra seating in a paved area to the rear. Q

Butcher's Arms

5 Wilberforce Street, Headington, OX3 7AN (from centre of Headington, past shark, first left, first right)
☎ (01865) 742470 butchersarmsheadington.co.uk
Fuller's London Pride, ESB; Gale's Seafarers Ale; 2 changing beers (often Fuller's)
A friendly, back-street, late-Victorian hostelry; the red-brick pub is a little hard to find but worth searching out. The long single room has the bar in the middle, and outside is a paved area. It offers a good range of Fuller's beers, traditional pub food and light lunch options. The inn sign, a parody of the arms of the Butchers' Company, and the motto, which means 'God gives us everything', are both of unknown origin. Q

St Austell Atkinson's Pale Ale; Sharp's Doom Bar; Thornbridge Jaipur IPA; 5 changing beers (sourced nationally; often Brakspear, Hook Norton) Ⓗ
Worth searching out, much of this Grade II listed pub dates back to the early 16th century when it was converted from a moneylender's tenement to a tavern, hence the name. Note the fine carvings, windows and the ceiling in the lower bar. There is an upstairs bar with an additional three handpumps, and a cobbled courtyard provides alfresco drinking, dining and smoking space.
Q❀◑◗♿⇌♣●🚌🐾📶

Fir Tree 🄻 ✔

163 Iffley Road, OX4 1EJ
☎ (01865) 245290
5 changing beers (sourced nationally; often Greene King, Morland, Plain) Ⓗ
Multi-level pub with a quiet snug at the back and a small patio garden and smoking area to the rear. There are some pavement tables at the front. The house speciality is pizza and a pop-up diner serves a vegan roast dinner on Sunday afternoon. The interior of this quirky pub still bears the scars of its days as a Morrells alehouse, with a whole bank of handpumps and a mishmash of finishes, artefacts and pictures. Handy as a before and after-match venue for Oxford University Rugby Union FC, whose ground is opposite. ❀◗♣●🚌(3)🐾📶

Gardener's Arms 🄻

39 Plantation Road, Walton Manor, OX2 6JE
☎ (01865) 559814 🌐 thegarden-oxford.co.uk
4 changing beers (sourced locally; often Little Ox, Loose Cannon, XT) Ⓗ
Established in the 1830s, this is a cosy pub down a narrow street off Woodstock Road. A popular and relaxing place to eat and drink, the small bar opens up to a spacious dining area, once two rooms, serving some of the finest vegetarian and vegan food in the city. At the rear is a large and pleasant garden as well as the outside toilets. The famous weekly quiz is on Sunday evening.
Q❀◑◗♣●🚌🐾📶

Lamb & Flag

12 St Giles, OX1 3JS
☎ (01865) 515787
Palmers IPA; Skinner's Betty Stogs; Theakston Old Peculier; house beer (by Palmers); 3 changing beers (sourced nationally; often XT) Ⓗ
Grade II listed building owned by the adjacent St John's College. Some of the profits from the pub support student scholarships. This is a classic city pub with no music, Wi-Fi or other distractions from friendly conversation. Beers from the South-West feature – the

Rose & Crown 🄻

14 North Parade Avenue, OX2 6LX (½ mile N of city centre, off Banbury Rd)
☎ (01865) 510551 🌐 roseandcrownoxford.com
Adnams Southwold Bitter; Hook Norton Old Hooky; Shotover Scholar; 1 changing beer (sourced locally) Ⓗ
Now a free house, this popular Victorian local on a vibrant north Oxford street is a time capsule with two small rooms and many original features. A friendly community pub, it has been run by the same landlords for over 30 years. No intrusive music or mobile phones are permitted. Its fame has even spread to Everest – see the photo on the wall. Identified by CAMRA as having a regionally important historic pub interior. Q❀◑◗♣🚌📶

Royal Blenheim 🏆 🄻

13 St Ebbes Street, OX1 1PT
☎ (01865) 242355 🌐 royalblenheim.co.uk
Everards Tiger; Titanic Plum Porter; White Horse WHB – White Horse Bitter, Stable Genius, Village Idiot; 5 changing beers (sourced nationally) Ⓗ
Single-room Victorian pub with a bright, airy interior, set on a street corner next to the Museum of Modern Art. It was built in 1889 on the site of two alehouses in what was then a very rough part of the city. The original Royal Blenheim was a stagecoach. The pub is owned by Everards but leased to Titanic, who run it in partnership with White Horse Brewery. Its 10 handpumps dispense a range of White Horse and Titanic beers, one from Everards, plus guests. Local CAMRA City Pub of the Year 2020. Q♿⇌♣●🚌🐾📶

St Aldates Tavern 🄻 ✔

108 St Aldate's, OX1 1BU
☎ (01865) 241185 🌐 staldatestavernoxford.co.uk
Hook Norton Hooky; XT Three; house beer (by West Berkshire); 3 changing beers (sourced regionally; often Box Steam, Flying Monk, Siren Craft) Ⓗ
Not the original St Aldates Tavern – that was at no.61 – but there was an inn recorded at this site in 1397. The pub has been rebuilt at least once since then and was a coaching inn in the 18th century. A friendly establishment opposite the town hall, it features up to seven well-kept real ales, with at least two from local breweries. Good-quality, freshly cooked food is served all day using locally sourced ingredients where possible.
Q◑◗⇌♣🚌🐾📶

White Hart

12 St Andrew's Road, Headington, OX3 9DL (opp church in Old Headington village)
☎ (01865) 761737 🌐 thewhitehartheadington.com

summer. Local CAMRA Pub of the Year in 2018. ☎❀◐♣●P🐾≋

Stoke Lyne

Peyton Arms

School Lane, OX27 8SD
☎ 07546 066160
Hook Norton Hooky, Old Hooky; 1 changing beer (often Hook Norton) Ⓖ
Enter this historic Hook Norton pub and step back in time. Up to three Hooky ales are served through a hatch, direct from casks. Simple filled rolls are usually available. A wealth of interesting memorabilia is all around. The bar area is for adults only and a relaxing place to enjoy to conversation with other drinkers by the fire; however, children are welcome in the garden. No dogs allowed. Opening hours can vary. Identified by CAMRA as having a regionally important historic pub interior. Q❀P

Sydenham

Inn at Emmington 𝕃

Sydenham Road, OX39 4LD (just off M40 jct 6)
☎ (01844) 351367 🌐 theinnatemmington.co.uk
Chiltern Beechwood Bitter; Rebellion IPA; 1 changing beer (sourced locally; often Loose Cannon, XT) Ⓗ

Royal Standard 𝕃

32 St Marys Street, OX10 0ET
☎ (01491) 599105 🌐 royalstandardwallingford.co.uk
Amwell Springs Chairman Dave, Easy Geez; 1 changing beer (sourced nationally; often Amwell Springs) Ⓗ
This much-loved 19th-century pub reopened in May 2019. It offers local ales from Amwell Springs and a great menu from a former Michelin-starred chef. On Tuesday to Friday it also serves as a coffee shop, with a soft play area for under-fives, but in the evening it has sports TV, quiz nights, entertainment and a warm atmosphere. The large beer garden has an 85-inch TV – perfect for those summer sports events. ☎❀⇌◐♿⚠🚌🐾≋

Wantage

King's Arms 𝕃 ✔

39 Wallingford Street, OX12 8AU (E of Market Sq)
☎ (01235) 765465 🌐 kingsarmswantage.co.uk
6 changing beers (sourced nationally)
This friendly, open-plan pub with polished wooden floors and panelling has been transformed by owners Oak Taverns, giving it a new lease of life. Six handpumps serve constantly changing beers, with six ciders also available. Outside, to the rear, is a large, grassy, sloping

OXFORDSHIRE

ENGLAND

Castle 𝕃 ✔

24 Paradise Street, OX1 1LD
☎ (01865) 248990 🌐 thecastleoxford.co.uk
Hook Norton Hooky, Hooky Gold, Old Hooky; 3 changing beers (sourced regionally; often Arbor, Big Smoke, Hook Norton) Ⓗ
Rebuilt in 1892 to a design by HG Drinkwater, the pub is now above the street after the realignment of Castle Street when the Westgate Shopping Centre opposite was first built. Some period features remain but the interior is modern with one long room and a pleasant half-cellar. Purchased by Hook Norton in 2016 for its first venture into the city and extensively refurbished, it now offers a range of real ales, not all from Hook Norton, and two ciders. Q☎◐◑⇌♣●🚌🐾≋

Chequers 𝕃 ✔

130A High Street, OX1 4DH (down narrow passageway off High St, 50yds from Carfax)
☎ (01865) 727463

house beer Lamb & Flag Gold is brewed by Palmers of Bridport. The pub has many literary links but is not the pub of the same name in Thomas Hardy's novel Jude the Obscure – that was the Turf Tavern. Q☎◐⇌●🚌

Mason's Arms 𝕃 ✔

2 Quarry School Place, Headington Quarry, OX3 8LH
☎ (01865) 764579 🌐 themasonsarmshq.co.uk
Castle Rock Harvest Pale; Harvey's Sussex Best Bitter; 3 changing beers (sourced nationally; often Castle Rock, Oakham, Rebellion) Ⓗ
Family-run community pub hosting many games leagues, including bar billiards and Aunt Sally. The guest ales are varied and turn over quickly, and a wide range of bottled beers is stocked. The pub is home to the Headington beer festival in September. A heated decking area and garden lead to the function room, which hosts music and comedy nights. A regular local CAMRA City Pub of the Year. ☎❀♣●P🚌(H2)🐾≋

garden with tables for drinkers. There is a small on-site microbrewery, Wantage Brewery, which plans to commence brewing in the near future.
Q

Lamb
59 Mill Street, OX12 9AB
☎ (01235) 766768 lambinnwantage.co.uk
Fuller's London Pride; Gale's Seafarers Ale; 1 changing beer (sourced nationally; often St Austell) H
A 17th-century inn near the mill, this is the second-oldest building in Wantage after the parish church, and the only thatched building in the town. The pub has never been sold and has had only two landlords in the last 50 years. It has now been extended at the rear and serves an extensive range of pub food, freshly made using ingredients from local suppliers. This family pub extends a warm and friendly welcome to all. P

Royal Oak
Newbury Street, OX12 8DF (S of Market Sq)
☎ (01235) 763129 royaloakwantage.co.uk
Wadworth 6X; West Berkshire Maggs' Mild, Dr Hexter's Healer; 8 changing beers (sourced nationally) G
This multi award-winning street-corner pub is a mecca for the discerning drinker. All beers are served by gravity, along with 30 ciders and perries. Photographs of ships bearing the pub's name are displayed. The lounge features wrought-iron trelliswork covered in pumpclips. Table football is played in the public bar. A repeat local CAMRA Pub of the Year and Cider Pub of the Year, including in 2020. Q

Shoulder of Mutton
38 Wallingford Street, OX12 8AX (E of Market Sq)
☎ (01235) 767158 theshoulder.pub
Butts Barbus Barbus; 9 changing beers (sourced nationally) H
Friendly and popular Victorian corner pub a short walk from the town centre, with 10 constantly changing beers on handpump to suit all tastes. The sympathetically renovated interior comprises public and lounge bars, a cosy snug and a 'lay-by' leading to a small courtyard and function room. A former local, county and regional CAMRA Pub of the Year, and identified by CAMRA as having a regionally important historic pub interior.
Q

Witney

Angel Inn
42 Market Square, OX28 6AL
☎ (01993) 703238
Brakspear Oxford Gold; Wychwood Hobgoblin Gold, Hobgoblin Ruby; house beer (by Marston's) H
A Grade II listed free house at one time owned by Joseph Early of the blanket manufacturing dynasty and a brewer. It has a fine front bar with low beams and a bay window with plenty of space for drinkers and diners beyond. Outside is a small paved and walled courtyard. The beer range is mostly from Marston's – its Wychwood Brewery is just around the corner, but the beer goes to Burton upon Trent to be casked. One of the regular beers is sometimes replaced by a guest. (S1,S2)

Drummers
8 Langdale Court, OX28 6FG (down passageway opp Blue Boar in town centre)
☎ (01608) 677717 oxbrewmicropub.co.uk
2 changing beers (sourced locally; often Church Hanbrewery, Goff's, Little Ox) H
Witney's first micropub is a venture run by a father and son team. In 2017 they started an eight-barrel brewery, Oxbrew, which has now merged with Little Ox Brewery. The pub, once a charity shop, serves the brewery's own beers alongside others from nearby small breweries via two handpulls from casks and six taps from kegs. Beers are kept in an air-conditioned cold room behind the bar. All Little Ox beers are gluten-free. QP(S1,S2)

Eagle Tavern
22 Corn Street, OX28 6BL
☎ (01993) 700121
Hook Norton Hooky, Hooky Gold, Old Hooky; 1 changing beer (sourced locally; often Hook Norton) H
The building has been an inn from the beginning of the 19th century – at first the Coach & Horses, then the Eagle Tavern in 1862. In the 1920s it was owned by Hunt Edmunds brewery, then bought by Hook Norton in 2001. The pub serves a range of Hook Norton beers, as well as malt whiskies and bourbons, gins and rums. The interior has three seating areas, lots of dark wood, and you can see the cellar through the window next to the bar.
Q(S1,S2)

Wychwood Brewery Tap
Eagle Maltings, The Crofts, OX28 4DP (S down alleyway off Corn St just after Chequers)
☎ (01993) 890800 wychwood.co.uk/brewery-tap
Wychwood Hobgoblin Gold, Hobgoblin Ruby; 2 changing beers (sourced nationally; often Brakspear, Ringwood, Wychwood) H
The brewery now has a taproom open to the public five days a week with a small room containing a bar and a larger room with some comfortable seating. As well as the mainstream offerings, it sometimes serves beer in cask that would normally only go for bottling. Keg and bottled beers are also available. QP

Woodstock

Black Prince
2 Manor Road, OX20 1XJ
☎ (01993) 811530 theblackprincewoodstock.com
Loddon Hullabaloo; St Austell Tribute; 2 changing beers (sourced nationally; often Gun Dog Ales, Vale) H
This lovely historic 16th-century riverside pub sits opposite the grounds of Blenheim Palace. Four ales – two regular and two changing, often locally sourced, brews – are available, alongside fresh well-cooked meals and snacks at reasonable prices. The interior boasts ancient fireplaces and a French suit of armour. Outside is a terrace with seating for warmer days, an ideal spot to watch the yearly mock mayor ceremony or June duck race. Aunt Sally is played, and families, walkers and well-behaved dogs are welcome. QP

Crown Inn
31 High Street, OX20 1TE (in centre of Woodstock on A44)
☎ (01993) 813339 thecrownwoodstock.com
Hook Norton Hooky, Hooky Gold; 1 changing beer (sourced nationally) H
Attractive Grade II listed 18th-century coaching inn in the centre of the historic town of Woodstock. Drinkers are welcome in the bar areas – one with wooden tables and chairs, the other with sofas and chairs. The latter is suitable for families and is dog-friendly. There is a small enclosed patio tucked away at the rear, and an airy conservatory restaurant. The pub has a wood-fired pizza oven. Hook Norton ales are available, with an additional guest in the spring and summer.
Q

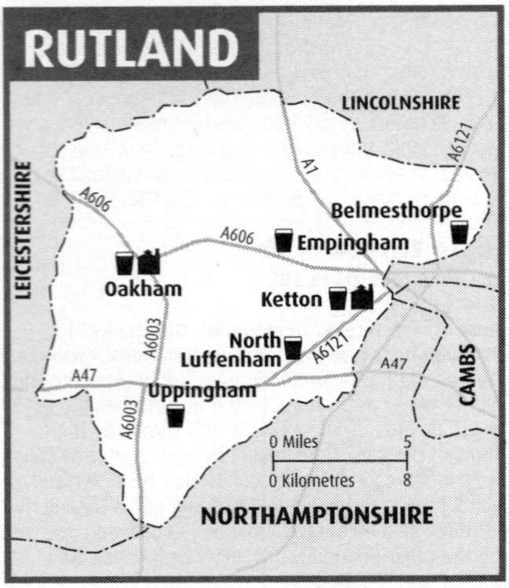

Belmesthorpe

Blue Bell

Shepherds Walk, PE9 4JG
☎ (01780) 753081
Draught Bass; Grainstore Ten Fifty; Greene King IPA; Oakham Bishops Farewell; 1 changing beer (often Abbeydale) H
The Blue Bell is a historic village pub – low ceilings, a roaring fire and stone walls are part of its charm. Six handpulls offer a wide range of well-kept guest beers, including at least one LocAle and a real cider. Dogs on leads are welcome in the bar area. Good honest home-made pub food is available Tuesday to Sunday lunchtimes (booking advisable). A former Rutland CAMRA Pub of the Year. Q P

Empingham

Empingham Cricket & Social Club

Exton Road, LE15 8QB
☎ (01780) 460696 🌐 empinghamcsc.com
Magpie Best; 3 changing beers (often Great Heck, Greg's, Stockport) H
Recently refurbished, the Cricket & Social Club is noted for the quality and variety of the ales served, many from microbreweries. It has limited hours, often extended by sporting and other functions – check the website for events. An annual beer festival is held to coincide with the final matches of the Six Nations rugby in March. A Rutland CAMRA award winner. Q P

Ketton

Railway

Church Street, PE9 3TA
☎ (01780) 721050
Grainstore Rutland Osprey, Ten Fifty; Oakham JHB H
A traditional village local situated in the shadow of the impressive church, serving good beer and wine in a welcoming and friendly atmosphere. The Grade II listed building is several hundred years old, with much character and more than a little charm. Food is not normally served but functions can be catered for. A fourth beer can be added at busy times. Local CAMRA Pub of the Year. Q P

North Luffenham

Fox

1 Pinfold Lane, LE15 8LE
☎ (01780) 720991 🌐 thefoxrutland.co.uk
Greene King IPA; Oakham JHB; house beer (by Grainstore); 1 changing beer (often Church End) H
Formerly owned by Courage, then Marston's, the Fox is now in private hands – it is from the same stable as the Horse & Jockey at Manton. The stone building has been opened out and completely refurbished with a clean and modern decor, while retaining the rural feel of a country inn. Happy hour is 5-7pm Monday to Thursday. A former Rutland CAMRA Pub of the Year. Q P

Oakham

Grainstore Brewery Tap

Station Approach, LE15 6EA
☎ (01572) 770065 🌐 grainstorebrewery.com
Grainstore Rutland Bitter, Rutland Panther, Cooking, Triple B, Daniel Lambert, Ten Fifty; 3 changing beers (often Grainstore) H
A pub and brewery in a cleverly converted small warehouse over four floors, retaining some original features. Brewery tours are available but must be booked in advance. Ten handpumps offer a range of beers, always including a mild. A range of bottle-conditioned Belgian beers is also stocked. Home-made food is served at lunchtime. Live bands feature regularly. Walkers and their dogs are welcome. A Rutland CAMRA award winner. Q P

Lord Nelson

12 Market Square, LE15 6DT
☎ (01572) 868340 🌐 kneadpubs.co.uk
Fuller's London Pride; Oakham JHB; 3 changing beers (often Bakers Dozen) H
A sympathetic refurbishment of Nick's Restaurant in the corner of the marketplace. Part of the Knead group of pubs, the Lord Nelson is a traditional tavern in a traditional town. It serves good beer and has become a popular addition to the county's real ale circuit. High-quality home-cooked food is available daily. A regular quiz night is hosted. A Rutland CAMRA award winner. Q

Uppingham

Exeter Arms

3 Leicester Road, LE15 9SB (follow High St W past school and turn right)
☎ (01572) 822900
Langton Inclined Plane Bitter; 1 changing beer (often Thornbridge) H
A friendly, recently refurbished, old-fashioned drinking establishment, situated to the west of the town centre. This pub is a real survivor and its furniture dates from a previous era. It divides into several different areas, one with a pool table. Sunday lunches are now served (booking is advisable). It can get extremely busy when rugby and football matches are shown on the large TV screen. The pub participates in the Uppingham Town Beer Festival. P

REAL ALE BREWERIES

Bakers Dozen Ketton
Grainstore Oakham

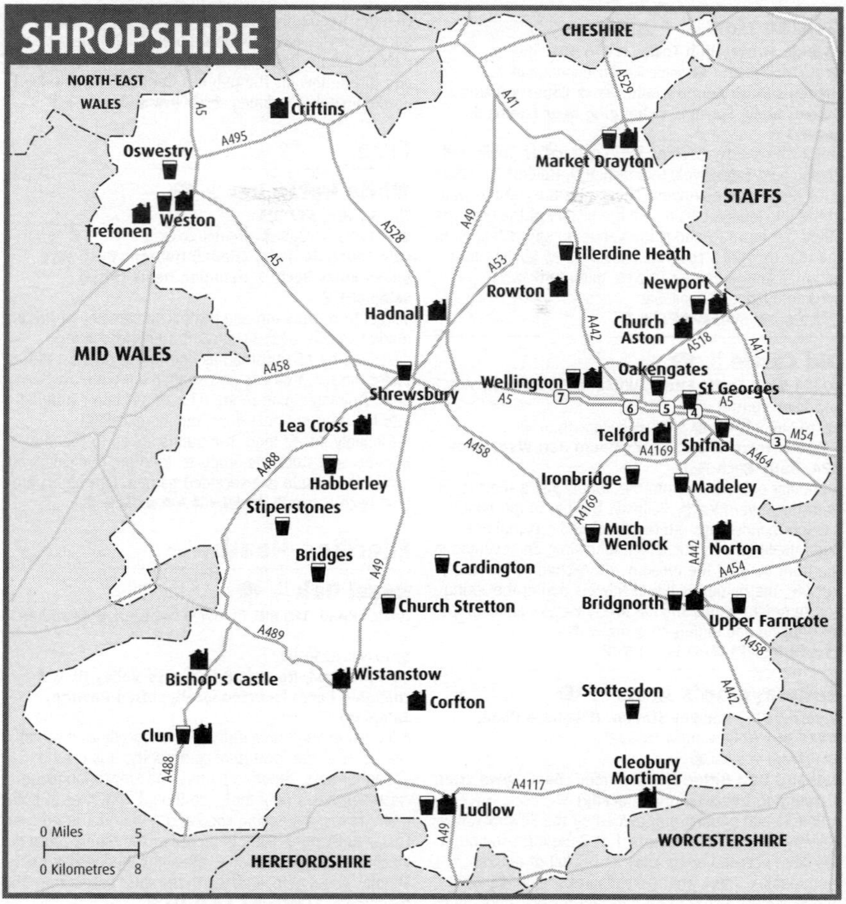

Bridges

Bridges

SY5 0ST (on back road from Shrewsbury to Bishops Castle via Longden)

(01588) 650260 thebridgespub.co.uk

Three Tuns Rantipole, XXX, Stout, Cleric's Cure; 3 changing beers (sourced locally; often Three Tuns)

This pub is a tied house belonging to the Three Tuns Brewery. A long, low building of some age, it nestles on the western edge of the Long Mynd on the banks of the River East Onny. Inside, there is a large dining area to the left, a bar area to the right, and beyond that a newly constructed room with a woodburner, used primarily for drinking. Six Three Tuns beers are regularly on offer. Walkers are welcome. Q P

Bridgnorth

Black Boy

58 Cartway, WV16 4BG

(01746) 769911

Hardys & Hansons Olde Trip; Ludlow Blonde; Morland Old Golden Hen; house beer (by Bewdley); 2 changing beers (sourced regionally)

Award-winning Grade II listed 17th-century alehouse, first licensed in 1790. It stands on the historic Cartway linking High Town with the quayside. Knowledgeable staff can advise on a range of ales from a selection of local brewers. Real ciders and traditional bar snacks are also available. At the rear is a partially covered patio with views overlooking the River Severn.

Q (SVR)

REAL ALE BREWERIES

All Nations Telford
Chapel Criftins
Church Aston Church Aston
Clun Clun
Corvedale Corfton
Finney's Wellington
Hobsons Cleobury Mortimer
Hop & Stagger Norton
Joule's Market Drayton
Ludlow Ludlow
Offa's Dyke Trefonen
Plan B Newport
Rowton Rowton/Wellington
Salopian Hadnall
Severn Valley Bridgnorth
St Annes Lea Cross
Stonehouse Weston
Three Tuns Bishop's Castle
Wood Wistanstow

Golden Lion 🅛

83 High Street, High Town, WV16 4DS
☎ (01746) 762016 🌐 goldenlionbridgnorth.co.uk
**Holden's Black Country Mild, Black Country Bitter,
Golden Glow, Special; 1 changing beer (sourced
locally)** Ⓗ

This 17th-century coaching inn has separate public and
lounge bars. Extensively refurbished by Holden's, it offers
a full range of the brewery's beers. Pictures on the walls
of the two lounge bars reveal the history of the pub. The
public bar has a TV and is the venue for sports teams. At
the rear there is a covered smoking area leading to a
patio drinking area near the car park. B&B
accommodation is available.
Q🌂🏵♿️🍴➤(SVR) ♣🚶P🚌🐕🏮

Old Castle 🅛 ✅

10/11 West Castle Street, WV16 4AB (between SVR
and town centre)
☎ (01746) 711420 🌐 oldcastlebridgnorth.co.uk
**Hobsons Town Crier; Sharp's Doom Bar; Wye Valley
HPA, Butty Bach** Ⓗ

A popular pub dating from the 1600s, just a short walk
from the Severn Valley Railway. The bar in the middle
has four handpumps offering local and regional ales.
Good-quality meals are served lunchtime and evening in
the front bar and the recently refurbished conservatory.
Outside, the garden is full of flowers during the spring
and summer months and has lovely views – an ideal spot
for drinking and dining on a sunny day.
🌂🏵🍴➤(SVR) 🚌(436,890) 🐕🏮

Railwayman's Arms 🅛 ✅

**Severn Valley Railway Station, Hollybush Road,
WV16 5DT** (follow signs for SVR)
☎ (01746) 760920 🌐 svr.co.uk
**Bathams Best Bitter; Hobsons Mild, Best, Town Crier;
4 changing beers (sourced locally)** Ⓗ

A unique and popular pub owned by the Severn Valley
Railway. Located on Platform 1 at Bridgnorth station, it
has been licensed since 1861 and is full of railway
memorabilia. There are 10 handpumps, eight serving
real ales from near and far and two for real cider. The
platform drinking area is an ideal place to soak up the
atmosphere of a steam railway. It gets busy at weekends
and holidays. Q🌂🏵♿️➤(SVR)🚶P🚌(436,101)🐕🏮

Cardington

Royal Oak

SY6 7JZ
☎ (01694) 771266 🌐 at-the-oak.com
Ludlow Best; Sharp's Doom Bar; 2 changing beers Ⓗ

The Royal Oak, dating back to the 15th century, is
reputedly Shropshire's oldest continually licensed pub,
and is the archetypal country inn. The single room is
multi-functional with a bar, lounge and dining area, and
has a relaxed ambience. It is low-beamed and
dominated by a large inglenook fireplace which provides
a home for various interesting artefacts. A good choice of
beers includes a mix of local and regional brews.
Q🏵🌂🍴A♣🚶P🚌(540) 🐕🏮

Church Stretton

Old Coppers Malt House

2 Shrewsbury Road, SY6 6DU
☎ (01694) 723336 🌐 theoldcoppersmalthouse.co.uk
Draught Bass; Rat White Rat; 4 changing beers Ⓗ

Revitalised inn in the centre of town offering fine ales
and good food. It has been freshly decorated while
retaining a traditional pub feel. The beer selection

changes frequently and includes a full range of styles. A
Randall device has been incorporated into one pump,
passing a base beer through additional dry hopping to
add to the flavour. The pub has three rooms, one kept
predominately for dining. 🌂🏵🍴➤🚶🚌(435)🐕🏮

Clun

White Horse Inn 🅛 ✅

The Square, SY7 8JA
☎ (01588) 640305 🌐 whi-clun.co.uk
**Clun Loophole, Pale, Citadel; Hobsons Best; Wye
Valley Butty Bach; 2 changing beers (often
Salopian)** Ⓗ

Sixteenth-century inn and posthouse standing in the old
market square, at the centre of a timeless town
described by AE Housman as one of the quietest places
under the sun. Inside is an L-shaped bar with low beams
and adjoining dining room, which has been extended
into the property next door, serving excellent,
reasonably priced food. The pub is linked to the Clun
Brewery and stocks its products. Rotating real ciders are
available. Outside is a secluded garden. Jam nights are
held once a month. 🌂🏵🍴🍴A♣🚶🚌🐕🏮

Ellerdine Heath

Royal Oak 🅛 ✅

Hazles Road, TF6 6RL (midway between A442 and A53)
SJ603226
☎ (01939) 250300
**Hobsons Best; Rowton Bitter; Wye Valley HPA; 3
changing beers (sourced locally; often Rowton,
Salopian)** Ⓗ

A long-standing Guide entry, known locally as the Tiddly.
The heart of the local rural community, it is used by
young farmers, shooting parties and French language
classes. It has a pool table, dartboard, real fires in both
main rooms, a smoking shed and a marquee used from
Easter to October. Food is served in the dining room –
lunchtimes weekends only, evenings Wednesday to
Sunday. A real gem, well worth the short detour from the
main roads. Q🌂🏵🍴A♣🚶P🐕🏮

Habberley

Mytton Arms 🅛

SY5 0TP
☎ (01743) 792490
**Hobsons Best; Three Tuns XXX; 2 changing beers
(often Hobsons, Joule's)** Ⓗ

Situated in a small village on the edge of the South
Shropshire Hills, somewhat off the beaten track, this
popular pub is worth seeking out. There are four low-
beamed rooms and a friendly rustic atmosphere – beer
and conversation predominate. Outside are seats to the
front and a paved area with a vine-covered pergola to
the side. A well-known local character and pub regular
features on the inn sign. The South Shropshire Hills
shuttle bus provides transport in summer. Q🏵♣🚶P🚌🐕

Ludlow

Blood Bay

13 High Street, SY8 1BS
☎ (01584) 872381
3 changing beers

This conserved Victorian property had been refurbished
to look exactly as it would in the 1800s. It has a public
bar, a tiny snug and a back bar. Up to three beers are
served – an IPA, a stout, brewed locally to authentic
recipes, and an occasional guest. Dogs on leads are

welcome on the ground floor only. Toilets are on the first floor. Under-16s, mobile phone use and smoking are prohibited. Q≹⊟🐾

Charlton Arms

Ludford Bridge, SY8 1PJ

☎ (01584) 872813 🌐 thecharltonarms.co.uk

Hobsons Best; Ludlow Gold, Stairway; Wye Valley Butty Bach; 1 changing beer (often Hobsons, Ludlow) Ⓗ

Recently extensively refurbished, this fine building overlooks the River Teme and is just across the historic Ludford Bridge, up towards Ludlow's last remaining fortified gate and the town centre. It has an attractive bar and a spacious lounge leading to a separate dining room with a terrace. The impressive function suite and roof bar offer fine views across the river towards the town. Accommodation is in 10 en-suite rooms. Dogs are allowed in the bar. Q≿❀⇔◑♿P⊡🐾

Ludlow Brewing Co 🄻

Station Drive, SY8 2PQ

☎ (01584) 873291 🌐 theludlowbrewingcompany.co.uk

Ludlow Best, Blonde, Gold, Black Knight, Boiling Well, Stairway Ⓗ

The Railway Shed is the brewery tap and visitor centre for the Ludlow Brewing Company. As the name suggests, the building was once a depot for railway goods. An imaginative conversion, it is built on two levels, with two huge mash tuns on the upper level, and comfortable seating and tables. On the ground floor there are hand-crafted timber tables and benches, together with a shop. Brewery visits are welcome and the centre is available for hire. Occasional beer festivals and events are hosted. Q≿❀◑♿≹●P⊟🐾

Rose & Crown

8 Church Street, SY8 1AP

☎ (01584) 875726 🌐 roseandcrowninnludlow.co.uk

Joule's Pure Blonde, Pale Ale, Slumbering Monk, Old No.6; 2 changing beers (often Hobsons, Hop Back) Ⓗ

Hidden away in a courtyard, the Rose and Crown is probably Ludlow's oldest pub, possibly 12th century. Recent refurbishment has created a much larger pub with exposed beams and fireplace. The Sun Room is open to the elements on one side and there is a garden area. A private room is available upstairs for small groups. Food is good honest pub grub, such as bangers and mash or bubble and squeak. There is a carvery on Sunday. ≿❀◑♿≹●⊟🐾

Wicked Grin 🄻

3 Fish Street, SY8 1TY

☎ 07766 185451

3 changing beers Ⓗ

This micropub opened in 2019 as a new addition to the Ludlow pub scene. It is tucked away at the end of Pepper Lane in the centre of town. The cosy downstairs room houses the servery and a couple of tables, and there are stairs leading up to a contemporary space with more seating. Three changing ales, usually including a dark beer, offer something for all tastes. Wine, gin, craft beer in bottles and cans, and a cask-served port are also available. ≹●⊟🐾

Market Drayton

Clive & Coffyne 🏆 ✔

6 Shropshire Street, TF9 3BY

☎ (01630) 657523

4 changing beers (sourced locally; often Hancocks, Hobsons) Ⓗ

A town-centre Tudor house originally built in 1753 and named after Market Drayton's famous son, Sir Robert Clive (of India), and a mutton pie, a coffyne, once served to customers. The Clive offers four changing ales plus a real cider, and is one of only four free houses in the town. It has three open fires and a large outside decking area for the summer. The pub holds regular music nights in the function room. ≿❀♿♣●P⊟(64,164)🐾

King's Arms

Shropshire Street, TF9 3DA

☎ (01630) 655413

Theakston Best Bitter; Timothy Taylor Landlord; Wadworth 6X; 1 changing beer (sourced regionally) Ⓗ

Originally an old coaching house built in 1865, the building has recently been tastefully extended and refurbished. A friendly every-man-and-his-dog's pub, it is smallish in size while maintaining two of the original rooms, one with a log fire. The Arms is very much into rugby and football, with major sports shown on TV. It serves three regular ales and is one of only four free houses in the town. Wheelchair access is at the rear via the car park. Q≿❀♿♣●P⊟(64,164)🐾

Red Lion 🄻 ✔

Great Hales Street, TF9 1JP

☎ (01630) 652602

Joule's Pure Blonde, Pale Ale, Slumbering Monk; 1 changing beer (sourced locally; often Joule's) Ⓗ

A previous winner of the CAMRA/English Heritage Pub Design Awards, this Joule's brewery tap is a former coaching inn built in 1623. Its unique features include the Mouse Room – a Robert Thompson-inspired function room featuring carved mice – and an illuminated well in the main bar. Log fires and oak beams create a comfortable atmosphere. Locally sourced food features on an extensive menu along with the Joule's range of beers produced in the adjacent brewery. Q≿❀◑♿P⊟(64,164)🐾

Salopian Star 🄻

21 Stafford Street, TF9 1HX

☎ (01630) 652530

Plan B New Alchemy, New Session IPA, Newport Pale Ale, Boscobel Bitter, Steam Stout Ⓗ

With its larger-than-life landlord, this is a friendly, no-frills boozer – what you see is what you get. It's a little gem if you like the kind of pub that offers traditional pub games and a fair pint. Three of the five ales are produced by one of Shropshire's newest breweries, Plan B, or New Brew as it is more commonly known, based in Newport. Outside is an attractive and colourful seating area for warmer weather. ❀♿♣⊟(64,164)🐾

Sandbrook Vaults 🄻

4 Shropshire Street, TF9 3BY

☎ (01630) 478405

Joule's Pure Blonde, Pale Ale, Slumbering Monk; 1 changing beer (sourced locally; often Joule's) Ⓗ

You are guaranteed a warm welcome at this Joule's pub, originally built in 1653. It has a familiar easy-on-the-eye Joule's interior and serves well-kept ales from the brewery close by. Free hot food is available at the weekend (with an optional donation to charity). The pub hosts high-quality live acoustic music nights on Thursday and Sunday featuring regional bands. Q❀◑♿♣⊟(64,164)🐾

Much Wenlock

George & Dragon 🄻

2 High Street, TF13 6AA

☎ (01952) 727009 🌐 thebestpubintheworld.com
Greene King Abbot; Hobsons Town Crier; Wye Valley HPA; 2 changing beers (sourced nationally) Ⓗ
Historic pub centrally located in this beautiful small market town and close to places of great interest like Wenlock Priory. Locals and visitors are all made welcome. The front bar has timber-backed settles, an original quarry-tiled floor and two open fireplaces. Whisky water jugs hang from the original beams, and interesting photographs are on the walls. The rear bar has an intimate atmosphere. A wide variety of food is available, with special offers most days (no food Mon or Sun eve). Dogs are welcome in the front bar.
Q🐎◐♿⛺♣P🚌(18,436)🐾📶

Newport

New Inn L
2 Stafford Road, TF10 7LX
☎ (01952) 812295 🌐 thenewinnnewport.co.uk
Joule's Pure Blonde, Pale Ale, Slumbering Monk; 2 changing beers (sourced locally; often Joule's, Ludlow, Wood) Ⓗ
Originally a coaching inn dating from 1792, the building was extended and refurbished by Joule's in 2016, while retaining some old features. There is a Yorkist fireplace in the snug area plus a central wood-burner for winter comfort. The New Inn is friendly and lively, with helpful staff and good food including vegetarian options. Two beer festivals are held each year in the extensive garden. Live music plays every Sunday from 6pm. Wheelchair access is via the Stafford Road entrance.
Q🐎❀◐♿♣●🚌(5,519)🐾📶

Oswestry

Bailey Head L
Bailey Head, SY11 1PZ (in Market Sq opp Guildhall)
🌐 baileyhead.co.uk
6 changing beers (sourced nationally; often Oakham, Salopian) Ⓗ
The pub is near the old castle and reopened as a free house in 2016. Seven constantly changing real ales, three KeyKeg beers and draught cider are on offer. Beers are sourced locally, regionally and nationally, usually from microbreweries, and served in thirds on request. Locally produced, traditional food is available, including vegan options. Events include Meet the Brewer and music and quiz nights. The market car park is close by.
🐎♿♣●▯🚌🐾📶

Black Lion L
Salop Road, SY11 2RJ (500yds S of town centre on B4579)
☎ (01691) 652745
Salopian Oracle; 4 changing beers (sourced locally; often Hobsons, Salopian, Wood) Ⓗ
Just inside the town's conservation area, this establishment is a true community pub and has a warm and friendly atmosphere. It is home to sports teams and social groups, with plenty of TVs for sports fans and tasting boards for beer lovers. The central bar divides the pub into a comfortable lounge at the front and public bar at the rear. Well-kept ales from various local and regional brewers can be enjoyed. Q🐎❀♣●P🚌🐾📶

Shifnal

Anvil L
22 Aston Road, TF11 8DU
☎ (01952) 462686
Black Country Bradley's Finest Golden, Pig on the Wall, Fireside; 5 changing beers (sourced regionally) Ⓗ
Reopened in 2018 after extensive refurbishment by Black Country Ales, and thoroughly brought up to date, including accessible toilets. The interior has been expanded, but the original fireplace remains, with coal fires in winter. The dartboard is in an enclosed booth. The bar has 10 handpulls, three devoted to Black Country Ales, five for guests and two for real cider. Generous bar snacks are available. Dogs are welcome, and children until 7pm. The shortest route to and from the railway station is via the station car park. Q❀♿⇌♣●P🚌🐾📶

Plough Inn L
26 Broadway, TF11 8AZ
☎ (01952) 463118 🌐 theploughinnshifnal.co.uk
Hobsons Mild, Best; 6 changing beers (sourced regionally; often Bathams, Sarah Hughes, Three Tuns) Ⓗ
Traditional, family-run free house dating back to the 17th century, with exposed beams and tiled floors. Ten handpulls offer an array of well-kept ales, always including one strong and one dark beer, as well as two draught ciders. Hearty home-cooked meals are served, with a popular roast on Sunday. The huge beer garden is a suntrap in the summer months, and a large function room is available to hire. The Wednesday night quiz is a must. Dogs are allowed in the garden.
Q🐎❀◐⇌♣●🚌🐾📶

White Hart L ✔
High Street, TF11 8BH
☎ (01952) 461161
Greene King Abbot; Salopian Shropshire Gold; Wye Valley HPA, Butty Bach; 5 changing beers (sourced regionally; often Enville) Ⓗ
This Grade II 17th-century timber-framed free house boasts 25 continuous years in the Guide. It offers a range of beers on nine handpumps and two ciders from the cellar. Evenings are for drinking and good conversation unspoilt by distracting games machines, while lunchtimes offer a popular food menu, except on Sunday, when a free cheeseboard is usually provided in the afternoon and snacks are available to order. Outside is a beer garden, walled patio area and large car park. Local CAMRA Pub of the Year 2019. Q🐎❀◐⇌♣●P🚌🐾

Shrewsbury

Abbey L ✔
83 Monkmoor Road, Monkmoor, SY2 5AZ
☎ (01743) 236788 🌐 theabbeyshrewsbury.co.uk
Bombardier; Sharp's Doom Bar; 6 changing beers Ⓗ
A large pub with several alcoves and multiple fireplaces. The publican is an ale enthusiast, running frequent Meet the Brewer sessions and several beer festivals a year. In between, he has expanded the range of guest ales and real ciders. Food is served until 10pm every night. There are regular community events including quizzes and occasional live music. 🐎❀◐♿♣●P🚌(1)📶

Admiral Benbow L
24 Swan Hill, SY1 1NF (just off Main Sq)
☎ (01743) 244423
Ludlow Gold; 5 changing beers (sourced locally; often Hobsons, Salopian, Wye Valley) Ⓗ
Spacious free house serving a range of Shropshire and Herefordshire beers plus a selection of ciders from Rosie's including Black Bart and Wicked Wasp. A good choice of Belgian, American and other foreign beers is also offered. A small room off the bar can be used for private functions, and there is a seating and smoking

area outside at the rear. Children are not permitted. The Admiral was a notorious 17th-century naval officer born in Shrewsbury. Q❀⇌♣●🚌ᯤ

Coach & Horses 🄻

23 Swan Hill, SY1 1NF

☎ (01743) 365661 🌐 coachswanhill.co.uk

Salopian Shropshire Gold, Oracle; Stonehouse Station Bitter; 3 changing beers Ⓗ

Set in a quiet street off the main shopping area, the pub is a peaceful haven in which to enjoy great LocAle beers, with magnificent floral displays in summer. Victorian in style, it has a wood-panelled bar, a small side snug area and a large lounge where meals are served lunchtimes and evenings. Bar snacks are also available at lunchtimes. Cheddar Valley or Sweeney Mountain cider is dispensed on handpull. Q◐♿⇌♣●🚌🐾ᯤ

Cross Foxes

27 Longden Coleham, SY3 7DE (close to River Severn)

☎ (01743) 355050

Draught Bass; Salopian Shropshire Gold; Three Tuns XXX; Wood Shropshire Lad Ⓗ

The pub has been a free house since its purchase from Mitchells & Butlers in the late 1980s, and run by the same family since 1985. It has one large, L-shaped room, with the bar and major drinking area on the large stroke, the smaller stroke occupied by the darts and another drinking area. The main part has an efficient wood-burner and the walls are adorned with sports trophies and a fine Bass mirror. Q♿♣🚌ᯤ

Loggerheads ★ 🄻 ✔

1 Church Street, SY1 1UG

☎ (01743) 362398

Banks's Amber Ale; Jennings Atomic Theory; Marston's 61 Deep; Young's London Gold; 2 changing beers (sourced nationally) Ⓗ

This 18th-century, Grade II listed, town-centre pub has a nationally important historic interior, with a small bar, servery and three other rooms. The bar to the left is served from a hatch and was Gents Only until 1975. The rear room, served from the same hatch, has portraits of Shropshire poets. The pub hosts regular folk and acoustic music events. Q⇌🚌🐾

Montgomery's Tower 🄻 ✔

Lower Claremont Bank, SY1 1RT

☎ (01743) 239080

Greene King IPA; Salopian Shropshire Gold; Wood Shropshire Lad; 4 changing beers (often Sadler's, Sharp's, Slater's) Ⓗ

Close to the Quarry Park and handy for Theatre Severn, this Lloyds No.1 offers a choice of two bars. To the left is a large open area rich in natural light, with a smoking area to the rear. The bar to the right provides quieter surroundings and subdued lighting, except on Friday and Saturday when there is a DJ. The walls display prints illustrating local history and famous Salopians. ➰❀◐♿⇌●🚌ᯤ

Nag's Head 🄻 ✔

22 Wyle Cop, SY1 1XB

☎ (01743) 362455

Hobsons Best; Timothy Taylor Landlord; Wye Valley HPA; 2 changing beers (often Titanic) Ⓗ

Situated on the historic Wyle Cop, the main architectural features of this Grade II listed, timber-framed building are best appreciated externally – in particular the upper-storey jettying and, in the beer garden to the rear, the timber remnants of a 14th-century hall house including a screened passage which provided protection from draughts (and now offers shelter for smokers). The old-style interior has remained unaltered for many years. The pub is said to be haunted and features on the Shrewsbury Ghost Trail. ❀⇌♣🚌🐾

Prince of Wales 🏆 🄻

30 Bynner Street, Belle Vue, SY3 7NZ

☎ (01743) 343301 🌐 theprince.pub

Hobsons Mild, Twisted Spire; Salopian Golden Thread; St Austell Tribute; Wainwright; 1 changing beer (sourced locally; often Rowton, Stonehouse, Wood) Ⓗ

Welcoming two-roomed community pub with a heated smoking shelter and a large suntrap deck adjoining a bowling green overlooked by a 19th-century maltings. Darts, dominoes and bowls teams abound. Beer festivals take place each year in February and May. Shrewsbury Town FC memorabilia adorn the building, with some of the seating from the old Gay Meadow ground skirting the bowling green. Westons Rosie's Pig is on handpull. The pub was judged as CAMRA's West Midlands Regional Pub of the Year for 2019. Q➰❀♿♣●P🚌🐾

Salopian Bar 🄻 ✔

Smithfield Road, SY1 1PW

☎ (01743) 351505

Hobsons Best; Oakham Citra; Salopian Oracle; 5 changing beers (often Oakham, Salopian) Ⓗ

A single-room pub popular with all age groups. The bar's management strives to vary the beer, cider and perry range to satisfy public demand. Regular cider and perry are provided by Westons and Thatchers, and an interesting and increasing range of bottled beer, including gluten-free, is also available. Large-screen TVs show coverage of major sporting events. Live music features on Friday evening. The pub will reopen in late 2020 following refurbishment due to flood damage. ♿⇌●🚌🐾ᯤ

Tap & Can

13 Castle Gates, SY1 2AB

☎ 07837 490495

4 changing beers Ⓗ

Opened in 2019, this single-room bar has the counter at the far end. Four handpumps offer a changing range of real ales, plus KeyKeg and keg craft beers. Cans are served from vast fridges near the bar, available to drink here or take away. The rear wall of the Gents is the exposed castle foundations and is over 900 years old. ⇌🚌🐾

Three Fishes 🄻

4 Fish Street, SY1 1UR

☎ (01743) 344793

Ludlow Best; Timothy Taylor Landlord; 3 changing beers (often Oakham, Salopian, Stonehouse) Ⓗ

Fifteenth-century building standing in the shadow of two churches, St Alkmund's and St Julian's, within the maze of streets and passageways in the town's medieval quarter. Freshly prepared food is available lunchtimes and early evenings Monday to Saturday. The pub offers a range of up to five local and national ales, usually including some dark beers, and a choice of real ciders and perries. Q◐⇌♣●🚌🐾ᯤ

Woodman 🄻

32 Coton Hill, SY1 2DZ

☎ (01743) 351007

Salopian Shropshire Gold; Wye Valley Butty Bach; 3 changing beers (sourced regionally; often Abbeydale, Ossett) Ⓗ

Part-brick and part-timbered black and white corner pub, originally built in the 1800s, destroyed by fire in 1923, and rebuilt in 1925. The building is reputedly haunted by the ex-landlady who died in the fire. The wonderful oak-

panelled lounge has two real log fires and traditional settles, and the separate bar has the original stone-tiled flooring, wooden seating, fire and leaded windows. The courtyard has a heated smoking area and seating. The bar specialises in pale, hoppy beers.
Q♘❀⇌♣●🚌🐾📶

Stiperstones

Stiperstones Inn

SY5 0LZ

☎ (01743) 791327 🌐 stiperstonesinn.co.uk

Three Tuns XXX; 1 changing beer (often Rowton, Six Bells, Stonehouse) [H]

A delightful and homely pub tucked away under the Stiperstones range. The public bar is rather plain but the little lounge has its own charm. There are also two separate dining rooms. Whinberries – the local delicacy that grow wild in the area – are used here to make home-made jam and as a gin flavouring. The pub is on the route of the Shropshire Hills shuttle bus during the summer months and welcomes walkers and their canine companions. ♘❀🛏◑♿♣P🚌(552)🐾📶

Stottesdon

Fighting Cocks Ⓛ

1 High Street, DY14 8TZ

☎ (01746) 718270 🌐 fightingcocks.co.uk

Hobsons Twisted Spire; Ludlow Blonde; Wye Valley HPA, Butty Bach [H]

A locals' pub set in the heart of rural south Shropshire and first licensed in 1830. A traditional bar serving local ales and warmed by a log fire leads to one of two dining rooms where locally sourced food is on the menu. Live music features on occasional weekends. Outside is a patio area and lawned garden with a children's play area. Walkers and cyclists are welcome. A shop/cafe/function room is at the rear of the premises. Winter opening hours may vary. ♘❀◑ɅP🐾📶

Telford: Ironbridge

Coracle Micropub & Beer Shop

27 High Street, TF8 7AD

☎ (01952) 432664

6 changing beers (sourced nationally; often Salopian, Tiny Rebel) [H]/[A]

Opened in 2018 by two beer enthusiasts, this is a quiet micropub with friendly and knowledgeable staff. The main room is semi-divided, creating two separate drinking areas and enhancing the cosy ambience. The well-stocked fridge contains up to 80 bottled and canned beers, listed on a beer menu, with more in the cellar. A good selection of locally sourced bar snacks is available, including a free cheeseboard on Sunday. Children are welcome until 7pm. The pub is central to Ironbridge, overlooking England's last coracle shed.
Q♘Ʌ♣●🚌🐾📶

Telford: Madeley

All Nations Ⓛ

20 Coalport Road, TF7 5DP (signed off Legges Way, opp Blists Hill Museum)

☎ (01952) 585747

House beer (by All Nations); 2 changing beers (sourced regionally; often Hobsons, Ludlow) [H]

Regulars and visitors love this pub for its cosy interior and friendliness. The historic 1852 brewhouse, an icon of home-brewing history, is still working at the back of the building. Four real ales, including the pub's own beers, plus cider or perry, are available. Freshly prepared bar snacks are on offer – bacon and brie, black pudding and cheese baps are particular favourites. Visitors can browse books and newspapers by the fire. The TV is in use only for international Rugby Union matches. Monday is quiz night, and live bands play in the summer.
Q♘❀🛏Ʌ●P🐾📶

Telford: Oakengates

Crown Inn Ⓛ ✔

Market Street, TF2 6EA

☎ (01952) 610888 🌐 crown.oakengates.net

Hobsons Twisted Spire, Best; 10 changing beers (sourced nationally; often Backyard, Beartown, Rudgate) [H]

Cosy, traditional, three-room town pub with real coal fires in the front and rear bars, close to Oakengates station. It has 14 cooled handpulls – with more for beer festivals in May and October, where some 18,000 beers have featured since 1995 – plus a large range of interesting continental bottled beers. There is a suntrap courtyard with wheelchair access plus a large municipal car park and bus station to the rear. The Crown hosts a comedy club, live music and traditional pub quizzes.
Q♘❀♿⇌♣P🚌🐾📶

Old Fighting Cocks Ⓛ

48 Market Street, TF2 6DU

☎ (01952) 615607

Everards Tiger; Rowton Ironbridge Gold, Area 51; 6 changing beers (sourced regionally) [H]

Popular family-run Rowton Brewery pub with 12 handpulls, four for the brewery's own beers, plus five changing beers and three ciders. The building retains many period features including stained glass and a horse-feeding hatch in the accessible toilet. As well as the two main rooms there is a rear room and a snug. The large outside area has a covered space. Bar snacks are available. There are a number of car parks nearby and the local bus station is less than 200m away.
Q❀♿⇌♣●🚌🐾📶

Station Hotel Ⓛ

42 Market Street, TF2 6DU

☎ (01952) 612949

Bathams Best Bitter; 8 changing beers (sourced nationally; often Abbeydale, Pictish) [H]

This multi-roomed local has been in the Guide for many years. It specialises in beers mainly from Yorkshire, though local beers do appear now and then. Home-made rolls, pies and cheeses are available, and a curry night is held on Wednesday. An open fire warms the bar. The floor is level throughout and give easy wheelchair access to modern toilets. Three beer festivals are held a year – over the May and August bank holidays and in December. Outside is a patio and a covered and heated smoking area. Q❀♿⇌♣🚌🐾📶

Telford: St Georges

St Georges Sports & Social Club Ⓛ

Church Road, St Georges, TF2 9LU

☎ (01952) 612911 🌐 stgeorgesclub.co.uk

Sharp's Doom Bar; 7 changing beers (sourced regionally; often Hobsons, Ludlow, Salopian) [H]

This friendly, welcoming private members' club is a frequent CAMRA branch Club of the Year. The spacious lounge bar shows live sport on three screens and has views of the sports fields. Eight handpulls dispense mostly regional beers. Food is served throughout the day. The club has a large function room available for hire

for weddings and parties, with bespoke bar and on-site catering services available. Show a CAMRA membership card or copy of this Guide for entry at any time.
ᗰ❀◑ᕹᗰ🗗🛜

Telford: Wellington

Pheasant Inn ❢ Ⅼ

54 Market Street, TF1 1DT
☎ (01952) 260683

Everards Tiger; Rowton Ironbridge Gold; 5 changing beers (sourced nationally; often Finney's, Rowton) Ⓗ
Family-run Rowton Brewery tap, situated near the historic market, with nine handpulls – three for Rowton's own ales, four for changing ales usually including a dark beer, plus two for ciders. The large beer garden next to the brewery has a covered area. Home-made food is served Monday to Saturday during the day plus bar snacks at any time. A popular cheese night is held on the last Tuesday of the month. Q ᗰ❀◑ᕹ✿⇄●🗗❀🛜

William Withering Ⅼ ⊘

43-45 New Street, TF1 1LU
☎ (01952) 642800

Greene King Abbot; Ruddles Best Bitter; Sharp's Doom Bar; 3 changing beers Ⓗ
Named after a local physician who is best remembered for discovering and developing Digitalis. This pub is a large single open-plan room with an interior styled as an 18th century study. The regular ales are joined by three changing ales from local, regional and national breweries, but with a focus tending on ales from the local area. Good value food is served and it is busy Saturday lunchtime with shoppers enjoying brunch.
ᗰ❀◑ᕹ⇄●🗗🛜

Upper Farmcote

Lion o' Morfe Ⅼ

WV15 5PS (½ mile from A458 signpost Claverley)
SO770919
☎ (01746) 389935

Enville Ale; Hobsons Town Crier; Wye Valley HPA; 2 changing beers (sourced locally; often Bewdley, Ludlow, Three Tuns) Ⓗ
This Georgian farmhouse became a pub in the early 1850s. After prolonged closure it was extensively refurbished and the conservatory was rebuilt. The doorway opens into the main bar with an open fire. To the rear is a snug with an old-fashioned range lit during winter. To the left is a traditionally decorated lounge. Meals are served daily (no food Sun eve). The garden area contains a boules piste and there is a large car park.
Q ᗰ❀◑ᕹ✤●P❀

Weston

Stonehouse Brewery Ⅼ

Stonehouse, Weston Road, SY10 9ES (just off A483 Oswestry bypass)
☎ (01691) 676457 ⊕ stonehousebrewery.co.uk

Stonehouse Sunlander, Station Bitter, Off the Rails; 1 changing beer Ⓗ
The family-run Stonehouse Brewery bar and shop is part of the brewery and is next to the preserved Cambrian Railway. The building has a pleasant rustic style and serves only Stonehouse products – at least four beers plus Sweeney Mountain Cider and Henstone spirits (whisky, gin, applejack) distilled on-site. Bottles, gift packs and 'fill your own' are available. Brewery tours are by appointment. Q ᗰ❀◑ᕹᕹ✤●P🗗❀🛜

Three Fishes, Shrewsbury (Photo: Nigel Parker/Flickr)

SOMERSET

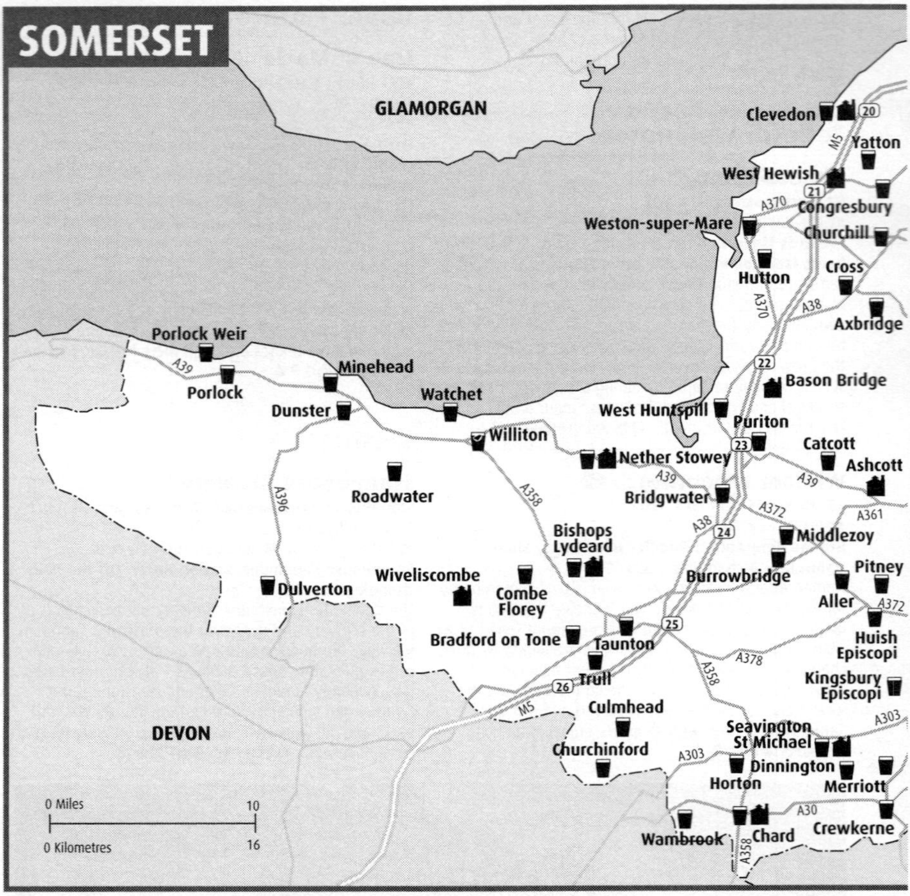

Aller

Old Pound Inn

1 High Street, TA10 0RA (centre of village)
☎ (01458) 250469 🌐 oldpoundinn.com
Butcombe Original; Teignworthy Reel Ale; 1 changing beer (sourced regionally; often Exmoor, Otter) H
This lovely 16th-century inn stands on the ground of the old village pound. A varying selection of three regional ales and a local cider are on handpump. A wonderful open Dutch fire is a feature in the centre of the bar. There is a separate restaurant/function room, public lounge and a delightful snug. Excellent food, including a Sunday carvery, is served in the bar or restaurant.
P (16)

Axbridge

Lamb ✔

The Square, BS26 2AP
☎ (01934) 732253
Butcombe Original; 3 changing beers (often Butcombe, Milestone) H
Lovely Butcombe-owned Grade II listed coaching house in the village square. Inside is a large low-beamed bar area with several smaller, quieter areas leading off it, where traditional pub games can be played. Outside drinking spaces are to the front, as well as to the rear via the courtyard. Real cider is sold and there is an interesting food menu, including bar snacks. Directly opposite is the National Trust's medieval King John's Hunting Lodge, where Hanging Judge Jeffreys held court.
Q (26,126)

Batcombe

Three Horseshoes Inn

BA4 6HE (off Back Lane) ST69023908
☎ (01749) 850359 🌐 thethreehorseshoesinn.co.uk
Butcombe Original; 3 changing beers H
A 400-year-old country pub which has a spacious bar with an inglenook fireplace and beamed ceiling, a stunning dining room with a vaulted ceiling and a lawned garden overlooked by the church tower. Food is from local suppliers. Open to all, it welcomes drinkers, foodies, walkers, children (with colouring books and games to keep them entertained) and dogs. Local cider is from Rich's. Q P

Bath

Bath Brew House ✔

14 James Street West, BA1 2BX
☎ (01225) 805609 🌐 thebathbrewhouse.com
Bath Brew House Gladiator, Emperor; 5 changing beers (sourced regionally; often Bristol Beer Factory, Siren) H

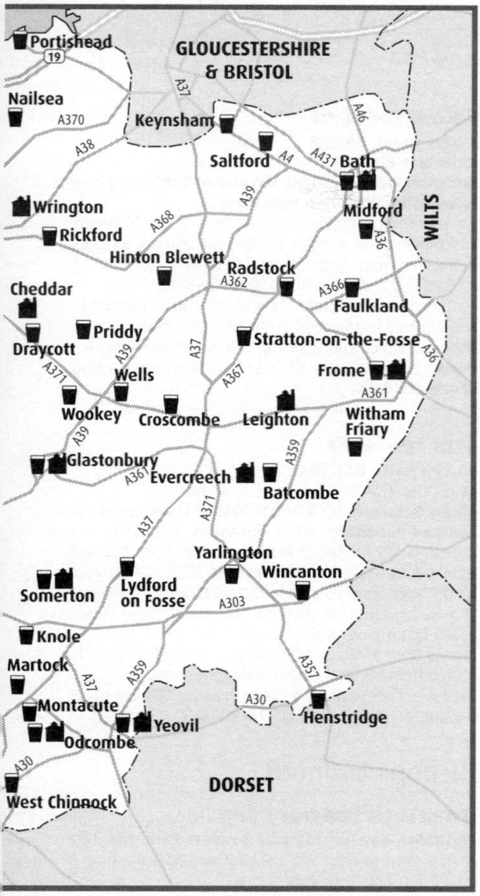

Refurbishment in 2013 saw the former Midland Hotel transformed into a City Pub Company brewpub. The on-site James Street Brewery produces two regular beers, the refreshing and malty Gladiator (3.9% ABV) and the hoppy, citrussy Emperor (4.4 ABV), and rotating seasonal ales. Five guests, usually from nearby micros, are complemented by four craft beers. A large L-shaped bar gives out on to a dining area and a good-sized beer garden. The upstairs room hosts sports TV, quizzes, comedy, and so on.

Bell

103 Walcot Street, BA1 5BW

(01225) 460426 thebellinnbath.co.uk

Abbey Bellringer; Bath Ales Gem; Box Steam Golden Bolt; Butcombe Original; Hop Back Summer Lightning; Otter Ale; 3 changing beers (sourced regionally; often Arbor, Cotswold Lion, Keystone)

Purchased by 536 of its regulars, fans and staff, following a community buy-out in 2013. The Bell has six regular ales plus three changing guests from local micros. Live music is a mainstay, with bands playing Monday and Wednesday evenings and Sunday lunchtimes. An open mic night is held on Thursday evening in the separate Back Bar. Features include bar billiards, board games and even a tiny launderette. At the rear is a walled garden with covered seating.

Coeur de Lion

17 Northumberland Place, BA1 5AR

(01225) 463568

Abbey Bath Best, Bath Pale Ale; 2 changing beers (sourced nationally; often Abbey)

In a passageway opposite the Guildhall in the centre of town, this pub claims to be the smallest in Bath. With just four tables in the tiny bar this may well be true. A fine stained-glass window forms the frontage. Traditional pub food is served at lunchtime. Seating capacity is increased in summer by placing tables outside. There is also an upstairs room used mainly for food. One guest beer is always from Abbey. Q

Cross Keys

Midford Road, Combe Down, BA2 5RZ

(01225) 849180 crosskeysbath.co.uk

Butcombe Original; 3 changing beers (sourced locally)

Historic inn dating from 1718 on the southern outskirts of the city, close to the beautiful Midford Valley and popular with walkers. It features four ales, including guests often from a local brewery of the month range of ales. Highly recommended, gastro-standard, home-made food is served at all sessions. The main bar on the left still has many original features and an open fire. The restaurant is on the right and split across three levels. Parking is a bit restricted. P (3,D2)

Crystal Palace

10-11 Abbey Green, BA1 1NW

(01225) 482666

Fuller's London Pride, ESB; 2 changing beers (often Butcombe, Wild Beer)

Set on the pretty Abbey Green, this pub was refurbished by Fuller's in 2014 and is now a city-centre venue with an upmarket feel. There are usually at least two Fuller's beers on plus a couple of guest ales, some local, others from further away, but all are from interesting breweries. Full table service is available in the lounge. There is a glass-covered seating area at the rear.

REAL ALE BREWERIES

Abbey Bath
Bason Bridge Bason Bridge
Bath Brewhouse Bath
Black Bear Wiveliscombe
Blindmans Leighton
Butcombe Wrington
Cheddar Cheddar
Clevedon Clevedon
Cotleigh Wiveliscombe
Electric Bear Bath
Epic (Pitchfork/3D) West Hewish
Exmoor Wiveliscombe
Fine Tuned Somerton
Frome Frome
Glastonbury Glastonbury
Isle of Avalon Ashcott
Odcombe Odcombe
Parkway Somerton (NEW)
Quantock Bishops Lydeard
Ralph's Ruin Bath
Stowey Nether Stowey
Tapstone Chard
Twisted Oak Bristol: Wrington
Wild Beer Evercreech
Windy Seavington St Michael
Yeovil Yeovil

King of Wessex ✓
5–10 James Street West, BA1 2BX
☎ (01225) 303380
Greene King Abbot; Ruddles Best Bitter; Sharp's
Doom Bar; 4 changing beers (sourced nationally) ⓗ
A large new-build Wetherspoon, refurbished in 2016, at
the entrance to a cinema complex. There are up to four,
sometimes five, real ales that change regularly, plus the
usual Spoons beers. Popular with the younger crowd, it
can get busy in the evenings. Both the food and the
beers are good value for the city centre. Alcoholic drinks
are served from 9am. ⏱◐➤●🖵🕏

Old Green Tree ★
12 Green Street, BA1 2JZ
☎ (01225) 448259
Butcombe Original; Pitchfork Golden Ale; house beer
(by Blindmans); 3 changing beers (sourced locally) ⓗ
A classic, unspoilt 300-year-old inn with three oak-
panelled rooms including a superb northern-style
drinking lobby. Although it can get crowded, there is
often space in the comfortable back bar. Guest beers are
generally from local microbreweries, with a stout or
porter usually on offer in the winter months. A local
farmhouse cider is also sold, along with a range of fine
wines and malt whiskies. Winter Sunday hours may be
longer. Q◐➤●🖵

Pulteney Arms ✓
37 Daniel Street, BA2 6ND (on corner of Daniel St and
Sutton St)
☎ (01225) 463923 ⊕ thepulteneyarms.co.uk
Bath Ales Gem; Timothy Taylor Landlord; Wye Valley
HPA; 2 changing beers (sourced nationally; often
Exmoor, Fuller's, Otter) ⓗ
Tucked away near the end of Great Pulteney Street, this
establishment has been open since 1792. The cat symbol
on the pub sign refers to the Pulteney coat of arms. There
are five gas light fittings (now sadly condemned) above
the bar. The decor has an emphasis on sport, particularly
rugby. The food menu is extensive and deservedly
popular (no food Sun eve). Guest beers are usually from
a national brewery. Winter hours vary.
⏱🕏◐♣●🖵🕏🕏

Raven
6-7 Queen Street, BA1 1HE
☎ (01225) 425045 ⊕ theravenofbath.co.uk
House beer (by Blindmans); 4 changing beers
(sourced regionally; often Gloucester, Moor Beer) ⓗ
A busy 18th-century free house in the heart of Bath,
voted the local CAMRA branch's Pub of the Year in 2018.
The six ales include two brewed exclusively by
Blindmans. Guest ales come from far and wide, with
several mini beer festivals a year. The main bar and the
quieter first-floor bar serve the same range of ales.
Famous for its sausages and Pieminister pies, the Raven
is one of the few pubs in Bath serving food on Sunday
evening. Q◐➤♣●🖵🕏

Royal Oak 🍺
Lower Bristol Road, Twerton, BA2 3BW (on A36 at
intersection with road to Windsor Bridge)
☎ (01225) 481409 ⊕ theroyaloakbath.co.uk
Ralph's Ruin Ivory Tower, Sirius, Dark Side of the
Ralph; 5 changing beers (often Butts, Downton,
Stonehenge) ⓗ
Up to three beers from its own brewery, Ralph's Ruin,
and up to six guest beers from microbreweries near and
far, are served here alongside an interesting range of
ciders, perries and bottled British and Belgian beers.
There is live music on Wednesday evening and most
weekends, and regular quiz nights, plus occasional beer

festivals. Outside is a small secluded garden and a small
car park. Local CAMRA City Pub of the Year 2019.
🕏➤●P🖵🕏

Salamander ✓
3 John Street, BA1 2JL
☎ (01225) 428889
Bath Ales Prophecy, Gem, Lansdown; 1 changing beer
(sourced locally; often Bath Ales) ⓗ
An 18th-century building, tucked away in a side street,
which opened as a coffee bar in 1957 and got a drinks
licence five years later. Taken over by St Austell in 2017,
it looks and feels like an inn that's been here for a
century or more. Wooden floorboards, wood panelling
and subdued lighting add to the ambience of the ground-
floor bar, which was originally several small rooms. A
popular restaurant upstairs uses local ales in its cooking.
◐➤♣●🖵🕏🕏

Star Inn ★ ✓
23 Vineyards, BA1 5NA
☎ (01225) 425072
Abbey Bellringer ⓖ; Draught Bass; 3 changing beers
(sourced nationally; often Robinsons, Titanic) ⓗ
A main outlet for Abbey Ales, this classic town pub was
fitted out by Gaskell and Chambers in 1928. Its four small
rooms have benches around the walls, wood panelling
and roaring fires. The smallest room has a single bench,
called Death Row, while the pub itself, which dates
around from 1760, is coffin-shaped. Abbey Bellringer is
served from the cask and complimentary snuff is
available. Cheese night is every Thursday and live music
features on Friday evening. Q♣●🖵🕏🕏

Bishops Lydeard

Quantock Brewery Tap ⓛ
Westridge Way, Broadgauge Business Park, TA4 3RU
(follow signs to West Somerset Railway WSR and shop is
on left just before railway station)
☎ (01823) 433812 ⊕ quantockbrewery.co.uk
Quantock Ale, QPA, Wills Neck, Plastered Pheasant; 1
changing beer (sourced locally; often Quantock) ⓗ
The brewery taproom, with up to six of its cask beers on
handpump. There are also two Quantock KeyKeg beers
always on the bar, plus a monthly small batch KeyKeg
(subject to availability). One or two guest KeyKeg beers
are also sold, typically from Northern Monk, Salopian,
Thornbridge or Weird Beard. A brewery shop supplies
takeaway bottles and other brewery gifts. There is an
annual beer festival in July and regular live band, comedy
and quiz nights. Street food is on offer Fridays and most
Saturday evenings. ⏱🕏🕏➤●P🖵(28)🕏🕏

Bradford on Tone

White Horse Inn ⓛ
Regent Street, TA4 1HF (off A38 between Taunton and
Wellington at World's End junction)
☎ (01823) 461239 ⊕ whitehorseinn.pub
3 changing beers (sourced regionally; often Exeter,
Otter, St Austell) ⓗ
A friendly, well-established and well-run free house with
real fires in winter warming both the bar and restaurant.
Three different ales are sourced locally and regionally.
Good home-cooked food is served at reasonable prices.
The beautiful large garden hosts a barbecue in summer,
and regular events include music, skittles matches, quiz
nights and gatherings of local interest groups. Closes
early on Sunday October-April. ⏱🕏◐🅰P🖵(22)🕏🕏

Bridgwater

West India House

101 Durleigh Road, TA6 7JE (top of Durleigh Rd hill)
☎ (01278) 452533 🌐 westindiahouse.co.uk
Butcombe Original; Sharp's Doom Bar; 1 changing beer (sourced locally; often Cheddar Ales) [H]
This building was constructed in 1936, although there has been a pub on the site for many years, with the name derived from the days when Bridgwater was a bustling port. For a quiet drink in cosy surroundings there is the lounge bar complete with open log fire, and for a more vibrant atmosphere try the saloon bar which has been extended and refurbished with modern decor. Three good ales are on offer from Butcombe, Sharp's and, occasionally, Cheddar Ales. **Q♘❀◐◑♣P🚌ᯤ**

Burrowbridge

King Alfred Inn [L]

Burrow Drove, TA7 0RB (on A361, 9 miles from Taunton)
☎ (01823) 698379 🌐 king-alfred.co.uk
Bristol Beer Factory Fortitude; Butcombe Original; Otter Amber [H]
A welcoming free house with a friendly atmosphere on the Somerset Levels between Taunton and Glastonbury. It is positioned under Burrow Mump where, allegedly, King Alfred famously burnt the cakes. The pub is a perfect stopping-off point for walkers on the River Parrett Trail. It serves good home-made food with many choices, all cooked to order, including specialist burgers with many fillings. The three cask ales rarely change but are always good quality, and there are usually a couple of local real ciders. There is a bus stop outside and a car park to the rear. **Q♘❀◐◑♿♣●P🚌**(29)**🐾ᯤ**

Catcott

Crown Inn

1 The Nydon, TA7 9HQ
☎ (01278) 722288 🌐 crowninncatcott.com
3 changing beers (sourced regionally; often Butcombe, Dartmoor, Exmoor) [H]
A traditional freehold country pub in this Polden Hills village, which lies just off the A39 between Bridgwater and Street. The original part of the building is over 400 years old and has a log fire, flagstone floors, cob walls and low-beamed ceilings. There is a large function room/skittle alley to the rear. A range of up to three cask ales is normally available, usually on handpump but sometimes on gravity. **♘❀◐◑⛺♣●P🐾ᯤ**

Chard

Cerdic ✔

47 Fore Street, TA20 1PT (on A30 in centre of town)
☎ (01460) 260070
Greene King Abbot; Ruddles Best Bitter; Sharp's Doom Bar; 4 changing beers (sourced nationally; often Dorset, Exmoor, Otter) [H]
A Wetherspoon pub that used to be a cinema of the same name before it closed in the 1960s. The well-kept guest beers are normally local and you may find a bigger selection at the weekend. In addition there are usually six real ciders. There is a bar area and a family dining area down some steps in a conservatory. A pleasant rear garden has been added (closed late evening).
♘❀◐◑♿●🚌ᯤ

Churchill

Crown Inn [L]

The Batch, Skinners Lane, BS25 5PP (off A38, 400yds S of A368 jct)
☎ (01934) 852995 🌐 the-crown-inn.co.uk
Bath Ales Gem; Butcombe Original; Exmoor Ale; Palmers IPA; St Austell Tribute; house beer (by St Austell); 1 changing beer [G]
Long-time Guide regular and winner of many CAMRA awards, the Crown is tucked away down a small lane close to the village centre. Several cosy rooms with stone-flagged floors are warmed by two log fires, and offer an assortment of seating. Excellent food is provided at lunchtimes using local ingredients. Up to eight beers, usually local, are served on gravity. Outside drinking areas are to the front and rear. Families are welcome away from the bar itself. An old, classic, unchanged pub.
Q♘❀◐⛺●P🚌(A2) **🐾ᯤ**

Churchinford

York Inn ✔

Honiton Road, TA3 7RF
☎ (01823) 601333 🌐 yorkinn.co.uk
Otter Bitter, Amber; Sharp's Sea Fury; 1 changing beer (sourced regionally) [H]
This is a traditional hostelry in the Blackdown Hills dating back, in some parts, to the 16th century, with an open fireplace and oak beams, but at the same time offering contemporary facilities. It serves a good range of four cask ales and one real cider. The menu offers good traditional home-cooked food including a specialist range of pies. **♘❀◐◑♣●P🐾ᯤ**

Clevedon

Fallen Tree Micropub [L]

43 Hill Road, BS21 7PD
☎ (01934) 310515 🌐 twistedoakbrewery.co.uk
Twisted Oak Fallen Tree, Spun Gold, Slippery Slope; 6 changing beers (sourced locally; often Bristol Beer Factory, Cheddar Ales, Pitchfork) [G]
A new micropub opened in 2018 in a shopping area up a hill from the Grade I listed Clevedon Pier. Between five and eight ales are served straight from casks in the wooden stillage behind the bar. It is owned by Twisted Oak Brewery and guest beers are usually from local breweries such as Pitchfork, Bristol Beer Factory and Cheddar Ales. The filled rolls served at weekends come from Murrays deli on the same road. **Q♘●🚌🐾**

Royal Oak ✔

35 Copse Road, BS21 7QN (behind ice cream parlour near pier)
☎ (01275) 563879 🌐 theroyaloakclevedon.co.uk
Butcombe Original; St Austell Tribute; Sharp's Doom Bar, Atlantic; 1 changing beer (often Cheddar Ales, Great Western, Palmers) [H]
Lively, friendly, mid-terrace pub close to the seafront and connected via an alley. It has a large front window and an unexpectedly large interior with many rooms. This community hub is home to cribbage and cricket teams, with a quiz on Monday and acoustic music on Wednesday. The winner of various awards, it hosts many events, including a street party every two years. Food is served lunchtimes including daily specials and a range of salads. **Q♘◐♣●🚌🐾ᯤ**

Combe Florey

Farmers Arms Ⓛ

TA4 3HZ (on A358 between Bishops Lydeard and Williton)

☎ (01823) 432267 🌐 farmersarmsatcombeflorey.co.uk

Exmoor Ale, Gold; Otter Ale; Quantock QPA [H]

A thatched 14th-century Grade II listed pub with cob walls, a medieval chimney and fireplace, and a restored staircase (in its original position from more than 200 years ago). The bar serves four cask ales and three real ciders plus some unusual keg beers, bottled beers and a large selection of gins and malt whiskies. The restaurant offers a good-quality menu with various evening specials. During the summer months there is a splendid marquee and a large pizza oven for special occasions.
Q🐎❀◑♿●P🚌🐾📶

Congresbury

Plough Ⓛ

High Street, BS49 5JA (off A370 at B3133 jct)

☎ (01934) 877402 🌐 the-plough-inn.net

Butcombe Original; St Austell Tribute [H]/[G]**; Twisted Oak Fallen Tree** [G]**; 4 changing beers (sourced locally)** [H]/[G]

Characterful village inn with flagstone floors and many original features, decorated with interesting local artefacts. Four guest beers, mainly from local breweries, are delivered from a row of old cask heads behind the bar. Up to 16 ciders are also stocked. The pub has a deserved reputation for the quality of its food, which is served lunchtimes and evenings, except Sunday evening, which is quiz night. The pub has real fires and a large garden. Mendip morris men meet here.
Q❀◑♿♣●P🚌(X1,X2) 🐾📶

Crewkerne

King William Inn

Barn Street, TA18 8BP (take A30 towards Chard and at fringe of town Barn St is on left)

☎ (01460) 074492 🌐 kingwilliamcrewkerne.com

3 changing beers (sourced nationally; often Bristol Beer Factory, Oakham, Tapstone) [H]

A short walk from the town centre towards Chard brings you to this well-hidden traditional inn. There are three changing and often interesting ales and two ciders, and the array of pumpclips adorning the beams indicates the huge range of beers served over time. Current beers are shown on Twitter. There is a happy hour every Monday and Wednesday. For music lovers there is an acoustic night on the last Wednesday of each month.
🐎❀♣●P🚌🐾

Croscombe

George Inn

Long Street, BA5 3QH (on A371 between Wells and Shepton Mallet)

☎ (01749) 342306 🌐 thegeorgeinn.co.uk

House beer (by Blindmans); 3 changing beers (often Cotleigh, St Austell, Yeovil Ales) [H]

An attractive 17th-century inn refurbished by the owner, serving at least four guest ales from West Country independents and hosting two beer festivals a year. Blindmans King George the Thirst and George and the Dragon are brewed exclusively for the pub. Four real ciders are sold, with Hecks Kingston Black and Thatchers the regulars. The pub has a large main bar, a snug with a fireplace, a family room and a separate dining room. A skittle alley/meeting room is to the rear and there is a large garden with a covered terrace. Food is home-cooked in a modern theatre kitchen using locally sourced ingredients. Q🐎❀🛏◑♿♣●P🚌🐾📶

Cross

New Inn ✔

Old Coach Road, BS26 2EE (on A38/A361 jct)

☎ (01934) 732455 🌐 newinncross.co.uk

Otter Bitter, Ale; 4 changing beers (often Box Steam, Bristol Beer Factory, Tiny Rebel) [H]

A 17th-century roadside inn on the A38, close to the historic medieval town of Axbridge. It is popular for its extensive food menu served all day, and its beer festival at Easter. Four guest beers, often rare for the area, are usually available. Families are welcome. The large hillside garden with children's play facilities offers a fine view of the Mendip Hills and Somerset Levels. There is a small car park opposite. 🐎❀◑⛺♣P🚌(126)🐾📶

White Hart

Old Coach Road, BS26 2EE

☎ (01934) 733108

Bath Ales Gem; St Austell Trelawny; 2 changing beers (often Bath Ales, St Austell) [H]

A 17th-century inn, reopened in 2019 after refurbishment. It is reputed to be haunted by one of Hanging Judge Jeffreys' victims. Inside there is a games bar with pool and darts, and a door leading to a lounge-style area. Beers come from the St Austell stable. The kitchen opens for lunches, with evening meals available for groups by arrangement. The nearby bus stop is a Hail and Ride halt, and there is a large car park opposite.
🐎❀◐⛺♣P🚌(491) 🐾📶

Culmhead

Holman Clavel Inn

TA3 7EA (¼ mile off B3170)

☎ (01823) 421070 🌐 theholmanclavelinn.co.uk

Butcombe Gold; Fuller's London Pride; Hanlons Yellow Hammer; Otter Bitter, Amber, Ale [H]

This is a real country pub set in the Blackdown Hills Area of Outstanding Natural Beauty, with six good ales straight from the barrel, Tricky cider, wine, food and company. There is neither a TV nor games machines, but children, dogs, walkers, cyclists and muddy boots are welcome. Food is from local farmers and suppliers, with gluten-free and vegetarian options on the menu. Local musicians play Irish-style sessions every first Thursday of the month. Q🐎❀🛏◑⛺♣●P🐾

Dinnington

Dinnington Docks Inn ✔

TA17 8SX (approx 3 miles E of Ilminster off B3168)

☎ (01460) 52397 🌐 dinningtondocks.com

Butcombe Original; Teignworthy Gun Dog; 3 changing beers (sourced locally; often Exmoor, Fine Tuned, Quantock) [H]

A quirky gem, this traditional Somerset country pub has beautiful views from the large garden. It wears its heart on its sleeve, supports the local community and offers a warm welcome to locals and visitors alike. A good selection of two permanent and three guest ales is available to suit all tastes, along with a wide choice of wines and spirits. The pub also offers a renowned menu of hearty meals, and is well worth a visit.
Q🐎❀◑♣●P🐾📶

Draycott

Cider Barn

Latches Lane Crossroads, Draycott Road, BS27 3RU

☎ (01934) 741837

1 changing beer (sourced locally; often Box Steam, Cheddar Ales) G

Quirky and relaxing bar, café and takeaway cider and ale barn on the main A371 near Cheddar. Up to 13 real ciders and one or two usually local real ales are available. It also offers coffee, tea and simple locally sourced home-cooked food and snacks including pizzas. There is live music on Sunday and open-mic sessions on Wednesday. Caravan hook-ups, camping and lodges are available nearby. Q P (126)

Dulverton

Bridge Inn

20 Bridge Street, TA22 9HJ

☎ (01398) 324130 thebridgeinndulverton.com

Exmoor Ale; St Austell Tribute; 2 changing beers (sourced regionally; often Bath Ales, St Austell) H

A warm, welcoming inn dating from 1845. As the name implies, it is close to a bridge, one that crosses the River Barle upstream from its confluence with the River Exe. In a delightful small town, it has a cosy single-room bar with a wood-burning stove and an extended restaurant area. There is always an interesting selection of national cask ales on offer, as well as bottled beers including some Belgian ones. Opening hours are restricted in winter – see the website for information.

Q P

Dunster

Luttrell Arms Hotel

36 High Street, TA24 6SG

☎ (01643) 821555 luttrellarms.co.uk

Exmoor Ale; Otter Amber; 2 changing beers (sourced locally; often Quantock) H

The hotel, with its 28 unique bedrooms, is on the site of three ancient houses dating back to 1443. The back bar has an open log fire and features some of the oldest glass windows in Somerset, and there is fine plasterwork on the lounge ceiling. You can dine in the à la carte restaurant or, if you prefer, order a bar snack. The view of Dunster Castle from the back garden is spectacular. Mini beer and cider festivals are held.

Q (28,198)

Faulkland

Tucker's Grave ★

BA3 5XF

☎ (01373) 834230

Butcombe Original G

A gem from a bygone age, with a nationally important historic pub interior, this place was built in the mid-17th century and has changed little since. It was named after Tucker, who hanged himself close by and was buried at the crossroads outside. He featured in a song by the Stranglers. There is no bar – the beers and Thatchers cider are served from an alcove. Shove-ha'penny is played and there is a skittle alley. Camping now in operation.

Q P

Frome

Griffin

Milk Street, BA11 3DB

☎ (01373) 228283 griffinfrome.com

Frome Funky Monkey, Zig-Zag Stout; 2 changing beers (often Frome) H

In the part of Frome known as Trinity, the Griffin was formerly the brewery tap for Milk Street (now Frome) Brewery, and serves up to four Frome ales or guests as well as a range of craft beers. Recently refurbished and under new management, the single bar retains some original features such as etched windows and wooden floors. Food is available daily, including burgers and street food featuring locally sourced ingredients and suppliers – Sunday lunch is popular.

P (184)

Just Ales

10 Stony Street, BA11 1BU

☎ (01373) 462493 justalespart2.com

4 changing beers (sourced nationally) H

Frome's first micropub opened in 2018 serving four real ales on handpump, as well as a large range of local ciders. Set in what was a small café, in the heart of Frome's vibrant St Catherine's District, this bar has a welcoming atmosphere and is run by the same team as Just Ales in Wells, including the friendly hound. Biltong is sold as a quick and tasty snack. Q

Three Swans

16-17 King Street, BA11 1BH

☎ (01373) 452009 thethreeswans.com

Abbey Bellringer; Butcombe Original; 1 changing beer (sourced nationally; often Butcombe) H

A 17th-century, Grade II listed two-bar pub in the centre of town. Quirky and traditional, it was extensively refurbished in 2013, and has a comfortable and inviting feel. The interior is heated by traditional gas burners; paintings and various ornaments adorn the wall. The back door leads out to a beautiful secluded courtyard. There is also an upstairs function room. Home-made pies are sold Thursday to Sunday.

Glastonbury

Beckets Inn

43 High Street, BA6 9DS (at top of High St in town centre)

☎ (01458) 832928 becketspubglastonbury.co.uk

Wadworth Henry's IPA, 6X; 1 changing beer (sourced regionally) H

A traditional town-centre pub named after Thomas Becket, with a pool room and three separate bar areas. There is no food, but customers are welcome to bring takeaways (plates and cutlery provided) to eat in or to have as a picnic in the garden. The pub will even do the washing up. Children are welcome until 5pm but, as there is a resident dog, only assistance dogs are permitted. Three well-kept Wadworth beers are on handpump.

George & Pilgrims

1 High Street, BA6 9DP (near Market Cross)

☎ (01458) 831146

Otter Bitter; St Austell Tribute; 2 changing beers (sourced nationally; often Bristol Beer Factory, Quantock) H

A three-storeyed Grade I listed establishment that boasts a panelled embattled frontage with mullion windows. On walking through the stout doorway of this stone-built gatehouse inn, there is a corridor leading to the rear patio and several tabled alcoves on the right. The Pilgrims Bar on the left oozes old-world charm and displays medieval artefacts. There are four well-kept real ales and a choice of ciders. It is worthwhile reading about the history of the inn over a pint. Q P

Hawthorns

8-12 Northload Street, BA6 9JJ (at bottom of Glastonbury High St turn into Northload St at Market Cross)
☎ (01458) 831255 hawthornshotel.co.uk
2 changing beers (often Fine Tuned, Moor Beer, Pitchfork)
A quirky hotel and bar in the centre of this historic town within walking distance of the Tor and abbey. It is a well-known music venue with an open mic session on Tuesday, blues jam on Sunday and regular music on Friday night. Hawthorns is famous for producing authentic curries from around the world, and the Sunday carvery is also popular. In May there is a well-supported beer festival with 20 ales and six ciders. P

Henstridge

Bird in Hand

Ash Walk, BA8 0QD
☎ (01963) 362255
Butcombe Original; 2 changing beers (often Sharp's)
Old stone village hostelry with low ceilings, beams, a fireplace at each end of an attractive long bar, and a games room housing a TV. There is an adjoining skittle alley. Excellent-quality ales and good-value snacks make a visit to this friendly place well worthwhile. At the heart of most village activities, this really is a true community pub. Thatchers cider is on handpump and there is more cider in boxes. Q P (58)

Hinton Blewett

Ring O' Bells

Upper Road, BS39 5AN (2 miles W of Temple Cloud from A37) ST594569
☎ (01761) 451245 ringobellshinton.co.uk
Butcombe Original; 3 changing beers (often Butcombe, Timothy Taylor)
Popular village pub dating from the 19th century. A dining/function room with its own garden was recently added, and blends nicely with the cosy bar and snug. Quality food is served, using local produce when possible. Local sports clubs meet here and much memorabilia is on show, particularly cricket-related. Free boules is played on Tuesday evening. Cyclists, walkers, children and dogs are all most welcome. Ashton Still, Cheddar Valley and other real ciders are served. Open all day from June to September. Q P

Horton

Five Dials Inn

Goose Lane, TA19 9QQ
☎ (01460) 55359
Otter Bitter; Sharp's Doom Bar; 1 changing beer (often Otter)
This old coaching inn, situated at the foot of the picturesque Blackdown Hills, has been given a contemporary facelift. It stocks three real ales and traditional local ciders from Perry's and Burrow Hill, including the famous Somerset Cider Brandy. Fresh seasonal food is served, with a specials board changing daily. There are six guest rooms, and the Inn was awarded 4 stars by Enjoy England. Open all day on bank holidays. P

Huish Episcopi

Rose & Crown ★

TA10 9QT (on A372 in village)
☎ (01458) 250494
Teignworthy Reel Ale; 2 changing beers (sourced regionally; often Fine Tuned, Hop Back, Otter)
A 17th-century thatched inn known as Eli's after the former owner, Eli Scott, who took over in 1920; it is still in the same family. The hub of the pub is the rare counterless flagstoned taproom which leads out to four parlours. Good-value meals are served (no food Sun eve). Live music is a regular feature and there is a meeting of the Elderflower Food Co-operative every Friday for the purchase of organic produce. The pub is an official Brit Stop for travellers. Q P

Hutton

Old Inn

Main Road, BS24 9QQ
☎ (01934) 812336
Fuller's London Pride; Otter Head; Palmers Dorset Gold; St Austell Tribute; 1 changing beer (often Palmers)
Genuine free house and thriving local, right at the heart of the local community. The pub is popular for its excellent and great-value food, particularly the Sunday carvery (booking advised). Food is served every lunchtime and evening except Sunday evening, which is quiz night. The guest beer is usually only on at weekends. Dogs are welcome in the bar. The car park at the back is accessed by narrow one-way lanes either side. P (4)

Keynsham

Old Bank

20 High Street, BS31 1DQ
☎ (0117) 904 6356
Severn Copper Ale; 4 changing beers
This Grade II listed building was originally a coaching inn, then a branch of Westminster Bank, before becoming a pub again. It is a free house with one large room for drinking, and a covered, heated outdoor area at the back. The landlord tries to have at least one dark, often strong, beer on at all times. There is a large TV screen for sport and the pub can sometimes get lively on late weekend openings. A small car park is to the rear. P

Kingsbury Episcopi

Wyndham Arms

Folly Road, TA12 6AT (4 miles S of Langport)
☎ (01935) 823239 wyndhamarms.com
Butcombe Original; 3 changing beers (sourced nationally; often Fine Tuned, Quantock, Yeovil Ales)
A 400-year-old inn that used to house the village bakery and the courtroom of the Bishop of Wells. Old settles and a magnificent log fire can be found in the bar area, which has a flagstone floor and a wealth of beams. The pub is a popular stopping-off point for cyclists and walkers drawn by the four ales and five real ciders on the bar. Check the website events page for details of live music and quizzes. Q P

Knole

Lime Kiln Inn

TA10 9JH

☎ (01458) 241242
Butcombe Original; 2 changing beers (often Butcombe) Ⓗ
A traditional inn with flagstoned flooring in the main bar area and a grand inglenook fireplace with a warming fire in winter. Adjoining is a recently refurbished and comfortable restaurant, now with large doors leading onto the garden for summer use. The restaurant is a more modern addition to this 200-year-old pub, which was first granted a licence in 1814. Excellent food is served from the main menu, with a changing specials board. There will be between one and three ales.
♨❀◑♿●P🐾📶

Lydford on Fosse

Cross Keys Inn 🄻

TA11 7HA (next to A37 between Yeovil and Shepton Mallet at traffic lights in village)
☎ (01963) 240473 🌐 crosskeysinn.info
House beer (by Otter); 1 changing beer (sourced regionally; often Bristol Beer Factory, Twisted Oak) Ⓖ
A traditional 18th-century pub with flagstone floors, blue lias stonework and a wealth of beams. It has an open-plan bar area with fireplaces at each end and a snug. This is a community venue with many events organised such as live music, a beer festival, comedy nights and charitable events. Camping is available on-site, with a shower block and toilets. There are up to five ales on gravity including the house beer.
Q♨❀🛏◑♿⛺♣●P🚌(667)🐾📶

Martock

White Hart Hotel 🄻

East Street, TA12 6JQ (centre of village)
☎ (01935) 822005 🌐 whiteharthotelmartock.co.uk
Otter Bitter; Sharp's Doom Bar; 1 changing beer (sourced regionally; often Exmoor, St Austell, Yeovil Ales) Ⓗ
This hamstone-built Grade II listed coaching inn dates from 1735. It is warm and welcoming and serves great chef-cooked food, with three real ales on handpulls, mainly from nearby breweries. Local societies such as music and film clubs use it as a meeting place. There is a main bar for drinks and a cosy restaurant for table service. The Hotel has 10 en-suite letting rooms including a family room. Q♨❀🛏◑♿♣P🚌(N9,N10)🐾📶

Merriott

King's Head

Church Street, TA16 5PR
☎ (01460) 78912 🌐 thekingsmerriott.com
Sharp's Doom Bar; 2 changing beers (sourced regionally; often Otter, Plain, Red Rock) Ⓗ
Traditional 17th-century inn with open-plan rooms and a mix of flagstones and wood flooring. A raised wood-burning stove in the flagstoned area makes it welcoming in winter. As well as cask ales, there is a selection of up to seven local ciders, and the owner stocks more than 80 gins. Outside is a large beer garden with a smoking area featuring a wood-burner. The pub is dog-friendly and popular with walkers. Q♨❀◑♣●P🚌🐾📶

Middlezoy

George Inn 🄻

42 Main Road, TA7 0NN (off A372, 1 mile NW of Othery, 5 miles E of Bridgwater)
☎ (01823) 698215 🌐 thegeorgeinnmiddlezoy.co.uk
House beer (by St Austell); 2 changing beers (sourced regionally; often Bath Ales, Cheddar Ales, Fine Tuned) Ⓗ
A 17th-century free house which has been in the Guide for over 20 years, with stone-flagged floors, exposed beams and log fires. Excellent locally sourced food is served Wednesday to Saturday evenings and Saturday lunchtime. A private dining room seating 12 can be reserved. Farmer Jims and Orchard Pig ciders are served. Live acoustic music takes place on the third Sunday of each month and there is a monthly bingo night. Accommodation is provided in three rooms.
Q♨❀🛏◗⛺♣●P🚌(16)🐾📶

Midford

Hope & Anchor

Midford Road, BA2 7DD
☎ (01225) 832296 🌐 hopeandanchormidford.co.uk
2 changing beers (sourced regionally; often Otter, Three Daggers, Twisted) Ⓗ
An ivy-clad building dating back to the 17th century. Formerly owned by Courage Brewery, it became a free house in 1976 and has been run by the same family for over 26 years. It is close to the Two Tunnels cycle path leading to and from Bath, via the old S&D railway route. The beers are usually from the West Country and vary according to the time of year. The cider comes from a local farm. ♨❀◑●P🚌(D2)🐾📶

Minehead

Kildare Lodge ✔

Townend Road, TA24 5RQ
☎ (01643) 702009 🌐 kildarelodge.co.uk
St Austell Tribute; 3 changing beers (sourced regionally) Ⓗ
A cracking local close to the town centre. The Grade II listed building, in the Arts & Crafts style, has a bar, two lounges and a dining room. Two beer festivals are held every year with up to 20 beers on tap. The pub is in the local boules and quiz leagues, and is a great base for exploring Exmoor National Park, Dunster and the coast. There are 12 en-suite rooms including a bridal suite with a four-poster bed. Q❀🛏◑♿⛺⇌♣●P🚌🐾

Montacute

Phelips Arms ✔

The Borough, TA15 6XB
☎ (01935) 822557 🌐 phelipsarms.co.uk
Palmers Dorset Gold; 3 changing beers (sourced nationally; often Palmers) Ⓗ
A lovely hamstone-built village pub just 200 yards from the National Trust's Montacute House and offering a warm and friendly welcome. Home-cooked meals and daily specials are made from locally sourced ingredients where possible. There is a walled garden. A selection of three or four Palmers cask ales is on the bar and the real cider on handpump is also from Palmers. Open daytime on bank holiday Mondays. ♨❀🛏◑♣●P🚌🐾📶

Nailsea

Nailsea MicroPub

Unit 4, Ivy Court, 63A High Street, BS48 1AW
☎ 07496 428350
6 changing beers (sourced locally) Ⓖ
Nailsea's first micropub, opened in September 2019 in a former opticians'. It serves up to eight ales straight from the cask, along with two real ciders. Beers of all styles are sourced from up and down the country, as well as

from local breweries. Bottled ciders, gins, wines and soft drinks are also available, as well as reasonably priced bar snacks, including filled rolls on busy weekends. Although there is no dedicated parking, there are ample public car parks nearby. Q♣●🚌🐾

Nether Stowey

George 𝕃
1 St Mary Street, TA5 1LJ
☎ (01278) 732248 🌐 georgestowey.com
2 changing beers (often Bays, St Austell, Stowey)
The George is the oldest pub in the village and can trace its history back to 1616, although the original building dates back another century. It is a friendly multi-roomed hostelry with a real fire, dark-wood interior, Tiffany lamps and historical photographs of the village on the walls. A function room is available upstairs. Live music features on occasion. Beers from the nearby Stowey Brewery are available. 👶❀🛏♣●🚌🐾📶

Odcombe

Masons Arms
41 Lower Odcombe, BA22 8TX (off Yeovil to Montacute road)
☎ (01935) 862591 🌐 masonsarmsodcombe.co.uk
Odcombe Spring, No.1, Drewer's Broop, Roly Poly [H]
A pretty hamstone and thatched pub set in a picturesque village, family-run and exuding a friendly ambience. Odcombe Microbrewery is on-site to the rear and provides a good range of four ales on handpump, brewed by the owners. Good local food is served every day, enhanced by meals from a wood-fired pizza oven Thursday to Sunday. With six en-suite bedrooms, a cottage, glamping in a shepherd's hut and camping pitches in the grounds, overnight stays are for everyone. Dogs are welcome in all areas of the pub.
Q👶❀🛏◑♿⛺●P🚌(81)🐾📶

Pitney

Halfway House 𝕃
Pitney Hill, TA10 9AB (on B3153 between Langport and Somerton)
☎ (01458) 252513 🌐 thehalfwayhouse.co.uk
Hop Back Crop Circle; Otter Bright; Teignworthy Reel Ale; 6 changing beers (sourced regionally; often Bristol Beer Factory, Pitchfork, Quantock) [G]
An outstanding establishment serving eight to 10 regional ales on gravity alongside many bottled beers and four real ciders, and serving superb home-cooked food. The inside is traditional, with flagstone flooring, old solid wooden tables and benches, and three real fires. This basic but busy pub deserves its many accolades and has featured in the Guide for over 25 years. Accommodation is now provided in the Hut.
Q👶❀🛏◑●P🚌(54)🐾📶

Porlock

Ship Inn 𝕃 ✔
High Street, TA24 8QD
☎ (01643) 862507 🌐 shipinnporlock.co.uk
Exmoor Beast; Otter Bitter; 6 changing beers (sourced regionally; often Cotleigh, Quantock, St Austell) [H]
Known locally as the Top Ship, the bar is a gem with its flagstone floor, open fire and settle seating. It has changed little since featuring in RD Blackmore's novel Lorna Doone. The pub dates from the 13th century and sits at the bottom of the notorious Porlock Hill that takes you up to Exmoor. Eight ales and a local cider are served and good food can be enjoyed in the restaurant or delightful three-tiered garden in summer.
Q👶❀🛏◑♿⛺♣●P🚌(10)🐾

Porlock Weir

Ship Inn 𝕃
TA24 8PB (take B3225 from Porlock)
☎ (01643) 863288 🌐 shipinnporlockweir.co.uk
Exmoor Ale, Stag; St Austell Tribute, Proper Job; 2 changing beers (sourced regionally; often Cotleigh, Otter) [H]
This 400-year-old inn in Exmoor National Park, next to the small harbour and pebbled beach, offers fantastic views of the Bristol Channel and South Wales coast. Set on the South West Coast Path, it is popular with walkers and gets busy in the summer. A beer festival is held early July with up to 50 ales on tap. Accommodation is dog-friendly. There is a Pay & Display car park opposite.
Q❀🛏◑♿⛺♣●P🚌(10)🐾📶

Portishead

Ship
310 Down Road, BS20 8JT
☎ (01275) 848400
Draught Bass; Otter Bitter; 1 changing beer [H]
A large pub with traditional opening hours on the coast road between Clevedon and Portishead with views over the Severn Estuary from an award-winning garden. The landlord has been at the pub he built since 1973, and is a fount of local knowledge. Meals are served lunchtime only, but you can get pasties in the evening. There is a small library of books on-site with a particularly good selection on local history. ❀◖♣P🚌🐾

Siren's Calling 𝕃
315 Newfoundland Way, Portishead Marina, BS20 7PT
☎ (01275) 268278 🌐 sirenscalling.co.uk
5 changing beers
A modern single-room waterside bar, opened in 2018, serving up to six cask ales and nine craft keg beers in a variety of styles. Some are from breweries in the Bristol area, others from further afield. Still ciders are also sold. The pub is simply furnished, with large front windows overlooking the many boats moored in the marina. Food is always available but limited to cheese platters, Scotch eggs, pork pies and sausage rolls. Regular beer festivals are held. 👶◑♿●🚌🐾📶

Windmill Inn 𝕃
58 Nore Road, BS20 6JZ (next to municipal golf course above coastal path)
☎ (01275) 818483
Butcombe Original; Fuller's Oliver's Island, London Pride; 3 changing beers (often Fuller's) [H]
Large split-level pub with a spacious patio to the rear, plus an extension enjoying panoramic views. It is above the coastal path on the edge of town, and the Severn Estuary and both Severn bridges can be seen on clear days. The Windmill was acquired by Fuller's in 2014 but one guest ale comes from a brewery outside the Fuller's stable. A varied menu is served all day with table bookings available. Monday is quiz night. Dogs are allowed in the main bar area only.
Q👶❀◑♿●P🚌🐾📶

Priddy

Hunters' Lodge
Old Bristol Road, BA5 3AR (at isolated crossroads 1 mile from A39 close to TV mast) ST549500

☎ (01749) 672275
Butcombe Original; Cheddar Ales Potholer; 1 changing beer (often Butcombe) [G]
The landlord of this timeless classic roadside inn has been in charge for 50 years. Priddy is the highest village in Somerset, and popular with cavers and walkers. The pub's three rooms include one with a flagged floor. All beer is served direct from casks behind the bar; local cider is also on offer. Simple home-cooked food is excellent and exceptional value. A folk musicians' drop-in session is held on Tuesday evening. The garden is pleasant and secluded. Mobile phones aren't welcome but dogs are. Q🐴❀◑♿♣●P🚌(683)🐾

Puriton

37 Club Ⓛ
1 West Approach Road, Woolavington Road, TA7 8AD (5 mins from jct 23 of M5 between Bridgwater and Wells)
☎ (01278) 685190 🌐 37club.co.uk
Otter Bitter, Ale; St Austell Tribute; 3 changing beers (sourced regionally; often Box Steam, Pitchfork, Quantock) [H]
On the site of the former Royal Ordnance Factory, which was allocated the number 37, this is a large club offering a great many facilities to members and visitors. It has two bars and its multi-roomed layout incorporates a concert room, two skittle alleys, a dining room, and a snooker room with five tables. Outside there is a beer garden, a fishing lake and a football pitch. CAMRA members are welcome with a membership card.
🐴❀◑▲♣●P🚌(75)

Radstock

Fromeway
Frome Road, BA3 3LG
☎ (01761) 432116 🌐 fromeway.co.uk
Butcombe Original [H]**; 2 changing beers (sourced nationally; often Otter, Twisted)** [H]/[A]
A friendly free house in the sixth generation of the same family and now in the capable hands of Emily, the youngest daughter of the present generation. The excellent selection of ales from all over the country changes weekly. There is an emphasis on food, with traditional classics as well as more contemporary dishes (booking is essential). Regular charity events, quiz nights and walks take place from month to month. The award-winning garden is lovely in summer.
🐴❀🛏◑♿●P🚌(768,178)🐾📶

Rickford

Plume of Feathers
Leg Lane, BS40 7AH (off A368, 2 miles from A38; approaching from Churchill, left U-turn into Leg Lane is extremely tricky)
☎ (01761) 462682 🌐 theplumeoffeathers.com
Butcombe Original; Cheddar Ales Potholer; 1 changing beer (often Butcombe, Cheddar Ales, Pitchfork) [H]
This 17th-century building has been a pub since the 1800s. The interior is divided into several areas, including a restaurant with a real fire. It provides a pleasant and convenient base from which to walk, fish or explore the Mendips. There is a garden to the rear and a stream running along the front, leading to a ford. Beers are always from local breweries. A popular charity duck race takes place in July. Car parking is limited.
Q🐴❀🛏◑▲♣●P🚆🚌(791)🐾📶

Roadwater

Valiant Soldier Ⓛ ✔
TA23 0QZ (off A39 at Washford)
☎ (01984) 640223 🌐 thevaliantsoldier.co.uk
Exmoor Ale; Greene King IPA; 1 changing beer (sourced locally; often Cotleigh) [H]
The pub dates back to 1720 and is ideal for country walks and exploring nearby Exmoor, the coast and Dunster. It has been run by Mike, the landlord, for over 30 years. This vibrant local has quiz, pool, darts and nine skittles teams to see it through the winter months. It is set by a small river where you can relax and watch the ducks and, if you're lucky, kingfishers. Good-quality locally sourced food is served. 🐴❀🛏◑♣●P🐾📶

Saltford

Bird in Hand ✔
58 High Street, BS31 3EJ
☎ (01225) 873335 🌐 birdinhandsaltford.co.uk
Butcombe Original; Sharp's Doom Bar; 2 changing beers (often Exmoor, Otter, Yeovil Ales) [H]
A convenient stopping-off point for cyclists on the Bristol to Bath Railway Path, this traditional 19th-century country inn is very close to the River Avon and only 400 yards from the A4. It has a long L-shaped bar and a pleasant conservatory with fine views across the garden to the hills beyond. Quality food is served lunchtimes and evenings, and all day at weekends, with gluten-free options. There is a pétanque piste in the garden.
🐴❀◑♿♣●P🚌🐾📶

Seavington St Michael

Volunteer Inn Ⓛ
New Road, TA19 0QE (on old A303 between South Petherton and Ilminster)
☎ (01460) 240126 🌐 thevolly.co.uk
Windy Drift, Tornado, Windward; 2 changing beers (sourced regionally) [H]
This cosy three-roomed pub has built a strong reputation with real ale enthusiasts for its Windy Brewery ales created on-site in a purpose-built building to the rear. After building their true brewpub, owners Colin and Ruth called the brewery after the bad weather encountered by the builders, and all their ales are named after the wind and weather. This fine establishment is well worth a visit. Q🐴❀🛏◑♣●P🚌(9)🐾📶

Somerton

Etsome Arms
6 West Street, TA11 7PS
4 changing beers (sourced locally; often Fine Tuned, Parkway, Yeovil Ales) [G]
A former café, this micropub is among the first of a breed in Somerset, and is local CAMRA branch runner-up Pub of the Year 2020. It is cosy, friendly and serves between four and six ales on gravity, depending on the time of week and year, with all changing regularly. Seating is comfortable sofas or traditional tables and chairs. Quality cold bar snacks are sourced locally and include a range of Scotch eggs and pies. Children and dogs are welcome. This micropub is well worth a visit. 🐴❀♣●🚌🐾📶

White Hart Inn
Market Place, TA11 7LX (in centre of village)
☎ (01458) 272273 🌐 whitehartsomerton.com
Cheddar Ales Potholer; 2 changing beers (sourced regionally; often Gritchie, Otter) [H]

The White Hart has been trading as an inn in Somerton's delightful market square since the 16th century. You can't miss it, as there is a large white hart on the entrance porch. It is much larger inside than you might first envisage and there are plenty of tables for dining or coffee and cakes. Excellent food from an award-winning chef is offered daily. A courtyard provides space for alfresco eating and drinking.
(54,77)

Stratton-on-the-Fosse

King's Arms

South Street, BA3 4RA
(01761) 233544 kingsarms-strattonotf.co.uk
4 changing beers (sourced locally; often Great Western, Yeovil Ales)
A smart and handsome establishment offering up to four weekly changing ales, mainly from local and other West Country breweries, plus a local cider. Meals are on offer in the evenings, lunchtimes too Friday to Sunday, and there are B&B rooms available. The village is set in beautiful countryside, and the pub is directly opposite Downside Abbey. P

Taunton

Bank

Middle Street, TA1 1SJ
(01823) 257788 thebanktaunton.co.uk
3 changing beers (sourced nationally; often Arbor, Moor Beer, Oakham)
Close to Somerset cricket ground, the Bank features three changing cask ales from small breweries. The pub has two floors: the ground is a cosy bar, and upstairs is reserved for diners, with doors opening on to a terrace. A popular choice of keg beers and cans is served in addition to the cask ales. Excellent food is on offer and can be described as modern British with an international influence. Bar meals reflect the quality of the main menu. Q

Coal Orchard

30-32 Bridge Street, TA1 1UD (near River Tone bridge in town centre)
(01823) 447330
Greene King Abbot; Ruddles Best Bitter; Sharp's Doom Bar; 4 changing beers (sourced regionally; often Dartmoor, Exmoor, Quantock)
North Town Wharf once stood behind this Wetherspoon house, next to the River Tone. Facing it was the Coal Orchard, the site of an orchard which became the landing place for Welsh coal. Latterly, the pub was converted from a former hardware store. One of Wetherspoon's smaller premises, the frontage has Art Deco styling and seating is arranged over a single open-plan level. There is a small garden and patio area at the rear.
Q

Racehorse Inn

East Reach, TA1 3HT
(01823) 327513
St Austell Trelawny, Tribute, Proper Job; 1 changing beer (sourced nationally)
A popular St Austell pub close to the town centre at the top of East Reach. It is a traditional community local with front and rear bars and a small lounge with comfortable armchairs. Skittles and darts are played regularly, and there is live music every week which is extremely popular. A large walled garden at the rear is ideal for a relaxing drink on warm summer days. No food is served.
P

Ring of Bells

16-17 St James Street, TA1 1JS
(01823) 259480 theringofbellstaunton.com
5 changing beers (sourced nationally; often Dark Star, Oakham, Otter)
Situated close to Somerset cricket ground, this pub is a favourite haunt of cricket fans. Wooden floored, there are two bar areas with open fires, a downstairs dining area, an upstairs restaurant and a large outside courtyard. The five cask beers are from local, regional and national breweries, and you may find some interesting keg beers if this is your preference. Excellent locally produced food is served (booking is recommended). Sporting events are shown on a TV in the bar area.

Trull

Winchester Arms

Church Road, TA3 7LG
(01823) 284723 winchesterarmstrull.co.uk
4 changing beers (sourced regionally; often Cotleigh, Otter, St Austell)
Thriving community free house on the outskirts of Taunton, near the Blackdown Hills. A comfortable bar area is separated from the long dining area by a fireplace. The locally sourced home-cooked food is excellent (booking is advised at peak times). The streamside gardens, perfect for families and dogs, also host entertainment and barbecues. A popular quiz takes place on Sunday night and there is occasional live music. The pub offers good-value accommodation.
Q P (97)

Wambrook

Cotley Inn

TA20 3EN (from A30 W out of Chard, by toll house, take left fork and almost immediately left again; following signs for pub continue for just over 1 mile on narrow lane)
(01460) 62348 cotleyinnwambrook.co.uk
Otter Bitter; 1 changing beer (sourced regionally; often Exmoor, Tapstone, Teignworthy)
A traditional country inn that is well worth finding. The bar area has a welcoming wood-burning stove to greet you during the winter months. To the right of the bar is a challenging skittles alley and to the left there are dining areas offering excellent food. Ales are served from gravity racking behind the bar. This pub is in a wonderful rural location and sitting outside is a delight. Dogs, owners, muddy boots and wellies are all welcome.
Q P

Watchet

Esplanade Club

5 The Esplanade, TA23 0AJ (opp marina)
(01984) 634518 esplanadeclub.net
House beer (by St Austell); 4 changing beers (sourced regionally; often Exmoor, Quantock, St Austell)
Built in the 1860s as a sailmaking factory and now home to the Boat Owners Association, the club is an archive of local history and memorabilia, with unique murals and even its own Tardis. There are great views over the marina and Bristol Channel. The Esplanade is a busy music venue with live acts every weekend, open mic on the first Tuesday of the month, and folk every fourth Wednesday. Winner of Somerset CAMRA Club of the Year in 2020. (28)

Pebbles Tavern

24 Market Street, TA23 0AN (in heart of town, near museum)

☎ (01984) 634737 🌐 pebblestavern.co.uk

Timothy Taylor Boltmaker, Landlord [H]**; 1 changing beer (sourced nationally)** [H]/[G]

This small, unique tavern has won numerous CAMRA awards for Cider Pub of the Year including in 2020, and in 2015 it was the National runner-up. As well as the ales there can be up to 30 ciders, 60 gins, 24 rums and 64 whiskies. You are allowed to bring in your fish and chips from the shop next door. Poetry night is the first Tuesday of the month and regular music nights include folk, sea shanty, acoustic and jazz. (28)

Star Inn L ✓

Mill Lane, TA23 0BZ

☎ (01984) 631367 🌐 starinnwatchet.co.uk

House beer (by Exmoor); 4 changing beers (often Butcombe, Dartmoor, Exmoor) [H]

Twice Somerset CAMRA Pub of the Year and runner-up in 2019, this inn has been in the Guide for over 19 consecutive years. Renowned for its congenial atmosphere and friendly staff, it hosts darts, quiz and boules teams, and holds music nights in the summer. The pub also holds port and cheese nights, and is home to the Sunday night Bad Boys club. Mick's beer tours have run over 100 trips.

Wells

City Arms ✓

69 High Street, BA5 2AG

☎ (01749) 677768 🌐 cityarmswells.co.uk

House beer (by Glastonbury); 2 changing beers (sourced regionally; often Cheddar Ales, Timothy Taylor) [H]

In 1810 the City of Wells jail closed and later became the City Arms. The main bar retains the small barred windows and low-vaulted ceilings of its former existence. The building encloses a courtyard on three sides, with outdoor seating. An extensive choice of food is served in the bar, bistro and restaurant, all made to order using fresh local produce. Between five and seven beers are normally on tap, mainly from local brewers.

Q

West Chinnock

Muddled Man L ✓

Lower Street, TA18 7PT

☎ (01935) 881235 🌐 themuddledmaninn.co.uk

3 changing beers (often Cheddar Ales, Quantock, Yeovil Ales) [H]

A popular, traditional free house in a picturesque village. Visitors and locals alike are assured of a warm welcome. Good home-cooked food is served by the friendly family team, with a variety of steaks the speciality. Sunday lunch is always popular and must be pre-booked. A good range of three well-kept ales and a real cider are available on handpump. Outside, the large beer garden has exceptional flower boxes, troughs and baskets.

Q

West Huntspill

Crossways Inn 🏆 L

Withy Road, TA9 3RA (on A38)

☎ (01278) 783756 🌐 thecrosswaysinn.com

St Austell Trelawny; 9 changing beers (sourced nationally; often Bristol Beer Factory, Dartmoor, Yeovil Ales) [H]

Fabulous 17th-century character inn, a well-deserved winner of local CAMRA Pub of the Year for the last six years. It has several charming bar areas, a dining room serving good pub food, two log fires in winter, plus an outside fireplace for smokers. A range of eight changing cask and two keg ales is on the bar, usually local but sometimes national, to ensure a wide choice of beer styles. Six real ciders are also available. A beer festival is held in July. P (21)

Weston-super-Mare

Bear Inn

66 Walliscote Road, BS23 1ED

☎ (01934) 641722 🌐 thebearinnweston.co.uk

4 changing beers (sourced regionally) [H]

A spacious and comfortable pub a few minutes' walk from the seafront. It was formerly called the Balmoral, and reopened in 2012 with its new name after a period of closure. Beers can be unusual for the area, and come in a variety of styles. Live music is popular every Saturday evening. Attractions include a skittle alley, a refurbished function room at the back with a stage, and 19 en-suite rooms. Sport is occasionally shown on TV.

P (5,7)

Black Cat

135 High Street, BS23 1HN

☎ (01934) 283286

6 changing beers [G]

A micropub opened in November 2018 in a former clothes shop at the Playhouse Theatre end of the High Street. Five cask ales are served, chosen from local breweries and a few further afield. Food, including pizzas and fish and chips, is available Wednesday to Saturday lunchtimes and on Friday and Saturday evenings. Dogs are welcome, as are children until later in the evening. There is reasonable access for those of limited mobility. Look for the impressive Black Cat mural.

Q

Brit Bar L ✓

118 High Street, BS23 1HP

☎ (01934) 632629

5 changing beers [H]

Formerly the Britannia, this long-standing town-centre pub was bought by the current owners at auction after a period of closure and has now been given a bright, modern makeover while retaining the important traditional elements. Five changing beers are served, always including some dark beers. Bag-in-box real cider is usually sold too. Live music features at weekends and families are welcome all hours in the covered courtyard, which is heated in cold weather.

Fork & Ale Taproom & Kitchen

18 Walliscote Road, BS23 1UG

☎ (01934) 384044 🌐 pitchforkales.com

6 changing beers (sourced locally; often 3D Beers, Pitchfork) [H]

This pub opened in November 2019, conveniently located in the town centre, close to both railway station and seafront. It has a modern look and feel, with an interior of wood, metal and brick, as well as a few comfy sofas. There is a big focus on the beer, with between four and six on at any one time, usually from Pitchfork and 3D. Food is a range of small plates of modern food. The toilets are upstairs.

Regency

22-24 Lower Church Road, BS23 2AG

☎ (01934) 633406 🌐 theregencyinn.co.uk

Butcombe Original; Courage Best Bitter; Dark Star Hophead; Draught Bass; Timothy Taylor Landlord; 1 changing beer (sourced nationally) Ⓗ
Comfortable, friendly town-centre local, attracting a mixed clientele including students at lunchtime. It has pool, skittles and crib teams, but also offers a quiet refuge for conversation. The pool room with TV and jukebox is separate from the main bar area, and children are welcome here. Keenly priced home-cooked food is served lunchtimes as well as curries on Wednesdays and grill evenings on Thursdays. There are patios to the front and rear. Pub outings feature, and live bands perform here occasionally. ♨❀◑♿♣🚌

Williton

Masons Arms 🄻
2 North Road, TA4 4SN
☎ (01984) 639200 🌐 themasonsarms.com
Exmoor Ale; St Austell Tribute; 1 changing beer (sourced regionally; often Dartmoor) Ⓗ
This beautiful thatched 16th-century inn has oak beams throughout and offers five en-suite rooms in the adjoining annexe. It hosts quiz teams in the local league. Outside is a pleasant beer garden where locals and visitors alike sit and relax. The pub has a good reputation for its food and the quality of its ales, and Rich's cider is always on offer. Close to the Quantock Hills, West Somerset Railway and a short drive from Exmoor National Park. Q♨❀🛏◑♿⛺♣●P🚌(28)🐾📶

Railway Inn 🄻
55 Long Street, TA4 4QY
☎ (01984) 632508
3 changing beers (sourced regionally; often Butcombe, Exmoor) Ⓗ
An old inn set beside the A39, with two bars, a small lounge and a games room. Internally, white walls are interspersed with black beams and stone fireplaces. It has teams in the local quiz, darts, skittles and pool leagues. It also hold its own quiz on Monday nights. By the skittle alley at the back is an outside seating area. The pub is close to the West Somerset Railway, the Quantock Hills and Exmoor.
❀🛏◑♿⛺⇌♣P🚌(28)🐾📶

Wincanton

Nog Inn
South Street, BA9 9DL
☎ (01963) 32998 🌐 thenoginn.com
Otter Bitter; house beer (by Sharp's); 2 changing beers (sourced regionally; often Cotleigh, Otter, Sharp's) Ⓗ
An attractive listed pub with a striking Georgian façade fronting a long, narrow building with parts dating back to the 16th century. A secluded sunny garden with covered seating can be found at the far end of the property. The guest ales are often seasonal and an extensive range of continental beers on tap is always available. Home-cooked pub classics are served using locally sourced and seasonal ingredients where possible.
♨❀◑♣P🚌(58,667)🐾📶

Witham Friary

Seymour Arms ★
BA11 5HF
☎ (01749) 684280
Cheddar Ales Potholer Ⓗ
A hidden rural gem, this inn has probably changed very little over the last 50 or so years. Built in the 1860s as a hotel to serve the nearby Mid-Somerset GWR branch railway station, it was part of the Duke of Somerset's estate. Sadly, in the 1960s Mr Beeching closed the station, and the hotel became a quiet country pub. One locally sourced beer and a cider are served from a glass-panelled hatch in the central hallway. Q♨❀♣●P🐾

Wookey

Ring o' Bells
High Street, BA5 1JZ
☎ (01749) 678079
Butcombe Original; Cheddar Ales Potholer; 1 changing beer (sourced locally) Ⓗ
A vibrant and friendly old pub in the village centre, serving a good range of four beers and two ciders. A pleasant terrace is out at the front and a small courtyard garden is to the rear. Formerly a Wadworth outlet, it is now a free house under new ownership since 2016. It has a large single bar, with the bar itself made from old cider barrels, and a small dining room adjoining. There is a skittle alley which also acts as a function room. Food is sourced locally. Q♨❀◑⛺♣●🚌(67)🐾📶

Yarlington

Stag's Head
Pounds Lane, BA9 8DG ST65462923
☎ (01963) 440393 🌐 stagsheadinn.co.uk
3 changing beers (often Bath Ales, Wriggle Valley, Yeovil Ales) Ⓗ
Local ales, Somerset cider and food made using local produce await you as you step over the threshold of this historic 18th-century inn, which first opened in the 1850s. The pub is set in a picturesque village with a beautiful church and a running stream, a working farm and circular walks. Dogs are more than welcome in the bar area and snug room. Q♨🛏◑●P🐾📶

Yatton

Butchers Arms 🄻
31 High Street, BS49 4JD
☎ (01934) 838754 🌐 thebutchersarms.info
Butcombe Original; St Austell Tribute; 2 changing beers (sourced locally; often Bristol Beer Factory, Pitchfork, Twisted Oak) Ⓗ
A traditional village pub free of tie, occupying a 14th-century building that retains many original features, including a bay window at the front. Mind your head as you go in – there are low ceilings throughout, with steps between bars and to the toilets. Up a step is the rear restaurant area with a beer garden beyond. The guest beer is usually from a local Bristol or Somerset brewery.
♨❀◑⛺●🚌(X2)🐾📶

Yeovil

Quicksilver Mail ✔
168 Hendford Hill, BA20 2RG (at jct of A30 and A37)
☎ (01935) 424721 🌐 quicksilvermail.com
Butcombe Original; Dartmoor Jail Ale; Sharp's Doom Bar; 2 changing beers (sourced nationally) Ⓗ
A roadside pub with a unique name commemorating a high-speed mail coach. It has been run by the same landlord since 2002 and has been in most editions of the Guide since then. There is a large single bar and a separate dining area serving excellent food and an attractively priced range of wine. The pub is a well-known live music destination and also holds comedy, bingo and quiz nights in the bar or function room.
♨❀🛏◑♣P🚌(40,96)🐾📶

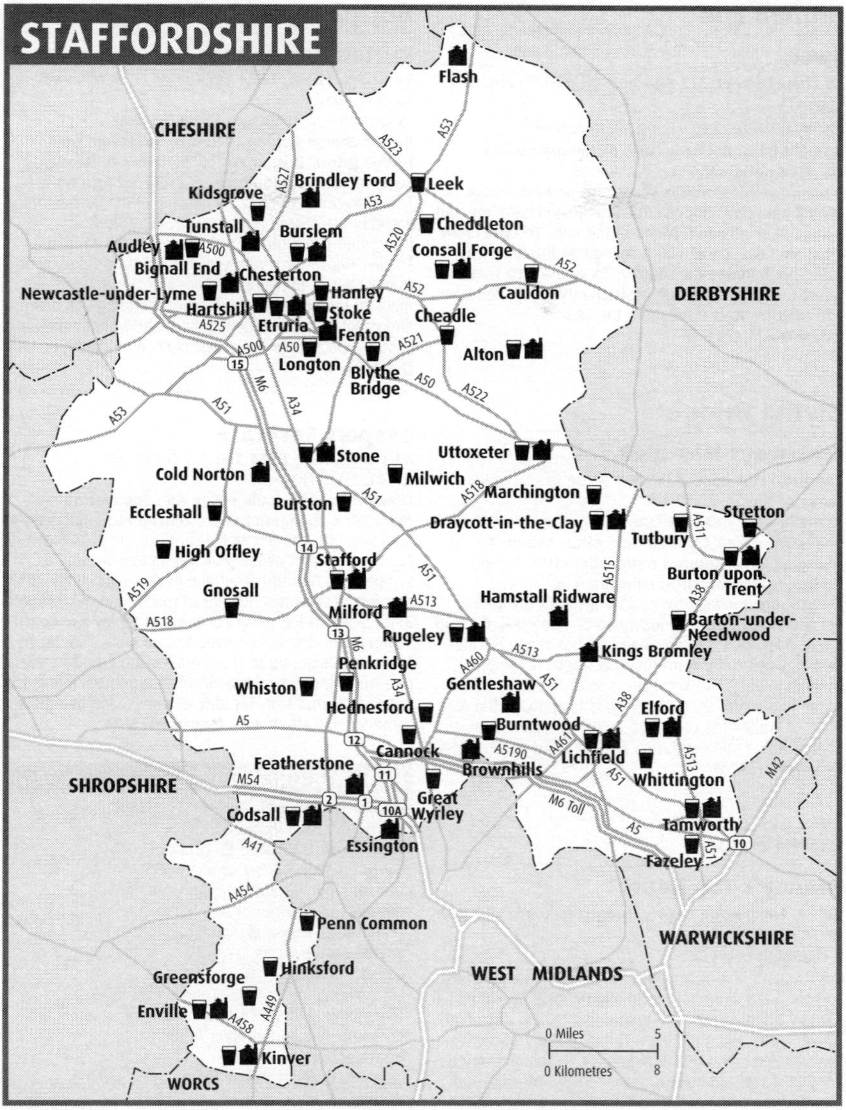

Alton

Talbot ✔

Station Road, ST10 4BX

☎ (01538) 269709

Draught Bass; Sharp's Doom Bar; 3 changing beers (sourced nationally) Ⓗ

A Grade II listed building, believed to be from the 17th century, in a village with several award-winning pubs. The building was closed and derelict for 16 years before it was reopened in 2018. Owned by the adjacent Alton Bridge Hotel, a previous Guide entrant, it shares several facilities such as the car park and garden. A warm and comfortable inn, fitted out in an olde-worlde style. Regular events take place such as games nights and live music. A carvery is served every Sunday lunchtime. Past winner of several local CAMRA branch awards.

Q ❀ ♿ ♣ P 🐾 📶

Barton-under-Needwood

Royal Oak ✔

74 The Green, DE13 8JD (½ mile S of B5016 via Wales Lane)

☎ (01283) 713852

Marston's Pedigree; 2 changing beers (sourced nationally) Ⓗ/Ⓖ

A bustling community local on the southern edge of the village, home to many traditional pub games teams and a base for several local sports teams. While parts of the building date back to the 16th century, the pub has only existed since the mid-1800s. Public bar and lounge customers are served from a central bar below the level of the rest of the ground floor. A separate conservatory offers access to the garden. Beers are poured on handpump or by gravity, direct from the cask, on request.

Q ❀ ♣ P 🚌 (811,812) 🐾 📶

Bignall End

Swan

58 Chapel Street, ST7 8QD (just off B5500 ½ mile E of Audley)
☎ (01782) 720622 🌐 theswaninn-stoke.co.uk
Draught Bass; Oakham Citra; 6 changing beers (sourced nationally) [H]
A warm welcome awaits you at this popular venue. The central bar serves both a large lounge and bar area, and a large beer garden is found to the rear. You can enjoy eight real ales, six of which change all the time and come from around the country. There are also several ciders to sample. The pub hosts charity nights and beer and cider festivals throughout the year.
♘❀♣●🚌(4,4E) 🐾 📶

Blythe Bridge

Crossways Micropub 𝕃

246 Uttoxeter Road, ST11 9LY (close to crossroads, in centre of town)
☎ 07376 259117 🌐 peakstonesrock.co.uk/crossways.html
Peakstones Rock Chained Oak, Alton Abbey; 1 changing beer (sourced nationally; often Burton Bridge, Leatherbritches, Milestone) [H]
This micropub owned by Peakstones Rock Brewery opened in 2015. Four handpulls serve three real ales and a real cider, plus a further bag-in-a-box range of cider. Two ales will come from the Peakstones range plus changing guests. No keg beer is sold. The building was formerly a motor spares outlet and is opposite the old Duke of Wellington pub, now a Tesco Express. Close to Blythe Bridge railway station and on a bus route.
Q⇌♣●🚌(6A) 🐾

Burntwood

Sankey's Tap House

Unit 1, Lambourne House, Bridgcross Road, WS7 2BX
☎ 07982 923744
4 changing beers [H]
Burntwood's first micropub, offering four changing ales and six ciders from both local and national breweries. A friendly place, there is no loud music or TVs, just good conversation and great beer. It has recently been redeveloped – two of the rooms are freshly decorated – and has a welcoming feel. Food consists of cobs, pork pies and the usual pub offerings. Closed on Monday except bank holidays. Q♘♿♣●P🚌(60,61)🐾📶

Burston

Greyhound Inn

ST18 0DR (just off A51 N of Sandon and 3 miles S of Stone)
☎ (01889) 508263 🌐 greyhoundinn.info
Lancaster Bomber; 2 changing beers (sourced regionally) [H]
A spacious and friendly family-owned pub 15 minutes' walk from the Trent & Mersey Canal at Bridge 86, refurbished in 2017 and not to be missed on travels around Staffordshire. It has a reputation for good food and beer, with a separate bar for those who just want a drink. The garden with farm animals helps make children welcome. Local CAMRA Rural Pub of the Year runner-up in 2019. ♘❀◐⛺♣P🐾📶

Burton upon Trent

Burton Bridge Inn

24 Bridge Street, DE14 1SY (on A511, at town end of Trent Bridge)
☎ (01283) 536596 🌐 burtonbridgeinn.co.uk
Burton Bridge Golden Delicious, Sovereign Gold, Bridge Bitter, Burton Porter, Stairway to Heaven, Festival Ale; 1 changing beer (sourced locally) [H]
This 17th-century pub is the flagship of the Burton Bridge Brewery estate and fronts the brewery itself. It incorporates two rooms served from a central bar: a smaller front room, with wooden pews and displaying many awards, brewery memorabilia, and framed old maps of Burton, and a back room featuring oak beams and panels. A small function room and a skittle alley are upstairs. Occasional live music plays on Saturdays.
Q❀♣●🚌🐾📶

Coopers Tavern ★

43 Cross Street, DE14 1EG (off Station St)
☎ (01283) 567246
Draught Bass [G]**; Joule's Pale Ale, Slumbering Monk** [H]**; 6 changing beers (sourced regionally)** [H]/[G]
A classic 19th-century alehouse, once the Bass Brewery tap but now part of the Joule's estate. Following a sympathetic refurbishment and expansion in early 2017, the pub incorporates five linked rooms, but the intimate inner taproom has retained its barrel tables and bench seating, with the beer served from a small counter by the cask stillage. Up to six ciders/perries (choice varies), plus fruit wines, are also available. Impromptu folk music regularly features on Tuesday evenings, and live music some Sunday afternoons. ♘❀⇌●🚌🐾📶

REAL ALE BREWERIES

Beowulf Brownhills
Blythe Hamstall Ridware
Brewhouse & Kitchen ▮ Lichfield
Burton Bridge Burton upon Trent
Burton Town ◆ Burton upon Trent
Consall Forge Consall Forge
Crown Brewhouse ▮ Elford
Enville Enville
Firs ▮ Codsall
Flash Flash
Front Row ◆ Brindley Ford
Gates Burton Burton upon Trent
Gentlewood Gentleshaw
Grey Friars Featherstone (brewing suspended)
Heritage Burton upon Trent
Inadequate ▮ Stoke-on-Trent: Etruria
Izaac Walton Cold Norton
Kinver Kinver
Lymestone Stone
Marston's Burton upon Trent
Morton Essington
Peakstones Rock Alton
Quartz Kings Bromley
RAN Stoke-on-Trent: Fenton
Roebuck Draycott-in-Clay
Shugborough Milford (brewing suspended)
Six Towns ▮ Tunstall
Slater's Stafford
Tamworth ◆ Tamworth
Titanic Stoke-on-Trent: Burslem
Tower ◆ Burton upon Trent
Townhouse Audley
Uttoxeter Uttoxeter
Vine Inn ▮ Rugeley
Weal Chesterton

Derby Inn ✔
17 Derby Road, DE14 1RU (on A5121, 350yds north of jct with A511)
☎ 07736 953206
Draught Bass; Marston's Pedigree; 2 changing beers (sourced nationally) [H]
Friendly, Victorian, two-roomed community pub, towards the northern edge of the town, offering a step back in time to a more relaxed pace of life. Popular with football supporters on match days since it is en route between the railway station and Burton Albion's Pirelli Stadium. Lunchtime meals are available only on Sundays and evening meals, with limited choice, only on Wednesdays, but fresh filled cobs are available to order at all times, plus hot snacks on match days. Quiz Night Tuesday. ❀◑♣●P🚌(V1,X38)🐾📶

Devonshire Arms 🏆
86 Station Street, DE14 1BT (on corner of jct with Milton St)
☎ (01283) 480022
Burton Bridge Bridge Bitter, Burton Porter, Stairway to Heaven; Draught Bass; 3 changing beers (sourced regionally) [H]
Popular old pub, now a free house, dating from the 19th century and Grade II listed. It comprises a public bar at the front, and a larger, more comfortable, split-level lounge to the rear, the latter featuring an 1853 map of Burton, old local photographs, and unusual arched wooden ceilings. An extended rear patio is adorned with flower borders and hanging baskets. Real cider, continental bottled beers and English fruit wines are also stocked. There is a themed food evening on a Tuesday – often fish, pies or steak. The pub welcomes football fans including away supporters. ❀◑⇌♣●P🚌🐾📶

Dog Inn
5 Lichfield Street, DE14 3QZ (opp Burton College, near jct with High St/New St)
☎ (01283) 517060
Black Country Bradley's Finest Golden, Pig on the Wall, Fireside; Draught Bass; 7 changing beers (sourced regionally) [H]
Attractive half-timbered terrace pub near the town centre, dating back to the early 19th century. Radically revitalised by Black Country Ales in 2015, an impressive selection of cask ales and ciders is offered. Internally, a large, comfortable, square single room surrounds a central bar and features a wood-framed ceiling and wood panelling on the walls, plus three real fires and numerous framed old photographs of Burton. Beers are listed on two boards on opposite sides of the room. May close early depending on custom on Sunday or Monday evening. ♿♣●🚌🐾📶

Last Heretic
95 Station Street, DE14 1BT (between Grant's Yard and Mosley St)
☎ 07715 097797 🌐 thelastheretic.co.uk
4 changing beers (sourced regionally) [G]
A smart micropub in a terrace of commercial properties close to the station, named after Edward Wightman, a resident of Burton, who in 1612 was the last person to be burnt at the stake in England for heresy. The comfortable single room features a small bar counter towards the rear, with the stillage visible through a glass door and window. Up to six beers are on offer, and up to seven ciders and perries, from various sources, are listed on boards near the bar. There is a narrow garden at the rear for outdoor drinking. Q❀♿⇌●🚌🐾📶

National Brewery Centre (Brewery Tap)
Horninglow Street, DE14 1NG (on A511, near jct with Guild St)
☎ (01283) 532880 🌐 nationalbrewerycentre.co.uk
Draught Bass; Heritage St Modwen Golden Ale, Masterpiece IPA; 3 changing beers (sourced locally) [H]
This tap for the National Brewery Centre (formerly Bass Museum and later Coors Visitor Centre) serves beers from the William Worthington's Brewery which are marketed under the name Heritage Brewing Company. The comfortable single-room bar is bright and airy, furnished in a modern style with much brewery memorabilia. Food is served in the bar and adjacent restaurant; a conservatory overlooks the garden and children's play area. Numerous events, including live music, are hosted (details on the NBC website). ❀◑♿P🚌(1)🐾📶

Cannock

Linford Arms ✔
79 High Green, WS11 1BN
☎ (01543) 469360
Greene King Abbot; Ruddles Best Bitter; Sharp's Doom Bar; 5 changing beers (sourced nationally; often Backyard, Beowulf, Salopian) [H]
Established town-centre Wetherspoon serving eight real ales and ciders. Its name originates from the builders' merchants that formerly occupied the premises. Food is served all day, and there is a seating area on two floors with quieter alcoves and a separate snug. Two ale festivals are held each year and local breweries feature regularly. There are good bus and rail links. A many-times local CAMRA Pub of the Year finalist in recent years, this pub is not to be missed if visiting Cannock. ◑♿●🚌📶

Newhall Arms
81 High Green, WS11 1BN
☎ 07852 573042
8 changing beers [H]
Cannock's first micropub, in the centre of the town. This is a friendly place with no loud music or TVs, just good conversation and great beer. The bar serves eight ales and two ciders – the beers changing all the time, sourced locally as well as nationally. Cobs are available as well as the usual snacks. A real gem, it is a local CAMRA branch Pub of the Year. Q❀♿●P🚌🐾📶

Cauldon

Yew Tree Inn 𝕃
ST10 3EJ (turn right at Ye Olde Crowne pub, Waterhouses, approx 1 mile from jct)
☎ (01538) 309876
Burton Bridge Bridge Bitter; Rudgate Ruby Mild; 1 changing beer (sourced nationally; often Blue Monkey, Dancing Duck, McMullen) [H]
Situated halfway between Leek and Ashbourne, this is possibly one of the most famous pubs in the country, and one of the few where even the local CAMRA committee would admit that the good real ale is the least of its attractions. Step back in time into an interior stuffed with antiques, guns, pianos, penny farthings, a working pianola and much more period bric-a-brac. The entrance is dominated by the eponymous yew tree.
Q❀◑⛺♣●P🚌(109)🐾📶

Cheadle

Bird in Hand
117 Tape Street, ST10 1ER
☎ 07812 375407
Burton Bridge Bridge Bitter; Dancing Duck 22; 2 changing beers (often Brunswick, Burton Bridge) 🄷
A well-deserved first entry into the Guide, this small, traditional, terraced street-corner pub occupies a main road position just outside the town centre. Two rooms have lovely coal fires. A large screen shows major sporting events, another room houses a dartboard, and a pool table is found in an ante-room. The cosy snug is quieter and also has a real fire. Outside is a patio for smokers. The licensees always give a warm welcome, as do the bar staff. Q♣🚌(32,32X)🐾

Huntsman L
The Green, ST10 1XS (at bottom of hill)
☎ (01538) 750502 🌐 thehuntsmancheadle.com
Brains Rev James; Marston's Pedigree; Sharp's Doom Bar; 3 changing beers (sourced regionally; often Geeves, Peakstones Rock, Slater's) 🄷
A Guide regular on the edge of this market town, ideal for visiting Alton Towers, the Potteries or the Peak District. Family-friendly, it has a stylish interior and a welcoming atmosphere; guest beers are sourced locally and regionally. A beer and music festival is held at the end of May, with gin and cider festivals later in the year. The food is cooked from scratch, with the beef and lamb coming from the neighbouring farm. Highly recommended. ❀🛏◐◑♿♣●P🚌(IN2)🐾📶

Cheddleton

Black Lion 🏆 L
12 Hollow Lane, ST13 7HP (turn off A520 into Hollow Lane opp Red Lion and pub is approx 100yds up hill on right next to church)
☎ (01538) 360620
Draught Bass; Timothy Taylor Landlord; 4 changing beers (often Salopian, Wincle) 🄷
A welcome new entry to the Guide, the Black Lion is a comfortable village pub, with real fires in the winter. It is close to the Flint Mill Museum and the Cauldon Canal, and beside the Grade II listed St Edward's Church, which has a Wardle family connection and Arts & Crafts features. Recently refurbished in a modern rustic style, outside there is a patio area to the front and an enclosed beer garden at the rear. An excellent range of well-kept beers is offered. Q❀◐⇌♣●P🚌(16)🐾📶

Codsall

Codsall Station L
Chapel Lane, WV8 2EJ
☎ (01902) 847061 🌐 HoldensCodsallStation.co.uk
Holden's Black Country Bitter, Golden Glow, Special; 3 changing beers (sourced regionally; often Holden's, Salopian) 🄷
Sensitively converted from the waiting room, offices and stationmaster's house, the Grade II listed building comprises a bar, lounge, snug and conservatory, and displays worldwide railway memorabilia. Steps lead to a drinking area outside with tables and benches overlooking the working platforms. Bar meals are served except Sunday and Monday and cobs and locally made pork pies are available all week. Beer festivals are held on the May and August bank holiday weekends. Q❀◐◑⇌P🚌(5,10B)🐾📶

Firs Club L
Station Road, WV8 1BX (entrance from shared Co-op car park off Station Rd)
☎ (01902) 844674 🌐 thefirscodsall.com
5 changing beers (sourced locally; often Hobsons, Ludlow, Wye Valley) 🄷
Local CAMRA branch Club of the Year 2020, with a bar area, quiet lounge and sports lounge with pool table. The range of five changing ales, mainly local, usually includes a mild, and occasionally a beer from the in-house brewery. A beer festival is held in November. The Firs Suite, a separate function area, is available to hire for weddings and events. A pedestrian entrance in Wood Road is handy for the bus stop. Q❀♿⇌♣P🚌(5,10B)📶

Consall Forge

Black Lion L
ST9 0AJ (off A522 follow signs to Consall Gdns, then Nature Reserve on hairpin bend; go straight on, ignore No Vehicular Access sign; at bottom of hill go left along track to car park)
☎ (01782) 550294 🌐 blacklionpub.co.uk
Peakstones Rock Black Hole; 3 changing beers (sourced regionally; often Consall Forge, Falstaff) 🄷
Walk, drive or travel by boat or train to visit this destination pub with its changing beer and cider selections; regular beer festivals are held, normally to coincide with a steam gala on the neighbouring Churnet Valley Railway. Typical pub food is served; arrive hungry as the portions are large. Set in an Area of Outstanding Natural Beauty, the pub is not easy to find by car but well worth the effort. Seek it out! Q❀◐◑⛺⇌♣●P🐾📶

Draycott-in-the-Clay

Roebuck ✔
Toby's Hill, DE6 5BT (at Toby's Hill/A515 jct, 600yds N of village)
☎ (01283) 821135 🌐 theroebuckdraycott.co.uk
Roebuck Blonde, Hopzester, Bitter, IPA; 1 changing beer (sourced locally) 🄷
Dating back to at least the early 19th century, this friendly country inn is now a privately owned free house, offering a warm welcome and a pleasant atmosphere. It has a comfortable single-room main bar and a separate smart restaurant beyond. The pub has gained a good reputation for food (no meals Sun eve). Beers from the associated Roebuck Brewery to the rear are served. ❀◐◑P🚌(402)🐾📶

Eccleshall

King's Arms Hotel ✔
17 Stafford Street, ST21 6BL
☎ (01785) 850294 🌐 kingsarmseccleshall.com
Marston's Pedigree; Wainwright; 4 changing beers (sourced nationally) 🄷
A former coaching inn once known as the Unicorn and then a local Inland Revenue office, it was restored and refurbished in 2017 and is now a friendly free house. Parts of the original building are visible. Various rooms are served by a central bar with an interesting selection of beers, both local and national, often including those from the nearby Izaak Walton Brewery. This is an excellent, well-run establishment, warm and cosy in winter, and one not to be missed. ❀🛏◐◑♿♣P🚌🐾

Elford

Crown Inn 𝕃

The Square, B79 9DB (600yds E of A513) SK189106
☎ (01827) 383602
Draught Bass; Purity Pure Gold; 2 changing beers (sourced locally; often Crown Brewhouse) Ⓗ
Grade II listed village pub, with a simple but cosy bar room, a plush snug, two small dining rooms, and a quirky little space which was formerly the above-ground cellar. Solid fuel heating gives a rosy glow in winter. A changing ale from the in-house Crown Brewhouse is occasionally offered. Food is served Wednesday to Saturday evenings and Sunday lunchtime. Children are welcome in a separate room on the car park side. ☖◐◑♣P🐾ᯤ

Enville

Cat Inn 𝕃

Bridgnorth Road, DY7 5HA (on A458)
☎ (01384) 872209 🌐 thecatinn.com
Enville Ale, Ginger Beer; Olde Swan Original; 4 changing beers (sourced nationally; often Enville, Froth Blowers, Skinner's) Ⓗ
Local CAMRA South Staffordshire branch Pub of the Year 2020. A picturesque and impressive country retreat with multiple drinking and dining areas all served by real fires. The majority of the cask offering comes from staple and seasonal Enville ranges, but you will also find a number of guest beers and up to two real ciders.
Q☖❀◐◑●P🐾ᯤ

Fazeley

Three Horseshoes

New Street, B78 3RD (near jct of A4091 and B5404)
☎ (01827) 289754
Draught Bass; St Austell Tribute; 1 changing beer Ⓗ
This is very much a traditional local, with a friendly welcome for all. The single room features a quarry-tiled bar room, with a smaller, cosier area to the side. There are several TVs showing sport. Towards the rear is a large enclosed garden which proves popular in the summer. The guest ale changes frequently and is often local. Parking is usually available on nearby streets.
❀♣🚌(110)🐾ᯤ

Gnosall

George & the Dragon 🏆

46 High Street, ST20 0EX
☎ 07779 327551 🌐 georgeandthedragongnosall.com
Holden's Golden Glow; Wood Shropshire Lad; 3 changing beers (sourced locally) Ⓗ
This lovely little pub opened in 2015 and soon received acclaim. The building dates from 1736, with a past life as a home, shop and off-licence. It has two rooms served by one bar. With no TVs, no music and no bandits, it has a good old-fashioned appeal. Tasty home-made snacks are available at the bar, but they do tend to sell out fast.
Q☖♣●🚌(5)🐾

Great Wyrley

Andys' Ale House 🏆

Unit 38, Quinton Court, WS6 6DS
☎ 07975 847318
5 changing beers (often Beowulf, Bristol Beer Factory, Sarah Hughes) Ⓗ
This new venue is Great Wyrley's first micropub, owned and run by two Andys, and located in the Quinton Court shopping centre. It is a friendly place – no loud music or TVs, just good conversation and great beer. Recently updated, one room has been freshly decorated. The five beers and four ciders are always changing, with local as well as national ales on offer. Cobs, pork pies and Scotch eggs are served, as well as the usual snacks. Local CAMRA 2019 Pub of the Year. ☖♿⇌♣●P🚌(2)🐾ᯤ

Greensforge

Navigation

Greensforge Lane, DY6 0AH
☎ (01384) 273721
Enville Ale; Three Tuns XXX; 2 changing beers (often Hobsons, Holden's, Olde Swan) Ⓗ
A welcoming pub-cum-restaurant continuing to attract a significant following of locals and ramblers due to the unspoilt interior and consistently good grub. On sunnier days drinkers can enjoy their beers on one of the many benches at the front of the premises, or on the various grass verges which offer relaxing views. There is a large car park directly opposite. Q☖❀◐◑P🐾ᯤ

Hednesford

Bridge Inn

387 Cannock Road, WS11 5TD (on jct of Belt Rd and Cannock Rd)
☎ (01543) 423651
Banks's Amber Ale; 6 changing beers (sourced nationally) Ⓗ
Close to Cannock Chase, this is a real ale-based pub that prides itself on a changing selection of ales as well as real cider. Food is served Thursday to Sunday, produced on-site and using only fresh local produce. The chips are triple cooked and the burgers are made to a special recipe. Theme nights and live music feature most Saturday nights, and pool and darts teams are also based here. ☖❀◐◑⇌♣P🚌🐾ᯤ

Cross Keys Hotel 𝕃

42 Hill Street, WS12 2DN
☎ (01543) 879534
Draught Bass; Holden's Golden Glow; Salopian Oracle; Wye Valley HPA; 5 changing beers (sourced nationally; often Beowulf, Ludlow, Three Tuns) Ⓗ
Serving up to eight real ales including several guests, this former coaching inn dates back to 1746. Hednesford Town Football Club was originally based behind the pub; the licensee is an ex-player and now assistant manager. Sporting and historic photographs decorate the walls, and monthly quiz nights are held. It is rumoured that the infamous highwayman Dick Turpin stopped here on his ride to York. Local CAMRA Pub of the Year many times.
❀🛏♣P▯🚌🐾ᯤ

High Offley

Anchor Inn ★

Peggs Lane, Old Lea, ST20 0NG (by Bridge 42 of the Shropshire Union Canal) SJ775256
☎ (01785) 284569
Wadworth 6X Ⓗ
An unspoilt example of a 19th-century canalside pub, built around 1830 on the Shropshire Union Canal, England's last narrow trunk canal. It has been run by the same family since 1870. The right-hand room has a quarry-tile floor, two high-back settles, a window bench, scrubbed tables and, in winter, a roaring fire, all of which creates a timeless atmosphere. Opening hours vary – check if travelling any distance. Q☖❀⛺♣●P🐾

Hinksford

Hinksford Arms ✓
Swindon Road, DY6 0BA
☎ (01384) 386069 🌐 hinksfordarms.co.uk
Enville Ale; Holden's Golden Glow; Wye Valley HPA; 2 changing beers (sourced nationally; often Bristol Beer Factory, Salopian, Thornbridge) [H]
Local CAMRA branch Pub of the Year 2020 finalist. Formerly the Old Bush, this recently renovated pub has broad appeal for drinkers, diners and followers of sport (both Sky and BT are shown). There are regular tap takeovers, as advertised on Facebook. Extensive grounds at the rear provide a good suntrap on warmer afternoons, where there is often a barbecue.
❀ ♿ P (16) 🐾 ᯤ

Kidsgrove

Blue Bell
25 Hardingswood, ST7 1EG (off A50 near Tesco)
☎ (01782) 774052
Whim Arbor Light; 5 changing beers (sourced nationally) [H]
Friendly traditional canalside pub offering six real ales and nine ciders, plus a warm welcome from the hosts. The main bar has two separate areas off it and a smaller room to the rear. The well-kept beer range features different styles, always including one dark ale. There is a beer garden to the rear. The pub holds an annual beer festival and seasonal and charity events. Popular with locals, walkers and canal users.
Q ❀ ♿ ♣ P (3,4A) 🐾 ᯤ

Kinver

Cross Inn
Church Hill, DY7 6HZ
☎ (01384) 878481
Black Country Bradley's Finest Golden, Pig on the Wall, Fireside; 4 changing beers (sourced nationally; often Fixed Wheel, Oakham, Salopian) [H]
A popular destination, with internal decor one would expect from a Black Country Ales outlet, including a real fire. Tasty and tempting food is served at the weekend including hot pork sandwiches and 'grey paes'. There is a large car park adjacent and Stourbridge buses stop nearby, but there is no service after 6pm or on Sunday.
♿ ♣ P (228) 🐾 ᯤ

Leek

Blue Mugge
17 Osbourne Street, ST13 6LJ (off A53 Buxton Rd)
☎ (01538) 384450
Draught Bass; 4 changing beers (sourced nationally; often Coach House, Slater's) [H]
Now an established entry just outside the town centre. Owned and run by the same family for over 40 years, this unassuming terraced street-corner local has several distinctly separate themed rooms, a result of three adjoining properties being knocked into one. The unique layout has bar service from a central octagonal pillar, with the beer pumps and taps behind the staff. Two handpulls are believed to be 120 years old. Constantly changing guest ales are listed on a blackboard. Good-value food is available lunchtimes. The bus station is nearby. Q ♣ 🐾 ᯤ

Fountain Inn
14 Fountain Street, ST13 6JR
☎ (01538) 387205
Draught Bass; St Austell Tribute; 6 changing beers (sourced nationally; often Exmoor, Front Row, Wincle) [H]
A magnificent bank of 10 handpulls greets the eye on entering this smart town-centre local, a former CAMRA regional Pub of the Year. Eight real ales change regularly and always include a darker, stronger brew. Two real ciders are also on sale. Live music on Sunday plus a beer raffle help make this a real gem of a friendly community pub. Two well-appointed rooms upstairs offer accommodation, with plenty of places to eat nearby.
Q ❀ ♣ 🐾 ᯤ

Roebuck
18 Derby Street, ST13 5AB (on main shopping street)
☎ (01538) 385602
Everards Tiger; Titanic Steerage, Iceberg, White Star, Plum Porter, Captain Smith's Strong Ale; 4 changing beers (sourced regionally; often Magic Rock, Salopian, Tiny Rebel) [H]
A well-deserved new entry to the Guide, in the town centre. With its distinctive black and white wooden-framed frontage, this Titanic Brewery-owned former coaching inn dates back to 1626. Up to 13 ales at busier times are mainly from the Titanic range, including the award-winning Plum Porter, plus four guest ales, real cider and a range of craft beers. Award-winning food is served all day, including breakfast. Regular live music and outdoor events take place in the large rear beer garden. Close to the bus station. Q ❀ P 🐾 ᯤ

Wilkes Head
15 St Edward Street, ST13 5DS
☎ 07976 592787
Whim Hartington Bitter, Hartington IPA, Flower Power; 2 changing beers (sourced nationally; often Broughton, Burton Bridge) [H]
Reputedly the oldest licensed premises near the main market square, this Whim Brewery-owned local is the longest continuous Guide entry in the area and displays a range of past CAMRA awards over the bar. Live jam music is held on Monday evening hosted by the accomplished musician landlord, and several other all-day music events are staged throughout the year in the large back yard. The beers are from Whim, plus changing guests usually including a darker, stronger brew. A good range of real cider is also available. Q ❀ ♣ P 🐾

Lichfield

Beerbohm
19 Tamworth Street, WS13 6JP
☎ (01543) 898252 🌐 beerbohm.co.uk
4 changing beers (sourced nationally) [H]
Atmospheric café-bar with a Belgian feel, decorated with beer enamels, gilded mirrors and globular chandeliers. The large, comfortable room upstairs offers the unusual view of three adjacent pubs on the opposite side of the road. Four changing ales are partnered by continental draught and bottled beers. Draught ales can be canned for takeout. Simple snacks are served, and customers are welcome to bring their own food. The unisex toilets are upstairs. Q 🐾 ᯤ

Bitter-Suite
55 Upper St John Street, WS14 9DT
☎ 07852 179340 🌐 bittersuite-micropub.co.uk
House beer (by Heritage); 4 changing beers (sourced nationally) [G]
This splendid micropub sits opposite the long-closed Lichfield Brewery building, and was in fact a pub over 30 years ago. There are three comfortable rooms, and service is to your table – make your choices from the

board. Four real ciders are usually available, plus five ales, including the house beer from Heritage. Gins, wines and bottled beers are also on offer, plus simple snacks. There is a large beer terrace to the rear. Children are welcome during the day. Q

Horse & Jockey

8-10 Sandford Street, WS13 6QA

☎ (01543) 410033

Holden's Golden Glow; Marston's Pedigree; Timothy Taylor Landlord; Wye Valley HPA; 4 changing beers (sourced nationally; often Izaak Walton)

Lichfield's longest-serving Guide entry attracts locals as well as visitors from afar. The four guest ales are generally from microbreweries. Various comfy areas surround the central bar, and there is a small suntrap beer terrace to the rear. Sports screenings are popular. Hot food is served Tuesday to Saturday lunchtimes, and a pork pie/cheeseboard selection is always available. A 21-plus age policy applies.

Whippet Inn

21 Tamworth Street, WS13 6JP

☎ 07922 581468

4 changing beers (sourced nationally)

This former dress shop is an outstanding micropub with a proven record. It takes its name from a cheeky boozer in a Carry On film. Four well-chosen, varying ales are complemented by two changing real ciders and a selection of craft keg beers. With seating for around 25 and a capacity of up to 40, the pub offers a friendly intimacy. Food is served only on Saturday – sandwiches, and cakes often flavoured with beer. Q

Marchington

Dog & Partridge

Church Lane, ST14 8LJ (250yds along Church Lane from High St)

☎ (01283) 820394 dogandpartridgemarchington.co.uk

Draught Bass; 3 changing beers (sourced locally; often Abbeydale, Gates Burton, Uttoxeter)

A gem of a village inn with Bass always on tap, plus a selection of local guest ales on several handpumps. Formerly a restaurant, the interior is split into four main areas with open fires. Food is served lunchtimes and evenings. A pleasant beer garden to the rear is popular in the summer months. The pub is renowned locally for its weekly live music sessions and regular beer festivals. Parking is available to the side and close by at the church. Children are welcome. Q P (402)

Milwich

Green Man

Sandon Lane, ST18 0EG (on B5027 in centre of village)

☎ (01889) 505310 greenmanmilwich.com

Draught Bass; 5 changing beers (sourced nationally)

A country inn well worth a visit, with 27 consecutive years in the Guide and a frequent local CAMRA Pub of the Year winner. The licensee has been in-situ since 1990 – he drinks Bass! There is usually a dark beer available. The enormous luxurious beer garden is used to host an annual free music festival. The pub is at the heart of a vibrant village community and is also popular with walkers and cyclists visiting the area. No food Monday or Tuesday. Q P

Newcastle-under-Lyme

Bridge Street Ale House

31 Bridge Street, ST5 2RY

☎ (01782) 499394 bridgestreetalehouse.com

5 changing beers (sourced nationally)

The first micropub in the area, this is a special place for regulars and newcomers alike, in the capable hands of Grum and his hospitable staff. The pub oozes charm and appeal, enhanced by the quirky décor. Five changing guest beers are served on handpull from various breweries, with more occasionally available straight from the barrel. Nine real ciders and an extensive range of speciality rums add to the individuality of this fantastic pub, a Newcastle real ale institution. Q

Cask Bar

1-2 Andrew Place, ST5 1DL

☎ (01782) 870560

Sarah Hughes Dark Ruby Mild; 4 changing beers (sourced nationally; often Kelham Island, Ossett, Rudgate)

Award-winning micropub just outside the town centre, which opened in July 2017. One room houses a variety of high and low seating. Five cask beers are stocked, plus a couple of real ciders, a good selection of bottled beers, a rotating craft keg selection, and one of the best gin ranges in the area. Evening food includes Monday curry night, Thursday pie and pub classics, and Friday fish and chips. Q

Hopinn

102 Albert Street, ST5 1JR

☎ (01782) 711121

Black Sheep Best Bitter; Draught Bass; Oakham Citra; 8 changing beers (sourced nationally; often Mallinsons, Northern Monk, Oakham)

Voted Pub of the Year for the last three years by the local CAMRA branch, the Hopinn offers an outstanding range of quality national and local beers. Bought from Punch Taverns in 2014, the pub is now a free house. Its three rooms are comfortably furnished, with Art Deco features to admire, all contributing to a wonderful atmosphere. Staff are ever attentive and a warm welcome is extended to all. The eight cask ales that adorn the bar are supplemented by five KeyKeg beers.

Lymestone Vaults

Pepper Street, ST5 1PR

☎ (01782) 615801

Lymestone Stone Cutter, Stone Faced, Foundation Stone, Stone the Crows; 3 changing beers (sourced regionally; often Derventio, Lymestone, Springhead)

A modern wine bar-style venue, the first to be owned by Lymestone Brewery of Stone. Accessed via an alleyway in between the estate agents' and Chatwins, it has a single L-shaped room with a mixture of chairs and sofas, plus a piano in the corner giving that old-fashioned feel. Up to eight beers and at least eight real ciders are available, advertised on a tall pole. A good lunchtime menu is served including the highly recommended local delicacy, Staffordshire oatcakes, sold with a range of fillings.

Mellards

Mellards Warehouse, Market Lane, ST5 1AA

☎ (01782) 610497

2 changing beers (sourced nationally)

Smart modern bar set in an old warehouse building. The pub is split level – the bar on the ground floor with high tables and chairs, the upper level with settees and armchairs. The bar prides itself on the three handpulls, one of which serves a cider, and six craft beers. A large selection of bottled beers and cans is also stocked. Outside, there is a large seating area to the front of the bar. ●🚌🐾📶

Wellers Ⓛ
3 Pepper Street, ST5 1PR
☎ (01782) 698080
Weal Ales Weller Weal, Centwealial Milk Stout; 4 changing beers (sourced nationally; often Weal Ales) ⊞
Wellers is the taphouse for Weal Ales and showcases its national award-winning ales alongside three nationally sourced rotating guests. Two real ciders, two craft ales and speciality gins and vodkas are also available. Just off the High Street, this is a modern, comfortable, family-friendly pub for a quality beer served by welcoming staff. Thursday is quiz night. No food is served but you can bring your own. Closed Monday except bank holidays.
🐎●🚌🐾📶

Penkridge

Star Inn ✔
Market Place, ST19 5DJ
☎ (01785) 712513 🌐 thestarpenkridge.wixsite.com/home
Lancaster Bomber; Marston's Pedigree; Wainwright; 4 changing beers (sourced nationally) ⊞
A popular and welcoming pub in the old Market Place in the village, this one-room establishment first traded as an inn in 1830. It closed in about 1908 and became a Co-op store, then a private residence, but was restored and converted back to a pub in 1981. Often busy, it has several distinct areas and a cosy feel, with a patio and seating area outside. Good pub food is served daily plus excellent Scotch eggs. 🐎❀◑⛺⇌●P🚌🐾📶

Penn Common

Barley Mow Ⓛ ✔
Pennwood Lane, WV4 5JN (follow signs to Penn Golf Club from A449) SO901949
☎ (01902) 333510
Greene King Abbot; Hobsons Town Crier; St Austell Tribute; Timothy Taylor Landlord; 2 changing beers (sourced regionally; often Salopian, Three Tuns) ⊞
On the edge of Penn Common and sharing an access driveway with Penn Golf Club, this charming inn is worth seeking out. Built around 1630, it has low-beamed ceilings and steps leading down into the drinking and dining areas. the pub is renowned for its steaks. The compact single bar has a display of beer mats and foreign banknotes, and offers a selection of six quality real ales. Thatchers Heritage cider is also on offer.
Q🐎❀◑●P🐾📶

Rugeley

Plaza Ⓛ ✔
Horsefair, WS15 2EJ
☎ (01889) 586831
Greene King Abbot; Ruddles Best Bitter; Sharp's Doom Bar; 7 changing beers (sourced locally; often Beowulf, Blythe, Salopian) ⊞
Previously a cinema originally known as the Picture House and dating from the 1930s, this spacious Wetherspoon pub retains much of the cinematic atmosphere and Art Deco flourishes of the period. The light and airy interior allows for three widely separated levels, accentuated by a large window area where the cinema screen once was. Outside is a drinking area with balcony, terrace and lawned beer garden. Around seven guest ales are offered, with brews from microbreweries such as Salopian proving popular. The small car park is Pay & Display. Q🐎❀◑♿⇌●P🚌📶

Rusty Barrel
Fernwood Shopping Centre, Green Lane, WS15 2GS
🌐 therustybarrel.co.uk
Backyard Gold; Beowulf Dark Raven; Blythe Palmers Poison; Slater's 1 Hop; 4 changing beers (sourced locally; often Goff's, Leatherbritches, Titanic) ⊞
The first micropub in this town, it has one room and a friendly atmosphere. The decor is simple painted brick, with a ceiling adorned with pumpclips showing the vast array of beers sold. There are four handpumps offering a changing selection of ales, and at least five ciders are on offer. A good selection of wine, gin and whisky is also available. Children are welcome until the evening.
Q🐎♿♣●P🚌(22,825) 🐾

Vine Inn
Sheep Fair Close, WS15 2AT
☎ (01889) 574443
Vine Inn EPA, Vanilla Porter, Grapefruit IPA; 1 changing beer (sourced locally) ⊞
An old boozer on a quiet street, retaining a traditional multi-room layout with a spacious bar to the front, a small snug behind the bar, plus a room to the rear with a pool table. There is a large function room upstairs. The Vine now has its own brewery. The bar feels pleasantly dated, with quarry tiles and an open log fire. A small beer yard is at the front, underneath the sign. The guest ale is generally Draught Bass. Q🐎❀♿♣🚌🐾📶

Stafford

Bird in Hand
Victoria Square, ST16 2AQ (corner of Victoria Square)
☎ (01785) 252198 🌐 birdinhandstafford.co.uk
Black Country Bradley's Finest Golden, Pig on the Wall, Fireside; 6 changing beers (sourced regionally) ⊞
Part of the Black Country Ales chain, the pub was refurbished in 2017 and has a traditional feel, with three rooms and open fires. It boasts the biggest beer garden in Stafford town centre. Good home-cooked food complements the quality ales. Live music is hosted on a Sunday evening. Part of the Bird's history is as a Joule's of Stone outlet, and the trademark cross can still be seen on the exterior door frames. Over-18s only.
❀◑⇌♣●🚌🐾📶

bod
57-59 Bodmin Avenue, ST17 0EF
☎ (01785) 661506 🌐 stafford.bodcafebars.co.uk
Titanic Steerage, Iceberg, Plum Porter; 3 changing beers (often Titanic) ⊞
The first of Titanic Brewery's bod chain of café bars opened in 2018, named after its location on Bodmin Avenue and providing, as it says, breakfast, brunch, lunch, dinner, snacks or even a well-deserved pint after a hard day's work. Four Titanic beers are on draught. The premises occupies a former Co-op shop; ironically, the new Co-op shop opposite is on the site of a former pub. Gluten-free and vegan options are available on the menu. Alcoholic drinks are served from noon.
Q🐎◑♿🚌🐾📶

Greyhound
12 County Road, ST16 2PU (off A34, opp jail)
☎ (01785) 222432 🌐 greyhoundfreehousestafford.co.uk
Bradfield Farmers Blonde; 7 changing beers (sourced nationally) ⊞

A short walk from the centre of Stafford, this two-room free house is well worth a visit. It dates from 1831 and a newspaper article from the day it opened is on display above the bar. A range of eight ales is on offer plus a choice of bottled ciders. The Greyhound has won a number of CAMRA awards including Pub of the Year. Q⚭♣🚌🐾

Shrewsbury Arms

75 Eastgate Street, ST16 2NG

☎ (01785) 248240

Black Country Bradley's Finest Golden, Pig on the Wall, Fireside; 6 changing beers (sourced nationally) 🄷

Part of the Black Country Ales chain and fully refurbished in 2016, the pub concentrates on offering a wide range of beers from local breweries and across the country to complement its own range. Two real ciders are also served. There are three open fires in cold weather and a conservatory available to hire for private functions. Light snacks are always on offer. There are rumours of a ghost. Over-18s only. Q⚭❀⚌♣●🚌🐾📶

Slater's Bar

28 Gaolgate Street, ST16 2NT

☎ 07977 982884 🌐 slatersales.squarespace.com/slaters-bar

Slater's 1 Hop, Premium, Haka; 2 changing beers 🄷

A straightforward micropub with friendly staff, converted from a former shop, selling real ale, craft lager, ciders, speciality gins and spirits, wine, tea and coffee. Set in a pedestrianised area with little traffic, it has a pavement drinking area with tables and chairs to enjoy the sun. No food is served but you are welcome to bring your own lunch. Open mic night is every Tuesday, quiz night is Thursday, live music plays on Saturday night, and drink and draw is held on Sunday evening. Q⚭♿⚌●🚌

Spittal Brook

106 Lichfield Road, ST17 4LP (1 mile SE of centre off A34 at Queensville Bridge)

☎ (01785) 251343 🌐 thespittalbrookstafford.co.uk

St Austell Tribute; 3 changing beers (sourced nationally) 🄷

Traditional, friendly, two-roomed local within walking distance of the town centre. Following a refurbishment and change of management in 2019, the pub is now thriving. The front room offers TV sports and darts – dogs are welcome here and in the spacious garden. The rear room is both lounge and restaurant where fresh home-cooked food is served daily. There are three constantly changing guest beers. The pub hosts a quiz on Wednesday, poker on Thursday and live entertainment most Saturdays. Q⚭❀🛏◐♣P🚌🐾📶

Sun

7 Lichfield Road, ST17 4JX

☎ (01785) 248361 🌐 thesunstafford.co.uk

Everards Tiger; Titanic Steerage, Anchor Bitter, Iceberg, White Star, Captain Smith's Strong Ale; 6 changing beers (sourced nationally) 🄷

One of Titanic Brewery's pubs, this is a multi-roomed, multi-level establishment with 12 handpumps. Food is served throughout the day, using locally sourced ingredients. The Sunday menu includes a traditional roast. An outdoor drinking area with its own bar is great on warmer days. Beer festivals are held in spring and late summer in a large marquee at the rear. Buses stop outside the front door. Q⚭❀◐⚌♣P🚌🐾📶

Stoke-on-Trent: Burslem

Bull's Head 🄻

14 St John's Square, ST6 3AJ

☎ (01782) 834153

Titanic Steerage, Iceberg, White Star, Plum Porter; 6 changing beers (sourced nationally) 🄷

The Titanic Brewery's tap offers 10 real ales, 10 ciders and perries served from the cellar, and a selection of draught and bottled Belgian beers. With a large central bar, customers can choose between the snug or the bar where bar billiards, a skittles table and a jukebox can be found. A beer garden is to the rear. The pub is close to Port Vale and opens early on home match days – all fans are welcome. It is also a supporter of community events in the area. Q⚭❀♣●🚌🐾📶

Stoke-on-Trent: Etruria

Holy Inadequate 🄻

67 Etruria Old Road, ST1 5PE

☎ 07771 358238

Inadequate NZ Pale Ale, Roundhouse Stout; Joule's Pale Ale; 5 changing beers (sourced nationally; often Inadequate) 🄷

On the outskirts of Hanley, this popular pub offers a warm welcome. An L-shaped lounge and bar area, a rear room – both with log-burners – and a covered beer garden provide a choice of places in which to enjoy the excellent variety of beer and real cider on offer. The in-house brewery goes from strength to strength. Scotch eggs and pork pies are available all day, and regular mini beer festivals are held. The pub is a regular recipient of local CAMRA awards including Pub of the Year on four occasions. ❀●P🚌(4,4A,17)🐾📶

Stoke-on-Trent: Hanley

BottleCraft

33 Piccadilly, ST1 1EN (next to Regent Theatre)

☎ (01782) 911819 🌐 bottlecraft.beer

14 changing beers (sourced nationally)

A modern, friendly, craft beer bar in the heart of the city centre with two cask ales on handpull, 12 KeyKeg beers and over 200 bottles and cans from around the world. If you're finding it hard to choose, the friendly and experienced bar staff are more than happy to help. Beer is served in third, two-third and pint measures. There is a larger seating area upstairs and an outdoor space at the front. Tasting events are run regularly (see website). Q⚭♿●🚌🐾📶

Coachmakers Arms ★

65 Lichfield Street, ST1 3EA (opp Hanley bus station)

Draught Bass; 3 changing beers (sourced nationally) 🄷

A hidden gem of a historic Victorian corridor-style pub, comprising four rooms off a main passageway, with the bar accessible from the rear room, drinking corridor and the small snug. The front right-hand room is cosy, with a real fire. The pub offers a fine selection of real ales on handpull, with Draught Bass plus three guests, including many local and national favourites. A selection of bottles including lagers is also available, and a significant range of real cider is in the fridge. Q⚭●P🚌🐾

Victoria Lounge 🄻

5 Adventure Place, ST1 3AF (next to Hanley bus station)

☎ (01782) 273530

Draught Bass; Salopian Oracle; 4 changing beers (sourced nationally) 🄷

Family run for 36 years, and with a well-established reputation for quality, this pub is popular with locals and travellers alike. It has a large split-level room with comfortable furnishings enhanced by the addition of Chesterfield settees. There are six handpulls on the bar –

Bass is the long-standing house beer and has been joined, on request, by Oracle. The four guest ales come from local and national brewers. Conveniently close to the main bus station and the theatres. Q

Stoke-on-Trent: Hartshill

Artisan Tap

552 Hartshill Road, ST4 6AF
☎ (01782) 618378
4 changing beers (sourced nationally) Ⓗ
Converted from an old workshop in 2017, this popular venue on the Hartshill Mile soon established itself as a firm favourite with drinkers, serving four draught beers, three real ciders and several keg beers across all styles. The raised area in the main bar hosts regular live bands and a Tuesday quiz. The pub appears small but is bigger on the inside, with a long and quirky rear lounge plus outside seating at the front. Dogs are welcome. Q

Greyhound

67 George Street, ST5 1JT
☎ (01782) 635814
Titanic Steerage, Iceberg, White Star, Plum Porter; 5 changing beers (sourced nationally; often Titanic) Ⓗ
The second pub in the Titanic fleet, this establishment holds its own in an area renowned for good beer. Nine handpulls showcase four Titanic beers plus five different guests from across the UK. Two real ciders are always on offer, along with a large selection of country wines and bottled beers. Three kegs are often used for tap takeovers. Tasty bar snacks are served. Entertainment includes regular live music from local bands and a quiz on Sunday evening. Q

Sanctuary

493-495 Hartshill Road, ST4 6AA
☎ (01782) 437523
4 changing beers (sourced nationally) Ⓗ
This extremely popular micropub is a must-visit if you enjoy good conversation in a relaxed atmosphere with your drink. Cosy and eclectically furnished, the single-room bar is adorned with memorabilia and many intriguing ornaments. It has a real charm that makes you want to linger a little bit longer. The four handpull beers are well chosen and change all the time, and are joined by four traditional ciders plus an array of gins.

Stoke-on-Trent: Longton

Congress Inn

14 Sutherland Road, ST3 1HJ (near Longton police station)
☎ (01782) 763667 congressinnlongton.co.uk
Adnams Broadside; Castle Rock Sheriff's Tipple; Townhouse Styrian Pale; 6 changing beers (sourced nationally; often Castle Rock, Townhouse) Ⓗ
A convivial, multi award-winning, two-roomed pub, just outside the centre of Longton, dedicated to the dispense of good-quality real ale from a whole host of microbreweries. The left-hand room contains the bar where the three permanent beers are joined by up to six guest beers. The right-hand room houses the dartboard, and is also used for meetings and the annual beer festival, held every May. It's hard for the real ale fan to go wrong in a place like this – four real ciders and a good selection of beer in bottles are also available.

Stoke-on-Trent: Stoke

bod

Stoke-on-Trent Railway Station, Station Road, ST4 2AA
☎ (01782) 749673 stafford.bodcafebars.co.uk
Titanic Iceberg, Plum Porter; 6 changing beers (sourced nationally; often Titanic) Ⓗ
Located in the listed former first class lounge at Stoke railway station, this is a Titanic Brewery bod café bar. Contemporary and quirky, it retains the original vaulted ceiling. A unique sliding gate separates platform side from street side, effectively forming two pubs in one. This is a wonderful place to start, break or finish a journey, with basic food and coffee available. Quality local award-winning Titanic beers are always on the bar. Closed on some match days. Alcoholic drinks are served from 8am. Q P

London Road Ale House

241 London Road, ST4 5AA
☎ (01782) 698070
6 changing beers (sourced nationally) Ⓗ
Enter through the telephone box door into this quirky one-room pub. You can choose from six different real ales and a range of ciders. There are also bottles and cans, which can be selected through the windows into the cellar. The seating varies throughout, from high tables to church pews, and there are a chess table and a piano that both get a lot of use. Large windows at the front depict scenes from the Potteries in years gone by. Q (21,21A)

White Star

63 Kingsway, ST4 1JB (off Church St, close to King's Hall)
☎ (01782) 848734
Everards Tiger; Titanic Steerage, Iceberg, White Star, Plum Porter; 5 changing beers (sourced nationally; often Titanic) Ⓗ
This popular, multi award-winning pub is one of the renowned Titanic Brewery fleet, with a well-established reputation for the quality of its beers. Internally, it has a large, comfortably furnished split-level bar, with photos and information about the Titanic adorning the walls and adding to the atmosphere. Five Titanic beers are supplemented by five changing guests. A menu of fresh home-cooked food is served lunchtimes and evenings. A function room is also available. Q

Stone

Borehole

Unit 5, Mount Road Industrial Estate, Mount Road, ST15 8LL
☎ (01785) 813581
Lymestone Stone Cutter, Stone Faced, Ein Stein, Stone the Crows; 3 changing beers (often Lymestone) Ⓗ
This traditional pub was once part of the Bent's Brewery site. It is small and friendly, with eight handpumps offering a range of Lymestone ales and the occasional guest beer, plus a range of bottled beers. Well-behaved children are welcome until mid-evening, and dogs too. A light menu of pork pies, paninis, pickled eggs and home-made cakes can be enjoyed around a log-burner. There is a small, enclosed beer garden to the rear. Car parking is limited. Q P

Royal Exchange

26 Radford Street, ST15 8DA (on corner of Northesk St and Radford St)
☎ (01785) 812685

Everards Tiger; Titanic Steerage, White Star, Plum Porter, Captain Smith's Strong Ale; 4 changing beers (sourced nationally; often Titanic) [H]
A one-roomed pub, refurbished sympathetically to a high standard, with four distinct drinking areas and real fires at either end. Ten real ales are always on tap including three changing guest beers, often Titanic seasonals. One real cider is also available. There are no TVs or piped music, just good conversation. Acoustic music nights are staged and many clubs meet here. Lunches are served Friday and Saturday. There is a set evening meal on Monday, and monthly quiz nights.
Q♨❀◐⇌♣●🚌🐾ᯤ

Swan Inn

18 Stafford Street, ST15 8QW (on A520 near Trent & Mersey Canal)
☎ (01785) 815570 🌐 swaninnstone.co.uk
House beer (by Coach House); 8 changing beers (sourced nationally) [H]
This thriving free house has nine handpumps serving a wide choice of beers. Four draught real ciders are also available plus bottled varieties. The pub has one long room with coal fires at each end. A multiple local CAMRA award winner, its themed beer festival each July is a mecca for beer lovers. Live, free music is hosted on Thursday and Saturday in a variety of styles, though often rock – sometimes national acts. Dogs are welcome. Over-18s only. ❀♿●🚌(101)🐾

Stretton

Junction

Unit 1A, 1 Main Street, DE13 0DZ (on corner of jct with Hillfield Lane, close to St Mary's Church)
☎ 07931 290879
Blythe Bagot's Bitter, Ridware Pale, Summer Breeze, Palmers Poison; 2 changing beers (sourced locally) [H]
A former hairdressing salon, converted into a single-room micropub by the owners of Blythe Brewery in 2018 to showcase its beers – it is the brewery's only significant outlet in the area. Up to five real ciders, from Hurst View and Yoxall, are also available. Unusual features include a slate-topped and metal-fronted bar counter, and some cinema-style folding seating. Children are welcome until the evening. There is no car park but free public car parks and some street parking are nearby. Q♨♿●🚌🐾

Tamworth

King's Ditch 𝕃

51 Lower Gungate, B79 7AS
☎ 07989 805828 🌐 kingsditch.co.uk
Changing beers (sourced nationally) [G]
Previously a cycle shop, this convivial micropub opened in 2015. Its primary focus is ale, with between four and six on offer, but it is also well known for cider, with up to 30 ciders and perries. The pub has been been a finalist in CAMRA's national Cider Pub of the Year competition several times. Occasional beer festivals are held. The single ground-floor room is plainly decorated, and there is an additional small drinking area upstairs. Simple snacks are served. Children are welcome until the evening. Q♨⇌●▯🚌🐾ᯤ

Sir Robert Peel 𝕃

13-15 Lower Gungate, B79 7BA
☎ (01827) 300910
5 changing beers (often Salopian) [H]
Busy town-centre free house celebrating its 17th consecutive year in the Guide. It is named after the former prime minister, known for his role in the creation of the police force and the Tamworth pig. Five changing ales are dispensed by friendly and knowledgeable staff. Three or more real ciders also feature, plus a good selection of foreign bottled beers. A large and peaceful beer garden is to the rear, with ancient stone walls, overlooked by the historic St Editha's Church. ❀⇌●🚌🐾

Tamworth Tap 🏆 𝕃 ✔

29 Market Street, B79 7LR
☎ (01827) 319872 🌐 tamworthbrewing.co.uk
8 changing beers (often Beowulf, Blythe, Tamworth) [H]
This elegant building is home to Tamworth Brewing Company. The cosy upstairs rooms have Tudor features, the historic courtyard beer terrace to the rear offers striking views of Tamworth Castle, and there is café-style seating to the front. Eight handpulls usually feature two Tamworth ales, the rest from near and far. Various snacks are offered, plus a wide range of gins, wines and bottled beers. Regular live music takes place. Winner of CAMRA Pub of the Year for Staffordshire in 2019. ❀⇌●▯🚌🐾ᯤ

Tutbury

Cross Keys ✔

39 Burton Street, DE13 9NR (E side of village, 300yds from A511)
☎ (01283) 813677
Burton Bridge Draught Burton Ale; 3 changing beers (sourced regionally) [H]
Privately owned 19th-century free house, overlooking the Dove Valley and providing a fine view of Tutbury Castle. The two split-level rooms – public bar and lounge – have a homely feel and are served from a similarly split-level bar. There is a separate large dining room to the rear serving evening meals Friday and Saturday, lunch on Sunday. This is the only pub in the area that has offered Draught Burton Ale since its launch by Ind Coope in 1976 through to its 2015 reincarnation by Burton Bridge. ♨❀◐♿♣P🚌🐾ᯤ

Uttoxeter

Horse & Dove

21 Market Place, ST14 8HY
☎ (01889) 735942 🌐 horsendove.co.uk
6 changing beers (sourced locally; often Heritage, Titanic, Uttoxeter) [H]
A warm welcome awaits visitors to the town's first micropub. A pleasant, traditional decor with plenty of hard and soft furnishings helps to create a cosy but vibrant atmosphere. There is an excellent selection of up to six real ales including many offerings from local breweries, plus a lengthy real cider list and a selection of gins. Friendly staff and regulars ensure an enjoyable drinking experience. ⇌●🚌🐾ᯤ

Plough Inn

Stafford Road, Blounts Green, ST14 8DW (on A518)
☎ (01889) 569777
Marston's Pedigree; Wainwright; 4 changing beers (often Bristol Beer Factory, Purple Moose, Uttoxeter) [H]
Warm, friendly and welcoming, this inn is situated on a main road a 15-minute walk from Uttoxeter centre, with several other good pubs nearby. The clientele is drawn mainly from the local community, supplemented by passing trade. The Plough serves both drinkers and diners, and no area is reserved for either. Up to six real ales are sourced from national and smaller breweries. Well worth dropping in if you are in the area.
Q♨❀◐♿♣P🐾ᯤ

Whiston

Swan at Whiston

Whiston Road, ST19 5QH SJ895144
☎ (01785) 716200 🌐 swanwhiston.co.uk
Holden's Black Country Bitter, Golden Glow; Wye Valley HPA, Butty Bach; 4 changing beers (sourced nationally) Ⓗ
Although in a remote location, the Swan is a thriving pub offering high-quality, well-kept ales and superb food. Built in 1593, burnt down and rebuilt in 1711, the oldest part of the building today is the small bar housing an inglenook fireplace. The lounge features an intriguing central double-sided log fire. Six acres of grounds include a children's play area, an aviary and a large beer garden which gets busy on summer evenings. Open all day on bank holidays. **Q**♉❀◑▲♣●**P**🚌(878,76)🐾📶

Whittington

Dog Inn ✔

2 Main Street, WS14 9JU
☎ (01543) 432601 🌐 doginnwhittington.com
Holden's Golden Glow; Marston's Pedigree; St Austell Tribute; 2 changing beers Ⓗ
Comfortable and spacious village pub with a long frontage. Two or three guest ales are offered, generally from well-known breweries. Perhaps unsurprisingly, the pub is dog friendly. Live music features occasionally, and Wednesday is quiz night. A good choice of food includes traditional Sunday lunch, theme nights and breakfast from 9.30am Friday to Sunday (no food Mon). Bus services dry up in the early evening, but there is reasonably priced accommodation.
♉❀🛏◑**P**🚌(765) 🐾📶

Yew Tree Inn, Cauldon (Photo: The Roaming Picture Taker/Flickr CC BY 2.0)

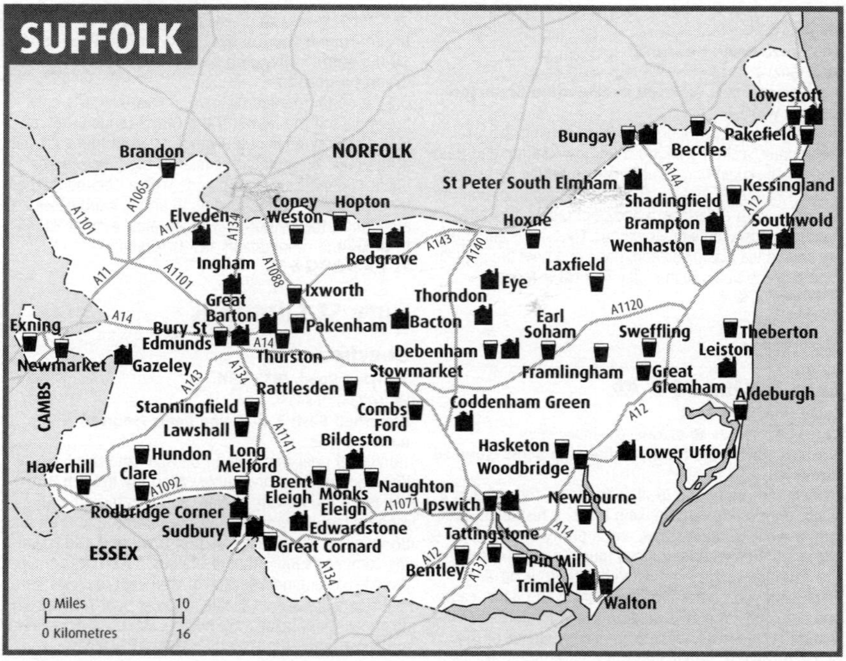

Aldeburgh

White Hart

222 High Street, IP15 5AJ

☎ (01728) 453205 whitehartaldeburgh.co.uk

Adnams Southwold Bitter, Ghost Ship, Broadside; 3 changing beers (often Adnams)

Friendly single bar, formerly used as a public reading room. Drinkers can buy fish & chips and eat them in the garden, when the weather permits, while supping a drink from the bar. Live music features on occasion. Families are welcome to use the garden in the summer months, with a covered barbecue and wood-fired pizza oven in use Easter to mid-September.

Beccles

Butchers Arms

51 London Road, NR34 9YT

☎ (01502) 712243 mypub.org.uk

Woodforde's Nelsons Revenge; 5 changing beers (sourced regionally; often Bull of the Woods, Greene King, Woodforde's)

Just a 10-minute walk from the town centre, this friendly pub serves up to six real ales mainly from local breweries. Live music, open mic evenings, charity and community-focused events are hosted. The pub originally had separate lounge and public bars but it has been extended and is now open plan. The bar and real fire are in the original area, with more seating and pool tables in the extension. No food is served except basket meals on occasion. P

Caxton Club

Gaol Lane, NR34 9SJ

☎ (01502) 712829

4 changing beers (sourced locally; often Green Jack, Greene King, Woodforde's)

Spacious club conveniently situated a short walk from the train and bus stations and close to the town centre. All members and guests receive a warm welcome (non-members pay a small fee to cover entertainment costs). It has a central bar, TV and darts room, and snooker room. There is also a large function room, garden with children's play area and a bowling green. Four real ales and a choice of real ciders are available. Guide dogs only are allowed.

REAL ALE BREWERIES

Adnams Southwold
Beccles Brampton (NEW)
Brewshed Ingham
Briarbank Ipswich
Bruha Eye
Cabin Bildeston (NEW)
Calvors Coddenham Green
Cliff Quay Debenham
Dove Street Ipswich
Earl Soham Debenham
Green Dragon Bungay
Green Jack Lowestoft
Greene King Bury St Edmunds
Humber Doucy Bacton (NEW)
Iceni Elveden
Kings Head Bildeston
Krafty Braumeister Leiston
Little Earth Project Edwardstone
Mauldons Sudbury
Mr Bees Trimley
Munson's Gazeley (NEW)
Nethergate Rodbridge Corner
Old Cannon Bury St Edmunds
Shortts Thorndon
St Judes Ipswich
St Peter's St Peter South Elmham
Star Wing Redgrave
Stow Fen Bungay (NEW)
Uffa Lower Ufford
Weird Sisters Great Barton

Ingate 🄻

108 Grove Road, NR34 9RE
☎ (01502) 712315
4 changing beers (sourced locally; often Green Jack, Lacons, Wolf) Ⓗ
Privately owned two-bar free house serving the local community, a short walk from the town centre and train station. The main bar, furnished with tables, bar stools and sofas, serves three real ales on handpump, and the front bar, with a dartboard and pool tables, has one handpump used only at weekends. Live sports and music are shown via plasma screen. Darts and pool are popular here and the pub's teams play in local leagues.
❀⇌♣●P🚌🐾📶

Bentley

Case Is Altered 🄻 ✔

Capel Road, IP9 2DW
☎ (01473) 805575 🌐 thecasepubbentley.co.uk
Adnams Southwold Bitter; 3 changing beers (sourced locally) Ⓗ
Owned and run by the local community, the pub has a single bar serving two drinking areas, a restaurant area with a wood-burning stove, and a pretty beer garden with plenty of seating. Various music evenings and themed food nights are hosted but there is no TV. Traditional pub games are played including darts, cards and dominoes. A quiz is held on the last Saturday of the month. Local artists' work is on display. Some of the produce used in the kitchen is grown at home by the local community. ♘❀◐♿♣P🚌🐾📶

Brandon

Ram

High Street, IP27 0AX
☎ (01842) 810275
Greene King Abbot; 6 changing beers (sourced nationally) Ⓗ
Said to be one of the oldest surviving buildings in Brandon, this attractive Grade II listed inn dates back 500 years in parts. A wonderful log fire greets you on entering this friendly free house, owned and run by one family. It is home to regular club nights for the Iceni Car Club, Classic Vehicle Club, Model Engineering Club, Brandon Speakers Club and the Champions Poker League.
♘❀🛏◐⛺⇌♣P

Brent Eleigh

Cock ★

Lavenham Road, CO10 9PB
☎ (01787) 247371
Adnams Southwold Bitter; Greene King Abbot; 2 changing beers (sourced locally; often Bishop Nick, Mauldons) Ⓗ
An unspoilt gem, well worthy of its place on CAMRA's National Inventory of Historic Pub Interiors. With just two small bars, conversation with the regulars is assured. The public bar has an old wooden bar, a main table deeply etched with shove-ha'penny grooves and a settle with a 'pinch penny' cut into it. The snug bar is ideal for families. Good home-cooked food service does not intrude on the classic pub ambience.
Q❀🛏◐♣●P🚌(111)🐾📶

Bungay

Green Dragon 🄻

29 Broad Street, NR35 1EE
☎ (01986) 892681 🌐 greendragonbungay.co.uk
Green Dragon Chaucer Ale, Gold, Bridge Street Bitter, Strong Mild; 1 changing beer (sourced locally; often Green Dragon) Ⓗ
On the northern edge of town, this is Bungay's only brewpub and the home of the Green Dragon Brewery, with ales brewed in outbuildings adjacent to the car park at the rear. The pub is a regular in the Guide. It has a public bar and a spacious lounge with a side room where families are welcome, leading to an enclosed garden. In addition to the five Green Dragon ales, a range of KeyKegs and canned craft ales is served.
♘❀⛺♣●P🚌🐾📶

Bury St Edmunds

Beerhouse 🄻

1 Tayfen Road, IP32 6BH
☎ (01284) 766415
Brewshed Best; 7 changing beers (sourced nationally) Ⓗ
Traditional beer house in an unusual semicircular Victorian building (previously called the Ipswich Arms), handy for the railway station, and refurbished with a modern feel. It serves its own beers from the Brewshed Brewery, which is located out of town and also supplies the company's four other local pubs. Seven beer engines provide a changing selection of well-kept real ales. Three real ciders are also available. Regular beer festivals and an annual cider festival are hosted. Major sporting events are shown on a big screen. ♘❀⇌●P🚌🐾📶

Dove 🄻

68 Hospital Road, IP33 3JU
☎ (01284) 702787 🌐 thedovepub.co.uk
Woodforde's Wherry Ⓗ**; changing beers** Ⓗ/Ⓖ
This early Victorian back-street community free house is just five minutes' walk from the town centre. It has six handpumps, plus jugged ales brought up direct from the cooled, brick-vaulted cellar, and the staff are knowledgeable about the ever-changing choice of local ales. A good selection of real ciders is also available. Truly traditional and basic, the Dove is just how pubs used to be – no lager, TVs, pool or gaming machines. A two-times winner of CAMRA Regional Pub of the Year.
Q❀♣●P🚌🐾

Nutshell ★ ✔

17 The Traverse, IP33 1BJ
☎ (01284) 764867 🌐 thenutshellpub.co.uk
Greene King IPA, Abbot Ⓗ
The Nutshell claims to be 'Britain's smallest pub', with an interior measuring only 15ft by 7ft, and is listed in the Guinness Book of Records. The main drinking area is crowded if more than six people are in it. The Grade II listed building dates from the mid-19th century and is a popular tourist attraction in the town. Good-quality Greene King Abbot and IPA are regularly available. There is a function room upstairs. Q🚌

Oakes Barn 🏆

St Andrews Street South, IP33 3PH (opp Waitrose car park)
☎ (01284) 761592 🌐 oakesbarn.co.uk
Oakham JHB; Woodforde's Wherry; 4 changing beers (sourced nationally) Ⓗ
A real ale free house and social hub near the town centre with some period features and historic links to the medieval town. Six real ales are always on the bar, including one dark beer alongside craft cider. Home-made food comprises lunchtime specials and snacks served all day, plus roasts on the first Sunday of the month. There is a covered smoking area outside and an

open courtyard with seating. Regular events are held in the bar, and an upstairs function room can be hired.

Rose & Crown

48 Whiting Street, IP33 1NP (on corner of Whiting St and Westgate)

☎ (01284) 361336

Greene King IPA, Abbot; 4 changing beers (sourced nationally; often Nethergate, Theakston, Timothy Taylor) [H]

This traditional inn is a Grade II listed building within the conservation area of Bury St Edmunds, and is recognised by CAMRA as having a regionally important historic pub interior. It has two bars and a separate off-sales hatch. A new landlord took over in September 2019 following the retirement of the previous tenants after 34 years' service. Good-value wholesome food is served lunchtimes Monday to Saturday. It is in sight of Greene King's Westgate Brewery, and a mild is always among the choice of beers. Q

Clare

Globe

10 Callis Street, CO10 8PX

☎ (01787) 278122

Young's London Original; 3 changing beers (sourced nationally) [H]

A phoenix risen from the ashes, the Globe reopened in 2013 after a two-year closure. Serving one well-kept regular beer and up to three changing guests, it is now a thriving local where beer and conversation dominate. Live music plays every other Saturday night and afternoon sessions every other Sunday. It has a separate pool room at the rear and a newly refurbished garden for summer drinking. No food is served. Q P

Combs Ford

Gladstone Arms

2 Combs Road, IP14 2AP

☎ (01449) 771608 gladstonearms.co.uk

Adnams Southwold Bitter, Broadside; Crouch Vale Brewers Gold; Fuller's London Pride; Sharp's Doom Bar; Woodforde's Wherry [H]**; 4 changing beers** [H]/[G]

A large open-plan pub serving consistently good beer. The owners also run the Dove Street Inn in Ipswich. The two pubs share a similar beer range, with between 12 and 14 ales, including house beers brewed in Ipswich. Four or five ciders and a wide range of craft lagers, imported foreign beers and whiskies are also available. Good-value snacks and meals are served with vegetarian options. There are board games, sports TV and regular live music. A beer festival features over the Easter weekend. At the rear is the riverside garden.
Q P

Coney Weston

Swan

Thetford Road, IP31 1DN

☎ (01359) 221900 swaninnconeyweston.com

Adnams Broadside; Greene King IPA; Wychwood Hobgoblin Ruby; 1 changing beer (often Adnams, Sharp's) [H]

The current building is about 100 years old, though there has been a pub on this site for many centuries – the original building burnt down. It serves a changing range of popular ales such as Draught Bass, Doom Bar and Hobgoblin. A full menu of traditional pub food is available. Regular events are hosted for charity, and the pub has its own bowling club. It is a camping and caravan stopover, and coaches are also welcome by arrangement. Q P (338)

Debenham

Woolpack

49 High Street, IP14 6QN

☎ (01728) 860516

Earl Soham Victoria Bitter [H]**, Sir Roger's Porter** [G]**; Fuller's London Pride; 1 changing beer (often Earl Soham)** [H]

Small one-bar wooden-floored pub with steps up from the road. Until recent years it was licensed as a beer house. Horse brasses, village photographs and miniature bottles decorate the bar area. Two TVs show terrestrial sport. Keenly priced home-cooked food is served. The pub is home to a darts team and hosts occasional live music, karaoke and quiz nights. There is a splendid view of the church from the patio – bell ringers meet here after practice on Tuesday.

Earl Soham

Victoria

The Street, IP13 7RL

☎ (01728) 685758 earlsohamvictoria.co.uk

Earl Soham Victoria Bitter; 2 changing beers (often Cliff Quay, Earl Soham) [H]

A popular, traditional pub that despite refurbishment has changed little over the years, with two small bars separated by a wood-burner, and an outside toilet. A varied menu with daily specials is offered lunchtimes and evenings, all home-cooked. The pub gets busy at weekends, especially on sunny days when even a seat in the garden can be hard to find. Dogs and children are welcome. The Earl Soham Brewery was originally behind the pub. Q P

Exning

White Horse

23 Church Street, CB8 7EH

☎ (01638) 577323 whitehorseexning.co.uk

3 changing beers [H]

Mentioned in the Domesday Book and a pub for 300 years, this fine free house has been run by the same family since 1935. Still retaining much original character, it comprises a public bar, cosy lounge and separate restaurant. At least 10 changing real ales are on offer each week, plus cider on draught, and a good choice of home-cooked food is served. A private room can be hired. Q P (10,10A)

Framlingham

Station Hotel

Station Road, IP13 9EE

☎ (01728) 723455 thestationframlingham.com

Earl Soham Gannet Mild, Victoria Bitter, Brandeston Gold; 2 changing beers (often Earl Soham) [H]

Cosy two-bar pub set in a former station buffet (the branch line closed in 1963). Beers and a guest cider are dispensed from a set of Edwardian German silver handpumps. The pub enjoys a good reputation for food, made with locally sourced ingredients and prepared on the premises – the ever-changing menu is displayed on chalkboards. On Sundays, brunch and beers are available. The garden bar has a wood-fired pizza oven. An annual beer festival is held in the summer. Children and dogs welcome. Q P

Great Cornard

Brook Inn

241 Bures Road, CO10 0JQ

☎ 07759 960051

5 changing beers (sourced nationally) Ⓗ

Friendly, welcoming, locals' pub, formerly owned by Greene King and now independent. Set in the country near the Suffolk/Essex border, it has a beer garden and a good-sized car park. There are two bars, one with low-key TV for sports events. Bar billiards and pool are played, with teams in local leagues. An open-mic music session is held on the third Sunday of each month. A good range of up to five real ales is served on handpump. ❀♿♣P🚌🐾📶

Great Glemham

Crown

The Street, IP17 2DA

☎ (01728) 663693 🌐 thecrowninnglemham.co.uk

6 changing beers (sourced locally) Ⓗ

Refurbished to a high standard, this multi-roomed pub has wood-burners, traditionally tiled floors and many lovely seating areas. Up to six beers are on offer during the busy summer months and at least four during quieter periods. Acoustic music sessions feature regularly. The pub hosts a local community lunch once a month and caters for private parties. All food is cooked on the premises, from bar snacks to an à la carte menu (no food Tue). ❀◐♣P🚌🐾📶

Hasketon

Turk's Head ✔

Low Road, IP13 6JG

☎ (01394) 610343 🌐 theturksheadhasketon.co.uk

Adnams Ghost Ship; Morland Old Speckled Hen; Woodforde's Wherry; 2 changing beers (sourced locally) Ⓗ

The pub has been much refurbished and extended in recent years but retains a cosy timber-framed bar with a large fireplace and wood-burner. A separate large restaurant and kitchen are to the rear. Good food includes renowned Sunday lunches. Three to five changing beers are on handpump. An annual beer festival is held in the summer. Events include quiz nights and themed food nights. The beautiful two-acre garden has seating and two pétanque pistes. ❀◐♣P🐾📶

Haverhill

Royal Exchange ✔

69 High Street, CB9 8AH

☎ (01440) 702155 🌐 theroyalexchangepub.co.uk

Greene King IPA; Nethergate Suffolk County Best Bitter; 3 changing beers (sourced nationally; often Nethergate) Ⓗ

Friendly town-centre local in a classic street-corner location. The Greene King-managed house has had the full makeover, with scrubbed floors and traditional furniture. It can be boisterous with sports fans watching the five TVs – glasses are available for those wishing to watch in 3D. A swift turnover helps sustain the good quality of the beer. There is a large public car park behind the Arts Centre opposite. ♿♣🚌🐾

Hopton

Vine

High Street, IP22 2QX

☎ (01953) 688581

Adnams Southwold Bitter; Greene King IPA, Abbot; Timothy Taylor Landlord; 5 changing beers (sourced locally; often Colchester, Lacons, Mauldons) Ⓗ

On the main road near the church, this village local has been revitalised since it was taken over by the current landlord in 2013. Nine ales including a selection of local and regional guests are offered at reasonable prices. A variety of ciders is also available. This welcoming pub, popular with locals and visitors, is a regular winner of local CAMRA branch Pub of the Year.
❀♿♣●P🚌(100)🐾📶

Hoxne

Swan Inn of Hoxne ✔

Low Street, IP21 5AS

☎ (01379) 668275 🌐 theswaninnofhoxne.co.uk

Adnams Southwold Bitter, Ghost Ship, Broadside; Timothy Taylor Landlord Ⓖ

The Swan reopened in 2016 after temporary closure and is once again a thriving village local. The 15th-century building has a colourful history – it claims to be both the former home of the Bishop of Norwich and later a brothel. There is a large open fire in the main bar and a wood-burner in the adjacent bar. The restaurant serves excellent home-cooked food, with an emphasis on local produce. To the rear is a large garden. An annual beer festival features in August. Buskers' night is Thursday.
❀◐♿♣P🚌🐾📶

Hundon

Rose & Crown

20 North Street, CO10 8ED (centre of the village)

☎ (01440) 786261 🌐 hundon-village.co.uk/roseandcrown.html

Sharp's Doom Bar; 3 changing beers (sourced nationally; often Fuller's, Mauldons, St Austell) Ⓗ

A traditional country pub comprising two bars with open fires. Home-cooked food is available Thursday to Sunday including popular Sunday lunchtime roasts. The deceptively large beer garden has a patio for alfresco dining leading to a lawned area with a stage. The outside bar is used for weddings, parties, an annual community music festival over the August bank holiday and other events. The morris men gathering on St George's Day is enjoyed by all. A proud previous winner of local CAMRA Community Pub of the Year. ❀◐♿♣P🚌🐾📶

Ipswich

Arcade Street Tavern

Arcade Street, IP1 1EX (behind Corn Exchange)

☎ (01473) 805454 🌐 arcadetavern.co.uk

2 changing beers (sourced regionally) Ⓗ

A stylish and highly popular multi-roomed café bar with a traditional wooden interior, and an emphasis on craft and imported beers. Two handpumps dispense a variety of ever-changing beers, mainly from East Anglia. There is no food in-house but the bar regularly hosts street-food Friday in conjunction with other local traders. There are heated seating areas outside and two function rooms – one used for product launches and tasting evenings. Artisan coffee is available. Q❀🚌📶

Briarbank Ⓛ

70 Fore Street, IP4 1LB

☎ (01473) 284000

Briarbank Perpendicular, Old Spiteful; 3 changing beers (sourced locally; often Briarbank) Ⓗ

A smart and modern first-floor drinking bar that opened in 2013 in a former bank above a small brewery. Many house beers are also available as craft ales. An outside seating area provides additional space when weather permits. Live music – usually jazz – features twice monthly, either in the bar or outside. TVs show sport – rugby, Formula 1, tennis or golf. Easter and summer beer festivals are hosted. ❀◑P🚌📶

Dove Street Inn 🄻 ✔

76 St Helen's Street, IP4 2LA

☎ (01473) 211270 🌐 dovestreetinn.co.uk

Adnams Broadside; Crouch Vale Brewers Gold; Fuller's London Pride; Greene King Abbot 🄷; changing beers (often Dove Street) 🄷/🄶

Popular multi-roomed inn with a large selection of ales including milds, bitters, seasonal beers, continental beers and ciders. Some ales are from its own Dove Street Brewery. There is also a gin bar. Home-cooked food and bar snacks are served at all times. Sports TV is shown in the conservatory. A covered and heated seating area outside hosts various events including three beer festivals. Well-behaved dogs and children are welcome. A sister pub to The Gladstone Arms in Combs Ford. Last admission is 10.45pm. ❀◑♿♣●🚌(66)🐾📶

Fat Cat

288 Spring Road, IP4 5NL

☎ (01473) 726524 🌐 fatcatipswich.co.uk

Adnams Southwold Bitter 🄷; Crouch Vale Brewers Gold 🄶; Timothy Taylor Landlord 🄷; 14 changing beers 🄶

A small, multi-roomed drinking bar, free from background music and games machines. Up to 14 beers and five ciders are dispensed from the taproom. Bar snacks include Scotch eggs and pasties cooked on the premises. An airy conservatory behind the main bar leads to the pretty garden, which provides extra space on sunny afternoons, and the occasional barbecue. A quiz is held monthly. Often voted the best pub in town by local CAMRA branch members. No under-16s. Q❀◑●🚌🐾📶

Greyhound

9 Henley Road, IP1 3SE

☎ (01473) 252862 🌐 thegreyhoundipswich.co.uk

Adnams Southwold Bitter, Ghost Ship, Broadside; 3 changing beers 🄷

This tied house has a small bar at the front and a much larger, more modern drinking and dining room to the side and rear. The recently expanded outside drinking space can be busy during the summer months and it occasionally hosts barbecues. A new kitchen offers freshly prepared food and various daily specials, including vegetarian options. On Sundays breakfasts are available. Quizzes take place twice a month on Sunday evenings. TVs are only used for sporting events. Free Wi-Fi. Q❀◑♿♣P🚌📶

Lord Nelson

81 Fore Street, IP4 1JZ

☎ (01473) 407510

Adnams Southwold Bitter, Ghost Ship; 3 changing beers (often Adnams) 🄶

Timber-framed building dating from the 17th century just a short walk from the historic waterfront. An unusual gravity-dispense system incorporates a row of wooden casks to good effect and guarantees temperature-controlled real ales. Freshly prepared food is served including daily specials. Outside is a small enclosed patio area to the rear, and families and dogs are welcome. Quiz nights are held twice a month. A sister pub to the Red Lion in Manningtree and Marlborough in Dedham. ❀◑♿♣🚌🐾📶

Thomas Wolsey

9-13 St Peters Street, IP1 1XF (300yds from bus station)

☎ (01473) 210055

Adnams Ghost Ship; Crouch Vale Brewers Gold; Woodforde's Wherry; 1 changing beer 🄷

Large lounge bar set in a historic Grade II listed building. It has a patio area to the side and two nicely furnished function rooms upstairs, used for a wide variety of events including story-telling nights, charity quizzes and meetings. Craft ales are available, plus over 25 bottled beers and 40 quality wines. Games are played including darts. Home supporters only on football match days. ❀⇌♣🚌📶

Woolpack ✔

1 Tuddenham Road, IP4 2SH

☎ (01473) 215862 🌐 woolpack-ipswich.co.uk

Adnams Southwold Bitter, Ghost Ship; 2 changing beers 🄷

Popular hostelry retaining a tiny snug at the front, flanked by a cosy lounge and a small public bar. A back room is mostly used for dining. There are usually five beers on handpump. An interesting selection of good-quality home-cooked food is served all week (including breakfast). The menu – all home-made – includes specials, bar snacks and vegetarian options. The pub hosts a regular Sunday night quiz and traditional music sessions. Outside, the patio area at the front is popular on sunny days. Q❀◑♣P🚌🐾

Ixworth

Greyhound ✔

49 High Street, IP31 2HJ

☎ (01359) 230887

Greene King IPA, Abbot; 3 changing beers (sourced nationally) 🄷

Situated on the village's attractive high street, this welcoming traditional inn has three bars, one a lovely central snug. The heart of the building dates back to Tudor times. Good-value lunches and early evening meals are served in the restaurant including a daily special. Dominoes, crib, darts and pool are played in leagues and for charity fundraising. Dogs and children are welcome. Q❀◑Å♣P🚌🐾

Kessingland

Sailors Home 🄻 ✔

302 Church Road, NR33 7SB

☎ (01502) 740245 🌐 sailorshome.co.uk

Adnams Southwold Bitter 🄷; 6 changing beers (sourced locally; often Green Jack, Lacons, Wolf) 🄷/🄶

On the sea front, with coastal views, the pub is popular in summer with holidaymakers from nearby caravan parks and guest houses. The interior has a mock-Tudor design with four adjoining rooms – one for diners serving value-for-money food, a large central bar area with a TV screen, a games room and a side room. Four handpulled beers are available and up to three on gravity, plus a changing real cider. ❀◑Å♣●P🚌(99)🐾📶

Lawshall

Swan

The Street, IP29 4QA

☎ (01284) 828477 🌐 swaninnlawshall.com

5 changing beers (sourced nationally; often Adnams, Colchester, Woodforde's) 🄷

Set in the heart of rural Suffolk, the Swan is a classic Suffolk country pub. The beautiful 18th-century thatched building with a low-beamed bar and an inglenook

fireplace has been lovingly restored and is crammed full of period features. On the menu you will find all the traditional pub classics and a few extra culinary delights. The large garden encourages children to play.
Q P

Laxfield

King's Head (Low House)

Gorams Mill Lane, IP13 8DW (walk through churchyard and exit via lower street gate; the pub is on your right)
(01986) 798395 laxfieldkingshead.co.uk
Green Jack Jackalope Golden Best; Shortts Skiffle; Timothy Taylor Landlord; 4 changing beers (sourced locally; often Shortts)
Local CAMRA's newest community pub. Also known as the Low House, bought from Adnams in 2018, this timeless thatched inn is always worth a visit. The main room features high-back settles set around a small fireplace – the beer is served on gravity from a small taproom to the rear. The separate dining room offers an interesting menu of locally sourced food, including roast lunch on Sunday. There is an enclosed garden and patio to the rear. Accommodation is available in an outbuilding. P

Long Melford

Crown Inn

Hall Street, CO10 9JL
(01787) 377666 thecrownhotelmelford.co.uk
Adnams Southwold Bitter, Ghost Ship; 2 changing beers (sourced nationally)
A busy family-run free house and cosy hotel set in this popular antiques centre. Two regular ales and two changing guests, together with real cider, are on handpump. A high-quality home-cooked menu is served in the spacious bar and separate restaurant. There is a large, attractive patio garden for summer dining and drinking. Eleven comfortable bedrooms are available for those wishing to stay and explore this picturesque area.
Q P

Nethergate Brewery Tap

Rodbridge Corner, CO10 9HJ
(01787) 377087 nethergate.co.uk
8 changing beers (sourced locally; often Nethergate)
Nethergate Brewery was founded in 1986 and its new visitor centre and taproom opened in 2017. The taproom has a bar offering a range of Nethergate ales on draught, and a shop selling bottled beers, wines and spirits. There is a window to view the brewery and tours can be booked. The members' club hosts regular events including beer festivals. Q P

Lowestoft

Norman Warrior

Fir Lane, NR32 2RB
(01502) 561982 thenormanwarrior.co.uk
Greene King IPA; 4 changing beers (sourced nationally; often Greene King, Lacons, Wolf)
Large estate pub on the northern side of town with ample parking, close to the bus stop and a 20-minute walk from Oulton Broad North train station. It comprises a public bar where pool and darts are played and a comfortable lounge leading to a spacious restaurant where home-cooked food is served daily. Outside is a terrace and garden where a beer and cider festival featuring live music is held over the August bank holiday weekend. A popular quiz takes place weekly.
Q P (102)

Stanford Arms

Stanford Street, NR32 2DD
(01502) 587444
10 changing beers (sourced locally; often Star Wing, Three Blind Mice, Wolf)
A quality free house that is a short walk from Lowestoft bus and train stations. The open-plan, L-shaped bar is heated by two wood-burners and has 10 handpumps serving beers mainly from East Anglia. A fine collection of beer trays adorns the walls. To the rear is a courtyard garden with an aviary and a wood-fired pizza oven (Friday is pizza night). Wednesday is often speciality food night (booking required), live music plays on Sunday afternoon, and an annual Easter weekend beer festival is held. Q

Triangle Tavern

29 St Peters Street, NR32 1QA
(01502) 582711 green-jack.com
Green Jack Jackalope Golden Best, Trawlerboys Best Bitter, Lurcher Stout, Gone Fishing ESB, Ripper Tripel; 2 changing beers (sourced locally; often Crouch Vale, Green Jack, Oakham)
This lively town-centre tavern is the brewery tap for Green Jack Brewery. The cosy parlour-style front bar is heated with a wood-burner in winter months and hosts live music every Friday evening and a quiz night monthly. A corridor leads to a back bar with a central pool table and a jukebox. Alongside the full Green Jack range are a guest ale, real ciders and continental keg beers. Customers are welcome to bring in their own food. Dogs and children are welcome.

Monks Eleigh

Swan

The Street, IP7 7AU
(01449) 744544 swaninnmonkseleigh.co.uk
Greene King Abbot; Mighty Oak Oscar Wilde; 2 changing beers (sourced regionally)
A welcoming, traditional country pub in the heart of Suffolk. Food and drink come from small and artisan producers, bringing a range of Suffolk ingredients to the table and bar, including local cask ales on handpump. The uppermost restaurant area has a large inglenook fireplace and there is a smaller real fire in the bar area. Events include comedy and quiz nights. Closed Monday but available to hire. (111)

Naughton

Wheelhouse

Whatfield Road, IP7 7BS (450yds off B1078 close to former airbase)
(01449) 740496 thewheelhouseatnaughton.co.uk
3 changing beers
A picturesque and recently redecorated pub with a thatched roof, low ceiling and traditional open fire. Many ancient timbers are in evidence – the building is reputed to have been a pub since the 12th century. It has a spacious public bar with a pool table. A varied and changing selection of ales makes it worth the visit. The garden to the rear is a nice place to relax on sunny days. The nearest bus stop is on the main road.
Q P (111)

Newbourne

Fox Inn

The Street, IP12 4NY
(01473) 736307 debeninns.co.uk/fox
Adnams Southwold Bitter; 3 changing beers

This picturesque timber-framed, two-bar village local is becoming increasingly popular, not just with ramblers and cyclists, but also with discerning diners. The refurbished kitchen offers a wide range of locally-sourced food, all home cooked from an à la carte menu, with vegetarian and gluten-free options plus daily specials. The large garden has a pond and shed which houses an old skittle alley – the only one in Suffolk. The restaurant has recently been extended in sympathy with the existing building. Extra car parking is available in summer. Q🍼❀◑♿⛺♣P🚌(179)🐾📶

Newmarket

Golden Lion ✔

44 High Street, CB8 8LB

☎ (01638) 672040

Adnams Ghost Ship; Greene King Abbot; 7 changing beers [H]

A large, bustling, 18th-century Wetherspoon town pub, situated on the main street. The pub's name is thought to have originated from King Henry I, who was known as the Lion of Justice. Knowledgeable and efficient staff serve up to seven real ales at any one time, including up to four guest ales. Real cider is also available. The pub is popular with the local horse-racing community. Children are welcome until 9pm in the family area.
🍼❀◑♿≢🍎P🚌📶

Pakefield

Oddfellows L

6 Nightingale Road, NR33 7AU

☎ (01502) 538415

Adnams Southwold Bitter; house beer (by Green Jack); 3 changing beers (sourced locally; often Green Jack, Lacons, Woodforde's) [H]

Situated close to the cliff top, this pub is popular with local drinkers, holidaymakers and walkers on the heritage coastal path. The interior comprises three open-plan areas including one for diners, and has wooden flooring and panelling throughout. Sporting events are shown on TV screens. Up to five ales are available from local breweries. In summer, a popular beer festival is hosted on the green opposite the pub and, in January, a small winter festival is held, with the Old Glory Molly Dancers performing. 🍼❀◑🚌🐾📶

Pakenham

Fox

The Street, IP31 2JU

☎ (01359) 230194 🌐 pakenhamfox.co.uk

Mighty Oak Kings; 3 changing beers (sourced locally; often Elmtree, Shortts, Star Wing) [H]

Traditional 18th-century pub in a picturesque village, beautifully restored with a handcrafted central bar. A free house, the Fox serves four well-chosen ales from local breweries and two real ciders on draught. The chef prepares lunches Wednesday to Sunday and evening meals Wednesday, Thursday and Saturday using local ingredients. Friday is home-made pizza night. The spacious beer garden, smokers' shelter and pétanque pitch overlook a wildflower meadow. Every second Tuesday is quiz night. Q🍼❀◑♿♣🍎P🚌🐾📶

Pin Mill

Butt & Oyster ✔

Pin Mill Road, IP9 1JW

☎ (01473) 780764 🌐 debeninns.co.uk/buttandoyster

Adnams Southwold Bitter, Ghost Ship, Broadside; 1 changing beer (often Adnams) [G]

Dating from the 17th century, this pub enjoys a famous setting, with magnificent views of the River Orwell from the main bar and patio. The interior comprises three separate rooms connected via a flagstoned corridor. High-backed settles and a wood-burner in the main room help to create an old-world charm on cold winter days. The patio at the front of the pub is often used by diners during busy sessions. Breakfast is served on weekends only. Q🍼❀◑♿♣P🚌🐾📶

Rattlesden

Five Bells

High Street, IP30 0RA

☎ (01449) 737373

3 changing beers (sourced locally; often Earl Soham, Elgood's, Woodforde's) [H]

Set on the high road through a picturesque village, this is a good old Suffolk drinking house – few of its kind still survive. Three well-chosen ales on the bar usually come direct from the breweries, often including a mild. The cosy single-room interior has a games area on a lower level and there is occasional live music. Pub games include shut-the-box and shove-ha'penny, plus pétanque in the garden in summer. Q❀♣🚌🐾

Redgrave

Cross Keys

The Street, IP22 1RW

☎ (01379) 779822 🌐 crosskeysredgrave.co.uk

Earl Soham Victoria Bitter; 3 changing beers (sourced locally) [H]

The building dates from the late-16th or early-17th century, with later extensions. It was reopened in 2018, having been bought by the community. It is staffed by a mixture of paid staff and volunteers. Earl Soham Bitter is the regular beer, complemented by three changing ales. Numerous events are held – see Facebook for details. Please check food service times ahead of your visit as they may vary. 🍼❀◑♿♣P🚌(304)🐾📶

Star Wing Tap Room 🏆 L

Hall Farm, Church Road, IP22 1RJ

☎ (01379) 890586 🌐 starwingbrewery.com

Star Wing Dawn on the Border, Gospel Oak, Spire Light, Red at Night, Four Acre Arcadia, Stain Glass Blue; 1 changing beer [H]

The Tap Room opened in May 2019 and has developed a reputation as an excellent place to enjoy Star Wing and guest ales. As well as offering the core range of six Star Wing craft ales on tap, it also offers a full bar featuring local suppliers including Betty's Gin from Heart of Suffolk and Harleston Cider based in Palgrave. There is also a fine keg wall. Based in an old sawmill, the bar retains many original features and has an on-site bakery.
❀◑♿🍎P🐾📶

Shadingfield

Fox L

London Road, NR34 8DD

☎ (01502) 575100 🌐 shadingfieldfox.com

8 changing beers (sourced locally; often Lacons, Nene Valley, Wolf) [H]

Just a short drive from Beccles, this charming and cosy rural inn dates from the 16th century. It has retained the original arched doors and carved fox heads on the beams. The interior comprises a bar with a large array of handpumps and comfortable seating, a conservatory, and a restaurant serving local produce and running speciality food events. Live music is performed on Friday evening. Outside is a garden and sun terrace with umbrellas and chimenea heaters. Two beer festivals are held annually. Q🐴❀◐◑P🐾📶

Southwold

Lord Nelson Ⓛ ✔

42 East Street, IP18 6EJ

☎ (01502) 722079 🌐 thelordnelsonsouthwold.co.uk

Adnams Southwold Bitter, Ghost Ship, Broadside; 2 changing beers (sourced locally; often Adnams) Ⓗ

There is no shortage of pubs selling Adnams beer in Southwold and they all have their merits, but this is a special place in which to drink the full range of Adnams ales, including its seasonal beers. A stone's throw from the sea and Southwold Sailors' Reading Room, the pub is always busy and lively. The central bar has a flagstone floor and open fireplace and is decorated with naval memorabilia. Children are welcome in a side room and there is a heated patio to the rear. 🐴❀◐◑⛺🚌🐾📶

Stanningfield

Red House

Bury Road, IP29 4RR

☎ (01284) 828330 🌐 theredhousesuffolk.co.uk

Greene King IPA; 2 changing beers Ⓗ

Red brick in construction and displaying the red dress uniform of the Suffolk Regiment on its sign, the Red House is a family-run free house at the heart of the village. Good-value lunches and early evening meals are home cooked. The pub supports darts, cribbage and bar billiards teams and hosts regular evening entertainment. 🐴❀◐◑♣P🐾📶

Stowmarket

Little Wellington

12 Stowupland Road, IP14 5AG

☎ (01449) 614174

Greene King IPA; St Austell Tribute; 2 changing beers Ⓗ

Good local community pub, convenient for the railway station, especially if travelling eastwards. The bar is accessed via a short flight of steps up from the street level. It has a central servery and a reputation for good-value Sunday lunches. Pizzas are cooked outside in the summer. The beer garden has a play area for children. Live music plays on Saturday evenings, and the pub hosts occasional events such horse-racing evenings and private parties. 🐴❀◐◑♿⇌♣P🚌🐾📶

Royal William Ⓛ

53 Union Street East, IP14 1HP

☎ (01449) 674553

Greene King IPA; 10 changing beers Ⓖ

An end-of-terrace back-street bar, tucked away down a narrow side street, a short walk from the town centre and railway station. Well supported by locals, it is worth seeking out. Ales are served by gravity dispense from the cellar behind the bar, with up to 10 beers and five ciders. There is a games room, home to dominoes, darts and crib matches, and a smoking area in the garden. Sport is shown on TV and traditional music hosted monthly. Home-made bar snacks are available. A winner of many local CAMRA awards. 🐴❀◐◑♿⇌♣●🚌🐾📶

Walnut 🏆

39 Violet Hill Road, IP14 1NE

☎ (01449) 401 6769

6 changing beers Ⓗ

Refurbished by the landlord and landlady in early 2019, this much-improved back-street pub offers a changing selection of real ales on handpump, along with ciders and craft beers listed on a large blackboard. The beer menu regularly features some unusual choices for the area. Good-value snacks are available. The pub holds regular quiz and vinyl nights. There are two beer gardens. 🐴❀♿⇌●🚌🐾📶

Sudbury

Bay Horse

61-65 Melford Road, CO10 1JS

☎ (01787) 377450 🌐 bayhorsesudbury.co.uk

Woodforde's Wherry; 8 changing beers Ⓗ

On the bar at this traditional family-run free house is an impressive array of nine handpumps. Outside, there is a heated patio and a large rear garden overlooking the water meadows and River Stour. Filled baguettes are available and free food for sport lovers on Sunday. Attractions include regular music sessions, a beer festival, and five en-suite letting bedrooms. The pub is a short walk from the town centre. 🐴❀🛏◐♿♣P🚌

Brewery Tap Ⓛ

21 to 23 East Street, CO10 2TP (200yds from market place)

☎ (01787) 370876 🌐 blackaddertap.co.uk

Mauldons Moletrap Bitter, Suffolk Pride, Black Adder Ⓗ**; 7 changing beers (sourced nationally)** Ⓗ/Ⓖ

The Mauldons Brewery tap is a haven for ale lovers. A good selection of the brewery's beers is always stocked, complemented by a range of national and locally sourced ales, up to 10 at any one time, on both handpump and gravity. Hearty snacks are served at lunchtime including pies and sandwiches. Beer festivals are held in April and October and quiz, music and comedy nights are regular attractions in a pub where conversation dominates. Q❀◐♿⇌♣●▯🚌🐾

Sweffling

White Horse Ⓛ

Low Road, IP17 2BB

☎ (01728) 664178 🌐 sweffling whitehorse.co.uk

3 changing beers Ⓖ

A cosy, traditional two-room pub, warmed by a wood-burner and wood-fired range. The owners have refurbished the building in an environmentally-friendly manner. Beers from local brewers are dispensed on gravity, served through a taproom door. Cider is also available, as well as fairtrade, organic and locally produced bottled beers. Hot and cold bar snacks are sold. Pub games include bar billiards, darts, crib and board games, and live music features twice a month. Horse and trap rides are offered in summer. A former CAMRA East Anglian Pub of the Year. Q🐴❀🛏◑⛺♣●P🐾📶

Tattingstone

Wheatsheaf Ⓛ

Church Road, IP9 2LY

☎ (01473) 805470 🌐 wheatsheaftattingstone.com

3 changing beers (sourced locally) Ⓖ

Comfortable open-plan single bar pub, refurbished by the current owners. It is located on the outskirts of a small village divided by the Alton Water Park reservoir. There is a large garden to the side – home to the annual charity music and beer festival in June. An interesting beer selection includes many from local brewers. Live music and quiz nights are always popular, as are themed food

evenings and Sunday roasts. The pub hosts local cribbage league matches and caters for private parties.
P(94,96)

Theberton

Theberton Lion

The Street, IP16 4RU

☎ (01728) 830185

Star Wing Gospel Oak; 2 changing beers (sourced locally)

Lively old village bar with patio seating outside at the front, various seating areas inside and a central fireplace. Many local pictures decorate the walls. The local beer club meets in the bar. Real ciders in bottle (BiB) are now available all year round including Giggler and Thistly Cross Traditional. The outdoor toilets have been retained. Two log cabins are available to let. Opening hours vary depending on the time of year. P

Thurston

Fox & Hounds

Barton Road, IP31 3QT

☎ (01359) 232228 thurstonfoxandhounds.co.uk

Greene King IPA; 5 changing beers (sourced nationally; often Cliff Quay, Green Jack, Tring)

A listed building, this popular local sits in the middle of the village a short walk from the railway station. The restaurant, serving good home-cooked food, is within the public bar area, and there is a separate bar for pool and darts. The pub holds regular quiz nights and bingo, and live music on bank holidays and special occasions. It has its own golf society. P

Walton

Half Moon

303 High Street, IP11 9QL

☎ (01394) 285586

Adnams Lighthouse, Southwold Bitter, Broadside; 3 changing beers (often Adnams)

An excellent, traditional, two-bar local community pub with wood panelling and an open fire in the public bar in winter. A meeting place for local groups, it has quiz nights, darts matches, cribbage and a selection of books to read. There are no gaming machines or music. The secure garden has a children's play area which is popular with families in the summer. Food is served lunchtimes only. Monthly folk nights are hosted as well as other live music on occasion. P

Wenhaston

Star Inn

Hall Road, IP19 9HF

☎ (01502) 478240 wenhastonstar.co.uk

Adnams Southwold Bitter; Green Jack Jackalope Golden Best; 4 changing beers (sourced locally; often Colchester, Green Jack, Wolf)

Free house situated on the outskirts of the village, with fine views of the Blyth Valley from the lawned garden. It has three small public rooms – the front bar is full of character with old enamel advertising signs and an open fire in winter. Good food is all home-cooked (no food Sun). Beer festivals are held over the late May and August bank holiday weekends. Camping is available by prior arrangement. QP(99A)

Woodbridge

Angel

2 Theatre Street, IP12 4NE

☎ (01394) 382660 theangelwoodbridge.co.uk

Adnams Southwold Bitter; 5 changing beers

A traditional two-bar drinking pub with beams and tiled floors. The regularly changing range of real ales is complemented by a selection of over 270 gins. There is seating outside and a former stables to the rear. No meals are served but there is a wood-fired oven in the garden for pizzas. Open mic is hosted on the second and fourth Wednesday of the month plus a DJ every Saturday evening and more live music. P

Cherry Tree

73 Cumberland Street, IP12 4AG

☎ (01394) 384627 thecherrytreepub.co.uk

Adnams Southwold Bitter, Ghost Ship, Broadside; Elgood's Black Dog; 5 changing beers (often Adnams)

Spacious family-friendly lounge bar/diner with a central servery and several cosy seating areas. Up to nine beers are usually on offer and an annual summer beer festival is hosted. The new kitchen provides home-cooked food all day every day, starting with breakfast, including vegetarian and gluten-free options. Board games and cards are available to play and a quiz is held on Thursday. The large garden has children's play equipment. Accommodation is in a converted barn.
P

Olde Bell & Steelyard

103 New Street, IP12 1DZ

☎ (01394) 382933 yeoldebellandsteelyard.co.uk

Greene King IPA, Abbot; 2 changing beers (often Greene King)

Large two-bar family-friendly pub with oak beams and a separate function room. The steelyard – a former cart weighbridge that still worked until hit by a lorry in 2018 – dates from 1650 and was on show at the Great Exhibition in 1851. Good home-cooked food is served. Traditional games include bar billiards, chess and bar skittles. Live rugby is shown on TVs in the side-bar area. To the rear of the building is a heated and covered patio area and wheelchair access.

Choosing pubs

CAMRA members and branches choose the pubs listed in the Good Beer Guide. There is no payment for entry, and pubs are inspected on a regular basis by personal visits; publicans are not sent a questionnaire once a year, as is the case with some pub guides. CAMRA branches monitor all the pubs in their areas, and the choice of pubs for the guide is often the result of democratic vote at branch meetings. However, recommendations from readers are welcomed and will be passed on to the relevant branch: write to Good Beer Guide, CAMRA, 230 Hatfield Road, St Albans, Hertfordshire, AL1 4LW; or send an email to: **gbgeditor@camra.org.uk**

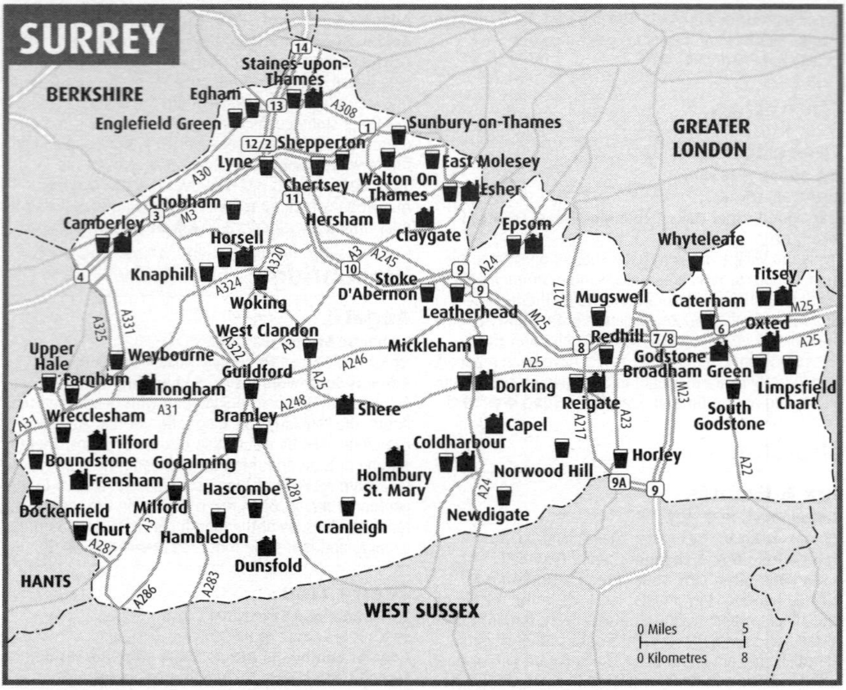

Boundstone

Bat & Ball L

15 Bat & Ball Lane, GU10 4SA (off Sandrock Hill Rd via Upper Bourne Lane) SU833444
☎ (01252) 792108 🌐 thebatandball.co.uk
Adnams Ghost Ship; Dark Star Hophead; Hop Back Summer Lightning; house beer (by Itchen Valley); 2 changing beers (sourced locally) H
A traditional country free house dating back 150 years, set in the Bourne Valley near Farnham. It has been run by the same family for two generations. The pub has several different rooms, with an open log fire, panelled walls and oak beams. The attractive garden has a children's play area and is popular with families on warmer days. There is an annual beer festival, a weekly quiz on Tuesday and live music once a month. An afternoon menu is served at weekends.
Q ❀ ♿ P (16,17)

Bramley

Jolly Farmer L

High Street, GU5 0HB
☎ (01483) 893355 🌐 jollyfarmer.co.uk
Greene King IPA; 7 changing beers (sourced nationally; often Crafty, Firebird, Heritage) H
A stagecoach inn that seems almost unchanged from yesteryear, with accommodation available in four en-suite rooms and a three bedroom flat. A privately owned free house it is full of character and has a cosy, welcoming atmosphere. Dark-wood beams hint of its long-ago upgrade from an entirely timber-framed construction. The decor is a celebration of the countryside and beer, featuring many historic beer mats and a large selection of pumpclips. The L-shaped bar offers a diverse range of up to eight real ales, plus real ciders in summer.
❀ ♣ P (53,63)

Broadham Green

Haycutter L

69 Tanhouse Road, RH8 9PE
☎ (01883) 776955 🌐 haycutter.co.uk
Brunning & Price Traditional Bitter; Harvey's Sussex Best Bitter; 3 changing beers H
A smart Brunning & Price pub that has been extended yet retains a cosy feel from its numerous small areas. Food is extremely popular but the main bar area's focus is as a community hub for locals. Guest beers, often from nearby breweries, are served alongside a house ale from Westerham. Outside is seating for summer dining plus a large garden for drinkers, featuring a children's play area.
Q ❀ ♿ ♣ P

Camberley

Claude du Vall L ✔

77-81 High Street, GU15 3RB
☎ (01276) 672910
Greene King Abbot; Ruddles Best Bitter; Sharp's Doom Bar; 4 changing beers (often Ascot, Tillingbourne, Windsor & Eton) H
The Claude du Vall is conveniently close to the station and bus stops, at the end of the High Street. The large, modern interior is divided into a number of different areas. The long bar offers three regular beers, four guests including at least one LocAle, and a real cider. Wetherspoon's reputation for good-value food and drinks attracts customers throughout the day, from breakfast onwards. Silent TVs generally show news programmes.
❀ ♿ ⇌

Caterham

King & Queen L

34 High Street, CR3 5UA (on B2030)

☎ (01883) 345438 🌐 kingandqueencaterham.co.uk
Fuller's London Pride, ESB; 1 changing beer Ⓗ
Traditional community pub that was originally three cottages dating back 400 years – as is evident from the inglenook fireplace and exposed beams – and that has been an inn since the 1840s. It now has three distinct areas in which to drink the superb beer. One bar is overlooked by portraits of King William and Queen Mary; another contains a dartboard. Live music features once a month. ♣P🚌🐾📶

Chertsey

Coach & Horses 🅛 ✔
14 St Ann's Road, KT16 9DG (on B375)
☎ (01932) 563085 🌐 thecoachandhorseschertsey.co.uk
Fuller's London Pride, ESB Ⓗ
An attractive, tile-hung Fuller's community local with linked drinking areas, built in 1860 as a school. Good-value food is served Tuesday to Friday but the landlady likes to keep a 'proper pub' for beer and conversation at weekends. The pub hosts league darts and has a sports TV. Outside, there is a garden to the rear and seating at the front. Abbeyfields park and Chertsey's cricket and football clubs are within walking distance and Thorpe Park is a short bus or car journey.
♣P🚌(446,456) 📶

Olde Swan
27 Windsor Street, KT16 8AY
☎ (01932) 562129 🌐 theoldeswanhotel.co.uk
Sharp's Doom Bar; Tring Side Pocket for a Toad; 2 changing beers (sourced nationally; often Thames Side, Timothy Taylor) Ⓗ
Refurbished when acquired by Mclean Inns, without spoiling its charm, the Olde Swan gives drinkers and diners a mellow experience with its shabby-chic decor. Four ales are usually on offer. The menu features stone-baked pizza, home-made burgers and sizzling steaks, with Mexican night on Friday. Accommodation includes double, twin and family rooms. Chertsey is handy for the M3 and Thorpe Park. P🚌(446,456)📶

Chobham

White Hart 🅛
58 High Street, GU24 8AA
☎ (01276) 857580 🌐 whitehart-chobham.co.uk
House beer (by St Austell); 4 changing beers (sourced locally) Ⓗ
A lovely rambling building with interesting nooks and crannies, next to the village church on an attractive and historic High Street with a cricket pitch behind the pub. Five ales are served in a range of strengths and styles. Brunning & Price Original is always available; guests could come from any of the many local breweries, with the distance from the pub prominently displayed. There are two restaurant areas and a less formal space for drinkers as you enter. Brunch is offered at weekends.
Q♿P🚌(73) 🐾📶

Churt

Crossways Inn 🅛
Churt Road, GU10 2JS
☎ (01428) 714323 🌐 weydonian.net/crossways
Arundel Sussex IPA; Hop Back Crop Circle; Loose Cannon Abingdon Bridge Ⓗ**; 4 changing beers** Ⓖ
Friendly two-bar pub with a homely ambience. At the centre of village life, it is popular with local groups as well as customers from further afield including ramblers and cyclists. Guest beers are fetched from their casks in the cellar, usually including local ales and a stout or porter. Good-value food is served lunchtimes, plus fish & chips on Wednesday night (no food Sun).
♣P🚌(19) 🐾

Coldharbour

Plough Inn 🅛
Coldharbour Lane, RH5 6HD
☎ (01306) 711793 🌐 ploughinn.com
Leith Hill Crooked Furrow, Smiler's Happiness, Surrey Puma; Tillingbourne Falls Gold; 1 changing beer Ⓗ
Home to the Leith Hill Brewery, this smart 17th-century inn is set in lovely countryside down narrow lanes close to Leith Hill. High-quality food, made with local produce where possible and changing with the season, is served lunchtimes and evenings (not Sun eve). The pub is understandably popular with walkers and cyclists. Its shop provides hot drinks and snacks alongside local produce. Six en-suite letting rooms are available.
Q♿P🚌(50,433) 🐾📶

Cranleigh

Three Horseshoes 🅛 ✔
4 High Street, GU6 8AE (on B2128)
☎ (01483) 276978
Harvey's Sussex Best Bitter; 5 changing beers Ⓗ/Ⓖ
This two-bar 17th-century pub features an inglenook fireplace with a roaring wood fire in winter. The long-gone Brufords Brewery used to stand behind the pub and some photos in the lounge bar show the building. You can get good home-made food each day (no food Sun eve). The garden has children's play equipment. Five constantly changing guest beers are sold, frequently served straight from the cask – check to see what is available. ♿♣P🚌🐾📶

Dockenfield

Bluebell 🅛 ✔
Batts Corner, GU10 4EX (½ mile N of Dockenfield village) SU820410
☎ (01252) 792801 🌐 bluebell-dockenfield.com
Langham Hip Hop; Triple fff Moondance; 2 changing beers (sourced locally; often Crafty Brewing, Hogs Back) Ⓗ
A 150-year-old hidden gem tucked away in a rural setting. The pub has a large garden, plenty of parking and is a truly independent family-run pub. The open-plan

REAL ALE BREWERIES

Ascot Camberley
Big Smoke ✎ Esher
Brightwater Claygate
Craft Brews ✎ Fresham
Crafty Brewing Dunsfold
Dorking Capel
Felday ▮ Holmbury St Mary
Fuzzchat ▮ Epsom
Godstone Godstone
Hogs Back Tongham
Leith Hill ▮ Coldharbour
Oxted Oxted
Pilgrim ✎ Reigate
Surrey Hills Dorking
Thames Side ✎ Staines-upon-Thames
Thurstons Horsell
Tilford ▮ Tilford
Tillingbourne Shere
Titsey Titsey

interior has a light, contemporary feel with three different seating areas for both formal and informal dining as well as drinking, with a real fire in winter. Beers are usually obtained directly from breweries within 15 miles. Q ❀ ◑ ♿ ▲ P 🐾 📶

Dorking

Cobbett's 🄻

23 West Street, RH4 1BY (on A25 one-way system eastbound)

☎ (01306) 879877 🌐 cobbettsrealales.com

6 changing beers Ⓗ/Ⓖ

In an old part of town, this excellent real ale off-licence and micropub offers the largest choice of ale in Surrey. The beer range, served by knowledgeable staff, is constantly changing, with up to six cask ales alongside six KeyKeg (one always from De Molen) and over 200 bottles and cans from Britain and beyond. The tiny bar (open from noon) in a back room has its own garden, and is a great place to drink and chat.
Q ❀ ≠(West) ● 🚌 🐾 📶

Cricketers 🄻 ✔

81 South Street, RH4 2JU (on A25 one-way system westbound)

☎ (01306) 889938 🌐 cricketersdorking.co.uk

Dark Star Hophead; Fuller's London Pride, ESB; 2 changing beers Ⓗ

Comfortable, small pub with a 'proper' feel. The single, L-shaped bar is covered with old mirrors, photographs and adverts. The terraced garden plays host to two beer festivals every year in May and in the autumn. This is a big rugby pub with all Six Nations matches and other internationals shown on TV. Classic films are often screened on Monday evening. Weekday lunchtime food is honest pub grub. Well over 10 years in this Guide is testament to the excellent quality and condition of the beer. ❀ ◑ ♣ 🚌 🐾 📶

East Molesey

Bell 🄻 ✔

4 Bell Road, KT8 0SS (off B369)

☎ (020) 8941 0400

Greene King IPA, Abbot; Morland Old Speckled Hen; 3 changing beers (often Hogs Back, Twickenham, Wimbledon) Ⓗ

A quirky, welcoming back-street inn, a short walk from the main shopping street. Several separate drinking areas make it ideal for a quiet pint or a larger gathering. The pub dates from 1460 and was later East Molesey's first post office. The 18th-century highwayman Claude Duvalier hid from the Bow Street Runners here. The large garden has a children's play area. Various TV screens show sport, which can be avoided if preferred. Quiz night is Tuesday. ❀ ◑ ♣ P 🚌 (411) 🐾 📶

Egham

Egham United Services Club 🄻

111 Spring Rise, TW20 9PE (close to A30 Egham Hill)

☎ (01784) 435120 🌐 eusc.club

Rebellion IPA; Surrey Hills Ranmore; 3 changing beers (sourced nationally; often Burning Sky, Thames Side, XT) Ⓗ

Local CAMRA Club of the Year and a previous National Club of the Year finalist. A changing range of guest ales includes something dark, and a wide choice of ciders is available from the cellar. Three beer festivals a year showcase an eclectic range of ales, mostly from the newest micros around. The club is comfortably furnished with sports TV, and hosts live music most Saturday evenings. Show a copy of this Guide or CAMRA membership card for entry. ❀ ♿ ≠ ♣ ● P 🚌 (8,441) 📶

Englefield Green

Happy Man 🏆 🄻 ✔

12 Harvest Road, TW20 0QS (off A30)

☎ (01784) 433265 🌐 thehappyman.co.uk

Hop Back Summer Lightning; 3 changing beers (sourced nationally; often Crouch Vale, Purity, Reunion) Ⓗ

In Victorian times two houses were converted to a pub serving workers building Royal Holloway College. Refurbished but virtually unchanged, this local CAMRA Pub of the Year is a popular haunt for students and locals. Alongside regular ale Hop Back Summer Lightning it serves three changing guests from local and national breweries. Beer festivals are held on the rear patio, which has a heated marquee. Darts and quiz nights are hosted and food is available every day.
❀ ◑ ♣ ● 🚌 (8,441) 🐾

Epsom

Assembly Rooms ✔

147-153 High Street, KT19 8EH (on A24 northbound)

☎ (01372) 737290

Fuller's London Pride; Greene King IPA, Abbot; Sharp's Doom Bar; 6 changing beers Ⓗ

A large, attractive building at one end of the marketplace in the centre of Epsom. Originally built as the town assembly rooms in the early 18th century, it became a Wetherspoon in 2002. The long bar runs across the rear, facing stone-paved and carpeted seating areas that drop down on slightly different levels. The single open area is broken up by dividing walls. Alcoholic drinks are served from 9am. Q ❀ ◑ ♿ ≠ ● 🚌 📶

Jolly Coopers 🄻

84 Wheelers Lane, KT18 7SD (off B280 via Stamford Green Rd)

☎ (01372) 723222 🌐 jollycoopers.co.uk

Surrey Hills Ranmore; 3 changing beers (sourced regionally; often Fuzzchat) Ⓗ

Close to Epsom Common, this pub is more than 200 years old. The interior is divided into two – a carpeted bar area to the left, and another larger area with polished parquet flooring to the right used more for dining, although not exclusively so. The decor is modern, with painted walls. There is a large paved garden at the rear. It can get busy at weekends but is quieter during the week. The Fuzzchat Brewery is in an outbuilding at the back. Varying ciders are sold in summer.
Q ❀ ◑ ♣ ● P 🚌 (E9,E10) 🐾 📶

Rifleman 🄻

5 East Street, KT17 1BB (on A24)

☎ (01372) 721244 🌐 therifleman.co.uk

Greene King London Glory; house beer (by Hardys & Hansons); 3 changing beers (sourced locally; often Dorking, Hogs Back, Windsor & Eton) Ⓗ

Small corner pub in the shadow of a bridge carrying the railway to and from London. It is decorated in a traditional style featuring two fireplaces and dark-green wood panelling, but also has some modern features such as bare brickwork and high tables at the front. There is a pleasant garden to the rear, an oasis of calm close to central Epsom. The name comes from the Surrey Rifle Volunteers who trained nearby. A changing cider is available. ❀ ◑ ≠ ● 🚌 🐾 📶

Esher

Albert Arms
82 High Street, KT10 9QS (on A307)
☎ (01372) 877117 🌐 thealbertarmsesher.co.uk
Dark Star Hophead; Fuller's London Pride; 1 changing beer (sourced regionally; often Fuller's) Ⓗ
A welcoming late 19th-century street-corner pub in the centre of Esher. It was named after Prince Albert, who at one time lived nearby. There is a large, wood-panelled bar area plus a smaller dining space where drinkers are also welcome. The TV is for major sporting occasions only. Two dining rooms upstairs can be hired for special events. Open for breakfast, with alcoholic drinks available from 10am.

Wheatsheaf L
40 The Green, KT10 8AG
☎ (01372) 464014 🌐 wheatsheafesher.co.uk
Harvey's Sussex Best Bitter; Surrey Hills Shere Drop; 2 changing beers (sourced locally) Ⓗ
Imposing inn about 200 years old opposite Esher Green. This is a smart, popular local with a vibrant atmosphere. Its spacious and modern interior comprises a large central bar and several seating areas. Drinkers and diners are equally welcome, with high-quality food available all day. The bar area has an open fire. A bicycle rack is provided at the rear. Changing guest beers include local ales. A former local CAMRA Pub of the Year.
P

Farnham

Hop Blossom
50 Long Garden Walk, GU9 7HX (between Waitrose and Castle St) SU838469
☎ (01252) 710770 🌐 hopblossom.co.uk
Fuller's London Pride, ESB; Gale's Seafarers Ale; 2 changing beers (often Dark Star, Fuller's, St Austell) Ⓗ
A hidden gem in the heart of Farnham, with a lovely welcoming feel and a log fire in winter. It has three distinct areas – the main bar, a conservatory and a back room. Seating includes some old pews; it has traditional floorboards underfoot. The pub can be crowded during events in the town. Dogs are welcome, as are children during the day and early evening.

Nelson Arms L ✔
50-52 Castle Street, GU9 7JQ
☎ (01252) 727222 🌐 thenelsonarmsfarnham.co.uk
Andwell Gold Muddler; Hogs Back TEA; Timothy Taylor Boltmaker; 1 changing beer (sourced nationally) Ⓗ
Originally three farm cottages belonging to the Bishop of Winchester's estate, this pub has plenty of history. Horatio Nelson is reputed to have stayed here while visiting Lady Hamilton, who lived nearby. There are many original dark beams and some exposed brickwork, with a log fire between the two main seating areas. The guest beer pump usually features a traditional amber bitter, or a golden ale in summer. Alongside the excellent beer the pub serves good food, including a grill night on Tuesday. (4)

Godalming

Star Inn ✔
17 Church Street, GU7 1EL
☎ (01483) 417717
Hardys & Hansons Olde Trip Ⓗ**; 9 changing beers (sourced nationally)** Ⓗ/Ⓖ
Dating from around 1830, the Star has a small public bar at the front and a main room to the side that leads to a patio garden and smoking area. There is a separate lounge with a bespoke cider bar, open Thursday to Sunday. Up to 10 real ales are stocked, some from the Greene King range. Beer festivals are held at Easter and Halloween. The pub is a regular winner of local and regional CAMRA cider awards.

Guildford

Drummond L ✔
55 Woodbridge Road, GU1 4RF
☎ (01483) 579395 🌐 thedrummondguildford.co.uk
Hogs Back TEA; St Austell Tribute; 2 changing beers (sourced regionally; often Ringwood) Ⓗ
A large open-plan pub whose interior features modern art, an eclectic range of furniture and an impressive selection of chandeliers. Classic pub food and modern dishes are served all day. Burger night is Wednesday, and booking is essential for the popular Sunday roasts. Major rugby matches are shown and a Sunday quiz is hosted. There is a garden and large heated patio behind the pub.

King's Head (Stoke Road)
27 King's Road, GU1 4JW (on A320 Stoke Rd)
☎ (01483) 568957 🌐 kingsheadguildford.co.uk
Dark Star Hophead; Fuller's London Pride, ESB; 1 changing beer (sourced nationally) Ⓗ
Built in 1860 as two cottages, which soon became a beer house, this pub is noted for its attractive hanging baskets. Its interior is deceptively spacious and now much enlarged. Service is from both sides of a central bar, with the full range of Fuller's beers available, including seasonals, and which is complemented by a draught cider. TV sport is screened in most areas. Acoustic music features on Tuesday, quiz night is Wednesday, and open mic night Thursday.
(London Rd) P

Rodboro Buildings L ✔
1-10 Bridge Street, GU1 4SB (opp Friary Centre)
☎ (01483) 306366
Greene King IPA, Abbot; Sharp's Doom Bar; 7 changing beers Ⓗ
This Wetherspoon maintains a range of up to 10 real ales, often from local breweries. It is spread over three levels in a Grade II listed former industrial building that was the original home of the Dennis car (later truck) company. The community noticeboard publicises a range of local events. The pub also hosts occasional Meet the Brewer nights and brewery battles.

Royal Oak
Trinity Churchyard, GU1 3RR (behind Trinity Church)
☎ (01483) 457144 🌐 royaloakguildford.co.uk
Fuller's London Pride; Gale's HSB; 3 changing beers (sourced nationally; often Dark Star, Fuller's, Windsor & Eton) Ⓗ
This pub has been serving real ale since 1870. It was built as an extension to the rectory next door, with a hall upstairs and rooms at ground level. These rooms are now the bar area and show the building's heavily beamed structure. Outside there is a patio area on one side, while a couple of tables overlooking Trinity churchyard are on the other. It does a take-away service, including for real ale. P

Wooden Bridge ✔
Woodbridge Hill, GU2 9AA (at bottom of Woodbridge Hill)
☎ (01483) 572708
Greene King IPA; 3 changing beers (sourced nationally; often Greene King, Hogs Back) Ⓗ

A former hotel, built in 1936 and featuring a more recent 50ft-long bar. Its interior blends traditional pub decor with contemporary elements – armchairs mixed with standard and high tables, and carpeted and wooden flooring. There are usually seven TVs showing sport, often with no sound and with music playing throughout the pub. Sunday is quiz night.
♨❀◑♿♣●P🚌(C,2)🐾📶

Hambledon

Merry Harriers 🄻 ✔

Hambledon Road, GU8 4DR SU967391
☎(01428) 682883 🌐 merryharriers.com
Surrey Hills Shere Drop; 3 changing beers (sourced locally; often Crafty, Dorking, Greyhound) 🄷
This impressive 16th-century country inn, popular with walkers and cyclists, takes you back in time. It is in the heart of this picturesque village, set against the backdrop of the Surrey Hills, surrounded by open fields, in a designated area of outstanding natural beauty. The free house is owned by local resident Peter de Savary. An open field at the rear is home to the pub's llamas.
Q♨❀🛏◑♣●P🚌(503)🐾📶

Hascombe

White Horse ✔

The Street, GU8 4JA
☎(01483) 208258 🌐 whitehorsepub.net
Harvey's Sussex Best Bitter; Hogs Back TEA; Otter Bitter; Surrey Hills Shere Drop; 1 changing beer (sourced locally) 🄷
A coaching inn dating from the 16th century, the White Horse has a traditional adults-only public bar, decorated with sporting photos and old agricultural tools. Several other rooms, where families are welcome, lead back to the garden. The guest beer is usually from a local brewery. Food is served lunchtime and evening every day, using locally sourced meat and game. The pub is on the Greensand Way and convenient for other local attractions. Q♨❀◑P🚌(42)🐾📶

Hersham

Bricklayers Arms

6-8 Queens Road, KT12 5LS (off A317)
☎(01932) 220936
Hogs Back TEA; Hop Back Crop Circle; Shepherd Neame Spitfire 🄷
This two-bar Victorian pub, just off the green, has built up a fine reputation. It is divided into a spacious public bar and comfortable saloon. Excellent food is served in the lounge, including daily specials. Features include wonderful external floral displays and a secluded rear garden. Two letting rooms are available. Parking can be difficult. ❀🛏◑♿♣🚌(458,515)🐾📶

Royal George

130 Hersham Road, KT12 5QJ (off A244)
☎(01932) 220910
Young's London Original, London Special; 1 changing beer (sourced locally) 🄷
The pub was built in 1964 – the name refers to a 100-gun ship from the Napoleonic Wars. It has one L-shaped bar with tartan carpet and upholstered banquette seating. A real fire adds to the comfortable atmosphere. The menu features excellent Thai food alongside more traditional British fare, with a roast on Sunday lunchtime. There are paved outdoor seating areas to the front and rear for the warmer months. Quiz night is Tuesday.
♨❀◑♿P🚌(555)🐾📶

Horley

Jack Fairman ✔

30 Victoria Road, RH6 7PZ (main shopping street nr Waitrose)
☎(01293) 827910
Greene King Abbot; Ruddles Best Bitter; Sharp's Doom Bar; 4 changing beers (sourced nationally) 🄷
This 1930s building in the centre of town, conveniently close to the station and bus stops, was formerly a garage used by local motor racing driver Jack Fairman. After a period as a Kwik Fit tyre centre the building reopened as a Wetherspoon pub, with racing-related historical items on the walls of the industrial-look interior. Food is available all day. Three TVs show news and sport.
Q♨❀◑♿⇌🚌📶

Horsell

Crown 🄻

104 High Street, GU21 4ST
☎(01483) 771719
6 changing beers (sourced locally; often Surrey Hills, Thurstons) 🄷
Welcoming two-bar community local with six real ales in the saloon bar. Three beers are from Thurstons, who started brewing in the Crown and are now located next door. Other ales come from independent local or regional breweries. Behind the pub is a sturdy smokers' shelter and beyond that a large garden with two pétanque pistes. Real cider is available occasionally, more often in summer. It hosts at least one beer festival a year. Local CAMRA Pub of the Year 2019. ♨❀♣●P🚌(48)🐾📶

Knaphill

Garibaldi ✔

134 High Street, GU21 2QH
☎(01483) 473374 🌐 thegaribaldiknaphill.co.uk
2 changing beers (sourced regionally) 🄷
Enterprising pub on the edge of Knaphill. Its compact interior has exposed beams and wooden floors. Two or three changing cask ales are served, with regional beers favoured. A real cider is available direct from the cellar. Monday is real ale club night, with beers sold at reduced prices. The pub hosts a Sunday evening quiz, a Tuesday curry night and a Thursday steak night. A beer festival is held over Easter. ♨❀◑●P🚌(34, 91)🐾📶

Royal Oak 🄻 ✔

Anchor Hill, GU21 2JH
☎(01483) 473330
5 changing beers (often Exmoor, Ringwood, St Austell) 🄷
An attractive 17th-century building set back from the road at the bottom of the hill. Up to seven ciders are served alongside the beers. Food is available Wednesday to Sunday, with a roast on Sunday. Behind the pub is a superb garden with a barbecue and children's play equipment. An outside bar opens at the weekend in summer. It hosts live music twice each month, plus an annual beer festival and two cider festivals.
♨❀◑♣●P🚌(48,91)🐾📶

Leatherhead

Running Horse 🏆 🄻 ✔

38 Bridge Street, KT22 8BZ (off B2122)
☎(01372) 372081 🌐 running-horse.co.uk
Shepherd Neame Master Brew, Spitfire; Surrey Hills Ranmore; 1 changing beer (sourced regionally; often Shepherd Neame) 🄷

Overlooking the River Mole, this Grade II* listed two-room pub, dating from 1403, features a real log fire, home-made food, a courtyard seating area plus a large back garden. Elizabeth I apparently spent the night here. The public bar has TV, pool table and dartboard, and the cosy lounge bar features low ceilings and exposed beams. Quiz night is Tuesday. Live jazz plays on Sunday lunchtime and live bands monthly, with a charity music event on May Day. Children are allowed until 9pm. Q⛭❀◑⇌♣P🚌🐾📶

Limpsfield Chart

Carpenters Arms 🄻

12 Tally Road, RH8 0TG (off B269)

☎ (01883) 722209

Westerham British Bulldog, 1965 – Special Bitter Ale, Summer Perle; 2 changing beers 🄷

This Westerham Brewery tied house is adjacent to the National Trust's Limpsfield Common and attracts both walkers and horse riders. The L-shaped bar has parquet flooring and the walls are adorned with an interesting collection of old photos and artwork. One side of the bar caters for diners enjoying the good food on offer. There is also a separate function room. The first Sunday of the month is quiz night. ⛭❀◑♣P🚌(594)🐾📶

Lyne

Royal Marine

Lyne Lane, KT16 0AN

☎ (01932) 873900 🌐 royalmarinelyne.co.uk

Greene King London Glory; Ruddles Best Bitter; 1 changing beer (sourced nationally; often Cotleigh, Goff's, Weltons) 🄷

The name of this rural pub commemorates Queen Victoria's review of her troops in 1853 on nearby Chobham Common. Royal Marine memorabilila, a collection of drinking jugs and other bric-a-brac are on display. Generous portions of home-cooked food are served Monday to Friday and Sunday lunchtime. Friday is bingo quiz night; note the pub is closed on Saturday. Occasional beer festivals are held. Q⛭❀◑♣P🐾📶

Mickleham

King William IV 🄻

4 Byttom Hill, RH5 6EL (off A24 Southbound behind Frascati restaurant)

☎ (01372) 372590 🌐 thekingwilliamiv.com

3 changing beers (sourced locally; often Crafty, Surrey Hills) 🄷

A quaint, welcoming country pub, nestled on a hillside and dating from 1790. The main bar is homely with a log fire and there is a smaller bar to the front. An attractive outside terrace, with some tables under cover, enjoys stunning views over the Mole Valley. Good home-made food is served – book ahead for lunch, especially on summer weekends. Steep steps can make access difficult. A shared car park is on the A24 southbound. Q⛭❀◑P🚌(465)🐾📶

Milford

Refectory 🄻

Old Portsmouth Road, GU8 5HJ

☎ (01483) 413820 🌐 refectory-godalming.co.uk

Firebird Festive 51; Surrey Hills Ranmore; house beer (by St Austell); 3 changing beers (often Hogs Back, Langham) 🄷

A large, open pub with exposed beams and several distinct areas, set in a fascinating building of uncertain age. Farming paraphernalia adorn the walls. Roaring log fires in the pretty fireplaces warm the pub in winter. The three guest beers are generally from local independent and micro breweries. Food is served. There is a courtyard garden to the rear. ⛭❀◑♿P🚌(70,71)🐾📶

Mugswell

Well House Inn 🄻 ✔

Chipstead Lane, CR5 3SQ (off A217) TQ25845526

☎ (01737) 830640 🌐 thewellhouseinn.co.uk

Fuller's London Pride; Hogs Back TEA; Surrey Hills Shere Drop; 2 changing beers 🄷

This secluded rural pub was originally three 1560s-built cottages and has had its current role since the 1950s. It comprises three small bars and a conservatory, with one bar set aside as a drinking area and the others given over to dining. Monday is steak night, Tuesday is quiz night. The two changing beers are generally from local micros. The pleasant garden contains St Margaret's Well, mentioned in the Domesday Book. ⛭❀◑♣P🐾📶

Newdigate

Surrey Oaks 🏆 🄻

Parkgate Road, Parkgate, RH5 5DZ (between Newdigate and Leigh) TQ20524363

☎ (01306) 631200 🌐 thesurreyoaks.com

Surrey Hills Ranmore, Shere Drop; 4 changing beers 🄷

This multi award-winning 16th-century inn is renowned for its commitment to good-quality real ale from microbreweries. Six cask beers including a dark ale, 12 KeyKeg beers and 12 ciders provide great choice. The numerous drinking areas feature low beams, flagstones and an inglenook fireplace with log-burning stove. Excellent home-cooked food includes daily specials. The large garden hosts popular late spring and August bank holiday beer festivals. Q⛭❀◑♣●P🚌(21,50)🐾📶

Norwood Hill

Fox Revived 🄻

Norwood Hill, RH6 0ET

☎ (01293) 229270 🌐 foxrevived.co.uk

Brunning & Price Traditional Bitter; Surrey Hills Shere Drop; 4 changing beers 🄷

Deceptively spacious country inn serving a good range of beer and food. There is a large and comfortable bar area as you enter, with several big tables. The guest ales change frequently and are mainly from local breweries. The restaurant is popular for its wide-ranging menu, served all day from midday. The pub's location on high ground gives a fine view to the north from the sizeable garden, with the North Downs and Box Hill ahead, rising towards Leith Hill in the west. ⛭❀◑♿●P🚌(22)🐾📶

Redhill

Garibaldi 🄻

29 Mill Street, RH1 6PA

☎ (01737) 773094 🌐 thegaribaldiredhill.co.uk

4 changing beers 🄷

The Garibaldi has been a pub for over 150 years and is now community owned and not for profit. Its single compact room has a central bar, with TV screens at each end for sporting events, and a small side area with a dartboard. Beers are primarily local and usually include at least one from Pilgrim Brewery. The large garden has views across Redhill. It hosts a variety of social events including two beer festivals each year. May open 4pm Monday to Thursday in winter.
⛭❀⇌(Earlswood) ♣🚌🐾📶

Plough Inn 🄻 ✔

11 Church Road, St Johns, RH1 6QE

☎ (01737) 766686 🌐 theploughredhill.com

Fuller's London Pride; Harvey's Sussex Best Bitter; 2 changing beers 🄷

Traditional and friendly establishment in a surprisingly rural setting, some parts dating from the 16th century. Rambling but compact, it is full of small rooms, low beams and changes in level. This gives it a remarkable character, made cosy by real fires in winter. The pub serves excellent food alongside its guest beers, one of which normally comes from a local brewery.
❀◐⇌(Earlswood) 🚌📶

Sun 🄻 ✔

17-21 London Road, RH1 1LY (on A25 in town centre)

☎ (01737) 766886

Greene King Abbot; Ruddles Best Bitter; Sharp's Doom Bar; 5 changing beers 🄷

Purpose-built Wetherspoon outlet whose name is an acknowledgement to 19th-century astronomer Richard Carrington, renowned observer of sunspots, who built an observatory in Redhill. The pub comprises a single large room with one long bar serving the vast space, a raised dining area at one end, and a section for families until 6pm. The chain's usual food menu is served all day. Several TV screens show sporting events with the sound turned off. Q🐴❀◐♿⇌●🚌📶

Reigate

Bell Inn 🄻 ✔

21 Bell Street, RH2 7AD (on A217)

☎ (01737) 244438 🌐 thebellreigate.co.uk

Greene King IPA; Morland Old Speckled Hen; 4 changing beers 🄷

Welcoming and comfortable pub in one of the oldest buildings in town. Its tiny frontage reveals a long, narrow interior with low ceilings and wooden tables and floors. Guest beers change frequently and are usually from local breweries. The menu includes more than a dozen speciality burgers supplied by a local butcher. Note the old Ordnance Survey map on the ceiling.
🐴❀◐⇌🚌🐾📶

Hop Stop Bar

73 Bell Street, RH2 7AN (on A217 S of town centre)

☎ (01737) 221781 🌐 hopstopbeers.co.uk

2 changing beers 🄷

Continental-style bar divided into several comfortable areas, specialising in beer, wine and spirits from small suppliers. It serves around 10 draught beers of various styles, from handpump, KeyKeg and keg. All are beautifully kept, with individual temperature control displayed on an electronic board. The bar also offers a wide and changing selection of bottled and canned brews. 🐴🚌🐾📶

Pilgrim Brewery Tap Room 🄻

11 West Street, RH2 9BL (off A25 towards Dorking)

☎ (01737) 222651 🌐 pilgrim.co.uk

Pilgrim Surrey, Session IPA, Progress, Quest; 2 changing beers 🄶

The cosy taproom of Surrey's oldest brewery occupies the converted office of an old Victorian bakery, hidden in a yard just off the town centre. It usually dispenses six cask ales plus a similar number of keg beers, some of them experimental. Food is not served but you are welcome to take in a pizza from across the road. Outside is a pleasant area overlooking Reigate Priory cricket ground.
Q🐴❀⇌♣P🚌🐾📶

Shepperton

Barley Mow 🄻

67 Watersplash Road, TW17 0EE (off B376 in Shepperton Green)

☎ (01932) 225326 🌐 thebarleymowshepperton.co.uk

Hogs Back TEA; Hop Back Summer Lightning; 3 changing beers (sourced locally; often Thames Side, Tillingbourne, Twickenham) 🄷

Friendly community local in Shepperton Green to the west of the main village centre. Five handpumps serve two regular beers plus up to three – usually local – guest ales. Many pumpclips adorn the bar and beams. Entertainment includes jazz on Wednesday, a quiz night on Thursday, live rock or blues bands on Friday or Saturday night, and a traditional charity meat raffle on Sunday afternoon. Outside is a covered, heated patio at the rear. ❀♣●P🚌(458)🐾📶

South Godstone

Fox & Hounds 🄻 ✔

Tilburstow Hill Road, RH9 8LY

☎ (01342) 893474 🌐 foxandhounds.org.uk

Greene King IPA; Hogs Back TEA; Pilgrim Surrey, Progress; 2 changing beers 🄷

This attractive building, with parts dating back to 1368, has been a pub since 1601. It features original beams throughout and a large inglenook in the restaurant. The low-ceilinged bar area is cosy, with high-back settles and a fire. The pub serves good-quality food alongside up to six beers, including guests from breweries rarely seen in the area. A pleasant rear garden has a children's play area. 🐴❀◐♣P🐾📶

Staines-upon-Thames

London Stone 🄻

14 Church Street, TW18 4EP

☎ (01784) 452012

4 changing beers (sourced nationally; often Thames Side, Tiny Rebel, Wild Beer) 🄷

Quirky town-centre local featuring regular live music and open mic nights. Its five handpumps dispense four ales plus a real cider. The pub also offers a wide range of craft beers from home and abroad, in bottle, can and on draught. The enthusiastic landlord is keen to hear customers' suggestions for new beers. Attractions include darts, table football, table tennis, retrogaming and a nifty arcade machine. ❀♣●📺🚌🐾📶

Swan Hotel

The Hythe, TW18 3JB (overlooking Thames by Staines Bridge)

☎ (01784) 452494 🌐 swanstaines.co.uk

Fuller's London Pride, ESB; 2 changing beers (often Dark Star, Fuller's) 🄷

Rambling 18th-century hotel a short walk from the town centre, much enlarged and refurbished over the years. Its warren of rooms includes two bars, a restaurant open every day, and 15 bedrooms. The walls display evocative pictures of Thames life, including local rowing events. The long riverside terrace by the hotel's moorings is ideally placed to watch the boats go by.
🐴❀🛏◐P🚌🐾📶

Thames Side Brewery & Tap Room 🄻

Bridge Street, TW18 4TG (on Thames towpath by Bridge St car park)

☎ 07749 204242 🌐 thamessidebrewery.co.uk

Thames Side Heron Ale, White Swan Pale Ale, Egyptian Goose India Pale Ale; 2 changing beers (sourced locally; often Thames Side) 🄷

Interesting views are guaranteed at this former Sea Cadets headquarters on the riverbank. Its downstairs taproom, which serves five real ales and a cider, overlooks the brewery. Historic Staines Bridge can be seen from the upstairs lounge, and from tables placed alongside the towpath in summer. Food includes artisan pies and bar snacks from local producers. The bar opens at noon on brewing days – check the website for details.

Wheatsheaf & Pigeon

Penton Road, TW18 2LL (corner of Wheatsheaf Lane and Penton Road)

(01784) 452922 wheatsheafandpigeon.co.uk

Bombardier; Fuller's London Pride; Otter Ale; 2 changing beers (sourced regionally; often Robinsons, Thames Side)

Community local situated between Staines and Laleham, a short signposted walk from the Thames Path, with Staines Town FC also nearby. Ales often include local micro or West Country guests. Good-value, interesting food is served every day, excluding Sunday and Monday evenings. The pub is dog friendly with water bowls provided. Outside seating is available at the front and back, plus a covered area. P (458,570)

Stoke D'Abernon

Old Plough

2 Station Road, KT11 3BN (off A245)

(01932) 862244 oldploughcobham.co.uk

Fuller's London Pride; Surrey Hills Shere Drop; 1 changing beer (sourced locally)

Dating from the late 16th century, this listed building was once a courthouse with the gallows outside, and the stables were used for hansom cab trade. The interior has been opened out but retains much of its original character, particularly at the front. An extension houses a dining area at the rear. The decor is a mix of bare brick, wood panelling and painted walls. There is a pleasant garden area to the side and rear. The pub has a good reputation for food, which makes it busy at times.

QP

Sunbury-on-Thames

Admiral Hawke

81 Green Street, TW16 6RD

(01932) 781326

Courage Best Bitter; Ringwood Razorback; Sharp's Doom Bar; Timothy Taylor Landlord

Traditional community local close to Hawke House, home of the 18th-century seafarer who gave the pub its name. When built in 1862 it was called the Railway, but the line ended up running some way to the north. Food is served in the evening only in winter. There is a rear garden, and additional seating out front. This is the closest pub to London Irish rugby club's headquarters, and only five minutes' walk from the Thames towpath. P

Titsey

Botley Hill Farmhouse

Limpsfield Road, Botley Hill, CR6 9QH (at top of ridge on B269) TQ39495554

(01959) 577154 botleyhill-farmhouse.co.uk

Titsey Gower Wolf, Gresham Hopper, Leveson Buck; 1 changing beer

An isolated location near the North Downs Way makes this the highest pub in the South-East and provides splendid views towards London. Once a farmhouse, the building dates from 1546 and offers a cosy blend of small rooms, low ceilings and three dining areas, warmed by real fires. The Titsey beers come from the brewery in a nearby building. The pub's extensive menu includes Sunday breakfast. P (595)

Upper Hale

Alfred Free House

9 Bishops Road, GU9 0JA

(01252) 820385 thealfredfreehouse.co.uk

Wantsum Montgomery; 4 changing beers (sourced nationally)

This friendly local pub, tucked away down a residential road, features a bar area and a restaurant/function room. The regular beer is supplemented by three or four guest ales, usually including a dark beer. Fresh home-made food, using locally sourced ingredients, is served Wednesday to Saturday evenings and Sunday lunchtime. The pub hosts events including charity quiz nights and two beer festivals each year, at Easter and in October.

QP (5)

Walton on Thames

Walton Village

29-31 High Street, KT12 1DG

(01932) 254431 thewaltonvillage.com

Fuller's London Pride; 1 changing beer (sourced nationally)

Modern high-street pub in a converted shop premises, featuring exposed brickwork and wood panels. The large front bar has a raised seating area and there is a room to the rear for private events. A wide range of food is served all day, prepared in an open-plan kitchen in the centre of the pub, and including vegan and gluten-free choices. Breakfast is available at the weekend. Poker night is Monday and quiz night Thursday. Attractions include a table tennis table.

Weir

Waterside Drive, KT12 2JB

(01932) 784530 weirhotel.co.uk

Greene King Abbot; 2 changing beers (often Belhaven, Park, Twickenham)

The Weir's superb riverside location, with extensive outside seating and free moorings, attracts walkers, cyclists, boaters and families. The Victorian-style bar area is mainly carpeted, with comfortable upholstered benches around the walls, and more intimate areas at the front and rear. The interior features copper pans, plates, ornaments and old pictures. Roasts are a highlight on Sunday. Accommodation is available in six rooms.

P (564)

West Clandon

Bull's Head

The Street, GU4 7ST

(01483) 222444

Hogs Back TEA; Surrey Hills Shere Drop; Young's London Original

Sixteenth-century village inn with several areas on different levels – beware of the low ceilings and oak beams. Food is an important part of the pub's trade and the focus is on traditional British cooking at reasonable prices (no food Sun eve). To the rear is a hedged garden where you can while away a secluded couple of hours enjoying the three regular beers.

QP (463)

Weybourne

Running Stream ✔

66 Weybourne Road, GU9 9HE

☎ (01252) 323750

Greene King IPA, Abbot; Hardys & Hansons Bitter; Morland Old Speckled Hen; 1 changing beer Ⓗ

A good old-fashioned friendly locals' pub. A horseshoe-shaped room surrounds a central bar, with basic tables dotted around the outer perimeter and stools at the bar. The handpumps dispense Greene King beers plus one free of tie, and usually a regular mild. It does lunchtime snacks and soup, or you can bring a takeaway, and there is a Canadian food van in the car park Wednesday-Saturday evenings. Attractions include a quiz on Wednesday and Sunday plus occasional live music. There is a pleasant garden at the rear. ❀P🚌🐾📶

Whyteleafe

Radius Arms

205 Godstone Road, CR3 0EL (on A22)

☎ 07514 916172

4 changing beers Ⓗ/Ⓖ

Welcoming micropub that thrives on eccentricity and its excellent, varying selection of beer and cider. At least four cask ales, four KeyKegs and about 15 ciders are always available. Quirky features include a pickled onion competition, a ceiling of hops and beer mats, and furniture recycled from the Olympic Park in London. There is also a small library. Local CAMRA Cider Pub of the Year. Q❀⇌(Whyteleafe/Upper Warlingham)🍎🚌🐾

Woking

Herbert Wells Ⓛ ✔

51-57 Chertsey Road, GU21 5AJ

☎ (01483) 722818

Courage Best Bitter; Greene King Abbot; Hogs Back TEA; Sharp's Doom Bar; 7 changing beers (sourced nationally) Ⓗ

A varied range of up to seven guest beers, plus six ciders and perries, are served at this popular town-centre Wetherspoon, which is close to bus stops and the railway station. The large open-plan bar is decorated with HG Wells-inspired features including an invisible man sitting in the window and its own time machine. A wealth of information about local history covers the walls of both the main bar and the smaller side room. Q◐♿⇌🍎🚌📶

Woking Railway Athletic Club

Goldsworth Road, GU21 6JT (behind offices at E end of Goldsworth Rd) TQ003585

☎ (01483) 598499

3 changing beers Ⓗ

Lively social club tucked away near Victoria Arch, serving three or four beers. One side of the bar is sports-oriented with darts, free-to-play pool and Sky Sports; the other side is quieter. Filled rolls are available on Saturday afternoon. Children are welcome at all times. Show a CAMRA membership card or copy of this Guide for entry. Local CAMRA Club of the Year 2019 and 2020.
🐴⇌♣🚌📶

Wrecclesham

Sandrock Ⓛ ✔

Sandrock Hill Road, GU10 4NS

☎ (01252) 447289 🌐 sandrockwrecclesham.co.uk

Bowman Swift One; Exmoor Gold; Fuller's London Pride; Hop Back Summer Lightning; Timothy Taylor Landlord; Triple fff Moondance; 1 changing beer (often Hogs Back, St Austell, Surrey Hills) Ⓗ

Traditional pub with a contemporary feel, benefiting from a refurbishment in 2018. The focus here is on dispensing quality real ale and serving Thai food in the separate restaurant, which has a set lunchtime menu and offers a takeaway service. The pub welcomes families and dogs. Outside is a patio garden and a small car park. Q🐴❀◐♿♣P🚌(16,17)🐾📶

King & Queen, Caterham (Photo: Andy Poole)

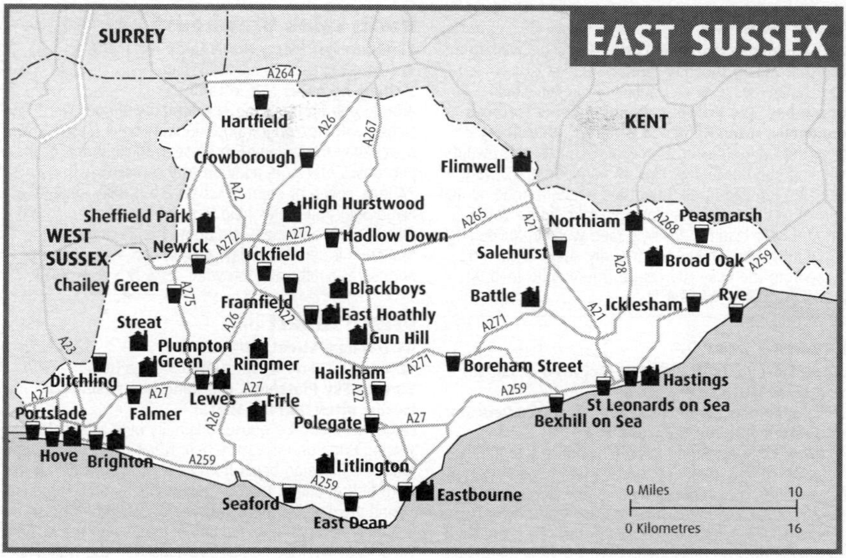

SUSSEX (EAST)

Bexhill on Sea

Albatross Club (RAFA)

15 Marina Arcade, TN40 1JS (on seafront 200yds E of De La Warr Pavilion)

(01424) 212916 bexhillrafa.co.uk

5 changing beers (sourced locally)

Many times local CAMRA branch Club of the Year, this popular and friendly Royal Air Forces Association club has five handpumps dispensing ales both local and national. Four real ciders are usually available. Beer festivals are held in June and November along with quizzes, jazz, ukulele and vinyl nights, notably on Fridays. Lunchtime food is served weekdays except Monday (the club is closed on Sun and Mon eves). CAMRA members are very welcome. Q (98,99)

Boreham Street

Bull's Head

The Strait, BN27 4SG

(01323) 831981 bullsheadborehamstreet.com

Harvey's Sussex Best Bitter; house beer (by Harvey's); 2 changing beers

On the main road, this traditional country inn boasts large grounds, including a beer garden, ample parking and a campsite. Charity events are often held here. Traditional English pub food is offered - the pub is renowned for its pies. Harvey's Sussex Best Bitter is always on tap, along with the exclusive Bull's Head Bitter, a seasonal and an occasional beer. Closing times may sometimes be a little earlier in the winter, especially if it's quiet Monday to Wednesday.
Q P (98)

Brighton

Basketmakers Arms

12 Gloucester Road, BN1 4AD

(01273) 689006 basket-makers-brighton.co.uk

Dark Star Hophead; Fuller's London Pride, ESB; Gale's Seafarers Ale, HSB; 4 changing beers (sourced nationally; often Butcombe, Fuller's)

Busy two-room street-corner pub on the edge of Brighton's famous bohemian North Laines. A much-loved Brighton institution, it is now under new management and is popular with young and old alike. Eight handpumps serve a selection of the Fuller's range plus guests. Locally sourced home-made food is available every day, including Seafood Saturday, and the traditional Sunday roasts are ever popular. The walls are adorned with old metal signs and tobacco tins. Live jazz music features on the first Sunday of every month.
Q

Battle of Trafalgar

34 Guildford Road, BN1 3LW

(01273) 327997

Fuller's London Pride; Harvey's Sussex Best Bitter; 3 changing beers (sourced nationally)

A locals' pub a minute's walk from Brighton railway station. A long narrow room leads down to the beer garden; another room is behind the bar. There are random prints on the walls, some appropriately sea-themed. The pub holds monthly Sunday music nights, a weekly quiz night, curry night every Wednesday and a monthly meeting of MENSA. The excellent menu includes vegan and gluten-free options plus a renowned Sunday roast. If you operate the Engine Room Telegraph you'll be expected to donate to the RNLI – the locals will insist!
Q

Brighton Bierhaus

161 Edward Street, BN2 0JB

(01273) 686386

Brighton Bier West Pier; 4 changing beers (sourced locally; often Brighton Bier)

This single-bar pub is the Brighton Bier brewery tap, centrally situated near the Royal Pavilion and Brighton Pier. It serves up to five changing beers and two ciders on handpump, along with keg and bottled beers. An extensive pizza range can be ordered from nearby to eat in the bar. There is a free cheeseboard on Sunday. The muted TV shows BT Sport. CAMRA branch Pub of the Year 2019.

Craft Beer Co

22-23 Upper North Street, BN1 3FG (short walk from Churchill Square shopping centre)

☎ (01273) 723736 🌐 thecraftbeerco.com/brighton

House beer (by Kent); 4 changing beers (sourced regionally; often Kent, Pig & Porter, Wild Beer) Ⓗ

Near the Grade II listed St Nicholas Church, this award-winning pub boasts five ales on handpump, 22 craft beers on tap and up to 90 bottled beers from home and abroad. A discount is available on take-home bottles. Tutored beer tastings are held (see website for details). The pub is comfortable and friendly, ideal for getting away from the busy city centre. There is no food on Monday.

Evening Star Ⓛ

55-56 Surrey Street, BN1 3PB (200yds S of station)

☎ (01273) 328931

7 changing beers (sourced regionally; often Dark Star, Northern Monk, Pig & Porter) Ⓗ

A classic, compact Brighton pub/alehouse five minutes from the station, majoring in good real ale and craft beers. Fairly basic in decor, it has a few tables outside on the street. It is no longer tied to Dark Star Brewery, as it was originally, with the brewery in the cellar, but Dark Star beers may be on, together with several interesting brews from around Britain. There are board games, window seats and the Trollburger van serves food Thursday to Saturday.

Free Haus Ⓛ

1 Howard Road, Hanover, BN2 9TP

☎ (01273) 692484

4 changing beers (often Brighton Bier) Ⓗ

Formerly the Reservoir, the Free Haus is the third in the small chain of Haus-branded pubs in Brighton Bier's portfolio. The bar offers plenty of seats and an open-plan kitchen. There is more seating downstairs, with access to the patio area. Food is available every day, mainly burgers, with a vegan menu on Monday and Tuesday. The four pumps serve a changing range of beers, mostly from Sussex.

Hanover Ⓛ

242 Queens Park Road, Hanover, BN2 9ZB

☎ (01273) 679902

Sharp's Doom Bar; 4 changing beers (sourced locally) Ⓗ

An estate pub from circa 1927, now opened out but retaining its well-used function/meeting room. The interior is quite large but there are discrete areas with a variety of seating and tables. Part of the Indigo chain, the pub serves a range of Sussex ales plus a local cider on handpump. Food is served all day – the bar area has a pizza oven. Sunday roasts are a highlight. Quiz night is Tuesday and there is occasional live music.

(21,23)

Haus on the Hill Ⓛ

58 Southover Street, Hanover, BN2 9UF

☎ (01273) 601419 🌐 hausonthehill.pub

Brighton Bier West Pier; 3 changing beers (sourced locally; often Brighton Bier, Hand) Ⓗ

This pub, situated at the top of a steep hill, is now operated by Brighton Bier. Conversation is the norm here and there is no TV or jukebox. A guest beer is always sold, along with three from Brighton Bier, plus a cider. A number of bottled beers and keg beers, both British and foreign, complete the range. The pub has two upstairs function rooms and a covered patio for smokers.

Q (18,23)

North Laine Brewhouse Ⓛ

27 Gloucester Place, North Laine, BN1 4AA

☎ (01273) 683666 🌐 northlaine.pub

3 changing beers (often Laine) Ⓗ

A large pub on the edge of Brighton's famous North Laines, with its own in-house brewery behind the bar. On a weekday the brewer can be seen making one of the pub's own brews. In addition to the cask ales there are 24 taps, seven or eight of which are usually KeyKeg. Large beer hall tables help to provide a party atmosphere, and there is a photo booth to record the fun. Food is served all day. A DJ or live music features and, occasionally, axe throwing.

Prince Albert Ⓛ

48 Trafalgar Street, BN1 4ED

☎ (01273) 730499 🌐 princealbertbrighton.co.uk

Burning Sky Plateau; 5 changing beers (sourced locally; often Burning Sky) Ⓗ

Large Victorian free house, originally built as a hotel serving Brighton railway station. It has six handpumps, mainly dispensing beers from local breweries or guests from further afield. The clientele is chiefly office workers during the day and all sorts in the evening. Live music or a DJ plays every night. The pub is famous for the Kissing Coppers artwork by Banksy previously on the wall. No food is available but customers may bring their own or order in a takeaway.

Prince George Ⓛ

5 Trafalgar Street, BN1 4EQ

☎ (01273) 681055 🌐 princegeorgebrighton.co.uk

Firebird Parody Ⓖ; 5 changing beers (often 360 Degree, Dorking, Gun) Ⓗ

This pub is famed for its vegetarian food – the Sunday roasts are particularly popular. The main bar dispenses five local ales and a cider, usually Westons. The Firebird Parody is served direct from a conditioning tank adjacent to the bar. Unfined beers are sourced whenever possible. The pub has several cosy drinking areas plus a covered, heated patio at the rear. Children are welcome until the evening. A DJ plays on Thursday and a quiz is hosted on Sunday.

REAL ALE BREWERIES

1648 East Hoathly
360° Sheffield Park
Battle Battle
Beak Lewes (NEW)
Bedlam Plumpton Green
Beer Me Eastbourne
Brewery at the Watchmaker's Arms Hove
Brewing Brothers Hastings
Brighton Bier Brighton
Burning Sky Firle
Cellar Head Flimwell
Engineer High Hurstwood
FILO Hastings
Franklins Ringmer
Gun Gun Hill
Hand Brighton
Harvey's Lewes
Laine Brighton
Long Man Litlington
Loud Shirt Brighton
Old Tree Brighton
Rectory Streat
Rother Valley Northiam
Three Acre Blackboys (NEW)
Three Legs Broad Oak
Unbarred Brighton

Chailey Green

Five Bells 𝕃

East Grinstead Road, BN8 4DA
☎ (01825) 722259 🌐 thefivebellschailey.co.uk
Harvey's Sussex Best Bitter; 3 changing beers (sourced locally; often Bedlam, Gun, Harvey's) Ⓗ
Built in 1590, the building became a coaching inn in 1752 and retains many original features including inglenook fireplaces, exposed beams and a large expanse of Tudor brick floor. Several areas open off the original core – cosy dining spaces behind, the bar and pool room to the side. The gardens are great for alfresco dining in warm weather. Real cider is available in the summer. Popular with motoring enthusiasts due to the roadside car park. Q🛝❀◑P🚌

Crowborough

Cooper's Arms 𝕃

Coopers Lane, TN6 1SN
☎ (01892) 654796
Harvey's Sussex Best Bitter; 3 changing beers (sourced nationally) Ⓗ
This friendly local drinkers' pub has been a regular Guide entry for many years. It offers changing beers, often local, and always serves them in top condition. More distant examples feature at the regular beer festivals, when all 12 handpumps are put to good use. A real cider is also sold. Food may be available on Sunday lunchtime but it is best to enquire first. Outside is a secluded rear garden. Q🛝❀🍎P🚌🐾📶

Wheatsheaf 𝕃 ✔

Mount Pleasant, TN6 2NF
☎ (01892) 663756 🌐 wheatsheafcrowborough.co.uk
Harvey's Dark Mild, IPA, Sussex Best Bitter; 1 changing beer (often Harvey's) Ⓗ
A quintessential 18th-century English pub in the quiet outskirts of Crowborough. Harvey's beers are served from the three-sided bar. There are log fires in each of the seating areas, where photos of the Wheatsheaf's history are on display. The well-attended annual beer festival at the end of May is staged in a marquee, and regular live music events are held. Many colourful hanging baskets adorn the outside seating area.
Q🛝❀◑⇌♣P🚌(228,229)🐾📶

Ditchling

White Horse 𝕃

16 West Street, BN6 8TS
☎ (01273) 842006 🌐 whitehorseditchling.com
Harvey's Sussex Best Bitter; Long Man Long Blonde; 3 changing beers (sourced locally) Ⓗ
This 12th-century inn lies below the parish church in a picturesque, historic village. Its cellar leads to a network of tunnels under the village, thought to have been used for smuggling in times past. Accommodation at the White Horse can cater for weddings, birthday parties or as a stopover while walking the South Downs Way. Log fires in winter, excellent food and quality guest beers are certain to fortify the traveller.
Q🛝❀🛏◑P🚌(167,168)🐾📶

East Dean

Tiger Inn 𝕃 ✔

The Green, BN20 0DA
☎ (01323) 423209 🌐 beachyhead.org.uk/the-tiger-inn
Harvey's Sussex Best Bitter; Long Man Long Blonde; St Austell Tribute; 3 changing beers (sourced locally) Ⓗ
Situated by the village green, with plenty of outside seating, this 15th-century inn is an ideal place to relax after a Downland walk. It features wooden beams and stone flooring, and serves good-quality food. The bar area is in the centre and has a log fire, the lower area has wheelchair access including for the toilets, and the snug is used for dining. At least one real cider is available. Several times winner of local CAMRA Country Pub of the Year. Q🛝❀🛏◑♿🍎P🚌🐾📶

East Hoathly

King's Head 𝕃

1 High Street, BN8 6DR
☎ (01825) 840238 🌐 thekingshead.org
1648 Triple Champion, Signature; Harvey's Sussex Best Bitter; 1 changing beer (often 1648) Ⓗ
Family-run free house that has been a pub for over 250 years. The 1648 Brewing Company was established in 2003 in the old stables next door; two of its beers are always on the bar, usually alongside a dark ale, as well as a changing cider. An extensive range of home-cooked food is served every day. There is a walled garden to the rear and additional outside seating to the front. Local CAMRA Cider Pub of the Year 2018 and Sussex Pub of the Year 2019. Q🛝❀◑⛺🍎P🚌(54)🐾📶

Eastbourne

Crown 𝕃 ✔

22 Crown Street, Old Town, BN21 1PB
☎ (01323) 724654
Gun Scaramanga Extra Pale; Harvey's Sussex Best Bitter; Shepherd Neame Spitfire Ⓗ; Young's London Special Ⓗ/Ⓖ; 1 changing beer Ⓖ
Traditional pub with a comfortable interior, in the Motcombe area of Eastbourne's Old Town. Popular with locals and visitors, it has separate public and saloon bars serving well-kept beer. There are log fires in winter and a separate pool room, and home-made bar snacks are served. Regular events include quiz nights, Sunday lunchtime competitions, three annual beer festivals and occasional live music. An enclosed rear garden has children's play equipment and is the setting for summer barbecues. 🛝❀♣🚌🐾📶

Hurst Arms 𝕃 ✔

76 Willingdon Road, Ocklynge, BN21 1TW
☎ (01323) 419440 🌐 thehurstarms.pub
Harvey's Forward's Choice, Sussex Best Bitter; house beer (by Harvey's); 2 changing beers (sourced locally) Ⓗ
This Harvey's tied house is a thriving drinkers' pub – Sussex Best is always available, plus two to four others according to the season. It has two bars – a smaller, comfortable lounge bar and a larger public bar. The latter houses a pool table, jukebox, dartboard and a TV showing BT Sport. Music events feature approximately fortnightly. No food is served. On-site parking is limited to four spaces. ❀♿♣P🚌🐾📶

Lamb Inn 𝕃 ✔

36 High Street, Old Town, BN21 1HH
☎ (01323) 720545 🌐 thelambeastbourne.co.uk
Harvey's Sussex Best Bitter, Armada Ale; 1 changing beer (sourced locally) Ⓗ
Many period features remain at this Harvey's inn in the Old Town, which dates back to 1180. Tours of the crypt (beer cellar) can be arranged. There are two bars serving Harvey's regular and seasonal ales. Food is available throughout the day, including vegetarian and vegan dishes. Live music, theatrical productions and comedy

nights are regular events. The pub has a function room for private parties as well as accommodation.
Q P

London & County

46 Terminus Road, BN21 3LX
(01323) 746310
Greene King Abbot; Ruddles Best Bitter; Sharp's Doom Bar; 3 changing beers (sourced nationally)
A Wetherspoon Lloyds No.1 bar occupying the former London & County Bank, arranged over two floors, each with a bar; the upstairs can be hired for functions. It is located in the town close to bus stops and the railway station. Varying guest beers are on offer, including at least one LocAle. Food is served all day. Muted TV screens display news, and music is played in the evening, with a DJ on Friday/Saturday evenings, when a smart casual dress code applies.

Falmer

Swan Inn

Middle Street, BN1 9PD (just off A27 in N of village)
(01273) 681842
Palmers Tally Ho!; 5 changing beers (sourced regionally; often Downlands, Long Man, Palmers)
This is a traditional family-run free house near the universities. It has three bar areas and a barn for functions. Food is served but times vary - check ahead. The pub gets busy when Brighton & Hove Albion play at home. Opening hours vary on match days - although usually closed on Monday it will open for evening games. There is a small courtyard area at the side.
Q P (28,29)

Framfield

Hare & Hounds

The Street, TN22 5NJ
(01825) 890118 hareandhounds.net
Harvey's Sussex Best Bitter
Cosy and welcoming village inn dating from 1428. Recently refurbished, it has separate dining, bar and snug areas, with an inglenook fireplace and comfy chairs. The pub has a good reputation for its food, especially Sunday roasts. Regular entertainment includes community events, quiz nights and live music. Children and dogs are welcome. With a good-sized garden and a play area, the pub offers something for all ages. No food on Monday. Q P

Hadlow Down

New Inn ★

Main Road, TN22 4HJ (on A272)
Harvey's IPA, Sussex Best Bitter; 1 changing beer (often Harvey's)
Quirky and friendly village inn, identified by CAMRA as having a nationally important historic pub interior. The back bar fittings, ceramic spirit casks and panelled counter date from 1885 when the pub was rebuilt following a fire. There is another bar at the back and a function room. The no-frills environment is more than compensated for by the warm welcome, conviviality and excellently kept beer. No food is available other than bar snacks. Q P (248)

Hailsham

George Hotel

3 George Street, BN27 1AD
(01323) 445120
Greene King Abbot; Ruddles Best Bitter; Sharp's Doom Bar; 2 changing beers (sourced nationally)
Busy town-centre pub that delivers Wetherspoon's model to a high standard, popular with locals and handy for visitors to Hailsham Pavilion cinema opposite. At least five real ales, including one LocAle, and up to 11 real ciders and perries are on the bar. There is a quiet enclosed patio to the rear and an outdoor terrace at the side. Local branch Cider & Perry Pub of the Year 2018 and 2019. Q

King's Head

146 South Road, Cacklebury, BN27 3NJ
(01323) 440447 kingsheadcacklebury.co.uk
Harvey's Sussex Best Bitter; 1 changing beer (often Harvey's)
Expect a warm welcome at this traditional community local which has been a tied Harvey's house since 1841. Inside, there are a quiet snug and two separate bars featuring exposed beams and a log fire; outside, the large garden has a covered, seated smoking area. A variety of traditional pub games and board games are played and live music events take place throughout the year, including the monthly open mic nights. Home-made food is served Friday to Sunday.
Q P

Hartfield

Anchor Inn

Church Street, TN7 4AG
(01892) 770424 anchorhartfield.com
Harvey's Sussex Best Bitter; Larkins Traditional Ale; 1 changing beer (sourced nationally)
Now the last pub in the village, the Anchor is a popular venue for locals and visitors to the area, close to Ashdown Forest and not far from Pooh Bridge. Originally a 15th-century manor house, it first opened as a pub in 1861 and has remained at the hub of the community ever since. Local cask ales are on tap in the combined drinking and dining areas. There is a separate restaurant to the rear, and use of the gardens in summer.
Q P (291)

Hastings

Albion

33 George Street, Old Town, TN34 3EA
(01424) 439156 albionhastings.com
Harvey's Sussex Best Bitter; 3 changing beers (often Bedlam, Three Legs)
A spacious refurbished former hotel with a drinks licence dating from 1730, featuring beautiful metal bar tops and stylish furniture, plus a stage for live music. The separate bar can be used as a function room. Previously a Younger's of Edinburgh outlet, the pub retains original 1940s wood panelling in the main bar, incorporating many clan tartans. Excellent food is served including home-made pies with unusual fillings. There is a large paved seating area on Marine Parade.
Q

Crown

64-66 All Saints Street, Old Town, TN34 3BN
(01424) 465100 thecrownhastings.co.uk
4 changing beers (sourced locally)
This award-winning pub, with its vast crown sculpture above the door, is just below the East Hill Country Park. Drinkers and diners can feel equally at home with four real ales from breweries in Sussex and Kent and a regularly changing food menu using locally sourced produce. The wooden floor, subdued paintwork and

hand-made furniture, together with two open fires, one in a small snug, help to create a relaxed atmosphere for all. Cider is usually from Seacider. ▦◑♣♨☐❦⬚

Dolphin 🅛 ✅
11-12 Rock-a-Nore Road, Old Town, TN34 3DW
☎ (01424) 434326 ⊕ thedolphinpub.co.uk
Dark Star Hophead; Harvey's Sussex Best Bitter; Young's London Special; 3 changing beers (sourced nationally) ⓗ
Traditional family-run pub next to Hastings' famous fishing huts and close to Europe's largest beach-launched fleet. It is adorned with memorabilia and old photographs of the local fishing community. Six cask beers are available including three regularly changing guests. There is a wood-burning stove, and a front terrace that is popular in summer. Fish and chip suppers are served on Monday evening. Live music, showcasing local bands, takes place on Tuesday, Friday and Saturday. Q▦❀◑♣♨☐❦⬚

First In Last Out 🅛
14-15 High Street, Old Town, TN34 3EY (near Stables Theatre)
☎ (01424) 425079 ⊕ thefilo.co.uk
FILO Brewery Crofters, Churches Pale Ale, Old Town Tom, Gold; 1 changing beer (sourced regionally) ⓗ
The FILO is a traditional pub, with a fireplace in the middle adding warmth during the winter months. A selection of six ales from its own FILO brewery is offered, plus a guest. The hostelry has very strong community ties, with many local patrons as well as visitors contributing to a convivial atmosphere in which to enjoy local beer. Good food is served daily. Live music features regularly (check website for details). Q▦◑♣☐❦⬚

Jenny Lind 🅛 ✅
69 High Street, Old Town, TN34 3EW
☎ (01424) 421392 ⊕ jennylindhastings.co.uk
Courage Directors; Old Dairy Uber Brew; Theakston Old Peculier; 5 changing beers (sourced nationally) ⓗ
This traditional Old Town pub is named after the Swedish opera singer who, it is reputed, stayed in Hastings in the 1880s. There are eight real ales, including up to five nationally sourced guests, and four traditional ciders. Free music events take place Friday to Sunday on a stage overlooked by a large mermaid figurehead. There is a separate cosy back bar with an open log fire and bar billiards. Upstairs to the rear is a terraced garden. ▦❀♨♣♨❦⬚

Jolly Fisherman
3 East Beach Street, Old Town, TN34 3AR
☎ (01424) 428811 ⊕ jollyfishermanhastings.com
3 changing beers ⓗ
A pub until the 1950s, then a café, and now Hastings' first micropub. At least three changing cask beers, together with six real ciders and perries, and keg beers, are supplemented by a large range of canned and bottled beers of UK and foreign origin. Home-made bar snacks are on offer Wednesday to Saturday, with free cheese on Sunday afternoon. The rustic furniture is arranged to help create a friendly atmosphere. Toad in the hole and shove-ha'penny can be played. ▦◑♣♨☐❦

Twelve Hundred Postcards
80 Queens Road, TN34 1RL
☎ 07883 408909
3 changing beers (sourced locally) ⓖ
One-room micropub incorporating benches and high stools on both sides, with novel ceiling lights made from green beer bottles in baskets. At the rear is a cool room

for the ales, cask and keg, with a large viewing window. Two or three real ciders are offered. The pub's name references a former sweet shop owner 100 years ago who sold illegal French postcards, resulting in his imprisonment and destruction of the postcards. ▦≈♨☐❦

White Rock Hotel 🅛
White Rock, TN34 1JU
☎ (01424) 422240 ⊕ thewhiterockhotel.com
4 changing beers (sourced locally) ⓗ
The hotel is on the seafront next to the White Rock Theatre, opposite the pier. Its bar overlooks the sea, with a terrace outside, superb in good weather. Four changing ales are served, all from Sussex, and at least one LocAle. Plenty of sofas and easy chairs provide a relaxing and comfortable seating area; there is restaurant-style seating for table service. Light snacks are available all day and a dinner menu in the evening. Q▦♨◑≈P☐❦⬚

Hove

Foghorn 🅛
55 Boundary Road, BN3 4EF
☎ (01273) 419362 ⊕ thefoghornmicro.com
5 changing beers (sourced regionally; often Brighton Bier, Burning Sky) ⓖ
This establishment is a quiet haven for drinkers on the busy corner of New Church Road and Boundary Road. Opened in December 2018, it has quickly become a go-to venue with its wide-ranging selection of beers. The new owners are happy to help and advise. The cellar sits just behind the bar and can be viewed through a glass partition. Furniture and decor is best described as minimalist. Q▦♿≈♨☐❦⬚

Neptune Inn 🅛
10 Victoria Terrace, BN3 2WB (on coast road E of King Alfred leisure complex)
☎ (01273) 736390 ⊕ theneptunelivemusicbar.co.uk
Dark Star Hophead; Greene King Abbot; Harvey's Sussex Best Bitter; 2 changing beers (sourced regionally) ⓗ
Friendly single-bar Victorian pub close to the King Alfred centre and Hove seafront. A reclining figure of Neptune rests above the old Courage signage at the front. Five beers are served including two changing guests. Children are welcome until the evening. Live music features strongly, with blues or rock every Friday and jazz on Sunday (see website for details). ☐(700)❦⬚

Watchmaker's Arms 🅛
84 Goldstone Villas, BN3 3RU
☎ (01273) 776307 ⊕ thewatchmakersarms.co.uk
5 changing beers (sourced regionally; often Brighton Bier, Downlands) ⓖ
This micro is handy for Hove station. The clock theme is recognised with old watches and timepieces on the wall – not always correct! Tall tables and benches line the walls. Pizzas from a local takeaway can be ordered – otherwise, sausage rolls and scratchings are the fare. Beercraft, a small on-site brewery, is now in full swing and its beers can be sampled here. Q≈♨☐(7,21)❦

Icklesham

Queen's Head 🅛
Parsonage Lane, TN36 4BL (opp village hall)
☎ (01424) 814552

Greene King Abbot; Harvey's Sussex Best Bitter; 4 changing beers (sourced locally; often Hardys & Hansons) [H]
Delightful 17th-century inn that has been in the Guide for over 30 years. Three changing ales, often local, and two ciders are normally on tap. Open fires and good-value home-made food make the pub popular with visitors, locals and walkers on the 1066 Country Walk. Live music features on Sunday and also at the mini beer festivals held on bank holidays. The large garden has sweeping views over the Brede Valley. There is a pétanque piste behind the pub. P (100)

Lewes

Black Horse ✔
55 Western Road, BN7 1RS
☎ (01273) 473653 theblackhorselewes.co.uk
Burning Sky Plateau; Greene King Abbot; Harvey's Sussex Best Bitter; Morland Old Speckled Hen; 3 changing beers (sourced regionally; often Dark Star, Greene King, Old Dairy) [H]
A Greene King Local Heroes venue that allows the licensee to stock Sussex ales and produce. This traditional community pub has feature bay windows and a large main bar with a real fire, together with a quieter back bar. Two TVs show most sporting events, and the pub's teams play a wide variety of games including toad in the hole and crib. Home-made food includes vegan options. (28,29)

Brewers Arms L
91 High Street, BN7 1XN (near Lewes Castle)
☎ (01273) 475524 thebrewersarmslewes.com
Harvey's Sussex Best Bitter; 4 changing beers (sourced regionally; often Burning Sky, Gun, Tring) [H]
The two rooms here have separate characteristics – the front bar is quiet and more food-oriented, the back bar offers sports TV, darts and pool. Food, starting with traditional breakfasts, is served until mid-evening. The venue is popular on match days with Lewes FC, Brighton & Hove Albion and away fans. The pub has a dwyle flunking team. An annual beer festival is hosted. The exterior commemorates the former owners, Page and Overton's Croydon Ales. (28,29)

Gardener's Arms L
46 Cliffe High Street, BN7 2AN
☎ (01273) 474808
Harvey's Sussex Best Bitter; 5 changing beers (sourced regionally; often Harvey's, Parkway, Rother Valley) [H]
Traditional, genuine free house near Harvey's Brewery. It is a one-roomed pub with a wooden floor and central bar. Five changing guest ales are dispensed, generally from small breweries across the country. Food consists of locally made pies and pasties. A real cider is always available, and a dark beer festival is held in March. No children allowed, but dogs are especially welcome. Popular with Lewes and Brighton FC fans on match days. (28,29)

John Harvey Tavern L ✔
1 Bear Yard, Cliffe High Street, BN7 2AN
☎ (01273) 479880 johnharveytavern.co.uk
Harvey's Dark Mild, IPA [H]**, Sussex Best Bitter** [G]**, Armada Ale** [H]**; 2 changing beers (sourced locally; often Harvey's)** [H]/[G]
Pub housed in a former stable block of the Bear Inn, opposite Harvey's Brewery and next to the River Ouse. The bar boasts wooden beams, a slate floor, log-burner and cosy seating areas. Children are allowed in the restaurant until 9pm. There is a large function/dining room upstairs. The outside tables are a suntrap in summer and therefore popular. There is a folk night on Tuesday and music on Sunday.
Q (28,29)

Lansdown Arms
36 Lansdown Place, BN7 2JU
☎ (01273) 470711
Gun Base Ejection Smoked Rye; Harvey's Sussex Best Bitter; Timothy Taylor Boltmaker; 1 changing beer (sourced locally; often Long Man, Timothy Taylor) [H]
Close to the railway station at the foot of a steep hill, this smallish venue is popular with fans and visitors from both Lewes FC and Brighton & Hove Albion on match days. The dark and cosy building dates from 1827, before the arrival of the railway in Lewes, and was at one time a Whitbread house. It hosts popular live music, regularly featuring local bands, and has a free jukebox. Local artists' work is displayed on the walls.

Lewes Arms ✔
1 Mount Place, BN7 1YH
☎ (01273) 473152 lewesarms.co.uk
Dark Star Hophead; Fuller's London Pride; Gale's Seafarers Ale, HSB; Harvey's Sussex Best Bitter; 2 changing beers (sourced regionally; often Adnams, Butcombe) [H]
Characteristic corner pub comprising three small rooms plus a central lobby with serving hatch, an upstairs function room containing a small theatre stage, and an outside terrace. Good food is served including excellent Sunday lunches. Toad in the hole is played here, and the pub is home to the world pea throwing championship, dwyle flunking, spaniel racing and other unusual events. A three-day music festival is hosted in August and an annual pantomime in March. Occasionally a real cider is on sale. Q (28,29)

Rights of Man L ✔
179 High Street, BN7 1YE
☎ (01273) 486894 rightsofmanlewes.com
Harvey's IPA, Sussex Best Bitter; 5 changing beers (sourced locally; often Harvey's) [H]
A small two-bar pub near the law courts. The front bar has two tall tables near the front windows, wonderful for enjoying a pint and watching the world go by. The decor includes dark oak-panelled walls and etched-glass screens to form booths. The small Martyr's Bar has pictures of each local bonfire society on the wall and more seating. Good-quality food is served lunchtimes and evenings. The roof terrace, with its artificial grass covering, is a suntrap in summer. (28,29)

Royal Oak
3 Station Street, BN7 2DA (at top of Station St)
☎ (01273) 474803 royaloaklewes.co.uk
Harvey's Sussex Best Bitter; St Austell Tribute; 2 changing beers (sourced locally; often Bedlam, Five Points, Gun) [H]
This single-room pub is the birthplace of Lewes FC (1875) and home to the Waterloo Bonfire Society. Good food is complemented by a range of five beers, at least one usually coming from Bedlam. The function room upstairs has its own bar and hosts regular live music sessions. There are DJs in the bar on Friday night, and karaoke sessions are held occasionally. The pub has a lovely secret garden.

Snowdrop Inn L ✔
119 South Street, BN7 2BU
☎ (01273) 471018

Harvey's Sussex Best Bitter; 3 changing beers (sourced locally; often Burning Sky, Cellar Head, Gun) 🄷
On the outer edge of the Cliffe area of this historic town, the Snowdrop is a popular and welcoming free house serving four cask ales (five in summer), one cider and four beers on KeyKeg. It has a central bar, with additional seating upstairs and two outside drinking areas. The pub is family friendly and serves good home-cooked food all day. There is a jazz night every Monday and music most Saturdays, and a beer festival is held in October.
♘❀◑≠♣🍎🚌(28,29) 🐾📶

Newick

Crown Inn 🄻 ✔
22 Church Road, BN8 4JX
☎ (01825) 723293 🌐 thecrownatnewick.co.uk
Harvey's Sussex Best Bitter; 2 changing beers (sourced regionally; often Harvey's, Pig & Porter) 🄷
This family-run free house is at the southern end of the village near the post office. The 121 bus stops just round the corner. There is a central bar with two smaller rooms off to either side and a pleasant garden to the rear. Good-value meals are served using local produce. With two other pubs on the village green, Newick is well worth a whole afternoon's stay, but don't miss the last bus home. ♘❀◑♣🍎P🚌(31,121)🐾📶

Peasmarsh

Horse & Cart Inn
School Lane, TN31 6UW
☎ (01797) 230034 🌐 thehorseandcart.co.uk
House beer (by Romney Marsh); 2 changing beers (sourced locally; often Three Legs) 🄷
A traditional country village inn with oak-beamed rooms, a single bar, a large restaurant area and a south-facing garden with plenty of seating at the rear. There is an extensive menu featuring home-cooked pub favourites, including pizza, using local and seasonal produce where possible. As well as the house beer from Romney Marsh Brewery, Horse and Cart Best, there is always a Three Legs Brewery ale on offer. Breakfast is served at weekends. Q♘❀🛏◑▲🍎P🚌(344)🐾📶

Polegate

Dinkum 🄻
54 High Street, BN26 6AG
☎ (01323) 482106
Harvey's Sussex Best Bitter; 2 changing beers (sourced locally) 🄷
With excellent nearby public transport, this Harvey's tied house is a lively, friendly pub with a loyal core of locals happy to welcome visitors. Patrons regularly organise card games in one of the two spacious bars, while in the other all the important sports events are shown, alongside the playing of darts, pool and toad in the hole. Pizzas, warm flatbread and nachos are on offer alongside typical bar snacks throughout opening hours.
♘❀≠♣🍎P🚌🐾📶

Portslade

Stag's Head Inn
35 High Street, Old Portslade, BN41 2LH
☎ (01273) 416058
Harvey's Sussex Best Bitter; Long Man American Pale Ale; 3 changing beers (sourced nationally; often Brains, Goddards) 🄷
Former brewery tap for the Dudney Brewery (closed 1930) which still stands nearby, this friendly two-bar community pub offers four beers. The regular ales are from Sussex, with guests mainly from outside the county. The old Watney's decor behind each bar is of interest. The pub hosts regular quiz nights and live music as well as TV sport and bar billiards, and is home to the local golf society (see Facebook for forthcoming events).
♘❀♣🚌(1,1A) 🐾📶

Stanley Arms
47 Wolseley Road, BN41 1SS (on corner of Wolseley Rd and Stanley Rd)
☎ (01273) 701738 🌐 thestanley.com
Harvey's Sussex Best Bitter; 5 changing beers (sourced regionally; often Downlands, Harvey's, Long Man) 🄷
A welcoming no-frills back-street pub, the hub of the local community, with a changing range of guest beers from Sussex and beyond. The first Monday of the month is cellar night, when you can visit the cellar, with reduced-price beers and free nibbles at the bar. TV sport is regularly shown. Quiz night is Wednesday and occasional beer festivals are hosted (see Facebook for events). Q♘❀≠♣🍎🚌(2,46)🐾📶

Rye

Standard Inn 🄻
The Mint, TN31 7EN
☎ (01797) 225231 🌐 thestandardinnrye.co.uk
House beer (by Old Dairy); 3 changing beers (often Romney Marsh, Three Legs) 🄷
Close to the town centre and riverside area, the Standard has recently been refurbished, revealing beautifully carved beams dating back to its 15th-century pub origins. Quarry-tiled floors, exposed brick, stone walls and open fires adorn the quaint interior. Locally sourced high-quality food is served, notably Rye Bay scallops. The house beer, Farmers Ale, is from Old Dairy, supplemented by LocAle from Three Legs and Romney Marsh. Five en-suite rooms are available. A recent local CAMRA branch Pub of the Year.
Q♘❀🛏◑≠♣🚌(100,101) 🐾📶

Waterworks 🏆 🄻
Tower Street, TN31 7AT
☎ (01797) 224110 🌐 ryewaterworks.co.uk
House beer (by Three Legs); 7 changing beers (sourced locally) 🄶
The Rye Waterworks is steeped in history. For 300 years it was a water pumphouse, then in the 1800s a soup kitchen, which has now been opened up as a feature. It then served as the town's public toilet before becoming the first micropub in the area. Now a family business serving eight real ales, including its own uRYEnal Best Bitter, and 12 ciders are available, all sourced within 30 miles. Pork pies and Scotch eggs are popular snacks. Current local CAMRA Pub of the Year.
Q♘❀♿≠♣🍎🚌🐾📶

Ypres Castle Inn 🄻
Gun Garden, TN31 7HH (accessed from A259 up a flight of steps; for fewer steps approach from Church Sq)
☎ (01797) 223248 🌐 yprescastleinn.co.uk
House beer (by Rother Valley); 3 changing beers (sourced locally) 🄷
An attractive weatherboarded pub, set just below the Rye Castle Museum and above the A259. The adjacent Gun Gardens give superb views across Romney Marsh, as do the outside drinking areas. There is one large bar with a log fire, and a smaller adjoining room. Quality bar snacks are offered alongside a simple menu centred

around gourmet sandwiches. The house beer from Rother Valley Brewery is Ypres Castle Bitter (ABV 3.8%). Real cider is from Nightingale's.

St Leonards on Sea

North Star Inn ✔

Clarence Road, Bohemia, TN37 6SD
☎ (01424) 436576
Harvey's Sussex Best Bitter; Timothy Taylor Landlord; 3 changing beers Ⓗ
Friendly local just off the main Bohemia Road. It has a large U-shaped bar and is decorated with railway memorabilia. The changing beers are both local and national. There is a meat raffle on Sunday, a cheese raffle on Saturday, a monthly bingo night and quiz night, and occasional live music. The pub has a pool table. A popular curry night is held on Wednesday; food is not available at other times. **Q**♣(99,100)

Tower

251 London Road, Bohemia, TN37 6NB
☎ (01424) 721773
Dark Star Hophead, American Pale Ale; 4 changing beers (sourced nationally) Ⓗ
Popular community pub with a lively, convivial atmosphere, offering six ales and up to seven ciders. All the main football, cricket and rugby matches are shown on HD screens. There is a pool table and wood-burning stove, and an annual beer festival is held in February. Occasional trips are arranged to breweries and sporting events. Local CAMRA branch Pub of the Year in 2019.
♣

Salehurst

Salehurst Halt 🄻

Church Lane, TN32 5PH (by church)
☎ (01580) 880620 🌐 salehursthalt.co.uk
Harvey's Sussex Best Bitter; 2 changing beers (sourced locally) Ⓗ
This delightful community village pub welcomes locals and visitors alike. Established in 1867, it was saved from closure by local families some years ago. Three real ales and a local cider are normally on offer, together with a varied menu of excellent fresh home-cooked food (booking advisable). Pizza is cooked on an outdoor wood-fired oven every Wednesday in summer. Upstairs is a function room for up to 20 people. The lovely garden has views over the tranquil Rother Valley.
Q♣

Seaford

Old Boot Inn 🄻

16 South Street, BN25 1PE
☎ (01323) 895454
Harvey's Sussex Best Bitter; 4 changing beers (sourced regionally; often Dark Star, Pitchfork, Thornbridge) Ⓗ
A deceptively large pub, under the same ownership as the Gardener's Arms in Lewes, with entrances in both South Street and High Street. There are plenty of tables and good food is served, with a variety of roasts on Sunday. Harvey's Best is always to be found on one of the six handpumps, along with Old Ale in season. Four changing guests and six bag-in-box ciders complete the range. Wheelchair access is possible.

Steamworks 🄻

Cafe Unit, Seaford Station, Station Approach, BN25 2AR
☎ 07541 858996
3 changing beers (sourced locally; often 360 Degree, Bedlam, Downlands) Ⓖ
Situated on the station platform, Steamworks is a two-room buffet bar that is busy early in the morning serving coffee to commuters, then becomes a micropub offering three interesting beers dispensed via an unusual gravity system. The decor and furniture is distressed industrial-style sanded-down woodwork. The toilet is down the platform, with the key hanging left of the door. Food is pasties. **Q**

Uckfield

Alma Arms 🄻 ✔

65 Framfield Road, TN22 5AJ (on B2102 from jct with High St)
☎ (01825) 762232 🌐 almaarmsuckfield.co.uk
Harvey's Dark Mild, Sussex Best Bitter; 2 changing beers (often Harvey's) Ⓗ
Within 10 minutes' walk of the railway and bus stations, this traditional town-centre pub has two separate bars and a large function room with its own facilities. The Alma dates from 1851 and was named after the 1854 Crimean battle. Westons Family Reserve is the regular draught cider. A quiz is held every Thursday and various other events take place from time to time. No food is served on Monday or Tuesday.
Q♣**P**(31)

SUSSEX (WEST)

Amberley

Bridge Inn 🄻 ✔

Houghton Bridge, BN18 9LR (on B2139 just W of railway bridge at Amberley station)
☎ (01798) 831619 🌐 bridgeinnamberley.com
Harvey's Sussex Best Bitter; Long Man Long Blonde; 1 changing beer (sourced nationally; often Timothy Taylor) Ⓗ
Close to Amberley Working Museum and Heritage Centre, the South Downs Way and the local station, this Grade II listed inn serves three real ales. Inside are a single cosy bar, open log fires in winter and a large dining area to the side, serving mainly locally sourced home-cooked produce. There is a patio at the front and an attractive gated beer garden. **Q****P**(73)

Balcombe

Half Moon

Haywards Heath Road, RH17 6PA
☎ (01444) 811582
Harvey's Sussex Best Bitter; 2 changing beers (sourced locally; often Dark Star, High Weald, Long Man) Ⓗ
A small pub with tables in the lower part as you enter, and the bar beyond up a couple of steps. The venue is food led. This is north Sussex's first community-owned establishment, with four handpumps. One normally has Harvey's Sussex Best, another a beer from High Weald, and the other two dispense rotating guests, which are mainly local. The pub also serves a varied range of locally sourced meals. **P**

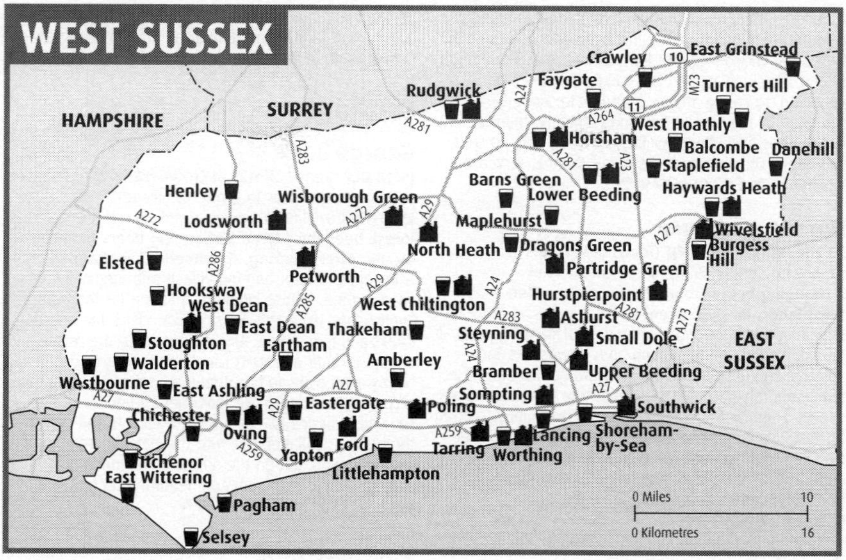

Barns Green

Queen's Head 𝕃

Chapel Road, RH13 0PS

☎ (01403) 730436

Fuller's London Pride; Long Man Best Bitter; 2 changing beers (sourced regionally) Ⓗ

A cosy 17th-century village pub, with old timber beams and a large inglenook fireplace used in winter. It is mainly open plan, with three seating areas and a small separate room. A garden with a covered seating area is at the back. There is a quiz night on the second Tuesday of the month, an open mic night on the first Thursday of the month, and a charity coffee morning on the last Friday of the month. Q ÅP

Bramber

Castle Inn Hotel 𝕃

The Street, BN44 3WE (just off A283, near S Steyning roundabout)

☎ (01903) 812102 🌐 castleinnhotel.co.uk

Downlands Bramber; Harvey's Sussex Best Bitter; Sharp's Doom Bar; 1 changing beer (sourced locally; often Dark Star, Riverside) Ⓗ

Set in a rural Sussex village, this historic inn has been called the Castle Inn Hotel since Victorian times, and there has been a coaching house or inn on the site since the early 13th century. The oldest part of the current building dates back to the 17th century. It is a family-run free house and 3-star B&B with good food and local ales on offer. There is a picturesque garden at the rear with a stream flowing through it. Q &P

Burgess Hill

Quench Bar & Kitchen 𝕃

2-4 Church Road, RH15 9AE

☎ (01444) 253332 🌐 quenchbar.co.uk

Harvey's Sussex Best Bitter; 2 changing beers (sourced regionally) Ⓗ

Close to the railway station and bus stops, this venue is at the top end of the town's original shopping street. It comprises a bar area together with a comfortable lounge. In addition to cask beers there is a varied range of bottled beers, spirits, teas and espresso coffees. There are old clocks above the bar and a display case of old cameras in the lounge. A limited number of tables and chairs is provided outside.

Chichester

Chichester Inn 𝕃

38 West Street, PO19 1RP (at Westgate roundabout)

☎ (01243) 783185 🌐 chichesterinn.co.uk

Harvey's Sussex Best Bitter; 3 changing beers (sourced regionally; often Bedlam, Vibrant Forest) Ⓗ

Pleasant two-bar pub with a real fire in the front bar surrounded by comfortable chairs, with a mix of seating and table types elsewhere. The larger public bar to the rear features regular live music on Wednesday, Friday and Saturday evenings. Outside is an attractive walled garden with a heated and covered smoking area. Four B&B rooms are available. Food includes Sunday lunches. There is a strong emphasis on LocAles.

♣P

Eastgate ✓

4 The Hornet, PO19 7JG (500yds E of Market Cross)

☎ (01243) 774877 🌐 eastgatechichester.co.uk

Dark Star Hophead; Fuller's London Pride; Gale's Seafarers Ale, HSB; 1 changing beer (sourced nationally; often Dark Star, Fuller's) Ⓗ

Welcoming town venue with an open-plan bar and tables for diners. Good-quality traditional pub meals are served daily. There is a heated patio garden to the rear, which is the venue for a beer festival in July. The pub attracts locals, holidaymakers and shoppers from the nearby market, with a warm welcome and traditional games such as darts, cribbage and pool. Music is turned up on Friday and Saturday late evenings. Live bands perform once a month. ♣(51,700)

Hole in the Wall

1A St Martins Street, PO19 1NP (just off East St, almost opp back door to Marks & Spencer)

☎ (01243) 788877 🌐 theholeinthewall-pub.co.uk

Big Smoke Solaris Session Pale Ale; 7 changing beers (sourced nationally; often Bristol Beer Factory, Gun, Harvey's) Ⓗ

A building that is believed to have started as an 18th-century debtors' prison and has been knocked through, so the bar wraps round to form three areas. The interior features brick pillars and half-height painted wood panelling, to create a cosy, friendly atmosphere. Operated by Big Smoke Brewing Company, there are 12 handpumps, including four for real cider, plus 20 craft keg beers. Quiz night is on Sunday. Food is served from lunchtime.

Hornet Alehouse

23 The Hornet, PO19 7JL (from market cross head due E)
(01243) 696387 thehornetalehouse.co.uk
5 changing beers (sourced nationally; often Downlands, Elusive, Siren) G
Busy split-level micropub with plenty of standing room at the bar in addition to seating both downstairs and upstairs. The upstairs room has board games and hosts twice-monthly quiz nights and monthly Meet the Brewer events. Friendly, knowledgeable staff are happy to offer tasters. Four ciders are always on sale as well as four craft keg taps. This pub is a wonderful addition to the city and a mecca for a changing range of cask ales served from a temperature-controlled cool room.
Q (700)

Crawley

Brewery Shades

85 High Street, RH10 1BA
(01293) 514255
Dark Star Revelation; Greene King Abbot; 8 changing beers H
Possibly the oldest building in Crawley High Street, the pub dates back to the 1400s and comes complete with two active ghosts. It is is wet-sales led. The licensee has a true passion for the trade, demonstrated by the inspired range of guest ales and ciders which are always in excellent condition. The haunted upstairs room is now available for meetings. Good food is served during the day and evening – check the specials board.

Danehill

Coach & Horses

School Lane, RH17 7JF
(01825) 740369 coachandhorses.co
Harvey's Sussex Best Bitter; 1 changing beer (sourced locally; often 360 Degree, Cellar Head, Franklins) H
A traditional country pub dating from 1847 and retaining many original features. The public and saloon bars have real fires and simple farmhouse-style furniture. Locally produced Black Pig cider is always on the bar, and occasionally its perry too. The separate restaurant area serves locally sourced, high-quality food. The large garden is a delight in summer and includes a children's play area. Q P (270)

Dragons Green

George & Dragon

Dragons Lane, RH13 8GE
(01403) 741320 thegeorgeanddragon.pub
Harvey's Sussex Best Bitter; Skinner's Betty Stogs; 1 changing beer (sourced locally; often Greyhound) H
Set in a tiny hamlet in the beautiful Sussex countryside near Shipley, the 16th-century George & Dragon, with its low beams and an inglenook fireplace, has greeted locals and travellers for over 200 years. A hidden gem, secluded and peaceful, it has a large garden and a children's play area. Recently renovated, it offers the best in traditional hospitality, combining excellent home-cooked pub food with a fine array of beers and wines.
Q P

Eartham

George

PO18 0LT (turn N off A27 at Crockerhill or W of Fontwell and proceed 2 miles to centre of village)
(01243) 814340 thegeorgeeartham.com
House beer (by Otter); 3 changing beers (sourced locally; often Dorking, Greyhound, Langham) H
A tastefully refurbished old village pub, originally a coaching inn, whose landlord's passion for the best of English, and especially Sussex, extends to the entire drinks and food menu. All changing beers are LocAle and always include one from Langham. Usually one is a hoppy golden ale and another is a porter, old ale or mild, according to season. The food menu features locally sourced ingredients. Popular with walkers and cyclists, the pub has collaborated with the National Trust on a four-mile walk throgh the adjacent Slindon Woods. A beer festival is held each April featuring LocAles and live music. Q P (99)

East Ashling

Horse & Groom

PO18 9AX (on B2178 in village) SU820077
(01243) 575339
Dark Star Hophead; Hop Back Summer Lightning; Young's London Original; 1 changing beer (sourced regionally; often Crafty Pint) H
Between the South Downs and the sea, and an inn for over 200 years, this fine country free house has a compact bar featuring flagstones, settles, half-panelled walls and a fine old range. Sympathetically extended and recently thoroughly renovated, it remains unspoilt. The beers are meticulously presented. A blackboard reveals the diverse, high-quality menu of hearty home-made dishes, all sourced locally (with roasts at Sunday

REAL ALE BREWERIES

81 Artisan West Dean
Adur Steyning
Arundel Ford
Brew Studio Sompting
Brewhouse & Kitchen Horsham
Brolly Wisborough Green
Chapeau Horsham
Dark Star Partridge Green
Downlands Small Dole
Firebird Rudgwick
Goldmark Poling
Greyhound West Chiltington
Gribble Oving
Hairy Dog Wivelsfield (NEW)
Heathen Haywards Heath
Hepworth North Heath
Hurst Hurstpierpoint
Kissingate Lower Beeding
Langham Lodsworth
Lister's Ford
Pin-Up Southwick
Polarity Worthing
Ridgeway North Heath
Riverside Upper Beeding
Top-Notch Haywards Heath
Vine Tarring (NEW)
Weltons Horsham
Wingtip Ashurst (NEW)

lunchtime). En-suite accommodation is dog-friendly, some in a converted 17th-century oak-beamed flint barn. Q❀🛏◐♿⛺♣P🚌(54)🐾📶

East Dean

Star & Garter 🄻 ✔

PO18 0JG (eastern end of village green)
☎ (01243) 811318 🌐 thestarandgarter.co.uk
Sharp's Doom Bar; 2 changing beers (sourced regionally) 🄶
An 18th-century free house situated by the duck pond in this charming downland village. The pub is renowned for good food, served in a dining area in the large bar. The menu features local seasonal produce, with fresh seafood a speciality (Sunday lunchtime booking essential). Beer is poured straight from the cask from a cold room behind the bar. There is a large walled garden to the rear which can host functions. ❀🛏◐♿P🐾📶

East Grinstead

Engine Room 🄻

The Old Mill, 45 London Road, RH19 1AW
☎ (01342) 327145
5 changing beers (sourced locally; often High Weald, Long Man, Titsey) 🄶
A bar operating as the brewery tap for High Weald, up a path between the shops close to Whitehall bus stop in London Road. The pub is a downstairs labyrinth of small seating areas, good for small groups to hold conversations. There is live music on Thursday evening; other attractions include a dartboard and a selection of board games. All real ales here are on gravity. Due to the downstairs location, access is not wheelchair-friendly. Q≠🍏🚌📶

Old Dunnings Mill ✔

Dunnings Road, RH19 4AT
☎ (01342) 821080 🌐 olddunningsmill.co.uk
Harvey's Sussex Best Bitter; 4 changing beers (often Harvey's) 🄷
This large pub on the edge of town is based in an old water mill. Separate bar and restaurant areas are on various levels but the main areas are wheelchair-friendly. A heated, covered area to the rear has a working water wheel. Two beer festivals a year are planned. The bar is basically a quiet place, although music plays on appropriate occasions. Families and pets are welcome. Q❀◐♿P🚌(84)🐾

East Wittering

Shore 🄻

Shore Road, PO20 8DZ (50yds from sea)
☎ (01243) 674454 🌐 theshorepub.co.uk
Hop Back Summer Lightning; Langham Hip Hop; Palmers Copper Ale, Dorset Gold; Sharp's Doom Bar; 1 changing beer (sourced regionally) 🄷
Friendly beachside pub popular with the locals (particularly dog owners) and the many summer visitors. Outside seating affords splendid sea views. There are two main bars selling good-value beers, a children's area and a fair-sized space for outside drinking as well as smoking. The good-quality lunchtime menu can be enjoyed either in the bar or restaurant, where extremely inviting dishes are on offer at fair prices (displayed on a blackboard). Occasional live music is hosted – see website for details. Q❀◐♿♣P🚌(52,53)🐾

Eastergate

Wilkes' Head 🄻 ✔

Church Lane, PO20 3UT (off A29 in old village, 350yds S of B2233 roundabout, 1⅓ miles W of Barnham station) SU943053
☎ (01243) 543380
Adnams Southwold Bitter; 5 changing beers (sourced nationally; often Bedlam, Downlands, Langham) 🄷
Small Grade II listed red-brick pub, built in 1803 and named after the 18th-century radical John Wilkes. There is a cosy lounge left of the central bar, and to the right a larger room with an inglenook fireplace, flagstones and low beams, plus a separate restaurant. At the rear is a permanent marquee with seating plus a heated smokers' shelter and a large garden. There are five well-chosen changing beers, and regular beer festivals are held. Q❀◐♿♣🍏P🚌🐾📶

Elsted

Elsted Inn

Elsted Road, Elsted Marsh, GU29 0JT (2 miles S of A272 between Midhurst and Petersfield) SU834206
☎ (01730) 813662 🌐 theelstedinn.com
3 changing beers (sourced nationally; often Bowman, Courage, Otter) 🄷
Elsted, or Halesteed in the Domesday Book, means the place where elder grows. Today this Victorian pub, built originally to cater for Elsted station on the Petersfield-Midhurst branch railway, is surrounded by the glorious countryside of the South Downs. In addition to the bar and restaurant, the pub has four en-suite rooms in a detached coach house alongside, at one time the home of Ballard's Brewery. At least three changing beers are usually sold, of which one is likely to be local. No food Sunday evening. Q❀🛏◐P🚌(91,92)🐾📶

Three Horseshoes

GU29 0JY (at E end of village)
☎ (01730) 825746 🌐 3hs.co.uk
Bowman Wallops Wood; Flower Pots Bitter; Young's London Original; 2 changing beers (sourced locally; often Hop Back, Langham, Red Cat) 🄶
Old and cosy rural inn divided into small rooms, including one reserved for dining and one with a blazing wood-burning stove in winter. Outside, the large, pleasant garden enjoys superb views of the South Downs. In summer there are five beers (mainly from local micros), and three in winter, all served by gravity from a stillage alongside the bar. Meals are substantial and of high quality. This is a popular and homely pub that you will be reluctant to leave. Q❀◐♣P🐾

Faygate

Frog & Nightgown 🄻

Wimland Road, RH12 4SS
☎ (01293) 852764 🌐 thefrogandnightgown.co.uk
Fuller's London Pride; 3 changing beers (sourced regionally; often Dark Star, Harvey's) 🄷
Vibrant pub that was comprehensively refurbished after changing hands in 2015. Regular events include quiz nights, classic car meets, live music, and open mic nights. Street food is often available on a Friday night. It is known as the fastest pub in West Sussex due to its motorsport connections. Q❀◐P🚌🐾📶

Haywards Heath

Lockhart Tavern 🄻

41 The Broadway, RH16 3AS

☎ (01444) 440696 🌐 thelockharttavern.co.uk
6 changing beers (sourced nationally; often Franklins, Heathen) Ⓗ
This often popular, centrally located free house is a conversion of a retail premises. It has two distinct areas – drinkers are catered for at the front with high tables and matching seating, and towards the rear there is a wood-panelled dining area. There are also picnic tables outside on the patio. Good food is served lunchtimes and evenings, with regular menu changes. The pub also offers a choice of wines, spirits, keg, canned and bottled beers. Q❀◐◑⇌🚌🐾📶

Henley

Duke of Cumberland 🄻
Henley Village, GU27 3HQ (off A286, 2 miles N of Midhurst) SU894258
☎ (01428) 652280 🌐 dukeofcumberland.com
Harvey's Sussex Best Bitter; Langham Hip Hop; Timothy Taylor Landlord; 1 changing beer (sourced locally; often Langham) Ⓖ
Stunning 15th-century inn nestling against the hillside in over three acres of terraced gardens with extensive views. The rustic front bar has scrubbed-top tables and benches, plus log fires at both ends; to the rear is a dining extension that blends in perfectly with the original pub and offers much-needed additional space. Outside is a smokers' shelter with its own wood-burner. A former local CAMRA Pub of the Year, this is a rural gem. May close winter Sunday evenings. Q❀◐◑♣P🚌(70)🐾📶

Hookswa y

Royal Oak
PO18 9JZ SU815163
☎ (01243) 535257 🌐 royaloakhooksway.co.uk
Langham Hip Hop; 3 changing beers (sourced nationally; often Hepworth, Langham) Ⓗ
An idyllic country pub, unspoilt and with great country walks, close to the South Downs Way. Popular with hikers, horseriders and people with young families, the pub has a large garden with a play area for children and is perfect for getting away from it all. In winter two lovely log fires greet you. There is an extensive menu catering for all tastes, including a varied children's menu. Also on offer are three permanent real ales and a regular guest, mainly from local breweries. Q❀◐◑P🐾

Horsham

Anchor Tap 🏆 🄻
16 East Street, RH12 1HL
☎ (01403) 713085
6 changing beers (sourced nationally) Ⓗ
Now free of tie, this popular pub continues to offer customers an eclectic choice of brews. The knowledgeable team behind the bar source interesting beers both local and from afar. There are six handpumps in use, plus a back bar dispensing 10 keg beers. The pub regularly hosts tap takeovers – check the Facebook page for details and additional opening hours. Bar snacks are available lunchtimes. 🐎♿⇌♣🚌🐾📶

King's Arms 🄻
64 Bishopric, RH12 1QN
☎ (01403) 451468 🌐 kingsarmshorsham.godaddysites.com
St Austell Tribute; 3 changing beers (sourced locally; often Chapeau, Hepworth, Weltons) Ⓗ
Near the town centre, this 18th-century coaching inn is close to the site of the former King & Barnes Brewery. A comfortable two-bar pub, it has long been popular with locals, and shows sports on TV at the weekend. There are five handpulls with at least three rotating local ales, and also a keg line that serves Brolly ale. ❀◐◑🚌📶

Malt Shovel 🄻
15 Springfield Road, RH12 2PG
☎ (01403) 252302
Surrey Hills Shere Drop; 4 changing beers (sourced regionally) Ⓗ
Close to the town centre, the pub has six handpumps on year round, plus two ciders and a mix of bottles and canned ales. It doesn't stock any regular ales, but has a focus on local beers and usually offers at least one dark ale. There is live music every Saturday night, as well as regular open mic and jam events. The landlord and his friendly staff takes great pride in the real ale. There is good parking for a town-centre pub. ❀◐♿♣●P🚌🐾📶

Piries Bar 🄻
Piries Alley, The Carfax, RH12 1NY
☎ (01403) 267846
Gun Scaramanga Extra Pale; Timothy Taylor Landlord; 1 changing beer (sourced locally; often Gun) Ⓗ
In a building dating from the 15th century with exposed original timber beams, the pub is tucked away down a narrow alley adjoining Horsham's Carfax. It comprises a small downstairs room, an upstairs lounge bar, and a small modern extension in character with the building. Regular charity events are organised. Evenings here can be lively, with karaoke on Sundays, quiz nights on Tuesdays and occasional live music. With two cask ales always on the go, this bar is well worth a visit.
🐎◐⇌🚌🐾📶

Itchenor

Ship
The Street, PO20 7AH (on main street, 100yds from waterfront)
☎ (01243) 512284 🌐 theshipinnitchenor.co.uk
Arundel Castle; Langham Hip Hop, Best; 1 changing beer (often Itchen Valley) Ⓗ
A popular hostelry in the main street of an attractive village on the shore of picturesque Chichester harbour. The cosy bar decorated with yachting memorabilia adds to the pub's character and is complemented by a pleasant patio, a suntrap in summer. The separate restaurant area offers a wide range, including local seafood. Accommodation is available in a two-bedroom apartment and a three-bedroom cottage.
Q🐎❀🛏◐◑♿♣P🐾📶

Lancing

Stanley Ale House 🄻
5 Queensway, BN15 9AY (200yds N of Lancing railway station)
☎ (01903) 366820 🌐 thestanleyalehouse.com
Langham Arapaho; 3 changing beers (sourced regionally; often Downlands, Franklins) Ⓗ
This former launderette opened as a family-run micropub/ale house in 2014. It is near local shops, and offers several changing ales, plus cider, wine and gin. The owners have listened to customers so now have both keg and cask beers. There is ample seating inside and out. Bar snacks are served. A weekly quiz, regular music nights, a takeaway night and other events are hosted, and a variety of board games is available.
Q🐎◑♿⇌♣●🚌🐾📶

Littlehampton

George Inn

14-18 Surrey Street, BN17 5BG (a five-minute walk E from station, close to pedestrianised area)
☎ (01903) 739863
Greene King IPA, Abbot; Sharp's Doom Bar; 7 changing beers (sourced locally; often Marston's, Shepherd Neame, Wychwood) H
Large town-centre pub named after an old inn nearby. Pictures of old Littlehampton adorn the walls inside, evoking memories of a past era. There is a variety of comfy seating in the two main areas; some of it is partitioned. Outside is a patio area for drinking. Eight handpumps serve ales from around the country including from local breweries. The normal range of Wetherspoon food and drinks is available.

New Inn

5 Norfolk Road, BN17 5PL (N from Sea Road)
☎ (01903) 713112
3 changing beers (sourced nationally) H
Friendly community pub offering three regularly changing ales, just a short walk from the beach. This traditional inn has two bar areas. The front bar has ample seating, a real fire and hosts weekly quizzes and regular charity events; the rear bar has a pool table and dartboard, and shows live sport. A free jukebox is a feature of Monday nights. There is a heated courtyard at the back.

Steam Packet

54 River Road, BN17 5BZ
☎ (01903) 715994 the-steam-packet.com
Fallen Acorn Pompey Royal; 3 changing beers (sourced locally; often Bedlam, Franklins, Vibrant Forest) H
One-bar pub with a pleasing, light seating area that makes good use of the available floor space. It overlooks the harbour, is near the river footbridge, and is a short distance from where a cross-Channel steam packet ferry service once operated from Littlehampton to Honfleur. All ales are from independent microbreweries, mainly locally sourced. Real ciders and craft beer in cans are on sale. Fresh food is prepared on the premises, with vegetarian, vegan and allergies catered for.
(700)

Lower Beeding

Kissingate Brewery

Pole Barn, Church Lane Farm Estate, Church Lane, RH13 6LU
☎ (01403) 891335 kissingate.co.uk
Kissingate Black Cherry Mild, Pernickety Pale, Chennai, Powder Blue; 2 changing beers (sourced locally) G
This is the taproom for the renowned Kissingate Brewery. You will find a selection of beers from the Kissingate range served on gravity, plus cider and perry from Black Pig and JB cider. On the last Friday of the month the bar opens later into the evening. Events including curry nights are held, and there is a function area upstairs.

Maplehurst

White Horse

Park Lane, RH13 6LL
☎ (01403) 891208 whitehorsemaplehurst.co.uk
Weltons Pride 'n' Joy; 4 changing beers (often Harvey's, Hepworth, Kissingate) H
Under the same ownership for 38 years, this splendid and welcoming country pub has featured in the Guide 35 times, and is popular with locals, cyclists and walkers. The cosy interior, with its unusually wide wooden bar, boasts real fires and many interesting artefacts and bric-a-brac. Good honest fare is provided, with the emphasis on beer and conversation. Many local ales feature, with a good selection of dark brews. Local JB cider is also available. QP

Oving

Gribble Inn

Gribble Lane, PO20 2BP (at W end of village)
☎ (01243) 786893 gribbleinn.co.uk
Gribble Flint's Full Glory, Ale, Fuzzy Duck, Reg's Tipple, Pig's Ear, Wobbler; 1 changing beer (often Gribble) H
Once home to a Miss Gribble, this attractive thatched cottage has been a traditional village pub for over 30 years and shares the premises with the Gribble Brewery. The full range of regular Gribble beers, complemented by seasonals, is always on the bar. The pub is cosy, with log fires in winter, and home-made food is served in the bar and restaurant. In summer a large attractive garden offers occasional weekend barbecues. The skittle alley is also available for functions.
QP (85,85A)

Pagham

Inglenook

255 Pagham Road, PO21 3QB
☎ (01243) 262495 the-inglenook.com
Fuller's London Pride; Young's London Special; 4 changing beers (sourced nationally; often Brighton Bier, Dark Star, Vibrant Forest) H
A 16th-century Grade II listed hotel, restaurant and free house, owned and run by the same family for over 40 years. There is always a selection of excellent well-hopped real ales on offer from highly regarded microbreweries, alongside local real ciders. The cosy bar areas have real fires and there is a large garden to the rear and a patio at the front.
QP (600)

Rudgwick

King's Head

Church Street, RH12 3EB
☎ (01403) 822200 kingsheadrudgwick.co.uk
Crafty Brewing Crafty One; 2 changing beers (often Harvey's, Morland) H
This 18th-century low-beamed pub can be found at the northern end of the village. It is opposite the Norman church and in a conservation area. There is a bar with a wood-burning stove and leather sofas at one end and a restaurant at the other. Food is freshly prepared for the Italian menu. The Downslink footpath passes nearby.
QP

Selsey

Crab Pot

153 High Street, PO20 0QB
☎ 07834 226751 crabpotmicropub.co.uk
3 changing beers (sourced regionally)
After two years in a former tea shop, the popular Crab Pot has moved down the street to larger premises, where a bigger cool room allows a wide range of real ciders to complement the three changing real ales. One of these is often from Brew Studio. The mixture of high

and low seating makes for a relaxed and friendly atmosphere; a warm welcome is assured for visitors and locals alike. There is a function room behind the bar where televised sport – especially rugby – can be watched. ⛺♣●▯🚌(51)🐾📶

Shoreham-by-Sea

Duke of Wellington 🏆 L

368 Brighton Road, BN43 6RE (on A259)
☎ (01273) 441297 🌐 dukeofwellingtonbrewhouse.co.uk/home
7 changing beers (sourced regionally) H
A place of contrasts: on some nights this former Dark Star pub is a quiet drinking emporium, on others it is packed to the gills with a ukulele band, the Wellington Wailers, or a local group. What is consistent is the beer quality and range. The original brewer has a small shrine of certificates together with copies of all the CAMRA Guides in a display case. There are original Kemp Town Brewery windows. 🐴❀⇌♣●🚌(2,700)🐾📶

Old Star Ale & Cider House L

Church Street, BN43 5DQ
☎ 07938 407320 🌐 oldstarshoreham.co.uk
3 changing beers (sourced regionally; often Brighton Bier, Burning Sky, Gun) G
This well-run micropub is just off the High Street. Three beers are served through the week with up to five on Saturday, almost always including one dark beer, sourced mainly from Sussex microbreweries, and poured direct from the casks on stillage behind the bar. There is also a range of real and craft ciders and perries. A cider festival is held over the autumn bank holiday. A complimentary cheese board is on offer every Saturday early evening. Q⇌♣●🚌(2,700)🐾📶

Staplefield

Jolly Tanners L ✔

Handcross Road, RH17 6EF
☎ (01444) 400335 🌐 jollytanners.com
Fuller's London Pride; Harvey's Sussex Best Bitter; 4 changing beers (sourced locally; often Dark Star, Tring, Wimbledon) H
On the north corner of the village green, this welcoming venue combines all the best elements of a village inn. The spacious bar is divided into two distinct areas, with two log fires adding to the cosy feel. There is an extensive range of guest beers, always including a mild, and real cider is also sold. A good range of tasty food is served at all sessions. This is a friendly place and still very much a locals' pub. Q🐴❀◐♿⛺♣●P🚌(271)🐾📶

Stoughton

Hare & Hounds L

PO18 9JQ (off B2146, through Walderton) SU803115
☎ (023) 9263 1433 🌐 hareandhoundspub.co.uk
Dark Star Hophead; Long Man Best Bitter; Otter Amber; 2 changing beers (sourced locally; often Fallen Acorn) H
Traditional country pub in a beautiful setting that makes it an ideal base for walking. The large dining room serves fresh local produce in comfortable surroundings, with an open fire in winter. A separate public bar has pictures of vintage racing cars and its own open fire, which attracts locals. The fires, stone-flagged floors and simple furniture create a wonderful atmosphere. Outside, the paved patio area complements a rear garden for dining and drinking. Two ciders are sold. Q❀◐♣●P🐾📶

Thakeham

White Lion Inn

The Street, RH20 3EP (300yds N of village, on B2139, turn right)
☎ (01798) 813141 🌐 whitelion-thakeham.co.uk
Harvey's Sussex Best Bitter; St Austell Tribute; 2 changing beers (sourced nationally; often Greyhound) H
A 16th-century inn, north of the village in the atmospheric conservation area. Stone steps lead up to the door, and inside is a delightful country pub interior, with an ornamental white lion on the bar. There are three separate bar areas and a room that doubles as a function room or restaurant. The pub is renowned for its food (no food Sun eve), with one of the fireplaces used to smoke local ham. It has a large south-facing patio and garden. Q❀◐●P🚌(72)🐾📶

Turners Hill

Red Lion L ✔

Lion Lane, RH10 4NU
☎ (01342) 715416 🌐 redlionturnershill.com
Harvey's Dark Mild, IPA, Sussex Best Bitter, Armada Ale; 2 changing beers (sourced locally; often Harvey's) H
A regular entry in the Guide, this place is still very much a village local, offering a warm welcome to all who enter. It has a split-level layout and features a large inglenook fireplace. Good-value and high-quality food is served lunchtimes (but not Thu). There is a popular fortnightly quiz on a Wednesday. The local CAMRA branch held its first meeting here in 1974. Children and dogs are welcome in the pub, and newspapers are available for customers. Q🐴❀◐♿♣P🚌(84,272)🐾📶

Walderton

Barley Mow

Breakneck Lane, PO18 9ED
☎ (023) 9263 1321 🌐 thebarleymow.pub
Dark Star Hophead; Harvey's Sussex Best Bitter; Otter Amber; Ringwood Fortyniner; 1 changing beer (sourced locally; often Harvey's) H
An attractive free house in the centre of this picturesque village, popular with walkers and visitors to the South Downs National Park. Much of this cosy, traditional pub caters for diners, but drinkers are most welcome in the large bar area. There are log fires in winter and the pretty garden alongside the River Ems is popular in summer. Five handpumps are usually in use, featuring two beers from Harvey's. The skittle alley can double as a function room. Q🐴❀◐♿P🚌(54)🐾📶

West Chiltington

Five Bells L

Smock Alley, RH20 2QX (approx 1 mile S of old village centre) TQ092171
☎ (01798) 812143 🌐 thefivebellsinn.com
5 changing beers (sourced nationally; often Harvey's, Jennings, Palmers) H
This friendly village free house is a Guide regular. Dating from 1935, the former King & Barnes outlet has been run by the same couple since 1983. Five handpumps are on what is probably Sussex's longest copper-top counter. Local and regional ales are served – one is usually a dark ale. There is also a large copper-hooded open fire. Locally sourced home-cooked food is served in the bar and large conservatory (not Sun eve). CAMRA branch Country Pub of the Year 2018. Q❀🛏◐●P🚌(1,74)🐾📶

West Hoathly

Cat

Queen's Square, North Lane, RH19 4PP
☎ (01342) 810369 🌐 catinn.co.uk
Firebird Parody; Harvey's Sussex Best Bitter; Larkins Traditional Ale; 2 changing beers (often Bedlam, Dark Star, Harvey's) H
Set in a picturesque hilltop village in the heart of the Sussex countryside, this 16th-century free house is within reach of several attractions. It retains oak beams and two inglenook fireplaces. There is an outside terrace, where food and drink can be consumed in the summer months. Five local ales are on the bar and good-quality food is cooked to order, using mostly local suppliers. This cosy pub has four letting rooms.
Q P (84)

Westbourne

Cricketers

Commonside, PO10 8TA
☎ (01243) 372647
Flack Manor Flack's Double Drop; Flower Pots Bitter; Greene King London Glory; 2 changing beers (sourced locally; often Itchen Valley, Langham) H
This 300-year-old local is the only true free house in the village. Situated on the northern outskirts, it is hard to find but well worth the effort. Conversation abounds in the single L-shaped, half-panelled bar. There is a suntrap garden to the side with a covered and heated smoking area. Up to two guest beers come from mainly Hampshire and Sussex micros. The beer range may vary a little. Q P

Worthing

Anchored in Worthing

27 West Buildings, BN11 3BS (close to seafront)
☎ (01903) 529100 🌐 anchoredinworthing.co.uk
3 changing beers (sourced locally; often Gun, Hand, Rother Valley) G
Look for the Tardis-style entrance to Sussex's original micropub, where you are assured of a warm welcome. High wooden tables are arranged to encourage conversation between customers. The ceiling is decorated with small wooden anchors as well as being adorned with pumpclips of the ales sold since opening. The walls have maps showing breweries and micropubs, plus CAMRA and local event information. All ale, cider, wine, gin and soft drinks sold are from Sussex producers. A free cheeseboard is offered on Sunday. Q

Brooksteed Alehouse

38 South Farm Road, BN14 7AE (100yds N of South Farm Rd level crossing, 5 mins' walk from Central station)
☎ 07484 840103 🌐 brooksteedalehouse.co.uk
House beer (by Arundel); 4 changing beers (sourced nationally; often Goldmark, Gun, North Riding Brewpub) G
Worthing's second micropub opened in 2014, with a change of ownership in 2017. It has a stylish and interesting decor, with high tables and comfortable seating inside, plus outside seating areas at the front and rear. With a strong community spirit, this popular pub organises events that include other local businesses. It has a good selection of regularly changing cask ales, KeyKeg and cider and perry from local and national brewers, plus a range of bottled beers, wines and gins. A cheeseboard is provided on Sunday.
Q P (16)

Corner House

80 High Street, BN11 1DJ (opp Waitrose)
☎ (01903) 216463 🌐 cornerhouseworthing.co.uk
4 changing beers (sourced regionally; often Goldmark, Harvey's, Shepherd Neame) H
The Corner House occupies a prominent position at the town centre's eastern edge. Originally called the Anchor, it dated back to 1805 and was one of Worthing's oldest pubs, but it was rebuilt in 1895. After several different names, it reopened as the Corner House in 2015 under new ownership, and quickly became popular. There is an emphasis on local suppliers for both food and drink, including for its Sunday roasts. The large heated beer garden is popular all year round.

Cricketers

66 Broadwater Street West, Broadwater, BN14 9DE (at S end of Broadwater Green on A24)
☎ (01903) 233369 🌐 cricketersworthing.co.uk
Fuller's London Pride; Greene King Abbot; Harvey's Sussex Best Bitter; Sharp's Atlantic; 2 changing beers H
A traditional inn close to Broadwater Green. A much older building dating from the 1700s was on the current site, and there has been a pub here since the 1800s. A single bar serves a number of rooms, including one where food is served, and there is a large beer garden and children's area. Ales are from local and national brewers, with changing guests. A popular beer festival in July coincides with the local carnival. P

Fox & Finch Alehouse

8 Littlehampton Road, BN13 1QE (on A259, N side of road, across from Thomas a Becket pub)
🌐 thefoxandfinch.co.uk
4 changing beers (often Arundel, Dark Star, Sussex Small Batch)
Worthing's fifth micropub opened in summer 2019 and quickly became popular. The building is decorated in a homely, traditional pub style with high and low tables and comfortable seating. The owners offer a warm welcome to all. A cold room behind the bar houses the ale served directly from the cask; the keg selection is from taps on the bar. There is a range of Belgian beers, fine wine and a small choice of spirits. Local CAMRA Pub of the Year 2020. (1)

Georgi Fin

54 Goring Road, BN12 4AD (on A259, N side in Goring Rd shops)
☎ (01903) 240933 🌐 thegeorgifin.co.uk
4 changing beers (sourced regionally; often Franklins, Gun, Thornbridge) G
This popular micropub opened in 2017. Named after the owner's children, it is in a busy shopping parade. It has a selection of high and low tables and seating. Unusually for a micropub, it has both ladies' and gents' toilets. The drinks are served from a purpose-built cold room and include ales from local and national brewers, traditional ciders, KeyKeg beers, and wines, plus a selection of English, Belgian and German bottled beers. There is a cheeseboard on Sundays. Q

Green Man Ale & Cider House

17 South Street, Tarring, BN14 7LG (40yds N of W Worthing railway crossing)
☎ 07984 793877
5 changing beers (sourced regionally; often Goldmark, Gun, Wantsum) G
Worthing's third micropub opened in 2016 in a former café. The temperature-controlled cellar is visible from the bar, which is furnished with high-level tables, benches and stools arranged to encourage chat. The place is

known for having a friendly atmosphere. Typically, it serves five gravity-dispensed ales, eight ciders and perries plus a whisky, a selection of gins, wines and soft drinks. CAMRA branch Pub of the Year and Cider Pub of the Year 2018 and 2019. Q⥆♣●🚌🐾

Old Bike Store 𝕃

65 Brighton Road, BN11 3EE

☎ (01903) 206311 🌐 theoldbikestore.co.uk

3 changing beers (sourced regionally; often Chapeau, Gun, Langham)

This small bar opened in a former bicycle shop, describing itself as a micropub since it has more keg than cask ale, but it fits the criteria in other respects. The interior decor has a bicycle theme, high and low tables, and comfortable chairs in a long, thin seating area. Typically, it dispenses three changing cask ales from local and national brewers, eight keg craft beers, three ciders, wines and gin. Pizza is available from a good takeaway to eat in the pub. ●🐾ᯤ

Park View

Salvington Road, BN13 2JR (corner of Salvington Rd and Durrington Lane)

☎ (01903) 521397 🌐 parkview-worthing.co.uk

Bath Ales Gem; 2 changing beers (sourced regionally; often Dark Star, St Austell) Ⓗ

Formerly the Lamb, the Park View reopened in 2018 as a community pub in the Durrington and Salvington area of Worthing. It has a sports bar showing live Sky Sports and BT Sport, an informal lounge bar and an extensive garden. A changing selection of real ales is on offer both from local and national breweries, along with good food. Regular events include a weekly quiz on Thursday and live music on Saturday nights. ❀◐♿♣🚌(5,6)🐾ᯤ

Parsonage Bar & Restaurant 𝕃 ✔

6-10 High Street, Tarring, BN14 7NN (at S end of Tarring High St – not to be confused with High St Worthing)

☎ (01903) 820140 🌐 theparsonage.co.uk

Burning Sky Plateau; Harvey's Sussex Best Bitter Ⓗ**; 2 changing beers (sourced locally; often Downlands, Harvey's, Lister's)** Ⓗ/Ⓖ

In the heart of Tarring village, this lovely Grade II listed 15th-century building was originally three cottages. It has been a quality restaurant since 1987 but the bar now has four well-kept local ales, two of which change regularly, always including a dark brew. Customers are welcome to drink without having a meal although the bar menu is good value. The courtyard garden is great for warmer weather. Q❀◐⥆🚌(6,16)🐾ᯤ

Selden Arms 𝕃

41 Lyndhurst Road, BN11 2DB (about 5 mins from centre of town and 2 mins from Worthing Hospital on Lyndhurst Rd)

☎ (01903) 523361 🌐 seldenarms.co.uk

6 changing beers (sourced nationally; often Burning Sky, Gun, Vibrant Forest) Ⓗ

This welcoming 19th-century free house has been in the Guide for 22 years. Six handpumps serve a changing selection of local and national ales, one of which is always a dark ale. There is also a choice of craft beers, both keg and in cans and bottles, plus an extensive range of bottled Belgian beers. A blackboard displays upcoming ales. Lunchtime food is served Monday to Saturday, with curry on Friday and Saturday evenings. An annual winter beer festival takes place in January. ◐♣●🚌🐾ᯤ

Yapton

Maypole 𝕃

Maypole Lane, BN18 0DP (off B2132 ½ mile N of village; pedestrian access across railway from Lake Lane, 1¼ miles E of Barnham station) SU978042

☎ (01243) 551417 🌐 themaypoleinnyapton.com

Bedlam Phoenix IPA; Lister's Best Bitter; 3 changing beers (sourced locally; often Bedlam, Cellar Head, Greyhound) Ⓗ

Small flint-built free house dating from about the 18th century, hidden away from the village centre, down a narrow lane ending in a pedestrian crossing over the railway. The cosy, often lively, lounge boasts a log-burner and a row of six handpumps dispensing beers from local micros. Real cider is served from the cellar. There is also a traditional public bar with pool and darts, plus a skittle alley/function room with bar billiards. Fresh filled rolls are on offer at lunchtimes.
Q❀◐♿⛺♣●P🚌🐾ᯤ

Albatross Club (RAFA), Bexhill on Sea, East Sussex (Photo: Peter Adams)

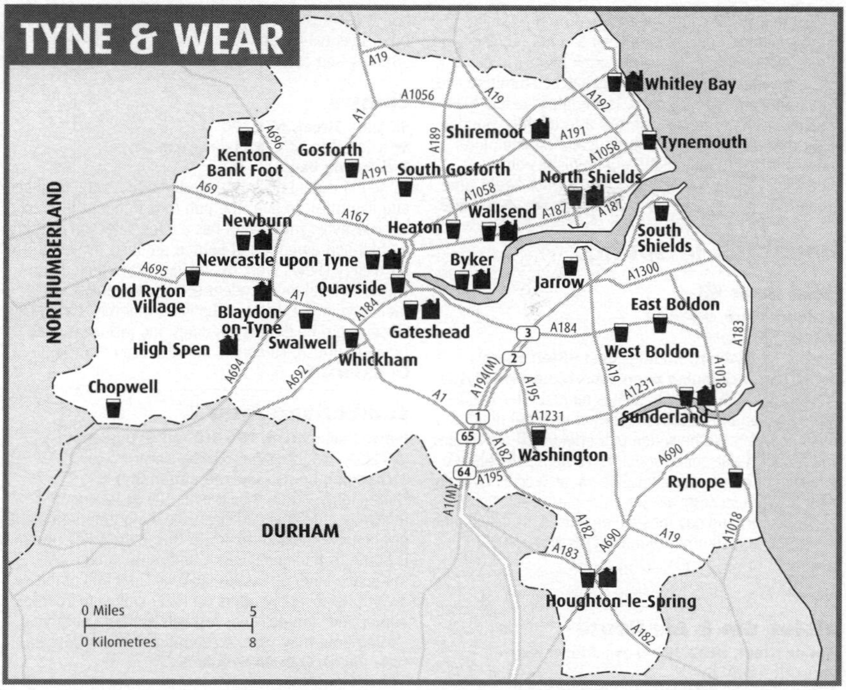

Chopwell

Red House

1 Millfield Terrace, NE17 7LL

☎ (01207) 560065 🌐 the-red-house-bar.business.site

3 changing beers (sourced nationally; often Great North Eastern) 🄷

This micropub is on the main street in the centre of the village and is a welcome addition to the real ale scene. Run by a fireman with a passion for real ales and ciders, the friendly community establishment is well worth a visit.

East Boldon

Grey Horse ✔

Front Street, NE36 0SJ

☎ (0191) 519 1796

6 changing beers (sourced nationally) 🄷

Distinctive mock-Tudor building with separate pleasant and comfortable lounge and bar areas and an upstairs function room. Up to six changing ales are available, from local and national breweries. Meals are served daily – Thursday is grill night. There are large-screen TVs in the bar for football and other sports. Quiz night is every Wednesday and the Boldon History Society meets on the last Tuesday of the month. Q♉❀◑♿♁P🚌🐾ᯤ

Gateshead

Old Fox 𝕃

10-14 Carlisle Street, Felling, NE10 0HQ

☎ (0191) 447 1980

5 changing beers (sourced nationally) 🄷

The Fox is a traditional community single-room pub with a roaring fire in the winter months, only a short walk from Felling Metro station. Ales are drawn both from national and local breweries. Snacks and Sunday lunches are available. There is live music over the weekend, and the dartboard is in frequent use. A friendly and welcoming pub with a beer garden at the rear. ♉❀≠♁♣🚌🐾ᯤ

Schooner 𝕃

South Shore Road, NE8 3AF (vehicular access only from E end of South Shore Rd)

☎ (0191) 477 7404 🌐 theschooner.co.uk

Rat White Rat; 5 changing beers (sourced nationally) 🄷

On the banks of the Tyne, the Schooner currently has six handpumps for cask ales and one for cask cider. The selection changes regularly to showcase the best local and national ales and ciders. Great-value home-cooked food is served throughout the week with traditional roasts on Sunday. Live music plays every Sunday afternoon, some Saturday nights, and on many other occasions. ♉❀◑♿♁♣●P🚌(93,94)🐾ᯤ

Station East 𝕃

Hills Street, NE8 2AS

☎ (0191) 435 3389

Hadrian Border Farne Island Pale Ale, Grainger Ale, Tyneside Blonde; 3 changing beers (sourced nationally; often Hadrian Border) 🄷

Occupying the site of the former Gateshead East Station and Railway Hotel, the building is now stripped back and enlarged with much structural work. Formerly a small pub, it is now open and spacious. There is a pleasant mezzanine floor above the main room and a further arched room to the rear below another railway bridge. A rear room is available for functions. Q♿♁🚌

Wheat Sheaf 𝕃

26 Carlisle Street, Felling, NE10 0HQ

☎ (0191) 597 2981

Big Lamp Bitter, Prince Bishop Ale, Sunny Daze; 1 changing beer (sourced locally) 🄷

Welcoming street-corner pub owned by Big Lamp Brewery and patronised by a loyal band of regulars who often travel quite a distance to drink here. The pub features some original details, mismatched furniture and, when needed, real coal fires. The outdoor toilets have original Victorian urinals. There is a fortnightly Monday night quiz, traditional folk music featuring keen local musicians on Tuesday night and dominoes on Wednesday night. An original CAMRA clock keeps time behind the bar. Snacks are available.

Houghton-le-Spring

Wild Boar

Frederick Place, DH4 4BN

(0191) 512 8050

Greene King Abbot; Ruddles Best Bitter; Sharp's Doom Bar; 4 changing beers (sourced nationally)

Previously a club, the Wild Boar is named after the Black Sabre boar on the crest of the former rector of Houghton. This open-plan Wetherspoon pub offers well-priced ales and a good-value food menu. Its 10 handpulls serve a selection of national and local beers, as well as two real ciders. Two beer festivals are held every year. Popular brewery visits and day trips are organised, usually during the spring and summer months. Q P

Jarrow

Albion Gin & Ale House

Walter Street, NE32 3PQ (behind town hall)

(0191) 489 7222

4 changing beers (sourced nationally)

A well-appointed conversion of the old Crusader, with an emphasis on wooden panelling, vintage photographs of the area and pub memorabilia. The pub serves four ales – note the blackboard near the entrance featuring an ale of the moment, offered at a discount. Nearly two dozen gins are also kept. Live music plays Thursday to Saturday evenings as well as Monday and Friday lunchtimes. A quiz and karaoke are held every Sunday evening. P

Newburn

Keelman

Grange Road, NE15 8NL

(0191) 267 1689 biglampbrewers.co.uk

Big Lamp Bitter, Keelman Brown, Prince Bishop Ale, Summerhill Stout, Sunny Daze; 1 changing beer (sourced nationally)

This tastefully converted, Grade II listed former pumping station is now home to the Big Lamp Brewery – the Keelman is the brewery tap. A conservatory restaurant serves excellent food, and quality accommodation is provided in the adjacent Keelman's Lodge and Salmon Cottage. Attractively situated by the Tyne Riverside Country Park, Coast-to-Coast cycleway and Hadrian's Wall National Trail. P (22,71)

Newcastle upon Tyne: Byker

Brinkburn Street Brewery Bar & Kitchen

Unit 1B, Ford Street, Ouseburn, NE6 1NW

(0191) 338 9039 brinkburnbrewery.co.uk

8 changing beers (sourced locally)

The main attraction here is the range and quality of beers available. Most ales are brewed on-site, alongside a couple of guests, often from Steam Machine. Food is also a major feature, with a kitchen that uses locally sourced ingredients and serves traditional local dishes. Upstairs hall is used as a venue for occasional beer festivalsand other events. The quirky bar features a collection of armoury and objets d'art.

Cluny

36 Lime Street, NE1 2PQ

(0191) 230 4474 thecluny.com

7 changing beers

Large industrial building converted into a pub, art gallery and live music venue. The pub runs frequent themed beer festivals and always has a good selection of British and foreign draught and bottled products available. The art gallery shows work of all kinds, from final degree shows to local independent established artists in all media, with the displays changing monthly. Live music sessions are held most evenings and include a wide range of British, European and American musicians. Q

Cumberland Arms

James Place Street, NE6 1LD (off Byker Bank)

(0191) 265 1725 thecumberlandarms.co.uk

6 changing beers (sourced nationally)

Three-storey venue rebuilt over 100 years ago and relatively little changed since, standing in a prominent position overlooking the lower Ouseburn Valley. The pub is home to traditional dance and music groups. A multiple winner of CAMRA regional Cider Pub of the Year awards, it generally offers up to 12 ciders and perries. Winter and summer beer festivals are held each year. Closing time may vary. Accommodation is in four en-suite rooms. Q P

Free Trade Inn

St Lawrence Road, NE6 1AP

(0191) 265 5764

7 changing beers (sourced nationally)

Unique former Scottish & Newcastle pub with wonderful views of the Tyne bridges and Newcastle and Gateshead quaysides. Up to nine beers and five ciders are available on the bar. Interesting ales come from far and wide, with regular tap takeovers and an extensive range of foreign bottled beers. The jukebox is classic and free, and the

REAL ALE BREWERIES

Almasty Shiremoor
Anarchy Newcastle upon Tyne
Big Lamp Newburn
Box Social Newburn
Brinkburn Street Newcastle upon Tyne: Byker
Cullercoats Wallsend
Darwin Sunderland
Dog & Rabbit Whitley Bay
Errant Newcastle upon Tyne
Firebrick Blaydon-on-Tyne
Flash House North Shields
Full Circle Newcastle upon Tyne (NEW)
Great North Eastern Gateshead
Hadrian Border Newburn
Maxim Houghton le Spring
Metalhead North Shields (NEW)
Newcastle Newcastle upon Tyne
Northern Alchemy Newcastle upon Tyne: Byker
Out There Newcastle-upon-Tyne
Stu Brew Newcastle upon Tyne
Tavernale Newcastle upon Tyne
Three Kings North Shields
TOPS High Spen
Two by Two Wallsend
Tyne Bank Newcastle upon Tyne
Whitley Bay Whitley Bay
Wylam Newcastle upon Tyne

beer garden is excellent. Regular pop-up food vendors. A former local CAMRA Pub of the Year and Cider Pub of the Year. Q (Q3)

Newcastle upon Tyne: City Centre

Bacchus

42-48 High Bridge, NE1 6BX

(0191) 261 1008

Anarchy Blonde Star; Fyne Ales Jarl; 7 changing beers (sourced nationally)

A winner of many CAMRA branch awards, this smart city-centre pub boasts nine handpumps offering a wide range of rapidly changing guest beers, with one pump dedicated to cider. A large selection of draught and bottled foreign beers is also available. Photographs and posters showing the industries in which this region used to lead the world cover the walls. (Monument)

Beer Street

Arch 10, Forth Street, NE1 3NZ

5 changing beers (sourced nationally)

Sited in a railway arch, this micropub with seating for 50 people opened in 2018. There is a main bar area with five handpumps. Stairs at the rear give access to a mezzanine floor above, with pump badges from former beers adorning the staircase. Interesting artwork covers the walls, apparently inspired by the famous Hogarth paintings Beer Street and Gin Lane. (Central)

Bodega

125 Westgate Road, NE1 4AG

(0191) 221 1552

Big Lamp Prince Bishop Ale; Fyne Ales Jarl; house beer (by Almasty); 5 changing beers (sourced nationally)

Two fine stained-glass domes are the architectural highlights of the pub, which is popular with football and music fans. TVs show sporting events and the pub can be busy on match days. The interior offers a number of standing and seating areas with separate booths for more intimate drinking. A number of old brewery mirrors adorn the walls. Eight handpumps include beers from Oakham and Fyne Ales, alongside a good selection of foreign bottled beers. (Central)

Box Social

Arch 11, Forth Street, NE1 3NZ

boxsocial.pub

Box Social Gentleman's Nectar Pale Ale; 3 changing beers (sourced nationally; often Box Social)

Micropub with a welcoming ambience, owned by Box Social Brewery and on the site formerly occupied by the Split Chimp. A mezzanine floor gives extra seating to the rear. The bar is constructed from scaffolding planks, with wooden bar-back fittings. There are 10 keg beer taps on the wall behind the bar and a colourful tap board provides details of what is on the handpumps and wall taps. Q (Central)

Bridge Hotel

Castle Square, NE1 1RQ

(0191) 232 6400

Anarchy Blonde Star; Sharp's Doom Bar; 7 changing beers (sourced nationally)

Large Fitzgerald pub situated next to Stephenson's spectacular High Level Bridge – the rear windows and patio have views of the city walls, River Tyne and Gateshead Quays. The main bar area, with many stained-glass windows, is divided into a number of seating areas, with a raised section at the rear. Guest beers come from far and wide. Meetings of what claims to be the oldest folk club in the country are among live music events hosted in the upstairs function room.
(Central)

Fitzgeralds

60 Grey Street, NE1 6AF

(0191) 230 1350

Anarchy Blonde Star; 5 changing beers (sourced nationally)

Large, open-plan pub that is much bigger inside than it appears from the outside owing to its depth, with the bar situated towards the back. There is plenty of seating in various areas, as well as a large standing area in front of the bar. Six handpulls serve local and national ales, usually including a dark beer. A former local CAMRA Pub of the Year. (Monument)

Lady Greys

20 Shakespeare Street, NE1 6AQ

(0191) 232 3606 ladygreys.co.uk

House beer (by Ridgeside); 7 changing beers (sourced nationally)

Close to the historic Theatre Royal and busy shopping areas, it is nice to see this pub, formerly The Adelphi, adding itself to the city-centre real ale scene. Beers are mainly from local brewers Hadrian Border, Allendale and Wylam, with guests from all over the country. Refurbishment has added two more handpumps for beer and two for real cider. Food is served all day.
(Monument)

Mean-Eyed Cat

1 St Thomas Street, NE1 4LE

(0191) 222 0952

Rat White Rat; 5 changing beers (sourced nationally)

Situated in a former newsagent's in the street opposite Haymarket bus station, this one-room micropub opened in 2018 with six handpumps. It serves beers from local, national and international suppliers, alongside a range of eight craft keg beers. A good selection of up to six ciders is available – traditional still and served from the 'cellar'. Mexican spirits are also on offer. There are street food pop-ups on occasion. (Haymarket)

Split Chimp

Arch 7, Westgate Road, NE1 1SA

splitchimp.pub

House beer (by Errant); 4 changing beers (sourced nationally)

Newcastle's first micropub opened in 2015 in a refurbished railway arch behind Central station opposite the site of the former Federation Brewery. It relocated to this larger arch on Westgate Road in 2016. More spacious than some micropubs and split over two levels, it has six handpumps serving a wide selection of real ales, with one dedicated to the house beer, Clever Chimp 2, from nearby Errant Brewery. A selection of real ciders is also available, as well as foreign bottled beers. Winter opening hours may vary. (Central)

Town Mouse Ale House

Basement, 11 St Mary's Place, NE1 7PG

townmousealehouse.co.uk

6 changing beers (sourced nationally)

This well-designed micropub is in the basement of what was a coffee shop and has space for around 50 people. The bar area is to the front with more seating to the rear. A large blackboard gives details of the four cask beers and larger range of keg and bottled beers. Local CAMRA branch Pub of the Year 2019. (Haymarket)

Tyneside Cinema Bar Café 𝕃

Pilgrim Street, NE1 6QG

☎ 0845 217 9909 🌐 tynesidecinema.co.uk/food-drink/tyneside-bar-cafe

4 changing beers (sourced nationally; often Wylam) Ⓗ

Part of Tyneside Cinema, the Bar Café is a large open-plan bar with its own curtained-off cinema screen. It has three handpumps serving a range of locally brewed cask ales including the house beer, 35mm from Wylam Brewery. Beers can be taken into cinema screenings. A tasty selection of cakes and pastries is also available. The cellar is in the vault of a former bank.
◑♿⇌🚇(Monument) 📶

Newcastle upon Tyne: Gosforth

County 𝕃 ✔

High Street, NE3 1HB

☎ (0191) 285 6919

Draught Bass; Great North Eastern Rivet Catcher; Greene King IPA, Yardbird; Hadrian Border Farne Island Pale Ale; Sharp's Doom Bar; 8 changing beers (sourced nationally) Ⓗ

A large L-shaped bar with pleasant stained-glass windows on the main road frontage. It attracts a variety of visitors, from office workers to students, and can get busy, especially at weekends. A separate quiet room at the back offers respite from the hustle and bustle of the main bar, and also doubles as a small meeting or function room. Several guest beers are available.
❀🍎P🚌🐾📶

Gosforth Hotel 𝕃 ✔

High Street, NE3 1HQ

☎ (0191) 285 6617 🌐 gosforthhotelnewcastle.co.uk

Anarchy Blonde Star; 7 changing beers (sourced nationally) Ⓗ

Located on the corner of a busy junction at the top of the High Street, this is a stalwart of the lively Gosforth pub scene. Popular with a wide clientele, from nearby office workers to locals and students, the pub often gets busy. The rear bar opens at 5pm Monday to Thursday and midday Friday to Sunday. A good range of local ales is always available. ◑♿🚇🚌📶

Newcastle upon Tyne: Heaton

Chillingham 𝕃

Chillingham Road, NE6 5XN

☎ (0191) 265 3992

Anarchy Blonde Star; Sharp's Atlantic; 8 changing beers (sourced nationally) Ⓗ

Close to Chillingham Road Metro station, this large two-roomed pub was extensively renovated, refurbished and reopened in 2016. It has a comfortable bar and lounge, with sport shown on TVs, appealing to the widest-possible clientele. An excellent choice of local microbrewery beers is offered – and look out for the bottled beer, whisky and wine of the month. The food menu is popular with locals and visitors alike. A function room upstairs hosts regular quiz nights.
◑🚇♣P🚌(62,63) 📶

Newcastle upon Tyne: Kenton Bank Foot

Twin Farms 𝕃

22 Main Road, NE13 8AB

☎ (0191) 286 1263 🌐 twinfarmsnewcastle.co.uk

Anarchy Blonde Star; 6 changing beers Ⓗ

Large stone farmhouse building standing in its own grounds. It has various comfortable areas inside and out – including a separate bar and family areas – to enjoy the extensive selection of beers on offer. Quiz night is Monday and an early-bird menu is offered on Thursday. Barbecues are hosted in summer. The pub supports reducing food miles – ingredients are locally sourced from named suppliers. Q🐴❀◑♿🚇P🚌(X77,X78)📶

Newcastle upon Tyne: Quayside

Crown Posada 𝕃

31 Side, NE1 3JE

☎ (0191) 232 1269

Allendale Pennine Pale; Hadrian Border Tyneside Blonde; house beer (by Hadrian Border); 3 changing beers (sourced nationally) Ⓗ

An architecturally fine pub, on CAMRA's Regional Inventory of Historic Pub Interiors. The narrow street frontage with its two impressive stained-glass windows leads to a small snug, bar counter and a longer seating area. There is an interesting coffered ceiling, as well as local photographs and cartoons of long-gone customers and staff on the walls. Local small brewers are enthusiastically supported, with three regular local ales.
⇌🚇(Central) 🚌📶

Newcastle upon Tyne: South Gosforth

Millstone 𝕃

Haddricks Mill Road, NE3 1QL

☎ (0191) 285 3429

Allendale Pennine Pale; Anarchy Blonde Star; Draught Bass; 4 changing beers (sourced nationally) Ⓗ

A modern, stylish two-roomed pub with a lounge to the front and a small public bar to the rear, offering beers from local microbreweries as well as national favourites. Bass has been popular with the regulars for many years. The free-to-hire function room upstairs has been renovated and hosts CAMRA events. Complimentary bar nibbles are served every Sunday from noon.
🐴❀◑🚇P🚌(55) 📶

North Shields

Enigma Tap

60 Bedford Street, NE29 0AR

☎ 07792 822063

4 changing beers (sourced nationally) Ⓗ

Micropub in a former shop unit just off the main Northumberland Square. There is a seating area near the entrance and a narrower raised area towards the rear incorporating the bar and craft beer tap board. Outside, there is a small patio in the back yard. 🐴❀🚇♣🚌🐾

Old Ryton Village

Olde Cross

Burnmoor Lane, NE40 3QP

☎ (0191) 447 3460 🌐 yeoldecross.co.uk

Timothy Taylor Landlord; 3 changing beers (sourced locally; often Firebrick) Ⓗ

This community-owned inn in the Tyne Valley is an attractive Edwardian half-timbered local in a lovely setting by the village green and the cross it is named after. The original Cross Inn dates from the mid-19th century and was partly rebuilt in 1909. The pub is a centre for the local community, hosting entertainment and activities. Two community events – the hirings, which take place in spring and autumn, and the annual carols at Christmas – are held on the village green. Winner of a CAMRA Pub Saving Award in 2020. 🐴♿♣🚌🐾📶

Ryhope

Guide Post 𝕃 ✔

Ryhope Street South, SR2 0RN
☎ (0191) 523 5735 🌐 theguidepost.co.uk
Maxim Double Maxim; 2 changing beers (sourced nationally) 🄷
This friendly, popular, street-corner local has three handpulls – the guest beers will always include one light ale. With a cask ale club, sports TV, a pool table, a Thursday quiz, regular weekend entertainment and dominoes and poker on Sunday, there is something for everyone here. Bar snacks are available. Outside at the back is a pleasant enclosed garden. 🐴❀♣🚌🐾📶

South Shields

Alum Ale House ✔

Ferry Street, NE33 1JR (next to Ferry Landing)
☎ (0191) 427 7245
Banks's Amber Ale; Brakspear Oxford Gold; Jennings Cumberland Ale; Ringwood Boondoggle; Wainwright; Wychwood Hobgoblin Gold; 1 changing beer (sourced nationally) 🄷
Traditional pub close to the River Tyne and Market Place. It is popular with local ale drinkers as a haven of good beer. There are 12 handpumps offering ales from the Marston's range plus a real cider. Note the large blackboard to the right of the bar with details of the beers. A lively Irish folk session is hosted on the first Sunday of each month. Bar snacks are available. Seating on the decking outside has views of the river. ❀🔥♣🍎🚌

Cask Lounge 𝕃

Charlotte Terrace, NE33 1QQ
☎ 07387 750551
4 changing beers (sourced nationally) 🄷
This micropub, a former housing office opposite the town hall, shares the premises with a vinyl album store/coffee shop. It is run by an experienced couple who value the principle of the micropub, encouraging conversation with no TVs or gambling machines. There are four handpulls dispensing changing real ales, and two real ciders are also available. The pub is light and airy and includes a comfortable sofa, soft carpeting and background music. ♿🔥🍎🚌📶

Marine 🏆 𝕃

230 Ocean Road, NE33 2JQ
☎ (0191) 455 0280
Allendale Golden Plover; Rat White Rat; 6 changing beers (sourced regionally) 🄷
Large 1840s pub opposite Marine Park, near the seafront. This family-run free house serves eight changing real ales and four real ciders. To the left of the bar are raised areas with plenty of seating, and to the right is a games area. Upstairs is a function room. Unobtrusive background music plays. Pub food is served daily. Local CAMRA Pub and Cider Pub of the Year 2020. ◐◑🔥♣🍎P🚌(E1,516) 🐾📶

Steamboat 𝕃 ✔

Mill Dam, NE33 1EQ (follow signs for Customs House)
☎ (0191) 454 0134
9 changing beers (sourced nationally) 🄷
Close to The Customs House and the Shields Ferry, this multi award-winning pub is full of character and has one of the largest selections of cask ales in South Shields. There are 13 handpumps dispensing nine ales from local and national breweries and four real ciders. Meet the Brewer events and beer festivals take place throughout the year, as well as regular music nights. The split-level bar and small lounge are decorated with a nautical theme. Q🔥🍎🐾📶

Wouldhave ✔

16 Mile End Road, NE33 1TA
☎ (0191) 427 6014
Greene King Abbot; Ruddles Best Bitter; 3 changing beers (sourced nationally) 🄷
Named after local boat builder William Wouldhave, co-inventor of the self-righting lifeboat, this town-centre Wetherspoon has had a major refit, extending the drinking and dining space and creating a new garden. The pub offers a selection of real ales and ciders from six handpumps, with two regular beers and a rotation of guests, alongside well-priced bar meals served all day. Beer festivals feature twice yearly. Five minutes from the public transport interchange. Q🐴◐◑♿🔥🍎P📶

Sunderland

Avenue

Zetland Street, Roker, SR6 0EQ (just off Roker Avenue)
☎ (0191) 567 7412 🌐 theavenue.pub
6 changing beers (sourced nationally) 🄷
Fifteen minutes' walk from the Stadium of Light, this local pub offers six changing real ales on handpull and several real ciders. It hosts various themed nights including poker, bingo, pool, a popular Thursday night quiz and a Sunday dominoes handicap. A snooker table and dartboards can be found in the upstairs games room. In 2020 a restaurant opened offering in-pub dining and a take-away service. Local CAMRA Cider Pub of the Year 2020. ❀◐◑♣🍎P🚌(E1)🐾📶

Chaplins

40 Stockton Road, SR1 3NR
☎ (0191) 565 3964
6 changing beers (sourced nationally; often Darwin) 🄷
A city-centre pub with six real ale handpulls and one for real cider. The house beer, Happy Chappy, is brewed at nearby Darwin Brewery. Good-value food is served every day. A quiz is held on Thursday evening. There is plenty of seating either side of the main entrance, as well as outside. Some tabletops depict scenes of Sunderland's industrial heritage. Handy for public transport, with Park Lane Interchange two minutes away. ❀◐◑♿🚆🔥🍎🚌📶

Chesters 𝕃 ✔

Chester Road, SR4 7DR
☎ (0191) 565 9952
6 changing beers (sourced nationally) 🄷
This popular pub just outside the city centre has a smart and comfortable interior, with a large main bar and a more intimate area at the back. Six handpulls invariably offer an ale from a local brewery as well as guest beers and a real cider. Meals are served all day. Outside is a pay car park (you can claim the charge back at the bar) and a large beer garden. A function room with a private bar is available. 🐴❀◐◑♿🔥🍎P🚌

Dun Cow ★ 𝕃

High Street West, SR1 3HA
☎ (0191) 567 2262
Anarchy Blonde Star; Sharp's Doom Bar; 5 changing beers (sourced nationally) 🄷
This Grade II listed building is an architectural gem and features on CAMRA's National Inventory of Historic Pub Interiors. It was a winner of two CAMRA/Historic England

awards for restoration and conservation following a refurbishment in 2014. Since then it has had a major external makeover. Real ale and cider feature on eight handpulls. The pub is next to the Sunderland Empire and can get very busy around performance times. There is a Tuesday buskers' night and a Thursday quiz. Meals are served upstairs. Q

Fitzgeralds

12-14 Green Terrace, SR1 3PZ

(0191) 567 0852

Titanic Plum Porter; 8 changing beers (sourced nationally)

This city-centre pub has been in the Guide since 1983. It serves two regular beers complemented by up to six guests and two ciders. The pub comprises a large main bar offering a number of different seating areas and the smaller, quieter, nautically themed Chart Room. Lunchtime meals are served daily. Live music features on Tuesday and Sunday nights, and a quiz is held every Thursday evening.

Harbour View

Harbour View, Roker, SR6 0NU

(0191) 567 1402

6 changing beers (sourced nationally)

A modern local pub with six handpulls offering regularly changing beers chosen by local CAMRA members. A board displays a tally of beers to date from 1 January – the aim is to offer in excess of 600 ales a year. A cask ale club is held every Wednesday evening. This is a relaxing pub for a drink, with additional seating outside to take in the sun. (E1,18)

Ivy House

7A Worcester Terrace, SR2 7AW

(0191) 567 3399

6 changing beers (sourced nationally)

Tucked away but five minutes' walk from the Park Lane public transport interchange, the Ivy House is well worth seeking out. Six varied guest ales and a cider are on offer, as well as extensive range of bottled international beers. Home-made pizzas and burgers are prepared in an open kitchen. There is a weekday happy hour from 5pm, themed meal nights and a Wednesday night quiz. Live music features on the second Saturday and last Sunday of the month. P

Ship Isis

26 Silksworth Row, SR1 3QJ

(0191) 514 7684

9 changing beers (sourced nationally)

Dating back to 1885, this place was restored to its original Victorian splendour by the former Jarrow Brewery in 2011 after lying dormant for two years. It has ten handpumps offering six or more cask beers, two real ciders and a perry, served by very knowledgeable staff. An extensive selection of bottled beers and craft gins means there is something for everyone. Opposite the main bar is a long, quieter lounge. There is live music on Sunday, a Monday quiz and buskers' night on Wednesday.

William Jameson

30-32 Fawcett Street, SR1 1RH

(0191) 514 5016

Greene King Abbot; Ruddles Best Bitter; 6 changing beers (sourced nationally)

Wetherspoon pub in what used to be a department store, opposite the Winter Gardens in the heart of the city centre. All the usual features associated with the chain can be found in this busy corner pub, including good-value meals served all day. Twelve handpumps offer up to six guest beers and a cider to complement the regular range. The pub is a keen supporter of local brewers and holds twice-yearly beer festivals. Q

Swalwell

Owa The Road

Unit 1, Spencer House, Market Lane, NE16 3DS

4 changing beers (sourced nationally)

Situated within the old Co-op building directly opposite the Sun Inn, this micropub has no music and no TV. It does have four changing beers on handpull though, two of which are generally beers from the wood. The owner is working with a number of breweries to bring beers to the pub that are not normally found in wooden casks. Real ciders are served from boxes. Local CAMRA branch Cider Pub of the Year 2020. QP

Sun Inn

Market Lane, NE16 3AL

6 changing beers (sourced nationally)

A hostelry in the heart of the historic village that spawned many internationally renowned engineers and industrialists, and of course the famous Swalwell cabbage. This truly no-nonsense community pub provides good company for locals and strangers alike. Sword dancers, darts, dominoes handicaps, a monthly pie competition and a buskers' night all feature. Bar food and snacks are available, free on Sunday. There is a regular bus service from Newcastle.

Tynemouth

Tynemouth Lodge Hotel

Tynemouth Road, NE30 4AA

(0191) 257 7565 tynemouthlodgehotel.co.uk

Caledonian Deuchars IPA; Draught Bass; Hadrian Border Tyneside Blonde; Marston's Pedigree; 1 changing beer (sourced locally)

This externally tiled 1799 free house, next to a former house of correction, has featured in every issue of the Guide since 1983. The comfortable pub has a U-shaped lounge with the bar on one side and a serving hatch on the other, and is noted in the area for its Draught Bass. An ideal stopping-off point for those completing the Coast-to-Coast cycle route. QP(1,1A)

Tynemouth Social Club

15/16 Front Street, NE30 4DX

(0191) 257 7542

2 changing beers (sourced nationally)

Formerly a Co-op, this well-established social club at the heart of Tynemouth has a full pub licence and welcomes visitors. After several attempts to sell real ale, the club now has a rotating guest beer policy which has stimulated demand. The ale is well kept by the bar/cellarman and the club is well worth a visit. Local CAMRA Club of the Year 2019.

Wallsend

Ritz

87/93 High Street West, NE28 8JD

(0191) 296 9600

Greene King Abbot; Ruddles Best Bitter; Sharp's Doom Bar; 4 changing beers (sourced nationally)

A welcome addition to Wallsend High Street, this pub opened in 2015. The building was originally the Ritz cinema and later a bingo hall before Wetherspoon took it over. Entering from the High Street, the original period decoration can be seen. Quiz night is Monday. There is a large car park at the rear.

Washington

Courtyard 𝕃
Biddick Lane, NE38 8AB
☎ (0191) 417 0445 🌐 artscentrewashington.co.uk/courtyard.aspx
8 changing beers (sourced nationally) 🄷
Located within the Washington Arts Centre, this light and airy café/bar offers a warm welcome to drinkers and food lovers alike. Eight changing handpulled beers, two real ciders and a perry are available. An extensive range of food is served lunchtimes and early evenings, with breakfast Monday to Saturday. Quiz night is Thursday. There is outdoor seating within the spacious courtyard. Popular beer festivals are held over the Easter and August bank holidays.

Sir William De Wessyngton
2-3 Victoria Road, NE37 2SY
☎ (0191) 418 0100
Greene King Abbot; Maxim Maximus; Ruddles Best Bitter; Sharp's Doom Bar; 4 changing beers (sourced nationally) 🄷
Large open-plan Wetherspoon that used to be a snooker hall and ice cream parlour. It is named after a Norman knight and lord of the manor whose descendants later emigrated to the United States. The pub offers value-for-money beer and the usual well-priced Wetherspoon menu. The regular ales are complemented by at least four guests and two real ciders. Twice-yearly beer festivals are held. A good selection of local and international bottled beers is available.
Q P

Steps
47 Spout Lane, NE38 7HP
☎ (0191) 415 0733
5 changing beers (sourced nationally) 🄷
Opened in 1894 as the Spout Lane Inn, the pub was renamed The Steps in 1976. The comfortable and friendly single-room lounge bar is divided into two drinking areas, with pictures of old Washington decorating the walls. Five varying beers are on offer, often selected by the regulars, with some from local microbreweries. A quiz is held on Tuesday night, and live entertainment features every first and last Saturday of the month. Opening hours vary. QP (84)

West Boldon

Black Horse
Rectory Bank, NE36 0QQ (off A184)
☎ (0191) 536 1814
Jennings Cumberland Ale; 1 changing beer (sourced nationally) 🄷
A former coaching inn and blacksmith's shop, this pub and restaurant traces its history back to the early 1700s or possibly to the Battle of Boldon in 1644. The bar has a musical theme created by owner Pete Zulu, a former member of punk band the Toy Dolls. Photographs by Pete are on display and for sale. The restaurant is popular and specialises in vegan food. P

Whickham

One-Eyed Stag 𝕃
5 The Square, NE16 4JB
☎ 07811 261924
5 changing beers (sourced nationally) 🄷
A fairly recent addition to the pubs in Whickham, this micropub has a tile-topped bar with four handpumps serving beer from local microbreweries. Blackboards adorn the wall behind the bar giving details of the beers and other drinks available. There is an interesting light fitting covering most of the ceiling and an electric stove in an alcove to the right. P

Whitley Bay

Dog & Rabbit 🏆 𝕃
36 Park View, NE26 2TH
☎ 07944 552716 🌐 dogandrabbitbrewery.co.uk
4 changing beers (sourced nationally) 🄷
It is good to have this micropub, converted from a women's clothing shop, adding to the number of pubs in the area. The corner bar has four handpumps serving mostly local beers. The owner's microbrewery has been installed in the pub brewing Dog & Rabbit beers. With no music, Wi-Fi or sports TV, conversation is encouraged among visitors. Local CAMRA Pub of the Year 2020.
Q

Split Chimp 𝕃
Unit 1, Ground Floor, Spanish City Dome, Marine Avenue, NE26 1BG
🌐 splitchimp.pub
House beer (by Errant); 4 changing beers (sourced nationally) 🄷
This micropub, opened in early 2019, occupies one of the external units of the recently refurbished Spanish City and overlooks the promenade along the North Sea coast. The single room has a long bar counter facing the entrance, with seating around the periphery. The house beer from Three Kings is supplemented by a changing range of four beers from near and far. Winter opening hours vary – check ahead of your visit.

Fishing for beer

Ah! My beloved brother of the rod, do you know the taste of beer – of bitter beer – cooled in the flowing river? Take your bottle of beer, sink it deep, deep in the shady water, where the cooling springs and fishes are. Then, the day being very hot and bright, and the sun blazing on your devoted head, consider it a matter of duty to have to fish that long, wide stream. An hour or so of good hammering will bring you to the end of it, and then – let me ask you avec impressement – how about that beer? Is it cool? Is it refreshing? Does it gurgle, gurgle and 'go down glug' as they say in Devonshire? Is it heavenly? Is it Paradise and all the Peris to boot? Ah! If you have never tasted beer under these or similar circumstance, you have, believe me, never tasted it at all.
Francis Francis, By Lake and River, 16th century

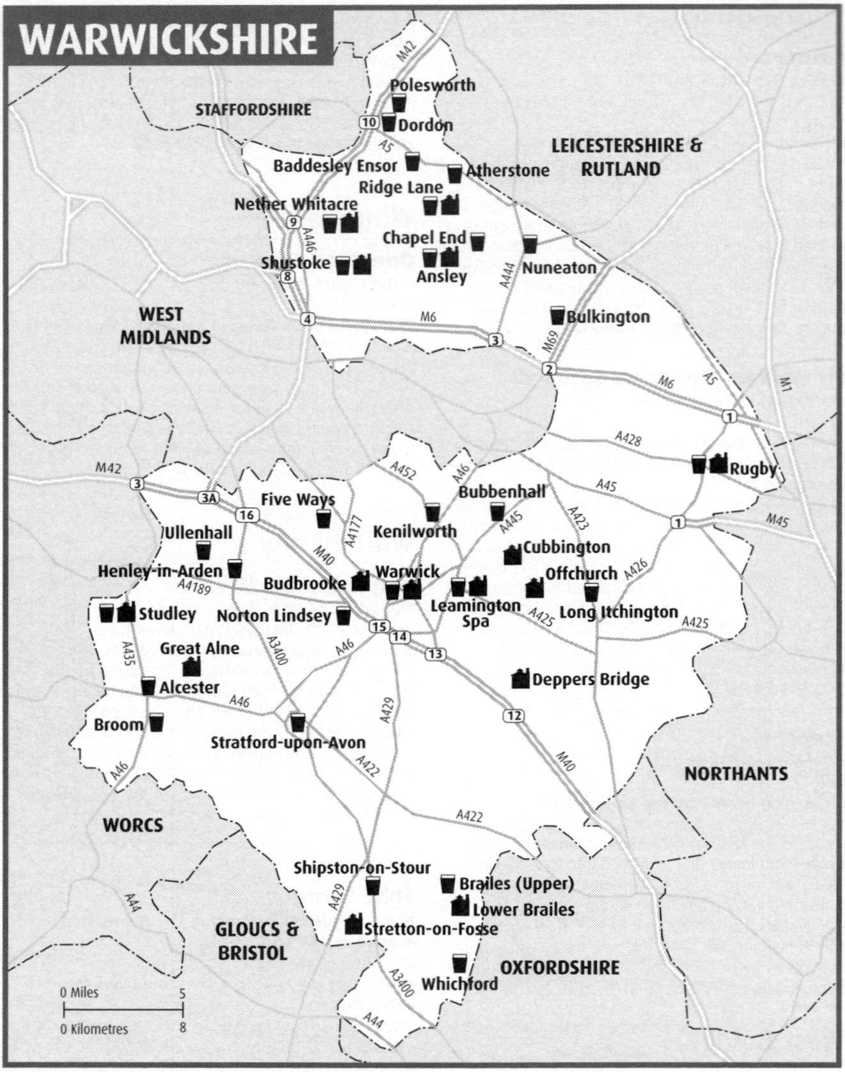

Alcester

Three Tuns

34 High Street, B49 5AB

☎ 07772 530119

Adnams Southwold Bitter; Hobsons Mild; Sharp's Atlantic; 3 changing beers (sourced regionally; often Bathams) Ⓗ

Nestled in the historic market town of Alcester on the high street. This welcoming single-bar pub with antique shop-style small-paned windows retains the original beams, stone-flagged floors and sections of wattle and daub. No food, no loud music, but a relaxed atmosphere, friendly staff and a fantastic selection of real ales, fine wines and an array of ciders await you. There is also a varied range of malt whiskies, speciality gins and special spirits, plus prosecco from the bottle and tap. The pub hosts monthly bake-off nights and ale, cider and whisky tasting nights as well as quizzes. Small parties can be catered for. There is seating outside for alfresco drinking.

Turk's Head

4 High Street, B49 5AD

☎ (01789) 765948 🌐 theturkshead.net

Wye Valley HPA; 3 changing beers (sourced nationally; often Purity, Salopian, Skinner's) Ⓗ

Central to the town, this busy pub is dedicated to real ale and is well worth a visit with its bare wood floors, exposed beams and roaring log fires. Beers served are from local breweries as well as Shropshire, Yorkshire and south Wales. Good food is a daily feature; there is a separate dining room as well as a quiet garden. The pub holds regular beer festivals and provides a bar during town festivals. Local CAMRA Pub of the Year 2018 and 2019. Q

Ansley

Lord Nelson Inn 🅻 ✔

Birmingham Road, CV10 9PQ

☎ (024) 7639 2305 🌐 thelordnelsoninnansley.co.uk

Sperrin Ansley Mild, Head Hunter, Band of Brothers, Third Party, Thick as Thieves; 3 changing beers H
This nautically-themed pub has been run by the Sperrin family since 1974, incorporating a brewery at the rear of the building since 2012. This is the pub's 27th consecutive entry in the Guide. Nine handpulls dispense its own Sperrin brews plus guests from microbreweries near and far. There is an extensive food menu with meal nights and tribute nights hosted. A monthly quiz is held in the Victory restaurant. The suntrap courtyard garden is a venue for a beer festival and barbecue in August. P

Atherstone

Angel Ale House

24 Church Street, CV9 1HA
☎ 07525 183056
Blythe Palmers Poison; Oakham Citra; 4 changing beers H
This attractive pub on the market square is a frequent local CAMRA Pub of the Year winner. Its interior features an inglenook fireplace with log-burning stove. The pub offers six real ales, often local and always including a dark beer, plus up to 10 real ciders. Wednesday is quiz night; music is via customer select-and-play from a large vinyl LP collection. There is a large free council car park to the rear. P

Baddesley Ensor

Red Lion

The Common, CV9 2BT (from Grendon roundabout on A5 go S up Boot Hill) SP273983
☎ (01827) 718186
Draught Bass; Greene King Abbot; Marston's Pedigree; 3 changing beers H
Popular village pub offering just ale and conversation. The comfy seating and log fire are enhanced by a music-free environment. Three guest ales are served, often from major concerns such as Greene King and Everards, but sometimes from small local breweries. The sparkler is willingly removed on request. Off-road parking is available opposite the pub. Lunchtime opening is weekends only. Q

Brailes (Upper)

Gate Inn

OX15 5AX (on B4035)
☎ 07973 853149
3 changing beers (sourced locally; often Prescott, Uley, Wye Valley) H
Traditional rustic free house with immense character. Well-liked and busy, it features a log fire in winter and a huge garden. Three cask ales are always served, along with Napton Recipe No.3 cask cider. Food is limited to crisps and nuts served at the bar but customers are welcome to bring their own – the landlord will supply plates and cutlery. Q P (3A)

Broom

Broom Tavern

32 High Street, B50 4HL
☎ (01789) 778199 broomtavern.co.uk
Purity Pure UBU; Wye Valley HPA; 2 changing beers H
A lovely brick and timber multi-room building which retains a great amount of character. It has been tastefully made over, keeping the cosy snug and log fire in winter. Run by two experienced chefs with a good pedigree in the kitchen, it serves great food lunchtimes and evenings, made with local ingredients. Local beers are frequently found here along with at least one real cider. There is a choice of beer gardens. Q

Bubbenhall

Malt Shovel

Lower End, CV8 3BW
☎ (024) 7630 1141
Church End Fallen Angel; Courage Directors; Greene King Abbot; 1 changing beer (sourced nationally) H
Traditional Grade II listed two-room village pub dating from the 17th century. Its bar is the hub of the community; the lounge is more food-oriented. Attractions include a dartboard and a well-kept bowling green behind the large car park. Local CAMRA Pub of the Year 2020. Q P (539)

Bulkington

Weavers' Arms

12 Long Street, CV12 9JZ
☎ (024) 7631 4415
Draught Bass; 1 changing beer H
Family-owned, two-roomed village pub converted from weavers' cottages. Well known for the quality of its Bass ale, it has a wood-panelled games room, log-burning fireplace and slate floor. Outside, the extensive, well-kept beer garden hosts barbecues in the summer. Children are welcome and private functions can be catered for. The Pork Pie Club, Weavers Walkers and Hillbilly Golf Society hold regular meetings here. (56)

Chapel End

Salutation

Chancery Lane, CV10 0PB
☎ (024) 7704 7573
Draught Bass; 2 changing beers H
Chapel End used to have five pubs but the only survivor is the Sally, a popular, award-winning community inn. Bass is served regularly, along with guest beers from a variety of breweries. The pub hosts quizzes and other events, and shows major football, rugby and boxing matches on TV. Live bands perform regularly, usually on Saturday night or Sunday late afternoon. P

REAL ALE BREWERIES

Atomic Rugby
Church End Ridge Lane
Church Farm Budbrooke
Clouded Minds Lower Brailes
Fizzy Moon Leamington Spa
Fosse Way Offchurch
Freestyle Shustoke
North Cotswold Stretton-on-Fosse
Old Pie Factory Warwick
Purity Great Alne
Slaughterhouse Warwick
Sperrin Ansley
Warwickshire Leamington Spa: Cubbington
Weatheroak Studley
Whitacre Nether Whitacre
Windmill Hill Deppers Bridge

Dordon

Mini Miner
13 Browns Lane, B78 1TR
☎ 07455 242415
3 changing beers (often Church End) ⊞
Now the only pub in Dordon, this small, single-roomed bar in a parade of shops provides much-needed refreshment for local drinkers. Its name refers to a former pub in the village, the Merrie Miner, later renamed the Cuckoo's Rest before closing for good. Two or three ales are served, typically including a local beer and a well-known brew. ⅍♣P🖵(65)❀

Five Ways

Case is Altered ⓛ
Case Lane, CV35 7JD (off Five Ways Rd nr A4141/A4177 jct) SP225701
☎ (01926) 484206
Old Pie Factory Pie in the Sky; Wye Valley Butty Bach; 3 changing beers (sourced locally) ⊞
A classic unspoilt country pub with a bar and separate snug, it has been identified by CAMRA as having a historic pub interior of regional importance. The current landlady has been here for more than 30 years, after taking over from her grandmother. The traditional bar billiards table still takes the old sixpences, which have to be bought from the bar. Monday is cribbage night. Do not miss the Victorian print of a former Leamington brewer in the bar plus a clock from another old local brewer. There is even a propeller from a World War I fighter plane on the ceiling. Q❀&♣P

Henley-in-Arden

Three Tuns
103 High Street, B95 5AT
☎ (01564) 792723
Church End Goat's Milk; Fuller's London Pride; Sharp's Doom Bar, Atlantic; Wye Valley Butty Bach ⊞
A 16th-century two-roomed inn with a single bar serving both areas. Popular with locals, this unpretentious drinkers' pub is usually busy and the atmosphere is always friendly. Five real ales are served in consistently good condition. Pub snacks plus home-made cobs and sausage rolls are usually on sale. Parking is on the street outside the pub. Q⅍&⇌♣🖵(X20)❀🛜

Kenilworth

Ale Rooms & Gin Bar ⓛ
7 Smalley Place, CV8 1QG
☎ (01926) 854585
5 changing beers (often Church End, Silhill)
Small pub opposite the clock tower at the top of Warwick Road – a new entry in this Guide and a welcome addition to the Kenilworth pub scene. Six handpumps dispense real ales, some from local breweries, and real cider in summer. The pub also offers keg beers plus a variety of gins, wines and spirits. Upstairs is a chill-out lounge. ⅍&⇌●🖵(11,X17)🛜

Gauntlet ✅
8 Oaks Precinct, Caesar Road, CV8 1DP
☎ (01926) 852110
Robinsons Trooper; St Austell Proper Job; Sharp's Sea Fury; 1 changing beer (sourced regionally) ⊞
A well-preserved example of a 1960s estate pub, recently given a more modern look. Run by a licensee with extensive local knowledge, it features in this Guide for the first time. The pub is renowned for quality home-

made food. It serves meals every evening except Monday, and is particularly popular at weekends when food is available all day. ⅍❀◑&P❀🛜

Old Bakery ⓛ
12 High Street, CV8 1LZ (nr A429/A452 jct)
☎ (01926) 864111 ⊕ theoldbakery.eu
Wye Valley HPA; 3 changing beers (sourced regionally) ⊞
Converted former bakery in the heart of the old town. The small two-roomed pub is cosy and welcoming, with beams and rustic furniture. It has a good mix of locals and visitors, with conversation the main entertainment. The owners plan to broaden the variety of beer styles and strengths further, and to extend the opening hours and offer afternoon teas and lunchtime snacks. Q❀⍃&P🖵(11) ❀🛜

Leamington Spa

Benjamin Satchwell ✅
112/114 The Parade, CV32 4AQ (almost opp town hall)
☎ (01926) 883733
Greene King Abbot; Ruddles Best Bitter; Sharp's Doom Bar; 4 changing beers ⊞
Named after a renowned local benefactor who discovered Leamington's second spring in 1784, this pub bears all the hallmarks of the Wetherspoon style. Converted from two shops, it is large, stretching back to Bedford Street. The building's split levels have been used well to create comfortable seating areas. The upper level hosts an impressively long bar. Wall panels depict local history and personalities. ⅍◑&⇌●🖵🛜

New Inn ✅
197 Leam Terrace, CV31 1DW
☎ (01926) 422861 ⊕ thenewinnleamington.co.uk
Eagle IPA; Sharp's Doom Bar, Atlantic, Sea Fury; 2 changing beers (often Byatt's) ⊞
A traditional pub in a wide Victorian terrace on the outskirts of town. The original pub has been extended into the next-door property. A central door opens directly onto the bar, with a seating area to the left and a games area to the right leading to an extension at the rear. Outside is a good-sized walled garden. Quality home-cooked food is served. A quiz is hosted fortnightly on a Wednesday. ⅍❀◑&♣🖵(63,64)❀🛜

White Horse ⓛ ✅
4-6 Clarendon Avenue, CV32 5PZ
☎ (01926) 426892 ⊕ thewhitehorseleamingtonspa.co.uk
Purity Pure UBU; Sharp's Doom Bar; 4 changing beers ⊞
Popular town pub that dates back to the 1830s and has been extended and modified over the years. The extended section now holds the main bar, serving a large selection of cask, craft and continental beers, while the original bar area is reserved for private functions. An arched stable entrance featuring a full-sized white horse leads to a courtyard and beer garden with covered and heated seating. ⅍❀◑&♣●🖵🛜

Long Itchington

Harvester ⓛ
6 Church Road, CV47 9PE (off A423 at village pond, then first left)
☎ (01926) 812698 ⊕ theharvesterinn.co.uk
3 changing beers ⊞
White-fronted pub near the village pond, on the corner of the square. Inside is a main bar, a small drinking area and a restaurant specialising in good-value steaks. The

ale range changes frequently, usually supporting smaller breweries. Real cider and a Belgian fruit beer are also on the bar. The pub hosts a beer festival each May bank holiday. A large walled courtyard garden to the rear has a wood-fired pizza oven. Gruntfuttocks Speciality Pickles can be purchased to take home.
(64)

Nether Whitacre

Dog Inn

Dog Lane, B46 2DU SP232930
(01675) 481318
Castle Rock Harvest Pale; Sharp's Doom Bar; Wye Valley Butty Bach; 1 changing beer (sourced nationally; often Castle Rock) H
A well-hidden black and white country pub, popular both with drinkers and diners. Its characterful interior features two intimate dining rooms. Brass knick-knacks abound, and there are two hefty log fires in winter. Occasional ales from the tiny on-site Whitacre Brewing Company disappear quickly. Half pints are sold at a premium; try-before-you-buy is offered on all ales. Free bar nibbles are provided at Sunday lunchtime. The peaceful beer garden includes a pets' corner. P

Norton Lindsey

New Inn

Main Street, CV35 8JA
(01926) 258411 thenewinn.pub
Greene King IPA; Timothy Taylor Landlord; 2 changing beers (sourced locally; often Church End, M&B, Slaughterhouse) H
Warwickshire's first community-owned pub opened in 2017 after fundraising resulted in it being saved from closure when it was purchased by a collective of more than 200 people. Located on a street corner in the heart of the village, the pub features a wooden floor and an open-plan interior that gives a light and airy feel. Food is locally sourced, with many specials on offer. Circular walks start and end at the pub. Q P

Nuneaton

Anker Inn

Weddington Road, CV10 0AN
(024) 7632 9193
Sharp's Doom Bar; Theakston Old Peculier; 1 changing beer H
This large community pub is known for the quality of its Theakston Old Peculier. Numerous sports teams are based here, and other activities include quizzes, pantos and a Wednesday afternoon coffee and crafts get-together. Sunday lunch is popular, with booking advisable. Beer festivals are hosted occasionally.
P

Felix Holt

3 Stratford Street, CV11 5BS
(024) 7634 7785
Byatt's Regal Blond; Greene King Abbot; Ruddles Best Bitter; Sharp's Doom Bar; changing beers (often Byatt's, Oakham) H
Large Wetherspoon outlet in the town centre. The pub takes its name from a novel by George Eliot and the literary theme is reflected in the decor of books and pictures of local history. Look out for the comical metal sculptures on the walls. A good range of guest beers includes local ales. Food is served. Outside are tables and chairs for alfresco drinking and eating, plus a heated area for smokers. Q

Lord Hop

38 Queens Road, CV11 5JX
(024) 7798 1869
4 changing beers H
Town-centre micropub on two levels, the upper one boasting settees, a small library and board games. Four or more real ales are served on handpull or straight from the cask, both from local and far-away breweries, alongside up to eight ciders or perries in the chiller. Wine, gins, bottled lager and soft drinks are also sold. Snacks are available, or bring your own takeaway. CAMRA magazines are provided for reading. No under-18s, and assistance dogs only. Local CAMRA Pub of the Year and Cider Pub of the Year. Q

Polesworth

Bull's Head

Tamworth Road, B78 1JH (by canal bridge on B5000)
(01827) 898990
3 changing beers (sourced nationally) H
Welcoming community local attracting boaters from the nearby canal. It comprises a traditional bar and a small lounge featuring unusual arches. Drinks served in the lounge usually include two or three real ales plus one real cider. With no music, the place is a conversational hub except occasionally when sport is screened. Pub games, quizzes and raffles are popular. Snacks are offered on darts nights and other occasions.
P

Ridge Lane

Church End Brewery Tap

CV10 0RD (2 miles SW of Atherstone)
(01827) 713080 churchendbrewery.co.uk
Church End Goat's Milk, Gravediggers Ale, What the Fox's Hat, Fallen Angel; 4 changing beers H
This brewery tap is hidden from the road, with access opposite Tom Piper Close. The brewery is visible from the bar area. Eight handpulls serve the bar and vestry, with a mild always among the beers. Ciders are dispensed direct from the barrel. Children are allowed in the vestry until 6pm, and are welcome in the meadow garden, which has ample seating. Regular events include a monthly quiz night. The pub opens on Wednesday in summer only. Q P

Rugby

Crafty Banker

11a Bank Street, CV21 2QE
07398 715365
XT Hop Kitty; house beer (by XT); 4 changing beers (sourced nationally; often Castor Ales, XT) H
Friendly venue serving quality ales in an atmosphere perfect for conversation. The pleasant, open-plan bar area has a retro feel. Six handpumps dispense a wide range of real ales, complemented by four craft beers. The pub also stocks more than 70 gins plus other spirits, sourced from independent producers. Customers are welcome to bring their own food on Tuesday to Thursday evenings, with plates and cutlery provided. Q

Merchants Inn

5-6 Little Church Street, CV21 3AW
(01788) 571119 merchantsinn.co.uk
Nethergate Venture; Oakham Bishops Farewell; Purity Mad Goose H**; 6 changing beers (sourced nationally)** H/G
Busy town-centre pub frequented by a varied local clientele. Flagstone floors and an open fire greet you on

entering – the interior is a museum of brewery memorabilia. Food is served Monday to Saturday, and traditional roasts on Sunday. Rugby and cricket are popular on the TV. Activities held around the calendar include Belgian and German nights, beer festivals and gin and cider weekends.

Rugby Tap Room

4 St Matthews Street, CV21 3BY (close to town centre, adjacent to A426 gyratory)
07514 771993
Changing beers (sourced locally; often Byatt's, Church End, Phipps NBC)
Micropub featuring a long room with a large selection of gravity-served draught ales and ciders racked at the far end. The atmosphere promotes conversation and there is no electronic entertainment, although acoustic music is performed on Thursday evening. The pub serves up to six LocAles plus canned craft beers. Traditional pub snacks are available. There is outside seating at the front.
Q

Seven Stars

40 Albert Square, CV21 2SH
(01788) 535478 sevenstarsrugby.co.uk
Everards Tiger, Old Original; Oakham JHB; 7 changing beers (sourced nationally)
Traditional multi-roomed community pub with a focus on quality beer and cider. Its 14 handpumps dispense ales including milds, stouts and porters, plus four ciders. Food features an impressive selection of pub-made Scotch eggs, which sell out quickly, plus filled rolls and locally produced pork pies. All can be enjoyed in the rear courtyard garden. Rugby is popular on the bar's TV. Local CAMRA Pub of the Year for the last three years. No children after 7pm. Q

Squirrel Inn

33 Church Street, CV21 3PU
(01788) 578527
4 changing beers (sourced nationally; often Dow Bridge, Marston's, Pitchfork)
A warm welcome is guaranteed at this historic free house, Rugby's jewel in the town. A real fire and pictures of old Rugby contribute to the intimate ambience. Ales from Dow Bridge, Cotleigh, Pitchfork and 3D breweries are frequently served alongside Marston's beers and four ciders. Live music is a regular attraction, with various genres performed on Saturday evening and an open mic night on Wednesday. Poetry features on the last Sunday of the month.

Town & County

12 Henry Street, CV21 2QA
07931 661840
Church End Gravediggers Ale; Greene King IPA; 2 changing beers (sourced nationally; often Donnington, Otter, Timothy Taylor)
Small town-centre club that has been trading since 1933 and is making its third appearance in this Guide. Its four handpumps include two dispensing changing guest ales from breweries near and far. The club hosts dominoes and skittles teams, and holds regular events including Tuesday bingo and monthly quizzes, plus occasional live music and coach trips. CAMRA members are welcome and guests may be signed in. Q

Victoria Inn

1 Lower Hillmorton Road, CV21 3ST
(01788) 544374 downthevic.com
Atomic Strike; Hook Norton Hooky; 5 changing beers (sourced nationally; often Abbeydale, Atomic, Titanic)
A beautiful Victorian pub just outside the town centre – a true gem and the last of its kind in the town. Built in a wedge shape, the multi-roomed local features a traditional bar, larger lounge and two relatively new snugs. Owned by the town's Atomic Brewery, the pub stocks two of its beers plus five rotating guests. It shows sport on TV and hosts quiz nights on Wednesday and Sunday.

Shipston-on-Stour

Black Horse Inn

Station Road, CV36 4BT
(01608) 238489 blackhorseshipston.co.uk
Prescott Hill Climb; Wye Valley Butty Bach; 3 changing beers (sourced regionally; often Marston's, North Cotswold, Young's)
This stone-built 15th-century inn is the oldest pub and only thatched building in Shipston, with a licence that dates back to 1540. Its welcoming and cosy lounge has a large inglenook log fire. Traditional pub games are popular in the left-hand bar, where sport is shown on TV. The excellent Thai restaurant operates a takeaway service. The enclosed rear garden has a large decking area, is well suited to children and dogs, and hosts live music in summer. Q P

Thirst Edition

46b Church Street, CV36 4AS
(01608) 664974 thirstedition.co.uk
4 changing beers (sourced regionally; often North Cotswold, Oakham, Thornbridge)
A micropub in this small market town serving up to four real ales, mostly local or regional, straight from the cask. Real ciders, craft beers, wines and six gins are also sold. Since opening in 2018 the pub has offered more than 350 real ales. It hosts regular live music including a singalong on the last Sunday of the month. The free-to-enter Thursday quiz has raised more than £3,000 for local causes. Q (50)

Shustoke

Griffin Inn

Church Road, B46 2LB (on B4116 on sharp bend)
(01675) 481205
Freestyle Griffin Dark; Oakham Citra; Theakston Old Peculier; Wye Valley Butty Bach; 8 changing beers (sourced nationally; often Freestyle, Oakham)
A renowned real ale venue with more than 25 consecutive years in this Guide. Its interior features a stone bar, inglenook fireplaces and beams decorated with old beer mats. No music is played. The pub serves up to eight guest beers, usually including Freestyle ales from the adjacent brewery. There is always one real cider, and up to four in summer. Children are welcome on the beer terrace and in the conservatory and meadow-style garden. Home-cooked lunches are served (no food Sun). Q P

Stratford-upon-Avon

Bear Freehouse

Swan's Nest Lane, CV37 7LT (S end of Clopton Bridge)
(01789) 265540 thebearfreehouse.co.uk
Hook Norton Old Hooky; North Cotswold Shagweaver; Silhill Blonde Star; Wye Valley Butty Bach; house beer (by North Cotswold); 3 changing beers (sourced regionally; often Church End, Purity)
Welcoming and delightful pub on the waterside, five minutes' walk from the town centre. Recently refurbished with a quiet room and a snug, it features a

wood-panelled interior and pewter bar. It dispenses up to eight real ales, some seasonal, with a focus on local and regional brewers. High-quality traditional pub cuisine is served in a friendly atmosphere.

Stratford Alehouse

12B Greenhill Street, CV37 6LF

07746 807966 thestratfordalehouse.com

4 changing beers (sourced nationally; often Byatt's, North Cotswold, Wye Valley)

A family-run, one-bar micropub serving the finest real ales, ciders and wines. There are no gaming machines to distract you here, just a friendly welcome in a relaxing environment for drinking, chatting, making new friends or reading the newspapers. More than 1,250 different beers have been served since the pub opened in 2013. Occasional TV sport is shown and there may be music events/bands, which include Stratford Folk Club (Wed) – check website for more details. Q

Studley

Weatheroak Tap House

21A High Street, B80 7HN

(01527) 854433 weatheroakbrewery.co.uk

Weatheroak Bees Knees, Victoria Works, Keystone Hops; house beer (by Weatheroak); 2 changing beers (sourced locally; often Beowulf, Church End, Weatheroak)

This popular and welcoming micropub with two small, cosy rooms opened in 2016 and is an outlet for the nearby Weatheroak Brewery. Basic snacks are available and there is a chip shop next door – you are welcome to bring in food. Off-sales from Weatheroak are also available. QP(x19,67,247)

Ullenhall

Winged Spur

Main Road, B95 5PA SP122674

(01564) 797396 thewingedspurullenhall.co.uk

4 changing beers (sourced regionally)

A quintessentially rural British pub in the heart of the village, with an emphasis on food and drink for families. The pub was fully refurbished and extended in 2018; its light and airy interior can seat more than 100 diners. The name derives from Robert Knight, a former local landowner, whose family crest was a spur – the medieval symbol of knighthood. QP

Warwick

Cape of Good Hope

66 Lower Cape, CV34 5DP (off Cape Rd)

(01926) 498138 thecapeofgoodhopepub.com

Church Farm Harry's Heifer; Hook Norton Hooky; Wye Valley Butty Bach; 3 changing beers

On the Grand Union Canal this historic alehouse, built in 1798, welcomes canal users and locals alike. The original building on the waterside is now the front bar, with a modern extension to the rear. Internal decorations feature canal memorabilia, including interesting maps. Three permanent real ales are offered along with three locally sourced guest beers. The friendly staff are knowledgeable, and proud to serve local ales and food. There is outside seating alongside the water next to a double lock that can get busy.

P(G1)

Four Penny Pub

27/29 Crompton Street, CV34 6HJ (nr racecourse, between A429 and A4189)

(01926) 491360 4pennyhotel.co.uk

6 changing beers

The pub is in a Georgian building dating from around 1800 and lies a short distance from the town centre, close to the racecourse and castle. Its name derives from the price of a cup of coffee and tot of rum that was charged to workers building the nearby Grand Union Canal in the early 1800s. The single, split-level room has a contemporary feel and a relaxed atmosphere, enhanced by the absence of machines or loud music.

QP

Old Post Office

12 West Street, CV34 6AN

07765 896155 oldpostofficewarwick.com

Slaughterhouse Saddleback Best Bitter; 3 changing beers /

Warwick's first alehouse offers a friendly, relaxed atmosphere and traditional beers served both on handpump and straight from the cask. Popular with real ale enthusiasts and local residents, the small bar is housed in a former shop just below the West Gate and within easy walking distance of the castle. It is decorated with a large collection of pub memorabilia. A good selection of ciders is also available. No food is served but you are welcome to bring your own.

Punch Bowl

1 The Butts, CV34 4SS

(01926) 403846 punchbowlwarwick.co.uk

5 changing beers

The building is an old coaching inn and hostelry dating back to the early 19th century. It has a large, open bar on different levels – a raised area serves as a stage for popular music events held every Thursday and Saturday. Sports events are shown on a large screen. The pub promotes real ale, with five changing guest beers available at all times. A blackboard behind the bar keeps a tally of all the different ales sold.

P(X17)

Wild Boar

27 Lakin Road, CV34 5BU

(01926) 499968 thewildboarwarwick.co.uk

Slaughterhouse Saddleback Best Bitter; 9 changing beers (often Everards, Slaughterhouse)

Award-winning Project William community pub, close to the railway station. An end-of-terrace Victorian building, it has a bar, snug and separate beer hall which was formerly a skittle alley. The pub is the taphouse for Slaughterhouse Brewery. Ten handpumps deliver Slaughterhouse, Everards and guest ales, with two real ciders also available. Outside is an attractive patio hop garden – the hops are used for Slaughterhouse's annual brew, the Green Hopper. Q(X17)

Whichford

Norman Knight

CV36 5PE (2 miles E of A3400 at Long Compton)

(01608) 684621 thenormanknight.co.uk

Hook Norton Hooky; Prescott Hill Climb; house beer (by Goff's); 2 changing beers (sourced regionally; often Purity, Timothy Taylor)

A friendly pub in the centre of this picturesque village, popular with locals and visitors. Its attractive decor and stone-flagged floor contribute to a cosy and comfortable ambience. The high-quality food is locally sourced where possible. The pub holds monthly music nights, and in summer hosts classic car meetings on the third Thursday of the month. Accommodation is available in high-specification glamping pods in the garden.

QP

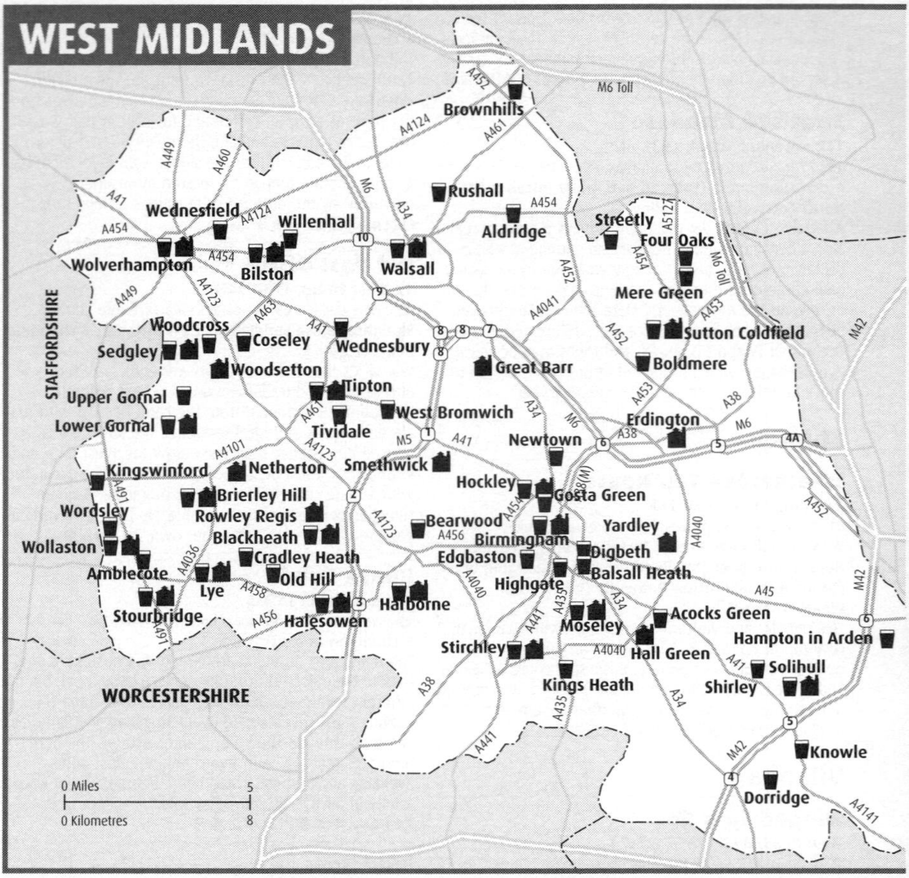

Aldridge

Turtle's Head

14 Croft Parade, WS9 8LY

☎ (01922) 325635 theturtleshead.co.uk

4 changing beers (sourced locally; often Backyard, Bristol Beer Factory, Dancing Duck)

This micropub with a warm welcome opened in 2015 in the centre of Aldridge. Four handpulls serve a range of ales from throughout the United Kingdom. Bar food includes freshly made rolls and snacks, with complimentary cheese and pâté on a Sunday. You can bring your own food if you are drinking. Discounts are offered on a Tuesday. Closed on Monday except bank holidays.

Amblecote

Robin Hood

196 Collis Street, DY8 4EQ (on A4102 one-way street off Brettell Lane A461)

☎ 07436 793462

Bathams Best Bitter; Holden's Golden Glow; St Austell Proper Job; Sarah Hughes Dark Ruby Mild; Titanic Plum Porter; Wye Valley HPA; 4 changing beers

Fine ales, quality food and a warm welcome – this is a fine traditional Black Country local. In 2015 the pub celebrated 160 years as a licensed house. The front rooms house a wonderful beer bottle collection including international and historic brews. Food is served at the weekend and occasional themed culinary nights are hosted. The bar offers some national guest ales but the LocAle scheme is emphasised – the permanent beers are mostly local. Q P

Bearwood

Bear Tavern

500 Bearwood Road, B66 4BX

☎ (0121) 429 1184

Greene King IPA; 5 changing beers (sourced nationally; often Fixed Wheel, Purity, Titanic)

Busy open-plan community local dominated by a central bar, with sports screens scattered throughout – live matches are often shown. Attentive staff serve an interesting range of nationally sourced real ales and up to two bag-in-box real ciders. There is a large wooden-floored function room upstairs, available to hire. Affordable classic pub food is served. The pub attracts a diverse clientele spanning all age groups.

Midland

526-528 Bearwood Road, B66 4BE

☎ (0121) 429 6958

Black Country Bradley's Finest Golden, Pig on the Wall, Fireside; changing beers (sourced nationally; often Beat, Downton, Magpie)

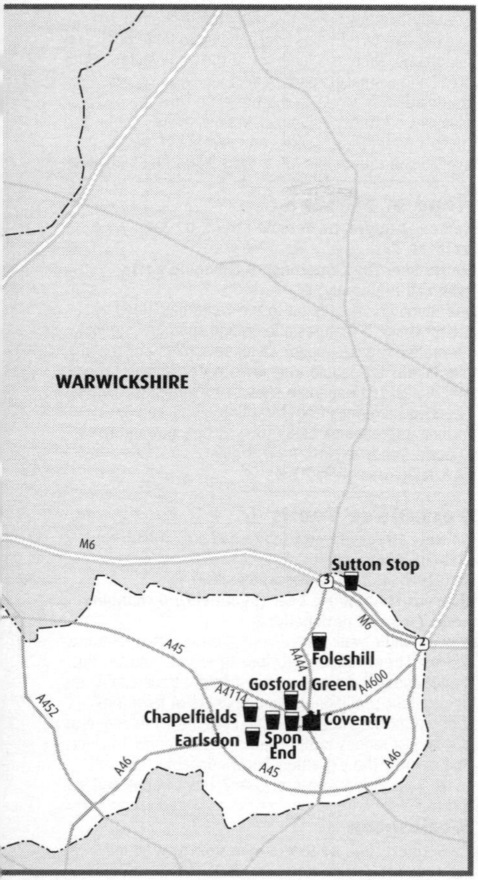

A former HSBC bank, the single-room, open-plan pub began trading in 2014 following a thorough refurbishment, and is now decorated in accordance with the established Black Country Ales theme to a high standard. It serves up to 13 real ales and three still ciders. It has a beer cellar on the same floor which can be viewed through a glass inspection panel. There is a quiz on Wednesday and live music every Thursday.
Q♣♣

Bilston

Cafe Metro

46 Church Street, WV14 0AH (opp St Leonard's Church, close to town hall)
☎ (01902) 498888
Thornbridge Jaipur IPA; Wye Valley Butty Bach; 4 changing beers (sourced nationally) Ⓗ
Friendly, busy high-street venue near both bus and Metro stations, operating more as a café during the day and a bar in the evening. The small, welcoming bar area at the front leads to a further room with seating. There is a large function room at the rear where regular beer festivals are held, also available for hire. QP

Birmingham: Acocks Green

Inn on the Green

2 Westley Road, B27 7UH
☎ (0121) 708 0108 🌐 innonthegreen.pub
6 changing beers (sourced nationally; often Wye Valley) Ⓗ
Run by a keen and passionate landlord, the Inn offers regular entertainment, with live sports and live music at the weekend. Four handpulls are in use during the week and six at weekends. The same beers are rarely on twice, so this is a great place to find beers from new breweries. Excellent beer festivals are held four times a year.
P

Birmingham: Balsall Heath

Old Moseley Arms

53 Tindal Street, B12 9QU (400yds off Moseley Rd)
☎ (0121) 440 1954 🌐 oldmoseleyarms.co.uk
Church End Goat's Milk; Enville Ale; Wye Valley HPA, Butty Bach; 1 changing beer (sourced nationally) Ⓗ
Another of Birmingham's hidden gems. The left bar has an 80in screen for sport, the right bar has a jukebox. Upstairs is for functions and the pool table, and there are comfy sofas in the covered garden/smoking area. A superb tandoori menu is served in the purpose-built extension in the evening and all day Sunday. Regular beer festivals feature 12 ales and two ciders. Live music showcases local talent upstairs or outside every Sunday evening. The bar gets busy when international and T20 cricket matches are played at Edgbaston (10 minutes' walk). ♣(50)

REAL ALE BREWERIES

AJ's Walsall
Angel Ales Halesowen
Attic Birmingham
Backyard Walsall
Banks's Wolverhampton
Bathams Brierley Hill
Beat Lye
Birmingham Birmingham
Black Country Lower Gornal
Brewhouse & Kitchen Sutton Coldfield
Burning Soul Birmingham: Hockley
Byatt's Coventry
Craddock's Stourbridge
Davenports Smethwick
Dhillon's Coventry
Dig Birmingham
Fixed Wheel Blackheath
Fownes Brierley Hill
Froth Blowers Erdington
Glasshouse Stirchley
Green Duck Stourbridge
Halton Turner Birmingham: Hall Green
Holden's Woodsetton
Indian Great Barr
Leviathan Sutton Coldfield
Mashionistas Coventry (NEW)
Moseley Moseley
Newbridge Bilston
Olde Swan Netherton
Ostlers Harborne
Pig Iron Rowley Regis
Printworks Stourbridge (NEW)
Red Moon Birmingham: Yardley
Rock & Roll Birmingham
Sarah Hughes Sedgley
Silhill Solihull
Toll End Tipton
Triumph Coventry
Twisted Barrel Coventry
Two Towers Birmingham
Websters Wollaston

Birmingham: City Centre

Bull

1 Price Street, B4 6JU (off St Chads Queensway)
☎ (0121) 333 6757
Hook Norton Old Hooky; Oakham Citra; 2 changing beers (sourced nationally) Ⓗ
A country pub in the city centre near Aston University, this popular back-street local with friendly staff is one of Birmingham's oldest venues and has a cosy, comfortable and homely feel. Two distinct drinking areas surround a U-shaped bar, with a smaller back room for more privacy, and there is a small garden at the rear. A large collection of jugs abounds, along with a number of old pictures and memorabilia. Traditional, hearty pub food is served and the guest beers change regularly. Eleven en-suite letting bedrooms are available at affordable rates.
Q❀🛏◐◑♿⇌Ω(St Chads) 🚌🐾📶

Cherry Reds 🄻

88-92 John Bright Street, B1 1BN
☎ (0121) 643 5716 🌐 cherryreds.com
3 changing beers Ⓗ
Stylish independent, open since 2010, near the Victoria, BrewDog, Railway, Stable and BoneHead, and within easy walking distance of New Street station. Expect three changing good-quality ales, often including one from Birmingham Brewing Co, and always a local offering, alongside a good range of bottled beer and keg products. Freshly cooked and interesting food is served every day, with a focus on local produce and vegan-friendly options. The bar has an upstairs area with more seating.
◐◑♿⇌Ω(Grand Central) 🚌📶

Colmore

116 Colmore Row, B3 3BD
☎ (0121) 238 1041 🌐 colmoretap.co.uk
9 changing beers (often Thornbridge) Ⓗ
Thornbridge Brewery has joined forces with Pivovar to convert and refurbish a former Lloyds bank as a bar. It offers a combination of Thornbridge beers on handpump, in draught and in bottle, with additional craft beers from Pivovar. This welcoming, stylish venue is family-friendly and serves fresh pizza made with Jaipur IPA. A range of craft beers is also available alongside wines and spirits, including no fewer than 20 gins. There is a pool table downstairs. ♉◐◑⇌Ω(Grand Central)🚌

Craven Arms 🄻

47 Upper Gough Street, B1 1JG (in side street near Mailbox)
☎ (0121) 643 2852
Black Country Bradley's Finest Golden, Pig on the Wall, Fireside; 8 changing beers (sourced nationally) Ⓗ
This early 19th-century former Holder's outlet, restored by Black Country Ales, sports an attractive blue-tiled exterior and a cosy interior. In addition to three permanent Black Country beers, between six and eight changing guest casks come from breweries often new to Birmingham. Beer festivals are held regularly. Customers are welcome to bring their own food. ◐⇌🍎P🐾📶

Gunmakers Arms 🄻

93 Bath Street, B4 6HG
☎ (0121) 236 8486 🌐 gunmakersarms.com
Two Towers Baskerville Bitter, Hockley Gold, Complete Muppetry, Chamberlain Pale Ale; 5 changing beers (sourced regionally; often Lincoln Green, Millstone, Stockport) Ⓗ
Small, pleasant, back-street pub just off the city's inner ring road, five minutes' walk from Snow Hill station. This Grade II listed Regency building, the Two Towers Brewery taphouse, was tastefully refurbished in 2017, and has five Two Towers beers and up to three guests on handpump. There is a large bar at the front, snug seating areas and a smaller room behind leading to a rear courtyard with access to the brewery. Cobs are served, plus pies on Tuesday evening. Various events are hosted (details on website, Twitter and Facebook). B&B is available at reasonable rates. ❀🛏◐◑⇌Ω(St Chads)♣🐾

Head of Steam 🄻

Somerset House, 36 Temple Street, B2 5DP
☎ (0121) 643 6824
House beer (by Camerons); 9 changing beers (sourced regionally) Ⓗ
The Birmingham addition to the Camerons' Head of Steam chain. It features a large and spacious interior decorated in a steampunk style, with plenty of seating and booths for people to enjoy a wide variety of food and drinks. Ten handpulls showcase Camerons' own beers and offerings from local breweries. Keg lines include international beers such as Delirium and La Chouffe. Tends to close early if quiet.
◐◑♿⇌Ω(Corporation St) 🐾

Post Office Vaults 🄻

84 New Street, B2 4BA (entrances are on both New St and Pinfold St)
☎ (0121) 643 7354 🌐 postofficevaults.co.uk
Hobsons Mild; house beer (by Kinver); 6 changing beers (sourced nationally) Ⓗ
A two-minute walk from the Stephenson Street entrance to New Street station and close to Victoria Square, this subterranean bar offers a range of eight traditional beers in excellent condition. It always stocks at least 350 different bottled beers from all over the world – one of the largest ranges in the country – and serves 14 ciders and perries. The extremely knowledgeable staff will make your visit a pleasure. Q⇌Ω(Town Hall)♣🍎🚌📶

Wellington 🄻

37 Bennetts Hill, B2 5SN (5 mins from New St and Snow Hill stations)
☎ (0121) 200 3115 🌐 thewellingtonrealale.co.uk
Black Country Bradley's Finest Golden, Pig on the Wall, Fireside; Oakham Citra; Purity Mad Goose; Wye Valley HPA; 10 changing beers (sourced nationally; often Froth Blowers, Titanic) Ⓗ
A stalwart of Birmingham's real ale scene, the Wellington has the feel of a community local in the heart of the city. There are 27 handpulls over two floors, dispensing well-kept ale and three traditional ciders. A huge range of whiskies is also available – the ground floor offering Scotch, the rest of the world represented on the first-floor bar. The suntrap roof terrace is a hidden urban gem. Regular quizzes, folk nights and cheese nights are held. There is no food but you can bring your own – plates, cutlery and condiments are provided.
Q❀♿⇌Ω(Grand Central) ♣🍎🚌📶

Birmingham: Digbeth

Spotted Dog 🄻

104 Warwick Street, B12 0NH
☎ (0121) 772 3822 🌐 spotteddog.co.uk
Castle Rock Harvest Pale; 4 changing beers (sourced nationally) Ⓗ
A multi-roomed traditional pub of Irish character, family-owned and with the same landlord since the 1980s. Rugby and Irish sports are shown on large-screen TVs. Outside is an extensive covered patio garden and smoking area with heaters, a large real fireplace, a barbecue, a projection screen and eclectic adornments. A traditional Irish music night takes place on alternate

Mondays, jazz night on Tuesdays, and the pub is the home of Na Madrai golf society and the Digbeth O'lympics. There is usually a cask mild on the bar. Often busy when Birmingham City play at home.

Woodman ★

New Canal Street, B5 5LG (opp old Curzon St station by Millennium Point)

☎ (0121) 643 4960 thewoodmanbirmingham.co.uk

Castle Rock Black Gold, Harvest Pale; 3 changing beers (sourced nationally)

Lovingly restored Victorian-era hostelry with original features preserved, including a gilded and etched mirror at the centre of the bar, period tiles and the old smoke room with (now discontinued) bell pushes in the wall for table service. Hearty pub food is served until the evening every day. The roof terrace overlooks Eastside Park, popular with local students and skateboarders. Regular live music showcases varied talent from the adjacent Royal Birmingham Conservatoire in the well-appointed function room. Student groups sit cheek by jowl with older regulars to create a lively and vibrant atmosphere. (Bull Street)

Birmingham: Edgbaston

Physician

Harborne Road, B15 3DH

☎ (0121) 272 5900

Brunning & Price Original; Purity Mad Goose; Timothy Taylor Landlord; 3 changing beers (sourced regionally)

Large historic former BMI building used to house the vast Sampson Gamgee Library for the History of Medicine, recently converted into a pub. It is an upmarket establishment with several drinking and dining areas. A range of ales is served, often featuring a lot of local brews, alongside a good selection of wines, gins and whiskies. P

Birmingham: Gosta Green

Sacks of Potatoes

10 Gosta Green, B4 7ER

☎ (0121) 503 5811 sacksofpotatoes.co.uk

Wye Valley HPA; 5 changing beers

This traditional pub strikes an interesting balance between serving the local student population while also appealing to the many staff at Aston University and the offices surrounding. It serves a good range of six real ales, always including Wye Valley HPA. The staff are friendly and happy to help. The regular Stonegate pub food menus are offered. All in all, a friendly bar where all are made to feel valued and welcome. P(66)

Birmingham: Harborne

Hop Garden

19 Metchley Lane, B17 0HT (100yds from High St, at back of M&S)

☎ (0121) 427 7904

5 changing beers (sourced nationally)

A small pub serious about craft beer, with few mainstream products. It serves five real ales from small and local breweries, seven craft beers and five craft ciders, as well as real cider. There is also an interesting selection of bottled beers. The décor is original and eclectic. There really are hops growing in the garden!

White Horse

2 York Street, B17 0HG

☎ (0121) 608 7641 whitehorseharborne.com

Greene King Abbot; Ostlers Terry's Gold; 7 changing beers (sourced regionally; often Bathams, Church End, Wye Valley)

Traditional community local just off the High Street, a former Festival Alehouse with a long history of real ale. It brews on the premises as Ostlers Ales. There are four rotating craft beers on KeyKeg – check what's on in real time via the website beerboard. Entertainment includes live music at the weekend, quizzes on Tuesday and Thursday, and Sky/BT sport.

Birmingham: Highgate

Lamp Tavern

157 Barford Street, B5 6AH (500yds from A441 Pershore Rd near bottom of Hurst St)

☎ (0121) 688 1220

Hobsons Mild; 4 changing beers (sourced nationally)

This hidden gem has one permanent real ale and four changing guests, often including one from Stanway as well as local breweries. It has been run by the friendly licensee for 27 years now and has a proper homely feel, with a folk club on Friday and a jazz club some Tuesdays. There is road parking only, but good bus routes nearby. Closes early if quiet. Q

Birmingham: Hockley

Burning Soul Brewery

Unit 1, Mott Street Industrial Estate, B19 3HE

☎ (0121) 439 7253 burningsoulbrewing.com

11 changing beers (sourced locally; often Burning Soul)

A changing list of smaller, experimental pilot brews is available here, so the brewery can capture at first-hand what people think of the beers – the favourites are rebrewed and sold outside the brewery. There is one handpump for cask ale plus 10 KeyKeg taps, with all Burning Soul beers meeting the CAMRA definition of real ale. Bottled mead is also sold. Brewery tours can be arranged. Card payment is preferred. P

Jewellers Arms

23 Hockley Street, B18 6BW

☎ (0121) 212 0347

Black Country Bradley's Finest Golden, Pig on the Wall, Fireside; 7 changing beers

Refurbished and reopened by Black Country Ales in 2017. It has 10 real ales and two ciders, and gets busy in the evenings. Food is limited to freshly made cobs. The interior is now all open plan, with a real fire at one end lit daily in winter. There is just one fruit machine. A function room is available upstairs. Q

Rock & Roll Brewhouse

19 Hall Street, B18 6BS

☎ 07969 759649

Rock & Roll Brew Springsteen, Thirst Aid Kit, Voodoo Mild

A quirky brewery taproom bedecked with music memorabilia. The bar staff and their knowledge of beer is excellent – the brewery's other shared love is music and a playlist of what you're hearing is on the wall. There is usually a choice of three vegan-friendly ales, always including a dark beer. Hogan's cider is also available. Open Thursday and Friday evenings and Saturday afternoon only. Check Facebook before visiting as the taproom is occasionally closed for music festivals.

Birmingham: Kings Heath

Hop & Scotch

9 Institute Road, B14 7EG

☎ (0121) 679 8807 🌐 hopscotchbrum.com

4 changing beers (sourced locally; often Green Duck, Kinver) Ⓗ

Friendly and welcoming microbar with three to four cask beers, often from local producers Green Duck and Kinver, together with an interesting range of KeyKeg beers from local breweries, some of which are vegan-friendly. Bottled and canned ales are also sold. Beers currently on offer are displayed on torn-off paper strips stuck on a side wall. There are various seating areas in various styles. The bar attracts a wide age range and can get busy in the evening. Dogs are welcome, with snacks offered. Opening hours vary – see the website for up-to-date times. 🚌🐾

Kings Heath Cricket & Sports Club

Charlton House, 247 Alcester Road South, B14 6DT

☎ (0121) 444 1913 🌐 kingsheathsportsclub.com

Wye Valley HPA, Butty Bach; 2 changing beers (sourced nationally) Ⓗ

Welcoming sports club where CAMRA members are permitted entry on production of a membership card (maximum 10 visits per year). The club has two rooms: the comfortable lounge for relaxed drinking, and the big room for watching sporting events on large screens and also housing two full-size snooker tables. The beer range always includes two rotating guest ales. Various social events are held throughout the year, including live music. Q🐴❀◑♿♣🍎P🚌📶

Birmingham: Moseley

Prince of Wales 𝕃 ✔

118 Alcester Road, B13 8EE

☎ (0121) 449 4198 🌐 theprincemoseley.co.uk

Oakham Bishops Farewell; Purity Mad Goose; Timothy Taylor Landlord; 2 changing beers (often Oakham, Titanic) Ⓗ

This traditional Victorian pub is a lively venue in the heart of Moseley village. At the front is a bar with 10 handpumps, a real fire and a TV showing sports. At the rear is a snug and cigar emporium. Outside is a large covered and heated area, ideal at any time of year. There is also an exterior bar selling cocktails, numerous foreign beers and various wines. ❀🍎🚌🐾📶

Birmingham: Newtown

Bartons Arms ★ ✔

144 High Street, B6 4UP

☎ (0121) 333 5988 🌐 thebartonsarms.com

Oakham JHB, Inferno, Citra, Bishops Farewell; 2 changing beers (sourced nationally; often Oakham) Ⓗ

This Grade II* listed building is a classic example of late-Victorian splendour. From the main bar the superb original stained-glass windows can be viewed, with the M&B logo as it was in 1901. There are ornate Minton tiles and a fancy tiled staircase. The restaurant is well known for its excellent Thai cuisine. As well as the regular Oakham beers and seasonals, at least one guest ale is usually served. The pub can get busy when Aston Villa are at home. 🐴◑🍎P🚌📶

Birmingham: Stirchley

Wildcat Tap

1381-1383 Pershore Road, B30 2JR

🌐 stirchleywildcat.co.uk

5 changing beers (sourced nationally) Ⓗ

This bar is much changed from the original Wildcat just down the road and is spacious for a micropub, with adequate seating, although it does get busy at weekends, attracting all ages. The beer range of cask and keg is adventurous and interesting, with five casks on handpump, a real cider and eight craft keg lines, complemented by a selection of bottled craft beers, gin, whisky and soft drinks. ≹🍎🚌

Blackheath

Britannia ✔

124 Halesowen Street, B65 0ES

☎ (0121) 559 0010

Exmoor Gold; Greene King Abbot; Ruddles Best Bitter; 6 changing beers (sourced nationally; often Backyard, Kinver, Slater's) Ⓗ

An L-shaped Wetherspoon outlet at the very heart of Blackheath. The garden at the rear of the property provides a pleasant space away from the main A4099. The exposed brick façade is often decorated with hanging baskets in the warmer seasons. Six changing beers are accompanied by three permanent beers. Pictures placed throughout the pub depict local monuments and historic characters. Food is served all day, every day. A small car park for customers can be accessed via Cross Street. 🐴❀◑♿≹♣🍎P🚌📶

Boldmere

Bishop Vesey 𝕃

63 Boldmere Road, B73 5XA

☎ (0121) 355 5077

Backyard Blonde; Greene King Abbot; Oakham Citra; Ruddles Best Bitter; Sharp's Doom Bar; 11 changing beers (sourced nationally; often Oakham) Ⓗ

A busy Wetherspoon whose consistent performance has earned it 20 consecutive years in the Guide. Named after the area's Tudor benefactor, who is credited with gaining royal status for Sutton Coldfield, it features a carved wooden pulpit by the entrance. Up to 11 interesting guest beers are offered, many from local microbreweries, plus a changing real cider. As well as extensive seating areas upstairs and down, there is a spacious rooftop garden, and a smaller beer garden downstairs. 🐴❀◑♿≹♣🍎🚌📶

Cask & Craft

56 Boldmere Road, B73 5TJ

☎ 07497 828911

2 changing beers (sourced nationally; often Tiny Rebel) Ⓟ

Friendly micropub opened in 2019, with craft beers and, usually, two real ales. No handpulls – the ales come through a keg tap but are fed by an electric pump. Wines, gins and cocktails also feature. The bar area is on the small side, but there's a larger room upstairs offering more seating. A well-stocked fridge has a range of craft beers, mostly canned. ≹🚌📶

Brierley Hill

Garrison

Waterfront E, DY5 1XL

☎ (01384) 349644

Enville Ale; Fixed Wheel Chain Reaction Pale Ale; Green Duck Duck Blonde; Salopian Shropshire Gold; house beer (by Salopian); 3 changing beers (sourced nationally; often Salopian, Tiny Rebel, Titanic) Ⓗ

This 1920s-themed saloon bar is a welcome addition to the Waterfront Business Park, which was once a hotspot for drinkers. The seven real ales include Garrison Gold (Salopian Shropshire Gold), Garrison Pale (Fixed Wheel Chain Reaction), Green Duck Duck Blonde, Enville Ale, and three changing beers. Real ciders, keg and lager lines, and a selection of top-shelf tipples complete the drinks offering. The bar has a Peaky Blinders mural, a jukebox, and a small stage to accommodate live acts. Q≒&♦P☐❀

Rose & Crown L
161 Bank Street, DY5 3DD (on B4179)
☎ (01384) 936166
Holden's Black Country Bitter, Golden Glow, Special; 1 changing beer (often Holden's) ⊞
This traditional pub was originally two terraced properties. One end of the bar is dominated by a dartboard. A conservatory provides extra space and is used as a function room, opening on to a small garden with tables and benches. There is a bus stop outside, or a five-minute walk takes you to Brierley Hill High Street, which is served by several bus routes. Holden's seasonal beers are rotated. Q≒✿♣P☐❀♥

Vine
10 Delph Road, DY5 2TN
☎ (01384) 78293
Bathams Mild Ale, Best Bitter ⊞
Unspoilt brewery tap with an ornately decorated façade proclaiming the Shakespearian quotation 'Blessing of your heart, you brew good ale'. An elongated pub with a labyrinthine feel, the front bar is staunchly traditional, while the larger rear room has its own servery, leather seating and a dartboard. The homely lounge was partly converted from former brewery offices. Black Country lunches, such as faggots and home-made pies, are served weekdays, with generously filled rolls and pork pies at all times. Q≒✿◑♣P☐(8)♥♥

Waterfront Inn ✔
6-7 The Waterfront, Level Street, DY5 1XE (between A461 and A4036)
☎ (01384) 262096
Greene King Abbot; 3 changing beers (sourced nationally; often Exmoor, Sharp's, Shepherd Neame) ⊞
Comparatively small single-room Wetherspoon outlet in an attractive location overlooking the Dudley Number One Canal basin, with a patio and garden enjoying a sunny aspect. Food is served from the standard menu all day. Bag-in-box real cider comes from the fridge. The pub now benefits from a recent resurgence in entertainment and drinks venues across the Waterfront Business Park. Q≒✿◑&♦P☐(8,81)♥

Brownhills

Jiggers Whistle L
5-7 Brownhills High Street, WS8 6ED
☎ 07854 356976
House beer (by Green Duck); 3 changing beers (sourced nationally; often AJ's Ales, Backyard, Green Duck) ⊞
Micropub opened in 2017, with one room divided into three interconnected drinking areas. It serves a wide range of cask and craft keg ales, and around eight real ciders, plus bar snacks at weekends. This venue has grown hugely in popularity and now has its own darts team. The owners offer customers a warm and friendly welcome and are keen to support local events. Q≒♣♦P☐(10)♥♥

Coseley

Old Chainyard L
63 Castle Street, WV14 9DW
2 changing beers (sourced regionally; often Kinver, Purity, Salopian) ⊞
Lively single-roomed community pub serving two rotating cask beers, at least one often from Salopian Brewery. The handpulls not in use advertise beers that are currently resting in the cellar and coming soon. A number of beer festivals feature throughout the year. The pub is a five-minute walk from Coseley train station and a three-minute walk from the A4123 – both of which offer direct links to Birmingham and Wolverhampton. ≒✿≈♣P☐♥♥

Coventry: Chapelfields

Hearsall Inn L
45 Craven Street, CV5 8DS (1 mile W of city centre, off Allesley Old Rd)
☎ (024) 7671 5729 ⊕ hearsallinn.com
Church End Goat's Milk; Draught Bass; 2 changing beers (sourced locally; often Byatt's) ⊞
Built in the 1850s to serve Chapelfields' historic watchmaking district, this free house has been run by the same family for 22 years. It has separate bar and lounge areas with a paved patio to the front. The pub is home to darts, dominoes and football teams and hosts traditional Irish music on Tuesday evenings. Four handpumps dispense local and regional beers. Freshly made batches are available throughout the day. The building has an externally mounted defibrillator. ≒✿♣☐♥♥

Nursery Tavern
38-39 Lord Street, CV5 8DA (1 mile W of city centre, off Allesley Old Rd)
☎ (024) 7667 4530
Fuller's London Pride; Otter Bitter; 4 changing beers (sourced nationally) ⊞
Boasting a long unbroken run in the Guide, this traditional mid-terrace local in the historic watchmaking area provides a comfortable retreat for beer, conversation and pub games. It has three separate and quite distinct rooms, complemented by a rear courtyard that is perfect for summer drinks and also hosts mini beer festivals twice a year. Good-value Sunday lunches are served. The pub regularly holds popular live music evenings showcasing local talent. Q≒✿◑♣♦☐(8,8A)♥♥

Coventry: City Centre

Earl of Mercia ✔
18 High Street, CV1 5RE
☎ (024) 7643 3990
Greene King Abbot; Ruddles Best Bitter; Sharp's Doom Bar; 5 changing beers (sourced nationally) ⊞
An inviting city-centre Wetherspoon housed in a former bank near to the imposing Council House. It is named after Leofric, Earl of Mercia, who, along with his wife Godiva, founded Coventry's St Mary's Priory in 1043. The pub is ideally situated for city centre shops and local attractions, and has seating split across ground floor and mezzanine levels, plus a small front patio area. A good selection of ales is on offer with local breweries regularly featured. ≒✿◑&≈☐♥

Gatehouse Tavern L
44-46 Hill Street, CV1 4AN (close to Belgrade Theatre and Spon St, near jct 8 of Ring Road)
☎ (024) 7663 0140

Draught Bass; Fuller's London Pride; 4 changing beers (sourced locally; often Byatt's, Church End, Purity) Ⓗ
A former gatehouse building for Leigh Mills, converted to a pub in 1995 by the current landlord. This long-standing Guide entry is sports-oriented, with most major events shown on several large screens. A stained-glass window portrays the emblems of all Six Nations rugby teams. Outside is an attractive grassed beer garden. Good-value home-cooked meals are served. One handpump is usually given over to real cider. ☋❀◑🍎🚌📶

Golden Cross 🄻 ✔
8 Hay Lane, CV1 5RF (near old cathedral ruins)
☎ (024) 7655 1855 🌐 thegoldencrosscoventry.co.uk
House beer (by Ringwood); 3 changing beers (sourced locally; often Adnams, Byatt's, Church End) Ⓗ
One of the claimants to being the oldest pub in Coventry, originally a mint in medieval times. The imposing black and white exterior is not matched by the interior, which was the victim of corporate vandalism in the 1960s. However, the most recent interior refurbishment has been carried out in sympathetic style. The pub is a handy refreshment stop after visiting Coventry's three cathedrals, which are adjacent. Live music features in the upstairs room at weekends, with open mic downstairs on Tuesday evening. ❀◑🍎🚌📶

Old Windmill 🄻 ✔
22-23 Spon Street, CV1 3BA
☎ (024) 7625 1717
Morland Old Speckled Hen; Theakston Old Peculier; Timothy Taylor Landlord; 4 changing beers (sourced locally; often North Cotswold) Ⓗ
A stunning 15th-century building in a medieval street, with a number of rooms that still hold clues to their former uses. One houses a stove within a large fireplace with an adjacent priest hole, another a Victorian brewhouse. One of two claimants to being the oldest pub in the city, it is still known locally as Ma Brown's in memory of an early 20th-century landlady. Recommended locally produced pork pies are served. Two beer festivals are held annually. ♣🍎🚌🐾📶

Town Wall Tavern ✔
Bond Street, CV1 4AH
☎ (024) 7622 0963
Brains Rev James; Draught Bass; Theakston Best Bitter, Old Peculier; Wye Valley HPA; 3 changing beers (sourced nationally; often North Cotswold) Ⓗ
Convivial traditional city centre local behind the Belgrade Theatre, now dwarfed by high-rise buildings, and often busy with theatregoers before and after performances. Open fires feature both in the bar and lounge, and discreet smaller areas add charm. Must-sees are the Donkey Box snug, which was fashioned out of the former off-sales counter, plus an internal window that bears the long defunct Atkinsons Brewery crest. Excellent pub food is served from Tuesday to Saturday, with roast lunches on Sunday. ❀◑🍎🚌🐾

Coventry: Earlsdon

City Arms 🄻 ✔
1 Earlsdon Street, CV5 6EP (on roundabout at centre of Earlsdon)
☎ (024) 7671 8170
Greene King Abbot; Ruddles Best Bitter; Sharp's Doom Bar; 7 changing beers (sourced nationally; often Byatt's, Grainstore, Purity) Ⓗ
A large mock-Tudor building housing a popular Wetherspoon in the heart of the bustling Earlsdon suburb. With excellent transport links to the city centre and local universities, it appeals to a mixed clientele and can get busy on weekend evenings. It has a large open-plan main room and a quieter smaller room, plus an attractive outdoor drinking area to the side. Good-value food is served. Beer and gin festivals feature regularly. ☋❀◑♿🍎P🚌(5,11) 📶

Coventry: Foleshill

Byatt's Brewhouse Bar 🄻
Unit 7-8, Lythalls Lane Industrial Estate, Lythalls Lane, CV6 6FL
☎ (024) 7663 7996 🌐 byattsbrewery.co.uk
6 changing beers (sourced locally; often Byatt's) Ⓗ
Contemporary brewery taproom located on a small industrial estate, comprising a ground-floor bar area plus mezzanine. Handpumps dispense up to six changing beers from the Byatt's portfolio, with three gravity ciders and bottle-conditioned beers and carry-out containers also available. There are occasional quiz and music nights plus brewery tours and tastings (book in advance). The bar opens some Sundays but only prior to Wasps home fixtures at the nearby Ricoh Arena. Check the website for seasonal variations. ☋♿🍎P🚌🐾📶

Coventry: Gosford Green

Twisted Barrel Brewery & Tap House 🄻
Fargo Village, Far Gosford Street, CV1 5ED
☎ (024) 7610 1701 🌐 twistedbarrelale.co.uk
Twisted Barrel Beast of a Midlands Mild, Detroit Sour City, God's Twisted Sister, Sine Qua Non, Naido; 18 changing beers (sourced nationally) Ⓗ/Ⓟ
Enjoy beer right where it's made at this brewery and bar in a renovated industrial unit within a creative arts development. All beers are vegan and a variety of styles is offered. Two handpumps and multiple KeyKeg lines dispense at least five of the core beers plus seasonal and special brews. There is also a good selection of guest beers. Regular events are held each month including quizzes, home-brew clubs, comedy and open mic nights. ☋♿🍎P🚌🐾📶

Coventry: Spon End

Broomfield Tavern 🏆 🄻
14-16 Broomfield Place, CV5 6GY (adjacent to rugby ground but hidden from main road)
☎ (024) 7663 0969
Church End Fallen Angel; Froth Blowers Piffle Snonker; 8 changing beers (sourced locally) Ⓗ
A unique pub with quirky brickwork features – its owners are gradually renovating, so the building remains a work in progress. The L-shaped front room is a mix of bar and lounge areas, while the back room is used for music and other events. It can get busy at weekends with rugby fans and when live music is hosted, but the attentive staff ensure service is prompt. A genuine free house, it is local CAMRA Pub of the Year in 2020. Q☋♣🍎🚌🐾

Coventry: Sutton Stop

Greyhound Inn
Sutton Stop, Hawkesbury Junction, CV6 6DF (off Grange Rd)
☎ (024) 7636 3046 🌐 thegreyhoundlongford.co.uk
Draught Bass; Greene King Abbot; 3 changing beers (sourced nationally) Ⓗ
Dating from the 1830s, the building overlooks Hawkesbury Junction where the Coventry and Oxford canals meet. This traditional award-winning pub is

popular with regulars and visitors alike. Real fires add to a cosy atmosphere for drinkers and diners in the winter. In the summer, a canalside patio and garden provide the perfect setting for watching the world, and boats, go by. An extensive menu of freshly cooked food is offered. Beer festivals are held twice-yearly. ⛑❀◑♣●P🐾ᯤ

Cradley Heath

Plough & Harrow

82 Corngreaves Road, B64 7BT
☎ (01384) 638351
Banks's Mild; Wye Valley HPA, Butty Bach; 3 changing beers (sourced nationally; often Abbeydale, Bristol Beer Factory, Fernandes) Ⓗ
Local CAMRA branch Pub of the Year 2020 finalist and Community Pub of the Year 2020. This tastefully modernised hostelry is a pleasant, comfortable place. Children are allowed until the evening. Dogs must remain on a lead. Baguettes and cobs are available. Sports TV is a background feature and does not detract from an enjoyable drinking environment. Three regular beers and three changing hoppy guest ales are all keenly priced. Q⛑❀⇌♣P🚌(18,14A)🐾ᯤ

Dorridge

Knowle & Dorridge Cricket Club

Station Road, B93 8ET (corner of Station and Grove Rd)
☎ (01564) 774338 🌐 knowleanddorridgecc.co.uk
3 changing beers (sourced nationally) Ⓗ
This established cricket club is set in an upmarket residential area, with outside seating to watch top-class cricket in the Birmingham league. Visitors are welcome to try the changing range of up to three cask-conditioned ales, always in excellent condition and often from interesting breweries. There are no entry restrictions, but drinks are reduced in price for club members. Bar snacks and filled rolls are usually available. CAMRA branch Club of the Year three years in succession.
⛑❀♿⇌●P🚌(S2,S3)🐾ᯤ

Four Oaks

Butlers Arms ✔

444 Lichfield Road, B74 4BL
☎ (0121) 308 0765 🌐 butlersarms.co.uk
4 changing beers Ⓗ
Family-run pub geared towards dining, though drinkers are always made welcome. The décor has an engagingly eccentric style, with mirrors, lamps, curiosities and colourful seating. The four guest ales change but often come from well-known breweries. There's an excellent wide-ranging food menu, with fish-lovers looked after particularly well. Live music is hosted on the last Friday of the month. A small beer terrace is to the front. Car parking is free but requires registration number entry at the bar. Q⛑❀◑♿⇌P🐾

Halesowen

Crafty Pint H'ales'owen 🄻

8 Wassell Road, B63 4JU
☎ 07823 880240
Wye Valley Butty Bach; 5 changing beers (often Oakham, Salopian, Titanic) Ⓗ
A micropub, now occupying the adjacent building as well, run by a local resident. It offers traditional ale, cider, wines and beverages plus pork pies. Coffee is generally available during the week, along with crusty cobs and sausage rolls. No children are allowed in the evening. Q⛑●P🚌🐾ᯤ

Hawne Tavern 🄻

76 Attwood Street, B63 3UG (just off Stourbridge Rd, down Short St opp Tesco Express)
☎ (0121) 602 6743
Bathams Best Bitter; Oakham Citra; Wye Valley HPA; 6 changing beers Ⓗ
A back-street locals' pub just off the main bus route. It has a large bar with a pool table and a TV showing sports (not Sky), with separate seating areas plus a smaller cosy lounge. There are three regular and up to six guest ales, many of which are from microbreweries, specialising in northern beers. Real cider is also sold. Baguettes are available in the evenings, hot sandwiches and chips at weekends. The enclosed rear garden has a smoking shelter. Q❀♣●🎯🚌🐾

King Edward VII 🄻 ✔

88 Stourbridge Road, B63 3UP
☎ (0121) 602 2537
Enville Ale; Holden's Golden Glow; 6 changing beers Ⓗ
Friendly, comfortable venue next to Halesowen Town football ground, on the main road just out of the town centre towards Stourbridge. There is a large front lounge and a smaller rear lounge with sports TV, both served by a central bar, selling eight real ales plus one cider. Bar snacks are available Wednesday to Sunday. This is one of several pubs in the locality selling quality real ale.
⛑❀♿●P🚌(9)🐾

Shell-ter 🄻

1A Nimmings Road, B62 9JJ
Enville Ale; Wye Valley HPA; 1 changing beer (sourced regionally) Ⓗ
A micropub near Shell Corner that opened in 2017, with a large single room big enough for up to 50 customers. Three real ales are always on, usually from local breweries, as well as a box of real cider. Cold snacks are served (cobs, samosas, etc). The comfortable interior decor is military themed, with a gas mask, German hand grenade, ammo box and replica plane in the roof space. There is no car park but plenty of street parking is available in the vicinity. ♿⇌●P🚌(14)🐾ᯤ

Waggon & Horses 🄻

21 Stourbridge Road, B63 3TU (on main A458, ½ mile from bus station)
☎ (0121) 585 9699
Black Country Bradley's Finest Golden, Pig on the Wall, Fireside; 10 changing beers (sourced nationally) Ⓗ
Former CAMRA branch Pub of the Year, the Waggon dates from the 1850s and was recently refurbished by Black Country Ales, retaining many of its historical features. One long bar serves three drinking areas. The main bar is very narrow, with a famous sloping floor. Eighteen handpulls dispense three regular ales and 10 guests, and five real ciders are also available. Cobs and snacks are served. There is no car park but there is adequate street parking nearby. Q♿●🚌(9)🐾ᯤ

Hampton in Arden

White Lion ✔

10 High Street, B92 0AA
☎ (01675) 442833 🌐 thewhitelioninn.com
Banks's Mild; Hobsons Best; Holden's Golden Glow; M&B Brew XI; Skinner's Betty Stogs; Wye Valley HPA Ⓗ
A charming 17th-century timber-framed building with Grade II status, the White Lion has been licensed since 1838. It has an L-shaped lounge and dining area with a

separate public bar, and lovely real fires. The dining space is light, airy and open plan, serving quality British pub food with a French accent lunchtimes and evenings. The quantity and quality of real ales is always of the highest level, with two beers rotating every five to six months. This traditional country venue is well worth a visit. Q P (82)

Kingswinford

Cottage ✔
534 High Street, DY6 8AW
☎ (01384) 287133
Enville Ale; St Austell Tribute; 2 changing beers (sourced nationally; often Exmoor, Three Tuns, Wye Valley) H
Comfortable pub set on two levels, with a homely and inviting interior. It offers a good food menu including lunchtime specials, as well as a carvery on Sunday which also supplies the meat for delicious sandwiches and cobs. The layout is L-shaped and diners and drinkers intermingle throughout this spacious hostelry. Guest beers are always pale and sessionable. A range of country wines is also stocked. Quiz night is Wednesday and Sunday. The frontage would not look out of place on a postcard. Q P (16)

Knowle

Ale Rooms ✔
1592 High Street, B93 0LF
☎ (01564) 400040
7 changing beers (sourced nationally; often Church End, Silhill) H
This micropub in a converted shop (formerly a funeral directors) is a welcome addition to the Knowle beer scene. It stocks at least one real ale from the local Silhill Brewery, along with one from Church End, plus guests. Real cider, wines and spirits, including speciality gins, are also available. The usual bar snacks are served. Regular live music is featured. Local CAMRA Pub of the Year 2018 and 2019, and West Midlands County Pub of the Year 2019. (S3)

Lower Gornal

Fountain Inn
8 Temple Street, DY3 2PE (on B4157 5 mins from Gornal Wood bus station)
☎ (01384) 596317
Greene King Yardbird, Abbot; Hobsons Town Crier; Wye Valley HPA, Butty Bach; 7 changing beers (sourced nationally; often Church End, Fixed Wheel, Malvern Hills) H
With separate areas for drinking and dining, in addition to a pretty courtyard at the rear, this is a pub for all occasions. It now serves 12 real ales, and an extensive food menu daily except Monday. Prior notice of upcoming beers is given on a blackboard opposite the central bar. There is wheelchair access via a ramp at the back. The pub reopened under new management in 2018.

Old Bull's Head
1 Redhall Road, DY3 2NU (at jct with Temple St, B4175)
☎ (01384) 231616
Black Country Bradley's Finest Golden, Pig on the Wall, Fireside; Hobsons Town Crier; 4 changing beers (often Fixed Wheel, Oakham, Salopian) H
The brewery tap for Black Country Ales, a choice of eight beers is available here. The rear lounge has a sports focus and is also used to host celebrations, while the front bar has a dartboard adjacent to the real fire. Large crusty cobs are a popular accompaniment to the ales. A variety of CAMRA reading materials is well-maintained by the management. Regular beer festivals are held in the garden, where there is additional seating.
P

Lye

Windsor Castle L ✔
7 Stourbridge Road, DY9 7DG (at Lye Cross)
☎ (01384) 897809 windsorcastleinn.co.uk
Printworks Helvetica, Bumble Bees, Verdana, Geneva; 6 changing beers (sourced locally) H
Formerly the taphouse and brewery for Sadler's Ales, the Windsor Castle now offers its own Printworks Brewery beers. The modern yet cosy interior has an atmosphere that is relaxed during the week and livens up at weekends. Home-made food is served daily including breakfast on Saturday. The adjoining brewery offers brewery tours. Accommodation is available. Ale is available to take away if you're frequenting one of the local curry houses. Q P (9,7)

Mere Green

Mare Pool L ✔
294 Lichfield Road, B74 2UG (behind shops on E side of Lichfield Rd)
☎ (0121) 323 1070
Greene King IPA, Abbot; Sharp's Doom Bar; 5 changing beers H
This is a busy Wetherspoon pub that works hard to keep its ale choices interesting. Local and national beers are featured, with an emphasis on change. The Mare pool was one of many pools that used to surround Sutton Coldfield – the watery theme is reflected in the decor, with hundreds of hanging glass droplets. The comfortable interior is complemented by café-style seating outside at the front, plus a beer terrace to the side. Q P

Old Hill

Wheelie Thirsty L
215 Halesowen Road, B64 6HE
Fixed Wheel Wheelie Pale; Oakham Inferno; 4 changing beers (often Fixed Wheel, Titanic) H
The second establishment operated by Fixed Wheel Brewery, joining the Brewery Tap in Blackheath. This single-room micropub opened in May 2019 and was previously a Mediterranean café. In addition to the six cask ales, there is a range of eight rotating craft keg beers and eight ciders. Quiz/cheese/pizza nights take place monthly, with music on alternate Sunday afternoons. Street parking is free and unconstrained after 6pm. Local CAMRA branch Pub of the Year finalist and Cider Pub of the Year 2020. (19,X10)

Rushall

Manor Arms ★ L ✔
Park Road, off Daw End Lane, WS4 1LG (off B4154 at canal bridge)
☎ (01922) 642333
Banks's Amber Ale, Sunbeam; Bombardier; Wainwright; 1 changing beer (often Young's) H
A canalside inn built around 1105, thought to have held a licence for ale since 1248 – it is one of the oldest establishments in the country. It retains period features including exposed beams and open fires in both bars. Known locally as the pub with no bar, beer pulls come

straight out of the wall. Although a little off the beaten track, this place is well worth a visit. A country park and nature reserve are close by. Q🚼❀P🚌🐾

Sedgley

Beacon Hotel ★ 🄻

129 Bilston Street, DY3 1JE (on A463)
☎ (01902) 883380 🌐 sarahhughesbrewery.co.uk
Sarah Hughes Pale Amber, Sedgley Surprise, Dark Ruby Mild; 3 changing beers (sourced nationally; often Bristol Beer Factory, Shiny, Vocation) Ⓗ
A unique destination brewery tap for Sarah Hughes, also offering progressive guest beers. It is a popular Grade II listed pub brimming with character – queues have been known to assemble ahead of opening time. The biggest selling beer by some margin is the award-winning Sarah Hughes Dark Ruby Mild. The large garden has children's play facilities at the rear and is used to host various annual events such as Black Country Day.
Q🚼❀P🚌(229,224)

Clifton ✔

Bull Ring, DY3 1RX (on A459)
☎ (01902) 677448
Greene King Abbot; Ruddles Best Bitter; changing beers (sourced nationally; often Backyard, Kinver, Salopian) Ⓗ
Multi-level JD Wetherspoon outlet at the heart of Sedgley. It last featured in the 2007 edition of the Guide, but a sustained and noticeable improvement in beer quality in recent years has led to its inclusion once again. Popular with drinkers and diners of all ages, it gets exceptionally busy at peak weekend times. The building opened as a cinema back in 1937 before becoming a bingo hall in the 1970s. Q🚼❀◐◑♿●P🚌📶

Mount Pleasant

144 High Street, DY3 1RH (on A459)
☎ 07950 195652
9 changing beers (sourced nationally; often Enville, Oakham, Wychwood) Ⓗ
Known locally as the Stump, this popular free house serves a selection of nine beers. It has a mock-Tudor frontage and a Tardis-like interior. The front bar is the first room off a long corridor. The lounge areas have an intimate feel, with two rooms on different levels housing various nooks and crannies, both with a real coal stove. The pub is on the main No.1 bus route, or a five-minute walk from the centre of Sedgley. Q❀♣P🚌(1)🐾

White Lion Inn

104 Bilston Street, DY3 1JF
☎ (01902) 685232
Oakham Bishops Farewell; 3 changing beers (often Olde Swan, Salopian, Thornbridge) Ⓗ
Large wet-only pub serving a range of pale and often hoppy beers, popular for spectators of sport, which is shown on TVs. What was previously the restaurant is now a quieter drinking lounge and can be used for meetings and functions. There is a garden with benches at the rear. The pub is served by a large car park next door, accessed via Claremont Road. ❀P🚌(229,224)📶

Shirley

Shaking Hand

Unit 24 Parkgate, Stratford Road, B90 3GG
☎ (0121) 733 1176
4 changing beers
A first entry in the Guide for this friendly, light and airy micropub in the Parkgate shopping centre. It is a single-room premises serving four regularly changing guest ales, usually two from local breweries and two from further afield. It ticks all the micropub boxes: no loud music, no sports TV, no electronic games, just plenty of chat, a warm welcome and great beer. Q🚼♿●P🚌📶

Solihull

Fieldhouse ✔

10 Knightcote Drive, B91 3JU
☎ (0121) 703 9209
Purity Pure UBU; St Austell Proper Job; house beer (by Brakspear); 3 changing beers (sourced nationally; often Black Sheep) Ⓗ
Part of the Ember Inns chain, this large, modern pub is tastefully decorated and comfortably furnished. It features three large fires (one real, two coal-effect) and pleasant patio areas. Six ales are usually available, including three guest beers from across the country, often unusual and changing frequently. Cask ales are sold at a discount on Monday. Often busy, the pub attracts a wide age range. It hosts quiz nights on Sunday and Tuesday, monthly tribute acts and occasional Meet the Brewer events. 🚼❀◐◑♿P🚌(S15,5)📶

Pup & Duckling

1 Hatchford Brook Road, B92 9AG
☎ (0121) 247 8358 🌐 pupandduckling.co.uk
6 changing beers (sourced nationally; often Fixed Wheel) Ⓗ
Solihull's first micropub, family run and opened in 2016 in a vacant shop. A garden area and another room have been added to the original two-room layout. Six rapidly changing real ales are on handpull, along with six ciders. The latest beers are listed on Facebook, but can sell out in an evening. Bar snacks are served and customers are welcome to bring in their own food from nearby Chinese, Indian and fish and chips takeaways. CAMRA branch Pub of the Year 2020. Q❀●🚌(73,957)🐾📶

Stourbridge

Queen's Head 🏆 🄻

111 Enville Street, DY8 3TQ
☎ (01384) 396283
Black Country Bradley's Finest Golden, Pig on the Wall, Fireside; 7 changing beers (sourced nationally) Ⓗ
Recently purchased by Black Country Ales, this is a real ale-centric pub with 12 handpulls, situated just a short walk from Stourbridge town centre. At the rear there is a comfortable heated smoking shelter, and a separate function room with a newly renovated skittle alley, ideal for events and private functions. Regular live music and comedy events now feature. Bar snacks are available. Current local CAMRA Pub of the Year. ❀♣●🚌🐾

Red House Boutique 🄻

21-26 Foster Street East, DY8 1EL
☎ (01384) 936430
Enville Ale; Holden's Golden Glow; 6 changing beers (sourced nationally; often Fixed Wheel, Three Tuns) Ⓗ
Large, single-bar free house near to Stourbridge Interchange. Originally part of the Hogshead chain, this refurbished pub has returned to being an alehouse. Beers from Enville, Fixed Wheel and Three Tuns will usually be on the bar but may change from those listed. A range of KeyKegs is also on sale. Gourmet snacks can be enjoyed at all times including Scotch eggs and flavoured scratchings. Fridges behind the bar are stocked with many bottles from around the world. ❀♿⇌●🚌🐾📶

Waggon & Horses

31 Worcester Street, DY8 1AT
(01384) 395398
Church End Goat's Milk; Enville Ale; Holden's Golden Glow; 4 changing beers
Recent refurbishment has created a comfortable, welcoming alehouse. There is a small cask ale bar to the front with a narrow passageway leading to a larger rear bar. To the side is a cider bar with a small serving hatchway, offering two or more real ciders. Parking can be difficult in the narrow surrounding streets.

Streetly

Brew House

49 Boundary Road, B74 2JR
(0121) 679 8512
4 changing beers
This basic micropub, opened in 2018, sits at the end of a parade of suburban shops and is an ale oasis in an area dominated by chain pubs. Up to four beers are offered, with a growing array of pumpclips showing those you've missed. Craft beers, real ciders and spirits are also stocked. Parking is available at the front.

Sutton Coldfield

Station

44 Station Street, B73 6AT (near Sutton station southbound platform)
(0121) 362 4961 craft-pubs.co.uk/thestationsuttoncoldfield
Black Sheep Best Bitter; Holden's Golden Glow; Timothy Taylor Landlord; 5 changing beers
Traditional rail-themed pub right next to the station, ideal for commuters, with a view of the departures board from the bar. Up to eight ales are offered on handpulls in both front and back bars – check the chalkboard for what's available. Monthly Meet The Brewer sessions reflect the often local ale choices. Quizzes, live music and comedy nights are among the entertainment. In summertime, the multi-level beer terrace to the rear hosts DJs and live music.

Tipton

Fountain

51 Owen Street, DY4 8HE
(0121) 522 3606
Greene King Abbot; Wye Valley HPA; 4 changing beers (often Holden's, Wadworth, Wye Valley)
Canalside pub attracting gongoozlers, boaters, families and lovers of real ale. Changing beers include national brands, namely Wadworth and Wye Valley, but also core range beers from Salopian and Hobsons. Lunchtime meals, such as beef & onion pie, are served Monday to Friday. Snacks are available all week including cobs and pork pies. The Fountain became a listed building in 1984. A small car park can be accessed from Factory Road.

Rising Sun

116 Horseley Road, DY4 7NH (off B4517)
(0121) 557 1940
Black Country Bradley's Finest Golden, Pig on the Wall, Fireside; 7 changing beers (sourced nationally; often Coach House, Froth Blowers, Malvern Hills)
A former CAMRA National Pub of the Year which reopened in 2013 following refurbishment by Black Country Ales. This imposing Victorian hostelry has two distinct rooms warmed by open fires, and a large yard at the rear with patio heaters and an outbuilding. There are seven changing guest beers plus the three Black Country Ales core beers and five traditional ciders. Cobs are served. Great Bridge is a 10-minute walk, which has frequent services to Dudley, West Bromwich and Birmingham. (22)

Tame Bridge

45 Tame Road, DY4 7JA (off A461)
(0121) 557 2496
Wye Valley HPA; 3 changing beers (sourced nationally; often Abbeydale, Oakham, Pictish)
Renowned for superior beer quality, the pub offers a varying range of guest beers, advertised in advance on a blackboard near the bar. The rear White Room is used for occasional live entertainment and can also be hired for events and meetings. Live sporting fixtures are shown on a flatscreen TV, below which is a real fire. The pub is part of the popular Red Pub Co regional portfolio. A local CAMRA branch Pub of the Year 2020 finalist.
(74)

Tividale

Tivi Ale

45-47 Regent Road, B69 1TL
Holden's Golden Glow; 3 changing beers (sourced nationally; often Bathams, Enville, Salopian)
Popular microbar which opened in 2018 in what was then a convenience store. One of the guest beers will be from a local brewery while the other two are national ales. Fresh cakes are available daily and afternoon tea can be served (book ahead). Regular family-friendly events are held throughout the year which often spill out on to the front terrace. A array of interesting gins and tonics is also on sale.

Upper Gornal

Britannia ★

109 Kent Street, DY3 1UX (on A459)
(01902) 883253
Bathams Best Bitter
Dating to the early 19th century, this inn has a nationally important historic pub interior because of the taproom at the rear with its wall-mounted handpulls. Service can be obtained from the front bar, itself a comfortable place to be. There is also a family/games room with a TV. Behind the building is the former brewhouse and the garden. Large cobs and pork pies are sold. The pub is on the main bus route between Wolverhampton and Dudley.
(1)

Jolly Crispin

25 Clarence Street, DY3 1UL (on A459)
(01902) 672 2209
Fownes Crispin's Ommer; 8 changing beers (sourced nationally; often Fat Cat, Fownes, Oakham)
A shoemaker's house in the 18th century, this has been an inn for 200 years. It sits on the top of the Black Country ridge, with distant views from the rear. Inside, the fires glow and dogs are welcome. The Fownes Brewing Company, which brews the house beer, is now in Brierley Hill, but started in a shed at the rear of the premises. Real ales are complemented by different real ciders, and cobs are served. (1)

Walsall

Black Country Arms

High Street, WS1 1QW (in market, opp Asda)

☎ (01922) 640588 🌐 blackcountryarms.co.uk
Black Country Bradley's Finest Golden, Pig on the Wall, Fireside; 13 changing beers (sourced nationally; often Fixed Wheel, Mallinsons, Salopian) Ⓗ
One of the town's oldest hostelries, a short walk from the train and bus station, dating back to as early as 1627. It offers an unrivalled and changing selection of real ales and ciders, and good food is available daily. The interior is open plan, with comfortable seating and various quieter areas. The staff offer a warm welcome to all. Entertainment is staged regularly on Saturday nights and there are sports TVs spread around. Dogs are welcome. ♉❀◐≉♣●P🚌🐾ᯤ

Butts Tavern 🄻
44 Butts Street, WS4 2BJ (200yds from Arboretum's Lichfield St entrance)
☎ (01922) 629332 🌐 buttstavern.co.uk
Holden's Golden Glow; Wye Valley Butty Bach; 2 changing beers (often Castle Rock, Church End, Marston's) Ⓗ
Large community-based local with a spacious main bar including a stage and sports TV. A smaller bar at the rear has a pool table and darts facilities, and there is an outside patio area for smoking and summer drinking. Local dominoes and crib teams are based here, and entertainment is often held on Friday or Saturday nights. A warm welcome is assured from the staff.
♉❀♿♣🚌ᯤ

Fountain Inn 🄻
49 Lower Forster Street, WS1 1XB (off A4148 Ring Rd)
☎ (01922) 633307
Backyard The Hoard, Blonde; 6 changing beers (sourced regionally; often Green Duck, Salopian, Titanic) Ⓗ
Family-run Backyard Brewery tap with up to eight real ales plus cider – a rare example of a lively wet-led venue. It has two comfortable rooms with log fires. Bar snacks are available (cobs, pork pies, crisps, nuts). Regular music nights are hosted, including indie, classic rock, reggae and vinyl, as well as monthly drawing classes. This is a superb back-street pub with friendly staff and a great atmosphere, situated an easy walk from the town centre. ♉≉♣●🚌🐾

Lyndon House Hotel 🄻
9-10 Upper Rushall Street, WS1 2HA (below St Matthew's Church)
☎ (01922) 612511 🌐 lyndonhousehotel.co.uk
Bathams Best Bitter; Burton Bridge XL Mild, Stairway to Heaven; Caledonian Deuchars IPA; Greene King Abbot; Holden's Golden Glow Ⓗ
At the top of the Walsall market, the old Royal Exchange pub was incorporated into an adjoining Salvation Army hostel and former leather works in 1995 to create this luxurious hotel. The comfortable bar has an island counter, cosy corners and old wood and brick, giving it a traditional feel. With its function room and outdoor terraces, the premises is unexpectedly spacious. Live music plays on Sunday afternoon and Monday evening. Delicious hot club sandwiches served at lunchtime are great value. Q❀🛏♿P🚌(7,51)ᯤ

Pretty Bricks 🄻
5 John Street, WS2 8AF (near magistrates' court, off B4210)
☎ (01922) 612553
Black Country Bradley's Finest Golden, Pig on the Wall, Fireside; 6 changing beers (sourced nationally) Ⓗ
This small, friendly, cosy pub on the edge of town dates from 1845 and has a front bar with a wood fire, lounge, upstairs function room and a small blue-brick courtyard. Originally called the New Inn, its current name derives from a part-glazed frontage. Cobs and pork pies provide sustenance alongside the great range of ales. A folk night is held every second Thursday of the month.
Q❀≉♣●🚌🐾ᯤ

St Matthew's Hall ✔
Lichfield Street, WS1 1SX (adjacent to town hall)
☎ (01922) 700820
Greene King Abbot; Ruddles Best Bitter; Sharp's Doom Bar; 4 changing beers (sourced regionally; often AJ's Ales, Backyard, Salopian) Ⓗ
A stunning Grade II listed Wetherspoon outlet in the centre of town, easily accessible by public transport and with plenty of parking nearby. A selection of national guest ales supplements the three regular beers. Regular beer festivals feature throughout the year, and entertainment is hosted every Friday and Saturday evening. There is a large beer garden at the side.
♉❀◐◑♿≉●🚌🐾ᯤ

Victoria 🄻
23 Lower Rushall Street, WS1 2AA
☎ (01922) 635866
Backyard Bitter; Banks's Sunbeam; Church End Gravediggers Ale; Wye Valley Butty Bach; 3 changing beers (sourced regionally; often AJ's Ales, Fixed Wheel, Salopian) Ⓗ
Popular two-roomed pub very close to the town centre, dating from 1845, with its former brewhouse at the rear. Bar snacks are available along with Sunday lunches. One real cider is permanently on offer. Open mic and quiz nights are held regularly, and there is live entertainment on Sunday evening. A pool table is upstairs, and a pleasant garden and smoking facilities to the rear. A large Pay & Display car park is at the back.
♉❀◐≉♣●🚌🐾ᯤ

Walsall Arms 🄻
17 Bank Street, WS1 2EP (off A34)
☎ (01922) 649839
Wye Valley Bitter, HPA, Butty Bach; 3 changing beers (sourced locally; often Salopian) Ⓗ
Recently refurbished back-street pub, situated just a short walk from the town centre, behind the Royal Hotel. It has a large, comfy, carpeted bar area with an open fire, old Walsall photographs and two TV screens. A fully refurbished patio at the rear is painted in an Italianate fashion. The pub holds a quiz on the first Monday of the month, a themed food event every Thursday and regular jazz nights. ❀◐◑♿♣P🚌(51,377)🐾ᯤ

Walsall Cricket Club
Gorway Road, WS1 3BE (off A34, by university campus)
☎ (01922) 622094 🌐 walsall.play-cricket.com
Wye Valley HPA; 1 changing beer (sourced regionally; often Backyard, Castle Rock) Ⓗ
On a fine summer day, the click of bat on ball welcomes you to a green oasis on the outskirts of town. The club room has had a major renovation and now provides luxurious comfort with a panoramic view of the field. Local cricket memorabilia is on display and there are two large sporting screens. Occasional entertainment is hosted and the venue is available to hire for functions. CAMRA members are welcome – show your membership card for entry. Hours are reduced on winter Sundays.
♉❀♿♣P🚌(51)🐾ᯤ

Wednesbury

Bellwether ✔
3-4 Walsall Street, WS10 9BZ

☎ (0121) 502 6404
Greene King Abbot; Oakham JHB; Ruddles Best Bitter; 7 changing beers (sourced nationally) [H]
Near the main shopping area and market, the pub attracts a wide clientele. The large open L-shaped room is on a split level with tables and chairs in front of the bar. More intimate seating is at the rear, leading to a tranquil garden area. The pub is decorated with images of historic events and characters associated with the town. Ten handpulls serve a large selection of guest ales. Q🐴❀◑♿♣🍎🚌📶

Olde Leathern Bottel ✔

40 Vicarage Road, WS10 9DW (just off A461; bus 311 from Walsall is 5 mins' walk)
☎ (0121) 505 0230
4 changing beers (sourced nationally; often Marston's, Wye Valley) [H]
The bar and snug are set in cottages dating from 1510, while a later extension contains a comfy lounge. The small snug is often used as a function room. Many old photos are on display throughout the four rooms, including a photo of the pub from 1887 in the bar, and a map of Wednesbury from 1846. The friendly staff are happy to help you, and there is entertainment on Saturday nights. 🐴❀◑♣P🚌(11)🐾📶

Wednesfield

Vine ★ 🄻

35 Lichfield Road, WV11 1TN
☎ (01902) 733529
Black Country Bradley's Finest Golden, Pig on the Wall, Fireside; 6 changing beers (sourced nationally) [H]
Built in 1938, this Grade II listed community local is a rare intact example of a simple inter-war working-class pub, with the original bar, lounge and snug. It has been identified by CAMRA as having a nationally important historic pub interior. Darts and dominoes are played and there are TVs showing sport and horse racing. Outside are a covered smokers' shelter and a beer garden. Cobs and pork pies are available at all times. On alternate Saturdays there is live music, and open mic on the first Tuesday of the month. 🐴❀♣🍎P🚌(59,60)🐾📶

West Bromwich

Crown & Cushion ✔

2 Lloyd Street, B71 4AT
☎ (0121) 553 4493
Castle Rock Harvest Pale; St Austell Tribute; 1 changing beer (sourced nationally; often Harviestoun) [H]
Family-friendly single-room hostelry on the outskirts of town, run by staff who make you feel at home. It is popular in the summer with visitors to the nearby park. Within easy walking distance of West Bromwich Albion's ground, it gets busy on match days – away supporters are always welcome. A quiz night is held on Thursday. 🐴❀♿♣🍎P🚌(47)🐾📶

Royal Oak 🄻 ✔

14 Newton Street, B71 3RQ (down side road off Hollyhedge Rd)
☎ (0121) 588 5857
St Austell Proper Job; Wye Valley HPA; 2 changing beers (sourced nationally) [H]
Traditional back-street local with two small rooms – the bar on the left is adorned with West Bromwich Albion memorabilia and on the right is the quieter lounge. TVs show sport in both rooms. There is a terrace in the rear yard for smokers, and two benches at the front for basking in the sun in summer. Bar snacks are available. Parking is in the street. 🐴❀♣🚌🐾📶

Three Horseshoes 🄻

86 Witton Lane, B71 2AQ
☎ (0121) 502 1693
Black Country Bradley's Finest Golden, Pig on the Wall, Fireside; 4 changing beers (sourced nationally) [H]
This refurbished one-room pub was taken on by Black Country Ales in 2016, with 10 handpulls added. The spacious interior is furnished in a traditional style, with TVs showing live sport. The warm welcome provided by the staff makes you feel right at home. There are bar snacks available and a beer garden for fine weather enjoyment. 🐴❀♿♣🍎P🚌(79,49)🐾📶

Willenhall

Falcon

77 Gomer Street West, WV13 2NR (off B4464, behind flats)
☎ (01902) 633378
Hobsons Town Crier; 3 changing beers (sourced regionally; often Castle Rock) [H]
A two-roomed inn with a lively public bar and quieter lounge at the rear, a short walk from the town centre. Dating back to 1936, the Falcon has been in the same family for over 30 years. Old pub memorabilia adorn both rooms. The beers are keenly priced. There is a beer garden at the rear, and plenty of on-street parking. 🐴❀♣🍎▯🚌(529)🐾📶

Robin Hood 🄻

54 The Crescent, WV13 2QR (200yds from A462/B4464 jct)
☎ (01902) 635070
Black Country Bradley's Finest Golden, Pig on the Wall [H], Fireside [H]/[G]; 6 changing beers (sourced nationally; often Backyard, Beowulf, Salopian) [H]
A traditionally styled public house with welcoming staff and a friendly clientele. The L-shaped venue has a fire adding warmth during the winter months. Up to nine real ales are on sale and three real ciders, and a variety of cobs, hot pies and pork pies is available throughout the day. A quiz is held on Thursday and a local archery club meets on adjacent land on Saturday.
❀♣🍎P🚌(529)🐾📶

Wollaston

Unicorn 🄻

145 Bridgnorth Road, DY8 3NX (on A458 towards Bridgnorth)
☎ (01384) 394823
Bathams Mild Ale, Best Bitter [H]
A former brewhouse purchased by Bathams, the Unicorn has barely altered in appearance since the Billingham family sold up in the early 1990s. It is a traditional two-bar drinking house, with a small back room where children are welcome, popular with all age groups and where conversation is the order of the day. The brewhouse remains but is no longer in use. Fresh cobs – with hot pork and stuffing on Saturday lunchtimes – are available on request. Bathams XXX is sold in the winter only. Q🐴❀♿P🚌🐾📶

Wolverhampton

Chindit

113 Merridale Road, WV3 9SE

☎ 07986 773487 🌐 thechindit.co.uk

Hop Back Summer Lightning; Wye Valley HPA; 3 changing beers (sourced regionally; often Ossett, Rat, Titanic) H

Built in the 1950s as an off-licence, the first landlord here served in the Chindit Regiment in Burma in WWII and named the pub after his comrades. It is thought to be the only place in the country honouring Major General Orde Wingate's WWII special forces; their history is on display in the lounge. The two-roomed pub has a small lounge and a bar featuring an original Wurlitzer jukebox stocking 60s and 70s 45rpm records. There is live music every Friday and open mic night is Sunday. P(3,15)

Combermere Arms

90 Chapel Ash, WV3 0TY (on A41 Tettenhall Rd)

☎ (01902) 421880

5 changing beers (sourced nationally; often Greene King) H

Grade II listed building with original sash windows. It comprises three charming rooms with cosy fireplaces replete with classic adverts. One locally brewed beer, four from the Greene King portfolio, and a varying cider are on sale. Pie, sausage and cheese-tasting festivals are held annually and there is occasional live entertainment. To the rear is a courtyard and beer garden. The renowned tree in the Gents is still growing despite being trimmed. Situated a short walk or bus ride from the city centre. QP

Great Western

Sun Street, WV10 0DG (pedestrian access from city centre via Corn Hill)

☎ (01902) 351090

Bathams Best Bitter; Holden's Black Country Mild, Black Country Bitter, Golden Glow, Special; 3 changing beers (sourced regionally) H

A previous CAMRA National Pub of the Year near the former low-level railway station. It attracts a varied clientele, including a rock-climbing club and railway groups. Plenty of railway and Wolverhampton Wanderers memorabilia is on display, and cosy real fires blaze in the winter. Meals are served at lunchtime (not Sun), and hot pork baps, gray pays and bacon, beef and vegetable stew, are available every day. A beer festival is held over November's Remembrance weekend. QP

Hail to the Ale

2 Pendeford Avenue, Claregate, WV6 9EF (at Claregate island)

☎ 07846 562910 🌐 hailtothealemicropub.co.uk

6 changing beers (sourced locally; often Morton) H

Welcoming one-room beer and conversation focused pub, the West Midlands' first micropub, opened in 2013 by Morton Brewery. Six handpulls serve at least two Morton beer, and guest ales usually come from local microbreweries. Also from the cellar are four ciders or perries. Locally sourced pies, cheese, sausage rolls and Scotch eggs are available, along with 10 fruit wines. Local CAMRA branch Pub of the Year five years running 2015-2019. QP(5,6)

Hogshead

186 Stafford Street, WV1 1NA

☎ (01902) 717955

10 changing beers (sourced nationally) H

A large 19th-century traditional city-centre building with an attractive brick terracotta exterior. A stained-glass window above the entrance displays the original name, the Vine. The large interior single room is divided into separate areas, with TVs showing sport throughout. A range of 10 guest ales is available, with regular brewery tap takeovers, and a large number of ciders, mostly from Lilley's. The pub is popular with all age groups. There is a quiz on Wednesday evening and a DJ on Saturday evening.

Keg & Comfort

474 Stafford Road, Oxley, WV10 6AN

☎ 07952 631032 🌐 kegandcomfort.co.uk

4 changing beers (sourced locally)

The city's second micropub opened in 2018 in a former bank. The main contemporary room has a striking bar, custom-built using coloured bottles, seating for around 40 and old barrels as tables for people who prefer to stand. A small side room houses a large sofa and a games cupboard. Four changing cask ales, one dark, five ciders or perries, and a selection of fruit wines are served. Live music plays on the first Wednesday of the month. Local CAMRA Cider Pub of the Year 2020. QP(3,54)

Lych Gate Tavern

44 Queen Square, WV1 1TX (off Queen Square between Nationwide and Barclays banks by St Peter's Church)

☎ (01902) 399516 🌐 lychgatetavern.co.uk

Black Country Bradley's Finest Golden, Pig on the Wall, Fireside; 6 changing beers (sourced nationally) H

Friendly, traditional city-centre pub housed in one of the oldest timber-framed buildings in Wolverhampton – the Georgian frontage dates from 1726 and the timber-framed rear from about 1500. The bar area is reached by a short flight of stairs down from street level. There is a function room for hire upstairs. Cobs are served but customers may bring their own food (plates and cutlery provided). A charity collection is made during the regular tap takeovers. All floors are accessible via a lift. Q

Posada

48 Lichfield Street, WV1 1DG

Hobsons Town Crier; Sharp's Doom Bar; 3 changing beers (often AJ's Ales, Salopian, Wye Valley) H

Little altered Victorian city-centre pub with a regionally important historic pub interior, having tiled walls and original bar fittings, including rare snob screens. It attracts a varied clientele and is quiet during the day but busy in the evenings and weekends, especially when Wolverhampton Wanderers are at home. There is a courtyard to the rear with a smoking area. Cobs are available and Westons Old Rosie is served on handpump.

Royal Oak

70 Compton Road, WV3 9PH

☎ (01902) 422845 🌐 theoakchapelash.com

Banks's Mild, Amber Ale, Sunbeam; Wainwright; Wychwood Hobgoblin Gold; 3 changing beers (sourced nationally; often Jennings, Ringwood, Wychwood) H

A friendly local, a short walk or bus ride from the city centre, which serves a wide range of real ales from the Marston's portfolio. The bustling pub hosts jam nights on Tuesdays, open mic evenings on Wednesdays and live bands on Fridays and Saturdays (also Sunday afternoons in summer). Part of the community, the venue raises money for local and national charities and is the headquarters of Old Wulfrunians hockey club. Pub and local history and maps are displayed on a wall. Cobs are served. P(10,9)

Starting Gate 🄻

134 Birches Barn Road, Penn Fields, WV3 7BG
5 changing beers (sourced regionally; often Ludlow, Sarah Hughes, Wye Valley)
Opened in 2018, this small outlet occupies a former bank branch and retains the original counter and wings. The impressive rear door to the garden also reflects its previous use. The small bar area leads to a cosy lounge, with another lounge upstairs reached by an open spiral staircase. The paintings, silks and other memorabilia reflect an interest in horse racing, hence the name of the pub. Q❀♿🍎🚌(2)🐾📶

Stile Inn 🄻 ✔

3 Harrow Street, Whitmore Reans, WV1 4PB (off Newhampton Rd E/Fawdry St)
☎ (01902) 425336
Banks's Mild, Amber Ale, Sunbeam; 1 changing beer (sourced nationally) 🄷
A typical late-Victorian street-corner pub built in 1900, featuring a public bar, smoke room and snug. It is a true community local with an emphasis on sports – darts and dominoes feature inside, Crown Green bowls on the unusual L-shaped green outside, and it gets busy with Wolverhampton Wanderers fans on match days. Excellent-value food, including Polish dishes, is served all day. Friday is disco night and Saturday is karaoke. Sky and BT Sports are shown in all rooms.
🐎❀◑♣🚌(5,6)🐾📶

Swan 🄻

Bridgnorth Road, Compton, WV6 8AE (at Compton Island, A454)
☎ (01902) 754736
Banks's Mild, Amber Ale, Sunbeam; Marston's Old Empire; Wainwright; 1 changing beer (sourced nationally; often Brakspear, Jennings, Wychwood) 🄷
Built around 1780, this Grade II-listed former coaching inn close to the Staffordshire & Worcestershire Canal and Smestow Valley Nature Reserve is popular with locals, boaters, ramblers and cyclists. It comprises a lively bar with local banter, a games room and a more sedate snug. The pub hosts a quiz on Tuesday and a darts team on Wednesday, charity dog shows and the local pigeon flyers' club. A sympathetic refurbishment was carried out in 2016. Q🐎❀♣P🚌🐾📶

Woodcross

Horse & Jockey 🄻 ✔

Robert Wynd, WV14 9SB
☎ (01902) 662268 🌐 horseandjockeywoodcross.com
Hobsons Twisted Spire, Town Crier; St Austell Tribute; 3 changing beers (sourced locally; often Salopian, Three Tuns) 🄷
Run by two CAMRA members, this friendly and thriving community pub comprises a bar, a large contemporary lounge with a seasonal open fire, a rear beer garden and a small smoking shelter at the front. Good-value home-cooked food, including vegetarian options, is served daily. Under-18s are allowed in the lounge area and the newly refurbished garden until the evening.
Q🐎❀◑♣🍎P🚌🐾📶

Wordsley

Bird in Hand 🏆

57 John Street, DY8 4AZ
☎ (01384) 865809
Enville Ale; Hobsons Town Crier; Holden's Golden Glow; 3 changing beers (sourced nationally; often Cotleigh, Fixed Wheel, Tiny Rebel) 🄷
Local CAMRA Pub of the Year 2020, this is an ambitious and inviting back-street local which ticks all the boxes on a CAMRA member's wish list. With a high turnover on the permanent cask range and a changing trio of national guest beers, there is always a tipple to please. Multiple teams and community groups meet here. The pub is part of the popular Red Pub Co regional portfolio. The homely garden at the rear has some sheltered seating.
Q🐎❀♣🍎🚌🐾📶

Fountain, Tipton (Photo: Elliott Brown/Flickr CC BY-SA 2.0)

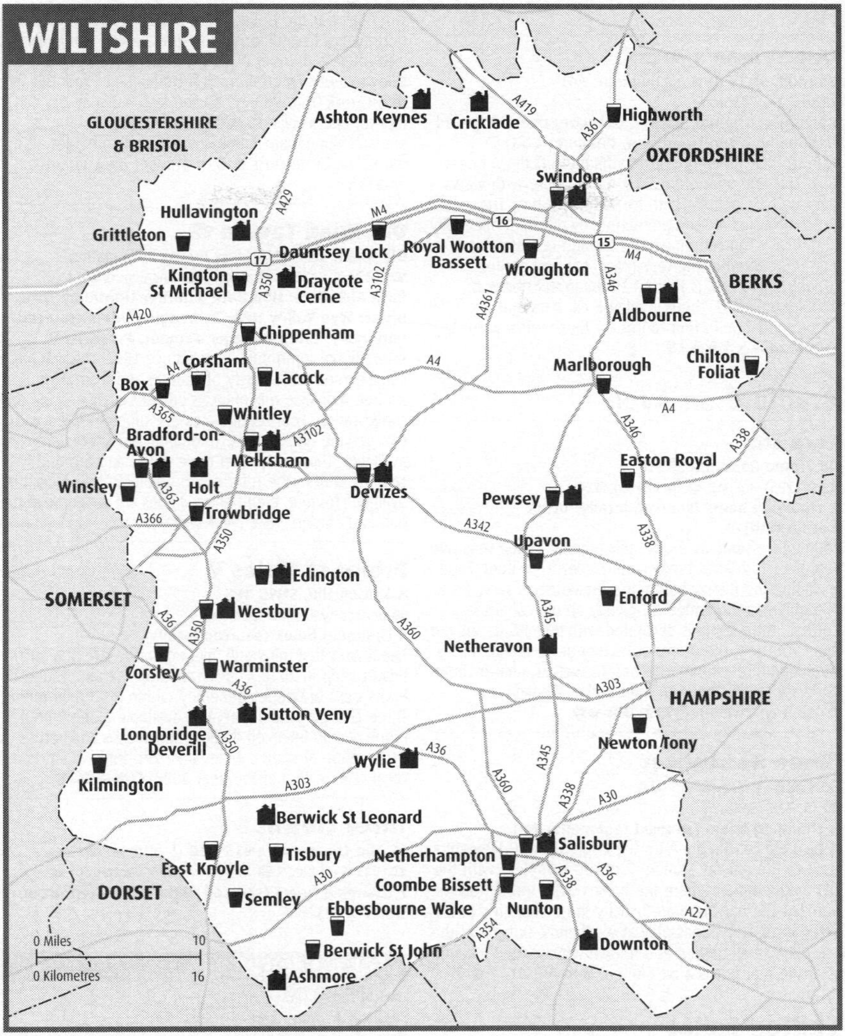

Aldbourne

Crown ✔

The Square, SN8 2DU

☎ (01672) 540214 🌐 thecrownaldbourne.co.uk

Sharp's Doom Bar; Shepherd Neame Spitfire; Timothy Taylor Landlord; 1 changing beer (sourced nationally) Ⓗ

The Crown is set in the middle of the village opposite the duck pond, with a Dalek standing guard outside. At the heart of the local community, it has a relaxed and pleasant atmosphere. The main bar is stylishly refurbished with a welcoming fire in winter. The smaller bar shows films on a Monday night. The restaurant serves freshly prepared food made from local produce where possible with daily specials, and a carvery on Sunday. Tuesday is quiz and bridge night, there is a meat raffle on Saturday afternoon, plus live music is hosted (check the website for details). Accommodation is available in five en-suite bedrooms. Situated a short drive from the historic market towns of Marlborough and Hungerford, and only a stone's throw from the ancient Avebury Rings, Silbury Hill and Stonehenge. An ideal base for walkers, the famous Roman Ridgway is nearby. ❀🛏◑⛺♣🚌(46,48)🐾📶

Berwick St John

Talbot

The Cross, SP7 0HA

☎ (01747) 828222 🌐 talbotinnberwickstjohn.co.uk

Sixpenny 6d Best Bitter; Wadworth 6X; house beer (by Ringwood); 1 changing beer (often Sixpenny) Ⓗ

In a small, peaceful, rural village, the Talbot opened circa 1832 despite vehement opposition from the local parson's wife. The building is predominantly stone-built with a long, low bar with beams and an inglenook fireplace. One of the regular beers is brewed by a local microbrewery. The more inquisitive visitor will find the dining room behind the inglenook; good, home-cooked food is offered. The pub is popular with walkers from the local downs, and cyclists on the 160-mile Wiltshire Cycleway. There is no mobile phone signal; however, there is internet access. Q❀◑P🐾📶

Box

Quarryman's Arms 🄻

Box Hill, SN13 8HN (signed from A4)
☎ (01225) 743569
Butcombe Original, Gold; 3 changing beers (sourced nationally; often Liberation, Oakham, VOG) 🄷
A Butcombe Brewery pub in a hamlet off the A4 near Box. This 300-year-old former miners' inn, with views over Bath, is popular with locals and visitors. The Butcombe ales are complemented by different nationally and locally sourced guest ales. A high-quality varied menu is served in the restaurant, bar and garden. Wheelchair access is limited although assistance is happily provided. There is a large car park and accommodation in four rooms for those wishing to stay. Q❀⇌◐◑♿Å♣●P📶

Bradford-on-Avon

Lock Inn

48 Frome Road, BA15 1LE
☎ (01225) 868068 🌐 thelockinn.co.uk
2 changing beers (sourced locally; often Kettlesmith) 🄷
Although essentially a café, this popular venue sells two real ales from local brewers and cider from Iford. Food, including the hearty boatman's breakfast, is served and is highly recommended. Originally an old canalside cottage, the interior is decorated with bric-a-brac and old signs. Outside, there are tables alongside the Kennet & Avon and three summerhouses, as well as a narrowboat. The café closes about an hour earlier weekdays in autumn and winter. Q❀◐◑⇌●🐾

Three Horseshoes

55 Frome Road, BA15 1LA
☎ (01225) 865876
3 changing beers (sourced regionally) 🄷
A nice old coaching inn on the edge of the town centre next to the railway station. It comes complete with the old wooden door where the horses went through to the yard. At the bar there are usually three changing beers, often local. Live bands play at weekends. Outside at the back is a small garden and terrace with seating. Parking is at the rear but is a bit limited. ❀⇌♣P🚌(D1)🐾📶

Chilton Foliat

Wheatsheaf 🄻 ✔

RG17 0TE
☎ (01488) 680936 🌐 thewheatsheafchiltonfoliat.co.uk
Ramsbury Gold; house beer (by Butts); 1 changing beer (sourced locally; often Hop Kettle) 🄷
This enterprise in an 18th-century Grade II building has been run by a local couple since 2015. It is an award-winning sustainable hub with a bar, music, first-floor art gallery and shop. There are three local real ales including a changing guest, and cider from Hungerford Park. The kitchen features a wood-fired oven for home-made pizza to complement the excellent menu of locally sourced food. Live music plays on the third Friday of each month. ❀◐◑●P🚌(46,46A)🐾📶

Chippenham

Flying Monk 🄻

6 Market Place, SN15 3HD
☎ (01249) 460662
North Cotswold Windrush Ale; 4 changing beers (sourced regionally) 🄷
The pub is in the town centre adjacent to the historic Buttercross. In addition to the real ales on handpump, it also offers a number of Belgian beers, craft beers and Lilley's ciders. Entertainment includes twice monthly live music, rock 'n' roll bingo on the last Thursday of each month, and a twice-monthly meat raffle. During the annual Chippenham Folk Festival the pub provides a cider bar in the Buttercross and an outdoor drinking area. ⇌●🚌📶

Old Road Tavern ✔

Old Road, SN15 1JA (over bridge from station)
☎ (01249) 247080 🌐 oldroadtavernchippenham.co.uk
Bath Ales Gem; Hop Back Summer Lightning; Otter Bitter; Wye Valley HPA; 2 changing beers (sourced nationally; often Adnams, Exmoor, Prescott) 🄷
A traditional community venue since 1842. The pub has a large garden with plenty of seating and a smoking shelter. A diverse mix of locals ensures lively and friendly conversation. Four regular ales are supplemented with two varying guest beers. Traditional bar snacks are available. There is frequent live music and a monthly comedy club in the refurbished adjoining hall, which is available for hire. Well-behaved dogs are welcome in the pub and garden. ❀◐⇌♣🚌🐾📶

Prince of Wales 🏆

8 Station Hill, SN15 1EG
🌐 princeofwalesmicropub.com
4 changing beers (sourced locally) 🄷
The town's first micropub opened on the site of a former flower shop in 2018. Four handpumps serve a range of beers from breweries generally within a 50-mile radius. Three changing ciders are also available along with a range of craft beers on draught and in cans and bottles. A small range of spirits, wines and soft drinks is stocked. Local CAMRA Pub of the Year 2020. Q⇌●🗍🚌🐾

Three Crowns 🄻

18 The Causeway, SN15 3DB (S of town centre)
☎ (01249) 449029 🌐 threecrownschippenham.co.uk
7 changing beers (sourced nationally; often Arbor, Slater's, XT) 🄷

REAL ALE BREWERIES

Arkell's Swindon
Ashton Ashton Keynes (NEW)
Blonde Brothers Wylie
Box Steam ◆ Holt
BrightBeer ▮ Swindon
Broadtown Swindon (NEW)
Dark Revolution ◆ Salisbury
Downton ◆ Downton
Gritchie Ashmore
Hop Back Downton
Hop Kettle ▮ Cricklade/Swindon
Hop Therapy Draycote Cerne (NEW)
Kettlesmith Bradford-on-Avon
Keystone Berwick St Leonard
New Flying Monk Hullavington
Plain Sutton Veny
Ramsbury Aldbourne
Shed Pewsey
Stealth Melksham
Stonehenge Netheravon
Three Castles Pewsey
Three Daggers Edington
Twisted Westbury
Wadworth ◆ Devizes
Wessex Longbridge Deverill
World's End ▮ Pewsey

Friendly, welcoming, 18th-century waggoners' pub with a main bar warmed by a real fire and a cider/snug bar. A proper pub without noisy distractions, it hosts quizzes, darts and a cheese club, and is popular with visitors and locals. Beers includes local ales and dark ales, alongside four ciders or perries. Filled rolls and pork pies are served. The quarterly beer festivals have 12 ales and eight ciders/perries plus more substantial hot and cold snacks. A multiple CAMRA award winner. Q≥♣●P⊡⊟❀ᯤ

Coombe Bissett

Fox & Goose L

Blandford Road, SP5 4LE

☎ (01722) 718437 🌐 foxandgoose-coombebissett.co.uk

Sharp's Doom Bar; Sixpenny 6d Best Bitter; 1 changing beer (sourced nationally) H

An 18th-century coaching inn on the A354, three miles south of Salisbury. This popular community pub has a loyal village clientele and a welcoming atmosphere. Divided into a bar and restaurant, it offers an extensive food menu with ever-changing specials. Outside, there are pleasant gardens to the rear and a covered smoking area. Guest ales are from local and national breweries. Q❀P⊟(20,29)❀ᯤ

Corsham

Flemish Weaver ✔

63 High Street, SN13 0EZ (next to town hall)

☎ (01249) 701929 🌐 flemishweaver.co.uk

House beer (by Wadworth); 4 changing beers (sourced nationally; often Marston's, Salopian, Wadworth) H

An intriguing pub and full of character that reveals itself through its many nooks and crannies. It was refurbished in 2017 and the garden is a pleasant and unexpected surprise. There is a focus on quality service and real ale, with six handpumps offering a regularly changing range. The building is in the oldest part of Corsham where you may notice locations from the TV series Poldark, some of which was filmed here. ❀♣⊟❀ᯤ

Corsley

Cross Keys Inn

Lye's Green, BA12 7PB

☎ (01373) 832406 🌐 crosskeyscorsley.co.uk

Three Daggers Daggers Ale; 3 changing beers (sourced locally; often Box Steam, Moles, Twisted) H

This rural gem in the shadow of Cley Hill (famed for its UFO sightings) has a large open fire and a warm, welcoming atmosphere. A good selection of guest ales, mainly from local breweries, is available, along with excellent bar food and restaurant meals. The cider is Cheddar Valley from Thatchers. In 2016 the pub was taken over by a village consortium. It is in an excellent walking area, close to the Somerset border, and near Longleat House and Safari Park. ❀Ă♣●P❀ᯤ

Dauntsey Lock

Peterborough Arms L

SN15 4HD (on B4069)

☎ (01249) 247833 🌐 peterborougharms.com

3 changing beers (sourced nationally; often Box Steam, Plain, Three Castles) H

Saved by the Wilts & Berks Canal Trust and restored by its volunteers, this place reopened in 2018 offering three real ales including a dark beer, plus real cider and good pub food. It is home to both skittles and darts teams and hosts regular quiz nights. There is a beer garden for the summer and a log-burner for the winter. It is alongside the old canal which is under restoration by the WBCT. Q♿♣●P⊡ᯤ

Devizes

British Lion ✔

9 Estcourt Street, SN10 1LQ (on A361 opp Kwik Fit)

☎ (01380) 720665 🌐 britishliondevizes.co.uk

4 changing beers (sourced nationally; often Palmers, Plain, Stonehenge) H

The British has been ever-present in the Guide for over 25 years. An unpretentious free house with wooden floors, cosy settles and an eclectic group of talkative regulars, it is an essential port of call in town. There are four handpumps and the beers change frequently throughout the week – time it right and you can savour eight different ales. The knowledgeable landlord is always pleased to offer his advice. The cider is often Cheddar Valley or Black Rat. ❀●P⊟ᯤ

Southgate Inn

Potterne Road, SN10 5BY

☎ (01380) 722872

Hop Back GFB, Crop Circle, Summer Lightning; 3 changing beers (sourced nationally; often Hop Back) G

The five-minute walk from the town centre is well worth it for the welcome you will receive here. The cosy, friendly pub has three separate bar areas, lots of nooks and crannies, and a large courtyard area. It usually has six ales – mainly from Hop Back but often a guest too – plus still ciders and a perry, all served straight from the cask. Live music features throughout the weekend, an acoustic jam session on Wednesday and a Friday afternoon ukulele group. Well-behaved dogs are positively encouraged. ♣●P⊟(49)❀ᯤ

Vaults

28A St John's Street, SN10 1BN (opp town hall)

☎ (01380) 721443 🌐 thevaultsdevizes.com

5 changing beers (sourced nationally; often Stealth) H

The Vaults maintains its high standards, with a long, galley-style bar usually offering at least two ales from Stealth Brew Co, normally at least one dark beer, plus up to three still ciders. Beer paddles are available and a selection of bottles and tins from around the world is also stocked. Conversation rules here – there is no loud music or fruit machines, just a great atmosphere. The large cellar is used for events ranging from quizzes to a poetry club and a Christmas story evening. ●⊟❀ᯤ

White Bear

33 Monday Market Street, SN10 1DN

☎ (01380) 727588 🌐 whitebeardevizes.co.uk

Wadworth Henry's IPA; 5 changing beers (sourced nationally; often Wadworth) H

Recently refurbished throughout, this old coaching inn with original beams and wood-burning stoves dates from the 1500s. It offers six real ales, two from Wadworth – IPA and a varying beer – plus four guests. A dark beer is usually among the selection, plus a changing still cider. Food is served all week. There is no car park but there is plenty of on-street parking and public car parks adjacent. ●⊟❀ᯤ

East Knoyle

Fox & Hounds

Wise Lane, The Green, SP3 6BN ST87113135

☎ (01747) 830573 🌐 foxandhounds-eastknoyle.co.uk

3 changing beers ⊞
Attractive old thatched black and white pub situated high on a hillside with extensive panoramic rural views, especially from the beer garden. Comfortable and cosy inside, the warm welcome is enhanced in winter by a blazing log fire in a huge inglenook fireplace. Three ales are always available, encompassing a wide range of strengths and varying continuously, with local beers given prominence. The cider is Harry's. Food is served at all sessions. An adjacent skittle alley doubles as a function room. Q⏰★🕙●P🌸

Easton Royal

Bruce Arms ★ Ⓛ
Easton Road, SN9 5LR
☎ (01672) 810216 ⊕ thebrucearms.net
Sharp's Atlantic; Stonehenge Pigswill; Wadworth 6X; 2 changing beers (sourced regionally) ⊞
Located in the heart of rural Wiltshire, this mid-19th century local has been identified by CAMRA as having a nationally important historic pub interior. It has a cosy bar with furniture that probably goes back to the 1850s, a small lounge with easy chairs and a piano, and a larger dining/function room at the back. The pub exists in splendid isolation, so its campsite with full facilities is an asset that makes it a good venue for meetings and rallies. Q⏰★Å♣P🚌(96,19)🌸🛜

Ebbesbourne Wake

Horseshoe
The Cross, SP5 5JF
☎ (01722) 780474 ⊕ thehorseshoe-inn.co.uk
Bowman Swift One; Gritchie English Lore; Otter Bitter; 1 changing beer (sourced nationally) Ⓖ
Unspoilt 18th-century inn in a remote rural setting at the foot of an old ox drove. This friendly pub has two small bars displaying an impressive collection of old farm implements, tools and lamps, plus a restaurant, conservatory and pleasant garden. Good local food is available Tuesday to Sunday and beers are poured direct from casks behind the bar. The original serving hatch just inside the front door is still in use. Real cider is usually available, often Orchard Pig Reveller or Wessex. CAMRA branch Country Pub of the Year 2019 and 2020. Q⏰★🕙Å♣P🚌(29)🌸

Edington

Three Daggers
Westbury Road, BA13 4PG
☎ (01380) 830940 ⊕ threedaggers.co.uk
Three Daggers Daggers Blonde, Daggers Ale, Daggers Edge; 1 changing beer (often Three Daggers) ⊞
This refurbished village pub is now the tap for the eponymous brewery, situated in an adjacent farm shop. The pub has a main bar with three distinct drinking areas, leading into a seating area and a dining room. Two mirrors hide TV screens that are occasionally used for sporting events. At the rear is a lovely garden. Regular seasonal beers are brewed, and carryouts and bottles are available in the shop. Q⏰★🕙Å♣P🚌(87)🌸🛜

Enford

Swan Ⓛ ✅
Long Street, SN9 6DD
☎ (01980) 670338 ⊕ theswanenford.co.uk
5 changing beers (sourced locally; often Stonehenge, Three Daggers) ⊞

Everyone is welcome at this 16th-century, Grade II listed pub purchased by villagers for the community in 1998. It is one of only a handful of pubs in the country with the inn sign hanging on a gantry over the road. Old beams, an inglenook fireplace, sloping walls and quiet nooks and crannies add to its character. Flights of three third-pints help you sample a selection of mainly local ales. ⏰★🕙♣●P🚌(X5) 🌸🛜

Grittleton

Neeld Arms
The Street, SN14 6AP
☎ (01249) 782470 ⊕ neeldarms.co.uk
St Austell Tribute; Wadworth 6X; 1 changing beer (sourced locally; often Plain) ⊞
Its motto 'Proud to be a proper pub' sums up this 17th-century, Grade II listed inn with its four handpumps, beamed ceiling, two stoves and bench tables in the bar. A reasonably priced lunch and evening menu includes an interesting specials board. An annexe can also be used for private functions. The owners of 19 years plan an event each month. Ample roadside parking is available. Accommodation is in six en-suite rooms. Q⏰★🕙🛏🕙P🌸🛜

Highworth

Rose & Crown
19 The Green, SN6 7DB
☎ (01793) 764699
5 changing beers (sourced nationally; often Sharp's) ⊞
Now a free house, this is one of the oldest pubs in Highworth. The interior features wooden beams decorated with hops, and an efficient wood-burner. There are five handpumps serving changing ales, with a Sharp's beer always on at some point in the week. The lunch menu is good quality and value. Cheerful, friendly staff add to the pleasant atmosphere. Occasional open mic and folk sessions are hosted. Outside is a boules pitch in the garden. ⏰★🕙♣P🚌(7)🌸🛜

Kilmington

Red Lion Inn Ⓛ ✅
BA12 6RP (on B3092 between Mere and Frome)
☎ (01985) 844263 ⊕ theredlionkilmington.co.uk
Butcombe Original; Wessex Stourton Pale Ale; 1 changing beer ⊞
A friendly, traditional free house with a low-beamed, flagstoned front bar featuring cushioned wall and window seats, curved high-backed settles and wood-burners. The larger back bar has tables for diners to enjoy the home-cooked food supplied by high-quality local food producers (some from the village itself). Thatchers cider is on handpump. Dogs are welcome to join their owners in the front bar or in the large, attractive garden which has fine views of White Sheet Hill. Q⏰★🕙♣●P🌸🛜

Kington St Michael

Jolly Huntsman Ⓛ
SN14 6JB (signed from A350)
☎ (01249) 750305 ⊕ jollyhuntsman.com
Moles Best; 2 changing beers (sourced locally; often Goff's, Ramsbury) ⊞
A former brewery situated on the village high street, this free house offers a warm and friendly welcome, with a large open fire in the winter. It serves a selection of locally brewed real ales and a choice of ciders, usually

from regional suppliers. An excellent menu is available lunchtimes and evenings, featuring a range of traditional fare and chef's specials, and there are occasional themed evenings. Accommodation is en-suite.
Q🚼🛏◑♿🍎P🚌(99)

Lacock

Bell Inn L

The Wharf, SN15 2PJ
☎ (01249) 730308 🌐 thebellatlacock.co.uk
House beer (by Great Western); 3 changing beers (sourced regionally; often Butts, Great Western, Plain) [H]
Popular free house just out of Lacock towards Bowden Hill. A regular local CAMRA Pub of the Year, it has two house beers, Beau Bell and Arlo's, as well as up to three guest ales. A wholesome and varied food menu is served in the restaurant, bar and conservatory. The spacious garden has a marquee and bar, and two beer festivals are held each year. Q🚼❀◑⛺♣🍎P📺🐾📶

Marlborough

Wellington Arms L ✔

46 High Street, SN8 1HQ
☎ (01672) 516697 🌐 thewellingtonarmsmarlborough.co.uk
Ramsbury Farmer's Best, Gold; 2 changing beers (sourced nationally; often Ramsbury) [H]
This friendly 18th-century pub with an open fire is the tap for Ramsbury Brewery. Pieminister pies are served. Entertainment includes a vinyl evening on Tuesday – bring your own records and get a 10 per cent discount on drinks – a weekly pub quiz and regular live music. To the rear is the garden which has a covered area.
🚼❀◑♣🍎🚌(X5,80) 🐾📶

Melksham

Hiding Place Micropub

15 High Street, SN12 6JY
☎ (01225) 899022
4 changing beers (sourced regionally; often Stealth, Tyne Bank) [H]
As Melksham's only micropub and only independent free house in the town centre, this new and innovative venue is much appreciated by those looking for interesting and diverse ales and ciders. It features mostly Stealth cask beers, supplemented by guest keg craft beers and lager, plus locally produced spirits. An open-plan design encourages conversation. Downstairs is bright and welcoming while upstairs offers more comfortable seating. Pizza nights are proving popular. Payment is by card only. 🍎🚌📶

Netherhampton

Victoria & Albert

Netherhampton Road, SP2 8PU
☎ (01722) 743174 🌐 victoriaandalbert.org
3 changing beers (sourced regionally) [H]
A long-established family business, with 17 consecutive years in the Guide and winner of numerous CAMRA awards, this welcoming English country pub is a classic. Nestling in the heart of the village, the building dates back to 1540 and features a thatched roof, spacious garden, large covered patio, flagstone floors, log fire and original timber beams. Snacks and full meals are available lunchtimes and evenings (excluding Sun eve). Black Rat and Lilley's ciders are served.
Q🚼❀◑♣🍎P🐾📶

Newton Tony

Malet Arms L

SP4 0HF
☎ (01980) 629279 🌐 maletarms.co.uk
4 changing beers (sourced locally; often Plain, Ramsbury, Stonehenge) [H]
Charming and historic pub, with a restaurant extension, in the conservation area of the village and with the River Bourne flowing past in winter. The window in the larger bar is reputed to come from a galleon. Celebrating 20 years at the pub, the landlord is as enthusiastic and proud of his high-quality food as he is of his ales. Four mainly local beers change weekly and Old Rosie cider is served. The pub welcomes walkers and dogs.
Q🚼❀◑🍎P🚌(67) 🐾

Nunton

Radnor Arms L ✔

SP5 4HS
☎ (01722) 329722 🌐 theradnor.com
Downton New Forest Ale; 3 changing beers (sourced locally) [H]
A popular, spacious pub dating from 1853 and named after the local landowner. The landlady and her staff offer a warm welcome to all, including families, children and dogs. Three dining areas adjoin the main bar and an extensive and regularly changing menu is provided to suit all tastes. The large open garden extends to the river and has a secure children's playground. The pub hosts an annual summer festival. Q🚼❀◑♿P🚌(44,X3)🐾📶

Pewsey

Coopers Arms L

37-39 Ball Road, SN9 5BL
☎ (01672) 562495
Ramsbury Gold; Wadworth 6X; 5 changing beers (sourced nationally; often Box Steam, St Austell, Skinner's) [H]
Worth seeking out, this down-to-earth thatched pub on the eastern edge of Pewsey has a historic interior with an open-plan bar, two side rooms and a warming fire in winter. Five real ales are served: two local regulars plus three changing guests, usually from the South-West. Real cider is available in summer. The pub hosts live music monthly on a Friday night and a quiz on the first Sunday of the month. No food, but snacks are available.
Q❀🛏♣🍎P🚌(X5) 🐾📶

Shed Alehouse L ✔

20 North Street, SN9 5EX
☎ 07769 812643 🌐 theshedalehouse.com
5 changing beers (sourced regionally) [H]
A former shop converted to a cosy micropub, the interior reflecting its name with a wood decor complete with tools. This is a free house with five handpumps serving a changing range of beers from local and regional brewers, often including Shed ales. The total number dispensed since 2015 exceeds 1,000. A craft pilsner and up to four real ciders are also offered. With room inside for around 20 people, you will soon get to know your fellow drinkers. No dogs allowed. Q🚼🚆♣🍎🚌(X5)

Royal Wootton Bassett

Five Bells 🏆 L ✔

Wood Street, SN4 7BD
☎ (01793) 849422

Black Sheep Special Ale; Fuller's London Porter; 4 changing beers (sourced nationally; often Sharp's, Timothy Taylor)
Dating from before 1841, this is a busy and cosy traditional thatched local with a beamed ceiling and open fires. It has been run by the same couple for over 20 years. The bar has seven handpumps for two regular beers, four guests and Old Rosie cider. Food is served lunchtimes and Tuesday and Wednesday evenings (booking recommended). The pub has darts and crib teams. Local CAMRA Pub of the Year.
Q P (55)

Salisbury

Deacons

118 Fisherton Street, SP2 7QT
(01722) 322866 deaconssalisbury.com
Hop Back GFB, Summer Lightning; Sharp's Doom Bar; 1 changing beer (sourced regionally)
A friendly, independently owned free house a stone's throw from Salisbury railway station and a short walk from the cathedral. The landlord collaborates with local breweries to showcase quality real ale. Sky and BT sport are shown in HD and the front room has a digital jukebox. The pub hosts live music, quiz nights and beer festivals – see the website for details. Local CAMRA Pub of the Year 2020.

Duke of York

34 York Road, SP2 7AS
07881 812218
Hop Back GFB; Sixpenny 6d Best Bitter; 5 changing beers (sourced locally; often Downton, Plain, Stonehenge)
A popular free house sporting local beers and two changing traditional ciders. The focus is on the community, with an informal Sunday night quiz, wine club, whisky club and thriving conversation. The pub is home to the Fisherton History Society who meet on the second Wednesday of the month and host occasional events. Live music plays every other Saturday. Barbecues are held at weekends during the summer.
(R1)

Haunch of Venison ★

1 Minster Street, SP1 1TB
(01722) 411313 haunchpub.co.uk
Courage Best Bitter; Hop Back GFB, Summer Lightning; 1 changing beer (sourced regionally)
A fine old inn, identified by CAMRA as having a nationally important historic interior. The main bar, the Commons, is timber-panelled and has a rare pewter-topped bar. A tiny second bar features original spirit taps and floor tiles recovered long ago from a refurbishment of the cathedral. On the mezzanine floor, the House of Lords area contains the mummified hand of a card cheat. Upstairs again, there are two separate dining rooms, one with an old fireplace dating back to 1588. A must for whisky drinkers, it offers up to 130 varieties of malts.

Rai d'Or

69 Brown Street, SP1 2AS
(01722) 327137 raidor.co.uk
2 changing beers (sourced locally)
Characterful 13th-century free house near the cathedral, with a fascinating history highlighted by a blue plaque recalling a 14th-century landlady. An inglenook fireplace and low ceilings make for an appealing ambience. Excellent, reasonably priced Thai food is complemented by two changing, usually local, beers, and Wessex Dry cider. The pub can be busy at mealtimes but drinkers are always welcome. There is a discount on food if you eat early. A former local CAMRA Town Pub of the Year, with 19 years in the Guide.

Rugby Club

Castle Road, SP1 3SA
(01722) 325317 salisburyrfc.org
Hop Back GFB, Crop Circle, Summer Lightning; 1 changing beer (sourced locally)
Occupying a corner of the large club house, this cosy, refurbished lounge bar is open to the public. Retaining its sporting roots, the bar features rugby memorabilia. Two TVs generally show rugby or other sport. The function room bar is open at busy times such as match days. The three Hop Back ales are often joined by a Hop Back or Downton seasonal brew. Quiz night is Wednesday. A beer festival is held in May. There are camping facilities close by. P

Village Freehouse

33 Wilton Road, SP2 7EF
(01722) 329707
Downton Quadhop; 4 changing beers (sourced nationally)
A lively pub near the train station. Microbrewery beers come from near and far, with customer requests welcome. There is always at least one dark brew – stout, porter or mild. Teams are fielded in the local crib, cricket and football leagues, and a TV shows BT Sport, with the sound off much of the time. Filled rolls are available or you are welcome to bring your own food. Local CAMRA Pub of the Year three times.

Winchester Gate

113-117 Rampart Road, SP1 1JA
(01722) 503362
4 changing beers (sourced regionally; often Downton, Plain, Red Cat)
Characterful free house, an inn since the 17th century, which once provided for travellers at the city's east tollgate. Four handpumps offer changing ales and often real ciders from across the country. Beer and cider festivals are held, sometimes in association with a live music event. A small lawned garden offers a pleasant area to sit out, particularly during the summer. The pub is renowned for live music every Friday and Saturday, and frequently on Thursday too. P

Wyndham Arms

27 Estcourt Road, SP1 3AS
(01722) 331026
Hop Back GFB, Citra, Crop Circle, Summer Lightning; 2 changing beers (sourced locally; often Hop Back)
The birthplace of the Hop Back Brewery, the pub is now celebrating 34 consecutive years in the Guide. A traditional ale house, it has a single bar serving a selection of Hop Back ales – normally Taiphoon in summer and Entire Stout in winter – alongside seasonal offerings and a fine selection of bottled beers and wines. Two small rooms off the main bar area provide quiet spaces and more seating. This is a pub for conversation, good-natured banter and fine ales. Branch CAMRA Pub of the Year 2019. (R2,R6)

Semley

Benett Arms

Village Green, SP7 9AS (1 mile E of A350) ST891270
(01747) 830221 thebenettarms-semley.co.uk
Exmoor Ale; 2 changing beers
A genuine free house sitting by the green and pond in a quiet village, with a single small bar and separate dining areas. The beer choice varies but there are usually three

to choose from, either on handpump or direct from the cellar. Excellent home-cooked food is available at all sessions. A warm welcome is extended to all, including families and dogs, in an area popular with walkers. There are three letting rooms. Twice local CAMRA Pub of the Year. Q🐴❀🛏◑♿P🚌(84,247)🐾📶

Swindon

Beehive ✔

55 Prospect Hill, SN1 3JS

☎ (01793) 523187 🌐 bee-hive.co.uk

Hardys & Hansons Olde Trip; house beer (by Hardys & Hansons); 4 changing beers (sourced regionally; often Greene King) [H]

This pub dates from 1871 and is built on a corner on a hill, giving a nearly triangular layout on five different levels. It serves six real ales including four changing guests, with a regional focus. A popular live music venue, it hosts performances on most Thursday and Friday nights, and a world music club on the last Wednesday of the month. The walls display pictures and other art for sale. Locally sourced pies are available lunchtime until early evening. ◑♣🚌(11,12)🐾📶

Blunsdon Arms ✔

Lady Lane, SN25 2NA

☎ (01793) 729801

St Austell Tribute; house beer (by Black Sheep); 6 changing beers (sourced nationally; often Bath, Butcombe) [H]

Opened in 2006 owned by Ember Inns, the Blunsdon Arms is a large, open-plan, popular pub with friendly, pleasant staff. It features an 18-plus area, where no children are allowed. The six guest beers rotate from a selection of 12 ales, which change quarterly. Three real ciders are also available. Food is served every day. There is a quiz on Wednesday and Sunday, poker on Monday and live music the last Saturday of the month.
🐴❀◑♿♣●P🚌(11,15)📶

Glue Pot

5 Emlyn Square, SN1 5BP

☎ (01793) 497420

Hop Back Citra, Fuggle Stone, Crop Circle, Entire Stout, Summer Lightning; 3 changing beers (sourced nationally; often Downton, Hop Back) [H]

An unspoilt inn, the last remaining pub in the historic stone-built Railway Village built in the 1840s. An Allsopp's Brewery logo adorns one window. Seven Hop Back or Downton ales are joined by one guest. Local CAMRA Cider Pub of the Year, it stocks 11 real ciders. A range of sandwiches, wraps and subs are available. Busy at weekends, there is a quiz on Wednesday, a price reduction on Monday and a beer festival at Easter.
Q❀⇌●🚌(1,5)🐾

Goddard Arms ✔

1 High Street, SN1 3EG

☎ (01793) 619090

Ringwood Fortyniner; St Austell Tribute; Sharp's Doom Bar; 2 changing beers (sourced nationally; often Prescott, Timothy Taylor) [H]

This Grade II listed building was the home of the magistrates court until 1852. The smart interior is spacious with comfortable seating. The bar features five real ales, two of them changing guests, and Lilley's cider. Good-value food is available all day, making the pub busy most of the time. Sports TV is screened in the background. There is accommodation and a separate function room upstairs. 🐴❀🛏◑♿●P🚌(12)📶

Hop Inn L

8 Devizes Road, SN1 4BH

☎ (01793) 976833 🌐 hopinnswindon.co.uk

House beer (by Ramsbury); 6 changing beers (sourced regionally; often Arbor) [H]

The pub that began the Devizes Road real ale boom, The Hop Inn moved two doors down from its original location in 2019 to larger premises. This free house now has eight handpumps serving six changing guest ales and Hop Inn Bitter brewed by Ramsbury. Two ciders from Hungerford Park are also sold. The interior is decorated in an eclectic style, including tables and chairs made from reclaimed wood. Wings and burgers are available from the Pick up Point. Q🐴❀◗●🚌(11,22)🐾📶

Little Hop L

7 Devizes Road, SN1 4BJ

☎ (01793) 976833

Arbor Shangri La, Blue Sky Drinking; 3 changing beers (sourced regionally; often Arbor) [H]

A rebirth for Swindon's first micropub in association with Arbor Ales. The Little Hop opened in August 2019 on the site of The Hop Inn, which in a former life was a sex shop. The small, brightly coloured, modern pub has five handpumps, three of which showcase the latest brews from Arbor. In the corner is a well-stocked bottle fridge featuring beers mainly from the Bristol area. Local art features on the walls. Q🐴♿●🚌(11,22)🐾📶

Wyvern Tavern ✔

49-50 Bridge Street, SN1 1BL

☎ (01793) 484924

Butcombe Original; 5 changing beers (sourced nationally) [H]

Large town-centre chain pub which unusually has a better-than-average interest in and sale of real ales and ciders, offering one regular and five changing guest beers alongside Lilley's cider. It can be very lively, especially later in the week and at the weekend. Essentially a sports bar, it has a number of TV screens showing various sports and news. Refurbished in 2019 with more seating, facilities are all on one level.
🐴❀◑♿⇌♣●🚌(1,8)🐾📶

Tisbury

Boot Inn L

High Street, SP3 6PS

☎ (01747) 870363

3 changing beers (sourced locally) [G]

Fine village free house, licensed since 1768 and run by the same family since 1976. A traditional, Chilmark stone building, it has a relaxed, friendly atmosphere and offers a cordial welcome to locals and visitors alike. Join in the conversation at the bar or find a quiet table at which to enjoy well-kept (mainly local) ales served from casks behind the bar. The beer range may increase at weekends and in summer. Excellent food is served and there is a spacious garden. The third Tuesday of the month is quiz night. Q❀◑⇌♣P🚌(25)🐾📶

Trowbridge

King's Arms

5 Castle Street, BA14 8AN

☎ (01225) 751310 🌐 thekingsarmstrowbridge.co.uk

Butcombe Adam Henson's Rare Breed; Sharp's Doom Bar; 2 changing beers (sourced regionally; often Brotherhood, St Austell, Wye Valley) [H]

Following an extensive refurbishment, this town-centre pub has reopened as a smart, welcoming free house. The single drinking area, served by a central bar, has partitions creating a number of separate snug-like areas. The patio at the back, with its listed tree, makes a pleasant spot for an alfresco drink. An interesting and varied food menu is offered. Four beers are usually available – including guest beers from larger micros in Wiltshire, Somerset or Devon – alongside a varied choice of real ciders. Q❀◑♿⛺⇌●🚌📶

Upavon

Ship 🄻

10 High Street, SN9 6EA

☎ (01980) 630313 🌐 theshipatupavon.co.uk

Butcombe Original, Gold; 4 changing beers (sourced locally; often Plain, Stonehenge, Three Castles) 🄷

This popular village pub is now locally owned and run. Parts of the Grade II listed building date from the 15th century. Inside, it combines traditional wooden beams with a light, open decor. The dining room has a huge model of the Cutty Sark. There are six real ales, four of them locally sourced. An extensive food menu makes use of local ingredients when available, with various theme nights. Live music features on occasion.
❀◑♿⛺♣🚌(X5) 🐾📶

Warminster

Fox & Hounds

6 Deverill Road, BA12 9QP

☎ (01985) 216711

Wessex Warminster Warrior; house beer (by Wessex); 2 changing beers (sourced regionally; often Bath Ales, Palmers) 🄷

A friendly two-bar local – the main bar with a pool table and sports TV is at the rear, and a quiet snug bar is to the right of the entrance. There is a large skittle alley and function room at the back. Guest real ales are usually from local and regional breweries. Regular ciders are from Thatchers and Rich's, plus up to five guests. Closing time may be later than 11pm. A local CAMRA multiple award-winning pub. Q❀♿♣●P🚌🐾📶

Organ Inn ✔

49 High Street, BA12 9AQ

☎ (01985) 211777 🌐 theorganinn.co.uk

3 changing beers (sourced regionally; often Kettlesmith, Plain, Stonehenge) 🄷

An inn until 1913, the Organ reopened as a pub in 2006. The welcoming interior comprises three rooms with a traditional feel, including a snug bar, games room and a skittle alley. The beer range constantly changes but will always include Organ Bitter (the brewery is a secret). At least five varying ciders are also available. A beer festival is held in September. Bar snacks are interesting and there is an art gallery upstairs. Local CAMRA Pub of the Year 2019 and Rural Pub of the Year 2018 and 2020.
Q❀♿⇌♣●🚌🐾📶

Westbury

Angel

3 Church Street, BA13 3BY

☎ (01373) 822648

4 changing beers (often Irving, Twisted) 🄷

Recently reopened, this traditional, welcoming pub has several rooms including a library for customers. It offers at least four beers, always including one from local brewer Twisted. Others come from the south and the West Country. A couple of ciders are also available. There are plans to serve food in the future.
❀🛏♣●🚌(D1) 🐾📶

Horse & Groom ✔

18 Alfred Street, BA13 3DY

☎ (01373) 859433 🌐 horseandgroomwestbury.co.uk

Sharp's Doom Bar; 2 changing beers (sourced regionally; often Twisted) 🄷

A large pub on the north-eastern edge of the town centre. There are two separate bars – one is essentially a restaurant. The pub has an attractive patio-style drinking area at the front, which can be a suntrap in the summer, as well as a large garden with plenty of seating and a good sized car park. Opposite is a skittle alley which can be used as a function room. ❀🛏◑♿♣P🚌🐾📶

Whitley

Pear Tree Inn 🄻

Top Lane, SN12 8QX (off B3353 on Purlpit/Atworth road)

☎ (01225) 704966 🌐 peartreewhitley.co.uk

Bath Ales Gem; 2 changing beers (sourced locally; often Box Steam, Brotherhood, Ramsbury) 🄷

Sympathetically refurbished in 2015, this 17th-century former farm is now a pub restaurant. There is a small rustic bar area with a large open fire, stone walls and flagstone floors. Three local ales and a local real cider are available. Restaurant areas are to the rear, where a wide range of food is served, with an emphasis on locally sourced, seasonal ingredients. There are extensive gardens including a vegetable plot that supplies the pub.
Q🐴❀🛏◑♿⛺●P🚌(D3) 🐾📶

Winsley

Seven Stars ✔

Bradford Rd, BA15 2LQ

☎ (01225) 722204 🌐 sevenstarswinsley.co.uk

Palmers IPA; 3 changing beers (sourced regionally; often Exmoor, Plain, Three Daggers) 🄷

This fine old village pub dates in parts back to the early 1700s. The four beers on include three changing guests usually from the West Country. The home-made food comes highly recommended and there is a peaceful garden and spacious car park. The D1 bus from Bath to Salisbury/Warminster (and back) stops right outside. Booking is recommended for those wishing to eat and note that all food can be ordered gluten free.
🐴❀◑♿⛺P🚌(D1) 🐾📶

Wroughton

Carters Rest 🄻

57 High Street, SN4 9JU

☎ 07816 134966

Ramsbury Deerstalker; 6 changing beers (sourced regionally) 🄷

First mentioned in 1671, this popular real ale pub was extensively altered around 1912 to give its current Victorian appearance, and was refurbished in 2017. There are 12 handpumps but currently the beer range is seven, with eight at the weekend. Beers are mainly from small independent breweries within a 50-mile radius, although occasionally they may be from further afield. Poker night is Tuesday and quiz night Thursday.
Q🐴❀♿♣P🚌(9,49) 🐾📶

> Give my people plenty of beer, good beer and cheap beer, and you will have no revolution among them. **Queen Victoria**

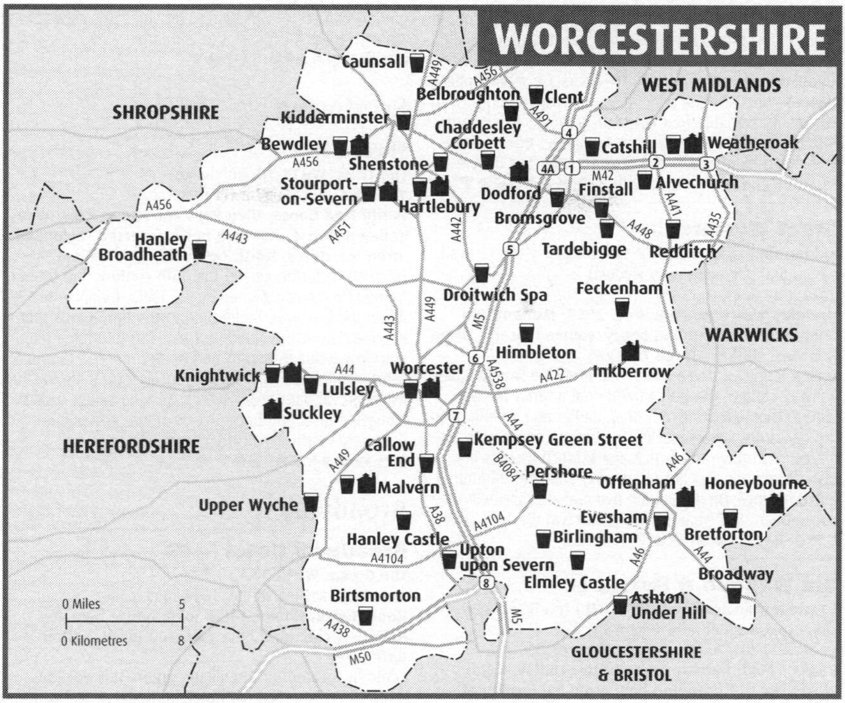

Alvechurch

Weighbridge

Scarfield Wharf, Scarfield Hill, B48 7SQ (follow signs to marina from village) SP022721

☎ (0121) 445 5111 the-weighbridge.co.uk

6 changing beers (sourced locally; often Hobsons, Kinver, Weatheroak) H

This cosy canalside pub has received many CAMRA awards. It has two small lounges, a public bar and a pleasant garden. Good-value, home-cooked food is served lunchtimes and evenings, with excellent Sunday lunches (no food Tue and Wed). A covered area outside can be used for functions. There are changing beers from Kinver, Weatheroak and Wye Valley, plus three changing guests from other breweries, one of which is a mild, as well as a real cider. Spring and autumn beer festivals are held. Q P

Ashton under Hill

Star Inn

Elmley Road, WR11 7SN

☎ (01386) 881325 thestar-ashtonunderhill.co.uk

Black Sheep Best Bitter; 2 changing beers H

A delightful pub on the edge of Bredon Hill, welcoming walkers for a pint and a meal. It serves home-made country food prepared using local produce, including meats from its own family farm. The pub has a traditional interior with a bar, warmed by an open fire, and a separate restaurant – food is served throughout. The large garden is popular with families. P

Belbroughton

Holly Bush Inn

Stourbridge Road, DY9 9UG (on A491 Stourbridge Rd)

☎ (01562) 730207

Hobsons Mild, Twisted Spire, Town Crier; 2 changing beers (sourced regionally; often Hobsons) H

This traditional inn, set back from the A491 dual carriageway, was originally terraced cottages built in 1845. Beers from the Hobsons range are served, along with a real Westons cider. The pub menu includes good-value steak and fish options. Full of character, it has a lounge/dining area, central bar section and a small raised restaurant. Cards and dominoes are frequently played. A winner of CAMRA awards including branch Pub of the Year. Q P (318)

Bewdley

Bewdley Brewery Tap

Bewdley Craft Centre, Lax Lane, DY12 2DZ

☎ (01299) 405148 bewdleybrewery.co.uk

Bewdley Worcestershire Way, Sir Keith Park, Worcestershire Sway; 2 changing beers (sourced locally; often Bewdley) H

Bewdley Brewery produces a range of six regular cask ales and a greater number of bottled beers, some for the Severn Valley Railway. The spacious taproom, to the rear of a former school building, is adorned with railway and brewery memorabilia, and has an old-fashioned feel. Five of the brewery's cask ales are served through half-pint pulls, giving each pint a perfectly clear dispense, and the full range of bottled beers is available. Open on bank holidays; winter hours may vary.

Black Boy

50 Wyre Hill, DY12 2UE (up Sandy Bank from Cleobury Rd at Welch Gate)

☎ (01299) 400088 theblackboybewdley.co.uk

Bewdley Worcestershire Way; Hobsons Town Crier; Three Tuns XXX; Wye Valley Bitter; 1 changing beer (sourced locally; often Hop & Stagger, Swan Brewery) H

Up a hill from the town centre, this friendly, ancient inn is worth the climb. The attractive, half-timbered building is the oldest pub in Bewdley, with a beamed interior and an open fire in winter. Up to five beers are served, plus a cider or two. Cobs and pork pies are always on offer, with hot meals available four evenings a week, plus Sunday. Attractions include bar skittles, bagatelle, board games and shove-ha'penny. A folk session is hosted on the second Monday of each month. Q♘❀▲♣●🚌🐾📶

Great Western 𝕃

Kidderminster Road, DY12 1BY (nr SVR station – walk past signal box and under viaduct)
☎ (01299) 488828
Bewdley Worcestershire Way, 2857; Morland Old Golden Hen; 2 changing beers (sourced locally; often Hobsons, Ludlow, Three Tuns) [H]
Conveniently located a short walk from the Severn Valley Railway station, the pub's traditional interior has a railway theme reminiscent of an earlier age. Overlooking the bar is an upper level from which to admire the fine glazed decorative tiling. Pub snacks such as cobs and tasty local pork pies are in keeping with the traditional pub ambience. On the bar are five real ales, including the house beer 2857 from Bewdley, and two Westons ciders. Q♘❀⇌(SVR)♣●P🚌🐾📶

Old Waggon & Horses 𝕃

91 Kidderminster Road, DY12 1DG (on Bewdley to Kidderminster road at Catchem's End)
☎ (01299) 403170 🌐 waggonbewdley.co.uk
Banks's Mild; Bathams Best Bitter; Ludlow Gold; Wainwright; 1 changing beer (sourced locally; often Enville, Hobsons, Holden's) [H]
Popular locals' and visitors' pub with a central bar serving three distinct areas. The small wooden-floored snug has a dartboard, the larger room a wood-burner and a roll-down screen for major sporting events, but at most times conversation prevails. An old kitchen range adds to the cottagey feel. Guest ales come from local independents. Pub food is available, plus a pie night and a tapas night once a month, and a carvery on Sunday. The attractive terraced flower garden is on many levels.
♘❀◐◑⇌(SVR)♣●P🚌🐾📶

Birlingham

Swan

Church Street, WR10 3AQ
☎ (01386) 750485 🌐 theswaninn.co.uk
2 changing beers (often Goff's, Purity) [H]
A delightful, thatched, food-oriented free house tucked away at the end of a lane in a quiet village. It has a separate bar and conservatory overlooking the fine garden, where food is served. The menu features fresh fish specials. The pub has been recently modernised inside but in a sympathetic manner in keeping with the age of the building. Q❀◐◑P🚌(382)🐾📶

Birtsmorton

Farmers Arms

Birts Street, WR13 6AP (off B4208) SO790363
☎ (01684) 833308 🌐 farmersarmsbirtsmorton.co.uk
Hook Norton Hooky, Old Hooky; 2 changing beers (sourced locally) [H]
Grade II listed black and white village pub dating from 1480, found down a quiet country lane. The large bar area features a splendid inglenook fireplace while the cosy lounge has old settles and low beams. Good-value, home-made food is on offer daily. A beer from a small local independent brewer is often available. The spacious garden, complete with swings, provides fine views of the Malvern Hills. A caravan site is nearby.
Q♘❀◐◑♿♣●P🚌(577)🐾📶

Bretforton

Fleece Inn ★ 𝕃

The Cross, WR11 7JE (nr church)
☎ (01386) 831173 🌐 thefleeceinn.co.uk
Purity Mad Goose; Uley Pig's Ear Strong Beer; Wye Valley Bitter; 4 changing beers (sourced regionally; often Marston's, North Cotswold, Wye Valley) [H]
Originally a farmhouse in the 15th century, the timber-framed Fleece was owned by the Taplin family until 1977 when the last Miss Taplin died in the bar. It was then bequeathed to the National Trust. The interior is filled with low wooden beams and open fires. The famous pewter collection was saved by locals from a fire in 2004. Its medieval barn hosts events. Serving seven cask ales alongside local and home-made ciders, the pub is definitely worth a visit if you are in the area.
Q♘❀🛏◐◑♿♣●P🚌🐾📶

Broadway

Broadway Hotel 𝕃 ✔

The Green, WR12 7AA
☎ (01386) 852401 🌐 broadway-hotel.co.uk
Hook Norton Hooky, Old Hooky; house beer (by Goff's); 1 changing beer (sourced locally; often Goff's) [H]
Centrally located on the village green, this opulent, refurbished 16th-century hotel, partly black and white, is a former coaching inn that once belonged to Pershore Abbey. A countryside ambience blends with cosy home furnishings and quirky decor, featuring comfy armchairs, a minstrels' gallery and a huge inglenook with log fire. Real ale and bar meals are served in the racing-themed Jockey Club Bar, seasonal food in the elegant award-winning brasserie. ♘❀🛏◐◑♿♣🐾

Crown & Trumpet Inn 𝕃 ✔

14 Church Street, WR12 7AE
☎ (01386) 853202 🌐 crownandtrumpet.co.uk
North Cotswold Green Man IPA, Shagweaver; Stroud Tom Long; Timothy Taylor Landlord; 1 changing beer (sourced locally; often North Cotswold) [H]
Picturesque 17th-century Cotswold-stone inn, just off the village green, with friendly staff and run by a landlord with 35 years' experience as a Guide licensee. This hostelry has an abundance of character, with oak beams, a log fire and Flowers Brewery memorabilia. Good honest home-made local dishes are offered at

REAL ALE BREWERIES

Ambridge Inkberrow
Bewdley ✈ Bewdley
BOA (Brothers of Ale) ✈ Stourport on Severn (NEW)
Boat Lane ✈ Offenham
Friday Beer Malvern
Hartlebury Hartlebury
Hop Shed Suckley
Lakehouse Malvern
Malvern Hills Malvern
Sociable ✈ Worcester
Teme Valley ▤ Knightwick
Weatheroak Hill Weatheroak
White Rabbit Honeybourne
Wintrip Worcester
Woodcote Manor Dodford
Worcester Worcester

reasonable prices alongside regular ales and guests plus ciders and perries. Entertainment includes midweek live jazz and blues nights. Q❀⇄◑♣●P ᯤ

Bromsgrove

Golden Cross Hotel 𝕃 ✔

20 High Street, B61 8HH (S end of High St)
☎ (01527) 870005
Greene King Abbot; Ruddles Best Bitter; Sharp's Doom Bar; 9 changing beers Ⓗ
A busy town-centre pub set in a former hotel and coachhouse. This split-level Wetherspoon has 12 booths with stained-glass surrounds and an open fire. Daily themed food deals and manager's specials are always on offer. Three regular core beers are served plus nine various guests, many from local breweries. The licensee asks for suggestions on beer choices and reacts to feedback. During seasonal festivals cask ales from across the UK are promoted. ❀◑♿●P ᯤ

Little Ale House

21 Worcester Road, B61 7DL (on corner of Station St)
☎ 07791 698641
6 changing beers (often Hobsons, Malvern Hills, Wye Valley) Ⓖ
A micropub with a cosy atmosphere. Up to six ales are served straight from the cask, from Hobsons, Malvern Hills, Wye Valley and Woodcote Manor. A range of ciders and perries is also stocked and take-away containers are available. Snacks include fresh cobs. A council car park is nearby and the bus station is parallel with the high street. Q♣● ᯤ

Callow End

Old Bush 𝕃

Upton Road, WR2 4TE (small lane off B4424) SO835497
☎ (01905) 830792 🌐 old-bush.com
Butcombe Original; Hobsons Twisted Spire; Wye Valley HPA; 1 changing beer (sourced locally) Ⓗ
Village local down a quiet lane off the main road with a pretty black and white exterior and a cosy interior with log-burner. The guest beer is usually local, and a guest cider is available in summer. Good home-made food is served in the separate dining area, though you can also eat in the bar. The large and attractively laid-out garden has country views, and a play area for children with a chicken run. The pub hosts regular live music and an annual blues festival. There is a camping and caravan site in the grounds. ❀◑Å♣●P ᯤ

Catshill

Royal Oak ✔

41 Barley Mow Lane, B61 0LU
☎ (01527) 870141 🌐 theroyaloakbromsgrove.com
4 changing beers (sourced regionally; often Enville, Timothy Taylor) Ⓗ
Popular local situated just off the main A38. The front bar incorporates a pool room and the larger lounge/restaurant to the rear extends into a sunny conservatory. The food menu offers excellent-value traditional English fare, and the beer menu normally includes up to four ales. The pub is close to the start of the three Royal Hunters' Walks around the local villages of Bournheath and Dodford. ❀◑♿♣P ᯤ

Caunsall

Anchor Inn 𝕃

DY11 5YL (off A449)
☎ (01562) 850254 🌐 theanchorinncaunsall.co.uk
Hobsons Best, Town Crier; Wye Valley HPA, Butty Bach; 1 changing beer (sourced regionally; often Hobsons, Three Tuns) Ⓗ
Friendly village inn renowned for its five real ales, traditional ciders and, especially, its well-filled cobs. A central doorway leads into the bar with its original 1920s furniture and horse-racing memorabilia. Outside, the garden is a suntrap in summer, and this popular pub can get busy, especially at lunchtimes and weekends. Easily reached from the nearby canal, this gem is well worth stopping off for. Local CAMRA Pub of the Year finalist 2014-2020. Q❀◑♣●P ᯤ

Chaddesley Corbett

Swan 𝕃

High Street, DY10 4SD SO892737
☎ (01562) 777302 🌐 theswanchaddesleycorbett.co.uk
Bathams Mild Ale, Best Bitter Ⓗ
Dating from 1606, this traditional pub sits at the heart of the village, featuring a public bar, side room with a real fire and an impressive lounge with a raised area for entertainment. Filled rolls and pies are available. Quiz night is held every Wednesday and jazz night every Thursday. There is a large garden and children's play area at the rear overlooking beautiful countryside. The pub is popular with walkers and cyclists alike. Bathams XXX is available in December. Q❀♿Å♣●P (42) ᯤ

Clent

Bell & Cross ★ ✔

Holy Cross Green, DY9 9QL (on five-way crossroads)
☎ (01562) 730319 🌐 thebellandcross.co.uk
Enville Ale; Timothy Taylor Landlord; Wye Valley HPA; 1 changing beer Ⓗ
Grade II listed whitewashed brick building of historic interest, featuring a quarry-tiled corridor, numbered rooms and a Victorian counter. A cosy, welcoming, traditional pub with modern touches, the small bar area has a real fire and the delightful and cosy snug can be booked for functions. Three separate charming dining rooms provide an à la carte menu and afternoon light bites. Outside is a sunny, enclosed rear garden. Close to the Clent Hills (NT). ❀◑P (197,318) ᯤ

Droitwich Spa

Old Cock Inn

77 Friar Street, WR9 8EQ (short walk from station and opp Norbury Theatre)
☎ (01905) 936771
Banks's Mild; Courage Directors; Marston's Pedigree, Old Empire; Wychwood Hobgoblin Gold; Young's Special London Ale Ⓗ
This pub, in the old part of the town, is Droitwich's oldest licensed premises, being first licensed in 1712. The central bar serves four open-plan rooms decorated with interesting old artefacts and local photographs. There is a small function room and a patio garden. The pub boasts a large range of Marston's beers that are not usually found in the area. Thatchers Heritage cider is on handpump. Live music is performed most Saturdays evenings. ❀◑≠♣●P (144) ᯤ

Elmley Castle

Queen Elizabeth 𝕃

Main Street, WR10 3HS
☎ (01386) 710251 🌐 elmleycastle.com

Purity Mad Goose; Wye Valley Bitter; 2 changing beers (sourced nationally; often Goff's, North Cotswold) 🄷
An old inn with a fresh, modern feel inside, named in honour of Elizabeth I's visit to the village in August 1575. This is a community pub, owned by a group of local residents who rescued it from closure. The bar has a flagstone floor, timber beams and a roaring fire, and normally serves one local beer. There is a comfortable lounge and a separate dining room. Themed food evenings are held and there are beer festivals on the May and August bank holidays. The café is open during the day Tuesday to Friday, and on Saturday for breakfast. Q🐴❀◑🍎P🚌🐾📶

Evesham

BCM
64 Bridge Street, WR11 4RY (courtyard off Bridge St)
☎ 07703 753064
House beer (by Birmingham); 4 changing beers (sourced locally; often Birmingham, Wye Valley) 🄷
At the end of a gated courtyard, this 16th-century, Grade II listed building houses a single bar room with tables and perimeter seating, decorated in a contemporary style with natural wood and exposed beams. The family-run pub offers five real ales including a house beer from Birmingham brewery and a regular Wye Valley special, together with craft beers. Quality bar food comes from a local butcher. 🐴❀♿▲⇌♣🚆🚌🐾📶

Red Lion 𝕃
6 Market Place, WR11 4RE
☎ (01386) 761688
Cannon Royall Arrowhead Bitter; White Rabbit Elwood's Dark; 3 changing beers (sourced locally; often Cannon Royall, White Rabbit) 🄷
Community local tucked away in the corner of Evesham's Market Square. It has a main bar, seating areas at the front and side, and a smaller snug at the rear with its own bar and an inglenook fireplace. The pub is now the sole stockist of Cannon Royall and White Rabbit beers. One real cider is always available, two in summer. Live music plays Friday evening and Sunday afternoon. There is no TV or piped music, no alcopops and no food – but you are welcome to bring in your own.
Q🐴⇌♣🍎🚆🚌🐾📶

Feckenham

Rose & Crown ✔
High Street, B96 6HS
☎ (01527) 892188 🌐 roseandcrownfeckenham.co.uk
Banks's Amber Ale; Brakspear Oxford Gold; 2 changing beers (often Ambridge, Marston's) 🄷
A welcoming family-run Grade II listed pub in the old village of Feckenham. Its traditional bar offers up to four real ales, plus at least one real cider. A wide menu of pub classics is served in the cosy lounge, with wooden settles for seating. There is a large enclosed beer garden at the rear. An annual beer festival is held over the August bank holiday. Parking is limited but there is a free car park 200 yards away. Q🐴❀◑♿♣🍎🐾📶

Finstall

Cross Inn 🏆 𝕃
34 Alcester Road, B60 1EW
☎ (01527) 577328
Black Country Bradley's Finest Golden 🄷**, Pig on the Wall** 🄷/🄶**, Fireside; 4 changing beers** 🄷
Taken over and refurbished by Black Country Ales in 2018. Nine handpumps dispense three beers from the brewery's range plus four guests, including one dark ale, and two ciders, displayed on a screen above the bar. Cobs, pork pies and local Scotch eggs are available. Crib and dominoes are played and the pub hosts fêtes, mini beer festivals and charity events for the Primrose Hospice. The garden incorporates a heated smokers' shelter. 🐴❀♿♣🍎P🚌(43,42)🐾📶

Hanley Broadheath

Fox Inn 𝕃
WR15 8QS (on B4204 E of Tenbury Wells) SO671652
☎ (01886) 853189
Bathams Best Bitter; Brakspear Oxford Gold; 1 changing beer 🄷
The main bar of this spacious 16th-century black and white timbered free house is decorated with hops and has a large fireplace with a wood-burning stove. The panelled dining area is separated from the bar by wood beams. The games room has a pool table, TV and darts. Home-made food, including Sunday lunch, is available, with bar snacks at any time. Q🐴❀◑▲♣P🚌(309)🐾📶

Tally Ho! 𝕃
WR15 8QX (on B4204 road E of Tenbury Wells) SO662655
☎ (01886) 853241 🌐 tallyhorestaurant.co.uk
Ludlow Gold; Wye Valley HPA; 3 changing beers (sourced nationally; often Malvern Hills, Wye Valley) 🄷
An inviting, cosy, 14th-century inn with an abundance of beams and stonework, featuring local beers on the bar. The separate restaurant in the conservatory has grand views of the countryside. A carvery is served on Sunday lunchtime (book ahead for food on Sun eve). The garden enjoys more panoramic views of Titterstone Clee Hill and the Teme Valley, and has a children's playground. Pool and darts are popular. 🐴❀🛏◑♿▲♣🍎P🚌(309)🐾📶

Hanley Castle

Three Kings ★ 𝕃
Church End, WR8 0BL (signed off B4211) SO838420
☎ (01684) 592686
Butcombe Original; Hobsons Best; 3 changing beers (often Beowulf, Malvern Hills, Slater's) 🄷
On CAMRA's National Inventory of Historic Pub Interiors, this unspoilt 15th-century country pub on the village green near the church has been run by the Roberts family since 1911. The three-room interior comprises a small snug with large inglenook, serving hatch and settle wall, a small side room, and Nell's Lounge with another inglenook, beams and its own entrance. Three guest ales are on offer, often from local breweries, plus Westons Old Rosie draught cider. Live music sessions feature regularly and a beer festival is held in November.
Q🐴❀♣🍎P🚌(363)🐾

Hartlebury

Tap House 𝕃
Station Road, DY11 7YJ (backs onto Hartlebury station platform)
☎ (01299) 253275 🌐 thetaphousehartlebury.co.uk
Enville Ale; Hartlebury Hooker, Off the Rails, APA; Wye Valley HPA; 3 changing beers (sourced regionally; often Hobsons, Holden's, St Austell) 🄷
A modern conversion of the former railway station, next to the platform at Hartlebury station. The lounge bar has comfortable bench seating reminiscent of old railway days, a large fireplace with wood-burner and railway-

style signs. Outside, tables on the terrace overlook the valley. Food is available all day including specials. Eight real ales are from national and local breweries including the adjacent Hartlebury Brewery.
❀◑♿≹P🚌(303)🐾📶

Himbleton

Galton Arms Ⓛ
Harrow Lane, WR9 7LQ
☎ (01905) 391672 🌐 thegaltonarms.co.uk
Banks's Amber Ale; Bathams Best Bitter; Prescott Hill Climb; Wye Valley HPA Ⓗ
Splendid rural pub situated on the edge of the village with a friendly welcome, attracting locals and visitors alike. Its unspoilt interior is warmed by open fires and retains the original beams that divide up the space. The bar area shows sports TV. Good-value food is served in two separate dining areas. The beer garden is suitable for children. Q❀◑♿P🚌(356)🐾

Kempsey Green Street

Huntsman Inn Ⓛ
Green Street, WR5 3QB (from A38 at Kempsey via Post Office Lane) SO868490
☎ (01905) 820336
Bathams Best Bitter; Greene King IPA; Morland Original Bitter Ⓗ
Cosy and friendly multi-roomed local that was previously a 300-year-old farmhouse with exposed beams. There is a small main bar with a real fire to the front and a larger bar down steps. A separate restaurant serves reasonably priced home-cooked food. There is also a skittle alley with its own bar, an attractive garden and a large car park. The pub is closed at lunchtimes during the week. Dogs are welcome in the bar and lounge. ❀◑♣P🐾

Kidderminster

Beer Emporium & Cider House
Oxford Street, DY10 1AR (between railway station and town centre)
☎ 07803 357362
4 changing beers (sourced nationally) Ⓖ
Micropub convenient for the station and the town centre. There is plenty of conversation around the room and table service is the norm. A chalkboard shows four real ales from around the country, usually including a dark one. Four ciders and two perries, a selection of foreign bottled beers, craft KeyKeg beers, wines and soft drinks ensure there's something for everyone. Local CAMRA Gold Cider Pub of the Year 2019 and 2020.
Q♿≹●P🚌🐾📶

King & Castle Ⓛ ✔
Comberton Hill, DY10 1QX (next to mainline station and part of SVR terminus)
☎ (01562) 747505
Bathams Best Bitter Ⓗ**; Bewdley Worcestershire Way** Ⓗ/Ⓟ**; Hobsons Mild, Town Crier; 3 changing beers (sourced regionally; often Exmoor, Three Tuns, Wye Valley)** Ⓗ
Atmospheric recreation of a GWR terminus station bar and gateway to the Severn Valley Railway. Eight handpumps dispense beers from local, regional and national breweries, and it has three ciders. Breakfast is served, then pub meals, cobs and snacks from the bar. Bottled beers from Bewdley are available on trains, and pubs along the line are an attraction for locals and visitors using the railway. Local CAMRA Gold Pub of the Year 2019. Q❀◑♿≹♣●P🚌🐾📶

Olde Seven Stars Ⓛ ✔
13-14 Coventry Street, DY10 2BG (opp Swan Centre)
☎ (01562) 228641
5 changing beers (often Draught Bass, Wye Valley) Ⓗ
With five changing real ales and two draught ciders, this historic town-centre pub is well worth visiting. The front and rear bars display many features from previous ages. Snacks include pork pies, and customers can bring their own food (there are plenty of takeaways nearby), with tableware and condiments provided. Live music plays on the last Friday of the month. Families are welcome and the rear garden is popular in summer. The pub's friendly atmosphere and excellent ales won it local CAMRA Bronze Pub of the Year 2019. ❀♣●🚌🐾📶

Weavers at Park Lane Ⓛ
40 Park Lane, DY11 6TG (opp Tesco)
☎ (01562) 742717
Wye Valley Butty Bach; house beer (by Woodcote Manor); 4 changing beers (sourced regionally; often Bathams, Ludlow, Swan) Ⓗ
Canalside inn with a beer garden overlooking the water – moorings are on the towpath a short walk from the nearby bridge. The pub offers cobs, pork pies and an impressive range of six well-kept real ales, including local and unusual beers from further afield, and six ciders and perries. Last orders are 20 minutes before closing time. Opening hours vary November to Easter. Local CAMRA Cider Pub of the Year 2018. Q❀♣●P🐾📶

Weavers Real Ale House Ⓛ
98 Comberton Hill, DY10 1QH (300yds down hill from railway station)
☎ (01562) 229413
Pig Iron Unbeweavable; Three Tuns XXX; Wye Valley Butty Bach; 5 changing beers (sourced nationally; often Bewdley, Fixed Wheel, Fownes) Ⓗ
A light and airy pub that is ideal for conversation and offers a warm welcome. Its walls display pictures of old Kidderminster alongside beer memorabilia. It serves eight excellent ales, four ciders and a perry on handpump, plus six craft beers. Cobs are always available. Close to the railway station, it is convenient for a pint and a chat on the way into town. CAMRA National Pub of the Year finalist in 2018 and Silver Cider Pub of the Year 2019. Q♿≹●🚌🐾📶

Knightwick

Talbot Ⓛ
WR6 5PH (on B4197, 400yds from A44 jct)
☎ (01886) 821235 🌐 the-talbot.co.uk
Teme Valley T'Other, This, That Ⓗ**; changing beers (often Teme Valley)** Ⓖ
This 14th-century former coaching inn has a large lounge bar divided into two by a fireplace, a separate taproom and a conservatory. The small wood-panelled restaurant serves an imaginative evening menu using local ingredients. The bar usually offers three or four beers from the Teme Valley Brewery behind the pub. There is a farmers' market outside on the second Sunday of the month. Beer festivals are held in April, June and early October (for green hop beers). Dogs and walkers are welcome. Q❀🛏◑♿⛺♣P🚌(420)🐾📶

Lulsley

Fox & Hounds Ⓛ
WR6 5QT
☎ (01886) 821228 🌐 foxandhoundslulsley.com
Hop Shed Sebright Golden Ale; Wye Valley Butty Bach; 2 changing beers (often Ambridge, Ledbury) Ⓗ

A purpose-built Victorian pub with two bars, a dining area and a conservatory, which has been renovated to a high standard. The two guest beers are usually locally sourced, as is the food on the menu. Behind the pub is an extensive garden and children's play area, with the River Teme beyond. A beer festival is held over the spring bank holiday weekend. Q P

Malvern

Great Malvern Hotel

Graham Road, WR14 2HN (by crossroads with Church St)
(01684) 563411 great-malvern-hotel.co.uk
Malvern Hills Black Pear; Wye Valley HPA, Butty Bach; 2 changing beers (often Draught Bass, Friday Beer, Lakehouse)
Popular hotel public bar, a short walk from the Malvern Theatres complex, ideal for pre- and post-performance refreshment. Meals are served in the bar and the adjoining brasserie, including breakfast and Sunday lunch. There is a comfortable lounge with lots of sofas, fresh coffee and daily newspapers. Live music sessions are hosted during the week. The Great Shakes cellar bar features sports TV and is available for hire. Parking is limited on site but there is plenty of public parking nearby. P

Morgan

52 Clarence Road, WR14 3EQ
(01684) 578575
Wye Valley Bitter, HPA, Butty Bach; 2 changing beers (sourced locally)
Named after the town's Morgan car factory, this Wye Valley Brewery-owned premises has an open-plan interior divided into a games area for darts, a drinking space and a slightly raised seating section with comfy settees. The landscaped patio has ample seating, a fish pond and 'Them Organ' gates. Activities include a monthly book club and weekly quizzes. The TV is only turned on for major sporting events. Up to two guest beers come from the Wye Valley range, often the stout.

Nag's Head

19-21 Bank Street, WR14 2JG (off Graham Rd at Link Top common)
(01684) 574373 nagsheadmalvern.co.uk
Banks's Amber Ale; Bathams Best Bitter; Wood Shropshire Lad; 5 changing beers (often Otter)
A free house where the permanent beers are joined by guests from all over the county plus two draught ciders. Mismatched furniture, nooks and crannies, newspapers and foliage create a homely environment, attracting visitors throughout the week. Quality food is served in the bar and separate restaurant. Outside is a large covered and heated area to the front and a garden to the rear. The small car park is backed up by ample street parking. Dogs are welcome and numerous.
P (44)

Pershore

Pickled Plum

135 High Street, WR10 1EQ
(01386) 556645 pickledplum.co.uk
Brakspear Gravity; Wye Valley Butty Bach; 4 changing beers (often Purity, Salopian)
A large, smart pub with a modern, airy interior, divided into several areas, with exposed beams and real fires creating a cosy old-world charm. The bar serves up to six real ales plus six real ciders. A three third-pints tasting option is offered. Food is available lunchtimes and evenings. The pub hosts a regular Sunday night quiz and an acoustic jam on the first Monday of the month.
P

Redditch

Black Tap

Church Green East, B98 8BP (nr top of Church Green East)
(01527) 585969 blacktapredditch.co.uk
Backyard Blonde; 3 changing beers (sourced locally; often Church End, Oakham)
A converted office building and former brewpub. The main bar has a roaring fire, which adds to the friendly atmosphere among regulars. Conveniently located near the town centre, a good mix of beer styles is usually available along with cider. A small side room can also be booked and live music usually features at weekends. The nearby Quadrant car park is free after 7pm.
P (57,58)

Rising Sun

4 Alcester Street, B98 8AE (opp town hall)
(01527) 62452
Greene King Abbot; Ruddles Best Bitter; Sharp's Doom Bar; 6 changing beers (sourced regionally; often Morland, Purity, Salopian)
Large open-plan town-centre pub in the Wetherspoon style with a raised seating area and booths, serving up to 10 cask ales and two ciders on handpull. Local histories of Redditch's manufacturing industries adorn the walls, and a large metal horse and rider stands in the centre. Outside, a glass canopy and café-style seating are ideal for people-watching. Screens at both ends of the pub show news and sports on terrestrial TV.
P

Shenstone

Plough

DY10 4DL (off A450/A448) SO865735
(01562) 777340
Bathams Mild Ale, Best Bitter
This traditional pub has been at the heart of the village since 1840. The long single bar serves both the public bar and the lounge, which has a real fire and memorabilia of the Parachute Regiment and the Falklands War. Bathams Mild and Bitter are served all year while the stronger XXX is available in December. Snacks include cobs and pork pies. A large enclosed courtyard serves as an overflow, and there is a small patio to the front. Q P

Stourport-on-Severn

Black Star

Mitton Street, DY13 8YP (off top end of High St)
(01299) 488838 theblackstar.co.uk
Wye Valley The Hopfather, HPA, Butty Bach, Wholesome Stout; 5 changing beers (sourced regionally; often Enville, Hobsons, Ludlow)
Situated next to the canal, the pub has a historic feel. The main bar has a real fire, beamed ceilings and cosy corners. Four beers are from Wye Valley, alongside five guest ales and two ciders. The varied home-cooked menu includes main meals, vegan options, doorstep sandwiches and baguettes. An attractive beer garden with a shelter, tables and raised flowerbeds overlooks the canal. Moorings are just through the bridge towards the basins. Local CAMRA Pub of the Year 2020.

Swan ✔

56 High Street, DY13 8BX
☎ (01299) 877832
Brains Rev James; Butcombe Gold; Hobsons Old Prickly; Wainwright; 2 changing beers (sourced nationally) Ⓗ
Former hotel with a large lounge bar decorated with vinyl LPs, which sets the scene as for a pub by day and music venue by night. Six ales grace the bar, along with a gin menu. At the back there's a tranquil secluded garden. The integral Mimi's Bistro serves food and Mediterranean specialities from a wood-fired oven during the day. Live music on most evenings has a loyal following. An interesting and unusual venue, well worth a visit.

Tardebigge

Alestones

Unit 23 Tardebigge Court, B97 6QW
☎ (01527) 275254 🌐 alestones.co.uk
Woodcote Manor SSS; 3 changing beers Ⓗ
A well-maintained micropub, opened in 2016, which sits in a courtyard alongside several small independent shops and businesses. There are usually four beers, including a golden ale, a dark beer and a best bitter, plus real cider and perry. Although opened out, the pub retains its cosy, convivial atmosphere. Local musicians play monthly on a Sunday. Pub snacks are usually available.
QP(43,42)

Upper Wyche

Wyche Inn L

Wyche Road, Malvern, WR14 4EQ (on B4218; follow signs from Malvern to Colwall)
☎ (01684) 575396 🌐 thewycheinn.co.uk
Wye Valley HPA; 3 changing beers (sourced regionally) Ⓗ
The highest pub in Worcestershire, this free house has panoramic views towards the Cotswolds. Ideally situated for hill walkers, it offers two bars – one with pool and darts, the other dedicated to drinking and dining. The range of real ales from smaller breweries always includes some locals. Home-cooked food is served lunchtimes and evenings, with themed nights Tuesday to Saturday. B&B, self-contained flats and a cottage provide accommodation. QP(675)

Upton upon Severn

Olde Anchor Inn L ✔

5 High Street, WR8 0HQ
☎ (01684) 593735 🌐 anchorupton.co.uk
Hobsons Best; Sharp's Doom Bar; St Austell Tribute; 2 changing beers (often Timothy Taylor) Ⓗ
Authentic old black-and-white timber-framed inn with oak beams and low ceilings, built in 1601 and mentioned in Cromwell's dispatches. The bar features a large fireplace and range, and a bar billiards table, and there is a separate restaurant area. An additional wood-panelled function room is available for meetings and parties. The remains of the Old Brew House, once used by the defunct Jolly Roger Brewery, are at the rear.
Q

Weatheroak

Coach & Horses L

Weatheroak Hill, B48 7EA (Alvechurch to Wythall road)
SP057740
☎ (01564) 823386 🌐 coachandhorsesinn.co.uk
Holden's Golden Glow; Hook Norton Old Hooky; Weatheroak Hill Gold, Icknield Pale Ale, Impossible IPA, Cofton Common; 4 changing beers (sourced nationally; often St Austell, Weatheroak Hill, Wood) Ⓗ
Traditional rural coaching inn with an idyllic beer garden. The bar remains untouched, with a log fire, tiled floor and old church pews, while a modern lounge offers comfy sofas and a restaurant. Four beers are usually stocked from the on-site brewery housed in the former stables, alongside a wider selection from regional independents. Freshly made rolls are always available. Sunday evening opening hours may vary in winter. The pub is adjacent to a historic Roman road.
P

Worcester

Bull Baiters

43-49 St Johns, WR2 5AG
☎ (01905) 427601 🌐 bullbaiters.com
6 changing beers (sourced locally) Ⓗ
A small bar housed in a medieval building with an interesting history, previously a hall house. A high beamed ceiling and a large stone fireplace add to the old-world ambience, and there is no music or TV. A small room upstairs provides additional seating and features an original painted wall and a mummified cat. Ever-changing beers – up to six – are usually local, and complemented by eight ciders and perries. Simple snacks are available. Q

Cardinal's Hat L

31 Friar Street, WR1 2NA
☎ (01905) 724006 🌐 the-cardinals-hat.co.uk
Purity Mad Goose; 4 changing beers (sourced locally) Ⓗ
Worcester's oldest pub is a period building set in the heart of the city centre. The main bar at the front has a scrubbed wooden floor, beams and leaded windows. A stone-flagged, panelled passageway leads to a patio at the rear. The atmospheric back room features wood panelling, more stone-flagged flooring, serving hatch and impressive fireplace with wood-burner and dribbly candles. A small snug has views of the bustling old street outside. Folk night is the first Tuesday of the month. Imaginative bar snacks are available.

Dragon Inn

51 The Tything, WR1 1JT (on A449, 300yds N of Foregate St station)
☎ (01905) 25845 🌐 thedragoninnworcester.co.uk
Church End Goat's Milk, Gravediggers Ale, What the Fox's Hat, Fallen Angel; 4 changing beers (often Church End) Ⓗ
A Georgian building on the edge of the city centre run by Church End Brewery. The bar is towards the back of the smart interior, while the front space offers the opportunity to watch the world go by on the busy street outside. Behind the pub is a large, quiet patio with a covered area in the old side passage. A changing variety of Church End beers is on the bar plus two guest ales from other small breweries. Pork pies and sausage rolls are always available. Q

Oil Basin Brewhouse

7 Copenhagen Street, WR1 2HB
☎ 07964 196194 🌐 wintripbrew.co
Wintrip Butchers Beastly Best; 3 changing beers (often Salopian, Teme Valley, Tiny Rebel) Ⓗ

A small, dimly lit bar with comfy chairs, wood-beamed ceiling, bare boards and a small brewery out the back. It serves a variety of interesting real ales, mostly local, and craft keg. A good selection of craft beers and ciders is also kept in the fridge. The pub is centrally located, just off the High Street. There is level access to the bar and toilets. Excellent pizzas cooked in a wood-fired oven are available upstairs. **Q◐◑⇌♣🚌🐾**

Plough 𝕃

23 Fish Street, WR1 2HN (on Deansway)

☎ (01905) 21381

Hobsons Best; Malvern Hills Black Pear; 4 changing beers (sourced regionally; often Salopian) Ⓗ

A Grade II listed pub near the cathedral. There is a short flight of steps leading to a tiny bar with rooms to either side. The beers usually come from breweries in Worcestershire and surrounding counties, but occasionally from further afield. Draught cider and perry are from Barbourne in the city. There is also a wide range of whiskies. Outside is a small patio area. Rolls are available at weekends and when the cricket is on, with cooked meals Friday to Sunday lunchtimes only. **🐴❀◐⇌♣🍎🚌🐾**

Postal Order ✔

18 Foregate Street, WR1 1DN

☎ (01905) 22373

Greene King Abbot; Ruddles Best Bitter; 10 changing beers (sourced nationally; often Bespoke, Lakehouse, Pershore) Ⓗ

A classic Wetherspoon pub, formerly the old Worcester telephone exchange. It serves a wide range of ales of different styles and strengths, some from local breweries. Beer festivals throughout the year add even more variety. A cider from local producer Barbourne and Old Rosie from Westons are always on the bar, plus two others. Good-value food is served daily from early on (alcoholic drinks from 9am). The volume on the TV may be turned up for important games. **Q🐴◐◑♿⇌🍎🚌📶**

Postal Order, Worcester (Photo: Elliott Brown/Flickr CC BY-SA 2.0)

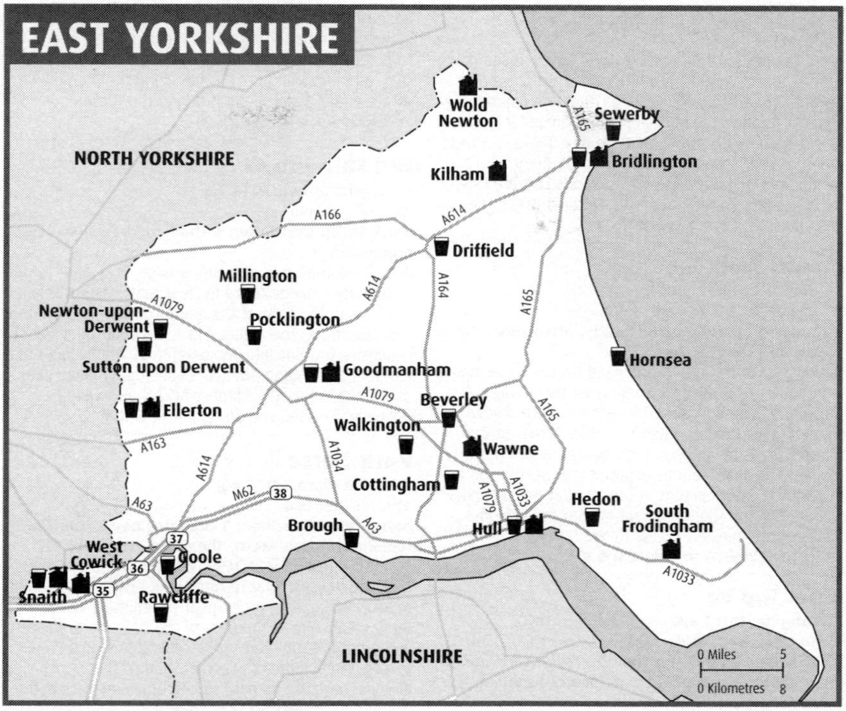

EAST YORKSHIRE

NORTH YORKSHIRE

Wold Newton
Sewerby
Kilham
Bridlington
A166
A614
Driffield
Millington
A614
A164
A165
Newton-upon-Derwent
A1079
Pocklington
Sutton upon Derwent
Goodmanham
A1079
Hornsea
Ellerton
A1079
Beverley
A165
Walkington
Wawne
A163
A614
A1034
Cottingham
A1079
A1033
Hedon
South Frodingham
A63
M62
38
Brough
A63
Hull
West Cowick
37
Goole
36
Snaith
35
Rawcliffe
A1033

LINCOLNSHIRE

0 Miles 5
0 Kilometres 8

YORKSHIRE (EAST)

Beverley

Chequers Micropub ⏚
15 Swaby's Yard, Dyer Lane, HU17 9BZ (off Saturday Market)
☎ 07964 227906
5 changing beers (sourced regionally; often Brass Castle, North Riding) Ⓗ
This is Yorkshire's first micropub, set in a former baker's shop near the bus station. Local breweries are well represented on the bar plus microbreweries from throughout the UK. Several ciders and perries are sold and there are three KeyKeg lines. Typically for a micropub, there is no lager. There is no TV or loud music either, making it a place for real conversation. A selection of board games is available. Local CAMRA branch Cider Pub of the Year 2019. Q❀≠♣●➡❀

Cross Keys ⏚ ✅
8 Lairgate, HU17 8EE
☎ (01482) 880388
Greene King Abbot; Ruddles Best Bitter; Sharp's Doom Bar; 5 changing beers (sourced nationally) Ⓗ
One of Beverley's historic pubs, saved from long-term closure. The main building dates from the mid 18th century and has been fully renovated with respect to its period features, although given a split-level layout with a large central area and smaller rooms off. Some areas can be used by groups by arrangement. Spacious outdoor areas at the rear further extend its capacity. The usual Wetherspoon menu and offers are available.
Q☎❀◑≠●➡❀

Dog & Duck ⏚
33 Ladygate, HU17 8BH (off Saturday Market adjacent to Brown's store, close to bus station)

☎ (01482) 862419 ⊕ bedandbreakfastbeverley.com
Black Sheep Best Bitter; John Smith's Bitter; Ossett Yorkshire Blonde; Timothy Taylor Boltmaker; 1 changing beer (sourced regionally; often Great Newsome) Ⓗ
The pub was built in the 1930s and has been run by the same family for 45 years. It comprises three areas: a bar with a period brick fireplace and bentwood seating, a front lounge with an open fire, and a rear snug. The good-value, home-cooked lunches are popular. Guest accommodation is in six purpose-built self-contained rooms to the rear. Dogs are welcome outside food service times. ⇘◑≠♣●➡❀☎

Green Dragon ✅
51 Saturday Market, HU17 8AA
☎ (01482) 889801 ⊕ thegreendragonbeverley.co.uk
Black Sheep Best Bitter; Sharp's Doom Bar; Timothy Taylor Landlord; Wainwright; 6 changing beers

REAL ALE BREWERIES

Aitcheson's Wawne (NEW)
All Hallows 🍺 Goodmanham
Atom Hull
Bone Machine ⚓ Hull
Bricknell Hull
Great Newsome South Frodingham
Half Moon ⚓ Ellerton
Old Mill Snaith
Raven Hill Kilham
Spotlight West Cowick
Vittles Hull
Wold Top Wold Newton
Woolybutt Hull
Yorkshire Brewhouse Hull
Yorkshire Coast 🍺 Bridlington (NEW)

(sourced nationally; often Adnams, Purity, Rudgate) [H]
A narrow-fronted Tudor timber-style inn accessed down a side passageway, with a further rear entrance off Lairgate. It was refurbished in 2018 and updated to increase its appeal to family diners, opening for breakfast and serving meals throughout the day. There is a wide range of beer styles to choose from on the 9-10 handpumps and further KeyKegs. Sports fans are catered for with several large-screen TVs. Quiz nights are Tuesday and Thursday.

Monks Walk

19 Highgate, HU17 0DN
☎ (01482) 864972 🌐 monkswalkinn.com
6 changing beers (sourced locally; often Atom, Brass Castle, Yorkshire) [H]/[G]
Dating back to the 13th century and built as a merchant's warehouse, records for this inn show there was a brewery attached in the 19th century. It was known as the George & Dragon until the 1980s. Access to the Minster Bar is by an open passageway, and it has a dining room that features exposed roof beams and an open fire. Conversation is encouraged at this genuine free house. The sheltered beer garden has splendid views of the minster. Access to the car park is off Eastgate. Q P

Tiger Inn

97 Lairgate, HU17 8JG (near Memorial Hall)
☎ (01482) 869040 🌐 tigerinnbeverley.co.uk
Black Sheep Special Ale; Timothy Taylor Landlord; Wainwright; 2 changing beers (sourced nationally; often Marston's, Wychwood) [H]
An attractive Grade II listed 18th-century building refronted in 1930s Brewers' Tudor by the now defunct Darley & Co, who once owned several pubs in Beverley. It has a multi-roomed interior with a public bar, snug, dining room/lounge and function room, all retained during a major refurbishment in 2017. Many local clubs and societies meet here and a folk music session is held on Friday evening. The large car park to the rear was once stables and outbuildings. Meals include a Sunday carvery. Q P

Bridlington

Board Inn

62 High Street, YO16 4QA
☎ (01262) 672087
Adnams Ghost Ship; Fuller's ESB; St Austell Proper Job; Tetley Bitter; Titanic Plum Porter; 2 changing beers (sourced nationally) [H]
Located in the Old Town, this lovingly restored historic inn dates back to the 18th century, with wood panelling, flagged and timber floors and four open fires. It has a multi-roomed interior with three comfortably furnished rooms and a snug upstairs. Music nights are hosted at weekends. To the rear, a taproom selling 10 craft-brewed beers has been established in converted stables, with further open fires. Recognised by CAMRA for the restoration undertaken, the pub is a real gem, not to be missed. Q P

Marine Bar

North Marine Drive, YO15 2LS (1 mile NE of centre)
☎ (01262) 675347 🌐 expanse.co.uk
Theakston Best Bitter; Timothy Taylor Landlord; 2 changing beers (sourced regionally; often Daleside, Rooster's, Wold Top) [H]
A large open-plan bar, part of the Expanse Hotel. Spectacular sea views are the perfect accompaniment to good home-cooked food served here daily. Attracting a good mix of regulars, a warm welcome also awaits the influx of summer visitors. Two regional guest beers complement the three regular ales, and real cider is also sold. Ample parking is available along the promenade, where a land train operates during the summer. P (512,513)

Old Ship Inn

90 St John Street, YO16 7JS
☎ (01262) 401906
Black Sheep Best Bitter; 5 changing beers (sourced regionally) [H]
A multi-roomed pub including a large, cosy and comfortable lounge (used for functions), with a smaller front bar to the right of the entrance as well as another separate room. The lounge has a plentiful collection of Frank Meadow Sutcliffe photographs of Whitby and some featuring Bridlington. There is a full programme of events during the week. The number of real ales varies dependent on the season.

Pack Horse

7 Market Place, YO16 4QJ
☎ (01262) 603502
Abbeydale Moonshine; 3 changing beers (sourced regionally; often Acorn, Theakston, Wold Top) [H]
This pub dates back to 1600, when it was a thatched coaching house. It was restored by its owners as a labour of love, to create an open-plan yet intimate layout with three areas: one to the right of the bar, one to the left, and a third at the rear. Home-cooked food is served (except Mon), with a carvery on Sunday. There is a paved area out back. The famous stocks remain in place in front of the pub. P (121,120)

Prior John

34-36 The Promenade, YO15 2QD (near bus station)
☎ (01262) 674256
Greene King Abbot; Ruddles Best Bitter; Sharp's Doom Bar; 6 changing beers (sourced nationally) [H]
This Wetherspoon pub was extended in 2019 and refurbished to provide an enlarged dining space suitable for families. Internal features include a spiral staircase to an upper floor, and a dome with original artwork by the main entrance. An outside area to the side and rear allows customers to enjoy the sea air. The pub is close to many of the seaside attractions for which Bridlington is well known. It is named after John de Tweng, who was a prior of Bridlington's medieval monastery.
Q

Stackhouse Bar

15a Promenade, YO15 2PY
☎ 07551 009294
3 changing beers (sourced regionally) [H]
An on-trend conversion from another business involving change of use, furnished with repurposed items that provide an eclectic atmosphere - a pub with a difference. It is very similar to and yet different from its sister establishment in Hornsea. In addition to real ales and ciders there are also craft keg products and a wide selection of fashionable spirits. The range of cask beers reduces in the winter, when there are also shorter opening hours – refer to social media for up to date information.

Brough

Centurion Arms

39 Skillings Lane, HU15 1BA
4 changing beers (sourced regionally; often Great Newsome, Half Moon, Wold Top) [H]

A converted shop unit, set among a number of small businesses supporting the local community. It is unlike any other pub in the village, and offers a changing range of real ale and cider. An extensive collection of pump badges is evidence of the variety, adding to the eclectic collection of paraphernalia decorating the interior. Social interaction and conversation is encouraged between regulars and visitors. Locally produced artwork is on show. Dogs are welcomed with snacks.
(158)

Cottingham

Hugh Fitz-Baldric of Cottingham

144 Hallgate, HU16 4BB
the-hugh-fitz-baldric-of-cottingham.business.site
Salopian Lemon Dream; Titanic Plum Porter; house beer (by Marston's); 3 changing beers (sourced nationally)
Converted from a shop in the busy main street, this is a one-room micropub with quiet corners and eclectic furnishings. A log-burner adds cosiness in winter. The pub is a quaint and peaceful place to enjoy a range of real ales, complemented by some real ciders and gins. Other drinks follow the trends as it caters for changing tastes. Local CAMRA Village Pub of the Year 2019.
Q

King William IV

152 Hallgate, HU16 4DB
(01482) 875996
Banks's Sunbeam; Jennings Cumberland Ale; Marston's Pedigree; Wainwright; Wychwood Hobgoblin Ruby; 2 changing beers (sourced nationally; often Brakspear, Ringwood, Wychwood)
Village-centre pub with a traditional bar and quiet lounge, hosting weekly quiz nights and a venue for Cottingham's annual music festival. At the rear, a former brewery has been converted into a function room offering live music and special events. The beer garden and side courtyard have covered smoking areas. Excellent-value meals are served in large and small portions. Thatchers cider is dispensed on handpump. Local CAMRA Village Pub of the Year runner-up for the last two years. Q

Driffield

Benjamin Fawcett

Middle Street North, YO25 6SW
(01377) 249130
Greene King Abbot; Ruddles Best Bitter; changing beers
Like most Wetherspoons, this is now a spacious one-room pub. It is a conversion from previous licensed premises on the site, and offers a choice of quieter and livelier areas. Family diners are welcome. The name comes from a local printer who was one of the first to print in colour, and framed examples are on display. The interior is decorated with artefacts that pay tribute to members of the armed forces stationed in the area during World War II. (121)

Butchers Dog

24 Middle Street South, YO25 6PS
(01377) 252229 thebutchersdog.co.uk
5 changing beers (sourced locally)
A one-room micropub with traditional pub values. Five real ales from local and regional breweries are served in oversized glasses (tasting paddles are available), alongside a wide selection of real ciders. Visitors are encouraged to rely on good conversation in an environment free from Wi-Fi and music. Simple bar snacks are on sale, and there is a free cheeseboard on Sunday afternoon, but customers may bring their own food. Local CAMRA Town Pub of the Year 2019.
QP(121)

Ellerton

Boot & Shoe

Main Street, YO42 4PB
(01757) 288346
House beer (by Dark Horse); 2 changing beers (sourced nationally; often Dark Horse)
A welcoming country village inn of character dating from the 17th century. The building wraps around a large tree and features low-beamed ceilings. There is a cosy bar area with exposed brick and an open fire, plus two separate intimate dining rooms. Three real ales are on offer in this free house, including two from Dark Horse Brewery. Food is served Friday and Saturday evenings and Sunday lunchtime (booking advisable). QP

Goodmanham

Goodmanham Arms

Main Street, YO43 3JA (close to Wolds Way footpath)
(01430) 873849 thegoodmanhamarms.co.uk
All Hallows Peg Fyfe Dark Mild; Hambleton Stallion Amber; Theakston Best Bitter; 3 changing beers (sourced regionally; often All Hallows, Oakham, Wold Top)
A unique village local, with the All Hallows Brewery attached. The cosy bar, dining room and kitchen are warmed by three log fires, and lit by candlelight during dark winter nights. An extension with vintage decorations has been added to meet demand for space. Hearty meals are served. The pub hosts events on bank holidays. Local CAMRA Village Pub of the Year winner many times, and runner-up in 2019. QP

Goole

Tom Pudding

20 Pasture Road, DN14 6EZ (2 mins walk from Goole station)
07762 525114
4 changing beers (sourced regionally; often Hambleton, Wold Top)
Opened in 2017, this micropub, once a newsagent, was started by two CAMRA members with an enthusiasm for real ale. It has interesting internal brickwork and an exposed wooden-beamed ceiling. It can accommodate up to 50 people, and is often sought out by travelling football fans on their way to Hull and Doncaster. It always has a gluten-free beer and up to four real ciders, often from Westons and Gwynt y Ddraig.
(155,X55)

Hedon

Hed'On Inn

7 Watmaughs Arcade, St Augustine Gate, HU12 8EZ
(01964) 601100
Black Sheep Best Bitter; 4 changing beers (sourced nationally)
A micropub next to a car park at the end of a shopping arcade in the centre of this old market town, converted from a disused carpet shop office. The premises are tastefully decorated with recycled fittings. There are two regular and four changing beers covering the full spectrum of styles, together with real ciders, bottled

beers and a range of spirits and wines. Acoustic music sessions take place on Tuesday nights and Sunday afternoons, and quiz and games nights on Wednesdays. Q♣●P🚌

Hornsea

Stackhouse Bar

8A Newbegin, HU18 1AG
☎ (01964) 534407
4 changing beers (sourced regionally) H
A former shop converted to a micropub in 2014, with an interesting choice of regional ales and a large range of real ciders. Attracting a mixed clientele, visitors are encouraged to engage in conversation. There is a separate function room. Although no food is provided, customers are allowed to bring in their own.
🐴Å♣●🚌(240,246)🐾📶

Hull

Admiral of the Humber L ✔

5-7 Anlaby Road, HU1 2NT
☎ (01482) 381850
Greene King Abbot; Ruddles Best Bitter; Sharp's Doom Bar; 6 changing beers (sourced nationally) H
Now a Wetherspoon hotel, the premises used to be a paint and wallpaper shop. Previously, the site was connected to Hull's seafaring past. The large single-room bar is mostly on one level. There is a large open-air rooftop garden (closes 10pm nightly). A designated area is set aside for diners during the day, and children are welcome until the evening. Q🐴❀🛏◑♿⇌●P🚌📶

Chilli Devil's L

Manor Street, HU1 1YP
☎ (01482) 961666 🌐 chillidevils.com
4 changing beers H
A small, well-appointed real ale and chilli micropub in the heart of the city, decorated with an extensive collection of photographs of Hull in bygone times. Cask ales and real ciders are the main offering, alongside a varied selection of bottled beers meeting LocAle criteria. Chilli infused cuisine is served featuring home-cooked dishes from all over the world, as well as sandwiches, burgers and hot dogs. ◑⇌●🚌🐾

Furley & Co L

18-20 Princes Dock Street, HU1 2LP (opp dockside entrance to Princes Quay shopping centre)
☎ (01482) 229649 🌐 furleyshull.co.uk
5 changing beers (sourced nationally; often Atom, Half Moon, North Riding)
Popular family-friendly bar overlooking the waterfront of the former Princes Dock. Historically, the premises were warehousing and offices for a local shipping company and the first bottled gas merchant in Hull. The decor is now neo-industrial, portraying music and film iconography on the walls. Local and regional cask and craft beers are available. Varied events include occasional live music and monthly visits from the chess society. Additional seating upstairs can be used as a function room. 🐴❀◑♿⇌♣●🚌🐾

George Hotel ✔

Land of Green Ginger, HU1 2EA
☎ (01482) 226373
6 changing beers (sourced regionally; often Abbeydale, Bradfield, Theakston) H
In the heart of the Old Town on Hull's most famous street, this pub was totally refurbished in early 2020. The downstairs real ale bar, with wood-panelled walls and ceiling beams, retains the period fittings. Other features of historic interest, such as the fine glazed leaded windows, have been retained. Of note is reputedly the smallest pub window in England, dating from the building's coaching days. Upstairs, a second bar has TVs for sporting events. A former CAMRA branch City Pub of the Year. ♣🚌

Head of Steam L

10 King Street, HU1 2JJ
☎ (01482) 217236
6 changing beers (sourced regionally; often Atom, Camerons) H
A single-roomed pub decorated with beer-related artefacts. Its large picture windows overlook Hull Minster and Trinity Square. An outdoor seating area to the front provides an ideal location to watch the world go by. The cask ales, which constantly vary, often promote new breweries, and are complemented by an extensive selection of craft products, reflecting the passion of the management team. The food menu includes a wide range of vegan dishes. 🐴❀◑⇌●🚌🐾

Hop & Vine L

24 Albion Street, HU1 3TG (250yds from Hull New Theatre and Central Library)
☎ 07507 719259
3 changing beers (sourced nationally; often Great Newsome, Isaac Poad, Wold Top) H
Atmospheric basement bar free house stocking three changing guest beers, largely from Yorkshire's independent breweries. The beer is served in oversized lined glasses. Unusual still ciders and perries are also on sale, and some continental bottled beers. A selection of freshly prepared food, including home-baked bread, is available. Shove-ha'penny, cribbage and shut the box games are played. Former CAMRA National Cider Pub of the Year and four times Yorkshire regional winner.
🐴◑Å⇌♣●🥤🚌🐾

Minerva Hotel L

Nelson Street, HU1 1XE
☎ (01482) 210025 🌐 minerva-hull.co.uk
Tetley Bitter; 5 changing beers (sourced regionally; often Bone Machine) H
Overlooking the Humber estuary and Victoria Pier, this famous inn, built in 1829, is a great place to watch the ships go by. Photos and memorabilia are a reminder of the area's maritime past. The central bar serves various rooms including a tiny three-seat snug. The former brewhouse was converted to provide an additional drinking area and is available for functions. The building is connected to The Deep visitor attraction by a footbridge at the mouth of the River Hull.
🐴❀◑🚌(16)📶

Olde White Harte ★ ✔

25 Silver Street, HU1 1JG (in alley between Silver St and Bowlalley Lane)
☎ (01482) 326363
Caledonian Deuchars IPA; Theakston Best Bitter, Old Peculier; 3 changing beers (sourced nationally) H
Historic pub in a 17th-century merchant's house, with strong connections to the English Civil War, hidden down an alley near Hull's Old Town. The existing ground floor interior dates back to a major refurbishment in 1881, which was an idealised re-creation of an old English inn, complete with massive inglenook fireplaces and stained-glass windows. The first floor features the Plotting Parlour and restaurant facilities, while a courtyard provides an outdoor drinking area. ❀♣🚌🐾

Pave

16-20 Princes Avenue, HU5 3QA
(01482) 333181 pavebar.co.uk
Tetley Gold; Theakston Best Bitter; 3 changing beers (sourced regionally; often Great Yorkshire, Saltaire, Scarborough)
The original pavement café in a popular area of the city, this continental-style bar attracts a diverse range of customers. As well as the regular ales, there are three guests, usually sourced regionally and including one stout, and a varied range of European draught and bottled beers. A changing Westons cider is sold. Home-cooked food including vegetarian and gluten-free options is served daily. Live music plays on Tuesday evening and Sunday afternoon.
(Interchange)

St John's Hotel

10 Queens Road, HU5 2PY
(01482) 341013 stjohnshull.com
Marston's 61 Deep; Wainwright; 3 changing beers (sourced nationally)
A classic Grade II listed street-corner local. The inside of the pub is one of the least altered in the city, and features in CAMRA's Regional Inventory of Historic Pub Interiors. The front corner public bar complements a quiet back room, with original bench seating. A basic larger room accommodates the pool table and is home to regular beer festivals. The pub is a community venue with two darts teams, a football team, and the Oddfellows cricket league which hosts quiz nights in the winter. Open mic night is Tuesday. Q P

Taphouse

70 Humber Street, HU1 1TU
(01482) 618000 taphousehull.co.uk
Yorkshire Almighty Festival Ale; 4 changing beers (sourced regionally; often Bone Machine)
The bar is a single spacious room, with an on-site brewery transformed from the previous brewhouse, which in turn was originally a fruit merchant's warehouse. The original on-site brewery was one of the first businesses in the area responsible for the area's early regeneration, and is consequently now at the heart of Hull's thriving Fruit Market. Food is provided by street vendors on a regularly changing basis, and there are bar snacks when the kitchen is closed.

Three John Scotts

Lowgate, HU1 1AA
(01482) 381910
Greene King Abbot; Ruddles Best Bitter; Sharp's Doom Bar; 7 changing beers (sourced regionally; often Great Newsome)
Originally an Edwardian post office, this open-plan Wetherspoon features modern decor and works of art. The name derives from three successive 19th-century vicars of St Mary's church opposite. The pub has established a broad customer base. Up to 10 real ales and two real ciders are served. Children are welcome until mid-evening. There is a large rear courtyard seating area that is a great suntrap in the summer.

Whalebone

165 Wincolmlee, HU2 0PA
07506 868461
Half Moon Old Forge Bitter; Rudgate Viking; 5 changing beers (sourced regionally; often Abbeydale, North Riding, Rat)
A rare gem sited within the old Greenland whaling trading area. Licensed since 1791, the current building dates from 1890, and has been a free house since 2002. Photos celebrating the city's sporting heritage and bygone Hull pubs adorn the walls. Artefacts showcasing the whaling industry are on display in the quiet room, which once contained the in-house brewery. A Moors' & Robson's Brewery sign from a previous era hangs outside. Local CAMRA City Pub of the Year 2019, and many times previously. Q

White Hart ★

109 Alfred Gelder Street, HU1 1EP
07793 710160 whiteharthullpub.co.uk
5 changing beers (sourced regionally; often Crafty Little, Great Heck, Revolutions)
Reopened in 2018 after many years of closure, this venue is located on the edge of Hull's Old Town. The White Hart has been identified by CAMRA as having a nationally important historic interior, with a rare bar front and many other original features. It is largely the brewery tap for Crafty Little Brewery, but it also showcases the more progressive breweries regionally, and has a number of craft and KeyKeg beers available. Runner-up local CAMRA Pub of the Year 2019.
Q P

Millington

Gait

Main Street, YO42 1TX
(01759) 302045 gait-inn-millington.co.uk
Black Sheep Best Bitter; Tetley Bitter; Theakston Best Bitter; 2 changing beers (sourced locally; often Great Yorkshire, Half Moon, Wold Top)
A delightful Yorkshire Wolds pub that provides a warm welcome, both to locals and to the many walkers enjoying the attractions of Millington Woods and Pastures. It has an idiosyncratic bar with a wood-burning stove in winter, filled with a range of ornaments and local pictures. Three regular beers are stocked plus at least one guest, often all from Yorkshire. Sit at kitchen-style tables to enjoy hearty, home-made food served from an extensive menu. The pub stages an annual beer festival with up to 35 beers. P

Newton-upon-Derwent

Half Moon

Main Street, YO41 4DB
(01904) 608883 thehalfmoonnewton.co.uk
Ainsty Flummoxed Farmer; Old Mill Traditional Bitter, Blonde Bombshell; Timothy Taylor Landlord; 1 changing beer
This free house has served the local community since 1743. Originally a single-storey thatched-roof building, it had taken on its present guise by 1904, and underwent some refurbishment in the 1930s. In the 1800s, inquests were conducted here, and from 1852 the Newton agricultural shows were held in the grounds. The pub serves traditional hearty food, made with fresh locally sourced ingredients. P

Pocklington

Feathers Hotel

56 Market Place, YO42 2AH
(01759) 303155 thefeathers-hotel.co.uk
Theakston Best Bitter; York Guzzler; 3 changing beers (sourced locally)
Steeped in history, this is an old posting and market inn dating back to Elizabethan times. It underwent extensive reconstruction in the early 19th century, while retaining some original features, and has benefited from refurbishment over the past couple of years under the

present ownership. A busy public bar in the centre of town, it offers a choice of five real ales, including three guests, usually from Yorkshire breweries. P

Market Tap

11-13 Market Place, YO42 2AS

(01759) 307783

Hop Studio Bitter, Porter, Mosaic, XS; 5 changing beers (often Hop Studio)

Overlooking the market place, this 19th-century building and former newsagent has recently been refurbished, providing a light, spacious and modern interior over two floors. An extensive range of nine cask and nine keg beers is on offer, including five cask regulars from Hop Studio as well as four changing guests. Wines, beers and ciders are also available to take away.

Rawcliffe

Jemmy Hirst at the Rose & Crown

26 Riverside, DN14 8RN (from village green turn N on Chapel Lane)

(01405) 837902

Timothy Taylor Landlord; 4 changing beers (sourced locally; often Bradfield, Brown Cow, Little Critters)

A free house in the heart of the village, well-established and recognised as an award-winning real ale local pub. The new owners have kept this hostelry in its traditional style while investing in modernising the cellar and redecorating to give it a fresh, cared-for and loved atmosphere. Customers old and new are assured of a warm and friendly greeting – families and dogs welcome. Q P (401)

Sewerby

Ship Inn

Cliff Road, YO15 1EW

(01262) 672374 shipinnsewerby.co.uk

Jennings Cumberland Ale; Mansfield Cask Ale; 3 changing beers (sourced nationally; often Banks's, Ringwood, Wychwood)

Village-centre pub featuring a wood-panelled bar with a beamed ceiling, a separate dining room and lounge. Popular with both locals and holidaymakers, it has a beer garden with a children's play area overlooking the sea. The restaurant serves traditional pub food – booking is recommended for the popular Sunday carvery (no food winter Mon). Nearby is a model village and Sewerby Hall, along with clifftop walks. A land train terminates close by. P (502,510)

Snaith

Yorkshire Ales Beer Café Bar

Selby Road, DN14 9HT (on edge of marketplace)

(01405) 860603

Bad Seed Session IPA; Brown Cow White Dragon; 4 changing beers (sourced regionally; often Brown Cow, Revolutions, Spotlight)

Yorkshire Ales promotes beers brewed by small, independent Yorkshire microbreweries. The building dates back to 1750 and has seating for 80 over two floors, plus a beer garden. Food is snacks only, but artisan chefs and street-food vendors are booked regularly. Music is at background volume and there are no TVs, helping to promote the art of conversation. Local cycling and photography clubs meet here regularly, and the weekly general knowledge quiz is popular.
Q (401)

Sutton upon Derwent

St Vincent Arms

Main Street, YO41 4BN

(01904) 608349 stvincentarms.co.uk

Fuller's London Pride; Greene King IPA; Theakston Old Peculier; Timothy Taylor Landlord; York Guzzler; 1 changing beer (sourced nationally)

Former winner of many local CAMRA awards, this pretty white-painted village free house on a bend in the road has been family owned and well run for generations. It has a consistent but large beer range, the changing beer usually from a local independent brewer. The cosy bar to the right, featuring a large Fuller, Smith & Turner mirror, is popular with locals. Another small bar to the left, with a serving hatch, leads to the dining rooms. Excellent food goes beyond the usual pub fare. Q P

Walkington

Barrel Inn

35 East End, HU17 8RX

07550 078833 barrelwalkington.co.uk

Thwaites IPA; Wainwright

Friendly drinkers' local in a quiet village, one of only a handful of Thwaites pubs in East Yorkshire. The front bar, with a log fire and a beamed ceiling, has a step leading to a connecting lounge, also with a log fire. To the rear is a secluded garden. Families and dogs are welcome. Although the pub is essentially quiet, major Premier League football matches and some other sporting events are shown. Thursday is quiz night.

YORKSHIRE (NORTH)

Acaster Malbis

Ship

Moor End, YO23 2UH

(01904) 703888

Black Sheep Best Bitter; Camerons Strongarm; Timothy Taylor Golden Best; 3 changing beers (sourced regionally; often Ossett, Theakston)

Located by the river (and attractively refurbished after the December 2015 floods), this friendly country pub serves a good range of real ales and quality food in a pleasant and relaxing location. The welcoming real fire inside and the riverfront garden offer choices depending on the weather. It is popular in spring and summer, with four nearby camping/caravan sites, and quieter the rest of the year. The York waterbus in the summer makes an interesting trip. Quiz night is Wednesday.
Q P (21)

Aldwark

Aldwark Arms

YO61 1UB

(01347) 838324 aldwarkarms.co.uk

House beer (by Daleside); 3 changing beers (sourced locally)

With its riverside setting and rural location, this family-owned dining pub caters for everyone, from locals and ramblers to cyclists and horse riders (it has a hitching rail and water buckets). Two of the three rooms are set out for dining, while the bar/lounge area has comfy leather chairs and sofas for drinkers – although tables here may be pressed into service for diners at peak times. The pub offers a warm and friendly welcome to all, and holds beer festivals, music festivals and the like. The beer range comes from Yorkshire breweries.
P (29)

Appleton Wiske

Lord Nelson

High Street, DL6 2AD

☎ (01609) 881351 🌐 lordnelsoninn.org.uk

Theakston Black Bull Bitter; 1 changing beer (sourced nationally) Ⓗ

A true locals' pub in the centre of this picturesque, award-winning village near Northallerton, facing the beautiful village green. It is divided into two rooms, one set out for meals and the other a welcoming bar for drinkers. Food is served Thursday and Friday evening and Sunday lunchtime. Two beers are always on – a traditional house bitter and a rotating local lighter beer. There is themed dining on Thursdays; check the website for details. ❀◑P🐾

Appletreewick

Craven Arms 🄻

BD23 6DA

☎ (01756) 720270 🌐 craven-cruckbarn.co.uk

Dark Horse Craven Bitter, Hetton Pale Ale, Night Jar; Theakston Old Peculier; Wharfedale Blonde; 2 changing beers (sourced regionally) Ⓗ

Dating from 1548, this multi-roomed free house has stone-flagged floors, oak beams and gas lighting. The bar features an original Yorkshire range, while the cosy taproom has an open fire and ring the bull. A snug behind the bar leads to the cruck barn, added in 2006 using traditional techniques. This can be hired for functions and hosts occasional events, including music and a beer festival in October. Two additional guest beers are added in summer. Accommodation is in three shepherd's huts. Q❀🛏◑♿⛺♣🍎P🚌(74A)🐾📶

Askrigg

Crown Inn 🄻 ✔

Main Street, DL8 3HQ

☎ (01969) 650387 🌐 crowninnaskrigg.co.uk

Black Sheep Best Bitter; John Smith's Bitter; Theakston Best Bitter; 2 changing beers Ⓗ

A three-roomed family-run pub at the top of the main street in the village. This busy, friendly Dales inn attracts a good mix of locals and visitors, and is particularly popular for its bar meals, sourced from local suppliers. The interior has been partly opened out but retains much of its traditional character, with an impressive range in the cosy snug, and open fires to warm cold walkers seeking shelter from the fells. 🛏◑⛺P🚌🐾📶

King's Arms 🄻

Main Street, DL8 3HQ

☎ (01969) 650113

Black Sheep Best Bitter; Theakston Best Bitter; 3 changing beers (often Yorkshire Dales) Ⓗ

This historic Grade II listed Dales free house starred as The Drover's Arms in All Creatures Great and Small. A huge open fireplace and a painting of the local friendly society add character to the stone-flagged bar. There are separate dining rooms, plus a vaulted games room to the rear and a small outdoor courtyard. Three house beers are from the Yorkshire Dales Brewery, a few hundred yards away. ❀◑⛺🍎🚌🐾📶

Austwick

Game Cock ✔

LA2 8BB (on road to Horton)

☎ (015242) 51226 🌐 gamecockinn.co.uk

Thwaites Mild, Original, IPA, Gold; 1 changing beer (often Thwaites) Ⓗ

Cosy, multi-roomed pub with the emphasis on good food. The old-fashioned bar, used mainly for drinking, has a warming real fire and is decorated with cartoons and old photos. Popular with locals, hikers and cyclists, it can be quite intimate, with conversation involving the whole room. There are two cosy snugs behind the bar, and the dining rooms extend into the small south-facing conservatory. Food specials include French night Wednesday, steak night Thursday, fish & chips Friday, and Sunday roasts. Q❀🛏◑⛺♣P🚌(581)🐾📶

Beck Hole

Birch Hall Inn ★ 🄻

YO22 5LE (approx 1 mile N of Goathland)

☎ (01947) 896245

Black Sheep Best Bitter; North Yorkshire Beckwatter; 1 changing beer Ⓗ

Unspoilt family-run rural gem, resting among a hamlet of cottages, run by a licensee now celebrating 40 years of continuous service to the trade. The interior comprises the Big Bar and the Small Bar, which sandwich a sweet shop. Pleasant outdoor drinking facilities overlook the Murk Esk. The house beer, Beckwatter, is brewed organically by North Yorkshire. Sandwiches, pies, beer cake and traditional sweets are always available. Opening hours change during the winter. Q❀♿♣🍎🐾

Beckwithshaw

Smith's Arms 🄻 ✔

Church Row, HG3 1QW

☎ (01423) 504871

Black Sheep Best Bitter; Greene King IPA; Morland Old Speckled Hen; 2 changing beers Ⓗ

A Chef & Brewer food-led venue in an 18th-century inn that, as the name suggests, was formerly a blacksmith's forge. Set in a quiet hamlet to the south-west of Harrogate, the pub comprises an L-shaped bar area and a separate restaurant. An excellent food menu with many seasonal dishes is offered throughout the day in both the restaurant and bar. The five handpumps serve three permanent beers and two widely sourced guest ales; flights of three thirds are available. ❀◑♿🍎P🐾📶

Bedale

Old Black Swan 🄻

19 Market Place, DL8 1ED

☎ (01677) 422973 🌐 oldblackswan.co.uk

John Smith's Bitter; Theakston Best Bitter, Old Peculier; 1 changing beer (sourced nationally) Ⓗ

This comfortable, traditional-style market town inn has several separate drinking areas on two levels, including an area to play pool. Popular with locals and visitors for both drinking and dining, it serves senior meals Monday to Friday. Handy for the Bedale's main bus stop, it is the town's rugby pub, and has a wide-screen TV for when Six Nations and autumn internationals are on. ◑♿⛺≈♣🚌🐾📶

Bishopthorpe

Bishopthorpe Sports & Social Club 🄻

12 Main Street, YO23 2RB

☎ (01904) 707185 🌐 bishopthorpeclub.co.uk

John Smith's Bitter; York Guzzler; 2 changing beers (sourced regionally) Ⓗ

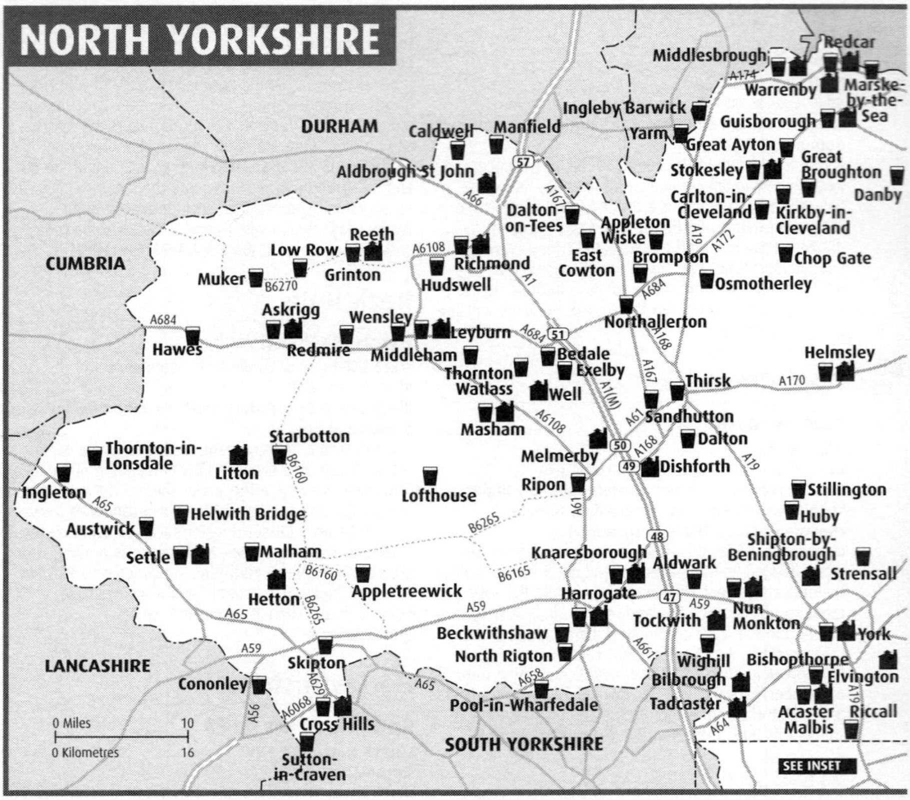

Over the past two decades, the stewards have established this club as a popular destination, and it has been voted CAMRA branch Club the Year on multiple occasions. Two regular ales are on the bar and one rotating guest, mainly regional. The annual St Patrick's beer festival, held in the refurbished function room, encourages non-members to enjoy an extended range of real ales and ciders, and to raise money for the local community sports teams. Close to the river, you can arrive by boat. ♿⛺♣P🚌🐾📶

Marcia 🄻 ✔

29 Main Street, YO23 2RA

☎ (01904) 706185 🌐 marciainnbishopthorpe.co.uk

Leeds Pale; Rooster's Yankee; 3 changing beers (sourced locally; often Atom, Half Moon, Treboom) 🄷

A popular village community local with a landlord who is passionate about real ale. Five handpumps serve mainly LocAle. An annual beer and cider festival takes place in the large rear garden, which has a children's play area. A good range of food is served every day – the pub is a former winner of The National Fish & Chips Awards. It was also voted Minster FM Best Pub. The Marcia has a relaxed and friendly atmosphere and hosts pub games and a Wednesday quiz night, as well as supporting local clubs and teams. Q🐴❀◐♿⛺♣P🚌(11)🐾📶

Brompton

Green Tree 🄻

Stokesley Road, DL6 2UA (on A684)

☎ (01609) 780251

Theakston Best Bitter; 3 changing beers (sourced locally) 🄷

On the edge of the village on the main Northallerton-Osmotherley road, this traditional single-room free house retains the feel of a friendly community local. There are two distinct drinking areas either side of a central bar, with real fires at both ends of the room. To the rear, a sheltered beer garden includes a quoits pitch and is a suntrap on a good day. Guest beers are usually from Yorkshire microbreweries. 🐴❀♣P🚌🐾📶

Burn

Wheatsheaf 🄻

Main Road, YO8 8LJ

☎ (01757) 270614 🌐 wheatsheafburn.co.uk

6 changing beers (often Brown Cow, Great Heck, Ossett) 🄷

A traditional country pub serving a varied range of guest beers mainly from Yorkshire breweries. It is popular for its excellent, reasonably priced food. There is a collection of artefacts from bygone days and memorabilia of 578 and 431 Squadrons stationed at Burn in WWII. The pub stages regular beer festivals, quiz nights and many other activities. Q🐴❀◐♿♣P🚌(476,405)🐾📶

Burythorpe

Bay Horse

Main Street, YO17 9LH

☎ (01653) 658302

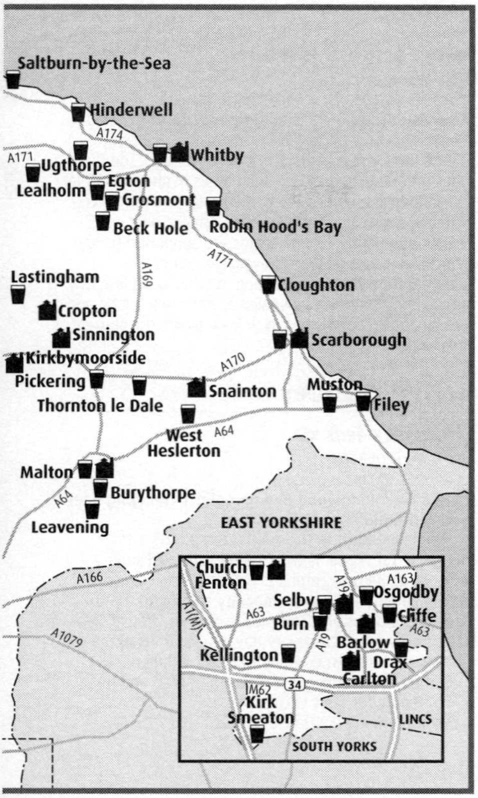

All Hallows Peg Fyfe Dark Mild, Ragged Robyn, No Notion Porter; 3 changing beers (sourced locally; often Hambleton, Ossett, Theakston) H
Nestled in the Yorkshire Wolds, the multi-roomed Bay Horse is homely, featuring farming paraphernalia, low lighting, multiple real fires, traditional furniture and a tiled floor. It was reopened following an extensive renovation in 2016 after a previously uncertain future. The range of beers includes three from the All Hallows Brewery at its sister pub in Goodmanham. The menu is wide-ranging and adventurous, using locally sourced ingredients, and is attractively priced. Tuesday is steak and pie night. Q❀◑♣P

Caldwell

Brownlow Arms

DL11 7QH
☎ (01325) 718471 🌐 brownlowarms.co.uk
Timothy Taylor Landlord; 2 changing beers (sourced nationally) H
Set in the quiet village of Caldwell, the Brownlow Arms could be described as the perfect country inn. It boasts a fine dining restaurant and two cosy bars, warmed by open log fires, where you are sure to find welcoming locals. Three cask ales are available, always including Timothy Taylor Landlord, the others ever changing, regularly from the Yorkshire Dales – requests are always welcome. A huge choice of home-cooked food is on offer to accompany your ale. A TV projector is used for unmissable game days and quiz night is the last Thursday of the month. Q❀◑P

Carlton-in-Cleveland

Blackwell Ox Inn

TS9 7DJ (800yds E of A172)
☎ (01642) 712287 🌐 blackwellox.co.uk
4 changing beers H
Set in a beautiful area on the northern edge of the North York Moors, with the same licensee for over 30 years, this popular, multi-roomed village inn is as renowned for its fine beers as it is for its authentic Thai food. Look out for the lunchtime and early-doors food offers. Drinkers can enjoy an eclectic range of beers in various styles on four handpumps. The garden has an extensive well-designed children's play area. Q❀◑P (89)

Chop Gate

Buck Inn L

TS9 7JL (on B1257 between Stokesley and Helmsley)
☎ (01642) 778334 🌐 the-buck-inn.co.uk
3 changing beers H
Set amid a walkers' paradise and close to the route of Wainwright's Coast-to-Coast walk, this picturesque family-run village pub offers a truly Yorkshire/Teutonic twist. Three locally sourced beers and seven specially imported draught lagers, brewed under the 505-year-old German Purity Laws, are served, together with real home-made food, again half-Yorkshire/half-German. There are six en-suite bedrooms, some designated dog-friendly, and free camping is offered to those who also dine here. Winter opening hours vary.
Q❀◑♣P (M4)

Church Fenton

Fenton Flyer L ✔

Main Street, LS24 9RF
☎ (01937) 558137
Rat White Rat; 4 changing beers (sourced regionally; often Ilkley, Leeds, Ossett) H
A friendly village pub featuring pictures of the nearby WWII airbase, which is now a commercial airport. The beers are chosen from the SIBA list and are often LocAle. Live music plays on the first Friday of each month, there is a monthly Saturday disco with karaoke, and a quiz night on Wednesday raising money for local charities. A Sky and BT Sports TV is in the main bar, and there is an adjacent games room with a pool table and darts. Beer festivals are held in June and November.
❀♣P (492)

Cliffe

New Inn L

York Road, YO8 6NN
☎ (01757) 633888
Theakston Best Bitter; 6 changing beers (sourced regionally; often Half Moon, Small World, Sunbeam) H
This cosy, welcoming, two-roomed country inn, close to the A63, offers seven real ales, mostly local and certainly from Yorkshire. There are regular quiz and dominoes nights, and the pub is home to the village football teams. With a real fire in winter and a welcoming beer garden in summer, you will always feel at home. Watch out for the now annual late-August charity beer festival with an eclectic choice of ales. ❀♣P

Cloughton

Bryherstones Country Inn

Newlands Road, YO13 0AR (½ mile up Newlands Rd off A171 at Cloughton)
☎ (01723) 870744 🌐 bryherstones.uk
Timothy Taylor Landlord; 1 changing beer (sourced regionally; often York) Ⓗ
A stone-built pub nestling between the North York Moors and the coast, just outside the village of Cloughton. Now back in the hands of the Shipley family, it has been restored to its former glory. Its many rooms are full of features, and there is a separate games room. An extensive locally sourced food menu is offered (booking is advised for evenings and Sunday lunchtimes). The pub welcomes children and dogs, and there is a play area in the spacious beer garden, as well as a large car park.
❀◐♣●P🚌🐾📶

Hayburn Wyke Hotel 🄻

Newlands Road, YO13 0AU (off Ravenscar road, 1½ miles N of jct with A171)
☎ (01723) 870202 🌐 hayburnwykeinn.co.uk
Black Sheep Special Ale; Theakston Old Peculier; 2 changing beers (sourced regionally) Ⓗ
An 18th-century coaching inn in woodland next to the disused Scarborough to Whitby railway, and only minutes away from the Cleveland Way coastal path and rocky beach. It is popular with cyclists and walkers. Home-made food is served lunchtimes and evenings (no food Mon eves), with the Sunday carvery a local favourite. En-suite accommodation is available. Outside is a well-provisioned children's play space and a sizeable heated smoking area. ❀🛏◐▲♣P🚌(115)🐾📶

Cononley

New Inn 🄻

Main Street, BD20 8NR
☎ (01535) 636302
Timothy Taylor Golden Best, Boltmaker, Knowle Spring, Landlord; 1 changing beer (often Timothy Taylor) Ⓗ
A real local community pub with mullioned windows and low-beamed ceilings. The bar area is warmed by a wood-burning stove in a huge stone fireplace, and pot plants and china animals adorn the shelves and window sills. The Archives room has a pool table and TV. Although just a short walk from Cononley railway station, if catching a train south allow time at the level crossing as the barriers often come down early. Quiz night is on Tuesday.
❀▲⇌♣🚌(78A) 🐾

Cross Hills

Gallagher's Ale House 🄻

1-3 East Keltus, BD20 8TD (in village centre)
☎ 07834 456134
5 changing beers (sourced nationally) Ⓗ
This popular micropub is located in what used to be Gallagher's bookmakers' shop. The five changing ales usually include a dark beer, a pale bitter, and a strong or speciality beer. The cellar can be viewed through a window to the left of the bar. No electronic music or TV disturb the conversation. Parking is available adjacent to the Co-op store round the corner. The pub's phone number is shared with the Beer Engine in Skipton.
Q♣●🚌(M4,66) 🐾📶

Dalton

Jolly Farmers Inn 🄻

2 Brookside, YO7 3HY
☎ (01845) 578053 🌐 ye-jolly-farmer-inn.business.site
John Smith's Bitter; 1 changing beer (often Leeds, Ossett, Timothy Taylor) Ⓗ
A large local in the heart of a working village. The three rooms offer drinking, dining and games, with sports TV in the bar and the games room. Two cask ales are served including a varying changing beer, often a dark one. Various pub games league teams are supported by the regulars. Accommodation is available across the courtyard from the main building in what were formerly outbuildings. Dalton is conveniently close to the A1M and A19, near the foot of the North York Moors escarpment.
❀🛏◐♣P🐾📶

Dalton-on-Tees

Chequers Inn ✔

The Green, DL2 2NT
☎ (01325) 721213
Bombardier; Ringwood Boondoggle; 1 changing beer (sourced nationally) Ⓗ
An inn dating back to the 1840s, comprising a bar, lounge and restaurant, with friendly and welcoming staff. It manages to combine both the atmosphere of a traditional pub and a contemporary restaurant. Up to three of the beers are Marston's mainstays, all well kept. Good food is available every day, and traditional roast lunches on Sundays. Overnight accommodation comprises five rooms overlooking the green and its pump. Handy for Croft Circuit.
Q❀🛏◐♣P🚌(X27) 🐾📶

Danby

Duke of Wellington 🄻

West Lane, YO21 2LY (300yds N of railway station)
☎ (01287) 660351 🌐 dukeofwellingtondanby.co.uk
Daleside Bitter; Whitby Saltwick Nab; 1 changing beer Ⓗ
This 18th-century inn is set overlooking the village green, in idyllic countryside, close to the Moors National Park Centre and the local traditional baker's shop. The venue was used as a recruiting post during the Napoleonic Wars. A cast-iron plaque of the first Duke of Wellington, unearthed during restorations, hangs above the fireplace. All beers are from Yorkshire. During the evening the kitchen offers traditional British home-cooked meals at their best, using local produce.
Q🛏◑⇌♣●🚌🐾

Drax

Drax Sports & Social Club 🄻 ✔

Main Road, YO8 8PJ
☎ (01757) 618041 🌐 draxsandsclub.co.uk
2 changing beers (sourced regionally)
Nestled in the shadow of the giant Drax power station, this club is full of life and enthusiasm. As well as the bar area, there is a huge function room which is often the venue for beer festivals and similar events. The club takes a little effort to get to but there are some buses from nearby Selby. A well-deserved former local CAMRA branch Club of the Year. ▲♣●P🐾

East Cowton

Beeswing ✔

Main Road, DL7 0BD

☎ (01325) 378349 🌐 thebeeswing.weebly.com
3 changing beers (sourced nationally) ⊞
Traditional country village inn with two bars, a pool room and a highly rated restaurant. Named after a locally bred champion racehorse, there are numerous racing references inside. Up to three changing ales are served from breweries countrywide and one craft beer. The staff are supportive and welcoming, and real fires create a relaxing atmosphere. The pub supports the local community with regular music events, quizzes and a pool table. Q P

Egton

Wheatsheaf Inn

YO21 1TZ
☎ (01947) 895271 🌐 wheatsheafegton.com
Black Sheep Best Bitter; Helmsley Striding the Riding; Timothy Taylor Landlord; 1 changing beer ⊞
Winner of many industry and CAMRA awards, this Grade II listed 19th-century pub only serves Yorkshire beers. It is now in its 21st year in the Guide, and remains under the stewardship of a licensee with over 30 years of continuous Guide recognition. Church pews, country collectables and a roaring range add to the ambience. The grassy areas are ideal for lazy summer drinking, while the renowned first-class restaurant always features local meat, fish and game. Q P (95)

Exelby

Exelby Green Dragon

High Row, DL8 2HA
☎ (01677) 427715 🌐 exelbygreendragonpub.co.uk
Black Sheep Best Bitter; Timothy Taylor Landlord; 2 changing beers (sourced nationally) ⊞
This pub was reopened at the end of 2018 following a community buy-out and renovations. The slightly altered new name distinguishes it from The Green Dragon in nearby Bedale. The knocked-through interior provides a number of different areas and a separate deli, and features two real fires. A spacious separate restaurant opens onto the decked beer garden. Music events include a twice-monthly folk club and weekly Wednesday singalongs, and numerous village activities include book, art and gardening clubs.
P

Filey

Bonhomme's Bar

Royal Crescent Court, The Crescent, YO14 9JH
☎ (01723) 515325
Rudgate Ruby Mild; house beer (by Isaac Poad); 1 changing beer (sourced nationally) ⊞
Located just off the fine Victorian Royal Crescent Hotel complex, the bar's name celebrates John Paul Jones, father of the American Navy. His ship, the Bonhomme Richard, was involved in a battle off nearby Flamborough Head during the War of Independence. Up to five handpumps dispense ale in summer, reducing to three in winter. Food is available daily except Monday. A quiz is held on Thursday evening and Saturday afternoon each week. (12,13)

Star Inn

23 Mitford Street, YO14 9DX
☎ (01723) 512031 🌐 thestarfiley.co.uk
Black Sheep Special Ale; Bradfield Farmers Blonde; Theakston Best Bitter; 3 changing beers (sourced nationally) ⊞
Located just off Filey town centre, the Star has a large main room incorporating a pool table to the left hand side, and a separate restaurant/function room to the rear. Three regular beers and three rotating guests are offered. Freshly cooked meals are served lunchtimes and evenings (except Mon). Live entertainment features occasionally, and pub teams participate in a local pool league. Smokers are catered for outside at both the front and rear. Parking is provided behind the pub.
P (12,13)

Great Ayton

Royal Oak Hotel

123 High Street, TS9 6BW (opp High Green)
☎ (01642) 722361 🌐 royaloakgreatayton.co.uk
Theakston Old Peculier; Timothy Taylor Landlord; Wainwright; 1 changing beer ⊞
A warm welcome is assured at this family-run 18th-century Grade II listed building which sits at the heart of the community. Always busy, the pub is as famed for its four beers as for its food – with breakfast, lunch and

REAL ALE BREWERIES

3 Non Beards York (NEW)
Ainsty Acaster Malbis
BAD Dishforth
Bad Seed Malton
Bilbrough Top Bilbrough
Black Sheep Masham
Brass Castle Malton
Brew York York
Brown Cow Barlow
Captain Cook Stokesley
Crooked Church Fenton
Daleside Harrogate
Dark Horse Hetton
Great British Breworks Kirkbymoorside
Great Yorkshire Cropton
Guisborough Guisborough (NEW)
Hambleton Melmerby
Harrogate Harrogate
Helmsley Helmsley
Hop Studio Elvington
Hops & Dots Middlesbrough
Jolly Sailor Selby
Lady Luck Whitby
LAMB Litton
Little Black Dog Carlton
Live Reeth (NEW)
Mithril Aldbrough St John
Naylor's Cross Hills
North Riding (Brewery) Snainton
North Riding (Brewpub) Scarborough
North Yorkshire Warrenby
Pennine Well
Play Brew Middlesbrough (NEW)
Redscar Redcar
Richmond Richmond
Rooster's Harrogate
Rudgate Tockwith
Ryedale Sinnington
Samuel Smith Tadcaster
Scarborough Scarborough
Settle Settle
Theakston Masham
Treboom Shipton-by-Beningbrough
Turning Point Knaresborough
Wensleydale Leyburn
Whitby Whitby
Yorkshire Dales Askrigg
Yorkshire Heart Nun Monkton

ENGLAND

dinner served, and various offers throughout the week, including pensioners' lunchtime specials on Monday. An enclosed courtyard to the rear, a function room, and four en-suite bedrooms are also available.
Q🛋❀🛏◐🚌(28,81)

Tannery ✔
The Arcade, High Street, TS9 6BW (continue for 50yds through archway next to baker's shop)
☎ (01642) 909030
4 changing beers H
This former hairdresser's shop has been tastefully refurbished and is now the village's micropub. Originally opened in 2018 by experienced licensees, it has always attracted a discerning clientele. Four rotating guest ales, several craft beers and an extensive gin menu are served by enthusiastic and knowledgeable bar staff. Third-pint beer bats are available. Free cheese and biscuit evenings are hosted on Wednesday, with donations going to the charities the pub supports. ♿🚌(28A,81)🐾

Great Broughton

Bay Horse L
88 High Street, TS9 7HA (at S end of village)
☎ (01642) 712319 🌐 thebayhorse-greatbroughton.co.uk
Camerons Strongarm; 3 changing beers H
Visitors and locals alike enjoy the welcoming hospitality offered by the friendly bar staff at this spacious and busy village inn, situated beneath one of the northern entrances to the North York Moors. There is an emphasis on good-value, freshly prepared, home-cooked meals, but drinkers are also well catered for. In addition to the Strongarm, which the pub has served for many years, three changing guest beers from the Marston's stable are also sold. Q🛋❀◐P🚌(89)

Grinton

Bridge Inn
DL11 6HH (on B6270, 1 mile E of Reeth)
☎ (01748) 884224 🌐 bridgeinn-grinton.co.uk
Jennings Cumberland Ale; Wainwright; 3 changing beers (sourced nationally; often Marston's) H
A friendly, well-run, historic inn close to a crossing of the River Swale, as its name suggests, lying beneath the towering hills of Fremington Edge and Harkerside. It has a comfortable lounge, a wood-panelled bar and two restaurant rooms offering home-made food, and is a haven for walkers and cyclists on the Coast-to-Coast and Inn Way walks and Dales Cycle Way; a Youth Hostel is half a mile up the hill. Guest beers are from the Marston's range. Closing time may be earlier at quiet times. Q🛋❀🛏◐♣●P🚌(30)🐾📶

Grosmont

Crossing Club
Co-operative Building, Front Street, YO22 5QE (opp NYMR car park – ring front door bell for entry)
☎ 07766 197744
4 changing beers H
Set amid beautiful scenery in the Esk Valley, this former local CAMRA branch Club of the Year is opposite the NYMR/Esk Valley railway stations in what was the village Co-op's delivery bay. Converted by dedicated villagers 22 years ago, a warm welcome always awaits CAMRA members. Over 1,300 different beers have been served during the club's history. For railway enthusiasts, both steam and diesel memorabilia adorn the walls. Open every evening in summer; hours may vary in winter.
Q⇌♣▯🐾

Guisborough

Monk L ✔
27 Church Street, TS14 6HG (at E end of Westgate)
☎ (01287) 205058
Timothy Taylor Landlord; 4 changing beers H
This contemporary venue is an upmarket addition to the town's social life and attracts a discerning clientele. It is opposite the ruins of Gisborough Priory, which was razed to the ground by King Henry VIII in 1540. The pub is aptly named as, legend has it, the 12th-century Black Monk made use of a tunnel here, discovered during recent renovations, for his nefarious night-time activities. The tunnel's access steps are now on view. Five beers and a real cider are served, and better-value four-drink paddles are available. ♿●🚌(5,X93)🐾📶

Harrogate

Blues Café Bar L
4 Montpellier Parade, HG1 2TJ
☎ (01423) 566881 🌐 bluesbar.co.uk
4 changing beers (often Daleside, Ossett, Rooster's) H
A small single-room café bar in the town centre overlooking the lovely Montpellier gardens, modelled on an Amsterdam café bar, which has been going for more than 30 years. Noted for live music seven days a week, with three sessions on a Sunday, it is popular with music lovers and can get busy. Upstairs is the Gin Bar – formerly an Egyptian restaurant – with seating in large booths where customers can watch the band on a TV screen while dining or drinking. ◐⇌🚌📶↺

Coach & Horses L
16 West Park, HG1 1BJ
☎ (01423) 561802 🌐 thecoachandhorses.net
Daleside Bitter, Blonde; Tetley Bitter; Timothy Taylor Landlord; 4 changing beers H
A busy, traditional pub popular with locals and visitors and overlooking Harrogate's famous Stray. The central bar is surrounded by snugs and alcoves, creating a cosy atmosphere. Tables are provided outside for customers in summer, while window boxes create a spectacular display adding year-round colour. Eight handpumps dispense four regular and four changing beers, and excellent meals are served lunchtimes. There are frequent themed food evenings which, together with a Sunday night quiz, have raised over £1 million for a local children's hospice. Q◐⇌🚌📶↺

Devonshire Tap House L
10 Devonshire Place, HG1 4AA
☎ (01423) 568702 🌐 devonshiretaphouse.business.site
Timothy Taylor Boltmaker; 7 changing beers (often Brass Castle, Harrogate, Wilde Child) H
A cosy old pub, rescued, restored and renovated in 2014, then refurbished and reopened again by new independent operators in 2019. It retains its original semicircular counter and stained-glass canopy, and has wood flooring throughout and a mix of wooden benches, tables and chairs. Four handpumps on each side of the bar dispense a largely changing selection of beers from Yorkshire and northern breweries, and there are 12 keg lines and a beer fridge. Food includes bar snacks and boards of British artisan meats and cheeses. 🛋❀⇌🚌🐾

Disappearing Chin 🏆
38 Beulah Street, HG1 1QH (opp bus station)
☎ 07539 942344 🌐 thedisappearingchin.co.uk
3 changing beers H
A new bar opened in 2019 in a shop unit opposite the bus station, accessible from either Beulah Street or

Station Parade. Long and narrow, it has soft seating at both ends in the windows, and stools at the bar, with some standing room. Three handpumps serve three changing cask ales, always including a dark beer, and there are eight craft keg fonts; sometimes there are tap takeovers. Card payments only. ఠ♿≹🚌🐾📶

Harrogate Tap Ⓛ

Station Parade, HG1 1TE

☎ (01423) 501644 🌐 harrogatetap.co.uk

11 changing beers (often Brew York, Harrogate, Rooster's) 🄷

Overlooking Harrogate station is this impressive transformation of a neglected railway building. The pub is of similar style to the Tapped Brew Company's other bars at York and Sheffield. It comprises a long bar room and a separate snug; the decor features dark-wood panelling, a tiled floor and tasteful Victorian-style fittings. A diverse range of cask ales is available on 12 handpumps, with one devoted to cider. The cask ales are complemented by craft kegs and bottled world beers. Bar snacks are served. ఠ♿≹●🚌🐾📶

Little Ale House

7 Cheltenham Crescent, HG1 1DH

☎ (01423) 391996 🌐 alehouseharrogate.co.uk

5 changing beers 🄷

Harrogate's first micropub, comprising one room with the counter at the back, and a downstairs cellar room. As with many micropubs, the beers are kept cool in a glass cabinet to one side. Five handpumps dispense cask ales, usually including a dark beer, and there is always at least one real cider. KeyKeg and local artisan gins are also sold. There is an outside seated area at the front as well as a pleasant yard with pub benches at the rear, with service at the window in summer. Q❀≹●🚌🐾📶

Major Tom's Social Ⓛ

The Ginnel, HG1 2RB

☎ (01423) 566984 🌐 majortomssocial.co.uk

4 changing beers (often Rooster's, Turning Point) 🄷

A café bar housed above a vintage shop in a former antiques emporium, providing real ale, craft keg, pizza, music and art. It is simply furnished, with wooden tables and chairs, and some bench seating. The décor is in a mix of styles to suit its eclectic customers, including artwork for sale. Four handpumps dispense a variety of ales, usually from a range of smaller breweries, often including the local Rooster's brewery, as well as Turning Point from nearby Knaresborough. ఠ◑≹🚌🐾📶

Old Bell Ⓛ ✔

6 Royal Parade, HG1 2SZ

☎ (01423) 507930

Ilkley Mary Jane; Theakston Best Bitter, Old Peculier; Timothy Taylor Boltmaker; 4 changing beers (often Ilkley, Leeds, Rooster's) 🄷

A Market Town Taverns establishment, the Old Bell opened in 1999 on the site of the Blue Bell Inn which closed in 1815 and was later demolished. President Bill Clinton visited the inn on a visit to Harrogate in 2001. Later the same year the pub expanded into the former Farrah's toffee shop, where there is a collection of Farrah's memorabilia. The interior was refurbished in 2017, with new leather armchairs and updated decor. Eight handpumps serve beers from local Yorkshire breweries, always including at least one dark beer and, occasionally, real cider. ఠ◑≹🚌🐾📶

Starling Independent Bar Café Kitchen Ⓛ

47 Oxford Street, HG1 1PW

☎ (01423) 531310 🌐 murmurationbars.co.uk

Rooster's Highway 51; 4 changing beers (often Harrogate) 🄷

A relaxed café bar with a contemporary feel and stripped-back brickwork throughout. A downstairs wall features a mural of a murmuration of starlings. The pallet-fronted counter holds six handpulls offering a well-chosen range of mainly Yorkshire beers in a good mix of styles and strengths, usually including a dark beer. The sixth pump is devoted to real cider. A large blackboard on the bar back lists the current beers and is updated regularly. Stone-baked pizzas are a favourite here. ఠ◑≹●🚌🐾📶

Winter Gardens Ⓛ ✔

4 Royal Baths, HG1 2RR

☎ (01423) 877010

Greene King Abbot; Ruddles Best Bitter; Sharp's Doom Bar; house beer (by Daleside); 6 changing beers 🄷

Converted from part of the Royal Baths complex in 2002, this magnificent building has a spacious interior reached from the Parliament Street entrance by a sweeping Hollywood-style double stone staircase. Wheelchair access is from the entrance in The Ginnel. In addition to the usual Wetherspoon core range of beers, numerous locally sourced guests are always dispensed across three sets of handpumps. The pub can get busy due to its location near Harrogate's conference and exhibition centre. ఠ❀◑♿≹●🚌📶

Hawes

Board Inn ✔

Market Place, DL8 3RD

☎ (01969) 667223 🌐 theboardinn.co.uk

Black Sheep Best Bitter; Theakston Best Bitter; Timothy Taylor Landlord; 1 changing beer (sourced nationally) 🄷

A comfortable and traditional pub located in the heart of this busy Dales centre, popular with walkers and other visitors. The main front bar has a warming coal fire in winter and there is also a pleasant dining room, plus an outdoor seating area at the front. Home-cooked food is served lunchtimes and evenings. There are five en-suite letting rooms. ఠ🛏◑⛺♣🚌🐾📶

Helmsley

Helmsley Brewing Co

18 Bridge Street, YO62 5DX

☎ (01439) 771014 🌐 helmsleybrewingco.co.uk

Helmsley Yorkshire Legend, Striding the Riding, Howardian Gold; 4 changing beers (sourced locally; often Helmsley) 🄷

The brewery tap for the Helmsley Brewing Company, close to the market square in a picturesque village. Four changing beers from the brewery's own range are on the bar. Brewery tours and the on-site shop complete the full beer experience. Helmsley is the only market town in the North York Moors National Park, and the perfect base for enjoying the wider area. 🚌

Helwith Bridge

Helwith Bridge Inn Ⓛ ✔

BD24 0EH (off B6479)

☎ (01729) 860220 🌐 helwithbridgeinn.co.uk

Thwaites Original; 4 changing beers (sourced nationally) 🄷

Despite its relative isolation in a tiny hamlet, this is a thriving, no-frills community local where the emphasis is on real ale. It has three separate rooms, all reached via the flagged main bar area. Adjacent to the River Ribble and the Settle and Carlisle railway line, the pub is the starting point of the Three Peaks cycle race. The house beer, Helwith Bridge Bitter, is Three Peaks Pen-y-Ghent. Self-catering accommodation is available in the adjacent bunk barn. ❀🛏◐◑♿▲♣P🚌(11)🐾📶

Hinderwell

Brown Cow

55 High Street, TS13 5ET (on A174)
☎ (01947) 840694
2 changing beers Ⓗ
Real pubs like this are hard to find! Wedged between the moors and the coast, this hostelry has been recently refurbished but retains an interior reminiscent of a 1960s front parlour. Visitors and locals alike are assured of a warm welcome. Two interesting rotating guest beers are served, as are good-value home-cooked meals. The pub supports darts teams, charity nights and dominoes drives, and hosts a quiz night on Sunday. Children and dogs are welcome, and smokers are well provided for. Reasonably priced accommodation is in four bedrooms. Q🐎❀🛏◐◑♿♣P🚆🚌(X4)🐾

Huby

Mended Drum 𝕃

Tollerton Road, YO61 1HT
☎ (01347) 810264 🌐 themendeddrum.com
Tetley Bitter; 4 changing beers (sourced locally; often Brass Castle) Ⓗ
This large, open-plan local, which takes its name from a Terry Pratchett novel, is bigger than it looks. Welcoming to families and cyclists, it is the lively centre of a rural community. The pub is popular for its interesting range of frequently changing local beers, served by knowledgeable staff, and good traditional pub food with a modern twist, including vegan, vegetarian and gluten-free dishes. With three beer festivals per year, it is well worth seeking out. Voted local CAMRA branch Pub of the Year 2019. 🐎❀◐◑♿▲♣●P🚌(40)🐾📶

Hudswell

George & Dragon 🏆 𝕃

DL11 6BL
☎ (01748) 518373 🌐 georgeanddragonhudswell.co.uk
Rudgate Ruby Mild; Wensleydale Falconer; 4 changing beers (sourced locally) Ⓗ
Rescued from closure by the local community in 2010, this homely, two-roomed village inn became CAMRA's National Pub of the Year just six years later. It now features its own library, shop, allotments and other local facilities, as well as great food, Yorkshire-brewed beers and a selection of nearly 70 whiskies. A large beer terrace to the rear offers stunning panoramic views over the Swale valley, and it is a pleasant hike from Richmond, so long as you do not mind the 300-plus steps. Open all day on bank holidays. Q🐎❀◐◑▲♣●P🚌(32)🐾📶

Ingleby Barwick

Beckfields ✔

Beckfields Avenue, TS17 0QA (W off A1045, along Ingleby Way, then first left along Beckfields Avenue)
☎ (01642) 766263
4 changing beers Ⓗ
If your passion is for well-known, stronger, best and premium beers, then this popular and uniquely named community venue will serve you well. It is at the heart of one of the six villages that make up what is reputedly Europe's largest private housing estate. Under the stewardship of a licensee with many years' service to the trade, four handpulls operate on a rotating guest basis. An extensive pub grub menu is also served. 🐎❀◐◑♿♣P🚌(15)🐾📶

Ingleton

Masons

New Road, LA6 3HL
☎ (015242) 42040 🌐 masonsismoran.co.uk
Sharp's Doom Bar; 4 changing beers Ⓗ
An early-Victorian building on the busy main road away from the centre of this popular tourist village. Extensively refurbished in 2016, Masons is now a true family-run free house. A small bar counter serves a long drinking space of linked areas with light and airy decor. The patio has a glazed roof and heating. Live music is featured, but not on a regular basis. ❀🛏◐◑▲P🚌(80)🐾📶

Kellington

Red Lion

1 Ings Lane, DN14 0NT (follow road from A19 into centre of village)
☎ (01977) 661008 🌐 redlionkellington.co.uk
Brown Cow White Dragon; 1 changing beer (sourced locally; often Brown Cow, Caledonian, Sharp's) Ⓗ
A friendly, family-run local at the heart of the village. It comprises an extensive lounge and an adjoining area with a pool table. There is also a function room and rooms to let. The pub plays an active part in the local community and runs three pool teams and hosts charity events. Sunday is quiz night. There is always a beer from Brown Cow Brewery as well as two changing guest beers. Parking is at the rear. Q🐎❀🛏♿♣P🐾📶

Kirk Smeaton

Shoulder of Mutton

Main Street, WF8 3JY (follow signs from A1)
☎ (01977) 620348
Black Sheep Best Bitter; 1 changing beer (sourced regionally; often Bradfield, Stancill) Ⓗ
Convenient for the Went Valley and Brockadale Nature Reserve, this welcoming, traditional village pub is popular with walkers and the local community. An award-winning free house, the beer comes direct from the brewery and the quality is superb. The interior comprises a large lounge with open fires and a cosy, dark-panelled snug. The spacious beer garden has a covered and heated shelter for smokers, and there is ample parking. Quiz night is Tuesday. Q🐎❀♣P🚌(409)🐾📶

Kirkby-in-Cleveland

Black Swan

Busby Lane, TS9 7AW (800yds W of B1257) NZ539060
☎ (01642) 712512 🌐 theblackswankirkby.co.uk
Bradfield Farmers Blonde; Sharp's Doom Bar; Timothy Taylor Landlord; Wainwright; 1 changing beer Ⓗ
Nestling at the foot of the Cleveland Hills, at the crossroads of an ancient village, this warm and cosy free house is under the stewardship of a licensee of 24 years' standing. A genuine welcome is assured from the friendly staff. The pub comprises a bar room, an adjacent pool room, a lounge/restaurant, a conservatory and a patio with seating. Four regular beers and a guest are on the bar. Good-value meals are served including daily specials and bar meals. 🐎❀◐◑♿♣P🚆🚌(89)🐾📶

Knaresborough

Blind Jack's 𝕃

19 Market Place, HG5 8AL

☎ (01423) 860475 🌐 blindjackspub.com

Black Sheep Best Bitter; 6 changing beers (sourced nationally) Ⓗ

Listed in the Guide since 1993, this is a Georgian listed building with bare-brick walls and wooden floorboards, comprising two small rooms on the ground floor and two similar rooms up a steep staircase. The pub provides a focal point both for locals and the many visitors who appreciate the excellent selection of ales, the cosy ambience and lively banter. The diverse beer range includes at least one dark and one gluten-free choice, as well as a range of craft kegs. A trompe l'oeil painting on the exterior features the pub's namesake, Blind Jack Metcalf. Q⇌🚌🐾ᯤ

Cross Keys ✔

17 Cheapside, HG5 8AX

☎ (01423) 863562

Ossett Yorkshire Brunette, Yorkshire Blonde, Silver King; Rat White Rat; 3 changing beers (sourced regionally; often Fernandes, Rat, Salt) Ⓗ

A former Tetley's house, refurbished by Ossett Brewery in its trademark style, with stone-flagged floors, bare-brick walls and stained glass. This traditional pub serves up to seven cask ales, mostly from the Ossett stable, which also includes Fernandes, Rat, Riverhead and Salt breweries. A guest beer is sometimes on the bar, and there is always a dark beer. Real ciders, eg Lilley's, are also served. Thursday is quiz night and a live band plays on most Saturday nights. ❀⇌🍎🚌🐾ᯤ↺

Half Moon 𝕃

1 Abbey Road, HG5 8HY

☎ (01423) 313461

Rooster's Yorkshire Pale Ale; 3 changing beers (sourced locally) Ⓗ

A lovingly restored independent free house, down by Low Bridge, providing a warm and welcoming atmosphere, with a real fire and a wood-burning stove. There is a small, attractive, enclosed outdoor space, with tables and chairs and some benches under a heated awning. Four handpumps dispense a varying range of beers, mostly from Yorkshire breweries. A grazing menu of meat and cheeseboards complements the beers, served throughout the day. Coffee and home-made cakes are also available. Dogs are welcome in the outside area. ❀◑⇌🚌(22)ᯤ

Mitre 𝕃 ✔

4 Station Road, HG5 9AA

☎ (01423) 868948

Ilkley Mary Jane; Timothy Taylor Boltmaker; 4 changing beers (often Rooster's) Ⓗ

Opposite Knaresborough's Grade II listed railway station and signal box, this Market Town Taverns pub offers a modern split-level bar with wooden flooring throughout. There is a side room mostly used for dining, a function room in the basement, and a sunny terrace at the back with views of the local church. The six handpumps dispense a range of Yorkshire ales and occasional beers from smaller national breweries, always including one dark. Food is served every day and well-behaved dogs and children are welcome. ❀🛏◑♿⇌🚌(1)🐾ᯤ

Six Poor Folk 𝕃 ✔

25 Castlegate, HG5 8AR

☎ (01423) 869918 🌐 sixpoorfolk.com

4 changing beers (often Timothy Taylor) Ⓗ

A former almshouse dating back to the 15th century, Six Poor Folk was converted from a restaurant to a bar in 2018. It now offers four real ales from a range of national and Yorkshire breweries, and there are also craft kegs and a wide selection of cans and bottles. The pub hosts a quiz on Wednesday, a DJ plays soul and funk music on Friday, and there is an open mic night each Sunday. Roasts are served on Sunday lunchtime. ❀◑⇌🚌🐾ᯤ

Lastingham

Blacksmiths Arms

Anserdale lane, YO62 6TN

☎ (01751) 417247 🌐 blacksmithsarmslastingham.co.uk

Saltaire Blonde; Theakston Best Bitter, Old Peculier; 1 changing beer (sourced regionally; often Daleside, Rudgate) Ⓗ

A pretty stone inn in a conservation village opposite St Mary's Church, famous for its 11th-century crypt. The interior comprises a cosy bar with a York range lit in winter, a snug, and two dining rooms. Excellent food including local game dishes is served alongside interesting guest beers and a changing guest cider, often Thistly Cross. A secluded beer garden is to the rear, which now includes a pizza oven. This remote hostelry is popular with locals, walkers and shooting parties. Dogs are welcome outside only. Q❀🛏◑🍎

Lealholm

Board Inn 𝕃

Village Green, YO21 2AJ

☎ (01947) 897279 🌐 theboardinn.com

3 changing beers Ⓗ

Overlooking the Esk, this family-run 17th-century inn is at the heart of village life. Three beers, six ciders and 60 whiskies are served. The pub comprises a locals' bar, a lounge/restaurant, and a riverside patio where an Easter beer festival is held. Almost all the food comes from no more than a mile away. The licensees air-cure their own hams, keep hens, ducks and livestock, and have salmon fishing rights. A recent winner of local CAMRA branch Community Pub and Cider Pub awards.
Q❀🛏◑♿⇌♣🍎🚌(95)🐾

Leavening

Jolly Farmers 𝕃

Main Street, YO17 9SA

☎ (01653) 658276

Timothy Taylor Landlord; York Guzzler; 2 changing beers (sourced locally; often Great Newsome, Half Moon) Ⓗ

A 17th-century hostelry on the edge of the Yorkshire Wolds between York and Malton. The pub is homely and welcoming, with low ceilings, tile flagged floors and an intriguing series of rooms. Serving locally sourced food and a range of ales from near and far, it is a popular stopping-off point for ramblers as well as locals. Annual beer and gin festivals are hosted. The outside drinking area has table football and a cask of drinking water for dogs complete with handpump. Q❀◑♿🍎P🐾ᯤ

Leyburn

Golden Lion 𝕃

Market Place, DL8 5AS

☎ (01969) 622161 🌐 goldenlionleyburn.co.uk

John Smith's Bitter; Wensleydale Semer Water, Gamekeeper; 1 changing beer (sourced locally; often Theakston) Ⓗ

Facing the main square of this busy and attractive Dales centre, this traditional market town pub is a short walk from the revived Wensleydale Railway, which has steam trains in summer. The comfortable main bar area is opened out and largely wood-panelled, with a real fire at each end, and there is a separate dining room to the rear, particularly popular for the Sunday carvery. There are tables outside for eating and drinking in fine weather.

King's Head

Grove Square, DL8 5AE

☎ (01969) 622798

Theakston Best Bitter; Wensleydale Semer Water

Set off the main marketplace, at the junction of the moor road and the Richmond road, this locals' pub is a rare example of a wet-led house in this tourist area, offering a selection of well-kept cask ales at attractive prices. It is an enthusiastic provider of sports TV, especially football, which is well supported, and also hosts regular live music. The rooms have been knocked through, but the bar, lounge and games room have the feel of separate areas. Attractions include a pool table, two dartboards, fruit machines, open fires, and the only jukebox in town.

Lofthouse

Crown Hotel

Thorpe Lane, HG3 5RZ

☎ (01423) 755206

Black Sheep Best Bitter; Theakston Best Bitter

A traditional Dales pub and hotel in the Nidderdale Area of Outstanding Natural Beauty, a short way uphill from the main part of the village on a road with spectacular views. There is an unusual panelled entrance corridor leading to a traditionally furnished, comfortable bar decorated with local pictures, maps and brassware; a more formal dining room is reached through the bar. There is also a rack of walking sticks for sale if required. There is no cellphone coverage indoors.

Q P

Low Row

Punch Bowl Inn

DL11 6PF

☎ 0333 700 0779 pbinn.co.uk

Black Sheep Best Bitter; Theakston Best Bitter; 1 changing beer

A smart, two-room, 17th-century inn with a focus on food, owned by the same people as the CB at Langthwaite. The bar area is pleasant, featuring a Mousey Thompson bar, bare floorboards and old pine tables, with comfortable leather settees around the stove. This is a pub that offers welcome R&R for walkers (provided muddy boots are removed). The guest beer is often from Rudgate. Q P

Malham

Lister Arms

Gordale Scar Road, BD23 4DB

☎ (01729) 830444 listerarms.co.uk

Lancaster Bomber; Thwaites Mild, Original; Wainwright; 3 changing beers (sourced locally; often Dark Horse, Settle, Thwaites)

Substantial stone-built Grade II listed inn dating from 1723 or earlier, overlooking the green. The tiled entrance hall opens to the stone-flagged main bar, with separate areas to left and right and a dining room/restaurant beyond. The large secluded garden at the rear has ample comfortable seating. Food is served all day, with breakfast and brunch on offer in the morning, and the main menu thereafter. Home-made cakes and cream teas are also available. Malham can get busy on weekends and school holidays. P

Malton

Blue Ball

14 Newbiggin, YO17 7JF

☎ (01653) 690692

Tetley Bitter; Timothy Taylor Landlord; 1 changing beer (sourced locally)

This Grade II listed establishment dating from the 16th century is in CAMRA Yorkshire's Real Heritage Pubs guide. It was named the Blue Ball in 1823. The low front elevation hides a maze-like interior, with the frontward cosy bar, compact servery and linking corridor retaining most of the historical flavour. A smoking area is at the rear. Home-cooked food is served daily (except Wed). The Blue Ball Folk Club meets here on the second Tuesday of each month. Q P (843)

Brass Castle Brewery Tap House

10 Yorkersgate, YO17 7AB

☎ (01653) 698683 brasscastle.co.uk

3 changing beers (sourced locally; often Brass Castle)

Formerly a town-centre temperance hotel, Malton's newest hostelry is a short walk from the railway station. The single-roomed bar is tastefully designed in a rustic style, with one wall partially adorned with barrel staves. Three regularly changing cask ales are offered together with six craft keg ales, alongside an extensive range of bottled beers. Snacks may be purchased at the bar. There is a smoking/drinking area to the rear of the premises and an upstairs seating area. Q

Manfield

Crown Inn

Vicars Lane, DL2 2RF (500yds from B6275)

☎ (01325) 374243

Draught Bass; Village White Boar; 5 changing beers (sourced nationally)

This 18th-century inn in a quiet village has been local CAMRA Country Pub of the Year 16 times, and previously Yorkshire Pub of the Year. It has two bars, a games room, a real log fire in the main bar, and an extensive beer garden. A mix of locals and visitors creates a friendly atmosphere. Up to six guest beers are sourced from microbreweries, alongside five ciders or a perry. Two seasonal beer festivals are held.

Q P (29)

Marske-by-the-Sea

Clarendon

88-90 High Street, TS11 7BA

☎ (01642) 490005

Black Sheep Best Bitter; Camerons Strongarm; Copper Dragon Golden Pippin; Theakston Best Bitter, Old Peculier; 1 changing beer

The Middle House, as it is also known, is a popular one-room locals' pub, where little has changed since the 1960s. Six beers are served from the mahogany island bar, a rarity on Teesside. The walls are adorned with interesting photographs of yesteryear. There is no TV, no pool table, no children or teenagers, just locals indulging in convivial conversation. There is no catering either, but tea and coffee are always available. Local CAMRA branch 2020 award winner. Q P (X3,X4)

ENGLAND

Masham

Bay Horse 🄻 ✔

5 Silver Street, HG4 4DX

☎ (01765) 688297 🌐 bayhorseatmasham.co.uk

Black Sheep Best Bitter; Theakston Best Bitter; house beer (by Hardys & Hansons); 3 changing beers (often Morland, Theakston, York) Ⓗ

Friendly pub welcoming tourists and locals alike with a range of ales unusual to Masham, although both the town's breweries are represented. As well as the front bar there is a dining area up a short flight of steps, a rear garden and five letting rooms. A wide variety of home cooked food is served with ingredients coming from local suppliers; note that meal times may vary in winter. Cask ends and pipework form a feature in the main front bar.

🔥❀🛏◐♣🚌🐾📶

White Bear 🄻 ✔

Wellgarth, HG4 4EN

☎ (01765) 689319 🌐 thewhitebearhotel.co.uk

Theakston Best Bitter, Black Bull Bitter, Lightfoot, Old Peculier; 1 changing beer (often Theakston) Ⓗ

Theakston's only pub, an award-winning venue and a great favourite with the locals as well as directors and staff from the brewery. A large dining area to the left and a cosy taproom to the right offer almost the full range of Theakston's beers. Unusually for the Yorkshire Dales, this building was a victim of wartime bombing, following which it was derelict for many years before it was rescued and renovated to a high standard. A popular beer festival is hosted in June featuring over 30 beers.

🔥❀🛏◐♿♣P🚌🐾📶

Middleham

Richard III Hotel 🄻

Market Place, DL8 4NP

☎ (01969) 623240 🌐 richard111hotel.co.uk

Black Sheep Best Bitter; John Smith's Bitter; Theakston Best Bitter; Wensleydale Semer Water; 1 changing beer Ⓗ

A small, comfortable 17th-century hotel overlooking the little market square in the centre of Middleham, a horse racing centre. You can be sure of a warm welcome from the local owners. The interior comprises an opened out front bar decorated with flock wallpaper, a real fire, and a separate dining room and snug to the rear. Tables are set out on cobbles at the front – the ideal spot to enjoy breakfast while racehorses trot by.

🔥🛏◐🚌(159,859) 🐾

Middlesbrough

Dr Phil's Real Ale House 🄻

10 Pilkington Buildings, Roman Road, Linthorpe, TS5 6DY (100yds N of The Crescent and Roman Road jct)

☎ 07883 072389

3 changing beers Ⓗ

The first micropub in this area is among a terrace of shops in the leafy suburbs of Linthorpe, a mile south of Middlesbrough. Opened in 2013 by an enthusiastic CAMRA member, it soon became a local CAMRA branch multi award-winner. The five-yards-square space accommodates an eclectic mix of drinkers, who have a choice of three changing beers, one of which is generally a porter or stout, as well as a real cider. Honesty box snacks are on offer Saturday and Sunday lunchtimes.

Q♿♣🍎🚌(11,17) 🐾📶

Infant Hercules 🏆 🄻

84 Grange Road, TS1 2LS (just S of Cleveland Centre and N of university campus)

☎ 07980 321626

4 changing beers Ⓗ

One of several micropubs in the town's original solicitors' quarter, all located in a series of parallel streets of Victorian terraced houses close to the law courts. It is named after Gladstone's description of the town in 1862, after he had witnessed the rapid expansion of the area's steel furnaces and shipbuilding industries. Third-pint tasting bats are available. Teesside University's Real Ale Society (TURAS) meets here on Thursday.

Q🔥❀🚆🍎🚌🐾📶

Isaac Wilson 🄻

61 Wilson Street, TS1 1SF (at N end of town, close to railway station)

☎ (01642) 247708

Camerons Strongarm; Sharp's Atlantic; 3 changing beers Ⓗ

A popular single room pub named after a 19th-century railway industry magnate and company director of the world's first railway, the Stockton and Darlington. The Isaac, a former Wetherspoon's conversion of the old law courts, has recently gained new owners and continues to follow, more or less, the chain's formula. Two regular beers, three local guests and several ciders are served, together with good-value food. Walls feature photographs of old Middlesbrough. Third-pint glasses are available. 🔥◐♿🚆🍎🚌📶

Muker

Farmers Arms 🄻

DL11 6QG

☎ (01748) 886297 🌐 farmersarmsmuker.co.uk

Black Sheep Best Bitter; Theakston Best Bitter, Old Peculier; Yorkshire Dales Muker Silver; 1 changing beer (sourced locally) Ⓗ

A traditional inn in the centre of a former lead-mining village, set in bleak but beautiful Swaledale countryside. Near both the Coast-to-Coast and Pennine Way routes, it attracts countless visitors. The stone-flagged bar with its open fire is popular with locals and walkers, cyclists and others. As well as the range of local ales there is a guest beer in summer, and home-prepared food is available every day. Closed Monday in winter.

Q🔥❀🛏◐⛺♣P🚌🐾

Muston

Ship Inn

West Street, YO14 0ER

☎ (01723) 514639

House beer (by Greene King); 2 changing beers (sourced nationally) Ⓗ

A popular village local two miles south-west of Filey – a favourite stopping point for people on the Yorkshire Wolds Way Walk. The main room is divided into drinking and dining areas. Two guest ales are offered, and home-cooked food is served all day in the summer (evenings and all day at weekends in winter). There are smoking and drinking areas outside at both the front and rear of the pub. Of note is the multiplicity of memorabilia displayed in the bar. Q🔥◐♣P🚌(12,13)🐾📶

North Rigton

Square & Compass 🄻 ✔

Rigton Hill, LS17 0DJ

☎ (01423) 733031 🌐 thesquareandcompass.com

Leeds Pale; Ossett Yorkshire Blonde; Theakston Best Bitter; Timothy Taylor Landlord; 2 changing beers (often Rooster's)
A large, elegant, open-plan pub with multiple spaces laid out for dining, although the main bar at the front is a pleasant area for drinking, furnished with tables and leather armchairs and overlooking a large sunny terrace. One area to the side of the bar features a large chandelier, and there is a bookshelf with second-hand books for sale. Six handpumps dispense beers from Yorkshire breweries, including one from the local Rooster's Brewery. P (747,X52)

Northallerton

Standard
24 High Street, North End, DL7 8EE (opp Sainsbury's on A167 N of town centre)
(01609) 772719 thestandard-pub.co.uk
Hambleton Stallion; Timothy Taylor Landlord; 2 changing beers
The Standard has a traditional single-room interior with bare stone and brickwork; three distinct areas feature many old photographs of the town. The pub is home to darts and dominoes teams and supports football and rugby teams, and hosts a golf society. Children and dogs are welcome. There is a Jet Provost aircraft in the pleasant beer garden to the rear!

Stumble Inn
4 Garthway Arcade, DL7 8NS (in pedestrian arcade off High St next to Grovers shop)
07817 568042
5 changing beers (sourced locally)
A friendly and cosy micropub hidden away near the Applegarth car park. It serves a selection of local ales, craft beers and up to 20 real ciders, and staff are keen to offer tasting advice and guidance. The choice always includes a dark beer. With no music, gaming machines, Wi-Fi, children or sports TV, you can enjoy good old-fashioned chat. A quiz is held on the last Sunday of each month, and seasonal beer and cider festivals. Q

Nun Monkton

Alice Hawthorn
The Green, YO26 8EW
(01423) 330303 thealicehawthorn.com
Black Sheep Pale Ale; Timothy Taylor Landlord, Landlord Dark
Originally called the Bluebell Inn, the Alice has been a pub since 1787, overlooking the green in this picturesque village. The current owners bought the premises in 2013 with a will to make it a cracking little place and to secure its future. It serves good-quality food made with local produce, and local cask ales from Yorkshire Heart, based just outside the village.

Osgodby

Wadkin Arms
Cliffe Road, YO8 5HU
(01757) 702391 wadkinarms.co.uk
Brown Cow White Dragon; Ossett Yorkshire Blonde; Timothy Taylor Landlord; 1 changing beer (sourced nationally; often Marston's)
A true community pub at the heart of the village, with five handpumps dispensing ales that mainly come from Yorkshire breweries. The Wadkin has a homely feel with open fires and a friendly welcome, and is home to locals and visitors alike. The nearby Trans Pennine cycle trail brings cyclist and walkers to the pub in the summer months, and a local bus service passes too. You will see much evidence of CAMRA sympathies on display.
P (4)

Osmotherley

Golden Lion
6 West End, DL6 3AA (in village centre, 1 mile E of A19)
(01609) 883526 goldenlionosmotherley.co.uk
Timothy Taylor Landlord; 2 changing beers (sourced locally)
Set in the centre of a picturesque village on the edge of the North York Moors National Park and at the start of the long-distance Lyke Wake Walk, this old inn is popular with hikers, casual visitors and locals. Much of the focus is on high-quality locally sourced food, but drinkers are always welcome, and the view from the outside drinking tables is an attraction on fine days. Regularly changing beers are from local breweries and there is a beer festival each November. Dogs are welcome.
Q (80,89)

Pickering

Sun Inn
136 Westgate, YO18 8BB (on A170, 400yds W of traffic lights in town centre)
(01751) 473661 thesuninn-pickering.co.uk
Tetley Bitter; 5 changing beers (sourced regionally; often Daleside, Hadrian Border, Saltaire)
Friendly local CAMRA Rural Pub of the Year, close to the steam railway. Six real ales are offered, often from Yorkshire micros, and several traditional ciders. A cosy bar with a real fire leads to a separate room, ideal for families and special events, where local artists display their work. The large beer garden is used for the annual beer festival in September. Regular events include fortnightly acoustic music, charity quizzes and monthly vinyl nights. Dogs (on leads), children and walkers are welcome. (128)

Pool-in-Wharfedale

Hunters Inn
Harrogate Road, LS21 2PS
Abbeydale Moonshine; Black Sheep Best Bitter; Morland Old Speckled Hen; 6 changing beers (often Bradfield, Rat)
Situated on the main Harrogate to Bradford road with views across lower Wharfedale, this is a single-storey building. The large open-plan interior incorporates a raised area at one end, with a warming real fire during the colder months. Nine handpumps dispense a varying selection of ales that mainly come from Yorkshire breweries. There is a pool table and video jukebox at one end and a small games room with fruit and pinball machines. Well-behaved children are allowed during the day. P

Redcar

Rita's Pantry
1 Esplanade, TS10 3AA (opp Beacon)
07730 445483
4 changing beers
A former amusement arcade, this is the town's first micropub. It is on the seafront, opposite Redcar's Beacon, from where the petrified forest can be seen at low tide. A warm welcome is extended to CAMRA members, locals and visitors alike. Three interesting beers are served, as well as real cider. Third-pint glasses are available. The amiable licensee hosts various social events, including a

music quiz on Sunday, and occasional Belgian beer nights. A recent local CAMRA award winner.
(X3,X4)

Redmire

Bolton Arms Inn

DL8 4EA
(01969) 624336 boltonarmsredmire.co.uk
Black Sheep Best Bitter; Theakston Best Bitter; Wensleydale Semer Water; 1 changing beer (sourced nationally)
This attractive village lies at the western terminus of the revived Wensleydale Railway and less than a mile from the historic Bolton Castle. The stone-built pub is a 10-minute walk from the station – trains provide a good way to travel as parking can be limited. Inside, lunchtime and evening meals are served in the large dining area, with snacks all day, as well as four real ales, usually locally brewed. P

Riccall

Greyhound

82 Main Street, YO19 6TE
(01757) 249101 thegreyhoundriccall.co.uk
Ossett Yorkshire Blonde; Tetley Bitter; Theakston Best Bitter, Old Peculier; 3 changing beers (sourced regionally; often Ossett, Rooster's, Rudgate)
Four miles north of Selby you will find the Greyhound, a welcoming inn in the heart of this historic village. It is a family-run village hostelry dating back to the late 1800s, and nowadays has up to seven cask beers on the bar. The pub is popular with locals and visitors alike, set in a location close to River Ouse walks and the Trans Pennine cycle trail. The large beer garden can get busy on warmer days. Food is served daily except Saturday. Check the website for winter opening hours and meal times.
P

Richmond

Holly Hill Inn

Sleegill, DL10 4RJ
(01748) 822192 holly-hill-inn.co.uk
Black Sheep Best Bitter; Sharp's Doom Bar; Timothy Taylor Landlord; 1 changing beer
A pleasant but strenuous walk half a mile south from the town centre, this popular pub lies beyond the castle, across the River Swale and high above it. The main bar is on two levels separated by a stone chimney breast with a cast-iron stove, while a large extension in the style of a baronial hall, with an impressive fireplace, is used as a restaurant and function room. Quiz night is Wednesday.
QP(30)

No.29 Alehouse & Gin Bar

29 Frenchgate, DL10 4HZ
(01748) 850491
number-29-alehouse-gin-bar.business.site
3 changing beers (sourced locally)
This real ale, craft beer, gin, wine and tapas bar opened in 2018. It is just off the foot of Richmond's market place, on the road down to the former station complex. The single small bar has simple decor and a wooden floor. The beers are usually local or regional. Food such as cured meat and cheese sharing boards, ploughman's and various tapas dishes are on sale. May close early if quiet.

Ripon

Royal Oak

36 Kirkgate, HG4 1PB
(01765) 602284 royaloakripon.co.uk
Saltaire Blonde; Timothy Taylor Golden Best, Boltmaker, Landlord, Landlord Dark; 1 changing beer (often Timothy Taylor)
This venue is in what was an 18th-century coaching inn, now beautifully renovated in a modern idiom, in the centre of historic Ripon between the cathedral and the Market Square. Timothy Taylor's most northerly tied house, the Royal Oak serves a top-quality range of the brewery's beers alongside a regular Saltaire Blonde. The pub is separated into relaxed dining areas with log-burning stoves and comfortable seating, and offers a first-class locally sourced menu. You can stay in one of the six stylish and comfortable bedrooms, and a hearty English breakfast is included. P(36)

Robin Hood's Bay

Bay Hotel

The Dock, YO22 4SJ (at end of very steep road, down towards bay from top car park; less able-bodied visitors can be dropped off by car)
(01947) 880278 bayhotel.info
Leeds Pale; Theakston Lightfoot, Best Bitter; Wainwright
This magnificent Grade II listed 1822 building is the finish line for Wainwright's Coast-to-Coast 192-mile walk. The bottom bar, named in his honour, gives access to the Dock patio, situated at the seawater's edge and providing superb panoramic views. With a licensee of 20 years' service, a friendly welcome awaits regulars, visitors, their children and their dogs. An extensive good-value home-cooked menu is served. Access to this part of the village is not easy for the less mobile.
(X93)

Saltburn-by-the-Sea

Saltburn Cricket, Bowls & Tennis Club

Marske Mill Lane, TS12 1HJ (next to leisure centre)
(01287) 622761 saltburn.play-cricket.com
3 changing beers
Visitors are made most welcome at this local CAMRA multi award-winner, now celebrating 25 years of continuous Guide recognition. Three interesting beers are served, often not even lasting the evening. An enthusiastic steward hosts a variety of events, including a monthly Blues Club, and the venue is well supported by the local community. The balcony, ideal for those lazy summer afternoons, overlooks the cricket field. On Saturday and Sunday match days, the club opens at noon. Please check winter opening hours.
P(X3,X4)

Sandhutton

King's Arms

YO7 4RW
(01845) 587887 thekingsarmssandhutton.co.uk
Black Sheep Best Bitter; 2 changing beers (sourced locally)
A well-appointed 200-year-old roadside inn in a small village. Although it retains a popular public bar, the focus here is largely on food served to a high standard, made with locally sourced ingredients and organic vegetables. Three beers are usually on offer, often including some from Rudgate, and the licensee is an enthusiastic

supporter of LocAle. Outside, an honesty box vegetable shop sells local produce and also offers bicycle spares and storage, gels and free air. P

Scarborough

Cellars

35-37 Valley Road, YO11 2LY
(01723) 367158 scarborough-brialene.co.uk/cellars.htm
Bradfield Farmers Blonde; Camerons Strongarm; Daleside Monkey Wrench; 3 changing beers (sourced nationally; often Rooster's)
Scarborough's most frequent Guide entry, this family-run pub was converted from the cellars of a Victorian town house. Six handpumps dispense guest beers from nationwide micros. Locally sourced home-cooked food is served lunchtimes and evenings, with Sunday lunches always popular. Quiz night is Tuesday, open mic night is Wednesday, local acoustic acts play on Thursday, and Saturday is live music night. The patio out front is popular in summer. Children and dogs are welcome and accommodation is available.
P (64)

North Riding Brew Pub

161-163 North Marine Road, YO12 7HU
(01723) 370004 northridingbrewpub.com
6 changing beers (sourced nationally; often North Riding Brewery, North Riding Brewpub)
Scarborough's only brewpub, serving at least six continually changing beers from local breweries and microbreweries around the UK. It always has one or more North Riding beers together with some brewed on the premises. These are complemented by three craft keg beers from around the world, and an extensive range of craft bottled beers. There is a public bar and quiet lounge, both with real fires. Quiz night is Thursday. Local CAMRA Town Pub of the Year 2019.
Q (9,9A)

Scarborough Borough Council Employees Welfare Club

Dean Road, YO12 7QS
(01723) 364593
3 changing beers (sourced locally; often North Riding)
Close to the town centre, this club comprises a large bar area with an adjacent snooker room and a 200-capacity function room upstairs. Three changing guest cask ales are offered. Live music features on Saturday night, usually on a monthly basis. Club teams participate in local snooker, darts and domino leagues. The club is family-friendly, with CAMRA members welcome subject to signing in. An outdoor drinking/smoking area is at the side. Local CAMRA Club of the Year 2019.
Q (8,8A)

Scholars Bar

6 Somerset Terrace, YO11 2PA
(01723) 372826
Hambleton Nightmare Porter; 5 changing beers (sourced regionally; often North Riding, Ossett)
A warm, friendly atmosphere prevails at this town-centre pub at the rear of the main shopping centre. The large front bar is dominated by TV screens showing major sporting events, and there is a smaller games area to the rear. Five rotating guest beers, usually from Yorkshire microbreweries, are offered, plus numerous ciders and perries. The Thursday night quiz is popular, with a first prize of 28 pints.

Stumble Inn

59 Westborough, YO11 1TS
07779 456662 stumbleinnmicropub.weebly.com/home.html
6 changing beers (sourced nationally)
The first micropub in Scarborough, this was a welcome addition to the local real ale scene, and quickly gained a positive reputation for its beer and cider. Located a short walk from the railway station, the former solicitors' office is a single-roomed venue offering six rotating guest ales, with local breweries always represented. Up to 26 ciders and perries are also stocked. An ideal place for a cosy chat and chill out, and dogs are welcome.

Valley Bar

51 Valley Road, YO11 2LX
(01723) 372593 valleybar.co.uk
Dark Star Hophead; 4 changing beers (sourced nationally; often Scarborough)
The bar, recently relocated adjacent to the original cellar bar, is a large room divided into several drinking areas. There is also a pool room and a separate function room. Of note is the remarkable décor utilising antique furniture. Four guest beers are offered, usually including one or more from Scarborough Brewery. Up to 10 real ciders and perries are also sold, together with a selection of Belgian bottled beers. Accommodation is available.
(64)

Wilsons

West Sandgate, YO11 1QL
07544 775051
8 changing beers (sourced nationally)
The Grade II listed Wilsons (formerly the Leeds Hotel) is close to the seafront and offers a warm welcome to locals and visitors. This is a single-roomed venue with a horseshoe bar adorned with numerous photographs relating to the local fishing industry. Up to eight cask ales are offered. Teams participate in the local darts league, and there is live music on Sunday afternoon. Runner-up in the local CAMRA Town Pub of the Year for 2019. En-suite accommodation is available in five letting rooms.

Selby

Doghouse

8 Park Street, YO8 4PW
07495 026173
Little Black Dog Yorkshire Bitter, Big Red American Amber, Oatmeal Stout; 3 changing beers (often Little Black Dog)
Selby's first craft beer café featuring six draught beers from its own brewery based at Carlton, together with four ciders and a large range of keg beers. The upstairs room is a meeting place for many local groups. The bar hosts a weekly quiz night, regular live music and occasional food from guest suppliers. You can be sure of a warm welcome at this family-run bar.

Giant Bellflower

47a Gowthorpe, YO8 4HF
(01757) 293020
Greene King IPA, Abbot; Sharp's Doom Bar; 4 changing beers (sourced nationally; often Adnams, Rudgate, Sharp's)
Busy town-centre pub named after the flower that was found on the banks of the town's river. Converted from a furniture showroom, it is modern and spacious, and displays artefacts and pictures of Selby's past. It offers typical Wetherspoon fare, a range of keenly priced beers, real ciders and LocAles.

ENGLAND

No.1 The Crescent
1 The Crescent, YO8 4PU
☎ (01757) 702968 🌐 no1selby.co.uk
Old Mill Traditional Bitter, Blonde Bombshell; 1 changing beer (often Old Mill) Ⓗ
One of the oldest pubs in town and close to Selby Abbey, owned by Old Mill Brewery. The bar has a contemporary feel and offers a good selection of bistro-style food. There is a small outside terrace seating area. Old Mill Brewery was established in 1983 as a small, independent, family-owned business, and is housed in an 18th-century former corn mill and maltings at Snaith in East Yorkshire. ◐⇌

Settle

bar 13 L
13 Duke Street, BD24 9DU
☎ (01729) 824356 🌐 bar13settle.co.uk
Goose Eye Chinook Blonde; 2 changing beers (sourced locally; often Kirkby Lonsdale, Wishbone, York) Ⓗ
On the main street between the square and the railway station, 13's narrow frontage hides a long, thin room with a well-stocked bar on the left-hand side. Created in 2005 from a small hardware store, it has a relaxed atmosphere and modern feel that attracts both locals and visitors to the town; you are as welcome in hiking boots as you are in high heels. Three LocAles are stocked, with the emphasis on pale, hoppier beers. ♿⇌🚌🐾📶

Golden Lion L ✔
Duke Street, BD24 9DU
☎ (01729) 822203 🌐 goldenlionsettle.co.uk
Thwaites Mild, Original, IPA, Gold, Amber; 1 changing beer (sourced locally; often Dark Horse, Kirkby Lonsdale, Settle) Ⓗ
Built around 1670, this old coaching inn has two comfortable high-ceilinged rooms for drinking. The main bar has wood panelling, a grand staircase and a huge fireplace. The Lion's Den is accessed from the bar or via a small door off the street. The separate dining area is bright and colourful. Outside seating is in the yard to the side. Folk sessions are on the second and fourth Thursdays of the month. ❀🛏◐⇌♣●🚌🐾📶

Talbot Arms L ✔
High Street, BD24 9EX
☎ (01729) 823924 🌐 talbotsettle.co.uk
Settle Mainline; Theakston Best Bitter; 3 changing beers (sourced regionally; often Saltaire, Wishbone, Worsthorne) Ⓗ
Just off the square, this family-run free house, claiming to be the oldest pub in town, has a welcoming and friendly atmosphere. In winter a stove glows in the large stone feature fireplace to the left, with an area with a pool table and dartboard beyond providing a base for teams in local leagues. A pleasant, terraced beer garden is at the rear. The guest beers are usually from Cumbria, Lancashire or Yorkshire. Good-value food is served until mid-evening all week. Live music plays most Fridays. ❀◐⇌♣●P🚌🐾📶

Skipton

Beer Engine L
1 Albert Street, BD23 1JD
☎ 07834 456134
5 changing beers (sourced nationally) Ⓗ
A well-established micropub in a tiny street between the town centre and the canal. Five handpumps dispense varying beers, always including one blonde or pale ale and one dark beer, plus a character beer. A still cider and a fruit cider are also on tap alongside a selection of bottled beers and wines. The beers are stored in refrigerated cabinets behind the bar. The ambience is friendly and welcoming, and closing time can be flexible. Well-behaved dogs welcome. Q⇌●🚌🐾📶

Boat House L
19 Coach Street, BD23 1LH
☎ (01756) 701660
5 changing beers (sourced regionally)
Tucked out of the way, access is through an arch from Coach Street or via the canalside path. The bar is light and airy, with picture windows looking onto the canal basin, and the decor has a canal theme. A cobbled outdoor drinking area offers the opportunity to enjoy a beer while watching the boats go by. An old-style stove keeps the bar warm in winter. One dark cask ale and keg craft beers are usually stocked. ❀♿⇌●🚌🐾📶

Narrow Boat L
36-38 Victoria Street, BD23 1JE (alleyway off Coach St near canal bridge)
☎ (01756) 797922
Ilkley Mary Jane; Okell's Bitter; Timothy Taylor Landlord; 5 changing beers Ⓗ
A long-standing Guide entry with eight handpulls dispensing an eclectic selection of cask ales – there should always be one to suit most tastes. Bottled and keg continental and craft beers, and up to three ciders or perries, complement this offering. Two separate rooms downstairs and an upstairs gallery and function room, plus a drinking/smoking area at the front, provide ample space. Note the unusual interpretation of the Leeds-Liverpool canal map on the wall. Children are welcome if eating. Skipton Folk Unplugged play on Monday. ❀◐♿⇌●🚌🐾📶

Starbotton

Fox & Hounds L
BD23 5HY
☎ (01756) 760269 🌐 foxandhoundsstarbotton.co.uk
Black Sheep Best Bitter; Wharfedale Blonde; 2 changing beers (often Naylor's, Wensleydale, Yorkshire Dales) Ⓗ
A family-run, whitewashed 17th-century inn, divided into two cosy rooms, with flagstone floors and a large stone fireplace enhancing the atmosphere. In fine weather the sheltered patio at the front provides additional seating. A locally brewed golden ale and dark beer are served alongside the regular beers. Lunch is available daily, with evening meals Wednesday to Sunday. There is a piano in the bar area which visitors are encouraged to play. The daytime community-run bus stops outside. ❀🛏◐♣P🚌(72B,874)🐾

Stillington

White Bear L
Main Street, YO61 1JU
☎ (01347) 810338 🌐 thewhitebearinn-york.co.uk
Leeds Pale; house beer (by Rudgate); 3 changing beers (sourced regionally) Ⓗ
Originally built as a house, the White Bear became an Inn in the 1700s and was used as a stopping point by Stagecoaches travelling from Leeds. You will always get a warm welcome in this historic hostelry. To the left is a gem of a restaurant for which you may need to book, and to the right is a classic bar. The staff are helpful and friendly, and it is definitely worth making the effort to visit if you are not already a lucky regular. ❀🛏◐♣P🚌(40)🐾📶↺

Stokesley

White Swan 🅛 ✅
1 West End, TS9 5BL (at W end of town, 150yds beyond shops)
☎ (01642) 714985 ⊕ whiteswanstokesley.co.uk
Captain Cook Endeavour, Slipway, Sunset; 5 changing beers 🅗
Home of the Captain Cook Brewery, this is a friendly 18th-century pub in a pretty market town. Eight handpulls serve six examples from the Captain Cook portfolio of 11 ales, together with two interesting guest beers, while two real ciders are also always available. Beer festivals are held at Easter and in October. Open mic night is Tuesday, quiz night is Wednesday, music night is Thursday. The sheltered outdoor drinking area overlooks the brewery. Over-18s only, please.
✿♣●🖵(81,89) 😺 ☎

Strensall

Ship
23 The Village, YO32 5XS
☎ (01904) 490302 ⊕ theshipinn-strensall.co.uk
Timothy Taylor Landlord; 3 changing beers (sourced regionally) 🅗
A family-run village inn near the River Foss, offering four real ales, one real cider and restaurant food. Open all day and late at the weekend, it is popular with walkers, cyclists and caravanners in summer, with outside seating and a children's play area at the rear. Although well known for its food, there is an area for people just wanting a quiet drink. Families and dogs are welcome. Regular events are held including music, quizzes and an annual spring beer festival. The bus stop from York is just across the road. 🌳✿🕪🕭&▲P🖵😺☎

Sutton-in-Craven

King's Arms 🅛 ✅
High Street, BD20 7LP (near jct with Main St)
☎ (01535) 636854
Black Sheep Best Bitter; 2 changing beers (sourced nationally) 🅗
The King's is a friendly, homely place. The main bar has two distinct areas: a smart carpeted room with high-backed settles, a fish tank and a real fire, and a smaller games area with darts. Note the interesting collection of clocks. The bar has three handpumps, two with rotating guest beers. There is a separate pool room at the rear, bookable for meetings, a covered patio, and a recently upgraded beer garden out back. A good range of malt whiskies is available. Regular jam sessions are held.
🌳✿♣🖵(66,78A) 😺 ☎

Thirsk

Little 3 🅛 ✅
13 Finkle Street, YO7 1DA
☎ (01845) 523782 ⊕ littlethree.co.uk
5 changing beers (sourced nationally) 🅗
Just off the Market Place, this old, low-beamed, characterful pub claims a history from 1214. It is a warren of nooks and crannies, all decorated in mock half-timbering, with an impressive fireplace in the main bar. Formerly the Old Three Tuns, it was renamed to avoid confusion with the nearby Three Tuns. Regularly changing guest beers are from local and national brewers, and there is a happy hour daily except Saturday. Food is served in the upstairs bistro and there is live music every Thursday and Saturday. 🌳✿🕪P🖵😺☎

Thornton le Dale

Buck 🅛 ✅
Chestnut Avenue, YO18 7RW
☎ (01751) 474212 ⊕ thebuckthorntonledale.co.uk
Tetley Bitter; Wainwright; 2 changing beers (often Whitby, Wold Top) 🅗
A welcoming, traditional venue with two guest beers (three in summer) that hail from Yorkshire and beyond. Whitby and Wold Top ales are often on the bar. Home-made food is served daily. Pool and darts matches and quizzes are held weekly. The beer garden is a suntrap in summer – the perfect place to relax after a day in Dalby Forest or on the moors, or just to sit soaking up the beautiful village atmosphere. 🌳✿🕪🕭&♣P🖵(128,840) 😺 ☎

Thornton Watlass

Buck Inn 🅛 ✅
Village Green, HG4 4AH
☎ (01677) 422461 ⊕ buckwatlass.co.uk
Black Sheep Best Bitter; Theakston Best Bitter; Timothy Taylor Landlord; Wensleydale Falconer; 1 changing beer 🅗
Overlooking the village green, this traditional country inn, with five letting rooms, features a cosy bar room with a real fire, a lounge/dining room and a large function room known as the Long Room. The building has been refurbished throughout by the owners, while retaining a village pub atmosphere. Excellent meals are available and four regular Yorkshire beers are served, with a changing ale added in summer. Live trad jazz music is hosted on Sunday lunchtimes once a month.
✿🛏🕪P🖵😺

Thornton-in-Lonsdale

Marton Arms
LA6 3PB (¼ mile from A65/A687 jct)
☎ (015242) 42204 ⊕ martonarms.co.uk
Black Sheep Best Bitter; 5 changing beers (sourced regionally; often Farm Yard, Timothy Taylor) 🅗
In a hamlet with a parish church, old stocks and little else, you will come across this independently owned free house. Behind the 1679 date stone and old oak door, a flagged passage leads to a modern bar refurbished in 2017. Alongside the beers there are 56 gins. The pub has an attractive little garden with a view of Ingleborough, and is 10 minutes' walk from the start of the Waterfalls Walk. ✿🛏🕪▲♣P🖵(80,581)😺 ☎

Ugthorpe

Black Bull Inn 🅛
Postgate Way, YO21 2BQ
☎ (01947) 840286 ⊕ blackbullwhitby.co.uk
Theakston Old Peculier; 1 changing beer 🅗
A warm welcome is assured at this Grade II listed, traditional, pantiled country inn, where photographs of yesteryear adorn the walls. It is a comfortable, family-run establishment that comprises a main bar, snug, restaurant and games room. The guest beers complement the Old Peculier, and change weekly. Portions of the home-cooked food are such that going home hungry is not an option. Diners travel from far and wide for the impressive Sunday lunch carvery, for which booking in advance is advised. Q🌳🕪&♣P

Wensley

Three Horseshoes L

DL8 4HJ (on A684)
☎ (01969) 622327 🌐 thethreehorseshoeswensley.co.uk
Black Sheep Best Bitter; Wainwright; Wensleydale Semer Water; 2 changing beers (sourced nationally) H
This traditional old country inn is full of atmosphere, with its small bar and dining room both featuring low beams and real fires. Outside, there is a terraced beer garden offering glorious views across Wensleydale, which is a real suntrap on fine days. Wholesome and reasonably priced lunchtime and evening meals are served daily, except Monday. Guest beers in busier months are usually from the Marston's range. Q☺❀◑♿♣●P🚌🐾📶

West Heslerton

Dawnay Arms

Church Street, YO17 8RQ
☎ (01944) 728507 🌐 dawnayarms.co.uk
Theakston Best Bitter; 2 changing beers (sourced regionally; often Wold Top) H
A village local just off the A64, with a main bar divided into drinking, eating and games areas, and a separate restaurant. One regular beer is offered together with two guests from Yorkshire microbreweries. Teams participate in local pool, darts and dominoes leagues. At the rear is a spacious beer garden and a partially covered smoking/drinking area. ☺❀♿Ⅹ♣P🚌(843)🐾📶

Whitby

Arch & Abbey

2-4 Skinner Street, YO21 3AJ (at S end of Skinner St, towards St Hilda's Terrace)
4 changing beers H
A recently opened micropub, close to Botham's Bakery, and operated by enthusiastic licensees who strive to adhere to the original micropub norms. This successful crowdfunded start-up is in what was a truly old-fashioned ladies' dress shop, and one that would not have looked out of place in a heritage museum. Four interesting beers, several real ciders, and light bites and snacks are served. Check ahead for winter opening hours. Children are allowed until mid-evening. Q☺⇌●🚌🐾📶

Black Horse L ✔

91 Church Street, YO22 4BH (on E side of swing bridge on way to Abbey steps, close to marketplace)
☎ (01947) 602906 🌐 the-black-horse.com
5 changing beers H
This little multi-roomed gem, dating from the 1600s, offers a warm welcome. The frontage, with its frosted glass, together with one of Europe's oldest public serving bars, was built in the 1880s and remains largely unchanged. Beer is dispensed from five handpumps. Snuff, tapas, olives, Yorkshire cheeses and hot drinks are always available, and hot lunches are served during the winter months. The cider is Westons Rosie's Pig. Accommodation is in four bedrooms.
Q☺🛏◐♿⇌♣●🚌(X93,840)🐾📶

Little Angel ✔

18 Flowergate, YO21 3BA (200yds W of swing bridge, 200yds N of railway and bus stations)
☎ (01947) 820475 🌐 littleangelwhitby.co.uk
5 changing beers H
Locals and visitors alike are afforded a genuinely friendly welcome at this extremely popular pub. It is rumoured the remains of the castle form part of the structure of the building. Now the home of Lady Luck Brewery, five beers and real cider are served to three separate rooms from a central bar. Sport is shown on large-screen TVs and live music plays regularly. There is a beer terrace outside, and even a horse mount for those requiring this facility. Local CAMRA branch Best Whitby Pub for three years running.
☺❀⇌♣●🚌🐾📶

Station Inn L ✔

New Quay Road, YO21 1DH
☎ (01947) 603937 🌐 stationinnwhitby.co.uk
Black Sheep Best Bitter; Ossett Yorkshire Blonde, Silver King; Theakston Old Peculier; Timothy Taylor Boltmaker; Whitby Jet Black; 2 changing beers H
Next to the harbour and marina, this is a popular multi-roomed venue. The enthusiastic licensees ensure that the eight beers, including two guests, always encompass an eclectic range of varying styles, while real cider and fruit wines mean there is something for everybody. Situated opposite the bus station and NYMR/Esk Valley railway station, this pub has become the discerning travellers' waiting room. Live music features three evenings a week, and there are three letting bedrooms.
🛏⇌●🚌(X93,840)🐾📶

Waiting Room L

2 Whitby Station, Langborne Road, YO21 1YN (by main entrance to NYMR/EVR station)
☎ (01947) 821640
5 changing beers H
On the platform used by the NYMR steam trains, Whitby's first micropub strives to adhere to the original micropub values – no craft beer or lager, no spirits, no jukebox, no TV. Friendly owners and plenty of convivial conversation promote a pleasant atmosphere, together with five handpumps and a dozen or more ciders. The six-yards-square room can be busy at times, so please don't be disappointed if there's no room inside. Local CAMRA branch Cider Pub of the Year winner.
Q♿⇌●🚌(X93,840)🐾📶

Wighill

White Swan L ✔

Main Street, LS24 8BQ
☎ (01937) 832217 🌐 thewhiteswanwighill.co.uk
3 changing beers (sourced locally) H
A well-decorated, cosy and friendly pub, with a roaring fire in winter. It serves well-kept cask ales along with excellent locally sourced food from the recently renovated kitchen, where you can watch the chefs create your meals. Walkers and cyclists are welcome. There is a large car park at the rear, accessed by a lane to the left-hand side. Q☺❀◑♿P🚌(37)🐾

Yarm

Ketton Ox L ✔

98-100 High Street, TS15 9AU (at N end of High St)
☎ (01642) 788311
Draught Bass; Timothy Taylor Landlord; 4 changing beers H
A historic 17th-century Grade II listed inn, once renowned for its illegal cock fighting and its upstairs morgue. The pub is named after a famous shorthorn ox, Comet, born in nearby Ketton Hall in 1796, who established the standards by which the breed has become defined. Recently refurbished, this contemporary outlet ticks all the boxes, including friendly staff, six handpulls and reasonably priced food. The large upstairs function room can be used for private parties. Third-pint glasses are available. ☺❀◑♿♣🚌(7,17)🐾📶

York

Ackhorne 🄻
9 St Martins Lane, YO1 6LN
☎ (01904) 671421
Rudgate Jorvik Blonde; 4 changing beers (often Ainsty, Bad Seed, Half Moon) 🄷
A traditional 18th-century hostelry, with six cask ales, hidden down a narrow cobbled lane at the bottom of Micklegate. It is partially open plan, with separate areas up a couple of steps or through an archway. There is a pleasant beer garden on a raised area to the back. The pub appeals to all age groups, with a friendly family atmosphere. It hosts a regular evening quiz, and lunch on a Sunday.

Blue Bell ★ 🄻 ✔
53 Fossgate, YO1 9TF
☎ (01904) 654904
Bradfield Farmers Blonde; Kelham Island Best Bitter; Rudgate Ruby Mild; Timothy Taylor Landlord; 4 changing beers (sourced locally; often Bad Seed, Half Moon, Rooster's) 🄷
This small, characterful Edwardian pub has a nationally important Grade II* historic interior dating from 1903, with a central bar supplying two small rooms and a side corridor. It can get full so entry may be restricted at busy times. House rules are enforced by the charismatic landlord and it has a no-groups policy. Permanent beers are complemented by a great range of rotating guests on eight handpulls. Bar snacks and pork pies are served.
Q♿♣

Brew York Tap Room 🄻
Unit 6, Enterprise Complex, Walmgate, YO1 9TT
☎ (01904) 848448 🌐 brewyork.co.uk
Brew York JARSA, Maris the Otter, Viking DNA; changing beers (sourced locally; often Brew York) 🄷
Brew York's taproom is inside the brewery and the beer hall in the adjacent old maltings. This multiple award-winning brewery offers over 50 regular, seasonal, experimental and collaboration real ales (including gluten-free ones), dispensed through 10 handpulls and 50 KeyKeg pumps. There is plentiful seating by the brew tanks and outside in the beer garden by the River Foss. Innovative fresh food is served, with good vegan choices.
♿

Golden Ball ★ 🄻
2 Cromwell Road, YO1 6DU
☎ (01904) 849040 🌐 goldenballyork.co.uk
Acorn Barnsley Bitter; Ainsty Assassin; Timothy Taylor Golden Best; 3 changing beers (sourced regionally; often Salamander, Salopian, Whitby) 🄷
A fine Victorian street-corner community-run local. The building has an impressive glazed-brick exterior and was extensively refurbished by John Smith's in 1929. Grade II listed, it has four very different rooms: a main bar, a back room, a comfortable lounge and a snug. Outside is a large south-facing beer garden. Seven handpumps supply three permanent ales complemented by a choice of changing guests. Local produce is on sale in the bar as well as Scotch eggs, pork pies and nuts. The pub hosts bar billiards games and community meetings, as well as music and quiz nights, and exhibitions by local artists.
Q♣

Maltings 🄻
Tanners Moat, YO1 6HU
☎ (01904) 655387 🌐 maltings.co.uk
Black Sheep Best Bitter; Treboom Yorkshire Sparkle; York Guzzler; 4 changing beers (sourced nationally; often Bad Seed, Hop Studio, Wilde Child) 🄷
A popular pub close to the station. Customers can choose from seven real ales and four traditional ciders. The three permanent beers are from Black Sheep, Treboom and York breweries. The four changing beers always include one from Rooster's. Cask ales from microbreweries, both local and further afield, change regularly. There is also a good selection of bottled and craft beer. An extension has provided more seating and a small outside area, while maintaining the original character. Local CAMRA Cider Pub of the Year 2020.

Market Cat
6 Jubbergate, YO1 8RT
☎ (01904) 637023 🌐 marketcatyork.co.uk
Thornbridge Lord Marples, Jaipur IPA; 6 changing beers (often Hawkshead, Tapped Sheffield, Thornbridge) 🄷
This bar, operated by Thornbridge and Pivovar UK, opened in 2018. The three-storey building has seating on all three floors, with excellent views across the Shambles market and towards the minster from the upper two. It offers a range of cask ales, as well as fresh home-made pizzas. The ales are served from eight handpumps and come variously from Thornbridge, Tapped and other breweries.

Phoenix
75 George Street, YO1 9PT
☎ (01904) 656401 🌐 phoenixinnyork.co.uk
Timothy Taylor Landlord; Wold Top Anglers Reward; 3 changing beers (sourced regionally; often Beer Monkey, Black Sheep, Phoenix) 🄷
An independently run pub with a regionally important historic pub interior, where a friendly welcome always awaits visitors and locals. It is close to the city walls, and Dick Turpin's grave is in the garden nearby. Relax in a traditional pub with no noisy gaming machines, TV or jukebox, where you can enjoy your beer while reading a newspaper or chatting with fellow drinkers. In the colder months warm yourself by an open fire in the front parlour. The rear room boasts bar games and weekly music events. A true gem, and not to be missed.
Q♣

Rook & Gaskill 🄻
12 Lawrence Street, YO10 3WP
☎ (01904) 674067 🌐 rookandgaskillyork.co.uk
Castle Rock Harvest Pale; Great Heck Blonde; 21 changing beers (sourced nationally; often Bad Seed, Brass Castle, Brew York) 🄷
This little treasure's unassuming exterior hides a thriving pub that is home to locals, students and beer aficionados. There is always a wide choice of ales on offer, ranging from dark to light, many of which are local, and all reasonably priced. Real ciders are sold and multiple KeyKeg taps ensure all tastes are catered for. A menu of fresh cooked food features generous portions at good-value prices. Local CAMRA branch Pub of the Year in 2018, this beer house is well worth a visit.
♣

Slip Inn 🏆 🄻
Clementhorpe, YO23 1AN
☎ (01904) 621793 🌐 theslipinnyork.co.uk
Leeds Pale; Rudgate Ruby Mild; Timothy Taylor Boltmaker; 5 changing beers (sourced regionally; often Great Heck, Revolutions, Ridgeside) 🄷
This independent free house is a thriving community local with two bars, a snug and a sheltered courtyard beer garden. A big scheme of investment in 2019 has doubled the beer range on the bar and created a dedicated outside festival bar. A hidden gem tucked away down York's historic Clementhorpe, the Slip hosts

regular beer festivals and events each year, including one jointly run with the Swan up the road. The pub supports traditional games including darts, dominoes and cribbage. Local CAMRA Pub of the Year 2020.
ᗡ🌣♣🖵(11) 😀 🛜

Swan ★ L
16 Bishopgate Street, YO23 1JH
☎ (01904) 634968 ⊕ theswanyork.co.uk
Tetley Bitter; Timothy Taylor Landlord; house beer (by Treboom); 4 changing beers (sourced regionally; often Half Moon, Revolutions, Salamander) ⊞
A thriving street-corner local, within sight of the city walls, which has been free of tie since 2017. Grade II listed, the traditional West Riding-style drinking lobby and two bars have a friendly and comfortable feel; the pub has been identified by CAMRA as having a nationally important historic interior. To the back is a heated and partially covered beer garden where an annual beer festival is hosted jointly with the nearby Slip Inn.
🌣♣🖵(11) 😀

Three-Legged Mare
16 High Petergate, YO1 7EN
☎ (01904) 638246
Black Sheep Special Ale, Riggwelter; York Guzzler, Yorkshire Terrier, Centurion's Ghost Ale; 5 changing beers (sourced regionally) ⊞
A modest frontage gives way to a roomy interior with plenty of seating, and there are views of the Minster from the seats by the door. The pub has been owned since late 2018 by Black Sheep Brewery, who now brew the York Brewery beers. The regular ales are supplemented by an interesting choice of guests in both cask and keg. A wide range of real ciders and perries is served direct from the box. A spiral staircase leads down to the toilets. ♿≕●🖵😀🛜

Volunteer Arms L
5 Watson Street, YO24 4BH
☎ (01904) 541945 ⊕ volunteerarmsyork.co.uk
Black Sheep Best Bitter; Brown Cow Mrs Simpsons Thriller in Vanilla; Leeds Yorkshire Gold; Saltaire Blonde; Timothy Taylor Dark Mild; 3 changing beers (sourced locally) ⊞
An independent free house just off Holgate Road, close to the centre of York. It has a real community feel, while welcoming all visitors. The beer range is excellent for a suburban hostelry, and the pub's loyalties are firmly with local breweries, emphasising its commitment to LocAle. There are five permanent beers and two ever-changing guests. Other attractions include live blues every Saturday night and a quiz every Sunday night.
Q🌣≕●🖵(1,10) 😀 🛜

York Tap
Railway Station, Station Road, YO24 1AB
☎ (01904) 659009 ⊕ yorktap.com
Timothy Taylor Golden Best, Boltmaker, Knowle Spring, Landlord; 18 changing beers (sourced nationally; often Anarchy, Tapped Sheffield, Thornbridge) ⊞
This pub, opened in 2010, is a conversion of the former Victorian tearooms on York station. The ornate ceiling, Art Deco stained-glass windows, terrazzo floors and stained-glass ceiling domes create an award-winning backdrop to the central round bar. Twenty handpumps offer 18 cask beers plus two ciders or perries. There is also a large range of keg and bottled beers. The parent company, Pivovar, sources the beers from many of Britain's finest breweries, and all styles and strengths are represented. No meals are provided, although you can get pies at the bar. 🌣♿≕●🖵😀

YORKSHIRE (SOUTH)

Armthorpe

Wheatsheaf
Church Street, DN3 3AG
☎ (01302) 835868
Purity Pure UBU; 2 changing beers (often Black Sheep, Woodforde's) ⊞
A roadside pub serving excellent beers and a variety of good-quality food. You are assured of a warm welcome here, and there is plenty of entertainment including darts, dominoes and pool. Food is served Tuesday to Saturday, lunchtimes and evenings, with a popular carvery on Sunday. There is a good-sized outside drinking area at the front. Sunday is quiz night.
Q🌣🌣🕪♿♣●P🖵(81) 😀 🛜

Aston

Roland Arms L
117 Mansfield Road, S26 2BR (corner of A618 Mansfield Rd and Lodge Lane, 1½ miles from M1 jct 31)
☎ (0114) 287 6199
5 changing beers (sourced regionally; often Chantry, Moorhouse's, Wadworth) ⊞
Friendly street-corner local that now sells up to five real ales. It retains a two-room layout supplied by a central bar. The comfortable lounge is complemented by a traditional taproom, and different beers are served in each room. Quality pub food is served including home-made curries and Sunday roasts. There is a quiz on Thursday evening, and live music and a music quiz at the weekend. Real ales often include those from Chantry, Moorhouse's or Wadworth breweries but may be local or from further afield. The location is handy for visiting Rother Valley Country Park and Gulliver's Valley Theme Park. 🌣🕪♿♣P🖵

Auckley

Eagle & Child ✪
24 Main Street, DN9 3HS
☎ (01302) 770406 ⊕ eagleandchildauckley.co.uk
Acorn Barnsley Bitter; Black Sheep Best Bitter; Timothy Taylor Landlord; 2 changing beers (sourced regionally; often Milestone, Welbeck Abbey) ⊞
A much-loved pub, on the main road in the village, and winner of numerous CAMRA awards. Dating from the early 19th century, it has real character. There are two bars, one with a TV, the other quieter, with tables for bar meals. The separate restaurant is decorated with photographs of local historic interest, and the home-cooked meals have a deserved reputation. There is an outside seating area and a beer garden. Robin Hood airport is just a mile away. Q🌣🌣🕪♣P🖵(57f)😀🛜

Barnsley

Jolly Tap on the Arcade L
31 The Arcade, S70 2QP
Jolly Boys Blonde; 3 changing beers (sourced locally; often Hilltop, Jolly Boys, Outhouse) ⊞
Barnsley's first micropub, opened by the owners of Two Roses Brewery. In the lovely Victorian Arcade, it was previously a cake shop. This tiny one-up one-down place is now owned by the Jolly Boys Brewery. The bar serves up to five real ales, all locally sourced. The staff are welcoming, and knowledgeable about the cask beers on offer. A large range of craft beers is also available.
Q≕🖵😀🛜

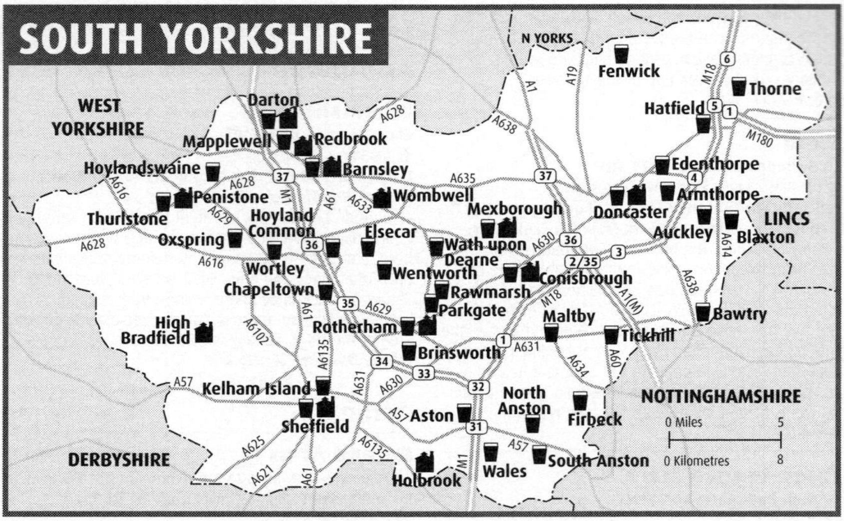

Miners Rest 🄻 ✔

Palm Street, S75 2SU (in the old town area)

☎ (01226) 282339

Bradfield Farmers Blonde; 2 changing beers (sourced nationally) 🄷

This local pub has three drinking spaces – a lounge to the left as you walk in and two areas to the right. The small bar efficiently serves all rooms. The extension and beer garden overlook the pub's bowling green. A wonderful place for warm summer evenings as well as cold winter nights. ❀♿♣P🚌🐾

Old No. 7 🏆 🄻

7 Market Hill, S70 2PX

☎ (01226) 244735 🌐 oldno7barnsley.co.uk

Acorn Barnsley Bitter, Blonde; 6 changing beers (sourced regionally; often Acorn) 🄷

This is the Acorn Brewery tap, offering up to six Acorn beers alongside two changing guest ales. The bar also has a choice of real ciders and perries, as well as a wide range of craft and continental beers. The downstairs bar is available for functions, meetings, and so on, and opens match days and busy Friday and Saturday evenings. There is regular live music. ⇌♣●🚌🐾📶

Tipsy Cow 🄻

Unit 2D, Gateway Plaza, Saville Street, S70 2RD

4 changing beers (sourced regionally) 🄷

This micropub near the entrance to the Gateway Plaza complex opened in 2018. It is split over two levels, with a mezzanine floor looking over part of the ground floor. The outside drinking area was added in 2019 and is popular in the summer months. The pub offers four changing real ales, craft beers and cider, and is renowned for its gin selection. No under-12s and no dogs allowed. ❀♿⇌P🚌📶

Bawtry

Ship ✔

Gainsborough Road, DN10 6HT (on A631 near traffic lights)

☎ (01302) 710275 🌐 theship-bawtry.com

Marston's 61 Deep; 4 changing beers (sourced nationally; often Jennings, Marston's, Wychwood) 🄷

One of the local CAMRA area's success stories, this previously run-down roadside pub was taken over in 2007 by the family of the present licensees. It has been extensively refurbished inside and outside, and has gained an enviable reputation for high-quality food and beer, winning several food awards. Two ales are always on tap, selected from the Marston's range, and regular beer festivals are held. ❀❀◑♿♣●P🚌(21,25)🐾📶

Blaxton

Station

Station Road, DN9 3AA

☎ (01302) 770055

3 changing beers (often Black Sheep, Navigation, Theakston) 🄷

A popular village local which in 2018 underwent a refurbishment under new owners, and was then reopened and relaunched in December of that year. It has since gained a reputation for good food and beer; two cask ales are on the bar, sourced from a range of breweries. Beers from Navigation have proved especially popular. The pub now offers accommodation and is handy for users of Robin Hood airport.
❀❀🛏◑♿P🐾📶

Brinsworth

Stop Inn Time 🄻

17 Brinsworth Lane, S60 5BS (close to the Tesco Express)

4 changing beers (sourced locally; often Dukeries, Little Critters) 🄷

A micropub opened in March 2019 in a former hardware shop in the centre of the village, providing an alternative to the nearby Three Magpies Hotel. A friendly welcome and warm atmosphere are assured within. The four changing real ales are often, but not exclusively, from local breweries, and are a mixture of light and dark styles. The decor is themed on timepieces – note the interesting ceiling and wall clocks. A new outside area was unveiled in 2020. Handy for events at the nearby Centre and playing fields. Q❀P🚌🐾

Conisbrough

Hilltop 🏆 L

Sheffield Road, DN12 2AY (on main A630)
☎ (01709) 868811 🌐 thehilltophotel.co.uk
Hilltop Classic Bitter, Blonde, Stout, Porter H
A traditional family-run free house standing alone on the Rotherham road, offering a relaxed and friendly atmosphere. The interior is divided into a public bar and lounge area. A wall of old Conisbrough photos includes pictures of a trolleybus. Four real ales are served, all from the on-site brewery. Quiz night is on a Wednesday and includes supper. The Hilltop has won several local CAMRA awards, has been in the Guide since 2014, and is District Pub of the Year 2020. Q P (X78)

Darton

Darton Tap L

70 Church Street, S75 5HQ
☎ (01226) 383444 🌐 dartontap.co.uk
Rat White Rat; house beer (by Molson Coors Burton); 2 changing beers (sourced locally) H
A welcoming micropub in the increasingly popular Darton and Mapplewell real ale corridor. This stylish venue has four cask lines, several draught lines and a large spirits selection. Drinkers can enjoy a beer in a modern and comfortable environment, close to transport links. Dogs are welcome here, with treats and foot towels available for them. Strictly over-18s only. P

Doncaster

Doncaster Brewery Tap L

7 Young Street, DN1 3EL
☎ (01302) 376436
Doncaster Sand House, Cheswold; 4 changing beers (sourced locally; often Doncaster) H
Convenient for the town centre, down a quiet side street, Doncaster Brewery Tap was opened in 2014. The brewery, originally launched in 2012, was relocated here, and provides up to six beers, all served in lined glasses. Guest beers are often available, as are six traditional ciders and perries. This welcoming pub always has something different going on, from quiz night on Tuesday and spoken word night on Thursday to ukulele singalong on Saturday. Local CAMRA Pub of the Year 2020. Q (15,81/82)

Draughtsman Alehouse

Station Court, DN1 1PE
☎ 07999 874660
3 changing beers (sourced regionally; often Allendale, Northern Monkey, Thornbridge) H
You will find this on Platform 3B of Doncaster station. It opened in 2017 and was highly commended in CAMRA's Pub Design Awards. The former Victorian buffet bar stood empty for 18 years before restoration. Be sure to inspect the Victorian tiles and mounted plan drawings of steam locomotives. Real ales on offer come mainly from regional brewers, with occasional collaborations and exclusives. Locally made pies and crisps are available. The bar arranges regular tap takeovers and special events. Q (21)

Hallcross 🏆

33-34 Hall Gate, DN1 3NL
🌐 hallcrossdoncaster.co.uk
Tetley Bitter; 2 changing beers (sourced nationally; often Dancing Duck, Elland, Welbeck Abbey) H
This pub has been recently refurbished, with real ale and cider reinstated after many years' absence. The front bar plays background music and shows sports (but with the sound on only for major events). There is a separate soundproofed function room for live music at weekends, a snug at the back, and a patio area. Hallcross is the home of the resurrected Stocks beers (brewed at Welbeck Abbey), which were previously brewed on the premises 20 years ago. (21,25)

Leopard ✔

2 West Street, DN1 3AA (less than 5 mins walk from station)
☎ (01302) 739460
4 changing beers (sourced regionally; often Acorn, Stancill, Titanic) H
A street-corner local, close to the town centre and railway station, which has been a regular CAMRA award-winner over the years. It has a superb tiled frontage, recalling its days as a Warwicks & Richardsons house. There are two rooms downstairs, and a large one upstairs that regularly hosts live music at weekends. The pub is owned by Doncaster Culture and Leisure Trust, and one of the five real ales on offer is from the trust's own 1086 Brewery. P (71,72)

Little Plough ★ L

8 West Laith Gate, DN1 1SF (close to Frenchgate shopping centre)
☎ (01302) 738310
Acorn Barnsley Bitter; Bradfield Farmers Blonde; 2 changing beers (sourced regionally; often Brains, Fuller's, Titanic) H
A friendly haven for anyone wishing to escape the town-centre bustle, where three real ales are served. The interior dates from 1934 and is mentioned in CAMRA's National Inventory of Historic Pub Interiors. The pub has a public bar at the front and a lounge to the rear. It is

REAL ALE BREWERIES

1086 Doncaster
Abbeydale Sheffield
Acorn Wombwell
Blue Bee Sheffield
Bradfield High Bradfield
Chantry Rotherham
Dead Parrot Sheffield
Don Valley Mexborough
Doncaster Doncaster
Exit 33 Sheffield
Fuggle Bunny Holbrook
Geeves Barnsley
Gorilla Mexborough (NEW)
Grizzly Grains Sheffield (NEW)
Heist Sheffield (NEW)
Hilltop Conisbrough
Imperial Mexborough
Jolly Boys Redbrook
Kelham Island Sheffield
Little Critters Sheffield
Lost Industry Sheffield
Loxley Sheffield
Nailmaker Darton
Neepsend Sheffield
On the Edge Sheffield
Sheffield Sheffield
St Mars of the Desert Sheffield
Stancill Sheffield
Tapped Sheffield
Toolmakers Sheffield
Triple Point Sheffield
True North Sheffield
White Rose Mexborough
Whitefaced Penistone

adorned with pictures of old agricultural scenes and has won many local CAMRA awards. Beer festivals are held twice yearly. Q❀⇌♣🚌🐾📶

Old Brewhouse

Cusworth Lane, DN5 7TU (inside grounds of Cusworth Hall)
☎ (01302) 639880
1086 Cuzeuuorde; 1 changing beer (sourced nationally; often Imperial) ⊞
Uniquely characterful and atmospheric, this brewpub was established in late 2018. It is in the original brewhouse of Cusworth Hall, a Grade I listed country house – now a museum. The old brewhouse is also home to the 1086 Brewery, and the fermenting vessels are to the rear behind the bar. Three 1086 beers are generally on offer, plus a traditional cider. Pizzas and various snacks are available, along with a selection of board games.
P🚌(41)

Queen Crafthouse & Kitchen

1 Sunny Bar, DN1 1LY (on corner of Sunny Bar and Market Place)
☎ (01302) 562908
5 changing beers (sourced nationally; often Acorn, Don Valley, Welbeck Abbey) ⊞
An old established market place pub, recently renovated under new ownership. An interior created out of unusual boarding sets the scene, attracting customers young and old to sample the real ales, atmosphere, and live music at weekends. Close by the historic Corn Exchange and market, this is a welcome addition to the town's real ale scene. Five changing beers are on the bar, usually from regional breweries, and two real ciders.
Q♿⇌●🚌(15)🐾📶

Edenthorpe

Eden Arms ✔

Eden Field Road, DN3 2QR (adjacent to Tesco)
☎ (01302) 888682
Abbeydale Moonshine; Thornbridge Kipling; house beer (by Sharp's); 3 changing beers (sourced nationally; often Black Sheep, Marston's, Thornbridge) ⊞
A fine, modern and busy estate pub, built in the late 1980s. Attractive and comfortable, it is one of the area's most CAMRA-friendly venues. On Monday all cask ales are generously discounted all day. Five real ales are usually on offer, with a display at the entrance informing customers about present and future cask beers. There is a large outside drinking area, and a pleasant gas-flamed fire indoors. Meet the Brewer evenings are popular. The pub is notable for its good-quality classic meals.
Q☕❀◐♿P🚌(87,8)📶

Elsecar

Crown Inn 𝕃 ✔

22 Hill Street, S74 8EL
☎ (01226) 361488
3 changing beers (sourced regionally; often Abbeydale, Ossett) ⊞
A community pub in a picturesque village. A recent refurbishment has added a new bar and opened up the main room. The TV usually shows football. The lounge to the rear leads to a large conservatory area which overlooks the garden and children's play area. Various local groups meet here. Close to the Elsecar Heritage Centre and train station. ☕❀◐♿⇌♣P🚌(66)🐾📶

Maison du Biere 𝕃

Wath Road, S74 8HJ (in Elsecar Heritage Centre, Unit 15)
☎ (01226) 805255 🌐 maisondubiere.com
Changing beers (sourced nationally)
A popular beer shop and tap in the heart of the historic heritage centre, serving up over 400 bottled and canned beers and ciders, 10 lines of craft/draught beers and real ales, and many real ciders. The knowledgeable staff can navigate you through a taste experience. The tap is popular with locals and visitors alike. Events take place monthly in the heritage centre.
☕❀♿⇌♣●P▯🚌(66,227)🐾📶

Fenwick

Baxter Arms

Fenwick Lane, DN6 0HA (between Askern and Moss)
☎ (01302) 702671
House beer (by Theakston) ⊞
This award-winning free house is truly a rural gem. It has been run by the same family for nearly 30 years, and you can be sure of a warm welcome. Three real ales from small independent breweries are always on sale, and reasonably priced locally sourced fresh food is served all day. Outside is a drinking area with seating, and there is ample parking. Quiz night is Wednesday.
Q☕❀◐▲♣P🐾📶

Firbeck

Black Lion 𝕃

9 New Road, S81 8JY (opp village hall)
☎ (01709) 812575
Chantry New York Pale; Timothy Taylor Landlord; 2 changing beers (sourced locally; often Abbeydale, Bradfield, Pheasantry) ⊞
A traditional village free house, reopened in 2017 following a period of closure. It attracts drinkers, diners, walkers and the local community. Four real ales are offered and two changing beers from local microbreweries, especially Pheasantry. The food is freshly cooked to order. Firbeck was the birthplace of the horse race that became the St Leger, and pictures of old Firbeck adorn the walls of the snug area. The pub is handy for the ruins of Roche Abbey and countryside walks. The No.20 bus serves the village Monday to Saturday daytime. Q☕❀◐♿♣P🚌(20)🐾

Hatfield

Jack Hawley at the Grange 🏆

Manor Road, DN7 6SB
☎ 07769 927603
Timothy Taylor Landlord; 4 changing beers (sourced regionally; often Kelham Island, Welbeck Abbey, York) ⊞
This micropub, local CAMRA District Pub of the Year 2020, is the project of a real ale enthusiast who was previously landlord of the Black Swan in Asselby. Access is via a staircase to the first floor. It has a long, narrow lounge with mixed seating. One wall displays four guitars, and the other has the story of Jack Hawley, a local character from the 19th century who was renowned for his hospitality. ❀●P🚌(84,87a)

Hoyland Common

Tap & Brew 𝕃

9 Hoyland Road, S74 0LT
☎ (01226) 824614
6 changing beers (sourced regionally) ⊞

A popular micropub converted from a tea room in 2017. This local serves a fine selection of cask ales, as well as a good range of bottled beers and artisan spirits. It doesn't serve meals but there is a wide choice of bar snacks, pies and pastries. Many local history books and board games are available. The Tap & Brew also hosts weekly quiz and music nights, and a popular open mic night, all adding to a great atmosphere. ❀♣🚌🐾📶

Hoylandswaine

Sports & Social Club L

Haigh Lane, S36 7JJ

☎ (01226) 765726

3 changing beers H

The club is in the heart of the village and popular with locals, and a warm welcome is assured. The fast-changing beers are from breweries in the locality. The terraced area with panoramic views is the ideal place to watch the world go by or to take in a game of cricket. Non-members ask to be signed in. Winter hours may vary. Q❀♣P🚌(20)

Maltby

Queen's Hotel ✔

Tickhill Road, S66 7NQ

☎ (01709) 812494

Greene King Abbot; Ruddles Best Bitter; Sharp's Doom Bar; 3 changing beers (sourced regionally) H

A former residential hotel at a busy crossroads, completely refurbished by Wetherspoon after a lengthy period of closure. Now firmly established, this spacious pub has an attractive family dining area and offers typical Wetherspoon value-for-money food and drink. The reopening of the Queen's led to a much-needed raising of the profile of real ale in Maltby, and regular Meet the Brewer nights are held. Next to Coronation Park and handy for Maltby Crags and Roche Abbey.
❀◐♿●P🚌📶

Mapplewell

Old Bakery L

16 Blacker Road, S75 6BN

☎ 07541 660287

5 changing beers (sourced regionally) H

A popular micropub in the heart of the real ale corridor of Mapplewell. The pub is in a converted bakery, its one-roomed bar serving up to five real ales, with ever-changing local and regional beers available, as well as craft beers and keg. There is an extensive beer garden at the rear and café seating to the front. Weekly and monthly events including quiz nights and vinyl music takeovers make this a popular destination.
Q❀♿●P🚌(1,97,x10)

Talbot Inn L ✔

Towngate, S75 6AS

☎ (01226) 385629 🌐 thetalbotmapplewell.co.uk

4 changing beers (sourced locally; often Acorn, Magic Rock, Nailmaker) H

This 17th-century coaching house pioneered the current real ale corridor of Mapplewell and Darton. It is popular with diners, serves bar meals, and has the 1776 restaurant upstairs. The bar has an extensive beer and wine list to complement the food, and sells four varying beers. It is accredited to a buy-local policy and has received numerous awards. The Talbot is the official tap for Nailmaker Brewing Co and Waterton's Reserve gin.
Q❀◐♣P🚌🐾📶

Wentworth Arms L ✔

Greenside, S75 6AU

☎ (01226) 390702 🌐 wentwortharms.co.uk

4 changing beers (sourced regionally; often Nailmaker) H

The sister of the Talbot Inn and the second official tap for Nailmaker Brewery. After a huge refurbishment, the former restaurant is now a community pub. The interior is open plan with ample seating including comfortable cushioned benches. Further renovations have created a second-floor Loft Bar, available to hire for private functions. Outside is a large beer garden with an external bar, and a raised terrace with large, round wooden benches. Now a popular local, the pub hosts live entertainment and quiz nights. ❀◐♿P🚌🐾📶

Mexborough

Imperial Brewery Tap L

Cliff Street, S64 9HU (opp bus station)

☎ (01709) 584000

Imperial Classical Bitter, Platinum Blonde, Bees Knees, Nah Then; 3 changing beers (sourced locally) H

A friendly brewery tap with a multitude of offerings. It comprises a main bar where all the entertainments are held, a cosy lounge area, and a games/function room. Eight handpumps only dispense quality ale: two permanent and six rotating beers from its own Imperial brewery, plus a plethora of ales from excellent breweries from around the country. Entertainment comes in the form of karaoke on Wednesday, an award-winning acoustic night on Thursday, and a wide range of live music on Friday and Saturday.
❀♿⇌♣🚌(220,221)🐾📶

North Anston

Little Mester L ✔

Nursery Road, S25 4BZ

☎ (01909) 562484

Greene King IPA; 4 changing beers (sourced locally; often Stancill, Welbeck Abbey) H

This modern estate pub, built in the 1960s, reopened in 2016 following refurbishment. The emphasis is now on real ale – beers may be from far and wide, but local breweries figure strongly among up to five guests. There is a cask ale club, with a free pint offered for every seven purchased. The pub gets active at the weekend, when a DJ and live entertainment feature. It is handy for visiting the nearby Butterfly Farm and for walks around Anston Stones. ❀◐♿P🚌

Oxspring

Smithy Arms L

Bower Hill, S36 8YA

☎ 07712 929011

3 changing beers (often Abbeydale, Acorn, Chantry) H

A popular micropub opened in 2017 in the extended garage of the owner's house. Its name comes from the fact that it is on the site of a former blacksmith's. Opening four days a week, it offers three changing real ales, usually from local breweries. It has a wood-burning fire for cosy winter nights and a small beer garden to the rear. Quiz night is Thursday. Q❀♿P🚌🐾

Parkgate

Little Haven Micro Bar 🄻

96 Broad Street, S62 6EN
☎ (01709) 710134
🌐 the-little-haven-micro-bar.business.site
Chantry New York Pale; 3 changing beers (sourced locally; often Chantry, Double Top, Exit 33) 🄷
Opened in 2018 in a former post office and hair salon, this micropub is compact and welcoming. Four handpumps are on the bar plus four craft taps, with local breweries favoured. Real cider is also sold. Nibbles are available, but meals are no longer served as the former kitchen was converted to a snug in 2020. Musicians play on Tuesday and Saturday evenings. There is a selection of board games. Outside seating is accessed via the bar lounge. Around 15 minutes' walk from the Parkgate tram/train stop. Q❀♣🚌🐾📶

Rawmarsh

Something Brew Inn 🄻

2 Stocks Lane, S62 6NL
Bradfield Farmers Blonde; Chantry New York Pale; Sharp's Doom Bar; 3 changing beers (often Abbeydale, Bradfield, Chantry) 🄷
Micropub and coffee house in a former office building behind the Star pub. It opened in 2018 in an area not renowned for selling real ale. The four changing real ales are often from Chantry and other local breweries. Craft keg and bottled beers are also sold. Tastefully decorated inside, it has a long bar, and outside there is seating at the front and back including deckchairs in the rear yard. A Sunday jam session and Wednesday night quiz are held. Q❀🚌🐾📶

Rotherham

Bluecoat 🄻 ✔

The Crofts, S60 2DJ (behind town hall, off A618 Moorgate Rd)
☎ (01709) 539500
Greene King Abbot; Ruddles Best Bitter; Welbeck Abbey Cavendish; 7 changing beers (sourced locally) 🄷
A former charity school, opened in 1776 by the Ffeofees of Rotherham, which became a pub named Ffeofees in 1981 and a Wetherspoon in 2001. Up to 10 handpulled beers are listed on a screen behind the bar, with a preference for local microbreweries among the guest beers. Three real ciders or perries are served from boxes. Regular Meet the Brewer nights are held, and special beers are brewed for the Bluecoat four times a year. A general knowledge quiz takes place on Wednesday night. The pub is a Guide regular and winner of numerous local CAMRA branch awards.
❀◐♿⇌♣●P🚌📶

Cutlers Arms 🄻

29 Westgate, S60 1BQ
☎ (01709) 382581 🌐 cutlersarms.co.uk
Chantry New York Pale, Iron and Steel Bitter, Diamond Black Stout; house beer (by Chantry); 2 changing beers (sourced locally; often Chantry) 🄷
Rebuilt for Stones Brewery of Sheffield in 1907 to the design of R Wigfull, with an impressive façade. On CAMRA's Regional Inventory of Historic Pub Interiors, the pub was saved from demolition in 2004 following statutory listing and restored to Edwardian splendour by Chantry Brewery, reopening in 2014. The original Art Nouveau windows, tiling and curved bar counter with its dividing screen have been retained. The full range of Chantry beers, two real ciders and quality craft beers are sold. There is live music Friday to Sunday, and student night on Thursday. Snacks are available.
Q❀◐⇌●🚌🐾📶

Dragon's Tap 🄻

477 Herringthorpe Valley Road, Broom, S65 3AD
☎ 07864 680301
Chantry New York Pale; 5 changing beers (sourced locally; often Elland, Little Critters, Magic Rock) 🄷
A micropub on two floors opened in April 2018 in a former DIY shop, offering a contrast to the nearby Stag. It is simply but tastefully decorated with modern art prints. Six changing beers come from local and national microbreweries, and there are also four craft keg beers plus real ciders and bottled beers. No food is served, save for snacks, but you can bring in food from nearby takeaways. There are tables outside at the front. A general knowledge quiz is held on Wednesday evening, and live acoustic music plays on the third Sunday of the month. Q❀♿●P🚌🐾

New York Tavern 🄻

84 Westgate, S60 1BD (at jct of Coke Lane)
☎ (01709) 371155 🌐 newyorktavern.co.uk
Chantry New York Pale, Iron and Steel Bitter, Diamond Black Stout; house beer (by Chantry); 2 changing beers (sourced locally; often Chantry) 🄷
This wedge-shaped house became a licensed premises in 1856. It was reopened by Chantry Brewery in 2013, renamed after a pub that was demolished when the nearby ring road was built. The focus is on real ales, with at least six Chantry beers and two real ciders or perries on offer at competitive prices. A large selection of foreign bottled beers is also stocked. Bar snacks are available. The pub is handy for New York Stadium, and has Rotherham United memorabilia on display. Occasional live entertainment features. Local CAMRA branch Town Pub of the Year 2014-2020. ⇌●🚌🐾

Sheffield: Central

Bath Hotel ★ 🄻 ✔

66-68 Victoria Street, S3 7QL
☎ (0114) 249 5151 🌐 beerinthebath.co.uk
Thornbridge Lord Marples; 5 changing beers (sourced regionally; often Thornbridge) 🄷
A careful restoration of the 1930s interior gave this two-roomed venue a conservation award, and it is on CAMRA's National Inventory of Historic Pub Interiors. The bar room lies between the tiled lounge, a small corridor drinking area and the cosy well-upholstered snug. There are usually three Thornbridge beers and three guests on the bar. Regular live music is hosted and a weekly quiz on Thursday. Light snacks are served. Q♣●🚌🐾

Dog & Partridge 🄻

56 Trippet Lane, S1 4EL
☎ (0114) 270 6156
Black Sheep Best Bitter; 3 changing beers (sourced locally; often Abbeydale, Blue Bee, Stancill) 🄷
Behind an impressive Gilmour's Brewery frontage and dating from 1796, this is a comfortable multi-roomed pub served from a central bar. To the right of the entrance is a spacious taproom with dartboard, and on the left a smaller seating area. Behind the bar is a cosy snug with a hatch for service, and at the rear the lounge often features live music. The three changing beers are usually from local breweries. ❀◗♣🚌🐾📶

Head of Steam 🄻

103-107 Norfolk Street, S1 2JE
☎ (0114) 272 2128

Camerons Strongarm; 7 changing beers (sourced regionally; often Abbeydale, Camerons, Magic Rock) H
A pub for some 20 years, this former bank was acquired by Camerons Brewery in 2015, and after extensive refurbishment was reopened as part of the Head of Steam chain. Behind the imposing frontage, the large single room is served by a central island bar, with a separate seating space at the rear leading on to an outside drinking area in Tudor Square. In addition to the brewer's own beers, the handpumps usually dispense ales from independents in Yorkshire and the North East. ❀◑♿⇌🚇(Cathedral) ●P🚌🐾📶

Old Queen's Head 🄻 ✔

40 Pond Hill, S1 2BG
☎ (0114) 327 0704 🌐 theoldqueenshead.co.uk
Thwaites Mild, IPA, Gold, Amber; 3 changing beers (sourced locally; often Abbeydale, Marston's) H
Dating from Tudor times, when it was the hunting lodge for the nearby Sheffield Castle, the pub is the oldest surviving domestic building in the city, and now adjoins the transport interchange. The central bar serves a U-shaped lounge and is next to a superb beamed dining room in the oldest part of the building. It is the meeting place for history groups, and is included in popular ghost tours. The menu includes Czech specials as well as the usual fare. ♨❀◑♿⇌🚇(Fitzalan Square)♣●🚌🐾📶

Red Deer 🄻 ✔

18 Pitt Street, S1 4DD
☎ (0114) 272 2890 🌐 red-deer-sheffield.co.uk
Abbeydale Moonshine; Little Critters Little Hopper; Moorhouse's Pride of Pendle; 5 changing beers (sourced regionally) H
A genuine, traditional local in the heart of the city. The small frontage of the original three-roomed pub hides an open-plan interior, extended to the rear with a gallery seating area. As well as the impressive range of eight cask beers, including five guest ales, there is also a selection of continental bottled beers. Meals are served lunchtimes and evenings daily. A popular quiz is held on Tuesday night, and an upstairs function room is available for bookings. Q❀◑🚇(West Street)●🚌🐾📶

Rutland Arms 🄻

86 Brown Street, S1 2BS
☎ (0114) 272 9003
Blue Bee Reet Pale; 6 changing beers (sourced regionally; often Blue Bee) H
Occupying a corner site in the Cultural Industries Quarter and near Sheffield's main railway station, the pub has operated as a free house since 2009. The comfortable interior provides ample seating either side of the central entrance, and the walls are covered in pumpclips and font badges from the huge number of guest beers that have featured over the years. The beers are mostly from local and regional microbreweries. Food is served throughout the day.
♨❀◑⇌🚇(Sheffield Station) ●🚌🐾📶

Sheffield Tap ★ 🄻

Platform 1B, Sheffield Station, Sheaf Street, S1 2BP
☎ (0114) 273 7558 🌐 sheffieldtap.com
Thornbridge Jaipur IPA; 9 changing beers (sourced nationally; often Tapped Sheffield) H
Opened in 2009, this was originally the First Class refreshment room for Sheffield Midland Station, built in 1904. After years of neglect the main bar area has been the subject of an award-winning restoration, retaining many original features. Further seating has been provided in the entrance corridor and to the right of the bar. Three beers are usually from the on-site Tapped Brewery, opened in 2013 in the impressive former dining room, which can be viewed behind a glass screen.
Q♨❀♿⇌🚇(Sheffield Station) ●🚌🐾📶

Sheffield: Chapeltown

Commercial 🄻

107 Station Road, S35 2XF
☎ (0114) 246 9066
Abbeydale Moonshine; 7 changing beers (sourced nationally; often Durham, Neepsend, White Rose) H
Built in 1890 by the long-closed local Strout's Brewery of Neepsend, this friendly well-established free house provides six guest beers, including a porter or stout, together with at least one real cider. A central island bar serves the games room, lounge and taproom. There is a rear outdoor area, and an upstairs function room that stages regular folk sessions. Beer festivals are held in May and November. Monthly tutored whisky tastings take advantage of the extensive range on offer. No meals Sunday evening.
♨❀◑⇌(Chapeltown) ♣●P🚌(265,31A) 🐾📶

Sheffield: Kelham Island

Bar Stewards

163 Gibraltar Street, S3 8UB
☎ (0114) 327 3580 🌐 thebarstewards.uk
4 changing beers (sourced nationally; often Abbeydale, Blue Bee, North Riding) H
Opened in a shop unit in 2017, the Bar Stewards is a modern-style bar and bottle shop, and a welcome addition to the Kelham Island circuit. The four well-chosen cask beers often include a local ale, and there is also a good range of keg beers, bottles and cans from independent breweries. The venue can be hired for private functions and a mobile bar service is available.
❀🚇(Shalesmoor) 🚌🐾📶

Crow Inn 🄻

35 Scotland Street, S3 7BS
☎ (0114) 201 0096
Abbeydale Heathen; 4 changing beers (sourced nationally; often Abbeydale, Arbor) H
The former Old Crown Inn, having spent several years as a hotel, reopened in summer 2019 as a free house under its new name. The old pub layout is still discernible, with two comfortably furnished seating areas either side of the entrance corridor which leads to the bar. The bar offers a wide range of cask and craft beers on five handpumps and 11 keg lines, together with a large choice of spirits including 40 malt whiskies. There are seven hotel rooms. ❀🛏♿🚇(Cathedral)●🚌🐾📶

Fat Cat 🄻

23 Alma Street, S3 8SA
☎ (0114) 249 4801 🌐 thefatcat.co.uk
Kelham Island Best Bitter, Pale Rider; Timothy Taylor Landlord; 8 changing beers (sourced nationally; often Kelham Island) H
Opened in 1981, this is the pub that started the real ale revolution in the area. Beers from around the country are dispensed alongside those from the adjacent Kelham Island Brewery. Vegetarian and gluten-free dishes feature on the menu (food is served lunchtimes and evenings Monday to Friday, daytime only at weekends). The walls are covered with many awards presented to the pub and brewery. An anniversary beer festival is held in August. Monday is curry and quiz night.
Q♨❀◑♿🚇(Shalesmoor) ●P🚌🐾

Harlequin 🄻

108 Nursery Street, S3 8GG

☎ 07794 156916 🌐 theharlequinpub.wordpress.com

Exit 33 Blonde, Northern Best; 8 changing beers (often Exit 33, North Riding) 🄷

Run by Exit 33 Brewing, the Harlequin takes its name from another former Ward's pub just around the corner, now demolished. The large open-plan interior features a central bar with seating on two levels. There are two regular and usually four other beers from Exit 33, as well as guests from far and wide, with the emphasis on microbreweries. A large range of real ciders is also available. Wednesday is quiz night and there is live music at weekends. 🐎❀◐🚋(Castle Square)♣🍎▯🚌🐾

Kelham Island Tavern 🏆 🄻

62 Russell Street, S3 8RW

☎ (0114) 272 2482 🌐 kelhamtavern.co.uk

Acorn Barnsley Bitter; Blue Bee Triple Hop; Pictish Brewers Gold; 10 changing beers (sourced nationally; often Abbeydale, Blue Bee, North Riding) 🄷

A former CAMRA National Pub of the Year and a regular regional and local winner, this small gem was rescued from dereliction in 2002. Thirteen handpumps dispense an impressive range of beers, always including a mild, a porter and a stout. In the warmer months you can relax in the multi award-winning beer garden. Regular folk music features on a Sunday evening and quiz night is Monday. No meals Sunday.
Q🐎❀◐🚋(Shalesmoor) ♣🍎▯🚌🐾

Shakespeare's Ale & Cider House 🄻

146-148 Gibraltar Street, S3 8UB

☎ (0114) 275 5959 🌐 shakespeares-sheffield.co.uk

Abbeydale Deception; Stancill Barnsley Bitter; 7 changing beers (sourced nationally; often Bad Seed, Blue Bee, North Riding) 🄷

Dating back to 1821, the building reopened as a free house in 2011 following a refurbishment that included incorporating the archway to the rear yard. The central bar serves three rooms, including the extension, and there is a further room across the corridor. The eight handpumps have featured more than 5,000 different beers over the last eight years, and over 100 whiskies are stocked. There is regular live music, and beer festivals twice a year. Q❀🚋(Shalesmoor)♣🍎🚌🐾📶

Wellington 🄻

1 Henry Street, S3 7EQ

☎ (0114) 249 2295

Neepsend Blonde; 6 changing beers (sourced regionally; often Neepsend) 🄷

A traditional two-roomed local opened as a free house in 1993. Now part of the small Sheaf Inns group of pubs, it is the brewery tap for the nearby Neepsend Brewery. Sympathetically refurbished following the takeover, the rooms are comfortably furnished and welcoming. Seven handpumps feature at least three Neepsend beers and up to three changing guests, mainly from micros, together with a real cider. An extensive range of malt whiskies is also on offer. Q❀🚋(Shalesmoor)♣🍎▯🚌🐾

Sheffield: North

Blake Hotel 🄻

53 Blake Street, Upperthorpe, S6 3JQ

☎ (0114) 233 9336

Neepsend Blonde; 5 changing beers (sourced regionally; often Blue Bee, Neepsend) 🄷

This community pub at the top of a steep hill (pedestrian handrails provided) reopened in 2010 after being closed for seven years. Although extensively restored, it retains many Victorian features, including etched windows and mirrors. There is a large decked garden to the rear. It has probably the largest selection of whiskies in Sheffield and a growing range of rums and other spirits. There are no electronic games, TV or jukebox. The pub is part of the local Sheaf Inns chain, along with the Sheaf View and the Wellington. Q❀🚋(Langsett)♣🍎▯🚌

Gardeners Rest 🄻 ✔

105 Neepsend Lane, Neepsend, S3 8AT

☎ (0114) 272 4978 🌐 gardenerscomsoc.wordpress.com

Sheffield Crucible Best, Five Rivers, Blanco Blonde; 6 changing beers (sourced locally) 🄷

Taken over by the Gardeners Rest Community Society in 2017, this friendly pub acts as the brewery tap for the nearby Sheffield Brewery. In addition to the regular range of ales, there are also at least six guest beers sourced nationwide from independent breweries as well as at least two real ciders. The cosy Dram Shop includes a bar billiards table, and to the rear is a conservatory leading to an eclectically decorated beer garden overlooking the River Don. There is live music at weekends and regular beer festivals. Local CAMRA Pub of the Year 2019. Q❀♿🚋(Infirmary Rd)♣🍎▯🚌🐾

New Barrack Tavern 🄻

601 Penistone Road, Hillsborough, S6 2GA

☎ (0114) 232 4225 🌐 newbarracktavern.com

Bradfield Farmers Bitter; Castle Rock Harvest Pale, Screech Owl; 6 changing beers (often Castle Rock) 🄷

A multi-roomed pub with an original 1936 floor plan, including a Gilmours-branded doorstep and distinctive colourful exterior tiles. In 2018 a new bottle/cider room was converted from a kitchen. The snug has a local sports theme, and the lounge features live bands at weekends and a monthly comedy club on the first Sunday. The function room has three handpumps. Outside is an award-winning heated and covered patio garden. CAMRA Yorkshire Cider Pub of the Year 2019.
Q🐎❀🚋(Bamforth St) ♣🍎🚌🐾📶

Wisewood Inn 🄻 ✔

539 Loxley Road, Loxley, S6 6RR

☎ (0114) 233 4310 🌐 wisewoodinn.co.uk

8 changing beers (often Acorn, Bradfield, Stancill) 🄷

The main bar has three rooms including a pool room, and below is the cellar bar, which is available for hire. A large garden to the rear overlooks the Loxley Valley. In addition to Loxley beers, the five handpumps invariably include local beers. There are also eight keg taps, often featuring Beavertown and Thornbridge. The extensive menu includes continental sausages, pizzas and tapas. Adjacent to the cellar bar is Loxley Brewery, which began production in 2018. 🐎❀◐♣P🚌(61,62)🐾📶

Sheffield: South

Ale House 🄻

187 Fraser Road, Millhouses, S8 0JP

☎ (0114) 274 5515

Saltaire Blonde; 5 changing beers (often Bad Seed, Dancing Duck) 🄷

A warm and friendly welcome awaits within this 1960s estate pub, which has been transformed in recent years into a real ale haven, home to many community activities. The six handpulled beers always include at least one from Saltaire together with a well-chosen changing range from small breweries across the country. Food is served Friday evenings, and traditional music and food events are held throughout the year.
🐎❀♿♣P🚌🐾📶

Beer Engine 🅛
17 Cemetery Road, Highfield, S11 8FJ
☎ (0114) 272 1356 🌐 beerenginesheffield.com
Neepsend Blonde; 5 changing beers (sourced nationally; often Bristol Beer Factory, Manchester) 🅗
This traditional-style multi-roomed pub, cosy and with a great atmosphere, reopened as a free house in 2015 following a sympathetic refurbishment. A generous choice of high-quality drinks is provided for its wide-ranging clientele. The five changing handpulled beers come from an interesting mix of microbreweries in Sheffield and across the country. Excellent mainly tapas-style food is served each evening and Friday and Saturday lunchtime, as well as a traditional roast on Sunday lunchtime. The large beer garden has a heated and covered area. ❀◑●🖨🐾☞

Broadfield 🅛
452 Abbeydale Road, Nether Edge, S7 1FR
☎ (0114) 255 0200 🌐 thebroadfield.co.uk
Abbeydale Moonshine; True North Blonde; 7 changing beers (sourced nationally; often Abbeydale, Ilkley, True North) 🅗
Dating from 1896, the Broadfield has established a deserved reputation for quality food, served all day every day, with an extensive menu including hearty meat pies and home-made sausages. There are nine cask ales including beers from owners True North, and large ranges of bottled beers and whiskies. The pub has a great atmosphere. Located in the city's Antiques Quarter, it is now a leading player in the local social scene. ☞❀◑🕎●🖨🐾☞

Brothers Arms 🅛 ✅
106 Well Road, Heeley, S8 9TZ
☎ (0114) 258 3544
Abbeydale Deception; house beer (by Abbeydale); 6 changing beers (sourced nationally) 🅗
A classic, traditional local. Although the interior is open plan, it is designed so that the various seating and games areas all feel individual and cosy. The pub's name reflects its association with locally renowned parody ukulele band, The Everly Pregnant Brothers, and live music is hosted every Thursday evening, supplemented by a folk session on the third Sunday of the month. The bar features eight real ales, with two regular beers and six changing guests, together with a real cider. ☞❀♣●🖨🐾☞

Sheaf View 🅛
25 Gleadless Road, Heeley, S2 3AA
☎ (0114) 249 6455
Neepsend Blonde; 7 changing beers (sourced regionally; often Neepsend, Pictish, Saltaire) 🅗
A 19th-century pub near Heeley City Farm, the Sheaf experienced a chequered history before becoming a real ale oasis since reopening as a free house in 2000. The walls and shelves are adorned with assorted breweriana and provide an ideal background for good drinking and conversation. A wide range of international beers, together with malt whiskies and a real cider, complement the eight reasonably priced real ales. The pub gets busy, especially on Wednesday quiz night and Sheffield United match days. Q❀🕎♣●🖨🐾☞

White Lion 🅛 ✅
615 London Road, Heeley, S2 4HT
☎ (0114) 255 1500 🌐 whitelionsheffield.co.uk
Abbeydale Moonshine; Tetley Bitter; Wychwood Hobgoblin Ruby; 9 changing beers (sourced nationally) 🅗
This Grade II listed pub has been respectfully refurbished over the years. A tiled central corridor links a number of delightful small rooms and leads to the larger rear concert room. A wide selection of cask-conditioned beers always includes a vegan option, and there is also a good choice of whiskies. The pub hosts many community events and has live music every night, except Wednesday, which is quiz night. ☞❀♣●🖨🐾☞

Sheffield: West

Ale Club 🅛
429 Ecclesall Road, Sharrow, S11 8PG
☎ (0114) 453 6818
5 changing beers (sourced regionally; often Bad Seed, Brew Foundation, Don Valley) 🅗
A busy micropub in the heart of the Ecclesall Road social scene, but only a stone's throw from the tranquil Botanical Gardens. It is comfortably furnished and has a cosy atmosphere, in contrast to the often spartan decor of many micropubs. Owned by the Brew Foundation, the brewer is often on hand to answer questions about the beers and advise on home brewing. In addition to the cask ales there is an extensive range of craft keg beers, bottles and cans from independent brewers. Q☞❀♣●🖨🐾

Beer House 🅛
623 Ecclesall Road, Sharrow, S11 8PT
6 changing beers (sourced nationally; often Abbeydale, Blue Bee, Exit 33) 🅗
Sheffield's first micropub opened in a small former shop unit in late 2014. The front room has level access from the street and contains the bar. Its bank of six handpumps displays a changing range of beers, mainly from microbreweries, with local breweries well represented. The rear room has seating focused around the fireplace. A quiz is held on Wednesday evening. Q☞❀♣●🖨🐾

Itchy Pig Ale House 🅛
495 Glossop Road, Broomhill, S10 2QE
☎ (0114) 327 0780 🌐 theitchypig.co.uk
5 changing beers (sourced regionally; often Abbeydale, Exit 33) 🅗
A cosy, friendly micropub with a relaxed atmosphere and a continental feel. The whitewashed walls are decorated with porcine-themed artwork, hop sacks and dried hops. There is craftsman-standard carpentry in evidence, including a bar made from Victorian-era doors, and a glass-covered bar top formed from 2p coins set in resin. A wide range of pork scratchings is available. Q☞♣●🖨(120) 🐾

Rising Sun 🅛 ✅
471 Fulwood Road, Nether Green, S10 3QA
☎ (0114) 230 3855 🌐 risingsunsheffield.co.uk
Abbeydale Daily Bread, Deception, Moonshine, Absolution; 7 changing beers (sourced nationally; often Abbeydale, Saltaire, Welbeck Abbey) 🅗
A large suburban roadhouse operated by a local brewer, Abbeydale. There are two comfortably furnished rooms, with a log-burning fire between the main bar and the glass-roofed extension, which also has glass panels in the end wall. A range of Abbeydale beers is always served, with up to six guests, mainly from micros, dispensed from the impressive bank of 13 handpumps. Quizzes are on Sunday and Wednesday evenings. The Sunfest beer festival is in July. Q☞❀◑🕎♣●🖨(120,83A) 🐾☞

University Arms 🅛
197 Brook Hill, Broomhall, S3 7HG
☎ (0114) 222 8969

Kelham Island Pale Rider 🄷; Welbeck Abbey Red Feather 🄷/🄶; house beer (by Acorn); 5 changing beers (sourced regionally) 🄷
Owned by the University of Sheffield, this former staff club has an open-plan lounge, with a bar at one end adjacent to a small alcove seating area, and a conservatory leading to the large garden. There is additional seating upstairs, with separate rooms for snooker and darts. The guest beers are mostly local, and there are regular beer festivals. Entertainment includes a quiz on Tuesday and open mic night on Wednesday, during term time. **Q🐴❀◑♿⛺♣●🚌**(51,52)**🐾📶**

South Anston

Loyal Trooper ✔

34 Sheffield Road, S25 5DT (off A57, 3 miles off M1 jct 31 heading for Worksop)
☎ (01909) 562203 🌐 loyaltrooperpub.co.uk
Abbeydale Moonshine; Timothy Taylor Landlord; 2 changing beers (often Black Sheep, Bradfield, Kelham Island) 🄷
A friendly oak-beamed village inn, parts of which date back to 1690. It sells a range of real ales and good wholesome locally sourced food at reasonable prices. Guest beers often come from local breweries. The interior was redecorated recently but the layout has remained unchanged since the 1960s. There is a public bar, snug and lounge, and a function room upstairs used by local groups including a thriving folk club. Close to St James's Church, the pub is on the Five Churches walk, handy for Anston Stones Wood and the nearby Butterfly Farm. **Q❀◑♿♣P🚌📶**

Thorne

Windmill ✔

19 Queen Street, DN8 5AA
☎ (01405) 812866
Kelham Island Pale Rider; Stancill Barnsley Bitter; 3 changing beers (sourced regionally; often Thornbridge, York) 🄷
A friendly community venue close to the town centre, on a street parallel with the main road. Four real ales from small independent breweries are sold. The interior comprises a smart lounge with a conservatory at the side, linked by an archway to another room with a pool table. Good-natured conversation between staff and clientele is assured. Outside is a large garden with play equipment, and there is ample parking. Sunday is quiz night. **🐴❀⇌♣●P🚌**(87,88a)**🐾📶**

Thurlstone

Huntsman 🄻

136 Manchester Road, S36 9QW
☎ (01226) 764892 🌐 huntsmanthurlstone.co.uk
Black Sheep Best Bitter; Timothy Taylor Landlord; 4 changing beers (sourced nationally) 🄷
The location of this village local on the main East-West Pennine route (the A628 towards Woodhead) provides an interesting mixture of customers from both regular and passing trade. Genuine and friendly drinking and talking are this pub's lifeblood. Throw in old-fashioned pub games, LocAle, and a seriously dog-friendly attitude, and you have a venue that just should not be passed by. Food is served Tuesday evening and Sunday lunchtime only. There is no jukebox or TV, but live music features on Wednesday evening. **Q🐴❀◑♣●🚌🐾📶**

Tickhill

Scarbrough Arms 🄻

Sunderland Street, DN11 9QJ (on A631 near Buttercross)
☎ (01302) 742977
Greene King Abbot; John Smith's Bitter; Timothy Taylor Landlord; 2 changing beers (sourced locally; often Abbeydale, Bradfield, Welbeck Abbey) 🄷
An entry in the Guide since 1990, this stone-built pub dates back to the 16th century. There is a taproom at the rear which features darts and sports TV, while a spacious lounge can be found at the front. Between the two is the Barrel Room snug, with barrel-shaped furniture. There is a covered smoking area and a large, attractive beer garden. Quiz nights take place on Monday and Thursday evenings, and summer beer festivals are held. **Q🐴❀♣●P🚌**(22,205)**🐾📶**

Wales

Duke of Leeds 🄻 ✔

16 Church Street, S26 5LQ (off A618 into School Rd, opp parish church)
☎ (01909) 515490 🌐 thedukeofleeds.co.uk
Bradfield Farmers Blonde; 3 changing beers (sourced regionally; often Abbeydale, Bradfield, Theakston) 🄷
A 300-year-old former coaching inn, extensively refurbished and reopened in 2015 under new ownership. The bar area leads to three further drinking and dining areas. The upstairs function room was recently converted into a snooker and pool room. Changing beers are sourced both locally and from further afield, and the food is freshly cooked to order. Outdoor seating offers views of the village. The pub is popular with walkers and is on the Five Churches walk. **🐴❀◑♣P🚌🐾**

Wath upon Dearne

Church House 🄻 ✔

Montgomery Square, S63 7RZ
☎ (01709) 879518
Greene King Abbot; Ruddles Best Bitter; 4 changing beers (often Acorn, Elland, Great Heck) 🄷
A large establishment with an impressive frontage, set in a pedestrianised square in the town centre, with excellent access to local bus services across the square. It was built in about 1810, consecrated by the nearby church in 1912, first became a pub in the 1980s, and then a Wetherspoon from 2000. It serves a wide variety of beers from national as well as local brewers, and real ciders or perries are also on handpull. Handy for exploring the RSPB Old Moor Wetlands Centre and for Manvers Commercial Park. **🐴❀◑♿●P🚌📶**

Wath Tap 🏆 🄻

49 High Street, S63 7QB
☎ (01709) 872150 🌐 wathtap.co.uk
6 changing beers (sourced locally; often Fernandes, Geeves, Ossett) 🄷
The first micropub in this area, opened in a former butcher's shop in 2016, with a warm welcome for all. The former walk-in cold store is now the cellar. Six changing real ales are served, mostly from local breweries, and five real ciders. These are listed on chalkboards by the bar. Food may be brought in from the surrounding takeaways. Seats outside at the front are protected from the rain by the original shop canopy. Jam sessions are sometimes held, and board games are available. Local CAMRA Pub of the Year 2017-2020. **Q♿♣●🚌🐾📶**

Wentworth

George & Dragon

85 Main Street, S62 7TN (stands back from road on B6090)

☎ (01226) 742440 georgeanddragonwentworth.com

Theakston Old Peculier; 7 changing beers (often Bradfield, Chantry, Geeves)

A village free house, licensed since 1804, offering eight changing real ales from local and national brewers. It has a front patio with a large garden and children's adventure playground at the rear, as well as a craft shop and a room for hire. Home-cooked food from an extensive menu is served, and a pop-up pie shop opens every Saturday and Sunday afternoon. The pub is a Guide regular, winner of numerous local CAMRA branch awards, and is handy for historic Wentworth Woodhouse, Needle's Eye and Hoober Stand. It is accessible from the parish church via the garden. Q P (44,136)

Wortley

Wortley Men's Club

Reading Room Lane, S35 7DB (in centre of village at back of Wortley Arms public house)

☎ (0114) 288 2066 wortleymensclub.co.uk

Timothy Taylor Landlord; 2 changing beers (sourced nationally)

This club is in a pretty rural village near Wortley Hall and gardens. With an opulent exterior and interior, features include exposed timber frames, ornate ceilings, wooden panelling and a real fire. Guest ales are from local and national breweries, and a guest cider is available. The club runs an annual beer festival in July. It is a multiple winner of CAMRA awards including regional, national and local Club of the Year. Show your CAMRA membership card or a copy of this Guide on entry.
Q P (23,23A)

YORKSHIRE (WEST)

Ackworth

Masons Arms

Bell Lane, WF7 7JD (Bell Lane is a turning off A628 by a defunct railway bridge)

☎ 07966 501827

Bradfield Farmers Blonde, Farmers Brown Cow; 2 changing beers (sourced regionally)

Grade II listed coaching house dating from 1682, built of locally quarried stone. A unique display of old photographs portrays the local social and industrial heritage. The central bar serves the main room, pool room and smaller lounge. Log-burning fireplaces in both the main rooms were discovered 15 years ago during a sensitive refurbishment. Live music takes place on Saturday and Sunday, bingo on Tuesday and a quiz on Thursday night, all well attended by locals and visitors alike. P

Altofts

Robin Hood

10 Church Road, WF6 2NJ (from Normanton town centre take road over railway into Altofts, continue through Lee Brigg, then High Green Rd and left onto Church Rd)

☎ (01924) 892911 robinhoodaltofts.co.uk

Acorn Barnsley Bitter; 5 changing beers (sourced locally; often Tarn 51)

Locally owned free house and brewpub at the top end of the village. It has a large patio area seating 70 people. Tarn 51 microbrewery plans to move into a new brewhouse next door. The pub is within easy reach of the Pennine Trail and Aire & Calder Navigation, and is only a mile from Stanley Ferry Marina. P

Armitage Bridge

Armitage Bridge Monkey Club

Dean Brook Road, HD4 7PB

☎ (01484) 522370 monkeyclub.co.uk

Goose Eye Bitter; 2 changing beers (sourced nationally; often Empire)

Refurbished and air-conditioned, this thriving and friendly little club in the hamlet of Armitage Bridge serves two guest beers. It is a regular local CAMRA Club of the Year. Well worth seeking out, the club is a great place to relax with a pint in the evening. It has plans for a one-day beer festival to be held annually in September.
P

Baildon

Bulls Head Inn

6 Westgate, BD17 5ES

☎ (01274) 976416

Goose Eye Chinook Blonde; Saltaire Blonde; Sharp's Doom Bar; Tetley Bitter; 1 changing beer (sourced nationally; often Nightjar)

Two-roomed traditional pub with log fires and a warming atmosphere. A very popular village local, it is frequented by a wide age range of customers, with visitors and well-behaved dogs always welcome. Local photos of Baildon adorn the walls. As well as the four regular ales, an ever-varying guest beer, usually of a darker style, is offered. Sunday and Tuesday evenings are quiz nights. Live music is played on fortnightly Saturdays. The separate tap room houses darts and dominoes. P

Junction

1 Baildon Road, BD17 6AB (on A6038/B6151 jct)

☎ (01274) 582009

Junction Blonde; Tetley Bitter; Timothy Taylor Landlord; 3 changing beers (sourced nationally; often Acorn, Box Steam, Junction)

A busy, three-roomed traditional local comprising a lounge, a public bar and a games area. Three regularly available beers, usually including at least one from the in-house Junction Brewery, are complemented by three guest ales. Bottled ciders and foreign beers are also sold. Sports events on TV are popular. Quiz nights take place on Tuesday and Thursday, and there is a piano for those wanting to provide impromptu live music and singalongs. A regular beer festival is held at the end of July.

Bingley

Chip N Ern

73 Main Street, BD16 2JA

☎ (01274) 985501

7 changing beers (sourced locally; often Bridgehouse, Goose Eye, Revolutions)

A traditionally styled micropub on Bingley's Main Street and a popular destination on the local real ale scene. The wood-panelled ground-floor bar has a distinctive and eclectic range of decorations. Additional seating is available in the upstairs room. The seven cask ales include a varying range from Bridgehouse, Goose Eye and other guest breweries. A range of ciders is also offered. The pub is close to the railway station and handy for exploring the famous Five Rise Locks on the adjacent Leeds-Liverpool Canal.

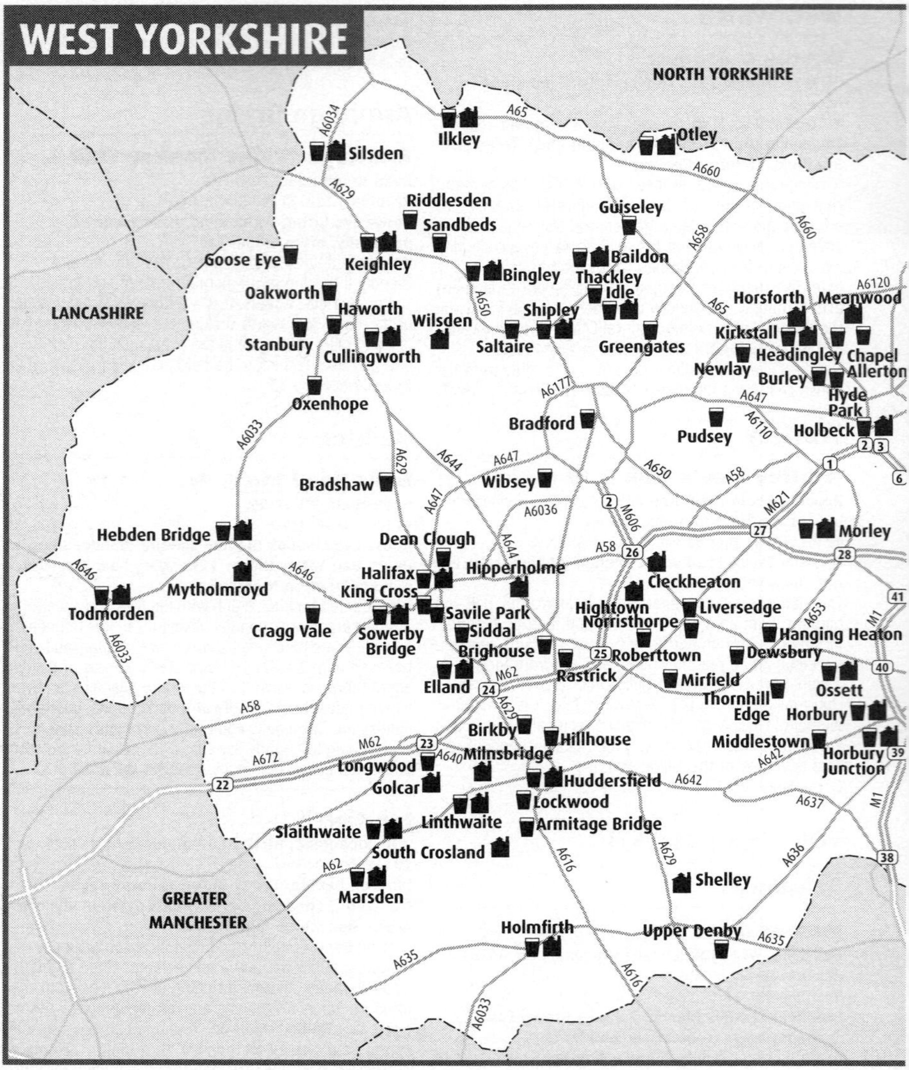

Platform 1¾

1 Burrage Street, BD16 1GH (close to railway station, off Chapel Lane)

☎ 07561 195586

8 changing beers (sourced regionally; often Empire, Manning, Phoenix)

A single-room pub where the decor includes some unusual recycling. Outside seating is available in good weather. Eight handpulls serve two regular house beers (a bitter and a blonde), and up to six varying guest beers, usually from the surrounding region. Lager and an extensive range of ciders are also offered. Dogs are welcome, as are children until mid-evening. Opening and closing times may vary depending upon demand.

Birkby

Magic Rock Brewery Tap

Willow Park Business Centre, Willow Lane, HD1 5EB

☎ (01484) 649823 magicrockbrewing.com

Magic Rock Hat Trick, Ringmaster, Dark Arts; 3 changing beers (sourced locally; often Magic Rock)

Following relocation from Quarmby, the brewery's meteoric rise has been mirrored by the Tap. Open every day, it offers five cask beers, always including a dark beer. Lower-strength beers double up on match days. The back wall has views into the brewery, and barrel-ageing beers are to one side. There is masses of outdoor seating under cover. Exhibitions, festivals and Saturday tours are organised. Street food outlets and other pop-up caterers are on-site every weekend. The Tap is less than 10 minutes' walk from the town centre, and enjoys a good bus service.

Bradford

Corn Dolly

110 Bolton Road, BD1 4DE

☎ (01274) 720219

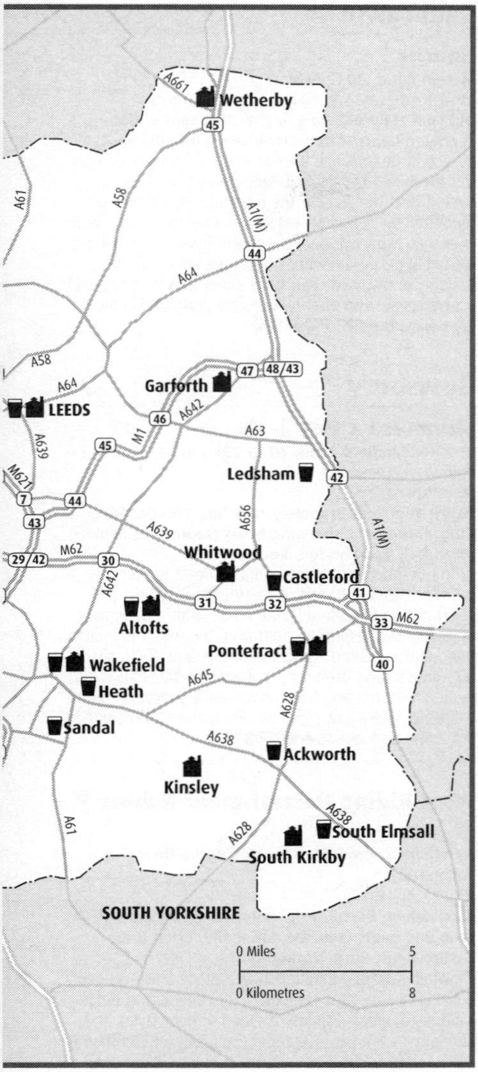

Everards Tiger; Moorhouse's White Witch; Timothy Taylor Boltmaker; 5 changing beers (sourced regionally; often Abbeydale, Pictish, Wishbone)
An award-winning traditional free house run by the same family for over 25 years, close to the city centre and Forster Square railway station. Previously called the Wharfe, due to its location near the former Bradford canal, it first opened its doors in 1834. An open-plan layout incorporates a games area at one end. A collection of pumpclips adorns the beams. Good-value food is served weekday lunchtimes. The pub has a friendly atmosphere and is popular before Bradford City matches. (640,641)

Exchange Craft Beer House

14 Market Street, BD1 1LH
☎ (01274) 306078
5 changing beers (sourced regionally; often Crooked, Nightjar, Stod Fold)
This establishment is located under the Victorian splendour that is the Wool Exchange building. Despite being a cellar bar, it has a light and airy feel. The interior is open plan, with a large seating area and bar under a brick barrel ceiling, and a smaller raised seating area near the entrance. The beer range usually includes one from its owners, Nightjar Brewery, alongside others from smaller regional breweries and sometimes from further afield, in a variety of styles.

Fighting Cock

21-23 Preston Street, BD7 1JE (close to Grattans, off Thornton Rd)
☎ (01274) 726907
Ilkley Mary Jane; Theakston Old Peculier; Timothy Taylor Golden Best, Boltmaker, Landlord; 7 changing beers (sourced nationally; often Millstone, Oakham, Vocation)
A drinkers' paradise in an industrial area, this multi-award winning traditional free house is 20 minutes' walk from the city centre and close to bus routes along Thornton Road and Legrams Lane. Twice-yearly beer festivals take place. Twelve real ales are usually on sale, including at least one dark beer. A variety of real ciders is stocked, and foreign bottled beers are also offered. Good-value lunches are served Monday to Saturday. Awarded CAMRA branch Cider Pub of the Year 2019.

Jacobs Beer House

14 Kent Street, BD1 5RL (by Jacobs Well Roundabout at end of Hall Ings)
☎ (01274) 395628
Abbeydale Deception; Half Moon Dark Masquerade; 6 changing beers (sourced regionally; often Bingley, Spotlight, Sunbeam)
A traditional real ale and cider free house, formerly known as Jacobs Well and dating from 1811. The layout is open plan but with a rustic feel, and there is a snug to the side of the bar. Nine handpulls offer a varying range of beers from local and regional independents and always feature some darker ales. Numerous ciders are available together with a good range of foreign bottled beers. Sit outside and watch the city bustle while enjoying good ale.

Old Bank

69 Market Street, BD1 1NE (nr city hall)
☎ (01274) 738218 🌐 theoldbankbar.co.uk
6 changing beers (sourced nationally; often Coach House, Empire, Moorhouse's)
A traditional city-centre pub located within an impressive building that was once a bank. There is a large ground-floor room, including a semi-enclosed room to the rear, finished with oak woodwork and neutral colours. An additional seating area upstairs, primarily for dining, has an opulent classical style to it. Good-value meals are offered throughout the day. Six handpulls serve a varying range of beers, often including one from Coach House Brewery. Sections of the venue can be hired.

Record Café

45-47 North Parade, BD1 3JH
☎ (01274) 723143 🌐 therecordcafe.co.uk
4 changing beers (sourced regionally; often Brass Castle, North Riding, Wilde Child)
An award-winning modern café bar in the city's independent quarter selling ale, ham and vinyl. Four handpulls serve real ales sourced regionally, in a range of styles and usually including a dark beer. Real cider and perry are offered and there are seven craft keg beers from independent brewers on tap. Food comes in

charcuterie style, specialising in hams and cheeses from Spain. Vinyl records are for sale in the upstairs mezzanine area. ♘❀◑♿⇌●🚌🐾📶↺

Bradshaw

Golden Fleece ✔

1 Bradshaw Lane, HX2 9UZ

☎ 07522 190990 🌐 goldenfleecebradshaw.co.uk

Saltaire Blonde; Tetley Bitter; 2 changing beers (sourced regionally; often Fuzzy Duck, Stod Fold) Ⓗ

Set in the heart of this picturesque village, the pub has a spacious, comfortable lounge and a separate room at the rear. A small snug leads out to a large beer garden with tables and chairs. Barbecues are held during the summer to take advantage of the scenic views. Local pool and dominoes teams are supported. Quiz night is on a Wednesday and there is a themed music night every Saturday. ♘❀♿▲♣P🚌📶↺

Brighouse

Market Tavern 🏆

2 Ship Street, HD6 1JX

☎ 07908 698360

6 changing beers (sourced regionally; often Abbeydale, Salopian, Squawk) Ⓗ

A single-storey former pork pie factory next to the canalside open-air market has been transformed into this micropub. There is seating in the bar, a small snug by the entrance, and a sheltered outside drinking area. At least one dark beer and one real cider, Thistly Cross Whisky Cask, are on sale at all times. Snacks are available for both people and dogs. Open bank holiday Mondays. Q♘❀⇌●🚌🐾📶

Castleford

Junction 𝕃

Carlton Street, WF10 1EE (enter Castleford on A655, pub is on corner with Carlton St at top of town centre)

☎ (01977) 277750 🌐 thejunctionpubcastleford.com

5 changing beers Ⓗ

A rejuvenated pub, handy for bus and train stations, that specialises in beers from the landlord's own wooden casks. Up to six guest ales are available in the wood from enterprising local brewers. The large L-shaped bar is kept warm with open fires, and the stove-heated snug can be used for functions. Folk night is on the last Sunday of each month and a live band plays on Friday evening. An annual Easter Woodfest beer festival is held. Q♘⇌♣●🚌🐾📶

Cragg Vale

Robin Hood 𝕃

Cragg Road, HX7 5SQ (on B6138 1½ miles S of Mytholmroyd)

☎ (01422) 885899

Timothy Taylor Boltmaker, Landlord; 3 changing beers (sourced regionally; often Goose Eye, Millstone, Oakham) Ⓗ

A warm welcome is assured at this friendly, two-roomed, split-level local in a beautiful wooded valley popular with walkers and cyclists. On entering, the cosy bar – with a real fire in winter – is to the right, while the larger dining room is to the left. Food is served Thursday to Sunday (times vary). Two Timothy Taylor beers are complemented by up to three guests from regional breweries (often Goose Eye, Millstone and Oakham). Real cider is sometimes available. Q♘❀◑▲🚌(900,901)🐾📶↺

Cullingworth

George 𝕃

Station Road, BD13 5HN

☎ (01535) 275566 🌐 thegeorgecullingworth.co.uk

Old Spot Light but Dark, Light, OSB, Spot o' Bother; 3 changing beers (often Great Newsome, Old Spot) Ⓗ

Rescued from oblivion in 2011 by local brewery owners, this lovely old-fashioned village pub has a pleasant setting near the church. The emphasis is primarily on food from an extensive and imaginative menu, but there is also an attractive bar area to the front. The taphouse for Old Spot, the brewery's beers are sold over the majority of the seven handpulls. Guest ales from regional breweries are also offered. Dogs are permitted in the bar area only. ♘❀◑♿P🚌🐾📶↺

Dewsbury

Shepherd's Boy 𝕃 ✔

157 Huddersfield Road, WF13 2RP (on A644 about ½ mile W of town)

☎ (01924) 454116

Ossett Yorkshire Brunette, Yorkshire Blonde, Silver King, Excelsior; 2 changing beers (sourced regionally; often Rat, Thornbridge, Vocation) Ⓗ

A fine Ossett Brewery reconstruction of a former Webster's establishment, it features four distinct and separate comfortable drinking areas, with a trademark brick arch separating the front from the rear. The hidden beer garden behind and below the pub provides shade on summer days. Monday is poker night, Thursday is quiz night. Fresh fruit and tasty home-made snacks are often available, while guest ales usually feature a renowned IPA and a dark ale. ❀♣●P🚌🐾📶↺

West Riding Refreshment Rooms 🏆 𝕃

Dewsbury Railway Station, Wellington Road, WF13 1HF

☎ (01924) 459193

Black Sheep Best Bitter; Timothy Taylor Landlord; 7 changing beers (sourced nationally; often Brass Castle, Magic Rock, Vocation) Ⓗ

This multi award-winning pub in a Grade II listed station building has recently celebrated 25 years in the Guide. Nine handpumps dispense a range of beer styles and strengths, a 10th is reserved for real cider. Good food is served daily – pizzas are available all day. Occasional beer festivals are held, and live music plays outside in summer. The pub gets busy on Saturday due to its prominent position on the Transpennine Rail Ale Trail. There are monthly Meet the Brewer sessions. ❀◑♿⇌♣●🚌🐾📶↺

Elland

Elland Craft & Tap

102 Southgate, HX5 0EP

☎ (01422) 370630 🌐 craftandtap.co.uk

Elland Blonde; 4 changing beers (sourced regionally) Ⓗ

On the main street of Elland, this bar has been busy since opening in 2018, and has made a good impression on local CAMRA members. It used to be a bank, and the main room still has the original ornamental features. There are stairs to a second room where you will find the bar. The pub supports various community groups and has a room upstairs for private meetings. Quiz night is every Wednesday. Q♘❀♿●🚌(501,503)🐾📶

Goose Eye

Turkey Inn

BD22 0PD SE028406

☎ (01535) 681339 🌐 theturkeyinn.com

Goose Eye Bitter, Chinook Blonde; Timothy Taylor Golden Best, Landlord; 6 changing beers (sourced nationally)

A friendly, historic pub in the centre of a tiny hamlet approached by steep roads or a riverside footpath. It has three snugs, each with a real fire to keep out the winter chill, and is a good base for exploring the surrounding countryside. The pub holds a quiz night on Wednesday, and hosts occasional live music and special theme nights. It has a pool table. Food is served every day.

P (K14,K16)

Greengates

Cracker Barrel

832 Harrogate Road, BD10 0RA

Tetley Bitter; 4 changing beers (sourced regionally; often Abbeydale, Great Newsome, Salamander)

Opened in 2017, this friendly, popular, family-run micropub has a cosy, homely feel. The bar is at the rear of the single room. Tetley Cask Bitter is the regular beer. The other four handpulls serve a varying range of real ales, often including a dark beer, from regional breweries. The pub welcomes families and dogs. Outside seating to the front is next to a busy main road.

New Line

60 New Line, BD10 9AP

☎ (01274) 613855 🌐 thenewline.co.uk

Timothy Taylor Landlord; 3 changing beers (often Abbeydale, Crooked)

Opened in 2018, this pub is an impressive high-quality conversion of a former 1800s residential property. The downstairs room contains the bar. There is an additional seating area upstairs (with table service at the weekend) with a TV and wood-burning stove. The original stonework and roof beams have been exposed and restored, and there are luxurious furnishings within. One regular and three guest real ales are served from the handpulls.

Guiseley

Coopers

4-6 Otley Road, LS20 8AH

☎ (01943) 878835

Ilkley Blonde; Rooster's Yorkshire Pale Ale; Timothy Taylor Landlord; 5 changing beers (sourced regionally; often Brass Castle, Hawkshead, Thornbridge)

A modern bar/diner converted from a former Co-operative store, Coopers has a bar with a separate dining area and an upstairs function room. Eight cask beers are served, generally from Yorkshire or northern breweries, with a dedicated pump for dark beer, and there is a large selection of other beers on tap and in bottles and cans. A

REAL ALE BREWERIES

Anthology Leeds
Barker's South Crosland (NEW)
Beer Ink Huddersfield
BEEspoke Shipley
Bingley Wilsden
Bone Idle Idle
Bosun's Huddersfield
Bridgehouse Keighley
Briscoe's Otley
Burley Street Leeds
Chin Chin South Kirkby
Cobbydale Silsden
Cooper Hill Leeds
Copper Dragon Keighley
Darkland Halifax
Eagles Crag Todmorden
Elland Elland
Empire Slaithwaite
Fernandes Wakefield
Five Towns Wakefield
Frisky Bear Leeds: Morley
Ghost Baildon
Goose Eye Bingley
Halifax Steam Hipperholme
Haworth Steam Cleckheaton
Henry Smith Pontefract
Hogs Head Sowerby Bridge
Horbury Horbury
Horsforth Leeds: Horsforth
Hungry Bear Leeds
Ilkley Ilkley
Junction Baildon
Kirkstall Leeds: Kirkstall
Lazy Turtle Holmfirth
Leeds Leeds
Legitimate Industries Leeds
Linfit Linthwaite
Little Valley Hebden Bridge
Lord's Golcar
Luddite Horbury Junction
Magic Rock Huddersfield
Mallinsons Huddersfield
Malt Brewhouse Horsforth
Meanwood Leeds
Mill Valley Hightown
Milltown Milnsbridge
Morton Collins Wakefield
Nightjar Mytholmroyd
Nomadic Leeds
Nook Holmfirth
North Leeds
Northern Monk Leeds: Holbeck
Old Moll Spring Huddersfield (NEW)
Old Spot Cullingworth
Ossett Ossett
Outgang Kinsley
Quirky Leeds: Garforth
Rat Huddersfield
Revolutions Whitwood
Ridgeside Leeds: Meanwood
Riverhead Huddersfield: Marsden
Salt Shipley
Saltaire Shipley
Shadow Otley
Small World Shelley
Stod Fold Halifax
Sunbeam Leeds
Tapped Leeds
Tarn51 Altofts
Three Fiends Holmfirth
Tigertops Wakefield
Timothy Taylor Keighley
Truth Hurts Leeds: Morley
Vocation Hebden Bridge
Wetherby Wetherby
Wharfedale Ilkley
Wilde Child Leeds
Wishbone Keighley

diverse range of meals is available. The large upstairs function room is used for events and also serves as extra dining space. Children are allowed during the day.
Q

Guiseley Factory Workers Club

6 Town Street, LS20 9DT
(01943) 874793 guiseleyfactoryworkersclub.co.uk
Tetley Bitter; 3 changing beers (sourced locally; often Goose Eye, Mallinsons, Rudgate)
A three-roomed multi award-winning club founded over 100 years ago. The bar serves both the lounge and the concert room, and has changing guest ales sourced both locally and nationally. There is also a snooker room and a large lawned beer garden. The club hosts many local clubs and organisations. A variety of musical acts occasionally performs on Friday and Saturday nights. CAMRA members are welcome on production of this Guide or a membership card. P

Halifax: Dean Clough

Stod Fold Dean Clough

Dean Clough, HX3 5AH
(01422) 355600
Stod Fold Gold, Best Yorkshire Bitter, West APA, Yorkshire Blonde, Dark Porter; 3 changing beers (sourced nationally; often Stod Fold)
A sympathetically restored industrial-chic bar tucked just inside Gate One of the architecturally significant Dean Clough Mills, formerly home to Crossleys Carpets. The bar has seven handpumps, mainly serving the core Stod Fold range, plus guest beers. Tasty food is served – usually burgers and ciabattas with a variety of fillings. The bar hosts live music every Sunday and monthly comedy nights introducing new talent. It is popular with Dean Clough office workers, particularly on Friday lunchtime.

Halifax: King Cross

Oddy's

158 Haugh Shaw Road, HX1 3BG
(01422) 351385 theoddyskingcross.co.uk
Cross Bay Sunset; John Smith's Bitter; 1 changing beer (sourced regionally; often Darkland)
Easily missed, this small pub is hidden away between King Cross Street and Aachen Way, in what was originally known as Back Land. Now refurbished and opened out into an L-shaped bar, drinkers can stand around the pillars that replaced the original walls. It features a pool table, wood-burning fire for the cold winter months and a beer garden. Although quiet and occupied by locals and regulars during the week, it can get busy at weekends when many people come to King Cross to eat. The pub hosts a quiz on Monday night and karaoke on Saturday evening.

Wainhouse Tavern

Upper Washer Lane, Pye Nest, HX2 7DR (take Edwards Rd off Pye Nest Rd)
(01422) 339998 wainhousetavern.co.uk
Wychwood Hobgoblin Gold; house beer (by Stod Fold); 5 changing beers (sourced regionally; often Elland, Mallinsons, Rudgate)
Former home to industrialist JFE Wainhouse, most famous for his nearby tower. The building was converted to a public house in the 1960s and saved from an uncertain future by the present owners. No two windows are alike in this Grade II listed Gothic-fronted building. A small lounge at the front opens up to a much larger bar at the rear. Private functions, live music and games nights take place here. Traditional home-cooked food is available in the evenings and at weekends.
P (579,560)

Halifax: Savile Park

Big Six

10 Horsfall Street, HX1 3HG (off A646 Skircoat Moor Rd at King Cross)
(01422) 350169
Old Mill Traditional Bitter; 4 changing beers (sourced regionally)
A characterful hidden gem in a row of terraces formed from two houses knocked together, adjacent to the Free School Lane recreation ground. The building has a regionally important historic pub interior, with a through corridor separating the bar and cosy snug from the games room and the two lounges. The emphasis in this friendly venue is on good beer and conversation. It serves a regular beer plus a regional ale and four rotating guest beers from local breweries or microbreweries. A large range of gins and malt whiskies is also stocked.
Q (577)

Halifax: Siddal

Cross Keys

3 Whitegate, HX3 9AE
(01422) 300348 crosskeyshalifax.co.uk
8 changing beers (sourced regionally; often Abbeydale, Salopian, Squawk)
This 17th-century tavern has a real traditional feel. There is a snug adjacent to the bar with an inglenook fireplace dividing the remaining area, and a taproom to the rear. Walkers and cyclists are welcome. Outside is a spacious, sheltered beer garden. The walls display various beer mats from many now-closed breweries. Live music is featured on Sunday afternoon.
Q (542,555)

Halifax: Town Centre

Grayston Unity

1-3 Wesley Court, HX1 1UH
07807 136520 thegraystonunity.co.uk
Goose Eye Chinook Blonde; 4 changing beers (sourced regionally; often Elland, Marble, Torrside)
A bar opposite Halifax's Town Hall in a listed Grade II building. There is a cafe-style seating area in front of the bar, a side room with comfy chairs, and a vestibule leading to an outside seating space. Officially the UK's smallest music venue, the bar hosts music nights, quizzes and local history talks. A bitter and a dark ale are always on tap, and on Sunday there is an ale of the day offer. Cutlery is provided if you bring your own food. Open all day on bank holiday Mondays.

Lantern

13-15 Alexandra Street, HX1 1BS
(01422) 341003 thelanternhalifax.co.uk
6 changing beers (sourced regionally; often Vocation)
The Lantern was founded in 2017 on the site of a former restaurant. The downstairs bar is set to the right of a rectangular room with an array of ceiling shelves full of books. It is well stocked with an interesting range of real and craft beers, offering six changing real ales and six KeyKeg beers. There is a music venue upstairs where national and international acts perform, and free live music downstairs on Sunday evening.

Three Pigeons ★ L ✔
1 Sun Fold, HX1 2LX
☎ (01422) 347001
Ossett Yorkshire Brunette, Yorkshire Blonde; Rat White Rat; house beer (by Ossett); 4 changing beers (sourced nationally; often Fernandes, Jennings) H
A striking octagonal drinking lobby forms the hub from which five distinctive rooms radiate in this Art Deco pub, built in 1932 by Websters Brewery. Sensitively refurbished and maintained by Ossett Brewery, this hostelry attracts a variety of local groups and societies along with football and rugby enthusiasts. Three Ossett beers are always on, the other one on a rota basis. Three guest beers also feature as well as a stout or porter.
Q❀≥♣●P⊟🐾ᯤ↺

Upper George ✔
Crown Street, HX1 1TT
☎ (01422) 353614
Greene King IPA; 5 changing beers (often Greenfield, Naylor's, BAD) H
A cosy and traditional pub, regarded by many as an institution, especially by those who have come here for 40 years or more. Friendly staff, loud music (with an eclectic selection on the jukebox) and an easy going atmosphere are all part of the appeal. There is a large-screen TV, a pool room and a spacious courtyard outside which is hugely popular in summer. Occasional music events are held. ❀◐≥♣⊟ᯤ

Victorian Craft Beer Café L
18-22 Powell Street, HX1 1LN (behind Victoria Theatre)
🌐 victorian.beer
9 changing beers (sourced nationally; often Squawk, Vocation) H
A busy, award-winning pub opened in 2014 after a complete refurbishment of a once-popular Italian restaurant. It offers nine rotating real ales from microbreweries nationwide, 18 keg lines, a choice of world bottled beers, and a draught cider. The main seating area has wooden floors and a tiled bar; to the left is a more secluded area and steps to an upper level with further seating. Many beer-themed events and tap takeovers take place (see website for details).
ᘐ≥●🐾ᯤ↺

Hanging Heaton

Hanging Heaton Cricket Club
Bennett Lane, WF17 6DB
☎ (01924) 461804
Ossett Yorkshire Blonde; Sharp's Doom Bar; 2 changing beers H
A long-established, welcoming community club, 2019 local CAMRA branch Club of the Year and Yorkshire runner-up. The successful cricket team plays in the local league, and snooker is taken seriously – the two snooker tables are well used and bring home prizes; there are frequent celebrity appearances. The handpumps have increased from one to four under the steward, who is knowledgeable and enthusiastic about real ale, and well-chosen guest beers come from far and wide. There are no regular meals but pizzas are available Friday to Sunday afternoons. ᘐ❀◐♿♣●P⊟(202)ᯤ↺

Haworth

Fleece Inn L ✔
67 Main Street, BD22 8DA
☎ (01535) 642172 🌐 fleeceinnhaworth.co.uk
Timothy Taylor Golden Best, Boltmaker, Knowle Spring, Landlord, Landlord Dark; 1 changing beer (often Timothy Taylor) H
A stone-built coaching inn on Haworth's famous cobbled Main Street, with spectacular views over the Worth Valley and close to the KWVR historic heritage railway. A cosy room to the right and a lower-level dining area offer quiet alternatives to the busy bar. Locally sourced food and accommodation are offered, and breakfast is available to all. The beer garden is three storeys up from the bar, on the roof. A Timothy Taylor tied house, popular with tourists and locals alike. ᘐ❀🛏◐♿⛺≥♣⊟🐾ᯤ

Heath

King's Arms ★ L ✔
Heath Common, WF1 5SL (at edge of Heath village on Heath Common, off A655 Wakefield-Normanton road)
☎ (01924) 377527 🌐 thekingsarmsheath.co.uk
Ossett Yorkshire Brunette, Yorkshire Blonde, Silver King; Rat White Rat; 3 changing beers H
Acquired by Clark's Brewery in 1989, this inn is now leased to Ossett Brewery. Built in the early 1700s and converted into a public house in 1841, it has three oak-panelled rooms with gas lighting, plus a conservatory and gardens to the rear. In the summer months you can sit outside and relax peacefully amid the acres of common grassland surrounding the area. There is a quiz on Tuesday. Time may be called early on quieter evenings. Qᘐ❀◐♿●P⊟(188)🐾ᯤ

Hebden Bridge

Fox & Goose L ✔
7 Heptonstall Road, HX7 6AZ (at traffic lights on jct of A646 and Heptonstall Rd)
☎ (01422) 648052 🌐 foxandgoose.org
Pictish Brewers Gold; 5 changing beers (sourced regionally; often Burton Bridge, Darkland, Eagles Crag) H
West Yorkshire's first community co-operative pub extends a warm welcome to locals and visitors alike. It has a single bar serving three different rooms and an upstairs hillside beer garden with great views. The main bar is warmed by a roaring coal fire in winter, while the room to the left exhibits the work of local artists and often hosts live music. The room to the right has a dartboard. At least one vegan beer and one dark beer are always served. Monday is quiz night.
Q❀♣●🚆⊟(590,592)🐾ᯤ

Nightjar L
New Road, HX7 8AD (next door to Picture House)
☎ (01422) 713015 🌐 nightjarhebden.co.uk
House beer (by Nightjar); 2 changing beers (sourced regionally) H
Opened in 2017, this is the brewery tap for Nightjar Brew Co, the Mytholmroyd-based brewery. The bar has a strong commitment to serving real ale in a friendly environment. It serves three handpumped real ales, usually two from its own brewery and another from one of the many other small independent breweries. Set in an area at risk of flooding, the decor is flood-proof in style. Q≥♣●🚆⊟(590,592)🐾ᯤ

Old Gate Bar & Restaurant L
1-5 Old Gate, HX7 8JP
☎ (01422) 843993 🌐 oldgatehebden.co.uk
Moorhouse's Pride of Pendle; Saltaire Cascade; Vocation Heart & Soul; 6 changing beers (sourced nationally; often Arbor, RedWillow, Thornbridge) H

A smart place with a modern downstairs bar and an upstairs restaurant. The bar has an impressive long copper-topped counter with 11 handpumps, one of which always dispenses a dark beer. Quality food is served all day. The bar area is furnished with a mixture of tables, chairs, benches and comfy sofas. The big picture windows and outside patio are great for people-watching. There is a comedy club on Friday evening and occasional live music at weekends.
Q♘❀◑⇌●🚌🐾ᯤ↺

Pub 𝕃
3 The Courtyard, Bridge Gate, HX7 8EX (from A646 turn into Bridge Gate, at start of pedestrian section turn into yard on right)
☎ 07421 768511 🌐 calansmicropub.co.uk
House beer (by Elland); 4 changing beers (sourced nationally; often Great Heck, Mallinsons) Ⓗ
Calderdale's first micropub, set in a suntrap courtyard just off the main pedestrianised shopping street, offers an intimate, friendly and welcoming experience. Four rotating ales, mainly from northern microbreweries, are complemented by cider. No piped music or other distractions disturb the conversation, but there are books, cards and dominoes to provide entertainment. Dogs are welcome. Q♘❀⇌♣●🐾ᯤ

Hillhouse

Slubbers Arms 𝕃
1 Halifax Old Road, HD1 6HW (off A641)
☎ (01484) 429032
Timothy Taylor Boltmaker, Landlord; 3 changing beers (often Potbelly) Ⓗ
A triangular corner-terrace pub on the edge of town, taking its name from the textile industry of the 1860s. It retains its multi-room features. There is a parlour with a V-shaped bar and open fire, a snug and quiet room with World War II and textile memorabilia, and a secluded beer garden. A regular winner of local CAMRA branch Mild Pub of the Year, it has a dedicated mild pump. Opens early on match days, when it can get busy.
Q♘❀◑♿●🚌🐾↺

Holmfirth

Nook 𝕃 ✔
7 Victoria Square, HD9 2DN (down alley behind Barclays bank)
☎ (01484) 682373 🌐 thenookbrewhouse.co.uk
Nook Baby Blond, Best, Blond, Oat Stout; 2 changing beers (often Nook) Ⓗ
The Nook, properly the Rose & Crown, dates from 1754, and is a well-known real ale outlet in the village. It has been dispensing beers from its own adjacent brewhouse since 2009. There are occasional guest beers, and Pure North ciders. Home-cooked food is served daily. A popular folk evening takes place every Sunday, and real ale festivals are held on the weekend before Easter and on the August bank holiday. The log fire is particularly warming on cold winter nights. ♘❀🛏◑♣●🚌🐾ᯤ↺

Horbury

Boons Horbury 𝕃 ✔
6 Queen Street, WF4 6LP (in town centre off B6128 Horbury-Ossett road, opp Co-op)
☎ (01924) 280442
Timothy Taylor Landlord; 7 changing beers (sourced regionally) Ⓗ
Popular community pub just off the High Street attracting people of all ages. The interior is based on a traditional layout around a central bar, with rugby league memorabilia on the walls. A guest cider is served alongside the ales. The sizeable outdoor drinking area is well used in summer. The pub has held a regular beer festival on the first weekend in June for more than 20 years. ❀♣●🚌ᯤ

Cherry Tree Inn
Church Street, WF4 6LT
☎ (01924) 262916
House beer (by Horbury); 2 changing beers (sourced locally) Ⓗ
Cask ale pub, craft beer bar, wine bar, gin bar, eatery and so much more... Not only home to the Horbury Ales Brewery, this establishment also serves great coffee, not to mention fantastic chef-prepared food including traditional classics as well as seasonal à la carte specials.
❀🛏◑P🚌🐾ᯤ↺

Cricketers Arms 🏆 𝕃 ✔
22 Cluntergate, WF4 5AG (a right fork off High St at its lower end)
☎ (01924) 267032
Timothy Taylor Landlord; house beer (by Elland); 6 changing beers (sourced regionally) Ⓗ
On the edge of the town centre, this former Melbourne/Tetley's pub is now a genuine free house, also stocking a range of craft and keg beers. It has a poker night on Monday, a quiz night on Wednesday and a meat raffle on Friday. Music is provided by way of an open mic night on the second Sunday and live music on the last Sunday of each month. The pub has won many awards including local CAMRA branch Pub of the Year 2018 and 2019.
❀♣P🚌🐾ᯤ

Horbury Junction

Calder Vale Hotel 𝕃
Millfield Road, WF4 5EB (from main A642 road follow signage through housing estate to Horbury jct industrial area; also walkable from canalside via tubular bridge)
6 changing beers (sourced locally; often Bad Seed, North Riding, Revolutions) Ⓗ
Established in 1874, this lovingly restored Victorian commercial hotel is steeped in local industrial history. Reopened in 2019, it is home to the Luddite Brewery, and has already been voted Yorkshire's dog-friendliest pub. It boasts Yorkshire stone floors, log-burning fires, a delightful garden and nearby canal walks. There are street-food weekends and occasional entertainment in an upstairs room. Q♘❀◑♿♣●P🚌🐾

Huddersfield

Cherry Tree ✔
14-18 John William Street, HD1 1BG
☎ (01484) 448190
Elland 1872 Porter; Greene King Abbot; Ruddles Best Bitter; 7 changing beers (sourced nationally; often Acorn, Saltaire, Sharp's) Ⓗ
Converted in 2001, this former bed shop is now a modern, town-centre Wetherspoon outlet. The prosaic architecture is outshone by the range and quality of the ales, and the pub has been listed several times in this Guide. Alongside the permanent beers are seven changing guest beers, regularly from Saltaire, Leeds, Adnams, Naylor's, Acorn and Moorhouses's. American craft beers on cask occasionally make an appearance at beer festivals. Three real ciders and one perry are always available. Food is served all day, alcohol from 9am.
♘◑♿⇌●🚌ᯤ

Grove

2 Spring Grove Street, HD1 4BP
☎ (01484) 430113 thegrove.pub
Kirkstall Pale Ale; Oakham Citra, Green Devil; 16 changing beers (often Hawkshead, Mallinsons, Northern Monk)
This establishment is the antithesis of everything mass market, with artwork, a snack range and live music that are unusual, to say the least. However, it is the array of 31 beers, lagers and a real cider that sets it apart, including a confusion-inducing 19 handpulled ales. Ranging from table beers through IPAs to imperial stouts, there is something for all. Also on offer are a superb menu of over 200 bottled beers and a comprehensive spirits range. The Grove is the area's must-visit pub.
Q

King's Head

St George's Square, HD1 1JF (in station buildings, on left when exiting station)
☎ (01484) 511058
Bradfield Farmers Blonde; Magic Rock Ringmaster; Timothy Taylor Golden Best, Landlord; 6 changing beers (sourced regionally; often Abbeydale, Oakham, Pictish)
A friendly welcome always awaits at this award-winning pub. Situated in a Grade I listed station and winner of a railway heritage award, the King's Head has been carefully restored, with features including a beautiful tiled floor, wood panelling and wood-burning stoves. It serves up four permanent and six rotating beers from breweries near and far; a mild and a dark beer are permanently on the bar, as is one real cider. Live music plays on Sunday afternoon, and hot food is served on match days.

Rat & Ratchet

40 Chapel Hill, HD1 3EB (on A616, just off ring road; car park is at rear)
☎ (01484) 542400
Ossett Yorkshire Blonde, Silver King; Rat White Rat, King Rat; 9 changing beers (sourced regionally; often Acorn, Fernandes, Riverhead)
A multi award-winning pub owned by Ossett, with the on-site Rat microbrewery. Eleven handpumps offer beers from a range of breweries including its own. The bar has two permanent dark beers, one cider pump, and a good choice of ciders and perries. The large open-plan main area still retains the feel of separate rooms. A further room at the back leads to an outside drinking area, and there is a dartboard and a pinball machine. Live music takes place regularly throughout the month. There is a quiz on a Wednesday, and regular beer festivals.
P

Sportsman ★

1 St John's Road, HD1 5AY
☎ (01484) 421929 beerhouses.co.uk/pub/the-sportsman
Timothy Taylor Boltmaker; 7 changing beers (sourced regionally; often Anthology, Three Blind Mice, Wilde Child)
This 1930s establishment, with a 1950s refit by Hammonds (note the windows), has won a CAMRA English Heritage Conservation Pub Design award. The superb, curved, central bar has a parquet floor and an interesting wooden entrance. Eight ales are arranged in order of strength. A dark beer is always available, along with two real ciders. Two rooms off are regularly used for meetings by poker, poetry and music clubs. A Meet the Brewer night is hosted on the last Tuesday of the month.

Idle

Idle Draper

28 The Green, BD10 9PX
☎ 07525 751574
3 changing beers (sourced regionally; often Bingley, Bone Idle, Parkway)
A modern microbar in the centre of Idle, housed within the premises of the former Briggs draper's. It comprises a single room containing the bar on the ground floor, with an additional lounge area above. The in-house Bone Idle Brewery is located in a converted barn to the rear. Three handpulls offer a varying range of real ales. The upstairs room and barn can be hired for private functions. The Bone Idle Men's Club meets here every Wednesday evening.

Ilkley

Flying Duck

16 Church Street, LS29 9DS (on A65)
☎ (01943) 609587
Dark Horse Hetton Pale Ale; Rooster's Yankee; Wharfedale Black, Blonde, Best; 4 changing beers (sourced regionally; often Goose Eye, Ilkley, Rooster's)
A beautifully refurbished Grade II listed venue close to the town centre. Originally constructed as a farmhouse in 1709, it is reputed to be Ilkley's oldest pub building. It retains many original features, including York stone and oak flooring, beamed ceilings, internal stonework and mullioned windows. Up to eight real ales, including four regulars, and two real ciders, are on the bar. Wharfedale Brewery is located to the rear. Food is served Tuesday to Sunday and also on bank holiday Mondays.

Keighley

Brown Cow

5 Cross Leeds Street, BD21 2LQ
☎ (01535) 382423
Timothy Taylor Golden Best, Landlord; 5 changing beers
A short walk from the town centre, this family-run free house is about quality, choice and the comfort of customers. Five guest beers come mainly from local micros, featuring at least one session beer, a strong one and a dark one. A quiz takes place on the second and last Wednesday of the month. Local CAMRA Pub of the Year 2020. A no bad language policy is in place.
Q P

Ledsham

Chequers Inn

Claypit Lane, LS25 5LP (close to All Saints church)
☎ (01977) 683135 thechequersinn.com
Leeds Best; Theakston Best Bitter; Timothy Taylor Landlord; house beer (by Brown Cow); 1 changing beer (sourced locally; often Brown Cow, Stod Fold)
A family-run pub dating from the 16th century, set at the heart of the village. Renowned for good food and Yorkshire beers, it is handy for the Fairburn Ings RSPB reserve and welcomes walkers and dogs. Various rooms lead off from the passageway, with low beams, alcoves, open fires, photographs, trinkets and unusual tabletops with interesting quotations. A marquee at the top of the garden is available for functions in the warmer months.
Q P (175)

Leeds: Burley

Cardigan Arms 🏆 ★

364 Kirkstall Road, LS4 2HQ
☎ (0113) 226 3154 🌐 cardiganarms.co.uk
Kirkstall Pale Ale, Three Swords, Dissolution IPA, Black Band Porter; 4 changing beers (sourced regionally; often Kirkstall, Track, Wylam) Ⓗ
Reopened in 2017 as a Kirkstall Brewery pub after a sensitive refurbishment, its fine woodwork, etched glass and ornamented ceilings are now displayed in their full glory. Originally built in 1896, this is a classic, Grade II listed Victorian establishment with four rooms off an L-shaped bar area. There is a first-floor function room. On the bar are eight cask ales and a good range of keg and bottled beers. The pub is named after the Cardigan family, who owned land locally. Q

Leeds: Chapel Allerton

Further North 🄻

194 Harrogate Road, LS7 4NZ (200yds N of centre of Chapel Allerton)
☎ (0113) 237 0962
North Session Pale; 1 changing beer (sourced locally; often Kirkstall, Vocation) Ⓗ
With a quirky retro look and feel, this is one of Leeds' first microbars. It is a welcoming, family-friendly, conversation-focused establishment with no TVs. There is an upstairs room free to hire for functions. Two cask beers are offered, one from North Brewing and the other a changing beer, usually from Yorkshire. There are seven UK and continental draught beers, and a fridge stocked with quality world beers. The food is a choice of cheeseboard or pies.

Leeds: City Centre

Assembly Underground

Civic Court, Calverley Street, LS1 3AB
Vocation Bread & Butter; 4 changing beers (sourced locally; often Kirkstall, Vocation) Ⓗ
This new development in the basement of a Grade II listed building features a Vocation Brewery bar with 50 taps, street food stalls, and a coffee bar. Bench seating is provided in the main area. The cask beers are from the taps at the right of the bar, and screens around the venue are regularly updated with the current beer range. There is a separate gin bar, the Staff Room, available for functions. Wheelchair access is at the rear on Alexander Street.

Brunswick 🄻

82 North Street, LS2 7PN
☎ (0113) 247 0546 🌐 thebrunswick.co.uk
5 changing beers (sourced locally; often Kirkstall, Saltaire) Ⓗ
You can spot the Brunswick by its funky exterior mural, and the modern vibe continues inside with hand-made furniture, bare boards, an upstairs gallery/dining area, a function room in the loft and sometimes a DJ. Alongside the six handpumps, one of which dispenses cider, are quality keg lines and fridges of packaged beer goodness. Burgers, dirty fries, brunch and mega Sunday lunches are all on the menu. Go for a quiet midweek coffee or a buzzing weekend bevvy. Loos are on the first floor.

Duck & Drake 🄻 ✔

43 Kirkgate, LS2 7DR
☎ (0113) 245 5432 🌐 duckndrake.co.uk
Brains Bitter; Bridgehouse Blonde; Rooster's Yankee; Theakston Old Peculier; Timothy Taylor Landlord; 10 changing beers (sourced locally; often Elland, Saltaire) Ⓗ
The guest beers, which come mainly from across Yorkshire, range from pale to dark in this traditional two-room corner pub. Wooden-floored throughout, the larger room has fixed seating around the outside and a small stage area that hosts live music five nights a week. Whole-wall mosaics depict numerous legends of the blues and rock music scene. There is a yard outside. Pie and peas are proudly served. The gents' lavatories are worth a visit for their traditional styling.

Foley's Tap House 🄻

159 The Headrow, LS1 5RG
☎ (0113) 242 9674
Black Sheep Best Bitter, Pale Ale; York Guzzler, Centurion's Ghost Ale; 8 changing beers (sourced locally; often Abbeydale, Black Sheep, Thornbridge) Ⓗ
A busy city-centre pub acquired by Black Sheep Brewery in 2019 as part of the York Brewery estate. Black Sheep beers now feature heavily, alongside up to eight guest ales, and there is an impressive range of real ciders from boxes stacked behind the bar. The building is a grand edifice, previously owned by the Pearl Assurance Company, founded by Patrick James Foley (see his statue atop the building). Coffees and cakes are served and beer tasting trays are available.

Head of Steam 🄻

13 Mill Hill, LS1 5DQ
☎ (0113) 243 6618
Camerons Strongarm; Timothy Taylor Boltmaker; 6 changing beers (sourced locally; often Camerons, Ilkley, Wilde Child) Ⓗ
A number of cosy semi-separate areas radiate from the central island bar. There are nine handpumps, one of which is dedicated to dark beer and another to a varying cider. Beers are normally from Yorkshire and the North-East. A wide range of beers from Belgium and the United States is also available, with empty boxes artistically displayed on a balcony above the spiral line of empty bottles leading from the bar. Regular live music and jazz are staged here.

North Bar 🄻

24 New Briggate, LS1 6NU
☎ (0113) 242 4540
3 changing beers (sourced locally; often Kirkstall, Magic Rock, North) Ⓗ
The North Bar has been showcasing craft beer since before it was called craft beer. The long, thin room has slatted walls to the left featuring local artwork, while to the right are some comfy settles from which to admire it. Further back are the bar's fridges, jam-packed with beers from all over the world. Themed beer festivals are held at various times of the year. Tea and coffee, and food provided by Little Bao Boy, are served, including to take out. A photo booth adds to the fun.

Reliance 🄻

76-78 North Street, LS2 7PN
☎ (0113) 295 6060 🌐 the-reliance.co.uk
House beer (by Acorn); 3 changing beers (sourced locally; often Magic Rock, Rooster's, Sunbeam) Ⓗ
Just outside the city centre, the Reliance is located on a street corner, easy to spot by its bicycle rack which is usually nearly full up. The pub has two bare-boarded rooms, with a third on the mezzanine level predominantly for eating. It is simply furnished throughout, with local artists' and photographers' exhibitions adding to the informal drinking and dining experience. Food includes home-made charcuterie.

Along with the real ale and cider there is a great selection of classic and modern bottled and canned beers and fine wines.

Scarbrough Hotel

Bishopgate Street, LS1 5DY

☎ (0113) 243 4590

St Austell Nicholson's Pale Ale; Tetley Bitter; 5 changing beers (sourced regionally; often Adnams, Great Heck, Vocation)

A busy ale house that provides a convenient spot in which to wait for a train from the nearby station. The building, with its impressive tiled frontage, dates from 1765, gaining a drinks licence in 1826. Possibly the most misspelt pub in Leeds, it is named after its first owner, Henry Scarbrough, rather than the seaside town. It is one of the few places still serving Tetley Bitter in central Leeds, while the selection of guest ales comes from around the country.

Tapped Leeds

51 Boar Lane, LS1 5EL

☎ (0113) 244 1953

10 changing beers (sourced nationally; often Kirkstall, Tapped Sheffield, Wild Beer)

Two or three beers come from the visible, on-site microbrewery or sister pub in Sheffield, while well-respected breweries from Yorkshire and across the country provide the remainder. The real-time online beer list and descriptions include two dark offerings. Fixtures and fittings blend retro and modern designs. Large windows open onto the street and a small seating area outside. Pizzas are served until an hour before closing. Under-18s are welcome until the evening, no football colours are allowed, and there is a dress code for Friday and Saturday nights (no shorts or tracksuit bottoms).

Templar

2 Templar Street, LS2 7NU

☎ (0113) 243 0318

Tetley Bitter; 7 changing beers (sourced locally; often Bradfield, Greene King, Kirkstall)

Recently awarded Grade II listing, with fine wood panelling from 1928 and exterior tiling, this is one of the few community locals in the city centre and offers traditional, honest values. The beers parallel this, with a focus on lower strength pales and bitters mainly from Yorkshire, and one or two from the Greene King stable. The landlord and many staff have served here for over 30 years. League darts and dominoes are played.

Town Hall Tavern

17 Westgate, LS1 2RA

☎ (0113) 244 0765

Timothy Taylor Dark Mild, Golden Best, Boltmaker, Knowle Spring, Landlord, Landlord Dark

A small, traditional inter-war pub dating from 1926, with a good reputation for its food and offering a full range of Timothy Taylor's beers. The single room has a bar to the left and open alcoves to the left and right of the door, with circular copper-topped tables and old photographs of Leeds. Dining tends to be to the rear of the room. The pub may close early if quiet, especially on Monday.

Victoria Family & Commercial Hotel

28 Great George Street, LS1 3DL (behind town hall)

☎ (0113) 245 1386

Leeds Pale; Sharp's Doom Bar; Tetley Bitter; 6 changing beers (sourced locally; often Kirkstall)

Built by the Victoria Hotel Company in 1865 as a 28-room hotel to accommodate visitors to the Assizes Court in Leeds Town Hall, the building has an impressive Victorian exterior and ornate interior with high ceilings. There is a long main bar area and two separate rooms, all of which feature an array of polished wood and shiny brass. Table service is available in Albert's Bar. Up to six guest ales are served.

Wapentake

92 Kirkgate, LS2 7DJ

☎ (0113) 243 6248 wapentakeleeds.co.uk

4 changing beers (sourced locally; often Kirkstall, Nomadic, Sunbeam)

Describing itself as a little piece of Yorkshire that welcomes grumpy old men, children and dogs, this bar effortlessly attracts a wide age range and has generated a community feel. Friendly and upbeat equally describes the bar staff and the unobtrusive background music. Beers, one of which is often dark, are usually from smaller breweries within the county. Eclectic framed prints and beer mats adorn the walls, and there is a sports TV upstairs. Food and cakes are home-made with locally sourced ingredients. Alcohol is served from 10am.

Whitelock's Ale House ★

Turk's Head Yard, LS1 6HB (off Briggate)

☎ (0113) 245 3950 whitelocksleeds.com

Five Points Best, Pale; Kirkstall Pale Ale; Theakston Old Peculier; Timothy Taylor Landlord; 6 changing beers (sourced nationally; often Acorn, Great Heck, Saltaire)

Hidden down an alleyway right in the middle of town, Whitelock's is a must-visit public house. Built in 1715, and with an interior dating from the late 1800s, stepping through the heavy wooden doors takes you back to Victorian England as you peer round the iron pillars to see the long, wide, tiled and copper-topped bar and mirrors featuring old hand-etched ads. The handpumps dispense a well-chosen mixture of classic local beers and interesting ales from quality brewers further afield.

Leeds: Headingley

Arcadia Ale House

34 Arndale Centre, Otley Road, LS6 2UE (corner of Alma Rd)

☎ (0113) 274 5599

Timothy Taylor Boltmaker; 7 changing beers (sourced locally; often Kirkstall, Northern Monk, Ridgeside)

This award-winning bar established the real ale scene in Headingley. There are two ground-floor rooms and more seating on an upstairs mezzanine level. A mural of local landmarks features above the bar. Eight real ales are on handpull along with a range of canned, bottled and draught beers, always including vegan beer options. Thee is also a wide selection of gins, some locally produced. Under-18s, large groups and fancy dress are not permitted. Dogs are positively encouraged.

Q

Leeds: Holbeck

Grove Inn

Back Row, LS11 5PL

☎ (0113) 244 2085 thegroveinnleeds.co.uk

Daleside Blonde; 7 changing beers (sourced regionally; often Acorn, Moorhouse's, Settle)

A stubborn relic of old Holbeck, now hidden away among modern office developments, this pub is well worth the short walk out of town. Eight real ales from local and regional breweries are served. There are two small side rooms providing quiet away from the busier taproom, home to the regulars. The Concert Room to the rear hosts a variety of music six nights a week including, on Fridays since 1962, reputedly the oldest folk club in the world. ❀◐⇌♣🍏🚌🐾📶

Leeds: Hyde Park

Brudenell Social Club 🄻

33 Queen's Road, LS6 1NY

☎ (0113) 275 2411 🌐 brudenellsocialclub.co.uk

3 changing beers (sourced locally; often Kirkstall, Ossett) 🄷

A legendary gig venue which retains the feel of a working men's club. However, the no-frills look belies a community-centred, family-friendly local with a lively atmosphere. It hosts two live music rooms, a large lounge showing televised sports, and a wood-panelled snooker and pool room with multiple tables. Local cask ales are served on handpump. Pies with all the trimmings are available, and food trucks frequently set up in the car park. ⛑❀◐◑♿⇌♣🍏P🚌(56)📶

Leeds: Kirkstall

Kirkstall Bridge Inn 🄻

12 Bridge Road, LS5 3BW

☎ (0113) 278 4044 🌐 kirkstallbridge.co.uk

Kirkstall Pale Ale, Three Swords, Dissolution IPA, Black Band Porter; 4 changing beers (sourced regionally; often Sunbeam, Thornbridge, Wylam) 🄷

Spread over two floors, with an extensive riverside beer garden, the pub offers a large range of Kirkstall Brewery cask ales and changing guests, plus a range of continental lagers and other beers on keg. Food is served every day (booking is advised for weekend dining). Events include the annual Kirkstapalooza music and beer festival and a hugely popular bonfire night. A selection of board games is available. Dogs are welcome in the downstairs bar. ❀◐◑♣P🚌🐾📶

West End House

26 Abbey Road, LS5 3HS

☎ (0113) 278 6332 🌐 thewestendhouse.co.uk

3 changing beers (sourced nationally; often Brains, Marston's, Timothy Taylor) 🄷

A busy local, this traditional 150-year-old pub is just down the road from Kirkstall Abbey and Museum. The bar room shows sports TV and the large lounge area does a roaring trade in quality, hearty food. The bar has four handpumps dispensing frequently changing cask ales and cider, alongside foreign beers and lagers. There is a well-stocked fridge and a wine rack. A small smoking area and drinking patio is outside. Regular quiz nights are hosted. ❀◐◑⇌🍏🚌🐾📶

Leeds: Newlay

Abbey Inn 🄻

99 Pollard Lane, LS13 1EQ (vehicle access from B6157 only)

☎ (0113) 258 1248

Leeds Pale; 8 changing beers (sourced locally; often Kirkstall, Ossett) 🄷

A historic ale house and celebrated community pub between the River Aire and the canal towpath, showcasing a selection of predominantly local ales, with pumps dedicated to dark ale and cider. Keg ales, international lagers, wines and whisky are also available. The Abbey bustles with friendly locals throughout the week, and hosts a folk night on Tuesday, live music on Saturday and quizzes on Thursday and Sunday. Ample seating outside attracts dog walkers and cyclists. Access is by road from Pollard Lane, on foot over Pollard Bridge, or along the canal from Kirkstall Forge station. ⛑❀◐♿⇌(Kirkstall Forge) ♣🍏P🐾📶

Linthwaite

Sair 🄻 ✔

139 Lane Top, HD7 5SG (top of Hoyle Ing, off A62)

☎ (01484) 842370

Linfit Bitter, Gold Medal, Special, Swift, Autumn Gold, Old Eli 🄷

Home of the Linfit Brewery, this traditional, multi-roomed, stone-built brewpub stands overlooking the Colne Valley. It is the ultimate in LocAle, with up to 10 different beers brewed on-site, including three dark beers, and it also sells a cider from Pure North. The central bar serves four rooms, each with a real fire. A popular meeting place for locals and visitors, the pub supports community events and is dog-friendly. A former CAMRA National Pub of the Year. Q❀♣🍏🚌🐾📶↺

Liversedge

Black Bull 🄻 ✔

37 Halifax Road, WF15 6JR (on A649, close to A62)

☎ (01924) 403779

Ossett Yorkshire Blonde, Silver King, Excelsior; house beer (by Ossett); 5 changing beers (sourced nationally; often Goose Eye, Riverhead, Saltaire) 🄷

Ossett Brewery's first pub. The five rooms each have a unique style, including one dubbed the Chapel, which has a high ceiling and reminders of local industrial heritage. Nine handpumps always include a dark ale plus guest beers from the group and wide-ranging independents. A regular Guide entry, the Black Bull is a popular, sociable community local with a warm welcome. Quiz night is Tuesday, and darts and dominoes are played on a Monday in the local league. Q⛑❀♿♣P🚌(254,254A) 🐾📶↺

Lockwood

Shoulder of Mutton

11 Neale Road, HD1 3TN

☎ 07595 457655

6 changing beers (sourced regionally) 🄷

Well-run back-street local offering a decent selection of real ales from brewers including Abbeydale, Beartown and Oakham. It has a medium-sized bar with two snug rooms either side and a pool room upstairs. A CAMRA award winner, the pub features in CAMRA Yorkshire's Heritage Guide, with its dark wood interior and lead-lined windows. Easily reached by a regular bus service and close to Lockwood train station. Q⛑❀⇌♣🚌🐾↺

Longwood

Dusty Miller Inn 🄻 ✔

2 Gilead Road, Longwood, HD3 4XH

☎ 07946 589645 🌐 dustymillerlongwood.com

Milltown Weaver's Bitter, Platinum Blonde, Black Jack Porter; Timothy Taylor Landlord; 3 changing beers (often Brunswick, Milltown, Newby Wyke) 🄷

Local historic photographs adorn the walls and stone floors dominate at this pub, the Milltown Brewery tap. The cosy interior is open plan but has three distinct areas. From the benches outside there are great views up the Colne Valley. Seven real ales are served, showcasing the Milltown brews, alongside two changing guests, always including a dark beer, plus a permanent real cider. The only food is locally made pies from Brosters Farm at Lindley Moor. Q🔥♣🍏🚌(356)🐾📶↺

Marsden

Riverhead Brewery Tap L ✔

Peel Street, HD7 6BR

☎ (01484) 844324 🌐 theriverheadmarsden.co.uk

Ossett Yorkshire Blonde, Silver King; Riverhead Butterley Bitter, March Haigh, Redbrook Premium; 5 changing beers Ⓗ

A modern brewpub producing up to six regular Riverhead beers and occasional specials. It is now owned by the Ossett Brewery. Upstairs there is a restaurant and another bar with comfy seating. Outside is a riverside terrace for alfresco drinking. The microbrewery is visible from the main bar. Ten beers are served, two from Ossett plus guests, as well as a dark beer and a real cider. A popular venue for locals and visitors, it gets busy on Saturdays. On the Real Ale Rail Trail.
🔥❀◐♿⇌🍏P🚌(185)🐾📶↺

Middlestown

Little Bull L

72 New Road, WF4 4NR (on A642 at crossroads in centre of village)

☎ (01924) 726142 🌐 thelittlebull.co.uk

Abbeydale Deception; 2 changing beers (sourced locally) Ⓗ

This free house has been established since 1814. A single bar services a number of smaller rooms and has an open fire in colder weather. A gin bar is hosted on the last Saturday of the month. All food is locally sourced and home-cooked. Lunchtime and/or evening meals are served throughout the week but times vary. Monday is fish night and Wednesday is pie night. A beer festival is held on the last weekend in July. The National Coal Mining Museum is nearby. 🔥❀◐P🚌(232,128)🐾📶

Mirfield

Flowerpot L ✔

65 Calder Road, WF14 8NN (over river, 400yds S of railway station)

☎ (01924) 496939

Ossett Yorkshire Brunette, Yorkshire Blonde, Silver King, Excelsior; Rat White Rat; 4 changing beers (often Acorn, Fernandes, Riverhead) Ⓗ

An award-winning 1807 pub with a typically sensitive, tasteful restoration by Ossett Brewery, featuring an impressive tiled flowerpot as the centrepiece. It boasts four separate drinking areas and a real fire. Outside, there is a terrace and a riverside beer garden. Nine ales are offered from Ossett's five breweries and independents, usually including a mild or stout, plus a cider. The pub is on the Transpennine Real Ale Trail and holds occasional beer and cider festivals. Quiz night is Tuesday. Q❀⇌♣🍏P🚌(262)🐾📶↺

Knowl Club L ✔

17 Knowl Road, WF14 8DQ

☎ (01924) 493301 🌐 knowlclub.co.uk

Old Mill Traditional Bitter; Rat White Rat; Sharp's Atlantic; 1 changing beer (sourced nationally) Ⓗ

The former Mirfield Liberal Club celebrated its 125th anniversary in 2013. It is an ideal place for a quiet pint and extends a friendly welcome both to its members and the public. A long well-furnished room houses the single bar, which offers up to four beers. There is also a private function room and a pool table downstairs, and a snooker room upstairs. The small car park at the rear is accessed down an adjacent narrow alley. Sky and BT sports are shown. 🔥♿⇌♣🍏P🚌🐾📶↺

Navigation Tavern

6 Station Road, WF14 8NL (next to Mirfield railway station)

☎ (01924) 492476 🌐 navigationtavern.co.uk

John Smith's Bitter; Theakston Best Bitter, Lightfoot, XB, Old Peculier; 3 changing beers (sourced nationally; often Small World) Ⓗ

A canalside free house with a large wood-burning fire adding to winter comfort. The pub is an ambassador for Theakston beers and offers up to three guests, mainly at weekends, all at keen prices. It features on the Transpennine Rail Ale Trail, hosts occasional fundraising events, puts on Saturday night entertainment (often Motown) and has active sports teams. A large function room and an en-suite B&B with a stairlift are available. Book ahead for Sunday lunch. 🔥❀🛏◐♿⇌♣P🚌📶↺

Old Colonial

Dunbottle Lane, WF14 9JJ (off A644 up Church Lane, 1 mile NE of station)

☎ (01924) 496920

Copper Dragon Best Bitter; 3 changing beers (sourced regionally; often JW Lees, Stancill) Ⓗ

A former club with fascinating colonial memorabilia, offering a cosy retreat, with sofas around the fire. A Royal British Legion memorial is in the prize-winning garden, and local charities are well supported. The spacious conservatory hosts functions and meetings. Guest beers are from a range of brewers and usually include a dark ale. Good-quality and excellent-value meals are served Thursday to Saturday and Sunday lunchtime. Opening times may vary so ring ahead.
🔥❀◐♿♣P🚌(202,205)📶↺

Morley

Oscar's Bar L

2A Queen Street, LS27 9DG

3 changing beers (sourced locally) Ⓗ

This small, friendly bar serves as the tap for the nearby Frisky Bear Brewery. Three handpumps offer cask beers both from local and regional brewers. There is also a range of draught beer, usually including one or more from Frisky Bear. Rums and gins are a house speciality. The single wooden-floored room has seating for 19 people, although more can fit in with care, and do at busy times. A regular CAMRA award winner, well worth the trip. 🔥⇌🍏🚌🐾📶

Norristhorpe

Rising Sun L

254 Norristhorpe Lane, WF15 7AN (0.4 miles off A62)

☎ (01924) 400190

Abbeydale Moonshine; Acorn Barnsley Bitter; Saltaire Blonde; Timothy Taylor Landlord; 3 changing beers (sourced locally; often Bradfield, Copper Dragon, Hawkshead) Ⓗ

This village local, under family ownership, is tastefully decorated, featuring a light and spacious bar area and cosy lounge areas with exposed brickwork and real fires. The beer range is mainly from Yorkshire but with guest ales from local and national sources. Every Tuesday there is a popular quiz with prizes; also occasional live music advertised on Facebook. There is a large well maintained beer garden with plenty of seating and extensive views over the valley towards Mirfield and Emley Moor.
🔥❀♣P🚌(261)🐾📶↺

Oakworth

Oakworth Social Club 🅛
Chapel Lane, BD22 7HY
☎ (01535) 643931
Saltaire Blonde; Timothy Taylor Golden Best; 1 changing beer (sourced locally) 🅗
Friendly and welcoming, this imposing Victorian building on the main thoroughfare was originally built as the Liberal Club in the late 19th century. Now a social club with a thriving membership, it has a comfortable front lounge and a back bar with traditional games and a TV. Upstairs, a third room caters for functions and meetings. Quiz night is Monday, and regular live music events are staged (see Facebook). CAMRA Yorkshire Club of the Year runner-up 2018, and local branch Club of the Year 2020.
🏷️🕮&Å⇌♣P🖥(K7,K10) ✿ 🛜

Ossett

Bier Huis 🅛
17 Towngate, WF5 9BL (in shopping parade which backs onto bus station)
☎ (01924) 565121 ⊕ bierhuis.co.uk
3 changing beers (sourced locally) 🅗
A specialist beer shop stocking over 500 bottled beers from many Yorkshire breweries, in addition to an extensive selection of foreign bottled beers with an emphasis on Belgian and German beers. It has an on-licence whereby the bottled beers can be drunk on-site, along with three changing draught beers, and it also has a wide range of draught ciders. CAMRA branch Cider Pub of the Year in 2018 and 2019. Q🏷️&♣P🖥🛜

Brewers Pride 🅛 ✅
Low Mill Road, Healey, WF5 8ND
☎ (01924) 273865
Ossett Yorkshire Blonde; Rat White Rat; Rudgate Ruby Mild; 6 changing beers (often Ossett) 🅗
Once found never forgotten, in what is now largely the Healey Mills industrial area beside the River Calder. This, one of the best free houses in the area for many years, was sold to Ossett Brewery in 2018. Under the guidance of Stephen (Chalky) Whyte, the pub is finding its feet again after the transition from free house to tied house. Good-value meals are served.
Q🏷️🕮🍴♣●🖥(102,121)✿🛜

Otley

Black Horse 🅛
Westgate, LS21 3AS
☎ (01943) 466383 ⊕ blackhorseotley.co.uk
Kirkstall Pale Ale, Three Swords, Dissolution IPA, Black Band Porter; 4 changing beers (sourced nationally; often Five Points, Hawkshead, Vocation) 🅗
An impressive building dating from the start of the 20th century with a Victorian interior. It is run as a partnership between Kirkstall Brewery and the Brudenell Social Club, and was refurbished in early 2019 with quality furniture, fittings and brewery mirrors. The ornate wooden bar has a large range of Kirkstall Brewery beers, changing guest cask ales, and a good selection of keg beers on draught. There is a large covered outside seating area.
Q🏷️🕮🍴🕮&🖥✿🛜

Old Cock 🅛
11-13 Crossgate, LS21 1AA
☎ (01943) 464424
Ilkley Mary Jane; Theakston Best Bitter; Timothy Taylor Landlord; 6 changing beers (sourced locally; often Brass Castle, Briscoe's, Five Towns) 🅗

An award-winning, genuine free house, cleverly converted from a former café in such a way that it feels like a pub that has been here for many years. There are two low-ceilinged rooms downstairs with stone-flagged floors, and a further room upstairs. The guest ales are mostly from local breweries, but some are from further afield. At least two real ciders are also served, plus a range of foreign beers. Frequent beer festivals are held. No under-18s. Q&🍴●🖥✿🛜

Oxenhope

Bay Horse 🅛 ✅
20 Uppertown, BD22 9LN (on A6033)
☎ (01535) 642921
Timothy Taylor Boltmaker, Landlord; 4 changing beers 🅗
A friendly village local that welcomes families and dogs. It has a pleasant single-bar setup with a real fire, a cosy room to the rear, and a separate seating area up a flight of steps. The four changing guest beers (five at weekends) come from local breweries such as Bowland, Goose Eye and Wishbone. Traditional ciders from Lilley's and Gwynt y Ddraig are also served. The pub is one of the main stopping points for the annual village charity Straw Race. Regular live music is a feature.
🏷️🕮⇌♣●P🖥✿🛜

Pontefract

Old Grocers 🅛
26 Beastfair, WF8 1AL
5 changing beers 🅗
A new micropub converted from a hair and beauty salon into a craft ale and gin bar, spread over the ground and first floor, with seats for around 60 customers. Before that it was a grocery shop, hence the name. The proprietor seeks to offer a niche establishment new to the town, with a good range of cask ales, cask cider and gins. Q🕮⇌●🖥

Robin Hood 🅛
4 Wakefield Road, WF8 4HN (at town end jct of A645 Wakefield Rd with roads to Barnsley and Doncaster)
☎ (01977) 702231
Timothy Taylor Landlord; 9 changing beers (sourced regionally; often Henry Smith, Revolutions) 🅗
Recently bought and totally refurbished by a local landlord, the Robin has been a pub since 1791, when it was owned by the Duchy of Lancaster. It is the home of the Henry Smith Brewery, named after the son of the present owner. The locals are invited to choose the guest beers. There is a folk session on Sunday and live music on Thursday. Q🏷️🕮&♣●🖥✿

Pudsey

Fleece 🅛 ✅
100 Fartown, LS28 8LU
☎ (0113) 236 2748 ⊕ fleecepudsey.co.uk
Tetley Bitter; Timothy Taylor Golden Best, Landlord; house beer (by Sunbeam); 1 changing beer (sourced locally; often Elland, North Riding, Stod Fold) 🅗
Located on the outskirts of town, the Fleece is community focused and no stranger to winning CAMRA awards, which are proudly displayed in the entranceway. To the left is a small, basic taproom with a flagged floor, known as the Snug. To the right is a relatively large lounge with plenty of comfy settles around the perimeter. Look around and see how many film stars you can name, and how many Laurels and Hardys you can spot. 🕮♣P🖥🛜

Manor Inn Ⓛ

Manor House Street, LS28 7BJ

Saltaire Blonde; 3 changing beers (sourced locally; often Brew York, North, Wishbone) Ⓗ

A mini modern alehouse round the back of the town hall, this little pub packs a lot in. The wooden-boarded single room has cushioned benches along one side and a bar along the other, with four pumps dispensing local and interesting ales. The fridge is full of quality beverages, the walls have large (but only occasionally noisy) TVs for music and sport, sometimes there is live music, and dogs are always welcome. 🚌🐾📶

Rastrick

Roundhill Inn Ⓛ ✔

75 Clough Lane, HD6 3QL (400yds from A643/A6107 jct towards M62 motorway bridge)

☎ (01484) 713418 🌐 roundhillinn.co.uk

Bradfield Farmers Blonde; Sharp's Doom Bar; Timothy Taylor Golden Best, Landlord; house beer (by Ashover); 2 changing beers (sourced nationally) Ⓗ

A two-roomed genuine free house and locals' pub lying on the edge of Rastrick, easily reached by bus from Brighouse or Huddersfield. In daytimes during the week it hosts private functions, often wakes as the crematorium in neighbouring Kirklees is nearby. Recently extended separate wheelchair access is provided (though staff need to be alerted) and accessible toilets are available through two doors. Q♣P🚌(547,549)📶↺

Riddlesden

Willow Tree Inn Ⓛ

Ilkley Road, BD20 5PN (on Bingley road at top of village)

Bridgehouse Blonde, Aired Ale; 2 changing beers (sourced locally) Ⓗ

Situated in a residential area, this two-room free house is very much part of the local community. The taproom to the right of the central bar features a TV, jukebox and a pool table. The comfortable lounge to the left is warmed by a multi-fuel stove. Look for the windows from the long-gone Heys Brewery. Children are welcome until the evening. There is a quiz on Tuesday, a cask ale club on Wednesday and a book club on the first Thursday of the month. The guest beers are usually from Bridgehouse. ❀◐♣P🚌(K13,K17)🐾📶

Roberttown

New Inn Ⓛ ✔

Roberttown Lane, WF15 7NP

☎ (01924) 500483 🌐 newinnroberttown.co.uk

Abbeydale Moonshine; Bradfield Farmers Blonde; Leeds Best; 3 changing beers (sourced nationally; often Mill Valley, Sharp's, Stod Fold) Ⓗ

A free house in the centre of Roberttown, originally a beer house. It has been part of the community for many years and new, experienced licensees took over in 2019. There is a main bar area, a cosy snug and a room suitable for functions. Outside is a sunny seating area and a covered smoking shelter. A popular quiz is hosted on Wednesday, occasional live music at weekends, and an annual charity mini beer and cider festival. ఠ❀♣●P🚌(229,228)🐾📶↺

Saltaire

Cap & Collar Ⓛ

4 Queens Road, BD18 4SJ

4 changing beers (sourced nationally; often Ilkley, Saltaire, Thornbridge) Ⓗ

A popular, modern micropub, with an open-plan layout in the style of a café, accommodating up to 35 customers. A beer garden and smoking area is at the rear. Four handpulls serve a changing range of real ales, many of them regional. Real cider is served on draught and there is a good selection of bottle-conditioned ales. Tap takeover events are held regularly and a homebrew club also meets here. Live music can be heard on Sunday afternoons and occasional evenings. Snacks are available. Qఠ❀≢●🚌🐾📶

Salt Cellar 🏆 Ⓛ

192 Saltaire Road, BD18 3JF (on A657)

☎ (01274) 955051

House beer (by Bingley); 5 changing beers (sourced regionally; often Eagles Crag, Small World, Stod Fold) Ⓗ

A traditional pub on the edge of the World Heritage Site of Saltaire village, with a friendly, cosy feel. It comprises a two-roomed Victorian house with comfortable seating, stained-glass partitions and bookshelves. Numerous pictures of old Saltaire adorn the walls. Six handpulls deliver a varying range of real ales from local and regional breweries, usually two blondes, two ambers and two dark beers. Closing time on Friday and Saturday may vary. ఠ❀♿≢P🚌🐾📶↺

Sandal

Star ✔

Standbridge Lane, WF2 7DY (near Asda on A6186 which links A61 and A636)

☎ (01924) 255254

6 changing beers (sourced regionally; often Morton Collins) Ⓗ

A cosy inn dating from 1821 with a streamside beer garden. It was recently leased from Enterprise Inns by Morton Collins – the brewery has now moved to the pub – and serves one or two of its own beers, plus four or five guest beers mainly from local breweries. The welcoming pub has an open-plan layout and open fires in winter. There is a function room available for hire. Quiz night is Tuesday, and an annual beer festival is held. Qఠ❀◐♿♣P🚌(110)🐾📶

Sandbeds

Airedale Heifer Ⓛ ✔

Bradford Road, BD20 5LY

☎ (01274) 515870 🌐 theairedaleheifer.co.uk

Bridgehouse Blonde, Aired Ale, Porter, Holy Cow; 2 changing beers (often Bridgehouse) Ⓗ

An extensive roadside hostelry with a substantial food presence, many dishes featuring the brewery's beers. It is the tap for Bridgehouse Brewery, situated in the car park behind. The pub is named after the famous Airedale heifer of the early 1800s, the heaviest cow in the UK (see the statue at the front). The open-plan layout has a single L-shaped bar and a sizeable south-facing garden with patio heaters. Children are welcome during the day, later if dining. Brewery tours can be arranged – see the website for details. ఠ❀◐♿P🚌(662,K17)🐾📶

Shipley

Beehive

1 Saltaire Road, BD18 3HH (on A657)

☎ 07738 098330

Half Moon Dark Masquerade; Stod Fold Best Yorkshire Bitter; Sunbeam Nigel's Plum Porter; 6 changing

beers (sourced regionally; often Abbeydale, Great Heck, North Riding) ⊞
A stone-built former Hammonds house, built in 1870, reopened under new ownership in 2018. This traditional local has two semi open-plan ground-floor rooms, divided by a central bar, and a snug to the rear. Up to nine real ales and 11 local ciders are offered. A large basement room can be hired for functions and events. Shipley railway station and bus interchange are nearby. The pub is closed for the first two weeks of January. ✿⇆●P🖪❀🗣♿

Fox 🅻
41 Briggate, BD17 7BP
☎ (01274) 594826 🌐 thefoxshipley.co.uk
BEEspoke Plan Bee, Shipley Stout; 4 changing beers (sourced regionally; often 3 Piers, Abbeydale, Great Heck) ⊞
A friendly independent café-bar with a single-room interior, simply but smartly furnished and featuring recycled church pews. Six handpulled ales include some from the in-house BEEspoke microbrewery. Real ciders, often from a local producer, are available, as is a wide range of international bottled beers. Live music takes place on Tuesday and Wednesday evenings, and frequently on Saturday nights, when the bar can get busy. A handy place to wait for a train as the station is close by. ♿✿⛵&⇆●🖪❀🗣

Hullabaloo
37-41 Westgate, BD18 3QX
☎ 07974 910838
4 changing beers (sourced regionally; often Magic Rock, Northern Monk, Wilde Child) ⊞
A popular, modern bar close to Shipley town centre and the bus interchange. Opened in 2017, it is open plan but with three distinct areas in a variety of styles over split levels. Four handpumps serve a range of real ales, usually from regional brewers and often different from what you might find in other pubs in the area. A further handpump is dedicated to cider. Artisan craft beers are also available on six keg taps. Children are welcome. ♿🍴⇆●🖪🗣

Sir Norman Rae 🅻 ✅
Victoria House, Market Place, BD18 3QB
☎ (01274) 535290
Elland 1872 Porter; Greene King Abbot; Ruddles Best Bitter; 7 changing beers (sourced nationally; often Goose Eye, Wychwood) ⊞
A typical conversion by Wetherspoon, this former Co-op department store originally opened as a Lloyds No.1 but later changed to the standard format. Ten handpumps dispense real ale – three regulars and seven guests – often focusing on local breweries. Meet the Brewer nights are occasionally held. The good-value food is from the usual Wetherspoon menu. The pub is nicknamed the Waiting Room as it is near Shipley bus interchange and the railway station. ♿🍴&⇆🖪🗣

Silsden

Counting House 🅻
23 Kirkgate, BD20 0AJ
☎ (01274) 405644
Dark Horse Hetton Pale Ale; 3 changing beers (sourced regionally; often Ilkley, Saltaire) ⊞
A brightly decorated bar with a welcoming atmosphere, previously the branch of a bank, hence the name. The interior features exposed brickwork, interesting light fittings, and multiple clocks and mirrors. The L-shaped drinking/dining area has plenty of tables and small standing spaces at the bar and by the door. Three guest

beers change weekly and are usually from local suppliers. Food service times vary so check ahead – special events nights are a regular feature. ♿✿🖪(62,903) ❀🗣

Slaithwaite

Commercial 🅻
1 Carr Lane, HD7 5AN (village centre, off A62)
☎ (01484) 846258
Empire Moonrakers Mild; house beer (by Empire); 5 changing beers ⊞
Since reopening in 2009, this village-centre free house has enjoyed deserved success. Nine handpumps provide ample variety, with the keenly priced house beers supplied by Empire Brewery. There are five rotating guests ales and a rotating guest cider. The Commercial is an essential stop for Transpennine Rail Ale trailers and welcomes ramblers and dogs. Downstairs, the open-plan drinking area has the feel of separate spaces, and there is also an upstairs pool room. Live sports are screened in the bar. ✿⇆♣●🖪❀🗣

South Elmsall

Barnsley Oak ✅
Mill Lane, WF9 2DT (off A638)
☎ (01977) 643427
Black Sheep Best Bitter; 1 changing beer ⊞
On the B6474 about a mile from the village centre, this is a thriving community pub run to high standards. Built in 1970, it has been smartly refurbished. Excellent-value food is served daily, freshly prepared and made with locally sourced produce. There are good views of the Elm Valley from the conservatory. Quiz nights and TV sport are popular. Guest ales are usually from Yorkshire breweries. ♿✿🍴&P🖪

Sowerby Bridge

Hog's Head Brew House & Bar 🅻
1 Stanley Street, HX6 2AH
☎ (01422) 836585 🌐 hogsheadbrewhouse.co.uk
Hogs Head Maltings Ale, 6 To 8 Weeks, White Hog, Hoppy Valley, Old Schnozzler; 3 changing beers (sourced regionally; often Goose Eye, Phoenix, Vocation) ⊞
Close to the centre of Sowerby Bridge, this bar was an 18th-century malthouse and has been extensively renovated. The brewery is at the back of the building and can be viewed from the bar area. Five core Hogs Head beers are on tap as well as guest ales. There is plenty of seating in the huge, sprawling room, where snacks are also served. Q&⇆🖪❀🗣♿

Hollins Mill 🅻
12 Hollins Mill Lane, HX6 2QG
☎ (01422) 647410
Phoenix Hopsack; Timothy Taylor Golden Best, Boltmaker, Landlord; 6 changing beers (sourced regionally; often Oakham, Phoenix, Vocation) ⊞
In a former joinery, this local won CAMRA's Best Conversion to Pub Use award in 2006. Situated beside the Rochdale Canal on the western side of the town centre, it has an open-plan design and features exposed beams and floorboards. The main room is large and has an L-shaped bar. There is a small room in one corner used to host live folk music monthly on a Thursday. Upstairs is another smaller bar which is available to book for meetings and entertainment. Q✿&⇆P🖪❀🗣♿

Jubilee Refreshment Rooms 🄻

Station Road, HX6 3AB (on railway station)
☎ (01422) 648285 🌐 jubileerefreshmentrooms.co.uk
3 changing beers (often Bingley, Goose Eye, Small World) Ⓗ
Located in the only surviving part of the 1876 station building, the café bar serves three changing local beers and is a pleasant place to while away the time. Refreshments are available from early on, alcohol is sold from midday, and hot food is served at lunchtime. The walls are adorned with interesting railway and brewery-related memorabilia, and events and talks take place frequently. Trains depart regularly from here for Leeds and Manchester. Please note – the landlord specifies when closing time is called. Q❀◑♿≹P🚌🐾📶

Stanbury

Wuthering Heights Inn 🄻 ✔

Main Street, BD22 0HB (in village centre)
☎ (01535) 643332 🌐 thewutheringheights.co.uk
Moorhouse's White Witch; Theakston Best Bitter; 2 changing beers (sourced regionally; often Abbeydale, Bradfield) Ⓗ
Set in a farming village, this popular, friendly inn dates from 1763. Warmed by log-burners, the traditional main bar displays photographs showing the history of the Stanbury. The cosy dining room has a Bronte theme, and there is a third room that can be booked for parties and meetings. The rear garden has spectacular views down the Worth Valley and a separate camping area (no caravans). There is a quiz every Thursday. Well-behaved dogs and children are welcome. ♨❀🛏◑▲♣P🚌🐾📶

Thackley

Black Rat 🄻

530 Leeds Road, BD10 8JH
☎ 07920 061671
4 changing beers (sourced regionally; often Millstone, Samuel Smith, Settle) Ⓗ
Previously a florist's, this micropub, with a capacity for approximately 15 people, opened in 2016. A friendly welcome is assured and there is a cosy atmosphere. As there is no music, TV or games machines, conversation is key. The bar offers a varying selection of four real ales, primarily from Yorkshire breweries. Also stocked are two craft keg ciders, four boxed ciders and two craft lagers, along with a range of artisanal gins. Q🍎🚌🐾

Thornhill Edge

Flatt Top 🄻

29 Albion Road, WF12 0HD (off B6117)
☎ (01924) 462883
Abbeydale Moonshine; Tetley Bitter; Wychwood Hobgoblin Ruby Ⓗ
An unusual castle-like building on the edge of a steep slope, affording excellent views. It is a free house, popular with locals and welcoming to visitors. Two ground-floor rooms serve as a public bar and a cosy lounge with character, while the lower ground floors host occasional functions. There is a large south-facing patio for enjoyment of the vista. The beer range may vary according to customer demand.
♨❀♿♣P🚌(280) 🐾📶↺

Todmorden

Pub

3 Brook Street, OL14 5AJ
☎ (01706) 812145
6 changing beers (sourced nationally) Ⓗ
Close to the market, Todmorden's first micropub opened in 2017 in what used to be a café. The décor – exposed stone walls, reclaimed wood bar – enhances the simple layout, making the most of the limited space. There are 20 seats downstairs, and a flight of steep stone steps leads to another small seating area, as well as the toilets. Six handpumps serve a constantly changing range of beers, with full tasting notes on a chalkboard by the stairs. Over 30 UK distilled gins are stocked, plus traditional cider; a couple of craft beers are recent additions. Q≹🍎🚌🐾📶

Upper Denby

George Inn 🄻 ✔

114 Denby Lane, HD8 8UE
☎ (01484) 861347 🌐 thegeorgeinn-upperdenby.co.uk
Tetley Bitter; Timothy Taylor Landlord; 1 changing beer (often Acorn, Empire, Small World) Ⓗ
This family-run village local is going from strength to strength since it became a free house in late 2012, and is a former winner of the local CAMRA Rural Pub of the Year. It hosts regular pie and pea walks, with a reward of home-made food at the end. Other entertainment includes jazz on Thursdays and folk on the first and third Mondays. Walkers and dogs are welcome, and families until mid-evening. Q♨❀◑▲♣P🚌🐾📶

Wakefield

Black Rock ✔

19 Cross Square, WF1 1PQ
☎ (01924) 375550
Oakham Citra; Tetley Bitter; 4 changing beers (sourced regionally) Ⓗ
An arched, tiled façade leads into this compact city-centre local, where a warm welcome is assured. The comfy interior includes photographs of old Wakefield. The Rock stands as one of the few proper pubs left in the middle of the clubs and bars of Westgate, and is popular with drinkers of all ages looking for a real pint. Customers are encouraged to suggest beers to try, with four regularly changing guest ales on the bar. There is a free function room for private use. Q≹🚌↺

Fernandes Brewery Tap & Bier Keller 🄻 ✔

5 AvisonYard, Kirkgate, WF1 1UA (turn right approx 100yds S of George St/Kirkgate jct near Scartop Pine)
☎ (01924) 386348
Fernandes Polaris, Black Voodoo; Ossett Yorkshire Brunette, Yorkshire Blonde; 4 changing beers (sourced regionally; often Fernandes) Ⓗ
An Ossett Brewery tied house with Fernandes Brewery in the cellar. Eight handpulls dispense four Fernandes beers, two from Ossett, and two guest beers, and there are two bag-in-box ciders. The Bier Keller, which opens Friday and Saturday evenings, has premier foreign beers on keg plus a draught Ossett beer and one bag-in-box cider. There is a quiz on Wednesday evening, and folk music on the first Sunday of each month. Q◑≹🍎🚌🐾📶↺

Harry's Bar 🄻

107B Westgate, WF1 1EL (turn right from Westgate station, cross road at traffic lights, and Harry's Bar is at back of car park on right)
☎ (01924) 373773
House beer (by Five Towns); 7 changing beers (often North Riding) Ⓗ

A small, one-roomed pub set in an alleyway just off Westgate. A bare-brick and wood interior and a real fire enhance this cosy venue. In addition to the draught ales, a selection of bottled Belgian beers adds to the temptation. There is also a fantastic view of Wakefield's famous 99-arch viaduct – if only steam trains were a regular feature! Q❀♿⇌●P🚌ᯤ

Henry Boons 🄻 ✔

130 Westgate, WF2 9SR (200yds below railway bridge on Westgate)

☎ (01924) 378126

Rat White Rat; Timothy Taylor Boltmaker, Landlord; 3 changing beers (sourced regionally; often Blue Bee, Five Towns, Nook) Ⓗ

Quiet in the daytime, this pub gets busy in the evenings as it is on what is known as the Westgate run. It is the brewery tap for Clark's, which is behind the building. Hogsheads are used as tables, and there many items of breweriana, plus a thatched bar. The pub caters for drinkers of all ages and features live music. Two function rooms are available for hire. ♘◐♿⇌♣🚌🐾ᯤ

Polka Hop

60 George Street, WF1 1DL

☎ (01924) 609760

4 changing beers (sourced locally) Ⓗ

Following major refurbishment, this pub reopened under its new name in 2018. The polka hop is a morris dance step – the owner is a long-time member of the local morris dancers. The bar has been relocated to a recess, creating a comfortable seating area with secluded corners, and a real fire complements the warm welcome. Numerous board games are provided. Access from the street is problematic for wheelchair users.
♘⇌♣●🚌(443,444) 🐾ᯤ

Wakefield Labour Club 🄻

18 Vicarage Street, WF1 1QX (at top of Kirkgate, round corner from Wakey Tavern)

☎ (01924) 215626 🌐 theredshed.org.uk

5 changing beers (sourced regionally) Ⓗ

The Red Shed, as the club building is known, is a secondhand army hut that has been extensively refurbished, and is home to many union, community and charity groups. It has three rooms, two of which can be hired for functions. Quiz night is Wednesday, and there is occasional live music on the second Saturday and an open mic folk music night on the last Saturday of each month. An extensive collection of Union plates and badges is displayed over the bar, and numerous CAMRA awards adorn the walls.
Q♘♿⇌(Kirkgate/Westgate) ♣P🚌🐾

Wibsey

Hooper Micropub 🄻

209 High Street, BD6 1JU

🌐 thehoopermicropub.co.uk

5 changing beers (sourced regionally; often Goose Eye, Moorhouse's, Salopian) Ⓗ

A cosy and friendly split-level micropub that has quickly established itself with local people in this urban village. The bar is situated on the upper level and there is comfortable seating in the lower part. Five handpulls offer a varying selection of beers, primarily from the Yorkshire region but also occasionally from further afield. Photographs of old Wibsey provide interest in an otherwise minimalist décor. Local snacks are available. Closing time may vary depending upon demand.
Q♘♣🚌🐾ᯤ

Fox & Hounds, Starbotton, North Yorkshire (Photo: Dermot Kennedy)

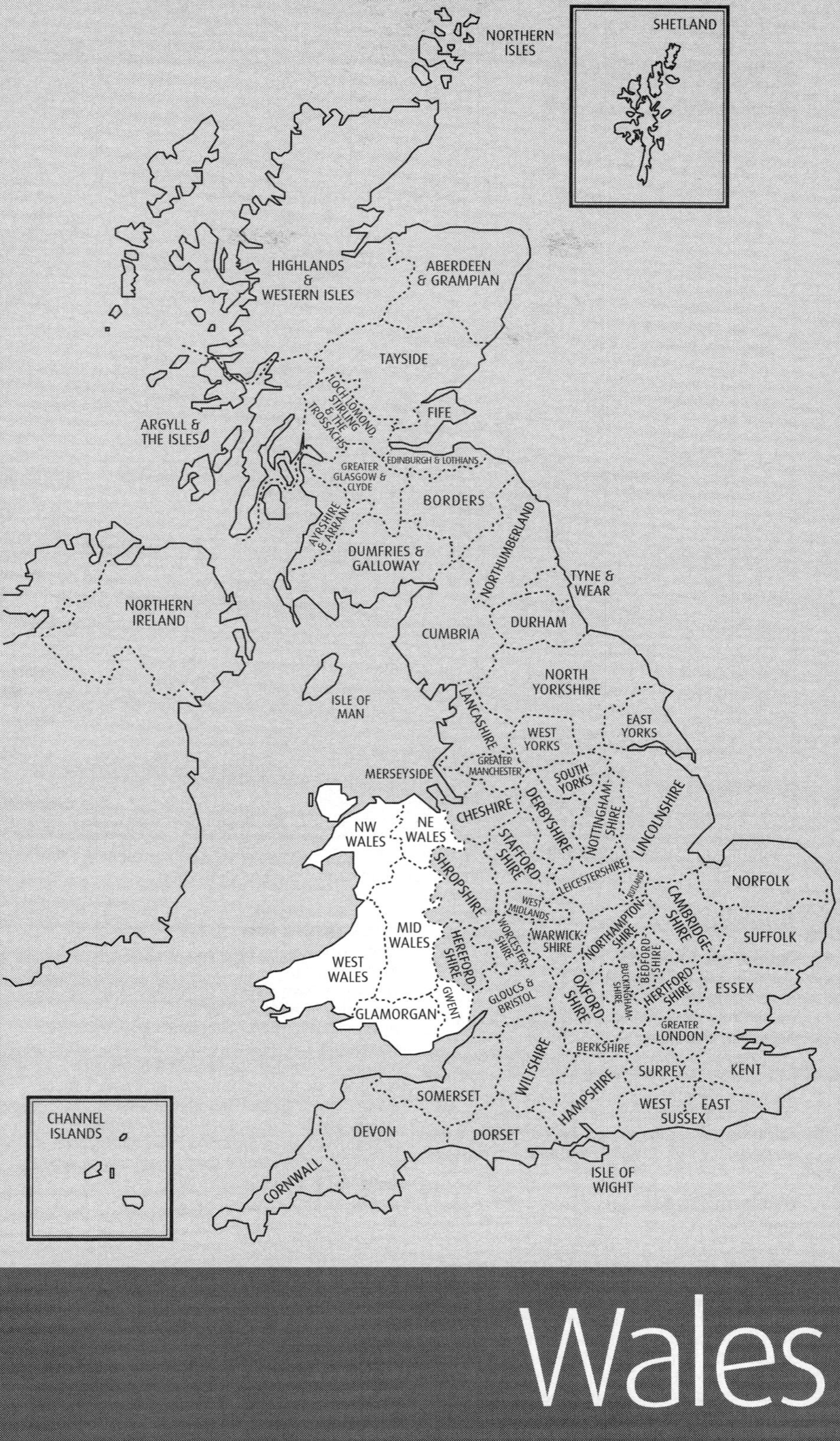

NORTHERN ISLES
SHETLAND
HIGHLANDS & WESTERN ISLES
ABERDEEN & GRAMPIAN
TAYSIDE
LOCH LOMOND, STIRLING & THE TROSSACHS
FIFE
ARGYLL & THE ISLES
EDINBURGH & LOTHIANS
GREATER GLASGOW & CLYDE
BORDERS
AYRSHIRE & ARRAN
DUMFRIES & GALLOWAY
NORTHUMBERLAND
TYNE & WEAR
NORTHERN IRELAND
DURHAM
CUMBRIA
NORTH YORKSHIRE
ISLE OF MAN
LANCASHIRE
WEST YORKS
EAST YORKS
GREATER MANCHESTER
SOUTH YORKS
MERSEYSIDE
CHESHIRE
DERBYSHIRE
NOTTINGHAMSHIRE
LINCOLNSHIRE
NW WALES
NE WALES
STAFFORDSHIRE
SHROPSHIRE
LEICESTERSHIRE
RUTLAND
NORFOLK
WEST MIDLANDS
CAMBRIDGESHIRE
MID WALES
HEREFORDSHIRE
WORCESTERSHIRE
WARWICKSHIRE
NORTHAMPTONSHIRE
BEDFORDSHIRE
SUFFOLK
WEST WALES
BUCKINGHAMSHIRE
HERTFORDSHIRE
ESSEX
GWENT
GLOUCS & BRISTOL
OXFORDSHIRE
GLAMORGAN
GREATER LONDON
BERKSHIRE
WILTSHIRE
SURREY
KENT
SOMERSET
HAMPSHIRE
WEST SUSSEX
EAST SUSSEX
CHANNEL ISLANDS
DEVON
DORSET
ISLE OF WIGHT
CORNWALL

Wales

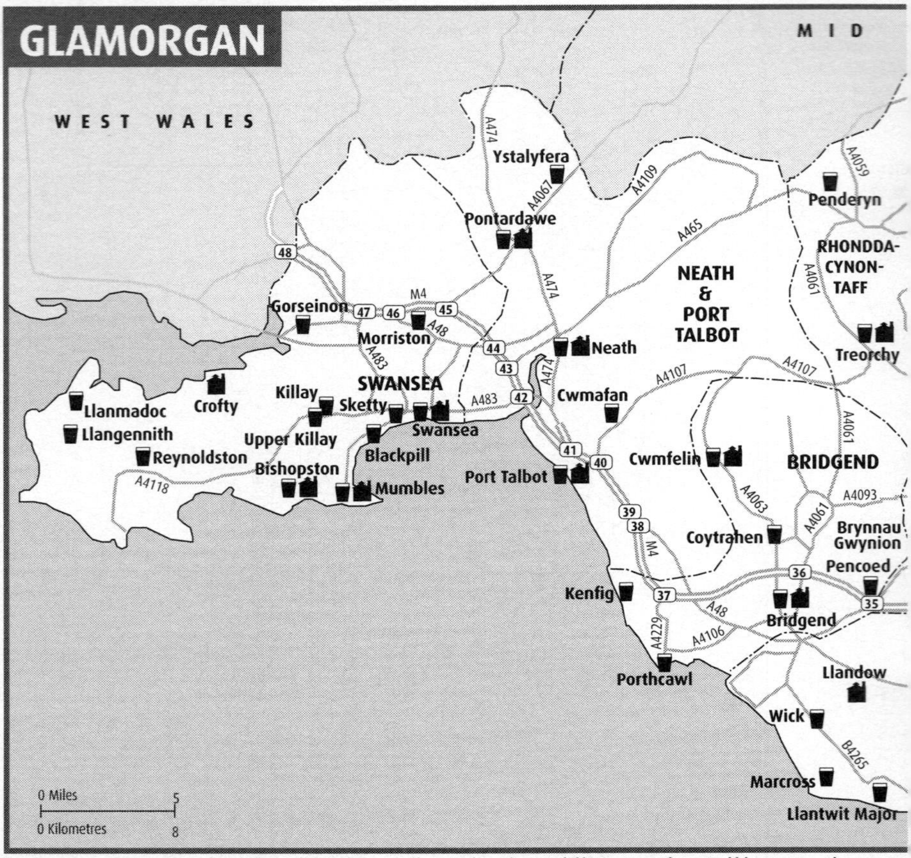

Authority areas covered: Bridgend UA, Caerphilly UA (part), Cardiff UA, Merthyr Tydfil UA, Neath & Port Talbot UA, Rhondda, Cynon & Taff UA, Swansea UA, Vale of Glamorgan UA

Aberdare

Ieuan ap Iago

6 High Street, CF44 7AA

(01685) 880080

Greene King Abbot; Ruddles Best Bitter; Sharp's Doom Bar; 4 changing beers (sourced nationally) H

Popular edge of town Wetherspoon, formerly the main post office. Ieuan ap Iago (Evan James) is the author of the words of the Welsh national anthem. Real cider is always available, together with a varied selection of national guest ales.The pub is a modest stroll from Dare Valley Country Park.

National Tap

Cross Street, CF44 7EG

(01685) 267310 greytreesbrewery.com

Grey Trees Caradog, Diggers Gold, Mosaic Pale Ale, Afghan Pale; 3 changing beers (sourced regionally; often Grey Trees, Purple Moose, Salopian) H

The first outlet for the award-winning Grey Trees Brewery, this micropub was established in 2019. It is housed in the former National School building in the centre of town. One wall features a superbly detailed 1950s image of the bustling street outside. The bar has already gained an excellent reputation for its outstanding ales and for being value for money. Budweiser Budvar is stocked plus a range of craft beer. Q

Whitcombe Inn

Whitcombe Street, CF44 7DA

(01685) 875106

Wye Valley Butty Bach; 2 changing beers (sourced nationally; often Sharp's) H

Traditional and friendly street-corner local, close to the town centre. The single bar backs on to a pool area at the rear. Sport often plays on TV screens but is rarely obtrusive except on rugby international days. Children are welcome until 9pm. Live music is hosted occasionally. The pub is approximately one mile from the picturesque Dare Valley Country Park, offering great walks and also pitches for campers and touring vans.

Aberthin

Hare & Hounds

Aberthin Road, CF71 7LG

(01446) 774892 hareandhoundsaberthin.com

Hancocks HB; Wye Valley HPA; 2 changing beers (sourced regionally; often Glamorgan Brewing Co) H

A characterful village pub with a cosy public bar with thick stone walls, wooden beams and log fire where the locals gather. The rustic dining area serves award-winning high-quality fare, with some ingredients grown by the chef. A full menu is also available in the bar. The

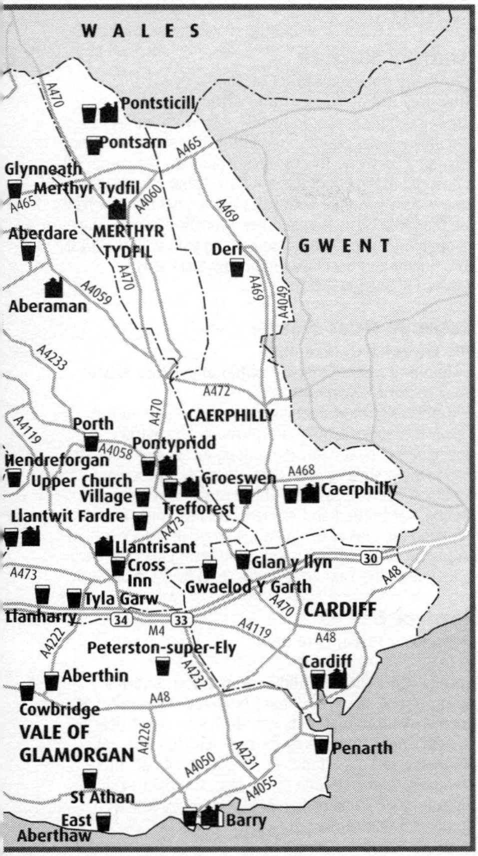

guest ales are mainly local, the ciders are from Llanblethian Orchards. Outside, the beer garden has its own bar shack and occasionally hosts live music. There is limited parking at the front of pub.
Q🝖❀◐♿♣🍎P🚌(321)🐾📶

Barry

Barry West End Club 🄻

54 St Nicholas Road, CF62 6QY

☎ (01446) 735739 🌐 barrywestendclub.webs.com

Sharp's Doom Bar; Wye Valley HPA; 2 changing beers 🄷

Multiple local CAMRA branch Club of the Year, this establishment is housed in a large multi-floored red-brick building overlooking the old harbour. Visitors are welcome and CAMRA members treated as honorary club members. Home to cricket, football, snooker and skittles teams as well as chess, scuba diving and fishing clubs, among others, there is always something going on here. Two beer festivals a year, live music at the weekend, pub grub and a friendly atmosphere makes this club an essential visit. Q🝖❀◐♿⇌♣🍎🚌(96,96A)📶

Butterfly Collector

50A Holton Road, CF63 4HE

☎ 07542 673794

10 changing beers (sourced nationally; often Box Steam, Grey Trees, Mumbles) 🄶

Formerly a shop, this is a single room with no bar – customers are served at their tables, with blackboards showing what's on offer. As well as up to eight predominantly Welsh cask ales on gravity, there are two craft keg beers and more than a dozen real ciders. The licensee is a fan of The Jam – the pub is named after one of their songs – and memorabilia includes a series of tiles in the toilet. Q♿⇌(Dock)🍎🚌🐾📶

Bishopston

Joiners Arms 🄻

50 Bishopston Road, SA3 3EJ

☎ (01792) 232658 🌐 thejoiners.info

Courage Best Bitter; Marston's Pedigree; Swansea Bishopswood Bitter, Three Cliffs Gold, Original Wood; 1 changing beer (sourced nationally) 🄷

Situated in the heart of the village, this 1860s free house remains popular with locals and visitors. Home of the Swansea Brewing Company, it has six cask handpumps in the rear area of the unpretentions, quarry-tiled bar. Good-value food is served lunchtimes and evenings (no food Mon and Sun eve) and there are occasional music events, usually around public holidays. Major sporting fixtures are shown on large screens. There is a small car park. 🝖❀◐♣P🚌(14)🐾📶

Valley ✔

41 Bishopston Road, SA3 3EJ

☎ (01792) 234820 🌐 valleyhotelbishopston.co.uk

Courage Best Bitter; 3 changing beers (sourced nationally; often Fuller's, Sharp's) 🄷

Traditional family-run country pub set in the heart of this Gower village. A large porch area (which doubles as the local bus shelter) leads to a split-level bar and dining area, with exposed beams, a hearth and an open fire. A wide variety of home-cooked meals using local

REAL ALE BREWERIES

Arcadian Cardiff
Bang-On ◆ Bridgend
Borough Arms ▮ Neath
Boss ◆ Swansea
Brains Cardiff
Brew Monster Caerphilly
Brewhouse & Kitchen ▮ Cardiff
Cerddin ▮ Cwmfelin
Coach ▮ Bridgend
Cold Black Label Bridgend
Crafty Dragon Pontsticill
Cwm Rhondda Treorchy (brewing suspended)
Dog's Window Bridgend
Freetime Swansea
Glamorgan Llantrisant
Gower Crofty
Grey Trees Aberaman
Little Goat Pontardawe
Mabby ▮ Trefforest
Mountain Hare ▮ Brynnau Gwynion
Mumbles Swansea
Neath Port Talbot
Pilot ▮ Mumbles
Pipes Cardiff
Swansea ▮ Swansea: Bishopston
Tomos a Lilford Llandow
Tomos Watkin Swansea
Twin Taff Merthyr Tydfil (brewing suspended)
Twt Lol Pontypridd
VOG Barry
Zepto Caerphilly
Zerodegrees ▮ Cardiff

ingredients is served daily and a Sunday lunch take-away service is available. Live music plays on occasion.
🐴❀◖◗♿♣P🚌(14) 🐾📶

Blackpill

Woodman ✔

120 Mumbles Road, SA3 5AS (near turn off for B4436, opp Blackpill Lido)
☎ (01792) 402700
Greene King IPA, Abbot; 3 changing beers (sourced nationally; often Greene King, Mumbles, Tomos Watkin) 🄷
Historic pub and restaurant dating back to 1819 and attractively refurbished. The deceptively spacious establishment, with its various nooks and alcoves, is on the main seafront road by the entrance to the beautiful Clyne Gardens. Popular with families and diners, the pub also welcomes those seeking only liquid refreshment. A changing range of ales is offered, including at least one from a local brewery. There are three outside seating areas including a small beer garden.
🐴❀◖◗♿P🚌(2,2A) 🐾📶

Bridgend

Coach

37 Cowbridge Road, CF31 3DH
Coach Bridgend Pale Ale 🄷**; 5 changing beers (often Grey Trees, New Bristol, Thornbridge)** 🄷/🄶
An incredible commitment to real ale, cider and independent producers has been the basis for the running of this pub since the current owners took it on. Basically furnished but comfortable, there is an art wall for local artists to display their work. Events include open mic nights, outings and two beer festivals a year. The owners began brewing in 2018 – the brewery is visible from inside the pub – and one Coach cask beer is usually on handpump. Q🐴❀≉♣●🚌(303,X2)🐾📶

Brynnau Gwynion

Mountain Hare

Brynna Road, CF35 6PG
☎ (01656) 860453
Wickwar BOB; 3 changing beers (sourced nationally; often Glamorgan, St Austell, Salopian) 🄷
A typical Welsh village inn that has featured in the Guide for more than 10 years. It is also a brewpub – the licensee began brewing in 2014 and conjures up some tasty treats. The inn has been owned by the same family for over 40 years and has a traditional public bar, games room and a lovely old stone-walled lounge. Sport is often on TV in this rugby lovers' venue. Staff and locals are most welcoming to visitors.
Q🐴❀◗♿♣●P🚌(64,404) 🐾📶

Caerphilly

Malcolm Uphill ✔

89-91 Cardiff Road, CF83 1FQ
☎ (029) 2076 0720
Greene King Abbot; Ruddles Best Bitter; Sharp's Doom Bar; 2 changing beers (sourced nationally) 🄷
Popular Wetherspoon at the top of the town, close to the main transport hub. It usually has one or two guest beers, particularly at the weekend, and up to two ciders, often including Gwynt y Ddraig Black Dragon. The pub can be crowded towards the weekend and hosts a popular quiz on quieter Sundays. Ring the main entrance doorbell if the separate accessible entrance is needed.
Q🐴◖◗♿≉●🚌📶

Cardiff

Andrew Buchan

29 Albany Road, Roath, CF24 3LH
Rhymney Hobby Horse, Dark, Bitter, Export; 1 changing beer (sourced locally; often Rhymney) 🄷
The only regular outlet in Cardiff for the award-winning Rhymney Brewery. This converted shop on the corner of a busy suburban street has a long, narrow bar. The front area is a cosy lounge with sofas and an open fire, while the rear area hosts frequent live acoustic sessions. Since its opening, the pub has forged strong links with the local community and hosts exhibitions by local artists.
❀♿≉(Cathays) ●🚌🐾📶

Cathays Beer House

109 Crwys Road, CF24 4NF
4 changing beers (sourced nationally; often Bristol Beer Factory, Liverpool) 🄶
With its welcoming, friendly atmosphere and no-frills decor, the quirky family-run micropub has quickly developed a loyal following among locals and students. Previously a street-corner post office, it now serves changing beers on gravity. There is also a choice of around 100 bottled and canned beers to enjoy while admiring the tank of exotic fish. A range of harder-to-find bag-in-box ciders has earned it the local CAMRA branch Cider Pub of the Year 2020 accolade. Q🐴❀♿●▯🚌🐾📶

Central Bar ✔

39 Windsor Place, CF10 3BW
☎ (029) 2078 0260
Greene King Abbot; Ruddles Best Bitter; Sharp's Doom Bar; 5 changing beers (sourced nationally) 🄷
Popular Wetherspoon pub just off Queen Street near its eastern end. A two-storey former nightclub, the upper storey is open most times as an additional bar. There is an outdoor drinking area at the rear. The bar usually has the full range of up to five guest beers, as well as a number of real ciders or perries.
🐴❀◖◗♿≉(Queen St) ●🚌📶

Chapter Arts Centre

Market Road, Canton, CF5 1QE
☎ (029) 2030 4400 🌐 chapter.org
Ringwood Fortyniner; 4 changing beers (sourced nationally; often Wye Valley) 🄷
Lively arts centre and cinema complex in a converted Victorian school, just off a busy main road. The five guest beers come from across the UK, usually from small independent breweries, as well as a local ale. A number of fridges contain an impressive range of bottled beers from continental producers, with the accent on German beers. Occasional beer festivals are held.
Q🐴❀◖◗♿≉(Ninian Park) P🚌📶

City Arms 🄻 ✔

10-12 Quay Street, CF10 1EA
☎ (029) 2064 1913
Brains Bitter, SA, Rev James; 7 changing beers (sourced nationally; often Beartown, Twisted Oak, VOG) 🄷
This flagship Brains pub has the ambience of a traditional Amsterdam brown bar. It is close to the Principality Stadium and gets extremely busy on match days. The three-sided bar serves the whole range of Brains beers plus up to seven guest ales, some rarely seen in the area and brought in from anywhere in the UK. A range of ciders and perries is also available. Q♿≉♣●🚌🐾📶

Flute & Tankard

4 Windsor Place, CF10 3BX
☎ (029) 2039 8315 🌐 thefluteandtankard.com

4 changing beers (sourced nationally; often Grey Trees) Ⓗ
You will find this pub just off the eastern end of Queen Street. Comfortable and quiet, it is just the ticket for anyone wanting a break from the hustle-bustle of city-centre activity. A choice of four regularly changing real ales can come from anywhere within the UK. Enjoy the live events in the upstairs function room most weekday evenings. Q❀⇌(Queen St)●

Grange
134 Penarth Road, CF11 6NJ
☎ (029) 2025 0669
4 changing beers (sourced nationally; often Cold Black Label, Grey Trees) Ⓗ
A real community establishment, this is a sister pub to the award-winning Lansdowne in Canton. The emphasis is on quality real ales and home-made food, and it seeks to provide an outlet for new small breweries. The interior is divided into two rooms separated by a central bar, with a decor on the plain, functional side. The skittle alley has recently been refurbished.
Q❀⇌(Grangetown) ♣●

Head of Steam
18-19 Church Street, CF10 1BG
☎ (029) 2037 2582
Camerons Strongarm; 5 changing beers (sourced nationally; often Castle Rock, Hydes) Ⓗ
Unlike the original Head of Steam pubs, the Cardiff bar is not close to a main railway station. A new venue on Cardiff's so-called pub mile, it offers a good range of cask and craft ales and a decent bottled selection of Belgian and German beers. It has a central island bar with seating around it, booths down one side and tables down the other. There is more seating in a spacious area upstairs.
♿⇌●

Heathcock
58-60 Bridge Street, Llandaff, CF5 2EN
☎ (029) 2115 2290 🌐 heathcockcardiff.com
Glamorgan Cwrw Gorslas/Bluestone Bitter; Wye Valley HPA; 3 changing beers (sourced regionally) Ⓗ
Roadside pub serving good beer and quality home-made food on the northern approach to Llandaff City. A central bar serves an adjoining public bar, lounge and pleasant outdoor area at the rear. The bar is cosy and traditional, with a small fireplace and a mix of furniture. The lounge is spacious and doubles as a dining room, albeit with a TV. ❀(25)

Lansdowne
71 Beda Road, CF5 1LX
☎ (029) 2022 1312
5 changing beers (sourced regionally; often Grey Trees) Ⓗ
An award-winning community pub with an open-plan layout, divided into three distinct areas. Five handpumps serve one dark beer and one local ale, with the remainder dedicated to independent brewers, often rare in the area. At least one keg beer from a local craft brewery is also offered, along with a traditional cider. A beer festival is held in mid-June. The pub is popular with families and serves good-quality food includes award-winning Sunday lunches.
❀♿⇌(Ninian Park) ♣●(96,X2)

Pen & Wig
1 Park Grove, CF10 3BJ
☎ (029) 2037 1217
8 changing beers (sourced nationally; often Bristol Beer Factory, Grey Trees, Mumbles) Ⓗ
Formerly a large Victorian terraced residence, just off the city centre and near the university and National Museum. The clientele is typically professionals and office workers during the day, students in the evening. The beer range comes from local, regional and national breweries. Monthly Meet the Brewer events and brewery takeovers are held. The large garden includes a covered section and a smokers' area. Prices are at the higher end for the area.
❀♿⇌(Queen St) ●

Romilly
69-71 Romilly Crescent, CF11 9NQ
☎ (029) 2025 6345
Brains Bitter, SA, Rev James; 1 changing beer (sourced nationally; often Timothy Taylor) Ⓗ
An attractive, comfortable locals' haunt with a variety of interconnecting rooms served by a single bar. Antique-style prints adorn the walls and there is a darts area towards the front. Outside, there is a front forecourt and a larger garden at the rear. Live music is hosted on Tuesday, a quiz on Sunday. The pub is CAMRA-accredited for serving consistently well-kept real ales.
❀♿♣(61)

St Canna's Ale House
42 Llandaff Road, CF11 9NJ
☎ 07890 106449
6 changing beers (sourced nationally; often Grey Trees, Tiny Rebel, Untapped) Ⓖ
Micropub in what used to be a corner shop, just off Cowbridge Road East, with two distinct rooms and an outdoor area. It serves up to six real ales on cooled gravity stillage, and four real ciders. The pub was founded to build community spirit and hosts regular activities such as tap takeovers, open mic nights and street food events. It has a piano and traditional board games to play. The yard, reached via a second room, has a covered smoking area.
Q❀♿⇌(Ninian Park) ♣●

Tiny Rebel
26 Westgate Street, CF10 1DD
☎ (029) 2039 9557
Tiny Rebel Fubar, Cwtch, Juicy, Stay Puft; 4 changing beers (sourced nationally; often Bristol Beer Factory, Thornbridge) Ⓗ
Multi-room city-centre pub in a historic building opposite the Principality Stadium. It is the Cardiff outlet for Rogerstone-based Tiny Rebel beers in cask and keg form. There are several rooms upstairs and downstairs, decorated in Tiny Rebel's unique style – some available for private hire. The pub holds regular quiz nights, bring your own vinyl nights and board game nights, as well as occasional brewery tap takeovers. There are four further handpumps for ciders and perries. ❀♿⇌●

Cowbridge

1 Town Hall Square
1 Town Hall Square, CF71 7DD
🌐 1townhallsquare.com
Wye Valley Butty Bach Ⓗ**; 3 changing beers (sourced nationally; often Coach, Grey Trees, Thornbridge)** Ⓗ/Ⓖ
Opened in 2017, this small pub is aimed at real ale enthusiasts. The small bar has seating off it while upstairs are another two rooms. The decor is traditional, with exposed stonework, tiled and wooden floors, and low beams. The entrance courtyard is a pleasant suntrap. No food is served but customers are welcome to bring their own. Butty Bach may be substituted by a beer from the Coach brewpub in Bridgend, which is under the same ownership. ❀♣●(X2,321)

WALES

Vale of Glamorgan Inn

51 High Street, CF71 7AE

☎ (01446) 772252

Glamorgan Jemima's Pitchfork; Hancocks HB; Wye Valley HPA, Butty Bach; 2 changing beers (sourced nationally; often Grey Trees, Salopian, VOG) Ⓗ

Popular pub where conversation is the main entertainment. The wooden-floored bar has a warming range fire; to the rear is a flagstone-floored area with another stove. Photographs and pictures of local interest adorn the walls. Outside is an attractive garden with a separate covered and heated smoking area. A now well-established annual beer festival coincides with the town's food and drink festival in May. Good-value home-made food is served at lunchtime (no food Sun). Real cider may sometimes be available.

Q❀◐●🚌(X2,321)🐾📶

Coytrahen

Nicholls Arms

Nicholls Road, CF32 0ED

☎ (01656) 724680

1 changing beer (often Sharp's, Wye Valley) Ⓗ

Grade II listed building on the Bridgend to Maesteg road. The truly stunning interior features wood-panelled and exposed stone walls, brass, paintings, a superb collection of Spode plates, and photographs commemorating the area's mining history. Seating includes luxurious old leather armchairs and settees. There is no music, games or TV. A friendly group of locals regularly enjoys the quality meals served in the dining room.

Q❀◐◑ÅP🚌(70,71)🐾📶

Cross Inn

Cross Inn Hotel ✔

Main Road, CF72 8AZ

☎ (01443) 223431

Hancocks HB; Wye Valley HPA; 2 changing beers (sourced nationally) Ⓗ

A welcoming, traditional pub which is popular with locals and visitors alike. Immaculately maintained throughout, the large single room is divided into a bar area and a comfortable lounge in which home-prepared meals are served. Sunday lunches are popular, as are themed food nights including cheese and grazing board evenings (booking recommended). There is a large car park at the rear. Q❀◐♿♣P🚌🐾📶

Cwmafan

Brit 𝕃 ✔

London Row, SA12 9AH

☎ (01639) 680247 🌐 thebrit.wales

3 changing beers (sourced regionally; often Grey Trees) Ⓗ

Local CAMRA branch Pub of the Year 2019, this is a cosy, dog-friendly establishment. It serves three rotating ales, often sourced locally, plus a real cider. The pub hosts summer and winter beer festivals and is also noted for its good food. Accommodation includes three bunk rooms plus a double en-suite, ideal for the Afan Valley mountain bikers. May occasionally close on a Monday in January and February. Q❀🛏◐◑♿●P🚌🐾📶

Cwmfelin

Cross Inn 🏆

Masteg Road, CF34 9LB

☎ (01656) 732476 🌐 cerddinbrewery.co.uk/cross-inn-maesteg.html

Cerddin Solar, Cascade; 3 changing beers (often Cerddin) Ⓗ

Home to Cerddin Brewery, this is a must-visit pub, with friendly locals and knowledgeable staff. Alongside the five cask beers, a range of bottle-conditioned beers is also available. The traditional two-roomed Valleys pub has a patio area outside the brewery. Its Tuesday night quiz raises money for the local food bank. Two times winner of CAMRA South Wales Pub of the Year.

Q❀⇌(Garth)♣●▯🚌(71)🐾📶

Deri

Old Club

93 Bailey Street, CF81 9HX

☎ (01443) 839333

Grey Trees Diggers Gold, Mosaic Pale Ale; 1 changing beer (sourced locally; often Grey Trees) Ⓗ

Friendly and informal independent bar – the club reference now purely historic. It is a rare regular outlet for award-winning Grey Trees beers, with a third ale occasionally added at weekends. A genuine community hub where locals come to relax, sports TV tends only to be turned on when there is interest. The bar is a short bus or taxi ride from Bargoed, or Sustrans route 469 offers a pleasant alternative on foot or bike. Cwm Darran Country Park is nearby in this pleasant semi-rural valley.

Å♣🚌(1)🐾📶

East Aberthaw

Blue Anchor

CF62 3DD

☎ (01446) 750329 🌐 blueanchoraberthaw.com

Brains Bitter; Theakston Old Peculier; Wadworth 6X; Wye Valley HPA; 1 changing beer (often Tomos Watkin) Ⓗ

Dating from 1380, this pub has been in the same family for over 75 years. Its thick stone walls and attractive thatched roof house a labyrinth of rooms, with stone floors, wooden beams and open fires adding to the character as well as to the pub's attraction for visitors. Up to five ales and award-winning food are served in the bar and upstairs restaurant. The guest beer and cider are often locally produced. Q❀◐◑●P🚌(303)🐾

Glan y llyn

Fagins Ale & Chop House 𝕃

9 Cardiff Road, CF15 7QD

☎ (029) 2081 1800

3 changing beers (sourced regionally; often Grey Trees, Twt Lol) Ⓗ

Quiet pub with a warm, friendly atmosphere enhanced by a log-burner and the buzz of pleasant chat. Handpulled beers come from several local suppliers including Grey Trees and nearby Twt Lol, as well as nationals. Two handpumps serve real cider. A selection of craft keg and bottled ciders is also sold. Good-value meals are available in the bar and rear dining area. A popular destination for dog walkers.

Q❀◐◑●🚌(26,132)🐾📶

Glynneath

Dinas Rock Hotel 𝕃

High Street, SA11 5AP

☎ (01639) 720105

2 changing beers (sourced regionally; often Evan Evans, Glamorgan, Tomos Watkin) Ⓗ

Traditional local in the centre of the village and a welcome refuge in an area where real ale is hard to find. Two wood-burning stoves and original stone walls make for a cosy atmosphere in winter. Live rugby including Six Nations and Ospreys fixtures on TV is ever-popular. Real cider hand-produced by one of the regulars is available seasonally. Live music often features at weekends.
Q☎❀♿♣●🚌(8,X7) ᯤ

Gorseinon

Mardy Inn ✔

117 High Street, SA4 4BR

☎ (01792) 890600

Greene King Abbot; Ruddles Best Bitter; Sharp's Doom Bar; 4 changing beers H

This Wetherspoon establishment was formerly a traditional high-street pub. Following a major refurbishment it is now modern in style, with a large single bar with several TVs for news and sport, and an adjoining airy extension overlooking the furnished patio area. Some interesting pictures of old Gorseinon adorn the walls, depicting the town and its inhabitants in years gone by. A good selection of local and national beers can be enjoyed in the beer garden.
☎❀◑♿●P🚌(110,111) ᯤ

Groeswen

White Cross Inn

CF15 7UT (overlooking Groeswen Chapel)

☎ (029) 2085 1332

4 changing beers (sourced nationally) H

Friendly little pub well worth finding, offering excellent choice and value. Six handpumps serve four changing beers and two ciders from local producer Williams Brothers. Four guest beers come in a diverse range of styles and strengths, with one always a dark brew. New and local breweries often feature, many making their debut here. The back room hosts meetings, including the popular Beer Bellies gathering, with visiting brewers and beer industry speakers. Occasional beer festivals are hosted. The road access is narrow. ☎❀♣●P🐾ᯤ

Gwaelod Y Garth

Gwaelod y Garth Inn 🏆

Main Road, CF15 9HH

☎ (029) 2081 0408 🌐 gwaelodygarthinn.co.uk

Wye Valley Bitter; 5 changing beers (sourced nationally; often Thornbridge) H

A characterful, stone-built, multi-award winning village local on the edge of Cardiff and on the lower slope of the Garth mountain. Frequented by locals, walkers and cyclists, it is the focus of the village. The pub offers a range of real ales along with two traditional ciders. There is a separate games room next to the main bar area along with a dining room upstairs. Local CAMRA Pub of the Year 2020. Q☎❀🛏◑♣●P🚌(26B)🐾ᯤ

Hendreforgan

Griffin Inn L

CF39 8YL

☎ (01443) 670379

Glamorgan Cwrw Gorslas/Bluestone Bitter, Jemima's Pitchfork H

You can be sure of a warm welcome at the Griffin (locally known as the Bog), which has been in the same family for generations. Recognised by CAMRA as a Real Heritage Pub of Wales, the immaculate decor features oak furniture, gleaming brasses and a Victorian counter with an 1870 till. The pub is a little difficult to find, but you will be rewarded by its quirky character and superbly kept beers. Q☎❀ÅP🚌(150,172)🐾

Kenfig

Prince of Wales

CF33 4PR

☎ (01656) 740356 🌐 princeofwalesinn.co.uk

Draught Bass; Gower Gold; Worthington's Bitter; 1 changing beer (sourced regionally) G

A heritage award-winning inn dating from the 15th century and steeped in local history. Visitors can expect three quality ales on gravity, good locally sourced food and a warm welcome. Family-friendly and popular with dog walkers, the pub is comfortable and cosy. Outside there is a stunning view over Kenfig Nature Reserve. The Draught Bass is renowned throughout the local area and outsells all the pub's lagers combined. Guest beers and cider are occasionally available.
Q☎❀◑●P🚌(63B) 🐾ᯤ

Killay

Village Bar Café

5-6 Swan Court, The Precinct, SA2 7BA

☎ (01792) 203311

Sharp's Doom Bar; 2 changing beers H

Situated in a small shopping precinct in Killay on the gateway to Gower, the Village has changed its focus from a traditional pub to a café bar. It retains a single, split-level bar, offering three real ales. There is a quiz on Sunday and Tuesday nights. The menu is varied and offers plenty of choice including vegetarian and vegan options. The kitchen is closed on Sunday and Monday, but the café/bar is open for coffee, cake and drinks.
☎◑♿♣P🚌(20,21) 🐾ᯤ

Llangennith

King's Head L

SA3 1HX

☎ (01792) 386212 🌐 kingsheadgower.co.uk

5 changing beers (often Evan Evans, Mumbles, Tomos Watkin) H

A row of three 17th-century stone-built cottages, this large pub has two separate bars and a variety of rooms for drinking and dining. Ales from local breweries are on the bar(up to five in summer, fewer in winter). An impressive variety of home-made food is served, with dishes inspired by fresh local produce. The pub is at the western end of the Gower Peninsular, a short distance from the sandy stretches of Llangennith Beach.
☎❀🛏◑Å♣●P🚌(116) 🐾ᯤ

Llanharry

Fox & Hounds

Llanharan Road, CF72 9LL

☎ (01443) 222124 🌐 foxandhoundsllanharry.co.uk

Courage Directors; 4 changing beers (sourced nationally; often Glamorgan, Oakham, Salopian) H

Traditional stone-built pub with a lounge containing an open fire and comfortable settees. There is also a games room and separate restaurant. The pub has a reputation for offering a good range of quality beers, with guests often modern in style, and has developed a keen following. It also has a growing reputation for serving good food. Live bands play on Saturday evenings. There is a car park to the side and beer garden at the rear.
☎❀◑♿♣P🚌(64,404) 🐾ᯤ

WALES

Llanmadoc

Britannia Inn ✔

SA3 1DB

☎ (01792) 386624 🌐 britanniagower.com

Gower Gold; Sharp's Doom Bar; 1 changing beer (sourced nationally) Ⓗ

Timbers from ships wrecked on the nearby coast were used in the construction of this pretty and popular 17th-century pub in a quiet corner of Gower. A cosy bar at the entrance serves good food and beer; the back bar area has been converted into a fine dining restaurant. Beer gardens to the front and rear offer stunning views over the nearby estuary, with an aviary and pet area popular with children. ❀◑▲♣P🚌(30)🐾📶

Llantwit Fardre

Bush Inn

Main Road, CF38 2EP

☎ (01443) 203958

Hancocks HB; 2 changing beers (sourced regionally) Ⓗ

Bustling pub in the centre of the village. The interior is semi open plan, with exposed stone walls and timber. Guest beers can be from national brewers, but are more often from independents, particularly larger Welsh providers. There is a quiz on Tuesday and Wednesday, plus a jam session on Thursday. A band often plays on Saturday, when the pub can get quite busy.
❀♿♣P🚌(100,400)🐾📶

Llantwit Major

Llantwit Major Rugby Club

Old Market, Boverton Road, CF61 1XZ

☎ (01446) 792276 🌐 llantwitmajor.rfc.wales

Sharp's Doom Bar; 2 changing beers (often Brains, Wye Valley) Ⓗ

A friendly community club, proud of its rugby history, which welcomes visitors. The regular beer and two changing guest ales are excellent value for money. There is a cosy, well-appointed lounge bar and a function room which hosts frequent live music and is available for hire. A small patio area is popular in summer and there is a covered smoking area. Dogs are welcome in the players' bar. ♿▲⇌P🚌(303,321)🐾📶

White Hart Inn 🏆 ✔

Wine Street, CF61 1RZ

☎ (01446) 796956 🌐 oldwhitehartllantwitmajor.co.uk

Ringwood Fortyniner; Wadworth Horizon; 1 changing beer (often Wainwright) Ⓗ

The Hart was awarded the local CAMRA County Community Pub of the Year in 2020, rewarding the licensees' participation in town events. Dating back to the 15th century, it is set in the picturesque town square. The cosy public bar has a large log-burner, two TVs and three ales on sale. There is a separate restaurant offering a range of traditional food. A large beer garden at the back hosts hugely popular music events and small beer festivals. ❀◑▲⇌♣🚌(303,95)🐾📶

Marcross

Horseshoe Inn

CF61 1ZG

☎ (01656) 890568 🌐 theshoesmarcross.co.uk

Sharp's Atlantic; Wye Valley Butty Bach; 2 changing beers (often Gower, VOG) Ⓗ

The Shoes is a beautiful 19th-century pub set in this hamlet. It usually has a range of three ales, one a Welsh brew. An extensive menu offers a choice of good pub fare. The bar is cosy on winter nights with a log-burner; the beer garden is delightful in summer. The pub and its friendly staff are popular with students from the local college. It is convenient for spectacular coastal walks, taking in the nearby Nash Point cliffs and lighthouse.
Q❀◑♣P🚌(303)

Morriston

Red Lion Inn ✔

49 Sway Road, SA6 6JA (opp fire station)

☎ (01792) 761870

Greene King Abbot; Ruddles Best Bitter; 6 changing beers (sourced nationally; often Draught Bass, Mumbles, Sharp's) Ⓗ

Deceptively spacious Wetherspoon pub with a large, comfortable, open-plan room featuring an open log fire at the front and high bar stools at the back. On the walls are a number of pictures depicting the long-gone industrial history of the area. A community board advertises trips to breweries and other local events. At least one guest ale comes from a local brewery.
❀◑♿●P🚌(4,X6)📶

Mumbles

Beaufort Arms 🄻

1 Castle Road, Norton, SA3 5TF

☎ (01792) 514246

Draught Bass; Glamorgan Jemima's Pitchfork; 2 changing beers (often Brains, Gower) Ⓗ

Charming 18th-century local with a welcoming atmosphere. Previously closed by its owning pub group, it was bought privately in 2017 by a couple who have renovated it and pleased the locals by increasing the range of beers on offer. The pub has a traditional main bar with TV and dartboard, and a small, comfortable lounge. Both rooms have real fires and there is a small beer garden at the rear. A quiz is held on Tuesday.
Q❀♣🚌(2A,3A)🐾📶

Mumbles Ale House

21 Westbourne Place, SA3 4DB

4 changing beers (sourced nationally; often Bristol Beer Factory, Glamorgan, Mantle) Ⓗ/Ⓖ

Traditional back-street corner local in the heart of Mumbles, dating from the 1860s and now specialising as an alehouse. Decorated in a traditional and comfortable style, it retains some original features of historic interest including a well in the bar area – the source of water in the days when the pub brewed its own beer. Live music plays most Sunday evenings. There is often a pop-up kitchen on a Monday evening. Q❀🚌(2A,3A)🐾

Park Inn 🄻

23 Park Street, SA3 4DA

☎ (01792) 366738

5 changing beers (sourced regionally; often Evan Evans, Mumbles, Tiny Rebel) Ⓗ

The convivial atmosphere in this small establishment in a village side street attracts discerning drinkers of all ages. Five handpumps dispense a varying range of beers, with particular emphasis on independent breweries from Wales and the west of England. Alongside a fine display of pumpclips are pictures of old Mumbles and its pioneering railway. A popular quiz is held on Thursday, with occasional music at weekends.
Q❀♣●🚌(2A,3A)🐾📶

Pilot Inn L

726 Mumbles Road, SA3 4EL
☎ 07897 895511 🌐 thepilotofmumbles.co.uk
Draught Bass; 6 changing beers (sourced nationally; often Pilot) H
Welcoming and friendly local on the seafront at Mumbles and home to the Pilot Brewery. Seven ales are always on the bar, usually including up to three rotating beers brewed on-site. A wide range of bottled ciders is also kept and hot drinks are served. This historic pub, built in 1849, is next to the coastal path and popular with lifeboatmen, locals, walkers and cyclists. A former Welsh CAMRA Pub of the Year. Q (2B)

Ty Cwrw

650 Mumbles Road, SA3 4EA
☎ 07488 298344
4 changing beers (sourced nationally; often Tenby, Tiny Rebel, Tomos Watkin) H
A new, independently owned and friendly pub – the name Ty Cwrw is Welsh for Beer House. It serves four real ales and six craft keg beers, all from a variety of Welsh breweries and listed on a large blackboard. Although the frontage appears to be narrow from the outside, there is a second room behind the front room and the long wooden bar. Both rooms have a light, modern decor including paintings from local artists. (2A,3A)

Neath

Borough Arms L

2 New Henry Street, SA11 1PH (off Briton Ferry rd, near Stockhams Corner roundabout)
☎ (01639) 644902
House beer (by Draught Bass); 4 changing beers (sourced regionally; often Glamorgan, Grey Trees) H
The emphasis in this welcoming local is very much on ales and conversation. The new landlord and brewer occasionally has his own ales on tap, but there is always a good choice from regional breweries. The pub holds an annual GlastonBorough festival in May featuring live music, plus a beer festival over the August bank holiday. Live acoustic music plays every Wednesday. Worth the 10-minute walk from the town centre. Q

David Protheroe L

7 Windsor Road, SA11 1LS (opp railway station)
☎ (01639) 622130
Greene King Abbot; Ruddles Best Bitter; Sharp's Doom Bar; 5 changing beers (sourced nationally; often Brains, Evan Evans, Grey Trees) H
A former police station and courthouse, the pub named after the first policeman to be posted in Neath. A Wetherspoon, it is ideally positioned in the centre of town, directly opposite the railway station and a short walk from the bus terminus. It has three permanent and up to five changing beers, often including a locally brewed ale. Ciders are also available.

Greyhound

11 Water Street, SA11 3EP
☎ 07896 418110
2 changing beers (sourced regionally) H
Around 400 years old, the pub has been attractively modernised and has an open-plan layout served by an L-shaped bar. It has a strong local following and is home to three darts teams. The choice of ales reflects customer preferences and usually includes a dark ale or stout. Live music features on Saturday and Sunday, karaoke on Friday. TV screens show live sport at an acceptable volume. The pub holds many charity events. Well worth visiting if in Neath town centre.

Penarth

Golden Lion

69 Glebe Street, CF64 1EF
☎ (029) 2070 1574
4 changing beers (often Glamorgan, Grey Trees, VOG) H
A genuine locals' pub with a reputation for serving some of the best-kept quality real ale in the area. Three or four beers from Welsh breweries are usually on tap, along with good-value food. The pub can sometimes be loud and lively with its popular jukebox and numerous sports TVs, and football and darts teams are among the regular customers. The small beer garden is a delight in warmer weather, with artificial grass and wall paintings depicting Penarth.

Pilot

67 Queen's Road, CF64 1DJ
☎ (029) 2071 0615
4 changing beers (often Grey Trees, Saltaire, VOG) H
The Pilot has established a reputation for high-quality beer, wine and food. Its ales are chosen from some of the best Welsh breweries, alongside more unusual offerings from around the country. The four handpumps usually serve up to three beers and often one real cider. The front bar is dog-friendly, there is pleasant seating outside at the front for warm weather, and the rear restaurant area with its log-fired stove is comfortable on winter days. Q

Windsor L

95 Windsor Road, CF64 1JE
☎ (029) 2070 8675
Brains Bitter, SA, Rev James; 3 changing beers (sourced nationally; often Brains) H
The Windsor was refurbished a few years ago to a high standard and has an emphasis on quality dining. It serves a selection of ales mainly from the core Brains range. The pub offers a relaxing environment, with a cosy front area with comfortable seating, a long dining/drinking space opposite the bar, and further tables to the rear. It is popular with families for Sunday lunch and lively on weekend evenings with live music acts.
Q (Dingle Rd) (92,93)

Pencoed

Little Penybont Arms

11 Penybont Road, CF35 5PY
☎ 07734 767937
3 changing beers (often 3 Piers, Beartown, VOG) G
Cosy micropub offering a couple of changing beers on gravity, craft keg beer, 10 ciders and more than 15 single malt whiskies and gins. The Steak & Stamp restaurant two doors down is under the same ownership and serves the same choice of drinks. The pub sells excellent bar snacks include pork pies, nuts and home-made pork scratchings. A quiz and pizza night is held on Wednesday. Since opening, the pub has built up a strong local following. Q

Penderyn

Red Lion

Church Road, CF44 9JR
☎ (01685) 811914 🌐 redlionpenderyn.com
Brains Rev James; Draught Bass; Fuller's ESB; Gower Gold; 1 changing beer (sourced nationally) G
Family-owned drovers inn on the edge of the Brecon Beacons National Park. Parts date back to the 12th century – at one time it was a Welsh longhouse. Much renovated over the last 40 years, there are two log fires

WALES

in the small but delightfully cosy bar. Darker, traditional ales predominate, with Fuller's ESB a stalwart for many years. Two or more local ciders and perries are always available. High-quality food is served (booking advised as it can get busy). Q❀◑♿●P🐾ᯤ

Peterston-super-Ely

Sportsman's Rest ⓛ

CF5 6LH

☎ (01446) 760675 🌐 thesportsmansrest.co.uk

Otter Ale; Wye Valley HPA; 2 changing beers (sourced nationally) Ⓗ

Attractive village pub with outdoor seating front and rear and a children's play area. The comfortable interior includes a bar area for drinkers and a split-level dining section. An emphasis on quality food – with special deals and themed food evenings – is balanced by a good range of real ales, some unusual for the area. Community and charity events are well supported, including an annual beer festival to coincide with the village duck race in May. ❀◑♿●P🚌(320)🐾ᯤ

Pontardawe

Pontardawe Inn ⓛ

123 Herbert Street, SA8 4ED

☎ (01792) 447562 🌐 pontardaweinnpub.co.uk

Marston's Pedigree; Ringwood Fortyniner; 5 changing beers (sourced nationally; often Banks's, Jennings, Mumbles) Ⓗ

Former Welsh longhouse later converted to a drovers' pub. A side room and stable were added in 1850 as a sorting depot for the Royal Mail. The central bar serves two regular and up to five changing ales, including a locally produced beer, as well as a range of real ciders. Good food is available daily. Seasonal beer festivals and music festivals are held, and live music features at weekends. The award-winning pub is alongside the River Tawe and local cycle path. ❀◑♿●P🚌(56,X6)🐾ᯤ

Pontsarn

Aberglais Inn

CF48 2TS (between Trefechan and Pontsticill) SO043098

☎ (01685) 377344 🌐 aberglais.com

Wye Valley Bitter, Butty Bach; 3 changing beers (sourced nationally; often Cold Black Label, Grey Trees) Ⓗ

Located on the way to Pontsticill Reservoir, the pub has a pleasant and relaxing main bar with a light decor and a cosy wood stove, and an adjoining restaurant area. It is popular with families, hikers, holidaymakers and cyclists on the nearby trails. Dogs are welcome in the bar and beer garden. Good food is served and booking is essential on Saturday and recommended at other times. ❀◑P🚌🐾

Pontsticill

Butchers Arms Restaurant, Bunkhouse & Brewpub

CF48 2UE

☎ (01685) 723544 🌐 butchersbunkhouse.com

3 changing beers (sourced regionally; often Crafty Dragon, Grey Trees, Twin Taff) Ⓗ

Located on the southern edge of the Brecon Beacons with spectacular views. A roaring log fire and traditional pub decor add to a cosy welcome. Food is served throughout the day. Bunkhouse accommodation is available, as well as bike hire to explore the many nearby trails. In-house Crafty Dragon beers are sometimes on offer, along with well kept and varied guest beers. There is seating outside and a large car park. Q❀🛏◑♣●P🚌🐾ᯤ

Red Cow

Main Road, CF48 2UN

☎ (01685) 387775 🌐 redcow.wales

Wye Valley Bitter; house beer (by Grey Trees); 1 changing beer (sourced regionally; often Boss, Cotleigh, Twt Lol) Ⓗ

A handsome and tranquil pub in the middle of Pontsticill with views of the Brecon Beacons. Warm, friendly and inviting, the bar is open plan and comfortably furnished, with a log fire in a cosy snug. Permanent beers are from Grey Trees and Wye Valley; the rotating guest is often from Twt Lol or Cotleigh. Popular for meals, food is served until 9pm. There is a garden and a large car park. Q❀◑P🚌🐾ᯤ

Pontypridd

Bunch of Grapes ⓛ ✔

Ynysangharad Road, CF37 4DA (off A4054)

☎ (01443) 402934 🌐 bunchofgrapes.org.uk

Grey Trees Diggers Gold; 9 changing beers (sourced nationally; often Oakham, Salopian, Tiny Rebel) Ⓗ

A short walk from the town centre, this popular pub has won multiple awards. The guest ales range always changes and includes at least one local beer. Two ciders are also sold. Events include beer, cider and food festivals. A popular quiz is held on Tuesday evening. The separate highly acclaimed restaurant has undergone recent refurbishment and serves locally sourced produce. Q❀◑⇌●P🚌🐾

Llanover Arms ⓛ

Bridge Street, CF37 4PE (opp N entrance to Ynysangharad Park, off A470)

☎ (01443) 403215

3 changing beers (sourced nationally; often Salopian) Ⓗ

Built around 1794 to serve thirsty boatmen on the newly opened Glamorganshire Canal, this historic free house has been owned by the same family for over a century. It has three rooms linked by passageways – all with their own distinct character and atmosphere. Nearby is the famous old town bridge and Ynysangharad Park with its restored National Lido of Wales. The Taff Trail passes close by. Q❀⇌♣P🚌🐾

Patriot Bar ⓛ

25B Taff Street, CF37 4UA

☎ (01443) 407915

Rhymney Bevans Bitter, Bitter, Export; 2 changing beers (often Rhymney) Ⓗ

A Rhymney Brewery tied pub, near the bus station and a short walk from the railway station. Its exceptionally well-kept beers include two guests from the Rhymney range. Trade is brisk, with beers turning over quickly, helped by the keen prices. Real cider is sometimes stocked. The pub is easy to find, located in a former shop in Taff Street. It is fondly known as the Wonky Bar, recalling its former twisted entrance. It can be loud and bustling but is a gem. ⇌🚌🐾ᯤ

Tumble Inn ✔

4-9 Broadway, CF37 1BA

☎ (01443) 484390

Greene King Abbot; Ruddles Best Bitter; Sharp's Doom Bar; 3 changing beers (sourced regionally; often Boss, Glamorgan, Rhymney) Ⓗ

A long single bar serves this large open-plan Wetherspoon/Lloyds No.1 Bar. The food service offers a varied choice and covers long hours. Monday is poker night, Wednesday is quiz night. The patio outside is divided into smoking and no-smoking areas. Handy for the town centre and railway station, several main bus routes pass by.

Port Talbot

Lord Caradoc

69-73 Station Road, SA13 1NW
☎ (01639) 896007
Greene King Abbot; Ruddles Best Bitter; Sharp's Doom Bar; 5 changing beers (sourced nationally; often Glamorgan, Rhymney, Tomos Watkin) [H]
On the main shopping street, this Wetherspoon has a relaxed atmosphere, with a spacious open-plan layout and family-friendly area. The choice of beers is open to suggestion from customers, with a wide range always available, frequently including a locally brewed ale. The walls are adorned with historic photographs of the town and famous local people. The pub has been recognised by Wetherspoon for its high standard of catering on several occasions. P

Porth

Rheola

Rheola Road, CF39 0LF
☎ (01443) 682633
Rhymney Bevans Bitter, Bitter, Export [H]
Acquired by the Rhymney Brewery in 2015, this friendly local sells a range of Rhymney beers. A large detached building, it is situated at the confluence of the two Rhondda rivers, and is well served by both rail and bus. The bar features a jukebox, pool table and dartboard, and is often quite lively. The comfortable lounge generally provides a quiet haven and tends only to get busy at weekends. Activities include a quiz, whist and monthly open mic nights. P

Porthcawl

Lorelei Hotel

36-38 Esplanade Avenue, CF36 3YU
☎ (01656) 788342 loreleihotel.co.uk
Draught Bass [G]**; Rhymney Export; 2 changing beers** [H]
Near the seafront, the town centre and the Grand Pavilion, this is the 22nd year the Lorelei has been in this Guide. Good-quality and value-for-money food is served evenings (no food Mon eve) and Sunday lunchtime. Four cask beers are available plus cider in summer. Beer festivals are held twice a year on Grand National and Halloween weekends. Built around the end of the 19th century, during World War I it was two separate buildings – one used as a hospice for injured soldiers.
Q

Reynoldston

King Arthur Hotel

Higher Green, SA3 1AD (on village green)
☎ (01792) 390775 kingarthurhotel.co.uk
Gower Gold; Sharp's Doom Bar; 2 changing beers (sourced nationally; often Glamorgan, Tenby, Tiny Rebel) [H]
Traditional family-owned hotel and acclaimed wedding venue, at the foot of Cefn Bryn in beautiful Gower, overlooking the village green. There is covered outdoor seating by the pub entrance and a large seating area on the green itself. The cosy, atmospheric main and rear bars are welcoming to drinkers and diners, serving home-cooked food made with local produce. Main meals and bar snacks are available all day, as well as breakfasts for non-residents. P (118,119)

St Athan

Roost

Rock Road, CF62 4PG
☎ (01446) 753715 theroostonrockroad.com
Hancocks HB; Wye Valley HPA; 1 changing beer (often Glamorgan) [H]
Formerly the Four Bells, a major refurbishment has given the pub a more modern style but some original features remain – the floorboards now form the bar front. Food is of a high standard and the menu is varied. Beer is always in top condition. Barbecues and other events are hosted on the patio and lawn outside in summer. Accommodation is in five rooms.
QP (304)

Sketty

Vivian Arms

106 Gower Road, SA2 9BT (at Sketty Cross, jct A4118 and A4216)
☎ (01792) 516194
Brains Bitter, SA, SA Gold, Rev James; 1 changing beer [H]
On the main crossroads in Sketty, the Vivs is a spacious pub that attracts a wide range of customers, young and old. It has a mixture of seating areas and plenty of TV screens throughout showing live sport. There is a small meeting room. A popular carvery is held on Sunday. Live music features on Friday and occasionally Saturday, a general knowledge quiz on Sunday and a music quiz on Wednesday. (20,21)

Swansea

Bank Statement

57-58 Wind Street, SA1 1EP
☎ (01792) 455477
Sharp's Doom Bar; 5 changing beers (sourced nationally; often Exmoor, Fuller's, Jennings) [H]
A former Midland Bank, sympathetically transformed by Wetherspoon while retaining its original ornate interior. Trading as a Lloyds No.1, the pub is at the heart of the city's popular bar quarter and has a large ground floor with plenty of seating. Attracting all ages, it is busy throughout the week. Sport is shown on its many screens. The bottled beer selection includes real ales.

Brunswick Arms

3 Duke Street, SA1 4HS (between St Helens Rd and Walter Rd)
☎ (01792) 465676 brunswickswansea.com
Butcombe Original; Courage Directors; Wye Valley Butty Bach [H]**; 2 changing beers (sourced nationally)** [H]/[G]
A side-street pub with the air of a country inn in the city. Wooden beams and comfortable seating create a traditional, relaxing atmosphere, and a local resident artist's work is displayed for sale. Up to six beers are usually available – one of the changing beers is dispensed on gravity, often from a local microbrewery. A popular quiz is held on Monday, live music on Thursday and Saturday, and an open mic session on the second Tuesday of the month. Food is served daily.
(200)

No Sign Bar
56 Wind Street, SA1 1EG
(01792) 465300 nosignwinebar.com
Gower Gold; 3 changing beers (sourced nationally; often Butcombe, Mumbles, Tiny Rebel)
Historic narrow bar established in 1690, formerly known as Mundays Wine Bar and reputedly a regular haunt of Dylan Thomas. The interior is divided into separate areas, with architectural remains from various periods of the pub's past still in evidence. Quality food and wine are sold, and up to five real ciders. Live music features in the bar on Friday, Saturday and often Sunday evenings. Bands also play in the Vault basement later at night.

Potters Wheel
85-86 The Kingsway, SA1 5JE
(01792) 465113
Adnams Broadside; Fuller's London Pride; Ruddles Best Bitter; Sharp's Doom Bar; 6 changing beers (sourced nationally)
A city-centre Wetherspoon outlet with a long sprawling bar area offering various seating arrangements, attracting customers of all ages and backgrounds. An interesting selection of guest beers is kept, with a commitment to local breweries. Real cider is always available. Photographs on the walls feature local dignitaries associated with the area's industrial past, particularly the ceramics and pottery industries. Look for the CAMRA board and beer suggestion box.

Queen's Hotel
Gloucester Place, SA1 1TY
(01792) 521531
Theakston Best Bitter, Old Peculier; 2 changing beers (sourced nationally; often Bristol Beer Factory, Fuller's, Glamorgan)
This vibrant free house is near the Dylan Thomas Theatre, City Museum, National Waterfront Museum and marina. The walls display photographs depicting Swansea's rich maritime heritage. The pub enjoys strong local support, and home-cooked lunches are popular. Evening entertainment includes a Sunday quiz, bingo on Wednesday and live music on Saturday. This is a rare local outlet for Theakston Old Peculier in addition to a seasonal guest beer, often from a local microbrewery. Local CAMRA Pub of the Year.

Uplands Tavern
42 Uplands Crescent, Uplands, SA2 0PG
(01792) 458242
Greene King IPA, Abbot; 2 changing beers (sourced locally)
Situated in the heart of Swansea's student quarter, the Tav attracts regulars from all walks of life. The large single-room pub is a former haunt of Dylan Thomas, who is commemorated in a separate snug area. The pub has a reputation for the quality and variety of its live music at weekends and open mic nights on Mondays. Quiz night is Tuesday. Shufl board (shuffleboard with a concave playing surface) is a popular new game here. There is a large heated outdoor drinking area.

Westbourne
1 Brynymor Road, SA1 4JQ
(01792) 476637 westbourneswansea.com
Greene King Abbot; Sharp's Doom Bar; 2 changing beers
Located on the western fringe of the city centre, this family-run street-corner pub has a single split-level bar; outside there is a heated terrace. Popular with diners, the menu includes vegan options (it is advisable to book for Sunday lunch). A quiz is held on Tuesday evening. The pub does not subscribe to sports TV channels but will show major sporting events on Freeview. (2,3)

Trefforest

Otley Arms
Forest Road, CF37 1SY (on gyratory system)
(01443) 402033 theotley.co.uk
Mabby Blue, Red, Black, Green; 3 changing beers (sourced regionally; often Grey Trees, Salopian, Tiny Rebel)
Hospitable and informal pub, a haven for students from the nearby university and locals alike. The open-plan bar has a log fire and leather sofas. A wide variety of guest and craft ales is on offer along with Mabby beers brewed on-site. Traditional food is of a high standard, and the service and atmosphere are always friendly. Board games are available and a quiz is held on Monday. The pub is well served by train and bus.
(90,100)

Rickards Arms
61 Park Street, CF37 1SN
(01443) 402305
3 changing beers (sourced nationally; often Grey Trees)
Close to Trefforest railway station and backing on to the railway line, the pub is popular with students at the nearby University of South Wales. It is divided into four areas, all served by a single bar. Three guest beers are available, one usually local and two national. Food is good value, especially the famous cooked breakfasts. The pub hosts regular quiz and music nights.
(90,100)

Treorchy

Pencelli Hotel
Pencae Terrace, CF42 6HL
(01443) 775181
5 changing beers (sourced nationally; often Glamorgan, Salopian, Tiny Rebel)
Two large rooms are served by a central bar offering a range of beer styles. A log fire adds warmth in winter. The pub has a strong musical following and hosts live bands on Thursdays, Saturdays and bank holidays. It is easily reached by bus or train and has ample car parking opposite. A winner of many local CAMRA awards, and Wales CAMRA Cider and Perry Pub of the Year 2020.

Tyla Garw

Boar's Head
Coedcae Lane, CF72 9EZ (600yds from A473 over level crossing)
(01443) 225400
Glamorgan Jemima's Pitchfork; 3 changing beers (sourced regionally; often Oakham, Salopian)
This award-winning pub includes a bar, two dining areas, a gin bar and Piglets lounge, which is a coffee bar during the day. A recently added zero waste shop (selling organic, vegan and gluten-free foods, and local food and drink) is in keeping with the pub's role as a community hub. Classic pub meals include Sunday lunch (booking advisable). Quiz night is every other Tuesday. Pontyclun railway station is a 10-minute walk. P

Upper Church Village

Farmers Arms ✔

St Illtyd Road, CF38 1EB

☎ (01443) 205766

Brains Rev James; 2 changing beers (sourced regionally) Ⓗ

Comfortable village local with one large bar and an attractive split-level beer garden and patio. The changing beers can include national brands but are more often unusual ales for the area. A popular quiz night is hosted on Tuesday, but beer and conversation are the main attractions. Traditional pub food is available most days (no food Sun). ❀◑◐P🚌(90)🐾

Upper Killay

Railway Inn Ⓛ

553 Gower Road, SA2 7DS

☎ (01792) 203946

Swansea Deep Slade Dark, Bishopswood Bitter, Three Cliffs Gold, Original Wood; 1 changing beer Ⓗ

Classic locals' pub set in woodlands in the Clyne Valley. The adjacent former railway line forms part of Route 4 of the National Cycle Network. There are two small rooms at the front – one the main bar and snug – and a larger lounge at the rear. In winter the fire in the lounge provides welcome warmth and cheer. At least one guest ale is kept alongside the Swansea Brewing Company beers. A large area outside hosts occasional barbecues and music events. Q❀♣●P🚌(118)🐾

Wick

Star Inn 🏆

Ewenny Road, CF71 7QA

☎ (01656) 890080 🌐 thestarinnwick.co.uk

Glamorgan Welsh Pale Ale; 2 changing beers (often Glamorgan) Ⓗ

Originally three farm cottages, the interior comprises a traditional bar with pew seating, a lounge/diner with flagstone flooring – both with log-burning fires – and an upstairs pool/function room. The friendly landlady, her staff and locals help make this a pleasant place to visit. Good food is available – the meat is supplied by an award-winning local farm butcher. Dogs are welcome in the bar. Local CAMRA Pub of the Year 2020.
Q♨❀◑◐♣●P🚌(303)🐾📶

Ystalyfera

Wern Fawr Ⓛ

47 Wern Road, SA9 2LX (on main top road through village)

☎ (01639) 843625

9 Lives Amber, Dark, Gold; 1 changing beer (sourced nationally) Ⓗ

Entering this quirky pub feels like stepping back in time. Run by the same family for three generations, the two-roomed inn is full of industrial memorabilia from the local area. It has a cosy lounge and a friendly locals' bar with an old-fashioned stove that keeps the room toasty in wintertime. The beers are brewed locally by 9 Lives Brewing, accompanied by one changing guest ale.
Q♣🚌(X6)🐾

WALES

Queen's Hotel, Swansea (Photo: Reading Tom/Flickr CC BY 2.0)

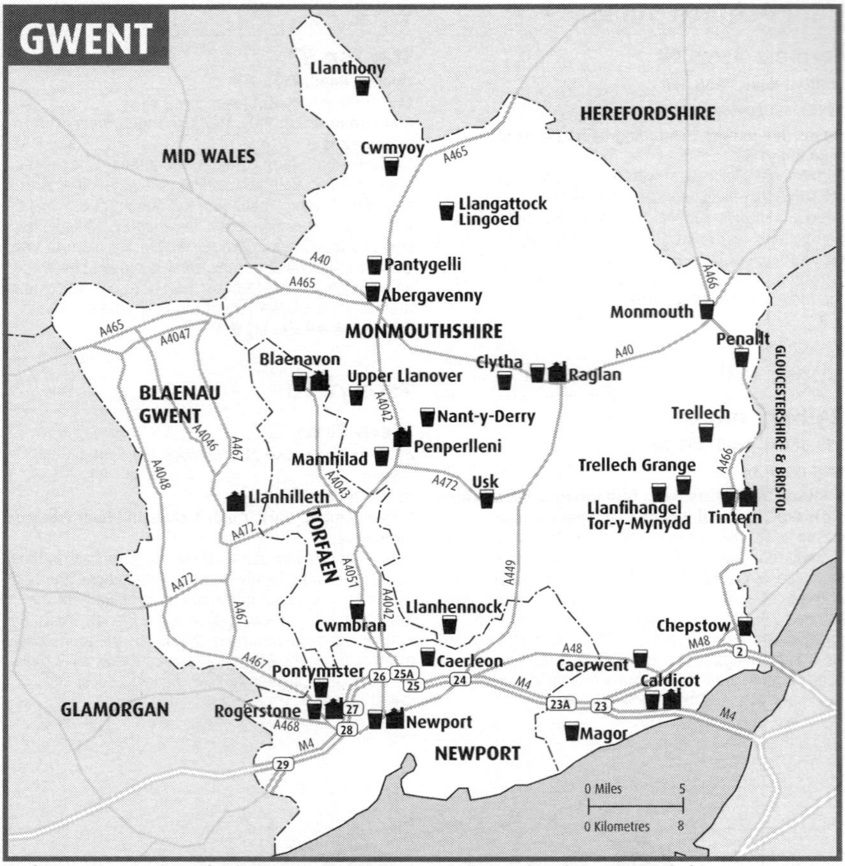

Authority areas covered: Blaenau Gwent UA, Caerphilly UA (part), Monmouthshire UA, Newport UA, Torfaen UA

Abergavenny

Cantreff Inn

61 Brecon Road, NP7 7RA

(01873) 855888

Grey Trees Diggers Gold; Wye Valley Butty Bach; 1 changing beer (often Grey Trees)

Low ceilings, a bay window, a large wall mirror and a variety of seating including a settee give character to the bar at this late 19th-century pub. It is the only permanent outlet for Grey Trees beers in the locality. Well-known for its good quality meals, served in a separate dining room at weekends. The licensees welcome pooches. To the rear, there is a pleasant garden. The pub is on the main road to Brecon and the local hospital.
P (X4)

Grofield

Baker Street, NP7 5BB

(01873) 858939 grofield.com

Rhymney Bevans Bitter; Sharp's Doom Bar; 1 changing beer (sourced nationally; often Kingstone, Untapped)

Close to the pedestrianised town centre, library and cinema, this pub is often busy throughout the day, and is a popular place for lunch (no food Mon). It has a single large U-shaped bar on two levels decorated with contemporary prints. To the rear is a well-maintained garden. A quiz is held every Sunday evening. This is a family-run free house with an experienced licensee.
(47,X4)

Station Hotel

37 Brecon Road, NP7 5UH

(01873) 854759

Draught Bass; Rhymney Bitter; Wye Valley HPA; 1 changing beer (sourced nationally)

One of CAMRA's Real Heritage Pubs of Wales, this two-roomed local has a long, thin bar and a small snug with a serving hatch. On the far wall of the bar, a large mural depicts a female jazz singer. Free music sessions are hosted every Friday evening and a regular quiz night on Wednesday. P (X4)

REAL ALE BREWERIES

Anglo Oregon Newport
Kingstone Tintern
Mad Dog Penperlleni
Rhymney Blaenavon
Tiny Rebel Rogerstone
Tudor Llanhilleth
Untapped Raglan
Zulu Alpha Caldicot

Blaenavon

Lion Hotel

41 Broad Street, NP4 9NH
☎ (01495) 792516 🌐 thelionhotelblaenavon.co.uk
Tudor Black Rock; house beer (by Tomos a Lilford) Ⓗ
A quality hotel for visitors to local world heritage sites as well as a place for regulars to enjoy. The interior is tastefully decorated with light wood and soft furnishing. The restaurant has an excellent reputation for its cuisine. The beer range includes a specially commissioned house ale alongside a Tudor guest ale that seems to have taken up residence! 🛋❀🛏◑P🚌(X24,30)📶

Caerleon

Hanbury Arms 🄻 ✔

Uskside, High Street, NP18 1AA
☎ (01633) 420361
Brains Bitter, SA Gold, Rev James; 2 changing beers (sourced locally; often Brains) Ⓗ
Caerleon's oldest inhabited building has a Norman tower forming part of its fabric. The large spacious interior offers a choice of connected drinking and dining areas, some with riverside views. Alfred, Lord Tennyson wrote his 'Idylls of the King' here, and there is a wall plaque to commemorate this event. Reasonably priced food is available all day, while the range of Brains beers is supplemented by a guest, often from the Brains craft brewery. Quiz nights are Sundays and Tuesdays.
Q🛋❀◑P🚌(27,28)🐾📶

Caerwent

Coach & Horses

Green Lane, NP26 5AX
☎ (01291) 420352 🌐 caerwent-coachandhorses.co.uk
Brains Rev James; Wye Valley HPA, Butty Bach; 1 changing beer (sourced regionally; often Gower) Ⓗ
Popular two-bar inn in a village with Roman fortress remains all around. A smart, dog-friendly public bar at the front links to a lounge behind, with plentiful comfortable space in the large dining area. A fourth handpump has expanded choice to two Wye Valley ales, Brains Rev James and a changing guest. Conversation rules and this thriving pub is well established as the centre of village life. Three B&B rooms are available.
🛋❀🛏◑♣P🚌(73)🐾📶

Caldicot

Cross Inn

1 Newport Road, NP26 4BG
☎ (01291) 409042 🌐 crossinncaldicot.co.uk
Sharp's Doom Bar; 2 changing beers (sourced nationally) Ⓗ
In the pedestrianised centre of Caldicot, this pub has a large bar that is lively from late afternoon and at weekends. A central wall with a TV above a fireplace separates the open-plan bar area from a secluded seating space. A large clock fixed to a pillar is useful if you have a bus to catch outside. A second, smaller bar has a pool table. Three real ales are served: Doom Bar plus two ever-varying guests. 🛋❀♿♣P🚌(62,74)🐾📶

Chepstow

Chepstow Athletic Club 🄻

Mathern Road, Bulwark, NP16 5JJ (off Bulwark Rd)
☎ (01291) 622126 🌐 chepstowac.co.uk
St Austell Cornish Best Bitter; Wye Valley Butty Bach; 2 changing beers (sourced regionally) Ⓗ
A friendly and comfortable meeting place for a broad cross-section of the local community. The Athy has gained a far-reaching reputation for the quality, consistency and value of its cask ales. Conversation rules, with two TV screens for avid sports viewers muted except for Wales rugby internationals, when the ale pumps work overtime. An upstairs function room also serves real ale and a suntrap patio is popular in summer. CAMRA members gain a particularly warm welcome. Opening hours may vary. 🛋❀♿♣P🚌(73,X74)

Queen's Head 🏆 🄻

Moor Street, NP16 5DD
☎ 07793 889613
8 changing beers (sourced regionally; often Gower, Grey Trees, Untapped) Ⓗ
A classic, basic and welcoming micropub where quality, mainly local beers – usually including a stout or porter – and ciders are the centre of attention. Although Welsh brews predominate, other nations' beers are periodically showcased. With no TV or games machines, the only regular entertainment is conversation. Pub crawls and outings to beer festivals are often arranged. Local CAMRA Pub of the Year for the last five years.
Q⇌●🚌(73,X74)🐾

Three Tuns Inn 🄻

32 Bridge Street, NP16 5EY
☎ (01291) 645797
5 changing beers (sourced regionally; often Kingstone, Wadworth, Wye Valley) Ⓗ
A pleasant walk from the town centre and close to the River Wye, this fine 16th-century inn sits in the shadow of the stunning Chepstow Castle, where open-air plays and concerts take place in the summer. Local beers are attractively priced, and locally sourced food is served at lunchtime. 🛋❀🛏◐⇌●P🚌(X74,73)🐾

Clytha

Clytha Arms 🄻

Groesonen Road, NP7 9BW
☎ (01873) 840206 🌐 clytha-arms.com
Uley Bitter; Untapped Whoosh, UPA; 3 changing beers (sourced nationally) Ⓗ
On the old road between Abergavenny and Raglan, this multi CAMRA award-winning pub has been in the Guide for well over a quarter of a century. Set in extensive grounds, the building started out as a dower house. It has a single bar, a separate dining area and good-quality accommodation. Beers from the nearby Untapped Brewing are always available, together with a wide and eclectic mix of regularly changing beers from around the country. Q🛋❀🛏◑▲♣●P🚌(83)🐾

Cwmbran

Bush Inn 🄻

Graig Road, Upper Cwmbran, NP44 5AN
☎ (01633) 483764 🌐 thebushuppercwmbran.co.uk
3 changing beers (sourced regionally; often Tudor, Twt Lol) Ⓗ
A cosy nook tucked into the slopes of Mynydd Maen, the split-level interior giving a clue that the pub was originally two cottages. Pictures of the inn and its formerly industrial locality adorn one wall. The front patio and decking give scenic views over Cwmbran and beyond. There is some form of entertainment most evenings – themed food nights (curry, pizza, steak) are always popular. An interesting beer range comes from breweries large and small, local and national.
🛋❀◑♣●P🚌(1,8)🐾📶

Mount Pleasant Ⓛ
Wesley Street, Old Cwmbran, NP44 3LX
☎ (01633) 712176
2 changing beers (sourced locally; often Kingstone, Mumbles, Rhymney) Ⓗ
Nestled among the churches of Old Cwmbran, the Mount is a traditional community hub in which to enjoy a drink, perhaps to accompany a meal. Compact, homely and open plan, the pub's three spaces provide informal dining and drinking areas. Sunday lunches are particularly popular. The handpumps favour local and independent breweries from south Wales and the English South-West. The front terrace gets busy in the warmer months. ♘❀◑♣●P🚌(6)🐾📶

Queen Inn
Upper Cwmbran Road, Upper Cwmbran, NP44 5AX
☎ (01633) 484252
3 changing beers (sourced regionally) Ⓗ
Set in an attractive location, with a mountain slope behind it and a rushing stream in front, the building was once a terrace of three cottages which are now a dining room, bar and lounge. The latter leads out to a well-designed smoking space, well-equipped children's play area and car park. Food is popular, with traditional dishes to the fore, while the beers are often from local breweries. Real cider is also popular.
♘❀◑♣●P🚌(1,8)🐾

Cwmyoy

Queen's Head
NP7 7NE SO311221
☎ (01873) 890241
Kingstone Classic Ⓗ
A venerable institution in the beautiful Llanthony valley, known locally as Billy's in honour of the landlord of 40 years' standing. Only a couple of miles off the main A465 at Llanvihangel Crucorney, yet in a truly rural spot, the pub looks over the River Honddu and up to the open hills beyond. Thick walls, heavy beams and flagstone floors reflect the building's ancient origins. This is National Park walking country, with sheep heavily outnumbering the local population. Q❀P

Llanfihangel Tor-y-Mynydd

Star on the Hill
NP15 1DT (near Llansoy)
☎ (01291) 650256 🌐 thestaronthehill.co.uk
Kingstone Gold; Tiny Rebel Cwtch; Wye Valley Butty Bach; 1 changing beer (sourced regionally; often Wye Valley) Ⓗ
The public bar of this traditional 16th-century inn is comfortably furnished with sofas and warmed by a large wood-burning stove. The separate restaurant extends into a large conservatory and has three more fireplaces. Quality home-cooked food is made to order. Disabled access is at the back. The pub produces its own cider and occasionally perry, which are sold seasonally. Well worth seeking out. ♘❀◑♿⛺♣P🐾

Llangattock Lingoed

Hunter's Moon Inn
NP7 8RR SO361201
☎ (01873) 821499 🌐 hunters-moon-inn.co.uk
Wye Valley HPA Ⓗ/Ⓖ**, Butty Bach** Ⓗ**; 1 changing beer (sourced regionally)** Ⓗ/Ⓖ
Set in a hamlet in rolling countryside next to a medieval church and the long-distance Offa's Dyke Path, this is a classic village pub. Heavy wooden beams, bare stone walls and flagstoned floors reflect the ancient nature of the building. It has a separate bar and dining area, with food served throughout the day. Outside, two contrasting and well-maintained garden areas provide excellent views. Q♘❀🛏◑♣P🐾📶

Llanhennock

Wheatsheaf
NP18 1LT ST353927
☎ (01633) 420468
🌐 thewheatsheafatllanhennock.webs.com
Fuller's London Pride; 2 changing beers (sourced regionally) Ⓗ
A fixture in this Guide for over 30 years, the pub has probably remained almost unchanged over that time. The main bar is to the right, with a slightly smaller, cosier bar to the left. The walls are festooned with old photographs, bric-a-brac and memorabilia. There are views of the hills miles away from front and back, plus a secluded garden. Boules is played seriously in the car park. There is usually a beer from a local brewery available. ♘❀⛺♣P🐾📶

Llanthony

Half Moon
NP7 7NN SO286279
☎ (01873) 890611 🌐 halfmoon-llanthony.co.uk
Wye Valley Butty Bach; 1 changing beer (sourced regionally; often Wye Valley) Ⓗ
In the heart of the Black Mountains close to the romantic ruins of medieval Llanthony Abbey, in an area considered to be among the most beautiful places in Wales. It has a single flagstone-floored bar and wood-burning stove, with a small curtained snug at the far end. There is a separate dining area and a garden space. Simple accommodation is available throughout the year; the bar will open for guests in winter. Q♘🛏◑⛺♣P🐾📶

Magor

Wheatsheaf Ⓛ ✔
The Square, NP26 3HN
☎ (01633) 880608 🌐 wheatsheafinnmagor.co.uk
4 changing beers (sourced regionally; often Rhymney, Tiny Rebel) Ⓗ
Village pub with a sense of longevity within its whitewashed walls and old wooden beams. It has a taproom, lounge and restaurant. The regulars tend to gather somewhere near the handpumps in the lounge. Family-run, the team ensures there is an interesting choice of ales from breweries near and far to complement the fresh food menu. A partly covered garden/patio is a pleasant spot on warm days.
♘❀◑♿♣P🚌(62,X74)🐾📶

Mamhilad

Horseshoe Inn ✔
Old Abergavenny Road, NP4 8QZ
☎ (01873) 880542 🌐 horseshoeinn.org
Tiny Rebel Cwtch; house beer (by Sharp's); 1 changing beer (sourced regionally) Ⓗ
A fine country hostelry and popular dining venue, well worth seeking out. Locally-brewed ales alongside other favourite beers, plus up to four ciders, provide a fine accompaniment to the excellent food. The menu offers a wide range of dishes, with extra choices on the specials board. Outside, admire the pleasant hillside country which brings in thirsty and hungry walkers to this traditional country inn. Q♘❀◑⛺●P🐾📶

Monmouth

Punch House ✔

4 Agincourt Square, NP25 3BT

☎ (01600) 713855

Brains Dark, Rev James Gold, Rev James Ⓗ

The traditional interior displays interesting artefacts including the door of the old town gaol. Food is very much to the fore, starting with breakfast/brunch, but drinkers are well catered for. Letting rooms are available, and live entertainment features on Friday evening. The family-friendly pub, well-loved for generations, welcomes children until 9pm. ❀🛏◐♿▲🚌(69)🐾📶

Nant-y-Derry

Foxhunter Inn

NP7 9DN

☎ (01873) 881101 🌐 foxhunterinn.com

Felinfoel Double Dragon; Untapped Whoosh; Wye Valley Butty Bach; 1 changing beer (sourced regionally; often Wadworth) Ⓗ

This fine old building once used to serve as the tea rooms for Nant-y-Derry station; the old station stands opposite. It has been a popular bar and restaurant for many years. The current licensee reopened the pub in 2015 and offers good food and drink as well as occasional entertainment. Curry night is every Tuesday, OAP lunch specials on Thursday (booking advisable). Accommodation is available in two adjoining cottages. 🐴❀🛏◐♿P🐾

Newport

Cellar Door

5 Clytha Park Road, NP20 4NZ

☎ 07930 857897

3 changing beers Ⓗ

Five minutes' walk from the railway station, this micropub opened in 2017 and swiftly became a hit with CAMRA members and locals. Three ales from microbreweries are augmented by up to eight chilled ciders from local producers. Chilled bottled ales from Newport's own Anglo-Oregon brewery are always on sale. There is live music each Thursday and Sunday. The recent transformation of a storage room has provided a much-needed overspill area. Q❀⇌♣🍎🚌🐾

Godfrey Morgan Ⓛ ✔

158 Chepstow Road, Maindee, NP19 8EG

☎ (01633) 221928

Brains SA; Greene King Abbot; Ruddles Best Bitter; Sharp's Doom Bar; 2 changing beers (sourced nationally; often Rhymney) Ⓗ

Taking its name from the 1st Viscount Tredegar, a survivor of the Charge of the Light Brigade, this large, open-plan Wetherspoon pub was once a cinema, and displays photos of film stars from a bygone-age with local connections. It stocks the usual range of national and regional ales, plus one or two more interesting options. The pub has a small car park at the rear, with some or all of the charge refundable when you buy your pint. Q🐴❀◐♿P🚌(8,73)📶

Olde Murenger House

52-53 High Street, NP20 1GA

☎ (01633) 263977

Samuel Smith Old Brewery Bitter Ⓗ

This listed mid-16th century building has served various purposes over the centuries, but is now firmly established as a popular public house, expertly restored and managed by Samuel Smith's brewery. Enjoy your keenly-priced Old Brewery Bitter while taking in the surroundings of wood panelling, old wooden settles and memorabilia of Newport's history commemorating iconic buildings and local celebrities past and present.
◐⇌🚌🐾

Pen & Wig Ⓛ

22-24 Stow Hill, NP20 1JD

☎ (01633) 666818 🌐 jwbpubs.com/penandwig

Draught Bass; 5 changing beers (sourced regionally; often Boss, Gloucester, Tudor) Ⓗ

Popular city-centre pub with several linked sections, some for dining, and most within sight of a TV for sport. The food offering is appetising and substantial; just the job to complement the interesting range of ales. The pub prides itself on showcasing Welsh and West Country ales alongside the Bass. A large upstairs function room is available for hire, and a deck patio at the rear is popular in fine weather. ❀◐⇌♣P🚌(151)🐾

St Julian Inn ✔

Caerleon Road, NP18 1QA

☎ (01633) 243548 🌐 stjulian.co.uk

Bombardier; Fuller's London Pride; Young's Bitter; 1 changing beer (sourced regionally; often Bath Ales, Ludlow, Wye Valley) Ⓗ

A perennial favourite attracting customers from miles around – its commanding position atop a bend of the River Usk with views towards tranquil countryside adding to its appeal. There are several areas arranged around a central bar in which to settle and savour tasty ale or a meal, including a lounge lined with wood recovered from a former ocean liner, and a riverside balcony. The regular ales are usually joined by a light, hoppy guest ale. 🐴❀◐♣P🚌(27,28)🐾📶

Tiny Rebel

22-23 High Street, NP20 1FX

☎ (01633) 252538

Tiny Rebel Cwtch; 5 changing beers (sourced nationally; often Tiny Rebel) Ⓗ

After a successful trial as a pop-up bar at the front of Newport Market, Tiny Rebel decided to open a pub here permanently. The ground-level bar is quite sparse but has some modern pop art-style artwork. Downstairs there are some comfortable settees to sink into, and a table tennis table. There are usually four Tiny Rebel ales on, plus two guests. Real ales are much reduced on Mondays. ❀◐♿⇌♣🚌🐾📶

Pantygelli

Crown Inn Ⓛ

Old Hereford Road, NP7 7HR

☎ (01873) 853314 🌐 thecrownatpantygelli.com

Draught Bass; Rhymney Bevans Bitter; Wye Valley HPA; 1 changing beer (sourced regionally; often Evan Evans, Grey Trees, Tomos Watkin) Ⓗ

CAMRA award-winning pub two miles north of Abergavenny with a long-standing reputation for high-quality beers and food. The largely open-plan interior is divided into separate dining and drinking areas. A well-balanced choice of permanent beers is supplemented by a frequently changing guest from a Welsh independent brewery. Situated between the Sugar Loaf and Skirrid mountains, the flower-decked patio with its views over the countryside is a lovely place to relax on warm days.
🐴❀◐♣P

Penallt

Boat Inn

Lone Lane, NP25 4AJ

☎ (01600) 712615 🌐 theboatpenallt.co.uk

WALES

Kingstone Gold; Wye Valley Butty Bach; 1 changing beer (sourced regionally; often Wickwar)
Pub locations do not come much more idyllic than this, set alongside the fast-flowing river amid wondrous Wye Valley scenery. Easiest access is across the old railway footbridge from Redbrook in England. One Wye Valley ale is always available as well as two varying guest beers, while at least 12 draught ciders provide fulsome choice. The home-cooked food is particularly popular.
P(69)

Pontymister

Commercial Inn
Commercial Street, NP11 6BA
(01633) 612608 thecommercialpontymister.com
3 changing beers (sourced nationally)
Busy locals' pub on the main road through the village, popular for reasonably priced and varied meals plus an ever-changing range of cask and craft keg ales. The room is somewhat dominated by TV sets on most walls, though these are mercifully muted unless there is a match on. A pool table is in one corner and there is a decent jukebox near the bar. The outside area is inviting in summer. (56,151)

Raglan

Beaufort Arms
High Street, NP15 2DY
(01291) 690412 beaufortraglan.co.uk
Untapped Border Bitter, Whoosh, UPA
Former coaching inn with good-quality accommodation, diagonally opposite the large parish church. The bar has a hunting and fishing theme and the larger lounge offers a relaxing atmosphere, while the elegant brasserie is modern but sympathetic to the older fabric of the building. The Mediterranean-inspired menu features locally sourced produce, with themed nights including pie Tuesday, curry Wednesday and seafood Thursday. Three beers come from the local Untapped Brewing.
P(60,83)

Rogerstone

Tiny Rebel Brewery Bar
Wern Industrial Estate, Wern Terrace, NP10 9FQ
(01633) 547378
Tiny Rebel Cwtch; 2 changing beers (sourced locally; often Tiny Rebel)
Modern, trendy barn of a place, with an upstairs balcony and views of the brewery through windows at the back. Much focus is on promoting the Tiny Rebel brand, with takeaways and merchandise. There is an impressive array of handpulls on the bar, though with some duplication. With a huge screen and a quality sound system, it can get noisy during sporting events.
P(151,56)

Tintern

Wye Valley Hotel
Monmouth Road, NP16 6SQ
(01291) 689441 thewyevalleyhotel.co.uk
Wye Valley Bitter; 1 changing beer (sourced locally; often Kingstone)
Set in a beautiful valley, here is a fine place to pause, drink and stay. A Wye Valley beer is always on offer along with something from the nearby Kingstone Brewery. The comfortable single bar has a multi-angled shape matching the distinctive 1920s pub itself, while an array of commemorative beer bottles lines a shelf around the room. Generous home-cooked meals are available in the bar and traditional restaurant. Opening times are extended in summer.
P(69)

Trellech

Lion Inn
Church Street, NP25 4PA
(01600) 860322 lioninn.co.uk
3 changing beers (often Kingstone, Wye Valley)
Traditional 16th-century hostelry, originally a coaching inn. The pub has a charming bar centred around a fireplace and, on a slightly higher level, a cosy lounge and dining room where good food is served from an interesting menu. Ales are from breweries local to the south Wales and West Country areas; beer and cider festivals with live music feature during the year.
Q P(65)

Trellech Grange

Fountain Inn
NP16 6QW SO503011
(01291) 689303 fountaininntrellech.co.uk
Glamorgan Cwrw Gorslas/Bluestone Bitter; Wye Valley Butty Bach; 1 changing beer (sourced locally; often Kingstone)
A fine 17th-century drovers' inn, in the countryside a few miles from Tintern Abbey, somewhat off the beaten track but well worth seeking out. Three well-kept ales are always available alongside one local cider. In winter two real fires keep you cosy, while in summer the garden with its own brook is welcoming. Hours may vary so check ahead. P

Upper Llanover

Goose & Cuckoo
NP7 9ER (follow handwritten signs to the Goose) SO292073
(01873) 880277 gooseandcuckooinn.wales
Rhymney Bitter; Untapped Monnow; 2 changing beers (sourced regionally; often Felinfoel, Wye Valley)
Local CAMRA Country Pub of the Year 2020, the Goose is on a hilltop at the end of a long single-track lane from Llanover. Unchanged over many years, stepping inside feels like entering a time warp. Outside, well-maintained gardens overlook many miles of the Usk Valley below. Beers from independent breweries, usually Welsh, are sourced carefully. Apart from annual beer and music festivals, nothing disturbs the tranquillity of this beautiful and remote spot. Q P

Usk

New Court Inn
62 Maryport Street, NP15 1AD
(01291) 671319 thenewcourtinn.co.uk
Draught Bass; Glamorgan Welsh Pale Ale; Wye Valley Butty Bach; 2 changing beers (sourced regionally)
Attractive bar restaurant with a cosy interior comprising a comfortable seating area near a warming fire, a small snug with a TV for major sporting events, and a restaurant with an eclectic mix of furniture. It is a popular venue for diners, drawn to the tempting dishes on an award-winning menu. Seven handpumps dispense up to five real ales, often including local beers, and two ciders. With en-suite accommodation available it is a handy base for visitors to the town.
Q (60,63)

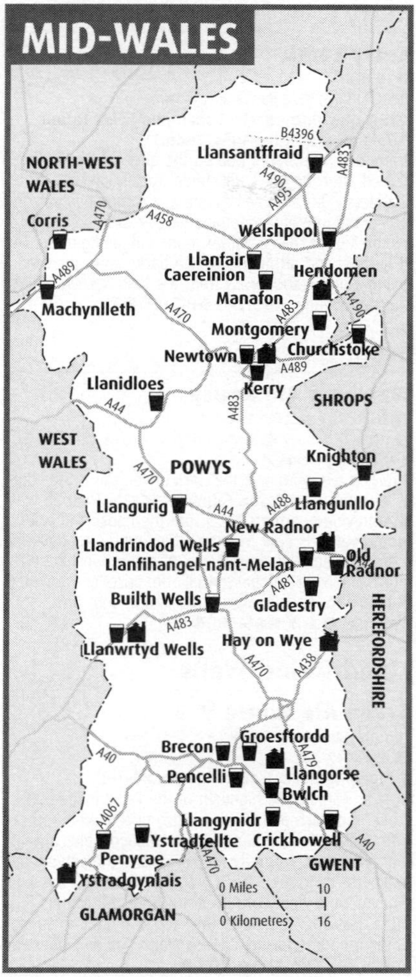

Authority area covered: Powys UA

Brecon

Brecon Tap

6 Bulwark, LD3 7LB
☎ (01874) 623888
4 changing beers (sourced regionally) Ⓗ
In a prime town-centre location, this contemporary bar has a light and airy feel, with comfortable seating throughout and walls lined with bottle-filled shelves. Three or four varying guest ales are served, often from Welsh breweries. There is also an interesting range of international and UK craft ales, plus simple food including sandwiches and pies. Bottled beers, wines, craft spirits and local artisan produce are available for off-sales.
Q (T4,X43)

Clarence

25 The Watton, LD3 7ED
☎ (01874) 622810 🌐 clarenceinn.co.uk
Wye Valley Bitter, Butty Bach; 1 changing beer (often Wye Valley) Ⓗ
Two-roomed town-centre community pub with a contemporary, welcoming and relaxed atmosphere. The front bar tends to be frequented by locals; the larger back bar is more popular with diners. Guest beers are generally from local breweries. A large-screen TV shows big sporting events. The spacious garden is a major attraction, especially during the annual Brecon Jazz Festival. (T4,X43)

George Hotel ✔

1 George Street, LD3 7LD (just off The Struet)
☎ (01874) 620250
Greene King IPA; Sharp's Doom Bar; 2 changing beers Ⓗ
Former 16th-century inn, now a Wetherspoon house. The interior has been expanded, creating a large bar area at the back and numerous rooms leading off it. Up to six ales are served, with national brews supplemented by beers from smaller breweries. Food is available all day and there are four letting bedrooms.
(T4,X43)

Builth Wells

Fountain Inn ✔

7-9 Broad Street, LD2 3DT
☎ (01982) 553888
Wye Valley Butty Bach; 3 changing beers (often Salopian, Tiny Rebel) Ⓗ
Town-centre pub that is popular with locals. Decorated in a modern style, it retains a traditional feel with stonework, exposed floorboards and a wood-burner. The pub serves up to four regularly changing real ales plus a real cider. Pool and darts are played in the bar, and sports TVs show major events. Next door is a café area and an upstairs terrace with a view of the River Wye. P

Bwlch

New Inn 🏆

Brecon Road, LD3 7RQ (on A40 between Brecon and Crickhowell)
☎ (01874) 730215 🌐 beaconsbackpackers.co.uk
Wye Valley Butty Bach; 2 changing beers (sourced regionally; often Grey Trees, Oakham, Salopian) Ⓗ
Lively and cosy village pub popular both with locals and visitors. A comfortable dining area sits to the side of the stone-flagged bar, with armchairs around a huge fireplace. Two interesting guest beers supplement the regular ale, and good-value home-cooked food is available at weekends – the pies are deservedly popular. It is an excellent base for exploring the surrounding Brecon Beacons and Black Mountains, with bunkhouse accommodation available. Local CAMRA Pub of the Year 2017-2020. Q P (43,X43)

Churchstoke

Horse & Jockey

SY15 6AE
☎ (01588) 620060
2 changing beers (sourced regionally) Ⓗ
A prominent stone-built pub on the edge of the village. It serves a changing range of guest ales, plus up to nine real ciders and perries during the summer. The wood-

REAL ALE BREWERIES

9 Lives Ystradgynlais
Heart of Wales Llanwrtyd Wells
Left Bank Llangorse
Lucky 7 Hay On Wye
Monty's Hendomen
Radnorshire New Radnor
Wilderness Newtown

beamed public bar hosts pool, darts and bar billiards. The carpeted lounge features comfortable armchairs and wall seating, and leads to a large, well-appointed restaurant. A stone fireplace with wood-burning stove provides winter warmth. (81)

Corris

Slaters Arms

Bridge Street, SY20 9SP

(01654) 761324 slatersarmscorris.co.uk

3 changing beers (sourced nationally; often Big Bog, Conwy, Cwrw Ogwen)

Named after what was once the main trade in Corris, this Grade II listed three-roomed village pub is popular with locals and visitors staying nearby. Its main bar has traditional slate flooring and a decorative mantelshelf above a large inglenook fireplace. The pub offers a third-pint platter for the price of a pint. There is a dining room to the left and a room for pub games at the rear. Walkers, families and well-behaved dogs are welcome. Take-away food is available. (34)

Crickhowell

Bear Hotel

High Street, NP8 1BW

(01873) 810408 bearhotel.co.uk

Brains Rev James; Caledonian Deuchars IPA; Wadworth 6X; 1 changing beer (sourced regionally; often Boss, Butcombe, Grey Trees)

Originally a 15th-century coaching inn, this is now an award-winning hotel. Its grand, multi-roomed bar features exposed beams, wood panelling, settles and an eclectic selection of furnishings and decorations. The two bar rooms have exposed fireplaces, as does one of the side rooms. Four ales are usually served, often including guests from smaller Welsh breweries. Food is excellent and the menu features much local produce.
Q (43,X43)

Gladestry

Royal Oak Inn

HR5 3NR

(01544) 370586 theroyaloakgladestry.co.uk

Wye Valley Butty Bach; 2 changing beers (sourced regionally)

A 17th-century village inn on Offa's Dyke Path National Trail, in the wilds of Radnorshire between Hay-on-Wye and Kington. In 2019 it was taken on by a new management team whose previous pub was a Guide regular. Three real ales are served, including two changing beers from Hobsons, Three Tuns or Ludlow. The pub welcomes walkers and dogs on leads, and opens most lunchtimes and evenings. Q

Groesffordd

Three Horseshoes

LD3 7SN (just off B4558 in centre of Village)

(01874) 665672 threehorseshoesgroesffordd.co.uk

St Austell Tribute; 2 changing beers (sourced regionally)

Busy village-centre pub in the heart of the Brecon Beacons, boasting superb views from its outdoor seating areas. The pub is only a 10-minute walk from the Brynich lock on the Monmouthshire & Brecon Canal and is a popular stop for boaters and other visitors. The emphasis here is on the excellent food but the ales are always varied and interesting. Brynich caravan site and the Brecon YHA are nearby.

Kerry

Kerry Lamb

SY16 4NP

(01686) 670226 thekerrylambpowys.co.uk

Wye Valley Butty Bach; 2 changing beers (often Purple Moose, Three Tuns, Tudor)

Prominent red-bricked pub on the edge of the village, named after the Kerry Hill sheep. Locally owned, it seamlessly flits between its role as a community pub and restaurant, offering something for all tastes. It consists of a large lounge/bar, a games room and dining room. The St Michael and All Angels church backs on to the rear, giving a picturesque view from the beer garden during warmer weather. (81)

Knighton

Watson's Ale House

24 High Street, LD7 1AT

(01547) 740017 watsonsalehouse.co.uk

3 changing beers

A former tea room near the clock tower, this is the home of Watson's Real Powys Farmhouse Cider. The pub was also previously a butcher's – spot the hooks and cold-room door. It is next to a chip shop, where food can be ordered to eat with your drinks. Attractions include pizza nights and an occasional special offer price for three pints of beer – for each drinker. Walkers and dogs are welcome. Q (46)

Llandrindod Wells

Arvon Ale House

Temple Street, LD1 5DP

07477 627267

5 changing beers (sourced regionally)

Now an established highlight of the Llandrindod pub scene, this micropub offers sensibly priced beers sourced from Wales, the borders and the Midlands, plus at least four real ciders. Formerly shop premises, the pub is small and perfectly formed. It is a proper alehouse for the quiet enjoyment of beer with no distractions. All-comers folk music sessions are held on the second and fourth Sunday of the month. A former CAMRA Welsh Pub and Cider Pub of the Year. Q (T4)

Middleton Arms

Tremont Road, LD1 5EB (corner of Trefonen Lane)

(01597) 822066

Worthington's Bitter; 1 changing beer (sourced regionally)

A friendly street-corner local at the north end of town on the road to Newtown, named after one of the town's Victorian developers. The guest beer changes weekly. The pub supports four darts teams as well as pool and dominoes teams, and screens sports channels on TV. There is an enclosed drinking area outside, and families and dogs are welcome. Q (461,T4)

Llanfair Caereinion

Goat Hotel

High Street, SY21 0QS (off A485)

(01938) 810428 thegoathotel.co.uk

3 changing beers (sourced locally; often Stonehouse, Wood)

An excellent 300-year-old beamed coaching inn whose welcoming atmosphere attracts both locals and tourists. The plush lounge, dominated by a large inglenook with open fire, features comfortable leather armchairs and sofas. The real ale selection usually includes a beer from

the Wood Brewery. Home-cooked food is served in the dining room, and there is a games room at the rear. Beware the low-beamed entrance to the Gents! Handy for the Welshpool & Llanfair Light Railway.
Q⛀❀⇆◑⇄♣P🚌(87)🐾ᯤ

Llanfihangel-nant-Melan

Fforest Inn

LD8 2TN (jct. of A44 and A481)
☎ (01544) 350526 🌐 theforest.co.uk
Morland Old Speckled Hen; 2 changing beers (sourced nationally) Ⓗ
Built in the 16th century as a drovers' inn, this pub is steeped in history and retains many original features. Three regularly changing real ales are served in summer, two in winter. The food menu features fresh local produce. Well-behaved dogs are welcome in the bar and, subject to prior arrangement, in the guest rooms.
Q⛀❀⇆◑P🚌(461)🐾

Llangunllo

Greyhound Ⓛ

LD7 1SP (off A488 on B4356)
☎ (01547) 550400
2 changing beers (sourced nationally; often Swan) Ⓗ
This unique 16th-century inn, set in picturesque countryside, is the first stop on the Glyndwr's Way long-distance trail. The beers are usually from regional breweries, and the cider is Westons Family Reserve. Regular music sessions are hosted. Opening times are approximate – ring the doorbell any time after midday and with luck you will be served. Q⛀❀⛺⇄♣●P🐾

Llangurig

Black Lion Hotel

SY18 6SG
☎ (01686) 440223 🌐 llangurig.org.uk
Three Tuns Best; 1 changing beer (sourced locally; often Three Tuns) Ⓗ
Originally a shooting lodge, the Black Lion was first licensed in 1633 and rebuilt as a hotel in the late 19th century. It has low ceilings and wooden beams, and is divided into two bars and a conservatory. The first bar acts as a games area, with pool and table skittles. The lounge/dining area has a stone fireplace, wall seating and settles. There is also a side room with comfortable armchairs. Q⛀❀⇆◑♿♣P🚌(X75,525)🐾ᯤ

Llangynidr

Red Lion

Duffryn Road, NP8 1NT (off B4558)
☎ (01874) 730223
Wye Valley The Hopfather; 2 changing beers (sourced regionally) Ⓗ
Popular village local, situated away from the main road, with a warm welcome for families and dogs, walkers and boaters – the Monmouthshire & Brecon Canal is a short walk away. The beer range changes regularly and good-value home-cooked food is served in the bar. A separate games area, outside seating and children's play area make this a pub for all. Regular quiz nights and live music also feature. ⛀❀⇆◑♣P🚌🐾ᯤ

Llanidloes

Crown & Anchor ★

41 Long Bridge Street, SY18 6EF
☎ (01686) 412398 🌐 crown-anchor-inn-pub.business.site
Wye Valley Butty Bach; 2 changing beers (sourced regionally; often Purple Moose, Wye Valley) Ⓗ
A Grade II listed pub affectionately nicknamed Ruby's after its long-serving landlady, who has now retired. It comprises five unspoilt rooms, one of which was a haberdasher's shop before becoming part of the pub in 1948. A small corridor links the rooms, one displaying guitars that visiting musicians are welcome to play. A middle room and snug are connected to the bar by glass serving hatches. Q⛀❀♣🚌(X75,525)🐾ᯤ

Llansantffraid

Sun Hotel

Waterloo Terrace,, SY22 6AR
☎ (01691) 828804
3 changing beers (often Hobsons, Monty's, Salopian) Ⓗ
A two-storey 19th-century village inn, this Grade II listed building has been sympathetically enlarged over the years while retaining its original character. The original part has three upper 16-pane sash windows with openings below. The ground floor has a central door with larger sash windows each side. Up to three real ales are served alongside two real ciders.
⛀◑♿●P🚌(72,74)🐾ᯤ

Llanwrtyd Wells

Neuadd Arms Hotel Ⓛ

The Square, LD5 4RB
☎ (01591) 610236 🌐 neuaddarmshotel.co.uk
Felinfoel Double Dragon; Heart of Wales Irfon Valley Bitter, Aur Cymru, Welsh Black, Noble Eden Ale; 4 changing beers (sourced locally) Ⓗ
This large Victorian hotel is the tap for the Heart of Wales Brewery. The Bells Bar features a large fireplace and an eclectic mix of furniture. The bells, formerly used to summon servants, remain on one wall, along with the winners' boards from some of the town's unusual and famous competitions. The lounge bar is more formal. A good range of real cider is served alongside the ales. The hotel takes part in local events, including a beer festival over two weekends in November. Q❀⇆◑⇄♣●P🐾

Machynlleth

Dyfi Forester

4 Heol y Doll, SY20 8BQ
☎ (01654) 703239
2 changing beers (sourced regionally; often Evan Evans, Wood, Wye Valley) Ⓗ
Friendly free house between the railway station and bustling town centre. It has a welcoming central bar featuring darts, pool and a jukebox. Pub games are played with enthusiasm here, and all-day pool and darts events are hosted occasionally. The quirky exterior features original stained glass. A rear patio enables outdoor drinking. ⛀❀⇄♣P🚌(X28,X85)🐾ᯤ

Manafon

Beehive Inn

SY21 8BL
☎ (01686) 651007
Salopian Shropshire Gold; Stonehouse Station Bitter Ⓗ
A timbered black-and-white Rhiw Valley local in the heart of the village, established in the 1650s as a drovers' inn with original beams and settles throughout. It was originally a lot smaller – other rooms have been brought into pub use over the years. The room on the

right was once a butcher's. There is a caravan park at the rear with the river running beside the large beer garden. The adjacent church creates a peaceful backdrop amid pleasant scenery. Q🐴❀♣●P📶

Montgomery

Dragon Hotel

Market Square, SY15 6PA

☎ (01686) 668359 🌐 dragonhotel.com

4 changing beers (sourced regionally; often Monty's) Ⓗ

Dating from the mid-1600s, this former coaching inn has a distinctive Tudor black-and-white half-timbered frontage. The bar has been relocated to the rear of the hotel, giving more space to the clientele. There are patio areas outside to the front and rear for alfresco drinking. The hotel boasts an indoor swimming pool and a large function room. Q🐴❀🛏◐♿●P🚌(T12,81)🐾📶

Newtown

Exchange

Broad Street, SY16 2NA

☎ (01686) 621814 🌐 theexchangenewtown.co.uk

Hobsons Town Crier; Salopian Oracle; Sharp's Atlantic Ⓗ

Previously the town flannel exchange, this bar was also the cellar of a cinema and nightclub for a number of years. Following refurbishment it is now an open-plan sports bar, with TVs showing a variety of sporting events. It has a central area with high tables, plus several comfortable drinking areas. Darts and pool are played in a games area at the far end. Three ales are usually served, two from Shropshire breweries. ⇌♣🚌🐾📶

Sportsman 🄻

17 Severn Street, SY16 2AQ (off A483)

☎ (01686) 623978 🌐 hophouseinns.co.uk/index.html

Monty's Old Jailhouse, MPA, Sunshine, Masquerade, Mischief; 3 changing beers (sourced nationally; often Purple Moose, Wye Valley) Ⓗ

Free house that was formerly Monty's taphouse. The pub is divided into three areas – a snug with comfortable wall seating, a main bar area with a wood-burning stove and a rear tiled games area with pool table, TV and darts. There is a patio at the rear for summer drinking. A former local CAMRA Pub of the Year and Welsh Cider Pub of the Year. Q❀♿⇌♣●🚌📶

Old Radnor

Harp Inn

LD8 2RH

☎ (01544) 350655 🌐 harpinnradnor.co.uk

2 changing beers (sourced regionally) Ⓗ

This early 15th-century Welsh longhouse commands a fine view over the Radnor Valley. The building was rescued and restored by the Landmark Trust in 1972, then sold on in 1983. The interior is a tasteful mix of old and new, including a modern restaurant. Beers are mainly from regional and local microbreweries. The food features locally sourced seasonal ingredients. Q🐴❀🛏◐▲♣●P🐾📶

Pencelli

Royal Oak

LD3 7LX

☎ (01874) 665396

Brains Rev James; 3 changing beers (sourced regionally; often Grey Trees, Tudor) Ⓗ

Friendly family-run pub in a quiet village alongside the Monmouthshire & Brecon Canal. Its extended opening hours are welcome in this part of the Brecon Beacons. The regular ale is supplemented with two or three others, usually from independent Welsh breweries. The pretty garden next to the canal is a delight on a sunny day. Popular with walkers, cyclists and boaters, with moorings adjacent to the garden. Q🐴❀◐▲P🚌🐾📶

Penycae

Ancient Briton

Brecon Road, SA9 1YY (on A4067 Swansea to Brecon road, N of Abercrave)

☎ (01639) 730273 🌐 ancientbriton.co.uk

Wye Valley Butty Bach; 8 changing beers (sourced nationally; often Draught Bass, Salopian, Wye Valley) Ⓗ

Warm and friendly pub in the Brecon Beacons National Park, on the Swansea to Brecon road. Up to eight ales are served regularly. The pub welcomes children, campers and walkers. It is close to the famous Dan yr Ogof show caves and Craig y Nos castle. There is plenty of car parking on-site, and an attached campsite. Former local CAMRA Pub of the Year on numerous occasions for both ales and ciders. 🐴❀🛏◐♿▲♣●P🚌(T6)🐾📶

Welshpool

Angel

12 Berriew Street, SY21 7SQ

☎ (01938) 553473 🌐 angelwelshpool.com

3 changing beers (sourced locally; often Hobsons, Salopian, Three Tuns) Ⓗ

Modernised town-centre pub with a small, comfortable snug near the main door as a reminder of how it once was. The long main bar leads to a rear section featuring a pool table and numerous TVs showing sport – there is even a TV in the Gents. The three ales served come from Shropshire breweries. Outside to the rear is an area for drinking and smoking. Happy hour is 4-8pm during the week. 🐴❀◐♿⇌♣🚌📶

Pheasant Inn

43 High Street, SY21 7JQ

☎ (01938) 553104 🌐 pheasantwelshpool.co.uk

3 changing beers (sourced locally; often Ludlow, Salopian, Three Tuns) Ⓗ

Vibrant pub in a terrace of 18th-century former town houses. The Grade II listed building is much modified internally, featuring a long room with wooden floor, pool table and dartboard, and comfortable seating at the far end. A rear door leads to the outside drinking area. Ales are usually from small or regional breweries, with a third guest beer often served at weekends. ❀⇌♣🚌📶

Ystradfellte

New Inn

CF44 9JE

☎ (01639) 721014 🌐 waterfallways.co.uk

2 changing beers (sourced locally; often Glamorgan, Grey Trees) Ⓗ

A 16th-century village pub in the middle of Waterfall Country, a popular walking area in the Brecon Beacons. With two log fires and a small beer garden, it offers a welcome whatever the weather. Two local ales are kept on tap. There is a strong focus on local produce, including spirits from Penderyn Distillery. Home-cooked food includes the popular Boozy Cow Pie. Friendly dogs and muddy boots are welcome. Q🐴❀◐▲●P🐾

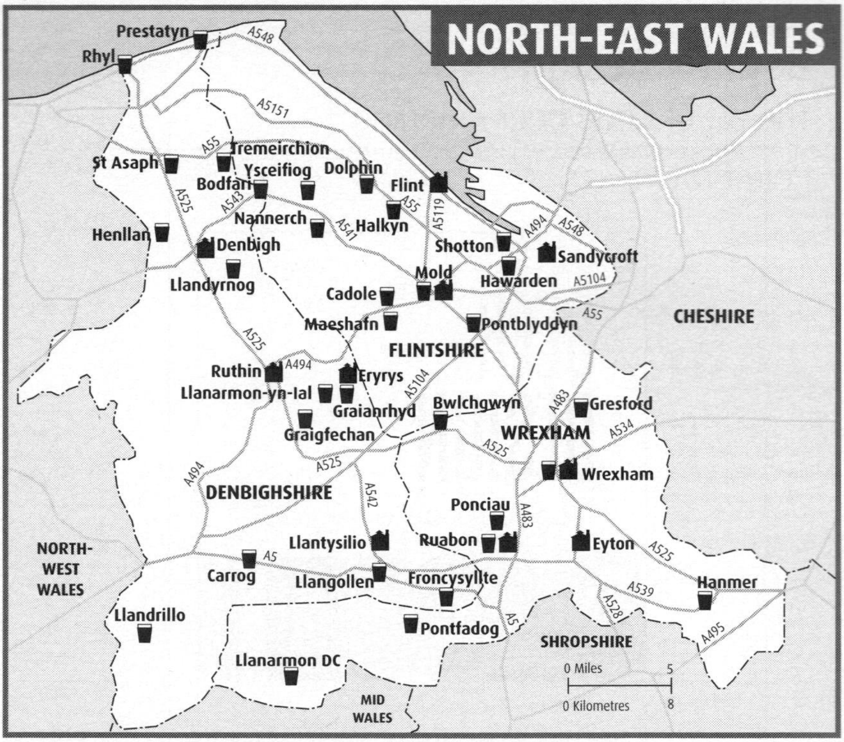

Authority areas covered: Denbighshire UA, Flintshire UA, Wrexham UA

Bodfari

Dinorben Arms 𝕃

LL16 4DA SJ092701

☎ (01745) 775090

Brunning & Price Original; Facer's North Star Porter; Timothy Taylor Boltmaker; 4 changing beers (sourced locally) Ⓗ

Reputedly established in 1640, the building was derelict for eight years before it was acquired by Brunning & Price. Its elevated position by the 16th-century church and tower offers fine views across the Vale of Clwyd. Primarily a destination pub popular for meals, the spacious interior has several dining areas in typical B&P style. Food is served all day, as well as a good selection of real ales including three regular beers and four guests usually from local micros. ❀◐♿P🚌(14)🐾📶

Bwlchgwyn

King's Head Inn 𝕃

Ruthin Road, LL11 5UT (on A525)

☎ (01978) 753089

2 changing beers (sourced locally; often Big Hand) Ⓗ

Friendly locals' free house standing on the main road through one of Wales' highest villages. It reopened in 2017 after an impressive and modern refurbishment. Entrance is through a neat and tidy room warmed by a large wood-burner, with the bar facing you. To the side is another comfortable room with banquette seating. The pub offers hearty meals to accompany two local beers on handpump, usually from Big Hand. Bus services are limited. ❀◐P🚌(X51)🐾📶

Cadole

Colomendy Arms

Village Road, CH7 5LL (off A494 Mold-Ruthin road)

☎ (01352) 810217

6 changing beers Ⓗ

A wonderful pub in the middle of the village, run by the same family for more than 30 years and featuring in the Guide for most of that time. It has two cosy rooms with real fires, festooned with local history and photographs. Conversation is king here. Its six beers will come from far and wide. A popular stop-off for walkers, with the Loggerheads Country Park close by. **Q**❀♣**P**🚌🐾

Carrog

Grouse Inn

LL21 9AT (on B5437, off A5 at Llidiart Y Parc)

☎ (01490) 430272 🌐 thegrouseinncarrog.co.uk

JW Lees Bitter, Founder's; 1 changing beer (often JW Lees) Ⓗ

Friendly family-run inn which was originally a farm and brewhouse and has a single bar serving several rooms. It was tastefully refurbished in 2020 without losing its fabulous character. Generous home-cooked food is served in most areas of the pub. The large covered patio offers splendid views of the Dee Valley, Berwyn Mountains and 1660 Carrog Bridge. Carrog station on the Llangollen Railway is a short walk away.
Q❀◐Å⇌♣**P**🚌(T3) 🐾📶

Dolphin

Glan yr Afon Inn 𝕃

Milwr, CH8 8HE

☎ (01352) 710052 🌐 glanyrafoninn.com
Facer's Dave's Hoppy Beer, Landslide Ⓗ
You can expect a warm welcome at this popular pub which first opened in the 16th century and is in an elevated position with views of the Dee Estuary and the Wirral Peninsula. A central bar serves four separate seating areas and the dining room, while the games room has its own bar. The inn also offers food and accommodation. Walkers and dogs are welcome and there is a real fire to keep you warm on cold days.
Q🚸❀🛏🍴♿♣P🚌(126)🐾📶

Froncysyllte

Aqueduct Inn ✔

Holyhead Road, LL20 7PY
☎ (01691) 777118
4 changing beers (sourced nationally; often Bathams, Slater's, Wood) Ⓗ
A welcoming free house on the busy A5. The small central bar leads to a games room with a TV to the right and a comfortable lounge with a wood-burning stove to the left. Outside, the veranda offers panoramic views of the Pontcysyllte Aqueduct on the Llangollen Canal. Up to four changing ales are available, with Bathams a favourite. Food is served daily, with a traditional roast on Sunday. 🚸❀🍴♣P🚌(64)🐾📶

Graianrhyd

Rose & Crown

Llanarmon Road, CH7 4QW (on B5430 off A5104)
☎ (01824) 780727 🌐 theroseandcrownpub.co.uk
Black Sheep Best Bitter; 2 changing beers Ⓗ
A traditional early 19th-century pub with a strong local following. The long bar serves two rooms – the main room has an open fire, copper-topped tables and a vast array of pumpclips. Guest beers are usually from local breweries. The pub is popular with tourists, walkers, cyclists and fell runners keen to fuel up on post-race chip baps following the local Dash in the Dark. It is also a stop-off on the Three Taverns Tour taken by the village choir each May. Q🚸❀🍴▲♣🍎P🚌(2)🐾

Graigfechan

Three Pigeons Inn L

LL15 2EU (on B5429 about 3 miles from Ruthin)
☎ (01824) 703178 🌐 threepigeonsinn.co.uk
4 changing beers Ⓗ
Fine old drovers' inn with parts originating from the 12th century. The interior is tastefully decorated, retaining the original features and open log fires. An extensive lounge area has a sports room to one side and a large dining area to the other. Cellars are ideal for keeping the cask ales that are still, on occasion, served in jugs. An outdoor area to the rear has great views over the Vale of Clwyd. Two self-catering apartments are available and a campsite is adjacent. 🚸❀🛏🍴▲♣🍎P🚌(76)🐾📶

Gresford

Griffin Inn

Church Green, LL12 8RG
☎ (01978) 855280
Courage Best Bitter; 1 changing beer (sourced nationally; often Moorhouse's, Weetwood) Ⓗ
Friendly community pub with an irregular, open-plan layout adorned with many interesting pictures. Lively conversation at the bar does not impinge on the quieter corners. Sited where pilgrims came to drink in the Middle Ages, opposite is All Saints Church, whose bells are one of the Seven Wonders of Wales. There is a lawned area to the side with seating. Bus No.1 (Chester-Wrexham) stops in the village less than half a mile away. The landlady has been running the pub since 1973. Q🚸❀♣P🚌(1)📶

Pant-yr-Ochain L

Old Wrexham Road, LL12 8TY (from A483 follow signs to The Flash)
☎ (01978) 853525
Purple Moose Cwrw Eryri/Snowdonia Ale; Timothy Taylor Landlord; Titanic Plum Porter; Weetwood Eastgate; house beer (by Phoenix); 4 changing beers (sourced regionally; often Big Hand, Castle Rock, Mobberley) Ⓗ
Impressive 16th-century dower house that retains many historic features and sits beside a small lake within extensive gardens. The central room, dominated by a large double-fronted bar, leads to a variety of seating areas including a garden room, a small snug behind a period inglenook fireplace, and the patio and lawn outside. Hugely popular for dining, the pub retains a quiet feel. Food is served all day and five regular beers are supplemented by four guests and often a draught cider. Happy hour is 5-7pm midweek.
Q🚸❀🍴♿♣🍎P🐾📶

Halkyn

Blue Bell Inn L

Rhosesmor Road, CH8 8DL (on B5123)
☎ (01352) 780309 🌐 bluebell.uk.eu.org
JW Lees Bitter; 3 changing beers (sourced locally) Ⓗ
Situated on Halkyn Mountain, the Blue Bell is a traditional rural inn and a good base for exploring the local countryside, with free guided walks around the area. Built in the 1700s and named after a local privateer's boat, the pub has a strong community focus, hosting regular events and societies. The beer range usually includes ales from north Wales breweries, often Facer's or Cwrw Llyn. A wide selection of real ciders is also available. Q🚸❀♿▲♣🍎P🚌(126)🐾📶

Hanmer

Hanmer Arms

SY13 3DE (just off A495 1 mile from jct with A525)
☎ (01948) 830458 🌐 hanmerarms.com
Hook Norton Hooky, Hooky Gold; Purple Moose Cwrw Ysgawen/Elderflower Ale; 4 changing beers (sourced nationally; often Hobsons) Ⓗ
This attractive hotel-restaurant just off the main Wrexham to Whitchurch road makes an ideal base for exploring the north Welsh borderlands, Shropshire and Cheshire. The hotel is a short stroll from the picturesque Hanmer Mere and is adjacent to the charming 12th-century St Chad's church. Hook Norton ales are regular,

REAL ALE BREWERIES

Big Hand Wrexham
Denbigh Denbigh
Dovecote Denbigh
Facer's Flint
Hafod ◆ Mold
Iâl Eryrys
Llangollen 🛢 Llantysilio
Magic Dragon Eyton
McGivern 🛢 Ruabon
Polly's Mold
Reaction Ruthin (NEW)
Sandstone Wrexham
Top Rope Sandycroft

WALES

complemented by beers from Purple Moose and other changing guests. Lunchtime and evening meals are available plus a popular Sunday carvery. Accommodation is provided in 11 en-suite bedrooms.
Q🚸❀🛏◐♿♣●P🚌(146) 🐾📶

Hawarden

Glynne Arms 𝕃

3 Glynne Way, CH5 3NS
☎ (01244) 569988 🌐 theglynnearms.co.uk
Facer's This Splendid Ale; 3 changing beers (sourced locally; often Big Hand, Facer's) 🄷
This 200-year-old coaching inn at the heart of the village is a comfortable place to try local beers and good-quality food. The semi-circular bar counter serves the bar area and adjacent dining room, and there is a separate restaurant with a real fire. The decor is sympathetic to the period of the building, with references to the village's most famous resident, William Gladstone. Popular with walkers visiting the nearby castle and park.
🚸❀◐♿⇌♣P🚌(4,11) 🐾📶

Henllan

Llindir Inn 𝕃

Llindir Street, LL16 5BH
☎ (01745) 812188
5 changing beers (sourced locally) 🄷
Rambling 13th-century Grade II listed thatched inn. On entry you are welcomed into a room with a long copper bar and an inglenook fireplace, with a comfortable TV lounge offset. Three steps take you up to another bar and a further three steps to a pleasant restaurant. The interior retains its original character with old beams, tiled floors, copper and brassware. Up to five guest beers are available. Q🚸❀◐♣P🚌(6)🐾📶

Llanarmon DC

Hand at Llanarmon

Llanarmon Dyffryn Ceiriog, LL20 7LD (end of B4500 from Chirk)
☎ (01691) 600666 🌐 thehandhotel.co.uk
2 changing beers (sourced locally; often Big Hand, Stonehouse, Weetwood) 🄷
Cosy free house in a very scenic location at the head of the stunning Ceiriog Valley. Look for the giant, wooden, carved hand outside. Two, usually local, real ales are always sold. Both food and accommodation are of a very high standard, and it has a recently opened spa. It is best to book at busy times. The bar is dog-friendly, with an open fire. Walkers, cyclists and tourists are all welcome. Q🚸❀🛏◐♿♣P🚌(64)🐾📶

West Arms

LL20 7LD (at end of B4500)
☎ (01691) 600665 🌐 thewestarms.com
4 changing beers (sourced nationally; often Big Hand, Timothy Taylor) 🄷
Historic hotel in a scenic location at the end of the Ceiriog Valley. The garden runs down to the infant River Ceiriog and offers excellent views. The lounge features settles and an inglenook while the narrow bar is often frequented by locals, dogs and walkers. Four changing ales often come from local breweries. Good-quality food is served lunchtimes and evenings (all day Sun), plus breakfast from early on and sandwiches in the afternoon. The accommodation has been recently refurbished.
Q🚸❀🛏◐♿♣P🚌(64) 🐾📶

Llanarmon-yn-Ial

Raven Inn 𝕃

Ffordd-Rhew-Ial, CH7 4QE (signed 500yds W of B5430)
☎ (01824) 780833 🌐 raveninn.co.uk
Purple Moose Cwrw Eryri/Snowdonia Ale; 2 changing beers (sourced locally) 🄷
Community-run by volunteers since 2009, this delightful old pub continues to go from strength to strength, with all profits used to benefit the community. There is a friendly and inviting ambience from the moment you enter. The bar serves two discrete carpeted areas and a tiled area to one side. The three guest beers are from local breweries. Excellent locally sourced home-cooked food is served Thursday to Sunday. Three self-catering bedrooms are available. Q🚸❀🛏◐♿♣●P🚌(2)🐾📶

Llandrillo

Dudley Arms Hotel 𝕃

High Street, LL21 0TL
☎ (01490) 440223 🌐 dudleyarms.wales
Stonehouse Station Bitter; 1 changing beer (sourced locally) 🄷
Traditional Welsh village inn nestling within the Berwyn mountains. The owners have carried out an extensive refurbishment to create a pub full of charm, with many period features and exposed oak beams. There are several discrete areas including a lounge, dining area and pool room with stone walls, tiled floors and cosy fires. The guest beer is always from a local brewery. B&B accommodation is available upstairs and in an adjacent refurbished cottage. 🚸❀🛏◐♣P🚌(T3)🐾📶

Llandyrnog

Kinmel Arms 𝕃

Waen, LL16 4HN
☎ (01824) 790291 🌐 kinmelarms.com
Marston's Saddle Tank; Young's London Special; 3 changing beers (often Big Hand) 🄷
A warm and traditional pub on the edge of the Clwydian Range and close to Offa's Dyke path and Moel Arthur hill fort. The front bar area features a large wood-burner. There is a separate dining space, children's play area and games room. The guest beers are usually from Cwrw Ial, Big Hand and Wild Horse breweries. Opening times are subject to change so check before visiting.
Q🚸❀◐♿⛺♣P🚌(76) 🐾📶

Llangollen

Chainbridge Hotel 𝕃

Berwyn, LL20 8BS (off B5103)
☎ (01978) 860215 🌐 chainbridgehotel.com
Stonehouse Station Bitter; 2 changing beers (sourced locally; often Purple Moose, Stonehouse) 🄷
Lying near the Horseshoe Falls, this comfortable, well-run hotel with cosy bar and dining areas is spectacularly set beside the turbulent River Dee with its chainbridge. Outside seating, bedecked in summer with colourful hanging baskets, makes the most of the dramatic riparian location. White water thrill-seekers and puffing steam locomotives on the Llangollen Railway provide further entertainment. Llangollen itself is a short train ride from Berwyn station perched opposite or a pleasant 30-minute stroll along the canalside towpath.
🚸❀🛏◐♿⇌P🚌(T3) 🐾📶

Ponsonby Arms

Mill Street, LL20 8RY (near steam railway)
☎ (01978) 447985

Bollington Long Hop; Elland White Prussian, 1872 Porter; 3 changing beers (sourced nationally; often Acorn, Titanic) Ⓗ
Under the same ownership as the nearby Sun, this is a community pub with an emphasis on good beer and conversation. The wide range of beers is made possible by the use of small casks. A real cider and a good selection of Belgian beers and gins are also on offer. Food is served April to September including traditional Sunday roasts. A large TV screen shows sporting events. Outside, the extensive garden overlooks the River Dee. A free ticket for the nearby car park can be obtained at the bar. Q🐴❀◐◑⛺⇌♣●P🚌(5,T3)🐾📶

Sun Inn Ⓛ
49 Regent Street, LL20 8HN (400yds E of town centre on A5)
☎ (01978) 860079
5 changing beers (sourced nationally; often Bollington, Rat) Ⓗ
A free house with a large front lounge with two open fires and a stage for live music. A smaller snug at the rear has mirrored panels and a large TV screen. This room is accessed via an enclosed partly covered terrace. The pub has a late licence, with music Wednesday to Saturday – last entry is 11pm. Quieter in the early evening, the pub can get busy later on, especially at weekends.
❀⛺⇌♣●🚌(5,T3)🐾📶

Three Eagles
Bridge Street, LL20 8PF
☎ (01978) 869595 🌐 thethreeeagles.co.uk
Sharp's Doom Bar; house beer (by Big Hand); 1 changing beer (sourced locally; often Purple Moose) Ⓗ
Formerly the Wynnstay Arms, this historic coaching inn is now a gastro-restaurant. The bar and main dining area are on the ground floor, with further dining areas on the upper two floors. The house beer is by Big Hand and the changing beer usually comes from a small local brewery. There is seating in the bar for those not dining. Features include a well by the entrance and a glass floor above the wine cellar. Q🐴❀◐◑♿⛺⇌🚌(5,T3)🐾📶

Maeshafn

Miners Arms
Village Road, CH7 5LR (off A494 in village centre)
☎ (01352) 810464 🌐 miners-arms-maeshafn.com
Facer's Flintshire Bitter, This Splendid Ale; Theakston Old Peculier; Timothy Taylor Boltmaker; Wainwright Ⓗ
Originally built in the 1820s as part of a local lead-mining development, this traditional inn in a small hamlet was taken over and refurbished in 2018 by new management. A double-sided wood-burning stove divides the central bar from the dining section, creating a warm atmosphere throughout. Surrounded by scenic countryside, the pub is particularly popular with hikers and has a pleasant seating area outside at the front. Theakston Old Peculier makes an occasional appearance.
🐴❀◐◑P🚌(2)🐾📶

Mold

Fat Boar Ⓛ
17 Chester Street, CH7 1EG
☎ (01352) 759890 🌐 thefatboar.co.uk
2 changing beers (sourced locally) Ⓗ
Formerly called the Boar's Head and closed for several years, the pub reopened as the Fat Boar following renovation. Now predominantly food-led, it has two local real ales on handpump. Two floors provide seating for around 80 people, and there is an additional outside space at the back of the building. The rear dining room has a TV for sports fans. Centrally situated in this market town, the pub is handy for local transport to and from the surrounding areas. 🐴❀◐◑♿🚌📶

Gold Cape ✔
8-8A Wrexham Street, CH7 1ES (next to Market Square crossroads)
☎ (01352) 705920
Greene King Abbot; Ruddles Best Bitter; Sharp's Doom Bar; 4 changing beers Ⓗ
A Wetherspoon named after a 4,000-year-old solid gold ceremonial cape found near Mold in 1831. There is a copy of the cape in Mold Library. The walls display pictures of the town's past, including local poet Daniel Owen. Q🐴◐◑⛺●🚌📶

Mold Alehouse Ⓛ
Unit 2, Earl Chambers, Earl Road, CH7 1AL
☎ (01352) 218188 🌐 moldalehouse.co.uk
4 changing beers (sourced locally; often Cwrw Ial, Facer's, Hafod) Ⓗ
Since opening in 2016, this micropub has won many CAMRA awards and gained a strong following based on sound principles of good beer, fellowship and conversation. It is in a Grade II listed building opposite the town hall and near Daniel Owen Square, named after the renowned Welsh novelist, and home to Mold museum and library. The four cask ales include a dark beer, and there are also five KeyKeg lines and four ciders.
Q●🚌🐾📶

Nannerch

Cross Foxes Ⓛ
Village Road, CH7 5RD
☎ (01352) 741464 🌐 cross-foxes.co.uk
3 changing beers (sourced locally; often Big Hand, Cwrw Ial) Ⓗ
This delightful village pub close to the church was built in 1780 and originally also served as a butcher's – the meat hooks still remain. The entrance leads to a main bar with a large fireplace. Off this is another small bar, a lounge and a function room. Three pumps serve changing beers, usually from local brewers including Big Hand and Cwrw Ial. Beer festivals are held in March and October.
🐴◐◑⛺♣P🚌(14) 📶

Ponciau

Colliers Arms
Chapel Street, LL14 1SE (off B5426)
3 changing beers (sourced regionally) Ⓗ
Splendid free house on a narrow terraced street with a convivial atmosphere. A rare cask ale outlet for around here, guest ales are often from local microbreweries. The front room has a slate floor, comfortable bench seating and cast-iron tables. There is also a small snug and a back room with a pool table. To the rear is a pleasant decked area and lawn. Public parking is available nearby. A former local CAMRA Pub of the Year. 🐴❀♿♣🚌(3)🐾📶

Pontblyddyn

Bridge Inn
Wrexham Road, CH7 4HN (on A541 3 miles S of Mold)
☎ (01352) 770087
2 changing beers Ⓗ
Fine old building at a crossroads, with the River Alyn at the rear. The unspoilt interior has a warm and cosy front

bar with a real fire, with another room leading off to the right and a separate restaurant to the left. There is also a courtyard area to the front and an extensive riverside beer garden and children's play area out the back.
Q🐎❀◑◐♿P🚌🐾📶

Pontfadog

Swan Inn

Llanarmon Road, LL20 7AR (on B4500 next to post office)
☎ (01691) 718273
2 changing beers (sourced locally; often Stonehouse) Ⓗ
Welcoming village free house in the scenic Ceiriog Valley. The cosy red-tiled bar, where the locals tend to congregate, features a central fireplace which separates the TV and darts area from the servery. The separate dining room leads to the outdoor area, which now has a terrace offering good views. On the bar are two changing ales from local breweries, often Stonehouse.
Q🐎❀🛏◑◐♿♣P🚌(64) 🐾📶

Prestatyn

Bar 236 L

236 High Street, LL19 9BP
☎ (01745) 850084 🌐 bar236.co.uk
4 changing beers (sourced locally; often Cwrw Ial) Ⓗ
This café bar at the top of the High Street opened in 2010 and was fully refurbished in 2014. The L-shaped room has a minimalist but pleasant feel with a wood-boarded floor and blue-tiled bar front. Glass-fronted on two sides, if offers open views inside and outside. TV sport is well catered for and there is live music at weekends, when it can be quite noisy. 🐎⇌🚌🐾📶

Halcyon Quest hotel L

17 Gronant Road, LL19 9DT (on A547 just E of town centre)
☎ (01745) 852442 🌐 halcyonquest-hotel.com
Facer's Flintshire Bitter; 3 changing beers (sourced nationally) Ⓗ
A longstanding supporter of cask beer, the HQ, as it is known, is at the southern end of town. It has just one room packed with sporting and other memorabilia, including a rowing boat suspended from the ceiling dedicated to JR Hartley of fly-fishing fame. The extensive garden patio at the rear has a covered area and is popular for drinking in the summer months.
🐎❀🛏⛺⇌●P🚌(35,36) 🐾

Rhyl

Cob & Pen L ✔

143 High Street, LL18 1UF
☎ (01745) 350446
Facer's Mountain Mild, Flintshire Bitter; 3 changing beers Ⓗ
A fine traditional town-centre pub close to the railway and bus stations with three separate areas to suit all tastes served from a central bar. The pub hosts darts, pool and dominoes teams and shows televised sports events, all adding to its popularity. Interesting novelty clocks are displayed in a side bar. The beers are usually from microbreweries including a cask mild – a rarity for these parts. Guest ales change every other day or so, giving customers more choice. 🐎❀◑⇌♣🚌📶

Dove at Rhyl L

2 St Margarets Buildings, St Margarets Drive, LL18 2HT (on A525)
☎ 07908 957116
4 changing beers (sourced locally; often Dovecote) Ⓗ
Situated on the outskirts of town, this welcome addition to the local pub landscape is the first in a small chain of pubs operated by Dovecote Brewery under the Dove umbrella. The interior is bright and airy, featuring a mural of Rhyl High Street, and the atmosphere is relaxed and friendly. The cask beer range includes at least two from Dovecote plus two guests from a local microbrewery.
Q🐎●🚌(51) 🐾

Ruabon

Bridge End Inn 🏆 L

5 Bridge Street, LL14 6DA
☎ (01978) 810881 🌐 bridgeendruabon.co.uk
8 changing beers (sourced nationally; often Ossett, Rat, Salopian) Ⓗ
Welcoming, traditional, community-focused local, close to Ruabon station, with three low-ceilinged rooms and a covered outside drinking area. It has deservedly won numerous awards since its revitalisation by the McGivern family, including CAMRA National Pub of the Year. The changing range of eight cask ales may include a brew from the on-site McGivern Brewery, plus porter and a stout. There is usually a real cider. Families and well-behaved dogs are welcome in the lounge.
Q🐎❀⛺⇌♣●P▯🚌🐾📶

St Asaph

New Inn ✔

Lower Denbigh Road, LL17 0EF
☎ (01745) 584600
JW Lees Bitter; 2 changing beers (often JW Lees) Ⓗ
The pub has a main lounge bar area leading to a pool room with a dartboard. The separate back bar has a real open fire and another dartboard. There is a raised outdoor space to the rear with a large landscaped garden below. The pub backs on to the River Elwy, with easy access for dog walkers. There is a large rear car park.
Q🐎❀◑♣P🚌(51) 🐾📶

Shotton

Central Hotel ✔

2-4 Chester Road West, CH5 1BX
☎ (01244) 845510
Greene King IPA, Abbot; Ruddles County; 3 changing beers (sourced nationally; often Big Hand, Hafod) Ⓗ
Built in 1943, this formerly rundown premises was refurbished by Wetherspoon in 2008. The interior is typical Wetherspoon mock-Edwardian, with the very large bar partially separated into three similarly furnished areas. There is an outdoor seating space to the front. Two or three guest beers come from local microbreweries such as Hafod or Big Hand. Occasional Meet the Brewer evenings are held. 🐎❀◑◐♿⇌P🚌📶

Tremeirchion

Salusbury L

LL17 0UN (1 mile S of jct 30 A55)
☎ (01745) 710532

> Where village statesmen talked with looks profound,
> And news much older than the ale went round.
> **Alfred, Lord Tennyson**

2 changing beers (often Dovecote) Ⓗ
Traditional old village pub with parts reputed to date back to the time of the Magna Carta. It has now under the ownership of the nearby Dovecote Brewery, who operate three pubs in north-east Wales. The interior divides into several discrete areas including dining rooms, a snug and a meeting room. Outside, there is a large space with a children's play area. Other beers from microbreweries are usually on the bar alongside the Dovecote range. Friday pie and fish night is popular.
♨❀◐♿⚠♣P🐾ᯤ

Wrexham

Elihu Yale ✔

44-46 Regent Street, LL11 1RR

☎ (01978) 366646

Greene King Abbot; Ruddles Best Bitter; Sharp's Doom Bar; 5 changing beers (sourced nationally) Ⓗ
Formerly the Majestic Cinema, this popular Wetherspoon town-centre pub is within walking distance of both railway and bus stations. It serves three regular beers plus at least five guest ales, one from a North Wales brewery, and up to two real ciders. There are various seating areas in the large room, with a quieter area near the front of the pub – look for the interesting skylight towards the front. Families are welcome until 10pm. Quiz night is Wednesday, Poker on Sunday.
Q♨◐♿⇌(Central/General) ●🚌ᯤ

Fat Boar L

11 Yorke Street, LL13 8LW

☎ (01978) 354201 🌐 thefatboarwrecsam.co.uk

4 changing beers (sourced locally; often Big Hand, Hafod) Ⓗ
A sister venue to the one of the same name in Mold, this stripped-down pub has a clean and bright feel with ceiling beams and exposed brick walls. It comprises a large L-shaped bar/lounge downstairs and a restaurant upstairs with a display of hanging potted plants. Up to four handpumps usually feature beers from local microbreweries. There is a large, stylish beer garden and smoking area at the rear. ◐⇌🚌ᯤ

Ysceifiog

Fox ★

Ysceifiog Village Road, CH8 8NJ (signed from B5121)

☎ (01352) 720241 🌐 foxinnysceifiog.co.uk

Tetley Bitter; 2 changing beers Ⓗ
Built around 1730, the Fox is well worth seeking out. The interior comprises four small rooms, two of them for dining. The bar has a sliding door that takes you back to the 1930s. There is a choice of four beers. A children's playground is adjacent to the outside drinking area. Identified by CAMRA as having a nationally important historic interior, this is a rare classic. Q♨❀◐♣P🐾ᯤ

All hands to the pumps

British beer is unique and so are the methods used for serving it. The best-known English system, the beer engine operated by a handpump on the pub bar, arrived early in the 19th century. It coincided with and was prompted by the decline of the publican brewer and the rise of commercial companies that began to dominate the supply of beer to public houses. In order to sell more beer, commercial brewers and publicans looked for faster and less labour-intensive methods of serving beer.

In The Brewing Industry in England, 1700-1830, Peter Mathias records that 'most beer had to be stored in butts in the publicans' cellars for the technical reason that it needed an even and fairly low temperature, even where convenience and restricted space behind the bar did not enforce it. This meant, equally inevitably, continuous journeying to and from the cellars by the potboys to fill up jugs from the spigots: a waste of time for the customer and of labour and trade for the publican. Drawing up beer from the cellar at the pull of a handle at the bar at once increased the speed of sale and cut the wage bill.'

The first attempt at a system for raising beer from cellar to bar was patented by Joseph Bramah in 1797. But his system – using heavy boxes of sand that pressed down on storage vessels holding the beer – was so elaborate that it was never used. But his idea encouraged others to develop simpler systems. Mathias writes: 'One of the few technical devices of importance to come into the public house since the publican stopped brewing his own beer was the beer engine. It was, from the first, a simple manually operated pump, incorporating no advances in hydraulic knowledge or engineering skill, similar in design to many pumps used at sea, yet perfectly adapted to its function in the public house.'

By 1801, John Chadwell of Blackfriars, London, was registered as a 'beer-engine maker' and soon afterwards Thomas Rowntree in the same area described himself as a 'maker of a double-acting beer-machine'. By the 1820s, beer engine services had become standard throughout most of urban England and Gaskell & Chambers in the Midlands had become the leading manufacturer, employing more than 700 people in their Birmingham works alone.

NORTH-WEST WALES

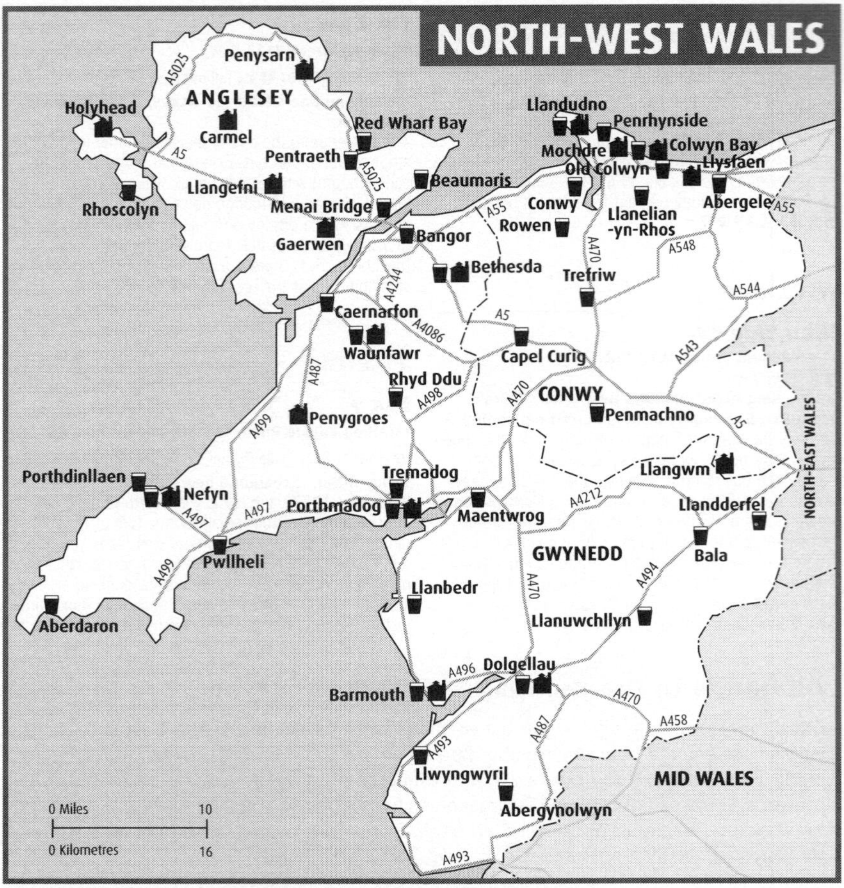

Authority areas covered: Anglesey UA, Conwy UA, Gwynedd UA

Aberdaron

Ty Newydd

LL53 8BE

☎ (01758) 760207 gwesty-tynewydd.co.uk

Purple Moose Calon Lan; 2 changing beers (sourced locally)

The hotel is at the centre of a picturesque and historic village at the end of the Llyn Peninsula. Beers are from two local breweries. Freshly caught Bardsey lobster and crab are on the menu, as well as afternoon teas. Eleven en-suite bedrooms are available, with stunning sea views. The Wales coastal footpath passes through the village. Bus services run from Pwllheli. Dogs are welcome in the Yellow Room and on the terrace, but are not permitted in bar/restaurant. Q

Abergele

Hoptimist

32 Market Street, LL22 7AA

5 changing beers (sourced locally; often Cwrw Ial, Dovecote)

An innovative conversion of a former building society, Abergele's first micropub – a joint venture between Cwrw Ial and Dovecote breweries – opened in 2018. Information regarding the beers and ciders, along with their prices and strengths, is clearly displayed on a large blackboard on the back wall. The bank of 13 taps dispenses five cask, five keg beers and three ciders, served in third-pint glasses on request. The large rear courtyard offers views into the small cellar.

Q (12,13)

Abergynolwyn

Railway Inn

Lichfield Terrace, LL36 9YW (on B4405)

☎ (01654) 782744

3 changing beers

Hospitable community local in the centre of the village not far from the Talyllyn Railway. You can still see the remains of the incline that brought goods down from the railway station to the village. Excellent food is served along with a choice of three draught beers and the occasional cider. The pub has stunning views of the nearby hills and there are wonderful walks in the valley.

Q P

Bala

Stori

101 High Street, LL23 7AE (opp Old Bull's Head and Co-op)

☎ (01678) 520501 storibeers.wales

3 changing beers (sourced locally; often Geipel) Ⓖ
This bottle shop and taproom is centrally situated in the popular town of Bala close to the lake and other attractions. The shop offers a wide range of beers and beer-related merchandise, with the emphasis on local products, and to the rear is the taproom. Cask and craft keg beers are available to either take away or enjoy in the cosy tasting room. Opening hours may be subject to seasonal variation. Q (T3)

Bangor

Blue Sky Bar & Café

236 High Street, LL57 1PA
☎ 07415 845599
2 changing beers (sourced locally) Ⓗ
Established in 2019, this taproom/microbar has a contemporary layout. It offers two draught beers from local breweries, up to 10 craft beers, plus a large range of predominantly Welsh bottled and canned beers. Drinks can be taken up to the café upstairs where food is served until 4pm every day. Live music plays on a monthly basis upstairs. Dogs are welcome downstairs in the taproom.

Patrick's

59 Holyhead Road, LL57 2HE
☎ (01248) 353062 patricksbar.com
4 changing beers (sourced regionally) Ⓗ
Situated in upper Bangor, this lively Irish-themed bar is popular both with the locals and students of Bangor University. Numerous TVs display sporting events. There are usually two local ales and one regional beer on the bar. There are extended opening hours for sports and late-night drinking. On the bus route towards the Menai Straits and near the railway station.

Barmouth

Royal Hotel

LL42 1AB
☎ (01341) 406214
4 changing beers Ⓗ
Located beneath the main hotel with access from the main road, the pub is on two levels, with the main bar next to the entrance, and the lower level primarily for playing pool. There is a beer garden to the rear. Beers are usually from Welsh breweries but occasionally come from just over the border.

Beaumaris

Castle Court Hotel

Castle Square, LL58 8DA
☎ (01248) 810078 castlecourtbeaumaris.co.uk
Facer's This Splendid Ale; 1 changing beer (sourced regionally) Ⓗ
In the centre of this historic town and overlooking the castle, this guest house was originally the White Lion Hotel. The owners have renovated the reception and dining areas. It has a small beer garden to the rear, and in spring and summer the courtyard outside the main door provides more seating. Facer's Splendid Ale is always available plus one guest beer from a small independent brewery. Lunchtime meals are served during school holidays only.

Bethesda

Y Sior

35-37 Carneddi Road, LL57 3SE
☎ (01248) 600072
4 changing beers (sourced locally) Ⓗ
A friendly locals' pub in the village of Carneddi just outside Bethesda. A short drive from the A5, there is plenty of parking nearby. Free of tie, the pub offers a variety of ales from the Marston's range as well as locally brewed beers. There are views across the valley to the local slate quarry, which has the longest zip wire in Europe. Q

Caernarfon

Bar Bach

Tan y Bont, LL55 2NF (just off square, behind Caffi Maes)
☎ (01286) 673111
2 changing beers (sourced locally) Ⓗ
Under the looming shadow of Caernarfon's imposing castle lies the self-proclaimed smallest bar in Wales. Part of Caffi Maes on Castle Square, its narrow entrance is found around the corner. A charmingly intimate place, it does indeed occupy a small area but it is deceptive in that the bar leads to another longer room on a lower level. Plenty of exposed stonework, a small fireplace and a mix of dark-wood furniture give it a lived-in feel.
Q(WHR)

Black Boy Inn

Northgate Street, LL55 1RW
☎ (01286) 673604 black-boy-inn.com
Draught Bass; 5 changing beers (sourced regionally) Ⓗ
The pub is set within the town walls between the marina and castle. This historic town, a World Heritage Site, is well worth a visit, ending with a welcome pint at the Black Boy. The public bar and small lounge are warmed by roaring fires. Good-value food is served and a guest beer usually comes from Purple Moose. There is a drinking area outside on the traffic-free street. Local CAMRA Pub of the Year.
(WHR) P (5C,S4)

Capel Curig

Plas y Brenin

LL24 0ET
☎ (01690) 720214 pyb.co.uk
3 changing beers (sourced locally) Ⓗ
Outdoor centre in an attractive rural area. The raised bar overlooks two lakes, Llynnau Mymbyr, with spectacular views of Mount Snowdon – the outdoor drinking area is the best way to enjoy the vista. The decor is basic but modern, with wooden floors, wooden tables and chairs and a TV. The large dining area offers a hearty and

REAL ALE BREWERIES

Anglesey Brewhouse Llangefni
Anglesey Brewing Carmel
Black Cloak Colwyn Bay
Cader Dolgellau
Conwy Llysfaen
Cybi Holyhead (NEW)
Druid Penysarn
Geipel Llangwm
Lleu Penygroes
Llyn Nefyn
Mona Anglesey: Gaerwen (NEW)
Myrddins Barmouth
Ogwen Bethesda
Purple Moose Porthmadog
Snowdon Craft Mochdre
Snowdonia Parc Waunfawr
Wild Horse Llandudno

WALES

reasonably priced food menu. Three handpumps dispense local beers from Conwy, Purple Moose and Snowdon Craft breweries. Q🐴❀🛏◑♿▲♣P📶

Tyn-y-Coed Inn 𝕃

Holyhead Road, LL24 0EE

☎ (01690) 720331 🌐 tyn-y-coed.co.uk

Purple Moose Cwrw Eryri/Snowdonia Ale, Cwrw Madog/Madog's Ale; 2 changing beers (sourced locally) 🄷

A spacious old multi-roomed pub with a hotel extension overlooking Moel Siabod. To mark its historic past on the coaching route, there is a majestic stagecoach opposite the entrance on the A5. It is popular with outdoor enthusiasts owing to its location in the Snowdonia National Park, with welcoming log fires warming three of the bar areas in the winter months. Locally sourced food, ales and a good selection of whiskies are available. Dogs are admitted on leads. Q🐴❀🛏◑♣P🐾📶

Colwyn Bay

Bay Hop 🏆 𝕃

17 Penrhyn Road, LL29 8LG

🌐 thebayhop.co.uk

5 changing beers (sourced regionally) 🄷

A multi award-winning micropub with a welcoming and friendly atmosphere. Furnishings include wooden settles and comfy chairs around larger tables, and tall barrel tables for those who prefer to stand. Five ciders and perries are available from a fridge in addition to an extensive range of beers in bottles and cans for drinking in or taking out. Thursday is cheese night. Local CAMRA Pub of the Year for the last four years, Cider Pub of the Year 2018 and North Wales Pub of the Year 2019. 🐴⇌♣●🚌(12,13)🐾📶

Black Cloak Taproom 𝕃

71 Abergele Road, LL29 7RU

☎ (01492) 330274

3 changing beers (sourced locally) 🄷

Brewpub opened in 2018 by two former employees of Heavy Industry Brewing, who are now producing their own beer on-site using a one-barrel plant. Beers are available on cask, keg and direct from a brite tank, and served in thirds, halves, two-thirds or pint measures. Guest beers are from quality breweries throughout the UK and bottled beers are also on offer. The taproom has comfortable seating and a convivial atmosphere. 🐴❀⇌♣🚌(12,13)🐾📶

Pen-y-Bryn 𝕃

Pen-y-Bryn Road, LL29 6DD

☎ (01492) 533360 🌐 penybryn-colwynbay.co.uk

Purple Moose Cwrw Eryri/Snowdonia Ale; house beer (by Phoenix); 4 changing beers (sourced regionally; often Timothy Taylor) 🄷

Large open-plan pub with bookcases, old furniture and real fires during the winter. The walls are decorated with old photographs and memorabilia from the local area. Panoramic views of the Bay of Colwyn and the Great Orme can be admired from the terrace and garden. The food menu changes daily and is served throughout the day. A boardroom-style function room for celebrations and meetings has been created in the cellar, opening onto the garden. Q🐴❀◑♿P🚌(23)🐾📶

Conwy

Albion Ale House ★ 𝕃

Upper Gate Street, LL32 8RF

☎ (01492) 582484 🌐 albionalehouse.weebly.com

10 changing beers (sourced locally) 🄷

Multi-room pub on CAMRA's National Inventory of Historic Pub Interiors, superbly refurbished by the current owners – each room retains original 1920s features and several have interesting fireplaces. There is no music or TV, just pleasant conversation. The pub is managed by three local brewers – Conwy, Purple Moose and Snowdon Craft – and showcases their beers as well as guests. There are up to 10 ciders and a good selection of wines and malt whiskies. CAMRA awards include local and Welsh Pub of the Year. Q❀⇌♣●🚌(5,19)🐾📶

Bank of Conwy 𝕃

1 Lancaster Square, LL32 8HT

☎ (01492) 573741 🌐 thebankofconwy.wales

4 changing beers (sourced regionally) 🄷

Craft beer bar in a Grade II listed former bank. It uses many fittings from the original building – the counter, the manager's office and the vault. Food is served daily. There is a wide selection of beers, with four cask and 13 keg pumps. An extensive selection of bottled beers, wines and gins is also available. Dogs are welcome with free sausages. Tuesday is jam night, Wednesday and Friday are music nights. 🐴◑⇌🚌(5,19)🐾📶

Erskine Arms 𝕃

Rosehill Street, LL32 8LD

☎ (01492) 593535 🌐 erskinearms.co.uk

Black Sheep Best Bitter; Conwy Clogwyn Gold; Timothy Taylor Boltmaker; 2 changing beers (sourced regionally; often Purple Moose) 🄷

Reopened in 2017 following a major refurbishment, the pub's name was changed back to the Erskine Arms – the family name of the owners. It was previously the Malt Loaf, in keeping with its sister pub the Cottage Loaf in Llandudno. The inn has two distinct dining areas, one on an upper floor, and there is a snug to the left and an outside drinking area. The decor includes traditional wooden features, open fires and pictures on the walls portraying local history. ❀🛏◑⇌●🚌(5,19)🐾📶

Dolgellau

Torrent Walk Hotel 𝕃

Smithfield Street, LL40 1AA

☎ (01341) 422858

Purple Moose Cwrw Eryri/Snowdonia Ale; Wychwood Hobgoblin Ruby; 3 changing beers (sourced nationally) 🄷

An 18th-century hotel in the narrow streets of the town centre, retaining most of its multi-roomed interior and old fireplaces, although the bar fittings date from circa 1970. Note the Coffee Room etched panel in the door from the lobby to the room on the right. A real cider is always served and up to five ales, mostly from local breweries. An ideal base for walking in the Cader Idris area. 🛏◑♣●🚌🐾📶

Llanbedr

Ty Mawr Hotel

LL45 2HH

☎ (01341) 241440 🌐 tymawrhotel.com

4 changing beers 🄷

Small country hotel set in its own grounds. The modern lounge bar has a slate-flagged floor and cosy wood-burning stove. Unusual flying memorabilia reflect connections with the local airfield. French windows open out onto a veranda and landscaped terrace with seating. A beer festival is held in a marquee on the lawn each year. Popular with locals and walkers, dogs and children are welcome. Meals are served all day. Q🛏◑▲♣🚌🐾

Llandderfel

Bryntirion Inn 🄻

B4401, LL23 7RA (on B4401 4 miles E of Bala)
☎ (01678) 530205 🌐 bryntirioninn.co.uk
Purple Moose Cwrw Eryri/Snowdonia Ale; 1 changing beer (sourced locally) 🄷
Dating back to 1695, this former hunting lodge and coaching inn overlooks the Dee Valley. The cosy and comfortable bar area with a log fire is open all day. There are a number of other rooms to accommodate diners and families including a large function room for special events. There is also a small covered and heated courtyard at the rear. The guest beer varies and may be from a local or national brewer. Two en-suite guest rooms are available upstairs. Q🐴❀🛏◑♣P🚌(T3)🐾📶

Llandudno

Albert 🄻 ✔

56 Madoc Street, LL30 2TW
☎ (01492) 877188 🌐 albertllandudno.co.uk
Timothy Taylor Golden Best; 4 changing beers (sourced regionally) 🄷
Just off the town centre and close to the railway station, this popular pub-restaurant has a modern decor with a range of interesting photographs and pictures on display. It offers five handpulled ales from local and independent breweries and a range of meals throughout the day. Current beers are displayed on blackboards above and beside the L-shaped bar, with third-pint glasses available. There is a heated and covered veranda with seating at the front. 🐴❀◑♿⇌●🚌(5,12)🐾📶

Palladium 🄻 ✔

7 Gloddaeth Street, LL30 2DD
☎ (01492) 863920
Greene King Abbot; Ruddles Best Bitter; Sharp's Doom Bar; 5 changing beers (sourced regionally) 🄷
When this huge Wetherspoon venue opened in 2001 it was the largest pub in the UK. Converted from a theatre originally built in 1920 on the site of the Market Hall, the boxes and upper seating remain although they are not in use. The walls are adorned with theatrical memorabilia including original programmes bearing the names of the stars of the day. There are spacious areas on split levels including a family dining room. A lift is available.
🐴◑♿⇌●🚌(5,12) 📶

Snowdon

11 Tudno Street, LL30 2HB
☎ (01492) 872166 🌐 thesnowdon.co.uk
Draught Bass; house beer (by Coach House); 4 changing beers (sourced regionally) 🄷
Reopened in 2019 following a major internal refurbishment, this is one of the oldest pubs in Llandudno. The large main drinking area has an attractive Snowdon mirror above the fireplace. Six real ales are on offer including Coach House Blue Sky house beer. The raised pavement garden gives a fine view of the Great Orme and the goats, if you are lucky. It is a repeat winner of the annual Llandudno in Bloom award for its floral displays. 🐴❀◑🚊(Great Orme)●🚌(5,12)🐾📶

Tapps 🄻

35 Madoc Street, LL30 2TL
☎ (01492) 870956
Conwy Welsh Pride; 4 changing beers (sourced regionally) 🄷
This micropub opened in October 2017 in what was a cake shop; it has an open-plan bar at the front with a small snug to the rear. Welsh beer is to the fore and there is a large bottled beer selection. Vinyl music is played on an old record player. One of the tables is a chessboard that transforms into a backgammon or card table, other board games are provided and there are books to borrow. 🐴❀⇌♣●🚌(5,12)🐾📶

Llanelian-yn-Rhos

White Lion Inn ✔

LL29 8YA
☎ (01492) 515807 🌐 whitelioninn.co.uk
Marston's Saddle Tank; 2 changing beers (sourced regionally) 🄷
A regular in the Guide for 29 years, this 16th-century inn situated in the hills above Old Colwyn, next to St Elian's Church, offers a warm welcome. Gracing the entrance are two white stone lions, leading into the bar area with slate-flagged flooring and large comfortable chairs around the log fires. Decorative stained glass is mounted above the bar in the tiny snug. The restaurant serves home-cooked food. Jazz night is Tuesday and quiz night Thursday. Q🐴❀◑♣●P🐾📶

Llanuwchllyn

Eagles Inn (Tafarn Yr Eryrod) 🏆 🄻

LL23 7UB
☎ (01678) 540278 🌐 yr-eagles.co.uk
4 changing beers (sourced locally; often Purple Moose) 🄷
An old stone-built village local opposite the church, this is a little gem with a friendly welcome for all. The bar area doubles as a shop and is open all day. It retains plenty of historic features including a wonderful stone floor. The adjacent restaurant serves highly rated locally produced food. The patio garden has good mountain views. It is a 10-minute walk to Llanuwchllyn station on the Bala Lake Railway. Opening times and beer range are reduced in winter. 🐴❀◑⛺⇌(Bala Lake)♣P🚌(T3)🐾📶

Llwyngwyril

Garthangharad Hotel

LL37 2UZ
☎ (01341) 251255 🌐 thegarthangharad.co.uk
3 changing beers (sourced regionally) 🄷
The only pub for miles around, the hotel is situated in the centre of the village. Built circa 1736 and extended in 1840, it has a front lounge, rear bar and outside courtyard/beer garden. Pub food and accommodation are available. The railway halt on the beautiful Cambrian Coast line is a 10-minute walk, and bus service 28 stops nearby. Opening hours are extended in summer – check the website. ❀🛏◑⇌P🚌(28)📶

Maentwrog

Grapes Hotel 🄻

LL41 4HN (on A496 near A487 jct)
☎ (01766) 590365 🌐 grapeshotelsnowdonia.co.uk
Purple Moose Cwrw Eryri/Snowdonia Ale; Sharp's Doom Bar; 1 changing beer (sourced locally) 🄷
A former coaching inn, this hotel dates back to the 17th century and overlooks the Vale of Ffestiniog. The interior comprises a lounge, public bar, veranda and large dining room; outside there is a sheltered beer garden to the rear. Most of the beers are local. Plas Halt railway station nearby is on the scenic Ffestiniog line. The village is an ideal base for visiting this beautiful area.
Q🐴❀🛏◑♿⛺⇌(Plas Halt)♣●P🚌

Menai Bridge

Liverpool Arms

St George's Pier, LL59 5EY

(01248) 712453

Facer's Flintshire Bitter; Purple Moose Cwrw Eryri/ Snowdonia Ale H/G, Ochr Dywyll y Mws/Dark Side of the Moose; 1 changing beer H

Refurbished to a high standard, the Livvy has four cask ales on offer and serves good-quality home-cooked food. This nautically themed pub is frequented by locals, students in term time and the local sailing fraternity. A short walk takes you beneath the famous Grade I listed suspension bridge and it is close to the quay for seasonal tourist boats. The Anglesey and Welsh Coast footpaths are nearby.

Nefyn

Bragdy Llyn

Ffordd Dewi Sant, LL53 6EG

(01758) 721981 cwrwllyn.cymru

Cwrw Llyn Brenin Enlli, Cwrw Glyndwr, Seithenyn; 1 changing beer (sourced locally) H

A friendly bar located within the Cwrw Llyn Brewery, open to the public all year round. Closing time may be later on Friday and Saturday depending on customer demand. Brewery tours are available on request which include a short film and tasters of the core range of ales. Near the coast and the National Trust village of Porthdinllean. P

Old Colwyn

Crafty Fox

355 Abergele Road, LL29 9PL

07733 531766

5 changing beers (sourced regionally) H

Previously two shops – a tattoo parlour and a butcher's – this welcoming micropub opened in 2018. The main entrance leads to the bar, with hops draped across the ceiling. The lounge is furnished with a mixture of leather sofas and stools. On the bar wall is an interesting set of photographs comparing the present street scene with a century ago. Loyalty cards are available for regular drinkers. Q (12,13)

Red Lion

385 Abergele Road, LL29 9PL

(01492) 515042

Courage Best Bitter; 6 changing beers (sourced nationally) H

In the Guide for 26 consecutive years, this free house serves up to six guest ales from independent and national brewers. It has an L-shaped lounge featuring antique brewery mirrors, local photographs and other memorabilia. There is a traditional public bar with a pool table, dartboard and several TVs. To the rear is a Victorian-style covered and heated smoking conservatory. Take a look at the pub sign on your way in. Q (12,13)

Penmachno

Eagles

LL24 0UG

(01690) 760177 eaglespenmachno.co.uk

Greene King IPA; 3 changing beers (sourced locally) H

Traditional inn in a peaceful village lying in a secluded valley at the heart of Snowdonia, four miles from Betws-y-coed. There are delightful views up the valley from the rear garden. The bar has a wood-burning stove ensuring a warm welcome in winter months. At least one local ale is always on offer. The pub prides itself on being at the centre of community activities, with local musicians performing on the first Wednesday of each month. Q (19)

Penrhynside

Penrhyn Arms

Pendre Road, LL30 3BY

(01492) 549060

Banks's Amber Ale; 4 changing beers (sourced regionally) H

Welcoming free house offering up to four guest beers, concentrating on new breweries and new beers, as well as local ciders and perries. The spacious single room has an L-shaped bar, comfortable seating, real fires and a widescreen TV. Food highlights include Wednesday pie and pint night and Thursday cheese night. Pizza is available on Friday and Saturday. The rear conservatory leads to a raised landscaped garden terrace with extensive views of the coastline. Live music features on occasional Saturdays. (14,15)

Pentraeth

Panton Arms

The Square, LL75 8AZ

(01248) 450959

Purple Moose Cwrw Glaslyn/Glaslyn Ale; 2 changing beers H

A spacious 18th-century coaching inn with a long lounge bar and separate taproom, popular with locals and tourists alike. Purple Moose Glaslyn is available all year round. The pub's location is ideal for walks in the nearby forest and it is served by a frequent no.62 bus service from the coast. Mid-week opening times can vary in the winter months. Q P (62)

Porthdinllaen

Ty Coch Inn

LL53 6DB (accessible by foot only)

(01758) 720498 tycoch.co.uk

Cwrw Llyn Brenin Enlli; Purple Moose Cwrw Ysgawen/ Elderflower Ale; 1 changing beer (sourced regionally) H

The Ty Coch has been named as one of the top 10 beach bars in the world. Set in an iconic position in this beautiful village, it opened as a pub in 1842 to serve local fishermen. It can only be reached on foot either along the beach or across the golf course. The single open-plan room is served by a central bar. Parking is available at the NT car park or the golf clubhouse. Check for out-of-season opening times.

Porthmadog

Australia

31-35 High Street, LL49 9LR

(01766) 515957

Purple Moose Cwrw Eryri/Snowdonia Ale, Cwrw Ysgawen/Elderflower Ale, Ochr Dywyll y Mws/Dark Side of the Moose; 2 changing beers (sourced locally; often Purple Moose) H

A pub since 1864, the Australia was taken over by the Purple Moose Brewery in 2017 and serves as its taphouse. Most of the core real ale range is available as well as seasonal and special beers. Two rooms are served by a long wooden bar with eight handpumps. There is a small outdoor seating area at the back. It is situated in the centre of town next to the bus stops and near the Ffestiniog & Welsh Highland Railways station. A former local CAMRA Pub of the Year. ♿≋🍎🚌🐾ᯤ

Pwllheli

Pen Cob ✔

Station Square, LL53 5HG
☎ (01758) 704970
Greene King Abbot; Ruddles Best Bitter; 4 changing beers Ⓗ
Wetherspoon pub opened in 2013 opposite the railway station at the start of the scenic Cambrian Coast Line. Formerly a clothing store, it has been attractively refurbished and is now a light and airy venue patronised by young and old. It gets especially busy with locals and tourists at weekends and during the holiday season. The area is popular for sailing. ♿≋🚌ᯤ

Red Wharf Bay

Ship Inn ✔

LL75 8RJ (off A5025 between Pentraeth and Benllech)
☎ (01248) 852568 🌐 shipinnredwharfbay.co.uk
Adnams Broadside; Brains SA; 2 changing beers Ⓗ
Red Wharf Bay was once a busy port exporting coal and fertilisers in the 18th and 19th centuries. Previously known as the Quay, the Ship enjoys an excellent reputation for its bar and restaurant, with meals served lunchtimes and evenings. It gets busy with locals and visitors in the summer. The garden has panoramic views across the bay to south-east Anglesey. The resort town of Benllech is two miles away and the coastal path passes the front door. Q❀♿P

Rhoscolyn

White Eagle

LL65 2NJ (off B4545 signed Traeth Beach)
☎ (01407) 860267 🌐 white-eagle.co.uk
Marston's 61 Deep, Pedigree; Weetwood Best Bitter; 2 changing beers Ⓗ
Saved from closure by the owners, this pub has been renovated and rebuilt with an airy, brasserie-style ambience. It has a fine patio enjoying superb views over Caernarfon Bay and the Llyn Peninsula to Bardsey Island. The nearby beach offers safe swimming with a warden on duty in the summer months. The pub is also close to the coastal footpath. Excellent food is available lunchtimes and evenings, all day during the school holidays. Q♿▲♣P

Rhyd Ddu

Cwellyn Arms

LL54 6TL
☎ (01766) 890321 🌐 snowdoninn.co.uk
Conwy Welsh Pride; 5 changing beers (sourced regionally) Ⓗ
A traditional Welsh country inn in a fabulous situation in this village at the foot of Snowdon. The pub's boast that it has nine real ales nine days a week is only slightly exaggerated. There are usually four handpulls in operation serving ales from local breweries. The lovely log fire makes the pub cosy and welcoming after a walk on Snowdon, or after a ride on the nearby Welsh Highland Railway. ❀♿▲≋(WHR)P🚌🐾

Rowen

Ty Gwyn ✔

High Street, LL32 8YU
☎ (01492) 650232
JW Lees Bitter; 2 changing beers (sourced regionally) Ⓗ
Community village inn in an idyllic setting with a warm welcome for locals and visitors alike. The comfortable lounge has horse brasses and old pictures on the walls, and there is a small restaurant area serving good food made with locally sourced ingredients. Traditional Welsh singing features on Friday evenings, live entertainment most Saturdays and charity quiz nights on occasion. There are two walled gardens, one with a stream running by. Opening times may vary seasonally.
❀▲♣P🚌(19A) 🐾ᯤ

Trefriw

Old Ship

LL27 0JH
☎ (01492) 640013
Banks's Amber Ale; 2 changing beers (sourced regionally) Ⓗ
Dating from the 16th century, this former custom house is now a busy village local. The small central bar serves an L-shaped lounge with an open fire, brass ornaments and pictures of historical and nautical interest. The separate dining room features an inglenook fireplace. Good home-cooked food is available from a changing menu. This genuine free house offers a range of guest beers from independent and local breweries. Outside, a grassed area leads down towards the River Conwy. Opening hours may vary seasonally. Q❀P🚌(19)

Tremadog

Union Inn ✔

7 Market Square, LL49 9RB
☎ (01766) 512748 🌐 union-inn.com
Big Bog Bog Standard Bitter; Purple Moose Cwrw Eryri/Snowdonia Ale; 1 changing beer Ⓗ
Friendly venue situated in the village square, with two separate cosy bars and a restaurant at the rear. The pub has a policy of using locally sourced produce, and the ale range mainly features local beers. Children are welcome and there are board games available. Excellent food is served in the bar and restaurant. Tremadog was the birthplace of Thomas Edward Lawrence (Lawrence of Arabia) in 1888. Frequent bus services pass nearby.
Q❀♿▲≋🍎🚌(1A,T2)

Waunfawr

Snowdonia Park

Beddgelert Road, LL55 4AQ
☎ (01286) 650409 🌐 snowdonia-park.co.uk
House beer (by Snowdonia Parc); 5 changing beers Ⓗ
Home of the Snowdonia Brewery, this is a popular pub for walkers, climbers and families, with children's play areas inside and out. Meals are served all day. The pub adjoins Waunfawr station on the Welsh Highland Railway – stop off here before continuing on one of the most scenic sections of narrow gauge railway in Britain. There is a large campsite adjacent on the riverside. A former local CAMRA Pub of the Year.
Q❀♿▲≋♣🍎P🚌🐾ᯤ

WALES

> Beer is proof that God loves us and wants us to be happy.
> **Benjamin Franklin**

WEST WALES

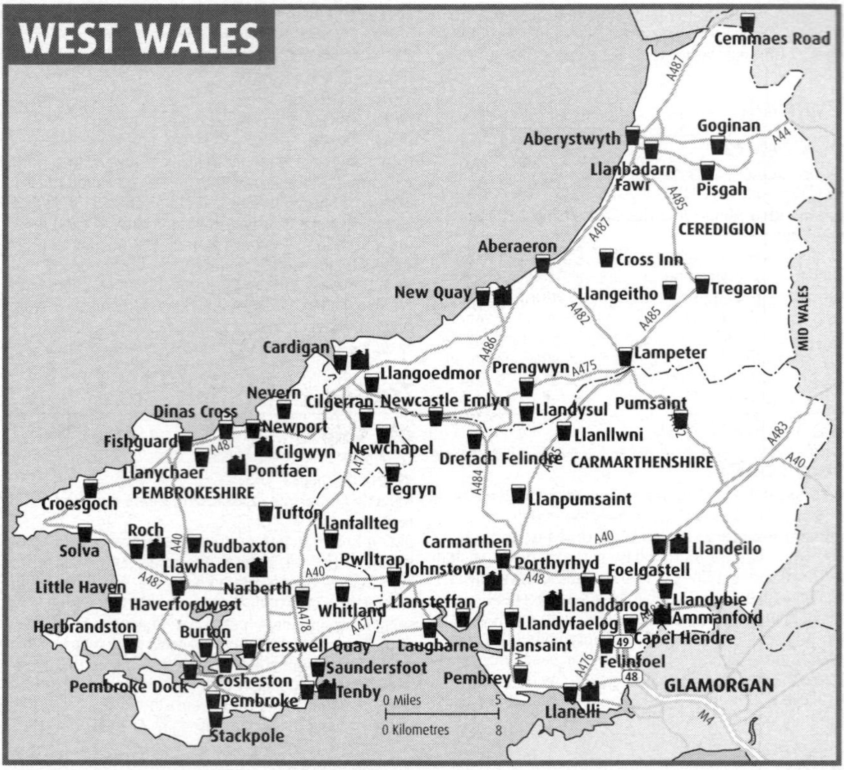

Cemmaes Road

Goginan
Aberystwyth
Llanbadarn
Fawr
Pisgah

CEREDIGION

Aberaeron
Cross Inn
New Quay
Llangeitho
Tregaron

Cardigan
Prengwyn
Llangoedmor
Lampeter
Nevern
Cilgerran
Newcastle Emlyn
Llandysul
Pumsaint
Dinas Cross
Newport
Llanllwni
Fishguard
Cilgwyn
Newchapel
Drefach Felindre
CARMARTHENSHIRE
Llanychaer
Pontfaen
PEMBROKESHIRE
Tegryn
Llanpumsaint
Croesgoch
Tufton
Llanfallteg
Roch
Carmarthen
Llandeilo
Solva
Rudbaxton
Pwlltrap
Johnstown
Porthyrhyd
Llawhaden
Foelgastell
Little Haven
Narberth
Llandybie
Haverfordwest
Whitland
Llansteffan
Llanddarog
Ammanford
Herbrandston
Burton
Llandyfaelog
Capel Hendre
Cresswell Quay
Laugharne
Llansaint
Felinfoel
Pembroke Dock
Cosheston
Saundersfoot
Pembrey
GLAMORGAN
Pembroke
Tenby
Llanelli
Stackpole

MID WALES

0 Miles 5
0 Kilometres 8

Authority areas covered: Carmarthenshire UA, Ceredigion UA, Pembrokeshire UA

Aberaeron

Cadwgan Inn
10 Market Street, SA46 0AU (off A487, overlooking harbour)
☎ (01545) 570149
Hancocks HB; 2 changing beers (sourced nationally; often Bluestone, Mantle, Tenby) ⊞
Named after the last ship to be built in this attractive Regency town, this old-fashioned single-bar pub offers a friendly welcome and lively conversation. It is popular for its sports coverage. The guest beers are chosen from a wide range of small and regional breweries. Gwynt y Ddraig bottled ciders are available. There is a colourful hidden garden at the rear, and the small pavement drinking area at the front is a suntrap. Opposite is a free but busy harbourside public car park. ✿▲♥(T1,T5)✿᯿

Aberystwyth

Glengower Hotel ⓛ ✅
3 Victoria Terrace, SY23 2DH (on seafront)
☎ (01970) 626191 ⊕ glengower.co.uk
Mantle Rock Steady; Wye Valley Butty Bach; 3 changing beers (sourced regionally; often Evan Evans, Purple Moose, Timothy Taylor) ⊞
Excellent coastal views of Cardigan Bay can be enjoyed from the suntrap front terrace at this seafront hotel. The central front bar is the main drinking area, with a log-burner for the winter months. Up to five ciders from Gwynt y Ddraig are served alongside regional guests. There is also a quieter dining area and a large rear games room. Food is locally sourced wherever possible.
Q✿᯿❀◑▲♥♠(03)✿᯿

Hen Orsaf ✅
Station Buildings, Alexandra Road, SY23 1LH
☎ (01970) 636080
Greene King Abbot; Ruddles Best Bitter; Sharp's Doom Bar; 6 changing beers (sourced nationally; often Evan Evans, Glamorgan, Purple Moose) ⊞
A recently refurbished, award-winning conversion of Aberystwyth's former GWR railway station, which dates from 1924. This excellent Wetherspoon pub offers up to six guest ales, usually including light and dark beers, and with a Purple Moose brew always available. Cider is from Westons and Gwynt y Ddraig. Drinks can be enjoyed outdoors on the old station concourse, which has access to the railway station. Convenient for trains, buses and taxis. ✿❀◑&▲♥♣♠᯿

Ship & Castle
1 High Street, SY23 1JG
☎ 07773 778785
Wye Valley HPA, Butty Bach; 3 changing beers (sourced nationally; often Oakham, Salopian, Tiny Rebel) ⊞
Aberystwyth's flagship pub offers microbrewery guests from the UK and Ireland. Small amounts of excellent beer in other formats are also on offer including craft keg, bottles (eg Wild Beer, Polly's) and cans, plus cider and perry from Gwynt y Ddraig. A five-pump platter of third-pint measures is available. Beer festivals in spring and autumn offer extended choice. The well-considered decor reflects the pub's name and history. The venue can be busy on rugby days, but is welcoming at all times.
▲♥♠♣P♠✿᯿

WALES

Burton

Jolly Sailor

SA73 1NX

☎ (01646) 600378 🌐 jollysailorburton.co.uk

Brains Rev James; Draught Bass; Morland Old Speckled Hen Ⓗ

Overlooking the River Cleddau and in the shadow of the toll bridge that traverses it, there has been a public house here for over 150 years. It was from this point that travellers would come to Burton to cross by rowing boat to Pembroke Dock, leaving their supply donkeys outside the Jolly Sailor until their return. The family- and food-oriented pub has a huge garden with a children's play area and an aviary. Winter opening times can vary – check ahead. P(308)

Capel Hendre

King's Head Hotel

Waterloo Road, SA18 3SF

☎ (01269) 842377

2 changing beers (sourced regionally; often Boss, Gower) Ⓗ

A village pub tucked away just three miles from junction 49 of the M4, and a couple of miles from the former mining town of Ammanford. It has a main bar and dining room, with a sliding door leading to a separate snug. Outside there is a garden and a large car park. Two or sometimes three real ales are from Wales, with Glamorgan, Bluestone and Neath breweries often represented. P(128,129)

Cardigan

Black Lion Hotel

High Street, SA43 1HJ

☎ (01239) 612532 🌐 blacklionhotelcardigan.com

Mantle Cwrw Teifi; Wadworth 6X; 1 changing beer (sourced locally) Ⓗ

Dating from 1105, the Black Lion is said to be the oldest coaching inn in Wales. Originally known as a Grogg Shope, it is an ideal stopping point for visitors and locals. There are three separate rooms – a traditional bar with real fire, a relaxing coffee room, and a restaurant. The pub serves ales from the local Mantle Brewery alongside guests. Opening times vary in winter.

Grosvenor

Bridge Street, SA43 1HY SN177459

☎ (01239) 613792

Greene King Abbot; Sharp's Doom Bar; 1 changing beer (sourced nationally) Ⓗ

Large pub on the edge of the town centre, next to Cardigan Castle and the River Teifi. It offers a good choice of ales, including a selection of bottled beers. The large open-plan bar/lounge provides various areas to relax, eat and drink, and there is an extra room upstairs for dining and functions. Good-value food is served lunchtimes and evenings every day. An outdoor patio area overlooks the river and the revamped quay.

Carmarthen

Coracle Tavern

1 Cambrian Place, SA31 1QG

☎ (01267) 468180

2 changing beers (sourced regionally; often Glamorgan, Mantle, Wye Valley) Ⓗ

In the centre of town, close to the main shopping area, this friendly free house offers a warm welcome to locals and visitors alike. Breakfast is served Tuesday to Saturday. The large open-plan bar area has comfy sofas, and there is a separate restaurant upstairs. Darts is popular and a number of teams play here.

Friends Arms

Old St Clears Road, SA31 3HH

☎ (01267) 234073

Mantle MOHO; Thornbridge Jaipur IPA; 2 changing beers (sourced locally; often Tiny Rebel) Ⓗ

Excellent hostelry half a mile from the town centre with a cosy and friendly atmosphere and a warm welcome, enhanced by two open fires. Popular with sports fans, it hosts darts and shows the main sports channels on TV. The pub has its own microbrewery which regularly produces good beer. An outbuilding on two floors has function rooms for meetings and parties. The local CAMRA branch meets here occasionally. (222,322)

Queen's Hotel

10 Queen Street, SA31 1JR

☎ (01267) 231800

3 changing beers (sourced regionally; often Evan Evans, Glamorgan) Ⓗ

A busy town-centre pub near Carmarthenshire County Hall with a bar and lounge. Local ales are always available. The public bar is popular with regulars and has TV for sporting events. There is a patio area that nestles beneath the castle walls and is a suntrap in summer. The local CAMRA branch occasionally meets in the upstairs function room.

Stag & Pheasant

34 Spilman Street, SA31 1LQ

☎ (01267) 232040

2 changing beers (sourced nationally; often Ringwood) Ⓗ

Busy pub on Carmarthen's main thoroughfare, with a warm and friendly atmosphere that is enjoyed both by locals and tourists. The landlady has the freedom to serve a selection of excellent ales. Two TVs make this a popular venue for watching sport. The pleasant rear beer garden has heaters for cold weather.

Yr Hen Dderwen ✔

47-48 King Street, SA31 1BH

☎ (01267) 242050

Glamorgan Jemima's Pitchfork; Greene King Abbot; Ruddles Best Bitter; 7 changing beers (sourced nationally; often Exmoor, Gower, Kelham Island) Ⓗ

Named after the local legend of Merlin and an ancient oak which is depicted throughout the premises. Local Welsh ales are always available alongside a good selection of beers from around the world, including bottled and canned craft ale. There are beer festivals in

REAL ALE BREWERIES

Bluestone Cilgwyn
Caffle Llawhaden
Coles Family Llanddarog
Evan Evans Llandeilo
Felinfoel Llanelli
Friends Arms Johnstown (brewing suspended)
Gwaun Valley Pontfaen
Harbwr Tenby Tenby
Mantle Cardigan
Penlon New Quay
Tenby Tenby
Tinworks Llanelli
Victoria Inn Roch
Zoo Ammanford (NEW)

the spring and autumn and a cider festival in the summer. Meet the Brewer sessions feature throughout the year. Food is served all day.

Cemmaes Road

Dovey Valley Hotel ★

SY20 8JZ

☎ (01650) 511335 doveyvalleyhotel.com

2 changing beers (sourced locally; often Evan Evans, Monty's) H

A gem of a pub built to serve the nearby railway. Boasting a nationally important historic interior, it comprises a cosy main bar and snug with features from the 1870s, including original slate floors and an Edwardian tiled fireplace, with log fire in winter. The pub is furnished with mirrors and brewery memorabilia. Spontaneous live music sessions occasionally take place. QP(T12)

Cilgerran

Masons Arms

Cwnce, SA43 2SR

☎ 07989 990461

Hancocks HB; Sharp's Doom Bar; 1 changing beer (often Mantle) H

Also known as the Rampin, this venue was thought to have opened in 1836. It is a small, cosy and friendly village pub with an open fire (an old kitchen range). Many local characters can be found here and a great atmosphere awaits your visit. Three real ales are on offer, one changing regularly, usually from a local brewery. Various charity events are held during the year along with an occasional musical evening. Winter opening times may vary – check ahead. P

Cosheston

Brewery Inn

SA72 4UD

☎ (01646) 686678 thebreweryinn.com

Brains Rev James; Coles Family Cwrw Blasus; 1 changing beer H

This Grade II listed free house was once accommodation for monks, with its own brewhouse in outbuildings behind (brewing ceased in 1889). The light and airy stone-built inn has a traditional slate floor and beamed ceiling. To one side is a cosy area for drinkers to enjoy a chat in front of the log fire. Ingredients for the extensive menu are sourced locally, including fresh fish. The pub has a solid reputation for good food and ales. QP

Cresswell Quay

Cresselly Arms L

SA68 0TE

☎ (01646) 651210

Sharp's Doom Bar H**; Worthington's Bitter** G**; house beer (by Caffle); 2 changing beers (sourced locally; often Bluestone, Mantle)** H

Situated on the Cresswell River, this 250-year-old ivy-covered hostelry is a throwback to the Victorian age. The homely farm kitchen interior, where a roaring fire burns in the hearth, is a haven for locals and visitors alike. Accessible by boat from the Milford Haven estuary at high tide, the pub also lies on a series of interesting walking routes. The house beer from Caffle is complemented by Worthington's Bitter dispensed from the barrel by jug. QP(361)

Croesgoch

Artramont Arms

SA62 5JP (on A487)

☎ (01348) 831309

2 changing beers (often Shepherd Neame) H

Friendly, family-run village local that has been licensed premises since the 1700s; in the past it also sold petrol and incorporated a post office. It now features a large public bar with tiled floor plus a lounge with dining area. There is also a small library for customers, and a pleasant garden outside. Good food is available from an interesting and varied menu. Check winter opening times before travelling. P(T11)

Cross Inn (Llanon)

Rhos yr Hafod Inn L

SY23 5NB (at B4337/B4577 crossroads)

☎ (01974) 272644

2 changing beers (sourced regionally; often Bluestone, Evan Evans, Mantle) H

A warm welcome and a varied range of guest ales await at this family-run pub. Its choice of drinking areas includes the front bar, popular in the early evening with lively locals, and the comfortable rear bar. For sunny days there is a large rear garden and a roadside drinking space. A traditional turntable and vinyl collection are available for customers' use. Various events are held throughout the year. Local CAMRA Pub of the Year. P

Dinas Cross

Freemasons Arms

Spencer Buildings, SA42 0UW (on A487 coast rd midway between Fishguard and Newport)

☎ (01348) 811674

Gower Gold; 1 changing beer (often Coles Family) H

Traditional sea captains' meeting place in the Pembrokeshire Coast National Park. This pub is conveniently placed for those who enjoy sailing or like to visit attractive beaches and walk the coastal path. It also has the advantage of being on a principal bus route. The main bar, tastefully refurbished while retaining its original character, features a cosy open fire and a dining area at the side. Check winter opening times before venturing forth. QP(T5)

Drefach Felindre

John Y Gwas

Drefach Felindre, SA44 5XG SN354383

☎ (01559) 370469

2 changing beers (sourced nationally; often Brains, Courage, Marston's) H

Early 19th-century village tavern with a striking yellow and black livery, attracting locals and tourists alike with snugs, a wood-burning stove, quality beer and cider, and a warm welcome, especially for dogs. Two ales are generally offered, alongside a wide variety of bottled beers and ciders. A beer festival, showcasing more than 10 different ales, is held over the August bank holiday weekend. P(460)

Felinfoel

White Lion Inn

Parkview, SA14 8BH (on main A476 in Felinfoel)

☎ (01554) 776644

Gower Gold; 4 changing beers (sourced nationally) H

A family-friendly split-level hostelry with defined drinking and dining spaces plus a function room. There are covered and open drinking areas outside. A selection of well-kept real ales is available, and a good-value carvery. Quiz nights are Sunday and Wednesday. National cycle and walking paths to the Swiss Valley and beyond are nearby. There is ample parking on the roadside. ✆✿❶&♣P🗑🛇

Fishguard

Royal Oak Inn ▼

Market Square, SA65 9HA

☎ (01348) 218632

Brains Rev James; Glamorgan Jemima's Pitchfork; 1 changing beer (sourced locally; often Bluestone) Ⓗ

This Grade II listed building is famous for its place in history – a French invasion attempt on the west coast of Wales in 1797 was thwarted by locals in the Battle of Fishguard; this was known as the last invasion attempt on Britain. A peace treaty was signed between the British and the French in the Royal Oak's bar area. The interior is sparingly decorated with exposed stone and wooden beams, but with little reference to its historic past. Q✆✿❶▲♣🗑

Foelgastell

Smiths Arms

Heol y Foel, SA14 7EL

☎ (01269) 842213 ⊕ thesmithsarms.co.uk

2 changing beers (sourced nationally; often Boss, Marston's, Rhymney) Ⓗ/🄶

A friendly locals' pub that also provides a handy stopping-off point for travellers on the A48, and visitors to the nearby National Botanic Garden of Wales. The beer selection varies but usually includes one or two real ales from local and national breweries. Real cider is often available. The pub is open from midday with food served lunchtimes and evenings except Sunday evening, featuring a choice of bar or restaurant menus. ✆✿❶&♣🗑P🗑(166) 🐾🛇

Goginan

Druid Inn Ⓛ

SY23 3NT (on A44 6 miles E of Aberystwyth)

☎ (01970) 880650

Mantle MOHO; Wye Valley Bitter; 3 changing beers (sourced nationally; often Purple Moose, Tenby, Wood) Ⓗ

A welcoming pub celebrating its 46th year in this Guide. The dining room and pool room flank an L-shaped main bar where dogs are welcome. Up to four real ales and four ciders are served, plus interesting bottles and craft beers on draught. Occasional music nights (sometimes with acts of more than local renown) and beer festivals are hosted. Food is popular and high quality. Buses run until early evening Monday to Saturday. A pub-owned B&B can be found next door. A former Wales CAMRA Pub of the Year. ✆✿❶♣🗑P🗑(525,X47)🐾🛇

Haverfordwest

Pembroke Yeoman

11 Hill Street, SA61 1QQ

☎ (01437) 762500

Draught Bass; 2 changing beers (sourced nationally) Ⓗ

This pub is at the top of town near St Thomas Green, which is also a car park. The name is taken from the Pembrokeshire Yeoman regiment, who gained military distinction for scuppering the last invasion of Britain by the French in Fishguard in 1797. Maintaining original features of wood beams, it is a quiet pub where conversation is the main entertainment, but there is also a jukebox if this fails. Recently refurbished, it's a 10-minute climb from the train and bus stations. However, it's quicker going back down the hill! ✆✿❶♣🛇P🐾

William Owen Ⓛ ✅

6 Quay Street, SA61 1BG

☎ (01437) 771900

Greene King IPA, Abbot; Sharp's Doom Bar; 5 changing beers (sourced regionally; often Bluestone, Boss, Caffle) Ⓗ

Pembrokeshire's first and only Wetherspoon pub occupies a handsome 19th-century building, formerly a shop, hotel and restaurant, with a spacious extension to the rear. It was reputedly built in 1856 for Joseph Thomas, a corn and manure merchant, by local architect William Owen. It has also been a saddler's and, more recently, the Wilton House Hotel. Beer from one of the county's breweries is regularly available. The pub offers the chain's standard menu and promotional deals, and opens early for breakfast. Q✆✿❶&♣🛇🗑🛇

Herbrandston

Taberna Inn Ⓛ

SA73 3TD (3 miles W of Milford Haven)

☎ (01646) 693498 ⊕ taberna.org.uk

Caffle Drop Squint; Purple Moose Ochr Tywyll y Mws/ Dark Side of the Moose; 1 changing beer (sourced nationally) Ⓗ

The Taberna was designed and built in 1963 by a local builder and carpenter with an eye to the area's rapidly developing oil and petrochemical industry at that time. A bus runs here from Millford Haven and the Marina, serving visitors and crews looking for a choice of real ales. The pub serves local, regional and national beers alongside Westons and Moles' Black Rat cider. It keeps a list of all guest ales sold throughout the year, with comments. Former local CAMRA Pub of the Year. Q✆✿❶&▲♣P🗑🗑(300,315)

Lampeter

Nag's Head

14 Bridge Street, SA48 7HG

☎ (01570) 218517

2 changing beers Ⓗ

Town-centre pub refurbished to add a modern and bright horseshoe-shaped bar area. Friendly and fun, it attracts a good mix of customers – locals, students and tourists. Most live sports events are screened, and live music often features. The pub also offers B&B, evening and lunchtime meals, and a function room. ✿❶▲♣🛇🛇

Laugharne

New Three Mariners Inn Ⓛ

Victoria Street, SA33 4SE

☎ (01994) 427426

1 changing beer (sourced locally; often Evan Evans) Ⓗ

The building is in the centre of this historic town and only yards from its early 11th-century castle. Dylan Thomas lived in Laugharne for a number of years and he and his wife Caitlin are laid to rest in the graveyard of St Martin's Church. The pub moved to its current site when the original ale house opposite was converted to a carpentry shop. Popular with locals, it serves evening meals and hosts a weekly quiz night. ✆✿❶&▲♣P🗑🐾🛇

Little Haven

Saint Bride's Inn 🄻

St Brides Road, SA62 3UN
☎ (01437) 781266 🌐 saintbridesinn.co.uk
Brains Rev James; Hancocks HB; 2 changing beers (sourced locally; often Bluestone, Caffle) Ⓗ
Little Haven is a quaint old fishing village in a conservation area of the Pembrokeshire Coast National Park. This family-run pub in the centre of the village is open all year round, selling a range of Welsh, often local, Pembrokeshire ales. It is noted for the ancient well in the cellar. The attractive interior includes a separate dining area, and there are heaters on the patio in the pretty suntrap garden for outdoor drinking.
Q❀◑⛺P🚌(311,400) 📶

Llanbadarn Fawr

Black Lion

SY23 3RA
☎ (01970) 636632
Wye Valley Butty Bach; 3 changing beers (sourced nationally; often Banks's) Ⓗ
Modernised pub in the village centre, a mile from Aberystwyth, popular with locals and students. Its spacious main bar has seating at one end, darts and pool at the other, plus a second bar and a function room at the rear. Local darts, pool and poker teams meet here regularly. The pub hosts a monthly karaoke night and a quiz every other Friday. The large rear garden, next to the village's ancient church, has a delightful air of rural seclusion. Q❀◐♣P🚌(526,X47)📶

Llandeilo

Cottage Inn

A40 Pentrefelin, SA19 6SD (on A40, 2 miles W of Llandeilo)
☎ (01558) 824645 🌐 cottageinnbandb.co.uk
3 changing beers (sourced regionally; often Glamorgan) Ⓗ
A popular family-run community pub on the A40, featuring a separate restaurant and function room. It dates back to the 1850s and was formerly a coaching inn and drovers' hostelry. Two or three guest ales are served. Attractions include a real fire and garden. The pub can get busy when sport is shown on TV. It hosts beer festivals in the last week of January and on August bank holiday. Accommodation is available, and there is a large car park with space for camping and caravans at the rear.
Q❀🛏◑♿⛺P🚌(280,281) 🐾📶

Salutation Inn

33 New Road, SA19 6DF
☎ (01558) 824255
Sharp's Doom Bar; Timothy Taylor Landlord; Titanic Plum Porter; Wye Valley Butty Bach; 1 changing beer (sourced regionally; often Gower) Ⓗ
A locals' pub near the town centre. Friendly staff dispense five well-kept ales. The interior is divided into two areas, with a pool table on one side and a wood fire on the other. Live music often features at weekends. There is a garden and function area to the rear. The pub hosts a beer festival in the summer. ❀♿🚆♣🚌🐾📶

White Horse

Rhosmaen Street, SA19 6EN
☎ (01558) 822424
Evan Evans Cwrw, Brittania, Warrior; 2 changing beers Ⓗ
Grade II listed coaching inn dating from the 16th century. The tap for the local Evan Evans Brewery, this multi-roomed hostelry is popular with all ages. There is a small outdoor drinking area to the front and a large council car park to the rear with access to the pub down a short flight of steps. A covered area is available for smokers with its own TV showing sport. A former local CAMRA Pub of the Year winner. 🚆●🚌(103,X13)🐾

Yr Hen Vic

82 New Road, SA19 6TB
☎ (01558) 822596
3 changing beers (sourced regionally; often Mumbles, Oakham) Ⓗ
A lively locals' pub with a warm welcome for all who pass through its doors. Originally a sports club, it has been a pub for more than a decade. Three well-kept, constantly changing beers are always available. Several large TVs show sport in the bar, and there is a separate pool room. To the front of the pub is a recently refurbished dining area. ◑🚆♣P🚌(X13,281)🐾📶

Llandybie

Ivy Bush

18 Church Street, SA18 3HZ (100yds from church)
☎ (01269) 850272
Timothy Taylor Landlord; 1 changing beer (sourced regionally; often Exmoor) Ⓗ
This friendly local, modernised several years ago, features a single bar with two comfortable seating areas. It usually serves Timothy Taylor's Landlord alongside at least one regularly changing guest ale. The pub hosts weekly games and quizzes, and shows sport on TV. The local birdwatching group meets here. The nearby railway station is on the scenic Heart of Wales line.
❀🚆♣●P🚌(103,X13) 📶

Llandyfaelog

Red Lion

SA17 5PP (300yds off A484)
☎ (01267) 267530 🌐 redlionllandyfaelog.co.uk
3 changing beers (sourced regionally; often Butcombe, Evan Evans, Glamorgan) Ⓗ
A family-run village hostelry that can truly be described as being at the heart of the community – it has an annexe that hosts the local choir's practice evenings and stages concerts and functions for the surrounding area. The large public bar, featuring darts and a pool table, is complemented by a restaurant and a family room. Food is served in both the bar and restaurant.
Q🛏◑♿⛺♣🚌(198,X12) 📶

Llandysul

Porth Hotel

Church Street, SA44 4QS SN418407
☎ (01559) 362202 🌐 porthhotel.co.uk
2 changing beers (sourced locally) Ⓗ
Set on the banks of the River Teifi, this former 17th-century coaching inn is now a family-run village hotel with a bar, restaurant and function room. The public rooms still retain the original oak beams and panels. Food and drink is sourced locally, where possible. At the rear of the hotel is a car park and lawned garden beside the river, with access to walks and fishing.
❀🛏◑♣●P🚌🐾📶

Llanelli

Stradey Arms ✔

1 Stradey Road, SA15 4ET
☎ (01554) 753332

Brains Bitter, SA, Rev James; 1 changing beer (sourced nationally) Ⓗ
A busy Brains pub on the outskirts of the town, with a comfortable bar and separate restaurant. Real ale is poured from up to four handpumps in the bar. A varied menu of freshly prepared food is served all day except on Sunday, when there is a lunchtime carvery. Friendly and welcoming staff add to the pleasant ambience in this pub. It is a popular venue for sporting events, especially rugby internationals.

Llanfallteg

Plash

SA34 0UN (off A40 at Llanddewi Velfrey)
☎ (01437) 563472 🌐 theplashinn.co.uk
Wye Valley Butty Bach; 2 changing beers Ⓗ
At the centre of village life, this terrace-style cottage pub has been an inn for more than 180 years. It holds a quiz night on Tuesday, a regular monthly folk night and other special nights. The guest beers are usually from small, independent breweries. The pub serves home-made food using locally sourced ingredients, with specials on Wednesday, Friday and Saturday. An accessible entrance is to the rear. A former local CAMRA Pub of the Year.
Q

Llangeitho

Three Horseshoe

SY25 6TW
☎ (01974) 821244
2 changing beers (sourced regionally; often Gower, Mantle, Wye Valley) Ⓗ
A traditional, family-run pub in this historic village. It has a main bar, dining area, function room and sunny outside seating. The friendly landlord is a keen supporter of real ale and offers a constantly changing range, with three real ales and two or three bag-in-box ciders from Welsh producers including Gethins and Marcherman. Excellent-value, home-cooked meals are served, with a popular special offer menu on Wednesday. Pool and darts are played, and there is a big screen for sporting events.
P(585)

Llangoedmor

Penllwyndu

SA43 2LY SN240458
☎ (01239) 682533
Hancocks HB; 2 changing beers (sourced regionally; often Brains) Ⓗ
Old-fashioned alehouse standing at an isolated crossroads where Cardigan's evildoers were once hanged – the pub sign is worthy of close inspection. The cheerful and welcoming public bar retains its quaintness, with a slate floor and inglenook with wood-burning stove. Good home-cooked food including traditional favourites is available all day in the bar and the separate restaurant. Free live music plays on the third Thursday evening of the month. P

Llanllwni

Talardd Arms

SA39 9DX SN487392
☎ (01559) 395633 🌐 talardd.co.uk
1 changing beer (sourced regionally) Ⓗ
There are records of this old inn dating back to 1626, when drovers would stop for refreshments for man and beast before driving their livestock over Llanllwni Mountain on their way to markets over the border. Now sympathetically modernised, Tafarn y Talardd continues to offer a traditional warm and friendly welcome in its bar, lounge and separate restaurant. P

Llanpumsaint

Railway Inn

SA33 6BU (by old railway bridge on main road through village)
☎ (01267) 253643
2 changing beers (sourced nationally; often Glamorgan, Wye Valley) Ⓗ
A warm and welcoming little pub-restaurant at the centre of the village, next to the former railway line. A thriving hub for locals and visitors alike, it has a cosy interior with comfortable sofas, decorated with old railway memorabilia. The pub is highly recommended for home cooking using local ingredients, and a great selection of home-made desserts. Food is served every evening except Sunday, when an excellent lunch is available. P(215)

Llansaint

King's Arms

13 Maes yr Eglwys, SA17 5JE
☎ (01267) 267487
Glamorgan Jemima's Pitchfork; Young's London Special; 1 changing beer (sourced nationally) Ⓗ
Friendly village hostelry that has been a pub for over 200 years. Situated near an 11th-century church, it is reputedly built from stone recovered from the lost village of St Ishmaels. Attractions include live music every Thursday and a TV for major sporting events. Good-value home-cooked food is served (book ahead, especially Sunday). Carmarthen Bay Holiday Park is a few miles away. P(198)

Llansteffan

Castle Inn

The Square, SA33 5JG
☎ (01267) 241225
Sharp's Doom Bar; house beer (by Evan Evans); 2 changing beers (often Evan Evans) Ⓗ
The Castle is a traditional inn committed to real ale, with a welcoming atmosphere and friendly staff. It has an open-plan layout but also plenty of cosy corners for customers to relax and unwind in relative peace and quiet. The pub hosts a number of local community groups. It offers bar snacks from an uncomplicated menu. There is an outside seating area overlooking the village square where locals and tourists mingle.
Q(227)

Llanychaer

Bridge End Inn

SA65 9TB (on B4313, 2 miles SW of Fishguard)
☎ (01348) 872545
Mantle Rock Steady, Cwrw Teifi, Dark Heart Ⓗ**; 1 changing beer (sourced locally; often Bluestone, Evan Evans)** Ⓗ/Ⓖ
Known locally as the Bont, this friendly country pub, over 150 years old, nestles in the beautiful Gwaun Valley at a bridging point across the river. The cosy bars with log fires serve mainly local real ales. The dining room is housed in the smithy, once run as a complementary business to the inn, and features an external water wheel. Home-made food includes popular Sunday lunches. Check ahead for winter hours and food service.
Q(345)

WALES

Narberth

Dingle Inn
Jesse Road, SA67 7DP
☎ (01834) 869979
3 changing beers (sourced regionally) Ⓗ
Friendly local next to a caravan and camping site, featuring plenty of Narberth's distinctive community spirit. Beer from the single handpump changes frequently, with regular customers' preferences guiding the selection of ales from the local area and further afield. The town boasts a range of specialist shops and attractions, including an award-winning museum, that would be the envy of many larger places.
🐎❀🛏◗⛺⇌P🚌(381)

Nevern

Trewern Arms
SA42 0NB (off A487, 2 miles N of Newport)
☎ (01239) 820395 🌐 trewernarms.com
3 changing beers (sourced nationally; often Bluestone, Harbwr, Mantle) Ⓗ
A picturesque 16th-century pub deep within a secluded valley astride the banks of the River Nevern. The village of Nevern is less than a mile from the beautiful fishing town of Newport. This multi-roomed pub caters for all, from those who just want a drink to large parties and wedding receptions. A great place to stay to experience some of the best walks in West Wales.
Q🐎❀🛏◖◗♿⛺♣P🚌(T5)🐾📶

New Quay

Black Lion Ⓛ
Glanmor Terrace, SA45 9PT
☎ (01545) 560122 🌐 blacklionnewquay.co.uk
2 changing beers (sourced locally; often Mantle, Purple Moose, Sharp's) Ⓗ
Perched atop a steep street, this striking pub has Dylan Thomas connections. Its contemporary interior features separate dining areas and a main bar that gets busy when big games are screened on TV. The large garden has a play area and stunning sea views (dogs welcome in the garden). Up to three, mostly Welsh, beers are served alongside bottled cider from Gwynt y Ddraig. Excellent food is on offer. Live music is hosted during New Quay's August festival. Accommodation is available in nine bedrooms. 🐎❀🛏◖◗⛺🚌📶

Newcastle Emlyn

Bunch of Grapes ✔
Bridge Street, SA38 9DU
☎ (01239) 711185
2 changing beers Ⓗ
A Grade II* listed building dating back to the 17th century, reputed to have been built from the ruins of the nearby 13th-century castle. Set in the heart of the community, the pub offers a warm and welcoming place to eat, drink and relax. Its enclosed rear garden features a children's play area and a covered smoking shelter.
🐎❀◖◗♿⛺♣●P🚌(460)🐾📶

Newchapel

Ffynnone Arms Ⓛ
SA37 0EH
☎ (01239) 841800 🌐 ffynnonearms.co.uk
Hancocks HB; Wye Valley Butty Bach; 1 changing beer (sourced locally; often Mantle) Ⓗ

Charming and traditional 18th-century pub on the borders of three counties – Pembrokeshire, Carmarthenshire and Ceredigion. Local ales are often available alongside the regional and national beers, and Welsh cider Gwynt y Ddraig is also sold. The landlady prides herself on serving good food using locally sourced ingredients where possible, with gluten-free, dairy-free and sugar-free options. Fish & chips night is Wednesday, and on Sunday there is a carvery. Welsh and English are spoken. Q🐎❀◖◗♿♣●P🚌

Newport

Royal Oak
West Street, SA42 0TA
☎ (01239) 820632 🌐 theroyaloaknewport.co.uk
Felinfoel Best Bitter; Gower Gold; 1 changing beer (sourced nationally) Ⓗ
A traditional Welsh country pub that retains all the charm and atmosphere of its roots, with oak beams, a tiled bar area and many original features. As well as offering quality real ales, the pub is renowned for its good home-made food, notably curries and fish & chips. A pensioners' lunch is served on Tuesday. Q🐎◖◗♿P🚌📶

Pembrey

Ship Aground Inn
Ashburnham Road, SA16 0TL
☎ (01554) 835724
4 changing beers (often Sharp's, Tiny Rebel) Ⓗ
A friendly husband and wife team offer a warm welcome to locals and visitors alike at this popular pub on the road between Pembrey and Burry Port. There is is an open-plan bar area plus a separate restaurant space. Real ale provision is a cornerstone of the premises, with four changing beers served. The pub also offers a wide range of locally sourced home-cooked food. 🐎❀◖◗P

Pembroke

Old King's Arms Ⓛ
Main Street, SA71 4JS
☎ (01646) 683611 🌐 oldkingsarmshotel.co.uk
Felinfoel Double Dragon; Marston's Old Empire; 2 changing beers (sourced locally; often Bluestone, Evan Evans) Ⓗ
This former coaching inn is allegedly the oldest inn in Pembroke, dating from around 1520. The hotel's Kings Bar is a small room with exposed stone walls, beams and a real fire. It has four handpumps serving local, regional and national beers. There is a separate lounge with a dining area, and a restaurant with room for larger groups. Locally sourced meat and fish products feature on the menu. Q🐎❀🛏◖◗♿P🚌🐾📶

Pembroke Dock

First & Last
London Road, SA72 6TX (on A477)
☎ (01646) 682687
Brains Rev James; Worthington's White Shield; 1 changing beer (sourced nationally; often Skinner's) Ⓗ
Friendly single-bar local run by the same family for more than 50 years. Formerly the Commercial, it acquired its more distinctive name in 1991 to reflect its edge-of-town location. The walls display an eclectic mix of photos and prints. The food is good pub fare. There is a popular quirky Sunday evening quiz. The pub is handy for the Cleddau Bridge, giving easy access to Haverfordwest, and close to the historic naval dockyard and Irish Ferries.
Q🐎❀◖◗⇌P🚌📶

Pisgah

Halfway Inn

SY23 4NE (on A4120 halfway between Aberystwyth and Devil's Bridge)
☎ (01970) 880631
Monty's Old Jailhouse, Sunshine; 1 changing beer (sourced locally; often Mantle) Ⓗ
Delightfully rustic and cosy pub with a flagstone floor and a bar that spans two rooms. This was the first pub in Wales to offer self-service beer although the practice has been discontinued. Good-value food is served in the evening, and at lunchtime in summer. Real cider is available seasonally. The pub was featured in the recent TV series Hinterland. P

Porthyrhyd

Mansel Arms

Banc y Mansel, SA32 8BS (on B4310 between Porthyrhyd and Drefach)
☎ (01267) 275305
Marston's Pedigree Ⓗ**; 5 changing beers (sourced nationally; often Courage, Evan Evans, Glamorgan)** Ⓗ/Ⓖ
Welcoming 18th-century former coaching inn with plenty of traditional character, featuring wood fires in both bars. The landlord is passionate about real ale and encourages customers to experience a variety of flavours. Beers are varied, and selected from local and national brewers, with a new ale every couple of days. The pub's cask ale members' club offers regular brewery visits. Excellent home-cooked food is served. CAMRA Welsh Pub of the Year 2019. P (129)

Prengwyn

Gwarcefel Arms

Prengwyn, SA44 4LU (on A475/B4476 crossroads) SN424442
☎ (01559) 363126 🌐 gwarcefelarms.co.uk
Sharp's Doom Bar; 1 changing beer (sourced nationally) Ⓗ
A traditional country inn with a friendly atmosphere where everyone is welcome, including families and dogs. Situated at the junction of five roads in Prengwyn, three miles north of Llandysul, the pub has a main bar with a wood-burning stove, cosy seating, a pool table and dartboard. A separate restaurant area, which caters for functions and parties, offers evening meals and Sunday lunches. The beer garden and large car park are to the rear. P

Pumsaint

Dolaucothi Arms

SA19 8UW (on A482 midway between Llanwrda and Lampeter)
☎ (01558) 650237
2 changing beers (sourced regionally; often Evan Evans, Purple Moose, Wye Valley) Ⓗ
A substantial stone-built inn, owned by the National Trust and tastefully restored in traditional style. Real cider and real ales are offered, with usually two beers from Welsh breweries. An excellent food menu features seasonal ingredients. The large beer garden provides views over the valley and the Rivers Cothi and Twrch. The Dolaucothi Gold Mines nearby are well worth visiting.
P

Pwlltrap

White Lion

SA33 4AT
☎ (01994) 230370 🌐 whitelion-pwlltrap.co.uk
Courage Directors; Greene King Abbot; Shepherd Neame Bishops Finger; Young's London Original; 1 changing beer (sourced locally) Ⓗ
This roadside pub, just outside St Clears on the road to Whitland, is warm and welcoming, with a real fire in winter. It has an old-world charm, with oak beams and panelled walls, and boasts a large restaurant serving good food. Two cask beers are available in winter, four in summer. Pool and darts are played and a large-screen TV shows sporting fixtures. The pub organises a range of events throughout the year. Q P (224,322)

Roch

Victoria Inn

SA62 6AW (on A487)
☎ (01437) 710426 🌐 thevictoriainnroch.com
Victoria Inn NewgAle, Fine & Dandy, WOW; 1 changing beer (sourced locally; often Victoria Inn) Ⓗ
A little gem with views across St Brides Bay, this locals' pub offers a warm welcome. The inn was established in 1851, although parts are older, and has retained much of its 19th-century appeal, with beamed ceilings and low doorways. The home-brewed house bitter is Fine & Dandy. Food is available every day except Monday, while curry and a pint night is Friday. For those in a hurry there is a beer carry-out service. Live music features occasionally. Q P (T11)

Rudbaxton

Corner Piece Inn

A40, SA62 5PG
☎ (01437) 742185
Caffle Drop Squint; Gwaun Valley Pembrokeshire Best Bitter Ⓗ
A cosy three-roomed pub serving good beer and food, run by owners who are enthusiastic about real ale. This is the first pub for two miles from Haverfordwest in one direction and Wolfs Castle in the other. The food offering includes pie night on Wednesday and fish night on Friday. There is seating and children's play equipment outside but the location on the busy A40 can be noisy.
Q P (T5)

Saundersfoot

Harbwr Bar & Kitchen

1 High Street, SA69 9EJ
☎ (01834) 811413
Harbwr MV Enterprise, North Star, RFA Sir Galahad; 1 changing beer (often Harbwr) Ⓗ
A modern pub and restaurant in the centre of this popular village, set in the Pembrokeshire Coast National Park a short walk from a long, sandy beach. The spacious interior features upstairs seating giving superb views, and the outlook from the patio stretches across the bay to Tenby. The pub serves the full range of Harbwr Brewery beers alongside a good selection of gins. It can get noisy when busy but is well worth a visit when in Saundersfoot. P

Solva

Royal George

13 High Street, SA62 6TF
☎ (01437) 720002 🌐 theroyalgeorgesolva.co.uk

Felinfoel Double Dragon; Sharp's Doom Bar; Wye Valley Butty Bach [H]
Set on the main road to St David's in Upper Solva, this friendly, imposing community pub commands stunning views over St Brides Bay. The one-roomed bar has a busy, homely feel, with rugby pictures on the walls. The furniture is both rustic and eclectic, which adds to the ambience. In winter a guest beer is only available on big occasions. A beer festival is held at least once a year. Chinese food is cooked to order at weekends.
P(T11)

Stackpole

Stackpole Inn

Jasons Corner, SA71 5DF (on B4319)
(01646) 672324 stackpoleinn.co.uk
Brains Rev James; Felinfoel Best Bitter, Double Dragon; 1 changing beer (sourced regionally; often Mantle) [H]
A multi award-winning pub three miles south of the historic town of Pembroke in the Pembrokeshire Coast National Park. The inn has a restaurant that focuses on local seafood dishes, and offers superb B&B accommodation. It is a short walk to the beautiful Pembrokeshire Coast Path, and when visiting you can also explore the Stackpole Estate, Bosherston Lily Ponds and the amazing Barafundle Bay and Broad Haven beach.
P

Tegryn

Butchers Arms

SA35 0BL
(01239) 698680
Gower Gold [H]**; Morland Old Speckled Hen** [G]**; Sharp's Doom Bar** [H]
A rural pub with a great atmosphere. It is well off the beaten track in a hard-to-find location, but on the National Cycle Network Route 47. The place has been attractively refurbished using local slate on the walls and floor. There is a games room featuring a mobile skittle alley plus other traditional pub games. A beer festival is held here every July. **Q P**

Tenby

Buccaneer Inn [L]

St Julian Street, SA70 7AS
(01834) 842273
Harbwr MV Enterprise, Caldey Lollipop, RFA Sir Galahad; 1 changing beer (sourced locally; often Harbwr) [H]
A pub in a quaint street which links the town square to the harbour and beaches. The bar area is large but has a cosy feel with beams, stove and Tenby memorabilia adorning the walls. A sunny walled beer garden is to the rear. It is the brewery tap for the adjacent Tenby Harbour Brewery, showcasing its full range of beers. Food is served all day with locally sourced produce, including fresh fish, on the menu.

Hope & Anchor [L]

St Julian Street, SA70 7AS
(01834) 842131
Felinfoel Double Dragon; Harbwr MV Enterprise, North Star [H]**, Caldey Lollipop** [G]**; Sharp's Atlantic; 2 changing beers (sourced nationally; often Bluestone, Mantle)** [H]
Welcoming pub in the old town on the way down to the harbour. The convivial atmosphere and interesting local decor make this an excellent place to relax over a beer. It serves four guest beers, mainly from Welsh breweries including Evan Evans, Mantle and Purple Moose; Wye Valley sometimes sneaks over the border. Ciders include Westons Old Rosie and Somerset Tree Shaker West Country Cider. Food is important and specials supplement the standard menu.

Tregaron

Talbot [L]

The Square, SY25 6JL
(01974) 298208 ytalbot.com
2 changing beers (sourced regionally; often Evan Evans, Ludlow, Mantle) [H]
A former drovers' inn of immense character in an unspoilt town on the edge of the Cambrian Mountains. It has a cosy front bar with a real fire, a beamed and flagstoned snug with an inglenook fireplace, a rear bar with TV and a restaurant. Two real ales are available in winter, three in summer, and three real ciders. Quality food includes locally reared meat and tempting desserts. The beautiful garden has fine views and a memorial to a circus elephant reputedly buried here.
Q P(585,588)

Tufton

Tufton Arms

SA63 4TU
(01437) 532692
Wye Valley Butty Bach [G]
A meeting place for the community, this locals' pub is the hub of a village where there are no other pubs or shops for two miles. Within easy reach of the Preseli Hills, it is a fine place to relax after a long walk. It hosts bingo on the third Wednesday of the month and a beer festival on the first Friday in July. **Q P**

Whitland

Station House Hotel

St Johns Street, SA34 0AP
(01994) 240556 stationhousewhitland.co.uk
5 changing beers (often Sharp's, Wye Valley, Young's) [H]
A smile and a warm welcome are always on tap at this friendly hostelry. It is very much a locals' pub for all ages and offers something for everyone, including pool and darts teams, and bingo on Sunday evening. A small room is available for people looking for a quiet corner. The outside drinking area is partly under cover. Car parking is to the rear and the railway station is close by.
P

By George!

It was my Uncle George who discovered that alcohol was a food well in advance of modern medical thought. **P G Wodehouse, The Inimitable Jeeves**

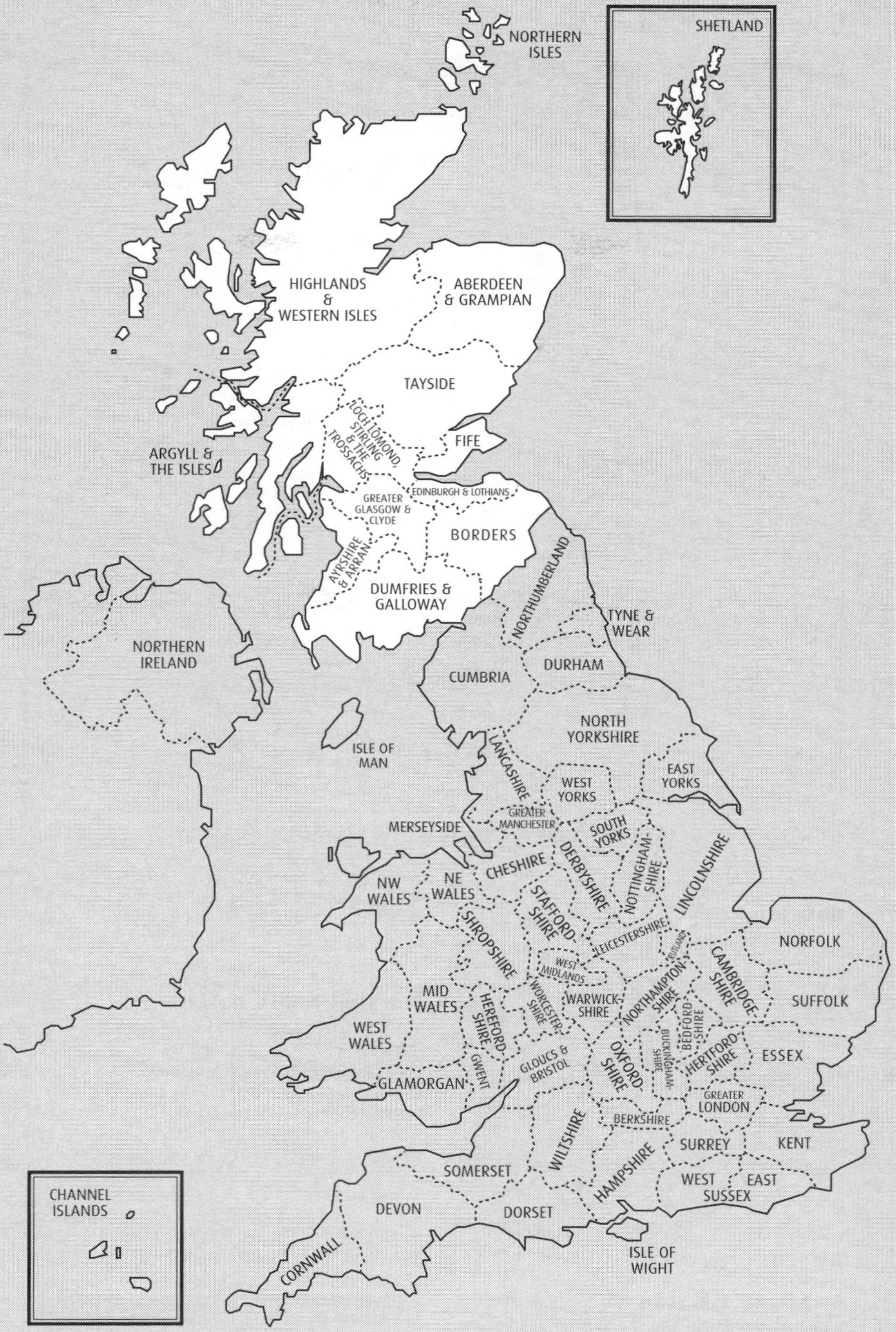
NORTHERN ISLES
SHETLAND
HIGHLANDS & WESTERN ISLES
ABERDEEN & GRAMPIAN
TAYSIDE
LOCH LOMOND, STIRLING & THE TROSSACHS
FIFE
ARGYLL & THE ISLES
EDINBURGH & LOTHIANS
GREATER GLASGOW & CLYDE
BORDERS
AYRSHIRE & ARRAN
DUMFRIES & GALLOWAY
NORTHUMBERLAND
TYNE & WEAR
NORTHERN IRELAND
DURHAM
CUMBRIA
NORTH YORKSHIRE
ISLE OF MAN
LANCASHIRE
EAST YORKS
WEST YORKS
GREATER MANCHESTER
MERSEYSIDE
SOUTH YORKS
CHESHIRE
DERBYSHIRE
NOTTINGHAMSHIRE
LINCOLNSHIRE
NW WALES
NE WALES
STAFFORDSHIRE
SHROPSHIRE
LEICESTERSHIRE
RUTLAND
NORFOLK
WEST MIDLANDS
CAMBRIDGESHIRE
MID WALES
HEREFORDSHIRE
WORCESTERSHIRE
WARWICKSHIRE
NORTHAMPTONSHIRE
SUFFOLK
BEDFORDSHIRE
WEST WALES
BUCKINGHAMSHIRE
OXFORDSHIRE
HERTFORDSHIRE
ESSEX
GWENT
GLOUCS & BRISTOL
GLAMORGAN
GREATER LONDON
BERKSHIRE
WILTSHIRE
SURREY
KENT
SOMERSET
HAMPSHIRE
WEST SUSSEX
EAST SUSSEX
CHANNEL ISLANDS
DEVON
DORSET
ISLE OF WIGHT
CORNWALL

Scotland

ABERDEEN & GRAMPIAN

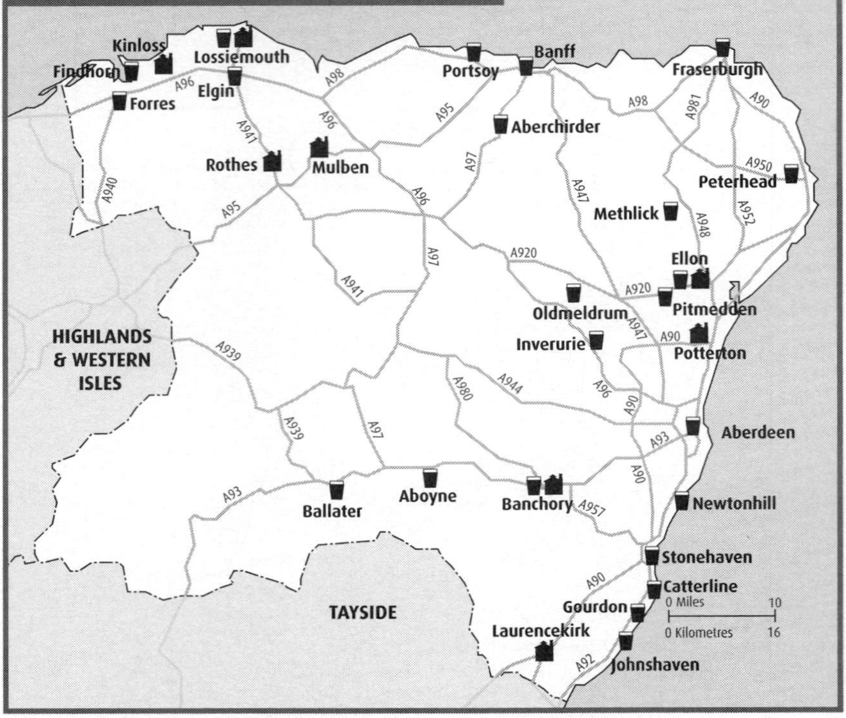

Authority areas covered: Aberdeenshire UA, City of Aberdeen UA, Moray UA

Aberchirder

New Inn

79 Main Street, AB54 7TB

☎ (01466) 780633 newinnaberchirder.co.uk

Windswept Wolf; 4 changing beers (sourced nationally; often Caledonian, Hambleton, Orkney) H

Traditional, friendly inn with wood-burning stoves, candlelit areas and a vintage atmosphere. It offers a changing selection of five quality ales from local and national breweries. Guest ales from Hambleton are often featured. A separate dining area provides home-made food prepared by the owner/chef using locally sourced produce. Families are welcome in the dining room until 9pm (booking recommended). Dogs are permitted in the bar but should be kept on a lead at busy times. Q P (301)

Aberdeen

Archibald Simpson ✓

5 Castle Street, AB11 5BQ (E end of Union St)

☎ (01224) 621365

Caledonian Deuchars IPA; Greene King Abbot; 9 changing beers (sourced nationally; often Orkney, Redcastle, Stewart) H

The former headquarters of Clydesdale Bank, this Wetherspoon is in one of the many monumental granite buildings in central Aberdeen designed by local architect Archibald Simpson. It has a pillared entrance and retains many original architectural features – the main room is a central hall with a high ceiling and additional seating areas to the side. Twelve handpumps offer beers from various Scottish breweries. There is a narrow outside drinking space on the pavement. Beer festivals are held several times a year.

Ferryhill House Hotel

169 Bon Accord Street, AB11 6UA (10 mins' walk from Union St)

☎ (01224) 590867 ferryhillhousehotel.co.uk

Caledonian Deuchars IPA; Orkney Corncrake, Dark Island; Timothy Taylor Landlord H

A small city-centre hotel in a quiet residential area, with tables and chairs in the extensive garden featuring a children's play area. There is a large, modern, lounge bar with a selection of more than 60 malt whiskies, a large restaurant and a conservatory. A wheelchair access ramp leads to the front door. The Dark Island pump may serve a varying beer. P (17,17A)

REAL ALE BREWERIES

Bodachra Potterton
Brewdog Ellon
Burnside Laurencekirk
Deeside Banchory
Keith Mulben
Quiet Banchory
Rothes Rothes
six˚north Laurencekirk
Spey Valley Mulben
Windswept ◆ Lossiemouth
WooHa Kinloss

Globe Inn

13-15 North Silver Street, AB10 1RJ (off Golden Sq)
(01224) 641171 the-globe-inn.com
3 changing beers (sourced regionally; often Cromarty, Swannay, Windswept)
This convivial open-plan pub reverted to private ownership in 2018 after being run by Belhaven for several years. With three new Angram pumps installed, it now serves beers from a variety of Scottish breweries. Live music plays on Friday and Saturday, ranging from pop and rock covers to acoustic blues. A quiz is held on Monday evening. The pub is convenient for nearby entertainment venues His Majesty's Theatre and Music Hall, and offers reasonably priced en-suite accommodation.

Grill ★

213 Union Street, AB11 6BA
(01224) 583563 thegrillaberdeen.co.uk
Fyne Ales Jarl; 4 changing beers (sourced regionally; often Cromarty, Orkney, Windswept)
With an exquisite interior redesigned in 1926, this is the only pub in the area listed on CAMRA's National Inventory of Historic Pub Interiors. It has been part of the McGinty's Group since spring 2019. The ale pumps have been moved to a central position, offering guest beers from various Scottish breweries. The large selection of whiskies has won numerous awards. Bar snacks are available. Musicians appearing at the Music Hall opposite often visit during concert breaks. A fomer CAMRA Branch Pub of the Year.

Krakatoa

2 Trinity Quay, AB11 5AA (facing quayside at bottom of Market St)
(01224) 587602 krakatoa.bar
8 changing beers (sourced regionally; often Cromarty, Spey Valley, Windswept)
This historic harbourside bar, formerly the Moorings, changes character from a friendly, laid-back local to a raucous rock bar on weekend evenings, when there may be a cover charge. The eclectic jukebox is popular with the varied clientele. A wide selection of Scottish ales is served on up to 12 American-style fonts to the far left of the bar, and a varied selection of Belgian beers and ciders is also available. Local CAMRA City Pub of the Year 2019.

Number 10 Bar & Restaurant

10 Queens Terrace, AB10 1XL
(01224) 631928 no10aberdeen.co.uk
Caledonian Deuchars IPA; Fyne Ales Jarl; Timothy Taylor Landlord; 1 changing beer (sourced regionally; often Inveralmond, Stewart)
Ten minutes' walk from the West End, this basement bar relaunched in 2015 following renovation. The contemporary interior features exposed granite walls, traditional herringbone floors and dark wood furnishings. It has two seating areas to the right and left as you come in, with several TV screens showing sports. The bar along the back wall has four handpumps. A wide choice of meals is available in the restaurant in the former Number 9, with an additional separate menu in the bar.

Prince of Wales

7 St Nicholas Lane, AB10 1HF (in lane opp Marks & Spencer)
(01224) 640597 princeofwales-aberdeen.co.uk
Greene King IPA, Abbot; 6 changing beers (sourced nationally; often Cromarty, Swannay, Windswept)
One of the oldest bars in Aberdeen, the Prince of Wales has possibly the longest bar counter in the city, a large following of regulars and a friendly atmosphere buzzing with conversation. The bar was refurbished in 2016 and is listed among CAMRA Scotland's True Heritage Pubs. It offers a varied selection of ales from mostly Scottish breweries, with tasters for the undecided. Good-value food is served daily including filled rolls. Folk music features every Sunday evening. Q

Queen Vic

126 Rosemount Place, AB25 2YU
(01224) 638500
Timothy Taylor Landlord; 3 changing beers (sourced nationally; often Fierce, Spey Valley, Windswept)
A cosy one-room locals' lounge bar slightly off the beaten track in a converted shop in the residential area of Rosemount. Sporting events are frequently shown, when the pub can get extremely busy and noisy. The cask ales are complemented by an extensive range of locally brewed bottled beers. A popular quiz featuring a Play Your Cards Right jackpot is held on Monday evening, live bands play occasionally at weekends and live jazz on one Sunday a month. Snacks include sandwiches, wraps and local Big Beefys Biltong. Local CAMRA Pub of the Year 2020. (3,3A)

St Machar Bar

97 High Street, AB24 3EN
(01224) 483079
Inveralmond Ossian; Stewart Pentland IPA; 1 changing beer (sourced regionally; often Orkney, Stewart, WooHa)
Located in the photogenic Old Aberdeen conservation area amid the university buildings and close to King's College, this friendly and historic bar is frequented by academia and locals alike. The bar features a splendid mirror from the long-gone local Thomson Marshall Aulton brewery and another from the original Devanha brewery may be spotted in the rear beside the toilets. Alongside the ales is a comprehensive selection of whiskies and gins. The bar is home to a darts team, university football team and rugby team. Traditional pub grub is now served from the tiny kitchen. (20)

Under the Hammer

11 North Silver Street, AB10 1RJ (off Golden Sq)
(01224) 640253
Cromarty Happy Chappy; Fyne Ales Jarl; 1 changing beer (sourced nationally; often Belhaven, Inveralmond, Orkney)
Located in a quiet side street near Golden Square just minutes from Union Street, this popular pub is in a basement next to Milne's auction house – hence the name. Guest beers come from a wide variety of Scottish breweries. Unobtrusive background music plays and open mic sessions are held every Wednesday evening. Works by local artists are on display and for sale. It is closed Sunday and Monday, and on the other days opens at 4pm. Q

Aboyne

Boat Inn

Charleston Road, AB34 5EL (N bank of River Dee next to Aboyne Bridge)
(01339) 886137 theboatinnaboyne.co.uk
3 changing beers (sourced nationally; often Belhaven, Cairngorm)
Popular riverside inn with a food-oriented lounge. Junior diners (and adults) may request to see the model train, complete with sound effects, traverse the entire pub at picture-rail height upon completion of their meal. The Shed public bar has a recess at the back used for live music nights. Three ales are served in summer, two in winter, usually at least one from Belhaven and another

SCOTLAND

from a local brewery. Breakfast is served. Fifteen twin rooms and a family room are available for overnight stays. Q P

Ballater

Alexandra Hotel

12 Bridge Square, AB35 5QJ

(01339) 755376 alexandrahotelballater.co.uk

Cairngorm Trade Winds; 2 changing beers (sourced regionally; often Cairngorm)

Originally built as a private home in 1800, this friendly, family-owned lounge bar became the Alexandra Hotel in 1915. It is popular both with locals and those visiting for bar suppers. Three Cairngorm ales are available in summer, generally just two in winter. Benches outside at the front are ideal for alfresco drinking. A handy stop-off on your way to Braemar for the Highland Games or on a visit with the royals at Balmoral. P

Glenaden Hotel

6 Church Square, AB35 5NE

(01339) 755488

3 changing beers (sourced regionally; often Windswept)

Situated on the far side of the picturesque town square, this small hotel displays a prominent external sign for its Barrel Lounge. It normally serves three beers in busy periods, usually Scottish, mostly from Windswept. Darker ales are apparently favoured by the locals.
Q P

Banchory

Douglas Arms Hotel

22 High Street, AB31 5SR (opp West church)

(01330) 822547 douglasarms.co.uk

Cairngorm Trade Winds; 1 changing beer (sourced nationally)

The public bar of this small hotel is a classic Scottish long bar with etched windows and vintage mirrors, and is one of CAMRA Scotland's True Heritage Pubs. Many TVs show sport and the bar is often used by the local rugby club. Known as the home of Deeside rugby, the lounge has a projector and screen for major matches and accommodates large numbers. There is a large decking area outside to the rear, ideal for fair weather drinking. The public bar is only open in the evening, and closed Monday to Wednesday at quiet times.
Q

Ravenswood Club (Royal British Legion)

25 Ramsay Road, AB31 5TS

(01330) 822347 banchorylegion.co.uk

2 changing beers (sourced nationally)

Large British Legion club with a comfortable lounge adjoining the pool and TV room and a spacious function room frequently used by local clubs and societies as well as members. Darts and snooker are popular and played most evenings. The two handpumps offer excellent value and the beer choice is constantly changing, with ales consistently the best quality in the village. An elevated terrace has fine views of the Deeside hills. Show a copy of this Guide or your CAMRA membership card for entry. P

Banff

Market Arms

5 High Shore, AB45 1DB

(01261) 818616

1 changing beer (sourced nationally; often Morland, Ruddles, Timothy Taylor)

This fine building is one of the oldest in historic Banff, dating back to 1585. The courtyard at the back retains many original features. The long public bar has several fine examples of historic brewery and distillery mirrors. One of the two handpumps always serves a changing beer – two beers are on at weekends and holidays. The impressive upstairs lounge is used mainly for meals.

Catterline

Creel Inn

AB39 2UL (on coast off A92, 5 miles S of Stonehaven)

(01569) 750254 thecreelinn.co.uk

3 changing beers (sourced regionally; often Cromarty, Fyne Ales, Swannay)

Set in a scenic clifftop location, the rear garden of this small village inn has fabulous views. Catterline is known as an artists' village, the most famous being Joan Eardley – one of her paintings is on display in the pub along with other artists' work. The Creel is primarily a food venue but the bar area serves as the village local, offering up to three beers, two in winter, usually from Scottish micros. Keg beers from local Six Degrees North are also available. Closed Monday-Friday afternoons.
P

Elgin

Muckle Cross

34 High Street, IV30 1BU

(01343) 559030

Caledonian Deuchars IPA; Greene King Abbot; Sharp's Doom Bar; 4 changing beers (sourced regionally; often Windswept)

A typical small Wetherspoon pub converted from what was once a bicycle repair shop. Refurbished in 2018, the pleasant long room has ample seating, a family area and a long bar. Deservedly popular, it can be busy, particularly at weekends. Eight handpumps offer a wide range of beers from national and Scottish microbreweries, and ciders are available during the annual cider fest. Two beer festivals are held annually, one Scottish and the other with world beers.
Q

Ellon

Tolbooth

21-23 Station Road, AB41 9AE

(01358) 721308

Greene King Abbot; 2 changing beers (sourced regionally; often Cairngorm, Cromarty, Strathbraan)

A large pub, popular with all ages, close to the centre of the town and just a short walk from the bus stops on Market Street. There are separate seating areas on split levels as well as an airy conservatory with barrel tables. One Scottish and one English guest ale are usually available. Several National Trust Scotland properties are nearby. No food is served but can be delivered via Meal Monsters app.

Findhorn

Kimberley Inn

94 Findhorn, IV36 3YG

(01309) 690492 kimberleyinn.com

2 changing beers (sourced regionally; often Cairngorm, Orkney)

The inn is situated on the shore of Findhorn Bay in a charming seaside village with a fine stretch of beach. It has three areas – a family room with wood-panelled walls, a snug with splendid views of the hills across the Moray Firth, and the bar, with an excellent log fire. Two ales are available, one in winter, mainly from Scottish micros. The extensive food menu features home-cooked meals, with local seafood the speciality, and local ice cream. Q✿☆❀◑&▲♣P🖂(31)☻

Forres

Mosset Tavern 🅛
Gordon Street, IV36 1DY
☎ (01309) 672981 ⊕ mossettavern.com
5 changing beers (sourced locally; often Spey Valley, Swannay, Windswept) 🄷
Described as 'the country pub in the heart of Forres', this smart, extremely popular Scottish lounge bar/restaurant is situated next to the Mosset burn and pond. Friendly, efficient staff serve ale from a single handpump in the lounge and up to five in the spacious, comfortable public bar, where there are pool tables and large screens showing sport. A large function room is also available, home to the Foot Tapper beer festival in April. Live music plays on Friday evening, and there is a pub quiz every Tuesday. ☆✿❀◑&≠♣P🖂(10)☻ 🛜

Red Lion
2-6 Tollboth Street, IV36 1PH
☎ (01309) 672716
2 changing beers (sourced nationally) 🄷
Dating from 1838 and known locally as the Beastie, this is one of the oldest real ale outlets in the north of Scotland. A popular venue, the modern and smart lounge offers two beers from the Belhaven list. The public bar has a pool table and features a rare mirror from Campbell & Co's Argyle Brewery. Live music plays on Saturday night. ☆◑&♣🖂(10,19A)☻

Fraserburgh

Elizabethan Bar & Lounge
36 Union Grove, AB43 9PH
☎ (01346) 510464
3 changing beers (sourced regionally; often Kelburn, Windswept, WooHa) 🄷
Set in the middle of a housing estate, with a mock-Tudor exterior, the pub has a public bar, games room with four dartboards and two pool tables, and a lounge bar with a large-screen TV usually featuring sport. The bar has a formidable reputation for offering a wide range of quality ales sourced from throughout the country, and also features well over 200 malts, the largest collection in the area. The beach, harbour and lighthouse museum are a mile away. A former CAMRA branch Pub of the Year. ☆&▲♣P🖂☻🛜

Saltoun Inn ✅
Saltoun Square, AB43 9DA
☎ (01346) 519548
Greene King Abbot; Sharp's Doom Bar; 5 changing beers (sourced nationally) 🄷
A Wetherspoon renovation of the historic Saltoun Arms Hotel, built in 1801, comprising several interconnecting low-ceiling rooms, including a lounge area to the left of the entrance. A garden area has been created to the rear. Accommodation is offered in 11 rooms, with reduced rates at weekends. The Scottish Lighthouse Museum is close by, as is the main fishing harbour, and the main surfing beach is one mile south. Q☆✿❀◑&▲🖂🛜

Gourdon

Harbour Bar
William Street, DD10 0LW
☎ (01561) 361337
1 changing beer (often Strathbraan) 🄷
Traditional seafaring decor abounds in this harbourside howff. It has a public bar, a smaller tap room, and a separate pool room with more seating. Nationally sourced beers are offered in winter and local ales during the summer season. The locally renowned Quayside Restaurant & Fish Bar is next door and the Maggie Law Maritime Museum nearby. ☆✿❀◑&▲♣P🖂(747)☻🛜

Inverurie

Gordon Highlander ✅
West High Street, AB51 3QQ
☎ (01467) 626780
Sharp's Doom Bar; 4 changing beers (sourced nationally; often Cairngorm, Inveralmond, Strathaven) 🄷
A fine Wetherspoon conversion of a splendid Art Deco building which used to be the Victoria Cinema. The name refers to a locomotive built at the now defunct Inverurie Locomotive Works, and there are many references to this throughout the pub. The famous Gordon Highlander Regiment also features prominently, with displays and a large mural. The books on the shelves are free to read and take home, with donations welcome. There are at least three guest ales and three real ciders, and the usual Wetherspoon beer festivals feature. ☆◑&≠🖂(10,37) 🛜

Johnshaven

Ship Inn
3 Castle Street, DD10 0ER
☎ (01561) 362257
1 changing beer (often Strathbraan) 🄷
While it may appear to be closed, check for a small light in the window near the door or just do battle with the door latch to the public bar. First licensed in 1763, this well-worn howff offers a warming welcome and beers from the Strathbraan range. The public bar has a traditional coastal decor complete with mixed fuel stove and bar counter water fonts. Children are allowed in the adjacent lounge, which has a pool table. The local knitting club meets here every Wednesday and the pub is a proud sponsor of the local shipwreck charity walk. ☆▲♣🖂(747) ☻🛜

Lossiemouth

Windswept Tap Room
13 Coulardbank Industrial Estate, IV31 6NG
☎ (01343) 814310 ⊕ windsweptbrewing.com/tap-room
2 changing beers (sourced locally; often Windswept) 🄿
This small industrial/office unit, converted to a taproom for the brewery next door, is now the only outlet for real ale in Lossiemouth. With an industrial chic decor, furniture is fashioned from pallets. A large adjacent marquee is used on busy nights. Two varying ales on cask are supplemented by eight KeyKeg beers. Coffee, tea, soft drinks, cakes and snacks are sold, as well as a range of bottled beers and brewery merchandise. The bar is available for private hire and may host the occasional weekend beer festival. Closed Sunday and from 5pm Monday-Thursday. ✿P🖂(33A,33C)🛜

Methlick

Ythanview Hotel

Main Street, AB41 7DT

☎ (01651) 806235 🌐 ythanviewhotel.co.uk

2 changing beers (sourced regionally; often Fyne Ales, Swannay) H

Traditional inn in the village centre, home to the Methlick Cricket Club at nearby Lairds. Log fires warm both the lounge bar at the front and the friendly sports-themed public bar at the rear. Beers are exclusively from Scottish micros. The restaurant is renowned for the owner's special chicken curry, and steak night on Thursday is popular. Meals are served all day at weekends. Live music and quiz nights take place on most Saturdays. Haddo House, Tolquhon Castle and Pitmedden Garden are nearby. Closed Monday-Friday afternoons. P (290,291)

Newtonhill

Newton Arms

10 Old Mill Road, AB39 3TZ

☎ (01569) 730227

1 changing beer (sourced regionally; often Cromarty, Orkney) H

Traditional village local with a classic, dark-wood panelled public bar featuring 1950s bar counters, an intriguing under-counter shelves for drinks and an original Devanha Brewery mirror. The lounge at the side has light-wood panelling and tables; you are welcome to bring in a curry from the Tandoori next door. Up to two beers are available in the public bar only, but usually just one. There is an east-facing patio to the rear for alfresco drinking.

Oldmeldrum

Redgarth

Kirk Brae, AB51 0DJ (signed off A947)

☎ (01651) 872353 🌐 redgarth.com

3 changing beers (sourced locally; often Cromarty, Fyne Ales, Swannay) G

Offering a warm welcome and excellent views of the eastern Grampian mountains, the Redgarth celebrated 30 years under the same ownership in 2020. The emphasis is on excellent beers served on gravity, with three handpumps on the bar to show which ales are available. Extra choice is offered during occasional Brewer in Residence evenings. Meals are served in the bar, and it has a restaurant area. A winner of many CAMRA awards, the pub retains a strong reputation for its imaginative choice of Scottish beers. Closed Monday-Saturday afternoons. P (35,X35)

Peterhead

Cross Keys

23-27 Chapel Street, AB42 1TH

☎ (01779) 483500

Greene King Abbot; Sharp's Doom Bar; 3 changing beers (sourced nationally) H

A typical Wetherspoon outlet in the centre of a bustling port, close to the local museum where you can learn about the town's maritime history. The pub is named after the chapel dedicated to St Peter that previously stood on the site. The long single room has the bar towards the front and a large seating area at the rear. A sheltered and heated area outside caters for hardy souls and smokers. Children are welcome until 9pm if dining. Q (69,63)

Pitmedden

Craft Bar

Tarves Road, AB41 7NX

☎ (01651) 842049 🌐 thecraftpitmedden.wordpress.com

2 changing beers (sourced regionally; often Orkney, Spey Valley, Windswept)

A one-room corner pub run by a local CAMRA member. Old church pews provide seating for some of the tables around the walls; other tables have bench seating. Two handpumps serve ales from Scottish breweries, supplemented by a wide variety of KeyKeg beers from UK breweries. There is also a comprehensive range of bottled and canned beer in the fridge. Occasional Brewer in Residence evenings are held. Snacks are available. P

Portsoy

Shore Inn

Church Street, AB45 2QR (overlooking harbour)

☎ (01261) 842831

2 changing beers (sourced regionally; often Kelburn, Spey Valley, Windswept) H

Cosy, comfortable, coastal howff with a warm welcome in winter and scenic outdoor views in summer. The pub overlooks the oldest harbour on Moray coast which was recently a location for the remake of Whisky Galore. The L-shaped room with low ceilings is a fine example of a nautical bar. Expect the pub to be busy each June during the Scottish Traditional Boat Festival.

Stonehaven

Marine Hotel

9-10 Shorehead, AB39 2JY (overlooking harbour)

☎ (01569) 762155 🌐 marinehotelstonehaven.co.uk

Timothy Taylor Landlord; house beer (by Six°North); 4 changing beers (sourced regionally; often Cairngorm, Cromarty, Windswept) H

Now the only outlet in the Six Degrees North empire that serves real ale, this is a former Scottish CAMRA Pub of the Year and a multiple branch winner. The small harbourside hotel features simple wood panelling in the bar and a rustic lounge with an open fireplace. Seating outside offers a splendid view of the harbour. Ales from Six Degrees North are served plus numerous Belgian beers and up to 18 craft keg beers. Historic Dunnottar Castle is one mile south and an open-air bathing pool one mile north. (747,X7)

Ship Inn

5 Shorehead, AB39 2JY (on harbour front)

☎ (01569) 762617 🌐 shipinnstonehaven.com

2 changing beers (sourced regionally; often Harviestoun, Strathaven, Strathbraan) H

Built in 1771, this harbour-front hotel has a maritime-themed, wood-panelled bar and a small seating area outside overlooking the water. The long, narrow bar features a mirror from the defunct Devanha Brewery. Two beers are offered, at least one from Strathbraan, and an extensive range of malt whiskies is stocked. A modern restaurant with panoramic harbour views is adjacent to the bar – fish is the speciality and food is served all day at the weekend. Accommodation is available in 11 guest rooms. (747,X7)

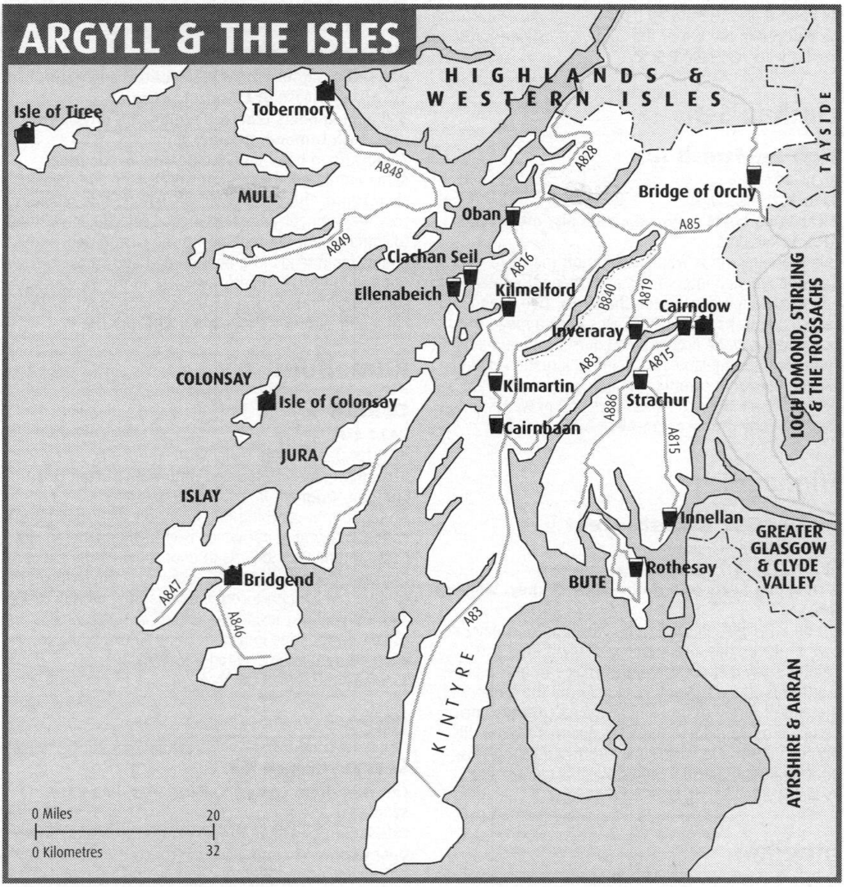

Authority area covered: Argyll & Bute UA

Bridge of Orchy

Bridge of Orchy Hotel

PA36 4AD

☎ (01838) 400208 🌐 bridgeoforchy.co.uk

Harviestoun Bitter & Twisted; 1 changing beer (sourced regionally; often Harviestoun) Ⓗ

Situated on the A82 that leads north to Glencoe, Fort William and Skye, and with a nearby railway station, this remote hotel is surprisingly accessible. With mountains and glens nearby it is popular with walkers, climbers and other outdoor types. The bar faces the road and features an iron stove, as does the comfortable lounge. The restaurant offers a panoramic view of the mountains. The menu includes local produce. P (915)

Cairnbaan

Cairnbaan Hotel

PA31 8SQ

☎ (01546) 603668 🌐 cairnbaan.com

3 changing beers (sourced regionally; often Fyne Ales) Ⓗ

The hotel was built in 1801 at the same time as the Crinan Canal – at its midpoint beside Lock 5 – and has been accommodating travellers visiting mid-Argyll ever since. The bar opens onto a conservatory furnished with comfortable sofas; outside there is a small seating area offering views of the canal and boats. In the summer three handpumps serve Fyne ales with two beers usually on offer in winter. The dark-painted bar and restaurant are housed in a more recent addition to one side. Q P

Cairndow

Fyne Ales Brewery Tap

Achadunan, PA26 8BJ (up side road at head of Loch Fyne)

☎ (01499) 600120 🌐 fyneales.com/brewery-tap

Fyne Ales Jarl; 4 changing beers (sourced locally; often Fyne Ales) Ⓗ

The brewery tap and shop opened in 2012 in what was originally a farm building. The bar, with its fine polished granite front, supports five handpumps selling a range of ales from the brewery along with a varied selection of bottled beers. Meat produced on the farm is available to

REAL ALE BREWERIES

Argyll Tobermory: Isle of Mull
Bun Dubh Sandaig: Isle of Tiree
Colonsay Scalasaig: Isle of Colonsay
Fyne Cairndow
Islay Bridgend: Isle of Islay

buy and is also used to fill the excellent pies, which can be enjoyed in the bar or the courtyard looking across to the brewery. Q❀♿P🐾📶

Clachan Seil

Tigh-an-Truish Inn

PA34 4QZ

☎ (01852) 300242

2 changing beers (sourced nationally; often Fyne Ales, Orkney) Ⓗ

This charming inn is worth veering off the A816 to visit. Its rustic wooden interior has an L-shaped counter with an unusual high bench seat, the Perch. Two handpumps (one in winter) serve Scottish ales from a range of breweries. A stone fireplace harbours a coal-burning iron stove, with a Highland sword and enigmatic wooden carving above. In summer the garden and patio are a delight. Check hours on weekdays and in winter before travelling any distance. Q❀🛏◐ΔP🚌(418)🐾📶

Ellenabeich

Oyster Bar & Restaurant

PA34 4RQ (by harbour)

☎ (01852) 300121 🌐 oysterbareasdale.com

2 changing beers (often Fyne Ales, Orkney, Williams Bros) Ⓗ

Set on an island, this little bar, which used to have its own brewery, has a reputation for good food and a unique view. It is not the easiest place to get to but is worth the effort. The pub is situated by the harbour at the end of a row of low whitewashed cottages once occupied by workers in the slate quarries around this historic village. Ale is generally from Scottish micros, often featuring unusual brews. Alcoholic drinks are available after 11am. Q❀◐♿🚌(418)🐾📶

Innellan

Osborne

44 Shore Road, PA23 7TJ

☎ (01369) 830820 🌐 theosborneinnellan.co.uk

St Austell Tribute; 2 changing beers (sourced nationally) Ⓗ

This whitewashed seafront hotel a few miles south of Dunoon was built in 1869 and has been completely refurbished in the past few years. The comfortable bar has a pool table to one side and a cosy lounge with a log fire. At the front a conservatory acts as the dining room and provides excellent views across the Firth of Clyde. Any good weather can be enjoyed in a small outdoor area to one side. ❀🛏◐🚌(489)📶

Inveraray

George Hotel

Main Street East, PA32 8TT

☎ (01499) 302111 🌐 thegeorgehotel.co.uk

3 changing beers (sourced regionally; often Caledonian, Fyne Ales, Inveralmond) Ⓗ

Attractive hotel developed from two private houses in 1860 by the Clark family, who still own it. The restaurants and bars have been completely restored but retain the original ambience with an abundance of dark wood, flagstone floors throughout and four roaring log and peat fires. Food has an emphasis on quality local produce, and the beers are mainly local too, served both in the main restaurant and the lively public bar (open from 5pm) alongside. Q❀🛏◐♿ΔP🚌(926,976)🐾📶

Kilmartin

Kilmartin Hotel

PA31 8RQ (on A816 10 miles N of Lochgilphead)

☎ (01546) 510250 🌐 kilmartin-hotel.com

3 changing beers (sourced regionally; often Fyne Ales, Loch Lomond, Orkney) Ⓗ

Whitewashed hotel on a promontory overlooking Kilmartin Glen and many sites of historic and religious significance. The small public bar to one side provides a cosy fireside nook and offers a good selection of whiskies to complement the real ale. To the rear, a pool and games room leads to a beer garden and smoking shed. Good home-made food is available in the evenings and some lunchtimes in the adjacent dining room, or in the garden in summer. ❀🛏◐♿ΔP🚌(423)🐾📶

Kilmelford

Cuilfail ★

PA34 4XA

☎ (01852) 200274 🌐 cuilfail.co.uk

3 changing beers (sourced nationally; often Loch Lomond, Orkney) Ⓗ

An old former coaching inn, now an established hotel with a welcoming bar which is virtually unaltered since being refitted in 1957. Its interior features the exposed boulders of the wall, an idea taken up in the facing of the counter (which also incorporates parts of whisky casks) and the wall just inside the entrance. Two real ales are usually served, one in winter. Enjoy a drink while you are warmed by the large wood-burning stove.
❀🛏◐♿P🚌(423)🐾📶

Oban

Corryvreckan

The Waterfront Centre, Railway Pier, PA34 4LW

☎ (01631) 568910

Caledonian Deuchars IPA; Greene King Abbot; Sharp's Doom Bar; 6 changing beers (sourced nationally) Ⓗ

Excellently located Wetherspoon named after the famous whirlpool between Jura and Scarba. It lies alongside the fishing boat berth, next door to both the rail station and ferry terminal and with views across Oban Bay. The interior has a wood-panelled roof and is open and spacious. The pub is enlivened by much nautical ephemera including a casting of a sea eagle. Opening time for breakfast is 7am but you will need to wait until at least 11am to sample the ale. ❀◐♿⇌🚌📶

Lorne

Stevenson Street, PA34 5NA

☎ (01631) 570020 🌐 thelornebaroban.co.uk

2 changing beers (sourced regionally) Ⓗ

A short walk through Oban's back streets will take you to this traditional pub in the Gateway to the Isles. Its impressive island bar features remarkable elephantine brass furniture. Beers are often sourced from the Hanging Tree Brewery in Drumnadrochit. A good selection of food is available. The sheltered garden area is a rarity. The pub is well worth a visit, and Oban can be reached on a day trip from Glasgow. ❀◐⇌🚌🐾📶

Oban Inn

1 Stafford Street, PA34 5NJ

☎ (01631) 567441

3 changing beers (often Fyne Ales) Ⓗ

This traditional corner local by the old harbour pier was shut for many years before being reopened in 2016. One of the most iconic and characterful pubs in town, the public bar remains unspoilt and retains its dark wood panelling and stone floors of Easdale slate. Old photographs and maritime artefacts decorate the walls, and banknotes from many nations cover the wooden beams. Real ale is only occasionally available in the comfortable lounge upstairs but it is still possible to admire the stained-glass panels acquired from an Irish monastery.

Rothesay: Isle of Bute

Black Bull Inn

West Princes Street, PA20 9AF (opp harbour)
☎ (01700) 502366
3 changing beers (sourced regionally; often Fyne Ales)
A pleasant ferry trip from Wemyss Bay rail station brings you to this well-known landmark, situated opposite the marina and within walking distance of all amenities including the Victorian toilets on Rothesay pier. The pub has two bars, a front and rear entrance and a separate dining area. It is always busy with yachtsmen and others looking for a meal. The real ales are often from Scottish microbreweries.

Strachur

Creggans Inn

PA27 8BX (on A815 at N end of village)
☎ (01369) 860279 creggans-inn.co.uk
2 changing beers (sourced locally; often Fyne Ales)
Convenient stopping place along Loch Fyne. MacPhunn's bar, named after a half-hung sheep rustler of yore, is comfortable with a real fire and plenty of room for dining. Two handpumps offer a changing selection of beers from Fyne Ales. Drinks may be taken to other lounges, the restaurant or games room, or enjoyed in the garden overlooking the loch. The games room and toilets are decorated with charts of the sea around Scotland and elsewhere. Q P (484,486)

Oban Inn, Oban (Photo: Draco2008/Flickr CC BY 2.0)

AYRSHIRE & ARRAN

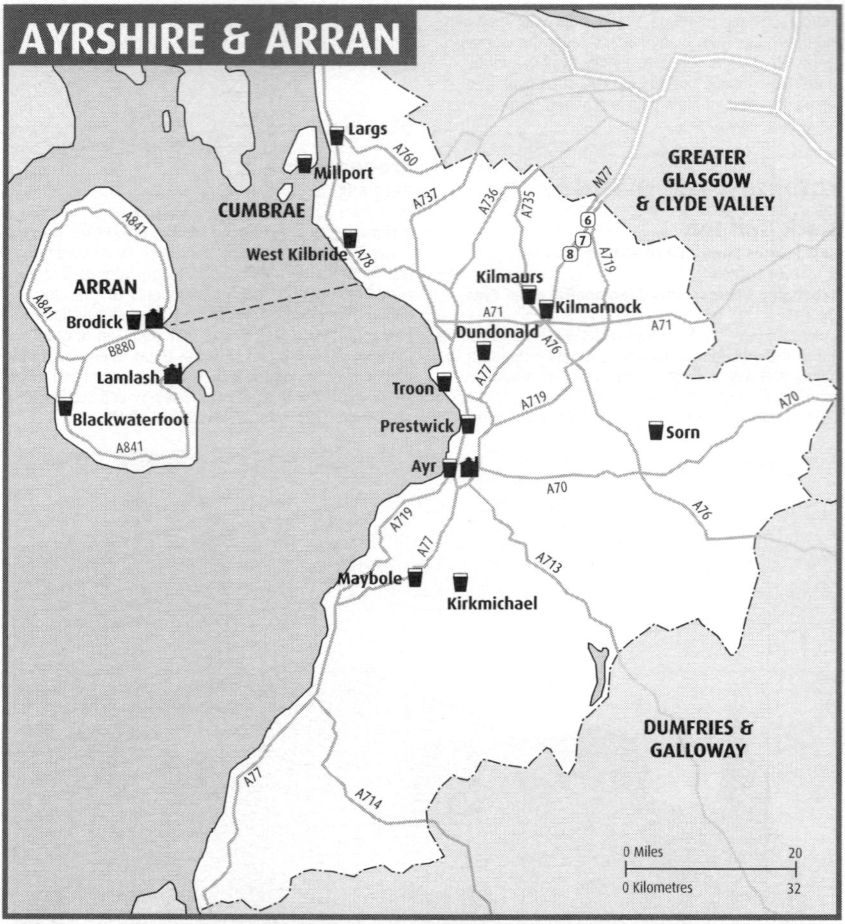

Authority areas covered: East Ayrshire UA, North Ayrshire UA, South Ayrshire UA

Ayr

Abbotsford Hotel

14 Corsehill Road, KA7 2ST

☎ (01292) 261506 🌐 abbotsfordhotel.co.uk

2 changing beers (often Fyne Ales, Wainwright) Ⓗ

Just under a mile south of Ayr town centre and a 20-minute walk from the rail station, this fine Scottish baronial-style building has been under the same ownership since 1966. The delightful and aptly named Copper Bar has the real ale. There is a pleasant dining room and a games room with TV showing sports. Book ahead for meals. The pub is close to the seafront, with golf courses, parks and Burns attractions nearby.

♿♣P🚌 (57,361) 🐾 📶

Chestnuts Hotel

52 Racecourse Road, KA7 2UZ (on A719, 1 mile S of centre)

☎ (01292) 264393 🌐 chestnutshotel.com

3 changing beers Ⓗ

This family-run hotel attracts both locals and visitors. Three changing real ales from a range of breweries are available in The 19th Hole, a delightful oak-beamed hall with an interesting history and a huge collection of whisky water jugs. Excellent food is served in the bar and separate restaurant. Open log fires add to the comfortable atmosphere in winter and a pleasant beer garden is popular when the weather allows.

♿P🚌 (9) 📶

Glen Park Hotel 𝕃

5 Racecourse Road, KA7 2DG

☎ (01292) 263891 🌐 theglenparkhotel.co.uk

Ayr Leezie Lundie, Jolly Beggars; 2 changing beers (often Ayr) Ⓗ

This comfortable lounge bar, in an attractive 1860s B-listed Victorian building, is the brewery tap for Ayr Brewing Company who brew in the rear of the building. The guest ales often include a seasonal from the brewery. Beers are usually also available to take away from a shop/bar at the rear of the dining room. Bar and restaurant meals are served daily except Monday.

♿≹P🚌 (9) 🐾 📶

REAL ALE BREWERIES

Arran Brodick: Isle of Arran
Ayr Ayr
Seagate Lamlash: Isle of Arran (NEW)

Wellingtons Bar
17 Wellington Square, KA7 1EZ
(01292) 262794 welliesbar.weebly.com
3 changing beers (often Born, Kelburn, Loch Lomond)
A large Wellington boot advertises the location of this basement bar. Close to the seafront, bus station and local government offices, it attracts tourists and office workers alike. The Wednesday evening quiz is popular and at the weekend there may be live music, or a DJ on Saturday and an acoustic session on Sunday. Three changing ales vary constantly between brewers. Bar food is served, with daily specials on the menu. Local CAMRA Pub of the Year 2019. Q

West Kirk
58A Sandgate, KA7 1BX (close to bus station)
(01292) 880416
Caledonian Deuchars IPA; Greene King Abbot; 5 changing beers
This Wetherspoon conversion of a former church retains many original features – you get to the toilets via the pulpit (there is an accessible toilet downstairs). Up to five changing guest ales are offered and local microbreweries are usually well represented. It does meals all day and breakfast from early on, and is licensed from 10am. Outside, the front drinking area has a shelter for smokers. Handy for Ayr bus station. Q

Blackwaterfoot: Isle of Arran

Kinloch Hotel
KA27 8ET
(01770) 860444 bw-kinlochhotel.co.uk
Ayr Uisge Dubh; 1 changing beer (often Ayr, Belhaven, Greene King)
A hidden gem in a quiet rural village on the west coast of Arran, offering coastal comfort and spectacular scenery. The family hotel has 37 bedrooms, a restaurant and three refurbished bars, and facilities including a heated indoor swimming pool, squash court and a fitness room and sauna. Fabulous local produce is served including fish and seafood. A beer festival is held in August.
P

Brodick: Isle of Arran

Ormidale Hotel
Knowe Road, KA27 8BY (off A841 at W end of village)
(01770) 302293 ormidale-hotel.co.uk
3 changing beers (often Arran)
This large red sandstone hotel with a small bar and spacious conservatory is set in seven acres of grounds. Beers are now served from handpumps rather than founts on the boat-shaped bar, although one original fount remains. Three ales are available in summer, often including Arran Blonde. Home-cooked meals are recommended. Entertainment includes discos and folk nights, and the attractive beer garden has views across Brodick Bay. P (322,324)

Dundonald

Auchans
29-31 Main Street, KA2 9HH (on B730)
(01563) 851472 theauchans.co.uk
2 changing beers (often Ayr, Fyne Ales, Kelburn)
Friendly family-run restaurant bar with a varied food menu including tapas and pizzas appealing to all tastes. The restaurant is to the rear and the comfortable lounge bar has views of the historic 14th-century castle. Up to two beers on handpump change regularly and tend to come from local and regional breweries. Dundonald is a pleasant village at the end of the historic smugglers' trail from Troon. Q P (10,110)

> I never drink water. I'm afraid it will become habit-forming.
> **W C Fields**

Kilmarnock

First Edition
50 Bank Street, KA1 1HA
(01563) 528833 firsteditionkilmarnock.co.uk
Caledonian Deuchars IPA; 3 changing beers (often Inveralmond, Strathaven, Wychwood)
Large town-centre pub in a former furniture shop in the historic core of Kilmarnock. Four ales are usually available including two from Scottish regional brewers. The large, recently renovated, modern pub serves food all day in bright surroundings. The recently revamped beer garden has table tennis and pool tables under cover. Numerous TV screens inside and three outside show sports, and a DJ features Friday to Sunday evenings.

Wheatsheaf Inn
70 Portland Street, KA1 1JG
(01563) 572483
Greene King Abbot; Sharp's Doom Bar; 6 changing beers
This sizeable town-centre Lloyds No.1 bar, originally the historic Wheatsheaf Hotel, is famous for its links to Robert Burns, who was first published in Kilmarnock. The bar is divided into various seating areas, with booths, sofas and a raised dining space. Six handpumps dispense a range of ales plus real cider; food is standard Wetherspoon fare. DJs entertain on Friday and Saturday, with karaoke early Friday evening, but otherwise conversation dominates. Licensed from 11am.

Kilmaurs

Weston Tavern
27 Main Street, KA3 2RQ
(01563) 538805 westontavern.co.uk
2 changing beers (often Cairngorm, Theakston)
Housed in the former manse of reformist minister David Smeaton, a contemporary of Robert Burns, this fully refurbished country pub and restaurant has a tiled floor, stone walls and a wood-burning fire. It sits beside the Jougs, a former jailhouse and tollbooth. Two handpumps serve ales from a rotating list of local breweries. The pub holds regular live music and quiz nights. Local CAMRA Pub of the Year 2019. P

Kirkmichael

Kirkmichael Arms
3-5 Straiton Road, KA19 7PH
(01655) 750200 kirkmichaelarms.co.uk
2 changing beers (often Ayr)
A friendly country pub at the heart of the community with a lounge bar, separate dining room and a small private dining room/function room. Two handpumps dispense an Ayr Brewing Co beer plus a guest. The pub serves excellent meals, using locally sourced ingredients where possible. Walkers and dogs are made welcome, and small functions are catered for. Well placed for accessing Galloway Forest Park to the south.
Q (358,361)

Largs

JG Sharps Bar

34-36 Nelson Street, KA30 8LW (off seafront at Nardini's)

(01475) 675515 jgsharps.co.uk

2 changing beers (often Redcastle, Sharp's)

Set back from the seafront, Sharps is located on the corner of Nelson Street and Boyd Street. It is a large, traditional pub with several drinking spaces. An open fire warms the bar area and there is a beer garden outside. Quality pub meals are served. Games and sport are shown on TV and live music plays occasionally.

Paddle Steamer

Gallowgate Street, KA30 8LX (on promenade nr Calmac ferry terminal)

(01475) 686441

Greene King Abbot; Sharp's Sea Fury; 4 changing beers (often Kelburn, Strathaven)

This seafront Wetherspoon's outlet has a nautical theme. There is a feature fire in the centre of the bar and a viewing window into the cellar. An outside balcony borders the promenade overlooked by wide windows with views to the Isles of Bute and Cumbrae, the ferry to the latter being only a minute away. Models of the world famous paddle steamer Waverley decorate the outside, while the real ship visits Largs throughout the summer. Licensed from 11am. (585,901,906)

Maybole

Maybole Arms

37 Whitehall, KA19 7DS

(01655) 883173

1 changing beer (often Ayr, Caledonian, Sulwath)

A welcome watering hole for those visiting an area which has few real ale pubs. This small, established local inn has a friendly clientele and offers good food from a family-friendly menu. Dogs are permitted, with water and biscuits supplied. A handy stop-off for nearby Culzean Castle & Country Park.
(58,60)

Millport: Isle of Cumbrae

Fraser's Bar

7 Cardiff Street, KA28 0AS

(01475) 530518

2 changing beers (often Jaw, Kelburn, Redcastle)

Well maintained and tidy, this pub caters for visitors to the island as well as locals. Buses meet every ferry from Largs and terminate just across the road. Two handpumps serve mostly light-coloured ales, usually including one from a local brewery. Good-value pub food is available lunchtime and early evening. The main bar has an open fire and a fine display of old Clyde steamer photographs. Children are welcome in the rear lounge until 8pm. (320)

Prestwick

Prestwick Pioneer

87 Main Street, KA9 1JS

(01292) 473210

Greene King Abbot; Sharp's Doom Bar; 8 changing beers

Modern Wetherspoon outlet in a former Woolworths store, named after the first Scottish Aviation Pioneer light aircraft, built in 1947 at the nearby international airport. The pub has an airy feel with a light-wood decor, and features photographs of early Open Championship golf at Prestwick, and of Elvis at the airport – the only place in the UK he set foot on. Ten handpumps serve local and national ales and food is available. Licensed from 10am.

Sorn

Sorn Inn

35 Main Street, KA5 6HU

(01290) 551305 sorninn.com

1 changing beer (often Orkney)

The pub is the community hub for this conservation village. It has an award-winning restaurant with a menu that offers a mix of fine dining and brasserie-style food, much of it featuring locally sourced ingredients. The bar provides seating for about 25 people and has one handpump, serving ale from Orkney brewery. Accommodation is offered in four en-suite rooms. Sadly it is not accessible by public transport.

Troon

McKay's

69 Portland Street, KA10 6QU

(01292) 737372

3 changing beers (often Fyne Ales, Greene King, Harviestoun)

A popular single-room town-centre bar with a large CAMRA award-winning beer garden, which is popular on sunny days. The bar hosts local dominoes competitions and shows live sports on TV. Dogs are welcome in the garden only. A former local CAMRA Regional Pub of the Year.

Number Forty Seven

47 Templehill, KA10 6BQ

(01292) 312814

Cairngorm Wildcat; Morland Old Speckled Hen; 3 changing beers (often Belhaven)

A long single-room bar which has recently been refurbished. Five handpulls dispense real ales from Scottish and English breweries, with a discount for over-60s on request. Quiz night is Thursday. There is a pool table, a jukebox and several TVs showing live sport. The gantry has a well stocked variety of spirits. On Friday and Saturday nights a DJ plays from 10pm and the bar moves into nightclub mode.

West Kilbride

Twa Dugs

71 Main Street, KA23 9AW

(01294) 822524

2 changing beers (often Ayr, Five Kingdoms, Kelburn)

Popular pub refurbished to a high standard and patronised by all age groups. Two handpulls dispense ales mostly from local breweries, and bar food is available Thursday to Sunday. There is a pool table, live music at the weekend and a regular quiz. Ziggy's restaurant next door is linked to the pub and serves meals Thursday to Sunday (booking advised). There is a bus stop opposite and the railway station is five minutes. Local CAMRA Pub of the Year 2019.
(585,585A)

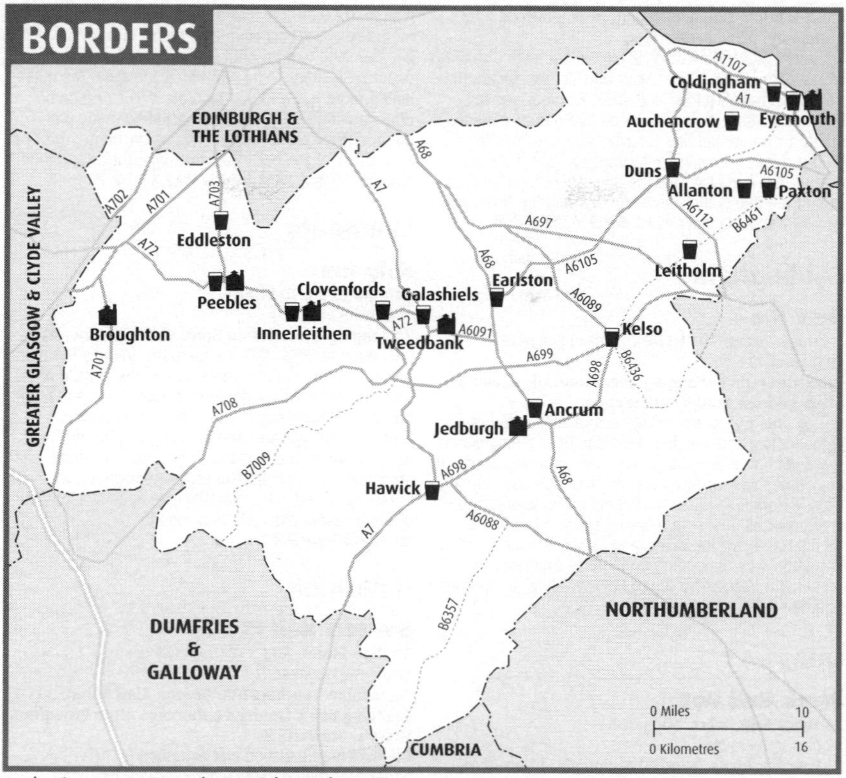

Authority area covered: Scottish Borders UA

Allanton

Allanton Inn

TD11 3JZ

☎ (01890) 818260 🌐 allantoninn.co.uk

2 changing beers (sourced nationally; often Born, Fyne Ales, Timothy Taylor) Ⓗ

An old coaching inn dating back to the 18th century with a bright, airy feel. Quality food is served in the dining room at the front. The small bar area, which overlooks the superb beer garden with views of the countryside beyond, may also be used for dining. It has an attractive decor with artworks and comfortable cushioned benches. Families are welcome – a children's menu and games are provided. Winter hours may vary.

Q❀◑♣P🚌(260) ᯤ

Ancrum

Ancrum Cross Keys

The Green, TD8 6XH (on B6400, off A68)

☎ (01835) 830242 🌐 ancrumcrosskeys.com

4 changing beers (sourced locally; often Born)

Perched on the Ale Water (yes really!), parts of this pub have been upgraded, but the front bar and its sliding door, as well as a real fire and pine panelling, have remained virtually untouched since 1906. There is also a comfortable drinking and dining area and a snug at the front. Owned by Born Brewery, the pub serves traditional food featuring local produce that is sometimes foraged. Families are welcome, with a children's menu, play area and games available. It is likely to be closed Monday-Friday afternoons. ❀◑♿Ⓐ♣P🚌(68,51)🐾ᯤ

Auchencrow

Craw Inn 🏆

TD14 5LS (signed from A1)

☎ (01890) 761253 🌐 thecrawinn.co.uk

Timothy Taylor Landlord; 3 changing beers (sourced nationally) Ⓗ

A revitalised and friendly 18th-century listed country inn. The real ales are usually from smaller breweries, as can be seen from the numerous pumpclips on show. The bar has a wood-burning stove and tables for dining and drinking. Excellent home-cooked food is served in both the bar and well-appointed restaurant. There is also an attractive rear area with comfy furniture and a separate games room with a pool table. Local CAMRA Borders Pub of the Year 2020. Winter hours may vary. It is likely to be closed Monday-Friday afternoons.

Q❀◑♣P🚌(34) ᯤ

Clovenfords

Clovenfords Hotel ✔

1 Vine Street, TD1 3LU

☎ (01896) 850203

REAL ALE BREWERIES

Aye Been Eyemouth (NEW)
Born Jedburgh
Broughton Broughton
Freewheelin' Peebles
Tempest Tweedbank
Traquair House Innerleithen

SCOTLAND

Sharp's Doom Bar; 1 changing beer (sourced nationally; often Stewart) [H]
Set in the heart of an old vineyard village with a striking white statue of Sir Walter Scott outside, this family-run hotel offers quality food and drink. Families are very welcome, with a children's menu and games provided. Meals are served all day Saturday and Sunday. Old photos adorn the walls, reflecting the hotel's literary history. The pub also runs the adjacent village shop as part of the Pub is the Hub initiative. Opening times may vary in winter. **Q**⛽❀🛏◑♿♣**P**🚌(62,X62)🐾📶

Coldingham

New Inn
1 Bridge Street, TD14 5NG (by village square)
☎ (01890) 771315
Fyne Ales Jarl; 1 changing beer (sourced regionally; often Hadrian Border, Orkney) [H]
A cosy little pub in the village centre with a corner bar, wooden floor and real fire. Steps lead up to a dining area. A second bar, reached by a separate entrance, opens at busy times and for functions. The two real ales are usually from Scottish or Northumbrian breweries. Meals are served all day in summer including a children's menu. Handy for the beach and St Abb's Head. Opening times can vary depending on custom, especially in winter. It is likely to be closed Monday-Friday afternoons.
⛽❀◑♿⛺🚌(235)🐾

Duns

Black Bull Hotel
15 Black Bull Street, TD11 3AR
☎ (01361) 883379
3 changing beers (sourced regionally; often Born, Fyne Ales, Tempest) [H]
This characterful, family-run, 200-year-old hotel is well worth seeking out. The cosy wood-panelled bar is popular with locals while the lounge is well suited to families. The restaurant specialises in fresh local produce, with an intimate, relaxed, candlelit atmosphere. The secluded beer garden with a gazebo and patio can be enjoyed during the summer. The bedrooms are named after local historical figures. No food is available on Mondays or winter Sunday evenings.
Q⛽❀🛏◑♿♣**P**🚌🐾📶

Earlston

Red Lion ✔
The Square, TD4 6DB
☎ (01896) 848994 🌐 redlionearlston.co.uk
2 changing beers (sourced locally; often Born) [H]
Dating from the 1800s, this former coaching inn has a spacious bar with a community noticeboard, a huge fireplace with open fire, a pool table and a dartboard. Food is available in the bar and attractive dining room, including breakfast on Saturday and Sunday. Families are welcome, with a menu and games for children. Real ale is promoted on blackboards. Handy for the local bus hub and countryside walks. Alcoholic drinks are served from 11am. ⛽❀🛏◑♣**P**🚌🐾📶

Eddleston

Horseshoe Inn
EH45 8QP
☎ (01721) 730225 🌐 horseshoeinn.co.uk
3 changing beers (sourced nationally; often Broughton, Orkney, Stewart) [H]
A large and welcoming free house with a separate dining room and snug, plus eight B&B rooms in an annexe. The bar and snug feature original flagstone floors, exposed beams and characterful old timber furniture; the quiet dining room has a more elaborate decor. The menu offers a wide choice of dishes including many pub classics. There are also light bites at lunchtime. The TV in one corner of the bar is just for major rugby and tennis matches. **Q**⛽❀🛏◑♿♣**P**🚌(X62,X70)🐾📶

Eyemouth

Ship Inn
Harbour Road, TD14 5HT
☎ (01890) 751495
2 changing beers (often Born, Cheviot, Stewart) [H]
Reopened in 2019, this is a pleasant, friendly bar and restaurant. The decor is modern and airy, with a nod towards the town's seafaring heritage. The varied food menu has something to suit everyone, including children's options. Situated on the quayside, the pub offers views of the harbour and Gunsgreen House. The accommodation is run as a separate business, with breakfast served in the pub. Likely to open at 10am, with alcoholic drinks available from noon.
⛽❀🛏◑♿⛺**P**🚌📶

Galashiels

Hunters Hall ✔
56 High Street, TD1 1SE (N end of centre)
☎ (01896) 759795
Caledonian Deuchars IPA; Greene King Abbot; 3 changing beers (sourced nationally; often Broughton, Sharp's, Stewart) [H]
Extensively refurbished and extended in 2019, this original Presbyterian Church and School has been sympathetically restored to expose much of the original stonework, high ceiling and the skylight roof panels. Historical photographs of Galashiels decorate the walls. No longer a Lloyds in the evening, it offers typical Wetherspoon fare for both food and drink and caters for families, locals and students. Meals are served all day. NOTE: Likely to open at 8am but alcohol drinks not served until 11am. **Q**⛽❀◑♿⛺⇌●**P**🚌📶

Ladhope Inn ✔
33 High Buckholmside, TD1 2HR
☎ (01896) 752446
1 changing beer (sourced regionally; often Black Sheep, Born, York) [H]
A comfortable, friendly local with a vibrant Borders atmosphere. Originating circa 1792, the pub has been altered considerably over the years and comprises one long single room, decorated with a large inked map of the area. One real ale is served, sometimes two at weekends. Three TVs ensure the bar is busy during sporting events, and live music is hosted on occasion. The pub is a community hub for locally arranged golf, horse racing and fishing trips. Children are not allowed. It is likely to close early afternoon Monday-Friday.
❀⛺⇌♣🚌🐾📶

Hawick

Exchange Bar (Dalton's)
1 Silver Street, TD9 0AD (off SW end of High St)
☎ (01450) 376067
2 changing beers (sourced regionally; often Belhaven, Born, Orkney) [H]
Tucked away near St Mary's Kirk, the pub used to overlook the Corn Exchange. However, a previous owner

was called Dalton and that name has stuck ever since. It is a Victorian gem, and the bar has original dark-wood panelling and ornate cornice work. It is popular with locals and there is a comfy back lounge used for parties, occasional karaoke and Sunday folk sessions. Children are not admitted. A CAMRA Borders Real Ale Quality Award runner-up. ❀▲♣P🚌🐾📶

Innerleithen

Traquair Arms Hotel

Traquair Road, EH44 6PD (B709, off A72)

☎ (01896) 830229 🌐 traquairarmshotel.co.uk

Traquair House Bear Ale; 2 changing beers (sourced nationally; often Stewart, Tempest) Ⓗ

Elegant 18th-century hotel in the scenic Tweed Valley offering accommodation in 16 en-suite rooms and two self-catering cottages. The comfortable lounge bar features a welcoming real fire, and a flagstoned sports bar with log-burner provides a great thawing-out space for mountain bikers, walkers and anglers. A bistro area and separate restaurant offer plenty of room for diners. Meals are served all day at weekends and there is a menu for children. One of the few outlets for draught real ale from Traquair House. The bar may close earlier if quiet. ❀🛏◑♿▲♣P🚌(X62)🐾📶

Kelso

Cobbles Freehouse & Dining

7 Bowmont Street, TD5 7JH (off NE side of town square)

☎ (01573) 223548 🌐 thecobbleskelso.co.uk

2 changing beers (sourced locally; often Tempest)

Diners and drinkers are equally well catered for at this popular, long-established gastro-pub. The cosy bar is on the right, featuring a real fire at the far end. The dining area is on the left, though food is served throughout, and is available all day at weekends. Both areas are bright and welcoming and there is a menu to suit all tastes, including children's options. The handpumps are dedicated solely to Tempest beers – some lined glasses are available. Please ask before bringing in your dog. Winter hours may vary. ❀🛏◑♿🚆🚌🐾📶

Leitholm

Plough Inn

Main Street, TD12 4JN

☎ (01890) 840408 🌐 theploughinnleitholm.co.uk

House beer (by Born); 1 changing beer (sourced nationally; often Cheviot, Greene King, Hetton Law) Ⓗ

Set in the main street of a quiet village, this formerly closed pub has been transformed into a charming and friendly family-run inn. The wooden-floored bar is decorated and furnished to create a bright, modern and welcoming ambience. A massive clock dominates the fireplace area. Children are welcome until 9pm. The beer garden overlooks fields. Opening hours may be extended in summer. It is likely to be closed Monday and Tuesday, and afternoons from Wednesday to Saturday. ❀🛏◑♣●P🚌(85,87)🐾📶

Paxton

Cross Inn

TD15 1TE (off B6461)

☎ (01289) 384877 🌐 thecrossinn.co.uk

Timothy Taylor Landlord; 2 changing beers (sourced regionally; often Hadrian Border) Ⓗ

A rejuvenated 19th-century village local with friendly staff. Its small, welcoming bar is stone-floored; the attractive larger dining and function area has floorboards and carpeting. Food is very much part of the pub's offering, with a menu that appeals to most tastes, as well as daily specials and Sunday roasts (no food Sun eve). Families are welcome and a children's menu provided. On occasion there is a real cider. It is likely to be closed Mondays and Tuesdays in winter, and afternoons Monday to Friday all year. ❀◑♿▲●P🚌(32,87)🐾📶

Peebles

Bridge Inn (Trust)

Portbrae, EH45 8AW

☎ (01721) 720589 🌐 thebridgeinnpeebles.co.uk

Fyne Ales Jarl; 3 changing beers (sourced nationally; often Born, Stewart, Tempest) Ⓗ

Cheerful, welcoming pub also known as the Trust and once called the Tweedside Inn. The bright, comfortable bar is decorated with jugs, bottles, pictures of old Peebles and displays relating to outdoor pursuits. There is a cosy corner with a log-burner and a small room to the rear. The suntrap patio overlooks the river and hills beyond. The Gents has superb old fittings. Children are not admitted. CAMRA Scotland and N Ireland Pub of the Year 2019. ❀▲♣🚌🐾📶

Cross Keys ✔

24 Northgate, EH45 8RS

☎ (01721) 723467

Caledonian Deuchars IPA; Greene King Abbot; Kelham Island Pale Rider; Sharp's Doom Bar; 2 changing beers (sourced nationally; often Broughton, Cairngorm, Harviestoun) Ⓗ

This old coaching inn is now a Wetherspoon pub and hotel. The pleasant, rambling, wood-panelled main area has low ceilings and a mix of tables and chairs, as well as booths with bench seating. The serving area is tucked away to the left of the entrance and has high tables and chairs. Steps lead up to the excellent beer garden. Food is available all day – children are permitted if dining. The cider is Westons Old Rosie. It is likely to open at 7am, with alcoholic drinks served from 11am.
Q❀🛏◑♿▲♣●🚌📶

Store of good ale

Though it was but about the middle of August, and in some places the harvest hardly got in, we saw the mountains covered with snow, and felt the cold very acute and piercing but we found, as in all these northern counties, the people had a happy way of mixing the warm and the cold together; for store of good ale which flows plentifully in the most mountainous parts of this country seem abundantly to make up for all the inclemencies of the season, or difficulties of travelling.

Daniel Defoe, A Tour Through the Whole Island of Great Britain, 1726

DUMFRIES & GALLOWAY

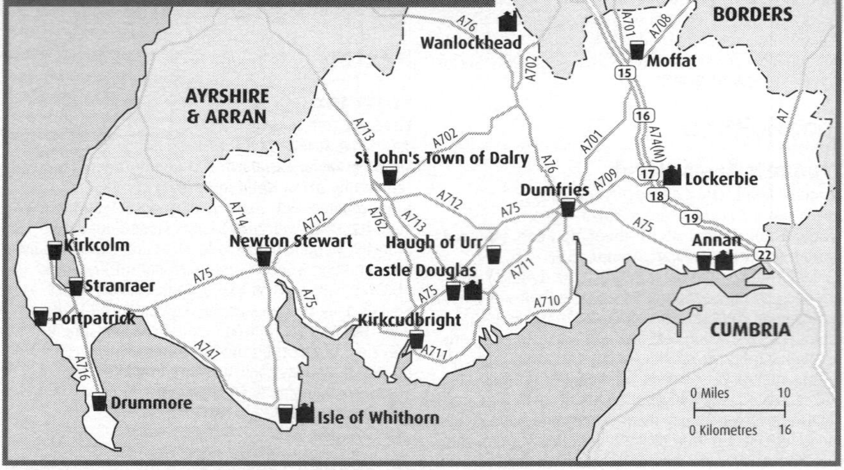

Authority area covered: Dumfries & Galloway UA

Annan

Blue Bell Inn 🏆

10 High Street, DG12 6AG

☎ (01461) 202385

Caledonian Deuchars IPA; 4 changing beers (sourced nationally; often Carlisle, Kelburn, Strathaven) Ⓗ

Former coaching inn dating from 1770 where Hans Christian Andersen is said to have stayed, and part of the Gretna State Management Scheme from 1917 to 1972 when pubs were nationalised. The red sandstone building retains some traditional features, notably the panelled interior and rear stables. The Gents has a panelled ante-room, tiled inner room and original Shanks urinals. The inn is home to many community activities along with annual beer and cider festivals. Motte & Bailey beers, brewed on-site, are only available in the Blue Bell. Local CAMRA Pub of the Year 2020.

P (79,383)

Castle Douglas

Sulwath Brewery Tap Room

209 King Street, DG7 1DT

☎ (01556) 504525 🌐 sulwathbrewers.co.uk

Sulwath Black Galloway; 5 changing beers (sourced locally; often Sulwath) Ⓗ

The visitor centre for Sulwath Brewery is a showcase for the brewery's beers (including its prize-winning Black Galloway) although not all are cask-conditioned. At times there may be guest beers from elsewhere. One draught cider, usually from Westons, is also available. Dried hop bines decorate the walls, and old wooden casks of various sizes provide some of the furniture. Brewery tours are available and there is an annual beer festival. Local CAMRA Pub and Cider Pub of the Year 2020.

QP

Drummore

Clashwhannon

DG9 9QE (on A716 S from Stranraer)

☎ (01776) 840632 🌐 clashwhannon.co.uk

3 changing beers (often Fyne Ales, Hadrian Border, Portpatrick) Ⓗ

This friendly and relaxing bar serves the adjacent caravan park and is open all year round. Demand from visitors and locals alike has seen the emergence of real ale in this remote location close to the Mull of Galloway. There is a bar area plus a large family room and restaurant where local produce is served at reasonable prices. Three handpumps are used in summer, one in winter. Music and variety events feature during the summer.

P (407)

Dumfries

Cavens Arms

20 Buccleuch Street, DG1 2AH

☎ (01387) 252896 🌐 cavensarms.com

Fyne Ales Jarl; Greene King Yardbird, Abbot; Morland Old Speckled Hen; Swannay Orkney IPA; 4 changing beers (sourced nationally) Ⓗ

Busy food-oriented pub, popular with diners for its range of good-value meals. A separate restaurant area has been created to cope with demand at peak times. Drinkers are welcome in the bar but seating can be limited during food service times. Guest ales are from a wide range of breweries, including some rarely seen in this locality. There are regular charity quizzes and other theme nights. Local CAMRA Town Pub of the Year 2020.

Coach & Horses

66 Whitesands, DG1 2RS

☎ 07746 675349

Draught Bass Ⓗ

A small, lively former coaching inn overlooking the River Nith. Situated next to the tourist information centre, the pub is handy for local attractions. The bar is small but service is always quick. The room features a flagstone floor with a warming open fire during the colder months.

REAL ALE BREWERIES

Five Kingdoms Isle of Whithorn
Lola Rose Wanlockhead
Lowland Lockerbie
Mote & Bailey Annan
Sulwath ◆ Castle Douglas

There is a great atmosphere in this gem of a pub, enhanced by regular live music sessions. Winter opening times may vary. ❀≠♣P🚌🐾

Globe Inn

56 High Street, DG1 2JA

☎ (013873) 23010 🌐 globeinndumfries.co.uk

Lowland Twa Dugs, Dryfe Blonde; 1 changing beer (often Lowland) ⊞

The Globe dates from 1610 and is the oldest inn in Dumfries. A busy town-centre pub steeped in tradition, it is up a close off the High Street, with a public bar, dining area and adjoining small snug. It has a close association with Scotland's National Bard, Robert Burns, who was a frequent visitor, is home to the world-famous Burns Howff Club, and holds much memorabilia; rooms associated with the poet can be visited by arrangement. Occasionally functions are held here, so checking before visiting might be advisable. Q❀◑≠🚌📶

New Bazaar

39 Whitesands, DG1 2RS

☎ (01387) 268776

Theakston XB; 3 changing beers (sourced nationally; often Fuller's, Greene King, Timothy Taylor) ⊞

Former coaching inn beside the River Nith with an attractive airy bar featuring a splendid Victorian gantry that displays an impressive malt whisky collection. The cosy lounge provides a quiet retreat and has a warming coal fire in winter. A small room is available for meetings. The pub is a favourite with football supporters attending nearby Palmerston Park and is ideally situated for car parking, local buses and tourist attractions. Winter opening times may vary. ❀♣P🚌🐾📶

Riverside Bar

Dock Park, DG1 2RY

☎ (01387) 254477

Morland Old Speckled Hen; 3 changing beers (sourced nationally) ⊞

The Riverside Bar is an established venue on the Dumfries real ale scene. Comfortable and friendly, it has seating on two levels and a large conservatory. Two outside seating areas include a terrace with open views over the Dock Park and down to the River Nith. The pub is accessible from the St Michaels area near the Robert Burns Mausoleum or from Dock Park. Guest beers can be from local brewers as well as from further afield. ☋❀♣🚌🐾📶

Robert the Bruce ✔

81 Buccleuch Street, DG1 2AB

☎ (01387) 270320

Caledonian Deuchars IPA; Greene King Abbot; Sharp's Doom Bar; 4 changing beers (sourced nationally) ⊞

This former Methodist church, sensitively converted by Wetherspoon, has a relaxed atmosphere and is a popular meeting place in the town centre. There is a pleasant outside seating area to the rear. The pub stands near the site where Robert the Bruce killed John Comyn in 1306 in an incident linked to Scotland's fight for independence. The food menu offers a range of good-value meals all day, every day. Alcoholic drinks are served from 11am. ☋❀◑♿≠♣●P🚌📶

Tam o' Shanter

113-117 Queensberry Street, DG1 1BH

☎ (01387) 267880

Broughton Clipper IPA, No.5 Proper IPA; 4 changing beers (sourced nationally; often Broughton, Sulwath) ⊞

Established in 1630, this 17th-century coaching inn with a connection to Robert Burns has been a mainstay of the Dumfries beer scene for many years. It is small and traditional, with a main bar and a couple of quiet cosy rooms including a games area behind. There are always guest beers from local breweries. An upstairs room hosts live music and other functions. The pub is well positioned just off the High Street. ☋≠♣P🚌🐾📶

Haugh of Urr

Laurie Arms Hotel

11-13 Main Street, DG7 3YA

☎ (01556) 660246 🌐 haugh-of-urr.co.uk

4 changing beers (sourced nationally; often Caledonian, Fyne Ales, Strathaven) ⊞

Welcoming family-run establishment in a charming, quiet village, popular for its range of beers and freshly cooked food featuring local produce. It has a good village-pub atmosphere, enhanced on winter nights by a warming log fire in the bar. Up to four beers are available depending on the season, mainly from independent breweries. National Cycle Route 7 passes nearby. It is on the bus route between Dumfries, Dalbeattie and Castle Douglas. A former local CAMRA award winner. Winter opening times may vary, so check before visiting. ☋❀◑♣P🚌(501) 🐾📶

Isle of Whithorn

Steam Packet Inn 🏆 ✔

Harbour Row, DG8 8LL (on B7004 from Whithorn)

☎ (01988) 500334 🌐 thesteampacketinn.biz

Morland Old Speckled Hen; 7 changing beers (often Five Kingdoms, Fyne Ales, Kelburn) ⊞

Traditional and historic family-run hotel overlooking the harbour, welcoming to all including families and pets. The public bar has stone walls and a multi-fuel stove, and there are pictures of the village and maritime events throughout. Four guest ales from a wide variety of breweries, along with up to four beers from in-house brewery Five Kingdoms, are available in both bars. Bottle-conditioned ales are also stocked. The extensive food menu features local produce. Local CAMRA Pub of the Year 2020. Q☋❀🛏◑♣●P🚌(415,416)🐾📶

Kirkcolm

Blue Peter Hotel

23 Main Street, DG9 0NL (on A718 5 miles N of Stranraer)

☎ (01776) 853221

2 changing beers (often Ayr, Born) ⊞

A small family-run hotel with two bars packed with memorabilia. Two handpumps dispense a constantly changing range of ales. Home-cooked food is served using fresh local produce, with takeaways available. Outside, the decked patio has views of abundant wildlife including red squirrels. The hotel is popular with real ale enthusiasts as well as walkers and wildlife watchers. It opens on Wednesday and Thursday evenings if darts or dominoes matches are held. Good-value B&B is available. Q☋❀🛏◗⛺♣🚌(408)🐾

Kirkcudbright

Masonic Arms

19 Castle Street, DG6 4JA

☎ (01557) 330517 🌐 masonic-arms.co.uk

2 changing beers (sourced nationally) ⊞

This friendly pub in the town has been a firm favourite with real ale enthusiasts for many years. One real ale is available all year round, two in the summer months. The tables and bar fronts are made from old malt whisky

casks from Islay's Bowmore Distillery. There is a smaller back bar, and a beer garden to the rear. A selection of more than 50 malt whiskies and over 230 gins is available, as well as a good range of world beers.
Q❀♿ÅP🚌🐾 ᯤ

Selkirk Arms Hotel ✓

High Street, DG6 4JG

☎ (01557) 330402 🌐 selkirkarmshotel.co.uk

2 changing beers (sourced nationally; often Sulwath) Ⓗ

Refurbished 18th-century hotel with a restaurant, bistro and lounge bar, renowned for locally sourced food, highlighted by the menus and photos of suppliers on the walls. The large garden area with tables is popular in summer. Two real ales are available, sometimes three in summer. A good selection of malt whiskies and gins is stocked. Robert Burns wrote his famous Selkirk Grace at the hotel in 1794. Kirkcudbright is notable for its artistic heritage and houses a number of interesting galleries and museums. Accommodation is in 16 en-suite bedrooms. Q❀🛏◑♿ÅP🚌🐾 ᯤ

Moffat

Star Hotel

44 High Street, DG10 9EF

☎ (01683) 220156 🌐 famousstarhotel.co.uk

2 changing beers (sourced regionally; often Sulwath, Greene King) Ⓗ

The Famous Star Hotel is recognised in the Guinness Book of Records as the narrowest detached hotel in the world. The building is 20 feet wide and 162 feet long but feels much bigger due to the clever use of internal space – there is a large public bar at the rear and a smaller lounge to the front. It has been run by the same family for over 30 years and offers excellent service. At least one beer is available all year round. Moffat is a good base for exploring the Southern Uplands.
❀🛏◑♿ÅP🚌🐾 ᯤ

Newton Stewart

Crown Hotel

102 Queen Street, DG8 6JW

☎ (01671) 402727 🌐 the-crown-hotel.com

1 changing beer (often Belhaven, Greene King) Ⓗ

A well-established hotel on the outskirts of town, popular with a wide mix of visitors and locals. Real ale is available from the Belhaven list, changing weekly. The interior is spacious and modern – the bar area has sports and seating areas. The restaurant offers good-value Scottish and traditional fare, from bar meals to an à la carte menu, plus a Sunday carvery. To the rear are a patio, decked area and beer garden. Accommodation comprises 15 en-suite rooms.
❀🛏◑♿Å♣P🚌(359,500) 🐾 ᯤ

Portpatrick

Crown Hotel

9 North Crescent, DG9 8SX (opp harbour)

☎ (01776) 810261 🌐 crownhotelportpatrick.com

2 changing beers (often Ayr, Portpatrick, Sulwath) Ⓗ

Hotel overlooking the picturesque and historic harbour with views on a clear day across to Ireland. The large comfortable bar area at the front is adorned with fine pictures and ornaments, and warmed by an open fire. Two regularly changing ales are sourced from breweries across the UK, including the local Portpatrick Brewery. Live music plays on Friday and Saturday nights, featuring both local and visiting musicians and groups.
❀🛏◑♿Å♣🚌(367) 🐾 ᯤ

St John's Town of Dalry

Clachan Inn

8-10 Main Street, DG7 3UW

☎ (01644) 430241 🌐 theclachaninn.co.uk

2 changing beers (sourced regionally; often Ayr, Fallen, Fyne Ales) Ⓗ

The Clachan has a reputation for excellent food, cosy, well-equipped bedrooms and a welcoming atmosphere. The menu is varied with excellent daily specials, and the kitchen makes use of local produce including organic lamb and venison. The pub has an attractive traditional main bar, a relaxing lounge bar and a separate restaurant – both bars have wonderfully warming open log fires in winter. A handy stop for walkers on the Southern Upland Way. Winter opening hours may vary, particularly on Mondays. Local CAMRA Pub of the Year 2018 and 2019.
Q❀🛏◑♿Å♣●P🚌(520,521) 🐾 ᯤ

Stranraer

Grapes

4-6 Bridge Street, DG9 7HY

☎ (01776) 703386

2 changing beers (often Ayr, Portpatrick) Ⓗ

Popular historic public bar, with an impressive mirror and gantry, which has altered little in over 50 years. It has a refurbished snug bar downstairs, an upstairs Art Deco lounge/function room, and a courtyard area with seating. Local musicians play in the public bar most Friday evenings, and touring American-style bands often perform upstairs. There is a strong commitment to real ales, sourced both locally and from all over the UK. Mini beer festivals are held twice yearly. ❀⇌♣🚌🐾 ᯤ

The ale diet

Boniface: Sir, I have now in my cellar ten tun of the best ale in Staffordshire; 'tis smooth as oil, sweet as milk, clear as amber, and strong as brandy; and will be just 14 years old the fifth day of next March, old style.
Aimwell: You're very exact, I find, in the age of your ale.
Boniface: As punctual, sir, as I am in the age of my children. I'll show you such ale: I have lived in Lichfield, man and boy, about eight-and-fifty years, and, I believe, have not consumed eight-and-fifty ounces of meat.
Aimwell: At a meal, you mean, if one may guess your sense by your bulk.
Boniface: Not in my life, sir, I have fed purely upon ale; I have eat my ale, drank my ale, and I always sleep upon ale.
George Farquhar, The Beaux-Stratagem, 1701

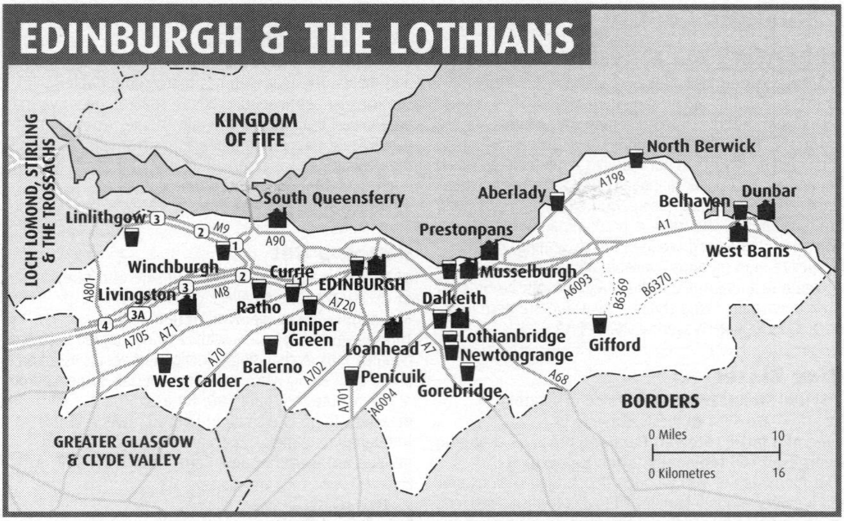

Authority areas covered: City of Edinburgh UA, East Lothian UA, Midlothian UA, West Lothian UA

Aberlady

Ducks Inn

Main Street, EH32 0RE

☎ (01875) 870682 🌐 ducks.co.uk

Sharp's Doom Bar; 1 changing beer (sourced nationally) Ⓗ

A well-appointed village hotel with a comfortable, compact and intimate bar, and numerous overspill areas. It is decorated with sporting and brewing memorabilia. Bar games include the unique Ducks Challenge putting contest. Meals are served all day and families are welcome until 8pm, with a children's menu and games provided. Three real ales are available in summer. Winner of CAMRA Lothian Real Ale Quality Award in 2019. The bar may close earlier if quiet. Likely not to be open until 4pm Monday-Thursday in winter.

Q ♿ ♣ P 🚌 🐾 📶

Balerno

Grey Horse

20 Main Street, EH14 7EH (off A70 in pedestrian area)

☎ (0131) 449 2888 🌐 greyhorsebalerno.com

4 changing beers (sourced regionally; often Alechemy, Orkney, Stewart) Ⓗ

Traditional stone-built village pub dating from the 18th century. The cosy public bar retains original features including wood panelling and a fine Bernard's mirror. A varied food menu is offered in the pleasant lounge and restaurant, with lighter options at lunchtime, a children's menu and Chinese specials (no food Mon). A folk session takes place one Tuesday evening a month. Dogs are allowed in the bar, with biscuits and water provided.

Q ♿ 🚌 🐾

Belhaven

Brig & Barrel

8 High Street, EH42 1NP

☎ (01368) 866847 🌐 thebrigandbarrel.com

2 changing beers (sourced nationally) Ⓗ

Close to Belhaven Brewery, the former Masons Arms is a bright, comfortable bar overlooking a superb beer garden with views to the Lammermuir Hills. Reopened and refurbished in 2019, it features a small horseshoe bar finished with reclaimed wood and barrels, a smart wooden floor and a real fire in winter. Meals are served all day (booking advisable at busy times). A good base for a walk round Belhaven Bay and Seafield Pond.

🚌 🐾 📶

Currie

Riccarton Inn

198 Lanark Road West, EH14 5NX

☎ (0131) 449 2230 🌐 riccartoninn.co.uk

4 changing beers (sourced nationally; often Inveralmond, Stewart, Timothy Taylor) Ⓗ

Originally a coaching inn, the pub has a long central bar with half-timbered walls and contemporary exposed stonework. The comfortable interior has attractive seating areas including booths next to the bar and a separate restaurant space. Meals are served all day including a children's menu. The decking at the front has southerly views to the Pentland Hills and the inn is handy for the Water of Leith Walkway. Likely to open at 11am on Sunday, although alcoholic drinks are only served from 12.30pm. P 🚌 (44,45) 🐾 📶

Dalkeith

Blacksmith's Forge ✔

5 Newmills Road, EH22 1DU

☎ (0131) 561 5100

Caledonian Deuchars IPA; Greene King Abbot; 5 changing beers (sourced regionally; often Broughton, Stewart, Strathaven) Ⓗ

Large open-plan multi-level Wetherspoon pub divided into several differently styled areas, with a mix of tables and chairs, high tables and booths with bench seating. Changing real ales are often from Scottish breweries. Food is served all day and children are welcome until 10pm (8pm Fri and Sat) if dining – menu and colouring books provided. Likely to open at 8am but alcoholic drinks are served from 11am (12.30pm Sun).

Q ♿ 🚌 📶

Edinburgh: Central

Abbotsford Bar & Restaurant ★
3-5 Rose Street, EH2 2PR
☎ (0131) 225 5276 theabbotsford.com
6 changing beers (sourced regionally; often Cromarty, Fyne Ales, Swannay) [H]/[A]
This traditional Scottish bar features a magnificent island bar and gantry in dark mahogany that have been fixtures since 1902. The ornate plasterwork and corniced ceiling are outstanding. The room is predominantly furnished with large tables and wooden bench seating. An extensive food menu is available all day in the bar. The separate restaurant is upstairs – real ale can be ordered from downstairs – and children over five are permitted here. Q (Waverley)

Blue Blazer
2 Spittal Street, EH3 9DX (SW side of centre)
☎ (0131) 229 5030 theblueblazer.co.uk
Fyne Ales Jarl [H]**; Stewart Pentland IPA** [A]**; 5 changing beers (sourced regionally; often Kelburn)** [H]
Two-roomed pub with wooden floors, high ceilings and old brewery window panels giving an old-fashioned feel, complemented by candles in the evening. Named after a local school uniform, it features a tiled blue blazer inlaid on the floor. The pub specialises in real ales from smaller Scottish breweries. The cider varies and is not always real. Snacks are available all day. Close to theatres and cinemas, the pub stays open later in August and December. Children are not admitted.

Bow Bar
80 West Bow, EH1 2HH (Old Town, off Grassmarket)
☎ (0131) 226 7667 thebowbar.co.uk
Fallen Odyssey; Loch Lomond Silkie Stout; Stewart 80/-; Tempest Armadillo; 4 changing beers (sourced nationally; often Cromarty, Fallen, Swannay) [A]
A re-creation of a classic Scottish one-roomed ale house, dedicated to traditional Scottish air pressure dispense and upright drinking. The real ales can be from anywhere in the UK. The walls are festooned with original brewery mirrors and the superb gantry does justice to an award-winning selection of almost 450 single malt whiskies and international bottled beers. Beer festivals are held in January and July along with frequent tap takeovers. Gourmet pies are available. Children are not admitted.
Q (Waverley)

Guildford Arms
1 West Register Street, EH2 2AA (off E end of Princes St)
☎ (0131) 556 4312 guildfordarms.com
Fyne Ales Jarl; Orkney Dark Island; Stewart Pentland IPA; Swannay Orkney IPA; 5 changing beers (sourced nationally; often Black Sheep, Loch Lomond, Timothy Taylor) [H]
A large establishment built in the golden age of Victorian pub design. The high ceiling, cornices, friezes, window arches and screens are spectacular. There is a large standing area around the canopied bar plus extensive seating areas. The diverse range of real ales includes many from Scottish micros. Simple bar snacks are available all day. Children over five are only allowed in the noteworthy upstairs gallery restaurant.
(Waverley)

Halfway House
24 Fleshmarket Close, EH1 1BX (up steps opp Waverley Station's Market St entrance)
☎ (0131) 225 7101
House beer (by Stewart); 4 changing beers (sourced nationally; often Broughton, Stewart, Strathbraan) [H]
Cosy, characterful bar hidden halfway down an Old Town close, decorated with railway memorabilia. The small, often busy, bar area at the front has window seats, stools and tables. The rear area has more comfortable semicircular booth seating where children over five may be allowed until 8pm if the pub is quiet. There are usually four interesting real ales from smaller Scottish breweries. Meals are served all day. The bar may stay open until 1am during busy times of year.
(Waverley)

Hanging Bat
133 Lothian Road, EH3 9AB (SW side of centre)
☎ (0131) 229 0759 thehangingbat.com
6 changing beers (sourced nationally) [H]
Three-level craft beer bar with cask ales served from bat-handled taps. A changing selection of beers is listed on a blackboard along with occasional specials dispensed on gravity – note that prices are for a two-thirds-pint measure. There is a small in-house brewery, visible through glass panels. Meals are served all day and families are welcome until 8pm.

Jolly Judge
7 James Court, 493 Lawnmarket, EH1 2PB (Old Town)
☎ (0131) 225 2669 jollyjudge.co.uk
3 changing beers (sourced nationally; often Cromarty, Tempest) [H]
Comfortable bar with an attractive painted ceiling just off the Royal Mile down an Old Town close. There are steps down to the entrance, as was common in the past. This is a welcome spot for refreshment after visiting the castle. The real ales are usually from smaller breweries UK-wide. A varying selection of four real ciders is also available. Dogs are permitted after 3pm, but no children inside. CAMRA Scottish Cider Pub of the Year 2019.
Q (Waverley)

Monty's
185 Morrison Street, EH3 8DZ (W edge of centre)
☎ (0131) 629 1104 montys.bar
Swannay Orkney IPA; 6 changing beers (sourced nationally; often Mallinsons, Oakham, Two by Two) [H]
Busy street-corner bar favoured by a younger clientele and keen to promote real ale. Cask ale is featured on the bar counter with keg beer on the back wall. The wood-panelled interior has large windows and a varied range of comfortable seating. There is also a cosy upstairs area with more seating. Bar snacks including cheese, charcuterie and toasties are served all day. Children are not allowed. Closing time may be later for national rugby matches. (Haymarket)

REAL ALE BREWERIES
Alechemy Livingston
Barney's Edinburgh
Belhaven Dunbar
Bellfield Edinburgh
Black Metal Loanhead
Caledonian Edinburgh
Campervan Edinburgh
Cross Borders Dalkeith
Eyeball Dunbar
Faking Bad Prestonpans
Ferry South Queensferry
Hanging Bat Edinburgh
Hurly Burly Musselburgh
Pilot Edinburgh
Stewart Loanhead
Top Out Loanhead
Winton West Barns (NEW)

Oxford Bar ★

8 Young Street, EH2 4JB (New Town, off Charlotte Sq)
☎ (0131) 539 7119
Caledonian Deuchars IPA; 3 changing beers (sourced regionally; often Belhaven, Fyne Ales, Inveralmond) Ⓗ
A basic, vibrant drinking shop that is little changed since the late 19th century. The bar counter nearly fills the small front room but the side room is more spacious and enhanced by a real fire and artworks for sale. The pub is renowned as a favourite of Rebus and his creator Ian Rankin, and a haunt of many other famous and infamous characters over the years. Children are not admitted. An autovac is only used for Deuchars IPA. Q

Teuchters

26 William Street, EH3 7NH (W edge of centre)
☎ (0131) 225 2973 🌐 teuchtersbar.co.uk
Fyne Ales Jarl; Stewart Pentland IPA; Swannay Dark Munro; Timothy Taylor Landlord; 1 changing beer (sourced regionally; often Fyne Ales, Inveralmond) Ⓗ
A cosy but deceptively roomy bar with a rustic feel, wooden beams and original stone walls. Seating includes chunky sofas and chairs around wooden tables. Small placename plates from Teuchterland create a frieze along the walls. Real ales are usually from Scottish micros. The gantry has an impressive range of single malt whiskies and an explanation of the pub's name. Bar snacks are offered and the restaurant serves fresh local produce. Likely to open 10.30am but alcoholic drinks are served from 11am. (Haymarket)

Thomson's Bar

182-184 Morrison Street, EH3 8EB
☎ (0131) 228 5700 🌐 thomsonsbaredinburgh.co.uk
Caledonian Deuchars IPA; Fyne Ales Jarl Ⓗ**; 4 changing beers (sourced nationally; often Oakham, Swannay, Tryst)** Ⓗ/Ⓐ
Superb single-roomed bar modelled on the style of Glasgow architect Alexander 'Greek' Thomson. The hand-made gantry and panelling are inlaid with scenes from Greek mythology. The walls are decorated with rare mirrors, adverts and point of sale material from long-forgotten breweries. A member of the Oakham Ales Oakademy, up to six often hoppy real ales are served from a variety of breweries. Superb pies are available on weekdays. Children are not admitted.
Q (Haymarket)

Edinburgh: East

Regent ✔

2 Montrose Terrace, EH7 5DL
☎ (0131) 661 8198
Caledonian Deuchars IPA; 2 changing beers (sourced nationally; often Born, Harviestoun, Stewart) Ⓗ
Large brightly decorated tenement bar with two rooms, popular with LGBT real ale drinkers. The comfortable seating includes banquettes, leather sofas and armchairs. Real ales are served without sparklers on request. The cider is Westons Old Rosie. Bar snacks and simple meals, including good vegetarian and vegan options, are available all day. A novel slant on pub games is the gymnastic pommel horse. Children over five are permitted until 8pm.

Edinburgh: North

Dreadnought 🏆

72 North Fort Street, Leith, EH6 4HL
☎ 07876 351535 🌐 dreadnoughtleith.com
4 changing beers (sourced nationally; often Brass Castle, Cromarty, Dark Revolution) Ⓗ
A welcoming one-roomed pub with big picture windows, a high ceiling with plaster cornicing, an attractive old-fashioned bar gantry and sports TV screens. A large photograph of HMS Dreadnought hangs on the wall along with other nautical items. The Brass Castle beers are all vegan. No food is prepared on-site, but pizza and burgers can be ordered from local outlets. A wheelchair ramp is available but there are no accessible toilets. Children are not admitted. Local CAMRA Edinburgh Pub of the Year 2020. Likely to be closed Monday-Thursday afternoons.

Kay's Bar

39 Jamaica Street West, EH3 6HF (New Town, off India St)
☎ (0131) 225 1858 🌐 kaysbar.co.uk
Caledonian Deuchars IPA; Fyne Ales Jarl; Theakston Best Bitter; Timothy Taylor Landlord; 3 changing beers (sourced nationally; often Cross Borders, Fallen, Stewart) Ⓗ
A cosy and convivial pub that retains many features from its days as a Victorian wine merchant and decorated with whisky barrels. Considering its size, it offers an impressive range of real ales. It also specialises in malt whisky, with a large selection behind the bar. If the front bar is busy, try the small room at the back. Lunches are mainly traditional Scottish fare. Children are not admitted. Dogs welcome outside food service hours.
Q

Malt & Hops

45 The Shore, Leith, EH6 6QU
☎ (0131) 555 0083
Hadrian Border Tyneside Blonde; 7 changing beers (sourced nationally; often Fyne Ales, Great Heck, Swannay) Ⓗ
Single-roomed, old-fashioned bar by the Water of Leith dating from 1747. It has a real fire and the walls are bedecked with mirrors, prints and beer-related artefacts. A large selection of pumpclips, many from long-lost breweries and distilleries, hangs from the ceiling along with hop bines renewed every harvest. The wide variety of real ales has an emphasis towards smaller breweries – beers are listed on the mirror behind the bar. Children are permitted until 6pm.

Old Chain Pier

32 Trinity Crescent, EH5 3ED
☎ (0131) 552 4960 🌐 oldchainpier.com
4 changing beers (sourced nationally) Ⓗ
The only Edinburgh pub directly on the seafront – the building was once the booking office of a pier destroyed by a storm in 1898. Panoramic windows and outdoor seats give superb views across the Firth of Forth. Drinkers should note that while there are a few seats at the bar, most of the pub is given over to dining. Food is served all day, with an emphasis on traditional Scottish ingredients. A children's menu is available.

Stockbridge Tap

2-4 Raeburn Place, Stockbridge, EH4 1HN
☎ (0131) 343 3000
Swannay Island Hopping; 5 changing beers (sourced nationally; often Alechemy, Cromarty, Cross Borders) Ⓗ
A multi CAMRA award-winning specialist real ale house, offering unusual and interesting ales from all over the UK and holding occasional beer festivals. The L-shaped room, with a bright bar area, boasts mirrors from lost breweries including Murray's and Campbell's. There is plenty of seating and also ample space for drinkers. Cold

SCOTLAND

snacks are served outside of main food times. A handy stop for those walking the Water of Leith path. Children are not admitted.

Teuchters Landing

1C Dock Place, Leith, EH6 6LU

(0131) 554 7427 aroomin.co.uk/teuchters-landing-bar-edinburgh

Fyne Ales Jarl; Inveralmond Ossian; Timothy Taylor Landlord; 2 changing beers (sourced regionally; often Fallen, Stewart, Tryst) H

Once the waiting room for the Leith to Aberdeen ferry, the attractive front bar has a wood-panelled ceiling edged with tiles featuring Scottish placenames from Teuchterland. There are two smaller rooms and a large conservatory opening out on to a pontoon floating on the Water of Leith. The varied food menu, available all day, features meals served in mugs. An excellent selection of malt whiskies is available. Children are allowed in the back rooms. Likely to open at 10.30am but alcoholic drinks are served from 11am.

Windsor

45 Elm Row, EH7 4AH (¾ mile N of centre)

(0131) 556 4558 windsoredinburgh.co.uk

Caledonian Deuchars IPA; 3 changing beers (sourced nationally; often Born) H

This late-Victorian locals' bar retains a traditional look and fine ceiling cornices but is now brighter and more open plan. Comfortable green leather armchairs and bench seating complement the extensive wood panelling; a raised area at the back features a mirror and window with the pub logo. The three changing real ales come from a range of Scottish and north-east English breweries. Simple bar snacks are served. Children are not admitted.

Edinburgh: South

Bennets Bar ★

8 Leven Street, EH3 9LG (just over ¾ mile SW of centre)

(0131) 229 5143 bennetsbaredinburgh.co.uk

6 changing beers (sourced regionally; often Stewart) H/P

One of the city's top pub interiors in a Grade B listed building, this is quintessential late-Victorian Edinburgh pub architecture – from the Jeffrey's Brewery etched door panels and window screens to the snug and a wonderful Bernard's mirror. The magnificent gantry houses a top-class range of malts and spirit barrels. A range of food is available all day in the bar and adjoining restaurant. Children are permitted until 8pm. Q

Cask & Barrel (Southside)

24-26 West Preston Street, EH8 9PZ

(0131) 667 0856 caskandbarrelsouthside.co.uk

Stewart Jack Back; Swannay Orkney Best; Tryst Drovers 80/-; 5 changing beers (sourced nationally; often Cross Borders, Fyne Ales, Loch Lomond) H

A modern recreation of a Scottish city or tenement bar. The single room, with windows front and back, is divided by a horseshoe bar with a dark-wood gantry adorned with decorative wooden casks. The walls support a fine range of old photos, advertisements and historic brewery and distillery mirrors. Sport is screened on multiple TVs with the sound off. This is a good place to try real ales from interesting breweries UK-wide. Children are not admitted. Winner of the CAMRA Edinburgh and SE Scotland Real Ale Quality Award in 2019.

Cloisters Bar

26 Brougham Street, EH3 9JH (just over ¾ mile SW of centre)

(0131) 221 9997 cloistersbar.com

Stewart Pentland IPA, Holy Grale; 8 changing beers (sourced nationally; often Stewart, Swannay, Thornbridge) H

Established in 1995 in the former All Saints Parsonage, many traditional features have been maintained in this warm and friendly bar. The real ales are generally from interesting breweries UK-wide. Frequent tap takeovers and Meet the Brewer events are held. The wide range of single malt whiskies, gins and rums does justice to the outstanding gantry. Freshly prepared meals are served lunchtime and evenings (no food Mon). Under-16s are not admitted. Q

Dagda Bar

93-95 Buccleuch Street, EH8 9NG (¾ mile S of centre)

(0131) 667 9773

Oakham Citra; 3 changing beers (sourced regionally; often Cromarty, Ferry) H

Small ground-floor bar in an 18th-century tenement terrace, in the heart of a university area. A stone-flagged floor surrounds the large rectangular counter which takes up at least a third of the room. The colourful, mirrored gantry blends with the cornice, the joins blurred by an extensive collection of pumpclips. The bar is often busy, especially on Tuesday evening when a quiz is held. Children are not admitted.

Edinburgh: West

Athletic Arms (Diggers) ✔

1-3 Angle Park Terrace, EH11 2JX (just over ¾ mile SW of centre)

(0131) 337 3822 athleticarms.com

Caledonian Deuchars IPA; house beer (by Stewart) A; **4 changing beers (sourced nationally; often Alechemy, Caledonian)** H

Dating from 1897, this legendary Edinburgh pub gained the name Diggers due to its location between two graveyards. Banquette seating lines the walls, and the wooden floor features a compass drawing. Children over five are allowed in the two smaller back rooms if eating. There is more seating here, and the larger room has a dartboard. The pub gets busy when Hearts are playing at home. Outstanding pies are available. Autovacs are only used with the tall founts.

Roseburn Bar ✔

1 Roseburn Terrace, EH12 5NG (1½ miles W of centre)

(0131) 337 1067 roseburnbar.co.uk

Fyne Ales Jarl; Stewart Pentland IPA; 2 changing beers (sourced nationally; often Cromarty, Tryst) H

A traditional pub that is popular with locals, and close to Murrayfield for rugby and Tynecastle for football. It boasts high ceilings and a largely wooden interior, with interesting mirrors and period photos on the walls. There are numerous comfortable booths along the walls and two separate lounge areas. Three TVs show sporting events, though the volume is typically kept low. Live music plays on Friday and Saturday evenings. Children are not admitted.

Gifford

Tweeddale Arms Hotel

High Street, EH41 4QU

(01620) 810240 tweeddalearmshotel.com

Hop Back Summer Lightning; 1 changing beer (sourced nationally; often Broughton, Stewart) H

Clad in traditional black and white and sitting opposite the village green, this hotel can be identified by its coat of arms sign suspended on wooden posts. The cosy locals' bar, with wood-burning stove, is where you will find the handpumps. The larger lounge bar is set up for dining, and there is also an elegant lounge area across the corridor. Food is served, with a children's menu available. (123)

Gorebridge

Stobsmill Inn (Bruntons)

25 Powdermill Brae, EH23 4HX (just over ¼ mile S of centre)
☎ (01875) 820202
1 changing beer (often Born, Cross Borders, Stewart) H

This small pub, built in 1866, is now the only pub in Gorebridge. The single-room bar has a long L-shaped counter with a row of bar stools, and an area with tables and chairs, benches, and a large clock. The décor and skylight help to create a bright and welcoming interior. Downstairs is an attractive dining area where meals are served all day. Entry is restricted to over-21s, unless dining. It is likely to be closed on Tuesdays.
P (29,48)

Juniper Green

Railway Inn

542 Lanark Road, EH14 5EL
☎ (0131) 458 5395 therailwayinnjg.com
Caledonian Deuchars IPA; Timothy Taylor Landlord; 2 changing beers (sourced nationally; often Alechemy, Hadrian Border, Stewart) H

Well-appointed single-room lounge bar in a late-1800s building, with a strong community spirit. The decor is clean and attractive throughout, with a mahogany bar counter and more modern gantry to match. Railway-themed pictures and memorabilia provide interest. The secluded patio and garden are popular in summer. A varied food menu includes steak pies, chicken, fish and lighter options. Children over five are permitted until 8pm. There is a quiz on Mondays at 8pm. Q

Linlithgow

Four Marys ✔

65-67 High Street, EH49 7ED
☎ (01506) 842171 fourmarys-linlithgow.co.uk
Belhaven St Andrew's Ale; Greene King IPA; 6 changing beers (sourced nationally; often Cromarty, Fyne Ales, Redcastle) H

Close to Linlithgow Palace, birthplace of Mary Queen of Scots, the building dates back to around 1500 and is named after Mary's four ladies-in-waiting. Initially a dwelling house, the building has had several changes of use over the centuries – it was once a chemist's run by the Waldie family whose most famous member, David, helped establish the anaesthetic properties of chloroform in 1847. The pub serves good-quality food and at least six real ales from breweries across Scotland and the UK. A frequent local CAMRA Pub of the Year. Q

Platform 3 ✔

1A High Street, EH49 7AB
☎ (01506) 847405 platform3.co.uk
Stewart Pentland IPA; 2 changing beers (sourced regionally; often Cairngorm, Harviestoun, Tryst) H

Small, friendly hostelry on the railway station approach, originally the public bar of the hotel next door and renovated in 1998 as a pub in its own right. Look out for the goods train that journeys from the station above the bar, with ducks waiting for a train that never comes. Two Scottish beers are served in addition to the regular ale. Dogs are welcomed with biscuits. A live departures board keeps travellers informed. Alcoholic drinks are served from 11am.

> How easy can the barley-bree
> Cement the quarrel.
> It's aye the cheapest lawyer's fee
> To taste the barrel.
> **Robert Burns**

Lothianbridge

Sun Inn

EH22 4TR (A7, nr Newtongrange)
☎ (0131) 663 2456 thesuninnedinburgh.co.uk
2 changing beers (sourced regionally; often Cross Borders, Ferry, Stewart) H

Award-winning gastro-pub overlooked by the impressive 23-span Waverley Line viaduct. At the front is the dining area – a mix of exposed stone, papered walls, wooden floors and carpets; to the rear is a more modern bar area for drinkers, and a coffee shop with various food stalls. Meals are served lunchtimes and evenings, all day on Sunday, and it does breakfast during the week. The bar may close earlier if quiet. It is likely to open at 8am but alcoholic drinks are available from 11am.
P (29,339)

Musselburgh

Levenhall Arms

10 Ravensheugh Road, EH21 7PP (1 mile E of centre)
☎ (0131) 665 3220
Inveralmond Ossian A**; 1 changing beer (sourced regionally)** H/A

A three-roomed hostelry dating from 1830 and close to the racecourse. Expect to find some interesting real ales from smaller, mainly Scottish, breweries. The lively, cheerfully decorated public bar is half timber-panelled and carpeted. Dominoes is popular here and there is a TV for sporting events. A smaller area leads off, with a dartboard and pictures of old local industries. The pleasant lounge, where families are welcome until 8pm, has comfortable seating. Q P

Volunteer Arms (Staggs)

81 North High Street, EH21 6JE (behind the Brunton)
☎ (0131) 665 9654 staggsbar.com
Loch Lomond Silkie Stout; Oakham JHB, Bishops Farewell; 4 changing beers (sourced nationally; often Fyne Ales, Loch Lomond) H

Superb pub run by the same family since 1858. Its bar and snug are traditional, with wooden floors, wood panelling, mirrors from defunct local breweries, and an attractive gantry topped with old casks. The more modern lounge opens at the weekend. Real ales change regularly and are mostly pale and hoppy. Black Rat real cider is also served. Local CAMRA Pub of the Year 2020, and winner of many previous awards.
P

Newtongrange

Dean Tavern

80 Main Street, EH22 4NA
☎ (0131) 663 2419 deantavern.co.uk
1 changing beer (sourced regionally; often Born, Cross Borders, Stewart) H

Superb pub run by trustees on Gothenburg principles, with profits returned to the local community. The spacious bar was designed to help miners recover from their day in darkness, with roof lights in a high ceiling supported by arched iron beams. There is also the Lamp Room restaurant and a function room with a large mural depicting the town's mining past. Meals are available all day; children are permitted until 8pm if dining. Likely to open at 10am but alcoholic drinks are served from 11am (midday Sun).

North Berwick

Auld Hoose

19 Forth Street, EH39 4HX
(01620) 892692 auldhoosenorthberwick.co.uk
2 changing beers (sourced nationally; often Greene King, Theakston, Timothy Taylor)
Interesting high-ceilinged and friendly traditional Scottish drinking shop with bare floorboards around a mahogany bar, carpeted areas and a welcoming atmosphere enhanced by a real fire in winter. The gantry has three carved pillars and supports six old numbered whisky casks. The through lounge has varied seating, a pool table and pictures of sporting heroes. Built in 1896 and said to be the oldest pub in town, it is certainly the closest to the sea, and supports the RNLI.

Nether Abbey Hotel

20 Dirleton Avenue, EH39 4BQ (just over ¾ mile W of centre)
(01620) 892802 netherabbey.co.uk
4 changing beers (sourced nationally; often Broughton, Greene King, Williams Bros)
Family-run hotel in a stone-built villa with a bright, contemporary, open-plan interior. The Fly Half Bar is in a split-level glass extension; large folding doors open out onto the patio. Real ales can be served without sparklers on request. The award-winning restaurant is famed for its freshly cooked and locally sourced food, available seven days per week and served all day Friday to Sunday. Children are welcome until 8pm (7pm in the bar). Likely to open at 9am but alcoholic drinks are served from 11am.

Penicuik

Navaar House Hotel

23 Bog Road, EH26 9BY (¼ mile W of centre)
(01968) 672683 navaarhouse.co.uk
Stewart Jack Back; 1 changing beer (sourced regionally; often Fyne Ales)
A lively pub with a strong community spirit. The large bar is open plan with a log/coal stove, TV screens and a pool table. A pleasantly decorated restaurant serves locally sourced food lunchtimes, evenings, and all day on Saturday and Sunday. Children (menu provided) are allowed in the restaurant only. There is a beer garden outside for warmer days. The bar opens at 3pm Monday to Friday, but real ale is served in the restaurant before then.

Ratho

Bridge Inn

27 Baird Road, EH28 8RA (by Union Canal, bridge 15)
(0131) 333 1320 bridgeinn.com
3 changing beers (sourced nationally)
Old canalside inn with a restaurant and outdoor dining area overlooking the Union Canal. Dating from 1750, the older part contains a separate bar for drinkers, and it has accommodation upstairs. A newer extension has views over the canal. Most real ales are from smaller Scottish breweries. Families with children are welcome until 8pm. The inn was a focal point during the canal restoration campaign. It is likely to open at 9am but alcoholic drinks are served from 11am (11.30am Sun). (20)

West Calder

Railway Inn ★

43 Main Street, EH55 8DL
(01506) 871691
2 changing beers (sourced nationally; often Black Sheep, Inveralmond, Timothy Taylor)
A listed building, circa 1895, with a prominent octagonal turret. The main bar has a large U-shaped timber counter with an ornamental central tiered wooden gantry. The coffered ceilings have elaborate cornicing and plastering and there are ornate coloured glass window panels. The jug bar has a coloured glass and ornamental finialled crown. The gents has an interesting marble slab urinal. Plenty of TVs, with sound kept low, ensure you do not miss any sports action.

Winchburgh

Tally Ho

7 Main Street, EH52 6TP
(01506) 891899 tallyhobar.co.uk
Caledonian Deuchars IPA; 1 changing beer (sourced nationally; often Marston's, Sharp's, Wychwood)
Recently renovated, this village-centre pub and restaurant is large and modern with a few rustic touches. The publican is keen to offer a good range of real ale. The interior is open plan but has various seating areas including a large conservatory. Families are welcome and there is an extensive beer garden with an excellent children's playground. The pub hosts regular live entertainment and community events including quiz and poker nights. Dogs are especially welcome, with treats and water.

Return trays

Also known as an Autovac or beer economiser, a return tray is a device that collects beer spilled in the pouring process, recycles it by mixing it with fresh beer, and returns it to the glass. It can be identified by a stainless steel drip tray below the nozzle on a handpump, with a pipe connected from the bottom of the tray to the draw line of the cask. They are commonly found in use in Yorkshire and parts of south-east Scotland and have been seen in north-east Scotland and north-west England.

A symbol will appear next to entries in the Guide where a return tray is in use on some or all of the beers (see inside cover key).

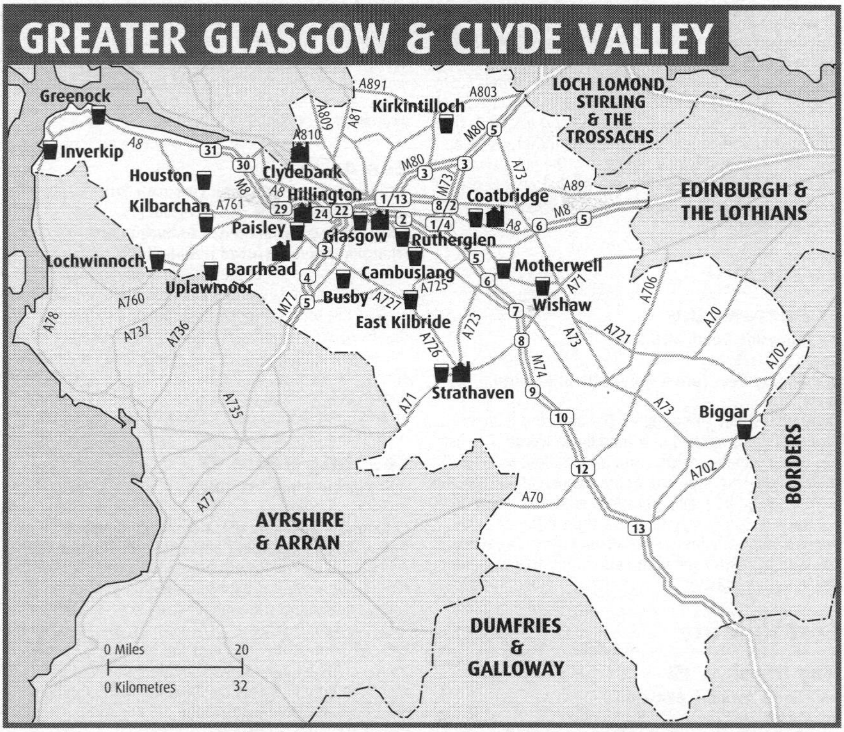

GREATER GLASGOW & CLYDE VALLEY

Authority areas covered: City of Glasgow UA, Dunbartonshire UAs, Inverclyde UA, Lanarkshire UAs, Renfrewshire UAs

Biggar

Crown Inn 🅛 ✓
109-111 High Street, ML12 6DL
☎ (01899) 220116 ⊕ thecrownbiggar.co.uk
House beer (by Broughton); 5 changing beers
(sourced nationally; often Broughton, Strathaven) ℍ
A pleasant and friendly inn in the centre of this market
town, the Crown has hundreds of years of tradition
behind it, officially dating from the mid-17th century. The
large bar area is directly accessed from the street and
there is a small, quiet room, conservatory and beer
garden to the rear. Six handpumps offer beers from a
range of breweries, including local brews from
Strathaven and Broughton. Beer festivals are held in May
and October, the latter coinciding with the Biggar
Festival. Folk music sessions are hosted on the second
Friday of the month. ♿❀◐🚆(91,191)♣🐾🛜

Elphinstone Hotel ✓
145 High Street, ML12 6DL
☎ (01899) 220044 ⊕ elphinstonehotel.co.uk
2 changing beers (sourced regionally; often
Broughton, Fyne Ales) ℍ
An old coaching inn dating from the 18th century with a
bright, modern public bar, a lounge bar, guest rooms and
a large outdoor drinking area. There are four handpumps
but in winter only two are in use to ensure that quality is
maintained. The beers come in rotation from Fyne Ales,
Broughton, Kelburn, Redcastle, Orkney and Strathaven.
The bar has a pool table and dartboard and features live
music on a Saturday. ♿❀🛏️◐🚆(91,191)♣🐾🛜

Busby

White Cart ✓
61 East Kilbride Road, G76 8HX
☎ (0141) 644 2711
Greene King IPA; 2 changing beers (sourced
regionally; often Belhaven, Kelburn, Williams Bros) ℍ
A lovely and lively Chef & Brewer pub, located in the
Busby conservation village, with a spacious bar and
restaurant area. The emphasis here is on food service,
but there are five handpumps serving three guest beers
plus Greene King IPA. A large patio area at the front is
popular in the summer and there is an area for families
inside. An added bonus is the roaring fire in winter.
♿❀◐🪑🅿️🚆🐾🛜

Cambuslang

John Fairweather ✓
50-60 Main Street, G72 7EP

REAL ALE BREWERIES
Drygate 🍺 Glasgow
Glasgow Beer Works Glasgow
Jaw Hillington
Kelburn Barrhead
Late Night Hype Clydebank
Ride Glasgow
Shilling 🍺 Glasgow
Simple Things Fermentations Glasgow (NEW)
Strathaven Strathaven
Veterans Coatbridge (NEW)
WEST 🍺 Glasgow

☎ (0141) 646 2411
Caledonian Deuchars IPA; Greene King Abbot; Sharp's Doom Bar; 3 changing beers (sourced nationally) [H]
Impressive Wetherspoon conversion of the former Savoy cinema and named after the man who designed it. Many original features have been retained and restored. The former ticket office leads to the bar and there is an area upstairs where the screen used to be. The pub is watched over by old moviegoers sitting in the balcony. Beers are available from both local and national breweries.
🐴❀◑♿⇌🍎🚌📶

Coatbridge

St Andrews Bar
37 Sunnyside Road, ML5 3DG
☎ (01236) 423773
1 changing beer (often Harviestoun, Kelburn, Tryst) [H]
Traditional street-corner public bar and cosy lounge where you are assured of a friendly welcome. The bar has a fine wooden gantry with an excellent selection of malt whiskies to complement the single real ale. The pub is well served by public transport, with both Coatbridge Central and Sunnyside stations a short distance away. Popular on match days when Albion Rovers are at home, it is also handy for the Summerlee Industrial Museum.
⇌(Sunnyside) 🚌🐾

East Kilbride

Hay Stook L ✔
26 Princes Avenue, G74 1JU
☎ (01355) 244323
Caledonian Deuchars IPA; Greene King Abbot; Sharp's Doom Bar; 5 changing beers (sourced nationally; often Broughton, Strathaven) [H]
This Wetherspoon pub is situated at the Brouster Gate entrance within the Princes Mall shopping centre, making it handy for shoppers and for the nearby cinema complex. Bare walls and a wooden ceiling give it a rustic air. The staircase up to the toilets divides the room, with the bar area to the right and family area to the left. There is a small beer garden beside the mall entrance. Up to six guest ales come from local and national breweries. Alcoholic drinks are available after 11am.
🐴❀◑♿⇌🍎🚌📶

Glasgow

Ben Nevis
1147 Argyle Street, Finnieston, G3 8TB
☎ (0141) 576 5204
2 changing beers (sourced nationally) [H]
Corner tenement pub established around 1880 but closed for a long time before it reopened in 1999. Now a small but popular bar with a highland theme, it has a large selection of malt whiskies, some of which appear to be precariously perched on sloping shelves. There is also a range of unusual canned and bottled beers. Folk music features on Wednesday, Thursday and Sunday evenings.
⇌(Exhibition Centre) 🚌(2,3) 🐾📶

Blackfriars L
36 Bell Street, Merchant City, G1 1LG
☎ (0141) 552 5924 🌐 blackfriarsglasgow.com
5 changing beers (sourced nationally; often Cromarty, Kelburn, Tryst) [H]
A vibrant bar in the Merchant City, close to the City Halls and Old Fruitmarket, Blackfriars has been in the Guide continuously for over 20 years. Five handpumps serve beers from all over Britain, usually including one from Kelburn and guests often from Tryst, Cromarty and Swannay. A fine selection of bottled beers is sourced from the US and Europe. Food is available. Aside from live music nights on Sunday and Tuesday, background music is unobtrusive and there is no TV.
◑♿⇌(High St) 🚊🚌🐾📶

Bon Accord L
153 North Street, Charing Cross, G3 7DA
☎ (0141) 248 4427 🌐 bonaccordpub.com
Caledonian Deuchars IPA, Edinburgh Castle 80/-; 8 changing beers (sourced nationally) [H]
One of the pioneers of the real ale scene in Glasgow, the Bon serves over 800 different beers each year. A dining area at the rear also hosts quiz, poker and live music nights. As well as ensuring there is a good choice of ale, the owner is passionate about malt whisky – the pub stocks 400 varieties on the bar and there is a whisky club and an online shop. Good-value food is served.
🐴❀◑♿⇌(Charing Cross) 🚊🍎🚌📶

Counting House ✔
2 St Vincent Place, G1 2DH
☎ (0141) 225 0160
Caledonian Deuchars IPA; Greene King Abbot; Sharp's Doom Bar; 12 changing beers (sourced nationally) [H]
A busy pub on George Square with a good view of the City Chambers. It has many fine features including a central dome and surrounding sculptures. In addition to the cask beers, there are up to 12 guest ales, sourced UK-wide. A bottle store in one of the bank's old strong rooms holds a large range of bottled and canned beers. Meet the Brewer nights are held regularly. Alcoholic drinks are available from 11am.
◑♿⇌(Queen St) 🚊🍎🚌📶

Drum & Monkey ✔
91-93 St Vincent Street, G2 5TF
☎ (0141) 221 6636
St Austell Nicholson's Pale Ale; 5 changing beers (sourced nationally; often Inveralmond) [H]
This corner pub housed in a former American-style bank has an opulent marble and wood-panelled interior and ornate ceilings. Convenient for both main railway stations and numerous bus routes, it is usually busy with a varied clientele. Family groups are welcome until 8pm when dining. The large P-shaped central bar features six handpulls offering a wide variety of styles, from local and national favourites to contemporary microbrews.
🐴◑♿⇌(Central) 🚊🚌🐾📶

Drygate L
85 Drygate, Dennistoun, G4 0UT (off John Knox St)
☎ (0141) 212 8815 🌐 drygate.com
Drygate Pale Duke, Seven Peaks [H]
Situated on the historic Wellpark Brewery site, this brewpub offers numerous cask, keg and bottled beers, firmly positioned towards the craft beer market and younger drinkers. Lively, with an industrial aesthetic, there are two bars over the ground and first floors, an outside terrace and a panoramic view of the brewery. Food is served throughout the day – the menu varies from modern British to street-inspired. Live music and comedy feature regularly in the upstairs beer hall.
🐴❀◑♿⇌(High St) P🚌🐾📶

Esquire House ✔
1487 Great Western Road, Anniesland, G12 0AU
☎ (0141) 341 1430
Caledonian Deuchars IPA; Greene King Abbot; Williams Bros Joker IPA; 3 changing beers (sourced nationally; often Broughton, Loch Lomond) [H]

A compact Wetherspoon, built 20 years ago in what was once a dry area of the city and replacing a function suite of the same name. There are six cask beers on offer, with guests usually from Scottish breweries, often Loch Lomond or Broughton. The pub caters for a mostly local clientele, with TV screens showing racing and football, and the community atmosphere is enhanced by the Monday quiz night. A Meet the Brewer event is held every six weeks. Alcoholic drinks are available from 11am. 👶✿◑♿⇌(Anniesland)🍎P🚌📶

Hengler's Circus

351-363 Sauchiehall Street, Charing Cross, G2 3HU

☎ (0141) 331 9810

Caledonian Deuchars IPA; Greene King Abbot; Sharp's Doom Bar; 7 changing beers (sourced nationally; often Broughton, Kelburn, Loch Lomond) [H]

A Wetherspoon pub named after the indoor circus that used to be on the other side of Sauchiehall Street nearer Charing Cross. It is an L-shaped pub, with the bar down both sides of the L, and a family area to the right of the entrance. Popular during the week with students and office workers, it is also busy at weekends as it is handy for the King's Theatre and other attractions. Alcoholic drinks are available after 11am.
Q👶◑♿⇌(Charing Cross) 🚇🍎🚌📶

Horse Shoe ★ ✔

17-19 Drury Street, G2 5AE

☎ (0141) 248 6368 🌐 thehorseshoebarglasgow.co.uk

Caledonian Deuchars IPA [H]; Harviestoun Bitter & Twisted [P]; 2 changing beers (often Fuller's, Timothy Taylor) [H]

Close to Central station, and busy in the evenings and at weekends, the downstairs bar has four handpumps, with Taylor Landlord and Fuller's London Pride often the guest beers. Dating from 1870, the Victorian pub is recognised by CAMRA as having a nationally important historic pub interior. The horseshoe theme is everywhere, from the shape of the long bar to the fireplaces, mirrors and clock. Good-value food is served in the bar and upstairs lounge/diner (where children are welcome).
👶◑♿⇌(Central) 🚇🚌📶

Inn Deep

445 Great Western Road, Hillhead, G12 8HH

☎ (0141) 357 1075 🌐 inndeep.com

3 changing beers (sourced nationally; often Williams Bros) [P]

Below Great Western Road on the banks of the River Kelvin, Inn Deep is set in the arches of an old railway station. The middle arch houses the bar, which stocks three guest cask ales. There is an extensive range of keg beers. The pub offers good food and hosts regular poetry nights and occasional music sessions. The outdoor seating beside the river and in the adjacent arch is handy for the many passing walkers and cyclists.
👶✿◑🚇🚌(20,6) 🐾📶

Koelschip Yard

686-688 Pollokshaws Road, Strathbungo, G41 2QB

☎ (0141) 423 2945 🌐 koelschipyard.beer

1 changing beer (sourced nationally; often Almasty, Cross Borders, Salopian) [H]

Cosy beer lovers' bar close to Queen's Park and the Tramway performance space. The single cask ale is usually pale, hoppy and around 4% ABV. There are 14 craft keg lines including Krausened, a hazy pilsner from Budvar, and IPAs, sours and stouts, some at higher strength. People travel from all over Glasgow and beyond to sample the extensive range of Belgian beers on draught and in bottle. Payment is by card only.
⇌(Queens Park) 🚌🐾📶

Laurieston Bar ★

58 Bridge Street, Tradeston, G5 9HU

☎ (0141) 429 4528

Fyne Ales Jarl; 2 changing beers (sourced locally; often Fyne Ales, Jaw) [H]

Unchanged over decades, a warm welcome is guaranteed at the Laurieston, which is owned and run by two brothers, assisted by family members. One of CAMRA Scotland's True Heritage Pubs, the horseshoe bar is surrounded by formica-top tables, with walls covered in vintage photographs, mirrors, memorabilia and the occasional painting. It is situated across from Bridge Street subway station and over the Clyde from Glasgow Central. Well-behaved dogs are welcome in the public bar. Glasgow CAMRA Pub of the Year 2019.
⇌(Central) 🚇🚌🐾📶

Pot Still

154 Hope Street, G2 2TH

☎ (0141) 333 0980 🌐 thepotstill.co.uk

4 changing beers (sourced regionally; often Ayr, Broughton) [A]

Near both main rail stations and major bus routes, this classic city-centre split-level bar is one of Scotland's leading whisky pubs, with a collection of around 300 malts. Listening to the staff describe the virtues of various drams to appreciative visitors is an education. Four handpumps offer Scottish beers, some not often seen in Glasgow. Food of the 'pie and beans' school is available during the day. 👶◑⇌(Central)🚇🚌🐾📶

Raven

81-85 Renfield Street, G2 1LP

☎ (0141) 332 6151 🌐 theravenglasgow.com

3 changing beers (sourced nationally; often Fyne Ales, Redcastle) [H]

Modern city-centre bar and restaurant close to the Royal Concert Hall, theatres and cinemas, and handy for the railway and bus stations. Three real ales are on offer, usually from Scottish breweries, as well as a selection of bottled and draught craft beer. Food is available until 9pm. Music can be loud in the evening but the atmosphere is relaxed in the daytime. Children and dogs are welcome until 9pm. 👶◑♿⇌(Queen St)🚇🚌🐾📶

Scotia Bar

112-114 Stockwell Street, G1 4LW

☎ (0141) 552 8681

Greene King IPA; house beer (by Greene King); 2 changing beers (often Broughton, Stewart, Strathaven) [H]

One of several pubs which claim to be the oldest in Glasgow, the Scotia certainly looks the part with its half-timbered frontage, wood panelling, dark wooden benches and low ceilings. It has been a firm fixture on the folk music scene for decades – the likes of Hamish Imlach and Billy Connolly performed here – and there are still regular sessions and live bands. There are three distinct areas: one closer to the band, one to the bar, and the cosy snug. ⇌(Argyle St)🚇♣🚌🐾📶

Sir John Moore ✔

260-292 Argyle Street, G2 8QW

☎ (0141) 222 1780

8 changing beers (sourced nationally) [H]

Close to Central Station's lower level Hope Street exit, with a live departure screen inside, this is an ideal place to wait for a train. Also handy for breakfast after a night on the sleeper, it serves the usual Wetherspoon fare. Converted from several shops, it has a number of distinct areas, and a pavement area outside. Alcoholic drinks are available from 11am. ✿◑♿⇌(Central)🚇🍎🚌📶

SCOTLAND

Sir John Stirling Maxwell ✔

136-140 Kilmarnock Road, Shawlands, G41 3NN

☎ (0141) 636 9024

Caledonian Deuchars IPA; Greene King Abbot; Sharp's Doom Bar; 3 changing beers (sourced nationally; often Broughton, Kelburn) Ⓗ

Wetherspoon pub named after a local benefactor and landowner, situated at the end of the Shawlands Arcade in what was previously a supermarket. Photographs of old local cinemas adorn the walls – at one time the Embassy was on this site. There is a TV-free family area up steps at the back. Usually at least seven handpumps are in use. Alcoholic drinks are available after 11am. ♿≠(Pollokshaws East)

Society Room ✔

151 West George Street, G2 2JJ

☎ (0141) 229 7560

Caledonian Deuchars IPA; Greene King Abbot; 4 changing beers (sourced nationally) Ⓗ

Wetherspoon's only Lloyds No.1 in Glasgow. It can be lively, however the music doesn't start until 8pm on weekdays and Sunday, and the pub is popular with older people during the day. On Saturday there is music from 5pm, with a DJ from 9pm. The building's low ceiling and lack of windows at the back give it a cavernous feel. Alcoholic drinks are available from 11am. ♿≠(Central)

State Bar 🏆

148 Holland Street, Charing Cross, G2 4NG (just off Sauchiehall St, opp Hengler's Circus)

☎ (0141) 332 2159

House beer (by Stewart); 6 changing beers (sourced nationally; often Oakham) Ⓗ

A regular winner of local CAMRA Pub of the Year, this popular and welcoming town-centre establishment gets busy at lunchtimes and weekends. Besides the regular beers from Oakham, the guest beers change often and tend to be ales rarely seen elsewhere in Glasgow. The pub has a traditional island bar, and its proximity to the King's Theatre is reflected by old pictures and show bills displayed on the walls. There is a blues session on Tuesday in the main bar and a comedy club downstairs on Saturday. ≠(Charing Cross)

Tennent's ✔

191 Byres Road, Hillhead, G12 8TN

☎ (0141) 339 7203 🌐 thetennentsbarglasgow.co.uk

Caledonian Deuchars IPA; Draught Bass; Fuller's London Pride; Marston's Pedigree; Stewart 80/-; Timothy Taylor Landlord; 2 changing beers (sourced nationally) Ⓗ

Large, traditional pub situated at a busy junction in the centre of the West End in the shadow of Glasgow University. It was established in the 1880s by a member of the Tennent family, but not originally associated with the brewery. The open-plan room is dominated by the rectangular bar and large TV screens mainly showing sporting events. A small lounge to one side provides extra seating. Food is served all day. ♿

Three Judges L ✔

141 Dumbarton Road, Partick, G11 6PR

☎ (0141) 337 3055 🌐 threejudges.co.uk

Sharp's Doom Bar; 8 changing beers (sourced nationally) Ⓗ

Traditional corner tenement pub on a busy junction at the bottom of Byres Road. Many customers come from the local community to watch the racing or listen to live jazz on the last Sunday afternoon of the month. But others come from further afield to enjoy the wide range of beers that has been a feature here for around 30 years, or sample the ciders, particularly during the annual cider festival. No food is available but it can be brought in. ≠(Partick)

Greenock

James Watt ✔

80-92 Cathcart Street, PA15 1DD

☎ (01475) 722640

Greene King Abbot; Sharp's Doom Bar; 4 changing beers Ⓗ

Situated in a former post office and close to transport links, this large open-plan Wetherspoon is named after one of Greenock's famous sons, who improved steam engine technology and had the SI unit of power named after him. The chain's standard value-for-money food is available all day and beer festivals are hosted at various times throughout the year. This pub is an oasis in a beer desert. ♿≠(Central)

Willow

203 Roxburgh Street, PA15 4DA

☎ (01475) 791775

2 changing beers (sourced nationally) Ⓗ

Located in the busy West Station area of Greenock, this friendly and welcoming free house has two handpumps dispensing beers from across the UK, with an emphasis on Scottish ales, often from local breweries. The pub is community focused, supporting a number of local causes and charities. A quiz night is held every Wednesday. ♿≠(West)

Houston

Fox & Hounds 🏆 L

South Street, PA6 7EN

☎ (01505) 808604 🌐 foxandhoundshouston.co.uk

Kelburn Goldihops; 4 changing beers (sourced nationally; often Fuller's, Fyne Ales, Kelburn) Ⓗ

Excellent traditional village pub established in 1779. The bar, lounge and restaurant are downstairs, a cocktail bar upstairs. A range of beers on five handpumps is available alongside a selection of canned and bottled craft beers and a wide choice of spirits including 130 whiskies. Gastro-pub food made wholly on the premises is served throughout the pub. An annual beer festival is held on the late May bank holiday weekend. There is a pool table upstairs and board games are played every Wednesday. Local CAMRA Pub of the Year.
Q♿♣P

Inverkip

Inverkip Hotel

Main Street, PA16 0AS

☎ (01475) 521478 🌐 inverkip.co.uk

Fyne Ales Jarl; 1 changing beer (sourced regionally; often Fallen, Fyne Ales) Ⓗ

Small family-run hotel located in the heart of a conservation village and just a short walk from the large Inverkip Marina, making it an ideal staging post for those just messing about on the river or passing through on the way to Largs and the Ayrshire coast. Food options range from snacks to special-occasion dining. Battle of the Brewer nights are extremely popular.
≠P(578,580)

Kilbarchan

Trust Inn

8 Low Barholm, PA10 2ET

☎ (01505) 702401 🌐 thetrustinn.com

3 changing beers Ⓗ
Small, popular, single-roomed pub in the centre of a
conservation village, with old village photographs
adorning the walls. A superior bar meal menu and
special promotions mean it can be busy at mealtimes.
Children are welcome until 9pm if dining. Regular live
events including local bands and other entertainment are
advertised via social media. ኈ◑🖨(38)☞

Kirkintilloch

Kirky Puffer ✅
1-11 Townhead, G66 1NG
☎ (0141) 775 4140
Caledonian Deuchars IPA; Sharp's Doom Bar; 3
changing beers (sourced nationally; often Kelburn,
Loch Lomond, Oakham) Ⓗ
The newly crowned Dunbartonshire CAMRA Pub of the
Year has developed a strong reputation for the quality
and range of its beers. The knowledgeable manager
endeavours to supplement the core and seasonal range
of Wetherspoon beers with those from a variety of
leading breweries, reflecting the clientele's preference
for pale, hoppy ales. This spacious, attractive pub sits
alongside the Forth & Clyde Canal and features an
extensive beer garden. Alcoholic drinks are served from
11am. ኈ🏵◑👌🖨☞

Lochwinnoch

Brown Bull
32 Main Street, PA12 4AH
☎ (01505) 843250
Harviestoun Bitter & Twisted; 3 changing beers
(sourced nationally; often Cromarty, Fyne Ales,
Kelburn) Ⓗ
More than 200 years old, this family-run pub attracts
locals and visitors throughout the year. A wide choice of
national ales is offered, with an emphasis of regional
breweries. At the rear is a quirky outdoor seating area
and garden. The upstairs restaurant uses local produce
and bar meals are also available. Quiz night is Tuesday
and live music features monthly. Located close to
Lochwinnoch RSPB nature reserve and Castle Semple
loch and visitor centre. Q ኈ🏵◑●🖨(X34,X36)🏵

Motherwell

Brandon Works ✅
45-61 Merry Street, ML1 1JJ
☎ (01698) 210280
Caledonian Deuchars IPA; Greene King Abbot; Sharp's
Doom Bar; 2 changing beers (often Kelburn, Loch
Lomond, Strathaven) Ⓗ
This central bar, handy for buses and trains, takes its
name from the ironworks that sat behind the pub's site
until the 1960s. There are five cask beers available. A
quiz night is held monthly and there are occasional Meet
the Brewer events. The pub has a display of prints
illustrating Lanarkshire's traditional industries and
influential historical figures, including Keir Hardie and
Robert Owen. Alcoholic drinks are available after 11am.
◑👌🖨☞

Paisley

Bull Inn ★ ✅
7 New Street, PA1 1XU
☎ (0141) 849 0472
4 changing beers (sourced regionally; often Jaw,
Kelburn, Loch Lomond) Ⓗ

Established in 1901 and identified by CAMRA as having a
nationally important historic interior, this is the oldest inn
in Paisley. The pub retains many original features
including stained-glass windows, three small snugs and a
spirit cask gantry, and boasts the only original set of spirit
cocks left in Scotland. Live sport is shown on large
screens in the main bar and the snugs. 👌🚲🖨🏵☞

Last Post Ⓛ ✅
2 County Square, PA1 1BN
☎ (0141) 849 6911
Caledonian Deuchars IPA; Greene King Abbot; Sharp's
Doom Bar; 6 changing beers Ⓗ
Large Wetherspoon pub converted from the town's main
post office. Open plan in design on two levels, there is
plenty of seating and good wheelchair access. The
standard Wetherspoon food menu is served and six guest
ales are usually available. Next to the railway station and
close to the bus station, it is a handy place to enjoy a pint
while you wait. ◑👌🚲(Gilmour St)●🖨(9,36)☞

Northern Way
13-19 Causeyside Street, PA1 1UW
4 changing beers (sourced nationally) Ⓗ
This Northern Way-branded Amber Taverns pub has
undergone a massive refurbishment from previous
incarnations and is extremely well appointed
throughout. It currently serves up to four ales, primarily
from the north of England, as well as a huge selection of
premium gins. Live sporting events are shown on a
number of largescreen TVs. Separate areas are available
to book for events. Children are not permitted. 👌🚲☞

Sandpiper ✅
Before Security, Glasgow Airport, PA3 2SW
☎ (0141) 842 7858
Greene King Abbot; 4 changing beers Ⓗ
Positioned on the ground floor, in the public area of the
airport, the Sandpiper is ideal if you are looking for an ale
before heading through security, waiting for family or
friends arriving on an incoming flight, or if you are a
plane spotter in need of refreshment. With six
handpumps you are spoilt for choice and can relax
watching one of the many TV screens showing 24-hour
news and sporting events. Opening hours are slightly
longer in the summer season. Q ኈ◑👌●P🖨☞

Wee Howff ✅
53 High Street, PA1 2AN
☎ (0141) 887 8299
2 changing beers (sourced nationally; often
Kelburn) Ⓗ
This place has appeared in more than 25 editions of this
Guide and is a little piece of heaven in an otherwise
crowded area of cheap drinking establishments. A small,
traditional pub with a loyal regular clientele, the Howff
offers up to three guest ales from all four corners of
Britain from a quarterly rotating list. It has an open mic
night on the first Monday of each month and a pub quiz
every Thursday. The jukebox caters for even the most
eclectic of tastes. 👌🚲🖨(9,36)🏵☞

Rutherglen

An Ruadh-Ghleann ✅
40-44 Main Street, G73 2HY
☎ (0141) 613 2370
Caledonian Deuchars IPA; Greene King Abbot; Sharp's
Doom Bar; 4 changing beers (sourced nationally) Ⓗ
Busy Wetherspoon pub at the start of the main street. It
has a long, narrow bar decorated in a contemporary
style, and a family area at the far end leading to the beer
garden. There is also a window into the cellar. The beer

SCOTLAND

garden is on two levels and affords a view of the Cathkin Braes. Six of the 12 handpumps are usually in use. Alcoholic drinks are available from 11am.
Q

Strathaven

Weavers

1-3 Green Street, ML10 6LT
4 changing beers (sourced nationally; often Strathaven)
A family-run pub in the centre of a small historic town with links to the 19th-century weaving industry. The single room has comfortable furnishings and is decorated with an assortment of black and white pictures of film stars. Four handpumps offer ales from a changing range, complemented by a selection of imported bottled beers. The pub is a community hub where local groups and clubs meet. (254,256)

Uplawmoor

Uplawmoor Hotel

66 Neilston Road, G78 4AF (off A736)
(01505) 850565 uplawmoor.co.uk
2 changing beers (sourced locally; often Kelburn)
In a tranquil village setting just over 10 miles from Glasgow, the building dates back to the 18th century. It was originally a coaching inn used by travellers and customs officers chasing smugglers en-route between Glasgow and the south-west coast of Scotland. Today the hotel continues to offer travellers the opportunity to relax and explore. The interior is rustic and cosy, with a public bar, pool room and lounge bar.
P (395,X44B)

Wishaw

Wishaw Malt

62-66 Kirk Road, ML2 7BL
(01698) 358806
Caledonian Deuchars IPA; Greene King Abbot; Sharp's Doom Bar; 3 changing beers
A town-centre bar converted from a furniture store 15 years ago, the Wishaw Malt has six handpumps, with guest beers from all over the UK supplementing the three regulars. Around the walls you'll find information panels and photographs of old Wishaw, and the pub name itself is of historical interest, being that of a 19th-century distillery and bonded warehouse. Ironically, a church to the rear of the pub once hosted the Wishaw Templar Lodge of Temperance. Alcohol is available from 11am.

Drum & Monkey, Glasgow (Photo: Reading Tom/Flickr CC BY 2.0)

Authority areas covered: Highland UA, Western Isles UA

Applecross

Applecross Inn

Shore Street, IV54 8LR NG70974444

☎ (01520) 744262 🌐 applecrossinn.co.uk

3 changing beers (sourced locally; often Applecross) H

This remote multi-award winning iconic inn is reached by a hair-raising road over one of the highest vehicular ascents in Britain or by a longer scenic coastal route. Renowned for its local seafood and venison, with a massive chalkboard menu, the pub is a must for foodies. Beers come from the new local microbrewery Applecross Ales. There are additional tables outside, with the Inn-Side-Out Airstream caravan offering light refreshments and takeaways. The pub is a popular stop-off on the North Coast 500. CAMRA branch Pub of the Year runner-up 2020.

Aviemore

Cairngorm Hotel L

77 Grampian Road, PH22 1PE (opp railway station)

☎ (01479) 810233 🌐 cairngorm.com

Cairngorm Stag, Gold H

Just over the road from the train station and bus stop, this is often the first watering hole for many after a long journey. The privately owned Cairngorm Hotel has a warm and familiar feel about it, with comfy seats in the lobby to the bar and seating under cover outside. Although not tied, Cairngorm beers feature on the two handpumps. Largescreen TVs show popular sporting events and there is Scottish entertainment for the many visitors most evenings. Food with a Scottish twist is available much of the day.

Old Bridge Inn L

23 Dalfaber Road, PH22 1PU

☎ (01479) 811137 🌐 oldbridgeinn.co.uk

4 changing beers (sourced locally; often Cairngorm, Caledonian, Windswept)

Close to the gently flowing River Spey, this gem of a pub off the main drag is worth seeking out. The cosy, intimate inn, converted from a cottage in 1982, is an ideal place to relax after a busy day on the hills, or even just touring in the area. Four handpumps offer a mix of local and regional beers. Booking is recommended for the restaurant, with a menu using produce with low food miles. Entertainment is hosted most nights. There is a bunkhouse adjacent and self-catering accommodation available. Handy for the Strathspey Steam Railway.

Winking Owl L ✔

123 Grampian Road, PH22 1RH

☎ (01479) 812368 🌐 thewinkingowl.co

6 changing beers (sourced locally; often Cairngorm, Caledonian) H

The Winky has been the brewery tap for the award-winning Cairngorm Brewery since 2014, with the addition of the Bothy Bar downstairs in 2018 massively increasing its popularity. Both bars offer four Cairngorm and two Caledonian beers. Hearty pub grub, international and Scottish dishes, including children's, vegetarian, gluten- and dairy-free, are served throughout. Live music plays in the Bothy. The rustic courtyard has a covered seating area made from upcycled materials and logs. Once a farmhouse, the pub is probably one of the oldest hostelries in Aviemore and Robert Burns is reported to have breakfasted here in 1787. ❀◑♿▲⇌P🚌🐾📶

Carbost: Isle of Skye

Old Inn

IV47 8SR (on B8009) NG379318

☎ (01478) 640205 🌐 theoldinnskye.co.uk

3 changing beers (often Cuillin, Isle of Skye) H

On the shores of Loch Harport, the Old Inn nestles on the tideline. Outside, trestle tables take advantage of the views that Skye is famous for – there can be no better place to enjoy a pint. The pub is busy all year round with an eclectic mix of outdoor folk, and those touring Skye or visiting the Talisker Distillery close by. Seafood is top of the menu, most of it coming from the loch.

Q❀🛏◑●P🚌🐾

Carrbridge

Cairn Hotel L

Main Road, PH23 3AS (just off A9 on B9153)

☎ (01479) 841212 🌐 cairnhotel.co.uk

3 changing beers (sourced regionally; often Cairngorm, Cromarty, Orkney) H

The Cairn Hotel is the hub of this small village, with the lure of a warming open fire and excellent gastro-pub style menus. The licensee selects the best cask ales from the Highlands and Islands for his three handpumps and deservedly the pub is popular with loyal locals and the many visitors to the area. There are 14 rooms for overnight stays – the 1717 Packhorse Bridge and Landmark Forest Adventure Park are in the village.

❀🛏◑♣P🚌🐾📶

Claddach Kirkibost: North Uist

Westford Inn

HS6 5EP (2½ miles NW of Clachan on A865) NF7751066195

☎ (01876) 580653 🌐 westfordinn.com

3 changing beers (sourced regionally; often Fyne Ales, Isle of Skye) H

The owners took on the Westford Inn in 2015 and have turned around its fortunes. The pub is very much the hub of the community, with live music and an annual beer festival. A second Skye ale is on rotation in winter, with three ales in summer, as well as a range of bottled beers. Good-quality pub food is served and also available to take away. Although probably one of the most remote pubs in the Guide, it is well worth making the effort to visit. Accommodation is in The Bothy, a former byre.

Q❀🛏◑▲♣P🚌🐾📶

Cromarty

Cromarty Arms L

Church Street, IV11 8XA

☎ (01381) 600230 🌐 cromartyarms.com

Cromarty Happy Chappy; 1 changing beer (often Cromarty) H

The Cromarty Arms is a family-run pub providing B&B accommodation and delicious home-made bar meals. A traditional music session is held on the second Friday of every month. The beers are from Cromarty Brewery less than three miles away. Just opposite is NTS Hugh Miller's Cottage and Cromarty Courthouse, or take a dolphin spotting tour from the harbour where you can also see the oil rigs in for maintenance. A two-car ferry operates during the summer to Nigg.

Q❀🛏◑♿♣P🚌(26,26A) 🐾📶

Drumnadrochit

Benleva Hotel L

Kilmore Road, IV63 6UH (signed off A82) NH513295

☎ (01456) 450080 🌐 benleva.co.uk

Hanging Tree First Light, Hangmans IPA; 3 changing beers (sourced regionally; often Hanging Tree) H

The 400-year-old sweet chestnut outside the Benleva was once a hanging tree, hence the name of the brewery in the bothy just outside. The bar in this 300-year-old former manse offers four Hanging Tree beers and a guest ale. Classic home-made dishes have a Scottish twist. Regular music and themed nights are held throughout the year and an annual beer festival in September. ❀🛏◑▲♣P🚌🐾📶

Fort William

Ben Nevis Bar

103 High Street, PH33 6DG

☎ (01397) 702295

Hanging Tree First Light, After Dark, Hangmans IPA H

Built in 1806 and under new ownership since April 2019, this pleasant two-roomed traditional locals' pub on the pedestrianised High Street is said to have a resident ghost in the loft. A decked area at the rear gives splendid views of Loch Linnhe. As well as the three ales, over 50 malt whiskies are stocked. A food menu of good honest pub favourites is available all day until 10pm. Live music plays at weekends. ❀◑♿⇌♣🚌🐾📶

Ben Nevis Inn L

Achintee Road, Claggan, PH33 6TE NN12477293

☎ (01397) 701227 🌐 bennevisbarfortwilliam.com

3 changing beers (sourced locally; often Cairngorm, Isle of Skye, River Leven) H

Traditional 200-year-old stone-built barn at the start of the Ben Nevis mountain path, popular with outdoor enthusiasts. The small bar counter has three handpumps offering beers from local breweries. The barn, with long beer hall-style tables and a beckoning stove, and decorated with mountaineering and skiing paraphernalia, is a warm, informal and friendly setting – an ideal venue for the regular live music. A hearty food menu is available until 9pm and changes daily. The adjacent bunkhouse sleeps 24 people. Check ahead for opening hours in winter (closed November).

Q❀🛏◑♿▲P

REAL ALE BREWERIES

Black Isle Munlochy
Cairngorm Aviemore
Cromarty Cromarty
Cuillin ▤ Sligachan: Isle of Skye
Dun Glenelg
Glen Spean Spean Bridge
Hanging Tree ▤ Drumnadrochit
Isle of Harris Borrisdale: Isle of Harris (NEW)
Isle of Skye Uig: Isle of Skye
John O'Groats John O'Groats
Knoydart Knoydart
Old Inn ▤ Gairloch
Plockton Plockton
River Leven Kinlochleven
Strathcarron Strathcarron
Two Thirsty Men Grantown on Spey
Wild Barn Annat (NEW)

Black Isle Bar

St Mary's House, Gordon Square, PH33 6DY
☎ (01397) 700876
Black Isle Goldfinch, Red Kite, Blonde Ⓟ
This is the second Black Isle Bar opened by the brewery. It follows the successful formula of offering a wall of 18 keg and up to three real ales – the latter may appear to be fonts, but are in fact electric pumps. Current ales are shown on a screen, with prices for pints, halves and thirds. Food is available throughout the day – home-made pizzas are the speciality. There is more seating upstairs.

Grog & Gruel

66 High Street, PH33 6AE (in pedestrianised area)
☎ (01397) 705078 grogandgruel.co.uk
6 changing beers (sourced locally; often Loch Lomond, River Leven) Ⓗ
The Grog alehouse is busy all day every day with a mix of locals and tourists. A regular in the Guide since 1997, the pub has up to six handpumps dispensing often local and sometimes regional beers, making it a draw for the real ale connoisseur. The bar menu offers imaginative and interesting food at affordable prices all day. After 5pm the restaurant upstairs opens, offering a wider selection for hungry hill walkers. Open mic features on most Friday evenings.

Fortrose

Anderson

Union Street, IV10 8TD (corner of High St)
☎ (01381) 620236 theanderson.co.uk
2 changing beers (sourced nationally; often Cromarty, Inveralmond) Ⓗ
A regular in the Guide since 2005, the Anderson offers well-chosen ales – mostly local or regional – drawn from the 200-year-old cellar. The whisky lounge has a single cider handpump and more than 250 single malts. The restaurant also has a reputation for excellence and is a popular destination for foodies. Regular music, quiz and special food nights feature throughout the year. Nine bedrooms are available, with local attractions including the golf course and dolphin watching at Chanonry Point. Closed before Christmas – phone ahead to check.
Q P (26,26A)

Glencoe

Clachaig Inn

PH49 4HX (3 miles SE of village, off A82) NN12705668
☎ (01855) 811252 clachaig.com
10 changing beers (sourced locally; often Cairngorm, Orkney, River Leven) Ⓗ
The Clachaig is a must for outdoor enthusiasts and beer lovers alike, set in a remote location among the spectacular hills and scenery of Glencoe. Having worked up a hunger on the hills, a huge choice of well-kept beers and hearty grub will replenish your energy. There are also more than 400 whiskies and 130 gins to distract you. On cooler days, wood-burning stoves keep the three bars and snugs warm. Beer festivals are held during the year and music hosted most weekend evenings.
P

Glenmore

Pine Marten Bar & Scran

PH22 1QU (on ski road by Loch Morlich) NH974098
☎ (01479) 861253 aviemoreski.co.uk
Cairngorm Trade Winds, Black Gold, Wildcat Ⓗ
Although it looks unassuming from the outside, this 'wee snug of a bar' has a welcoming wood-burning stove and a bar topped with three handpumps. The minimalist building is designed to emulate mountain refuges in Austria, Switzerland and Bavaria, and ice axes and skis decorate the walls along with quirky artefacts from across Europe. The kitchen serves some great grub, and there is also a shop, ski hire and accommodation including glamping pods and a tree house. Live music plays most Friday and Saturday nights.
P

Inverness

Black Isle Bar

68 Church Street, IV1 1EN
☎ (01463) 229920 blackislebar.com
Black Isle Yellowhammer, Red Kite; 1 changing beer (sourced locally; often Black Isle) Ⓟ
Popular right from the start, this bar opened in 2016, offering up to three real ales and 23 craft font beers. Two big screens show the eclectic beer menu, mostly from Black Isle but some guests, with prices for pints, halves and thirds. The open-plan bar area offers a mix of seating. Upstairs, the secret garden utilises upcycled pallet tables and stools under a cover of reclaimed corrugated iron. Organic ingredients from the brewery farm are used in an interesting food menu, with pizzas the speciality. Q P

Castle Tavern

1 View Place, IV2 4SA (top of Castle St)
☎ (01463) 718178 castletavern.pub
5 changing beers (sourced regionally; often Cromarty, Isle of Skye, Windswept) Ⓗ
Just a short walk from town, the Castle Tavern is popular with tourists visiting the castle opposite and locals who know their beer. Six handpumps offer an interesting rolling selection of beers, mostly from Scottish independents, and a changing cider. There is plenty of seating inside but the covered canopy area outside is always busy, even in winter, with panoramic views along the River Ness. Bar meals are available all day; the restaurant upstairs opens in the evening.
P

Clachnaharry Inn

17-19 High Street, Clachnaharry, IV3 8RB (on A862 Beauly road)
☎ (01463) 239806 clachnaharryinn.co.uk
Fyne Ales Jarl; Harviestoun Bitter & Twisted; Inveralmond Ossian; 2 changing beers (sourced nationally; often Cairngorm) Ⓗ
The Clach has featured in the Guide for more than 35 years and is where many have enjoyed their first pint of real ale. The 17th-century coaching inn offers a warm welcome to all, with an open fire most days. Food is available in both the bar area and the quieter restaurant. Quiz and music nights feature regularly. Outside, the occasional train rumbles by or boat using the Caledonian Canal. Beyond are stunning views of the Beauly Firth and Ben Wyvis, often snowcapped.
Q P (28,28A)

Hootananny

67 Church Street, IV1 1ES
☎ (01463) 233651 hootanannyinverness.co.uk
Black Isle Yellowhammer, Red Kite Ⓗ
There is a great craic every night at Hoots – this lively and popular multi-award winning pub celebrates Scottish folk music and all things Scottish. Live music plays downstairs most nights from 9.30pm and on weekend afternoons. On Friday and Saturday nights there is often a music or

comedy act upstairs, too. Two handpumps serve real ale alongside craft keg from Black Isle Brewery. A Scottish-themed food menu offers something for everyone.

King's Highway

72-74 Church Street, IV1 1EN
(01463) 251830
Caledonian Deuchars IPA; Fuller's London Pride; Greene King Abbot; Sharp's Doom Bar; changing beers
Situated centrally, this Wetherspoon pub has offered good-value fare since 2001 and is now in its 11th year in the Guide. Up to 10 handpumps feature mainly Scottish beers, many of them local to the area. A popular meeting point, it is handy for the town's buses and train station. Even when busy, you can always find a quiet place to sit and enjoy a pint. There is now a decked area outside. Accommodation is available. Alcoholic drinks are served from 11am.

MacGregor's

109-113 Academy Street, IV1 1LX (corner of Friars Lane)
(01463) 719629 macgregorsbars.com
2 changing beers (often Cromarty, Spey Valley, Swannay)
Crowdfunding allowed Blazin' Fiddles musician Bruce MacGregor's pub to become an instant hit on opening in 2017, offering an insight into Scottish history, culture, food and drink. Two handpumps and a font gantry feature beers from local breweries, alongside an extensive menu of bottled beers, gins and whiskies. A simple but elegant Scottish-themed food menu is served all day. Wood-burning stoves warm both the main bar and side whisky room. There is a patio area outside. Bruce is often in the bar playing his fiddle on a Sunday afternoon.

Number 27

27 Castle Street, IV2 3DU (opp castle)
(01463) 241999 number27inverness.uk
4 changing beers (sourced regionally; often Windswept)
Opposite the castle, the entrance to the pub is on the corner, leading you into a bar area with a mix of seating, then on to a raised area towards the rear for dining. Four handpumps normally offer ales from the Windswept Brewery, with beers from other local breweries making an occasional appearance, alongside an extensive selection of keg and bottled beers. Food menus cater for both a quick pub lunch and a more substantial offering in the evening, including an all-day children's menu.

John o' Groats

Seaview Hotel

County Road, KW1 4YR (A99/A863 jct) ND380727
(01955) 611220 seaviewjohnogroats.co.uk
John o' Groats Swelkie; 1 changing beer (sourced locally; often John o' Groats)
The family-run Seaview Hotel must be the most northerly pub on the UK mainland and is also the tap for John o' Groats brewery, with two handpulls on the bar. Meals are served throughout the day. Accommodation is available in the hotel itself, the annexe and cottage over the road, and pods with hammocks. The pub is a popular stop-off for End to Enders and the many visitors with John o' Groats on their bucket list. The surrounding area, including Duncansby Head, offers great views and walking.

Kinlochewe

Kinlochewe Hotel (Beinn Eighe Bar)

IV22 2PA (on Gairloch Road) NH028619
(01445) 760253 kinlochewehotel.co.uk
6 changing beers (sourced locally; often Cromarty, Orkney, Windswept)
An 18th-century coaching inn set amid the majestic Torridon Mountains – the approach from Achnasheen offers one of the most dramatic views in the Highlands. The hotel bar has six handpumps offering a tempting range of beers mainly from craft breweries of northern Scotland, as well as an excellent selection of whiskies and gins. Quality meals are served in the evening, with the focus on fresh and local ingredients. Rooms in the hotel and adjacent bunkhouse are popular with those doing the North Coast 500.

Mallaig

Steam Inn

Davies Brae, PH41 4PU (off Station Rd)
(01687) 462002 steaminnmallaig.co.uk
2 changing beers (often Isle of Skye)
In summer, hanging baskets adorn the striking frontage of this pub. The bar has a wood-burner at one end and an open fire at the other for cooler days. The beer garden at the rear comes into its own in fine weather, particularly when the pub fills up because the Skye ferry docks or the Hogwarts Express arrives – both just a short walk away. An extensive food menu features locally caught seafood, bar food and children's options.

Nairn

Bandstand

Crescent Road, IV12 4NB (E end of town towards beach)
(01667) 452341 braevalhotel.co.uk
5 changing beers (sourced nationally; often Cairngorm, Cromarty, Orkney)
Overlooking the green, with its bandstand and the Moray Firth beyond, the bar has five handpumps offering a great selection of local and regional Scottish beers, including the occasional English ale. The annual free beer festival in May is said to be the biggest independent event in the UK, with around 150 ales and ciders from all over the UK, accompanied by themed food and music acts over three days. The restaurant offers good-value quality food. Live music plays at the weekend. CAMRA branch Pub of the Year 2020.

Newtonmore

Glen Hotel

Main Street, PH20 1DD (S of village)
(01540) 673203 theglenhotel.co.uk
4 changing beers (often Cairngorm, Caledonian, Cromarty)
The Glen was a trailblazer in the Highlands when it started serving real ale and has appeared in the Guide for 18 years. With four handpumps offering both local and regional beers, it is an oasis for CAMRA members in the area. Good honest pub grub is served in the bar, restaurant and dining tables outside. A handy stop-off while exploring the Cairngorms National Park, Highland Wildlife Park and Folk Museum. Accommodation is available in eight rooms. Alcohol is served from 11am (12.30pm Sun).

Plockton

Plockton Hotel ✔

41 Harbour Street, IV52 8TN NG80293343
☎ (01599) 544274 🌐 plocktonhotel.co.uk
5 changing beers (often Cromarty, Fyne Ales, Swannay) 🄷
Plockton was the setting for TV's Hamish Macbeth, which is a draw for visitors to this pretty village, many of whom arrive by train on the picturesque Kyle Line. The bar proudly offers four handpumps dispensing both local and regional beers, which can be enjoyed on the terrace with views of the sea. The food menu features locally sourced seafood, beef and venison. A real ale and gin festival is held in May. Closed throughout January.
Q❀♿P🚌📶

Plockton Inn L ✔

Innes Street, IV52 8TW NG802333
☎ (01599) 544222 🌐 plocktoninn.co.uk
2 changing beers (sourced locally; often Plockton) 🄷
Set in a picture postcard Highland village, this popular inn has been owned and run by a local family for many years. A regularly changing selection of real ales includes locally brewed beers from Plockton Brewery. Locally caught fish and shellfish take pride of place on the menu – the seafood platter includes fish smoked on the premises. Every Tuesday (and Thursday in summer) live music plays in the public bar. There is outdoor seating in the garden behind and tables at the front.
Q❀♿♣P🐾

Roy Bridge

Stronlossit Inn L ✔

Main Street, PH31 4AG (on A86) NN27228117
☎ (01397) 712253 🌐 stronlossit.co.uk
3 changing beers (sourced locally; often Cairngorm, Isle of Skye, Orkney) 🄷
The location of the Stronlossitt makes it attractive to those keen on the outdoors, and with the railway station just over the road, you can abandon the car and arrive by train from Fort William or London. The train can also take you for a day trip to Corrour to walk around Loch Ossian. Up to four handpumps spoil real ale fans, with beers from varying Scottish breweries including the local Glen Spean. Great food is available all day, and rooms for all budgets. Q❀♿⇌P🚌📶

Strathcarron

Strathcarron Hotel

IV54 8YR (on A890 at head of Loch Carron) NG941421
☎ (01520) 722227 🌐 strathcarronhotel.com
2 changing beers (often Strathcarron) 🄷
The Victorian railway hotel bar offers up to two ales, mainly from the nearby Strathcarron Brewery. Take your beer outside to one of the trestle tables and you may catch sight of the excursion train that chugs the spectacular Kyle Line from Inverness to Kyle of Lochalsh. The hotel is a popular destination for motorcyclists, and cyclists and walkers are all equally welcome.
Q❀♿⇌♣P🚌(164) 📶

Ullapool

Morefield Motel L

North Road, IV26 2TQ (signed off A835)
☎ (01854) 612000 🌐 morefieldmotel.co.uk
3 changing beers (sourced locally; often Cairngorm, Cromarty) 🄷
Although principally a restaurant, there is room at the bar for a beer and everyone is welcome. The three handpumps offer a selection of Scottish ales, boosted to 20 in late October during the popular annual beer and cider festival, with music in the evenings. Locally landed seafood is a speciality in the lounge and conservatory restaurants. The motel rooms are an ideal base for exploring the spectacular and dramatic west coast of Scotland. Q❀♿♣P🚌🐾📶

Waternish: Isle of Skye

Stein Inn L

MacLeod's Terrace, IV55 8GA (N of Dunvegan, on B886) NG26255643
☎ (01470) 592362 🌐 stein-inn.co.uk
3 changing beers (often Caledonian, Isle of Skye) 🄷
Dating back to 1790, the Stein is reported to be the oldest pub on Skye. Nestling on the shore of Loch Bay, the low door of the white terraced building opens into the beamed bar where a double-sided stove keeps the room toasty on cooler days. Up to three beers are available from local and regional breweries. The regularly changing food menu features seafood, meat and game – all local, fresh and reasonably priced. You can dine in the bar, lounge or alfresco.
Q❀♣P🐾📶

Wick

Alexander Bain ✔

Market Place, KW1 4LP (in pedestrianised area just off High St)
☎ (01955) 609920
Caledonian Deuchars IPA; 2 changing beers 🄷
This most northerly Wetherspoon in the UK opened in 2003, taking over the old post office. It was due to be sold in 2019, but received a reprieve. The large single-room bar has many side areas and quiet corners, and there is decking outside. The bar sports six handpumps, although only three are in operation, two in winter. Offering the chain's usual reasonably priced drinks and meals, it is popular with locals. Music groups play regularly. Alcoholic drinks are served from 11am.
Q❀♿⇌P🚌📶

The discreet barman

Over the mahogany, jar followed jorum, gargle, tincture and medium, tailor, scoop, snifter and ball of malt, in a breathless pint-to-pint. Discreet barman, Mr Sugrue thought, turning outside the door and walking in the direction of Stephen's Green. Never give anything away – part of the training. Is Mr so-and-so there, I'll go and see, strict instructions never to say yes in case it might be the wife. Curious now the way the tinge of wickedness hung around the pub, a relic of course of Victorianism, nothing to worry about as long as a man kept himself in hand.

Jack White, The Devil You Know

SCOTLAND

KINGDOM OF FIFE

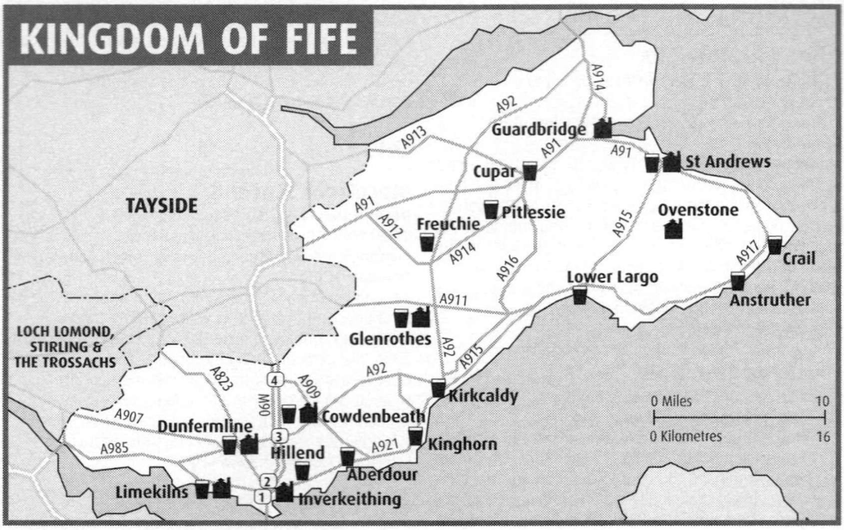

Authority area covered: Fife UA

Aberdour

Foresters Arms ✔

35 High Street, KY3 0SJ

☎ (01383) 861245 🌐 theforestersarms.pub

3 changing beers (sourced nationally; often Adnams, Born in the Borders, Robinsons) 🄷

Corner pub in the middle of the village, conveniently located for the railway station, castle, west sands and the old harbour. Customers are a mix of locals, coastal path walkers and visitors to the area. A monthly meat raffle is held for good causes. Bingo is played every Sunday afternoon and a monthly quiz night is popular. You will also find a jukebox, pool table and live sporting events on a big screen. ❀♿⇌♣🚌(7)🐾📶

Anstruther

Boathouse 𝕃 ✔

28 Shore Street,, KY10 3AQ

☎ (01333) 312105 🌐 at-the-shore.co.uk

3 changing beers (sourced locally; often Orkney, Timothy Taylor) 🄷

Situated on the harbour front, this busy pub is convenient for visiting yachtsmen, tourists and coastal path walkers. The spacious bar hosts live music, TVs, sports and other entertainment. An adjoining bistro offers a food menu that makes use of local produce and changes seasonally. Breakfast is served in the café from 9am. Food service times vary during the winter. There is an attractive beer garden at the rear. Accommodation is in three rooms, two with spectacular views across the harbour.

❀🛏◑⛺♣P🚌(X60,95)🐾📶

Dreel Tavern ✔

16 High Street, KY10 3DL

☎ (01333) 279238 🌐 dreeltavern.co.uk

3 changing beers (sourced nationally; often Adnams, Redcastle, Stewart) 🄷

A traditional pub, popular with locals and walkers. An open fire in winter creates a cosy atmosphere. Three nationally sourced real ales are normally available, along with an extensive range of whiskies and gins. Food menus make extensive use of produce from local farms and fishermen, and are updated with the changing seasons. At the rear is a sunny beer garden overlooking the Dreel Burn, from which the pub takes its name. Check opening times as they may vary in winter.

Q❀◑♣🚌(95,X60)🐾📶

Cowdenbeath

Woodside Hotel 𝕃

109 Broad Street, KY4 8JR

☎ (01383) 511598

1 changing beer (sourced nationally; often Coul, Swannay, Timothy Taylor) 🄷

A typical working men's pub at the top end of this old mining village. Set on its own, the grand building has a large, spacious bar, with a lounge area at the front with two handpumps – one available at all times – and a games area, pool and darts. Plasma screens show a wide range of live sporting events including football, rugby, golf and horse racing. A warm, friendly atmosphere prevails, with live music on Saturday and Sunday evenings. ❀🛏♿⇌♣P🚌(19,33)🐾📶

Crail

Golf Hotel ✔

4 High Street, KY10 3TD

☎ (01333) 450206 🌐 thegolfhotelcrail.com

3 changing beers (sourced nationally; often Harviestoun, Kelburn) 🄷

This historic building is a listed coaching inn dating from the early 1700s, making it one of the oldest inns in Scotland. The bar retains the original low-beamed ceiling, wooden floors and a 16th-century fireplace with

REAL ALE BREWERIES

Beath Cowdenbeath
Brew Shed Limekilns
Coul Glenrothes
Eden St Andrews Guardbridge (brewing suspended)
Inner Bay Inverkeithing
Ovenstone109 Ovenstone
Seven Kings Dunfermline
St Andrews Brewing St Andrews

a marriage lintel over it bearing the initials of the original owners. For golfers, Crail has two links courses and is well situated for a trip to St Andrews. Set in a picturesque village, scenic coastal paths nearby offer the opportunity to explore the coastline. Winter hours may vary.
P (95)

Cupar

Boudingait
43 Bonnygate, KY15 4BU
☎ (01334) 654681 🌐 theboudingaitcupar.co.uk
2 changing beers (sourced nationally; often Loch Leven, Orkney) H
A traditional pub in the centre of the market town, with exposed stonework and a stripped-back interior. Three real ales are always available. Food is served all day, every day, featuring fresh locally sourced ingredients. Families are welcome and the pub gets busy at weekends, especially when the local farmers' market comes to town. Live music and a quiz feature weekly.
Q

Dunfermline

Commercial Inn
13 Douglas Street, KY12 7EB
☎ 07500 119408
Caledonian Deuchars IPA; Inveralmond Ossian; Orkney Dark Island; Stewart 80/-; 2 changing beers (sourced nationally; often Harviestoun, Orkney) H
Located at the heart of the town centre, close to the main retail area, this 19th-century listed building is full of character. Formerly a hotel, it retains the high ceilings and decorative cornices of that period. A spiral staircase leads down to the lower levels. The pub attracts an eclectic clientele, and gets busy on match days. Local CAMRA Pub of the Year on numerous occasions, and a former Scottish runner-up.

East Port ✔
7 East Port, KY12 7JG
☎ (01383) 736678 🌐 greatukpubs.co.uk/eastportbar
4 changing beers (sourced nationally; often Born in the Borders, Stewart, Timothy Taylor) H
On the high street, just a short distance from the main shopping area, this pub is worth a visit when out and about in Dunfermline. A sports bar with plasma screens showing sport from football to golf, it is also a great place to relax, with many cosy booths. Soft background music usually plays. The interior features wood panelling and a wooden bar and gantry.

Guildhall & Linen Exchange ✔
79-83 High Street, KY12 7DR
☎ (01383) 625960
8 changing beers (sourced nationally; often Caledonian, Redcastle, Sharp's) H
This Wetherspoon outlet was indeed originally a guildhall and linen exchange, when Dunfermline was synonymous with fine-quality table linen. The category A listed building is now a split-level pub and hotel. The interior is decorated with a mix of modern and Art Deco features, and displays numerous pictures highlighting the historic past of the town. In the middle of the busy retail area, this is a great place to stop for a pint and a bite to eat. Alcoholic drinks are served from 10am.

Freuchie

Albert Tavern
2 High Street, KY15 7EX
☎ 07876 178863 🌐 alberttavern.wixsite.com/albert
5 changing beers (sourced nationally; often Fuzzy Duck, Stewart) H
A multi local award-winning pub for beer and cider and twice Scottish CAMRA Pub of the Year. This cosy two-roomed traditional village inn reminds you of an old English village pub with its low-beamed ceiling and welcoming atmosphere. The bar features five handpumps with ales sourced from throughout the UK, and up to three real ciders. The lounge has a TV and hosts a quarterly malt whisky society and regular gin nights. The famous pie night is on a Thursday. Q

Glenrothes

Golden Acorn ✔
1 North Street, KY7 5NA
☎ (01592) 755252
Caledonian Deuchars IPA; Greene King Abbot; Sharp's Doom Bar; 2 changing beers (sourced nationally) H
This pub is located at the heart of Glenrothes, only a few minutes' walk from the bus station, the Kingdom shopping centre and the local Rothes Halls theatre. A typical Wetherspoon outlet, it has a large open-plan bar area and a smaller family part. Seven handpumps serve real ale and at least one cider. Many large TV screens show sporting events and rolling news. There is a hotel attached. Alcoholic drinks are available from 10am.
P

Hillend

Hillend Tavern 🏆 L ✔
37 Main Street, KY11 9ND
☎ (01383) 415391 🌐 hillendtavern.co.uk
4 changing beers (sourced nationally; often Greene King, Stewart, Timothy Taylor) H
A small, welcoming village pub with two real fires. In addition to the traditional bar there is a spacious recently refurbished room at the rear and a large covered area outside. The Hillend, or Tav, is community-focused and hosts many village events. Live music nights and two quiz nights each month are well attended. Sporting events are shown on TV screens. A frequent local CAMRA Pub of the Year, including for 2020.
(7,87)

Kinghorn

Crown Tavern ✔
55-57 High Street, KY3 9UW
☎ (01592) 890340
2 changing beers (sourced nationally; often Elland, Sharp's) A
Affectionately known as The Middle Bar by locals, this two-roomed venue is right in the middle of this pleasant coastal village, only a short walk from the train station. Very much a pub at the heart of the community, it offers two ales from traditional Scottish tall founts, as well as three real ciders. A sports bar at heart, a number of sports can be viewed on a big screen and on smaller screens. Darts and pool are played at the back of the bar.
(7)

Kirkcaldy

Betty Nicols
297 High Street, KY1 1JL

(01592) 642083 bettynicolsbarandbistro.co.uk
Fyne Ales Jarl; 1 changing beer (sourced regionally)
Betty Nicols has long been one of Kirkcaldy's most popular places to enjoy a drink in a relaxed and comfortable atmosphere. This traditional bar attracts a varied clientele due to its location on the High Street. Live music nights are popular, as is the quiz which is held twice a month on a Thursday night. The modern bistro serves lunchtime meals and afternoon teas (booking essential).

Harbour Bar
471-475 High Street, KY1 2SN
(01592) 264270
6 changing beers (sourced nationally; often Fyne Ales, Mallinsons, Oakham)
A pub on the edge of the town's old harbour, a short distance from the main shopping area. A late 19th-century building, it was originally a ship's chandler and converted to a pub in 1924. The building still has the grade C listed jug bar at the entrance. A wide range of ales and a number of real ciders is always available. It is a previous winner of local and Scottish CAMRA Pub of the Year and a former national finalist. Q (X60)

Limekilns

Ship Inn
Halketts Hall, KY11 3HJ
(01383) 872247
3 changing beers (sourced nationally; often Greene King, Inveralmond)
A wee gem on the way out of Limekilns, which in its early days was a fishing village. The pub sits on the River Forth with views of the three bridges spanning the water. Three ales are available, which can be enjoyed in the bar or in a small, cosy alcove. Numerous artefacts relating to ships and shipping are on display, including the engine order telegraph that takes pride of place on the bar. Meals are served lunchtimes, with fish and seafood the speciality. Q P (6)

Lower Largo

Railway Inn
1 Station Wynd, KY8 6BU
(01333) 320239 railwayinnlargo.co.uk
5 changing beers (sourced regionally; often Born in the Borders, Coul, Stewart)
The Railway is a friendly and traditional village public house, established since 1749, located in a picturesque village. It rests in the shadow of the old railway viaduct, with views of Largo harbour. The small two-roomed interior is warmed by a cosy real fire. A champion of LocAle, you can usually find an ale from a Fife brewery on one of the five handpulls. Kingdom of Fife CAMRA Pub of the Year and Scottish Pub of the Year finalist 2019. Q (95)

Pitlessie

Village Inn
Cupar Road, KY15 7SU
(01337) 830595 pitlessievillageinn.com
1 changing beer (sourced nationally)
This traditional old coaching inn on the main road between Cupar and Glenrothes is right at the heart of the community. The family-run restaurant and bar offers locally sourced food and a relaxed dining experience. The wood-panelled, stone and plaster-walled interior is decorated with pictures of the maltings that was once opposite. A real fire adds to the cosy atmosphere. The function room doubles as a pantry kitchen offering coffee and tea, and sells produce from the surrounding area. P

St Andrews

Central Bar
77 Market Street, KY16 9NU
(01334) 478296 centralbar-standrews.co.uk
6 changing beers (sourced nationally; often Kelburn, Orkney, Stewart)
The pub is situated in the busy cobbled Market Square of this historic university town. The bar has a Victorian-style interior with an island bar, ornate ceiling and a fine collection of historic brewery mirrors. Customers are a mix of locals, tourists, students and golfers. A wide selection of real ales is available, mainly from Scottish breweries. There is seating outside at the front of the building.

Criterion
99 South Street, KY16 9QW
(01334) 474543 criterionstandrews.co.uk
6 changing beers (sourced nationally; often Caledonian, Coul, Stewart)
This small establishment dates from 1874, and is one of the few remaining family-run pubs in the area. On one of the main shopping streets, it is popular with locals, tourists and golfers. Regular music nights and quizzes are held and live sporting events are shown on a number of screens. A locally sourced menu is served, with the famous Cri pies available all day. In addition to the five cask ales, a large selection of whiskies and gins is stocked.

Whey Pat Tavern
1 Bridge Street, KY16 9EX
(01334) 477740 wheypat-standrews.co.uk
Greene King IPA; 4 changing beers (often Broughton, Inveralmond, Timothy Taylor)
A busy corner pub adjacent to the West Port and convenient for the bus station. It has a busy front public bar, a spacious lounge to the rear and a small courtyard outside, and is popular with the usual mix of locals, tourists and golfers found in the town. Live sporting events are shown on screens. The pub is the birthplace of the Fife branch of CAMRA.

A quart a day keeps the doctor away

A judicious labourer would probably always have some ale in his house, and have small beer for the general drink. There is no reason why he should not keep Christmas as well as the farmer; and when he is mowing, reaping, or is at any other hard work, a quart, or three pints, of really good fat ale a-day is by no means too much.
William Cobbett, Cottage Economy, 1822

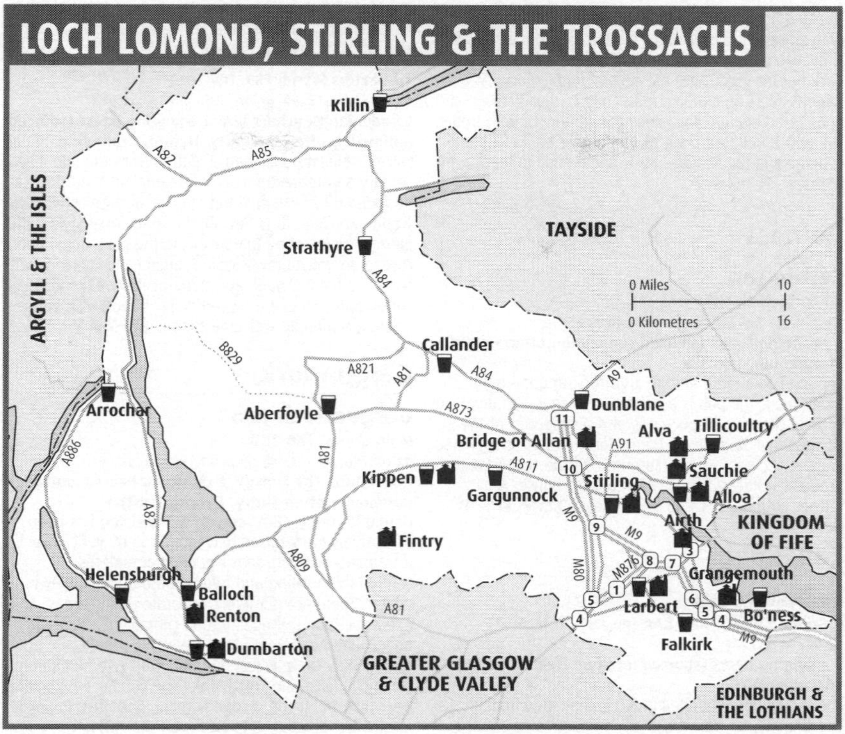

Aberfoyle

Forth Inn ✔

8 Main Street, FK8 3UQ

☎ (01877) 382372 🌐 forthinn.com

Harviestoun Schiehallion; 3 changing beers (sourced regionally; often Belhaven, Cairngorm, Fallen) Ⓗ

This 100-year-old, family-run inn is by the River Forth within the Trossachs National Park. The cosy wood-panelled bar is decorated with historic local photographs and is a magnet for tourists and locals alike. The pub proudly serve only Scottish ales from up to four handpumps (just one in January and February), with third-pint taster glasses available. The restaurant offers wholesome food featuring locally sourced produce. There is a separate dining room and a baronial dining hall. Accommodation is in six en-suite bedrooms.
Q🐴❀🛏◑♿⛺♣P🚌(X10A)🐾

Alloa

Bobbing John ✔

46 Drysdale Street, FK10 1JL

☎ (01259) 222590

Caledonian Deuchars IPA; Greene King Abbot; Sharp's Doom Bar; 3 changing beers (sourced regionally; often Harviestoun, Hybrid, Williams Bros) Ⓗ

The building dates from 1895 and is named after locally born John Erskine, who created industrial Alloa, developing the town as a coal-mining centre. He was twice Secretary of State for Scotland under Queen Anne; however, his frequent changes of political allegiance earned him the nickname Bobbing John. Much of the building's original stonework has been retained and a Victorian shopfront reintroduced. Alcoholic drinks are served from 11am. Q🐴❀◑♿⇌♣🚌📶

Arrochar

Village Inn ✔

Shore Road, G83 7AX (down A814 from A83 jct)

☎ (01301) 702279 🌐 villageinnarrochar.co.uk

5 changing beers (sourced nationally; often Fallen, Fyne Ales, Loch Lomond) Ⓗ

A popular haven for walkers to the Arrochar Alps, the inn affords fine views of Loch Long and the Cobbler. The bar to the left is welcoming and warm, and serves a wide range of ales from both local and more distant breweries. Accommodation and meals are available. The pub can be reached by rail or bus, and the journey is well worth the effort. 🐴❀🛏◑♿⛺♣P🚌(926,976)🐾📶

Balloch

Dog House Bar

54 Balloch Road, G83 8LE

☎ (01389) 607300 🌐 doghouseballoch.co.uk

1 changing beer (often Loch Lomond)

REAL ALE BREWERIES

Allanwater 🛢 Bridge of Allan
Black Wolf Stirling
Devon 🛢 Sauchie
Fallen Kippen
Fintry Fintry
Harviestoun Alva
Hybrid Grangemouth
Lennox Dumbarton (NEW)
Loch Lomond Renton
SLOPEmeisteR Airth (NEW)
Tryst Larbert
Williams Bros Alloa

The Dog House is a good combination of a traditional bar with a fire at the back and a modern bar to the front. Ale is available in the front bar but will be brought to the back bar for you. There are several large sports TV screens and frequent live music nights, plus karaoke and open mic. Canine companions are welcomed with treats. The pub is situated close to the bonnie banks of Loch Lomond and the National Park, and is easy to reach from Glasgow. ▲⇌➡😋🛜

Bo'ness

Corbie Inn
84 Corbiehall, EH51 0AS
☎ (01506) 825307 ⊕ corbieinn.co.uk
6 changing beers (sourced regionally; often Hybrid, Strathbraan, Tryst) ⊞
The Inn has a large lounge area serving good home-made food. The pub is a community venue and involved in local charity projects – it is also a supporter of the Bo'ness real ale festival. Handy for the Bo'ness & Kinneil Railway, Bo'ness Motor Museum and the Hippodrome, Scotland's oldest purpose-built picture house. A former local CAMRA Pub of the Year. Q👪❀◖▶P➡🛜

Callander

Engine Room
9 Bridge Street, FK17 8AA (on A81 off Main St)
☎ 07814 051321
3 changing beers (sourced locally; often Fallen, Tryst, Windswept) ⊞
The Engine Room opened in 2019, converted from a café. The friendly, no-frills micropub is one of only a small number in Scotland. It has a comfortable mix of benches and chairs, with plenty of railway memorabilia on display. Beers and opening hours are reduced November to March – check before visiting. Q▲➡(59)❀

Dumbarton

Captain James Lang 🅻 ✅
97-99 High Street, G82 1LF
☎ (01389) 742112
Greene King Abbot; 4 changing beers (sourced nationally; often Loch Lomond) ⊞
Few pubs in the Glasgow area boast a beer garden but this well-designed Wetherspoon features a large outdoor area overlooking the River Leven. The pub was converted from a Woolworths store and has a light, open layout with a variety of seating options. It is named after the renowned captain of the paddle steamer Leven, which was built in the town. Regular trains and buses serve the area. Alcoholic drinks are served from 11am. 👪❀◖&⇌(Central) ➡🛜

Dunblane

Tappit Hen ✅
Kirk Street, FK15 0AL
☎ (01786) 825226 ⊕ thetappithen-dunblane.co.uk
Greene King IPA; 3 changing beers (sourced regionally; often Broughton, Inveralmond, Kelburn) ⊞
Taking its name from a type of Scottish pewter drinking vessel, this is a traditional one-room pub with a friendly atmosphere. Refurbished in 2019 to an excellent standard, it is situated opposite one of Scotland's oldest cathedrals. The pub holds charity and community events, and a real ale festival once or twice a year. The railway station and car parking are both close by. 👪⇌➡❀🛜

Falkirk

Wheatsheaf Inn ✅
16 Baxters Wynd, FK1 1PF
☎ (01324) 638282 ⊕ wheatsheaffalkirk.co.uk
Caledonian Deuchars IPA; 3 changing beers (sourced nationally; often Cromarty, Hybrid, Orkney) ⊞
Falkirk's oldest public house, dating from the late 18th century and retaining much of its original character, can be found off the High Street via one of the vennels. The wood-panelled bar is furnished in traditional style with plenty of interesting features from the past. Guest beers come from microbreweries in Scotland and England, with two on offer midweek and three at the weekend. Tea, coffee and snacks are served daily. A must-visit venue, offering a friendly welcome for all. ❀⇌➡❀🛜

Gargunnock

Gargunnock Inn
Main Street, FK8 3BW
☎ (01786) 860333 ⊕ gargunnockinn.co.uk
House beer (by Fintry); 2 changing beers (sourced nationally; often Fintry, Hybrid, Tryst) ⊞
Dating from the 18th century, this building has been extensively modernised to create a roomy yet cosy pub/restaurant. The bar room has original features, comfortable seating and two wood-burning stoves in winter. There are numerous separate dining areas. An extensive menu of quality food (notably chicken with haggis and Aberdeen Angus steaks) is served throughout. There is just one bar, with two handpumps serving at least one Scottish ale. The pub hosts an annual beer festival on the second Sunday in August. Popular local walks abound. Q👪❀◖&♣P➡(X10)❀🛜

Helensburgh

Ashton
74 West Princes Street, G84 8UG
☎ (01436) 675900
Stewart Pentland IPA; 2 changing beers (sourced nationally) ⊞
A warm welcome awaits at this genuine local. The bar has been tastefully modernised and decorated with a nautical theme while retaining its original charm. There is a small room for playing darts. A changing selection of ales from Scottish microbreweries is complemented by quality English beers. Live music is a regular Saturday night feature. ⇌(Central)♣➡(1B,316)❀🛜

Henry Bell ✅
19-29 James Street, G84 8AS
☎ (01436) 863060
Greene King Abbot; changing beers (sourced nationally; often Loch Lomond) ⊞
Close to the recently revamped town centre and esplanade, this sympathetic Wetherspoon conversion of an old furniture showroom has now established itself as an important real ale outlet in the area. Offering a wide range of beers from across Britain, it is a busy and popular venue both with locals and visitors. The walls are adorned with TVs in homage to Helensburgh-born John Logie Baird and the decor is in the style of Charles Rennie Mackintosh. Alcoholic drinks are available from 11am. Q👪❀◖&⇌(Central) ➡(1B,316) 🛜

Killin

Coach House Hotel
Lochay Road, FK21 8TN
☎ (01567) 820349 ⊕ hotelkillin.co.uk

2 changing beers (sourced regionally; often Fyne Ales, Kelburn, Strathbraan) ⊞
Small family-owned hotel, amid magnificent scenery, frequented by locals and tourists. The comfortable bar has a wood-burning stove, pool table and a parrot. Good reasonably priced food is available. Two handpumps feature Scottish beers (one in winter). The gantry boasts a large selection of whiskies. There is a Caravan Club site opposite. Children are welcome until 8pm. From March to October the bar hosts live music on a Friday or Saturday night. Winter hours vary.
ॐ✿☎◑Å♣P☐✿ 🛜

Falls of Dochart Inn
Gray Street, FK21 8SL
☎ (01567) 820270 ⊕ fallsofdochartinn.co.uk
3 changing beers (sourced regionally; often Coul, Fyne Ales, Hybrid) ⊞
This historic coaching inn is set in a prime position by the bridge over the Falls of Dochart. The bar features a large open fireplace, stone-tiled floor and three handpumps (fewer in winter). Good food is served in the bar and dining rooms. Along with the bedrooms in the inn there is also self-catering accommodation at the rear of the hotel. Children and dogs are welcome. Opening hours vary during the winter – check before travelling.
ॐ✿☎◑ÅP☐✿ 🛜

Kippen

Cross Keys
Main Street, FK8 3DN
☎ (01786) 870293 ⊕ kippencrosskeys.com
House beer (by Fallen); 2 changing beers (sourced locally; often Fallen) ⊞
Comfortable old coaching inn with a rustic feel – one of the oldest of its kind in Stirlingshire. A locals' pub with a traditional feel, it has low ceilings, wood-panelled walls and a wooden floor. Log fires warm the bar in winter and the beer garden has great views in summer. It is popular with walkers, cyclists, golfers and fishermen. Ideal as a stopover whether travelling north or south, it is near Loch Lomond & the Trossachs National Park, with Stirling close by. Q ॐ✿☎◑♣☐ (X10)✿ 🛜

Larbert

Station Hotel ✅
2 Foundry Loan, FK5 4AW
☎ (01324) 557186 ⊕ stationhotellarbert.com
5 changing beers (sourced nationally; often Black Iris, Mallinsons, Titanic) ⊞
A popular local next to the railway station and on regular bus routes. It prides itself on the help it gives to a number of community groups. Three to five cask ales are usually on offer and efforts are made to provide a variety of local, regional and national ales. Largescreen TVs show sporting events. It has a cosy lounge area and a large enclosed beer garden. The pub is a supporter of CAMRA's Larbert Real Ale Festival in nearby Dobbie Hall in the spring. ✿☎◑&☐P☐

Stirling

Birds & Bees
Easter Cornton Road, FK9 5PB (off Causewayhead Rd)
☎ (01786) 473663 ⊕ thebirdsandthebees-stirling.com
3 changing beers (sourced regionally; often Fallen, Inveralmond, Williams Bros) ⊞
Welcoming rustic converted farmstead between the historic Wallace Monument and Stirling Castle. An award-winning gastropub, it serves locally sourced food. Three

handpumps dispense a variety of good-quality Scottish real ales. Two large beer gardens feature a barbecue area in the courtyard and a pétanque pitch. A popular pub with a good mix of locals and tourists. ✿◑♣P☐✿

Portcullis Hotel
Castle Wynd, FK8 1EG (adjacent to Stirling Castle)
☎ (01786) 472290 ⊕ theportcullishotel.com
2 changing beers (sourced nationally; often Cairngorm, Hybrid, Timothy Taylor) ⊞
Historic building dating from 1787, originally the grammar school and now a popular pub/hotel adjacent to Stirling Castle esplanade. James VI of Scotland was educated on this site. Exposed stone walls and an open fireplace with ornate surround help create a warm welcome in the heart of old Stirling. Frequented by tourists and supported by locals, it is renowned for its food and regularly changing selection of Scottish and English ales. Always busy, diners are advised to reserve a table. ॐ✿☎◑≠P☐ 🛜

Settle Inn
91 St Marys Wynd, FK8 1BU
☎ (01786 463403)
3 changing beers (sourced nationally; often Castle Rock, Oakham, Titanic) ⊞
Warm, friendly and atmospheric inn frequented by a mix of locals, students and tourists. Situated on a hill descending from Stirling Castle, it was built in 1733 and is the oldest pub in Stirling. There is music on Monday, Wednesday, Friday and Saturday evenings, and a quiz on Sunday. The pub hosts an annual beer festival.
ॐ≠♣☐✿ 🛜

Strathyre

White Stag
Main Street, FK18 8NA
☎ (01877) 384224 ⊕ thewhitestag.co.uk
3 changing beers (sourced nationally; often Harviestoun, Orkney, WooHa) ⊞
Cosy pub that serves meals in its bar and bistro, all made with local produce. The beers are mainly Scottish, with a few from England. Dogs and children are welcome in the bar. Hill walking, fishing, golf and watersports are all close at hand, and Stirling, Callander and the Trossachs are within easy travelling distance. Accommodation is available on-site. Opening hours are reduced in winter – check before travelling. Local CAMRA branch Pub of the Year in 2018. Q ॐ✿☎◑Å♣P☐ (C60,160,S60)✿ 🛜

Tillicoultry

Royal Arms
2 High Street, FK13 6AE
☎ (01259) 753037
3 changing beers (sourced nationally; often Morland, Stewart, Timothy Taylor) ⊞
This unpretentious, drinks-only pub continues to thrive under an enthusiastic owner. The bar caters mainly for local trade, with a dartboard, large sports TVs and fruit machine. It is furnished with comfortable seating, bar stools and a Victorian fireplace with log-burner. A quieter side room with service via a small counter is ideal for families. Three handpumps are in use, dispensing changing beers. The pub is well served by regular bus routes to Stirling and Alloa. ॐ✿♣☐✿ 🛜

NORTHERN ISLES

UNST

YELL

A968

SHETLAND

A970

A971

MAINLAND

Lerwick

A970

ORKNEY

Swannay   Rousay

Quoyloo   A966

Stromness   A965   A961   Kirkwall

HOY   MAINLAND

0 Miles   20
0 Kilometres   32

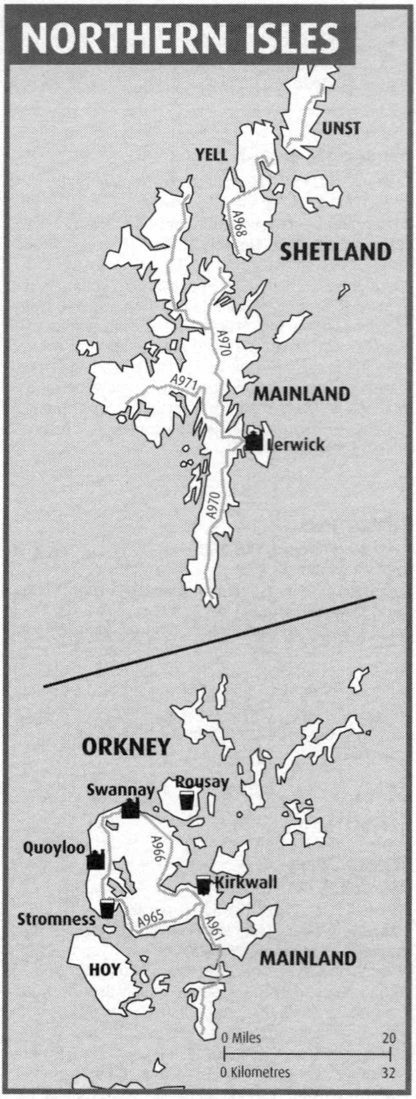

Kirkwall: Orkney

Auld Motor Hoose
26 Junction Road, KW15 1AB
☎ (01856) 871422 ⊕ auldmotorhoose.co.uk
Swannay Scapa Special ℍ
A friendly motor-themed pub with a single bar room, featuring lots of motoring memorabilia and car parts scattered throughout. The jukebox tends to blast out rock classics. There is regular live music, mainly at weekends, and the pub is one of the venues for the Orkney Rock Festival. Outside, the patio has a smoking area. It is the sister bar to the Torvhaug in Bridge Street and convenient for the bus station. Two-times CAMRA Northern Isles Pub of the Year. 🏵🕭♣▲🚌(X1)🏵🐾🛜

Ayre Hotel
Ayre Road, KW15 1QX
☎ (01856) 873001 ⊕ ayrehotel.co.uk

Swannay Scapa Special ℍ
Overlooking Kirkwall harbour, the Ayre dates back to 1791 in parts and was at one time a Temperance Hotel. There are plenty of comfortable seats in the lounge to relax with a pint after a day exploring local visitor attractions. Meals are served lunchtimes and evenings featuring Orkney beef, fish and other local produce. A new conservatory is used for dining (booking advised for meals). Close to the bus station and ferries to the outer isles of Orkney. 🏨🕭🕭♿▲♣🚌🛜

Helgi's Bar
14 Harbour Street, KW15 1LE (by harbour)
☎ (01856) 879293 ⊕ helgis.co.uk
Swannay Scapa Special; 2 changing beers (sourced locally; often Swannay) ℍ
Converted from a former shipping office, this small, smart bar has the look of a modern café with wood panelling and a floor of local stone. There is always one dark beer available. Special food nights where food is matched with ales are a highlight. Regular music sessions and a weekly Thursday quiz night are also hosted. Set on the harbour front where seafood is landed daily, this is a handy place to fill in time before island hopping on the many ferries to outlying parts. A former local CAMRA Pub of the Year. No under-18s. 🕭♿▲🚌🛜

Shore
Shore Street, KW15 1LG (on harbour road)
☎ (01856) 872200 ⊕ theshore.co.uk
Swannay Scapa Special ℍ
This smart, modern bar at the pier head may be the ideal place to recuperate after a rough ferry crossing from a north isle or it could be the first experience of a Scottish bar for cruise ship passengers. The main street is just round the corner where a wide range of shops can be found and also St Magnus Cathedral, which was founded in 1137 by the Viking Earl Rognvald. Cross over the road to catch a ferry to many other Northern Isles. 🏨🕭🕭♿▲🚌🐾🛜

St Ola Hotel
Harbour Street, KW15 1LE
☎ (01856) 875090 ⊕ stolahotel.co.uk
Swannay Scapa Special; 1 changing beer (sourced locally; often Swannay) ℍ
Built overlooking the harbour on the site of the Inns of Sinclair dating back to the 14th century, the Ola is a short walk from all of Kirkwall's major attractions. It has a traditional public bar complete with a roaring fire in winter and the larger lounge to the rear where food is served. Ales are available in both bars along with an extensive range of whiskies. A music session is held on the last Sunday afternoon of the month. 🏵🏨🕭♿▲♣🐾🛜

Rousay: Orkney

Taversoe
Frotoft, KW17 2PT (2 miles W of ferry) HY405273
☎ (01856) 821325 ⊕ taversoehotel.co.uk
1 changing beer (often Swannay)
The Taversoe is a little gem on the island of Rousay, run almost single-handedly by the owner. It offers an enticing selection of reasonably priced home-cooked food including Orkney beef and locally caught seafood.

REAL ALE BREWERIES

Lerwick Lerwick: Shetland
Orkney Quoyloo: Orkney
Swannay Orkney: Swannay

The stunning view from the dining area is worth the trip in itself. There is a meet-and-greet from the Tingwall ferry, otherwise the inn is around a two-mile walk. The island, dubbed The Egypt of the North, has more than 160 archaeological sites. Q❀⇆◑♿ÅP🐾ᯤ

Stromness: Orkney

Ferry Inn

10 John Street, KW16 3AD (across from ferry terminal)
☎ (01856) 850280 🌐 ferryinn.com
Swannay Scapa Special; 2 changing beers (sourced locally; often Orkney, Swannay) Ⓗ
An easy walk from the harbour front, the Ferry is handy for buses to Kirkwall and the mainland ferry from Scrabster. It is popular with locals and visitors, including divers who come to Orkney to explore the sunken German fleet at Scapa Flow. Various attractions nearby include the Ring of Brodgar and Skara Brae village. Annual folk and blues festivals are held, with a marquee erected outside complete with an ale pump. A previous local CAMRA Pub of the Year winner.
❀⇆◑Å♣P🚌🐾ᯤ

Stromness Hotel

15 Victoria Street, KW16 3AA (opp pier head)
☎ (01856) 850298 🌐 stromnesshotel.com
Swannay Scapa Special; 2 changing beers (sourced locally; often Swannay) Ⓗ
On the first floor of this imposing hotel you will find the Hamnavoe Lounge, with windows and a small balcony giving commanding views of the harbour. In winter a roaring fire and comfy settees welcome visitors and there is a separate whisky bar with over 100 bottles to choose from. The Flattie Bar downstairs, open all year round, is complete with a flattie (a small boat) hanging from the ceiling and serves a Swannay ale. Jazz, blues and beer festivals are held throughout the year. The hotel and upstairs bars are closed November to March.
❀⇆◑ÅP🚌

SCOTLAND

Scottish beer

Just as monks call their Lenten beers 'liquid bread', it's tempting to call traditional Scottish ales 'liquid porridge'. They are beers brewed for a cold climate, a country in which beer vies with whisky for nourishment and sustenance. Brewers blend not only darker malts with paler grains, but also add oats, that staple of many foodstuffs in the country. In common with the farmer-brewers of the Low Countries and French Flanders in earlier centuries, domestic brewers in Scotland tended to use whatever grains, herbs and plants were available to make beer. The intriguing use of heather in the Fraoch range of ales recalls brewing practice in Scotland from bygone times.

The industrial revolution arrived later in Scotland than in England, and industry tended to concentrate in the Lowland belt around Alloa, Edinburgh and Glasgow. As a result, brewing remained a largely domestic affair for much longer and – as with early Irish ales – made little use of the hop, which could not grow in such inhospitable climes.

Brewing developed on a commercial scale in the Lowlands in the early 19th century at the same time as many French emigres, escaping the revolution, settled in the Scottish capital. They dubbed the rich, warming local ales 'Scottish Burgundy'. Real wine from France, always popular in Scotland as a result of the Auld Alliance, become scarce during the Napoleonic Wars, and commercial brewing grew rapidly to fill the gap and to fuel the needs of a growing class of thirsty industrial workers.

Traditionally, Scottish ales were brewed in a different manner to English ones. Before refrigeration, beer was fermented at ambient temperatures far lower than in England. As a result, not all the sugars turned to alcohol, producing rich, full-bodied ales. As hops had to be imported from England at considerable cost, they were used sparingly. The result was a style of beer markedly different to English ones: vinous, fruity, malty and with only a gentle hop bitterness. Many of the new breed of ales produced by microbrewers in Scotland tend to be paler and more bitter than used to be the norm. For the true taste of traditional Scottish ales you will have to sample the products of the likes of Belhaven, Broughton, Caledonian and Traquair.

The language of Scottish beers is different, too. The equivalent to English mild is called Light (even when it's dark in colour), standard bitter is called Heavy premium bitter Export, while strong old ales and barley wines (now rare) are called Wee Heavies. To add to the complexities of the language differences, many traditional beers incorporate the word Shilling in their names. A Light may be dubbed 60 Shilling, a Heavy 70 Shilling, an Export 80 Shilling, and a Wee Heavy 90 Shilling. The designations stem from a pre-decimalisation method of invoicing beer in Victorian times. The stronger the beer, the higher the number of shillings. Until recent times, cask-conditioned beer in Scotland was served by air pressure. In the pub cellar a water engine, which looks exactly the same as a lavatory cistern but works in reverse, used water to produce air pressure that drove the beer to the bar. Sadly, these wonderful Victorian devices are rarely seen, and the Sassenach handpump and beer engine dominate the pub scene.

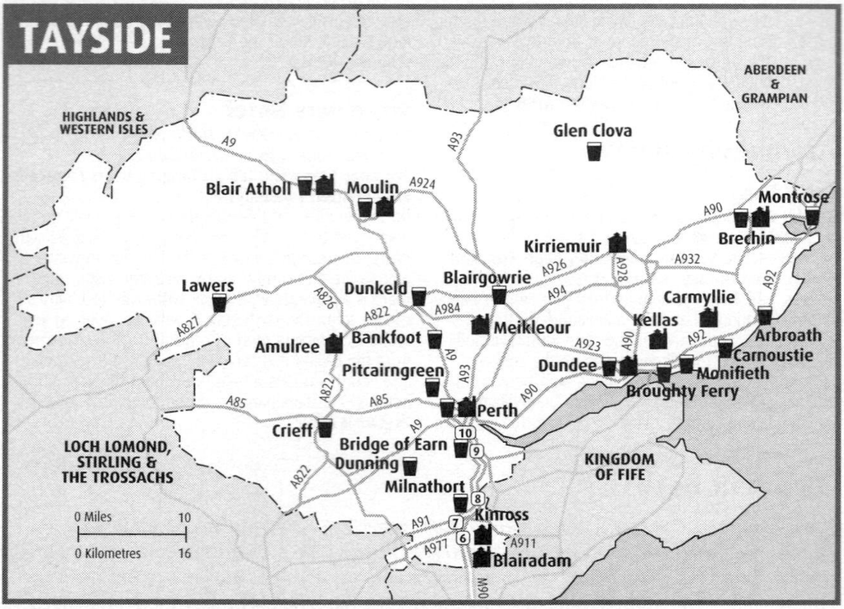

Authority areas covered: Angus UA, City of Dundee UA, Perth & Kinross UA

Arbroath

Corn Exchange

14 Olympic Centre, Market Place, DD11 1HR

(01241) 432430 .

Caledonian Deuchars IPA; Greene King Abbot; Sharp's Doom Bar; 3 changing beers (sourced nationally)

Located just off the High Street, this Wetherspoon is in what used to be a corn exchange in the 19th century. Although it is largely open plan there are a number of booths providing some privacy. A varied selection of real ales is always available, with alcoholic drinks served from 11am. Boat trips offering fishing or a visit to the 200-year-old Bell Rock lighthouse can be taken from the nearby harbour.

Bankfoot

Bankfoot Inn

Main Street, PH1 4AB

(01738) 787243 bankfootinn.co.uk

Inveralmond Ossian; 2 changing beers (sourced regionally; often Cromarty, MòR Beers, Strathbraan)

Real ale and a commitment to local breweries are features of this pub. It comprises a public bar, small lounge and adjoining restaurant, all warmed by two real fires in winter. Good food is available, with fish and chips a highlight either to eat inside or take away. There is a large whisky selection. Outdoor seating at the front of the pub catches the sun on fine days.
(23,27)

Blair Atholl

Atholl Arms Hotel

PH18 5SG

(01796) 481205 athollarmshotel.co.uk

Moulin Light, Braveheart, Ale of Atholl, Old Remedial

A characterful hotel with an imposing façade in the traditional Highland style. Its Bothy Bar serves four ales produced by the local Moulin Brewery, as well as freshly cooked food. Blair Atholl and the surrounding area are popular for walking, climbing, biking and sightseeing. The Bothy Bar's opening hours may be shorter out of season but all four ales can be brought through to the lounge bar. Q P (M91,87)

Blairgowrie

Ericht Alehouse

13 Wellmeadow, PH10 6ND

(01250) 872469

6 changing beers (sourced nationally)

Classic town-centre pub with a friendly atmosphere, close to the River Ericht. It has two seating areas separated by a well-stocked bar. A wide range of different ales and ciders is served, alongside increasing numbers of Scottish gins, malts and rums. No food is available but customers are welcome to bring their own. A winner of local CAMRA Pub of the Year several times over the past two decades. Q

REAL ALE BREWERIES

71 Brewing Dundee
Blunt Chisel Blairadam
Cullach Perth (NEW)
Dalrannoch Meikleour
Inveralmond Perth
Kirrie Kirriemuir (brewing suspended)
Law Dundee
Loch Leven Kinross
MòR Kellas
Moulin Moulin
Park Brechin (brewing suspended)
Redcastle Carmyllie
Strathbraan Amulree
Wasted Degrees Blair Atholl

Fair o' Blair 🄻 ✔
25-29 Allan Street, PH10 6AB
☎ (01250) 871890
Caledonian Deuchars IPA; 4 changing beers (sourced regionally; often Inveralmond, Redcastle, Stewart) Ⓗ
Town-centre Wetherspoon run by a real ale enthusiast. It features a small beer garden to the rear on two levels, the lower of which is accessible by wheelchair. The pub is near the Wellmeadow, the grassy triangular plot that has been a venue for markets and outdoor entertainment since 1824. Alcoholic drinks are served from 11am. 🐴◐♿♣●📶

Stormont Arms 🄻
101 Perth Street, PH10 6DT
☎ (01250) 873142
1 changing beer (sourced regionally; often Kelburn, Strathaven, Strathbraan) Ⓗ
Real ale is served from two handpulls in this traditional Scottish two-roomed pub, with Strathbraan ales featuring more than most. The friendly bar has wooden bench seating and a dartboard, and hosts a darts league during the week. A small seating area outside includes space for smokers. The pub may close early if quiet so check before travelling. A 10-minute walk from the town centre but many buses stop nearby. Q♣🚌🐾📶

Brechin

Brechin Arms
44 St David Street, DD9 6EQ
☎ (01356) 625405
1 changing beer (sourced regionally; often Orkney, Stewart) Ⓗ
Small, cosy pub in the town's main street, with a mixed clientele. The single handpump serves a regularly changing real ale. The interior features a lounge and quiet alcoves with easy access from the bar. Brechin has historically been described as a city due to its cathedral. Hence the local football club is Brechin City, reputedly the only senior side in Europe whose ground has a hedge along one of its perimeters. ♿♣🐾

Bridge of Earn

Cyprus Inn 🄻
Back Street, PH2 9AB
☎ (01738) 812313
1 changing beer (sourced locally; often Loch Leven Brewery, Strathbraan) Ⓗ
A friendly wee pub that has a great community atmosphere, with a separate lounge/function room and a large beer garden. The small, cosy bar area has fixed bench seating and a low ceiling. The inn itself dates back to around 1790 and is a Category C listed building. Original rings on external walls for tying up horses are now used by cyclists! It only has one handpull but the landlord changes the barrels over quickly so you never have long to wait for the next ale. Q🐴❀🛏🚌🐾📶

Broughty Ferry

Fisherman's Tavern
12-16 Fort Street, DD5 2AD
☎ (01382) 775941 🌐 fishermanstavern-broughtyferry.co.uk
Greene King IPA; house beer (by Belhaven); 4 changing beers (sourced nationally) Ⓗ
Licensed since 1857, this famous hostelry was originally three fishermen's cottages, later converted into a small hotel. The bar is to the right of the entrance, and a snug is to the left, leading to the dining room/lounge, warmed by a real fire. The lounge to the rear has wheelchair access from Bell's Lane. This Belhaven/Greene King-managed house serves ales from Scottish and English breweries. It hosts an annual beer festival in July. 🐴❀🛏◐♿⇌🐾📶

Jolly's Hotel ✔
43a Gray Street, DD5 2BJ
☎ (01382) 734910
Caledonian Deuchars IPA; Greene King Abbot; Sharp's Doom Bar; 3 changing beers (sourced nationally) Ⓗ
Named after John Jolly, its proprietor for two decades in the late 19th century, this Wetherspoon hotel has expanded considerably over the years. It features two large areas, one for drinking and dining, the other principally for dining. The numerous handpulls serve a wide selection of ales to a mixed clientele. The TV screens are usually muted. An outdoor patio area has a number of tables. 🐴❀🛏◐♿⇌●🚌(73)📶

Ship Inn
121 Fisher Street, DD5 2BR
☎ (01382) 779176 🌐 theshipinn-broughtyferry.co.uk
Timothy Taylor Landlord; 2 changing beers Ⓗ
Traditional free house on the waterfront, giving views over the Tay towards Fife. Dating back to 1847, when it was first listed as a spirit dealer serving the fisher folk of Broughty Ferry, this cosy retreat is atmospheric and interesting, with several nautical features. Three well-kept real ales are usually served. A range of tasty bar meals is on offer and there is a restaurant upstairs. Pavement seating outside the pub is available for fine weather. 🛏◐⇌🐾📶

Carnoustie

Station Hotel
103-105 Dundee Road, DD7 6AR
☎ (01241) 852447 🌐 stationhotelcarnoustie.com
Inveralmond Ossian; Timothy Taylor Landlord; 1 changing beer (sourced nationally; often Fuller's, Shepherd Neame) Ⓗ
Beside Carnoustie railway station on the East Coast Main Line, the Station has long been a feature of the town. It is now established as a real ale pub, serving two regular beers plus one constantly changing guest in both the public and lounge bars. The pub is a 15-minute walk from the town's famous golf course, a venue for the Open Championship. 🛏◐⇌♣P🚌(73)🐾📶

Crieff

Quaich Bar 🄻
47 High Street, PH7 3HT
☎ (01764) 656136 🌐 thequaichbar.co.uk
2 changing beers (often Inveralmond, Strathbraan) Ⓟ
Relaxed and informal family-run bar, grill and coffee house. The atmosphere is quiet, with no TV or jukebox – just a log-burning stove that is more than welcome in the winter months. Two ales are usually available on electric pump. A selection of books is provided for customers. Q🐴◐♿🚌(15)🐾📶

Dundee

Bank Bar ✔
7-9 Union Street, DD1 4BN
☎ (01382) 205037 🌐 thebankbardundee.com
Fyne Ales Jarl; house beer (by Marston's); 2 changing beers (sourced nationally) Ⓗ
A former bank with bare-board floors, wooden furnishings and a series of alcoves with tables, in the tradition of older Scottish city pubs. Two or three ales are

usually available and food is served until 7pm every day. Quality live music features on most Friday and Saturday nights. ◑⇌🚌🐾📶

Market 𝕃

7-9 Seagate, DD1 2EG

☎ (01382) 224591 🌐 marketdundee.co.uk

4 changing beers (sourced nationally; often Law) Ⓗ

Formerly the Capitol cinema, built in 1945, but then converted into a large public house. A staircase rises to the large upper seating area, which is primarily earmarked as the family area. Popular with both shoppers during the day and lively on Friday and Saturday evenings with occasional live music. Also showing Sky sports and BT sports on 10 TVs plus big screen. Six handpulls with local ale from Law often on. ♘◑♿⇌🚌(73) 📶

Phoenix

103 Nethergate, DD1 4DH

☎ (01382) 200014

Caledonian Deuchars IPA; Timothy Taylor Landlord; 3 changing beers (sourced nationally) Ⓗ

One of Dundee's oldest pubs, this traditional inn has a great atmosphere. Subdued lighting, sturdy wooden tables and chairs, green leather benches and a rare Ballingall Brewery mirror give the place character. Five ales are on offer, along with excellent pub food at sensible prices. The location is handy for the Rep Theatre, Dundee Contemporary Arts and Bonar Hall. Warm and cosy, like pubs used to be. ◑⇌🚌(73)🐾📶

Speedwell Bar (Mennies) ★ ✔

165-167 Perth Road, DD2 1AS

☎ (01382) 667783 🌐 speedwell-bar.co.uk

3 changing beers (sourced nationally) Ⓗ

Built in 1903 for James Speed, this pub is known as Mennie's after the family who ran it for more than 50 years. The L-shaped bar is divided by a part-glazed screen and has a magnificent mahogany gantry and counter, dado-panelled walls and an anaglypta Jacobean ceiling. There are usually three ales to choose from, alongside a selection of Belgian bottled beers and around 150 malt whiskies. You can take in your own food. 🚌🐾📶

Dunkeld

Perth Arms 𝕃

High Street, PH8 0AJ

☎ (01350) 727270

Strathbraan Due South, Head East Ⓗ

Cosy one-room establishment serving a mix of locals and tourists. This friendly place has been in the same family for almost 50 years and is the area's oldest trading pub, dating back to 1795. Its two handpulls dispense ales that are mostly from local breweries. The beer garden at the back has an area for smokers. ♘❀◑🚌🐾📶

Royal Dunkeld Hotel 𝕃

Atholl Street, PH8 0AR

☎ (01350) 727322 🌐 royaldunkeld.co.uk

3 changing beers (sourced regionally; often Cairngorm, Loch Leven Brewery, Strathbraan)

On the main street, this former coaching inn is now a comfortable hotel featuring a restaurant, lounge bar and public bar with an open fire. A pool room with dartboard is adjacent. Two local and one changing guest ale are available on three handpumps. Good food is served in the bar and restaurant. The large beer garden is a suntrap in summer. The hotel is an ideal base for outdoor activities including walking, fishing and golf. ♘❀🛏◑♣P🚌🐾📶

Dunning

Dunning Hotel 𝕃

2 Station Road, PH2 0RH

☎ (01764) 684242 🌐 thedunninghotel.com

Harviestoun Schiehallion; 1 changing beer (often MòR Beers) Ⓗ

A welcoming and cosy village inn near the steeple of St Serf's Church, dating from the early 18th century. According to legend, the Dunning dragon was slain by St Serf, hence the pub's dragon logo. Around a mile west of the village stands a 20ft-high stone cross, a memorial to Maggie Wall who was burned here as a witch in 1657. ❀🛏◑🚌(17) 🐾

Kirkstyle Inn ✔

Kirkstyle Square, PH2 0RR

☎ (01764) 684248 🌐 thekirkstyleinn.co.uk

House beer (by Marston's); 2 changing beers (sourced nationally) Ⓗ

A traditional village inn dating from 1760, overshadowed by the impressive Norman steeple of St Serf's Church, home to the ancient Dupplin Cross and other Pictish relics. One or two ales in the cosy public bar come from a variety of Scottish independents, as well as English and Welsh regional breweries. The pub also serves its house ale, Risky Kelt. There is a separate restaurant. ♘❀◑🚌(17) 🐾📶

Glen Clova

Glen Clova Hotel 𝕃

Milton of Clova, DD8 4QS

☎ (01575) 550350 🌐 clova.com

House beer (by Burnside); 1 changing beer (sourced regionally) Ⓗ

Situated near the head of one of Scotland's most beautiful glens, this hotel is popular with walkers after a day on the hills. Its bar has a large log-fired stove and plenty of character. Two handpumps supply the ales, usually from Scottish breweries. Local food, including lamb, pheasant and venison, is served in both the bar and adjoining restaurant. The hotel offers a range of accommodation from bunkhouse to self-catering luxury lodge. ♘🛏◑P🐾📶

Lawers

Ben Lawers Hotel 𝕃

Loch Tay, PH15 2PA

☎ (01567) 820436 🌐 benlawershotel.co.uk

3 changing beers (often Strathbraan)

In the heart of one of Scotland's most beautiful and accessible unspoilt areas, this small hotel provides fantastic views over Loch Tay. It is popular with walkers, having the Ben Lawers mountain range, including numerous Munros, on its doorstep. Its handpulls serve Strathbraan ales, alongside Helles lager and a selection of bottled and canned Tempest beers. Good food and accommodation are offered. Closed in January, and on Tuesday and Wednesday all winter. ♘❀🛏◑P🐾📶

Milnathort

Village Inn

36 Wester Loan, KY13 9YH

☎ (01577) 863293

3 changing beers (sourced nationally) Ⓗ

Friendly local with a semi open-plan interior featuring classic brewery mirrors and local historical photographs. The comfortable lounge area has low ceilings, exposed joists and stone walls, and the bar area is warmed by a log fire. The pub has been family-owned since 1985 and usually serves three beers, mostly locally sourced. Milnathort links some great cycling routes through the Ochils, via Burleigh Castle, to the more leisurely Loch Leven Heritage Trail.

Monifieth

Milton Inn

Grange Road, DD5 4LU

(01382) 532620 themiltoninn.co.uk

3 changing beers (sourced nationally)

The only premises in Monifieth serving real ale, which it does with a passion. There are usually three beers to choose from, alongside good home-made food at fair prices. The pub is set back from the road, with large gardens and a sunny decked area to the rear providing a nice sheltered spot for a pint in the fresh air. Entertainment features regularly. Q P (75)

Montrose

Market Arms

95 High Street, DD10 8QY

(01674) 673384

2 changing beers (sourced regionally; often Inveralmond, MòR Beers, WooHa)

Stylishly renovated a few years ago, this busy town-centre pub provides a comfortable retreat for its wide mix of customers. Two handpulls are sited on a long bar near the entrance in the main open area. Several TVs show live sport, and there is a snug at the front for those wishing to enjoy a quiet pint. Beers are mostly sourced from Scottish brewers. Convenient for visitors to the nearby Montrose Air Station Heritage Centre.

Moulin

Moulin Inn

11-13 Kirkmichael Road, PH16 5EH

(01796) 472196 moulininn.co.uk

Moulin Light, Braveheart, Ale of Atholl, Old Remedial

First opened in 1695, the inn is the oldest part of the Moulin Hotel, situated within the village square at an ancient crossroads just east of Pitlochry. Full of character and charm, it is traditionally furnished and has two log fires. A good choice of home-prepared local fare is available, along with four Moulin beers, brewed in the old coach house behind the hotel. There is an area outside for dining and drinking in good weather. An ideal base for outdoor pursuits, with several marked walks nearby. Q P

Perth

Capital Asset

26 Tay Street, PH1 5LQ

(01738) 580457

Caledonian Deuchars IPA; Greene King Abbot; Sharp's Doom Bar; 3 changing beers (sourced nationally)

A Wetherspoon pub that was formerly a savings bank. High ceilings and ornate cornices have been retained; pictures of old Perth adorn the walls of the open-plan lounge which overlooks the River Tay. A large safe from the building's banking days can be seen in the family area. Six ales are dispensed, with food available all day. Local ale drinkers enjoy the twice-yearly beer festivals. Q (7)

Cherrybank Inn

210 Glasgow Road, PH2 0NA

(01738) 624349 cherrybankinn.co.uk

Harviestoun Bitter & Twisted; Inveralmond Ossian; 3 changing beers (sourced nationally)

This 250-year-old former drovers' inn is a popular watering hole and stopover for travellers. Five ales from Inveralmond and other Scottish independents are dispensed in the public bar or the larger L-shaped lounge. Good bar lunches and evening meals are served. There is a large, sunny elevated wooden decking to the rear. The inn has seven en-suite rooms, and golf can be arranged for residents. P (7)

Old Ship Inn

31 High Street, PH1 5TJ

07956 924767 oldshipinnperth.co.uk

House beer (by Belhaven); 2 changing beers (often Belhaven, Fyne Ales, Harviestoun)

Said to be the oldest pub in Perth, having traded under the same name since 1665. This was the city's oasis for real ale in the 1980s, and now serves one regular beer and two changing ales. A large oil painting of a sailing ship adds interest in the timber-lined bar, which is lightened by a frieze and white-painted ceiling. The upstairs lounge was closed for 20 years before reopening in 2018. (7)

Pitcairngreen

Pitcairngreen Inn

PH1 3LP

(01738) 583022 pitcairngreeninn.co.uk

2 changing beers (sourced locally; often Strathbraan)

A fairly large establishment with several different areas including a snug warmed by an open log fire. The inn has a real enthusiasm for good beer, served on three handpulls. This is also the finest place in Tayside to enjoy real ciders and perries, presented professionally and with passion. The car park is just across the road. Local CAMRA Cider Pub of the Year. Q P (14,15)

Choosing pubs

CAMRA members and branches choose the pubs listed in the Good Beer Guide. There is no payment for entry, and pubs are inspected on a regular basis by personal visits; publicans are not sent a questionnaire once a year, as is the case with some pub guides. CAMRA branches monitor all the pubs in their areas, and the choice of pubs for the guide is often the result of democratic vote at branch meetings. However, recommendations from readers are welcomed and will be passed on to the relevant branch: write to Good Beer Guide, CAMRA, 230 Hatfield Road, St Albans, Hertfordshire, AL1 4LW; or send an email to: **gbgeditor@camra.org.uk**

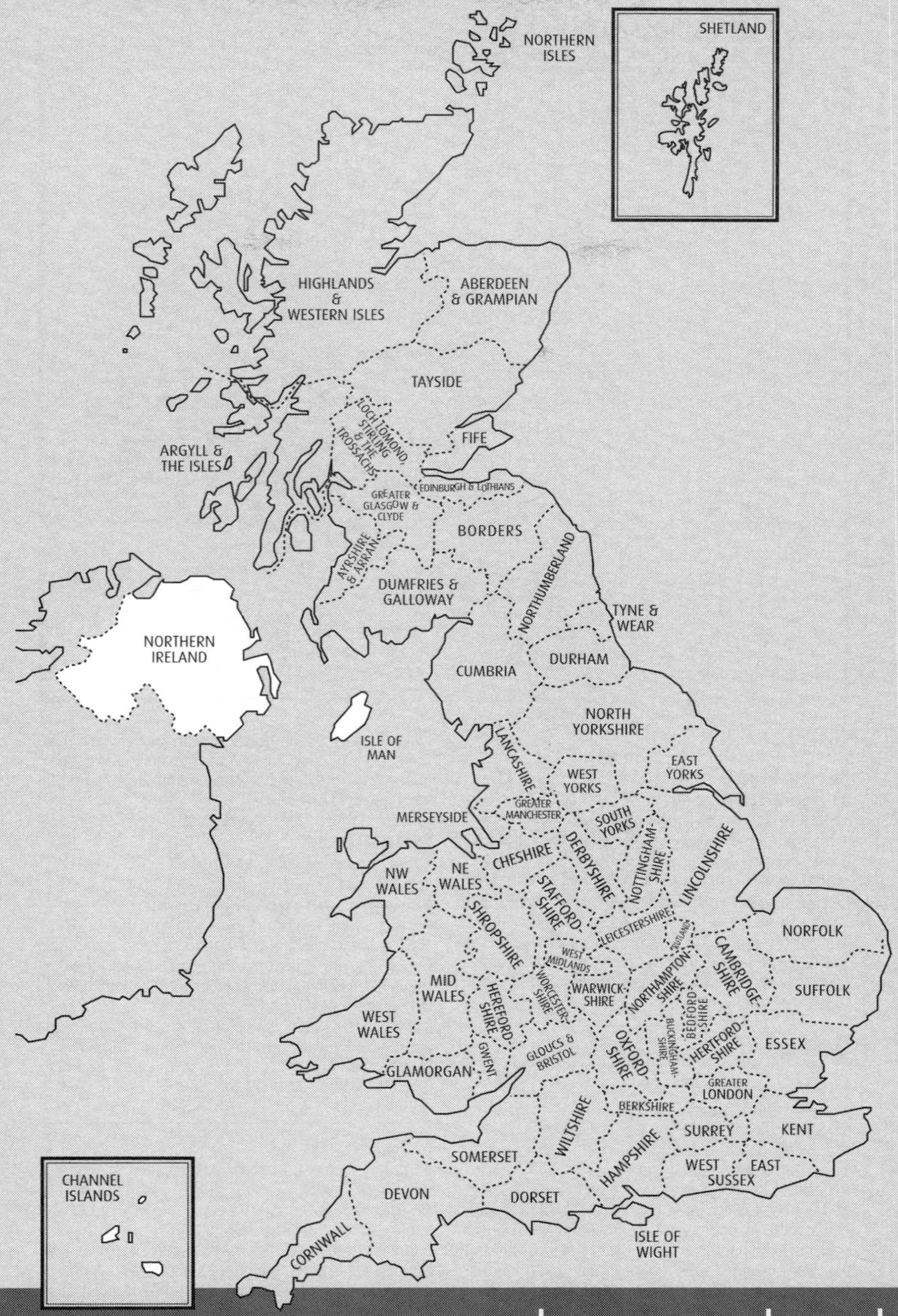
NORTHERN ISLES
SHETLAND
HIGHLANDS & WESTERN ISLES
ABERDEEN & GRAMPIAN
TAYSIDE
LOCH LOMOND, STIRLING & THE TROSSACHS
FIFE
ARGYLL & THE ISLES
EDINBURGH & LOTHIANS
GREATER GLASGOW & CLYDE
BORDERS
AYRSHIRE & ARRAN
DUMFRIES & GALLOWAY
NORTHUMBERLAND
TYNE & WEAR
NORTHERN IRELAND
DURHAM
CUMBRIA
NORTH YORKSHIRE
ISLE OF MAN
LANCASHIRE
EAST YORKS
WEST YORKS
GREATER MANCHESTER
SOUTH YORKS
MERSEYSIDE
CHESHIRE
DERBYSHIRE
NOTTINGHAM-SHIRE
LINCOLNSHIRE
NW WALES
NE WALES
STAFFORD-SHIRE
SHROPSHIRE
LEICESTERSHIRE
RUTLAND
NORFOLK
WEST MIDLANDS
CAMBRIDGE-SHIRE
MID WALES
HEREFORD-SHIRE
WORCESTER-SHIRE
WARWICK-SHIRE
NORTHAMPTON-SHIRE
SUFFOLK
BEDFORD-SHIRE
BUCKINGHAM-SHIRE
WEST WALES
GWENT
GLOUCS & BRISTOL
OXFORD-SHIRE
HERTFORD-SHIRE
ESSEX
GLAMORGAN
GREATER LONDON
BERKSHIRE
WILTSHIRE
SURREY
KENT
SOMERSET
HAMPSHIRE
WEST SUSSEX
EAST SUSSEX
CHANNEL ISLANDS
DEVON
DORSET
ISLE OF WIGHT
CORNWALL

Northern Ireland
Channel Islands
Isle of Man

NORTHERN IRELAND

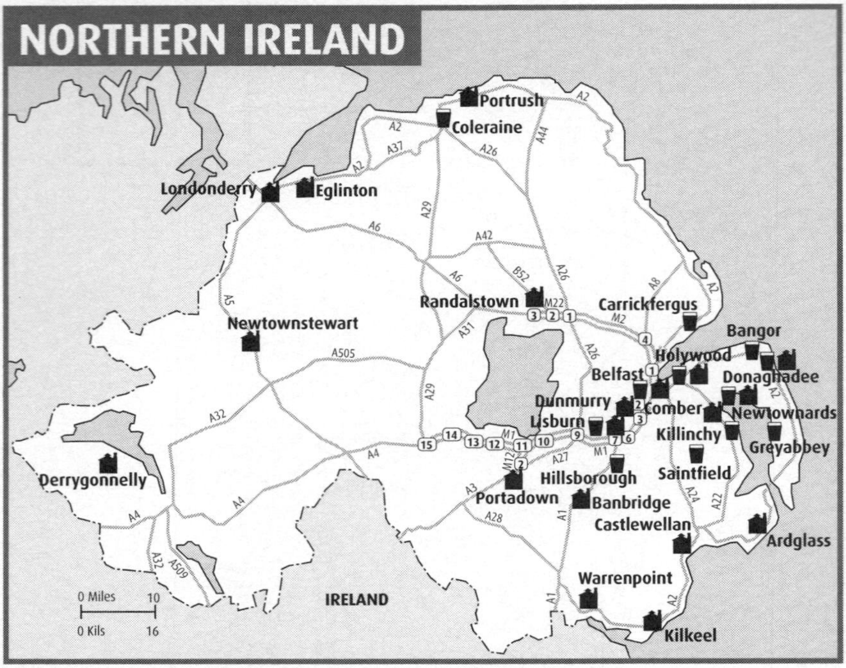

Bangor

Jenny Watts
41 High Street, BT20 5BE
☎ (028) 9127 0401 🌐 jennywattsbar.com
1 changing beer (sourced regionally; often Lacada) Ⓗ
Bangor's oldest pub has a traditional interior, with a central bar plus stone walls and flooring. It has served real ale for years and its single handpump now dispenses Sharp's Doom Bar or occasionally a local ale. Good food is available every day. The pub hosts live music Wednesday to Friday and jazz on Sunday afternoon. Ruby's Lounge upstairs hosts 80s and 90s nights. There is a beer garden to the rear. Q🐴❀◐◑♿⇌

Belfast

Bridge House ✔
37-43 Bedford Street, BT2 7EJ
☎ (028) 9072 7890
Greene King Abbot; Sharp's Doom Bar; changing beers (sourced nationally) Ⓗ
Reputed to be one of Wetherspoon's busiest bars, the Bridge House sells a wide choice of real ale from eight handpumps. Its bar area has been brightened over the years and the beer quality improved. There is a dining area upstairs and a beer terrace to the rear. Open from 8am, with alcoholic drinks served from 11.30am (12.30pm Sun). Q🐴❀◐◑♿⇌🍎🚌📶

Crown ★ ✔
46 Great Victoria Street, BT2 7BA (opp Europa Hotel and Great Victoria St station)
☎ (028) 9024 3187
Mourne Mountains Mourne Gold; St Austell Nicholson's Pale Ale; 4 changing beers (sourced nationally) Ⓗ
This historic pub is an architectural masterpiece and a top spot for quality real ale. Its six handpumps serve Nicholson's Pale Ale alongside a mixture of local and national beers. Bag-in-box cider is occasionally available. There are also three handpumps upstairs in the dining rooms; good food can be obtained both here and in the main bar. Q◐◑♿⇌🍎🚌

Errigle Inn
312-320 Ormeau Road, BT7 2GE
☎ (028) 9064 1410 🌐 errigle.com
5 changing beers (sourced locally; often Farmageddon, Knockout Brewing, Whitewater) Ⓗ
The Errigle Inn is a beer enthusiast's haven. Ale and food can be enjoyed in peace in the quiet back bar, the Oak Lounge. It has five handpumps mainly supporting local breweries – beers from Hilden, Whitewater, Farmageddon, Knockout, Bullhouse, Beer Hut and Lacada are frequently available along with some national brands, and often handpulled cider. There are also tap takeovers and occasional beers from the wood. CAMRA Northern Ireland Pub of the Year 2019. Q◐◑♿🍎🚌📶

John Hewitt
51 Donegal Street, BT1 2FH (100yds from St Anne's Cathedral)
☎ (028) 9023 3768
Shepherd Neame Master Brew Ⓗ
Named after the poet, this is a busy single-room bar with a large snug in one corner and a stage area in another. It differs from most bars in that it is run by the Belfast Unemployed Resource Centre; its profits fund the Centre's charitable work. The pub is also a popular venue for live traditional music and art exhibitions. Its single handpump dispenses a Shepherd Neame beer or a local brew from Hercules. Q🐴◐♿🚌

McHughs
29-31 Queens Square, BT1 3FG (near Albert Clock)
☎ (028) 9050 9999 🌐 mchughsbar.com
Whitewater Maggie's Leap IPA Ⓗ
Housed in Belfast's oldest building, McHughs is a lively pub with several different drinking and dining areas. The

main public bar has a handpump exclusively dispensing ales from Whitewater Brewery. Next to it is the restored old bar where wall paintings depict scenes from Belfast's history. Good food is served and TV sport is a big draw. Music is a regular feature – often folk or traditional – and the basement hosts a variety of acts.
Q (Central)

Northern Lights

451 Ormeau Road, BT7 3GQ
(028) 9029 0291 galwaybaybrewery.com/northernlights
1 changing beer (sourced regionally) H
Galway Bay Brewery's first pub in Northern Ireland is very much a modern craft beer bar. It serves up to 20 changing beers on draught, roughly half from its own portfolio and the rest from a range of Northern Ireland breweries. One handpump dispenses cask ales from a number of Irish breweries. An impressive selection of bottled and canned beers is also available. Local CAMRA Pub of the Year 2020. Q

Sunflower

65 Union Street, BT1 2JG
(028) 9023 2474 sunflowerbelfast.com
1 changing beer (sourced locally; often Hilden) H
This busy corner bar is one of the few that has replaced Ireland's most famous beverage with Double Stout from Hercules Brewery. There is also a handpump with a variety of beers from Hilden, plus a selection of craft beers. Music takes place seven days a week and beer events are hosted. The large beer garden is a popular attraction where pizza is available Thursday, Friday, and Saturday evenings. Q

Carrickfergus

Central Bar

13-15 High Street, BT38 7AN (opp castle)
(028) 9335 7840
Greene King IPA; Sharp's Doom Bar; 3 changing beers (sourced nationally) H
Lively market-town community local with a loyal clientele. This Wetherspoon pub has a ground-floor public bar of robust character and a quieter family-friendly first-floor loggia-style sitting room with exposed timber trusses, affording fine views from its many windows over Belfast Lough and the adjacent 12th-century castle. Handpumps on both levels serve two house beers and three guest ales, usually from mainland micros, or local beers such as Whitewater. Alcoholic drinks are served from 11.30am (12.30pm Sun). Q

Coleraine

Fairley's Bar

62-64 Railway Road, BT52 1PF
(028) 7032 0047
4 changing beers (sourced locally; often Lacada) P
A bar and off-licence near Coleraine's railway station. Its interior features a bar that opens up to a quieter area, leading to a lounge with real fire. The real ale is exclusively from the Lacada Brewery in Portrush and dispensed from KeyKegs. Drinks can also be purchased from the well-stocked off-licence and consumed in the bar.

Donaghadee

Moat Inn

102 Moat Street, BT21 0ED
(028) 9188 3297 themoatinn.com
Whitewater Belfast Ale; 1 changing beer (sourced locally; often Whitewater) H
A long-established hostelry conveniently near landmarks on the Ards Peninsula. It offers a public bar, lounge, Henry's Bistro and a beer garden. The bar is compact though comfy and is populated with rugby-loving locals. There are two handpumps with beers from Whitewater Brewery. In addition good food is available in the lounge and bistro. Q

Greyabbey

Wildfowler Inn

1 Main Street, BT22 2NE (6 miles S of Newtownards on A20)
(028) 4278 8234 wildfowlerinn.co.uk
Ards Scrabo Gold; 1 changing beer (sourced locally; often Ards) H
This is a restaurant with a small public bar situated on the east coast of the Ards Peninsula. It has a tiled and stone floor, exposed oak beams and stained-glass windows. The real ale is on two handpumps, one in the public bar and one in the restaurant, offering a changing choice of brews from Ards Brewing Company, less than two miles away. Phone ahead to find out which beers are on.
Q P

Hillsborough

Hillside

21 Main Street, BT26 6AE
(028) 9268 9233 hillsidehillsborough.co.uk
Hilden Twisted Hop; house beer (by Hilden) H
A bar and restaurant about 12 miles from Belfast. There are a number of comfortable areas to drink and dine in. The front bar houses two handpumps with ales mainly from Hilden Brewery, often the house beer, Hillside Embers. The late summer beer festival is popular, and during the year the bar plays host to musical acts, quizzes and curry nights. It is notably dog-friendly.
Q

Holywood

Dirty Duck Ale House

3 Kinnegar Road, BT18 9JN

REAL ALE BREWERIES

Ards Newtownards
Baronscourt Newtownstewart (NEW)
Beer Hut Kilkeel
Black Mountain Lisburn (NEW)
Boundary Belfast
Bullhouse Newtownards
Farmageddon Comber
Fermanagh Derrygonnelly
Hercules Belfast
Hilden Lisburn
Hillstown Randalstown
Knockout Belfast
Lacada Portrush
Lecale Ardglass (NEW)
MashDown Banbridge (NEW)
McCracken's Portadown (NEW)
Modest Holywood (NEW)
Mourne Mountains Warrenpoint
Norn Iron Dunmurry
Northbound Eglinton
Rough Brothers Londonderry (NEW)
Twisted Kettle Donaghadee (NEW)
Whitewater Castlewellan

☎ (028) 9059 6666 🌐 thedirtyduckalehouse.co.uk
House beer (by Hilden); 3 changing beers (sourced nationally; often Inveralmond, Sharp's, Shepherd Neame) Ⓗ
A single-room bar with a restaurant upstairs. Three regularly changing ales are served, and good food is available in the bar and upstairs restaurant. Attractions include a great view over Belfast Lough, collections of pumpclips and plastic ducks, and a corner in honour of local golf star Rory McIlroy. A summer beer festival is held every year in the roomy beer garden.
Q🚼❀◐♿⇌📶

Killinchy

Daft Eddy's 𝕃
Sketrick Island, BT23 6QH (2 miles N of Killinchey at Whiterock Bay)
☎ (028) 9754 1615 🌐 dafteddysni.co.uk
1 changing beer (sourced locally; often Farmageddon) Ⓗ
Refurbishment has enhanced this establishment. The lounge bar area, warmed by a wood-burning stove, has a modern feel; the former public bar is now Little Eddy's coffee bar. Beers dispensed by the handpump on the restaurant side of the bar include brews from the nearby Farmageddon Brewery. The restaurant serves quality local food, with oysters and lobster among the specialties. There is also an alfresco dining area.
Q🚼❀◐♿P🐾📶

Lisburn

Tap Room Hilden
Hilden House, Grand Street, Hilden, BT27 4TY
☎ (028) 9266 3863 🌐 taproomhilden.com
2 changing beers (sourced locally; often Hilden) Ⓗ
The Tap Room is alongside the Hilden Brewery, in the grounds of the Scullion family's Georgian mansion near Lisburn. It is a restaurant with a bar and seating areas, and offers alcohol only with meals. High-quality seasonal, locally sourced food is served alongside two ales from the brewery. Many events are hosted including an annual music and beer festival, brewery tours and separate taproom functions. Q🚼❀◐♿⇌(Hilden)🚌

Tuesday Bell ✔
4 Lisburn Square, BT28 1TS
☎ (028) 9262 7390
Greene King Abbot; Sharp's Doom Bar; 2 changing beers (sourced nationally) Ⓗ
A city-centre Wetherspoon pub spread over two floors, close to the bus station. It is well established as a part of Lisburn's social life, and a popular location for eating and drinking, especially at the weekend. There are five handpumps downstairs and three upstairs dispensing a changing range of beers. A bag-in-box cider is regularly offered. Alcohol is available from 11.30am (12.30pm Sun). Q🚼◐♿⇌🍎P🚌📶

Newtownards

Spirit Merchant ✔
54-56 Regent Street, BT23 4LP (next to bus station)
☎ (028) 9182 4270
Greene King Abbot; Sharp's Doom Bar; 2 changing beers (sourced nationally) Ⓗ
Near the bus station, about 10 miles from Belfast, this Wetherspoon pub has a long bar with booths on the right and a large outside area on the left. Its five handpumps dispense two regular beers and a changing range of guests. The ale is always kept in good order by the manager and staff. Alcohol is available from 11.30am (12.30pm Sun). Q🚼❀◐♿▲🚌📶

Saintfield

White Horse
49-53 Main Street, BT24 7AB
☎ (028) 9751 1143 🌐 whitehorsesaintfield.com
Whitewater Copperhead, Maggie's Leap IPA Ⓗ
This former coaching inn and Whitewater Brewery tap is now a busy food-oriented establishment. A bar, restaurant and pizza parlour are housed in a bright white-painted building at the end of the main street. Two Whitewater ales are on handpump, often Copperhead and Maggie's Leap. There is music at weekends and the pizza parlour is open Thursday to Saturday. Q🚼❀◐♿🚌

Crown, Belfast (Photo: K.Mitch Hodge/Unsplash)

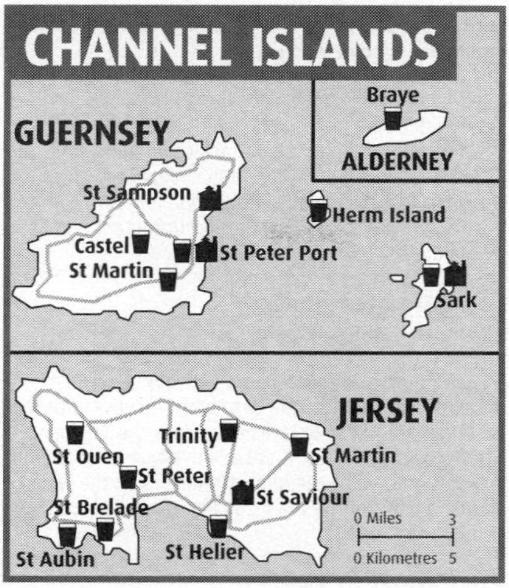

ALDERNEY

Braye

Divers Inn

Braye Street, GY9 3XT

☎ (01481) 822632 🌐 brayebeach.com

2 changing beers (sourced nationally; often Fuller's, Sharp's) Ⓗ

Traditional pub with a great atmosphere, attached to the Braye Beach Hotel. It serves two real ales and has a good bar menu. The interior features wooden tables, chairs and counter, and is warmed by real fires. Walking through the bar area reveals sea views and a superb outdoor seating space overlooking the beach. Themed and musical events attract locals and visitors alike, and make this a must-visit location when on Alderney. 🛏◐⚌♣

GUERNSEY

Castel

Fleur du Jardin ✔

Kings Mills, GY5 7JT

☎ (01481) 257996 🌐 fleurdujardin.com

3 changing beers (sourced regionally; often White Rock) Ⓗ

A building of unique charm with two bars – one traditional, small and cosy, attached to the restaurant, the other renovated in a more contemporary style to create a comfortable, relaxing area to enjoy a beer. A door leads to a large covered patio and out to the garden. Menus in both the bar and restaurant feature fresh local produce. The car park can be busy in summer. Q🐴❀🛏◐♿P🚌🐾

Rockmount Restaurant & Bar

Cobo Coast Road, GY5 7HB

☎ (01481) 252778 🌐 therocky.gg

4 changing beers (often Randalls) Ⓗ

The pub comprises a large lounge bar and a taproom that shows sport on TV. The lounge has an emphasis on food, served lunchtimes and evenings, but there are comfy chairs near the fire for drinkers. Five handpumps offer a changing range of beers and you can also try a tasting paddle of different ales. Q🐴❀◐♿🍎P🚌(41,42)🐾📶

Herm Island

Mermaid Tavern ✔

GY1 3HR

☎ (01481) 750050 🌐 herm.com/mermaid

House beer (by Liberation); 2 changing beers Ⓗ

A welcoming inn on the beautiful island of Herm, a short trip by ferry from Guernsey. The large courtyard is a popular spot in summer; an open fire adds to the charm in winter. The house beer is Liberation's Herm Island Gold, brewed specially for the island. The pub holds regular themed music and food events, and hosts real ale and cider festivals in June and September. 🐴❀◐⛺♣🍎🐾📶

St Martin

Les Douvres Hotel

La Fosse, GY4 6ER

☎ (01481) 238731 🌐 lesdouvreshotel.co.uk

3 changing beers (often White Rock) Ⓗ

Former 18th-century manor house, set in private gardens in St Martin near the south coast, two and a half miles from St Peter Port, with cliff walks and a tiny fishing harbour. A well-maintained, changing range of beers is offered on three handpumps, and real cider during the season. Excellent meals, including pizzas, are served in the bar and separate restaurant. Live music features on Friday night and occasional Wednesdays. ❀🛏◐🍎P🚌

St Peter Port

Cock & Bull

Lower Hauteville, GY1 1LL

☎ (01481) 722660 🌐 cockandbullguernsey.com

5 changing beers (often Marston's, Randalls) Ⓗ

The pub is just up the hill from the town church. It serves a good mix of local and national ales, with Marston's beers a regular feature, plus real cider in summer. Seating is on three levels, with a pool table on the lower level. Live music features throughout the week, with blues, jazz or baroque on Monday, open mic on Tuesday and Irish folk on Thursday. A meat draw is held on Friday. Open on Sundays when rugby is on. 🍎🚌📶

Golden Lion 🏆

7 Market Street, GY1 1HF

☎ (01481) 726634 🌐 thegoldenlion.gg

4 changing beers (sourced nationally) Ⓗ

Town-centre pub opposite the former market. The single room has a long bar serving up to six real ales and four real ciders, with the feel of a modern craft beer bar. (The beer range is reduced in winter.) Gluten-free ales are available in bottles. Live music is performed at weekends. The first floor Lions Den is open in the evenings and available for private hire. Local CAMRA Pub of the Year 2019 and 2020 and Cider Pub of the Year 2020. 🍎🚌📶

Pickled Pig, Duke of Normandie Hotel

Lefebvre Street, GY1 2JP

☎ (01481) 721431 🌐 dukeofnormandie.com/pickled-pig

Liberation Ale Ⓗ

REAL ALE BREWERIES

Isle of Sark La Seigneurie: Sark
Liberation St Saviour: Jersey
Randalls Guernsey: St Peter Port
White Rock Guernsey: St Sampsons

ISLANDS

Pub on the ground floor of a town-centre hotel just off the High Street. Its three rooms offer different seating areas that are easily accessible to each other. There is an emphasis on dining, but you are welcome to come in just for a drink, with stools and armchairs available. Gluten-free beer is sold in bottles and there are gluten-free options on the menu. ❀⇌◑P ᯤ

Red Lion

Les Banques, GY1 2RX

☎ (01481) 724042

4 changing beers (often Randalls) Ⓗ

Friendly pub on the outskirts of St Peter Port, with two bar areas – a lounge overlooking Belle Greve Bay to the front and a public area at the rear. Gluten-free beer is available in bottles, and real cider is served in summer. Numerous TVs show sport. Meat draws are held on Friday and Saturday evenings. The pub is on several bus routes and the cycle route between St Peter Port and St Sampson. ❀◑●🚌🐾ᯤ

Slaughterhouse

Castle Pier, GY1 1AN

☎ (01481) 712123 🌐 slaughterhouse.gg

6 changing beers (often Randalls) Ⓗ

Popular harbourside pub offering fine views over Havelet Bay and the harbour from its mezzanine restaurant and large outdoor terrace. The Randalls-managed pub serves a changing range of up to six real ales, some from small breweries. Winner of a CAMRA design award in 2019 for its conversion from an abbatoir. ❀◑♿

JERSEY

St Aubin

Trafalgar Inn ✔

Charing Cross, JE3 8AA

☎ (01534) 741334 🌐 trafalgarinn.com

5 changing beers (often Butcombe, Liberation, St Austell) Ⓗ

A traditional community pub with a strong nautical theme. There are two bars – a saloon at the front and a sports bar with pool, darts and TV behind. The five handpumps in the sports bar serve a rotating selection of ales, nearly always including one from Liberation Brewery. This is the local rugby pub – the Jersey Reds often drink here after Saturday home matches. ♿♣🚌🐾

St Brelade

Old Smugglers Inn ✔

Le Mont du Ouaisne, JE3 8AW

☎ (01534) 741510 🌐 oldsmugglersinn.com

Draught Bass; house beer (by Liberation); 2 changing beers (often Marston's, Ringwood, Skinner's) Ⓗ

Perched on the edge of Ouaisne Bay, the Smugglers has been the crown jewel of the Jersey real ale scene for many years. Steeped in history, dating back to when pirates came to enjoy an ale or two here, it is set within granite-built fishermen's cottages with foundations reputedly from the 13th century. Up to four ales are available including one from Skinner's, and mini beer festivals are held regularly. The pub is known for its good food including fresh daily specials. Q◑●P🐾

St Helier

Biere Atelier

Bath Street, JE2 4ST

☎ (01534) 874059 🌐 labastille.bar

Purity Pure Gold, Pure UBU; 1 changing beer (sourced nationally; often Purity) Ⓗ

This bar on the corner of Bath Street and Hilgrove Street could be described as Jersey's first micropub. A single room with a few tables and stools around the walls, it has a small bar counter with real ales on handpump and a craft beer wall behind. The pub is popular with office workers and is becoming a destination for real ale lovers. It is linked with the nearby Bastille restaurant and bar where the beers are also available. ♿

Lamplighter L ✔

9 Mulcaster Street, JE2 3NJ

☎ (01534) 723119

8 changing beers (sourced nationally) Ⓗ

A traditional pub with a modern feel. The gas lamps that gave the pub its name remain, as does the original antique pewter bar top. An excellent range of up to eight real ales is served – the largest selection on the island – including one from Skinner's. A real cider is sometimes also on offer. ●🐾ᯤ

Post Horn L ✔

Hue Street, JE2 3RE

☎ (01534) 872853

Butcombe Original; Draught Bass; Liberation Ale, IPA; 1 changing beer (often Liberation) Ⓗ

Busy, friendly pub adjacent to the precinct and five minutes' walk from the Royal Square. It is particularly popular at lunchtimes, with its own nucleus of regulars. Up to four draught ales are served alongside a good selection of freshly cooked food. The spacious L-shaped public bar extends into the lounge area featuring an open fire and sports TV. There is a large function room on the first floor, a drinking area outside and a public car park nearby. ❀◑♿🐾ᯤ

Prince of Wales Tavern

8 Hilgrove Street, JE2 4SL

☎ (01534) 737378

Courage Best Bitter; Fuller's London Pride; Ringwood Boondoggle; Sharp's Doom Bar; Wychwood Hobgoblin Gold; 5 changing beers (sourced nationally; often Shepherd Neame) Ⓗ

A traditional pub next to the market, offering a large selection of up to eight cask ales advertised on blackboards. The Victorian-style interior features a bright and sparkling bar-back displaying a large selection of whiskies. The beer garden at the rear is a pleasant spot to relax with a pint. ❀●🐾

St Martin

Royal

La Grande Route de Faldouet, JE3 6UG

☎ (01534) 856289

Bombardier; Courage Directors Ⓗ**; 1 changing beer** Ⓖ

Originally a coaching inn, this large country-style hostelry is located at the centre of St Martin with sizeable public and lounge bars, a restaurant and a spacious alfresco area. The interior features traditional furnishings, cosy corners and a real fire in colder months. Owned by Randalls Brewery, it serves guest ales from the Marston's, Sharp's and Skinner's stables. Quality food is popular with locals and visitors alike, with a good menu available lunchtimes and evenings (no food Sun eve). ❀◑♿▲♣P🚌(3) 🐾

Rozel Bar & Restaurant L

La Valle de Rozel, JE3 6AJ

☎ (01534) 863438 🌐 rozelpubanddining.co.uk

Draught Bass; Fuller's London Pride; Liberation Ale; 1 changing beer Ⓗ

A charming pub tucked away in the north-east corner of the island in the picturesque fishing village of Rozel. Bar meals are served in the public bar and snug, where there is a wood-burning stove in winter. A Liberation Group partner pub, it often offers guest ales from Skinner's and Ringwood. The excellent restaurant upstairs can be used for private functions. Outside is a delightful beer garden. P(3)

St Ouen

Farmers Inn

La Grande Route de St Ouen, JE3 2HY
(01534) 485311
Draught Bass; 2 changing beers (often Liberation) H
Friendly community local in the hub of St Ouen, near the war memorial and parish hall. There is a good chance of hearing Jersey French (Jerriais) spoken at the bar in this typical country pub, which offers up to three ales as well as a locally made cider when available (usually April to July). Traditional pub food is served in generous portions. There is seating outside at the front. P

Moulin de Lecq

Le Mont de La Greve de Lecq, JE3 2DT
(01534) 482818 moulindelecq.com
House beer (by Liberation); 2 changing beers (often Marston's, Skinner's) H
A free house, the Moulin is a converted 12th-century watermill in the valley above the beach at Greve de Lecq. The waterwheel is still in place and the turning mechanism can be seen behind the bar. A large restaurant adjoins the mill and can be hired for functions. There is a pool table in the second-floor games room. The children's play space and a barbecue area are used extensively in the summer. QP

St Peter

Tipsy

La Route de Beaumont, JE3 7BQ
(01534) 485556 thetipsy.co.uk
6 changing beers (sourced nationally; often Castle Rock, Elland, Liberation) H
The Tipsy, formerly The Tipsy Toad, was the site of the original Skinner's Brewery before it moved to Cornwall. The friendly pub has recently been refurbished to provide a main bar with comfortable seating. Six handpumps dispense a rotating selection of ales, often including a house beer from Liberation, Tipsy Toad Ale. A large selection of gins is also available. The separate restaurant offers an extensive menu. Outside is a heated patio area. There are plans to reopen the microbrewery.
P(9)

Trinity

Trinity Arms

La Rue es Picots, JE3 5JX
(01534) 864691
Liberation Ale; 1 changing beer (often Butcombe, Liberation) H
Sporting the parish's ancient symbol of the Trinity, this 1976-built establishment is modern by Jersey country pub standards but has plenty of character. Owned by the Liberation Group, it is central to village community life. It has a public bar and restaurant where food is served lunchtimes and evenings, and it opens early for breakfast. There is seating outside, a children's play area and car parking. Close to Jersey Zoo.
P(4)

SARK

Sark

Bel Air

Harbour Hill, GY10 1SB
(01481) 832052
Shepherd Neame Spitfire; 1 changing beer (sourced locally; often Randalls) H
Popular, family-friendly pub that is at the top of Harbour Hill but worth the walk. It serves two real ales and real cider, and offers food all day. There is a cosy fire for cold weather, and a large beer garden and courtyard where food and drink can be enjoyed on warm days. Barbecues and live music feature at the weekend in summer.

The language of beer

Nose: the aroma. Gently swirl the beer to release the aroma. You will detect malt: grainy and biscuity, often likened to crackers or Ovaltine. When darker malts are used, the nose will have powerful hints of chocolate, coffee, nuts, vanilla, liquorice, molasses and such dried fruits as raisins and sultanas. Hops add superb aromas of resins, herbs, spices, fresh-mown grass and tart citrus fruit – lemon and orange are typical, with intense grapefruit notes from some American varieties. Sulphur may also be present when waters are 'Burtonised': i.e. gypsum and magnesium salts have been added to replicate the famous spring waters of Burton-on-Trent.
Palate: the appeal in the mouth. The tongue can detect sweetness, bitterness and saltiness as the beer passes over it. The rich flavours of malt will come to the fore but hop bitterness will also make a substantial impact. The tongue will also pick out the natural saltiness from the brewing water and fruit from darker malts, yeast and hops. Citrus notes often have a major impact on the palate.
Finish: the aftertaste, as the beer goes over the tongue and down the throat. The finish is often radically different to the nose. The aroma may be dominated by malt whereas hop flavours and bitterness can govern the finish. Darker malts will make their presence felt with roast, chocolate or coffee notes; fruit character may linger. Strong beers may end on a sweet or biscuity note but in mainstream bitters, bitterness and dryness come to the fore.

The Family Brewers of Britain

A celebration of British brewing heritage

Roger Protz

A lavishly illustrated hardback book celebrating and examining the contribution to British brewing made by its family brewers. They are the often-overlooked flag bearers for real ale and have fascinating stories to tell of the early days of commercial brewing.

Fully-illustrated, with modern and archive photography of the breweries, their pub estates, people and beers, this book explores the past, the present and the future of these great brewing companies and helps to highlight the important part they continue to play in the nation's brewing story.

RRP: £25.00 **ISBN:** 978-1-85249-359-2

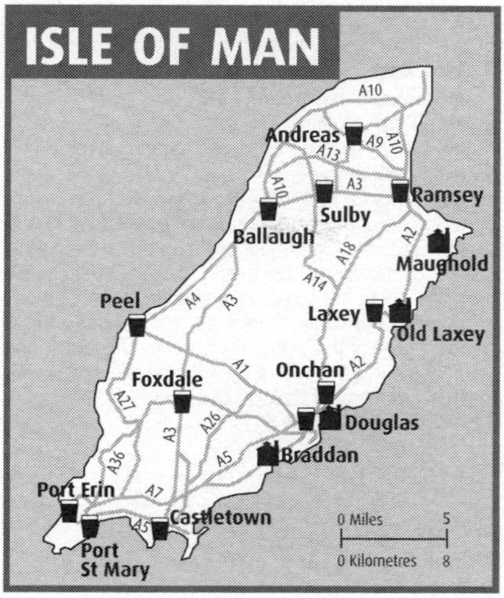

Andreas

Grosvenor Country Inn

Andreas Road, IM7 4HE
☎ (01624) 888007
Odin Manx Mild; Okell's Bitter; 1 changing beer (sourced nationally) H
The Isle of Man's most northerly pub is popular for both drinking and dining. The Tap Room public bar has a real sense of period charm and timeless character. Okell's bitter and Odin Manx Mild are served alongside a guest beer. There is a separate dining section and function room. Darts is played and quiz nights and musical events are held frequently. A large collection of old Shell advertising pictures is on display. P

Ballaugh

Raven ✔

The Main Road, IM7 5EG
☎ (01624) 896128
Okell's Bitter; house beer (by Okell's); 1 changing beer (sourced nationally) H
Village-centre pub next to Ballaugh Bridge on the TT course. There is a comfortable main bar area with dining spaces off to the right and left. To the rear is a separate darts, pool and TV room. Seating space outside is heavily used in summer especially during race periods, when motorbikes leap over the bridge. The house beer is Ravens Claw, a rare Okell's brew exclusively available in this pub. Q P (5,6)

Castletown

Castle Arms ✔

The Quay, IM9 1LD
☎ (01624) 824673
Okell's Bitter, Dr Okell's IPA; 2 changing beers H
Also known locally as the Glue Pot, this two-roomed pub is superbly located between the castle and harbour. It is featured on the Manx £5 note – the only pub in the British Isles to appear on a banknote. One room houses nautical memorabilia; the other celebrates the TT races with photographs and paintings. The patio overlooking the picturesque harbour is popular in summer.
Q (1,2)

Sidings

Victoria Road, IM9 1EF (next to railway station)
☎ (01624) 823282
Bushy's Castletown Bitter, Ruby (1874) Mild, Bitter; Okell's Bitter; 8 changing beers (sourced nationally) H
The former ticket office for the Heritage Steam Railway Station, the Sidings is handily placed for visitors to the many Manx National Heritage attractions in Castletown including Castle Rushen, Old House of Keys, Old Grammar School and Nautical Museum. There is a large bar area with a real fire in winter, an adjacent dining area, a separate games and TV room, and a beer garden at the rear. An unashamedly beer-oriented traditional pub with unpretentious food on offer daily.
Q P (1,2)

Douglas

Albert Hotel ✔

3 Chapel Row, IM1 2BJ (close to bus stands and indoor market)
☎ (01624) 673632
Bushy's Castletown Bitter; Okell's Bitter; 2 changing beers (sourced locally) H
The Albert is a traditional and well-maintained pub close to Douglas Harbour, and the one nearest to the sea terminal. It has an interior recognised by CAMRA as being of regional historic importance. A central bar area serves two rooms – the one to the right features pool, darts and sports TV; to the left is a quieter bar with photographs of Steam Packet boats adorning the walls. The cellar areas are thought to be some of the oldest structures in Douglas. Q

Horse & Plough ✔

Isle of Man Business Park, IM2 2QZ (in Bradden at jct with Vicarage Rd)
☎ (01624) 626060
Okell's Manx Pale Ale, Bitter, Dr Okell's IPA; 1 changing beer (sourced nationally) H
Superbly designed Heron & Brearley business park pub near a housing estate. The spacious interior comprises a large conservatory, a dining area, a comfortable lounge with sports TV and a quieter raised area. There is a beer garden outside. The pub is a popular venue for functions and uses in-house catering for both formal and informal occasions, serving good-value food to a high standard. There is occasional live music. The four real ales are always from Okell's Brewery. P

Old Market Inn

Chapel Row, IM1 2BJ
☎ 07624 381076
Bushy's Bitter; 2 changing beers (often Bushy's) H
Under the same ownership for many years, the Market has the smallest bar on the island, serving two separate rooms. The landlord is a keen TT supporter and the pub's walls are adorned with photos of the races. Two ales are normally on offer, usually from Bushy's. Friendly and very popular with locals, it is close to both the bus station on Lord Street and the ferry terminal, so it makes an ideal waiting room.

REAL ALE BREWERIES

Bushy's Braddan
Odin Maughold (NEW)
Okell's Douglas
Old Laxey Old Laxey

Prospect Hotel ✔

Prospect Hill, IM1 1ET

☎ (01624) 616773

Okell's Manx Pale Ale, Bitter; 6 changing beers (often Okell's) 🅗

Opened in 1857 in the finance sector of the island's capital, this large single-room pub has different areas, some decorated with pictures of the law profession, reflecting its proximity to the law courts. There are eight handpumps in two banks of four on separate sides of the bar. Guest ales change regularly and occasionally real cider and perry are available. Wednesday is quiz night. The rear area known as the Library is full of bookshelves and can be quieter. ◖≠♣🚌 (3,11)🐾📶

Rosemount Hotel ✔

Woodbourne Road, IM1 3HH

☎ (01624) 618500

Okell's Manx Pale Ale, Bitter; 1 changing beer (sourced nationally) 🅗

The Rosemount has three large rooms all served from a central area with separate bar counters. There is a focus on real ale, with three beers usually available. The back room hosts darts and there is a front room with a pool table. A variety of entertainment includes karaoke on Sunday afternoon and live music on Friday and Saturday nights. Q≠♣🚌 (2)🐾📶

Rovers Return

11 Church Street, IM1 2AG

☎ (01624) 676459

Bushy's Bitter; 5 changing beers 🅗

Fascinating pub tucked away in a street behind Douglas Town Hall, featuring handpumps fashioned from fire hoses, a traditional coal fire, and a shrine to Blackburn Rovers in a back room. The almost warren-like series of rooms is frequented by a truly eclectic and loyal clientele. Rare and unusual guest ales complement the Bushy's regular and seasonal beers, with real cider also always available. Famously large food portions are served at lunchtime. ❀◖≠♣●🚌🐾📶

Terminus Tavern ✔

Strathallan Crescent, IM2 4NR

☎ (01624) 624312

Okell's Bitter; 3 changing beers (sourced nationally; often Okell's) 🅗

Found at the Manx Electric Railway station at the northern end of the prom, the Terminus has an extensive and comfortable front bar with large bay windows, and another bar for games at the rear. Decoration in the front bar illustrates interesting architectural features. Okell's Bitter is offered alongside guest beers. Excellent food is served and the pub is often busy. Outside at the front is a large patio with views over Douglas Bay.
Q♨◖◗♿≠♣P🚌 (1,10) 🐾📶

Woodbourne Hotel ✔

Alexander Drive, IM2 3QF (in Woodbourne area of Douglas)

☎ (01624) 676754

Okell's Manx Pale Ale, Bitter, IPA; 3 changing beers (sourced nationally) 🅗

Built in 1895, the Woodbourne is a fantastic example of a large Victorian pub, set in a residential area within walking distance of Douglas town centre. It has three bars ready to serve a wide range of cask ales. Its interior is laid out to a high standard, featuring sports TV in two bars, plus accessible toilets. Q♿♣●🚌🐾📶

Foxdale

Baltic Inn

1 Glentramman Terrace, IM4 3EE

☎ (01624) 801305 🌐 balticinn.pub

Okell's Manx Pale Ale, Bitter; 1 changing beer (sourced nationally) 🅗

The only pub in a former mining town, with one main room divided into separate seating areas. A roaring real fire in winter adds to the atmosphere. Up to three real ales are on handpump along with Okell's IPA and Maclir in bottles. There are some fascinating historical photos on the walls of Foxdale during the mining boom. This friendly village pub is unlike any other on the island, and has undergone a significant revival over the years without losing any of its local character.
Q♨❀🛏◗♿⛺♣🚌 (4) 🐾📶

Laxey

Bridge Inn

6 New Road, IM4 7BE

☎ (01624) 862414

Bushy's Bitter; Odin Manx Mild; 2 changing beers (sourced nationally) 🅗

A traditional pub in the heart of Laxey, dating back to at least 1857. It has two bars, the main one to the right on entering, with pool, darts and a large TV screen for sport. The separate bar room to the left is used at busier periods. In 1897 after the Snaefell mining disaster, in which 20 men perished, the cellars were used as a temporary morgue. The pub is reputedly haunted.
Q♨❀🛏⛺≠♣●🚌🐾📶

Mines Tavern

Captains Hill, IM4 7AY

☎ (01624) 861484

Okell's Manx Pale Ale, Bitter; 1 changing beer (sourced locally) 🅗

Former mine captain's home in a picturesque setting alongside Laxey's historic tram station, with an unusual bar made from a 1902 tram car. A warming fire welcomes visitors in winter; in good weather the garden is popular. Trams run to Douglas, Ramsey and the summit of Snaefell, the island's mountain. The pub is close to the famous Laxey Wheel, and features memorabilia from the local mines and railways. Food is served except in winter, when the opening time is 4pm on weekdays. ❀◖◗⛺≠♣🚌 (3A,3)

Onchan

Manx Arms ✔

Main Road, IM3 1BE

☎ (01624) 675484

Okell's Manx Pale Ale, Bitter, Dr Okell's IPA; 2 changing beers (sourced nationally) 🅗

Traditional village pub on the main road with two separate bar areas. There are large TV screens for sporting fixtures, live music most Saturday evenings and occasional karaoke. Traditional games are played including pool, darts and dominoes. This pub is on the former motorcycle racing Clypse Course and displays racing photographs from the 1950s on the walls. There are attractive heated patios at the front and rear. An extensive choice of real ciders is available.
Q♿♣●P🚌 (3,23) 🐾📶

Peel

Central

12-14 Castle Street, IM5 1AN

☎ (01624) 844143 🌐 thecentral.im
Okell's Bitter; Timothy Taylor Landlord [H]
This small, unspoilt local near the promenade in central Peel was one of the island's first pubs when it was established in 1608. Recently reopened under a new licensee, it is a quiet place where conversation is paramount and there is a focus on real ale. Food is now served, including special offers for the Thursday steak night and Friday fish night. Q🛏◗●🐾ᯤ

Royal Hotel
Atholl Street, IM5 1HG
☎ (01624) 842217
Okell's Manx Pale Ale, Bitter; 2 changing beers (sourced nationally) [H]
For those entering for the first time, the unusual layout of the Royal comes as a surprise. The bar is set deeply to the rear of the building, at the end of a long, narrow corridor within the well-furnished drinking area. Although guest ales have come from breweries from all over in the past, the landlord's intention is to get all his beers from island brewers Bushy's and Okell's.
❀♣🚌(5,6) ᯤ

Two Fellas Micropub
33 Michael Street, IM5 1HD
☎ 07624 324058
4 changing beers (sourced nationally) [H]
The island's first micropub opened in 2018 in the premises of a small converted shop. It is run by two beer enthusiasts who set out to provide a venue where customers could enjoy a variety of different ales. The pub is a popular place for conversation because there is no distracting music or noise of any sort. Isle of Man CAMRA Pub of the Year 2019. Q●🚌(5,6)🐾

White House Hotel Ⓛ ✔
2 Tynwald Road, IM5 1LA (200yds from bus station)
☎ (01624) 842252
Bushy's Bitter; Odin Manx Mild; Okell's Bitter, Dr Okell's IPA; Timothy Taylor Landlord; 4 changing beers (sourced nationally) [H]
Popular community-focused stalwart featuring a public bar area, multiple pool tables, darts and a larger room for TV sport plus live music at the weekend. Through an unusual sliding door is a cosy snug with its own bar. The real ales are complemented by a vast malt whisky collection. A frequent winner of Isle of Man CAMRA Pub of the Year. Q❀♣●P🚌(5,6)🐾ᯤ

Port Erin

Station Hotel ✔
Station Road, IM9 6AE
☎ (01624) 838991
Okell's Manx Pale Ale, Bitter, Dr Okell's IPA; 1 changing beer (sourced nationally) [H]
Opposite the steam train station and near bus stops only a hundred yards from the stunning bay, the Station is an ideal first or last pub to visit in Port Erin. Traditionally and informally furnished, it has a relaxed atmosphere and offers the town's largest Okell's beer selection. Drinkers and diners mingle comfortably in the spacious main bar area, also using the large function room at busier times. 🛏◖◗♿⇌P🚌🐾ᯤ

Port St Mary

Albert Hotel
Athol Street, IM9 5DS (opp harbour)
☎ (01624) 832118
Bushy's Bitter; Okell's Bitter; 2 changing beers (sourced nationally) [H]
A hidden gem in the heart of this coastal village, the Albert boasts impressive views over the harbour. It has a public bar with games area, a cosy lounge bar heated by a wood-burning stove, and an overflow area of tables and seating. Immaculately decorated and furnished, it features walls adorned with many paintings by local artists who frequent the pub. An upstairs apartment is available for hire. Q❀🛏♣P🚌ᯤ

Shore Hotel
Shore Road, Gansey, IM9 5LZ
☎ (01624) 832269 🌐 theshore.im
Bushy's Old Bushy Tail; Okell's Bitter; 1 changing beer (sourced nationally) [H]
A prominent building with stunning views over Gansey or Carrick Bay. The hotel has a wooden bar area fashioned from ship's timbers and door panelling, with mixed seating and tables. The outside seating area is sheltered from the wind, which can be biting. The Gents incorporates some interesting fittings. Food is served throughout the day. This is a rare permanent outlet for Old Bushy Tail. ❀🛏◖◗⇌●P🚌🐾ᯤ

Ramsey

Central Hotel ✔
Bowring Road, IM8 2LL
☎ (01624) 813177
Okell's Bitter; house beer (by Okell's) [H]
A traditional drinkers' pub externally decorated as a house for Castletown Brewery, which closed in 1986. Its central bar area serves two rooms, the front featuring a TV and the rear which leads to outside seating and the car park. Pool and darts are played in the games room behind. Okell's Bitter is sold out of season, with additional guest beers added at busier periods. Popular at TT time due to its location on the outside of the course.
Q⇌(Plaza) ♣P🚌ᯤ

Mitre
16 Parliament Street, IM8 1AP
☎ (01624) 813045
Okell's Bitter; house beer (by Okell's); 2 changing beers (sourced locally) [H]
Welcoming pub that gives its friendly clientele a fine view of Ramsey's quayside and illuminated swing bridge. The first-floor Harbour Bar serves Okell's Jough; the refurbished basement Schooner Bar opens on Saturday night 10pm-1am. Food includes a Sunday lunchtime carvery – booking advised (no food Mon). The pub can also be accessed from the quay, which has ample parking. ◖⇌(Plaza)♣🚌(3,3A)🐾ᯤ

Trafalgar Hotel Ⓛ ✔
West Quay, IM8 1DW
☎ (01624) 814601
Moorhouse's Black Cat; Okell's Bitter; house beer (by Joseph Holt); 2 changing beers (sourced nationally) [H]
Traditional twin-room pub on the harbour, offering a warm welcome and a choice of excellent beers. The house ale is a rebadged Manchester beer, unusually for the island. A mild, such as Moorhouse's Black Cat, is normally available. Sport is shown on TVs downstairs; an upstairs room with fruit machines is open only during the day. Well-behaved dogs are welcome.
Q🛏⇌(Plaza) ●▯🚌🐾ᯤ

ISLANDS

Sulby

Ginger Hall

Ballamanagh Road, IM7 2HB

☎ (01624) 897231

Okell's Bitter; 1 changing beer (sourced nationally) Ⓗ

This welcoming landmark on the TT course used to be recognisable by its colour but has been repainted white. Its interior features a real fire and an impressive beer engine that dispenses two local real ales plus regularly changing guests. Attractions include historic TT pictures, a large mirror behind the bar and a huge circuit map on the ceiling – do not spill your beer while admiring it. The pub has a restaurant and en-suite accommodation.
❀⇔◐▲♣P🚌🐾📶

Sulby Glen Hotel ✔

Main Road, IM7 2HR

☎ (01624) 897240

Bushy's Bitter; Okell's Bitter; 2 changing beers (sourced locally) Ⓗ

Large, rural pub split into two lounges and a separate dining area, on the TT circuit's Sulby straight, close to accommodation and camping. Interesting local and TT photos help attract race enthusiasts. A motorcycle engine set up on the main bar dispenses four keg beers. The excellent home-cooked food uses local ingredients. Other features include a sports TV, pool table and warming open fire. A popular beer festival usually takes place the third week of July. Buses to Ramsey and Peel stop outside. **Q❀⇔◐♿▲♣P🚌**(5,6)

Albert Hotel, Port St Mary (Photo: Rick Pickup)

The Breweries

BREWERIES OVERVIEW

Brewing and pub retailing were defined, shaped and distorted in 2020 by the coronavirus pandemic. Roger Protz takes a look at what's been happening in the brewing industry over the past year.

Never before, even during the privations of world war, have the nation's pubs been locked and barred. The shutdown caused major changes to brewing practice. With no pubs to supply, breweries had to change course in order to survive. Many switched to packaged beer, others offered takeaway draught beer from taprooms and also made door-step deliveries to consumers' homes.

But one aspect of brewing and retailing was not stopped by the pandemic. The growing domination of global interests continued apace. When Fuller's sold their brewing interests to the Japanese giant Asahi in 2019, the question on many lips was: 'Who will be next?' The answer came long before COVID-19 struck. In August 2019, Greene King, one of the country's oldest breweries, with a lineage stretching back to 1799, was bought by Hong Kong property developers for £2.7 billion.

The pandemic didn't prevent further shock waves. In May 2020, Marston's, the revered Burton brewing group with its roots in the pale ale revolution of the 19th century, rocked the industry by merging with Carlsberg in a deal that leaves the global lager giant in the box seat.

Both deals give cause for concern. Greene King is now owned by CK Asset Holdings, based in Hong Kong but registered in the Cayman Islands. The company is owned by Li Ka-Shing, one of the world's richest men with a war chest of HK $60 billion to buy properties and companies. In Britain, he owns Superdrug pharmacies, Three Mobile and properties in some of the wealthiest areas of London.

CK has no known interest in brewing and its over-riding reason for buying Greene King is its vast estate of 2,700 pubs, restaurants and hotels. A year on from the takeover, little has happened but in the long term there must be worries about the future of pubs that could be converted to other retail use such as mini-markets, betting shops or pharmacies. And will all the beers in the large GK portfolio survive, including such short-run but popular brands as XX Mild and Strong Country Bitter?

In the longer term, there must be concern about the future of the brewery in Bury St Edmunds. The new owners could decide to concentrate on a few key beers, such as IPA and Abbot Ale, and have them produced under licence while the brewery, close to the centre of the historic town, is converted into retail outlets or housing.

'MARLSBERG'

The merger of what is now nicknamed 'Marlsberg' is more complex and no less worrying. If the deal is approved by the competition authorities, Carlsberg will control 60 per cent of the business. Marston's will receive £273 million from Carlsberg, which will go some way to easing the Burton company's crippling level of debt, running at £1.4 billion.

The devil, as always, is in the detail. The merger document says, 'annual synergies of £24 million will be achieved by the end of the third year'. This means costs will be reduced by running the slide rule over existing plants and brands. Carlsberg's giant lager factory in Northampton is sacrosanct but will all Marston's six breweries survive?

Marston's says the Ringwood brewery in

Greene King is now owned by CK Asset Holdings

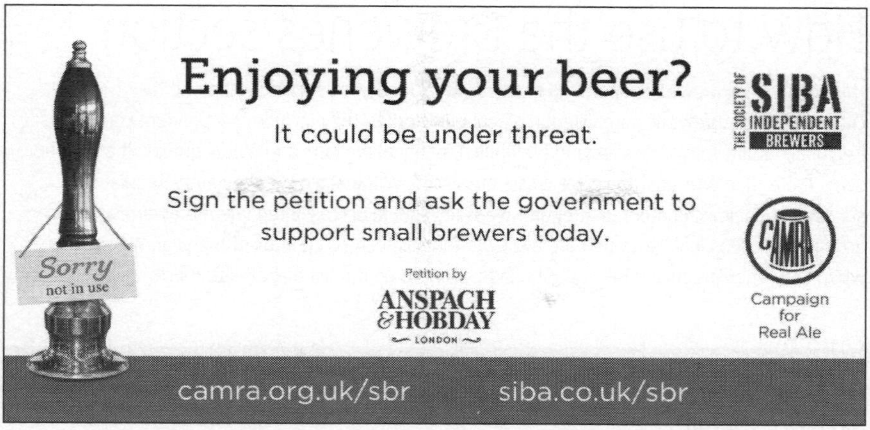

Enjoying your beer?
It could be under threat.
Sign the petition and ask the government to support small brewers today.
Sorry not in use
Petition by
ANSPACH &HOBDAY
LONDON
THE SOCIETY OF SIBA INDEPENDENT BREWERS
CAMRA
Campaign for Real Ale
camra.org.uk/sbr
siba.co.uk/sbr

CAMRA joined the fight against changes to Small Brewers' Relief announced by the Treasury in July 2020

Hampshire is 'flying' while the Wychwood plant in Oxfordshire is working to full capacity. But there has been speculation for years about the long-term viability of the cramped Jenning's plant in Cumbria and a large question mark hangs over the Eagle Brewery in Bedford. It was bought from Charles Wells in 2017 but Bedford council has drawn up a strategic plan for the area that includes modern housing and space for leisure activities that may not sit comfortably with a large brewery.

LOCKDOWN RENT WOES

Pub tenants were hit by a double whammy during lockdown of having no income but being charged full rent by their landlords, in most cases large national pub companies and big brewers. None of the biggest pub operators cancelled rents entirely but some, such as Greene King and Heineken's Star Bars and Pubs, allowed deferrals or made reductions. Marston's said it would support its tenants on a case-by-case basis, including rent reductions of up to 50 per cent. Admiral Taverns at first cancelled all rents but then brought in a graduated scheme that brought rents back as its pubs reopened. CAMRA held top-level meetings with the pub operators in an attempt to win further concessions for their tenants.

The Campaign hailed as heroes those brewers and pub operators who cancelled rents completely during the lockdown. They were: Adnams, Arkells, Brains, Donnington, Everards, Fuller's, Gray & Sons, Hall & Woodhouse, Holdens, JC Palmer, Holts, McMullen, Robinson, Shepherd Neame, St Austell, Timothy Taylor, Wadworth, Wells & Co and Young's.

SMALL BREWERS' RELIEF & PUB CODE REVIEW

Small brewers faced a major problem, too. In July, the Treasury announced changes to Small Brewers' Relief. It was hoped any changes would aid the 'squeezed middle' of breweries that lie between the national giants and the small producers. Instead, the Treasury planned to reduce the threshold for small brewers that produce between 2,100 and 5,000 hectolitres a year, meaning they would pay higher levels of duty.

Both SIBA – the Society of Independent Brewers – and CAMRA criticised the plan, with SIBA saying some 150 breweries could go out of business if they faced an increased tax burden. The Treasury will consult brewers of all sizes in autumn 2020 and it's hoped commonsense will prevail.

The autumn was also due to see a review of the Pubs Code by the Pubs Code Adjudicator, who oversees relations between tenants and their landlords. It's hoped the review will crack down hard on those landlords, mainly national pubcos, who have put major road blocks in the way of tenants being able to choose the Market Rent option that allows them, if they pay a higher rent, to buy beer free of the tie and give their customers greater choice.

The great unknown, as the lockdown eased and pubs reopened, was the fate of real ale. As a draught beer available only in pubs, production came to a halt for several months. A testing time lies ahead for our heritage beer, but it has withstood many challenges in the past and the *Good Beer Guide* is convinced it will revive again and go on to even greater appreciation.

Former editor of the *Good Beer Guide*, **Roger Protz** is considered one of the leading beer writers in the world, with a long career in journalism and publishing, and having won multiple awards. Roger has authored many books on beer and pubs, including *300 Beers to Try Before You Die*. Follow him on Twitter **@RogerProtzBeer** and **protzonbeer.co.uk**.

How to use the Breweries section

This section lists breweries operating in the United Kingdom, the Isle of Man and the Channel Islands. Breweries are listed in alphabetical order. They include independent companies (regional, family, micro-brewers and brewpubs), national brewers and global groups. If a brewery owns more than one site, these are cross-referenced. Within each brewery entry, regular beers are listed in increasing order of strength. Websites should be consulted when breweries produce occasional or seasonal beers that are available for less than six months of the year. We mention when breweries produce bottle-conditioned beers but do not list or evaluate them.

KEY TO BREWERY ENTRIES

BREWERY SYMBOLS

Brewpub: a pub that brews beer on the premises

A CAMRA Beer of the Year in 2019

Serve with tight sparkler: the brewery's beers can be acceptably served through a 'tight sparkler' attached to the nozzle of the beer pump, designed to give a thick collar of foam on the beer

Do not serve with tight sparkler: the brewery's beers should NOT be served through a tight sparkler. CAMRA is opposed to the growing tendency to serve southern-brewed beers with the aid of sparklers, which aerate the beer and tend to drive hop aroma and flavour into the head, altering the balance of the beer achieved in the brewery. When neither symbol is used it means the brewery in question has not stated a preference

Brewery tours available: check with individual breweries for details

Brewery shop: beer available to take away. Check opening hours in advance

RAIB **Real Ale in a Bottle:** the brewery produces bottle-conditioned beer (known by CAMRA as Real Ale in a Bottle)

♦ **Seasonal beers:** the brewery produces seasonal beers in addition to its regular range

V **Vegan:** the brewery produces vegan beers (check with brewery for further details. Not all beers produced may be vegan)

GF **Gluten free:** the brewery produces gluten-free beers (check with brewery for further details. Not all beers may be gluten free)

Taproom: the brewery features an on-site taproom (always check ahead with brewery for up-to-date information about opening times and events)

ABBREVIATIONS

ABV Stands for Alcohol by Volume, which is a measure of the percentage of alcohol in finished beer

SIBA Indicates a member of the Society of Independent Brewers

IFBB Indicates a member of the Independent Family Brewers of Britain

NOTE: The Breweries section was correct at the time of going to press and every effort has been made to ensure that all regularly available cask-conditioned beers are included.

The Breweries

The breweries listed in this section include micro, small, family, regional, national and global companies. Please use the Beer index (p866) to help locate beers.

1086

Old Brewhouse, Cusworth Hall, Cusworth Lane, Doncaster, South Yorkshire, DN5 7TU
☎ (01302) 639880

Office: Doncaster Culture & Leisure Trust, The Dome, Doncaster Lakeside, Bawtry Road, Doncaster, South Yorkshire, DN4 7PD 🌐 1086brewery.co.uk

1086 was established in 2018, in the original brewhouse of Cusworth Hall, an 18th century, Grade I country house in Cusworth, near Doncaster. The brewery shares space with its popular brewery tap, the Old Brewhouse. Beers are available in the taproom, and occasionally at the Leopard in Doncaster.

1648 SIBA

Old Stables Brewery, Mill Lane, East Hoathly, East Sussex, BN8 6QB
☎ (01825) 840830 🌐 1648brewing.co.uk

The 1648 brewery, set up in the old stable block at the King's Head pub in 2003, derives its name from the year of the deposition of King Charles I. One pub is owned and more than 40 outlets are supplied. ♦ RAIB

Hop Pocket (ABV 3.7%)
Triple Champion (ABV 4%)
Signature (ABV 4.4%)
Laughing Frog (ABV 5.2%)

3 Brewers of St Albans SIBA

The Potato Shed, Symonds Hyde Farm, Symonds Hyde Lane, Hatfield, Hertfordshire, AL10 9BB
☎ (01707) 271636 ☎ 07941 854615
🌐 3brewers.co.uk

Launched in 2013 by three brewers from St Albans who turned a potato shed into an eight-barrel brewery. Spent malt becomes compost for the farm. Its range of seven permanent beers is supplied to pubs, beer festivals, markets and other events in Hertfordshire and surrounding counties.

Dark Mild (ABV 3.6%)
Golden English Ale (ABV 3.8%)
Classic English Ale (ABV 4%)
Blonde (ABV 4.2%)
Ruby English Ale (ABV 4.3%)
IPA (ABV 4.6%)
Special English Ale (ABV 4.8%)

3 Non Beards (NEW)

Rook & Gaskill, 12 Lawrence Street, York, YO10 3WP ☎ 07980 994210 🌐 3nonbeards.co.uk

Launched in 2019 as a partnership of three friends, this one-barrel plant is in the basement of the Rook and Gaskill pub. Advised by innovative local brewers the range of beers can be found in the pub and at beer festivals. Around 30 brews per year means an eclectic range of mainly one-offs and frequent single hop beers. ♦

3 Piers

19 Cocker Avenue, Poulton Industrial Estate, Poulton-le-Fylde, Lancashire, FY6 8JU ☎ 07977 469326
🌐 3piersbrewery.com

Brewing began in 2017 using a 15-barrel plant. A wide range of beers is produced and delivered direct all over the UK. ♦

Old Station Porter (ABV 4.5%)
West Coast Blonde (ABV 4.6%)
Central Citra (ABV 5%)

360° SIBA

Unit 24b, Bluebell Business Estate, Sheffield Park, East Sussex, TN22 3HQ
☎ (01825) 722375 🌐 360degreebrewing.com

Brewing began in 2013, adjacent to the famous Bluebell Railway at Sheffield Park, East Sussex, using a six-barrel plant. Its goal is to produce as wide a range of beers as it can with the best ingredients, brewing in small batches. Beers are available across Sussex, the South East and London. ♦

Pale (ABV 3.9%)
Sussex Best (ABV 4.2%)
West Coast Pale Ale (ABV 5%)
Rye Pale (ABV 5.2%)

3D Beer

See Epic Beers

4 Mice

Coach & Horses, Main Street, Bolton-by-Bowland, Lancashire, BB7 4NW
☎ (01200) 447331
🌐 coachandhorsesribblevalley.co.uk

A four-barrel brewery in a gastro-pub, situated in the Trough of Bowland.

4Ts SIBA

Unit 20, Manor Industrial Estate, Lower Wash Lane, Latchford, Warrington, Cheshire, WA4 1PL
☎ (01925) 417820 ☎ 07917 730184
🌐 4tsbrewery.co.uk

4Ts returned to Warrington in 2015 and in 2019 the brewing plant was replaced with a new 12-barrel brew kit. Tipsy Angel beers are brewed by 4Ts. Beers can usually be found in the Tavern, Warrington, the brewery's tap and consist of a core range and many one-off beers. ♦

EPA (ABV 3.7%)
SPA (ABV 3.8%)
APA (ABV 4%)
WSB (ABV 4.2%)
IPA (ABV 4.6%)
Panzer Pils (ABV 4.8%)
Big Bro IPA (ABV 5%)
English Stout (ABV 5%)
Big Daddy DIPA (ABV 7.2%)

Brewed under the Tipsy Angel Brewery name:

Angels Mild (ABV 3.8%)
George Shaw Premium (ABV 4.3%)
Angels Folly (ABV 5.2%)
Taipur (ABV 5.9%)

40FT SIBA

Bootyard, Abbott Street, Dalston, London, E8 3DP

Office: The Printhouse, 18-20 Ashwin Street, Dalston, E8 3DL 🌐 40ftbrewery.com

Six-barrel microbrewery 40FT began brewing in 2015. It is located in a 40-ft shipping container in a disused car park close to Ridley Road Market. Beers are produced for its taproom as well as pubs, bars, restaurants and off-licences. Output is nearly all keg and cans. Expanded taproom open every Wednesday-Saturday. ◆

71 Brewing

36-40 Bellfield Street, Dundee, DD1 5HZ
☎ (01382) 203133 🌐 71brewing.com

Brewing began in 2016, principally brewery-conditioned lagers. In 2018 71 Brewing was commissioned to produce a cask-conditioned festival ale and is now producing a range of cask-conditioned beers. A taproom and bottle shop is open daily. !! ♦V◆

Aurora Burst (ABV 4.1%)
Breakfast Toast (ABV 4.5%)
Cloud Fall (ABV 4.5%)
Mandarina Sky (ABV 5%)

8 Sail SIBA

Heckington Windmill, Hale Road, Heckington, Lincolnshire, NG34 9JW
☎ (01529) 469308 ☎ 07866 183479
🌐 8sailbrewery.co.uk

8 Sail Brewery was established in 2010 and operates on a six-barrel brew plant. The brewery nestles in the shadow of Heckington Windmill, Britain's only eight-sailed windmill, from where the brewery takes its name. The Mill is now working and helps to mill malted grain for the brewery. The brewery shop stocks bottle-conditioned beers alongside local ciders. The front of the brewery has been converted into a Victorian-style bar, which has beer on handpump at the weekend. Regular events are held using the bar as a base. ♦RAIB ◆

Ploughmans Lunch (ABV 3.8%)
Windmill Bitter (ABV 3.8%)
Blonde (ABV 4%)
Fenman (ABV 4.1%)
Inn Keeper (ABV 4.2%)
Rolling Stone (ABV 4.3%)
Red Windmill (ABV 4.4%)
King John's Jewels (ABV 4.5%)
Millstone (ABV 4.5%)
Windy Miller (ABV 4.6%)
Fen Slodger (ABV 4.8%)
Damson Porter (ABV 5%)
Victorian Porter (ABV 5%)
Old Colony – Deacon John Ales (ABV 5.3%)
Black Widow (ABV 5.5%)
John Barleycorn IPA (ABV 5.5%)

81 Artisan

The Courtyard, Crowshall Farm, Chilgrove Road, West Dean, Chichester, West Sussex, PO18 9HP
☎ (01243) 527444 🌐 81artisan.com

Brewing began in 2017 using a 10-barrel plant.

9 Lives

Unit 303, Ystradgynlais Workshops, Trawsffordd Road, Ystradgynlais, SA9 1BS ☎ 07743 559736
🌐 9livesbrewing.co.uk

9 Lives Brewing was established in 2017 by Robert Scott, formerly the brewer at the now defunct Bryncelyn Brewery, using the same six-barrel plant. A number of beers are replications of former Bryncelyn beers which have been renamed. !! ♦RAIB V

Amber (ABV 4%)
Pale amber with a hoppy aroma. A refreshing hoppy, fruity flavour with balancing bitterness; a similar lasting finish. A beer full of flavour for its gravity.
Dark (ABV 4%)
Dark brown with an inviting aroma of malt, roast and fruit. A gentle bitterness mixes roast with malt, hops and fruit, giving a complex, satisfying and lasting finish.
Gold (ABV 4.5%)
An inviting aroma of hops, fruit and malt, and a golden colour. The tasty mix of hops, fruit, bitterness and background malt ends with a long, hoppy, bitter aftertaste. Full-bodied and drinkable.
Hot Tin Roof (ABV 4.5%)
Witti Kitti (ABV 4.6%)
Pale (ABV 4.7%)
Special (ABV 5%)

A-B InBev

Porter Tun House, 500 Capability Green, Luton, LU1 3LS
☎ (01582) 391166 🌐 inbev.com

No real ale.

Abbey SIBA

Abbey Brewery, Camden Row, Bath, BA1 5LB
☎ (01225) 444437 🌐 abbeyales.co.uk

Founded in 1997 Abbey Ales was the first brewery in Bath for more than 50 years. It supplies more than 80 regular outlets within a 20-mile radius and its beers are more widely available in the South West via wholesalers. Four pubs are operated in Bath. ♦

Bath Best (ABV 4%)
Bath Pale Ale (ABV 4.2%)
Bellringer (ABV 4.2%)
A notably hoppy ale, light to medium-bodied, clean-tasting, refreshingly dry, with a balancing sweetness. Citrus, pale malt aroma and a dry, bitter finish.

Abbeydale SIBA

Unit 8, Aizlewood Road, Sheffield, South Yorkshire, S8 0YX
☎ (0114) 281 2712 🌐 abbeydalebrewery.co.uk

Established in 1996, Abbeydale, the second oldest, and one of the largest breweries in Sheffield, produces more than 220 barrels a week. Recent investment and expansion has enabled substantial growth. In addition to the core range, at least one new beer is produced weekly. While many are widely available, some small batch brews are barrel-aged in Abbeydale's 'Funk Dungeon' project. One pub is owned; the Rising Sun, Nether Green. ♦V

Daily Bread (ABV 3.8%)
Deception (ABV 4.1%)
Heathen (ABV 4.1%)
Moonshine (ABV 4.3%)
Absolution (ABV 5.3%)
Black Mass (ABV 6.66%)

Abernyte

South Latch Farm, Abernyte, Perthshire, PH14 9SU ☎ 07827 715915 🌐 abernytebrewery.com

Established in 2016, the brewery overlooks the Carse of Gowrie. Brewing features a step mashing process in small batch, producing a range of unfiltered and naturally carbonated craft beers, packaged mainly in bottles. V

Abington

Buckingham Garden Centre, Tingewick Road, Buckingham, MK18 4AE 🌐 abingtonales.com

Started by Peter Brown as a home brewery, commercial production began in 2016 in 50-litre batches at the family garden centre in Buckingham. Beer is sold in bottles exclusively at the garden centre. RAIB

Abyss SIBA

Unit 12, Squires Farm Industrial Estate, Palehouse Common, Framfield, East Sussex, TN22 5RB ☎ (01825) 840561 ☎ 07919 445345 🌐 abyssbrewing.co.uk

Started in 2017, this small brewery moved to its present premises later the same year, using a plant purchased from Black Cat when it ceased brewing. Recently two new fermentation vessels were commissioned, giving a total of five, and a single brew capacity of eight barrels, and the ability to carbonate naturally in the new tanks. Alongside the four regular beers, new experimental brews are produced. All are suitable for vegetarians and vegans, but remain only available in Keykeg or cans. V

Accidental

The Old Stables, Bulk Street, Lancaster, LA1 1PU 🌐 accidentalbrewery.com

Brewpub located on the edge of Lancaster city centre in an 18th century converted stable block. A 140-litre brewplant is used. Occasional cask ale is produced.

Acid (NEW)

c/o 21 Rylands Gardens, Glasgow, G32 0RY ☎ 07896 812143 ✉ ciaran@acidbrewingcartel.com

A small nomadic brewery which creates sour, wild and farmhouse ales, focussing on merging historical techniques and traditional yeasts in a modern context. RAIB V

Acorn SIBA

Unit 3, Aldham Industrial Estate, Mitchell Road, Wombwell, Barnsley, South Yorkshire, S73 8HA ☎ (01226) 270734 🌐 acorn-brewery.co.uk

Acorn was set up in 2003 with a 10-barrel expanding to a 20-barrel plant when the brewery moved to larger premises. It currently has a 160-barrel a week capacity. All beers are produced using the Barnsley Bitter yeast strain, dating back to the 1850s. !! ♦ RAIB

Yorkshire Pride (ABV 3.7%)
Golden session beer with pleasing fruit notes. A mouthwatering blend of malt and hops create a fruity taste which leads to a clean, bitter finish.
Barnsley Bitter (ABV 3.8%)
Brown bitter with smooth, malty bitterness throughout, and notes of chocolate and caramel. Fruity, bitter finish.
Blonde (ABV 4%)
A clean-tasting, golden, hoppy beer with a refreshing bitter and fruity aftertaste.
Barnsley Gold (ABV 4.3%)
Golden ale, with fruit in the aroma, with a hoppy and fruity taste throughout. A well-hopped, clean, dry finish.
Old Moor Porter (ABV 4.4%)
A rich-tasting porter, smooth throughout with a hint of chocolate and a hint of liquorice. This is a moreish porter.
Gorlovka Imperial Stout (ABV 6%)
Black stout, rich, smooth and full of chocolate and liquorice flavours, with a fruity creamy finish.

Ad Hop

18 Severs Street, Liverpool, L6 5HJ ☎ 07957 165501

Ad Hop started life in 2014 at the Clove Hitch pub, moving a couple of times before ending up in much larger premises in 2017 where a 5.5-barrel plant was added to its existing 2.5-barrel one. ♦RAIB V

Liverpool Pale (ABV 3.8%)
Liver Bird (ABV 4.2%)
Merseyful (ABV 4.2%)
Aotearoa Pale (ABV 4.4%)
Paddy's Wigwam (ABV 4.6%)
Robusta (ABV 5%)
Enigma (ABV 5.5%)
Equinox (ABV 5.5%)

Adnams SIBA

Sole Bay Brewery, East Green, Southwold, Suffolk, IP18 6JW ☎ (01502) 727200 🌐 adnams.co.uk

Established in 1872 and still based in Southwold, Suffolk. More than 35 pubs are owned around East Anglia, with national distribution. Beers are from a 300-barrel plant within the confines of the present site. !! ♦

Lighthouse (ABV 3.4%)
A quaffable beer with bitterness predominating.
Southwold Bitter (ABV 3.7%)
Aromas of toffee apple, caramel and sulphur. Taste is a complex mix of malt toffee and roast bitterness with hops. Malty bitter and apple flavours linger into the aftertaste.
Mosaic (ABV 4.1%)
Tropical fruit nose, intensely fruity flavour with complex hop characteristics, which linger in the aftertaste.
Ghost Ship (ABV 4.5%)
Broadside (ABV 4.7%)
Rich, malty aroma with blackberries and dried fruit. Rich and full flavours of malt and fruit, with roast and caramel notes and subtle hops. Well-balanced, long-lasting aftertaste.

Adur

Brick Barn, Charlton Court, Mouse Lane, Steyning, West Sussex, BN44 3DG ☎ (01903) 867614

Office: 2 Sullington Way, Shoreham-by-Sea, BN43 6PJ 🌐 adurvalleycoop.com

Adur Brewery, nestled in the heart of the South Downs, was launched in 2008 on a 5.5-barrel plant, marking the return of brewing to the Adur Valley after an interval of nearly 100 years. The brewery was sold to the Adur Valley Co-Operative in 2012, including the Adur Brewery name and recipes. A large part of the output is sold as bottle-conditioned beer. !! ♦RAIB

Ropetackle Golden Ale (ABV 3.4%)
Hop Token: Amarillo (ABV 4%)

THE BREWERIES

Hop Token: Summit (ABV 4%)
Velocity (ABV 4.4%)
Black William (ABV 5%)
Robbie's Red (ABV 5.2%)

Affinity

Grosvenor Arms, 17 Sidney Road, Brixton, London, SW9 0TP ☎ 07904 391807 affinitybrewco.com

Established in 2016 using a 2.5-barrel plant, Affinity became part of the Bermondsey Beer Mile after moving to take over an arch of the vacated Partizan Brewery in 2017. This was sold in 2020 and Affinity have set up a new brewery at the Grosvenor Arms in Brixton.

Ainsty SIBA

Manor Farm, Intake Lane, Acaster Malbis, York, North Yorkshire, YO23 3UJ
☎ (01904) 703233 ☎ 07983 604989
ainstyales.co.uk

Established in 2014 as a cuckoo brewery, its own 10-barrel brewery opened in 2016 in the ancient York and Ainsty Wappentake, a few miles south-west of York. Homegrown hops are used in the beers, which can be found in York, across Yorkshire and as distant as the South of England. ‼ ♦

Angel (ABV 3.7%)
Flummoxed Farmer (ABV 4%)
Bantam Best (ABV 4.2%)
Assassin (ABV 4.9%)

Aitcheson's (NEW)

Windham Farm, Ferry Road, Wawne, East Yorkshire, HU17 0TB ☎ 07456 063670

Office: 2 Wheelhouse Court, Hull, HU6 5BF

Formerly the East Yorkshire Beer Company, Aitcheson's was established by Steve Aitcheson in 2020 after relocating from Beverley. Ingredients are sourced as locally as possible, grains malted in Bridlington and Castleford and UK hops used where possible. The beer range is named after historic Hull and East Yorkshire pubs. Brewing experience days can be booked. ♦

Top House Mild (ABV 3.8%)
King Billy Bitter (ABV 4.2%)
Earl de Grey IPA (ABV 4.5%)
Full Measure Porter (ABV 4.5%)
Star of the West Pilsner (ABV 4.6%)
Odd Fellows Irish Red (ABV 4.7%)

AJ's

Unit 12, Ashmore Industrial Estate, Longacre Street, Walsall, West Midlands, WS2 8QG ☎ 07860 585911
✉ ajs-ales@hotmail.com

AJ's was established in 2015 and use a four-barrel plant with three fermenting vessels and a cool room. It brews three times a week and mainly supplys local Black Country pubs, local wholesalers and Wetherspoon pubs. ♦

Blackjack Mild (ABV 3.6%)
Stuck on Blondes (ABV 3.9%)
Best Bitter (ABV 4%)
Dukey's Delight (ABV 4.1%)
SPA (ABV 4.2%)
Gold (ABV 4.3%)
Stuck in the Mud (ABV 4.3%)
Ruby (ABV 4.4%)
IPA (ABV 4.6%)
Stuck in the Doghouse (ABV 4.7%)

Alcazar

See Shipstone's

Aldwark Artisan

Lydgate Farm, Aldwark, Matlock, Derbyshire, DE4 4HW
☎ (01629) 540720 ☎ 07834 353807
aaabrewery.co.uk

Housed in an old milking shed on a rural working farm, this 10-barrel plant produced its first beers in 2017 using water from the farm's own borehole.

Pale IPA (ABV 4.8%)

Alechemy SIBA

Unit B, 1 Gregory Road, Kirkton Campus, Livingston, EH54 7DR
☎ (01506) 413634 ☎ 07748 156973
alechemy.beer

Dr James Davies, a keen traditional brewer and chemist, started brewing in 2012. A 12-barrel plant is used. New beers are being produced regularly. Beers can be found in shops and pubs across the UK. Alechemy is now part of the Consolidated Craft Breweries group, which opened its first bar in 2019, the Froth & Flame in Edinburgh. ♦RAIB

Charisma (ABV 3.7%)
Ritual (ABV 4.1%)
Well-balanced golden ale. A strong hop character, balanced by malt and fruit with a long, dry finish.
Photon (ABV 4.2%)
Light pale ale with lots of American hops.
Five Sisters (ABV 4.3%)
Flavoursome tawny beer with excellent balance of malt, hops and fruit plus hints of roast and caramel. Lingering distinctive finish.
10 Storey Malt Bomb (ABV 4.5%)
Bad Day at the Office (ABV 4.5%)
Secret Citra (ABV 5.7%)

Ales of Scilly

2b Porthmellon Industrial Estate, St Mary's, Isles of Scilly, TR21 0JY ☎ 07737 721599 alesofscilly.co.uk

Opened in 2001, Ales of Scilly is the most south-westerly brewery in Britain. Several island pubs and restaurants are regularly supplied, plus the occasional mainland outlet, and beer festivals across the country. Special one-off beers are produced in celebration of significant island events. ‼ ♦V

Schiller (ABV 3.9%)
Challenger (ABV 4.2%)
Amber best bitter with faint malt and hop nose. A refreshing, light beer with apricot flavours throughout, and gentle malty bitterness.
Association (ABV 4.5%)

Alfred's

Unit 6, Winnall Farm Industrial Estate, Easton Lane, Winchester, Hampshire, SO23 0HA
☎ (01962) 859999 alfredsbrewery.co.uk

Alfred's is a nine-barrel, state-of-the-art brewery located close to the centre of Winchester. Production of Saxon Bronze is complemented by returning favourites and experimental beers. ‼ ♦

Saxon Bronze (ABV 3.8%)

All Day

Salle Brewery Barns 14-16, Salle Moor Hall Farm, Wood Dalling Road, Salle, Norfolk, NR10 4SB
☎ (01603) 327656 ☎ 07825 604887
alldaybrewing.co.uk

Housed in a centuries old barn, the brewery has its own hop yard and an adjoining organic orchard. Many of the beers are barrel-aged, or sours, or involve fruit grown at the brewery. They are available in the taproom and kitchen, along with vegan food, pizza, real cider, and raw kombucha. Home of the the Norfolk Hop Festival. !! ♦ RAIB

All Hallows

Main Street, Goodmanham, East Yorkshire, YO43 3JA
☎ (01430) 873849 goodmanhamarms.co.uk

Abbie Logozzi, landlady of the Goodmanham Arms, started brewing in 2012 in outbuildings behind the pub. The ex-Goodmanham Brewery buildings were purchased and a five-barrel plant installed. The brewery name comes from the adjacent 12th-century All Hallows Church. Local legendary characters are used in the naming of some of the beers. Brews are supplied to the pub and its sister pub, the Bay Horse, Burythorpe. ♦

All Nations

20 Coalport Road, Madeley, Telford, TF7 5SU
☎ (01952) 585747 allnationsinn@btinternet.com

A famous brewpub established in 1832 and run by just two families for the first 151 years. The latest 10-barrel plant has brewed since 2016.

Allanwater

Queens Lane, Bridge of Allan, FK9 4NY
☎ (01786) 834555 ☎ 07831 224242
allanwaterbrewhouse.co.uk

Originally named Tinpot and then Wash House, the brewery was established in 2009 using a one-barrel plant designed to brew speciality beer. From 2018 all beers and branding are under the Allanwater Brewhouse name. The beer range varies depending on season and demand, which is increasing every year. !! ♦ RAIB GF

Allendale SIBA

Allen Mill, Allendale, Northumberland, NE47 9EA
☎ (01434) 618686 allendalebrewery.com

Established in 2006, the brewery is a 20-barrel plant in a historic lead smelting mill in the heart of the North Pennines Area of Outstanding Natural Beauty. Many of the beers reflect the heritage and identity of the local area. !! ♦

Wagtail Best Bitter (ABV 3.8%)
Amber bitter with spicy aromas and a long, bitter finish.
Golden Plover (ABV 4%)
Light, refreshing, easy-drinking blonde beer with a clean finish.
Pennine Pale (ABV 4%)
GFPA (ABV 4.7%)
Wolf (ABV 5.5%)
Full-bodied, red ale with bitterness in the taste giving way to a fruity finish.

AllGates

See Wigan

Almasty

Unit 11, Algernon Industrial Estate, New York Road, Shiremoor, NE27 0NB
☎ (0191) 253 1639 almasty.co.uk

Opened in 2014, Almasty now has two sites, both brewing on 10-barrel kits, one running a mixed/natural fermentation and a barrel-aging programme and the other producing unfined, unfiltered beers with a continuously changing output, including heavily-hopped pale ales, IPAS and stouts. A taproom and shop located at Benfield Business Park is open weekends. Pumpclips are made from screen-printed, hand-sawn logs. Beers are supplied nationwide. !! ♦ V

Alnwick SIBA

Unit E-F, Hawkhill Business Park, Lesbury, Northumberland, NE66 3PG
☎ (01665) 830617 ☎ 07788 433499
alnwickbrewery.co.uk

Brewing started in the 1860s in the centre of Alnwick, the capital of Northumberland. The brewery was acquired in 1978 by Scottish brewer Dryboroughs, who closed it in 1986, but relaunched in 2003 with the assistance of the Duchess of Northumberland. Beers are also brewed under the Holy Island name. More than 50 outlets are supplied in the north of England.

Alpha Delta (NEW)

18 Riversdale Court, Newburn, Newcastle upon Tyne, NE15 8SG alphadeltabrewing.com

Alpha Delta Brewing launched in 2019 in the Newburn district of Newcastle. Producing modern-style, high gravity beers in keg and can, the beers are unfined, unfiltered and unpasteurized. Collaborations with various breweries across Europe take place.

Alpha State

The Heath, Horsmonden, Kent, TN12 8JE
alphastatebeer.com

Alpha State was founded in 2012 by brewer Jonathan Queally, producing mainly bottled beer. In 2019 it launched a range of beer produced in collaboration with comedian Bob Mortimer. Beers are unfiltered and unpasteurised, supplied in bottles and KeyKeg. RAIB

Alphabet SIBA

99 North Western Street, Ardwick, Manchester, M12 6JL
☎ (0161) 272 6532 alphabetbrewing.co.uk

Founded in 2014, Alphabet Brewing Company is based in central Manchester in a railway arch with an on-site taproom. It focuses mainly on hop-forward, fruit-led session beers in keg and KeyKeg, which are unfiltered and unpasteurised. !! ♦ V

Altarnun SIBA

Inner Trenarrett, Altarnun, Launceston, Cornwall, PL15 7SY
☎ (01566) 86069 penpontbrewery.co.uk

Formerly known as Penpont, Altarnan began brewing in 2008 and has steadily increased its range and production since then. The award-winning brewery currently uses a 25-barrel plant, with an eight-barrel plant for special brews. Beers are available in pubs across Cornwall. Beer is also brewed under the Firebrand Brewing label. !! ♦ RAIB

St Nonna's (ABV 3.7%)
Tawny-coloured session bitter with floral nose and balanced malt and hop bitterness throughout with roast and sweet notes. Bitter finish.
Cornish Arvor (ABV 4%)
Golden bitter with good malt and pine/resin/earthy hop presence. Complex mix of stone fruit and esters. Dry finish.
Creation Pale Ale (ABV 4.2%)
Gold bitter with hop aroma. Quite hoppy taste with sweet peach, citrus zing and roast malt. Bitter, slightly dry finish.
Shipwreck Coast (ABV 4.4%)
Gold bitter with sweet malt, well-balanced by citrus and tropical fruit hop flavours. Dry finish.
Roughtor (ABV 4.7%)
Copper, strong ale with malt and citrus hop aroma. Hop bitterness balanced by malt, plum and marmalade. Bitter, dry finish.
Beast of Bodmin (ABV 5%)
Tawny, strong ale. Burnt sugar, tobacco and leather with stone fruit flavour. Mellow toffee/caramel and earthy hop finish.
Stormer IPA (ABV 5.2%)

Brewed under the Firebrand Brewery name:
Big Hop, Little Beer (ABV 3.6%)
Cross Pacific Pale Ale (ABV 4%)
Graffiti IPA (ABV 5%)

Alter Ego (NEW)

Unit 11, Small Business Centre, Adams Close, Heanor, Derbyshire, DE75 7SW ☎ 07989 655828
✉ matt@alteregobrewing.co

Alter Ego is a 2.5-barrel brewery producing small batch beers. The brewery tap is the Tip Inn micropub, Loscoe.

Echo Chamber (ABV 3.8%)
Mr Brown (ABV 4.2%)
Sidekick (ABV 4.5%)
Vigilante (ABV 4.8%)
Incognito (ABV 5.8%)

Amazing

Ship Inn, 65 High Street, Sandgate, Kent, CT20 3AH ☎ (01303) 248525

Amazing was set up in 2016 using a four-barrel plant and is situated at the Ship Inn, Sandgate. The pub and local beer festivals are supplied. The brewery can be viewed from inside the pub. ‼

Ambridge

Unit 2a, Priory Piece Business Park, Priory Farm Lane, Inkberrow, Worcestershire, WR7 4HT ☎ 07498 628238 🌐 ambridgebrewery.co.uk

Ambridge commenced brewing in 2013, initially for the family pub, The Bulls Head in Inkberrow. Expansion was achieved by acquiring the Wyre Piddle Brewery. The range of beers has continued to change with specials brewed especially to support charities and events. Some small run bottling is also carried out. ‼ ♦ RAIB

Flower Power (ABV 4%)
Sticky Dog (ABV 4%)
Best Bitter (ABV 4.3%)
Gold (ABV 4.3%)

Amity (NEW)

15-16 Festoon Rooms, Sunny Bank Mills, Farsley, Leeds, West Yorkshire, LS28 5UJ 🌐 amitybrew.co

Launching in 2020 with their online shop, Amity Brew Co was founded by an ex-BrewDog, Buxton, North Brewing Co and Beer Hawk team member, Russ Clarke. Originally cuckoo brewing, its brewpub opened later the same year sporting a 10-hectolitre brew kit, producing modern interpretations of classic beer styles, as well as more experimental brews. No real ale. ‼ V

Ampersand SIBA

Camphill Farm, Middle Road, Earsham, Bungay, Norfolk, NR35 2AH ☎ 07791 086689
🌐 ampersandbrew.co

A small batch brewery established in 2017 and based on a family farm in South Norfolk.

uIPA (ABV 2.9%)
Bidon (ABV 3.9%)
On The Wing (ABV 4.7%)
Cocow (ABV 4.8%)
Camphillisner (ABV 4.9%)
Pulpit Pale (ABV 5%)

Amwell Springs SIBA

Westfield Farm House, Cholsey, Wallingford, Oxfordshire, OX10 9LS ☎ 07812 396619
🌐 asbco.co.uk

Brewing began in 2017 on a 70-litre plant using water from a spring in the farmhouse grounds. Capacity expanded in 2019 to six barrels. Beers are available in local pubs. RAIB

Chairman Dave (ABV 3.5%)
Stay Jammy (ABV 3.8%)
Easy Geez (ABV 4.5%)
Mad Gaz (ABV 5.2%)

Anarchy SIBA

Unit A1, Benfield Business Park, Newcastle upon Tyne, NE6 4NQ 🌐 anarchybrewco.com

A 20-barrel brewery, started in 2012 in Morpeth, and moved to Newcastle upon Tyne in 2018. Its focus is on session beers, plus an eclectic mix of one-offs and collaborations with a host of breweries from the UK and across the globe. RAIB V

Blonde Star (ABV 4.1%)
Citra Star (ABV 4.1%)
Skin Deep (ABV 4.2%)
Halfway Dead (ABV 4.7%)
New Age Crisis (ABV 4.8%)
Boot Boys (ABV 5%)
X-Ray Eyes (ABV 5.1%)
Hollow Heroes (ABV 5.3%)
Hopped Up and Ready To Go (ABV 5.3%)
Cult Leader (ABV 5.5%)
Demon Fangs (ABV 5.6%)
Cell Phone Zombies (ABV 5.9%)
Hit the Juice (ABV 6%)

Anchor House (NEW)

c/o 3 Osmand Gardens, Plympton, Devon, PL7 1AA ☎ 07940 270918

A new family-run brewery, established in 2019, to brew small-batch vegan-friendly, experimental beers using spare capacity at other local breweries. All ingredients are locally sourced where possible. A number of local charities are supported. V◆

Andwell SIBA

Andwell Lane, Andwell, Hampshire, RG27 9PA
☎ (01256) 761044 ⊕ andwells.com

⊗ Brewing commenced in 2008 on a 10-barrel plant. The brewery relocated and expanded in 2011 to an idyllic riverside location with a new bespoke 20-barrel plant. Beer is distributed within a 40-mile radius to Hampshire, Surrey, Wiltshire, Berkshire, Greater London and the Isle of Wight. More than 200 outlets are supplied. ‼ ♦◆

Resolute Bitter (ABV 3.8%)
An easy-drinking, session bitter. A malty aroma, leads into an initially malty flavour with some bitterness and sweetish finish.
Gold Muddler (ABV 3.9%)
Light, golden standard bitter. Aroma of hops and malt; characteristics carried into flavour with solid bitterness and dry, biscuity finish.
King John (ABV 4.2%)
Malty best bitter, low in hops with short initial bitterness and underlying sweetness, leading to some dryness in the finish.
Ruddy Darter (ABV 4.6%)

Angel

Angel, 7 Stoney Street, Nottingham, NG1 1LG
☎ (0115) 948 3343

Situated inside one of Nottingham's oldest, haunted, and cave-filled pubs. The Angel Microbrewery uses a 2.5-barrel plant, nestled in the taproom of the 400-year-old pub. Beers are available at the Angel, and the Golden Fleece in Nottingham. GF V

Angel Ales SIBA

62a Furlong Lane, Halesowen, West Midlands, B63 2TA ☎ 07986 382919 ⊕ angelales.co.uk

Angel Ales began commercial brewing in 2011. The brewery building has been a chapel of rest, a coffin makers' workshop and a pattern makers' before becoming a brewhouse. Beers are produced using organic ingredients where possible. ♦RAIB V

Ale (ABV 4.1%)
Ginger Stout (ABV 4.8%)

Angels & Demons

Great Cauldham Farm, Cauldham Lane, Capel-le-Ferne, Kent, CT18 7HQ
☎ (01303) 255666 ⊕ fantasticbeer.co.uk

Brewing began in 2016 using a 20-barrel plant. The brewery produces two ranges of beers, the McCanns range of traditional ales and the Angels & Demons range of more experimental brews.

49 Horses (ABV 2.8%)
Bombay Social (ABV 3.8%)
Racing Tiger (ABV 4.2%)
Panama Jazz (ABV 4.8%)
I Spy Dragonfly (ABV 5%)
ADH Me (ABV 5.2%)
Goldilocks is Dead (ABV 5.3%)
Black Taxi to the Moon (ABV 5.4%)

Brewed under the McCanns brand name:
Harry Hop (ABV 3.7%)
Folkestone Best (ABV 4%)
Hockley Soul (ABV 4.2%)

Anglesey Brewhouse SIBA

Unit 12, Pen Yr Orsedd, Industrial Estate Road, Parc Bryn Cefni, Llangefni, LL77 7AW
☎ (01248) 345506 ☎ 07748 650368
⊕ angleseybrewhouse.co.uk

Microbrewery established in 2017 in the centre of Anglesey by a former homebrewer. The brewery relocated to larger premises in 2019 with a 10-barrel plant. Currently producing three bottle-conditioned beers sold direct from the brewery or in shops around North Wales.

Anglesey Brewing

Chwaen Ddu, Carmel, LL71 7DE
☎ (01248) 717734 ☎ 07943 697881
⊕ angleseybrewingcompany.co.uk

Brewing began in 2014 in Llanbadrig as Bragdy'r Bwthyn, producing bottle-conditioned beers. In 2017 the brewery relocated to Carmel under the Anglesey Brewing Co name and cask production began. Beers are mostly sold at events and outlets across Anglesey. RAIB

Anglo Oregon

3 Traston Lane, Newport, NP19 4RR ☎ 07854 194966
✉ aobrewingco@gmail.com

Set up in 2015 in Parkend (Forest Of Dean) the brewery moved to its current location in Nash, on the eastern outskirts of Newport, two years later. The name comes from the fact one of the owners is English and the other (in whose garage the brewery is located) is from Oregon. They have three fermenters and the brewing capacity is just 100 litres. Only bottle-conditioned ale is brewed (every few weeks, when necessary) in 330 ml bottles. RAIB

Animal

See XT

Anomaly

59 Glebe Gardens, Old Malden, KT3 5RU ☎ 07903 623993 ⊕ anomalybrewing.co.uk

Founded in 2017, beers started to appear at the end of 2018 brewed on a 100-litre home kit. Most production is available locally in bottles but cask is sometimes available at beer festivals.

Anspach & Hobday SIBA

118 Druid Street, Bermondsey, London, SE1 2HH
☎ (020) 8617 9510

Croydon: Unit 11, Valley Point Industrial Estate, Beddington Farm Road, Croydon, CR0 4WP
⊕ anspachandhobday.com

⊗ Best known for its porter, Anspach & Hobday began brewing in 2014. In early 2020 a new brewery was commissioned in Croydon with its existing seven-barrel kit and a canning line. Its original railway arch site (on the Bermondsey Beer Mile) is now the home of its barrel-aged and sour beers. The brewery also has a bar in Camberwell called the Pigeon. ‼ RAIB V◆

The Ordinary Bitter (ABV 3.7%)
The Patersbier (ABV 4.1%)
The London ESB (ABV 5.5%)
Seville marmalade aroma and flavour with zesty bitterness balanced by sweetness, spicy hops and roast. Hoppy, bitter and lingering finish.

The Smoked Brown (ABV 5.5%)
Smoked nose with traces of coffee. Flavour has damsons, toffee, dark chocolate, an underlying smoked character and lasting dry roastiness.
The IPA (ABV 6%)
Grapefruit, orange and lemon zesty, American-style beer with spicy hops and sweet biscuit providing balance to the increasing bitterness.
The Porter (ABV 6.7%)
Black/brown beer with roasted notes throughout with caramel, dark fruit and hops in the flavour and finish which is slightly dry.
The Stout Porter (ABV 8.5%)

Anstey

46a Albion Street, Anstey, Leicestershire, LE7 7DE
☎ 07960 776843 🌐 ansteyale.co.uk

Anstey Ale Brewery started as a one-barrel, part-time garage plant in 2015. It became full-time and upgraded some equipment, later moving to new premises and increased plant size to 2.5-barrels in 2017. On-site taproom, the Mash & Press, opened in 2019 in conjunction with Charnwood Ciders (Tue-Sun). Regular one-off brews are released under the Anstey (cask) and Monstex (keg) brands. Beers are occasionally available at local freehouses. A new beer garden and plans for increased capacity are planned for 2020-2021. ♦◆

Lakeside (ABV 3.9%)
Neddy's (ABV 3.9%)
Brewsters Bitter (ABV 4%)
Packhorse Bridge (ABV 4%)
Fluthered (ABV 4.5%)
Darkroom (ABV 4.7%)
Nook IPA (ABV 5%)

Anthology

Unit 6, Armley Link, Armley Road, Leeds, West Yorkshire, LS12 2QN ☎ 07594 975245
🌐 anthologybrewing.co.uk

Established in 2018, Anthology is a small batch brewery based in Leeds with a 2.5-barrel kit. Liam brews an ever-evolving range of beers with a focus on bold flavours. Beers are available in outlets around the city with some distributed further afield. V◆

Appleby

Unit 10, Castle Mills, Aynam Road, Kendal, Cumbria, LA9 7DE
☎ (01539) 726800 ☎ 07885 171210

Established by Fred Mills in 2015, the brewery outgrew its original premises in Appleby and moved to a former horse stable in a local village in 2016. It was taken over in 2018 and moved to shared premises at Bowness Bay Brewing, Kendal. The beers are available at selected pubs across Cumbria, but mainly in the Eden Valley area. ‼

Haweswater Blonde (ABV 3.6%)
Senior Moment (ABV 3.9%)
Midlife Crisis (ABV 4.2%)
Middle Aged Spread (ABV 5.2%)

Arbor SIBA

181 Easton Road, Easton, Bristol, BS5 0HQ
☎ (0117) 329 2711 🌐 arborales.co.uk

Founded in 2007, Arbor has a brew length of 20 barrels with 12 fermenting vessels. Willing to experiment, more than 300 beers have been produced. The current range reflects modern tastes and leans towards hoppy pale ales and IPAs plus some interesting red and dark ales. ♦RAIB GF

Mosaic Gluten Free (ABV 4%)
Shangri La (ABV 4.2%)
Yellow best bitter with hoppy aroma, light malt and tropical fruit on the palate, and a clean, refreshing, bitter finish.
Blue Sky Drinking (ABV 4.4%)
Malty aroma and background flavour with hints of berry fruits and spice. Hop bitterness increases in the short, balanced finish.
C Bomb (ABV 4.7%)
The Devil Made Me Brew It (ABV 5.5%)
A velvety speciality beer in stout style. Floral and citrus hops in the aroma, coffee and slightly burnt toffee flavours. Sweet but with a bitter finish.
Why Kick a Moo Cow (ABV 5.5%)
A strong, amber ale with malt and hops on the nose, flavours of tropical fruit and a dry bittersweet aftertaste.
Yakima Valley American IPA (ABV 7%)
A strong, full-bodied IPA. Hoppy and very fruity. Sweetness which is well-balanced with bitterness, lasting into a soft bitter aftertaste.

Arcadian

Bridge Studios, 454 Western Avenue, Cardiff, CF5 3BL
☎ 07748 802320 / 07468 612225
🌐 arcadianbrewing.com

Arcadian began brewing in 2018 using a 2.5-barrel brew plant. All beers are unfiltered and unpasteurised, and are available in keg and bottle. No core beer range; it changes seasonally but with a beer in each of the following categories: Pale/IPA, dark, Belgian & specialities. Beers available mainly locally. ♦

Archers

See Evan Evans

Ards

34B Carrowdore Road, Greyabbey, Newtownards, Co Down, BT22 2LX ☎ 07515 558406
✉ ardsbrewing@blackwood34.plus.com

Ards began brewing in 2011 using a 100-litre plant. A five-barrel plant is now in operation, allowing cask production in addition to the increasing range of bottle-conditioned and KeyKeg beers. Very much a local brewery with beers generally only supplied within a 15-mile radius. RAIB

Citra (ABV 4.8%)
Scrabo Gold (ABV 4.8%)
Hip Hop (ABV 5%)
Pig Island (ABV 5.2%)

Argyll

Unit 8a, Baliscate Industrial Estate, Tobermory, Isle of Mull, PA75 6QA
☎ (01688) 302821
✉ isleofmullbrewing@btinternet.com

Argyll Breweries was formed in 2010 following the merger of Oban Bay and Isle of Mull breweries, continuing to trade under those names. A small brewing plant now supports the Isle of Mull beers in Tobermory, primarily producing bottles but some cask-conditioned ale is still available.

Arkell's SIBA IFBB

Kingsdown, Swindon, Wiltshire, SN2 7RU
☎ (01793) 823026 🌐 arkells.com

⊗ Arkell's Brewery was established in 1843 by John Arkell. The Arkell family still brew in the original Victorian brewhouse. The brewery owns nearly 100 pubs across Wiltshire, Gloucestershire, Oxfordshire, Berkshire and Hampshire. In 2018 a brewery shop and visitor centre was opened on-site to mark its 175th anniversary. Seasonal beers are brewed frequently, often linked to sporting and other national events. ‼ ♦

Wiltshire Gold (ABV 3.7%)
3B (ABV 4%)
A medium brown beer with a strong, sweetish malt and caramel flavour. The hops come through strongly in the aftertaste, which is lingering and dry.
Hoperation IPA (ABV 4.2%)
Moonlight (ABV 4.5%)

Arran SIBA

Cladach, Brodick, Isle of Arran, KA27 8DE
☎ (01770) 302353

Office: 100 Wellington Street, Glasgow, G2 6DH
🌐 arranbrewery.com

The brewery opened in Brodick in 2000 using a 20-barrel plant with water sourced from the nearby mountains. In 2019 an additional 27-barrel plant was acquired for its proposed Loch Earn Brewery site, where cider is also produced. Its Arran View brewery site in Dreghorn has a 2.5-barrel plant for producing sour beers. Around 400 outlets around the UK are supplied direct. Beers are also produced under the Devil's Dyke Brewery name. ‼ ♦RAIB

Guid Ale (ABV 3.8%)
Dark (ABV 4.3%)
A well-balanced, malty beer with plenty of roast and hop in the taste, and a dry, bitter finish.
Sunset (ABV 4.4%)
Blonde (ABV 5%)
A hoppy beer with substantial fruit balance. The taste is balanced and the finish increasingly bitter. An aromatic, strong bitter that drinks below its weight.
Brewery Dug (ABV 5.5%)

Brewed under the Devil's Dyke Brewery name:
Devil's Blonde (ABV 4%)
Pale Ale (ABV 5%)

Arrow

c/o Wine Vaults, 37 High Street, Kington, Herefordshire, HR5 3BJ
☎ (01544) 230685 ✉ deanewright@yahoo.co.uk

Brewer Deane Wright continues to brew behind the Wine Vaults in Kington High Street, the only outlet for the beer.

Art Brew SIBA

Art Brew Barn, Brightwater Farm, Sutcombe, Holsworthy, Devon, EX22 7QE ☎ 07881 783626
✉ artbrewdevon@gmail.com

⊗ Brewing started in 2008 on a five-barrel plant near the Jurassic Coast in Dorset. In 2016, the brewery relocated to Devon, with a brewery tap, brewing 1,200 litres per week and distributing to more than 20 pubs and other outlets. Camping is available for 10 tents and four caravans/motorhomes all year round. Beer festivals are held at Easter and the first weekend in August. ♦RAIB V

Baby Anarchist (ABV 3.2%)
Pale (ABV 3.2%)
Raspberry Pale (ABV 4.4%)
Milk Stout (ABV 4.5%)
Ab6 (ABV 4.6%)
Black Cherry Chocolate Porter (ABV 4.8%)
Ginger & Chilli IPA (ABV 6%)
Love or Nothing (ABV 6%)
Orange IPA (ABV 6%)

Artisan

Building 1a, Aston Down Business Park, Minchinhampton, Gloucestershire, GL6 8GA ☎ 07780 449102 🌐 artisan-ales.co.uk

⊗ Artisan is located in a former fire station next to the gatehouse of a business park. It brews a range of beer styles, which are available for members of the public to purchase from the shop on most Fridays. ‼ ♦RAIB V

PA03 (ABV 3.6%)
BB01 (ABV 3.7%)
PA02 (ABV 3.9%)
BB02 (ABV 4.2%)
St01 (ABV 4.5%)
St02 (ABV 4.5%)
St03 (ABV 4.5%)
PA04 (ABV 4.7%)
PA01 (ABV 4.9%)
DB01 (ABV 5.2%)

Arundel SIBA

Unit C7, Ford Airfield Industrial Estate, Ford, Arundel, West Sussex, BN18 0HY
☎ (01903) 733111 🌐 arundelbrewery.co.uk

⊗ Founded in 1992, Arundel Brewery is the historic town's first brewery in 70 years. A brewery shop opened in 2014 by the quayside with a good selection of beers, both its own and from other breweries. It also brews for the Bison Crafthouse, Brighton. ‼ ♦

Black Stallion (ABV 3.7%)
A dark mild with a well-defined chocolate and roast character. The aftertaste is not powerful but the initial flavours remain in the clean finish.
Castle (ABV 3.8%)
A pale tawny beer with fruit and malt noticeable in the aroma. The flavour has a good balance of malt, fruit and hops, with a dry, hoppy finish.
Sussex Gold (ABV 4.2%)
A golden-coloured best bitter with a strong, floral hop aroma. The ale is clean-tasting and bitter for its strength, with a tangy citrus flavour. The initial hop and fruit die to a dry and bitter finish.
Sussex IPA (ABV 4.5%)
Stronghold (ABV 4.7%)
A smooth, full-flavoured premium bitter. A good balance of malt, fruit and hops comes through in this rich, chestnut-coloured beer.
Wild Heaven (ABV 5.2%)

Ascot SIBA

Unit 5, Compton Place Business Centre, Surrey Avenue, Camberley, Surrey, GU15 3DX
☎ (01276) 686696 🌐 ascotbrewing.co.uk

⊗ Ascot started production in 2007 on a four-barrel plant in a small industrial unit. The brewery has successfully expanded over the years and 2017 saw the brewery with new owners. ‼ ♦RAIB

Starting Gate (ABV 3.8%)

A pale brown, session bitter with malt flavours present throughout. Dry, with a lasting sharp, bitter finish.
Gold Cup (ABV 4%)
A lemony aroma leads to a dry, bitter taste, with more citrus flavours. Hoppy finish with a hint of sweetness.
Final Furlong (ABV 4.2%)
A best bitter with balancing biscuity malt sweetness. Some citrus fruitiness and a clean hoppy aftertaste.
5/4 Favourite (ABV 4.6%)
Some grapefruit in the aroma, with hop and bitterness in the taste and plenty of balancing biscuit in the aroma and aftertaste.
Front Runner (ABV 4.8%)
Shadowfax (ABV 4.8%)
Anastasia's Stout (ABV 5%)
Burnt coffee aromas lead to a roast malt flavour in this black beer. Notably fruity throughout, with a bittersweet aftertaste.

Ashley Down

c/o 15 Wathen Road, St Andrews, Bristol, BS6 5BY
☎ (0117) 983 6567 ☎ 07563 751200
✉ ashleydownbrewery@gmail.com

⊗ Ashley Down began brewing in 2011 using a 5.5-barrel plant in the owner's garage. It suffered a major fire in 2017 and uses spare capacity at other breweries while looking for new premises. ♦RAIB V

Ashleyhay

Royal Oak, North End, Wirksworth, Derbyshire, DE4 4FG
☎ (01629) 823000 ☎ 07708 050019
✉ jim@ashleyhaybrewery.co.uk

⊗ Brewing began in 2014, a 2.5-barrel plant is used.

Ashover SIBA

Unit 1, Derby Road Business Park, Clay Cross, Derbyshire, S45 9AG
☎ (01246) 251859 🌐 ashoverbrewery.com

⊗ Brewing began in 2007 on a 3.5-barrel plant in the garage of the cottage next to the Old Poets' Corner, Ashover. Since its acquisition of a 10-barrel brewery in the neighbouring village of Clay Cross in 2015, Ashover now brews at both sites. The brewery serves local freehouses across Derbyshire and further afield as well as the Old Poets' Corner. !! RAIB

Light Rale (ABV 3.7%)
Light in colour and taste, with initial sweet and malt flavours, leading to a bitter finish and aftertaste.
Font (ABV 3.8%)
Poets Tipple (ABV 4%)
Complex, tawny-coloured beer that drinks above its strength. Predominantly malty in flavour, with increasing bitterness towards the end.
Littlemoor Citra (ABV 4.1%)
The Fabrick (ABV 4.4%)
Rainbows End (ABV 4.5%)
Slightly smooth, bitter golden beer with an initial sweetness. Grapefruit and lemon hop flavours come through strongly as the beer gets increasingly dry towards the finish, ending with a bitter, dry aftertaste.
Red Lion (ABV 4.6%)
Coffin Lane Stout (ABV 5%)
Excellent example of the style, with a chocolate and coffee flavour, balanced by a little sweetness. Finish is long and quite dry.
Butts Pale Ale (ABV 5.5%)
Pale and strong, yet easy-drinking, golden bitter. Combination of bitter and sweet flavours mingle with an alcoholic kick, leading to a warming yet bitter finish and aftertaste.
Milk Stout (ABV 6%)

Ashton (NEW)

Cove House Gardens, Ashton Keynes, Wiltshire, SN6 6NS ☎ 07796 445822

Ashton Brewing Co was established in 2019.

Mosaic (ABV 4.4%)
Shot in the Dark (ABV 4.6%)

Atlantic

Treisaac Farm, Treisaac, Newquay, Cornwall, TR8 4DX
☎ (01637) 880326 🌐 atlanticbrewery.com

⊗ Specialist microbrewery producing organic and vegan ales. All ales are unfiltered and finings-free. There are eleven core brews including four food-matched dining ales developed with Michelin chef Nathan Outlaw. Casks are supplied locally and to London, with bottle-conditioned beers available nationally. ♦RAIB V

Soul Citra (ABV 4%)
Azores (ABV 4.2%)
Unfined golden ale. Citrus and resinous hops dominate the aroma and taste with tropical fruits. Refreshing bitter and dry finish.
Earl Grey PA (ABV 4.5%)
Cloudy, amber, organic, speciality ale. Hop aroma leads to powerful citrus fruit flavours becoming intense. Fairly bitter and dry.
Elderflower Blonde (ABV 4.5%)
Pale yellow, light, crisp floral beer with elderflower nose. Elderflower and gooseberry fruits with soft citrus and pine hops flavours.
Mandarina Cornovia (ABV 4.5%)
Pale gold, speciality beer with full mandarin citrus flavour matched by firm biscuit malt and resin/earthy hop notes.
Masala Chai PA (ABV 4.5%)
Sea Salt Stout (ABV 4.5%)
Simcotica (ABV 4.5%)
Blue (ABV 4.8%)
Smooth, rich porter with heavy roast malt aroma and taste. Smoky liquorice, bitter coffee and chocolate flavours with sweet fruit.
Honey Ale (ABV 4.8%)
Fistral (ABV 5.2%)
Full-flavoured, copper, wheat beer. Sweet, stone-fruit flavours blend with biscuit malt and citrus hops. Malt finish with hops and dryness.

Atlas

See Orkney

Atom

Unit 4, Food & Tech Park, Malmo Road, Sutton Fields Industrial Estate, Hull, East Yorkshire, HU7 0YF
☎ (01482) 820572 🌐 atombeers.com

⊗ Atom Brewing Co was founded in 2014 by Allan Rice and Sarah Thackray. Most of its production goes into can and keg, but cask ales are produced in rotation or on demand, around a core range of four. Atom's ethos is science and education based so, working with local colleges to inspire the next generation of scientists, it runs regular brewing schools and classes. All beers are unfined and unfiltered (so naturally hazy). !!♦V

Schrodingers Cat (ABV 3.5%)
Blonde Ale (ABV 4%)
Dark Matter (ABV 4.5%)

Critical Temperature (ABV 5.5%)

Atomic

c/o Alexandra Arms, 72-73 James Street, Rugby, Warwickshire, CV21 2SL
☎ (01788) 542170 ☎ 07876 195895
atomicbrewery.com

Founded in 2006, by Nick Pugh and Keith Abbis, Atomic is located in the Alexandra Arms' outbuildings. The six-barrel plant was initially leased by the pub landlord, who also brewed Alex Ales on it. The Victoria Inn was acquired in 2007. At the end of 2010 the Alexandra Arms was put up for sale, threatening the existence of Atomic, but after some bargaining it bought its second freehold property including the brewery. !! ♦

Attic

29B Mary Vale Road, Stirchley, Birmingham, B30 2DA
atticbrewco.com

A natural progression from homebrewing, Attic Brewery Co was launched in 2018 by two friends. Its taproom is open Friday evening and all day Saturday. Beer is mostly available in the tap but there are plans to expand into the local trade market. ◆

Aurora

Unit 6, Gallows Industrial Park, off Furnace Road, Ilkeston, Derbyshire, DE7 5EP ☎ 07740 783631

Aurora was established in 2016. Joint owner Mark Derbyshire, formerly of Hardy & Hanson's, brews on a 10-barrel plant. Many local outlets, and a few further away, are supplied direct. The brewery swaps beers with other breweries throughout the UK, many of which can be found in its micropub, the Ilson Tap.

Austendyke

The Beeches, Austendyke Road, Weston Hills, Spalding, Lincolnshire, PE12 6BZ ☎ 07866 045778

Austendyke Ales began brewing in 2012 using a seven-barrel plant. The brewery is operated on a part-time basis by brewer Charlie Rawlings and business partner Nathan Marshall, who handles sales. The brewery owns and runs micropub the Prior's Oven, Spalding.

Long Lane (ABV 4%)
Sheep Market (ABV 4%)
Bakestraw Bitter (ABV 4.1%)
Bake House (ABV 4.5%)
Holbeach High Street (ABV 4.5%)
Hogsgate (ABV 5%)

Autumn SIBA

8 East Cliff Road, Spectrum Business Park, Seaham, County Durham, SR7 7PS autumnbrewing.co.uk

Autumn produce keg and bottled gluten free beers. No real ale. GF

Avalanche (NEW)

5 Goodwood Close, Burton Latimer, Northamptonshire, NN15 5WP
avalanchebrew.co.uk

Avalanche Brew Co is a nanobrewery formed by two home brewers, Matt and Rob, producing modern, hoppy beers. The custom-built 200-litre brewhouse with fermentation capacity of around 400 litres produces beers that are unfined and unfiltered. Primarily cask and keg but occasional small batches are available in bottle and can. V

Late to the Party (ABV 4.5%)

Avid SIBA

Red Moss Farm, Quernmore Brow, Quernmore, LA2 0QW ☎ 07814 206881 avidbrewing.co.uk

Avid was established in 2015 by two experienced homebrewers. The 7.5-barrel microbrewery is based in picturesque Quernmore, near Lancaster. Water is used from a local borehole.

Golden Ale (ABV 3.9%)
American Pale (ABV 4%)
New Zealand Pale (ABV 4%)
Milk Stout (ABV 4.5%)
IPA (ABV 5%)
TropicAle (ABV 5%)
Irish Coffee Stout (ABV 6%)

Axholme

See Docks

Aye Been (NEW)

Masons Wynd, Eyemouth, TD14 5HG
✉ hello@ayebeenbrewing.com

Aye Been is a four-barrel brewery established in Eyemouth in 2020.

Aye PA (ABV 3.8%)

Ayr

5 Racecourse Road, Ayr, KA7 2DG ☎ 07834 922142
ayrbrewingcompany.com

Ayr began brewing in 2009 on a five-barrel plant and is located at the Glenpark Hotel. As well as the hotel, around 50 other outlets are supplied throughout Scotland and England. ♦ RAIB V

Leezie Lundie (ABV 3.8%)
A pale golden session ale with hints of grapefruit, and a dry lingering finish.
Uisge Dubh (ABV 3.8%)
Otto & Griselda (ABV 4%)
Boing! (ABV 4.1%)
Jolly Beggars (ABV 4.2%)
A complex best bitter with plenty of character and a lingering malty aftertaste.
Complicated Maisie (ABV 4.3%)
Rabbie's Porter (ABV 4.3%)
Award-winning, robust, full-bodied porter with well-balanced toffee, fruity maltiness and a slightly smoky finish.

B&T SIBA

The Brewery, Shefford, Bedfordshire, SG17 5DZ
☎ (01462) 815080 banksandtaylor.com

Banks & Taylor, now just B&T, was founded in 1982. It produces thirteen regular beers, plus monthly specials and occasional beers (see website for details), in an industrial unit close to the town centre. There are four tied houses, all sell B&T beers plus several guest beers & real cider. !! ♦

Two Brewers Bitter (ABV 3.6%)
Bronze-coloured bitter with citrus hop aroma and taste and a dry finish.
Plum Mild (ABV 3.8%)

THE BREWERIES

Shefford Bitter (ABV 3.8%)
A pale brown beer with a light hop aroma and a hoppy taste leading to a bitter finish.
Shefford Dark Mild (ABV 3.8%)
A dark beer with a well-balanced taste. Sweetish, roast malt aftertaste.
Golden Fox (ABV 4.1%)
Black Dragon Mild (ABV 4.3%)
Black in colour with a toffee and roast malt flavour, and a smoky finish.
Dunstable Giant (ABV 4.4%)
Dragon Slayer (ABV 4.5%)
A golden beer with a malt and hop flavour and a bitter finish. More malty and less hoppy than is usual for a beer of this style.
Edwin Taylor's Extra Stout (ABV 4.5%)
A complex black beer with a bitter coffee and roast malt flavour, and a dry bitter finish.
Fruit Bat (ABV 4.5%)
A warming straw-coloured beer with a taste of apricots and a bitter finish.
Shefford Pale Ale (SPA) (ABV 4.5%)
A well-balanced beer with hop, fruit and malt flavours. Dry, bitter aftertaste.
SOD (ABV 5%)
SOS (ABV 5%)
A rich mixture of fruit, hops and malt is present in the taste and aftertaste of this beer. Predominantly hoppy aroma.

Bacchus

Bacchus Hotel, 17 High Street, Sutton-on-Sea, Lincolnshire, LN12 2EY
☎ (01507) 441204 ⊕ bacchushotel.co.uk

Bacchus began brewing in 2010 and now has a two-barrel plant supplying the Bacchus Hotel. !! RAIB

Backyard SIBA

Unit 8a, Gatehouse Trading Estate, Lichfield Road, Brownhills, Walsall, West Midlands, WS8 6JZ
☎ (01543) 360145 ⊕ tbb.uk.com

Backyard began brewing in 2008 and expanded in 2012 to a 12-barrel plant brewing up to 50 barrels a week. Two pubs are owned: the Fountain, Walsall and the Saddlers Arms, Solihull. A half-barrel experimental plant is also in operation and a tap house is open every Friday (1-8pm). !! ♦

Bitter (ABV 3.8%)
The Hoard (ABV 3.9%)
Blonde (ABV 4.1%)
Americana (ABV 4.3%)
Gold (ABV 4.5%)
IPA (ABV 5%)
Antipodean (ABV 5.6%)

BAD SIBA

Unit 3, North Hill Road, Dishforth, North Yorkshire, YO7 3DH
☎ (01423) 324005 ⊕ wearebad.co

BAD Co commenced brewing in 2014, originally using a 13-barrel plant, since upgraded to cope with demand. A new and evolving Off Tempo range has been developed, focusing on experimental and radical brews. ♦V

DIPA 3
Pale Aura (ABV 3.8%)
Yorkshire Bitter (ABV 3.8%)
Love Over Gold (ABV 4.1%)
Wild Gravity (ABV 5.2%)
Dark Necessities (ABV 5.5%)
Boston Tea Party (ABV 5.8%)
Milkshake IPA (ABV 5.8%)

Bad Bunny (NEW)

26 Bullbridge Cottage, Ambergate, Derbyshire, DE56 2EW ☎ 07519 605362
⊕ badbunnybrewery.co.uk

Founded by husband-and-wife team Mike and Clare Chettle using a self-built 300-litre brewery in the back garden of their family home. Brewing commenced in 2019. RAIB

Bad Joke

Unit 2Ca, Penn Street Works, Penn Street, Amersham, Buckinghamshire, HP7 0FA ☎ 07791 937737
✉ badjokebrewco@gmail.com

Production started in 2018. A variety of styles of bottle-conditioned beers are produced, which can only be obtained at the brewery, by prior arrangement. RAIB

Bad Seed

7 Rye Close, York Way Industrial Estate, Malton, North Yorkshire, YO17 6YD
☎ (01653) 695783 ⊕ badseedbrewery.com

Bad Seed produce an award-winning range of new wave and traditional beers in cask, keg and can. Established in 2013, the brewery is based in Malton, the 'food capital' of Yorkshire, and operates on a 12-barrel brew kit. Alongside the core range it makes regular specials, unique brews and collaborations with other cutting-edge breweries. All beers are unfined, unfiltered and vegan friendly. !! ♦V

Kiwi (ABV 3.8%)
Dalliance (ABV 4%)
Session IPA (ABV 4%)

Badger

See Hall & Woodhouse

Bakehouse

See Warwickshire

Bakers Dozen SIBA

Unit 5, Ketton Business Estate, Pit Lane, Ketton, PE9 3SZ
☎ (01780) 238180 ⊕ bakersdozenbrewing.co.uk

Brewing takes place on a five-barrel plant installed in 2015 by the owners of the Jolly Brewer, Stamford, where the beers are always available. ♦V

Jentacular (ABV 3.5%)
Magic Potion (ABV 3.8%)
Stamford Pale (ABV 4%)
System of a Brown (ABV 4.1%)
Straight Outta Ketton (ABV 4.5%)
Electric Landlady (ABV 5%)

Ballard's

See Greyhound

Bang the Elephant

Unit 14, Bailey Brook Industrial Estate, Amber Drive, Langley Mill, Derbyshire, NG16 4BE ☎ 07539 652055
✉ bangtheelephantbrewing@hotmail.com

Bang The Elephant are a neo-victorian, steam punk-inspired, six-barrel brewery, creating small batch beers for the cask, keg and bottle market. ♦V

Gigglemug (ABV 4%)
Podsnappery (ABV 4%)
Half Rats (ABV 4.4%)
Sons of Liberty APA (ABV 5%)
Kali Yuga (ABV 5.9%)
Odissi (ABV 6%)

Bang-On

Unit 3, George Street, Bridgend Industrial Estate, Bridgend, CF31 3TS
☎ (01656) 760790 bangonbrewery.beer

Established in 2016, this five-barrel plant produces a variety of unique beers. An on-site taproom offers tours and brew day experiences. Limited edition beers are also available. A bespoke service is offered with personalised labels (minimum of six bottles). !! V

Tidy (ABV 4%)
Cariad (ABV 4.1%)
Bohemian Pilsner (ABV 4.2%)
Fuster Cluck (ABV 9.5%)

Bank Top SIBA

The Pavilion, Ashworth Lane, Bolton, BL1 8RA
☎ (01204) 595800 banktopbrewery.com

Bank Top was established in 1995. Since 2002, the brewery has occupied a Grade II-listed tennis pavilion housing an 11-barrel plant. Bank Top Brewery Estates was formed in 2010 and now owns three pubs, Bank Top Brewery Tap, Bank Top Ale House and Olde England Forever. !!♦

Draymans Draught (ABV 3.6%)
Bad to the Bone (ABV 4%)
Dark Mild (ABV 4%)
Coffee roast aroma. Smooth mouthfeel, with roasted malt prominent throughout and some fruit. Moderate bitterness in aftertaste.
Flat Cap (ABV 4%)
Amber ale with a modest fruit aroma leading to a beer with citrus fruit, malt and hops. Good finish of fruit, malt and bitterness.
Pavilion Pale Ale (ABV 4.5%)
A yellow beer with a citrus and hop aroma. Big fruity flavour with a peppery hoppiness; dry, bitter yet fruity finish.
Palomino Rising (ABV 5%)
Port O Call (ABV 5%)
Dark brown beer with a malty, fruity aroma. Malt, roast and dark fruits in the bittersweet taste and finish.

Banks's

Park Brewery, Wolverhampton, West Midlands, WV1 4NY
☎ (01902) 711811 bankssbeer.co.uk

Banks's was founded as maltsters in 1840, commencing brewing in 1874 and moved to the current Park Brewery in 1875. It became the principal brewery of Wolverhampton and Dudley Breweries (W&DB), founded in 1890. In 2007 the Marston's name was adopted following the takeover by W&DB in 1999. Whilst continuing to produce its traditional beers, Banks's now also produce Wainwrights, Lancaster Bomber, Bombardier, Courage Best and Courage Directors at Park Brewery, as well as contract brewing. Part of Marston's PLC. !!

Mild (ABV 3.5%)
An amber-coloured, well-balanced, refreshing, session beer.
Amber Ale (ABV 3.8%)
A pale brown bitter with a pleasant balance of hops and malt. Hops continue from the taste through to a bittersweet aftertaste.
Sunbeam (ABV 4.2%)

Brewed for Marston's:
Wainwright (ABV 4.1%)
Lancaster Bomber (ABV 4.4%)

Brewed under the Bombardier brand name:
Bombardier (ABV 4.1%)
A heavy aroma of malt and raspberry jam. Traces of hops and bitterness are quickly submerged under a smooth, malty sweetness. A solid, rich finish.
Gold (ABV 4.1%)

Brewed under the Courage brand name:
Directors (ABV 4.8%)

Brewed under the Mansfield brand name:
Cask Ale (ABV 3.9%)
Best Bitter (ABV 4%)

Barefaced SIBA

7 Norwich Road, Bournemouth, Dorset, BH2 5QZ
☎ 07435 157767 barefacedbrewing.co.uk

Barefaced Brewing was started in 2017 by two friends, Nick Horne and Tom Cooper, in one of their garden sheds in Wimborne. The brewery has since expanded and moved to Bournemouth using a 3.5-barrel plant. !!♦RAIB

Big Bang Blueberry Cream Ale (ABV 4.4%)
So You've Travelled (ABV 4.4%)
Heartbreak Stout (ABV 5.4%)
Flash IPA (ABV 6.2%)
Sucker Punch Saison (ABV 6.4%)

Barker's (NEW)

14 Midway, South Crosland, West Yorkshire, HD4 7DA
☎ 07876 540211 ✉ jimrbarker1978@me.com

James Barker started as a homebrewer four years ago, producing beers for friends. With invaluable help and guidance from Summer Wine Brewery and Neil at Milltown Brewery, he made the leap from homebrewer to commercial production in 2019. He continues to use his handbuilt 60-litre brewplant, bottling a core range of seven beers. RAIB V

Barn Owl

Buildings Farm, Faringdon Road, Gozzard's Ford, Oxfordshire, OX13 6QH ☎ 07724 551086

Located in a spacious barn on a farm just outside Abingdon, brewing began in 2016 using a four-barrel plant. Beers can be found in local free trade outlets.

Old Scruttock's Bitter (ABV 3.9%)
Golden Gozzard (ABV 4%)
Gozzard's Guzzler (ABV 4.4%)
Old Scruttock's Dirigible (ABV 5%)

Barnaby's

The Old Stable, Hole Farm, Staverton, Devon, TQ11 0LA
☎ (01803) 762730 barnabysbrewhouse.com

Soil Association-certified organic brewery established in 2016. Occasional cask ale production. Expansion is planned. ♦V

Dark Dunkel (ABV 4.8%)
Pilsner (ABV 4.8%)
Red Helles (ABV 4.8%)
English IPA (ABV 5.4%)
Green Tomato Saison (ABV 6%)

Barnard Castle SIBA

Quaker Yard, Rear of 24 Newgate, Barnard Castle, DL12 8NG ☎ 07591 236210
barnardcastlebrewing.com

Brewing commenced in 2017 on a 3.6-barrel plant situated in one of the many yards that feature in Barnard Castle. A bottle shop and taproom is planned while a mobile bar enables the brewery to take beers to events further afield. Beers are named after local themes.

Quaker Yard (ABV 3.5%)
Deliberation (ABV 3.7%)
Mechanical Swan (ABV 4.5%)
ArchAleOlogy (ABV 4.8%)
Peg Powler (ABV 5.6%)

Barnet

Barnet Brewery, C/O The Black Horse, 80 Wood Street, High Barnet, Hertfordshire, EN5 4BW
☎ (0208) 4492230 blackhorsebarnet.co.uk

Opened in 2013, it is a small 2.5-barrel plant behind the Black Horse. Four beers are regularly brewed on a rotating basis, using traditional recipes from long since closed breweries. Seasonal beers are brewed occasionally. The beers are mainly supplied to the Black Horse, but small quantities may be found in other local pubs.

Barney's

Summerhall Brewery, 1 Summerhall, Edinburgh, EH9 1PL ☎ 07512 253660 barneysbeer.com

The only microbrewery in Edinburgh's city centre, Barney's Beer was founded in 2010 and now brews on the site of the original 1800s Summerhall Brewery. Summerhall is Edinburgh's centre for the arts and science. !! RAIB

Good Ordinary Pale Ale (ABV 3.8%)
Extra Pale (ABV 4%)
Red Rye (ABV 4.5%)
Warming spicy notes from the rye malt create an interesting twist.
Volcano IPA (ABV 5%)
Nice floral aroma to this moderately bitter IPA.

Barngates SIBA

Barngates, Ambleside, Cumbria, LA22 0NG
☎ (01539) 436575 barngatesbrewery.co.uk

Barngates was established in 1997 to supply only the Drunken Duck Inn. It became a limited company in 1999. Expansion over the years, plus a new purpose-built, 10-barrel plant in 2008, means it now supplies more than 150 outlets throughout Cumbria, Lancashire and Yorkshire. !!

Pale (ABV 3.3%)
A well-balanced, fruity, hoppy bitter with plenty of flavour for its strength.
Cat Nap (ABV 3.6%)
Pale beer, unapologetically bitter, with a dry, astringent finish.
Cracker (ABV 3.9%)
A full-bodied, hoppy beer with some balancing sweetness and fruit. There is plenty of taste in this brown beer. Cleverly constructed.
Brathay Gold (ABV 4%)
Attractive sweet and rich aroma is followed by plenty of fruit and hops then a long, bitter finish.
Goodhew's Dry Stout (ABV 4.3%)
The inviting roast aroma leads to an easy-drinking, full-bodied, well-balanced roasty stout.
Tag Lag (ABV 4.4%)
This traditional bitter is full on: fruit, noble hops, malt balance, good body with a crisp, clean finish.
Red Bull Terrier (ABV 4.8%)
An assertive, roasty, red beer with full mouthfeel. Initial sweetness and luscious fruit, give way to a lingering, bitter finish.

Baronscourt (NEW)

38 Baronscourt Road, Newtownstewart, County Tyrone, BT78 4EY ☎ 07734 267164
baronscourtbrewery.com

Beers are produced using locally sourced ingredients and it is one of the first craft beer producers with a zero carbon footprint.

Barsham SIBA

Estate Office, West Barsham, Norfolk, NR21 9NR
☎ (01328) 864459 ☎ 07760 551056
barshambrewery.co.uk

Barsham Brewery purchased Jo C's Brewery business in 2017. Maris Otter is grown on-site and a private bore hole supplies water for the brewery. ♦RAIB V

Oaks (ABV 3.6%)
Norfolk Topper (ABV 3.8%)
Mr Shanks (ABV 4%)
Pilgrims Ale (ABV 4%)
BOB (ABV 4.3%)
Stout Robin (ABV 4.6%)
Golden Close IPA (ABV 5%)

Barum SIBA

c/o Reform Inn, Pilton High Street, Pilton, Barnstaple, Devon, EX31 1PD
☎ (01271) 329994 barumbrewery.co.uk

Barum was established in 1996 by Tim Webster and is housed in a conversion attached to the Reform Inn, which acts as the brewery tap and main outlet. Distribution is exclusively within Devon. !!♦RAIB

Basement Beer (NEW)

Meriton Foundry, Meriton Street, Bristol, BS2 0SZ
☎ 07702 430808 ✉ info@basementbeer.co.uk

New brewery established in the St Michael's Hill area of Bristol in 2019.

Bason Bridge SIBA

Unit 1 & 2, 129 Church Road, Bason Bridge, Highbridge, Somerset, TA9 4RG
☎ (01278) 787210 7daycellar.co.uk

⊗ Brewery founded in Somerset in 2018. Initially, two beers were brewed, but after the successful launch, a third is now available. All beer is brewed on the 12-barrel plant.

Batemans SIBA IFBB

Salem Bridge Brewery, Mill Lane, Wainfleet, Lincolnshire, PE24 4JE
☎ (01754) 880317 🌐 bateman.co.uk

Bateman's Brewery is one of Britain's few remaining independent family-owned and managed brewers. Established in 1874, it has been brewing award-winning beers for four generations. Justifiably proud of its heritage it is, nevertheless, forward-looking and progressive. All 62 tied and managed houses serve cask-conditioned beer. See website for seasonal and speciality beers brewed throughout the year. ‼ ♦

XB (ABV 3.7%)
A well-rounded, smooth, malty beer with a blackcurrant-fruity background. Hops flourish initially before giving way to a bittersweet dryness that enhances the mellow malty ending.
Gold (Also known as Yella Belly Gold) (ABV 3.9%)
Salem Porter (ABV 4.8%)
A black and complex mix of chocolate, liquorice and cough elixir.
XXXB (ABV 4.8%)
A brilliant blend of malt, hops and fruit on the nose with a bitter bite over the top of a faint banana maltiness that stays the course. A russet-tan brown classic.

Bath

Hare Brewery, Southway Drive, Warmley, Bristol, BS30 5LW
☎ (0117) 947 4797 🌐 bathales.com

⊗ Established in 1995, Bath Ales was taken over by St Austell in 2016. Since 2018 Bath Ales beers have been brewed in a new high-tech brewery with state-of-the-art bottling and kegging lines in the headquarters building. Eight venues are operated in the Bristol/Bath area, all serving cask ale. ‼ ♦ RAIB

Prophecy (ABV 3.9%)
Straw-coloured, refreshing bitter with fruity aroma. Bittersweet taste blends subtle citrus fruits with pine notes. Crisp, dry, bitter finish.
Gem (ABV 4.1%)
Pale brown best bitter with sweet fruit and malt flavours, and a hint of caramel. Little aroma, but a balanced taste with a short, bitter finish.
Lansdown (ABV 5%)
Hop-forward IPA with some light malt balancing citrus, pine and grassy notes which continue into the satisfying bitter finish.

Bath Brewhouse

City Pub Company, 14 James Street West, Bath, BA1 2BX
☎ (01225) 805609

Office: City Pub Group Plc, Essel House, 2nd Floor, 29 Foley Street, London, W1W 7TH
🌐 thebathbrewhouse.com

⊗ Previously known as the James Street Brewery, Bath Brewhouse opened in 2013 and is owned by the City Pub Company, which owns several other pubs and brewpubs around the country. The compact brewery is on the ground floor, with the fermenting vessels and conditioning tanks on the first floor. The on-site brewer produces a wide range of beers. The company's other pub, the Cork, Bath, is also supplied. ‼ ♦

Bathams IFBB

Delph Brewery, Delph Road, Brierley Hill, West Midlands, DY5 2TN
☎ (01384) 77229 🌐 bathams.com

A classic Black Country small brewery established in 1877. Tim and Matthew Batham represent the fifth generation to run the company. The Vine, one of the Black Country's most famous pubs, is also the site of the brewery. The company has 12 tied houses and supplies around 30 other outlets. Batham's Best Bitter is delivered in 54-gallon hogsheads to meet demand. A sixth generation family member, Tim's daughter, Claire, has joined the on-site team as Business Development Manager. ♦

Mild Ale (ABV 3.5%)
A fruity, dark brown mild with malty sweetness and a roast malt finish.
Best Bitter (ABV 4.3%)
A pale yellow, fruity, sweetish bitter, with a dry, hoppy finish. A good, light, refreshing beer.

Battersea

12-14 Arches Lane, Battersea Power Station, Nine Elms, London, SW11 8AB
☎ (020) 8161 2366 🌐 batterseabrew.co.uk

Opening in 2018, the brewery consists of two railway arches, one for the brewery and one for the taproom. A changing range of beers is produced in cask and keg available at the taproom and pubs owned by the brewery owners, the Mosaic Pub Company.

Battle

The Calf House, Beech Farm, North Trade Road, Battle, East Sussex, TN33 0HN
☎ (01424) 772838 🌐 battlebrewery.co.uk

Battle Brewery is an eight-barrel brewery with on-site taproom and bottle shop, located at the heart of 1066 country in the historic town of Battle, East Sussex. Established in 2017, local pubs, cafés and shops are supplied. V

Tostig (ABV 3.2%)
Conquest (ABV 4%)
One Hop Wonder (ABV 4%)
Black Arrow (ABV 4.5%)
Stigand (ABV 4.9%)
Abbey Pale (ABV 5%)
Russian Imperial Stout (ABV 8.3%)

Battledown SIBA

Coxhorne Farm, London Road, Cheltenham, Gloucestershire, GL52 6UY ☎ 07734 834104
🌐 battledownbrewery.com

⊗ A family brewery since 2005, the future is now guided by the next generation with the release of the Cotswold range. Long term beers have had some minor tweaks and are listed under the Heritage title. A new 13-hectolitre plant was installed in 2020, supplied by spring water from the Cotswold hills; spent malt is used on the farm. More than 250 outlets are supplied. ‼ ♦ RAIB V

Pale (ABV 3.8%)
California Spring Lager (ABV 4.4%)
Original (ABV 4.4%)
Tipster (ABV 4.4%)
London Road IPA (ABV 5.2%)

West Coast IPA (ABV 5.2%)
Four Kings (ABV 7.2%)

Battlefield

See Tunnel

Bays SIBA

Aspen Way, Paignton, Devon, TQ4 7QR
☎ (01803) 555004 🌐 baysbrewery.co.uk

Bays Brewery is a multiple award-winning, family-run business based in Torbay on the Devon coast. Its passion is to brew premium ales using the finest local ingredients whilst also supporting the community and protecting the environment. ‼🛒♦

Topsail (ABV 4%)
A tawny, session bitter with complex aroma. Malty, bitter taste leading to a long, dry and refreshing aftertaste.
Gold (ABV 4.3%)
Smooth, golden ale. Light aroma and taste of hops, malt and caramel. Lingering hoppy aftertaste.
Breakwater (ABV 4.5%)
Trunk Ale (ABV 4.5%)
Devon Dumpling (ABV 5.1%)
Strong ale, easily drinkable. Light aromas of hops and fruit continue through taste and lingering aftertaste.

Beach

See Milton

Beacon Brauhaus

Pilgrims Coffee, Falkland House, Marygate, Holy Island, Berwick upon Tweed, TD15 2SJ
☎ (01289) 389109 🌐 pilgrimscoffee.com

Nanobrewery situated on Holy Island, the first brewery to be based there in around 500 years. Local outlets are supplied. Brewing is currently suspended.

Beak (NEW)

Unit 14, Cliffe Industrial Estate, Lewes, East Sussex, BN8 6JL ☎ 07985 708122 🌐 beakbrewery.com

Originally a gypsy brewery, with recipes tested on a nano-kit, Beak now has its own 15-barrel brewery and taproom in Lewes. ♦

Bear Claw

Unit 3, Meantime Workshops, Spittal, Northumberland, TD15 1RG ☎ 07919 276715
🌐 bearclawbrewery.weebly.com

Bear Claw began brewing in 2012 using a two-barrel plant, producing a variety of mainly highly-hopped, cask-conditioned ales, and many bottle-conditioned beers, including continental styles. Beers are available in the Green Shop and Curfew pub in Berwick upon Tweed. RAIB

Beartown SIBA

Bromley House, Spindle Street, Congleton, Cheshire, CW12 1QN
☎ (01260) 299964 🌐 beartownbrewery.co.uk

Beartown began brewing in 1994 and uses a 25-barrel plant. It supplies more than 250 outlets. It is now in partnership with Manning Brewers (qv), also of Congleton. ‼🛒♦

Glacier (ABV 3.6%)
Best Bitter (ABV 3.7%)
Bluebeary (ABV 4%)
Ginger Bear (ABV 4%)
Kodiak (ABV 4%)
Hops and fruit dominate the taste of this crisp, yellow bitter and these follow through to the dryish aftertaste. Biscuity malt also comes through on the aroma and taste.
Skinful (ABV 4.2%)
Biscuity malt dominates the flavour of this amber best bitter. There are hops and a hint of sulphur on the aroma. A balance of malt and bitterness follow through to the aftertaste.
Peach Melbear (ABV 4.4%)
Lit (ABV 4.5%)
Atlas (ABV 4.8%)
Creme Bearlee (ABV 4.8%)
Polar Eclipse (ABV 4.8%)
Classic black, dry and bitter stout, with roast flavours to the fore. Good hop on the nose follow through the taste into a long dry finish.
Quantock (ABV 5%)
Wojtek (ABV 5.5%)

Beat SIBA

9 Old Forge Trading Estate, Dudley Road, Lye, West Midlands, DY9 8EL ☎ 07821 132297

Office: 11 Sydenham Hill, Bristol, BS6 5SL
🌐 beatales.com

Beat Ales has been remarketed as Beat Brewery. Originally brewing in North Curry, it moved to Lye in the Black Country in 2018. Beer names reflect the owners musical inspiration, taking in different genres. Music can be played from the pumpclips. Its taproom is open Friday and Saturday afternoons. ♦RAIB V

Raver (ABV 3.8%)
New Wave (ABV 4.5%)
Metal Head (ABV 4.8%)
Rocka (ABV 5.3%)
Funk (ABV 5.5%)
Cosmic Pop (ABV 6%)

Beath SIBA

54 Foulford Road, Cowdenbeath, KY4 9AS ☎ 07792 369678 🌐 beathbrewing.com

Beath began brewing in 2016, originally with a 20-litre capacity upgraded to 100-litre within a few months. There are plans for a further expansion. The beer range varies from week to week. RAIB

Mad World (ABV 4%)
Are You With Me (ABV 4.5%)
Ella Ella Ella (ABV 4.5%)
Funky Town (ABV 5%)

Beatnikz Republic

Unit 15, Red Bank Court, Green Quarter, Manchester, M4 4HF ☎ 07437 018918 🌐 beatnikzrepublic.com

Beatnikz Republic brews out of a railway arch near Manchester Victoria Station. Beers are available unfiltered in keg, can and cask. Its brewery tap opened in Manchester's Northern Quarter in 2018. 🛒♦GF V

2am Poet (ABV 3.8%)
Boardwalk (ABV 4%)
Light and hoppy beer, balanced with a sweet fruitiness and a fruity aroma. Dry finish.
Tropic Fiesta (ABV 4%)
Leather Soul (ABV 4.3%)
Midtown (ABV 4.9%)
Beach Bum (ABV 5%)

Dry and hoppy with pronounced bitterness.
Kentucky Riot (ABV 5%)

Beavertown

Units 17 & 18, Lockwood Industrial Park, Mill Mead Road, Tottenham Hale, London, N17 9QP
☎ (020) 8525 9884

Tottenham Hotspur: Stadium, 748 High Road, Tottenham, London, N17 9QP
beavertownbrewery.co.uk

Beavertown began brewing in 2014. Beers are mostly sold in KeyKeg and cans. The brewery is open to visit most Saturday afternoons. After selling a large minority stake to Heineken in 2018, expansion is planned for 2020, including moving to 'Beaverworld' in Ponders End, its fourth home. An on-site brewery and bar opened in the newly built Tottenham Hotspur's football ground in 2019 with access only to ticket holders. ♦ RAIB

Beccles (NEW)

The Studios, London Road, Brampton, Suffolk, NR34 8DQ ☎ 07400 786888 becclesbrewco.co.uk

The brewery is owned and run by two friends alongside existing jobs. It has a production run three times a week with a 700-litre capacity. Regular trial production runs of new beers can be found in local pubs. There are plans to bottle and can beers for sale in the local area.

Beckstones

Upper Beckstones Mill, The Green, Millom, Cumbria, LA18 5HL
☎ (01229) 314900 ☎ 07544 883802
info@beckstonesbrewery.co.uk

On the site of an 18th-century mill, with its own water supply, this five-barrel operation continues to win awards. Beer names have connections to the long-closed Millom Iron Works or local characters, and the brewer designs the distinctive pump clips. ♦

Leat (ABV 3.6%)
Rich, fruity, light mild with refreshing hops in the finish.
Barley Blonde (ABV 3.7%)
Full-flavoured, beautifully-balanced, emphatically-fruity, hoppy beer.
Black Dog Freddy Mild (ABV 3.9%)
A full-bodied, beautifully-balanced, ruby dark mild, replete with fruit and roast malt.
Border Stones (ABV 4.1%)
An old-fashioned-style, tawny bitter with a sweet start, some bitter notes and plenty of aftertaste.
Iron Town (ABV 4.1%)
Creamy, sweet, amber ale which fills the mouth with well-balanced fruit and hop.
Rev Rob (ABV 4.6%)
Well-balanced and distinctive best bitter. Fills the mouth with sweet malt fruit and complementary hops, leaving a pleasing finish.

Bedlam SIBA

St Helena Farm, St Helena Lane, Plumpton Green, East Sussex, BN7 3DH
☎ (01273) 978015 bedlambrewery.co.uk

Eco-friendly Bedlam Brewery operates from the heart of the South Downs on a farm with solar power. All spent grain is donated to cattle on the farm and hops are composted. More than 1,000 pubs and bars are supplied across London and the South of England. !! RAIB

Phoenix IPA
Benchmark (ABV 4%)
Golden (ABV 4.2%)

Beer Brothers SIBA

335 Ranglet Road, Walton Summit Centre, Bamber Bridge, Lancashire, PR5 8AR ☎ 07921 519129
beerbrothers.co.uk

Brewing began in 2015. The brewery expanded to a 10-barrel plant using nine fermenting vessels, with an on-site taproom. Several limited edition experimental beers are brewed. Bottled beers are available in local Booths and Spar stores. !! V

Gold (ABV 3.8%)
True Brit (ABV 3.8%)
Session IPA V3.3 (ABV 3.9%)
Sinatra (ABV 4%)
Hop Chocolate (ABV 4.3%)
Simply Red (ABV 4.4%)
Chinook (ABV 4.5%)
Pretty Fly (ABV 4.5%)
Spruce'd Up (ABV 4.6%)
Gunslinger (ABV 4.7%)
Stouty McStoutface (ABV 4.7%)
Miami Nice DDH IPA (ABV 4.9%)
Hefeweizen (ABV 5%)
Interstellar NZ Pale Ale (ABV 5.6%)
Dunkel Storm (ABV 6.5%)

Beer Engine SIBA

Newton St Cyres, Devon, EX5 5AX
☎ (01392) 851282 thebeerengine.co.uk

The Beer Engine was established in 1983 and is the oldest working microbrewery in Devon. The brewery is visible downstairs in the pub through multiple viewing windows. Several outlets are supplied, as well as local beer festivals. !! ♦

Beer Hut

6 Riverside Park, Kilkeel, BT34 4NA
andrew@beerhutbrewing.co.uk

Microbrewery situated near Kilkeel harbour. Established in a flat pack hut using a 100-litre kit, it has since upscaled twice and now operates using a 1,000-litre plant. Further expansion is planned. V

Citra Ella (ABV 4.5%)
Fluffy Bunny (ABV 5%)
Wahey IPA (ABV 5.6%)
There's Something in the Water (ABV 6%)
Simcoe Simon (ABV 6.5%)
Ahoy Captain (ABV 7.4%)

Beer Ink

Plover Road Garage, Plover Road, Lindley, Huddersfield, West Yorkshire, HD3 3HS
☎ (01484) 643368 ☎ 07885 676711 sales@beer-ink.co.uk

The Beer Ink Brewery is based in Lindley and opened in 2015 using an eight-barrel plant. It specialises in barrel-aged beers. Regularly collaborates with other forward-looking breweries. On-site taproom and facilities were expanded and improved in 2020. ♦

Vellum (ABV 4%)
Gutenberg (ABV 4.2%)
Typo (ABV 4.4%)
Lampblack (ABV 4.6%)
Scrawler (ABV 5%)

Beer Me

▮ The Belgian Café, 11/23 Grand Parade, Eastbourne, East Sussex, BN21 3YN
☎ (01323) 729967 ⊕ thebelgiancafe.co.uk

⊗ Beer Me was launched in 2014 by the owners of the Belgian Café in Eastbourne, building on 10 years in the catering industry. It uses a 2.5-barrel plant and produces continental-style beers which are served direct from the brewery. ‼♦

Beer Nouveau

75 North Western Street, Ardwick, Manchester, M12 6DY ⊕ beernouveau.co.uk

◎ Beer Nouveau has been producing heritage and experimental beers since 2015. Barrel-aging and beers from the wood are a strong focus, and always feature at its Friday and Saturday brewery tap. A passion for sustainability sees one-off brew runs using hops or fruit grown in Manchester, and the brew tap caters from a 'waste food' social enterprise. The brewery tap frequently hosts special events, often posited as alternatives to the mainstream. ‼♦ RAIB V◆

Peterloo Porter (ABV 4%)
Sunny Lowry (ABV 4.1%)

Beer Studio

See Hydes

Beerblefish SIBA

Unit 6, Georgiou Business Park, Second Avenue, Edmonton, London, N18 2PG ☎ 07594 383195
⊕ beerblefish.co.uk

Starting at UBrew in Bermondsey in 2015, the Edmonton site began production in 2016. Bottled beers were the main output, but cask has appeared regularly in London pubs and CAMRA festivals since. A range of Victorian heritage beers was launched in 2018 comprising an IPA, an ESB and a Porter. ◆

Pan Galactic Pale (ABV 4.6%)
Floral nose with hints of sweet biscuit. Malty, tropical fruit overlaid with a developing hoppy spiciness, and some dry bitterness.
1820 Porter (ABV 6.6%)
Aged, dark brown porter. Malty with supporting fruit (blackcurrant) and bitterness in the taste. Malty, bitter, fruity finish.
1892 – IPA (ABV 6.9%)
Rich, with hints of Demerara sugar and blood orange complementing the hops. Flavours slowly fade in the warm, oaky finish.

Beercraft Brighton

See Brewery at the Watchmaker's Arms

Beermats SIBA

New Yard, Winkburn, Nottinghamshire, NG22 8PQ
☎ (01636) 639004 ⊕ beermatsbeer.co.uk

◎ Brewing began in 2017 on the Winkburn Estate in old dairy buildings using a 10-barrel plant. The brewery was established by three friends with experience in the trade. Beers are named around the theme of the humble beermat. ‼ ⚑ V

Charismatic (ABV 3.8%)
Pragmatic (ABV 3.8%)
Format (ABV 3.9%)
Team Mates (ABV 3.9%)
Soul Mate (ABV 4.2%)
Diplomat (ABV 4.6%)
Ultimate (ABV 4.9%)

Beerology

See Blue

BeerRiff

Pilot House Wharf, Swansea, SA1 1UN ☎ 07897 895511 ⊕ beerriffbrewing.com

⊗ The proprietors of Pilot Brewery, Mumbles, have set up this four-barrel brewery mainly producing beer in keg and can. All beers are unfined, unfiltered and of a wide variety or styles. The taphouse bar has great views over the Swansea Marina. V◆

BEEspoke

▮ The Fox, 41 Briggate, Shipley, West Yorkshire, BD17 7BP
☎ (01274) 594826 ⊕ thefoxshipley.co.uk

◎ Brewing began in 2015 in the cellar of the Fox pub using a one-barrel plant. Beers are available in the pub and at local beer festivals. Shiny Cowbird Gin now also produced. ♦

Beeston SIBA

Fransham Road Farm, Beeston, Norfolk, PE32 2LZ
☎ (01328) 700844 ☎ 07768 742763
⊕ beestonbrewery.co.uk

⊗ The brewery was established in 2006 in an old farm building using a five-barrel plant. Brewing water comes from a dedicated borehole and raw ingredients are sourced locally whenever possible. ‼ RAIB

The Squirrels Nuts (ABV 3.5%)
Cherry, chocolate and vanilla aroma. A malt and cherry sweetness comes to the fore but quickly fades. Short finish.
Worth the Wait (ABV 4.2%)
Hoppy throughout with a growing dryness. Complex and grainy with fruit notes, malt and understated bitterness.
Stirling (ABV 4.5%)
The Dry Road (ABV 4.8%)
Village Life (ABV 4.8%)
Copper-coloured with a nutty character. Malty throughout, a bittersweet background gives depth. Strong toffee apple finish.
On the Huh (ABV 5%)
A fruity raisin aroma. A bittersweet maltiness jousts with caramel and roast. A dry hoppiness adds to a strong finale.
Old Stoatwobbler (ABV 6%)

Contract brewed for Brancaster Brewery:
Best (ABV 3.8%)
Malthouse Bitter (ABV 4.2%)

Beeston Hop

Windmill Lane, Sneinton, Nottingham, NG2 4QB
✉ john@beestonhop.co.uk

⊗ A nanobrewery launched in 2015 producing mainly bottle-conditioned beers. Cask beers are occasionally produced for festivals using capacity at other breweries. The beers are unfined, unfiltered and unpasteurised. RAIB

Belgian Brewer, The

Unit 11, The Links Business Centre, Raynham Road, Bishop's Stortford, Hertfordshire, CM23 5NZ
☎ (01279) 507515 ⊕ thebelgianbrewer.co.uk

Situated just outside Bishop's Stortford town centre, The Belgian Brewer is a small brewery and taproom. Established in 2018, it produces Belgian-style beers brewed to traditional Belgian methods using family recipes. Currently producing under 5,000 litres per month, demand is increasing week by week, especially for its speciality fruit beers. ‼ ⛟ ◆ RAIB V◆

Belhaven

Brewery Lane, Dunbar, EH42 1PE
☎ (01368) 862734 ⊕ belhaven.co.uk

☺Belhaven brewery is one of the oldest brewing sites in Scotland. Established in Dunbar in 1719, it brews beers made with water from its own well and local Scottish barley. Part of Greene King PLC. ‼ ⛟

60/- Ale (ABV 2.9%) 🍺
A fine example of a Scottish light. This bittersweet, reddish-brown beer is dominated by fruit and malt with a hint of roast and caramel, and increasing bitterness in the aftertaste.
IPA (ABV 3.8%)
80/- Ale (ABV 4.2%)
One of the last remaining original Scottish 80 Shillings. Malt is the predominant flavour characteristic, though it is balanced by fruit and a little hop. A complex ale, true to the 80/- style.
Black (ABV 4.2%)
A smooth, balanced, dry stout with a malty body and roast notes of dark chocolate and coffee.
1719 (ABV 4.5%)
St Andrew's Ale (ABV 4.9%)
A bittersweet beer with lots of body. The malt, fruit and roast mingle throughout with hints of hop and caramel.

Bell Street

🍴 57-59 Bell Street, Henley-on-Thames, Oxfordshire, RG9 2BA
☎ (01491) 570200 ⊕ bellstreetbrewery.co.uk

Bell Street Brewery opened in 2013 at the rear of Brakspear pub company's Bull on Bell Street on a four-barrel plant. The beers, both regulars and specials, are sold at the pub and through the Brakspear estate. Brewing is currently suspended. ◆

Belleville

Unit 36, Jaggard Way, Wandsworth Common, London, SW12 8SG
☎ (020) 8675 4768 ⊕ bellevillebrewing.co.uk

Belleville began brewing in 2012. It was formed by a group of parents who met in the playground at a local primary school. It specialises in American-style beers, and currently only occasionally brews cask-conditioned beer. Its nearby taproom is open Thursday-Sunday. ‼◆

Bellfield SIBA

46 Stanley Place, Edinburgh, EH7 5TB
☎ (0131) 656 9390 ⊕ bellfieldbrewery.com

☺Bellfield was established in 2014 and was the UK's first certified gluten-free brewery. It is accredited by Coeliac UK and registered with the Vegan Society. A new site with taproom opened in 2019. ‼◆GFV◆

Session Ale (ABV 3.8%)

Light citrus tones flavour this balanced bitter.
Lawless Village IPA (ABV 4.5%)
Jex-Blake Mosaic IPA (ABV 5.6%)

Bellinger's SIBA

Station Road, Grove, Oxfordshire, OX12 0DH
☎ (01235) 772255 ⊕ bellingersbrewery.co.uk

⊠ Established in 2011 by the late Mike Bellinger and now run by his nephew and son-in-law, Bellinger's is a five-barrel plant producing mainly bottled beer with the occasional cask-conditioned ale. All beers, when available, are sold in the garage forecourt shop and other local farm shops. ‼ ⛟ ◆ RAIB

Original Bitter (ABV 4.1%)
Arnhem (ABV 4.4%)
Cavalry (ABV 4.6%)
IPA (ABV 5%)
Gallipoli Stout (ABV 5.3%)

Belvoir SIBA

Crown Park, Station Road, Old Dalby, Leicestershire, LE14 3NQ
☎ (01664) 823455 ⊕ belvoirbrewery.co.uk

Belvoir (pronounced 'beaver') Brewery was set up in 1995 by former Shipstone's and Theakstons brewer Colin Brown. Long-term expansion has seen the introduction of a 25-barrel plant that can produce 120 barrels a week. The visitors centre incorporates brewery memorabilia, a bar, restaurant and shop. Around 150 outlets are supplied direct. ‼◆RAIB

Dark Horse (ABV 3.4%)
Whipling (ABV 3.6%)
Star Bitter (ABV 3.9%)
Reminiscent of the long-extinct Shipstone's Bitter, this mid-brown bitter lives up to its name as it is bitter in taste but not unpleasantly so.
Gordon Bennett (ABV 4.1%)
Beaver Bitter (ABV 4.3%)
A light brown bitter that starts malty in both aroma and taste, but soon develops a hoppy bitterness. Appreciably fruity.
Oatmeal Stout (ABV 4.3%)
Peacock's Glory (ABV 4.7%)
Old Dalby (ABV 5.1%)

Contract brewed for Hoskins Brothers:
Hob Bitter (ABV 4%)
IPA (ABV 4%)

Contract brewed for Steamin' Billy:
Tipsy Fisherman (ABV 3.6%)
Bitter (ABV 4.3%)
1485 (ABV 5%)
Skydiver (ABV 5%)

Bentley Brook

Unit 3, Lumsdale Mill, Lumsdale, Matlock, Derbyshire, DE4 5EX ☎ 07483 831640
Office: 1 Hilltop Terrace, The Cliff, Matlock, DE4 5FY
⊕ bentleybrook.co.uk

⊠ Formed in 2018, this 1.5-barrel brewery is located in the heart of Lumsdale Valley and named after the local brook. It offers unfined, small batch beers available to purchase in the local area. RAIB ◆

Beowulf

Forest of Mercia, Chasewater Country Park, Pool Lane, Brownhills, Staffordshire, WS8 7NL

THE BREWERIES

☎ (01543) 454067 ☎ 07714 291226
🌐 beowulfbrewery.co.uk

Beowulf Brewing Company is based at the Chasewater County Park. Beers appear as guest ales across the country. ‼♦RAIB V

Beorma (ABV 3.9%)
A perfectly-balanced, session ale with a malty hint of fruit giving way to a lingering bitterness. Background spice excites the palate.
Black & Blueberry (ABV 4.5%)
Boomer (ABV 4.5%)
Pale brown with lots of caramel aroma. Bitter start then a sweet, malty background, which develops to a mouthwatering finish with dry lips.
Chase Buster (ABV 4.5%)
Dark Raven (ABV 4.5%)
Dark in colour with apple and bonfire in the aroma, sweet and smooth like liquid toffee apples, with a sudden bitter finish.
Swordsman (ABV 4.5%)
Pale gold, light fruity aroma, tangy hoppy flavour. Faintly hoppy finish.
Folded Cross (ABV 4.6%)
Malt and caramel aroma and taste with hints of fruity biscuit, nudged aside by robust hops, which give a lingering bitter edge.
Hurricane (ABV 4.6%)
Chocolate Porter (ABV 4.7%)
Dragon Smoke Stout (ABV 4.7%)
Black with a light brown creamy head. Tobacco, chocolate, liquorice and mixed fruity hints on the aroma. Bitterness fights through the sweet and roast flavours and eventually dominates. Hints of a good port emerge.
Finn's Hall Porter (ABV 4.7%)
Dark chocolate aroma, after dinner mints, coffee and fresh tobacco. Good bitterness with woodland hints of autumn. Long late bitterness with lip-drying moreishness.
Mercian Shine (ABV 5%)
Amber to pale gold in colour with a good bitter, hoppy start and a hint of nutmeg. Plenty of caramel and hops with background malt leading to a good bitter finish with caramel and hops lingering in the aftertaste.
Clout (ABV 6%)
Nordic Noir (ABV 6%)
Dark brown in colour with a full liquorice aroma. Rich liquorice tastes with subtle notes of chocolate and cinnamon. Gently moreish.
IPA (ABV 7.2%)
Killer Stout (ABV 7.3%)

Bere

Bere Alston, Devon, PL20 7JA
☎ (01822) 840382 🌐 berebrewery.co.uk

Established in 2016 by growers Jerry and Buffy on their smallholding on the Bere Peninsula in the Tamar Valley. The brewery produces bottle-conditioned beers using home-grown hops, with a 1.3-barrel plant and a 50-litre small batch kit. Beers are sold at Tavistock Farmers' Market, by arrangement from the brewery, and at the Olde Plough Inn, Bere Ferrers. ♦RAIB V

Bespoke SIBA

Unit 5, The Mews, Mitcheldean, Gloucestershire, GL17 0SL
☎ (01594) 546426 🌐 bespokebrewery.co.uk

⊗ Brewing commenced in 2012 on a 5.5-barrel plant on the site of the former Wintles Brewery, which closed in the early 1900s. In 2014 capacity was increased to 12 barrels. Speciality-labelled bottles are offered for celebratory occasions. An on-site brewery tap opens Friday and Saturday. ‼♦

Saved by the Bell (ABV 3.8%)
Forest Gold (ABV 4%)
Beware the Bear (ABV 4.2%)
Going Off Half-Cocked (ABV 4.6%)
Money for Old Rope (ABV 4.8%)
Over a Barrel (ABV 5%)

Bestens

Unit 17, Church Lane Estate, Church Lane, Lower Beeding, West Sussex, RH13 6LU
☎ (01403) 892556 🌐 bestensbrewery.co.uk

The brewery opened in 2018 in Lower Beeding as a one-barrel plant, increasing to four-barrel capacity in 2020. A percentage of all beer sold is donated to a community fund, which supports local charities and initiatives. The brewery operates a mobile taproom in Haywards Heath, as well as hosting events at the brewery itself. No real ale. V

Bewdley SIBA

Unit 7, Bewdley Craft Centre, Lax Lane, Bewdley, Worcestershire, DY12 2DZ
☎ (01299) 405148 🌐 bewdleybrewery.co.uk

⊗ Bewdley began brewing in 2008 on a six-barrel plant in an old school. This was upgraded to a 10-barrel plant in 2014. Beers are brewed with a railway theme for the nearby Severn Valley Railway. The brewery has an on-site tap and shop. Element gin is also produced. ♦RAIB

Worcestershire Way (ABV 3.6%)
Refreshing golden ale with a citrus, faintly orange peel aroma, leads to a balanced hop, malt and grapefruit taste and a lingering, hoppy finish.
Baldwin (ABV 4.2%)
Jubilee (ABV 4.3%)
Pale colour, fruit and citrus aroma, sweet malt with underlying citrus taste.
Sir Keith Park (ABV 4.5%)
Pale amber colour, full fruity and balanced flavour, followed by a long hoppy finish.
Worcestershire Sway (ABV 5%)
Complex amber-coloured bitter, sometimes badged as 2857. Fragrant malty aroma, well-balanced slightly sweet malt and hops taste with hints of toffee and marmalade, malt with citrus and meadow grass finish.
William Mucklow's Dark Mild (ABV 6%)
Dark in colour, malty, sweetish fruity flavour with slight liquorice finish.

Bexar County

8 Belgic Square, Padholme Road, Peterborough, Cambridgeshire, PE1 5XF ☎ 07934 722584
🌐 bexarcountybrewery.com

Bexar was established in 2012, brewing an ever-changing range of American-style beers. V

Papa Steve (ABV 9%)

Bexley SIBA

Unit 18, Manford Industrial Estate, Manor Road, Erith, Kent, DA8 2AJ
☎ (01322) 337368 🌐 bexleybrewery.co.uk

Bexley Brewery was founded in 2014. Brewers Cliff and Jane Murphy produce regular, seasonal and experimental brews as well as selling own-brand beer mustard. The Bird & Barrel in Barnehurst, opened in 2018, replacing the taproom as the main source of the beers locally. ‼ ♦V

Session Golden Ale (ABV 3.6%)
Refreshing golden ale with grapefruit and some honey notes. There is a little peppery hop, and a bitter finish.
Session Ruby Ale (ABV 3.7%)
Malt and dark fruit on the nose. Taste is malty, biscuity and hints of smoke. Hoppy, long and dry aftertaste.
Session Pale Ale (ABV 3.8%)
Refreshing beer with a zesty, citrus flavour. Limited sweetness and some bitterness in the taste.
Golden Acre (ABV 4%)
Smooth golden ale with citrus aroma. Flavour is of grapefruit, hops and a strong bitterness, continuing in the dry-fruity finish.
Bexley's Own Beer (ABV 4.2%)
Pale brown beer with a balance of fudge, floral hop, stone fruit and some bitterness growing in the dry finish.
Redhouse Premium (ABV 4.2%)
Copper best bitter with roast and sweet orange marmalade. Dry finish with a touch of chocolate in finish and aroma.
Anchor Bay IPA (ABV 4.8%)

Bianca Road

83-84 Enid Street, Bermondsey, London, SE16 3RA
☎ (020) 3221 1001 ⊕ biancaroad.com

After starting in 2016 in Peckham, the brewery moved to a bigger site in 2017, and again in 2019 to two arches along the Bermondsey Beer Mile which double up as the taproom. Output is mostly keg and cans. The Cellar Boys brewery from New Cross now use the kit rather than its own. ♦

Bicester

Angel, 102 Sheep Street, Bicester, Oxfordshire, OX26 6LP
☎ (01869) 360410 ⊕ theangelbicester.co.uk

Brewing commenced in 2017 in an outhouse behind the Angel, Bicester. Beers are supplied solely to the pub.

Big Bog SIBA

74 Venture Point West, Evans Road, Speke, Merseyside, L24 9PB
☎ (0151) 558 0290 ☎ 07867 792466
⊕ bigbog.co.uk

Big Bog started life in Waunfawr, Wales in 2011, sharing its site with the Snowdonia Parc brewpub. Due to growth and expansion in 2016, the brewery moved to its present location in Speke, Liverpool, into a custom-built plant with a 10-barrel brew length. The brewery has its own licenced bar and is open to the public on Fridays. ♦♦

Bog Standard Bitter (ABV 3.6%)
Mire (ABV 3.8%)
Pride of England (ABV 3.8%)
Blonde Bach (ABV 3.9%)
Hinkypunk (ABV 4.1%)
Full-flavoured golden ale. Fruity (citrus) hoppy aromas, dry hoppy beer, slightly sweet with a little pepperiness and a satisfying bitter finish.
Stog (ABV 4.1%)
Jack O Lantern (ABV 4.2%)
Welsh Pale Ale (ABV 4.2%)
Morast (ABV 4.3%)
Billabong (ABV 4.4%)
Blueberry Hill Porter (ABV 4.5%)
Swampy (ABV 4.7%)
Will O the Wisp (ABV 4.7%)
Peat Bog Porter (ABV 4.9%)
Bayou (ABV 5%)
Quagmire (ABV 6%)

Big Clock

Grants, 1 Manchester Road, Accrington, Lancashire, BB5 2BQ
☎ (01254) 393938 ☎ 07766 163497
⊕ thebigclockbrewery.co.uk

Brewing commenced at the iconic Grants Pub and Brewhouse just off Accrington town centre in 2014. The specially commissioned six-barrel plant can be viewed from the bar area. Beer is supplied to around a dozen outlets across East Lancashire.

Big Drop SIBA

Office: 46 St Nicholas Street, Ipswich, Suffolk, IP1 1TT
⊕ bigdropbrew.com

Established in 2016 this company contract brews low-alcohol bottled beers of no more than 0.5% ABV at a variety of breweries around the country. No real ale.

Big Fish

c/o 45 Glenury Crescent, Stonehaven, AB39 3LF
☎ (01569) 760227

A gypsy brewery established in 2017.

Big Hand SIBA

Unit A1, Abbey Close, Redwither Business Park, Wrexham, LL13 9XG
☎ (01978) 660709 ☎ 07946 514238
⊕ bighandbrewing.co.uk

Big Hand began brewing in 2013 and continues to operate via a 10-barrel plant on the outskirts of Wrexham. Its broad-ranging selection of beers have won several awards and are widely available throughout North Wales and West Cheshire as well as at the Big Hand Alehouse in Chester. ‼♦

Seren (ABV 3.7%)
Pale, full-flavoured and hoppy with a fruity aroma and taste
Pila Pala (ABV 3.8%)
Pendragon (ABV 3.9%)
Copper-coloured and well-balanced with a smooth rich taste, juicy mouthfeel and hints of spice in the finish.
Super Tidy (ABV 4%)
A pale brown bitter beer with some citrus notes in the taste and peppery hops in the finish.
Bastion (ABV 4.2%)
A dry, malty best bitter, mahogany in colour with a full mouthfeel. Biscuity flavours and faint roast notes feature throughout.
Domino (ABV 4.4%)
A smooth and fruity stout, quite hoppy and roasty with hints of berries in the initial sweetness, leading to a satisfying hoppy finish.
Appaloosa (ABV 4.5%)
A full-bodied pale ale, some initial sweetness with strong New World hop flavours in the taste and spicy finish.
Havok (ABV 5%)
A powerfully-hopped American IPA with strong and tangy citrus fruit bitterness throughout.

Big Lamp

Grange Road, Newburn, Newcastle upon Tyne, NE15 8NL
☎ (0191) 267 1689 ⊕ biglampbrewers.co.uk

Big Lamp started in 1982 and relocated in 1997 to a 55-barrel plant in a former water pumping station. It is the oldest microbrewery in the North East of England. Around 160 outlets are supplied and two pubs are owned, one of which, the Keelman, is attached to the brewery. Beers are contract brewed for Stables Brewery. !! ♦ RAIB

Sunny Daze (ABV 3.6%)
Golden, hoppy session bitter with a clean taste and finish.
Bitter (ABV 3.9%)
A clean-tasting bitter, full of hops and malt. A hint of fruit with a good, hoppy finish.
Lamplight Bitter (ABV 4.2%)
Summerhill Stout (ABV 4.4%)
A rich, tasty stout, dark in colour with a lasting, rich roast character. Malty mouthfeel with a lingering finish.
Prince Bishop Ale (ABV 4.8%)
A refreshing, easy-drinking bitter. Golden in colour, full of fruit and hops. Strong bitterness with a spicy, dry finish.
Premium (ABV 5.2%)
Hoppy ale with a good bitter finish.
Keelman Brown (ABV 5.7%)

Big River

Building 1a, Aston Down Business Park, Stroud, Gloucestershire, GL6 8GA ☎ 07939 273697
bigriverbrew.co

Formed in 2018, using spare capacity at the now closed Ciren Ales, in Cirencester. Three core beers are available, all of which are brewed with a gluten-reducing enzyme. The brewery relocated to Stroud in 2019. ♦ RAIB

Pale Ale (ABV 3.6%)
All About Citra (ABV 4%)
Rolling Hills (ABV 4%)

Big Smoke SIBA

Unit D3, Sandown Industrial Estate, Esher, Surrey, KT10 8BL
☎ (01372) 469606 ☎ 07859 884190
bigsmokebrew.co.uk

Brewing began at the Antelope, Surbiton, in 2014. In 2019 Big Smoke moved to a new purpose-built 30-hectolitre brewery in Esher with an on-site taproom. ♦ V

Solaris Session Pale Ale (ABV 3.8%)
Unfined golden ale with bitter grapefruit flavour, some malt and a long, dry, bitter finish. Hoppy fruity nose.
Dark Wave Porter (ABV 5%)
Creamy, black porter with a dry roasty bitter character balanced by a caramelised sweetness.
Electric Eye Pale Ale (ABV 5%)
Underworld Milk Stout (ABV 5%)
Sweet, smooth stout with hints of chocolate and coffee in the aroma and taste coupled with toasted nuts and vanilla.

Big Stone (NEW) SIBA

Ashen Clough, Maynestone Road, Chinley, Derbyshire, SK23 6AH ☎ 07867 652062
bigstonebeer@gmail.com

Established in 2019 producing beers from the heart of the Peak District, using water from its own spring. RAIB V

Downfall (ABV 4.3%)

Biggar

Queens Arms Courtyard, Biggar Village, Cumbria, LA14 3YG
☎ (01229) 474335 biggarbrewing.co.uk

This 2.5-barrel brewery, an independent co-operative of several shareholders, opened in 2015 in the courtyard of the Queens Arms, Biggar Village on Walney Island. The beer names are themed on Barrow's shipbuilding heritage, and the brewery logo features a representation of Barrow's dockside cranes, a strong visual motif of the town's history. Brewing is currently suspended.

Bilbrough Top

St James House, Main Street, Bilbrough, North Yorkshire, YO23 3PH

A one-person microbrewery, Bilbrough Top began brewing in 2016. It produces only one beer on a six-barrel plant, available at the Three Hares, Bilbrough, and frequently at other pubs around the area.

Top Beer (ABV 3.9%)

Billericay SIBA

Essex Beer Shop, 54c Chapel Street, Billericay, Essex, CM12 9LS
☎ (01277) 500121 ☎ 07788 373129
billericaybrewing.co.uk

Billericay Brewing opened at its present site in 2014, using a 4.5-barrel plant. A micropub and beershop are next door. !! ♦ RAIB

Zeppelin (ABV 3.8%)
Blonde (ABV 4%)
Dickie (ABV 4.2%)
Vanilla Woods (ABV 4.2%)
Woody's Wag (ABV 4.2%)
Rhythm Stick (ABV 4.8%)
Sex & Drugs & Rock & Roll (ABV 5%)
Chapel Street Porter (ABV 5.9%)
Chilli Porter (ABV 5.9%)
Mayflower Gold (ABV 6.5%)

Binghams SIBA

Unit 10, Tavistock Industrial Estate, Ruscombe, Berkshire, RG10 9NJ
☎ (0118) 934 4376 binghams.co.uk

Binghams began brewing in 2010, producing 40 firkins in each batch. The brewery is situated in an industrial unit on the site of a former brickworks – hence the name of one of the beers. Founded by CAMRA member Chris Bingham, it was amicably sold as a going concern in 2020. !! V

Twyford Tipple (ABV 3.7%)
Tawny-coloured session bitter with a malt and hop aroma with a fruity, balanced flavour. Malty finish with lingering dry citrus hops.
Brickworks Bitter (ABV 4.2%)
Hop Project (ABV 4.5%)
Coffee Stout (ABV 5%)
Doodle Stout (ABV 5%)
Hot Dog Chilli Stout (ABV 5%)
Macchiato Stout (ABV 5%)
Space Hoppy IPA (ABV 5%)
Golden ale with malt, citrus hops, fruit and caramel aroma. Sweeter taste and aftertaste leads to a slight bitter finish.
Vanilla Stout (ABV 5%)

Black speciality stout with a strong vanilla and malt flavour throughout. These linger with a fruity, sweet aftertaste.

Bingley SIBA

Unit 2, Old Mill Yard, Shay Lane, Wilsden, West Yorkshire, BD15 0DR
☎ (01535) 274285 ⊕ bingleybrewery.co.uk

Bingley is a small, family-run brewery that opened in 2014 using a six-barrel plant. It is located in a rural setting in the village of Wilsden, part of Bingley Rural Ward. Beers are distributed coast to coast and as far south as Derby. ‼

Endeavour (ABV 3.7%)
Goldy Locks Blonde (ABV 4%)
Azacca (ABV 4.1%)
Aire Gold (ABV 4.2%)
Session IPA (ABV 4.2%)
Steady State (ABV 4.2%)
Centennial (ABV 4.4%)
Tri State (ABV 4.5%)
1848 Stout (ABV 4.8%)
Jamestown APA (ABV 5.4%)

Birch Cottage

Birch Cottage, Wilne Road, Sawley, Derbyshire, NG10 3AP ☎ 07966757407
✉ birchcottagebrewery@outlook.com

Birch Cottage is a nanobrewery established in 2018 brewing small batch beers. Its brewery tap, Sawley Junction, opened in 2018.

Birchover

∄ Red Lion, Main Street, Birchover, Derbyshire, DE4 2BN
☎ (01629) 650363 ⊕ red-lion-birchover.co.uk

⊗ Brewing started at the Red Lion pub in the picturesque Peak District village of Birchover in 2016, and upgraded to a five-barrel plant by enthusiastic pub/brewery owner in 2017. Core range beers are named after local Stanton Moor landmarks and are to be found alongside seasonal specials on the pub's bar. ◆RAIB

Birdhouse (NEW)

Revell Road, Downham Market, Norfolk, PE38 9SE
☎ 07858 628183 ⊕ birdhousebrewery.co.uk

Established in 2019 by Paul Bird, Birdhouse is a picobrewery based in Downham Market. It produces only 70 bottle-conditioned beers per batch, making it one of the smallest breweries in the country. RAIB V

Birmingham SIBA

Unit 15, Stirchley Trading Estate, Hazelwell Road, Birmingham, B30 2PF ☎ 07717 704929
⊕ birminghambrewingcompany.co.uk

Birmingham Brewing Co was established in 2016 and is based in a small unit on a trading estate in Stirchley. Production is a mix of cask and keg. ‼◆

Pale Brummie (ABV 4%)
Bitter Brummie (ABV 4.1%)

Bishop Nick SIBA

33 East Street, Braintree, Essex, CM7 3JJ
☎ (01376) 349605 ⊕ bishopnick.com

⊗ Bishop Nick was launched in 2011 by Nelion Ridley, a member of the family that started Ridley's brewery near

Chelmsford in 1842. In 2013 a new brewery was established in Braintree using a 20-barrel plant. ☞◆RAIB

Ridley's Rite (ABV 3.6%) ⊡
Heresy (ABV 4%)
1555 (ABV 4.3%) ⊡
Devout (ABV 4.5%)
Martyr IPA (ABV 5%)
Divine (ABV 5.1%)

Bishop's Crook

51 Woodcroft Close, Penwortham, Lancashire, PR1 9BX ☎ 07977 220742
⊕ bishopscrookbrewery.com

A small brewery based at the home of the owner. It started brewing commercially in 2013 and gradually built up a handful of regular outlets. Due to construction work the brewery was out of action for a lengthy period from 2017, and subsequently was mothballed, re-commencing production in 2020.

Bitter End

See Tirril

Black Bear SIBA

∄ c/o Bear Inn, 8-10 North Street, Wiveliscombe, Somerset, TA4 2JY
☎ (01984) 623537 ⊕ blackbearbrewery.co.uk

Originally established in 2014 at the Northbrook Arms, East Stratton, Hampshire, before relocating to the Bear Inn, Wiveliscombe, Somerset in 2015. Five beers are currently regularly brewed for the pub and a small but growing number of other local outlets. ◆

Black Cloak

∄ 71 Abergele Road, Colwyn Bay, LL29 7RU ☎ 07701 031121

Office: Glog Ddu Llangernyw, Abergele, LL22 8PS

Black Cloak opened in 2018 in a former café using a one-barrel plant producing cask and keg beer. Beers are usually only available in the bar. ◆◢

Black Country IFBB

∄ Rear of Old Bulls Head, 1 Redhall Road, Lower Gornal, West Midlands, DY3 2NU
☎ (01384) 401820

Office: 69 Third Avenue, Pensnett Trading Estate, Kingswinford, DY6 7FD ⊕ blackcountryales.co.uk

⊙A compact brewery located at the back of the Bull's Head in Lower Gornal, which recommenced brewing in 2004. In 2012 much of the old equipment was replaced with a new kit, which can brew up to 15 barrels at a time. Its sister company, Black Country Inns, now has 37 pubs in its portfolio. ‼◆

Bradley's Finest Golden (ABV 4.2%)
Pig on the Wall (ABV 4.3%)
Fireside (ABV 5%)

Black Dog

See Hambleton

Black Falls

See Neath

Black Flag

Unit 1D, New Road, Perranporth, TR6 0DL
☎ (01872) 858004 ⊕ blackflagbrewery.com

⊗ Black Flag began brewing in 2013 using an eight-barrel plant. Much use is made of New Zealand and American hops. ♦RAIB ◆

Fisher King (ABV 3.8%)
Fruity, gold beer with changing variety of citrus hop types. Tropical fruit flavours with light malt and a bitter hop finish.
Fang (ABV 4%)
Crisp pale ale with citrus/marmalade/resin hop flavours, balanced by faint bready malt and hints of caramel toffee. Long, bitter finish.
Naughty Pilchard (ABV 4%)
Copper bitter with malt aroma. Dominant biscuit malt flavour with a sharp bite of crisp hops. Short malty, bitter finish.
Crab Claw (ABV 5%)
Red, premium bitter with intense hop fruit nose. Powerful citrus hop flavour, lightly bittersweet. Dry hop and sweet finish.
Galaxy & Amarillo Pale Ale (ABV 5.5%)
Mosaic IPA (ABV 5.7%)
Smooth, easy-drinking golden beer with heady citrus hop nose. Powerful, grassy and citrus hop flavours throughout, with mango fruit and bitterness.
White Cross IPA (ABV 5.7%)
Amber IPA with full malty fruit aroma and flavours. Vibrant citrus and tropical fruits hops. Crisp, bitter finish.
Black IPA (ABV 6%)
Export Stout (ABV 6.3%)
Captain Haddock (ABV 6.5%)

Black Hole SIBA

Unit 3a, Old Hall Mill Business Park, Alfreton Road, Little Eaton, Derbyshire, DE21 5EJ
☎ (01283) 619943 ☎ 07812 812953
⊕ blackholebrewery.co.uk

⊗ Black Hole was established in 2007 with a 10-barrel plant in the former Ind Coope bottling stores in Burton-on-Trent, but moved to its current location in 2017. Fermenting capacity of 36 barrels enables the production of up to four brews per week, some of which are marketed under the Little Eaton Brewery name. Around 400 outlets are supplied direct, and many more via wholesalers. Since 2014, the brewery has been owned by GHH Llp, which also owns Mr Grundy's Brewery (qv). ‼♦

Bitter (ABV 3.8%)
Amber glow and malt and spicy hop aroma. Fresh lively session beer hopped to give a clean, crisp finish of hoppy dryness and touch of astringency.
Cosmic (ABV 4.2%)
Almost golden with an initial malt aroma. The complex balance of malt and English hops give lingering tastes of nuts, fruit and dry hoppy bitterness.
Supernova (ABV 4.8%)
Pure gold. Like marmalade made from Seville oranges and grapefruit the aroma mimics the sweet start but gives into the hops which deliver a dry, lingering bitter finish.
IPA (ABV 5.2%)
Milky Way (ABV 6%)
Honey and banana nose advises the sweet taste but not the sweet, dry, spicy finish from this wheat beer.

Brewed for Small Beer (Lincoln):
Lincoln Imperial Ale (ABV 3.8%)

Brewed under the Little Eaton brand name:
Bates' Pale Ale (ABV 3.8%)
Bagnall Bros Bitter (ABV 4.2%)
Delver's Drop IPA (ABV 4.8%)
Old Mill Stout (ABV 5%)

Black Iris SIBA

Unit 1 Shipstone Street, New Basford, Nottingham, NG7 6GJ
☎ (0115) 979 1936 ✉ blackirisbrewery@gmail.com

⊛ Black Iris began brewing in 2011 using a six-barrel plant behind the Flowerpot pub in Derby. It expanded to a brand new 10-barrel plant in 2014 and relocated to premises in Nottingham. Beers are distributed nationally through wholesalers and by direct order to the local free trade. Innovation and collaboration ensure that new beers are consistently being added to the range.

Snake Eyes (ABV 3.8%)
Golden-coloured ale, with intense hoppy aroma and taste, with a lingering bitter finish.
Bajan Breakfast (ABV 4%)
Endless Summer (ABV 4.5%)
Golden in colour with a tropical citrus fruit presence throughout, from aroma to aftertaste with a gentle bitter finish.

Black Isle

Old Allengrange, Munlochy, IV8 8NZ
☎ (01463) 811871 ⊕ blackislebrewery.com

⊛ Black Isle Brewery was set up in 1998 in the heart of the Scottish Highlands. It expanded substantially in 2011 with a new brewhouse and bottling line. All beers are organic with Soil Association certification. The Black Isle Bar in Inverness is open Saturdays. ‼⛟♦V

Yellowhammer (ABV 3.9%) 🗍
A refreshing, hoppy golden ale with light hop and peach flavour throughout. A short bitter finish.
Red Kite (ABV 4.2%)
Tawny ale with light malt on the nose and some red fruit on the palate. Slight sweetness in the taste.
Heather Honey (ABV 4.6%)
Very sweet, honey-flavoured brew.
Porter (ABV 4.6%)
A hint of liquorice and burnt chocolate on the nose, and a creamy mix of malt and fruit in the taste.
Blonde (ABV 5%)

Black Lodge

Kings Dock Street, Baltic Triangle, Liverpool, L1 8JU
☎ 07565 299879 ⊕ blacklodgebrewing.co.uk

Small-batch and one-off brewery producing beers that can be drunk in its own taproom. It moved premises in 2019 and now uses the ex-Mad Hatter brewery kit. Collaboration and special brews are frequent. ♦◆

Black Market

🍺 The Workman's, 43 High Street, Warsop, Nottinghamshire, NG20 0AE ☎ 07824 363373

Beers first appeared from Black Market in 2016. The 2.5-barrel plant is situated in the basement of the brewery tap, the Workman's/Black Market Venue in Warsop. There are three regular beers brewed. Nearly all the brews are consumed on-site, though a few go to pubs and beer festivals in the locality.

Black Metal SIBA

Unit 4, 6b Dryden Road, Loanhead, EH20 9LZ

☎ (0131) 623 3411 ☎ 07711 295385
⊕ blackmetalbrewery.com

Black Metal Brewery was established in 2012 by two old friends – metalheads and inspired brewers. Equipment was shared with Top Out (qv) brewery but it has now moved next door to its own site. ◆ RAIB

Will-o'-the-Wisp (ABV 6%)
Blood Revenge (ABV 6.6%)
Yggdrasil (ABV 6.6%)

Black Mountain (NEW)

🍺 47 Derriaghy Road, Lisburn, BT28 3SH
☎ (028) 9061 1113 ⊕ speckledhenlisburn.com

Small brewery attached to the Speckled Hen pub, the beer is only available in the pub, with a new ale every week.

Black Sheep SIBA

Wellgarth, Masham, North Yorkshire, HG4 4EN
☎ (01765) 689227 ⊕ blacksheepbrewery.co.uk

☺Established in 1992 by Paul Theakston, a member of Masham's famous brewing family, the brewery operation is now run by his two sons. It is situated in the former Wellgarth Maltings and uses the traditional Yorkshire Square fermenting system. The company supplies the free trade across Yorkshire and the North, with national supply through pubcos and wholesale channels. It acquired York Brewery in 2018 and six pubs/bars are owned in Yorkshire. !! 🏭 ◆

Best Bitter (ABV 3.8%)
A hoppy and fruity beer with strong bitter overtones, leading to a long, dry, bitter finish.
Pale Ale (ABV 4%)
Special Ale (ABV 4.4%)
Riggwelter (ABV 5.9%)
A fruity bitter, with complex underlying tastes and hints of liquorice and pear drops leading to a long, dry, bitter finish.

Brewed for Ember Inns:
Pale Ale (ABV 4%)

Black Storm

Unit 14, Stella Gill Industrial Estate, Pelton Fell, DH2 2RG ☎ 07725 762102
⊕ blackstormbrewery.com

Beers were originally contract brewed by Hadrian Border Brewery (qv) but the former Blackhill brewery was purchased in June 2019 with brewing commencing shortly afterwards.

Blonde (ABV 4%)
Gold (ABV 4.3%)
Porter (ABV 5.2%)
IPA (ABV 5.5%)

Black Tor SIBA

Units 5-6, Gidley's Industrial Estate, Christow, Exeter, Devon, EX6 7QB
☎ (01647) 252120 ⊕ blacktorbrewery.com

⊠ This independent, family-run brewery is located on the eastern edge of the beautiful Dartmoor National Park and has been under the current family ownership since 2015. Several changes of ownership and brewery name have occurred since brewing began on-site in 1998, with the present Black Tor name established in 2013. ◆

Pride Of Dartmoor (ABV 4%)
Raven (ABV 4.2%)

Devonshire Pale Ale (ABV 4.5%)

Black Wolf

Unit 7c, Bandeath Industrial Estate, Throsk, Stirling, FK7 7NP
☎ (01786) 437187 ⊕ blackwolfbrewery.com

☺Established in 2005, the brewery is located in a former torpedo factory on the shores of the River Forth. In 2014 the brewery changed its name from Traditional Scottish Ales to Black Wolf Brewery and rebranded its range of beers. All Black Wolf beers are brewed on demand all year round at Throsk. The brewery also bottles beers for other breweries. ◆

Blackedge SIBA

Moreton Mill, Hampson Street, Horwich, BL6 7JH
☎ (01204) 692976 ☎ 07795 654895
⊕ blackedgebrewery.co.uk

☺Blackedge Brewery brews at a 10-barrel plant visible through a viewing window on the ground floor beneath the Brewery Bar – one of its two outlets. Its CAMRA and SIBA award-winning beers are available throughout NW England and beyond. The brewers are influenced by both British traditions and by the US Pacific West Coast. A strong core range is supplemented by seasonal and experimental brews in both cask and unfiltered keg formats. !! 🏭◆RAIB ◆

Session (ABV 3.5%)
Refreshing citrus hops, with a full-bodied citrus hop aroma. Clean, dry finish with lingering bitter hops.
Zinc (ABV 3.5%)
Hop (ABV 3.8%)
Dark Mild (ABV 3.9%)
Pleasant chocolate and malt aroma leads to a full-bodied beer with dark fruits, sustained malt presence and roasty finish.
NZP3 (ABV 3.9%)
Black (ABV 4%)
Well-rounded and creamy dark beer with roast malt and balanced sweetness. Dry, bitter, roast finish.
Cascade (ABV 4%)
Pike (ABV 4%)
Smooth, copper-coloured beer with bitter hops and balanced sweetness, leading to a dry bitter finish.
West Coast (ABV 4.1%)
Citrus hop aroma and flavour. Sweet fruitiness balances lasting bitter hops.
American (ABV 4.2%)
Platinum (ABV 4.4%)
Blonde (ABV 4.5%)
Ginger (ABV 4.5%)
Amber-coloured, with fresh ginger prominent in aroma and taste. Spiciness balanced against sweet malt. Dry, bitter finish.
Dark Rum (ABV 4.6%)
Rich roast aroma and strong, dry, roast flavour. Accompanying taste of dried fruit and drawn-out, sweet finish.
IPA (ABV 4.7%)
Intense bitter hops with a long, drying finish.
Black Port (ABV 4.9%)
Black beer with malty, fruity aroma. Rich, with chocolate and dark fruits to taste with a slightly drier finish.
Kiwi (ABV 5%)

Blackened Sun

3 Heathfield, Stacey Bushes, Milton Keynes, Buckinghamshire, MK12 6HP ☎ 07963 529859
⊕ blackenedsunbrewing.co.uk

Blackened Sun began brewing in 2017 and has mainly focused on brewing beers using Belgian yeast. It is involved in other brewing projects including mixed fermentation and brewing with local home brewers. ♦RAIB V

Blackjack SIBA

36 Gould Street, Manchester, M4 4RN
☎ (0161) 819 2767 🌐 blackjack-beers.com

One of the longest established of Manchester's new wave of craft brewers, Blackjack have been brewing in a railway arch in the city's Green Quarter since 2012. The beer range was relaunched in 2019, concentrating on a core range in cask and keg, followed by a new brew kit installation in 2020. Beers are widely available across the North of England and nationally as well as in its own Smithfield Market Tavern and three Jack in the Box food market bars. ♦V

Mosaic Light (ABV 3.6%)
Carousel Blonde (ABV 4%)
Pale (ABV 4%)
Pub Ale (ABV 4%)
Amber beer with hops and tart fruit in aroma and taste. Good bitterness throughout.
Golden Bitter (ABV 4.2%)
Citrus hop aroma. Sharp hop bitterness balanced with sweet malt. Dry, bitter finish.
Manchester Stout (ABV 4.5%)
Session IPA (ABV 4.5%)
IPA (ABV 5.4%)

Blackpit

Blackpit Farm, Silverstone Road, Stowe, Buckinghamshire, MK18 5LJ
☎ (01280) 827244 🌐 blackpitbrewery.co.uk

Three friends, Ben, Duncan & Oly, began brewing in 2017 in a converted stable yard on Blackpit Farm, one mile south of Silverstone. !! ♦

Day Tripper (ABV 3.8%)
Cloud Nine (ABV 3.9%)
Loosehead (ABV 4.2%)
Goshawk (ABV 4.4%)

Blackwater

See Maldon

Blimey!

Branksome House, 166 St Clements Hill, Norwich, NR3 1RS ☎ 07775 788299
✉ adriankbryan@googlemail.com

Brewing began in 2017.

Son of Pale Face (ABV 4%)
Eleven APA (ABV 4.5%)
Solid orange citrus notes dominate aroma and taste. Full-bodied and robust with malt adding balance. Short bittersweet finish.
TEN DDH APA Cryo (ABV 4.5%)
The Pale Face (ABV 4.5%)
Thirteen (ABV 4.5%)
First Born IPA (ABV 5.2%)

Blindmans SIBA

Talbot Farm, Leighton, Frome, Somerset, BA11 4PN
☎ (01749) 880038 🌐 blindmansbrewery.co.uk

Established in 2002 in a converted milking parlour and purchased by its current owners in 2004, this five-barrel brewery has its own water spring. In addition to its core range of ales, which are available locally and nationally, the brewery produces bespoke branded beers for pubs and other customers. ♦

Buff Amber (ABV 3.6%)
Funny Farm (ABV 4%)
Golden Spring (ABV 4%)
Mine Beer (ABV 4.2%)
Icarus (ABV 4.5%)

Block

Wenlock Arms, 26 Wenlock Road, Hoxton, London, N1 7TA
☎ (020) 7608 3406 🌐 wenlockarms.com

Block is based in the cellar of the award-winning Wenlock Arms. Launched at the end of 2016, the beer is available at the pub in cask and keg formats.

Blonde Brothers

Great Bathampton Farm, Wylie, Wiltshire, BA12 0QD
☎ 07538 872379 🌐 blondebrothers.beer

Established in 2019 on an organic family farm, it uses home-grown barley and water drawn from its own chalk aquifer borehole.

Blue (NEW)

Unit G21, The Avenues, Eleventh Avenue, North Team Valley Trading Estate, Gateshead, Tyne & Wear, NE11 0NJ
☎ (0191) 491 0221 🌐 bluebrewing.co.uk

Gypsy brewery using spare capacity at other breweries. Established in 2019 it acquired the rights to the Mordue brand. Beerology branded beers are produced for the eponymous bar in Newcastle.

Brewed under the Mordue Brewery brand name:
5 Bridges (ABV 3.6%)
Blonde (ABV 4%)
Howay in a Manger (ABV 4.3%)
Workie (ABV 4.5%)
Radgie (ABV 4.8%)
IPA (ABV 5.1%)

Blue Anchor

50 Coinagehall Street, Helston, Cornwall, TR13 8EL
☎ (01326) 562821 🌐 spingoales.com

15th-century thatched brewpub, the oldest continuously brewing in the country. Home of the famous Spingo ales which are produced from the well water beneath the pub. All regular brews are also available bottle-conditioned. !! ♦RAIB

Flora Daze (ABV 4%)
Pale brown, session bitter with light, flowery aroma and balanced malt, fruit and hops in the mouth. Gentle, lingering finish.
Jubilee IPA (ABV 4.5%)
Amber, premium bitter with malty, fruity hop nose and taste, balanced by fresh hop bitterness. Gentle bitter finish, with sweet malt.
Ben's Stout (ABV 4.8%)
Creamy dark stout with coffee roast aroma. Roast malt with liquorice and cherry flavours. Bittersweet finish with apples and cloves.
Spingo Middle (ABV 5%)

Heavy, red ale with dominant malt and balancing, peppery hop bitterness. Nuts, spices and dates flavours. Long, malty, dry finish.
Spingo Special (ABV 6.6%)
Smooth, red, strong old ale. Red wine aroma. Powerful flavours of sweet stone fruits, malt and hops. Vinous but delicate.

Blue Bee SIBA

Unit 29-30, Hoyland Road Industrial Estate, Sheffield, South Yorkshire, S3 8AB ☎ 07375 659349
bluebeebrewery.co.uk

Established in 2010, this independently-owned, 10-barrel brewery supplies throughout Yorkshire and the East Midlands, although it is often seen further afield. Blue Bee produce regular innovative specials and collaborate frequently with other like-minded breweries. Many beers have an emphasis on New World hops and an IPA is always available. ♦

Hillfoot Best Bitter (ABV 4%)
Reet Pale (ABV 4%)
American 5 Hop (ABV 4.3%)
Triple Hop (ABV 4.3%)
Ginger Beer (ABV 4.5%)
Tempest Stout (ABV 4.8%)

Blue Bell

Cranesgate South, Whaplode St Catherine, Lincolnshire, PE12 6SN
☎ (01406) 540300 ☎ 07788 136663
thebluebell.net

Founded in 1998 behind the Blue Bell Pub. The brewery is owned by the pub after previously operating as a separate business. Beers are only available at the pub and to private customers. !! ♦ RAIB

Blue Monkey SIBA

10 Pentrich Road, Giltbrook Industrial Park, Giltbrook, Nottinghamshire, NG16 2UZ
☎ (0115) 9385899 bluemonkeybrewery.com

Blue Monkey was established in 2008 as a 10-barrel plant but moved in 2010 to a bigger site to meet increasing demand. It now brews around 15,000 pints a week to supply more than 200 local outlets and selected national distributors. The brewery has four pubs called the Organ Grinder, in Nottingham, Arnold, Loughborough, and Newark. !!

Marmoset (ABV 3.6%)
BG Sips (ABV 4%)
Pale golden, hoppy beer, brewed mainly with Brewers Gold hops. Very fruity and bitter.
Primate Best Bitter (ABV 4%)
Funky Gibbon (ABV 4.1%)
Tawny-coloured, malty ale, dried fruit aroma and a gentle bitter finish.
Howler (ABV 4.5%)
Infinity (ABV 4.6%)
Golden ale packed with Citra hops.
Chocolate Amaretto (ABV 4.9%)
Chocolate Guerilla (ABV 4.9%)
Guerrilla (ABV 4.9%)
A creamy stout, full of roast malt flavour and a slightly sweet finish.
Plum Stout (ABV 4.9%)
Ape Ale (ABV 5.4%)
Intensely-hopped, strong golden ale with dry, bitter finish.
Infinity Plus 1 (ABV 5.6%)

Blue Square

See Truth Hurts

Blueball

The Old Bakery, 31-33 Ashridge Street, Runcorn, Cheshire, WA7 1HU
☎ (01928) 775628

Founded by Alex Haycraft in 2010, Blueball relocated to its current site in Runcorn in 2017. The brewery and on-site taproom (Society Tap Room), is situated in a former bakery and local Co-op building underneath railway arches, a short walk from the station. ◆

Indie Girl (ABV 3.8%)
Gold Digger (ABV 4%)
Penny Black (ABV 4.5%)
Tropical IPA (ABV 5%)
Zeppelin (ABV 5.5%)
Spank (ABV 6%)

Bluestone SIBA

Tyriet, Cilgwyn, Pembrokeshire, SA42 0QW
☎ (01239) 820833 bluestonebrewing.co.uk

A family-run business established in 2013 on a working hill farm in the Preseli Hills, within the Pembrokeshire Coast National Park. The 10-barrel brewery was installed in a renovated 200-year-old stone barn, which doubles as a visitor facility and office (open daily). The surrounding yard is an events venue in the summer. The brewery's private water supply filters down through the Preseli Hills. A number of local outlets as well as wholesalers around the UK are supplied. !! ♦ RAIB

Rockhopper (ABV 3.9%)
Bedrock Blonde (ABV 4%)
Hammerstone IPA (ABV 4.5%)
Rocketeer (ABV 4.6%)
Preseli Pils (ABV 4.7%)

Blunt Chisel

Phoenix Mill, Sawmill Road, Blairadam, KY4 0JG
thebluntchisel.co.uk

A nanobrewery set up in a former sawmill on the north bank of the Kelty Burn. A range of bottle-conditioned beers is on sale at the monthly Kinross Farmers' Market and at Leith Market. RAIB

Blythe SIBA

Blythe House Farm, Lichfield Road, Hamstall Ridware, Staffordshire, WS15 3QQ
☎ (01889) 504661 ☎ 07483 248723
blythebrewery.co.uk

Blythe began brewing in 2003 using a 2.5-barrel plant in a converted barn. Only organic ingredients are used wherever possible. 15 outlets are supplied direct. !! ♦ RAIB

Bagot's Bitter (ABV 3.8%)
Amber in colour with a fruit start and sweetness which develops to a smooth, bitter finish. A lightly-hopped, easy-drinking beer.
Ridware Pale (ABV 4.3%)
Bright and golden with a bitter floral hop aroma and citrus taste. Good and hop-sharp, bitter and refreshing. Long, lingering bite with ripples of citrus across the tongue.
Summer Breeze (ABV 4.3%)
Staffie (ABV 4.4%)

THE BREWERIES

Hoppy and grassy aroma with hints of sweetness from this amber beer. A touch of malt at the start is soon overwhelmed by hops. A full hoppy, mouth-watering finish.

Palmers Poison (ABV 4.5%)
Refreshing darkish beer. Tawny but light-headed. Coffee truffle aroma, pleasingly sweet to start but with a good hop mouthfeel.

Gold Rush (ABV 4.6%)
Dark Horse (ABV 4.7%)
Knobbled Horse (ABV 4.7%)
Dark Ruby (ABV 5%)
Johnsons (ABV 5.2%)
Black with a thick head. Refreshingly hoppy and full-bodied with lingering bitterness of chocolate, dates, coal smoke and liquorice.

BOA (Brothers of Ale) (NEW)

Unit 3, Anglo Buildings, Baldwin Road, Stourport on Severn, Worcestershire, DY13 9AX
☎ (01299) 488100 ☎ 07725 724934
🌐 brothersofale.co.uk

What started as a hobby soon became a passion and BOA Brewery was established in 2018 before opening its doors in 2019. It is situated in the heart of Stourport on Severn producing hop-forward, New World-style beers. ◆

Peace Out (ABV 3.6%)
The 7 (ABV 4.2%)
2 Step (ABV 4.4%)
VVD Oatmeal Stout (ABV 4.7%)

Boat Lane

Unit 3, Streamside Business Park, Boat Lane, Offenham, Evesham, Worcestershire, WR11 8RS
☎ (01386) 48212 🌐 boatlanebrewery.co.uk

A microbrewery established in 2017 by Ian Hazeldene in a small village near Evesham. An ever-changing range of beers are brewed, with up to eight available in the brewery bar at weekends. ◆

Bodachra SIBA

57 Denview Road, Potterton, AB23 8ZL ☎ 07590 579844 ✉ robin@cityoftruro.free-online.uk

Bodachra is a small batch craft brewery established in 2018.

Boden (NEW)

Unit 3, 95 Boden Street, Glasgow, G40 3QF ☎ 07511 022231 🌐 bodenbrewing.co.uk

Launched in 2019, Boden Brewing is a one-man operation based in the east end of Glasgow. Six core beers are available in bottle and keg. V

Bog Brew SIBA

11 High Street, Old Town, Stevenage, Hertfordshire, SG1 3BG ☎ 07973 673040
🌐 bogbrew.co.uk

⊗ Brewing began in 2017. Currently using a 1.5-barrel plant, there are plans for expansion. Beers are available at local beer festivals, free houses around Hertfordshire and Bedfordshire and in the brewery tap, the Broken Seal. RAIB

Bohem

Unit 5, Littleline House, 41-43 West Road, Tottenham, London, N17 0RE
☎ (020) 8617 8350 ☎ 07455 502976
🌐 bohembrewery.com

Traditional Bohemian lagers brewed by Czech expats in North London. The brewery moved to larger premises in 2018. Beers are supplied to local outlets, including the taproom near the original brewery site. A second outlet was added in 2020, Bohemia House in West Hampstead replacing the former Czech club. No real ale, and cans are becoming a popular choice. ◆

Boilerhouse

See JW Lees (under L)

Bollington SIBA

Adlington Road, Bollington, Cheshire, SK10 5JT
☎ (01625) 575380 🌐 bollingtonbrewing.co.uk

⊗ Bollington began brewing in 2008 with the Vale Inn, Bollington, as the brewery tap. The Park Tavern, Macclesfield, and the Cask Tavern, Poynton, are also owned. Around 40 outlets are supplied direct. !! ◆ RAIB

Chinook & Grapefruit (ABV 3.6%)
Ginger Brew (ABV 3.6%)
White Nancy (ABV 3.6%)
Long Hop (ABV 3.9%)
Bollington Best (ABV 4.2%)
Dinner Ale (ABV 4.3%)
Oat Mill Stout (ABV 5%)
Eastern Nights (ABV 5.6%)

Bond Brews

Units 3 & 4, South Barns, Gardeners Green Farm, Heathlands Road, Wokingham, Berkshire, RG40 3AS
☎ (01344) 775450 🌐 bondbrews.co.uk

⊗ An award-winning brewery, Bond Brews was established in 2015 using a six-barrel plant. Beers are delivered to pubs within a 30-mile radius. Brewery tours and experience days are available by arrangement with the brewer. !! ◆ RAIB

Goldi-hops (ABV 3.9%)
A golden-coloured pale ale with a fruit and hop aroma. Bramble and apple flavours lead to a lingering fruity, dry bitter aftertaste.

Best of British (ABV 4%)
A tawny-coloured bitter with malt, hops and fruit aroma. Dried fruit, earthy and caramel flavours lead to a sweet, nutty aftertaste.

Bengal Tiger (ABV 4.3%)
A golden-coloured premium pale ale with a hoppy, fruity aroma. Initial fruity flavour leads to an earthy bitterness and a long, dry, bitter finish.

Railway Porter (ABV 4.5%)
A brown-coloured porter with roast malt and fruit aroma. Bitter and hoppy flavour with an earthy, peppery and bitter chocolate aftertaste.

Bone Idle

28 The Green, Idle, Bradford, West Yorkshire, BD10 9PX ☎ 07525 751574

Established in 2018 in a converted barn situated in the heart of Idle village. The brewery offers the public the opportunity to try brewing. All beers produced are sold exclusively in the Idle Draper pub next door. A mezzanine floor has a mini cinema/function room.

Bone Machine

20 Pier Street, Hull, East Yorkshire, HU1 1ZA
☎ (01482) 618000
✉ beer@bonemachinebrewing.com

Originally established in Pocklington in 2017, Bone Machine transferred operations to Hull's Fruit Market in 2019, brewing on an eight-barrel plant. Finnish brothers Marko and Kimmo previously worked at Atom and Brass Castle Brewery before setting up on their own. Beers are mainly available in keg and can, with a small amount in cask. V

Back Bone (ABV 3.7%)
Cloud Piercer (ABV 4.7%)
Dream Machine (ABV 5.2%)

Boot

12 Boot Hill, Repton, Derbyshire, DE65 6FT
☎ (01283) 346047 thebootbeer.co.uk

A 10-barrel brewery operating from the rear of the Boot Inn, Repton. The brewery supplies three pubs within the Bespoke Inns group and free trade outlets across the Midlands. !! ♦ RAIB V

Clod Hopper (ABV 3.9%)
Flying Pig (ABV 3.9%)
Bitter (ABV 4.3%)
Solstice (ABV 4.4%)
Tuffer's Old (ABV 4.6%)
ESB (ABV 4.8%)
Beast (ABV 6.7%)

Boot Town

c/o Copper Kettle Brewing, Bosworths Garden Centre, 110 Finedon Road, Burton Latimer, Northamptonshire, NN15 5QA
☎ (01536) 725212 boottownbrewery.co.uk

A microbrewery established in 2017 and based on the old Copper Kettle Brewery site, producing an ever-changing range of beers.

Bootleg

See Joseph Holt

Born SIBA

Lanton Mill, Jedburgh, TD8 6ST
☎ (01835) 830495 ☎ 07802 416494
bornintheborders.com

Scotland's original plough-to-pint brewery, it started brewing as Scottish Borders Brewery in 2011 using barley from its own farm before changing name to Born in the Borders Brewery. Beyond its core range of ales, projects have included the 'Wild Harvest' initiative, which sources locally-foraged ingredients for its ales. The brewery has a visitor centre, offering brewery tours, a café/restaurant and retail units featuring Borders beer, produce and food. A further name change to Born Brewery occurred in 2020. !! ♦

Blonde (ABV 3.8%)
Amber (ABV 4%)
IPA (ABV 4.3%)
Black (ABV 4.5%)

Born in the Borders

See Born

Borough Arms

2 New Henry Street, Neath, SA11 2PH
☎ (01639) 644902 boroughbreweryneath.com

The Borough Arms and Borough Brewery were bought by new owners in 2019, the brewery is at the rear of the pub and has been refurbished. Beers brewed are only available in-house at the Borough Arms.

Boss SIBA

176 Neath Road, Landore, Swansea, SA1 2JT
☎ (01792) 450978 ☎ 07825 525735
bossbrewing.co.uk

The brewery opened in 2015 by Roy Allkin and Sarah John, using a 10-barrel plant. It relocated in 2017 to larger premises opposite the Liberty Stadium which now include an on-site brewery tap – the Brewery Bar. Expansion has resulted in the setting up of bottling, canning, kegging as well as casking facilities. 250 outlets are supplied, bottles and cans are distributed to national retailers. In a further trade expansion, exports to France and Germany commenced in 2017. !! ♦ RAIB

Blonde (ABV 4%)
Blaze (ABV 4.5%)
Beetlejuice (ABV 4.8%)
Bare (ABV 5%)
Black (ABV 5%)

Bosun's SIBA

Unit 4, Prospect Business Centre, Prospect Street, Huddersfield, West Yorkshire, HD1 2NU
☎ (01484) 412300 ☎ 07513 112188
bosunsbrewery.co.uk

The first brew was produced in 2013 by a father-and-son team who had both served in the armed forces. The brewery relocated from Horbury to Huddersfield in 2018. The regular beers are produced on a 10-barrel plant with some given military-themed names. !! ♦

Tell No Tales (ABV 3.8%)
Bosun's Blonde (ABV 3.9%)
Maiden Voyage (ABV 3.9%)
Down The Hatch (ABV 4%)
King Neptune (ABV 4.3%)
Bosun's IPA (ABV 5.6%)

Botley

Botley Mills, Mill Hill, Botley, Hampshire, SO30 2GB
☎ (01489) 784867 ☎ 07909 337212
botleybrewery.com

Botley Brewery was established in 2010 and uses a five-barrel plant. A small bar next door, appropriately named the Hidden Tap, serves three of its ales Thursday-Saturday. ♦ RAIB

Hampshire Pale Ale (ABV 3.8%)
Pommy Blonde (ABV 4.3%)
English IPA (ABV 5.1%)
Stinger Porter (ABV 5.2%)

Bottle Brook

Church Street, Kilburn, Belper, Derbyshire, DE56 0LU
☎ (01332) 880051 ☎ 07971 189915

A sister brewery to Leadmill (qv), Bottle Brook was established in 2005 using a 2.5-barrel plant on a tower gravity system. New World hops are predominantly used. The core range of beers is supplemented by one-off brews.

THE BREWERIES

Columbus (ABV 4%)
Heanor Pale Ale (ABV 4.2%)
Roadrunner (ABV 4.8%)
Mellow Yellow (ABV 5.7%)
Rapture (ABV 5.9%)
Sand in the Wind (ABV 6.1%)

Boudicca

The Old Store, Walsingham Road, West Barsham, Norfolk, NR21 9NP
☎ (01328) 863854 ☎ 07864 321732
🌐 boudiccabrewing.co.uk

⊗ Established in 2015, Boudicca Brewery was based on a North Norfolk estate until mid 2020 and is planning to use a Norfolk contract brewer until a new home is located. It is an award-winning, independent brewery exclusively producing vegan beers, supplied to free trade outlets across East Anglia, including cafés, delis and off-licences. ‼ ♦ RAIB V

Queen of Hops (ABV 3.7%)
Three Tails (ABV 3.9%)
Golden Torc (ABV 4.3%)
Malty bouquet with a hint of grassy hop. Biscuity beginning with a growing zesty, citrus background. Clean grapefruit finish.
The Red Queen (ABV 4.5%)
Spiral Stout (ABV 4.6%)
Burnt toast on the nose and black malt in the taste define this traditional dry stout. Strong finish.
Prasto's Porter (ABV 5.2%)

Boundary SIBA

Unit A5, 310 Portview Trade Centre,, Newtownards Road, Belfast, BT4 1HE 🌐 boundarybrewing.coop

Boundary is a cooperative brewery based in Belfast, established in 2014. A taproom is open to the public. ♦ ◈

APA (ABV 3.5%)
Export Stout (ABV 7%)
IPA (ABV 7%)

Boutilliers

The Hop Shed, Macknade Fine Foods, Selling Road, Faversham, Kent, ME13 8XF ☎ 07743 372434
🌐 boutilliers.com

Founded in 2016, Boutilliers is a small brewery specialising in left field brews. Its beers are mainly bottled or canned. Cask-conditioned beers are supplied to a few local pubs and are sometimes available at the brewery on open days. ♦

Bowland SIBA

Holmes Mill, Greenacre Street, Clitheroe, Lancashire, BB7 1EB
☎ (01200) 443592 🌐 bowlandbrewery.com

⊛ Founded in 2003, this family-run business uses a 30-barrel plant together with a nanobrewery for experimental brews. The site features a beer shop and beer hall with 42 handpumps featuring beers from Lancashire and beyond. ‼ 🛒 ♦ RAIB

Pheasant Plucker (ABV 3.7%)
Gold (ABV 3.8%)
Well-balanced, pale, hoppy ale with delicate citrus hop notes and a long, dry, bitter finish.
Boxer Blonde (ABV 4%)
Bumble (ABV 4%)
Hen Harrier (ABV 4%)
Gentle aromas of malt, hops and fruit start this satisfying, fruity bitter which has a lasting, rich finish.
Buster IPA (ABV 4.5%)

Bowman SIBA

Wallops Wood, Sheardley Lane, Droxford, Hampshire, SO32 3QY
☎ (01489) 878110 🌐 bowman-ales.com

⊗ Brewing started in 2006 in converted farm buildings. The brewery supplies more than 100 outlets. A 40-barrel plant came on stream in 2013, which works alongside the original 20-barrel plant. Bowman also brew the Suthwyk Ales range of beers. ‼ ♦ RAIB

Swift One (ABV 3.8%)
Easy drinking bitter, well balanced with sweet maltiness leading to a bittersweet finish & slightly dry hoppy aftertaste.
Meon Valley Bitter (ABV 3.9%)
Well balanced copper coloured bitter; sweet with an initial maltiness in taste and aroma leading to a more bitter finish.
Yumi (ABV 3.9%)
Wallops Wood (ABV 4%)
No particular flavour dominates this well-crafted beer. Malt flavours throughout balanced by toffee notes, sweetness and slightly dry finish.

Contract brewed for Suthwyk Ales:
Old Dick (ABV 3.8%)
Pleasant, clean-tasting pale brown bitter. Easy-drinking and well-balanced. Brewed for Suthwyk using ingredients grown on its farm.
Liberation (ABV 4.2%)
Skew Sunshine Ale (ABV 4.6%)
An amber-coloured beer, brewed for Suthwyk using its homegrown ingredients. Initial hoppiness leads to a fruity taste and finish.
Palmerston's Folly (ABV 5%)

Bowness Bay SIBA

Unit 10, Castle Mills, Aynam Road, Kendal, Cumbria, LA9 7DE
☎ (01539) 726800 ☎ 07823 347763
🌐 bownessbaybrewing.co.uk

⊛ Bowness Bay Brewing moved to Kendal in 2015 and increased capacity from five to 16 barrels. The original five-barrel plant is used for small experimental brews. The brewery now has its own on-site taphouse, the Barrel House. In 2020 grant funding allowed further expansion into keg beers. ‼ ♦ ◈

Lakeland Blonde (ABV 3.7%)
Swift Best (ABV 3.8%)
A tawny bitter where caramel sweetness dominates, leading to a gentle bitter finish.
Swan Blonde (ABV 4%)
Sweet, fruity mild beer with gentle bittering hops.
Fellrunner (ABV 4.1%)
Raven Red (ABV 4.2%)
Swan Gold (ABV 4.2%)
Swan Black (ABV 4.6%)
Stout-like beer with a fruity, raisiny middle, grainy mouthfeel and roast bitter finish.
Tern IPA (ABV 5%)
Well-balanced IPA with some sweet malt and fruit to balance the lingering hoppy finish.

Bowtie (NEW)

78 Church Road, Watford, Hertfordshire, WD17 4PU
🌐 bowtiebrewers.co.uk

A 0.25-barrel nanobrewery founded in 2018 in a specially designed brewshed. Commercial brewing began in 2019, offering three ranges of small batch beers; traditional, craft and speciality. Beers are mostly available in bottles but cask-conditioned beer is occasionally produced.

Box Social

18 Riversdale Court, Newburn, Newcastle upon Tyne, NE15 8SG
☎ (0191) 340 4394 ☎ 07803 791761
⊕ boxsocial.pub

Launched in 2015, this family-run brewery has a licence and is open to the public most days. In 2016 it opened a micropub-cuterie based in Forth Street, Newcastle. ‼ ▦ ◆ RAIB

Hybrid Theory (ABV 3.5%)
Gentlemans Nectar Pale Ale (ABV 4.2%)
Sticky Beak (ABV 4.2%)
A Certain Shade of Green (ABV 6%)

Box Steam SIBA

15 The Midlands, Holt, Wiltshire, BA14 6RU
☎ (01225) 782700 ⊕ boxsteambrewery.com

⊗ Founded in 2004, the brewery boasts a Fulton steam-fired copper, hence the name. New ownership since 2006 meant expansion and increased capacity with the brewery moving to larger premises in Holt in 2011. Two pubs are owned and more than 100 outlets supplied. ‼ ▦ ◆ V ⬥

Golden Bolt (ABV 3.8%)
Soul Train (ABV 4%)
Tunnel Vision (ABV 4.2%)
Piston Broke (ABV 4.5%)

Boxcar

Unit 1, Birkbeck Street, Bethnal Green, London, E2 6JY
⊕ boxcarbrewery.co.uk

After being located in Homerton for two years, it moved to Bethnal Green in 2019 opening a larger brewery and taproom close to Old Street and Mechanic breweries. Keg and cans form the majority of production with bottles occasionally. No real ale. ⬥

Br3wery

253 Beckenham Road, Beckenham, BR3 4RP
⊕ br3wery.com

Established in 2019 producing bottle-conditioned beers, bigger batches of keg beer were later brewed at Birmingham Brewery. A new brewhouse and taproom opened in 2020. RAIB ⬥

Brack'N'Brew

⬛ **Brackenrigg Inn, Watermillock, Cumbria, CA11 0LP**
☎ (01768) 486206 ⊕ brackenrigginn.co.uk

⊕ Brewing started in 2015, set up in the old stable block at the rear of the Brackenrigg Inn, on the shores of Ullswater in the Lake District. A four-barrel plant is used to produce cask and bottled beers, which are sold across Cumbria and the north of England.

Bradfield SIBA

Watt House Farm, High Bradfield, Sheffield, South Yorkshire, S6 6LG
☎ (0114) 285 1118 ⊕ bradfieldbrewery.co.uk

⊕ Established in 2005, this family-run business is based on a working farm in the Peak District using pure Millstone Grit spring water. The delivery area covers the North of England from Northumberland to Northampton, east to west coast. Beer is also supplied further afield. The Nag's Head has been the brewery tap since 2009. In 2018 the brewery obtained the King & Miller, Deepcar, and the nearby Wharncliffe Arms a year later. Monthly specials are available. ▦ ◆ RAIB

Farmers Bitter (ABV 3.9%)
Farmers Blonde (ABV 4%)
Farmers Brown Cow (ABV 4.2%)
Farmers Steel Cow (ABV 4.5%)
Farmers Stout (ABV 4.5%)
Farmers Pale Ale (ABV 5%)
Farmers Sixer (ABV 6%)

Brains IFBB

Dragon Brewery, Pacific Road, Cardiff, CF24 5HJ
☎ (029) 2040 2060 ⊕ sabrain.com

⊕ Brains, still in family ownership, was established in 1882 at the Old Brewery in the City Centre, moving in 1999 to the former Hancock's brewery site (soon to be part of the Central Quay development area). The redundant Craft Brewery will be developed into a visitor's centre. The new Dragon Brewery in Cardiff Bay, relaunched in 2019. Brains runs more than 160 pubs throughout Wales and is also involved in sponsoring charities and Welsh sport. ◆

Dark (ABV 3.5%)
A tasty, classic, dark brown mild, a mix of malt, roast, caramel with a background of hops. Bittersweet, mellow and with a lasting finish of malt and roast.

Bitter (ABV 3.7%)
Amber-coloured with a gentle aroma of malt and hops. Malt, hops and bitterness combine in an easy-drinking beer with a bitter finish.

Rev James Gold (ABV 4.1%)
SA (ABV 4.2%)
A mellow, full-bodied beer. Gentle malt and hop aroma leads to a malty, hop and fruit mix with a balancing bitterness.

SA Gold (ABV 4.2%)
A golden beer with a hoppy aroma. Well-balanced with a zesty hop, malt, fruit and balancing bitterness; a similar satisfying finish.

Rev James Rye (ABV 4.3%)
Rev James (ABV 4.5%)
A faint malt and fruit aroma with malt and fruit flavours in the taste, initially bittersweet. Bitterness balances the flavour and makes this an easy-drinking beer.

Contract brewed for Molson Coors:
M&B Brew XI (ABV 3.6%)
Hancock's HB (ABV 3.7%)
Worthington's Bitter (ABV 3.7%)

Brakspear

Eagle Maltings, The Crofts, Witney, Oxfordshire, OX28 4DP
☎ (01993) 890800 ⊕ brakspear-beers.co.uk

Brakspear beers have been brewed in Oxfordshire since 1779. They continue to be traditionally crafted at the Wychwood Brewery (qv) in the historic market town of Witney using the original Victorian square fermenters and the renowned double drop fermenting system. Part of Marston's PLC. ‼ ▦ ◆ RAIB ⬥

Gravity (ABV 3.4%)
Oxford Gold (ABV 4%)

Brampton SIBA

Units 4 & 5, Chatsworth Business Park, Chatsworth Road, Chesterfield, Derbyshire, S40 2AR
☎ (01246) 221680 ⊕ bramptonbrewery.co.uk

☺The original Brampton Brewery closed in 1955. In 2007 a new brewery was established, and brewing commenced on an eight-barrel plant. Three tied houses are situated close to the brewery. ‼ ⧓ ◆ RAIB

Golden Bud (ABV 3.8%)
Crisp, refreshing, golden bitter with a pleasant balance of citrus, sweetness and bitter flavours. Light and easy to drink.
1302 (ABV 4%)
Griffin (ABV 4.1%)
Best (ABV 4.2%)
Classic, drinkable bitter with a predominantly malty taste, balanced by caramel sweetness and a developing bitterness in the aftertaste.
Impy Dark (ABV 4.3%)
Strong, roasted coffee aroma and a rich flavour of vine fruit and chocolate combine to make this a tasty mild ale.
Jerusalem (ABV 4.6%)
Tudor Rose (ABV 4.6%)
Wasp Nest (ABV 5%)
Strong and complex with malt and hop flavours and a caramel sweetness.
Speciale (ABV 5.8%)

Brancaster

See Beeston

Branscombe Vale SIBA

Branscombe, Devon, EX12 3DP
☎ (01297) 680511 ⊕ branscombevalebrewery.co.uk

⊠ The brewery was set up in 1992 in cowsheds at the back of a National Trust-owned farm, overlooking the sea at Branscombe. The brewery owners converted the sheds, digging their own well. In 2008 a new 25-barrel plant was shoehorned in through the roof to increase capacity. ◆ RAIB

Branoc (ABV 3.8%)
Amber session bitter. Hops and malt throughout with good bitterness in taste and aftertaste.
Golden Fiddle (ABV 4%)
Summa This (ABV 4.2%)
BVB White Label (ABV 4.6%)
Red/brown-coloured beer with a fruity aroma and taste, and bitter/dry finish.
Summa That (ABV 5%)

Brass Castle SIBA

10a Yorkersgate, Malton, North Yorkshire, YO17 7AB
☎ (01653) 698683 ⊕ brasscastle.co.uk

☺The brewery is based in the centre of Malton with a 12-barrel plant, having begun life in 2011 on a one-barrel kit in the owner's garage. It has an on-site taproom with many beers available for on and off-sales. ‼ ⧓ ◆ GF V✿

Northern Blonde (ABV 3.9%)
Misfit (ABV 4.3%)
Bad Kitty (ABV 5.5%) ⌷
Sunshine (ABV 5.7%)
Disruptor (ABV 7.4%)

Breakwater

St Martin's Yard, Lorne Road, Dover, Kent, CT16 2AA

☎ (01304) 410144 ☎ 07979 867045
✉ andrea@breakwater.brewery.co.uk

⊠ Breakwater is a brewery and taproom established in 2016 behind Buckland Corn Mill in former industrial premises and on the site of the former Wellington Brewery. ◆ RAIB

Dover Pale Ale (ABV 3.5%)
Hellfire Corner (ABV 4.1%)
Castle on the Hill (ABV 4.4%)
Cowjuice Milk Stout (ABV 4.4%)
Mogul West Country IPA (ABV 5.6%)

Brecon

See Cold Black Label

Brentwood SIBA

Calcott Hall Farm, Ongar Road, Pilgrims Hatch, Brentwood, Essex, CM15 9HS
☎ (01277) 200483 ⊕ brentwoodbrewing.co.uk

⊠ Since its launch in 2006 Brentwood has steadily increased its capacity and distribution, relocating to a new purpose-built brewery unit in 2013 with a visitor centre. Seasonal and special beers are also available including more unusual beer styles under the Elephant School brand name. ‼ ⧓ ◆ RAIB ✿

IPA (ABV 3.7%)
Marvellous Maple Mild (ABV 3.7%)
Brentwood Legacy (ABV 4%)
Best (ABV 4.2%)
Gold (ABV 4.3%)
Hope & Glory (ABV 4.5%)
Lumberjack (ABV 5.2%)
Chockwork Orange (ABV 6.5%)

Brewed under the Elephant School brand name:
Mallophant (ABV 4.1%)
Cheru Kol (ABV 4.5%)
Sombrero (ABV 4.5%)

Brew Buddies

Unit 14, Highlands Farm Business Park, Highlands Hill, Swanley Village, Kent, BR8 7NA ☎ 07962 369717
⊕ brew-buddies.co.uk

⊠ Owned and run by husband and wife Simon and Rebecca, Brew Buddies Brewery are brewing for cask, keg, bottle and can. Beers range from traditional to modern, and are unfined and vegan-friendly. Beers are available in the brewery tap room as well as venues across London and the South of England. ‼ ⧓ V✿

Brew By Numbers

79 Enid Street, Bermondsey, London, SE16 3RA
☎ (020) 7237 9794 ⊕ brewbynumbers.com

Established in 2012, Brew By Numbers (BBNo) has produced over 400 different beers across 38 styles. BBNo currently has three taprooms; the main site, located in the centre of the famed Bermondsey Beer Mile, is visited by over 1,000 people per week. ⧓ RAIB V✿

Brew Foundation

c/o Wincle Brewery, Toll Barn, Wincle, Cheshire, SK11 0QE
☎ (0114) 282 3098 ☎ 07545 618894

Office: 18 Jarrow Road, Sheffield, S11 8YB
⊕ thebrewfoundation.co.uk

A father-and-son brewery, currently using spare capacity at Wincle Brewery (qv). Beer is distributed both east and west of the Pennines.

Pop (ABV 3.6%)
Little Bitter That (ABV 3.8%)
Hops & Dreams (ABV 4%)
Laughing Water (ABV 4.3%)
First Light (ABV 4.6%)
Janet's Treat Porter (ABV 4.8%)
Hop & Glory (ABV 4.9%)
Bitter That (ABV 5%)

Brew Monster SIBA

Unit 1, Lon Y Twyn, Caerphilly, CF83 1NW ☎ 07772 869856 ⊕ brewmonster.co.uk

⊠ Having launched in 2017, this brewery has gone from strength to strength. The original core range of four ales has grown to six and are available in all forms. The 'White Label' series introduces new one-off or seasonal beers. The first 'tap' bar was opened in Cardiff city centre in 2019 and another has since opened in Cardiff Bay, with more to follow. The brewery relocated to Caerphilly from Cwmbran in 2020 and plans to open a restaurant/taproom on site.

Leviathan IPA (ABV 4%)
Phoenix (ABV 4.5%)
Daemon Red Ale (ABV 4.6%)
Tiamat IPA (ABV 5%)
Black Widow (ABV 5.4%)
Mephisto IPA (ABV 5.6%)

Brew Shack

Sixpenny Handley, Dorset ☎ 07580 120258 ⊕ thebrewshack.co.uk

⊠ Brewing began in 2015 on a 1.5-barrel plant in purpose-built premises, later upgraded to 10 barrels. The brewery is located on a working farm so there is no access for the general public. V

Bills Bitter (ABV 3.8%)
A traditional-style bitter with fruity aroma, good malt balance and moderate hoppiness leading to a hoppy, dry finish.
Pale Ale (ABV 4.5%)
Intense hop citrus taste with some fruit coming through. Leads to a pleasant, slightly dry, stringent finish. Unfined.
Eight Grain Porter (ABV 5%)
Light, drinkable, porter with prominent roast notes in the aroma and taste. Roast notes add astringency in the taste, leading to a fruity aftertaste.

Brew Shed

Wellheads House, Sandilands, Limekilns, KY11 3JD ☎ 07484 727672 ⊕ brewshedbeers.wordpress.com

Brewing began in 2016 in a tiny brewery behind the owner's house, the first brewery in Limekilns since 1849. Brew Shed Beers revives a tradition of local breweries serving the neighbourhood.

Brew Studio

39 Meadowview Road, Sompting, West Sussex, BN15 0HU

⊠ Brew Studio started off as a 0.5-barrel nanobrewery in 2017 and has recently upgraded to a 2.5-barrel plant. Around 20 outlets are supplied direct.

Brew Toon SIBA

72a St Peter Street, Peterhead, AB42 1QB
☎ (01779) 560948 ⊕ brewtoon.co.uk

Established in 2017, beers are brewed in small batches. The brewery has an on-site café/bar. V◆

Brew Yonder

Rookery Farm, Binegar, Radstock, Somerset, BA3 4UL
☎ 07967 649766 ⊕ brewyonder.co.uk

A farmhouse-style brewery founded by Stuart Winstone and Jasper Tupman, formally of Wild Beer fame, in 2018. They focus on wild yeasts, foraged ingredients and barrel-aging. All ingredients are sourced locally, within about 40 minutes of the brewery.

Brew York SIBA

Enterprise Complex, Walmgate, York, YO1 9TT
☎ (01904) 848448 ⊕ brewyork.co.uk

☺ Established in 2016, Brew York was born out of two friends passion for beer and brewing. The brewery is located within York's historic city walls, a 15-minute walk from the station. A unique taproom and beer hall (including kitchen) with riverside beer garden has been constructed alongside the brewhouse. ‼️💺◆GFV◆

JARSA (ABV 3.7%)
FOSSA (ABV 4.1%)
Tonkoko (ABV 4.3%)
Haze of Thunder (ABV 4.6%)

BrewBoard SIBA

Unit B3 Button End Industrial Estate, Harston, Cambridgeshire, CB22 7GX ⊕ brewboard.co.uk

Founded in 2017. Now brewing with 150-hectolitre plant. No real ale. ‼️💺

Brewdog

Balmacassie Industrial Estate, Ellon, AB41 8BX
☎ (01358) 724924

Tower Hill: Unit 3, Minister Building, 21 Great Tower Street, Tower Hill, EC3N 5AR ⊕ brewdog.com

Established in 2007 by James Watt and Martin Dickie. Most of the production goes into bottles and keg. In 2016 a KeyKeg initiative began, described as 'real ale for modernists'. More than 50 bars now exist in the UK. Beer is now also served as 'cask', conditioned in a KeyKeg. ‼️💺

Dead Pony (ABV 3.8%)
5am Saint (ABV 5%)

Brewers Folly

Ashton Farm House, Stanbridge, Wimborne, Dorset, BH21 4JD ⊕ brewersfolly.co.uk

⊠ Dean and Rufus have been avid homebrewers for a very long time. They began brewing on a 1.4-barrel system bought from Brew Shack in 2017. They currently work full-time and brew part-time, but hope to go full-time and expand the range in the future. ‼️◆V

Session Pale Ale (ABV 4.2%)
10w-40 (ABV 5%)
V1 Simco IPA (ABV 5.5%)
V2 Ekuanot IPA (ABV 5.5%)
V3 Galaxy (ABV 5.5%)

THE BREWERIES

Brewery at the Watchmaker's Arms

84 Goldstone Villas, Hove, East Sussex, BN3 3RU

Hove's first micropub has its own 100-litre microbrewery, producing under the Beercraft Brighton brand name. Beer is primarily for the Watchmakers but is available in other local pubs.

Brewery58

58 Wantage Road, Wallingford, Oxfordshire, OX10 0LY
☎ (01491) 838262 ☎ 07798 674724
brewery58.com

A nanobrewery that started when the owner was given a brewing kit as a retirement present. Commercial production began in 2018. Bottle-conditioned ales are available at a few local pubs and shops. RAIB

Brewhouse & Kitchen SIBA

Bedford: 115 High Street, Bedford, MK40 1NU ☎ (01234) 342931

Bournemouth: 154 Commercial Road, Bournemouth, Dorset, BH2 5LU ☎ (01202) 055221

Bristol: 31-35 Cotham Hill, Bristol, BS6 6JY ☎ (0117) 973 3793

Cardiff: Sophia Close, Pontcanna, Cardiff, CF11 9HW ☎ (029) 20371599

Cheltenham: Unit 7, The Brewery, St Margaret's Road, Cheltenham, GL50 4EQ ☎ (01242) 509946

Chester: Forest House, Love Street, Chester, CH1 1QY ☎ (01244) 404990

Dorchester: 17 Weymouth Avenue, Dorchester, DT1 1QY ☎ (01305) 265551

Gloucester Quays: Unit R1, St Anne Walk, Gloucester Quay, Gloucester, GL1 5SH ☎ (01452) 222965

Highbury: 2a Corsica Street, Highbury, London, N5 1JJ ☎ (0207) 226 1026

Horsham: 38 East Street, Horsham, RH12 1HL ☎ (01403) 788140

Hoxton: 397-400 Geffrye Street, Hoxton, E2 8HZ ☎ (020) 3861 8920

Islington: 5 Torrens Street, Islington, London, EC1V 1NQ ☎ (0207) 837 9421

Lichfield: 1 Bird Street, Lichfield, WS13 6PW ☎ (01543) 224740

Milton Keynes: 7 Savoy Crescent, Milton Keynes, MK9 3PU ☎ (01908) 049032

Nottingham: Trent Bridge, Nottingham, NG2 2GS ☎ (0115) 986 7960

Poole: 3 Dear Hay Lane, Poole, BH15 1NZ ☎ (01202) 771246

Portsmouth: 26 Guildhall Walk, Portsmouth, PO1 2DD ☎ (023) 9289 1340

Southampton: 47 Highfield Lane, Southampton, SO17 1QD ☎ (023) 8055 5566

Southbourne: 147 Parkwood Road, Southbourne, Bournemouth, BH5 2BW ☎ (01202) 055209

Southsea: 51 Southsea Terrace, Portsmouth, PO5 3AU ☎ (023) 9281 8979

Sutton Coldfield: 8 Birmingham Road, Sutton Coldfield, B72 1QD ☎ (01217) 966 838

Wilmslow: 6-12 Swan Street, Wilmslow, SK9 1HE ☎ (01625) 441850 brewhouseandkitchen.com

Brewing started in 2013 in Portsmouth, the first in the growing Brewhouse & Kitchen chain. There are now 22 brewpubs, each producing its own particular range of beers and with its brewery on open display in the bar area. Local freehouses and beer festivals can be supplied. Carry outs and brewery experience days are available at all venues. V

Brewing Brothers

Imperial, 119 Queens Road, Hastings, East Sussex, TN34 1RL brewingbrothers.org

⊗ Brewing began in 2016 in the Imperial, Hastings. The brewery has a 2.5-barrel capacity with four fermenting vessels. A wide range of brother-themed beers have been brewed to date, including a core range of seasonal beers, and a collaboration with Half Man Half Burger. ♦V

Brewis (NEW)

Unit 4, Coquet Enterprise Park, Amble, Northumberland, NE65 0PE
☎ (01665) 714818 brewisbeer.co.uk

Brewis Beer Co is a family-run nanobrewery featuring a bottle shop and taproom. ◆

Building Bridges (ABV 4.5%)
Helm (ABV 4.7%)
Just Like Heaven (ABV 5.7%)
Turning Tides (ABV 5.8%)
Ebb & Flow (ABV 6.5%)

Brewshed SIBA

Place Farm, Ingham, Suffolk, IP31 1NQ
☎ (01284) 848066 brewshedbrewery.co.uk

⊗ Brewshed began brewing in 2011 using a five-barrel plant in buildings located behind the Beerhouse, one of its outlets. It's now located in the nearby village of Ingham, using a 12-barrel plant, resulting in greater capacity and a wider beer range. The brewery continues to increase production and supplies bottled beers to Hotel Chocolat. ♦V

Pale (ABV 3.9%)
Best (ABV 4.3%)
American Blonde (ABV 5.5%)

Brewsmith

Unit 11, Cuba Industrial Estate, Stubbins, Ramsbottom, Bury, BL0 0NE
☎ (01706) 829390 brewsmithbeer.co.uk

Brewsmith is a 10-barrel microbrewery established in 2014 by the Smith family – James, Jennifer and Ted. It produces a range of cask and bottle-conditioned ales in traditional British beer styles. !! ♦ RAIB

Mosaic (ABV 3.5%)
Amarillo (ABV 3.8%)
Bitter (ABV 3.9%)
New Zealand Pale (ABV 4.2%)
Pale (ABV 4.2%)
APA (ABV 5%)
Oatmeal Stout (ABV 5.2%)
IPA (ABV 6%)

Brewsters SIBA

Unit 5, Burnside, Turnpike Close, Grantham, Lincolnshire, NG31 7XU
☎ (01476) 566000 brewsters.co.uk

⊗ Brewster is the old English term for a female brewer and Sara Barton – who was named Brewer of the Year by the All Party Parliamentary Beer Group 2018 - is a modern example. Originally established in the Vale of Belvoir in 1998, moving to Grantham in 2006, Brewster's produces a range of traditional and innovative beers with two regularly-changing ranges. ‼ ♦

Hophead (ABV 3.6%)
Marquis (ABV 3.8%)
A well-balanced, refreshing session bitter with maltiness and a dry, hoppy finish.
Aromantica (ABV 4.2%)
Hop A Doodle Doo (ABV 4.3%)
Decadence (ABV 4.4%)
Aromatic Porter (ABV 4.5%)
Stilton Porter (ABV 4.9%)
Rutterkin (ABV 5%)

Briarbank SIBA

70 Fore Street, Ipswich, Suffolk, IP4 1LB
☎ (01473) 284000 🌐 briarbank.org

The Briarbank Brewing Company was established in 2013, and is situated on the site of the old Lloyds Bank on Fore Street, Ipswich. The brewery is a two-barrel plant, and the bar above offers a core range of beers – including some speciality ales. ‼♦V

Brick SIBA

Units 13-14, Deptford Trading Estate, Blackhorse Road, Deptford, SE8 5HY ☎ 07747 787636
🌐 brickbrewery.co.uk

Established by owner and former homebrewer Ian Stewart in 2013. Due to continued expansion, the brewing operation relocated from Peckham to larger premises in nearby Deptford in 2017. The original Peckham railway arch site is retained as an expanded taproom. Numerous local and regional outlets are supplied. Frequent one-off and collaboration brews are produced. ♦

Kinsale (ABV 4%)
Fruity, tawny-coloured best bitter, with a little nutty, roast character and hops throughout. Sweetish with a little honey on palate.
Peckham Pale (ABV 4.5%)
Dark gold beer with hoppy, floral aroma. Malt, hops, bitterness, citrus and floral flavours. Long, bitter, fruity, hoppy, dryish finish.
Blenheim Black (ABV 5.3%)
Roasted notes throughout with black cherry and blackcurrant and a trace of hops. Finish is bitter dry and some malt.

Bricknell

Bricknell Avenue, Hull, East Yorkshire, HU5 4ET
☎ 07729 722953 🌐 bricknellbrewery.co.uk

Bricknell's range comprises of 12 bottle-conditioned, vegan-friendly ales. Some hops are grown on-site, some sourced locally. Everything is hands-on, from brewing, to hand-bottling and labelling, to delivery. Brewing takes place twice a week, and includes many ales from 19th-century recipes. Beers are available in local outlets and a select few further afield, plus at local beer festivals. RAIB V

Cascade Pale (ABV 4.5%)
Anchor Pale Ale (ABV 4.7%)
Bosphorous 1875 Ruby Ale (ABV 5.6%)
Double Anchor IPA (ABV 5.9%)
Chocolate Porter (ABV 6.5%)

Bridgehouse SIBA

Airedale Heifer, Bradford Road, Sandbeds, Keighley, West Yorkshire, BD20 9LY
☎ (01535) 601222

Office: Unit 1, Aireworth Mills, Aireworth Road, Keighley, BD21 4DH 🌐 bridgehousebrewery.co.uk

Bridgehouse began brewing in 2010 using a 10-barrel plant. The brewery purchased the recipes and branding of Old Bear Brewery in 2014 and moved into its premises in Keighley. In 2015 the brewery relocated again to its present address behind the Airedale Heifer pub in Sandbeds, which it also operates. A bespoke 15-barrel brewery is used and the site includes a visitor centre. ‼♦

Tequila Blonde (ABV 3.8%)
Initially sweet with hints of lime, finishing with a slight tingling aftertaste.
Blonde (ABV 4%)
A strong fruity aroma with a sharp burst of grapefruit on the tongue and a touch of sweetness in the background. Bitter finish.
Aired Ale (ABV 4.1%)
Brown beer with malty aroma. Malt, hops and fruit in equal balance with lingering fruitiness in a long, bitter finish.
Porter (ABV 4.5%)
Black beer with red hints. Aromas of malt and liquorice lead to coffee, chocolate and wine fruit flavours, which carry through to a bitter finish.
Landlady IPA (ABV 5.1%)
Holy Cow (ABV 5.6%)
Strong ale with juicy malt and full hop flavour, citrus overtones. Light hop aroma and a bitter finish.

Bridgetown SIBA

Albert Inn, Bridgetown Close, Totnes, Devon, TQ9 5AD
☎ (01803) 863214 🌐 albertinntotnes.com/bridgetown-brewery

⊗ Bridgetown started brewing in 2008 using a two-barrel plant in the outbuildings of the Albert Inn, Totnes. Beers are available in an increasing number of local outlets. ‼♦RAIB

Albert Ale (ABV 3.8%)
Pale bitter, malt dominating throughout. Roast and caramel in aroma, taste and aftertaste, with a little bitterness on the tongue.
Bridgetown Bitter (ABV 4.2%)
A tawny-coloured bitter with malt on the nose. The taste is malt and slightly fruity with a bitter, malty, dry finish.
Cheeky Blonde (ABV 4.5%)
Shark Island Stout (ABV 4.5%)
Smooth stout with strong malt and roast throughout. Touches of liquorice and chocolate lead to a bitter finish.
West Coast IPA (ABV 4.7%)

Briggs Signature

c/o Unit 1, Waterhouse Mill, 65-71 Lockwood Road, Huddersfield, West Yorkshire, HD1 3QU ☎ 07427 668004 🌐 briggssignatureales.weebly.com

⊗ Briggs Signature Ales started brewing in 2014 using spare capacity at Mallinsons (qv). Nick Briggs, also a member of the Mallinsons brewing team, produces a number of modern, hop-forward beers. RAIB

Northern Soul (ABV 3.8%)
Rock & Roll (ABV 4%)
Hip Hop (ABV 4.2%)
Techno (ABV 4.2%)
Blues (ABV 4.6%)

THE BREWERIES

Metal (ABV 5%)

BrightBeer

Weighbridge Brewhouse, Penzance Drive, Swindon, Wiltshire, SN5 7JL ☎ 07413 007022

Correspondence: 38 Andrews Way, Salisbury, Wiltshire, SP2 8QR 🌐 brightbeer.com

Rod Macdonald, original brewer at Exmoor Ales, started brewing at the Weighbridge, Swindon, in 2019 under the name BrightBeer Ltd. Global beer styles are designed and brewed on rotation as cask ales and naturally carbonated craft cellar beer, available at the pub, online and at local events. Tastings and beer design sessions are also available at the Weighbridge. !! ♦ V

Brighton Bier

Unit 10, Bell Tower Industrial Estate, Roedean Rd, Brighton, East Sussex, BN2 5RU ☎ 07967 681203 🌐 brightonbier.com

Brighton Bier was established in 2012. It operates a 15-barrel brewery close to the centre of the city and also owns the Brighton Bierhaus pub, Brighton. Beers are available throughout the UK and exported to Europe and Asia.

Thirty Three (ABV 3.3%)
Brighton Bier (ABV 4%)
West Pier (ABV 4%)
Underdog (ABV 4.2%)
IPA (ABV 5%)
No Name Stout (ABV 5%)
Grand Porter (ABV 5.2%)

Brightside SIBA

Unit 10, Dale Industrial Estate, Radcliffe, M26 1AD ☎ (0161) 725 9644 ☎ 07870 207442 🌐 brightsidebrewing.co.uk

Brightside is a 20-barrel, family-run brewery producing real ales, craft beers and lager. A broad range of styles is produced, from traditional best bitters, blonde ales and IPAs to beers brewed with unusual yeasts, fruit oils or flavours under its Wildside label. Brightside prides itself on working as sustainably as possible, by limiting energy expenditure, recycling and reusing waste. ♦ GF V

Odin Blonde (ABV 3.8%)
Refreshing bitter hops, with bitterness carrying into finish. Peachy hop aroma with some malt.
B-Side Gold (ABV 4.2%)
Academy Ale IPA (ABV 4.5%)
Manchester Skyline Gold (ABV 4.6%)
Maverick IPA (ABV 4.8%)
Topaz IPA (ABV 5%)

Brightwater

9 Beaconsfield Road, Claygate, Surrey, KT10 0PN ☎ (01372) 462334 ☎ 07802 316389 🌐 brightbrew.co.uk

Established in 2013 at Claygate in Surrey, Brightwater is a five-barrel brewery producing traditional beers. The range is available at its brewery tap, Platform 3, outside Claygate Station, and other Surrey and South London pubs.

Little Nipper (ABV 3.3%)
A rather thin, hoppy bitter with a hint of a citrus taste and a bitter, slightly dry finish.
Top Notch (ABV 3.6%)
Citrus notes dominate the aroma of this mid-brown bitter. It has a reasonably well-balanced taste with some bitterness in the finish.
Ernest (ABV 3.7%)
TPL (ABV 3.7%)
Village Green (ABV 3.7%)
Daisy Gold (ABV 4%)
Golden-coloured ale with a moderate, tropical fruit, hoppy character and some balancing malt leading to a bittersweet finish.
Liquorice & Blackcurrant Stout (ABV 4%)
Wild Orchid (ABV 4%)
All Citra (ABV 4.3%)
Lip Smacker (ABV 4.3%)
Coal Porter (ABV 4.9%)

Brimstage SIBA

Home Farm, Brimstage, Merseyside, CH63 6HY ☎ (0151) 342 1181 🌐 brimstagebrewery.com

Neil Young began brewing in 2006 using a 10-barrel plant in the heart of the Wirral countryside. Wirral's first brewery since the closure of the Birkenhead Brewery in the late 1960s. Since Neil passed away in 2018, his two sons now own the brewery. Outlets are supplied across the Wirral, Merseyside, Cheshire and North Wales. !! ♦

Sandpiper Light Ale (ABV 3.6%)
Trapper's Hat Bitter (ABV 3.8%)
A nicely-balanced beer, strong malt aromas, sweet, hoppy malt flavours and a smooth bitter finish.
Rhode Island Red (ABV 4%)
Red, smooth, well-balanced, malty beer with a good, dry aftertaste. Some fruitiness in the taste.
Elder Pale (ABV 4.1%)
Scarecrow Bitter (ABV 4.2%)
This best bitter has a good balance of flavours, some bitterness and sweetness along with a little fruit, these flavours develop in the finish with increased hops.
Oyster Catcher Stout (ABV 4.4%)
Shed Day Session IPA (ABV 4.4%)
IPA (ABV 6%)

Brinkburn Street SIBA

3 Hume Street, Byker, Newcastle upon Tyne, NE6 1LN ☎ (0191) 338 9039 🌐 brinkburnbrewery.co.uk

Brewing began in 2015, much influenced by West Coast US beer styles. Citrus flavours and highly-hopped bitterness is a feature of many of its beers. The brewery relocated to a new site in 2018, which also incorporates a brewery tap. ♦

Fools Gold (ABV 3.8%)
The Pursuit of Hoppiness (ABV 3.9%)
Byker Brown Ale (ABV 4.8%)

Briscoe's

16 Ash Grove, Otley, West Yorkshire, LS21 3EL ☎ (01943) 466515 ✉ briscoe.brewery@talktalk.net

The brewery was launched in 1998 by microbiologist/chemist Dr Paul Briscoe in the cellar of his house with a one-barrel brew length. He is currently producing one brew per week on his original plant, several beers are produced on an irregular basis. The beers are available in local Otley pubs.

Otley Gold (ABV 3.9%)

Bristol Beer Factory SIBA

Unit A, The Old Brewery, Durnford Street, Ashton, Bristol, BS3 2AW

☎ (0117) 902 6317

Office: Bristol Beer Factory, 291 North Street, Ashton, Bristol, BS3 1JP ⊕ bristolbeerfactory.co.uk

⊠ A 30-barrel microbrewery in a part of the former Ashton Gate Brewing Co, which closed in 1933. 50 outlets are supplied, with output and brewing capacity steadily increasing. Focusing on cask ale, it produces specials every 2-3 weeks. A brewery visitor centre opened in 2016. ‼♥◆RAIB

Notorious (ABV 3.8%)
Fruity hop aroma, flavours of pale malt overlaid with tropical fruit and hop bitterness before a lasting, dry, bitter finish.

Fortitude (ABV 4%)
Amber ale with light malt and hop nose, mildly fruity flavours balanced with hop bitterness and a short, dry finish.

Milk Stout (ABV 4.5%)
Very sweet, full-bodied, black stout with lactose creaminess. Finishes with smoky, roast bitterness.

Independence (ABV 4.6%) ⬠
Initial hop aroma, well-balanced flavours blend the fruity citrus hops with a malty backbone leaving a clean bittersweet aftertaste.

BritHop

c/o 133 Parsonage Manorway, Belvedere, DA17 6NG ☎ 07883 223127 ✉ info@brithopbeer.com

Started in 2018, with Franklins Brewery (qv), beers are available around South East London and further afield. A penchant for the Britpop music scene of the 90s comes through in the beer names. There are plans for a move to its own plant. V

King of the Kerb (ABV 3.2%)
Sandstorm (ABV 3.8%)
One to Another (ABV 4.1%)
Sweet Symphony (ABV 4.2%)
Shakermaker (ABV 4.4%)

Britt

See Pig Iron

Brixton

Arch 547, Brixton Station Road, Brixton, London, SW9 8PF
☎ (020) 3609 8880 ⊕ brixtonbrewery.com

The brewery opened in 2013 in a railway arch in central Brixton, with beer names and branding reflecting this. An investment by Heineken in 2017 enabled a major expansion into a nearby industrial unit. The original arch is now used for seasonal and experimental brews, while an adjacent arch houses the taproom. The bulk of production is in KeyKeg, cans and bottles. ‼♥◆RAIB V◆

Reliance Pale Ale (ABV 4.2%)
Tropical notes and a little malt are noticeable in this refreshing, amber-coloured beer. A gentle bitterness grows on drinking.

Low Voltage Session IPA (ABV 4.3%)
Effra Ale (ABV 4.5%)
Dry, copper-coloured best bitter with peppery hops and fruit in flavour and bitter finish. A little caramel malt provides balance.

Windrush Stout (ABV 5%)
Smoky, roast and blackcurrant aroma, which is in the flavour with sweet chocolate and liquorice. Aftertaste is dry, dark roast.

Atlantic APA (ABV 5.4%)

Hops and strong aroma of flowery hops, melon and citrus. Biscuit, grapefruit and melon flavours, with a little bitterness. Dry, complex finish.

Electric IPA (ABV 6.5%)
Sweet biscuit balances the bitterness in this golden ale. Strong citrus, passionfruit and melon with spicy hop flavours. Dry, hoppy aftertaste.

Broadtown (NEW)

29 Broad Town Road, Swindon, Wiltshire, SN4 7RB
☎ 07889 078648 ⊕ broadtownbrewery.co.uk

Opened in 2019, Broadtown is brewing in the old coach house of the 19th-century brewery of the same name. 117 years on, the village has a brewery again. Jason, the brewer, who is an engineer by training, brews on a 500-litre brew kit from the defunct Stratford-on-Avon Brewery. The brewery is home to three alpacas. GF V

Brockley SIBA

Unit 28, Chiltonian Industrial Estate, Manor Road, Hither Green, London, SE12 0TX ☎ 07814 584338 ⊕ brockleybrewery.co.uk

Established in 2013, in a converted workshop, the original Brockley site now focuses on Brewschool and specialist blueprint brewing. An on-site bar is open evenings Wednesday to Friday and all day Saturday and Sunday. In 2019 the bulk of production was relocated to a new, 20-barrel brewery situated on the site of the old Chiltonian Biscuit factory in Hither Green. Here, the taproom hosts special events. The brewery concentrates on supplying outlets within a six-kilometre radius. ♥◆♦

Pale Ale (ABV 4.1%)
Hints of citrus and lychee in the flavour with a sweetness and slight notes of spice in the bitterish finish.

Porter (ABV 4.3%)
Roast malt with a hint of blackcurrant becoming more hoppy and bitter late in the taste and aftertaste.

Red Ale (ABV 4.8%)
Smoky aroma on this well-balanced, sweet, fruity red ale, with a growing spiciness overlaid with dry-roasted, bitter character.

Broken Drum

Heron Hill, Upper Belvedere, DA17 5ER ☎ 07803 131678 ⊕ thebrokendrum.co.uk

Homebrewer that started trial brewing for the Broken Drum micropub in Blackfen, going commercial in 2018, brewing small batches.

Brolly

Lowfold Farm, Wisborough Green, West Sussex, RH14 0ES ⊕ brollybrewing.co.uk

Brolly was established in 2017 by keen homebrewer Brook Saunders. Beers are available in local pubs and at the brewery's on-site bar. V◆

Little Pearl (ABV 3.5%)
New England Pale Ale (ABV 3.6%)
Lowfold Wissy (ABV 3.8%)
Chub IPA (ABV 4.3%)
COW (ABV 4.8%)
Natural Spring Water (ABV 5%)

Brooks

17 Birkenhead Road, Hoylake, Merseyside, CH47 5AE
⊕ brooks-brewhouse.co.uk

Brewing starting in 2017 at this nanobrewery, which predominately produces bottle-conditioned beers. RAIB

Broughton SIBA

Main Street, Broughton, ML12 6HQ
☎ (01899) 830345 🌐 broughtonales.co.uk

Founded in 1979, Broughton Ales was then one of the first microbreweries. Broughton has developed since then and though more than 60% of production goes into bottle for sale in Britain and abroad, it retains a sizeable range of cask ales. All beers are suitable for vegetarians. ‼ ♦

Merlin Scottish Pale Ale (ABV 3.6%)
Crisp, fruity and malty ale. A darker shade of pale.
HOPO Session IPA (ABV 3.8%)
Dry-hopped pale ale with slightly tart, fruit taste and distinctive tang.
Wee Jock (ABV 4.6%)
Pleasant 80/- style. Light fruit and a malty sweetness.
Stout Jock (ABV 4.8%)
HOPO Proper IPA (ABV 5%)

Brown Cow

Brown Cow Road, Barlow, Selby, North Yorkshire, YO8 8EH
☎ (01757) 618947 🌐 browncowbrewery.co.uk

Brewing since 1997, Brown Cow has won awards at many festivals. Keith and Sue Simpson operate a six-barrel plant. Handcrafted cask beers brewed using traditional methods are delivered to the local area direct from the brewery. ♦V

Sessions (ABV 3.6%)
White Dragon (ABV 4%)
Mrs Simpsons Thriller in Vanilla Porter (ABV 5.1%)

Broxbourne

See Fallen Angel

Bruha SIBA

Unit 4, Progress Way, Eye, IP23 7HU
☎ (01379) 882230 🌐 station119.co.uk

Brewing started in 2014 graduating to the current brewery and taproom premises in Eye, Suffolk in 2017. In 2018 a 12-barrel brewhouse was installed. Beers are modern in style and consist of a small core range to allow for lots of seasonal variations throughout the year. All the beers are unfiltered, so are hazy and suitable for vegans. Brewery name changed from Station 119 to Bruha Brewing in 2020. RAIB V

Brumaison SIBA

Unit 7, Crest Industrial Estate, Pattenden Lane, Marden, Kent, TN12 9QJ ☎ 07831 704089
🌐 brumaison.beer

The name Brumaison came about from ideas to set up in a small village in France. However, Peter and Caroline decided to keep their 'Brewing Maison' in England after another brewery got there first. Trading since 2016 using a 10-barrel plant, Peter started brewing full time in 2017.

BB Traditional Ale (ABV 3.6%)
Flaxen XPA (ABV 3.8%)
GB Golden Blonde Ale (ABV 4.4%)
Bullion (ABV 4.5%)
Beulter (ABV 4.6%)
1770 (ABV 4.7%)

Brunning & Price

See Phoenix & St Austell

Brunswick SIBA

1 Railway Terrace, Derby, DE1 2RU ☎ 07534 401352 🌐 brunswickbrewingcompany.co.uk

Derby's oldest brewery. It is a 10-barrel tower plant built as an extension to the Brunswick Inn in 1991. Bought by Everards in 2002, the brewery is now run separately yet in conjunction with the pub. It supplies the Brunswick Inn, Dead Poets Inn, Everards, wholesalers and the free trade within 100 miles. Brunswick also swaps with other breweries. Beers are also produced under the Engine Shed Project brand name. ‼♦RAIB

White Feather (ABV 3.6%)
Triple Hop (ABV 4%)
The Usual (ABV 4.2%)
Railway Porter (ABV 4.3%)
Rocket (ABV 4.7%)
Black Sabbath (ABV 6%)

Brewed under the Engine Shed Project brand name:
Ubiquitous (ABV 6%)

Brythonic

14 Sandford Terrace, Aylburton, Gloucestershire, GL15 6DW ☎ 07766 652837
✉ doug.morgan@hotmail.co.uk

One of the new breed of nanobreweries, having begun brewing in a Bristol suburb on a small scale in 2015, the brewery relocated to the Gloucestershire/Welsh border village of St Briavels, and later to Aylburton. Beers can be found at the Doghouse, Coleford. RAIB

Raven (ABV 5.3%)
Spark (ABV 5.3%)

BRZN (NEW)

Unit 2, Cobblers Thumb, 10 New England Road, Brighton, East Sussex, BN1 4ZR
✉ buybrzn@gmail.com

Brewing began in 2020 in a shipping container on the site of a now demolished pub, producing mostly canned beers.

Buckland

Higher Thornhill Head, Bideford, Devon, EX39 5NU
☎ (01805) 601625 ☎ 07882 019255
🌐 thebucklandbrewers.co.uk

Brewing began in 2016. The original plant was replaced in 2018 with a new purpose-built microbrewery. It specialises in Belgian-style bottle-conditioned beers, which are now supplied to more than 40 local pubs, farm shops, restaurants and visitor attractions. ‼♦RAIB GF V

Bucks Star

23 Twizel Close, Stonebridge, Milton Keynes, Buckinghamshire, MK13 0DX
☎ (01908) 590054 🌐 bucksstar.beer

A solar-powered brewery, Bucks Star opened in 2015 using a 10-barrel, purpose-built plant. Only organic malt is used and no sugars or syrups are added. The beers are unfiltered and primarily available through Bucks Star's own zero-waste drinks innovation, called Growler Swap, where its range of beers are conditioned inside reusable glass growlers. These are available in farmers' markets, locally, various London locations, or through a local home delivery scheme. The brewery tap opened in the opposite unit in 2020. ‼ ⚑ RAIB V◆

Copernicus (ABV 3.8%)
No. 1 Pale Ale (ABV 4%)
Attenborough (ABV 4.1%)
Steenbrugge (ABV 4.8%)
Evolve Lager (ABV 5%)

Bull of the Woods

Brook Farm, Kirby Cane, Bungay, Norfolk, NR35 2PJ
☎ (01508) 518080 ☎ 07833 702658
✉ info@botwbc.co.uk

⊗ After 10 years of planning Bull of the Woods started brewing in 2017 using a four-barrel plant. ♦RAIB

Rock Steady (ABV 3.8%)
Vapour Trail (ABV 4.3%)
Inca Gold (ABV 4.4%)
Twisted Wheel (ABV 4.5%)
Shine A Light IPA (ABV 5.7%)

Bulletproof (NEW)

c/o 91 Mutley Plain, Plymouth, Devon, PL4 6JJ
☎ 07703 733570

Office: Highlands, 1 Queen's Road, Lipson, Plymouth, Devon, PL4 7PJ 🌐 bulletproofbrewing.co

Small-scale brewery established in an outbuilding in 2016 using a 50-litre pilot plant to refine recipes before upscaling using spare capacity at larger breweries. All beers are unfiltered and unfined. V◆

Bullfinch

Arches 886 & 887, Rosendale Road, Herne Hill, London, SE24 9EH ☎ 07899 795823
🌐 thebullfinchbrewery.co.uk

Bullfinch began brewing in 2014 using a 2.5-barrel plant with an on-site taproom. Production is mainly keg but cask and bottle-conditioned beers are available. In 2019 the brewery opened a pub called the Bull & Finch, which is located opposite Gypsy Hill station. ‼ ⚑ RAIB V◆

Swift (ABV 4%)
Dark Side of the Moon (ABV 4.5%)
Chocolate and vanilla on the nose, fading to a bitterness. Chocolate, roast, black cherries and liquorice flavours. Light, dry finish.

Bullhouse SIBA

10 Greengraves Rd, Newtownards, BT23 5AG

Bullhouse was set up in 2016 by beer enthusiast and homebrewer William Mayne. It has since expanded from a 2.5-barrel plant to a custom built, 1,000 litre brewhouse with a fermention capacity of 25,000 litres per year.

Road Trip (ABV 4%)
Small Axe (ABV 4.3%)
Frank the Tank (ABV 5%)
The Dankness (ABV 5.5%)
Merc Bro (ABV 6.5%)

Bumbling

See Xtreme

Bun Dubh SIBA

Ceabhar, Sandaig, Isle of Tiree, PA77 6XG
☎ (01879) 220684 ☎ 07808 220684

Duncan Castling began brewing on his picobrewery in 2016, catering solely for his restaurant, Ceabhar. Beer is produced in 200-litre batches. With an enviropunk ethos all production goes into reuseable containers, no bottles or cans, and distribution remains exclusive to the island. The brewery expanded into the adjoining guesthouse in 2019.

Buntingford

Greys Brewhouse, Therfield Road, Royston, Hertfordshire, SG8 9NW
☎ (01763) 250749 ☎ 07851 743799
🌐 buntingfordbrewery.com

⊗ Brewing commenced on the current site in 2005 and has expanded to a capacity of around 60 barrels per week. Regular beers are brewed year round alongside seasonal/occasional brews and various themed specials. The beers are brewed using water from an on-site well and all liquid waste is treated in a reed bed. The brewery is located on a conservation farm and there is a wide variety of bird life visible from the doors of the brewhouse, often including rare and endangered species. ♦

Twitchell (ABV 3.8%)
Single Hop varieties (ABV 4%)
Hurricane (ABV 4.3%)
Polar Star (ABV 4.4%)

Burley Street

Fox and Newt, 7-9 Burley Street, Leeds, West Yorkshire, LS3 1LD
☎ (0113) 245 4527 🌐 burleystreetbrewhouse.co.uk

Burley Street Brewhouse is in the cellar of the Fox & Newt pub where the first brewery was installed by Whitbread in the 1980s. The freehold was purchased by the current owners and brewing recommenced in 2010 and then, after a two-year break, again in 2015. The Fox & Newt pub is the only regular outlet for the beers.

Burning Sky SIBA

Place Barn, The Street, Firle, East Sussex, BN8 6LP
☎ (01273) 858080 🌐 burningskybeer.com

⊗ Burning Sky started brewing in 2013 using a 15-barrel plant, based on the Firle Estate in the South Downs. It is owned and run by Mark Tranter (ex-Dark Star head brewer). The brewery has its own yeast strains suited to the beer styles. It specialises in pale ales and Belgian-inspired farmhouse beers and has an extensive barrel-aging programme. RAIB

Plateau (ABV 3.5%)
Aurora (ABV 5.6%)

Burning Soul

Unit 1, 51 Mott Street, Hockley, Birmingham, B19 3HE
☎ (0121) 439 1490 ☎ 07793 026624
🌐 burningsoulbrewing.com

Established in 2016, the name Burning Soul reflects a passion for beer and brewing. A five-barrel full mash brewery with an on-site brewery tap less that one mile from Birmingham City centre, offering KeyKeg beer on tap. The core range is always available along with various special brews. Beers are regularly released into the trade in cask form. ‼ ⚑ ♦V◆

THE BREWERIES

Low Clarity (ABV 3%)
Mosaic Session IPA (ABV 4.5%)
OCT IPA (ABV 6.7%)
Belgian IPA (ABV 6.8%)
Coconut Porter (ABV 6.9%)

Burnside SIBA

Laurencekirk Business Park, Laurencekirk, AB30 1EY
☎ (01561) 377316 🌐 burnsidebrewery.co.uk

Burnside began brewing in 2010 using a 2.5-barrel plant and by 2012 had expanded to a 10-barrel plant. Since then the focus has been to establish the brand and range of cask-conditioned ales locally and to develop a range of bottle-conditioned beers. Further expansion is planned. ‼ RAIB

Black Katz (ABV 3.6%)
No. 1 Pale Ale (ABV 3.6%)
3-BULLZ (ABV 3.8%)
Mad Dogz (ABV 3.8%)
A light mix of roasted malt and citrus hops.
Golden X (ABV 4.1%)
Wild Rhino (ABV 4.5%)
Chieftains Export (ABV 4.6%)
India Pale Ale (ABV 4.8%)
Full on citrus hop aroma declining through the taste.
After Dark (ABV 5%)
M-PIRE (ABV 5.2%)
Sweetish peachy hoppy brew. Very warming.
Stealth (ABV 6%)

Burnt Mill

Unit 10, Woodlands Dairy, Badley, Ipswich, Suffolk, IP6 8RS 🌐 burntmillbrewery.com

Brewing began in 2016 in a former grain shed. Beers are available in KeyKeg and cans.

Burscough

See Hop Vine

Burton Bridge SIBA

24 Bridge Street, Burton upon Trent, Staffordshire, DE14 1SY
☎ (01283) 510573 🌐 burtonbridgebrewery.co.uk

The brewery was established in 1982 by Bruce Wilkinson and Geoff Mumford and owns three pubs in the local area, including its award-winning brewery tap. More than 300 outlets are supplied direct. ‼ ♦ RAIB

Golden Delicious (ABV 3.8%)
A Burton classic with sulphurous aroma and well-balanced hops and fruit. An apple fruitiness, sharp and refreshing start leads to a lingering mouth-watering bitter finish with a hint of astringency. Light, crisp and refreshing.
Sovereign Gold (ABV 4%)
Sweet caramel aroma with a grassy hop start with malt overtones. Fresh and fruity with a bitterness that emerges and continues to develop.
XL Bitter (ABV 4%)
Another Burton classic with sulphurous aroma. Golden with fruit and hops and a characteristic lingering aftertaste, hinting of toffee apple sweetness.
XL Mild (ABV 4%)
Black treacle initial taste after liquorice aroma. Sweet finish with a touch of bitterness.
Bridge Bitter (ABV 4.2%)
Gentle aroma of malt and fruit. Good, balanced start, finishing with a robust hop mouthfeel.
Burton Porter (ABV 4.5%)
Chocolate aromas and sweet, smooth taste of smoky, roasted grain and coffee.
Damson Porter (ABV 4.5%)
Faint roast, caramel and dark fruit nose. Cough mixture and Blackjack beginning. Uncomplicated profile with a fractious mix of bitter fruitiness and yeasty maltiness.
Draught Burton Ale (ABV 4.8%)
Fruity orange aroma leads to hoppy start, hop and fruit body then fruity aftertaste. Dry finish with fruity hints.
Bramble Stout/ Top Dog Stout (ABV 5%)
Smoky aroma with a fruit hint from black liquid. Roast start with briar dry fruit emerging, then a sharp blackfruit taste emerges to balance the burnt effect. Sweetish, dry blackberry finish, with prolonged mouth-watering.
Stairway to Heaven (ABV 5%)
Golden bitter. A perfectly balanced beer. The fruity and hoppy start leads to a hoppy body with a mouthwatering finish.
Festival Ale (ABV 5.5%)
Caramel aroma with plenty of hop taste balanced by a full-bodied, malty sweetness.
Thomas Sykes (ABV 10%)
Kid in a sweetshop aroma. Rich, fruity, spirited tastes – warming and dangerously drinkable.

Burton Town

Unit 8, Falcon Close, Burton upon Trent, Staffordshire, DE14 1SG
☎ (01283) 510839 ☎ 07428 968702 🌐 burton.town

Open since 2015, Burton Town Brewery is run by head brewer Steve Haynes from converted premises off Hawkins Lane. The brewery is currently a six-barrel plant, though there are plans for expansion. An on-site taproom is open to the public. ‼ V

Swan/Albion (ABV 3.9%)
Scorned Woman (ABV 4%)
Kolsch (ABV 4.5%)
Modwena (ABV 4.8%)
Thomcat (ABV 5.1%)
Burton IPA (ABV 5.6%)
Black as your Hat (ABV 6.2%)

Burtonwood

Bold Lane, Burtonwood, Warrington, Cheshire, WA5 4TH
☎ (01925) 220022 🌐 thomashardybrewery.co.uk

Thomas Hardy's only brewery was acquired by Molson Coors in 2015. Currently producing no real ale, and operating solely as a contract brewer.

Burwell (NEW)

17 The Paddocks, Burwell, Cambridgeshire, CB25 0HQ
☎ 07788 311908 🌐 burwellbrewery.com

Richard Dolphin and Paul Belton established Burwell Brewery in 2019 in a purpose-built timber brewery at the bottom of Richard's garden. The recently upgraded 2.5-barrel plant, together with three conditioning tanks, produces beer for cask, bottle and bag-in-box. ‼ ♦ V

Beer Fuggled (ABV 4%)
Stefans' Muhle (ABV 4.4%)
Sunshine (ABV 5.5%)

Bushy's SIBA

Mount Murray Brewery, Mount Murray, Braddan, Isle of Man, IM4 1JE

☎ (01624) 661244 🌐 bushys.com

Launched in 1986 as a brewpub, Bushys relocated in 1990 when demand outgrew capacity. Bushys goes one step further than the Manx Pure Beer Law preferring the German Reinheitsgebot (Pure Beer Law). The brewery hosts a successful festival during the TT period at Villa Marina Gardens, Douglas. !! ♦

Castletown Bitter (ABV 3.5%)
Ruby (1874) Mild (ABV 3.5%)
Classic, full-bodied, malty, ruby mild with sweet caramel flavours throughout, and well-balanced hops.
Bitter (ABV 3.8%)
A traditional malty and hoppy beer with good balance. The fruit lasts through to the bitter finish.
Old Bushy Tail (ABV 4.5%)
Red (ABV 4.7%)

Buswells

Lime Kilns Pub, Watling Street, Burbage, Leicestershire, LE10 3ED
☎ (01455) 631158 🌐 limekilnsinn.co.uk

Brewing started at the Lime Kilns pub, Burbage, in 2016 as a small batch brewery. It expanded to a two-barrel plant in 2017, providing up to 14 ales for the pub and other outlets, on demand. Bespoke brews are provided for events including several local beer festivals. V

Butcombe SIBA

Cox's Green, Wrington, Somerset, BS40 5PA
☎ (01934) 863963 🌐 butcombe.com

Originally established in 1978, Butcombe moved to a purpose-built brewery with a 150-barrel plant in 2005. The brewery was bought by the Jersey-based Liberation Group for a reported £15m in 2015. Around 500 outlets are supplied direct and similar numbers via wholesalers and pub companies. Butcombe opened a new distribution centre with a bottling line in Bridgewater in 2018. The brewery has an estate of around 20 managed and 20 tenanted pubs. !! ♦

Adam Henson's Rare Breed (ABV 3.8%)
Subtle aroma of unripe fruit with sulphurous hints. Malty flavour is masked by dry bitterness which continues into the finish.
Original (ABV 4%)
A brown bitter with little aroma. Sweet and malty taste with faint fruit notes. The hop gradually asserts itself leaving a slightly bitter finish.
Gold (ABV 4.4%)
Amber golden ale with light aroma of fruit and hops, leading to well-balanced flavours of malt, pale fruit and hops. Bitter aftertaste.

Butts

Northfield Farm, Wantage Road, Great Shefford, Berkshire, RG17 7BY
☎ (01488) 648133 🌐 buttsbrewery.com

The brewery was set up in a converted barn in 1994. In 2002 the owners took the decision to become dedicated to organic production; all the beers brewed use organic malted barley and organic hops and are certified by the Soil Association. ♦ RAIB

Jester (ABV 3.5%)
A pale brown, session bitter with a hoppy aroma and a hint of fruit. The taste balances malt, hops, fruit and bitterness with a hoppy aftertaste.
Traditional (ABV 4%)
A pale brown bitter that is quite soft on the tongue with hoppy, citrus flavours accompanying a gentle bittersweetness. A long, dry aftertaste is dominated by fruity hops.
Barbus Barbus (ABV 4.6%)
Golden ale with a fruity, hoppy aroma and a hint of malt. Hops dominate taste and aftertaste, accompanied by fruitiness and bitterness, with a hint of balancing sweetness.

Buxton

Units 4 A & B, Staden Business Park, Staden Lane, Buxton, Derbyshire, SK17 9RZ
☎ (01298) 24420 🌐 buxtonbrewery.co.uk

Set up in 2009 as a five-barrel plant, Buxton now uses a 20-barrel plant. Its brewery tap is in Buxton and there is a tasting room at the brewery with views of the Derbyshire countryside. A wide range of small-batch beers is brewed throughout the year. ♦ RAIB V

Moor Top (ABV 3.6%)
Low Tor (ABV 3.8%)
Buxton SPA (ABV 4.1%)

Bwthyn

See Anglesey Brewing

By The Horns SIBA

Units 21-27, Summerstown, London, SW17 0BQ
☎ (020) 3417 7338 🌐 bythehorns.co.uk

By the Horns began in 2011 with a 5.5-barrel plant, since upgraded to 12-barrels, and now capable of brewing up to 20,000 pints per week. Beers are available in cask, keg and cans. Located in industrial units near the new AFC Wimbledon Stadium, the Brewery Tap is open six days a week (Tue-Sun) and regularly shows TV sporting events. Pizzas are available during bar opening hours.

Stiff Upper Lip (ABV 3.8%)
Classic, amber-coloured bitter, well-balanced with hops throughout with hints of citrus and honey. Dry, bitter finish.
Hopadelic (ABV 4.3%)
Smooth golden ale with grapefruit, gooseberry, citrus and lemon rind notes overlaid with hops. Building bitterness in the lingering finish.
Lambeth Walk (ABV 5.1%)
Well-balanced, black porter with hops and a little fruit throughout. The roasted bitterness is complemented by the malt notes.

By The Mile

22 Detling Avenue, Broadstairs, Kent, CT10 1SL
☎ 07900 954680 ✉ jon@bythemilebrewery.co.uk

By the Mile began brewing in 2016 in domestic premises. Brewing is currently suspended. V

Byatt's SIBA

Unit 7-8, Lythalls Lane Industrial Estate, Lythalls Lane, Coventry, CV6 6FL
☎ (024) 7663 7996 🌐 byattsbrewery.co.uk

Byatt's was established in 2011, and expanded in 2016. An extensive beer list is brewed throughout the year together with an increasing range of seasonal beers. A brewhouse bar with six handpulls also serves ciders on draught or gravity. Tours and tasting sessions can be booked and private hire is available. Ricoh arena is nearby. ‼ ♦ RAIB V

XK Dark (ABV 3.5%)
Liquorice aroma, soft smoky tastes. Sweet but hoppy.
Coventry Bitter (ABV 3.8%)
Platinum Blonde (ABV 3.9%)
Brewhouse Best (ABV 4.1%)
Phoenix Gold (ABV 4.2%)
Crystal Cookie (ABV 4.4%)
Urban Red (ABV 4.5%)
Playtime Chocolate Milk Stout (ABV 5%)
Regal Blond (ABV 5.2%)

Cabin (NEW)

44 Brooksfield, Bildeston, Suffolk, IP7 7EJ ☎ 07990 845855 🌐 cabinbrewery.co.uk

Owner and brewer Chris Smith has been brewing since 2013, with Cabin Ales available commercially since 2015. Demand soon outgrew the original plant and a new two-barrel kit was designed and installed in 2018.

Autumn Leaf (ABV 3.8%)
Gold Rush (ABV 4%)
Mark's Gold (ABV 4%)
Pete's Porter (ABV 4.2%)
Red Nek (ABV 4.3%)
Mary Celeste (ABV 4.5%)
INNspiration (ABV 5%)

Cader SIBA

Unit 4, Parc Menter, Marian Mawr Enterprise Park, Dolgellau, LL40 1UU
☎ (01341) 388080 ☎ 07546 272372
🌐 caderales.com

Cader Ales was founded in 2012 by a husband-and-wife team. In the following years, the business has expanded to the point where it is now using the five-barrel, purpose built plant to its optimum. The brewery is situated close to the centre of the picturesque market town of Dolgellau. Deliveries are made to the licensed trade in North and Mid-West Wales and beers in cask or bottle are available to the general public direct from the brewery. ‼

Cregennan (ABV 3.8%)
Gold (ABV 3.8%)
Machlyd Mawddach (ABV 3.9%)
Arran Fawddy (ABV 4%)
Idris Bitter (ABV 4.1%)
Talyllyn Pale Ale (ABV 4.4%)
Red Bandit (ABV 5%)

Caffle

The Old School, Llawhaden, Narberth, SA67 8DS
☎ (01437) 541502
Office: Park View, Ropewalk, Llawhaden, Fishguard, SA65 9BT 🌐 cafflebrewery.co.uk

Started in 2013, Caffle is a four-barrel brewery which produces small batch crafted ales, mainly for the local market. Production consists of a range of core and seasonal cask and bottle-conditioned ales, with an annual green hop ale produced using Pembrokeshire-grown hops via the brewery's hop co-op. ‼ RAIB

Skirp Gold (ABV 3.8%)
Quay Ale (ABV 4%)
Sholly Amber (ABV 4%)
Sprilly Maid (ABV 4%)
Kift Blonde (ABV 4.3%)
In The Grip (ABV 4.7%)
Skaddly Pluck (ABV 4.8%)
Drop Squint (ABV 5.2%)

Cairngorm SIBA

Unit 12, Dalfaber Industrial Estate,, Aviemore, PH22 1ST
☎ (01479) 812222 🌐 cairngormbrewery.com

Cairngorm brews using a 20-barrel plant. Now with its own bottling line, it supplies the free trade as far south as the central belt and nationally via wholesalers. In 2016, in partnership with the Cobbs Group, it bought the brands of the Loch Ness Brewing Co and now brews selected beers under the Loch Ness brand name. ‼ ♦

Nessies Monster Mash (ABV 4.1%)
A fine best bitter with plenty of bitterness and malt flavour and a fruity background. Lingering bitterness in the aftertaste with diminishing sweetness.
Stag (ABV 4.1%)
A fine best bitter with plenty of roast and hop throughout. This tawny brew also has plenty of malt in the lingering, bittersweet aftertaste.
Trade Winds (ABV 4.3%)
Award-winning brew with a citrus, fruity hop and elderflower nose following on through to the bittersweet finish.
Black Gold (ABV 4.4%)
Roast malt dominates throughout, slight smokiness in aroma leading to a liquorice and blackcurrant background taste giving it a background sweetness. Very long, dry, bitter finish. A worthy Championship winner.
Gold (ABV 4.5%)
Fruit and hops to the fore with a hint of caramel in this sweetish brew.
Highland IPA (ABV 5%)
Refreshing, light-coloured, citrus American and South Pacific-hopped IPA. Some background biscuit and caramel.
Wildcat (ABV 5.1%)
A full-bodied, warming, strong bitter. Malt predominates but there is an underlying hop character through to the well-balanced aftertaste. Drinks dangerously less than its ABV.

Caledonian

42 Slateford Road, Edinburgh, EH11 1PH
☎ (0131) 337 1286 🌐 caledonianbeer.com

The brewery was founded by Lorimer and Clark in 1869 and was sold to Vaux of Sunderland in 1919. In 1987 the brewery was saved from closure by a management buy-out and became independent. It was purchased by S&N in 2004, and became part of Heineken in 2008. Guest beers, sometimes of an unusual style, are produced for occasions throughout the year, and there is a rolling programme of special beers covering each of the seasons. A pilot brewery 'Wee George' named after the founding father George Lorimer, was opened in 2015 to allow small scale brews of new recipes. ♦

Deuchars IPA (ABV 3.8%)
Golden session ale with hop aroma and dry, bitter finish. Balanced, with malt adding body and fruit balancing sweetness.
Edinburgh Castle 80/- (ABV 4.1%)
A predominantly malty, brown beer with soft roast and caramel throughout. Fruit gives sweetness, typical of a Scottish 80/-.

Contract brewed for Heineken:
John Smith's Bitter (ABV 3.5%)

Calverley's SIBA

23a Hooper Street, Cambridge, CB1 2NZ
☎ (01223) 312370 ☎ 07769 537342
🌐 calverleys.com

This small central Cambridge brewery was started in 2013 by brothers Sam and Tom Calverley. It is located in a converted stable yard close to the city centre. The brewery is open to the public for on and off-sales (Thursday-Saturday). A large proportion of the production is sold on the premises, and local pubs are also supplied. Most of the beers are keg (various styles), but the brewery remains committed to cask ale and its porter is usually available. ‼ ◆

Porter (ABV 5.1%)

Calvors SIBA

Home Farm, Coddenham Green, Suffolk, IP6 9UN
☎ (01449) 711055 🌐 calvorsbrewery.com

Calvors Brewery was established in 2008 and brews three craft lagers, as well as cask-conditioned beers. V

Lodestar Festival Ale (ABV 3.8%)
Smooth Hoperator (ABV 4%)

Cambridge

1 King Street, Cambridge, CB1 1LH
☎ (01223) 858155 🌐 thecambridgebrewhouse.com

Brewing began in 2013 at the on-site microbrewery in the Cambridge Brew House. ♦

Camden Town

Unit 1, Navigation Park, Morson Road, Ponders End, London, EN3 4NQ
☎ (020) 7485 1671 🌐 camdentownbrewery.com

Bought by A-B InBev in 2016. A modern, automated brewhouse situated in railway arches underneath Kentish Town West railway station with an on-site brewery tap. A second brewery in Ponders End opened in 2017 is the main production site with a large taproom open for special events. No real ale. ‼ ◆

Camel (NEW)

Aberaeron, SA46 0BB ☎ 07539 466105
✉ alistair@cwrwcamel.com

Established in 2019, Cwrw Camel uses spare capacity at Bluestone Brewing Co (qv). V

Camerons

Lion Brewery, Stranton, Hartlepool, County Durham, TS24 7QS
☎ (01429) 852000 🌐 cameronsbrewery.com

Camerons was founded in 1865, and is a family-owned business. Brewing is done by various members of the Camerons team from office staff to brewery staff. The brewery produces a range of cask ales in association with the RNLI, throughout the year. It also produces a number of limited run ales through its Tooth & Claw pilot brewery. It has a pub estate of more than 70 pubs including the Head of Steam pubs. ‼ ♦V

Sanctuary Pale Ale (ABV 3.8%)
Strongarm (ABV 4%)
A well-rounded, ruby-red ale with a distinctive, tight creamy head; initially fruity, but with a good balance of malt, hops and moderate bitterness.
Old Sea Dog (ABV 4.3%)
Boathouse Premium Blonde Beer (ABV 4.4%)
Road Crew (ABV 4.5%)

Campervan

Unit 4, Bonnington Business Centre, 112 Jane Street, Edinburgh, EH6 5HG
☎ (0131) 553 3373 ☎ 07786 566000
🌐 campervanbrewery.com

Campervan began brewing in 2016 in a private garage but also in a 1973 VW campervan, hence the name. The van is used as a mobile sales outlet at beer festivals and other outdoor events. It expanded to a new 10-barrel facility in Edinburgh in 2017. A taproom is open Thursday-Saturday. ◆

Blonde Voyage (ABV 3.8%)
All Shook Up (ABV 4%)
Mutiny on the Bounty (ABV 4.2%)
Leith Juice (ABV 4.7%)
Juicy IPA, full of orange flavour and a strong dose of citrus hops. Naturally hazy.
West Coast IPA (ABV 5%)

Cannon Royall

See White Rabbit

Canopy

Arch 1127, Bath Factory Estate, 41 Norwood Road, Herne Hill, London, SE24 9AJ
☎ (020) 8671 9496 ☎ 07792 463386
🌐 canopybeer.com

Canopy started brewing in a railway arch in Herne Hill in late 2014 with the taproom following in 2015 (open five days a week). Mostly available in keg and bottles, cask does get out into pubs around south London and the taproom is the best place to get the widest range including the regular specials. ‼♦RAIB ◆

Sunray Pale Ale (ABV 4.2%)
Floral, fruity, hoppy aroma. Flavour is citrus with floral hops and sweet biscuit character. Bitterness and dryness builds on drinking. Smooth mouthfeel.
Snapper (ABV 4.8%)
Refreshing, smooth, yellow beer. Mango, lemon and green pine notes lead to a dry bitterish aftertaste with hints of tobacco/smokiness.
Full Moon Porter (ABV 5%)
Strong malt aroma with raisins, figs, dark vintage marmalade and coffee. Roasted flavour with dark treacly, dark chocolate sweetness.

Canterbury Ales SIBA

Canterbrew Ltd, Unit 7 Stour Valley Business Park, Ashford Road, Chartham, Kent, CT4 7HF
☎ (01227) 732541 ☎ 07944 657978
🌐 canterbury-ales.co.uk

Brewing commenced in 2010. An eight-barrel plant is used. ‼♦

The Wife of Bath's Ale (ABV 3.9%)
A golden beer with strong bitterness and grapefruit hop character, leading to a long, dry finish.
The Reeve's Ale (ABV 4.1%)
The Miller's Ale (ABV 4.5%)

Canterbury Brewers SIBA

Foundry Brew Pub, 77 Stour Street, Canterbury, Kent, CT1 2NR
☎ (01227) 455899 🌐 thefoundrycanterbury.co.uk

⊗ Canterbury Brewers started brewing in the Foundry Brewpub in the heart of Canterbury in 2011. The eight-barrel plant is purpose-built. Popular events are held there including the Kent Green Hop Festival (late September/early October). A wide range of spirits are now distilled in the brewpub and three ciders are produced. ‼♦RAIB

Caps Off (NEW)

17 Chester Street, Bishop Auckland, County Durham, DL14 7LP ☎ 07900 551754 🌐 capsoff.co.uk

Established in 2020, supplying the Caps Off micropub in Bishop Auckland. The brewery produces a wide variety of hop-forward beers and tasty stouts. A barrel-ageing and wild fermentation project is planned. There are also plans for an onsite taproom.

Pale (ABV 4.3%)
IPA (ABV 5%)
Brown Ale (ABV 7.4%)

Captain Cook

White Swan, 1 West End, Stokesley, North Yorkshire, TS9 5BL
☎ (01642) 714985 🌐 whiteswanstokesley.co.uk

⊕Having celebrated its 20th anniversary in 2019, the Captain Cook Brewery is located behind the 18th-century White Swan pub. The brewery, which supplies the pub, uses a four-barrel plant. Since 2018, it has been under new ownership, but with the same brewer. ‼♦

Navigator (ABV 4%)
Sunset (ABV 4%)
Slipway (ABV 4.2%)
Endeavour (ABV 4.3%)
Skippy (ABV 4.3%)
Black Porter (ABV 4.4%)
Sandwich Islands (ABV 4.5%)
APA (ABV 4.7%)
Schooner (ABV 4.7%)
IPA (ABV 5.1%)

Carlisle SIBA

Unit 2, 12a Kingstown Broadway, Kingstown Industrial Estate, Carlisle, Cumbria, CA3 0HA
☎ (01228) 594959

Office: Spinners Arms, Cummersdale, Carlisle, CA2 6BD 🌐 carlislerealale.com

⊕Carlisle Brewing Company is a family-run brewery established in 2013. Initially using a 2.5-barrel plant in a shed behind the owner's freehouse, by 2015 it had expanded to a 10-barrel plant in an industrial unit. Beer is available in the Spinners Arms and other local outlets. ‼♦

Cumbrian Bitter (ABV 3.7%)
Bell (ABV 3.8%)
Citadel (ABV 3.8%)
Spun Gold (ABV 4.2%)
Flaxen (ABV 4.5%)
Magic Number (ABV 4.5%)
Nut Brown (ABV 4.7%)
Sweet, mild, characterful amber ale with predominately nutty and roasty flavours making for a quaffable strong ale.
Oatmeal Stout (ABV 4.7%)
Herkules (ABV 4.8%)

Carlsberg-Tetley

Jacobson House, 140 Bridge Street, Northampton, NN1 1PZ
☎ (01604) 668866 🌐 carlsberg.co.uk

International lager brewery, which whilst brewing no real ales is a major distributor of cask beer. The Tetley-owned real ales are mostly brewed by Marstons. Some Tetley beers are brewed at Leeds Brewery.

Carnival (NEW)

Unit 2, King Edward Industrial Estate, Gibraltar Row, Liverpool, L3 7HR 🌐 carnivalbrewing.me

Brewery and taproom opened in 2019 by keen homebrewers Dominic Smith and Adrian Burke. It brews specialist styles and supplies a few outlets in Liverpool as well as beer festivals. ◆

Castle SIBA

Unit 9a-7, Restormel Industrial Estate, Liddicoat Road, Lostwithiel, Cornwall, PL22 0HG ☎ 07880 349032
🌐 castlebrewery.co.uk

⊗ The brewery was established in 2007 using a one-barrel plant. It was re-equipped in 2016 with a new 200-litre plant. All brews are unfined. The brewery carries out its own bottling, and some for other breweries. ♦RAIB V

Restormel Gold (ABV 4.1%)
Cornish Best Bitter (ABV 4.2%)
Once a Knight (ABV 5%)

Castle Eden SIBA

8 East Cliff Road, Spectrum Business Park, Seaham, SR7 7PS
☎ (0191) 581 5711 ☎ 07768 044484
🌐 castleedenbrewery.com

Using the name of the former Castle Eden Brewery having acquired the intellectual rights and recipes, a new 20-barrel commercial plant was installed in 2015 along with a bottling/kegging plant. Besides its own brand production, the brewery also contract bottles for several local and national breweries. ♦

Blond (ABV 3.9%)
Ale (ABV 4.2%)
Red (ABV 4.4%)
Black (ABV 4.6%)

Contract brewed for HB Clark Brewery:
Classic Blonde (ABV 3.9%)
English Pale Ale (ABV 4%)
Merrie City Atlantic Hop (ABV 4%)
Merrie City Crystal Gold (ABV 4.2%)

Castle Rock SIBA

Queensbridge Road, Nottingham, NG2 1NB
☎ (0115) 985 1615 🌐 castlerockbrewery.co.uk

Castle Rock was established in 1998 and developed a reputation for producing high quality, consistent cask beers, with three from the core range winning awards at national level. Throughout the year, Castle Rock brew an eclectic range of special and one-off beers in cask, keg and can, from the traditional to the more experimental and modern styles. ‼♦RAIB

Black Gold (ABV 3.8%)
A dark ruby mild. Full-bodied and fairly bitter.
Harvest Pale (ABV 3.8%)
Pale yellow beer, full of hop aroma and flavour. Refreshing with a mellowing aftertaste.

Session (ABV 4%)
Preservation (ABV 4.4%) 🗂
A traditional, copper-coloured, English best bitter with malt predominant. Fairly bitter with a residual sweetness.
Sherwood Reserve (ABV 4.5%)
An earthy, yet smooth-tasting dark stout with a smoked roastness through to a roast bitter finish.
Elsie Mo (ABV 4.7%)
A strong golden ale with floral hops evident in the aroma. Citrus hops are mellowed by a slight sweetness.
Midnight Owl (ABV 5.5%)
Black IPA with roast malts, fruity hops and a slightly sweet finish.
Screech Owl (ABV 5.5%)
A classic golden IPA with an intensely hoppy aroma and bitter taste with a little balancing sweetness.

Castor SIBA

30 Peterborough Road, Castor, Cambridgeshire, PE5 7AX
☎ (01733) 380337 ⊕ castorales.co.uk

This three-barrel brewery, established in 2009, is located in a specially converted outhouse in the garden of the founder brewer. Several local outlets feature the beers as well as many national beer festivals. ‼◆

Roman Gold (ABV 3.7%)
Hopping Toad (ABV 4.1%)
Old Scarlett (ABV 4.6%)

Cat Asylum

12 Besthorpe Road, Collingham, Nottinghamshire, NG23 7NP
☎ (01636) 892229 ☎ 07773 502653
✉ henry.bealby@lineone.net

Established in 2017, Cat Asylum is a microbrewery specialising in historic recipes from Britain and around the world.

Cellar Boys

🏢 83-84 Enid Street, Bermondsey, London, SE16 3RA
⊕ cellarboysbrewery.com

Starting out as PWA (Paddies With Attitude), the name was changed to Cellar Boys in 2018. During 2019 brewing at the pub ceased with all production coming from Bianca Road. Only available in keg, the pub is the main place to find beers, along with Howl at the Moon, Hoxton, N1.

Cellar Head SIBA

The Barn, Pillory Corner, Flimwell, East Sussex, TN5 7QG ☎ 07391 557407 ⊕ cellarheadbrewing.com

⊠ Cellar Head is a microbrewery in the heart of the Weald countryside. ‼☲◆

Sub Three (ABV 2.7%)
Session Bitter (ABV 3.5%)
Amber Ale (ABV 4%)
Session Pale Ale (ABV 4.2%)
Single Hop Pale (ABV 4.6%)
India Pale Ale (ABV 5%)

Celt Experience

See Evan Evans

Cerddin

🏢 c/o Cross Inn, Maesteg Road, Cwmfelin, CF34 9LB
☎ (01656) 732476 ☎ 07949 652237
⊕ cerddinbrewery.co.uk

Established in 2010 using a 2.5-barrel plant in a converted garage adjacent to the owner's pub, now enlarged to a four-barrel plant. Beer is usually only available in the pub. Seasonal beers brewed. ‼◆RAIB

Cerne Abbas SIBA

Chescombe Barn, Barton Meadows Farm, Cerne Abbas, Dorset, DT2 7JS
☎ (01300) 341999 ☎ 07506 303407

Office: Cerne Abbas Brewery, The Mill House, Mill Lane, Cerne Abbas, Dorset, DT2 7LB
⊕ cerneabbasbrewery.com

⊠ Established in 2014 by Vic Irvine and Jodie Moore. Operating on a five-barrel plant, the beers are made as naturally as possible using chalk-filtered water from its own spring. All beers are brewed with organic, locally-sourced barley. Some non-conventional ingredients are used in seasonal brews. On the last Saturday in September, a community brew is produced using hops grown by people living in the village and surrounding area. ‼☲◆◆

Responsibly (ABV 3.2%)
Ale (ABV 3.8%)
Blonde (ABV 4.2%)
Tiger Tom Ruby Mild (ABV 4.4%)
Watercress Warrior (ABV 4.5%)
Gurt Stout (ABV 6.2%)
Gurt Coconuts Rum Stout (ABV 7.2%)

Chadlington SIBA

Blaythorne Farm, Chadlington, Oxfordshire, OX7 3NE
☎ (01608) 676823 ☎ 07931 482807
⊕ chadlingtonbrewery.com

Based in the Cotswolds, brewing was small to start with, producing small-batch brews, but the new brewhouse which opened in 2019 is capable of supplying a growing range of customers. The brewery utilises renewables and pure spring water. It is family-owned, making visitors very welcome, hosting events and holding brew-your-own days. They plan to build a tap room in the future.

Golden Ale (ABV 4%)
Oxford Blonde (ABV 4%)
Oxford Blue (ABV 4.2%)

Chain House

20 Brookdale, New Longton, Lancashire, PR4 4XL
☎ 07732 688121 ⊕ chainhousebrewingco.uk

Brewing began in 2017. In the past year beers have become more available in local pubs, and there have been successful collaborations with other breweries like Rivington and Farm Yard Ales.

Chalk Hill

🏢 Rosary Road, Norwich, NR1 4DA
☎ (01603) 477078 ⊕ thecoachthorperoad.co.uk

⊠ Chalk Hill began production in 1993 on a 15-barrel plant. It supplies local pubs and festivals. A small plant is used to brew experimental beers, which if popular become part of the regular range. ‼◆

Tap Bitter (ABV 3.6%)

A biscuity backbone throughout. Hints of hop and red fruits develop before a dry, watery, astringency grows in the ending.
Black Anna (ABV 4%)
Well-balanced and complex with a sweet roasty character. Echoes of caramel, coffee and chestnut in a long, smooth finale.
CHB (ABV 4.2%)
Gentle rolling mix of malt, hop, and apricot with caramel on the nose. Lingering finish with hops to the fore.
Gold (ABV 4.3%)
A light hoppy nose. Grapefruit, banana and hops mingle in a well-balanced beginning. The finish develops a growing bitterness.
Dreadnought (ABV 4.9%)
Red-brown beer with a malty, sulphurous nose. Malty with fruit and nut notes. Full-bodied with a long finish.
Flintknapper's Mild (ABV 5%)
Malt and caramel on the nose. Watery mix of sweet fruitiness with a gentle nutty overhang. Short, drying finish.

Chantry SIBA

Unit 1 & 2, Callum Court, Rotherham, South Yorkshire, S62 6NR
☎ (01709) 711866 ☎ 07815 727285
chantrybrewery.co.uk

Brewing returned to Rotherham with the opening of Chantry in 2012 using the latest brewing technology in a 20-barrel plant built by Sheffield-based Moeschle UK. As well as the brewery tap, Cutlers Arms, two other pubs are owned; New York Tavern, Rotherham, and Chantry Inn, Handsworth. !!

New York Pale (ABV 3.9%)
Iron & Steel Bitter (ABV 4%)
Steelos (ABV 4.1%)
Full Moon (ABV 4.2%)
Diamond Black Stout (ABV 4.5%)
Kaldo (ABV 5.5%)
Mighty Millers (ABV 5.5%)
Special Reserve (ABV 6.3%)

Chapeau

Unit 8, Redkiln Close, Horsham, West Sussex, RH13 5QL
☎ (01403) 252459 chapeaubrewing.com

Chapeau Brewing is a microbrewery based in Horsham, West Sussex. Beers are available direct from the brewery and in local pubs.

Slip Stream (ABV 3.5%)
Rouleur (ABV 4%)
Summit (ABV 4%)
Open Road (ABV 4.5%)
Hard Yards (ABV 4.6%)
Attrition (ABV 5.5%)

Chapel

Dinesfield, Chapel Lane, Criftins, Shropshire, SY12 9LZ
☎ (01691) 690412 ☎ 07928 682174
chapelbrewery.co.uk

Chapel began brewing in 2013 using a one-barrel plant behind the owner's bungalow. In 2016 the brewery expanded to larger premises. Occasional specials are brewed for festivals.

Angels Share (ABV 4%)
Miracle (ABV 4.4%)

Chapel Street

Thatched House, Ball Street, Poulton-le-Fylde, Lancashire, FY6 7BG
☎ (01253) 891063
thethatchedhousepoulton-le-fylde.co.uk

This four-barrel plant is situated in the coach house of the award-winning Thatched House pub in Poulton-le-Fylde and has been brewing since 2014. The beers are only available in the pub.

Chapel-en-le-Frith

5 Market Place, Chapel-en-le-Frith, Derbyshire, SK23 0EW ☎ 07951 524003
timboothman@aol.com

Opened in 2016, this small brewery is located at the rear of Chapel-en-le-Frith Post Office. The brewing kit consists of a single 200-litre capacity integrated system supplemented by a 20-litre trial kit. Bottles and five-litre mini casks are available from the post office. Cask ales are available from a limited number of local outlets. V

Siena (ABV 4.1%)
Rye the Hell Not (ABV 4.3%)
Isambard (ABV 4.4%)
Busted Monkey (ABV 4.6%)
Leningrad (ABV 5%)
Elysium Amber Ale (ABV 5.4%)
Acadian (ABV 5.6%)
Hoppy as Funk (ABV 5.8%)
Sinamarian Black IPA (ABV 6%)

Chapter SIBA

Unit 2a, Sutton Quays Business Park, Clifton Road, Sutton Weaver, Cheshire, WA7 3EH ☎ 07791 516948
chapterbrewing.co.uk

Award-winning Chapter Brewing was established in 2016, using a 10-barrel brew plant. It produces diverse 'fictional beers' inspired by literature from pales to sours, smoked porters to Belgian styles and beyond. !! ♦ RAIB V

02. Bread & Circuses (ABV 3.8%)
17. Taller Than a House (ABV 3.9%)
18. Unconsenting Soul (ABV 4.2%)
A fruity and hoppy bitter beer with plenty of impact on the palate and sweetness drying out in the finish.
09. Temos Tanta (ABV 4.4%)
08. Parabola (ABV 4.7%)
11. That Old Rope (ABV 5.4%)
03. Dead Man's Fist (ABV 5.5%)
14. Her Musket (ABV 5.7%)
04. I Said Doctor (ABV 6%)
01. As Lazarus (ABV 7.2%)

Charles Wells

See Eagle

Charnwood SIBA

22 Jubilee Drive, Loughborough, Leicestershire, LE11 5XS
☎ (01509) 218666 ☎ 07872 651561
charnwoodbrewery.co.uk

Family-run, 10-barrel brewery established in 2014. Three core beers are complemented by three monthly specials with a wide range of styles. All beers are widely available locally, including at its micropub, the Sorrel Fox, in Mountsorrel. The front of the brewery has been fitted out with a shop, selling brewery merchandise, bottled beers, and local gins, and as well as a bar with three hand pumps and large glass windows giving a good view into the brewery. ‼ ♦

Salvation (ABV 3.8%)
Vixen (ABV 4%)
APA (American Pale Ale) (ABV 4.8%)

Chasing Everest

15 Ponteland Square, Blyth, NE24 4SH
chasingeverestbrew.com

Founded in 2018 by Zak Everest, focusing on small batch brews. Many of the beers are dry-hopped, giving bold, hoppy flavours.

Plus One (ABV 3%)
Sideswiper (ABV 4%)
Joana, in Five Acts (ABV 4.2%)
Square Hammer (ABV 6.8%)

Cheadle

George & Dragon, 1 High Street, Cheadle, SK8 1AX

Using the former Hogarth's kit from Bolton, the brewery was established in 2018. Brewer Jonathan Winchcombe is still in charge and Amber Inn pubs are supplied.

Checkstone

First & Last Inn, 10 Church Street, Exmouth, Devon, EX8 1PE
(01395) 263275

Checkstone Brewery, named after the Checkstone reef outside the Exe Estuary, is a one-barrel plant inside the First & Last pub, Exmouth, established in 2016. Like the brewery, the beers are named after various sea features around Exmouth. ♦

Cheddar SIBA

Winchester Farm, Draycott Road, Cheddar, Somerset, BS27 3RP
(01934) 744193 cheddarales.co.uk

Established in 2006 in the heart of the Mendips, Cheddar Ales has expanded capacity to enable it to brew up to 100 barrels a week. Production is split approximately 75% cask-conditioned ale, 25% bottle-conditioned. Its bottling plant produces around 120,000 bottles annually and all bottled ales are gluten-free. Around 450 outlets are supplied including pubs, clubs and the off trade. A visitor centre and brewery tap opened in 2020. ‼ ♦ RAIB GF

Bitter Bully (ABV 3.8%)
Light session bitter with flowery hops on the nose and a dry, bitter finish.
Gorge Best (ABV 4%)
Malty bitter with caramel and fruit notes followed by a short, bittersweet aftertaste.
Potholer (ABV 4.3%)
Refreshing flavours combine soft fruit sweetness with hop bitterness on a light malt background before a clean, balanced finish.
Hardrock (ABV 4.4%)
Fruity hop aroma, balanced flavours of tropical fruit and bitterness on a pale malt background before a clean, bitter ending.
Totty Pot (ABV 4.5%)
Roasted malts dominate this smooth, well-flavoured porter. Hints of coffee and rich fruits follow with a well-balanced bitterness.
Crown & Glory (ABV 4.6%)
Lightly-hopped aroma, background malt balanced with fruity hops in the crisp, bittersweet flavour before a dry and bitter finish.
Goat's Leap (ABV 5.5%)
Light malt aroma with enticing toffee and red liquorice hints. Traditional hop flavours and fruity sweetness, clean, bitter finish.

Chelmsford

2 Brewery Fields, Church Street, Great Baddow, Chelmsford, Essex, CM2 7LE 07972 145611
blueshackbeers.com

Chelmsford was established in 2017 by a former homebrewer who used to brew in a little blue shack at the end of his garden.

Cheshire Brew Brothers

See Oaks

Cheshire Brewhouse SIBA

Units 13, Daneside Business Park, River Dane Road, Congleton, Cheshire, CW12 1UN
(01260) 274788 cheshirebrewhouse.co.uk

Cheshire Brewhouse was established in 2012 using a five-barrel plant, expanding in 2014 to a 10-barrel one. The brewery moved to a larger unit in 2018. ‼ ♦

Cheshire Pride (ABV 3.6%)
Cheshire Gap (ABV 3.8%)
Engine Vein (ABV 4.2%)
Lindow (ABV 4.5%)
DBA (ABV 4.6%)
Bluesbreaker (ABV 4.8%)
Govinda Chevallier Edition (ABV 6.8%)

Chevin

Office: 1 Mount Pisgah, Otley, West Yorkshire, LS21 3DX

Chevin is an Otley-based brewery specialising in small batch, hand crafted, artisan beers, primarily available in bottles.

Cheviot

Ford & Etal Estate, Cornhill on Tweed, Slainsfield, Northumberland, TD12 4TP 07778 478943
cheviotbrewery.co.uk

Brewing commenced in 2018 on a 7.5-barrel plant acquired from Goose Eye Brewery in West Yorkshire. The beers are named after local landmarks.

Upland Ale (ABV 3.8%)
Harbour Wall (ABV 4.3%)
Trig Point (ABV 4.5%)
Holy Bounty (ABV 4.8%)
Menhir (ABV 5.1%)
Flodden Thirst (ABV 5.4%)
The Schil (ABV 6%)

Chickenfoot

Barley Mow Inn, The Dale, Bonsall, Derbyshire, DE4 2AY
(01629) 825685 barleymowbonsall.co.uk

A purpose-built, 2.5-barrel plant housed in the car park of the Barley Mow Inn, in the picturesque rural village of Bonsall. The brewery supplies a range of hen-named ales for the pub which is famed as the Home of the World Hen Racing Championship. ♦

Chiltern SIBA

Nash Lee Road, Terrick, Aylesbury, Buckinghamshire, HP17 0TQ
☎ (01296) 613647 🌐 chilternbrewery.co.uk

Founded in 1980, Chiltern was one of the first microbreweries in the country. It is also the oldest independent brewery in Buckinghamshire and the Chiltern Hills, growing from a capacity of five to its present 10-barrel plant. A major expansion is planned. Now run by the second generation of the Jenkinson family, George and Tom, it supplies around 100 outlets including its own brewery tap, the Farmers' Bar, at the historic King's Head in Aylesbury. !! ♦ RAIB GF

Chiltern Pale Ale (ABV 3.7%)
An amber, refreshing beer with a slight fruit aroma, leading to a good malt/bitter balance in the mouth. The aftertaste is bitter and dry.
Beechwood Bitter (ABV 4.3%)
This pale brown beer has a balanced butterscotch/toffee aroma, with a slight hop note. The taste balances bitterness and sweetness, leading to a long, bitter finish.

Chin Chin

Unit 53F Lidgate Crescent, Langthwaite Grange Industrial Estate, South Kirkby, West Yorkshire, WF9 3NS ☎ 07896 253650
✉ david@chinchinbrewing.co.uk

Chin Chin was established in 2016 by brothers David and Andrew Currie. Brewing began on a one-barrel plant based in a domestic garage, relocating to larger premises with a five-barrel plant in 2018. An expanding range of small batch brews is supplied across Yorkshire and to beer festivals nationwide. !!

Chorlton

Office: 69 North Western Street, Ardwick, Manchester, M12 6DX 🌐 chorltonbrewingcompany.com

Brewing ceased at Ardwick in late 2019. The beers are now contract-brewed in Belgium. Main production concentrates on canned sour beers although bottle-conditioned Dark Matter has an annual release. RAIB

Church Aston

Church Aston, Shropshire, TF10 9EJ ☎ 07806 671436
✉ beer@churchastonbrewery.co.uk

A small indepedent brewery established in 2013. In addition to the regular beers, bespoke brews are available on request.

Lower Bar Bitter (ABV 3.8%)
Upper Bar Bitter (ABV 4.5%)

Church End SIBA

Ridge Lane, Nuneaton, Warwickshire, CV10 0RD
☎ (01827) 713080 🌐 churchendbrewery.co.uk

The brewery started in 1994 in an old coffin shop in Shustoke. It moved to its present site in 2001 and has expanded over the years, it currently operates a 24-barrel purpose-built plant. Many one-off specials and old recipe beers are produced. Its award-winning beers are available throughout the Midlands. !! ♦ RAIB

Brewers Truth (ABV 3.6%)
Cuthberts (ABV 3.8%)
A refreshing, hoppy beer, with hints of malt, fruit and caramel taste. Lingering bitter aftertaste.
Goat's Milk (ABV 3.8%)
Gravediggers Ale (ABV 3.8%)
What the Fox's Hat (ABV 4.2%)
A beer with a malty aroma, and a hoppy and malty taste with some caramel flavour.
Vicar's Ruin (ABV 4.4%)
A straw-coloured best bitter with an initially hoppy, bitter flavour, softening to a delicate malt finish.
Stout Coffin (ABV 4.6%)
Fallen Angel (ABV 5%)

Church Farm SIBA

Church Farm, Budbrooke, Warwickshire, CV35 8QL
☎ (01926) 411569 ☎ 07939 607027
🌐 churchfarmbrewery.co.uk

Brewing began in 2012. The original kit, converted from dairy farm equipment, was replaced five years ago with a modern 20-barrel plant in a purpose-built facility. The brewery has an emphasis on local ingredients, using water from an on-site well and some of the barley grown on the farm. Regular outlets in Warwickshire and surrounding counties are supplied, plus some further afield towards Bristol and London. RAIB

Pale Ale (ABV 3.8%)
Session IPA (ABV 3.8%)
The Imp (ABV 3.8%)
Ren's Pride (ABV 4%)
Brown's Porter (ABV 4.2%)
Harry's Heifer (ABV 4.2%)
IPA (ABV 5%)

Church Hanbrewery

Unit F2, New Yatt Business Centre, North Leigh, Oxfordshire, OX29 6TJ
☎ (01993) 774986 ☎ 07907 272617

Office: Tithe Barn South, Church Hanborough, OX29 8AB 🌐 churchhanbrewery.com

Brewing commenced in 2016 on a small scale in the owner's kitchen . A year later, a 2.5-barrel plant was installed in a small industrial unit in New Yatt. Some beers are brewed for keg and bottling only. One-off brews regularly appear in the brewery's nano bar in Oxford's Indoor Market. Brewery open days are well supported by the local community. RAIB

Ale X IPA (ABV 4.5%)
Rauk (ABV 5%)
Red Beetter (ABV 5%)
Bluenette (ABV 5.5%)
Mat Black (ABV 5.5%)

City of Cambridge

See Wolf

Clanconnel

Unit 5, 2 New Line, Gibson's Hill, Co Armagh, BT66 8TA ☎ 07711 626770

Office: PO Box 316, BT65 9AZ
🌐 clanconnelbrewing.com

Beers are contract brewed by the Rye River Brewery in Co Kildare in the Republic of Ireland under the McGraths Craft Beer Brand. No real ale.

Clark's

See Castle Eden

Clarkshaws

Arch 497, Ridgway Road, Loughborough Junction, London, SW9 7EX ☎ 07989 402687
🌐 clarkshaws.co.uk

Clarkshaws, established 2013, is a small brewery focusing on using UK ingredients for its core beers and reducing beer miles. The beers are suitable for vegetarians and are accredited by the Vegetarian Society. All beers are unfined and may be hazy. A small taproom operates on the premises for most of the year, check before travelling. V◆

Gorgon's Alive (ABV 4%)
Unfined, golden-coloured beer with spicy hops throughout. The flavour has hints of orange and peach with a dry bitterness.
Phoenix Rising (ABV 4%)
Tawny beer with a creamy toffee nose. Bananas, pineapple, hops and caramel flavours. Dryish, short, fruity, biscuit finish.
Strange Brew No. 1 (ABV 4%)
Easy-drinking, yellow-coloured pale ale. Flavour is of peppery hops, tropical fruits and biscuit sweetness with a trace of bitterness.
Four Freedoms (ABV 4.3%)
Coldharbour Hell Yeah Lager (ABV 5.3%)
Hops and mango notes that are also present on the flavour with some butterscotch. Dryish palate.
Hellhound IPA (ABV 5.5%)
Spiced and citrus notes in this unfined, amber beer with a bitterness in the flavour and finish, which is dry.

Clavell & Hind SIBA

The Old Haulage Yard, Old Cirencester Road, Birdlip, Gloucestershire, GL4 8JL
☎ (01452) 238050 🌐 clavellandhind.co.uk

Clavell & Hind is a 20-barrel brewery based in the Cotswold countryside with an on-site taproom. ◆

Coachman (ABV 3.8%)
Wicked Lady (ABV 4%)
Blunderbus (ABV 4.2%)
Rook Wood (ABV 4.4%)

Clay Brow

256 Carfield, Skelmersdale, WN8 9DW ☎ 07769 581500 ✉ claybrownano@gmail.com

Nanobrewery that started production in 2017.

Eclipse (ABV 5.4%)
Mr P's (ABV 5.7%)
Mrs P's (ABV 6%)

Clearwater SIBA

Unit 1 Little Court, Manteo Way, Gammaton Road, Bideford, Devon, EX39 4FG
☎ (01237) 420492 🌐 clearwaterbrewery.co.uk

⊗ Established in 1999, Clearwater is a 10-barrel brewery regularly supplying more than 250 outlets across the south west and nationally with its Devon's Own-labelled beers. Beers are also available at the brewery tap, the Champ, Appledore. ‼♦RAIB

Expedition Ale (ABV 3.5%)
Real Smiler (ABV 3.7%)
Broad Reach (ABV 4%)
Fruity aroma leads to crisp and fruity, yet bitter taste. The aftertaste continues a balanced sweet/fruit/bitterness, which is slightly dry.
Mariners (ABV 4.2%)
Proper Ansome (ABV 4.2%)
A dark brown bitter, malty-flavoured, slightly sweet. In the style of a winter warmer.
Riff (ABV 4.2%)
Voyager (ABV 4.5%)

Clevedon SIBA

Unit 1, Tweed Road Trading Estate, Clevedon, Somerset, BS21 6RR ☎ 07907 583415
✉ cheers@clevedonbrewery.co.uk

Founded in the Chilterns by Howard Tucker in 2016 as Red Kite, the brewery relocated to Clevedon in 2017, changing its name to Glede. Following the retirement of Howard in 2019 and subsequent sale, the brewery underwent a complete rebranding, becoming Clevedon in the process. All beers are now named with a twist to Clevedon. All of the malts used are British, as are most of the hops. ‼♦◆

Gold (ABV 3.8%)
BS21 (ABV 4.1%)
Clevedon's Best (ABV 4.4%)
Percy's Porter (ABV 4.4%)
Roasted malt with coffee and chocolate, balanced with blackberry and liquorice notes on the palate. before a short, dry finish.
IPA (ABV 5%)
Blonde (ABV 5.2%)

Cliff Quay

Unit 1, Meadow Works, Kenton Road, Debenham, Suffolk, IP14 6RT
☎ (01728) 861213 🌐 cliffquay.co.uk

⊗ Cliff Quay was established in 2008 by Jeremy Moss (parliamentary brewer of the year in 2005) and John Bjornson (owner of Earl Soham Brewery) in part of the historic Tolly Cobbold brewery in Ipswich. In 2012 the brewery relocated to Debenham, a small, picturesque market town, due to redevelopment of the Cliff Quay brewery site. It now operates alongside Earl Soham brewery, with shared production, offices and distribution facilities. ‼♦

Bitter (ABV 3.4%)
Pleasantly drinkable, well-balanced, malty, sweet bitter with a hint of caramel, followed by a sweet/malty aftertaste. A good flavour for such a low gravity beer.
Anchor Bitter (ABV 4%)
Black Jack Porter (ABV 4.2%)
Unusual dark porter with a strong aniseed aroma, and rich liquorice and aniseed flavours, reminiscent of old-fashioned sweets. The aftertaste is long and increasingly sweet.
Tolly Roger (ABV 4.2%)
Well-balanced, highly-drinkable, mid-gold summer beer with a bittersweet hoppiness, some biscuity flavours and hints of summer fruit.
Tumble Home (ABV 4.7%)
Aroma of marzipan and dried fruit. Flavour reminiscent of Amaretto, leading to a short, bitter, slightly spicy aftertaste.
Sea Dog (ABV 5.5%)
Dreadnought (ABV 6.5%)

Cloak & Dagger (NEW)

Highfield Farm, The Broyle, Ringmer, West Sussex, BN8 5AR ☎ 07378 300570
🌐 cloakanddaggerbrewing.com

Cloak & Dagger was established by three friends from Brighton in 2017. Beers are available in can and keg. The brewery tap is Cloak Room, Kemptown. 🛒

Clockwork

See Tryst

Clouded Minds

Unit 5B Brailes Industrial Estate, Winderton Road, Lower Brailes, Warwickshire, OX15 5JW ☎ 07530 998149 🌐 cloudedminds.co.uk

Brewing began in 2013 using spare capacity at various breweries around London and Derbyshire. In 2015 the brewery moved to its own site near Banbury using a 10-barrel plant. The London area is mainly supplied but also some outlets in Birmingham, Nottinghamshire, Warwickshire and Oxfordshire. Wholesalers also distribute the beers more widely. RAIB

N29 (ABV 3.7%)
N253 (ABV 3.9%)
99 steps (ABV 4%)
N18 (ABV 4%)
Luppol (ABV 4.2%)
Clout Stout (ABV 4.5%)
Hazelnutter (ABV 5%)
Elisir (ABV 5.3%)
Black Pike (ABV 6.1%)
Dolce Vita (ABV 6.2%)
Double Clout Stout (ABV 6.6%)

Cloudwater

Units 7-8 Piccadilly Trading Estate, Manchester, M1 2NP
☎ (0161) 661 5943 🌐 cloudwaterbrew.co

Cloudwater specialises in making modern, seasonal beers and also produce collaborative brews. One-off specials for beer festivals, experimental, canned and bottled beers are also available. Its beers now travel far and wide, from the UK to the US. The modern brewery tap is adjacent. ‼♦

Clun SIBA

White Horse Inn, The Square, Clun, Shropshire, SY7 8JA
☎ (01588) 640021 🌐 whi-clun.co.uk

Formerly a tiny brewery, capacity was increased to 2.5-barrels in 2010. Established behind the White Horse in Clun, beers (including specials) are produced for the pub and, increasingly, the local trade. ♦

Loophole (ABV 3.5%)
Pale (ABV 4.1%)
Solar (ABV 4.3%)
Citadel (ABV 5.9%)

Coach

37 Cowbridge Road, Bridgend, CF31 3DH

Office: 2 Oldfield Road, Bocam Park, Bridgend, CF35 5LJ

The Coach Brewing Co is based out of the award-winning free house the Coach. Launched in 2018, it is in the middle of the pub for all to see. Occasional seasonal additions are brewed. Beers are also available in keg.

Coach House SIBA

Wharf Street, Howley, Warrington, Cheshire, WA1 2DQ
☎ (01925) 232800 🌐 coachhousebrewery.co.uk

Established in 1991 by three former employees of Greenall Whitley Brewery, Coach House was bought by Martin Bailey in 2015. The 40-barrel plant produces up to 240-barrels per week. ♦

Coachman's Best Bitter (ABV 3.7%)
A well-hopped, malty bitter, moderately fruity with a hint of sweetness and a peppery nose.
Gunpowder Mild (ABV 3.8%)
Aromas of roast malts and caramel attract you to a pleasant sweet and toasty tasting mild with a gentle finish.
Honeypot Bitter (ABV 3.8%)
Farrier's Best Bitter (ABV 3.9%)
Cromwells Best Bitter (ABV 4%)
Blonde (ABV 4.1%)
Cheshire Gold (ABV 4.1%)
Dick Turpin (ABV 4.2%)
Malty, hoppy, pale brown beer with some initial sweetish flavours leading to a short, bitter aftertaste. Sold under other names as a pub house beer.
ClIPAty Hop (ABV 4.3%)
Hoppy, fruity, bitter beer with balancing sweetness and a dry finish.
Flintlock Pale Ale (ABV 4.4%)
Innkeeper's Special Reserve (ABV 4.5%)
A darkish, full-flavoured bitter. Quite fruity, with a strong, bitter aftertaste.
Postlethwaite (ABV 4.6%)
Blueberry Classic Bitter (ABV 5%)
Posthorn Premium (ABV 5%)
Blunderbus (ABV 5.3%)

Cobbydale

Red Lion, 47 Kirkgate, Silsden, West Yorkshire, BD20 0AQ
☎ (01535) 930884 ☎ 07965 569885
🌐 cobbydalebrewery.co.uk

Brewing began in 2017 at the Red Lion, Silsden. Originally only brewing one beer, others are now brewed on an occasional basis.

Cocksure

See Tapestry

Colchester SIBA

Viaduct Brewhouse, Unit 16, Wakes Hall Business Centre, Wakes Colne, Essex, CO6 2DY
☎ (01787) 829422 🌐 colchesterbrewery.com

Set up in 2012 by three friends, Tom Knox, Roger Clark and Andy Bone, using the double drop process. Popular during the early 20th century this process requires additional brewing vessels in a two-tier system resulting in clean beer with pronounced flavours. ‼🛒♦RAIB

AKA Pale (ABV 3.7%)
Metropolis (ABV 3.9%)
Jack Spitty's Smuggler's Ale (ABV 4%)
No. 1 (ABV 4.1%)
Red Diesel (ABV 4.2%)
Brazilian Coffee & Vanilla Porter (ABV 4.6%)
Cat's Whiskers (ABV 4.8%)
Old King Coel London Porter (ABV 5%)

Cold Bath SIBA

46 Kings Road, Harrogate, North Yorkshire, HG1 5JW ☎ 0330 880 7009 coldbathbrewing.com

Launched in 2018, Cold Bath's on-site brewery can be viewed on the mezzanine level above the bar. All beers are exclusively available in the pub. **V**

Cold Black Label SIBA

Guardian House, 5 Squire Drive, Brynmenyn Industrial Estate, Bridgend, CF32 9TX
☎ (01656) 728081 coldblacklabel.co.uk

Cold Black Label was initially founded in 2004, concentrating on its eponymous lager brand, and expanded into cask-conditioned beers 10 years later. In 2018, Cold Black Label and Brecon Brewing merged, with Buster Grant taking over all brewing, and 14 new beers were created. In 2019, Lithic Brewing joined the group, with these gluten free beers mainly available in keg and can, with the occasional release of casks. **GF**

Glyder Fawr (ABV 4.2%)
Singing Sword (ABV 4.2%)
Harlech Castle (ABV 4.4%)
Uncle Phil's Ale (ABV 4.4%)
Bwlch Passage (ABV 4.5%)
Miners Ale (ABV 4.5%)
Chirk Castle (ABV 4.6%)
Sand Storm (ABV 4.6%)
Guardian (ABV 4.7%)
Crib Goch (ABV 5%)
Nutty Ale (ABV 5%)
Pirate Bay (ABV 5%)
Red Beast (ABV 6%)
Miners Imperial Ale (ABV 7.5%)

Brewed under the Brecon Brewing name:
Three Beacons (ABV 3%)
Welsh Beacons (ABV 3.7%)
Dark Beacons (ABV 3.8%)
Copper Beacons (ABV 4.1%)
Gold Beacons (ABV 4.2%)
Red Beacons (ABV 5%)
Mind Bleach (ABV 10%)

Cold Town SIBA

8-10 Dunedin Street, Edinburgh, EH7 4JB

A Signature Pubs venture that began brewing lager in 2018. A brewpub has been opened at Cold Town House, Grassmarket, Edinburgh. No real ale.

Coles Family

White Hart Thatched Inn & Brewery, Llanddarog, SA32 8NT
☎ (01267) 275395 thebestpubinwales.co.uk

The brewery is based at the ancient White Hart Inn, built in 1371, which historically had an on-site brewery. Brewing started again in 1999 on a nine-gallon plant. A one-barrel plant was fitted in 2000. In 2012 the brewery was opened to the public. Cider is also produced. ♦

College

See Hilden

Collyfobble SIBA

Peacock, Hackney Lane, Barlow, Derbyshire, S18 7TD
☎ (01142) 890 340 collyfobblebrewery.com

Collyfobble began brewing in 2018. ‼

Colomendy

See Dovecote

Colonsay

The Brewery, Scalasaig, Isle of Colonsay, PA61 7YT
☎ (01951) 200190 colonsaybrewery.co.uk

Colonsay began brewing in 2007 on a five-barrel plant. Beer is mainly bottled or brewery-conditioned for the local trade. RAIB

Combe (NEW)

Unit 4, Lundy View, Mullacott Cross Industrial Estate, Ilfracombe, Devon, EX34 8PY
☎ (01271) 867030 ☎ 07973 488409
combebrewingcompany.co.uk

Combe Brewing Co was established in early 2020, in a recently closed brewery, just before the Covid-19 lockdown was put in place. Despite this inauspicious start, it continued brewing, producing bottle-conditioned ales to meet its small but growing client base. The owners, Richard and Michelle, have previous experience in the trade. A five-barrel plant is used. Bottle label artwork is designed by a local artist, Karen French, from Combe Toons. ‼ RAIB

Harbour (ABV 3.7%)
Beach Blonde (ABV 4.1%)
Dark & Stormy (ABV 5%)

Concrete Cow

59 Alston Drive, Bradwell Abbey, Milton Keynes, Buckinghamshire, MK13 9HB
☎ (01908) 316794 ☎ 07889 665745
concretecowbrewery.co.uk

Concrete Cow opened in 2007 on a 5.5-barrel plant. The beers are named after aspects of local history. The brewery supplies pubs, farmers' markets, local shops and restaurants. English single malt whisky is also available, produced from the brewery's own malt at a local distillery. ‼ ♦RAIB

Pail Ale (ABV 3.7%)
Fenny Popper (ABV 4%)
Cock 'n' Bull Story (ABV 4.1%)
Cloven Hoof (ABV 4.5%)
Old Bloomer (ABV 4.7%)

Concrete Island (NEW)

c/o 13 Pavilion Terrace, Wood Lane, North Kensington, London, W12 0HT ☎ 07720 078122
concreteislandbrewery.co.uk

Established as Small Beer Brewing in 2016 and rebranded as Concrete Island Brewery in 2020. Run from a private flat in West London and with a brewlength of just 25 litres, it is probably the smallest commercial brewery in the country. Unpasteurised, unfiltered beers are available in bottles. **V**

Coniston

Coppermines Road, Coniston, Cumbria, LA21 8HL
☎ (01539) 441133 conistonbrewery.com

A 10-barrel plant started in 1995 behind the Black Bull Inn in Coniston, it now brews 40 barrels a week and supplies numerous outlets locally and nationally. Some bottle-conditioned Coniston beers are brewed using Ridgeway Brewery. ‼ RAIB

Oliver's Light Ale (ABV 3.4%)
A fruity, hoppy, straw-coloured bitter with plenty of flavour for its strength.
Bluebird Bitter (ABV 3.6%)
A yellow-gold, predominantly hoppy and fruity beer, well-balanced with some sweetness and a rising bitter finish.
Asrai (ABV 4%)
Crisp on the palate, a gently-hopped beer with a full-bodied finish.
Bluebird Premium XB (ABV 4.2%)
Well-balanced, hoppy and fruity golden bitter. Bittersweet in the mouth with dryness building.
Old Man Ale (ABV 4.2%)
Delicious fruity, winey beer with a complex, well-balanced richness.
Special Oatmeal Stout (ABV 4.5%)
A well-balanced, easy-drinking stout, fruity with a balanced ratio of malt to hop bitterness. A good starting point for novice stout drinkers.
K7 (ABV 4.7%)
Balanced fruity hoppy bitter, plenty of body and a long, hoppy, bitter finish.
Golden Bitter (ABV 4.8%)
Thurstein Pilsner (ABV 4.8%)
True to style; mild but unusually sweet, with a hoppy fruitiness.
Blacksmiths Ale (ABV 5%)
A tawny ale which holds both roastiness and fruitiness in a pleasing balance.
Infinity IPA (ABV 6%)
High impact strong bitter. Fruity aromas persist in the powerful but well-balanced hoppiness and sweetness with nothing being lost in the finish.
No. 9 Barley Wine (ABV 8.5%)
Hops and alcohol dominate with appropriate sweetness and fruit on the tongue. A full-bodied and beautifully-balanced beer.

Connoisseur

(Rear of) Wolverhampton House, 121-125 Church Street, St Helens, Merseyside, WA10 1AJ ☎ 07921 838831 🌐 connoisseurales.com

Launched in 2014 by a family team of award-winning licencees, the brewery was run by Mark Yates until his death in 2017. The torch then passed to son Kevin who reinvigorated the range with a selection of new recipes to complement existing brews. Brewing is currently suspended while new premises are sought.

Consall Forge

3 Railway Cottages, Consall Forge, Staffordshire, ST9 0AJ

A one-barrel brewery set in the heart of the Staffordshire Moorlands adjacent to the Churnet Valley Railway. The Black Lion at Consall Forge is a regular outlet.

Dark Ruby Mild (ABV 5.2%)
Equilibrium (ABV 6%)

Consett SIBA

Grey Horse Inn, Consett, County Durham, DH8 6NE ☎ (01207) 591540 🌐 consettaleworks.co.uk

The brewery opened in 2006 in the stables of a former coaching inn at the rear of the Grey Horse, Consett's oldest pub. The name and branding commemorates the former steelworks, which closed in 1980. The brewery expanded in 2006 and 2017 to supply regionally and nationally. ‼♦

Steel Town Bitter (ABV 3.8%)
Steelworkers Blonde (ABV 4%)
White Hot (ABV 4%)
Cast Iron (ABV 4.1%)
Men of Steel (ABV 4.3%)
Stout (ABV 4.3%)
Red Dust (ABV 4.5%)

Consortium

Consortium, 13C & D Cornmarket, Louth, Lincolnshire, LN11 9PY ☎ (01507) 600754 🌐 theconsortiumlouth.co.uk

The Consortium Brewing Company was setup in 2016 to serve the Consortium micropub and tasting lounge. Situated in the Cornmarket of Louth down a small passageway close to the Masons arms, a large range of ale styles are brewed upstairs in the brewery (over 100 different ales since production started). ‼♦

Conwy SIBA

Unit 2, Ty Mawr Enterprise Park, Tan y Graig Road, Llysfaen, LL29 8UE ☎ (01492) 514305 🌐 conwybrewery.co.uk

Conwy started brewing in 2003, and was the first brewery in Conwy for at least 100 years. In 2013 it increased capacity and moved to bigger premises in Llysfaen with its own brewery tap. Around 100 outlets are supplied. Monthly seasonals are available as well as the West Coast range showcasing American style beers. ‼♦ RAIB

Clogwyn Gold (ABV 3.6%)
A full-flavoured golden ale featuring strong citrus fruit flavours throughout. Hoppy bitterness dominates the full mouthfeel and lasting finish.
Welsh Pride (ABV 4%)
Beachcomber Blonde (ABV 4.2%)
A pale beer with a citrus taste, initially sweetish with delicate hoppiness in the lingering bitter finish.
Honey Fayre (ABV 4.5%)
Rampart (ABV 4.5%)
A dark, fruity beer with a sweetish initial taste. Fruit flavours accompanied by the underlying hoppiness continue into the bittersweet aftertaste.
San Francisco (ABV 5.5%)

Cooper Hill

Highcliffe Industrial Estate, Bruntcliffe Lane, Morley, Leeds, LS27 9LR ☎ 0800 783 2989 🌐 cooperhillbrewery.co.uk

Commenced brewing in 2018 on equipment from the former Trinity Brewery, now relocated to Morley.

Copper Dragon

Lee Mills, St Pauls Road, Keighley, West Yorkshire, BD21 4QW ☎ (01756) 243243 🌐 copperdragon.co.uk

Copper Dragon are now brewing back in Yorkshire on a 15-barrel plant with the original team of brewers, Gordon Wilkinson, Matt Taylor and Dave Sanders. As well as the core range of Copper Dragon beers, Recoil Craft beers are also brewed.

Penny Pale (ABV 3.5%)
Best Bitter (ABV 3.8%)
Golden Pippin (ABV 3.9%)

Golden session beer, fruity and hoppy in aroma and taste. Citrus comes through in the aftertaste which is increasingly bitter.
Black Gold (ABV 4%)
Silver Myst (ABV 4%)
Scotts 1816 (ABV 4.1%)
Sidewinder (ABV 4.2%)

Brewed under the Recoil Craft brand name:
Boom Slang (ABV 3.7%)
Back to Best (ABV 3.8%)
Blonde Avenger (ABV 3.9%)
Collision (ABV 4%)

Copper Street

8 Copper Street, Brewery Square, Dorchester, DT1 1GH ☎ 07970 766622
✉ copperstreetbrewery@outlook.com

⊗ Anthony and Ann Buckton started this 2.5-barrel brewery in 2018, after moving from King Alfred Ales (now closed). It is situated in the new Brewery Square development, ex Eldridge Pope, next to Dorchester South station. The brewery can be seen from the shop, which sells a good selection of bottled beers. Nine or ten ales are produced throughout the year. A taproom is open Thursday-Saturday. ⛿♦◆

871 (ABV 4.3%)
Egbert's Stone (ABV 4.3%)
Shield Wall (ABV 4.3%)
Aethel Sword (ABV 4.5%)
Saxon Gold (ABV 4.7%)
Dark Ages (ABV 5.5%)

Corinium

Unit 1a, The Old Kennels, Cirencester Park, Cirencester, Gloucestershire, GL7 1UR ☎ 07716 826467 🌐 coriniumales.co.uk

⊗ Established in 2012, Corinium Ales brew classic and contemporary award-winning ales on a 2.5-barrel plant located in small, historic old kennels in Cirencester Park, just outside the town centre. An on-site taproom showcases the range, which is also available at a growing number of local outlets, events and pubs. !! ⛿ ♦ RAIB V◆

Firebird VI (ABV 4%)
Gold I (ABV 4.2%)
Plautus V (ABV 4.5%)
Bodicacia IV (ABV 4.7%)
Centurion II (ABV 4.7%)
Ale Caesar III (ABV 5%)

Corless

c/o Station Road, Scorton, Lancashire, PR3 1AN
☎ 07983 563917

Brewing began in 2018 using spare capacity at other brewers, mostly Avid.

Cornish Crown SIBA

End Unit, Badger's Cross Farm, Badger's Cross, Penzance, Cornwall, TR20 8XE
☎ (01736) 449029 ☎ 07870 998986
🌐 cornishcrown.co.uk

⊗ This six-barrel brewery was launched in 2012 on a farm high above Mounts Bay by the brewer, and landlord, of the Crown Inn, Penzance, which acts as the brewery tap. Beer is available locally and as far as the Southampton Arms in London. RAIB ◆

Golden (ABV 4%)
Causeway (ABV 4.1%)
Tawny bitter with a malty, caramel nose. Initially malty with resinous and citrus hop bitterness gradually emerging. Long, bitter finish.
One Hop One Grain (ABV 4.1%)
Amber best bitter. Fresh bread/marmalade aroma. Roast malt and citrus hop flavours with peardrops and honey hints. Long, dry finish.
Helter Skelter (ABV 4.2%)
Fruity, hoppy golden beer. Biscuit malt, pine hops and a touch of caramel honey provide a refreshing bitterness.
Honeyfuggle (ABV 4.5%)
Golden speciality honey beer. Light, subtle honey and caramel flavours evolving into a refreshing sweet, yet bitter beer.
SPA (ABV 4.8%)
Amber strong ale. Well-hopped with citrus, peach and grassy notes. Hints of honey leading to dry, bitter finish.
Porter (ABV 5.2%)
Dark vanilla porter. Roasted malt aromas. Molasses, treacle, liquorice flavours with raisin, fig/plum fruits and earthy hops. Roast, dry finish.
IPA (ABV 5.5%)
Amber India Pale Ale with hop aroma. Powerful, earthy hop bitter and persistent malt flavours. Kaleidoscope of fruitiness. Long bitter finish.
Red IPA (ABV 5.9%)
Strong, tawny speciality ale. Resinous hops, biscuit malt, with plums, raspberries and oranges and later smoky hints. Long fruity finish.

Corvedale SIBA

Sun Inn, Corfton, Shropshire, SY7 9DF
☎ (01584) 861239 🌐 corvedalebrewery.co.uk

Brewing started in 1999 behind the pub. Landlord Norman Pearce is also the brewer and uses only British malt and hops, with water from a local borehole. Beers are brewed for the pub and wider distribution. !! ♦ RAIB

Golden Dale (ABV 4.2%)
Oatmeal Stout (ABV 4.5%)
Dark & Delicious (ABV 4.6%)

Cotleigh SIBA

Ford Road, Wiveliscombe, Somerset, TA4 2RE
☎ (01984) 624086 🌐 cotleighbrewery.com

Established in 1979, Cotleigh is based in the historic town of Wiveliscombe. It supplies direct to 750 pubs, 200 retailers and selected wholesalers and is contracted to supply South West region Co-ops. A visitor centre is now established and available for functions. Monthly events include folk, jazz, open mic and curry nights. !! ⛿ ♦ RAIB

Harrier (ABV 3.5%)
Tawny Owl (ABV 3.8%)
Well-balanced, tawny bitter with malt and fruity aroma, major malt taste followed by hop fruit, developing to satisfying bitter finish.
Commando Hoofing (ABV 4%)
Cotleigh 25 (ABV 4%)
Golden Seahawk (ABV 4.2%)
Gold, well-hopped golden ale with flowery hop aroma and fruity hop flavour, clean mouthfeel, leading to a dry, hoppy finish.
Cotleigh IPA (ABV 4.4%)
Barn Owl (ABV 4.5%)
Mid-brown beer with well-balanced malt and hop aroma; a smooth, full-bodied taste where hops dominate, balanced by malt.
Honey Buzzard (ABV 4.5%)
Old Buzzard (ABV 4.8%)

THE BREWERIES

Cotswold SIBA

College Farm, Stow Road, Lower Slaughter, Bourton-on-the-Water, Gloucestershire, GL54 2HN
☎ (01451) 824488 ☎ 07760 889100
🌐 cotswoldbrewco.uk

An independent producer of craft lager and speciality beers. The brewery was established in 2005 and expanded in 2010. More than 150 outlets are supplied, mainly in the Cotswolds and London. !! ♦ RAIB

Cask (ABV 4%)

Cotswold Lion SIBA

Grain Store 5, Dowmans Farm, Coberley, Gloucestershire, GL53 9QY
☎ (01242) 870164 🌐 cotswoldlionbrewery.co.uk

⊗ The 10-barrel plant is located in a grain store on a farm in the Cotswolds, but may relocate during the currency of this Guide. RAIB

Shepherd's Delight (ABV 3.6%)
Hogget (ABV 3.8%)
Best in Show (ABV 4.2%)
Golden Fleece (ABV 4.4%)
Drover's Return (ABV 5%)

Cotswold Spring

See Severn

Cotton End

Pomfret Arms, 10 Cotton End, Northampton, NN4 8BS
☎ (01604) 765544

⊗ Established in 2015, Cotton End Brewery is located in the garden of the Pomfret Arms, Northampton. A one-barrel plant, it brews specialist beers on sale at the pub as well as other local outlets. While it produces a variety of beers, the regular range has been trimmed to just three.

Coul

22 Laggan Crescent, Glenrothes, KY7 6FY
🌐 coulbrewing.co.uk

Coul is a family owned and run brewery in the heart of Fife producing small batch craft beers.

Milestone (ABV 4%)
Baby Badger (ABV 4.2%)

Country Life SIBA

The Big Sheep, Abbotsham, Bideford, Devon, EX39 5AP
☎ (01237) 420808 ☎ 07971 267790
🌐 countrylifebrewery.co.uk

⊗ Country Life is based at the Big Sheep tourist attraction. The brewery offers a beer show and free samples in the shop during the peak season (Apr-Oct). A 15.5-barrel plant was installed in 2005, making Country Life the biggest brewery in North Devon. Regular, seasonal and bottle-conditioned beers are available at approximately 100 outlets, the brewery shop and online. !! ♦ RAIB

Old Appledore (ABV 3.7%)
Reef Break (ABV 4%)
Shore Break (ABV 4.4%)
Black Boar/Board Break (ABV 4.5%)

Complex, well-balanced aromas. Unusual dry bitter hop taste leading to softer aftertaste with unexpected roasted malt and caramel.

Golden Pig (ABV 4.7%)
Country Bumpkin (ABV 6%)

Courtyard

Gosfield Cottage, The Street, Gosfield, CO9 1TP
☎ (01787) 475993 ☎ 07710 230662
🌐 courtyardbrewery.co.uk

Courtyard Brewery uses a six-barrel plant designed to prefectly fit into a 19th century coach house in the north Essex village of Gosfield. It is run by two brewers passionate about producing ales traditionally, but with a 21st century twist.

IPA (ABV 3.8%)
Gold (ABV 4.1%)
Dark (ABV 5%)

CrackleRock

The Old Cooperage, High Street, Botley, Hampshire, SO30 2EA ☎ 07733 232806 🌐 cracklerock.co.uk

⊗ Cracklerock began brewing in 2014 at the Old Cooperage in the centre of Botley. Its taproom moved to larger premises near the brewery in 2018. !! ♦

Crackerjack (ABV 3.8%)
Verified (ABV 4%)
Fire Cracker (ABV 4.2%)
Gold Rush (ABV 4.5%)
Dark Destroyer (ABV 4.9%)
Crafty Shag (ABV 5%)
Crackatoa IPA (ABV 6.2%)

Craddock's

Duke William, 25 Coventry Street, Stourbridge, West Midlands, DY8 1EP
☎ (01384) 440202 🌐 craddocksbrewery.com

⊗ Craddock's brews exclusively for its four pubs; the Duke William and Plough & Harrow in Stourbridge, the King Charles, Worcester, and the Talbot, Droitwich. In 2019 a fifth venue, the Good Intent, was opened in Birmingham city centre as a not-for-profit enterprise selling Craddock's and other beers with the proceeds donated to charity. !! ♦ RAIB

Craft, The

29a Part Street, Southport, Merseyside, PR8 1HY
☎ 07870 160934 🌐 thecraftbrewery.com

The Craft is a small-batch, independently-owned microbrewery producing vegan-friendly, unfined, hand-crafted ales using traditional techniques. ♦ V

Crafty Gold (ABV 4%)
Crafty Ale (ABV 4.5%)
Crafty IPA (ABV 4.5%)
Crafty Devil (ABV 5%)
Crafty Smoke (ABV 5%)

Craft Academy

Florence, 131-133 Dulwich Road, Herne Hill, London, SE24 0NG 🌐 florencehernehill.com/brewery

Craft Academy was set up by Greene King in 2016 as an apprentice-led scheme offering young people the chance to learn the art of brewing. The brewery was installed at the Florence in 2017 and the beers were brewed by the students. Brewing is currently suspended.

Craft Brews

The Old Dairy, Pierrepont Home Farm, The Reeds, Frensham, Surrey, GU10 3BS ☎ 07774 982174
craftbrews.uk

Originally known as Frensham, Craft Brews Brewery & Taproom is a microbrewery founded in 2014 and situated in a 17th-century restored barn on a working dairy farm.

i. PL (ABV 3.2%)
RPA (ABV 3.7%)
USB (ABV 4.3%)
i.PA India Pale Ale (ABV 5.3%)
CAB (ABV 6.3%)

Crafty Beers

The Stables, Hall Farm, Stetchworth, Cambridgeshire, CB8 0TY
☎ (01223) 813938 craftybeers.co.uk

Crafty Beers has been brewing since 2012. Production moved to an old stable building near Stetchworth in 2016 in order to increase capacity. A range of beers is brewed and are available at pubs in the Cambridge and Newmarket areas and beyond. RAIB V

Carpenter's Cask (ABV 3.8%)
A well-balanced, amber brew with biscuit malt character giving way to hops on the palate and a long finish.
Incognito (ABV 4%)
Wilbraham (ABV 4.1%)
Sauvignon Blonde (ABV 4.4%)
APA (ABV 4.6%)

Crafty Brewing SIBA

Thatched House Farm, Loxhill, Dunsfold, Surrey, GU8 4BW
☎ (01483) 276300 ☎ 07702 305595
craftybrewing.co.uk

Opened in 2014 and situated on Luke Herman's family farm behind Dunsfold's famous aerodrome, Crafty expanded into a new 30-barrel plant in 2019. It supplies more than 175 regional pubs plus local events and markets. Its Pints with a Purpose range helps to support regimental charities and local community groups.

Loxhill Biscuit (ABV 3.8%)
Golden bitter which belies its strength. Initial malty aroma and taste with a dry, bitter finish, from the Challenger hops.
Dunsfold Best (ABV 4%)
A deep red-coloured, English bitter, with initial toffee and caramel aromas, which leads to a slightly vinous flavour and a sweetish taste, with Fuggles and First Gold hops used. The finish is shorter but with the caramel notes still present.
Crafty One (ABV 4.2%)
Golden-yellow beer with Chinook and Sorachi Ace hops. Tropical fruits aroma, leads to a full bitterness, with a dry finish.
Five Hop IPA (ABV 4.2%)
Hop Tipple (ABV 4.2%)
Brewed for Upham Brewery:
Tipster (ABV 3.6%)
An easy-drinking and light golden ale. Initial hoppiness and fruit is balanced by maltiness that lasts into the finish.
Punter (ABV 4%)

Crafty Devil

Unit 3, The Stone Yard, Ninian Park Road, Cardiff, CF11 6HE
☎ (029) 2240 4355 ☎ 07766 014550
craftydevilbrewing.co.uk

Brewery relocated to existing premises in 2017, which increased its capacity. Currently only regularly producing bottled, canned and keg beer, supplying to markets and a number of other outlets in the city. It operates two micro bars in Cardiff and has recently opened a third in Penarth.

Crafty Dragon

8 Castell Morlais, Ponsticill, CF48 2YB
☎ (01685) 723544 ☎ 07967 274272
butchersbunkhouse@gmail.com

Crafty Dragon began brewing in 2017 and is situated within the Brecon Beacons National Park. Its brewery tap is the Butchers Arms in Pontsticill.

Goldings Bitter (ABV 3.8%)
Session IPA (ABV 3.8%)
Bramling (ABV 4%)
Session IPA (ABV 4.2%)
Pen Y Fan Chocolate & Rum Porter (ABV 4.5%)
Chocolate & Rum Porter (ABV 5%)
Cwrw Coch (ABV 5%)
Red IPA (ABV 5%)

Crafty Little SIBA

Office: 109 Alfred Gelder Street, Hull, East Yorkshire, HU1 1EP
☎ (01482) 661393 thecraftylittlebrewery.co.uk

This family-run business, based in East Yorkshire, was founded in 2017. It is currently utilising contract brewing while new premises are sought. V

Apex Predator (ABV 3.8%)
ChamAleon (ABV 4%)
Red Tale (ABV 4.5%)
Silk Stout (ABV 4.5%)
Black Ryeno (ABV 4.6%)
Perky Porter (ABV 4.8%)
Wolf Bite APA (ABV 4.8%)
Snake Charmer (ABV 5.5%)
Brewed for Three Sisters Brewery:
Session Ale (ABV 4%)

Crafty Monkey SIBA

Benknowle Farm, Elwick, Hartlepool, TS27 3HF
craftymonkey.beer

Brewing commenced in 2018 on a plant supplied by Oban Ales.

Black Celebration (ABV 5%)

Crafty Pint

c/o Half Moon, 130 Northgate, Darlington, DL1 1QS
☎ (01325) 469965 ☎ 07804 305175

Established in 2013 in the cellar of the Half Moon in Darlington. Originally a 10-gallon brew length, it was upgraded to a one-barrel plant in 2015. One-off beers are produced solely for the pub. ♦

Crankshaft SIBA

17e Boxer Place, Leyland, Lancashire, PR26 7QL
☎ 07827 289200 crankshaftbrewery.co.uk

The brewery, a 2.5-barrel plant, launched in 2016, moved to new premises in 2017, and expanded into the next unit in 2018. Capacity has been doubled with the addition of two 1,000-litre fermenters. A core range of beers, in cask and bottle, is supplemented by a number of special occasional beers. A keg range has also been developed. A microbar, Cann Bridge Ale House, Higher Walton opened and a popular taproom is open Fridays/Saturdays. ■♦♦

Propshaft (ABV 3.8%)
Foggy Gold (ABV 4%)
Ribble 100 (ABV 4.2%)
Millstone (ABV 4.3%)
Crankcase (ABV 5%)
Tenterhook (ABV 5%)
Leyland Tiger Cub (ABV 5.5%)
Leyland Badger (ABV 5.8%)

Creative Juices (NEW)

Woodoaks Farm, Denham Way, Maple Cross, Hertfordshire, WD3 9XQ
☎ (01923) 771779
⊕ creativejuicesbrewingcompany.com

A craft brewery, taproom and beer garden that opened in 2019 in a renovated dairy building on a farm in Hertfordshire. V♦

Creaton Grange

Old Wash House, Creaton Grange, Grooms Lane, Creaton, Northamptonshire, NN6 8NN ☎ 07943 595829 ⊕ creatongrangeales.co.uk

Microbrewery started in 2017 and based in a converted disused building on a family farm in rural Northamptonshire.

Four Sons (ABV 3.5%)
Pheasant Tale (ABV 3.8%)
March Yard (ABV 4.2%)

Credence SIBA

Unit 16B, Coquet Enterprise Park, Amble, Northumberland, NE65 0PE
☎ (01665) 714855 ⊕ credencebrewing.co.uk

Credence began brewing in 2015. A barrel-aging programme is being established and a new trade counter is the first step in opening up the brewery to the public. Around 100 outlets are supplied direct. ♦

Blonde (ABV 4%)

Croft

32 Upper York Street, Stokes Croft, Bristol, BS2 8QN
☎ (0117) 214 1990 ⊕ croftales.com

⊠ Croft began brewing in 2017 in a former faggot factory in Bristol's vibrant Stokes Croft area, from which the brewery takes its name. The brewery also serves as a taproom, which holds regular tasting events and launches of its seasonal ales, often accompanied by DJs and pop-up food vendors. !!■♦V♦

BS2 (ABV 4%)
Hazy, unfined golden ale with grassy hop aroma. Clean, yet slightly sweet, citrus flavours, and a balanced, somewhat dry bitter finish.

Beast (ABV 4.2%)
Hint of malt on the nose with some added hop bitterness on the tongue, slightly tart, bittersweet aftertaste.

Backjump (ABV 4.5%)
Hazy, straw yellow beer with a citrus aroma, grapefruit flavours dominate with hints of pineapple, which both fade in the short finish.

Westide (ABV 4.5%)
Copper-coloured ale with earthy hops on the nose, fresh-tasting bitterness on the palate and a lingering, balanced aftertaste.

Deep Red (ABV 5.5%)
Hoppy, red ale combining rye with sweetish malt and pine notes on the palate, finishing with a lingering bitterness.

Cromarty

Davidston, Cromarty, IV11 8XD
☎ (01381) 600440 ⊕ cromartybrewing.co.uk

Cromarty began brewing 2011 in a purpose-built brewhouse, installed another two large fermenters during 2014, and further fermenter/conditioning tanks in 2015. A fully automatic bottling line was commissioned in 2017 and a warehouse was built on-site in 2018 to help cope with demand. !!■♦

Whiteout (ABV 3.8%)
Happy Chappy (ABV 4.1%)
An excellent golden ale with plenty of hop character. Floral, citric hop aroma with a good bitter taste which increases in aftertaste and balanced with malt.

Red Rocker (ABV 5%)
Red-coloured, rye, speciality, hop monster with a malty background leading to a bitter finish.

Rogue Wave (ABV 5.7%)
Easy-drinking, strong, peachy, hoppy bitter.

Ghost Town (ABV 5.8%)
Classic, dark-roasted, malty porter with blackcurrant and liquorice background.

AKA IPA (ABV 6.7%)
Strong IPA with a smooth, citrus, hoppy taste.

Cronx SIBA

Unit 6, Vulcan Business Centre, Vulcan Way, New Addington, CR0 9UG
☎ (020) 3475 8848 ☎ 07793 974395
⊕ thecronx.com

⊠ Cronx began brewing in 2012 and is the first commercial brewery in the area since 1954. The standard range and specials are available in cask, keg and bottles. The taproom was opened in 2016 at Boxpark Croydon. !!■♦

Standard (ABV 3.8%)
Easy-drinking, brown bitter with sweetish fudge and spicy hoppiness notes throughout. A malty bitter finish with a dryness that remains.

Kotchin (ABV 3.9%)
Grapefruity beer with pleasant hoppy notes. A little sweetness is balanced by a crisp, bitter finish that grows on drinking.

Nektar (ABV 4.5%)
Full-bodied dark gold best bitter. Peach with citrus, sweet biscuit and floral hops, gently fade in the lingering bitter finish.

Pop Up! (ABV 5%)
Smooth, amber APA with strong, tropical and grapefruit throughout. Hoppy and bitter on the palate and dry finish.

Entire (ABV 5.2%)
Dark brown porter with chocolate roast notes in the aroma, flavour and finish. The fruit character is of caramelised raisins.

Crooked

Units 12-15 The Garages, Leeds East Airport, Church Fenton, LS24 9SE ☎ 07890 526505
crookedbrewing.co.uk

After teaching homebrewing, Steve, Andy, Hudson and Mark started brewing in 2017 on the old RAF airfield at Church Fenton. Beers are increasingly available in a number of city centre pubs and bars in York and Leeds and many brews are canned for wider distribution. The brewery tap, Crooked Tap, opened in 2019 at Acomb Green in York. ♦

Spokes (ABV 4%)
The Lash (ABV 4.4%)
Rufus (ABV 4.8%)

Cropton

See Great Yorkshire

Cross Bay

Unit 1, Newgate, White Lund Industrial Estate, Morecambe, Lancashire, LA3 3PT
☎ (01524) 39481 crossbaybrewery.co.uk

Cross Bay commenced brewing in 2011 on a 28-barrel brew plant. An on-site taproom opened in 2018. The beers are widely available across north-west England. ‼ ♦

Halo (ABV 3.6%)
A crisp, hoppy, pale bitter.
Vesper (ABV 3.8%)
RIPA (ABV 4%)
Omega (ABV 4.2%)
Sunset (ABV 4.2%)
Sweet bitter with a rising bitter finish.
Zenith (ABV 5%)
Gentle bitterness and fruity sweetness with some dryness in the finish.
Guell (ABV 5.1%)

Cross Borders SIBA

28-1, Hardengreen Industrial Estate, Dalkeith, EH22 3NX
☎ (0131) 629 3990 crossborders.beer

Established in 2016 by childhood friends Jonathan Wilson and Gary Munckton. Cross Borders brews BRAW traditional Scottish ales without pretension. The brewery has an on-site tap open Fridays and Saturdays. ‼

Hop Series Pale (ABV 3.8%)
Notes of citrus on the nose with a balanced bitter finish.
Wee BRAW (ABV 4%)
A fresh, fruity beer with lots of hops creating a great aroma and a lightly bitter aftertaste.
Heavy (ABV 4.1%)
A malt-forward 'heavy', fruity with a slight bitterness not found in a traditional 80/-.
Bill's Beer (ABV 4.2%)
Session IPA, a pale, full-flavoured ale with zesty fruits and a clean finish.
Porter (ABV 4.2%)
Flavours of coffee and chocolate come through in the finish of this easily drinkable porter.
Stout (ABV 5%)
BRAW (ABV 5.2%)
Enticing citrus and tropical notes in the aroma of this juicy, refreshing golden ale.
IPA (ABV 6%)

Crossed Anchors

c/o Grapevine, 2 Victoria Road, Exmouth, Devon, EX8 1DL
☎ (01395) 222208 ☎ 07843 577608
crossedanchors.co.uk

Crossed Anchors was established in 2015. In 2016 a six-barrel plant became operational in the old stables of the Grapevine in Exmouth town centre. Beers are available across Devon and the South-west, as well as in the Grapevine. ‼ ♦

Bitter Exe (ABV 4%)
American Pale Ale (ABV 4.6%)
Weisse Guy (ABV 4.7%)

Crosspool Ale Makers Society

c/o 442 Manchester Road, Sheffield, South Yorkshire, S10 5DR crosspoolalemakers@gmail.com

Crosspool Ale Makers Society began brewing in 2019, taking over premises from Hopscotch Craft brewery. It began using spare capacity at Exit 33 Brewery (qv) in 2020. ♦ RAIB

Sandygate (ABV 3.6%)
Crosspale (ABV 4%)

Crouch Vale SIBA

23 Haltwhistle Road, South Woodham Ferrers, Essex, CM3 5ZA
☎ (01245) 322744 crouchvale.co.uk

Founded in 1981 by two CAMRA enthusiasts, Crouch Vale is well established as a major player in Essex brewing, having moved to larger premises in 2006. The company is also a major wholesaler of cask ale from other independent breweries, which it supplies to more than 100 outlets, as well as beer festivals throughout the region. A tap room (Tap Room 19) is on the brewery site. One tied house, the Queen's Head in Chelmsford, is owned. ‼ ♦ RAIB

Blackwater Mild (ABV 3.7%)
A dark bitter rather than a true mild. Roasty and very bitter towards the end.
Essex Boys Best Bitter (ABV 3.8%)
Brewers Gold (ABV 4%)
Pale golden ale with a striking citrus nose. Sweet fruit and bitter hops are well matched throughout.
Yakima Gold (ABV 4.2%)

Crown

Crown, Green End, Little Staughton, Bedfordshire, MK44 2BU
☎ (01234) 376260 thecrownstaughton.com

Brewing began in 2017 in a building behind the Crown public house in Little Staughton. The brewery is owned and run by the landlord of the Crown with the beers only being produced for the pub and local events. ♦

Crown Brewhouse

The Square, Elford, Staffordshire, B79 9DB
☎ (01827) 383602 bluecatsup@hotmail.com

A one barrel plant, established in 2017, housed in a former store room attached to the Crown pub. Beers are brewed almost exclusively for the pub, but can be found at local beer festivals and events.

Crumbs

See Goddards

Cuillin

Sligachan Hotel, Sligachan, Carbost, Isle of Skye, IV47 8SW
☎ (01478) 650204 ☎ 07795 250808
cuillinbrewery.com

The five-barrel brewery opened in 2004 and is situated in central Skye at the foot of the Cuillin mountains. The water from the Cuillins provides a distinctive colour and taste to the ales. Beers are available on-site at the Sligachan Hotel and at several other pubs and hotels on the Isle of Skye. The brewery is open by appointment only in winter (Nov-Mar). !! ♦

Cullach (NEW)

50 Princes Street, Perth, PH2 8LJ ☎ 07929 325890
cullachbrewing.co.uk

The brewery opened in 2019 in an industrial unit on the outskirts of Perth. It has recently moved into a retail unit closer to the town centre allowing a welcoming tap room to be set up for direct on-site sales. All draught beers are real ale in Keykeg. Some cans are also produced. RAIB ◊

Cullercoats SIBA

Westfield Court, 19 Maurice Road Industrial Estate, Wallsend, Tyne & Wear, NE28 6BY ☎ 07895 692881

Office: 17 St Oswins Avenue, Cullercoats, NE30 4PH
cullercoatsbrewery.co.uk

Established in 2011, brewing takes place twice a week. The brewery champions English hops. ♦

Shuggy Boat Blonde (ABV 3.8%)
Lovely Nelly (ABV 3.9%)
Polly Donkin Oatmeal Stout (ABV 4.2%)
Jack the Devil (ABV 4.5%)
Grace Darling Gold (ABV 5%)

Cumberland

See Great Corby

Cumbrian SIBA

Old Hall Brewery, Hawkshead, Cumbria, LA22 0QF
☎ (01539) 436436 cumbrianales.com

First established in 2003, the brewery is located in an idyllic position in a renovated barn on the shores of Esthwaite Water. The success of Loweswater Gold has meant the brewery is thriving. !! ♦

Esthwaite Bitter (ABV 3.8%)
Robust, refreshing bitter with plenty of hops, lasting well into the finish.
Langdale (ABV 4%)
Fresh grapefruit aromas with hoppy, fruity flavours and a crisp, long hop finish, make for a well-balanced beer.
Grasmoor Dark Ale (ABV 4.3%)
Dark, fruity beer with complex character and roast nutty tones leading to a short, refreshing finish.
Loweswater Gold (ABV 4.3%)
A dominant fruity body develops into a light, bitter finish. A beer that belies its strength.
American Invasion (ABV 5%)
Well-balanced, gold-coloured beer with big hop impact and long fruity finish.

Curious

Unit 1, Victoria Road, Ashford, TN23 7HQ
☎ (01580) 763033

Office: Level 2, Civic Centre, Tannery Lane, Ashford, TN23 1PL curiousbrewery.com

Situated next to Ashford International Railway station, this multi-million pound investment by parent company Chapel Down opened in 2019. It is a modern, state-of-the-art brewery, with a shop, tasting room (ground floor), bar and 120-seater restaurant (upstairs) featuring the Curious Brew core range and special/seasonal brews. Products are widely available in keg, bottle and can, but were previously contract brewed. Fresh unpasteurised, filtered beer from the brewery is served from tanks above the bar. Tours and tastings offered. !!

Cwm Rhondda

Fforch Farm, Cemetry Road, Treorchy, CF42 6TF
☎ (01443) 777491 cwmrhonddaales.co.uk

Cwm Rhondda Ales is a family-run brewery, situated on a farm in the Rhondda Valleys. Brewing commenced in 2015 on a 2.5-barrel plant, using the brewery's spring water, which gives a unique taste to the ales. Brewing was suspended in 2020. The proprietors have yet to decide the future of the brewery and have not ruled out the recommencement of brewing.

Cybi (NEW)

4 Bryn Annex, Williams Street, Holyhead, LL65 1RN
☎ (01407) 769651 bragdycybi.cymru

Nanobrewery established in 2020 using a 200-litre brew kit. It produces bottle-conditioned beers for local distribution on Anglesey. RAIB

Daleside SIBA

Camwal Road, Starbeck, Harrogate, North Yorkshire, HG1 4PT
☎ (01423) 880022 dalesidebrewery.com

Daleside was established in the mid-1980s, and moved to its current site at Starbeck in 1992. Daleside Brewery beers are sold to local, regional and national customers and export markets include Denmark, Sweden and Australia. ♦

Bitter (ABV 3.7%)
Pale brown in colour, this well-balanced, hoppy beer is complemented by fruity bitterness and a hint of sweetness, leading to a long, bitter finish.
Blonde (ABV 3.9%)
A pale golden beer with a predominantly hoppy aroma and taste, leading to a refreshing hoppy, bitter but short finish.
Old Leg Over (ABV 4.1%)
Monkey Wrench (ABV 5.3%)

Dalrannoch

Unit 16, The Old Dairy, Meikleour, Perth, PH2 6FB
☎ 07481 062862 dalrannochbrewing.co.uk

Brewing began in 2016 using a five-barrel plant.

Dancing Duck SIBA

1 John Cooper Buildings, Payne Street, Derby, DE22 3AZ
☎ (01332) 205582 ☎ 07581 122122
dancingduckbrewery.com

⊗ Dancing Duck was established in 2010 by Rachel Mathews using a 10-barrel brew plant. Its name comes from the local greeting 'ay up me duck'. The Exeter Arms in Derby is the brewery tap. ‼ ♦ V

Ay Up (ABV 3.9%)
Waitangi (ABV 4%)
Ginger Ninja (ABV 4.1%)
Nice Weather (ABV 4.1%)
Back, Sack & Quack (ABV 4.2%)
22 (ABV 4.3%)
DCUK (ABV 4.3%)
Dark Drake (ABV 4.5%)
Waddle It Be? (ABV 4.5%)
Indian Porter (ABV 5%)
Quack Me Amadeus (ABV 5%)
Abduction (ABV 5.5%)
Imperial Drake (ABV 6.5%)

Dancing Man

Wool House, Town Quay, Southampton, Hampshire, SO14 2AR
☎ (023) 8083 6666 dancingmanbrewery.co.uk

⊗ Dancing Man began brewing in 2011 in the Platform Tavern. In 2015 the brewery moved to the historic Wool House, the only surviving freestanding medieval building in Southampton, in order to expand and include an on-site bar and restaurant. One-off and rare brews are available throughout the year. ‼ ♦ RAIB V

Dancing Men

Hill House Inn, The Hill, Happisburgh, Norfolk, NR12 0PW
☎ (01692) 650004 ☎ 07818 038768
hillhouseinn.co.uk

⊗ Brewing began in 2014 at the 16th-century Hill House Inn on Happisburgh's fast-eroding clifftop. The microbrewery is named in honour of a Sherlock Holmes story by Sir Arthur Conan Doyle after he visited the pub in 1903. The five-barrel plant was acquired from Bees Brewery after its partial destruction during the tidal surge events in Walcott in 2013. New recipes have been crafted using exclusive hops and barley including locally-grown Norfolk varieties. ‼ ♦

Dark Horse SIBA

Coonlands Laithe, Hetton, Nr. Skipton, North Yorkshire, BD23 6LY
☎ (01756) 730555 darkhorsebrewery.co.uk

Dark Horse began brewing in 2008. The brewery is based in an old hay barn within the Yorkshire Dales National Park. Around 50 outlets are supplied direct.

Craven Bitter (ABV 3.8%)
Well-balanced bitter with biscuity malt and fruit on the nose continuing into the taste. Bitterness increases in the finish.
Blonde Beauty (ABV 3.9%)
Hetton Pale Ale (ABV 4.2%)
Earthy bitterness on the palate overlaying a malty base and a spicy citrus character.
Night Jar (ABV 4.2%)
A malty, fruity bitter in aroma and taste. Caramel and dark fruits lace the finish.

Dark Revolution

Unit 3-5, Lancaster Road, Salisbury, Wiltshire, SP4 6FB
☎ (01722) 326993 darkrevolution.co.uk

Dark Revolution started commercial brewing in 2015 using a one-barrel plant; the owner had been homebrewing for the previous decade. It upgraded to a 15-barrel brew plant in 2017, with more fermenting vessels added in 2019 retaining the smaller plant for trial brews and short runs. A canning line is now operational. An on-site taproom is also now open Fridays and Saturdays. Barrel-aging is a speciality. ♦ RAIB

Orbital (ABV 3.5%)
So.LA (ABV 4.5%)
Velveteen (ABV 4.8%)
A smooth, rich, black stout, served unfined. Noticeable malt and roast in the taste with balanced bitterness through to the finish.
Sonic (ABV 4.9%)
A citrus, hop-forward, pale and unfined premium ale with pronounced grapefruit taste from the American hops used.

Dark Star

22 Star Road, Partridge Green, West Sussex, RH13 8RA
☎ (01403) 713085 darkstarbrewing.co.uk

⊗ The Dark Star Brewing Co is named after a Grateful Dead song and was established in the cellar of the Evening Star in Brighton back in 1994, moving to its current home in Partridge Green in 2010. Purchased by Fuller's in 2018 and subsequently sold to Asahi in 2019, the 45-barrel plant produces a wide range of beers. ‼ ♦ RAIB

The Art of Darkness (ABV 3.5%)
Hophead (ABV 3.8%)
A golden-coloured bitter with a fruity/hoppy aroma and a citrus/bitter taste and aftertaste. Flavours remain strong to the end.
Partridge Best Bitter (ABV 4%)
Espresso (ABV 4.2%)
American Pale Ale (ABV 4.7%)
Festival (ABV 5%)
Original (ABV 5%)
Revelation (ABV 5.7%)

Dark Tribe

Dog and Gun, High Street, East Butterwick, Lincolnshire, DN17 3AJ
☎ (01724) 782324 darktribe.co.uk

Situated on the banks of the River Trent in the Dog & Gun pub, this 2.5-barrel brewing plant produces beers for the pub and local outlets. The award-winning brewery has been established since 1996. A range of one-off beers is produced throughout the year. ‼ ♦

Darkland

Unit 4c, Ladyship Business Park, Mill Lane, Halifax, HX3 6TA
☎ (01422) 320100 darklandbrewery.co.uk

A microbrewery hidden away in a corner of an industrial estate. Regular and seasonal beers are named after ancient runes and are available at the brewery tap, Pallet Bar, Boothtown (open Friday 5pm-9pm, Saturday 5pm-10pm).

Bohemian Raspberry (ABV 3.8%)
Reddish, amber-coloured fruit ale. Subtle flavours of malt and raspberries develop in the mouth and become more intense in the aftertaste.
Othala (ABV 3.8%)
Isa (ABV 4%)

A pale ale with a hoppy citrus aroma. It is a smooth-tasting beer with a long, dry bitter finish.
Wolfenbrau (ABV 4%)
A malty, traditional bitter with a subtle roast flavour. Sweet fruit quickly develops into a strong bitter aftertaste filling the mouth with depth of flavour.
Niflheim (ABV 4.2%)
Drakkar (ABV 4.5%)
A dark and rich ale with complex, toasted, rich malt flavours. It has a robust and bitter farewell.
Jera (ABV 5%)
Refreshing, well-balanced, hoppy, strong pale ale. Crisp and fruity with a developing bitter finish.

Dartford Wobbler SIBA

St Margaret's Farm, St Margaret's Road, South Darenth, Kent, DA4 9LB
☎ (01322) 866233 🌐 dartfordwobbler.com

John and Miriam Millis started with a 0.5-barrel plant at their home in Gravesend. Demand outstripped the facility and Millis moved in 2003 to its current location – a former farm cold store – using a 10-barrel plant. It supplies around 40 outlets within a 50-mile radius. ♦RAIB

Curiously Dark (ABV 3.6%)
Guinea Guzzler (ABV 3.7%)
Peddlars Best (ABV 4%)
Golden Wobbler (ABV 4.1%)
Dartford Wobbler (ABV 4.3%)
Thieves and Fakirs (ABV 4.3%)
Penny Red (ABV 4.4%)
Country Wobbler (ABV 4.8%)

Dartmoor SIBA

The Brewery, Station Road, Princetown, Devon, PL20 6QX
☎ (01822) 890789 🌐 dartmoorbrewery.co.uk

Formerly named Princetown, Dartmoor Brewery was established in 1994 and is the highest brewery in England at 1,465 feet above sea level. In 2006 the brewery moved to a purpose-built building, and in 2012 capacity was increased to 360 barrels a week by the addition of another 60-barrel fermenter with a further increase in 2013. All beer is brewed using locally-grown barley. ‼ ♦

Best (ABV 3.7%)
IPA (ABV 4%)
Flowery hop aroma and taste with a bitter aftertaste to this full-bodied, amber-coloured beer.
Dragon's Breath (ABV 4.4%)
Sweet, winter warmer best bitter. Full-bodied, sweet, fruity with treacle hints. Malt, roast and caramel from start to finish.
Legend (ABV 4.4%)
Complex beer full of aromas and flavours. Malt and caramel dominate, balanced in an aftertaste of bitter hops. Well-rounded.
Jail Ale (ABV 4.8%)
Stronger session ale with complex notes dominated by malty sweet bitterness. Well-rounded caramel and fruit with a pleasant aftertaste.

Darwin SIBA

1 West Quay Court, Sunderland Enterprise Park, Sunderland, SR5 2TE
☎ (0191) 549 9450 🌐 darwinbrewery.com

Established in 1994, Darwin is based in purpose-built premises in Sunderland with a 3.5-barrel brew plant. A range of established Darwin beers are produced frequently, with core beers and seasonal offerings available around the North East. Some beers produced are based on analysis of historic recipes. Darwin Brewery supports students on brewing courses at sister company, Brewlab, who produce many unique specialist and international beers. ‼♦RAIB

Expedition (ABV 3.8%)
Evolution (ABV 4%)
Beagle Blonde (ABV 4.1%)
Rolling Hitch (ABV 5.2%)
Galapagos (ABV 6%)

Davenports SIBA

Unit 5, Empire House, 11 New Street, Smethwick, West Midlands, B66 2AJ
☎ (0121) 565 5622
✉ info@davenportsbrewery.co.uk

Davenports brewery occupies part of a distribution warehouse in an industrial unit in Smethwick on the outskirts of Birmingham. The 7.5-barrel plant produces a selection of beers under the Davenports brand with some occasional beers from the former Highgate brewery of Walsall. ♦

Mild (ABV 3.5%)
Gold (ABV 3.9%)
Original Bitter (ABV 4.2%)
IPA (ABV 4.4%)

Dawkins SIBA

Unit 2, Lawnwood Industrial Units, Lawnwood Road, Easton, Bristol, BS5 0EF
☎ (0117) 955 9503 🌐 dawkinsales.com

The established Dawkins Taverns group of independent Bristol pubs bought the Somerset-based Matthews Brewery in 2009. New premises in Easton, Bristol, opened in 2015 with a 20-barrel plant. The brewery distributes to its own five pubs and directly to another 80 outlets in the area. A sister company was set up in Edinburgh in 2017, reviving the long-defunct Steel Coulson brewing name for a bar in Leith. ‼ ♦RAIB

Bristol Blonde (ABV 3.8%)
Pale yellow-coloured golden ale. Citrus aroma. Refreshing lemon taste with grassiness, which fades to astringent bitterness.
Bristol Best (ABV 4%)
Copper-coloured bitter with malty aroma and taste. Hints of apple. Astringent aftertaste.
Bristol Gold (ABV 4.4%)
Light hop aroma, pale malt with hops, spice and a hint of apple on the palate before a crisp, bitter finish.
Easton IPA (ABV 4.4%)
Hazy, golden yellow, unfined ale. Hop and ripe apple aroma. Slightly sour citrus on the palate. Dry and bitter aftertaste.
Foresters Black (ABV 4.8%)
Resolution IPA (ABV 5%)
Naturally hazy, golden yellow with aromas of tropical fruit. Flavours of grapefruit and lemon continue into the bitter finish.

Dead End Brew Machine (NEW)

Office: Flat 1-2, 10 Lawrence Street, Glasgow, G11 5HQ 🌐 deadendbrewmachine.com

Dead End Brew Machine produce small batch artisinal beers specialising in brettanomyces and saccharomycetes blends augmented with fruit and spices. Beers are available in bottle and can. ♦RAIB

Dead Parrot

44 Garden Street, Sheffield, South Yorkshire, S1 4BJ

Established in 2018. An on-site taproom is planned.

Deeply Vale

Unit 25, Peel Industrial Estate, Chamberhall Street, Bury, BL9 0LU ☎ 07749 856043
🌐 deeplyvalebrewery.com

⊛Deeply Vale is a family-run business established in 2012. The brewery's name immortalises the Deeply Vale area near Bury, famed for legendary 1970s music festivals. The range of traditional beers with a modern twist produced from the six-barrel plant are distributed largely across North West England and West Yorkshire. ♦

Equilibrium (ABV 3.8%)
Crisp and refreshing bitter with a pale malt flavour and clean bitter hops. Dry finish with lingering hops.
Hop (ABV 3.8%)
Obsession (ABV 3.9%)
Citra Storm (ABV 4%)
Ripper (ABV 4%)
Optimum (ABV 4.2%)
DV8 (ABV 4.8%)
Supple, fruity sweetness accompanying luscious coffee roast. Clean, gentle malt finish, with lingering sweetness. Coffee and raisin aroma.

Deeside

The Steading, Lochton of Leys, Banchory, AB31 5QB
☎ (01330) 825598 🌐 deesidebrewery.co.uk

First established in 2005, a change of ownership and location in 2012 led to substantial growth in the Scottish retail sector as well as export markets in Europe, USA, the Middle East and Asia, while maintaining its independent status. V

Macbeth (ABV 4.1%)
Roasted malt and hops coming through in the taste in this best bitter.

Delphic (NEW)

26 The Martins, Thatcham, RG19 4FD ☎ 07595 386568 🌐 delphicbrewing.com

Thatcham's first craft brewery, established in 2019 by head brewer Tom Broadbank. It is a 2.5-barrel plant brewing many seasonal beers destined for cask and keg. Availability is predominantly in local Berkshire pubs.

Level Crossing (ABV 4.2%)
World's End (ABV 4.6%)

Denbigh

Crown Workshop, Crown Lane, Denbigh, LL16 3SY
☎ (01745) 817021 ☎ 07850 687701
🌐 bragdybinbych.co.uk

Brewing commenced in 2012 at the rear of the Hope & Anchor pub relocating in 2015 to a dedicated brew house in the town. Output is cask and bottle in equal proportions. A tied micro pub, Y-Goron-Fach, is located next to the brewery. ♦RAIB

Dent SIBA

Hollins, Cowgill, Dent, Cumbria, LA10 5TQ
☎ (01539) 625326 🌐 dentbrewery.co.uk

⊛Dent was set up in 1990 in a converted barn next to a former farmhouse in the Yorkshire Dales National Park. In 2005 the brewery was completely refurbished and capacity expanded. One pub is owned. More than 150 outlets are supplied direct. !! ♦

Golden Fleece (ABV 3.7%)
Light, hoppy and fruity, with a bitter aftertaste.
Porter (ABV 3.8%)
A veritable malt feast for the beer's strength. A complex porter ending with roast highlights.
Aviator (ABV 4%)
This amber ale is characterised by citrus, caramel and hop flavours that evolve into a bitter finish.
Dales Way IPA (ABV 4%)
Rambrau (ABV 4.5%)
Ramsbottom Strong Ale (ABV 4.5%)
A well-balanced, malty best bitter.
Kamikaze (ABV 5%)
Hops and fruit dominate this full-bodied, golden, strong bitter, with a dry bitterness growing in the aftertaste.
T'owd Tup (ABV 6%)
A rich, full-flavoured, strong stout with a coffee aroma. The dominant roast character is balanced by a warming sweetness and a raisiny, fruitcake taste that lingers on into the finish.

Derby SIBA

Masons Place Business Park, Nottingham Road, Derby, DE21 6AQ
☎ (01332) 365366 ☎ 07887 556788
🌐 derbybrewing.co.uk

A family-run microbrewery, established in 2004 in the old Masons paintworks varnish shed by Trevor Harris, founder and former brewer at the Brunswick Inn, Derby (qv). The business has grown over the years and four venues are now owned across Derbyshire and Staffordshire. More than 400 outlets are supplied including major retailers. In addition to the core range there are at least three new beers each month. !! ♦

Hop Till You Drop (ABV 3.9%)
Triple Hop (ABV 4.1%)
Business As Usual (ABV 4.4%)
Double Mash (ABV 4.6%)
Penny's Porter (ABV 4.6%)
Dashingly Dark (ABV 4.8%)
Mercia IPA (ABV 5%)
Quintessential (ABV 5.8%)

Derventio SIBA

The Brew Shed, Darley Abbey Mills, Darley Abbey, Derbyshire, DE22 1DZ
☎ (01332) 380199 ☎ 07975 944242
🌐 derventiobrewery.co.uk

⊗Established in 2005, commercial brewing began in 2006 at Trusley Brook Farm. Derventio moved to a Grade I listed mill complex in 2011, which is part of the Derwent Valley Mills World Heritage site. A fiercely independent family brewer it is always open to new ideas. !! ♦

Gold (ABV 4.2%)
Cleopatra (ABV 5%)
Barbarian Stout (ABV 5.5%)
Lucretius (ABV 5.5%)

Derwent

Units 2a-2c, Station Road Industrial Estate, Silloth, Cumbria, CA7 4AG
☎ (01697) 331522 🌐 derwentbrewery.co.uk

Derwent was set up in 1996 in Cockermouth and moved to Silloth in 1998. Owners Mark and Allie Johnston bought the brewery in 2013. ♦

Cote Light (ABV 3.6%)
Carlisle State Bitter (ABV 3.7%)
Malty, biscuity, hoppy beer with a gold colour.
W&M Mild (ABV 3.7%)
Parsons Pledge (ABV 4%)
Amber ale with a biscuity tang and a slightly fruity finish.
Blonde (ABV 4.2%)
Hudson Bay (ABV 4.2%)
Reaper (ABV 4.3%)
Mutineer (ABV 4.4%)
W&M Pale Ale (ABV 4.4%)
A sweet, fruity, hoppy beer with a bitter finish.
Marshall Port Stout (ABV 5.2%)

Deviant & Dandy SIBA

Arch 165, Nursery Road, Hackney, London, E9 6PB
deviantanddandy.com/

Initially cuckoo-brewed at Enfield Brewery for the Off Broadway bar in London Fields, brewing started at its current premises in 2018. Beer is available in bars and bottle shops and at the on-site taproom, open at the weekend.

Devil's Dyke

See Arran

Devon

Mansfield Arms, 7 Main Street, Sauchie, FK10 3JR
☎ (01259) 722020 devonales.com

Established in 1992 to produce cask ales for the Mansfield Arms, Sauchie, Devon is the oldest operating brewery in the county. A second pub, the Inn at Muckhart, was purchased in 1994 and the only beers sold there are from the Devon Ales brewery. The brewery also sells beer to the open market. ‼

Devon Earth SIBA

Buckfastleigh, Devon ☎ 07927 397871

Office: 7 Fernham Terrace, Torquay Road, Paignton, TQ3 2AQ ✉ info@devonearthbrewery.co.uk

Devon Earth brewery is located on the banks of the River Dart on the edge of Dartmoor and is run on a part-time basis. The brewery is proud to support local charities and supplies local and national beer festivals and free houses. ♦

Devon Earth (ABV 4.2%)
Grounded (ABV 4.7%)
Lost in the Woods (ABV 5.2%)

Devon's Own

See Clearwater

DEYA

33-34 Lansdown Industrial Estate, Gloucester Road, Cheltenham, Gloucestershire, GL51 8PL
☎ (01242) 269189 ☎ 07887 537356
deyabrewing.com

DEYA Brewing Company was established in 2016. It brews innovative, hop-forward beers, all of which are unfiltered, unfined and unpasteurised and available in keg and cans, with occasional casks. Expansion plans are underway and a range of barrel-aged beers is being developed. V

Dhillon's SIBA

14a Hales Industrial Estate, Rowleys Green Lane, Longford, West Midlands, CV6 6AL
☎ (024) 7666 7413 dhillonsbrewery.com

Originally named Lion Heart, the brewery was established in 2014. It relaunched as Dhillon's in 2016 with a new range of beers brewed on a five-barrel plant. The main focus is on craft bottled beers but cask ales are also brewed. The brewery tap is open Friday evenings and before rugby and football matches at the nearby Ricoh Arena. ‼♦

Bright Eyes GPA (ABV 3.8%)
Fair Lady (ABV 4.5%)
The Ambler Gambler (ABV 4.5%)
Red Rebel IPA (ABV 6.2%)

Dig

43 River Street, Digbeth, Birmingham, B5 5SA
☎ (0121) 773 2111

Dig Brew Company is a craft brewing project founded by Oliver Webb and Peter Towler of Mad O'Rourkes Pie Factory. The brewery and taproom is housed within a repurposed industrial unit in Digbeth, Birmingham. Beers available throughout the area.

Mad O'Rourkes Lump Hammer Bitter (ABV 3.6%)
9th July (ABV 4%)
Mad O'Rourke's Lump Hammer Gold (ABV 4.2%)
Space is the Place (ABV 4.5%)
Mad O'Rourke's Sledge Hammer IPA (ABV 5.6%)

Digfield SIBA

Lilford Lodge Farm, Barnwell, Northamptonshire, PE8 5SA
☎ (01832) 273954 digfield-ales.co.uk

Digfield Ales started brewing in 2005 and has continually expanded brewing capacity to keep up with demand. In 2012 they moved to a larger premises near Barnwell, where a reed bed was installed and the brewhouse was equiped with a new 15-barrel plant. More than 40 free houses are supplied. ♦

Fools Nook (ABV 3.8%)
The floral aroma, dominated by lavender and honey, belies the hoppy bitterness that comes through in the taste of this golden ale. A fruity balance lasts.
Chiffchaff (ABV 3.9%)
An amber-gold pale ale with a distinct hoppy aroma.
Barnwell Bitter (ABV 4%)
A fruity aroma introduces a beer in which sharp bitterness is balanced by dry, biscuity malt.
Old Crow Porter (ABV 4.3%)
A rich, full-bodied porter with a balanced, roasted malt finish.
Shacklebush (ABV 4.5%)
This amber brew begins with a balance of malt and hop on the nose which develops on the palate, complemented by a mounting bitterness. Good, dry finish with lingering malt notes.
Mad Monk (ABV 4.8%)
Fruity beer with bitter, earthy hops in evidence.

Distortion (NEW)

647 Portslade Road, Battersea, London, SW8 3DH
☎ 07557 307452 / 07765 328900
distortionbrewing.co.uk

Inspired by founder Andy North's visit to the West Coast of America, Distortion Brewery and Tank Bar, located beneath Wandsworth Road station, opened in 2020. ◆

Docks

The Church, King Edward Street, Grimsby, DN31 3JD ☎ (01472) 289795 🌐 docksbeers.com

Brewing began in 2018 using a 15-barrel plant in a converted Edwardian Church in Grimsby. ‼◆

Brewed under the Axholme Brewery brand name:
Magnitude (ABV 3.9%)
Hard Graft (ABV 4%)
Cleethorpes Pale Ale (ABV 4.2%)
Lightning Pale Ale (ABV 4.3%)
Graveyard Shift (ABV 4.5%)
Never Say Die (ABV 6%)
Special Reserve (ABV 7.2%)

Dog & Rabbit

Dog & Rabbit Micro Brew Pub, 36 Park View, Whitley Bay, Tyne & Wear, NE26 2TH ☎ 07944 552716 🌐 dogandrabbitbrewery.co.uk

The Dog & Rabbit Brewery was established in 2015 and relocated to its current premises as a small one-barrel micro brewpub in 2016. RAIB

Dog Falls (NEW) SIBA

Scaniport, IV2 6DL 🌐 dogfallsbrewing.com

Microbrewery founded by Bob Masson in 2019, Dog Falls brew modern interpretations of international beer styles. Beers are unfined and unfiltered, available mainly in can. V

Dog's Window

8 Nant-Yr-Adar, Llangewydd Court, Bridgend, CF31 4TY ☎ 07929 292930 🌐 dogswindowbrewery.com

Dog's Window is a small batch brewery which started production in 2018, producing a range of craft beers to its own recipes. It has a core range of eight beers with an ever-changing list of limited editions under the banner of the Experimental Series. The mainstay of production is bottled beers, with the occasional keg. The brewery can sell bottles direct to the public by appointment (see website). ♦RAIB V

Dolphin (NEW)

8 Corby Close, Woodley, Reading, RG5 4TL

A new 130-litre brewery operating on a small scale from the garage of one of the brewer's parents, producing bottled keg beers, mainly sours.

Dominion

c/o Red Fox Brewery, Upp Hall Farm, Salmons Lane, Coggeshall, Essex, CO6 1RY

Office: Queen Street Brewhouse, Colchester, Essex, CO1 2PG 🌐 dominionbrewerycompany.com

Dominion Brewery was established in 2012 by Andy Skene. He was renting the premises and Pitfield brand names from the founder of Pitfield, Martin Kemp. In 2018 Dominion Brewery moved and is now using spare capacity at Red Fox Brewery (qv). RAIB V

Yukon Gold (ABV 9.7%)
Mad Trappiste (ABV 10%)

Brewed for the Woodbine Inn, Waltham Abbey:
Woodbine Racer (ABV 4.2%)
Woodbine Racer Turbo (ABV 6.2%)

Brewed under the Pitfield Brewery brand name:
Shoreditch Stout (ABV 4%)

Contract brewed for Billericay Brewery:
A Mild With No Name (ABV 5.5%)

Don Valley SIBA

Unit 3 Canalside Industrial Estate, Cliff Street, Mexborough, South Yorkshire, S64 9HU ☎ (01709) 580254 🌐 donvalleybrewery.co.uk

The brewery, established in 2016, changed ownership in 2018, and is based in an old rustic building alongside the Don Navigation in Mexborough. The brewery tap is open daily in Doncaster Wool Market. ‼♦

Bit o' That (ABV 4%)
Atomic Blonde (ABV 4.3%)
Gongoozler (ABV 4.5%)
Go Your Own Way (ABV 5%)

Doncaster SIBA

7 Young Street, Doncaster, South Yorkshire, DN1 3EL ☎ (01302) 376436 ☎ 07921 970941 🌐 doncasterbrewery.co.uk

Established in 2012 and initially based at an industrial unit in Kirk Sandall, Doncaster, the brewery moved to new premises in 2014 using a 15-barrel plant, and opened a micropub taproom. The brewer frequently trials new recipes for beers. ♦RAIB ◆

Sand House (ABV 3.8%)
Cheswold (ABV 4.2%)

Donkeystone SIBA

Units 17-18, Boarshurst Business Park, Boarshurst Lane, Greenfield, OL3 7ER ☎ (01457) 238710 🌐 donkeystonebrewing.co.uk

Donkeystone is a 10-barrel brewery set up in 2017 at the edge of the Peak District National Park featuring an on-site brewery tap and gin distillery. Former homebrewers Richard Thomas and Tom Phelan use a custom-built stainless steel plant supplied by Oban Ales, and also have a small kit for experimental brews. Beer is also brewed for the Pickled Pheasant, Holmbridge. ‼♦◆

Ferris Muler (ABV 3.7%)
Hoppinsesh (ABV 3.7%)
APA (ABV 3.8%)
Bad Ass Blonde (ABV 3.8%)
Bray (ABV 4%)
Hoppy beer with prominent fruit and bitterness, ending in a fruity finish.
Cotton Clouds (ABV 4%)
DPA (ABV 4.7%)
Neddy (ABV 4.9%)
Javanilla (ABV 5%)
Kaihe (ABV 5%)
Madagaska (ABV 5%)
Light-bodied stout. Moderate bitterness with vanilla flavour.

Brewed for the Pickled Pheasant, Holmbridge:
Blonde (ABV 3.8%)
American Pale (ABV 4%)
Bitter (ABV 4%)

Donnington IFBB

Upper Swell, Stow-on-the-Wold, Gloucestershire, GL54 1EP
☎ (01451) 830603 🌐 donnington-brewery.com

Thomas Arkell bought a 13th-century watermill in 1827 and began brewing on-site in 1865. The waterwheel is still in use. Thomas's descendant Claude owned and ran the brewery until his death in 2007, supplying 20 outlets direct. It has now passed to Claude's cousin, James Arkell, also of Arkells Brewery, Swindon (qv). RAIB

BB (ABV 3.6%)
A pleasant amber bitter with a slight hop aroma, a good balance of malt and hops in the mouth and a bitter aftertaste.
Donnington Gold (ABV 4%)
SBA (ABV 4.4%)
Malt dominates over bitterness in the subtle flavour of this premium bitter, which has a hint of fruit and a dry, malty finish.

Donzoko

Hartlepool, County Durham ☎ 07463 863647
🌐 donzoko.org

Donzoko Brewing Company, founded by Reece Hugill in 2017, takes its inspiration and influences from Germany and translates this beer tradition, combined with techniques from modern UK and US craft brewing, into its beers. It is a cuckoo brewery that has teamed up with Gipsy Hill (qv) to produce its flagship lager in London. Other beers are brewed at various breweries in the North East. No real ale.

Dopey Dick

Skeoge Industrial Estate, Derry, BT48 8SE
☎ (028) 7141 8920 ✉ dopeydickderry@gmail.com

A microbrewery founded by the proprietors of the Grand Central Bar in Londonderry. Beers are contract brewed.

Dorking SIBA

Aldhurst Farm, Temple Lane, Capel, Surrey, RH5 5HJ
☎ (01306) 877988 🌐 dorkingbrewery.com

⊗ Dorking started brewing in 2008 at premises in Dorking. In 2017 production moved to a new, larger site in Capel with a 30-barrel brew plant capable of producing 35,000 pints per week. Beers can be found in Surrey, West Sussex and South London. ‼ ♦

Surrey XPA (ABV 3.8%)
Washington Gold (ABV 3.8%)
Pilcrow Pale (ABV 4%)
Smokestack Lightnin' (ABV 4%)
DB One (ABV 4.2%)
Hoppy best bitter with underlying orange fruit notes. Some balancing malt sweetness in the taste leads to a dry, bitter finish.
Black Noise (ABV 4.5%)
Lunar White (ABV 4.6%)
Red India (ABV 5%)
Buffalo Buffalo (ABV 5.1%)
Five Claw (ABV 5.1%)

Dorset (DBC) SIBA

Unit 7, Hybris Business Park, Warmwell Rd, Crossways, Dorset, DT2 8BF
☎ (01305) 777515 🌐 dbcales.com

⊗ Founded in 1996, Dorset Brewing Company started in Hope Square, Weymouth, which was once the home of the Devenish and Groves breweries. In 2010 it moved to purpose-built premises near Dorchester. Here spring water is used in its state-of-the-art brewing equipment. Beers are available in local pubs and selected outlets throughout the South West. ‼ ♦ ◆

Dorset Knob (ABV 3.9%)
Complex, bitter ale with strong malt and fruit flavours despite its light gravity.
Jurassic (ABV 4.2%)
Clean-tasting, easy-drinking bitter. Well-balanced with lingering bitterness after moderate sweetness.
Origin (ABV 4.3%)
Durdle Door (ABV 5%)
A tawny hue and fruity aroma with a hint of pear drops and good malty undertone, joined by hops and a little roast malt in the taste. Lingering bittersweet finish.

Double-Barrelled SIBA

Unit 20, Stadium Way Industrial Estate, Tilehurst, Reading, Berkshire, RG30 6BX
☎ (0118) 942 8390 🌐 doublebarrelled.co.uk

Brewing began in 2018 on a 15-barrel plant, focusing on stouts, sours and session beers. An on-site taproom opened in 2019. ‼ ◆

Dove Street SIBA

82 St Helens Street, Ipswich, Suffolk, IP4 2LB
☎ (01473) 211270 ☎ 07880 707077
🌐 dovestreetbrewery.co.uk

⊗ Dove Street began brewing in 2011 using a 2.5-barrel plant in a garage opposite the Dove Street Inn. The pub, its sister pub and beer festivals are supplied. ‼

Underwood Mild (ABV 3.2%)
Gladstone Guzzler (ABV 3.6%)
Citra (ABV 3.9%)
Incredible Taste Fantastic Clarity (ABV 4%)
Dove Elder (ABV 4.1%)
Apples & Pears (ABV 4.2%)
Ed Porter (ABV 4.5%)
Thirsty Walker (ABV 4.6%)

Dovecote

Unit 2, Denbigh Enterprise Centre, Colomendy Industrial Estate, Denbigh, LL16 5TA
✉ dovecote.brewery@gmail.com

⊗ Also known as Bragdy Colomendy, named after the industrial estate where it is located. Owner and head brewer Richard Green commenced brewing in 2017 on a five-barrel plant. All beers brewed are unfined and unfiltered. The brewery owns three pubs in North Wales and also runs the chain of Hoptimist micropubs. RAIB V

Dove Dark (ABV 3.6%)
Dove Ale (ABV 4%)
Dove From Above (ABV 4.2%)
Dove Down Under (ABV 4.8%)
Dove Pale (ABV 4.8%)

Dovedale

Damgate Farm, Stanshope, Derbyshire, DE6 2AD
☎ 07714 105035 ✉ info@dovedalebrewing.co.uk

⊗ Dovedale is a microbrewery situated on a farm, established in 2019. Recent expansion has seen an increase in capacity. RAIB

Echo Beach (ABV 3.8%)
Pale (ABV 3.8%)
Stout (ABV 4.6%)

IPA (ABV 5.6%)
Blonde (ABV 5.9%)

Dow Bridge

2-3 Rugby Road, Catthorpe, Leicestershire, LE17 6DA
☎ (01788) 869121 ☎ 07790633525
⊕ dowbridgebrewery.co.uk

Dow Bridge commenced brewing in 2001 and takes its name from a local bridge where Watling Street spans the River Avon. The brewery uses English whole hops and malt with no adjuncts or additives. Seasonal and bottle-conditioned beers are also available. ⌷◆RAIB

Bonum Mild (ABV 3.5%)
Complex dark brown, full-flavoured mild, with strong malt and roast flavours to the fore and continuing into the aftertaste, leading to a long, satisfying finish.
Acris (ABV 3.8%)
Centurion (ABV 4%)
Legion (ABV 4.1%)
Ratae'd (ABV 4.3%)
Tawny-coloured, full-bodied beer with bitter hop flavours against a grainy background, leading to a long, bitter and dry aftertaste.
Dark (ABV 4.4%)
Gladiator (ABV 4.5%)
Fosse Ale (ABV 4.8%)
Praetorian Porter (ABV 5%)
Onslaught (ABV 5.2%)

Downham Isle

1 Matthew Wren Close, Little Downham, Cambridgeshire, CB6 2UL
☎ (01353) 699695 ☎ 07732 927479
⊕ downhamislebrewery.co.uk

Downham Isle Brewery opened in 2016. Brewing real and craft ales, the customer base spans the Isle of Ely, Cambridge and Dusseldorf. The brewery is open most days for sales on and off site. Opportunities to take part in brewery days available. One or two are usually available on draught in the taproom. Please call to check. ‼⌷◆RAIB V◆

Duneham Ale (ABV 4%)
Goose Ely (ABV 4%)
Nelson Blonde (ABV 4%)
Moturiki-Blowhole Pale Ale (ABV 5%)

Downlands SIBA

Unit Z (2a), Mackley Industrial Estate, Small Dole, West Sussex, BN5 9XE
☎ (01273) 495596 ⊕ downlandsbrewery.com

▨ A 10-barrel brewery set up in 2012 distributing beers across the south east of England. ‼◆

Root Thirteen (ABV 3.6%)
Best (ABV 4.1%)
Bramber (ABV 4.5%)
Devils Dyke Porter (ABV 5%)
Devils Dyke Salted Caramel (ABV 5%)

Downton SIBA

Unit 11, Batten Road, Downton Industrial Estate, Downton, Wiltshire, SP5 3HU
☎ (01725) 513313 ⊕ downtonbrewery.com

▨ Downton was set up in 2003. The brewery has a 20-barrel brew length and produces around 1,500 barrels a year. Around 100 outlets are supplied direct. A range of regular beers is produced together with speciality and experimental beers. The brewery offers an off-site

mobile bar service and has an online shop. A regular bar is open on Fridays and sales are available on-site. ⌷RAIB◆

New Forest Ale (ABV 3.8%)
An amber-coloured bitter with subtle aromas leading to good hopping on the palate. Some fruit, and predominate hoppiness in the aftertaste.
Quadhop (ABV 3.9%)
Pale golden session beer, initially hoppy on the palate with some fruit and a strong hoppiness in the aftertaste. Its all about the hops.
Elderquad (ABV 4%)
Golden yellow bitter with a floral fruity aroma leading to a good well-hopped taste with hints of elderflower. Dryish finish with good fruit and hop balance.
Honey Blonde (ABV 4.3%)
Straw-coloured golden ale, easy-drinking with initial bitterness giving way to slight sweetness and a lingering, balanced aftertaste.
Nelson's Delight (ABV 4.5%)
Dream (ABV 4.8%)
A premium pale ale with East European influences. Hoppy on aroma and taste with a particularly dry finish and a hint of lemon citrus notes.
Moonstruck (ABV 5.5%)
A dark, ruby-coloured premium bitter with malt and caramel in the aroma and taste, which also carries notes of dried fruit and plum. A dry finish with some bitterness and lingering taste.
Chimera IPA (ABV 6.8%)
Golden yellow, strong bitter with good balance of hops and fruit, slight sweetness and some malt notes, all through to the aftertaste.

Dowr Kammel

Deaconstowe, Lower Lank, St Breward, Cornwall, PL30 4PW ☎ 07774 427635

Office: 9 Tregarne Terrace, St Austell, PL25 4DD
✉ dowrkammel@btinternet.com

▨ Brewing began in 2016. A small number of local free houses are supplied. RAIB

Blisland Dark (ABV 3.5%)
Blisland Gold (ABV 3.6%)
Light blond ale with strong citrus aroma. Dominant citrus and grassy hops with summer fruit sweetness. Long, bitter hop finish.
Amber Rambler (ABV 4%)
Demelza (ABV 4.2%)
Devil's Jump (ABV 4.6%)
Balanced, golden best bitter with malt and hops aroma. Assertive malt and bitterness in the mouth with smooth, zesty lemon hops.
Delank Dynamite (ABV 5.1%)
Black porter with chocolate malt nose. Smooth roast coffee and smoky malt flavour balanced by plums and a flash of bubblegum.
Brewards Droop IPA (ABV 6%)
Golden IPA with citrus aroma. Overpowering citrus hop with bitterness, balanced by malt and strong orange fruit through to the end.
Big Cat (ABV 7.7%)

Dragonfly

⚑ George & Dragon, 183 High Street, Acton, W3 9DJ
☎ (020) 8992 3712 ⊕ georgeanddragonacton.co.uk

▨ Brewing began in 2014 with a Chinese-built, vertically-stacked brewing kit installed in the back bar of the George & Dragon. After a short time in 2019 being run by Portobello, the kit is currently unused but is available for use by other breweries (brewing suspended).

Draycott (Cambridgeshire)

Low Farm, 30 Mill Road, Buckden, Cambridgeshire, PE19 5SS
☎ (01480) 480 812 404 ☎ 07740 374710
draycottbrewery.co.uk

The brewery was set up in 2009 by Jon and Jane Draycott and is located in an old farm complex where they live. The focus is on bottle-conditioned beers, which are available in a full one-pint, traditionally shaped bottle. Four regular beers are available along with a cask beer brewed for the Grafham Trout pub, or to order. RAIB

Grafham Trout Bitter (ABV 3.8%)

Draycott (Derbyshire) SIBA

Ladywood Lodge Farm, Spondon Road, Dale Abbey, Derbyshire, DE7 4PS ☎ 07834 728540
draycottbrewingcompany@yahoo.co.uk

Microbrewery established in 2014, supplying local pubs and beer festivals. Relocation to new premises in 2015 saw beer range and capacity increased. A tap house in Draycott village is also operated.

Top Of The Hops (ABV 3.8%)
Lamb & Flag (ABV 4%)
Butcher's Bitter (ABV 4.2%)
California Steam Beer (ABV 4.2%)
Piano Man Blues (ABV 4.2%)
Lord Have Mercy (ABV 4.5%)
Obsidian (ABV 4.5%)
Tap House Tipple (ABV 4.5%)
Minnesota North Star American Red Ale (ABV 4.7%)
Irish Red Ale (ABV 5%)

Driftwood Spars SIBA

Driftwood Spars Hotel, Trevaunance Cove, Cornwall, TR5 0RY
☎ (01872) 552591 driftwoodsparsbrewery.co.uk

Established in 2000, production on the custom-built five barrel plant expanded with the installation of additional fermentation and conditioning capacity. Annual production now stands at 1,500-barrels. All brews produced are gluten free. !! ♦ RAIB GF

Bawden Rocks (ABV 3.8%)
Refreshing amber bitter. Grassy/honey aromas. Malt and citrus/resin hop taste with honey and stone fruits. Long, dry finish.
Blackheads Mild (ABV 3.8%)
Dark mild with coffee aroma. Silky, smoky roast malt, raisins and liquorice flavours persist to the finish with dry bitterness.
SPARS (ABV 3.8%)
Refreshing, copper, session bitter with a balance of sweet malt and earthy hops, plum and orange flavours. Rising bitter finish.
Blue Hills Bitter (ABV 4%)
Pale brown session bitter. Aroma of orange/marmalade. Peach, grapefruit and floral hop flavour. Long, bitter finish.
Booskor (ABV 4.2%)
Smooth, red, strong mild. Malt and fruit nose. Roasted malt/caramel, blackberry and light hop flavour. Rich malt/dried fruits finish.
Forest Blond (ABV 4.3%)
Light, refreshing, golden ale. Citrus fruit aroma. Fruits (tropical, grapefruit) and gentle hop flavours provide a balanced and easy-drinking beer.
Bolster's Blood (ABV 4.8%)
Full-bodied, dark brown porter. Coal-smoke and peaty malt flavour with dark chocolate and dried fruits. Bitterness and burnt malt persist.
Lou's Brew (ABV 5%)
Golden beer laden with orange and grapefruit flavours with spice and pepper notes. Tropical fruit aromas give way to a long-lasting, tangy grapefruit bitterness.
JSB (ABV 5.2%)
Full-flavoured, copper, strong bitter with perfumed hop aroma. Assertive bitterness, woody malt and spicy hops. Marmalade and pears. Lasting bitterness.
Alfie's Revenge (ABV 6.5%)
Rich, strong, red ale with dominant malt aroma and flavour. Kaleidoscope of dried and stone fruit, bittersweet flavours. Long, dry finish.

Drone Valley SIBA

Unstone Industrial Complex, Main Road, Unstone, Derbyshire, S18 4AB ☎ 07794 277091
dronevalleybrewery.com

Community-owned, five-barrel brewery that began brewing commercially in 2016. All the brewing is carried out by volunteers under the supervision of qualified, experienced brewers. Profits go to local good causes. New owner members are always welcome. The brewery is open every Saturday and holds open days throughout the year. !! ♦ RAIB

Dronny Bottom Bitter (ABV 3.7%)
Gosforth Gold (ABV 4%)
Dronfield Best (ABV 4.3%)
Coal Aston Porter (ABV 4.5%)
Fanshaw Blonde (ABV 4.8%)
Stubley Stout (ABV 5%)
IPA (ABV 5.2%)
Candelriggs (ABV 5.8%)
Carr Lane Black Label (ABV 6%)

Drop Bear (NEW)

Gower House, Tir Y Farchnad, Gowerton, SA4 3GS

The brewery opened in 2019, specialising in low alcohol novelty bottled beers. Presently brewing is undertaken at Hambleton (qv), but some beers, especially for canning, may be produced at Boss (qv).

Drop The Anchor

9 East Close Farm, Lyndhurst Road, Hinton, Dorset, BH23 7EF ☎ 07806 789946
droptheanchorbrewery.co.uk

Neil Hodgkinson began brewing in 2017 using a 2.5-barrel plant situated in the loft area of the Christchurch Emporium. This has now relocated to Hinton. Beer is available in a number of local pubs, and a small bar and shop is situated in the brewery (open Fri-Sun). All beers are unfined. ♦ RAIB

Silent Stones (ABV 4.7%)
Tucktonia (ABV 4.7%)
Priest Hole Porter (ABV 4.9%)
Fusee Chain (ABV 5%)

Druid

4 Dinorben Terrace, Penysarn, LL69 9YR ☎ 07766 608889 alan@druidbrewery.co.uk

A microbrewery, in the north of the Isle of Angelsey. It is fitted into an early 19th century cottage that was built to house miners working in the historic copper mines of the nearby Parys Mountain. It is also the home of the brewery owners. The beers and ciders are produced in a purpose-built brew room using the latest German and British fermenters. Bespoke beers can be supplied for special events. ♦RAIB

British Summer Time (ABV 3.8%)
No. 9 Dream IPA (ABV 5%)

Drygate

85 Drygate, Glasgow, G4 0UT
☎ (0141) 212 8810 🌐 drygate.com

Restaurant, bar and microbrewery, Drygate is a joint venture of Tennent's and Williams Bros, though operationally independent. The on-site brewery began production in 2014. A core range of keg and bottled beers has been launched. The brewery is also committed to cask ale, at least one permanent cask is on at all times. !! ♦RAIB

Dukeries SIBA

18 Newcastle Avenue, Worksop, Nottinghamshire, S80 1ET
☎ (01909) 731171 ☎ 07500 119299
🌐 dukeriesbrewery.co.uk

Founded in 2012, the brewery is located in the Dukeries tap premises using a five-barrel plant. Brewing capacity is restriced to three brews each week. ♦

Elsi Pale (ABV 3.6%)
Blonde (ABV 3.8%)
Chapmans Map (ABV 3.9%)
A Ray of Sunshine (ABV 4.2%)
Castle Hill (ABV 4.2%)
De Lovetot (ABV 4.2%)
Lime Tree Porter (ABV 4.4%)
Mining Stout (ABV 4.5%)
Bolt out of the Blue (ABV 5%)
Farmers Branch (ABV 5%)
Gunsmoke (ABV 5.5%)
Bess of Hardwick (ABV 5.7%)

Dun

Corrary Farm, Glen Beag, Glenelg, Kyle, IV40 8JX
☎ (01599) 522333 🌐 dunbrewing.co.uk

Established in 2018, this four-barrel brewery is named after the two neighbouring Iron Age brochs (forts) – Dun Telve and Dun Trodden. Using its own spring water, Soil Association-certified, 100% organic ingredients, and 100% renewable energy, the environmentally sustainable ales are unfiltered and naturally carbonated. Beers are only available locally at present. RAIB

Dunham Massey

100 Oldfield Lane, Dunham Massey, WA14 4PE
☎ (0161) 929 0663 🌐 dunhammasseybrewing.co.uk

Opened in 2007, Dunham Massey brews traditional North-western ales using only English ingredients. Around 30 outlets are supplied direct, along with the brewery tap, Costello's Bar, Altrincham. A sister brewery, Lymm (qv), opened in 2013 with Costello's Bar in Stockton Heath tied to both breweries. ♦RAIB V

Castle Hill (ABV 3.5%)
Walker's Bitter (ABV 3.5%)
Little Bollington Bitter (ABV 3.7%)
Straw-coloured, light ale with malt and citrus fruit taste and a dry, bitter finish.
Chocolate Cherry Mild (ABV 3.8%)
Dunham Dark (ABV 3.8%)
Dark brown beer with malty aroma. Fairly sweet, with malt, some roast, hop and fruit in the taste and finish.
Big Tree Bitter (ABV 3.9%)
Obelisk (ABV 3.9%)
Dunham Milk Stout (ABV 4%)
Landlady (ABV 4%)
Dunham Stout (ABV 4.2%)
Dunham XPA (ABV 4.2%)
Stamford Bitter (ABV 4.2%)
Deer Beer (ABV 4.5%)
Cheshire IPA (ABV 4.7%)
Dunham Porter (ABV 5.2%)
East India Pale Ale (ABV 6%)
Dunham Gold (ABV 7.2%)

Duration (NEW)

Abbey Farm, West Acre, Norfolk, PE32 1TX
☎ (01553) 635000 🌐 durationbeer.com

Following two years of wandering collaborative brewing, Anglo-American founders Bates and Miranda unveiled their own brewery in 2019 in a repurposed 16th-century barn located near the Nar Valley in North Norfolk. Duration is a modern farmhouse brewery producing wild and natural ales. ♦V

Durham SIBA

Unit 6a, Bowburn North Industrial Estate, Bowburn, County Durham, DH6 5PF
☎ (0191) 3771991 🌐 durhambrewery.com

Established in 1994, County Durham's oldest brewery has a portfolio of around 40 beers, some permanent, some on rotation and with new beers appearing regularly. Beers are available throughout the North East. !! RAIB

Magus (ABV 3.8%)
Pale malt gives this brew its straw colour but the hops define its character, with a fruity aroma, a clean, bitter mouthfeel, and a lingering dry, citrus-like finish.
Citra Nova (ABV 3.9%)
Pale Ice (ABV 3.9%)
Apollo (ABV 4%)
White Gold (ABV 4%)
White Amarillo (ABV 4.1%)
Columbus IPA (ABV 4.2%)
White Velvet (ABV 4.2%)
Evensong (ABV 5%)
White Stout (ABV 7.2%)

Dynamite Valley

Unit 6, Viaduct Works, Frog Hill, Ponsanooth, Cornwall, TR3 7JW
☎ (01872) 864532 ☎ 07775 570235
🌐 dynamitevalley.com

Dynamite Valley was set up in 2015 following a successful crowdfunding campaign and is located close to a historic gunpowder site near Falmouth. Beers are influenced by European and US beer styles. The brewery has broadened its horizons by expanding into bottling. It also acquired the Rebel Brewery brand name and beers. V

Gold Rush (ABV 4%)
Smooth, gold-coloured bitter with a light malt nose. Malt dominates throughout with bitterness, honey, lemon and apricot flavours. Long malty, bitter finish.

THE BREWERIES

Kennall Vale Pale (ABV 4.3%)
TNT IPA (ABV 4.8%)
Robust, amber-coloured American-style IPA with malt and fruity hop aroma. Heavy hop bitter taste with sweet toffee apples and malt balance.
Black Charge (ABV 5%)
Black, oatmeal-style, sweet stout. Powerful flavours of roast coffee, dark chocolate, malt and molasses throughout. Smooth, but short finish.

Brewed under the Rebel Brewery brand name:
Surf Bum IPA (ABV 3.5%)
Golden ale with fruity hop nose. Dominant grassy hop bitterness with grapefruit, apples and apricots. Lingering hop bitterness and a little dryness.
Rebel Gold (ABV 3.8%)
Refreshing golden ale with light grassy hop and fruit nose. Sweet grapefruit and citrus marmalade throughout. Bitter and hoppy finish.
Bal Maiden (ABV 4%)
Tawny best bitter with malt aroma. Full malt and bitter ale with apple and lemon flavours. Lingering bitter finish. Dry throughout.
Penryn Pale Ale (ABV 4.3%)
Pale brown best bitter with mainly hop aroma. Bitter taste, citrus fruit, and biscuit malt. Short, fresh, hop bitter finish.
Rebel Red (ABV 4.5%)
Red best bitter with biscuit malt and toffee dominating the taste with bitter hop and light fruit. Light bitter finish.
80/- Scotch Ale (ABV 5%)
Dark brown porter with roast malt aroma. Smoky roast and biscuit malt balanced by sweet plum and bitterness. Long finish.

Eagle

Havelock Street, Bedford, MK40 4LU
☎ (01234) 272766 🌐 eaglebrewery.co.uk

Founded in 1876 and remained with the Wells Family until 2017 when the brewery and its brands were acquired by Marston's and renamed Eagle Brewery. It has brewed Young's beers since 2007 after the closure of the Ram Brewery, McEwans since 2011 and the popular Bedfordshire Ale, Eagle IPA, and forges strong links with the local area. Marston's supply the Wells & Co and Young's pub estates with beers from the Eagle Brewery and from the other Marston's owned Breweries. Part of Marston's PLC. ‼♦

IPA (ABV 3.6%)
A refreshing, amber session ale with pronounced citrus hop aroma and palate, faint malt in the mouth, and a lasting dry, bitter finish.

Brewed under the Bombardier brand name:
Burning Gold (ABV 4.1%)

Brewed under the Young's brand name:
London Original (ABV 3.7%)
Light-drinking, amber bitter. Citrus initially on the palate with sweet malt and a hint of hops that linger into a slightly dry and bitter finish.
London Gold (ABV 4%)
A dark gold beer with a smooth mouthfeel. Citrus and malt in the low aroma, coming through more strongly on the palate and aftertaste with a little peach. Dry finish.
Cityscape (ABV 4.1%)
London Special (ABV 4.5%)
Pale brown in colour, this rounded premium bitter has citrus throughout plus some slight creamy toffee, which balances the bitterness that grows in the aftertaste.

Eagles Crag

Unit 21, Robinwood Mill, Todmorden, West Yorkshire, OL14 8JA
☎ (01706) 810394 🌐 eaglescragbrewery.com

Eagles Crag is named after and overlooked by a prominent landmark, famous in local folklore. Its eight-barrel plant is situated in a former textile mill. Commercial brewing began in 2017 and the two founders both have 35 years of brewing experience. Beers are delivered direct to 170 outlets in Lancashire, Yorkshire and Manchester. ♦

The Eagle's Feather (ABV 3.8%)
Pale Eagle (ABV 4%)
Easy-drinking,very well-balanced pale ale. Light citrus notes offset by a touch of sweetness giving a smooth, bitter finish.
Eye of the Eagle (ABV 4.3%)
An amber, traditional best bitter with malt and fruit to the fore, lingering, dry finish.
Eagle of Kindness (ABV 4.4%)
Black Eagle (ABV 4.6%)
The Eagle has Landed (ABV 4.6%)
An amber best bitter with a good balance of fruit and malt. Moderate bitterness with a lingering malty finish.
Golden Eagle (ABV 4.7%)
A fruity, full-flavoured golden ale. Hoppy bitterness dominates the full mouthfeel and lasting finish.
Eagle of Darkness (ABV 5%)
Refreshing, dark brown porter. A subtle blend of chocolate malt and raisin-like fruit develops into a mellow, sweet aftertaste.
Bald Eagle (ABV 6.9%)

Ealing (NEW)

Unit 2, The Ham, Brentford, TW8 8EX
☎ (020) 8568 9906 🌐 ealingbrewing.com

A four-barrel brewery with an on-site taproom situated in Brentford, brewing beer for the Owl & the Pussycat and elsewhere. RAIB V

EB Bitter (ABV 4.2%)
A smooth, light pale bitter with a subtle fruity flavour, hops and a bitter finish.

Earl Soham SIBA

Meadow Works Cross Green, Cross Green, Debenham, Suffolk, IP14 6RP
☎ (01728) 861213 🌐 earlsohambrewery.co.uk

Earl Soham was set up behind the Victoria pub in 1984 and continued there until 2001 when the brewery relocated, moving again in 2013 to Debenham. Around 30 outlets are supplied and two pubs are owned. ‼♦RAIB

Gannet Mild (ABV 3.3%)
A beautifully-balanced mild, sweet and fruity flavour with a lingering, coffee aftertaste.
Victoria Bitter (ABV 3.6%)
A light, fruity, amber session beer with a clean taste and a long, lingering hoppy aftertaste.
Elizabeth Ale (ABV 4%)
Sir Roger's Porter (ABV 4.2%)
Roast coffee aroma and berry fruit introduce a full-bodied porter with roast/coffee flavours. Dry roast finish.
Albert Ale (ABV 4.4%)
Brandeston Gold (ABV 4.5%)
Popular beer brewed with local ingredients. Lovely, sharp, clean flavour, malty/hoppy and heavily laden with citrus fruit. Malty finish.

Earth Ale

Unit A007, The Chocolate Factory, 5 Clarendon Road, Wood Green, London, N22 6XJ ☎ 07508 553546
⊕ earthale.com

After periods of brewing at various London breweries, it took on a unit in the Chocolate Factory complex in Wood Green in 2019. Its main outlet and notional home is the bar in a converted London bus, the Earth Tap, at Blue House Yard nearby. Foraged wild ingredients add to the eco-friendly ethos of the brewery.

East London SIBA

Unit 45, Fairways Business Centre, Lammas Road, London, E10 7QB
☎ (020) 8539 0805 ⊕ eastlondonbrewing.com

⊠ East London Brewing Company is an award-winning, 25-barrel brewery established in 2011 by Stu and Claire. The brewery brews a core range of regular beers available for cask, keg, bottles and can, as well as regular "specials", including an annual green-hopped beer produced each September in collaboration with Walthamstow Beer, a collective of small-batch hop growers. ◆ RAIB

Pale Ale (ABV 4%)
Amber best bitter with spicy hops, bitter lemon, tropical fruits and biscuit that are there in the dry aftertaste.
Foundation Bitter (ABV 4.2%)
Well-balanced, brown bitter with hoppy aroma and flavour overlaid with caramelised orange, fudge and tropical fruit. Short, bitter marmalade finish.
Peacock English Pale Ale (ABV 4.2%)
Light-drinking, gold-coloured beer with a strong flavour of resinous hops, which are also on the bitter, dryish finish.
Nightwatchman (ABV 4.5%)
Dark ruby-brown, complex best bitter. Peach, caramelised fruit, and toffee balanced by bitter, nutty and roasted malt flavours. Dry aftertaste.
Cowcatcher American Pale Ale (ABV 4.8%)
Fruity, hoppy, rich golden ale with honey sweetness, mango and hints of passionfruit, lingering in the dry, bitter finish.
Jamboree (ABV 4.8%)
Golden, strong, smooth bitter with hoppy, citrus and sweet biscuit aroma, and peach flavour. Dry, bitter, sweetish aftertaste.
Quadrant Oatmeal Stout (ABV 5.8%)
Smooth, rich oatmeal Stout with liquorice, mocha and caramelised fruit. Roasted coffee aroma. A dry, slightly roasted, bitter finish lingers.

Eden River SIBA

Hawksdale House, Hartness Road, Penrith, Cumbria, CA11 9DB
☎ (01768) 210565 ☎ 07729 677692
⊕ edenbrewery.com

Originally named Eden Brewery, the name changed to Eden River in 2018. Set up in 2011, the brewery is run by Jason Hill, assisted by Linda and Chris. The five-barrel plant was located at historic Brougham Hall but moved in 2017 to premises on a Penrith industrial estate. !! ◆ RAIB

Eden Best (ABV 3.8%)
A traditional bitter, with a hoppy beginning; a malty, bittersweet middle, and a gentle finish.
Eden Fuggle (ABV 3.8%)
Initially sweet, a gently-hopped, pale beer with a more bitter finish.
Blonde Knight (ABV 4%)
Eden Dynamite (ABV 4%)

Eden Atomic Blonde (ABV 4.1%)
The initially inviting aroma of hops is followed by an intense hop flavour with some fruitiness.
Eden Gold (ABV 4.2%)
Gentle fruity and honey aromas to start, leading to a well-balanced, sweet beer with a lasting, hoppy finish.
Eden First Emperor (ABV 4.6%)
Fascinatingly fruity beer, with balanced malt and hops and a hint of butterscotch combining to a rich, bitter finish.

Eden St Andrews SIBA

Main Street, Guardbridge, KY16 0UU ☎ 07786 060013 ⊕ edenbrewerystandrews.com

☺The brewery was established in 2012 using a five-barrel plant in part of the former Guardbridge paper mills. In 2014 a new 20-barrel plant and distillery was installed. Brewing is currently suspended. !! ➤ RAIB

Edinburgh Beer Factory SIBA

Unit 15, 32 Bankhead Drive, Edinburgh, EH11 4EQ
✉ info@edinburghbeerfactory.co.uk

Family run brewery established in 2015, its packaging is inspired by Leith-born artist Eduardo Paolozzi. No real ale. !! ➤ ◆

Eel Pie

Ricardo's Cellar, 44-45 Church Street, Twickenham, TW1 3NT
☎ (020) 8891 3020 ⊕ ricardoscellar.com

Eel Pie is located in Ricardo's Cellar bottle shop and runs courses teaching brewing on the inhouse kit. Students get their beers bottled to take away. Some brews are sold through the shop from time to time but other beers are brewed locally at Belleville and Twickenham.

Eight Arch

Unit 3a, Stone Lane Industrial Estate, Wimborne, Dorset, BH21 1HB
☎ (01202) 889254 ☎ 07554 445647
⊕ 8archbrewing.co.uk

⊠ This award-winning brewery commenced in 2015 on a five-barrel plant on a small industrial estate on the outskirts of Wimborne. It has recently expanded into the unit next door with an on-site brewery bar. The ales are distributed to local pubs and clubs as well as nationally. !! ➤ ◆ RAIB V✦

Square Logic (ABV 4.2%)
Easy Life (ABV 5%)
Corbel (ABV 5.5%)
Strong golden ale with hops dominating, yet balanced with bitterness.

Electric Bear SIBA

Unit 12, Maltings Trading Estate, Locksbrook Road, Bath, BA1 3JL
☎ (01225) 424088 ⊕ electricbearbrewing.com

Electric Bear began brewing in 2015 using a purpose-built 18-barrel plant, expanding capacity in 2016, 2018 and 2020. Its brewery tap showcases a selection of the range, including exclusive one-offs. Beers are available in cans, kegs and occasionally cask and all are unfiltered, unfined and unpasteurised. !! ➤ ◆ RAIB V✦

Werrrd! (ABV 4.2%)
Howdy Ho (ABV 5.1%)

Elements

Upton Downs Farm, Upton, Burford, Oxfordshire,
OX18 4LY ☎ 07384 308670
⊕ elementsbrewery.co.uk

Began brewing in 2018 on a six-barrel plant, producing
small-batch, hop-forward beers initially in keg. A
taproom opened in 2019. No real ale. ■◆

Elephant School

See Brentwood

Elgood's SIBA

North Brink Brewery, Wisbech, Cambridgeshire,
PE13 1LW
☎ (01945) 583160 ⊕ elgoods-brewery.co.uk

⊠ The North Brink brewery was established in 1795.
Owned by the Elgood family since 1878, the fifth
generation are now involved in running the business.
Elgood's has approximately 30 tied pubs within a 50-mile
radius of the brewery and a substantial free trade.
Lambic style beers are produced using the brewery's old
open cooling trays as fermenting vessels. Off-sales
are available all year round from the shop in the brewery
office when the visitor centre is closed. ‼■◆V

Black Dog (ABV 3.6%)
Black-red mild with liquorice and chocolate. Dry roasty
finish.
Cambridge Bitter (ABV 3.8%)
Fruit and malt on the nose with increasing hops and
balancing malt on the palate. Dry finish.
Blackberry Porter (ABV 4.5%)
Plum Porter (ABV 4.5%)

Elixir

Livingston, EH54 9BX ☎ 07760 330122
⊕ elixirbrew.com

Established in 2012, Elixir Brew Company is an
experimental brewery that produces collaboration beers
with a variety of brewers throughout the UK.

Elland SIBA

Units 3-5, Heathfield Industrial Estate, Heathfield
Street, Elland, West Yorkshire, HX5 9AE
☎ (01422) 377677 ⊕ ellandbrewery.co.uk

☺Orginally formed in 2002 as Eastwood & Sanders by
the amalgamation of the Barge & Barrel, and West
Yorkshire Breweries, the company was renamed Elland
in 2006 to reinforce its links with the town. The brewery
has a capacity of 50 barrels (200 firkins) a week with
further expansion planned. The brewery tap, Elland Craft
& Tap, opened in Elland in 2018. ‼◆RAIB

White Prussian (ABV 3.9%)
A straw-coloured, lightly-flavoured, easy-drinking and
refreshing lager-style, speciality beer.
Blonde (ABV 4%)
Creamy yellow, hoppy ale with hints of citrus fruits.
Pleasantly strong, bitter aftertaste.
Beyond the Pale (ABV 4.2%)
Gold-coloured, robust, creamy beer with ripe aromas of
hops and fruit. Bitterness predominates in the mouth and
leads to a dry, fruity and hoppy aftertaste.
Nettlethrasher (ABV 4.4%)
Smooth, amber-coloured beer. A rounded nose with
some fragrant hops notes followed by a mellow nutty,
fruity taste, and a dry finish.
1872 Porter (ABV 6.5%)

Creamy, full-flavoured porter. Rich liquorice flavours with
a hint of chocolate from roast malt. A soft but satisfying
aftertaste of bittersweet roast and malt.

Elliswood

See New Buildings

Elmesthorpe

Church Farm, Station Road, Elmesthorpe,
Leicestershire, LE9 7SG ☎ 07754 321283

Elmesthorpe was established in 2017 by a beer
enthusiast and pub landlord. The brewery has gone from
strength to strength and now supplies many pubs and
taprooms in Leicestershire, Nottinghamshire,
Warwickshire, Derbyshire and Staffordshire.

Tight Bar Steward (ABV 3.7%)
CAPA (ABV 3.8%)
Aylmers Ale (ABV 4.1%)
Barons Best Bitter (ABV 4.3%)
Lord Cullens Ruby (ABV 4.5%)
Ale O Clock (ABV 5.2%)
Taking the Biscuit (ABV 5.3%)

Elmtree SIBA

Unit 10, Oakwood Industrial Estate, Harling Road,
Snetterton, Norfolk, NR16 2JU
☎ (01953) 887065 ⊕ elmtreebeers.co.uk

⊠ Established in 2007, Elmtree brews on a six-barrel
plant. More than 120 free trade outlets are supplied
directly. The brewery specialises in high quality ales
made with the best ingredients. Some of the strongest
beers are only available in bottled-conditioned form.
Bespoke beers for individual pubs are also brewed.
‼■◆RAIB V

Burston's Cuckoo (ABV 3.8%)
Gentle malt airs. Biscuity, sweet beginning with delicate
lime hints. Full-bodied, short, sweet finish.
Bitter (ABV 4.2%)
Norfolk's 80 Shilling Ale (ABV 4.5%)
Mixed fruit nose introduces a sweet fruity bitter with a
bitter counterbalance. Short, drying finish.
Dark Horse Stout (ABV 5%)
Solid coffee and malt aroma. A cornucopia of vanilla,
dark chocolate, and roast with a sweet foundation. Long,
strong finale.
Golden Pale Ale (ABV 5%)
Full-bodied, with a swirling malty aroma. Lime fruit adds
depth to the sweet malty character. Short, sweetening
finish.
Nightlight Mild (ABV 5.7%)
A heavy mix of liquorice, roast and malt infuses aroma
and first taste. A sweet spiciness slowly develops.

Elusive SIBA

Unit 5, Marino Way, Hogwood Lane Industrial Estate,
Finchampstead, Berkshire, RG40 4RF ☎ 07917
541718 ⊕ elusivebrewing.com

Elusive is a five-barrel brewery, which began brewing in
2016. With a fermenting capacity of 28 barrels, it
produces a diverse range of cask, KeyKeg, bottled and
canned beers and continues to be involved in many
collaborations. Its on-site taproom has three flatscreens
with controls for people to play retro computer games
and sells the range of beers, beers from other breweries
plus other related merchandise. ■◆RAIB ◆

Punch Out (ABV 4.3%)
Sphere of Destiny (ABV 4.4%)

Level Up (ABV 5%)
Shadow of the Beast (ABV 5%)
Overdrive (ABV 5.5%)
Spellbinder (ABV 6%)

Empire SIBA

The Old Boiler House, Unit 33, Upper Mills, Slaithwaite, West Yorkshire, HD7 5HA
☎ (01484) 847343 ☎ 07966 592276
empirebrewing.com

Empire Brewing was set up 2006 in a mill on the bank of the scenic Huddersfield Narrow Canal, close to the centre of Slaithwaite. In 2011 the brewery upgraded from a five-barrel to a 12-barrel plant. Beers are supplied to local free houses and through independent specialist beer agencies and wholesalers. !! ♦ RAIB

Golden Warrior (ABV 3.8%)
Moonrakers Mild (ABV 3.8%)
Strikes Back (ABV 4%)
Smoking Pistol (ABV 4.3%)
Porter (ABV 5%)

Emsworth

Unit 45, Basepoint Business Centre, Havant, Hampshire, PO9 1HS ☎ 07840 876854
theemsworthbrewhouse.co.uk

Emsworth Brewhouse was launched in 2015 as a half-barrel plant, and upgraded to 1.5-barrels in 2016. It was sold in 2017 and is now in the capable hands of Jonathan Khoo, who has moved it to larger premises in Havant with a shop and taproom. The brewery has moved away from bottles and now sells all its beers in cans. All beers are unfined and vegan-friendly. V

Mainsail (ABV 3.8%)
Starboard (ABV 4%)
Flotilla (ABV 4.4%)
Wodehouse (ABV 4.8%)
Portside (ABV 5.2%)
SkIPA (ABV 5.4%)

Enfield SIBA

Unit 17a, Eley Road, Edmonton, London, N18 3BB
☎ (020) 8807 1533 enfieldbrewery.co.uk

Brewing started in 2015 concentrating on bottled and keg beers with cask beers following in 2017. The beers use the brewery's well water and are sold under the Enefeld name, the Saxon spelling for Enfield. The range has been expanded during 2019 with availability increasing around North London and beyond, the beers proving popular in local Wetherspoon pubs.

Brewed under the Enefeld brand name:
EB (ABV 4%)
Light-bodied, amber, traditional bitter with caramel and slightly spicy hops aroma. Bready, caramel taste with hoppy notes. Bitter finish.
Iron Brew (ABV 4.2%)
A rich, smooth malty sweet beer with a floral aroma, some fruit notes and lasting, hoppy finish.
Speculation (ABV 4.8%)
London Pale Ale (ABV 5%)
London Porter (ABV 5.5%)
Ovaltine and cocoa aroma. Chocolate flavour with damsons and a little apple. Dark chocolate with a little fruit that fades.
London IPA (ABV 6.5%)
Smooth, gold beer with spicy hops. A developing bitterness overlaid with sweet honey and tangerine in the lingering, dry aftertaste.

Engine Shed Project

See Brunswick

Engineer

Russetts, Burnt Oak Road, High Hurstwood, East Sussex, TN22 4AE ☎ 07841 669096
theengineerbrewery.co.uk

A brewery that provides a wide variety of historic, traditional and contemporary beer styles to three local pubs. Beers can also be enjoyed at local beer festivals, and are available in bottles at the Cooper's Arms, and Five Ash Down Post Office. V

Ennerdale SIBA

Chapel Row, Rowrah, Cumbria, CA26 3XS
☎ (01946) 862977 ☎ 07918 626652
ennerdalebrewery.co.uk

This family-owned brewery began brewing in 2010 as a 10-barrel brewery in a converted barn. In 2016 the brewery moved to larger premises with plans for expansion. It distributes throughout Cumbria and the North of England. The brewery tap is open daily. !! ♦

Blonde (ABV 3.8%)
A sweet, fruity, light-coloured beer with gentle bitterness.
Darkest (ABV 4.2%)
Sweet, roasty, black mild with a fruity hoppy flavour.
Ennerdale Wild (ABV 4.2%)

Enville SIBA

Coxgreen, Hollies Lane, Enville, DY7 5LG
☎ (01384) 873728 envilleales.com

Enville Brewery is sited on a picturesque Victorian, Grade II-listed farm complex, using natural well water, traditional steam brewing and a reed and willow-effluent plant. Enville Ale is infused with honey and is from a 19th-century recipe for beekeeper's ale passed down from the former proprietor's great-great aunt. ♦

Nailmaker Mild (ABV 4%)
Simpkiss (ABV 4%)
Caramel-smooth start, caramel body with sweet malt and hop bite. Fruity hop finish, easing finish and satisfying.
American Pale Ale (ABV 4.2%)
White (ABV 4.2%)
Yellow with a malt, hops and fruit aroma. Hoppy but sweet finish.
Ale (ABV 4.5%)
Sweet malty aroma and taste, honey becomes apparent before bitterness finally dominates.
Old Porter (ABV 4.5%)
Black with a creamy head and sulphurous aroma. Sweet and fruity start with touches of spice. Good balance between sweet and bitter, but hops dominate the finish.
Ginger Beer (ABV 4.6%)
Golden bright with gently-gingered tangs. A drinkable beer with no acute flavours but a satisfying aftertaste of sweet hoppiness.

Epic Beers

The Brewery, West Hewish, Somerset, BS24 6RR
☎ (01934) 384044 pitchforkales.com / 3D-beer.com

Epic Beers was formed in 2017 on the site of the former RCH brewery, with several of the original staff, including head brewer Graham Dunbavan. Epic trade under two distinct brands. Pitchfork beers are cask-conditioned and made only with 100% British ingredients. Many specials add to the regular brews. 3D Beers produce monthly specials using international hops (mostly cask but some keg too). It opened its first pub in Weston-Super-Mare in 2019. ‼🍴◆RAIB

Brewed under the Pitchfork Ales brand name:
Goldbine (ABV 3.8%)
PG Steam (ABV 3.9%)
Light malt and faint hop aroma. Pale fruit combines with dry bitterness in the flavour, before a lasting, dry aftertaste.
Pitchfork (ABV 4.3%)
Pale gold-coloured, some hops on the nose, flavours combine light malt with citrus hop bitterness, lingering dry and bitter aftertaste.
Old Slug Porter (ABV 4.5%)
East Street Cream (ABV 5%)

Epic Brewing

Unit 2, Ty Mawr Enterprise Park, Tan Y Graig Road, Conwy, LL29 8UE
☎ (0161) 468 2775

Office: Beehive Mill, Jersey Street, Manchester, M4 6JG ⊕ epicbrewing.co.uk

Epic Brewing was started in 2018 by two brewing and cask beer enthusiasts, one of whom is a successful publican. Beer is brewed using spare capacity at Conwy Brewery. Monthly guest brews supplement the core range of ales. Outlets are supplied throughout North Wales and the North West of England. Brewing is currently suspended.

Errant

Arch 8 King Edward Bridge, off Pottery Lane, Newcastle upon Tyne, NE1 3TQ ☎ 07736 333303
⊕ errantbrewery.com

⊗ Brewing began in 2015 in an old Victorian railway arch. A range of speciality beers is available seasonally or on request. ◆

Escape (NEW)

922 Wigan Road, Bolton, BL3 4RN ☎ 07341 810387

Office: 48 Longworth Road, Horwich, Bolton, BL6 7BE
✉ phil@escapebrewery.co.uk

Small brewery launched officially in 2019. Currently brewing four regular beers and one occasional beer on a one-barrel plant.

Erik Weisz (ABV 4.4%)
Frank Morris (ABV 4.5%)
Tom, Dick & Harry (ABV 4.5%)
Virgil Hilts (ABV 5%)

Essex Street

🍴 **46 Essex Street, Temple, London, WC2R 3JF**
☎ (020) 7936 2536 ⊕ templebrewhouse.com

☺Opened in 2014 within the Temple Brew House pub. Beers are neither filtered nor pasteurised. The City Pub Group also operates sister brewpubs in Bath, Bristol, Cambridge and Norwich. ‼◆

Evan Evans SIBA

The New Brewery, 1 Rhosmaen Street, Llandeilo, Carmarthenshire, SA19 6LU
☎ (01558) 824455 ⊕ evanevansbrewery.com

⊗ Evan Evans has been in operation since 2004. The range of beer brands produced includes: Evan-Evans, J Buckley, which focusses on hop flavour, Artisan, a US-style craft beer brand; Fire-Island, Celt Experience and Archers. The brewery also bottles its own brands as well as bottling product of other independent breweries. The brewery now markets its own traditional and berry flavour cider in standard and low alcohol lines as well as its own Liberty lager. ‼🍴◆RAIB

WPA (Welsh Pale Ale) (ABV 4.1%)
Cwrw (ABV 4.2%)
Brittania (ABV 4.6%)
Warrior (ABV 4.6%)
Organic Welsh Gold (ABV 5%)

Everards

Office: Everards Meadows, Leicestershire, LE19 2AN
☎ (0116) 201 4100 ⊕ everards.co.uk

Everards was established in 1849 by William Everard and remains an independent fifth generation family-owned company. It has a pub estate of more than 173 throughout the East Midlands. Its new state of the art brewery, comprising of offices, beer hall and shop is due to open in late 2020. Its beers are, in the interim, brewed by Robinsons and Purity (qv). Its limited edition beers are brewed by selected brewing partners.

Exale (NEW)

Unit 2C, Uplands Trading Estate, Blackhorse Lane, Walthamstow, London, E17 5QJ ⊕ exalebrewing.com

Originally started as Hale Brewery in Tottenham in the former Affinity brewery container in 2017. 2019 saw expansion by starting a new brewery in Walthamstow with a new name. The site doubles as a busy taproom at the weekend and is one of four breweries within walking distance of each other. ◆

Exe Valley SIBA

Land Farm, Silverton, Exeter, Devon, EX5 4HF
☎ (01392) 860406 ⊕ exevalleybrewery.co.uk

⊗ Exe Valley was established as Barron's Brewery in 1984. The brewery is located in a converted barn overlooking the Exe Valley and Dartmoor hills. Locally sourced malt and English hops are used, along with the brewery's own spring water. Around 100 outlets are supplied within a 45-mile radius of the brewery. Beers are also available nationally via wholesalers. ◆RAIB

Bitter (ABV 3.7%)
Mid-brown bitter, pleasantly fruity with underlying malt through the aroma, taste and finish.
Barron's Hopsit (ABV 4.1%)
Straw-coloured beer with strong hop aroma, hop and fruit flavour and a bitter hop finish.
Dob's Best Bitter (ABV 4.1%)
Delicate aroma, well-balanced taste with malt, hops and sweet fruit continuing into a bitter, hoppy aftertaste.
Fryer's Thirst (ABV 4.3%)
Devon Glory (ABV 4.7%)
Mr Sheppard's Crook (ABV 4.7%)
Smooth, full-bodied, mid-brown beer with a malty-fruit nose, and a sweetish palate leading to a bitter, dry finish.
Exeter Old Bitter (ABV 4.8%)
Mid-brown old ale with a rich, fruity taste, and slightly earthy aroma and bitter finish.
It's Phil's Ale (ABV 4.8%)

Exeter SIBA

Unit 1, Cowley Bridge Road, Exeter, Devon, EX4 4NX

☎ (01392) 259059 🌐 exeterbrewery.co.uk

⊗ Exeter began brewing in 2003 and is the largest brewery in the city, supplying more than 600 outlets in Devon, Cornwall, Dorset and Somerset. It moved to its present site in 2012, having outgrown its previous location. ‼ ♦

Lighterman (ABV 3.5%)
Tomahawk (ABV 3.5%)
Slight biscuit/malty aroma, biscuit and a tinge of orange, and a slight toffee, bitter finish.
Avocet (ABV 3.9%)
A lager-coloured bitter, fruity and sweet from nose to aftertaste. Slight maltyness balances pineapple. Light session ale.
'fraid Not (ABV 4%)
Ferryman (ABV 4.2%)
Lovely-flavoured, session bitter, a mix of sweet/bitterness.
County Best (ABV 4.6%)
Darkness (ABV 5.1%)
Full-bodied stout. Roasted malt dominates the aroma. Complex taste with roast chocolate. Hints of liquorice in a bitter finish.

Exile

See Exmoor

Exit 33

Unit 1, Petre Drive, Sheffield, South Yorkshire, S4 7PZ ☎ (0114) 270 9991 🌐 exit33.beer

This eight-barrel brewery was founded in Sheffield in 2008 as Brew Company but rebranded in 2014. The brewer is also a joint partner at the Harlequin pub. Regular house beers are brewed for local pubs. Beers are available nationally. ♦V

Thirst Aid (ABV 4%)
Mosaic (ABV 4.1%)
Northern Best (ABV 4.2%)
Hop Monster (ABV 4.5%)
Oat Stout (ABV 5%)

Exmoor SIBA

Golden Hill Brewery, Old Brewery Road, Wiveliscombe, Somerset, TA4 2PW ☎ (01984) 623798 🌐 exmoorales.co.uk

Somerset's largest independent brewery was founded in 1980 in the old Hancock's brewery, which closed in 1959. In 2015 it moved to new, larger premises within 100 yards of the original site, doubling capacity. More than 250 outlets in the South West are supplied, plus others nationwide via wholesalers and pub chains. In 2017 it developed a sub-brand, Exile Ales, to represent a new, modern breed of beers. ‼♦

Ale (ABV 3.8%)
Mid-brown, medium-bodied, session bitter. Mixture of malt and hops in the aroma and taste lead to a hoppy, bitter aftertaste.
Fox (ABV 4.2%)
Gold (ABV 4.5%)
Golden best bitter with balance of malt and fruity hop on the nose and palate, with sweetness following. Bitter finish.
Stag (ABV 5.2%)
A pale brown beer, with a malty taste and aroma, and a bitter finish.
Beast (ABV 6.6%)

Experimental

See Dog's Window

Eyam

Unit 4, Eyam Hall Craft Centre, Main Road, Eyam, Hope Valley, Derbyshire, S32 5QW ☎ 07976 432682 🌐 eyamrealalecompany.com

Brewing began in 2017 using a 1.5-barrel plant producing keg and bottle-conditioned beers. Most output goes to its shop and events but 10 local outlets are also supplied.

Eyeball

The Works, Implement Road, West Barns, Dunbar, EH42 1UN ☎ 07764 606510 🌐 eyeballbrewing.co.uk

Eyeball Brewing was established in 2016 by James Dempsey, who developed a passion for lager while travelling through Germany. Inspired, he built a brewery in his home and began to experiment. Now housed in a new brewery on the East Lothian coast, Eyeball produces three lagers in cask, keg and bottle.

Fable

c/o George's Brewery, Common Road, Great Wakering, Essex, SS3 0AG 🌐 fablebrewery.com

A cuckoo brewery specialising in vegan beers. V

Genesis Pale Ale (ABV 3.8%)
Let's Get Lost in the Woods Together (ABV 4.5%)

Facer's

A8-9, Ashmount Enterprise Park, Aber Road, Flint, CH6 5YL ☎ 07713 566370 🌐 facers.co.uk

Set up in 2003 by the now retired Dave Facer, the brewery is now operated by long-time employee Toby Dunn, It is the oldest brewery in Flintshire. Sales average some 30 barrels per week to around 100 outlets in North Wales and north west England. ‼♦

Mountain Mild (ABV 3.3%)
A fruity dark mild, not too sweet, with underlying roast malt flavours and a full mouthfeel for its low ABV.
Clwyd Gold (ABV 3.5%)
Clean-tasting session bitter, mid-brown in colour with a full mouthfeel. The malty flavours are accompanied by increasing hoppiness in the bitter finish.
Flintshire Bitter (ABV 3.7%)
Well-balanced, session bitter with a full mouthfeel. Some fruitiness in aroma and taste with increasing hoppy bitterness in the dry finish.
Abbey Blonde (ABV 4%)
Abbey Original (ABV 4%)
A sweetish golden beer with a good hop and fruit aroma, juicy taste and a dry hoppy finish.
Abbey Red (ABV 4%)
A darker version of Abbey Original, copper-coloured with a sweet, malty taste and a bittersweet aftertaste.
North Star Porter (ABV 4%)
Dark, smooth, porter-style beer with good roast notes and hints of coffee and chocolate. Some initial sweetness and caramel flavours followed by a hoppy bitter aftertaste.
Sunny Bitter (ABV 4.2%)
An amber beer with a dry taste. The hop aroma continues into the taste where some faint fruit notes are also present. Lasting, dry finish.
DHB (Dave's Hoppy Beer) (ABV 4.3%)

THE BREWERIES

A dry-hopped version of Splendid Ale with some sweet flavours also coming through in the mainly hoppy, bitter taste.
This Splendid Ale (ABV 4.3%)
Refreshing, tangy best bitter, yellow in colour with a sharp hoppy, bitter taste. Good citrus fruit undertones with hints of grapefruit throughout.
Landslide (ABV 4.9%)
Full-flavoured, complex premium bitter with tangy orange marmalade fruitiness in aroma and taste. Long-lasting hoppy flavours throughout.

Fairy Glen

5 The Corn Store, Heol Ty Gwyn, Maesteg, CF34 0BG
☎ 07968 847878

Office: 60 Oaklands Avenue, Bridgend, CF31 4ST
🌐 fgbltd.co.uk

Brewing began in 2018. No real ale.

Faithless

See RedWillow

Faking Bad

Prestoungrange Gothenburg, 227-229 High Street, Prestonpans, EH32 9BE 🌐 fakingbadbrewery.co.uk

Faking Bad was established in 2018 by chemistry teachers and avid homebrewers Gareth Evans and Gordon Kidd. All beers are unfined and unfiltered and are available in the Prestoungrange Gothenburg. RAIB V

Fallen

Kippen Station, Kippen, FK8 3JA ☎ 07507 862167
🌐 fallenbrewing.co.uk

Fallen began brewing in 2014 using a 10-barrel plant and now brews four times a week. The brewery has also installed a canning line. Electricity is from 100% renewable sources. All waste malt goes to local farmers for cattle feed, while waste hops are composted for the garden. Beers are supplied throughout central Scotland (and further afield) and its beer can always be found at the Cross Keys in Kippen. ♦RAIB

Local Motive (ABV 3.9%)
Odyssey (ABV 4.1%)
Grapevine (ABV 5.4%)
Chew Chew (ABV 6%)
Platform C (ABV 6.3%)

Fallen Acorn SIBA

Unit 7, Clarence Wharf Industrial Estate, Mumby Road, Gosport, Hampshire, PO12 1AJ
☎ (023) 9307 9927 🌐 fallenacornbrewing.co

Fallen Acorn is a 15-barrel microbrewery based in Gosport, resurrected from the ashes of the Oakleaf brewery in 2016. With 25 years experience in brewing, the brewing team is able to explore a multitude of styles and flavours including traditional ales, real lagers and flavoured beers. !! ♦ RAIB V

She Sings Sea Shanties (ABV 3.7%)
Twisted Oak (ABV 4%)
Pompey Royal (ABV 4.3%)
Black Hearted (ABV 4.7%)
Hole Hearted (ABV 4.7%)
Amber-coloured with a strong floral hop aroma continuing into the flavour, with some malt, leading to a long, bittersweet finish.
Expedition IPA (ABV 5.5%)
Crimea River (ABV 9%)

Fallen Angel SIBA

Unit 21c, Reeds Farm Estate Roxwell Road, Writtle, CM1 3ST
☎ (01245) 767220 🌐 fallenangel-brewery.co.uk

Formerly known as the Broxbourne Brewery, a name change to Fallen Angel occured in 2017. Brewing began in 2013 using a 12-barrel plant. A 15-barrel plant has been in operation since the brewery's move from Hertfordshire to Essex in 2015.

Falstaff

24 Society Place, Normanton, Derby, DE23 6UH
☎ (01332) 342902 ☎ 07947 242710
🌐 falstaffbrewery.co.uk

Attached to the Falstaff freehouse, the brewery dates from 1999 but was refurbished and reopened in 2003 under new management. More than 30 outlets are supplied. ♦

Faringdon

1 Park Road, Faringdon, Oxfordshire, SN7 7BP
☎ (01367) 241480

Faringdon brewery opened in 2010 using a one-barrel plant with brewing on a larger scale beginning in 2011. After a period of closure, brewing restarted in 2019. All beers are supplied to the brewery tap, the Swan, when available. ♦

Farm Yard

Gulf Lane, Cockerham, LA2 0ER
☎ (01253) 799988 ☎ 07717 081170
🌐 farmyardales.co.uk

This family-run brewery commenced brewing in 2017 and has now expanded to 12 barrels with a canning plant. It also provides contract brewing services. !! ♦

Holmes Stead (ABV 3.4%)
TVO 54 (ABV 3.7%)
Haybob (ABV 3.9%)
Sheaf (ABV 4.1%)
Hoof (ABV 4.3%)
Chaff (ABV 4.7%)
Gulf IPA (ABV 5.8%)

Farmageddon

25 Ballykeigle Road, Comber, BT23 5SD ☎ 07966 809481 🌐 farmageddonbrewing.com

Co-operative brewery, formed in 2014. All beers are unfiltered with no preservatives. ♦RAIB V

Gold (ABV 4.2%)
Session (ABV 4.8%)
India Export Porter (ABV 5.2%)
IPA (ABV 5.5%)
Mosaic IPA (ABV 6.3%)

Farmer's

See Maldon

Farr Brew SIBA

Unit 7, The Courtyard, Samuels Farm, Coleman Green Lane, Wheathampstead, Hertfordshire, AL4 8ER
☎ 07967 998820 🌐 farrbrew.com

⊠ Farr Brew began brewing in 2014. The beers proved popular necessitating a move to a brand new 10-barrel brewery in 2016. Ecological and environmental concerns are at the forefront of everything Farr Brew creates. A micropub and bottle shop, the Reading Rooms, opened in Wheathampstead in 2018 and the Rising Sun, Slip End, in 2019. ‼◆

Chief Jester (ABV 3.6%)
Our Greatest Golden (ABV 4.1%)
Our Most Perfect Pale (ABV 4.2%)
The Best Bitter (ABV 4.2%)
Black Listed IBA (ABV 4.5%)
Our Most Potent Porter (ABV 5%)

Farriers Arms

▤ The Forstal, Mersham, Kent, TN25 6NU
☎ (01233) 720444 ⊕ thefarriersarms.com

Brewing commenced in 2010 in this brewpub owned by a consortium of villagers. ‼◆

Fat Belly

Unit 8, Commercial Point, Mullacott Cross Industrial Estate, Ilfracombe, Devon, EX34 8PL
☎ (01598) 753496 ⊕ thecottageinnlynton.co.uk

⊠ Established in Lynbridge in 2016 at the Cottage Inn, using a three-barrel plant located at the rear of the pub. It relocated to its current premises in 2018, installing a new 10-barrel plant. As well as the pub it also supplies a growing number of outlets in the Exmoor area. Further beers are planned. ◆RAIB V

FPA Pale Ale (ABV 3.8%)
Guzzler (ABV 3.8%)
Ocean Gold (ABV 4.2%)
Carver Doone (ABV 4.5%)

Fat Cat

▤ Fat Cat Brewery Tap, 98-100 Lawson Road, Norwich, NR3 4LF
☎ (01603) 788508 ☎ 07795 633368
⊕ fatcatbrewery.co.uk

⊠ Established in 2005 by the mini pub chain's founder, the brewery is based at the Fat Cat Brewery Tap in Norwich. Beers can be sampled in the other pubs in the Fat Cat chain. ‼◆RAIB

Fat Pig

▤ Fat Pig, 2 John Street, Exeter, Devon, EX1 1BL
☎ (01392) 437217 ⊕ fatpig-exeter.co.uk

⊠ Brewing commenced in 2013 using a 2.5-barrel plant to supply the Fat Pig pub. It is run as an experimental brewery, constantly playing with combinations of malts, hops and temperatures to improve the range of beers, and to push the boundaries. In 2018, the brewery briefly relocated to below St Thomas station in Exeter, alongside the distillery making gin and Exeter's first whisky but in 2019 returned to the basement of the Fat Pig pub. ◆V

Faversham Steam

See Shepherd Neame

Fearless Nomad (NEW)

▤ Black Dog Beer House, 17 Albany Road, Brentford, TW8 0NF
☎ (020) 8568 5688 ⊕ blackdogbeerhouse.co.uk/ fearless-nomad

The Fearless Nomad Brewery is owned by Pete Brew who previously helped to set up the Big Smoke Brewery. Beginning in 2020, it is a small one-barrel brew plant producing a variety of different beers served in the Black Dog Beer House. There are plans to increase brewing capacity, distribute to other venues and introduce a canned range.

Federation

▤ 48 Greenwood Street, Altrincham, WA14 1RZ
☎ (0161) 696 6870 ⊕ conclubuk.com

Located in the Con Club, a pub with restaurant that was formerly Altrincham Working Mens Conservative Club, this is a small 2.4-barrel plant that began brewing in 2017. Several new seasonal and speciality beers have been produced in addition to the core range. Brewing is currently suspended.

Felday

▤ Royal Oak, Village Green, Felday Glade, Holmbury St. Mary, Surrey, RH5 6PF
☎ (01306) 730654 ⊕ feldaybrewery.co.uk

Brewing began in 2017 on a custom-made plant in a small, purpose-built, building next to the Royal Oak pub car park. Almost all of the beer is supplied to the pub although it may very occasionally be seen elsewhere. ◆

Felinfoel SIBA

Farmers Row, Felinfoel, Llanelli, SA14 8LB
☎ (01554) 773357 ⊕ felinfoel-brewery.com

Founded in the 1830s, the company is still family-owned and is now the oldest brewery in Wales. The present buildings are Grade II*-listed and were built in the 1870s. It supplies cask ale to half its 84 houses (though some use top pressure dispense), and to approximately 350 free trade outlets. ‼🍴◆

Felinfoel IPA (ABV 3.6%)
Celtic Pride (ABV 3.9%)
Double Dragon (ABV 4.2%)
This pale brown beer has a malty, fruity aroma. The taste is also malt and fruit with a background hop presence throughout. A malty and fruity finish.
Stout (ABV 5%)

Fell

Unit 27, Moor Lane Business Park, Flookburgh, Cumbria, LA11 7NG
☎ (01539) 558980 ☎ 07967 503689
⊕ fellbrewery.co.uk

⊠ Fell Brewery was founded in 2012 by homebrewer Tim Bloomer and friend Andrew Carter, brewing beers inspired by their travels in the US and Belgium. Production capacity has now increased from 12 to 15 barrels. It has three retail outlets situated in Chorlton (near Manchester), Kendal and Penrith. ◆

Ghyll (ABV 3.7%)
A yellow, highly-drinkable, hoppy session bitter with a long, drying, bitter finish.
Crag (ABV 3.8%)
Tinderbox IPA (ABV 6.3%)

Fellows

2 Leopold Walk, Cottenham, Cambridge, Cambridgeshire, CB24 8XS
☎ (01954) 250262 ⊕ fellowsbrewery.co.uk

⊗ Fellows began production in 2010 though brewer Mark Burton had been developing recipes for a year or so before. Five regular beers are available with plans for a series of special ales. Beers are increasingly visible in the local free trade.

Cambridge Fellow (ABV 3.8%)
Gulping Fellow (ABV 4.2%)
Burton Snatch (ABV 4.8%)
Jolly Fellows (ABV 5%)
Clever Fellow (ABV 5.2%)

Fengate

23 Fengate, Marsham, Norfolk, NR10 5PT
☎ (01263) 479953 ☎ 07884 960697
✉ fengatebrewery@gmail.com

Fengate Brewery was established in 2019.

Nightjar Rye & Oat Stout (ABV 3.6%)
Sunstone Pale Ale (ABV 3.8%)
Three Threads (ABV 4%)
Opus (ABV 4.2%)
John Barleycorn Bitter (ABV 4.4%)
California Common Ale (ABV 4.7%)
Pacific Gem (ABV 4.8%)
Jamadhar (ABV 5.5%)

Fermanagh

75 Main St, Derrygonnelly, BT93 6HW
☎ (028) 6864 1254

Now known as Fermanagh Beer Company but still using the Inishmacsaint brand, this small-scale brewery has been producing a range of bottle-conditioned beers since 2009. RAIB

Fernandes

5 Avison Yard, Kirkgate, Wakefield, West Yorkshire, WF1 1UA
☎ (01924) 291709 ⊕ ossett-brewery.co.uk

Opened in 1997 and housed in a 19th-century malthouse, Ossett Brewing Company purchased the brewery and tap in 2007 but independent brewing continues. Around 90 different beers are brewed each year. The tap sells Fernandes and Ossett beers as well as guest ales; the former are more widely available through Ossett's supply chain. ‼♦

Polaris (ABV 3.9%)
Black Voodoo (ABV 5.1%)

Ferry Ales SIBA

Ferry Hill Farm, Ferry Road, Fiskerton, Lincolnshire, LN3 4HU ☎ 07790241999 ⊕ ferryalesbrewery.co.uk

Ferry Ales Brewery (FAB) began brewing in 2016 using a five-barrel plant. It is situated just outside Fiskerton, Lincolnshire. Beers can be found in the Lincoln area and beyond.

Just Jane (ABV 3.8%)
Spirit of Jane (ABV 3.8%)
Lincoln Lager (ABV 4.3%)
Golden Fleece (ABV 4.5%)
Witham Shield (ABV 4.5%)
Slippery Hitch (ABV 4.7%)
49 SQN (ABV 4.9%)
Smokey Joe (ABV 4.9%)

Ferry Brewery SIBA

Bankhead Farm, Steading, Bankhead Road, South Queensferry, EH30 9TF
☎ (0131) 331 1851 ⊕ ferrybrewery.co.uk

The first brewery in South Queensferry since 1851, Ferry Brewery was established in 2016 by Mark Moran and has an on-site taproom and shop. Its beers combine traditional and historic beer recipes with a contemporary twist as well as modern-style beers. Brewery tasting tours are also available for group bookings. ‼ ♦ RAIB V

Fair (ABV 4%)
Light and fruity with some bitterness. A complex, golden session ale.
Smokey Jack (ABV 4%)
Smoked malt gives this beer the characteristic taste of a rauchbier. Sweetness in the initial taste followed by a smoky bitter aftertaste.
40/- Fine (ABV 4.2%)
A light take on a traditional 80/- style. Malty with a balance of sweetness and bitterness.
Crossing (ABV 4.5%)
Refreshing, fruity golden ale with good malt balance. A fruity aroma and taste followed by increasing bitterness.
Three Bridges (ABV 4.5%)
Witches Brew (ABV 4.5%)
Full-bodied, brown bitter with distinctive malt flavour and bittersweet finish.
Stout (ABV 4.9%)
Well-balanced stout with hints of chocolate and subtle roast coffee flavours.
Thomas Miller 1785 (ABV 5.5%)

Fierce

Unit 49, Howe Moss Avenue, Dyce, Aberdeen, AB21 0GP
☎ (01224) 035035 ⊕ fiercebeer.com

The multi-award-winning Fierce Beer was established by Dave Grant and David McHardy, brewing its first beer in 2016. It produces a range of hoppy, fruity, dark and speciality beers plus a limited range of spirits. Production is KeyKeg and bottles. Two bars are owned, in Aberdeen and Edinburgh.

Fierce & Noble

25 Mina Road, St Werburgh's, Bristol, BS2 9TA
☎ (0117) 955 6666 ⊕ fierceandnoble.com

Founded in 2017 to supply beer to the Grounded community café chain in Bristol, beers can now be found across Bristol and the South West. A range of IPAs and occasional specials are brewed on an eight-barrel plant. The on-site tap room and brewery shop regularly hold events, and are open year round on Fridays, Saturdays and Sundays. ‼

Session IPA (ABV 4.2%)

FILO

The Old Town Brewery, Torfield Cottage, 8 Old London Road, Hastings, East Sussex, TN34 3HA
☎ (01424) 420212 ⊕ filobrewing.co.uk

⊗ The brewery at the First In Last Out public house was established in 1985, with the current owners taking over in 1988. In 2011 the brewery relocated two minutes' walk away, remaining in the Old Town. The First In Last Out (FILO) is still supplied direct together with pubs throughout Sussex and Kent. ‼♦

Crofters (ABV 3.8%)
Churches Pale Ale (ABV 4.2%)
Old Town Tom (ABV 4.5%)
Gold (ABV 4.8%)

Fine Tuned SIBA

Unit 16, Wessex Park, Bancombe Trading Estate, Bancombe Road, Somerton, Somerset, TA11 6SB
☎ (01458) 897273 ☎ 07872 139945
finetunedbrewery.com

Established in Langport, Somerset in 2016, but relocated to its current site in 2017. ♦RAIB

Pitch Perfect (ABV 3.8%)
Langport Bitter (ABV 4%)
Sunshine Reggae (ABV 4.2%)
Free Style (ABV 4.5%)
Twist & Stout (ABV 4.5%)
Hop Culture (ABV 5%)

Finney's

51 Wrockwardine Road, Wellington, Shropshire, TF1 3DA
☎ (01952) 412224 ✉ finney@blueyonder.co.uk

A microbrewery of a half-barrel capacity, which supplies local pubs.

Fintry SIBA

23 Main Street, Fintry, G63 0XA
☎ (01360) 860224 ☎ 07833 662820
✉ bill@fintrymusos.co.uk

Fintry Brewery was established in 2013 in premises at the Fintry Inn. After expansion in 2015, it now uses an 18-barrel plant. The beers are always available in the Fintry Inn (different ownership) as well as throughout Stirlingshire and selected outlets in Glasgow and southern Scotland. The brewery has now expanded its outlets into Carlisle and the Northern Lake District. !!♦

Kiltrochan Ale (ABV 3.6%)
Clachertyfarlie (ABV 3.9%)
Corrie of Balglass (ABV 4.6%)

Firebird SIBA

Old Rudgwick Brickworks, Lynwick Street, Rudgwick, West Sussex, RH12 3UW
☎ (01403) 823180 firebirdbrewing.co.uk

Firebird began brewing in 2013 and has grown rapidly with new beers, new vessels, an extended warehouse and an expanded team. There is a comfortable upstairs bar on-site. !!♦RAIB V

Two Horses (ABV 3.8%)
Heritage XX (ABV 4%)
Parody (ABV 4.5%)
Festive 51 (ABV 4.8%)

Firebrand

See Altarnun

Firebrick SIBA

Units 10 & 11, Blaydon Business Centre, Cowen Road, Blaydon-on-Tyne, Tyne & Wear, NE21 5TW
☎ (0191) 447 6543 firebrickbrewery.com

Firebrick began brewing on a 2.5-barrel plant in 2013, expanding to a 15-barrel plant in 2014. Beers are mostly available in pubs within the Tyne & Wear area and a few outlets further afield. ♦

Blaydon Brick (ABV 3.8%)
Coalface (ABV 3.9%)
Elder Statesman (ABV 3.9%)
Tyne 9 (ABV 3.9%)
Pagan Queen (ABV 4%)
Little Belgium (ABV 4.2%)
Trade Star (ABV 4.2%)
Stella Spark (ABV 4.4%)
Toon Broon (ABV 4.6%)
Cushie Butterfield (ABV 5%)
Wey – Aye P. A. (ABV 5.8%)

Firehouse

13 Thames Street, Louth, Lincolnshire, LN11 7AD
☎ (01507) 608202 ☎ 07961 772905
firehouse-brewery.co.uk

Owned by Jason Allen and Louise Darbon, Firehouse Brewery was founded in 2014 and started production in the village of Manby on part of the site of the former RAF station. In 2016 a 2.5-barrel plant was purchased from Fulstow Brewery and relocated to the Thames Street Brewery in Louth, where both brewery's beers are brewed. Beers are available in the free trade and from the bar located at the brewery, the Gas Lamp Lounge. ♦

Mainwarings Mild (ABV 3.6%)
Marsh Mild (ABV 3.8%)
FGB (ABV 3.9%)
Northway IPA (ABV 4.2%)
Woodman Pale Ale (ABV 4.4%)
Pride of Fulstow (ABV 4.5%)
Wobbly Weasel (ABV 4.9%)
Lincolnshire Country Bitter (ABV 5.1%)

FireRock

20-24 Outram Street, Sutton in Ashfield, Nottinghamshire, NG17 4FS ☎ 07875 331898
✉ firerock@mail.co.uk

FireRock Brewing Co is an independent microbrewery and craft beer bar specialising in hop-forward craft beers.

Firs

Station Road, Codsall, Staffordshire, WV8 1BX
☎ (01902) 844674 thefirscodsall.com

Beers are brewed on-site in the CAMRA award-winning Firs club and are exclusive to the club.

First & Last SIBA

Bird in Bush, Village Green, Elsdon, NE19 1AA
☎ (01830) 520804 ☎ 07757 286357
firstandlastbrewery.co.uk

First & Last was established in 2016 by Red Kelly, a founder member of Stu Brew (qv) in Newcastle upon Tyne. It was upgraded to a five-barrel plant in 2018, relocating from Rochester to the Bird in Bush, Elsdon. Other outlets in Northumberland and the Scottish Borders are supplied. !!♦

First Chop

B2 Barton Hall Business Park, Hardy Street, Eccles, M30 7NB ☎ 07970 241398
firstchopbrewingarm.com

Brewing began at Outstanding Brewery (qv) in Bury in 2012 before transferring to Salford in 2013. The brewery relocated again to Eccles in 2017 with increased capacity. It specialises in producing gluten-free beers. GF

AVA (ABV 3.5%)
POD (ABV 4.2%)
SYL (ABV 6.2%)

Fish Key (NEW)

c/o Woodlark Inn, Church Street, Nottingham, NG4 4QB
☎ (0115) 931 2535 ☎ 07814 019250
woodlarkinn.co.uk/micro-brewery

The brewery was originally established in East Looe by Pete and Elaine Delaney in 2016, getting its name from its location on the old fish quay in Looe. It has now relocated into one of the cellars at the Woodlark Inn, Lambley.

Fishponds

Star, 539 Fishponds Road, Fishponds, Bristol, BS16 3AF

Brewing began in 2018 at the family-run pub, the Star, where brothers Eimhin and Cillian look after the brewery while their father, Eimear, runs the attached pub.

Five Kingdoms SIBA

22 Main Street, Isle of Whithorn, DG8 8LF
☎ (01988) 500334 fivekingdomsbrewery.com

Five Kingdoms was established in 2015 by Alastair Scoular, owner of the Steam Packet Inn, using a 2.5-barrel plant. It is situated in the harbourside village of Isle of Whithorn, the most southerly point of the Wigtownshire peninsular in Galloway and a tourist and sailing hotspot. The Brewery supplies numerous local and Scottish outlets, selected national beer festivals, and the Steam Packet Inn. ‼♦

Bright Idea (ABV 3.8%)
Bitter X Blonde (ABV 4%)
Captain Morrison IPA (ABV 6.5%)
Dark Storm Stout (ABV 6.9%)

Five Points SIBA

3 Institute Place, Hackney Downs, London, E8 1JE
☎ (020) 8533 7746 fivepointsbrewing.co.uk

Five Points commenced brewing in 2013 on a 10-barrel plant in a railway arch under Hackney Downs Railway Station. Expansion has been continuous including an off-site depot used for events. 2018 saw successful crowdfunding to continue expanding and to buy the Pembury Tavern, over the road from the brewery (now considered the brewery tap). Cask Ale Care sessions were launched in 2020 to Five Points stockists. RAIB

XPA (ABV 4%)
Golden ale with strong citrus fruitiness, a developing bitterness and a sweet biscuity flavour providing balance. Lingering dry, bitter finish.
Best (ABV 4.1%)
Full-flavoured, amber bitter with earthy hoppy aroma. Dry roasty character overlaid with caramel and orange. Lingering, dry, bitter finish.
Pale (ABV 4.4%)
Quaffable, strong, fruity, bitter golden ale with citrus and tropical fruit fading in the aftertaste where the bitterness lingers.
Railway Porter (ABV 4.8%)
Full-bodied, dark brown porter. Dark chocolate throughout softened by a peppery treacly sweetness and caramelised fruit. Finish mirrors the taste.
Brick Field Brown (ABV 5.4%)
Full-flavoured, ruby-brown beer. Dry-roasted, nutty chocolate notes are balanced by sweet fruity toffee. Dry, bitter, lingering aftertaste.
Hook Island Red (ABV 6%)
Treacle notes on nose and flavour linger in the dry bitterness, which builds on drinking. The mouthfeel is creamy.

Five Towns

651 Leeds Road, Outwood, Wakefield, West Yorkshire, WF1 2LU
☎ (01924) 781887
malcolmbastow@googlemail.com

Five Towns began production on a 2.5-barrel plant in 2008, supplying outlets mainly in Yorkshire but as far afield as Berkshire and the North East. As well as the standard beers a range of themed and speciality brews are also produced. ♦RAIB

Mi Usual (ABV 3.7%)
Middle Un (ABV 4.6%)
Owt'll Do (ABV 4.6%)
Nowt (ABV 6.7%)
One At T'End (ABV 6.7%)
Summat Else (ABV 7.2%)

Fixed Wheel SIBA

Unit 9, Long Lane Trading Estate, Long Lane, Blackheath, West Midlands, B62 9LD ☎ 07766 162794 fixedwheelbrewery.co.uk

Set up in 2014 by cycling and brewing enthusiasts Scott Povey and Sharon Bryant, this full mash brewery is situated on a trading estate on the Blackheath/Halesowen border. It brews several times a week using an eight-barrel plant. Alongside the core range, there are regular single hop and other specials brewed. The award-winning ales are available throughout the Midlands and further afield. ‼♦RAIB

Through & Off (ABV 3.8%)
Wheelie Pale (ABV 4.1%)
Chain Reaction Pale Ale (ABV 4.2%)
Century Gold (ABV 4.8%)
Blackheath Stout (ABV 5%)
Mild Concussion (ABV 5.5%)
Ruby in colour with a creamy head. Aroma is red fruit with a rich, balanced taste and satisfying finish.
No Brakes IPA (ABV 5.9%)

Fizzy Moon

Fizzy Moon, 35 Regent Street, Leamington Spa, Warwickshire, CV32 5EE
☎ (01926) 888715 fizzymoonbrewhouse.com

Fizzy Moon is a bar and microbrewery in the heart of Leamington, brewing a range of small batch beers, exclusively for consumption in the bar.

Flack Manor SIBA

8 Romsey Industrial Estate, Greatbridge Road, Romsey, Hampshire, SO51 0HR
☎ (01794) 518520 flackmanor.co.uk

Flack Manor commenced brewing in 2010 using a 20-barrel plant purchased from Canada. The brewery employs the double drop method of fermentation. Beers are supplied to local outlets within 50 miles of Romsey and may also be found in Wetherspoon pubs. ‼♦RAIB

Flack's Double Drop (ABV 3.7%)
A classic amber session bitter. Hops, malt and some bitterness in the taste, with more hop and some malt in the finish.
Flack Catcher (ABV 4.4%)

A well-balanced, amber best bitter with some fruit aroma and throughout with good hop bitterness in the balanced taste and finish.
Hedge Hop (ABV 4.9%)
Amber-coloured best bitter, some fruit and hop in the aroma with biscuit malt balnced with fruit and spice flavours right through in the taste.

Flagship

c/o Ship & Mitre, 133 Dale Street, Liverpool, L2 2JH
☎ (0151) 236 0859

Launched in 2016, the Ship & Mitre Brewing Co rebranded as Flagship Beer in 2017, and primarily supplies the iconic city centre pub, the Ship & Mitre, with some sales locally and nationally. Beers are brewed using spare capacity at other breweries. ♦

Sublime (ABV 3.7%)
Lupa (ABV 3.8%)
Silhouette (ABV 4.5%)
Vanilla and liquorice aromas with strong malt roast dominating the flavours, a good dry stout with a malt bitter finish.
Jar (ABV 4.7%)
Roast and prune aroma, dry through to finish with bitter roast flavours.
Century (ABV 5%)
Appealing golden beer, very hoppy with light citrus flavours and a dry hoppy finish.

Flash

Moss Top Farm, Moss Top Lane, Flash, Staffordshire, SK17 0TA ✉ flashbrewery@hotmail.com

The brewery is located high in the Peak District and was founded by two friends who brew on a part-time basis. All natural ingredients are used including spring water and seaweed finings which make the beer suitable for vegans. Three bottle-conditioned beers are produced and are sold at Leek Market (only sales outlet). RAIB V

Flash House

Unit 1a, Northumberland Street, North Shields, NE30 1DS ☎ 07481 901875
flashhousebrewing.co.uk

Flash House was set up by Jack O'Keefe in 2016, after a life-long appreciation of ale, influenced by family associated with North East real ale pubs. It aims to bring the best beer styles the world has to offer to the North East, and continues to produce new guest ales. The Brewery and taproom are situated a short walk from the revamped North Shields Fish Quay. ‼ ♦

Kolsch (ABV 4.4%)
Tiny Dancer Pale Ale (ABV 5.4%)

Flipside

c/o Magpie Brewery, Unit 4 Ashling Court, Iremonger Road, Nottingham, NG2 3JA
☎ (0115) 987 7500 ☎ 07958 752334

Office: Old Volunteer, 35 Burton Road, Carlton, NG4 3DQ flipsidebrewery.co.uk

Andrew and Maggie Dunkin established this six-barrel brewery in an industrial unit in Colwick in 2010, expanding to 12-barrels in 2013 in a larger adjacent unit. The brewery opened its own tap, the Old Volunteer, Carlton, in 2014. In 2016 it relocated again to share the plant at Caythorpe Brewery (qv). With the closure of that brewery it now shares with Magpie Brewery (qv). ♦RAIB V

Sterling Pale (ABV 3.9%)
Golden ale with a citrus aroma and hoppy taste, leading to a bitter and peppery finish.
Dark Denomination (ABV 4%)
Bitcoin (ABV 4.1%)
Copper Penny (ABV 4.2%)
Golden Sovereign (ABV 4.2%)
Franc in Stein (ABV 4.3%)
Golden ale with a floral hop aroma, leading to a hoppy and bitter finish.
Random Toss (ABV 4.4%)
Kopek Stout (ABV 4.5%)
Full-bodied, dark stout with a coffee aroma, assertive roast flavours throughout and a balanced bitterness.
Flipping Best (ABV 4.6%)
Brown-coloured, malty, strong bitter with lasting malt, bitterness and subtle hop flavours.
Dusty Penny (ABV 5%)
Clippings IPA (ABV 6.5%)
Russian Rouble (ABV 7.3%)
Strong dark stout with balanced malt, roast and fruit flavours.

Flower Pots SIBA

Brandy Mount, Cheriton, Hampshire, SO24 0QQ
☎ (01962) 771534 theflowerpots.co.uk

Flower Pots began production in 2006. The 10-barrel brewery, and neighbouring pub of the same name, are in a pretty Hampshire village. Besides the three core beers, it brews a variety of seasonal/ special beers. In 2019 the brewery and pub were taken over by three local partners, whilst the two sibling pubs (Wheatsheaf and Albion) were retained by the original owners. ♦

Perridge Pale (ABV 3.6%)
Very pale, easy-drinking golden ale. Honey-scented with high hops, grapefruit and bitterness throughout. Crisp with some citrus notes.
Pots Bitter (ABV 3.8%)
Dry, earthy hop flavours balanced by malt. Good bitterness with some hop in aroma and sharp, bitter finish. Refreshing bitter.
Goodens Gold (ABV 4.8%)
Complex, full-bodied golden ale, bursting with hops and citrus fruit and a snatch of sweetness, leading to long, dry finish.

Flowerhorn (NEW)

The Bridge Studios, 454 Western Avenue, Cardiff, CF5 3BL flowerhornbrewery.co.uk

Established in 2019 by two friends, Andrew and Arran. Brewing was initially on a gypsy basis and beers were available in bottle and keg only. In 2020 the brewery moved to its own premises in Cardiff with a bespoke five-barrel plant. There are plans for expansion and for cask-conditioned beers to be offered occasionally for beer festivals.

Flying Monk

See New Flying Monk

Fonthill

c/o George, 29 Mount Ephraim, Tunbridge Wells, Kent, TN4 8AA
☎ (01892) 539492
thegeorgepubtunbridgewells.co.uk

Fonthill is a small batch brewery located in the George pub. Beers are available in the pub as well as its two sister pubs in Tunbridge Wells.

Fool Hardy SIBA

▤ Hope Inn, 118 Wellington Road North, Heaton Norris, SK4 2LL
☎ (0161) 637 6191 ⊕ foolhardyales.co.uk

😊Martin Wood installed the brewery in the cellar of the Hope Inn. The first beers went on sale in 2013. 2020 saw a totally new beer range due to a change of yeast. Beers are supplied to the free trade, local pubs and festivals.
‼ ➡ ◆ RAIB

#Fooligan (ABV 4.2%)
Dead Man Walking (ABV 5%)

Foraged & Found

See Welbeck Abbey

Forest Road (NEW)

Unit 1a, Elizabeth Industrial Estate, Juno Way, South Bermondsey, London, SE14 5RW
☎ (020) 7249 7033 ⊕ forestroad.co.uk

Forest Road's first brew in 2015 was with the Leroy family in Belgium. Since then the brewery, founded by Pete Brown, has brewed its output in England, settling down in South Bermondsey on the site of the historic Mazawattee tea company. It's taphouse is at Arch 355, Hackney. No real ale. V

Forge

Wilderland, Woolley, Cornwall, EX23 9PW ☎ 07837 487800 ⊕ forge-brewery.co.uk

⊠ This multi-award-winning brewery was set up near Bideford in Devon by Dave Lang, who commenced brewing in 2008 using a five-barrel plant. The brewery relocated to Cornwall in 2017. ◆ RAIB

Discovery (ABV 3.8%)
Gold-coloured bitter bursting with hops from start to finish. Some subtle hints of fruit to the discerning palate too.
Blonde (ABV 4%)
Pale ale with light citrus aroma. Zesty citrus hop in the mouth balanced by a little malt. Bitter and dry.
Litehouse (ABV 4.3%)
Pale ale with faint tropical fruit hop aroma. Light balance of sweet malt and hop bitterness fading into a short finish.
IPA (ABV 4.5%)
Rev Hawker (ABV 4.6%)
Tamar Source (ABV 4.6%)
Premium bitter with malt and earthy hop aroma. Dominant crystal malt with bitterness and sweet stone fruit flavours. Bitterness rises.

Fosse Way SIBA

Unit 5a, Manor Farm, Hunningham Lane, Offchurch, Warwickshire, CV33 9AG ☎ 07956 179999
⊕ fossewaybrew.co.uk

⊠ Housed in a converted barn on Manor Farm, near Offchurch, is the 5.5-barrel plant now operated by Fosse Way Brewing Co. Originally established in 2013, the new owner has made continued improvements to the equipment. The core beer range includes a lager influenced by the owner's extensive experience in South Africa.

Aurora (ABV 3.6%)
Sentinel (ABV 4.5%)
Dark Side (ABV 4.8%)

Four Candles

▤ 1 Sowell Street, St Peters, CT10 2AT ☎ 07947 062063 ⊕ thefourcandles.co.uk

⊠ Based in the cellar of the micropub of the same name, Four Candles uses a 2.5-barrel plant and produces up to 10 nine-gallon casks with each brew. Never brewing the same ale twice, the brewery supplies the micropub, which is named after the well known Two Ronnies sketch. ‼

Four Kings

Unit 15g, Newton Moor Industrial Estate, Lodge Street, Hyde, SK14 4LD ☎ 07951 699428
⊕ fourkingsbrewery.com

😊Four Kings is a six-barrel brewery opened in 2016 in Hyde by five friends with a mutual love of beer. Regular open days are held at the brewery's on-site bar, which is also available for private functions. Beers can typically be found in pubs across Tameside and High Peak and at beer festivals held in Greater Manchester and Yorkshire.
‼ ➡ ◆ RAIB V◆

Gold (ABV 4%)
IPA (ABV 4%)
Bitter (ABV 4.5%)
Porter (ABV 5.2%)

Fourpure

22 Bermondsey Trading Estate, Rotherhithe New Road, South Bermondsey, London, SE16 3LL
☎ (020) 3744 2141 ⊕ fourpure.com

Fourpure began brewing in 2013. Beers are available in cans and kegs, unfiltered, unpasteurised and unfined. In 2018 the brewery was bought by Lion of Australia, part of Kirin of Japan. A substantial taproom opened along from the brewery in 2019, becoming a star of the Bermondsey Beer Mile. ➡ RAIB ◆

Fowey

Unit 3F, 3-4 Restormel Industrial Estate, Liddicoat Road, Lostwithiel, Cornwall, PL22 0HG
☎ (01208) 871385 ☎ 07443 504644

Office: Pawton Mill, St Breock, St Breock, PL27 7LH
⊕ foweybrewery.co.uk

Fowey began brewing in 2016, initially producing bottle-conditioned beers only. It relocated to a larger unit on the same industrial estate in 2017, allowing for a new eight-barrel plant. Cask-conditioned ales are occasionally available. ◆ RAIB

Lostwithiel Amber (ABV 4.9%)

Fownes

Unit 2, Two Woods Estate, Talbots Lane, Brierley Hill, West Midlands, DY5 2YX ☎ 07790 766844

Office: 42 The Ridgeway, Sedgley, DY3 3UR
⊕ fownesbrewing.co.uk

😊The brewery was established in 2012 by James and Tom Fownes in premises to the rear of the Jolly Crispin in Upper Gornal. A recent expansion saw the brewery moved to a new site in Brierley Hill. Frequent specials along a 'Dwarfen Ales' theme are brewed in addition to the core range. ‼ ◆ RAIB

Elephant Riders (ABV 4%)
Gunhild (ABV 4%)
Bright with creamy lingering head. Smooth mouthfeel. Pleasant earthy aroma with hints of blackcurrants and

honey. Peardrops and caramel with some malt and blackcurrant flavour. Dry malty aftertaste
Crispin's Ommer (ABV 4.1%)
Frost Hammer (ABV 4.6%)
Blonde and bright with a clingy head. Pine resin, nutmeg, malt, lemon and floral aroma. Dry mouthfeel with coffee, sweet malt and grapefruit flavours. Grapefruit and hoppy aftertaste.
Firebeard's Old Favourite No. 5 Ruby Ale (ABV 5%)
Creamy head, red colour. Malty, rich, fresh earth, rhubarb and some coffee in the aroma. Smooth mouthfeel, Dark chocolate and plum dominate flavour with hints of malt and coffee. A pleasant dryness in the aftertaste, with hints of coffee, plum and cocoa.
King Korvak's Saga (ABV 5.4%)
Peardrop and cocoa aroma with hints o coffee. Coffee, toasted malt, blackcurrant and slight cocoa taste, with rich malty tones in the aftertaste.

Fox

■ 22 Station Road, Heacham, Norfolk, PE31 7EX
☎ (01485) 570345 ⊕ foxbrewery.co.uk

⊠ Based in an old cottage adjacent to the Fox & Hounds pub, Fox Brewery was established in 2002 and now supplies around 30 outlets as well as the pub. All the beers are brewed using malt from Crisps in Great Ryburgh. A hop garden next to the brewery, trialled during 2009, has been enlarged. ‼ ☞ ◆ RAIB

Heacham Gold (ABV 3.9%)
Red Knocker (ABV 3.9%)
Norfolk Lad (ABV 4%)
A well-balanced, malty brew with a hoppy, bitter background. Long finish with a growing sultana-like fruitiness.
Nelson's Blood (ABV 4.7%)
Grizzly Bear (ABV 4.8%)
IPA (ABV 5.2%)

Foxfield SIBA

■ Prince of Wales, Foxfield, Foxfield, Cumbria, LA20 6BX
☎ (01229) 716238 ⊕ princeofwalesfoxfield.co.uk

☺Foxfield is a 4.5-barrel plant in old stables attached to the Prince of Wales. Several other outlets are supplied. Tiger Tops in Wakefield is also owned. The beer range constantly changes. Brewing is currently suspended. ‼ ◆

Framework

The Old City Depot, 72-74 Friday Street, Leicester, LE1 3BW ⊕ frameworkbrewery.com

⊠ Framework is a six-barrel brewery in an historic Victorian red-brick City Centre building that started brewing in 2016. Alongside its core range of ales it also offers changing seasonal beers, collaboration and one-off experimental brews. Both traditional and modern hop-forward beers are available. ‼ V✿

Jackpin US Pale Ale (ABV 4%)
We'll Meet Again Bitter (ABV 4.2%)
Semper NEPA (ABV 4.4%)
Keep the Faith WCIPA (ABV 5.5%)

Frank & Otis

See Hanlons

Franklins SIBA

Highfields Farm, The Broyle, Ringmer, East Sussex, BN8 5AR ⊕ franklinsbrewery.co.uk

⊠ Owned by Steve Medniuk, Franklins moved to a new site in Ringmer in order to aid expansion. A 10-barrel brew plant is currently used. Beers are available throughout the South East, London and beyond. ‼ V✿

Lawless (ABV 3.8%)
Eclipse (ABV 4%)
What Mama Don't Know (ABV 4.1%)
Kaleidohop (ABV 5%)

Contract brewed for Veterans Brewery (South East):
American Pale (ABV 4%)
No Mans Land (ABV 4.1%)
Dambuster (ABV 5.6%)

Freedom SIBA

1 Park Lodge House, Bagots Park, Abbots Bromley, Staffordshire, WS15 3ES
☎ (01283) 840721 ⊕ freedombrewery.com

Freedom specialises in producing hand-crafted English lagers, all brewed in accordance with the German Reinheitsgebot purity law. No real ale. ‼ ☞

Freestyle

■ Church Road, Shustoke, Warwickshire, B46 2LB
☎ (01675) 481205 ⊕ griffininnshustoke.co.uk

Griffin Inn started brewing in 2008 in the old coffin shop adjacent to the pub. In 2017 the brewery was updated to a modern, more efficient 2.5-barrel plant. At this time the name was changed to Freestyle though the business is still owned by the Pugh family who run the Griffin. Beers are available for the free trade as well as selling through the pub. ‼ ◆

Freetime

19 St Lukes Court, Clarke Way, Winch Wen, Swansea, SA1 7ER
☎ (01792) 713731 ☎ 07291 253227
⊕ hello@freetimebeer.co

Microbrewery operations began in 2016, brewing small batches of craft beer available in bottles, keg and cask, under the name West by Three. A broad variety of styles are produced using the finest ingredients and tasty Welsh water. Beers are always unfined, using instead a combination of time, temperature and, if appropriate, filtering to achieve the specific clarity for the style.

Freewheelin'

Peebles Hydro, Innerleithen Road, Peebles, EH45 8LX
☎ 07802 175826 ⊕ freewheelinbrewery.co.uk

Freewheelin' began brewing in 2013 and is based in Peebles. It is located in a former joiners shed in the grounds of the Peebles Hydro Hotel. Local spring water is used in the brewing process. ‼ ◆

Blonde (ABV 3.8%)
IPA (ABV 4.2%)
Ruby (ABV 4.4%)
Stout (ABV 4.4%)

Frensham

See Craft Brews

Friday Beer

Unit 4, Link Business Centre, Link Way, Malvern, Worcestershire, WR14 1UQ
☎ (01684) 572648 ⊕ thefridaybeer.com

Founded in 2011, the Friday Beer Co primarily produces bottle-conditioned ales. The range of bottles now sells across the region and to a growing number of outlets, from Birmingham to London, and south of the M4 corridor (including local restaurants and venues). Cask-conditioned ales are only available in a few local pubs or from the brewery for events. ‼ RAIB

Jubilee (ABV 3.1%)
Summer Hill Blonde (ABV 4.3%)
Pinnacle (ABV 4.5%)
WR14 (ABV 4.7%)
Friday Gold (ABV 5.6%)

Friends Arms

Old St Clears Road, Johnstown, Carmarthen, SA31 3HH
☎ (01267) 234073 ⊕ thefriendsarms.co.uk

⊗ Friends Arms Brewery opened in 2011 on the premises of the Friends Arms, a traditional local community pub, which acts as the brewery tap. Brewing has stalled for more than a year, and to date, there is no sign that brewing will resume soon.

Frisky Bear

Unit 1, Vantage Point, Howley Park Road East, Morley, Leeds, West Yorkshire, LS27 0SU
⊕ friskybear.com

Established in 2016, Frisky Bear upgraded from a one-barrel to a six-barrel plant and relocated in 2019. The beers are available on a rotating brewing schedule. Regularly available in Oscar's Bar, Morley, but also around West Yorkshire. RAIB V

Grizzly Bear (ABV 4.5%)

Frome SIBA

Unit L13, Marshall Way, Commerce Park, Frome, Somerset, BA11 2FB
☎ (01373) 467766 ⊕ fromebrewingcompany.com

⊗ Formerly Milk Street Brewery, the business changed its name in 2018. The brewery was established in 1999 behind the Griffin, Frome, before moving to an industrial unit on the edge of town in 2016, and increasing its capabilities to 60 barrels. Beer is supplied direct to local outlets and wholesalers are used to distribute further afield. ‼♦V

Same Again (ABV 3.9%)
Funky Monkey (ABV 4%)
Ra (ABV 4.1%)
The Usual (ABV 4.4%)
Zig-Zag Stout (ABV 4.5%)
Gulp IPA (ABV 4.8%)
Beer (ABV 5%)

Front Row SIBA

Unit A3, The Old School, Outclough Road, Brindley Ford, Staffordshire, ST8 7QD ☎ 07861 718673
⊕ frontrowbrewing.co.uk

After starting operations in Congleton in 2012 on a 2.5-barrel plant, Front Row expanded to an eight-barrel plant in 2014, and moved to its current location at the end of 2018 to allow for further increase in capacity. There is an on-site brewery tap (call for current opening times). ‼♦

Number 8 (ABV 3.7%)
Crouch (ABV 3.8%)
LOHAG (Land of Hops and Glory) (ABV 3.8%)
Touch (ABV 4%)
Sin Bin (ABV 4.2%)
Try (ABV 4.2%)
Half-Time (ABV 4.5%)
Pause (ABV 4.5%)
Red Roses (ABV 4.5%)
Pride (ABV 4.6%)
Blindside (ABV 4.7%)
Crafty Flanker (ABV 4.7%)
Rucked (ABV 5.2%)
Converted (ABV 5.4%)
Lomu (ABV 5.4%)
Oblensky (ABV 7.3%)

Froth Blowers SIBA

Unit P35, Hastingwood Industrial Park, Wood Lane, Erdington, West Midlands, B24 9QR ☎ 07966 935906
⊕ frothblowersbrewing.com

⊗ Froth Blowers began brewing in 2013, the name derived from the Ancient Order of Froth Blowers, an organisation dedicated to 'Lubrication in Moderation'!. The brewery has the capacity to brew 20 barrels at a site only metres away from its original one with most of the beers being consumed within 30 miles of the brewery. ♦

Piffle Snonker (ABV 3.8%)
Straw-coloured. Aroma is almost jammy with a little malt and hop. Taste is well-balanced with a slightly hoppier aftertaste.
Bar-King Mad (ABV 4.2%)
Wellingtonian (ABV 4.3%)
John Bull's Best (ABV 4.4%)
Gollop With Zest (ABV 4.5%)
Hornswoggle (ABV 5%)

Fuddy Duck

Unit 12, Kirton Business Park, Willington Road, Kirton, Lincolnshire, PE20 1NN ☎ 07881 818875
⊕ thefuddyduckbrewery.co.uk

Small brewery based in Kirton near Boston, where brewing commenced in 2016.

Pale Ale (ABV 4%)
American Red Ale (ABV 4.5%)
Blonde Ale (ABV 4.5%)
Dark Porter (ABV 4.5%)
German Ale Altbier (ABV 4.5%)
Biere De Garde (ABV 6.5%)

Fuggle Bunny SIBA

Unit 1, Meadowbrook Park Industrial Estate, Station Road, Holbrook, Sheffield, South Yorkshire, S20 3PJ
☎ (0114) 248 4541 ☎ 07813 763347
⊕ fugglebunny.co.uk

⊗ Fuggle Bunny was established in 2014 and is an independent, family-run brewery. The plant, originally obtained from Flipside Brewery, has since been expanded. The core range is supplemented by occasional seasonal and special brews. Beers are delivered direct within a 40-mile radius of the brewery and are available nationally through wholesalers. Its first pub opened in Worksop in 2017. ‼

Chapter 5 Oh Crumbs (ABV 3.8%)
Chapter 9 La La Land (ABV 3.9%)

Chapter 2 Cotton Tail (ABV 4%)
Chapter 6 Hazy Summer Daze (ABV 4.2%)
Chapter 8 Jammy Dodger (ABV 4.5%)
Chapter 1 New Beginnings (ABV 4.9%)
Chapter 3 Orchard Gold (ABV 5%)
Chapter 7 Russian Rare-Bit (ABV 5%)
Chapter 4 24 Carrot (ABV 6%)

Full Circle (NEW) SIBA

Hoults Yard, Walker Road, Newcastle upon Tyne, NE6 2HL
☎ (0191) 481 4114 🌐 fullcirclebrew.co.uk

Brewing began in 2019 in Hoult's Yard in Byker, another addition to the real ale scene in this area. It also incorporates a taproom plus the Pip Stop bottled beer shop. ◆

Full Mash

17 Lower Park Street, Stapleford, Nottinghamshire, NG9 8EW
☎ (0115) 949 9262 🌐 fullmash.net

Brewing commenced in 2003 and has grown steadily since, with a gradual expansion in outlets and capacity. ♦

Horse & Jockey (ABV 3.8%)
Easy-drinking, golden ale with moderate hoppy aroma and finish.
Whistlin' Dixie (ABV 3.9%)
Séance (ABV 4%)
Predominantly hoppy golden beer, with a refreshing bitter finish.
Illuminati (ABV 4.2%)
Gently-hopped golden ale with initial hops and bitterness giving way to a short, bitter finish.
Wheat Ear (ABV 4.2%)
Warlord (ABV 4.4%)
Amber-coloured beer with an initial malt taste leading to a dry, bitter finish.
Apparition (ABV 4.5%)
A pale hoppy bitter brewed with Brewers Gold hops.
Northern Lights (ABV 4.7%)
Manhattan (ABV 5.2%)
Bhisti (ABV 6.2%)

Fuller's

Griffin Brewery, Chiswick Lane South, Chiswick, London, W4 2QB
☎ (020) 8996 2000 🌐 fullers.co.uk

⊗ The Griffin brewery has stood for more than 360 years with the Fullers name coming from the partnership formed in 1845. Gales of Horndean was bought in 2005 and closed a year later, the beers are now brewed at Chiswick. Dark Star of Sussex was bought in 2018 and brewing continues there. Fullers sold its brewing interests to Asahi in 2019 but will keep its pubs and hotels. ‼ ♦ RAIB

Oliver's Island (ABV 3.8%)
Well-balanced golden ale with fruity aroma and flavour. Gentle bitter hoppiness balances a sweet malty character flavour and short finish.
London Pride (ABV 4.1%)
Well-balanced, smooth best bitter with orange citrus fruit, malt and hops in aroma and flavour, which linger into a slightly bitter aftertaste. Honey and toffee develop as the beer matures.
Bengal Lancer (ABV 5%)
Rich, creamy and well-balanced pale brown IPA with a gold hue. Hops with a dryish bitterness harmonise with the fruit and malty sweetness that linger into the aftertaste.
ESB (ABV 5.5%)
Bitter orange marmalade with hops, creamy toffee and some raisins are all present in this multifaceted strong brown bitter. A satisfying, long, bitter and dry finish balanced by a malty sweetness.

Brewed under the Gale's brand name:
Seafarers Ale (ABV 3.6%)
A pale brown bitter, predominantly malty, with a refreshing balance of fruit and hops that lingers into the aftertaste where a dry bitterness unfolds.
HSB (ABV 4.8%)
Dates and dried fruit with some spicy hops in the nose adding to the caramelised orange and treacle in the flavour of this smooth brown beer. Malty throughout with a bittersweet finish.

Fulstow

See Firehouse

Funk Dungeon

See Abbeydale

Funky Hop Donkey

See Silver

Furnace

9 Duke Street, Derby, DE1 3BX
☎ (01332) 385981

Six-barrel brewhouse in the beer garden of the Furnace Inn on Duke Street. Supply is mainly for the pub, but beers can be seen at beer festivals and specialist pubs across the UK. V

Futtle (NEW)

Unit 2, The Bowhouse, St Monans, KY10 2FB
🌐 futtle.com

Organic farmhouse brewery producing European-style beers. A 1,000-litre 'coolship', a shallow open fermentation vessel, has been installed in the rafters of the brewery.

Fuzzchat

Jolly Coopers, 84 Wheelers Lane, Epsom, Surrey, KT18 7SD
☎ (01372) 723222 🌐 fuzzchatbrewery.co.uk

⊗ Fuzzchat is Epsom's first brewery in more than 90 years. Housed behind the Jolly Coopers, it used to be an old blacksmith's cottage, recently restored after being derelict for several years. A Fuzzchat is anyone born on Epsom Common. ‼ ♦

Fuzzy Duck SIBA

18 Wood Street, Poulton Industrial Estate, Poulton-le-Fylde, Lancashire, FY6 8JY ☎ 07904 343729
🌐 fuzzyduckbrewery.co.uk

Fuzzy Duck was established in 2006. It relocated to Poulton-le-Fylde later that year, expanding capacity to an eight-barrel plant. The brewery delivers over a wide area of north-west England and Yorkshire. Most beers are available bottle-conditioned. ‼ ♦ RAIB

Golden Cascade (ABV 3.8%)
Mucky Duck (ABV 4%)

THE BREWERIES

Pheasant Plucker (ABV 4.2%)
Cunning Stunt (ABV 4.3%)
Ruby Duck (ABV 5.3%)

Fyne SIBA

Achadunan, Cairndow, PA26 8BJ
☎ (01499) 600120 ⊕ fyneales.com

Fyne Ales has been brewing since 2001 and is situated at the head of Loch Fyne. In 2012 an on-site brewery tap was added. Expansion has allowed for the production of experimental brews. FyneFest runs annually, celebrating local fare and showcasing other breweries. !! ♦ RAIB

Jarl (ABV 3.8%)
Maverick (ABV 4.2%)
Full-bodied, roasty, tawny best bitter. It is balanced, fruity and well-hopped.
Hurricane Jack (ABV 4.4%)
Vital Spark (ABV 4.4%)
Avalanche (ABV 4.5%)
This true golden ale starts with stunning citrus hops on the nose. Well-balanced, with good body and fruit balancing a refreshing, hoppy taste, it finishes with a long, bittersweet aftertaste.
Highlander (ABV 4.8%)
Full-bodied, bittersweet ale with a good dry hop finish. In the style of a Heavy although the malt is less pronounced and the sweetness ebbs away to leave a bitter, hoppy finish.
Sublime Stout (ABV 6.8%)
Superior IPA (ABV 7.1%)
Mills & Hills (ABV 9.5%)

Gadds

See Ramsgate

Gale's

See Fuller's

Gallus (NEW)

Glasgow ⊕ gallusbrewing.scot

Gallus is a Glasgow-based gypsy brewery established in 2016.

Gan Yam (NEW)

Hillingdon Street, Walworth, London, SE17 3JH
⊕ ganyambrew.co.uk

Small home-based commercial brewery that started in 2018 with occasional beers available in London on keg but usually bottled. Links with Cumbria where they hope to relocate, beers sometimes seen in Kendal. No real ale.

Garden City

22 The Wynd, Letchworth Garden City, Hertfordshire, SG6 3EN ☎ 07932 739558
⊕ gardencitybrewery.co.uk

A brewbar established in 2016 using a 2.5-barrel plant, serving a selection of its own ales plus guests on gravity.

Gasworks

First Street, Manchester, M15 4FN

Gasworks is a six-barrel brewpub from the team behind Dockyard, opened in 2016. It supplies Gasworks Tap, Dockyard, Salford Quays and Dockyard, Spinningfields.

Gates Burton

Reservoir Road, Burton upon Trent, Staffordshire, DE14 2BP
☎ (01283) 532567
✉ gatesburtonbrewery@talktalk.net

The Gates Burton Brewery was established in 2011 using a one-barrel plant. This has now expanded to a three-barrel plant, representing cottage brewing at its finest. !! ♦

Reservoir (ABV 4.6%)
Pale brown with a malty aroma and roast hint. Caramel and malt lead to a sweet hop balanced taste. Hops arrive late on the palate to urge another mouthful
GBA (Gates Burton Ale) (ABV 4.8%)
Damn (ABV 5%)
Reservoir Gold (ABV 7.5%)

Geeves SIBA

Unit 12, Grange Lane Industrial Estate, Carrwood Road, Stairfoot, Barnsley, South Yorkshire, S71 5AS
☎ 07859 039259 ⊕ geevesbrewery.co.uk

Geeves began brewing in 2011 using a 5.5-barrel plant with recipes developed when the owners lived on a narrow boat. !! ♦ RAIB

Evolver (ABV 3.8%)
Renaissance (ABV 4.1%)
Aurelian (ABV 4.2%)
Cadenza (ABV 4.3%)
Clear Cut (ABV 4.4%)
Oaty McOatface (ABV 4.5%)
Smokey Joe Stout (ABV 5%)
Fully Laden (ABV 6%)

Geipel SIBA

Pant Glas, Llangwm, LL21 0RN
☎ (01490) 420838 ☎ 07549 526287 ⊕ geipel.co.uk

Geipel commenced brewing in 2013 producing unpasteurised and unfiltered beers. The brewery specialises in lagers, drawing inspiration from the classic styles of Germany and beyond. Available in keg, KeyKeg and bottle. RAIB V

Gemstone

See Nelson

Gentlewood

Fir Tree Cottage, Tithe Barn, Gentleshaw, Staffordshire, WS15 4LR ☎ 07544 146900

Gentlewood began in 2018 and is co-owned and run by Darren Williams and Ben Colthorpe, it is a Staffordshire-based brewery specialising in traditional cask ales using British hops and grain.

Heritage (ABV 4.2%)

George Samuel

Unit 3, Norland House Business Centre, Shildon, DL4 1HE ☎ 07840 892751

Named after the brewer's two sons, the brewery originally set up as a two-barrel plant in 2014 at the Duke of Wellington pub in Welbury near Northallerton before moving to Spennymoor and closing in late 2018. The brewery reopened as an eight-barrel plant in 2020 in Shildon, the 'Cradle of the Railways', in a unit which formerly housed the offices of Shildon Wagon Works. Plans include a taproom.

Locomotion No. 1 (ABV 4%)
Leaves on the Line (ABV 4.2%)
Travelling Light (ABV 4.5%)
Harvey (ABV 5.2%)
Terminus (ABV 5.5%)

George's SIBA

Common Road, Great Wakering, Essex, SS3 0AG
☎ (01702) 826755 ☎ 07771 871255
⊕ georgesbrewery.com

⊠ George's Brewery and Hop Monster Brewing Company (qv) are owned by the same brewer, using the same plant. George's concentrates on traditional styles and Hop Monster on the more unusual. ‼🏭◆RAIB

Wallasea Wench (ABV 3.6%)
Wakering Gold (ABV 3.8%)
8-bit Bitter (ABV 4%)
Best (ABV 4%)
Cockleboats (ABV 4%)
Empire (ABV 4%)
Figaro (ABV 4%)
Banshee Porter (ABV 4.4%)
Broadsword (ABV 4.7%)
Excalibur (ABV 5.4%)
Merry Gentlemen (ABV 6%)
Excalibur Reserve (ABV 7.2%)

Brewed under the Hop Monster Brewery name:
Rakau (ABV 4.2%)
Snake Oil Stout (ABV 5%)

German Kraft

Mercato Metropolitano, 42 Newington Causeway, Borough, London, SE1 6DR ⊕ germankraftbeer.com

Initally beer was imported from its German brewery in Bavaria, Steinbach, in 2017. In early 2018 the brewery officially opened and beers are replicated on-site. The keg beers are of varied German styles. A second brewery will open at the new Mercato Metropolitano site in Mayfair during the currency of this Guide. No real ale.

Ghost

Unit D, Tong Business Centre, Otley Road, Baildon, West Yorkshire, BD17 7QD
☎ (0113) 418 2002 ☎ 01896 097882
⊕ ghostbrew.co.uk

Ghost Brew Co is the creation of Steve Crump and James Thompson.

Gibberish

≣ 15 Caryl Street, Liverpool, L8 5AA ☎ 07871 645864

Gibberish is a brewpub that opened in 2017 in Liverpool's Baltic Triangle.

Gil's

12 Greenfield Avenue, Dinas Powis, CF64 4BW
☎ 07882 076321

Brewing began in 2018. Beer is available in kegs and bottles. No real ale.

Gipsy Hill SIBA

Units 7-11, Hamilton Road Industrial Estate, 160 Hamilton Road, West Norwood, London, SE27 9SF
☎ (020) 8761 9061 ⊕ gipsyhillbrewing.com

Gipsy Hill opened in 2014 at the same time and on the same site as London Beer Factory. It has since expanded into adjacent units and the taproom moved across the yard. Its pop up pub, the Douglas Fir, is now permanent. No real ale. ‼◆RAIB ✦

Glamorgan SIBA

Unit B, Llantrisant Business Park, Llantrisant, CF72 8LF
☎ (01443) 406080

Office: Unit J, Llantrisant Business Park, Llantrisant, CF72 8LF ⊕ glamorganbrewingco.com

⊚This family-owned and run brewery moved to its present site in 2013. Production capacity has increased significantly year-on-year and a new, bigger brewery is anticipated. A range of year-round and seasonal ales are produced, with additional special brews to mark notable events. The brewery shop is open daily and brewery tours are available for groups by prior arrangement. Direct deliveries are made throughout Wales and distributed further afield by selected wholesalers and breweries. 🏭◆

Cwrw Gorslas/Bluestone Bitter (ABV 4%)
Welsh Pale Ale (ABV 4.1%)
Jemimas Pitchfork (ABV 4.4%)
Thunderbird (ABV 4.5%)

Glasgow Beer Works SIBA

Block 23, Unit 2, Queenslie Industrial Estate, Glasgow, G33 4JJ

Office: Pavilion 1, Finnieston Business Park, Minerva Way, Glasgow, G3 8AU ⊕ glasgowbeerworks.com

Established in 2017 as Merchant City Brewing using a 12-barrel plant, Glasgow Beer Works moved and rebranded in 2020. In addition to the core range, small pilot batches and barrel aged beers are produced. 25 outlets are supplied direct plus specialist off-licences across central Scotland. A pop-up bar in Osborne Street, beneath the John Byrne mural of Billy Connolly opened in 2020. ◆

Pilsner Lager (ABV 4%)
American Pale Ale (ABV 4.7%)
New World IPA (ABV 5.2%)

Glasshouse

Unit 6b, Waterside Business Park, Stirchley, B30 3DR

Glasshouse opened in 2018 run by Josh Hughes. Brewing mainly keg and keykeg beers in a broad range of exciting new styles, there will be the occasional casks sold to the local trade.

Glastonbury

Park Corner Farm,, Glastonbury, Somerset, BA6 8JY
☎ (01458) 830750 ⊕ glastonburyales.com

Established in 2002 as Glastonbury Ales on a five-barrel plant, they changed ownership and moved to Somerton, increasing capacity to a 20-barrel plant. Cider is also produced. In 2019 it relocatied to Glastonbury. ‼◆RAIB

Glede

See Clevedon

Glen Affric

Unit 2 & 3 Lightbox, Knox Street, Birkenhead, Merseyside, CH41 5JG ☎ 07742 020275

THE BREWERIES

Office: 53 Wood Street, Ashton-under-Lyne, OL6 7NB
glenaffricbrewery.com

Established in 2016, a small batch brewery producing only keg beers.

Glen Spean SIBA

Tirindrish Steading, Tirindrish, Spean Bridge, PH34 4EU ☎ 07487 953714
glenspeanbrewing.com

Based in a converted steading, brewing began in 2018.

Globe

144 High Street West, Glossop, Derbyshire, SK13 8HJ
☎ (01457) 852417 globepub.co.uk

Globe was established in 2006 by Ron Brookes on a 2.5-barrel plant in an old stable behind the Globe pub. Grandson Toby now has a major role in the brewery under the watchful eye of Ron. The beers are mainly for the pub but special one-off brews are produced for beer festivals. ♦

Gloucester SIBA

Fox's Kiln, West Quay, The Docks, Gloucester, GL1 2LG
☎ (01452) 668043 ☎ 07503 152749
gloucesterbrewery.co.uk

Situated in the historic Gloucester Docks, brewing began in 2011. The brewery expanded into larger premises in the docks area to cope with increased demand while retaining and sympathetically restoring its original converted stables site for experimental brews and a bar named Tank. The full range of beers is regularly available in pubs throughout Gloucestershire and beyond. Beers are brewed in cask, keg and bottled format, most are unfined. A range of gins is distilled on site. !! ♦ RAIB V

Session Pale (ABV 3.7%)
Gold (ABV 3.9%)
Cascade (ABV 4.2%)
Session IPA (ABV 4.5%)
Six Malt Porter (ABV 4.5%)
Dockside Dark (ABV 5.2%)
New England IPA (ABV 5.2%)

Goacher's

Unit 8, Tovil Green Business Park, Burial Ground Lane, Tovil, Maidstone, Kent, ME15 6TA
☎ (01622) 682112 goachers.com

A traditional brewery that uses only malt and Kentish hops for all its beers. Phil and Debbie Goacher have concentrated on brewing good wholesome beers without gimmicks. Two tied houses and around 30 free trade outlets in the mid-Kent area are supplied. Special is brewed for sale under house names. !! ♦

Real Mild Ale (ABV 3.4%)
A rich, flavourful mild with moderate roast barley and a generous helping of chocolate malt.
Fine Light Ale (ABV 3.7%)
A pale, golden brown bitter with a strong, floral, hoppy aroma and aftertaste. A hoppy and moderately malty session beer.
Special/House Ale (ABV 3.8%)
Best Dark Ale (ABV 4.1%)
Dark in colour but light and quaffable in body, this ale features hints of caramel and chocolate malt throughout.
Crown Imperial Stout (ABV 4.5%)
A good, well-balanced roasty stout, dark and bitter with just a hint of caramel and a lingering creamy head.
Gold Star Strong Ale (ABV 5.1%)
A strong pale ale brewed from 100% Maris Otter malt and East Kent Goldings hops.

Goddards SIBA

Barnsley Farm, Bullen Road, Ryde, Isle of Wight, PO33 1QF
☎ (01983) 611011 goddardsbrewery.com

Anthony Goddard established what is now the oldest active brewery on the Isle of Wight in 1993. Originally occupying an 18th-century barn, a new brewery was built in 2008, quadrupling its capacity, which has since been further increased. Goddards' remain a locally-focused business distributing ales on the Isle of Wight and the easily accessible counties of southern England. Beers are also contract brewed for Crumbs Brewery, where breadcrumbs replace about a quarter of the malt usually used in the brewing process. ♦

Ale of Wight (ABV 3.7%)
Starboard (ABV 4%)
Wight Squirrel (ABV 4.3%)
Fuggle-Dee-Dum (ABV 4.8%)
Brown-coloured strong ale with plenty of malt and hops.

Godstone SIBA

Flower Farm, Oxted Road, Godstone, Surrey, RH9 8BP
☎ 07791 570731

Office: 3 Willow Way, Godstone, RH9 8NQ
thegodstonebrewers.com

The Godstone Brewers was established in 2015 using a one-barrel plant but moved to larger premises on a farm in Godstone, using a 12-barrel plant. Beers are named with local themes. Local outlets are supplied. A taproom is planned. ♦ RAIB V

Trenchman's Hop (ABV 3.8%)
Redgate (ABV 4%)
Pondtail Pale (ABV 4.1%)
Junction 6 (ABV 4.2%)
Rusty's Ale (ABV 4.4%)
Tunnel Vision (ABV 4.6%)
Buzz (ABV 4.7%)
Bitter Entropy (ABV 5.3%)
Polly's Potion (ABV 6.5%)

Goff's SIBA

9 Isbourne Way, Winchcombe, Cheltenham, Gloucestershire, GL54 5NS
☎ (01242) 603383 goffsbrewery.com

Goff's is a family concern that has been brewing cask-conditioned ales since 1994. The ales are available regionally in more than 200 outlets and nationally through wholesalers. ♦

Lancer (ABV 3.8%)
Jouster (ABV 4%)
A drinkable, tawny-coloured ale, with a light hoppiness in the aroma. It has a good balance of malt and bitterness in the mouth, underscored by fruitiness, with a clean, hoppy aftertaste.
Tournament (ABV 4%)
Dark golden in colour, with a pleasant hop aroma. A clean, light and refreshing session bitter with a pleasant hop aftertaste.
Fallen Knight (ABV 4.4%)
Cheltenham Gold (ABV 4.5%)
White Knight (ABV 4.7%)

A well-hopped bitter with a light colour and full-bodied taste. Bitterness predominates in the mouth and leads to a dry, hoppy aftertaste.

Golden Duck

Unit 2, Redhill Farm, Top Street, Appleby Magna, Leicestershire, DE12 7AH ☎ 07846 295179 ⊕ goldenduckbrewery.com

Golden Duck began brewing in 2012 using a five-barrel plant. It is run by the father-and-son team of Andrew and Harry Lunn. Beers have a cricket-related theme and are always available in Mushroom Hall, Albert Village and Cellar Bar, Sir John Moore Hall, Appleby Magna (Fri evenings only). ◆RAIB

Hayles' Ale (ABV 3.8%)
Extra Pale (ABV 4.2%)
LFB (Lunns First Brew) (ABV 4.3%)
Lunnys No. 8 (ABV 4.8%)

Golden Triangle SIBA

Unit 9, Watton Road Industrial Estate, Norwich, NR9 4BG
☎ (01603) 757763 ☎ 07976 281132 ⊕ goldentriangle.co.uk

⊠ Golden Triangle, named after an area of Norwich, has been brewing modern, hop-forward ales on a 10-barrel plant since 2011. The brewery continues to add new beers to its range. Beers are mainly found in pubs across Norwich. The Artichoke, Norwich, purchased by owner and brewer Kevin Tweedy in 2018, is the brewery tap (two beers permanently available). ◆

Table Bitter (ABV 3.3%)
Mosaic City (ABV 3.8%)
Full-bodied lemon citrus character throughout. Hops provide depth throughout. A subtle, malty bitterness quickly fades.
Simcoe City (ABV 3.8%)
Peach and lemon nose. A full-bodied and fruity sweet malt beginning. A notable bitter edge to the finish.
Citropolis (ABV 3.9%)
Equinoxity (ABV 3.9%)
Understated melange of hop, pineapple and lemon throughout. Gentle malt airs arrive in a short, sweet finish.

Goldmark SIBA

Unit 23 The Vinery, Arundel Road, Poling, West Sussex, BN18 9PY
☎ (01903) 297838 ☎ 07900 555415. ⊕ goldmarks.co.uk

⊠ Ex-biochemist and homebrewer Mark Lehmann began commercial brewing in 2013 using an 11-barrel plant. !!RAIB

Ebony Mild (ABV 3.5%)
Liquid Gold (ABV 4%)
Wurst Bitter (ABV 4%)
Pheonix (ABV 4.1%)
Red IPA (ABV 4.3%)
American Hop Idol (ABV 4.4%)
Warrior (ABV 4.6%)
Black Lion Porter (ABV 4.8%)
GSB (ABV 4.8%)
Vertigo Craft Lager (ABV 4.8%)
Pitch Shifter IPA (ABV 5%)

Good Chemistry

Unit 2, William Street, St Philips, Bristol, BS2 0RG

☎ (0117) 903 9930 ⊕ goodchemistrybrewing.co.uk

⊠ Good Chemistry was established in 2015 in a warehouse in St Philips, Bristol by Bob Cary and Kelly Sidgwick, using a 10-barrel plant. As the name suggests, all brewery and beer logos have a scientific theme. Brewery open days are held. RAIB V

Natural Selection (ABV 4%)
Hops and pale malt aromas. Initially sweet body is followed by hoppy bitterness which continues into the short, dry finish.
Kokomo Weekday (ABV 4.3%)
Hazy, golden-coloured ale with hop and sweet fruit aroma which continues onto the palate before a short, bitter finish

Good Stuff

⊟ Abdication, 89 Mansfield Road, Daybrook, Arnold, Nottingham, NG5 6BH ⊕ theabdication.co.uk

A nanobrewery located inside the Abdication micropub. Capacity is 0.5-barrels so occasional beers can only be found at the pub and local beer festivals.

Good Things SIBA

Rendlye Farm, Sandhill Lane, Eridge, TN3 9LP
☎ (020) 7780 7499 ⊕ goodthingsbrewing.co

Brewing began in 2018. Good things is a sustainable brewery, meaning that its aim is to be energy-efficient, with everything recycled and reused. Beer is available in kegs and cans in more than 100 outlets. No real ale.

Goodalls

⊟ Lodge Inn, 88 Crewe Road, Alsager, ST7 2JA
☎ 07484 113610
✉ simonturner@goodallsbrewery.com

Goodall's is a community microbrewery, brewing on a 2.5-barrel plant. Mainly seasonal ales are brewed. !!◆

Goodness (NEW)

Unit 5, Olympia Industrial Estate, Coburg Road, Wood Green, London, N22 6TZ ⊕ thegoodnessbrew.co

After a time cuckoo brewing at Sentinel, and more recently at the local House Brewery, Goodness opened in a large industrial unit in 2019, doubling as a taproom and events venue. Proud to brew cask as well as keg, a green hop beer is brewed with the local hop co-operative. ◆

Goodwood SIBA

The New Brewery, Stane Street, North Heath, West Sussex, RH20 1DJ ⊕ goodwood.com/estate/home-farm/goodwood-brewery

Beers are available in bottle and keg in restaurants and bars across the Goodwood estate. The beer is brewed by Hepworth (qv) using ingredients grown on the estate.

Goody SIBA

Bleangate Brewery, Braggs Lane, Herne, Kent, CT6 7NP
☎ (01227) 361555 ⊕ goodyales.co.uk

Goody Ales began brewing in 2012 using a 10-barrel plant. A wood-burning boiler is used to heat the water for the brews using wood from its copse, thereby minimising the use of non-renewable fuel. An on-site bar and shop, the Cathedral, is open (limited hours). ◆RAIB

Good Evening (ABV 3.4%)
Genesis (ABV 3.5%)
Good Health (ABV 3.6%)
Good Life (ABV 3.9%)
Good Heavens (ABV 4.1%)
Good Sheppard (ABV 4.5%)
Goodness Gracious Me (ABV 4.8%)
Good Lord (ABV 5%)

Goose Eye SIBA

Unit 5, Castlefield Industrial Estate, Crossflatts, Bingley, West Yorkshire, BD16 2AF
☎ (01274) 512743 🌐 goose-eye-brewery.co.uk

Goose Eye is a family-run brewery established in 1991, supplying numerous regular outlets, mainly in Yorkshire and Lancashire. The beers are available directly or through national wholesalers and pub chains. Goose Eye moved in 2017 to a custom-built brewery which has enabled them to increase production with a 20-barrel brew run. The new brewery bar is open every Friday and Saturday. ♦◆

Springwell (ABV 3.6%)
Bitter (ABV 3.9%)
Traditional Yorkshire brown session bitter, well-balanced malt and hops with a pleasingly bitter finish.
Blackmoor (ABV 3.9%)
Chinook Blonde (ABV 4.2%)
Assertive grapefruit hoppiness in the aroma and tropical flavours
Golden Goose (ABV 4.5%)
Over & Stout (ABV 5.2%)
A full-bodied stout with roast and malt flavours mingling with hops, dark fruit and liquorice on the palate. Look also for tart fruit on the nose and a growing bitter finish.
Pommies Revenge (ABV 5.2%)
Golden, strong bitter combining grassy hops, a cocktail of fruit flavours, a peppery hint and a hoppy, bitter finish.

Goose Island

222 Shoreditch High Street, Shoreditch, London, E1 6PJ
☎ (020) 3657 6555 🌐 gooseislandshoreditch.com

The Chicago-based Goose Island brewery opened its London brewpub in 2018. The on-site kit brews a range of continually changing beers only available at the pub, including a bourbon barrel-aged version of the Shoreditch Porter (the barrel can be seen behind the bar). Real ale has been experimented with but is not the norm.

Gorgeous

Bull, 13 North Hill, Highgate, London, N6 4AB
☎ 07754 925562 🌐 gorgeousbrewery.com

Formerly the home of London Brewing (qv), Gorgeous inherited the brewing kit on the purchase of the pub in 2017. At the beginning of 2018 a newly-built brewhouse at the rear of the pub came on stream. This extra capacity has seen a wider range of beers, including collaborations, available in the pub and further afield in more than 25 other pubs. V

Greedyguts (ABV 3.5%)
Glowfly (ABV 4%)
Pale brown, easy-drinking bitter with apples and orange aroma. Hops, orange and caramel flavours with a lingering, peppery bitter finish.
Geekhunter (ABV 4.2%)
A refreshing, light-drinking, dryish golden ale with a hint of honey sweetness and citrus, which is also in the aroma with some hops.
Gunpowder (ABV 4.8%)
Amber-coloured, smooth beer with hoppy tangy nose. Flavour is orange and biscuit with notes of bitter, earthy hops.
Gravedigger (ABV 5%)
Smooth, vanilla milk stout with some fruit, black treacle and subtle vanilla notes. Slightly sweet finish with some vanilla.

Gorilla (NEW)

Unit 3, Glasshouse Lane, Cliff Street, Mexborough, South Yorkshire, S64 9HU ☎ 07747 484368
🌐 gorillabrewing.co.uk

Co-founders Jason White and Phil Paling launched Gorilla Brewing in 2020 next to the Sheffield and South Yorkshire Navigation canal. ◆

Silverback Blonde (ABV 3.8%)
Monkey Magic (ABV 4.5%)
Orang-A-Tang (ABV 4.5%)
Vanilla Gorilla (ABV 5%)
Kong (ABV 6%)

Gower SIBA

Unit 25, Crofty Industrial Estate, Penclawdd, SA4 3RS
☎ (01792) 850681 🌐 gowerbrewery.com

Established in 2011 on a five-barrel brew plant at the Greyhound Inn, Llanrhidian. Moved to a new 20-barrel brewery in Crofty, Gower in 2015. Seasonal and speciality ales are brewed alongside established beers. !! ♦

Brew 1 (ABV 3.8%)
Best Bitter (ABV 4.5%)
Gold (ABV 4.5%)
Rumour (ABV 5%)
Shipwreck (ABV 5.1%)
Power (ABV 5.5%)

Grafham (NEW)

30 Breach Road, Grafham, Cambridgeshire, PE28 0BA
☎ 07590 836241 🌐 grafhambrewing.co

Grafham Brewing Co is a 1.8-barrel brewery that began commercial production in 2019.

Hodders Panama (ABV 4.8%)

Grafton SIBA

Walters Yard, Unit 4 Claylands Industrial Estate, Worksop, Nottinghamshire, S81 7DW
☎ (01909) 476121 ☎ 07436 282779

Office: 8 Oak Close, Crabtree Park Estate, Worksop, S80 1BH 🌐 graftonbrewing.co.uk

Grafton is a 12-barrel brewery established in 2007. In 2017 the brewery took over the operation of the former Hale's Brewery, which was based in an adjacent unit, but utilised the Grafton plant, and now produces Hale's beers as a sub-brand within its portfolio. The brewery tap is its micro bar, the Malt House on Potter Street. !!♦

Framboise (ABV 4%)
Golden ale with a raspberry aroma and taste, leading to a sweet and slightly bitter finish.
Silhouette (ABV 4%)
Lady Julia (ABV 4.3%)
Bananalicious (ABV 4.5%)
Lady Catherine (ABV 4.5%)
Lady Ruby (ABV 4.5%)

Apricot Jungle (ABV 4.8%)
Blondie (ABV 4.8%)
Mint Chocolate Stout (ABV 4.8%)
Caramel Stout (ABV 5%)
Coco Loco (ABV 5%)
Dark-coloured, smooth-drinking ale, infused with coconut. Gentle bitterness.

Grain SIBA

South Farm, Tunbeck Road, Alburgh, Harleston, Norfolk, IP20 0BS
☎ (01986) 788884 🌐 grainbrewery.co.uk

⊗ Grain Brewery was launched in 2006 by Geoff Wright and Phil Halls in a converted dairy in the Waveney Valley. It upgraded to an 18-barrel plant in 2012. Four pubs are owned: the Plough and the Cottage, Norwich, the Locks Inn, Geldeston, and the Spread Eagle, Ipswich. ‼ ♦ RAIB

Oak (ABV 3.8%)
Good balance of malt, toffee and bittersweet fruitiness. Caramel in initial taste fades as biscuit and bitterness dominate the aftertaste.
ThreeOneSix (ABV 3.9%)
Booming hop and citrus notes in aroma and taste. Initial maltiness fades as a piquant bitterness develops into crisp dryness.
Best Bitter (ABV 4.2%)
Brazil nut and malt introduce this well-balanced complex bitter. Bittersweet caramel notes flourish before a gently tapering, malty finish.
Redwood (ABV 4.3%)
A fruity aroma introduces a smooth, full-flavoured bitter. A malty fruit base defined by bitter undertones. Lingering bitter finish.
Slate (ABV 6%)
Roast and dark fruits dominate throughout. Caramel and sweet malt add complexity and balance. Full-bodied with a short finish.
Lignum Vitae (ABV 6.5%)
Solidly orangy and hoppy throughout. Imposing oily character with a definite marmalade bias. A bittersweet blast enlivens the towering finale.

Grainstore SIBA

Station Approach, Oakham, Rutland, LE15 6RE
☎ (01572) 770065 🌐 grainstorebrewery.com

Grainstore, the smallest county's largest brewery, has been in production since 1995, founded by Tony Davis and Mike Davies. After 45 years in the industry Tony decided to retire, handing the reins to his son, William. More than 200 outlets are supplied. ‼ ♦

Rutland Bitter (ABV 3.4%)
Rutland Panther (ABV 3.4%)
This superb reddish-black mild punches above its weight with malt and roast flavours combining to deliver a brew that can match the average stout for intensity of flavour.
Cooking (ABV 3.6%)
Tawny-coloured beer with malt and hops on the nose and a pleasant grainy mouthfeel. Hops and fruit flavours combine to give a bitterness that continues into a long finish.
Red Kite (ABV 3.8%)
Rutland Osprey (ABV 4%)
Steelback IPA (ABV 4.2%)
Triple B (ABV 4.2%)
Initially hops dominate over malt in both the aroma and taste, but fruit is there, too. All three linger in varying degrees in the sweetish aftertaste of this brown brew.
GB Best (ABV 4.3%)
Ten Fifty (ABV 5%)
Pungent banana and malt notes on the nose. On the palate, rich malt and fruit is joined by subtle hop on a bittersweet base. Dry malt aftertaste with some fruit.
Rutland Beast (ABV 5.3%)
Nip (ABV 7.3%)

Brewed under the Stoney Ford brand name:
Sheepmarket Supernova (ABV 3.8%)
PE9 Paradise Pale (ABV 4%)
All Saints Almighty (ABV 4.2%)

Grampus

Grampus Inn, Lee Bay, Devon, EX34 8LR
☎ (01271) 862906 🌐 thegrampus-inn.co.uk

⊗ Grampus was established in 2014 at the back of the Grampus Inn by Bill Harvey, the pub owner and brewer. It is a small plant using traditional brewing methods, but combining unique and unusual ingredients. All beers are available in the local area. ♦ RAIB

Granite Rock

Unit 19, Kernick Road Industrial Estate, Penryn, Cornwall, TR10 9EP
☎ (01326) 379251 ☎ 07436 817974
🌐 graniterockbrewery.co.uk

⊗ Granite Rock was established in 2013 as a brewery and homebrew shop. Located on an industrial estate in Penryn, the recently upgraded five-barrel plant currently supplies the free trade in West Cornwall. Sadly the homebrew shop has now closed. ‼ ♦ RAIB

Penryn Company Pale Ale (ABV 4%)
Copper bitter with fruity hop and malt nose. Assertive bitterness, resinous hops, spicy notes. Lasting bitterness with vine fruit hints.
Summer Solstice (ABV 4%)
Golden ale with a citrus and pineapple aroma. Refreshing orange, citrus and pineapple notes, honey flavours leading to dry finish.
Granite IPA (ABV 4.3%)
Penryn Pride (ABV 4.5%)
Tawny best bitter. Grainy mouthfeel with biscuit malt. Complex flavours, traces of toffee and caramel, hoppy bitterness and spice notes.
Driller IPA (ABV 5.1%)
Refreshing golden IPA, apricot and orange peel aromas. Citrus hops with hints of pine and resin balanced with honey notes.
Bronescombe's Vision (ABV 5.2%)
Well-balanced, red-coloured, strong bitter with malt and hop bitterness. Pronounced malt flavour with prunes and a lingering, dry malt finish.
Glasney College Porter (ABV 5.4%)
Black porter with roast malt aroma. Full-bodied taste of mocha coffee and dark chocolate, liquorice and pear drops. Light finish.

Grasmere

Lake View Country House, Lake View Drive, Grasmere, Cumbria, LA22 9TD
☎ (01539) 435572 ☎ 07840 059561
🌐 grasmerepub.com

Brewing began in 2017 in old farm buildings at Lake View Country House. Beers are available at its nearby taproom and restaurant, the Good Sport.

Helles Lager (ABV 3.8%)
Pale Ale (ABV 4%)
Bitter (ABV 4.1%)
Stout (ABV 5%)
IPA (ABV 5.5%)

Grasshopper

Unit F2, Langley Bridge Industrial Estate, Linkmel Road, Langley Mill, Derbyshire, NG16 3RZ
☎ (01773) 530224 ☎ 07900 806277
🌐 grasshopperbrewery.co.uk

Grasshopper commenced brewing in 2017 using a purpose-built, 10-barrel plant. Beers started appearing in local pubs shortly after and have been well received. Its core range (five beers) can be found in pubs and at festivals throughout Nottinghamshire, Derbyshire, Leicestershire, Staffordshire and beyond.

Knee High (ABV 3.8%)
Nymph (ABV 4.2%)
Cricket (ABV 4.5%)
Devil's Horse (ABV 4.8%)
Kung Fu (ABV 5.8%)

Gravity Well

Arch 142, Tilbury Road, Leyton, London, E10 6RE
☎ 07833 226373 🌐 gravitywellbrewing.co.uk

The brewery was installed during 2018 in a railway arch under the Gospel Oak to Barking overground line. A taproom is open at weekends and real ale is being considered following its success at local beer festivals. ◆

Great British Breworks

34 Dove Way, Kirkby Mills industrial Estate, Kirkbymoorside, North Yorkshire, YO62 6QR ☎ 07876 827475

Office: c/o The Black Swan Hotel, 18 Birdgate, Pickering, YO18 7AL 🌐 blackswan-pickering.co.uk/breworks

Brewing started on a permanent basis in the yard of the Black Swan in 2016, on a 2.5-barrel plant. In 2020, the brewery expanded by taking over the 12-barrel brewing plant in Kirkbymoorside previously used by Turning Point brewery. The core range of three ales has been supplemented by Kirkby Gold, previously brewed by the defunct Kirkbymoorside Brewery. An enlarged range of seasonal and experimental brews are now available. Beer is supplied to the Black Swan, Pickering and others in Ryedale. ♦

Great Scot (ABV 3.8%)
Istanbul (ABV 4.5%)
Coal Porter (ABV 4.6%)
Simcoe Pale (ABV 5.2%)

Great Central

Unit B, Marlow Road Industrial Estate, Leicester, LE3 2BQ ☎ 07584 435332 🌐 gcbrewery.co.uk

Brewing restarted in 2019 on a two-barrel plant primarily to supply the brewery tap, the Wheeltapper, Loughborough. Beers are named with a railway theme. ♦

Great Corby SIBA

The Forge, Great Corby, Cumbria, CA4 8LR
☎ (01228) 560899 🌐 greatcorbybrewing.co.uk

Established in 2009, with a bespoke, 10-barrel plant, the brewery was situated in The Old Forge (originally a farriers shop, dating back to 1833). Alltech purchased the brewery in 2015 and, in 2017, brewing operations moved across the village green to a former honey factory. The Forge buildings were retained for office space and cask washing. Monthly special beers commenced during 2018. ‼♦

Session Ale (ABV 3.8%)
A fruity session beer with sweetness leading to gentle bitterness in the aftertaste.
Blonde (ABV 4%)
Some fruit in the aroma and then a sweet fruity and lightly bittered taste which continues for a short time.
Lakeland Summit (ABV 4%)
Signal Peak APA (ABV 4.4%)
Stout (ABV 4.5%)
Fruity aroma, sweet roast middle and dry finish.
Fox Brown Ale (ABV 4.6%)
A pleasing brown ale with a slight bitter finish.

Great Newsome SIBA

Great Newsome Farm, South Frodingham, East Yorkshire, HU12 0NR
☎ (01964) 612201 🌐 greatnewsomebrewery.co.uk

Nestled in the Holderness countryside, Great Newsome began brewing in 2007 in renovated farm buildings. A range of beers is now brewed using barley from the farm and brewing can be seen from a viewing area. Expansion into other farm buildings in 2018 and again in 2019 increased brewing capacity to 20-barrels. Beer is distributed throughout the UK and overseas. ‼ ♦ GF

Sleck Dust (ABV 3.8%)
Pricky Back Otchan (ABV 4.2%)
Frothingham Best (ABV 4.3%)
Holderness Dark (ABV 4.3%)
Jem's Stout (ABV 4.3%)
Liquorice Lads Stout (ABV 4.3%)

Great North Eastern SIBA

Contract House (Unit E), Wellington Road, Dunston, Gateshead, NE11 9HS
☎ (01914) 474462 🌐 gnebco.com

Brewing began in 2016 on a 10-barrel plant. In 2017 the brewery expanded into the adjacent premises and a tap and shop was opened, with an events space for live entertainment. Beers are supplied direct throughout the North-East, and nationally via wholesalers. ♦◆

Claspers Citra Blonde (ABV 3.8%)
Styrian Blonde (ABV 3.8%)
Gold (ABV 4%)
Rivet Catcher (ABV 4%)
Taiheke Sun (ABV 4.2%)
Delta APA (ABV 4.5%)
Foxtrot Premium Ale (ABV 4.5%)
GNE Stout (ABV 4.6%)
Graphite (ABV 4.6%)
Hopnicity (ABV 5%)

Great Oakley SIBA

Ark Farm, High Street South, Tiffield, Northamptonshire, NN12 8AB
🌐 greatoakleybrewery.co.uk

Award-winning brewery established in 2005 in Great Oakley, relocating to Tiffield in 2012. It is run by Guy Jenkins who took over in 2017. More than 60 outlets are supplied, including brewery tap, the George, Tiffield. ‼♦ RAIB

Welland Valley Mild (ABV 3.6%)
Egret (ABV 3.8%)
Wagtail (ABV 3.9%)
Wot's Occurring (ABV 3.9%)
Tiffield Thunderbolt (ABV 4.2%)
Harpers (ABV 4.3%)

Gobble (ABV 4.5%)
Delapre Dark (ABV 4.6%)
Abbey Stout (ABV 5%)
Tailshaker (ABV 5%)

Great Orme

See Snowdon Craft

Great Western SIBA

Stream Bakery, Bristol Road, Hambrook, Bristol, BS16 1RF
☎ (0117) 957 2842 🌐 gwbrewery.co.uk

Great Western is a 12-barrel brewery set up in 2008 by Kevin Stone in a former bakery. The property has been renovated resulting in a bespoke showpiece brewery retaining many of the building's original features. The brewery owns a single pub – the Rising Sun, Frampton Cotterell – and 500 outlets are supplied. !! ♦

HPA (ABV 4%)
Hoppy, yellow bitter with zesty citrus flavours and hints of tropical fruit, leading to a moreish, bittersweet finish.
Maiden Voyage (ABV 4%)
An amber bitter with a light aroma of malt and fruit which continues to the palate before leading to a strong bitter finish.
Old Higby (ABV 4.8%)
Full-bodied, malty bitter with roast notes on the nose. Hints of fruit flavour give way to a bitter hop finish with some astringency throughout.
Moose River (ABV 5%)
Light citrus aroma, delicate hop taste with long-lasting bitter finish.

Great Yorkshire

New Inn, Cropton, North Yorkshire, YO18 8HH
☎ (01751) 417330
🌐 thegreatyorkshirebrewery.co.uk

Established in 1984, the brewery was built behind the New Inn in 1994. In 2010 Cropton Brewery rebranded as Great Yorkshire for its export markets. Beers are available throughout Yorkshire and nationally through wholesalers. !! ♦ RAIB

Yorkshire Classic (ABV 4%)
Yorkshire Golden (ABV 4.2%)
Yorkshire Blackout (ABV 5%)

Green Dragon

Green Dragon, 29 Broad Street, Bungay, Suffolk, NR35 1EF
☎ (01986) 892681

The Green Dragon is Bungay's busiest pub and oldest existing brewery, established in 1991 by brothers Robert and William Pickard. In 1994 the plant was expanded and moved to a converted barn. The doubling of capacity allowed the production of a larger range of ales. !! ♦

Chaucer Ale (ABV 3.8%)
Gold (ABV 4.4%)
Bridge Street Bitter (ABV 4.5%)
Strong Mild (ABV 5.5%)

Green Duck SIBA

Unit 13, Gainsborough Trading Estate, Rufford Road, Stourbridge, West Midlands, DY9 7ND
☎ (01384) 377666 🌐 greenduckbrewery.co.uk

Green Duck began brewing in 2012 and relocated to its present site in Stourbridge in 2013. Experimental beers are brewed alongside a core range. The brewery has an on-site brewery tap, the Badelynge Bar, where the brewing equipment is visible through a glass partition. Private events and quarterly beer festivals are hosted as well as being open to the public at weekends (check social media for times). !! ♦

Session IPA (ABV 4%)
Pale gold with a tropical aroma derived from mosaic hops. Very refreshing with a dry pine and resin aftertaste.
Blonde (ABV 4.2%)
Gold with a sharp fruity aroma. Lots of passionfruit in the taste. Aftertaste is balanced with fruit sweetness and hops.
American Pale (ABV 4.5%)

Green Jack SIBA

Argyle Place, Love Road, Lowestoft, Suffolk, NR32 2NZ
☎ (01502) 562863 ☎ 07902 219459
🌐 green-jack.com

After 10 years at Oulton Broad, Green Jack moved to the Triangle Tavern, Lowestoft in 2003 and then to a nearby 35-barrel plant in 2009. One pub is owned and more than 150 outlets supplied. !! ♦ RAIB

Jackalope Golden Best (ABV 3.8%)
Nightingale (ABV 4%)
LGM1 (ABV 4.2%)
Orange Wheat Beer (ABV 4.2%)
Marmalade aroma with a hint of hops, leading to a well-balanced blend of sweetness, hops and citrus with a malt background. Mixed fruit flavours in the aftertaste.
Trawlerboys Best Bitter (ABV 4.6%)
Tawny beer with aroma of apple, sultana and malt plus hints of caramel and hops. Rich fig and plum base with malt and roast overtones. Strong finish with a sticky mouthfeel.
Lurcher Stout (ABV 4.8%)
Pleasant malt, roast and fruit aromas. Blackberry, raisin and port flavours. Long, dry, bitter, roast finish.
Red Herring (ABV 5%)
Gone Fishing ESB (ABV 5.5%)
Mahseer IPA (ABV 5.8%)
Ripper Tripel (ABV 8.5%)
Baltic Trader Export Stout (ABV 10.5%)
Worthog (ABV 11%)

Green Mill SIBA

Harewood Arms, 2 Market Street, Broadbottom, SK14 6AX ☎ 07967 656887 🌐 greenmillbrewery.com

Green Mill started brewing in 2007 on a 2.5-barrel plant and moved in 2010 to the Cask & Feather in Rochdale. The brewery relocated again in 2013 to the Harewood Arms in Broadbottom. A number of occasional beers are brewed. Around 40 outlets are supplied. ♦

Greene King

Westgate Brewery, Westgate Street, Bury St Edmunds, Suffolk, IP33 1QT
☎ (01284) 763222 🌐 greeneking.co.uk

Greene King has been brewing in the market town of Bury St Edmunds since 1799. It brews its beers using water drawn from artisan chalk wells below its brewhouse as well as local East Anglia malt. Beers are also brewed under the Tolly Cobbold brand name. !! ♦ RAIB

XX Mild (ABV 3%)

THE BREWERIES

IPA (ABV 3.6%)
Hop-infused fruit cake aromas. Complex flavours of malt, caramel and hop with both sweetness and bitterness. A lingering, mellow aftertaste with blackberries.
London Glory (ABV 4%)
Yardbird (ABV 4%)
St Edmunds (ABV 4.2%)
Abbot (ABV 5%)
Strong malt, toffee and caramel aromas. Rich, malty, caramel flavours with vine fruit and a little hop bite. Heavy, sweet finish with a subtle hint of bitterness in the aftertaste.

Brewed under the Hardys & Hansons brand name:
Bitter (ABV 3.9%)
Olde Trip (ABV 4.3%)

Brewed under the Morland brand name:
Original Bitter (ABV 4%)
Old Golden Hen (ABV 4.1%)
Old Speckled Hen (ABV 4.5%)
Smooth, malty and fruity, with a short finish.

Brewed under the Ruddles brand name:
Best Bitter (ABV 3.7%)
An amber/brown beer, strong on bitterness but with some initial sweetness, fruit and subtle, distinctive Bramling Cross hop. Dryness lingers in the aftertaste.
County (ABV 4.3%)
Sweet, malty and bitter, with a dry and bitter aftertaste.

Greenodd

Ship Inn, Main Street, Greenodd, Cumbria, LA12 7QZ
☎ (01229) 861553 ☎ 07782 655294
theshipinngreenodd.co.uk

Established in 2010 at the Ship Inn on a two-barrel plant. The majority of production goes to the Ship with the remainder going to the local free trade. ‼♦

Greenwich

Up The Creek Comedy Club, 302 Creek Road, Greenwich, London, SE10 9SW
☎ (020) 8858 4581

Greenwich began brewing in 2018 using a three-barrel plant and is situated in the front part of the bar area of the Up the Creek Comedy Club. The beers are available in the bar. Please note that entrance may be restricted to ticket holders for some events in the club area. RAIB

Greg's

Dambusters Inn, 23 High Street, Scampton, Lincolnshire, LN1 2SD
☎ (01522) 730123

Established in 2013, the microbrewery is situated on the premises of the Dambusters Inn. A number of house ales are produced by publican Greg Algar. ♦

Grey Friars

Featherstone Hall Farm, New Road, Featherstone, Staffordshire, WV10 7NW
☎ (01785) 840093 ☎ 07966 361443

Office: 17 Cranbrooks, Wheaton Aston, ST19 9PZ
greyfriarsbrewery@gmail.com

Established in 2014 and using equipment originally from Upham Brewery in Hampshire, the three-barrel plant is installed in a barn, formerly used as a snooker room and which still contains the original wood panelling. Brewing is currently suspended.

Grey Trees SIBA

Unit 5-6, Gas Works Road, Aberaman, Aberdare, CF44 6RS
☎ (01685) 267077 greytreesbrewing.com

National award-winning small brewery from the Welsh heartlands. Now in its tenth year, its reputation as a giant killer is large and well deserved. Grey Trees recently opened National Tap in Aberdare town centre has released urgently needed space at the brewery. Plans for expansion should come to fruition during the currency of this Guide. Beers are available from more enlightened local free houses, and sometimes further afield. ♦RAIB

Caradog (ABV 3.9%)
Black Road Stout (ABV 4%)
Diggers Gold (ABV 4%)
Drummer Boy (ABV 4.2%)
Mosaic Pale Ale (ABV 4.2%)
Chinookan VPA (ABV 4.3%)
Valley Porter (ABV 4.6%)
JPR Pale (ABV 4.7%)
Afghan Pale (ABV 5.4%)

Greyhound SIBA

Watershed, Smock Alley, West Chiltington, West Sussex, RH20 2QX ☎ 07973 625510
greyhoundbrewery.co.uk

Established in 2015 by husband-and-wife team Nick and Sarah Allen, Greyhound is a 7.5-barrel brewery. In 2017 the brewery took over production of Ballard's Brewery beers, and continue to make its traditional ales alongside the Greyhound range. ‼♦RAIB

Good Ordinary Bitter (ABV 3.8%)
Blonde Bird (ABV 3.9%)
Amber Eyes (ABV 4.2%)
B-46 (ABV 4.6%)
Tree Frog (ABV 4.9%)
White Bird (ABV 5.2%)

Brewed under the Ballard's Brewery name:
Best Bitter (ABV 4.2%)
Nyewood Gold (ABV 5%)

Greywood (NEW)

Sandford Avenue, Wood Green, London, N22 5EJ
greywoodbrewery.co.uk

Commercial brewing began in 2020. The name Greywood Brewery is a nod to the brewery's origins in Haringey and derives from the Anglo Saxon expression meaning 'enclosure of the grey wood'.

The Longest Road (ABV 5.2%)

Gribble

Gribble Inn, Oving, West Sussex, PO20 2BP
☎ (01243) 786893 gribbleinn.co.uk

Established in 1980 using a five-barrel plant, the Gribble Brewery is the longest-serving brewpub in the Sussex area, independently owned and run by the licensees since 2005. A number of local outlets are supplied. ♦

Griffin

See Freestyle

Gritchie SIBA

Ashgrove Farm, Ashmore, Wiltshire, SP5 5AW

☎ (01747) 828996 ⊕ gritchiebrewingcompany.co.uk

⊗ Owned by film director Guy Ritchie, this 20-barrel brewery, in converted farm buildings on the Ashcombe Estate, started brewing in 2017, using its own borehole water and estate-grown barley. Expansion to 40-barrel capacity and a tap room are planned. Both cask and KeyKeg beers are produced, with new beers being developed regularly. There are three five-barrel fermenters for experimental beers. The beers are distributed locally with plans to expand nationally. The Lore of the Land, Fitzrovia, London, is the brewery tap. ♦

Moon Lore (ABV 3.6%)
Summer Lore (ABV 3.6%)
English Lore (ABV 4%)
A copper-coloured bitter with some hint of fruit in the aroma. A sweet slightly bitter taste which diminishes quickly.

Grizzly Grains (NEW)

342 Walkley Bank Road, Sheffield, South Yorkshire, S6 5AR ☎ 07807 242545
✉ sambrewsbeers@gmail.com

Having purchased the equipment from Crosspool Alemakers in 2019 Sam Bennett commenced brewing in the Walkley area of Sheffield in 2020. ♦

Grounding Angels SIBA

6 Rear Battle Hill, Hexham, Northumberland, NE46 1BB ☎ 07508 175512 ⊕ grounding-angels.com

Brewing commenced in 2018.

GT

Unit 5, The Old Aerodrome, Chivenor Business Park, Braunton, Devon, EX31 4AY
☎ (01271) 267420 ☎ 07909 515170 ⊕ gtales.co.uk

⊗ GT Ales was established in Barnstaple in 2013, producing only bottle-conditioned beers, before relocating to larger premises in Braunton in 2015. All six regular award-winning ales are now available in cask. One-off specials of 20 barrels are regularly produced. ‼♦RAIB

Thirst of Many (ABV 4.2%)
North Coast IPA (ABV 4.3%)
Blonde Ambition (ABV 4.5%)
Dark Horse (ABV 4.5%)
Battleaxe (ABV 4.7%)
Crimson Rye'd (ABV 4.8%)

Guisborough (NEW)

14 South Buck Way, Guisborough, North Yorkshire, TS14 7FJ ☎ 07703 002858
✉ info@guisboroughbrewery.co.uk

⊗ Established in 2020, using a five-barrel plant. The core range consists of five beers using a variety of traditional and more contemporary hops, together with the finest malts. Events are held regularly and visitors, by arrangement, are made most welcome. ‼

Delight (ABV 3.7%)
Alchemy (ABV 3.8%)
Phoenix (ABV 4%)
Elixir (ABV 4.7%)
Vypa (ABV 5.5%)

Gun SIBA

Hawthbush Farm, Gun Hill, East Sussex, TN21 0JY
☎ (01323) 700200 ☎ 07900 683355
⊕ gunbrewery.co.uk

⊗ Gun Brewery is located on a 140-acre, organic, mixed farm in the Sussex Weald. It generates much of its own power from a 15-kW solar array and heating comes from a wood-powered boiler. Spent grains keep the local livestock happy and all the water used for brewing comes from the brewery's spring. More than 30 outlets are supplied. RAIB V

Scaramanga Extra Pale (ABV 3.9%)
Parabellum Milk Stout (ABV 4.1%)
Chummy Bluster Best Bitter (ABV 4.4%)
Project Babylon Pale Ale (ABV 4.6%)
Base Ejection Smoked Rye (ABV 4.7%)
Spin Drift IPA (ABV 5.7%)
Zamzama IPA (ABV 6.5%)

Gun Dog

See Phipps

Gwaun Valley

Kilkiffeth Farm, Pontfaen, SA65 9TP ☎ 07854 767383
⊕ gwaunvalleybrewery.com

Gwaun Valley began brewing in 2009 on a four-barrel plant in a converted granary. The brewery offers views of the Preseli Hills and has a campsite, a holiday cottage and pitches for five caravans. Folk music sessions are held every Saturday evening. The owners retired early in 2019 and the business has been relaunched by a new tenant brewer who will retain some core range of beers and add others. ‼ 🛒

Farmhouse Ale (ABV 4%)
Cwm Gwaun Porter (ABV 4.3%)
Cwrw Melyn (ABV 4.3%)
King of the Road (ABV 4.5%)
Pembrokeshire Best Bitter (ABV 4.5%)
Sir Benfro Bitter (ABV 4.5%)
Blodwen (ABV 4.7%)
Cascade (ABV 4.7%)

Gyle 59 SIBA

The Brewery, Sadborow Estate Yard, Thorncombe, Dorset, TA20 4PW
☎ (01297) 678990 ☎ 07508 691178 ⊕ gyle59.co.uk

⊗ Gyle 59 is a 10-barrel brewery that began commercial production in 2014. Bottling takes place on-site with bottles being available by mail order. ‼ 🛒 ♦RAIB V

Take It Easy (ABV 2.5%)
Freedom Hiker (ABV 3.7%)
Thoroughbred (ABV 3.7%)
Toujours (ABV 4%)
C59's Special (ABV 4.2%)
Vienna Session Lager (ABV 4.2%)
Capitalist Hippie – Skinny (ABV 4.3%)
Capitalist Hippie – Far Out (ABV 5%)
Halcyon Daze (ABV 5%)
IPA (ABV 5.3%)
Nettle IPA (ABV 5.3%)
Dorset GIPA (ABV 5.4%)
Capiltalist Hippie – Summer of Love (ABV 6.6%)
Starstruck (ABV 6.6%)
The Favourite (ABV 6.6%)
Double IPA (ABV 7.3%)

Contract brewed for Lyme Regis Brewery:
Ammonite (ABV 3.7%)
Cobb (ABV 3.9%)
Lyme Gold (ABV 4.2%)

Dorset Pearl (ABV 4.3%)
Town Mill Best (ABV 4.5%)
Black Ven (ABV 5%)
Revenge (ABV 5.3%)

Hackney SIBA

Arch 358, Laburnum Street, Haggerston, London, E2 8BB
☎ (020) 3489 9595 ⊕ hackneybrewery.co.uk

⊗ Founded in 2011, Hackney Brewery is the oldest brewery in the area and continues to release new exciting beers monthly. The majority of the output is packaged in keg and can. Cask versions of the core beer range are available by special order. RAIB

Hackney Church

Arches 16 & 17 Bohemia Place, Hackney, London, E8 1DU
☎ (020) 8985 3496 ⊕ hackneychurchbrew.co

Formerly known as St John at Hackney Brewery. Comprising two railway arches, the brewery almost fills one arch, the other being the taproom. With an experienced brewing team, the recipies are being continually refined. Available only in the tapoom for quality control, beers come from kegs or the tanks above the bar. All profits are used by the trust for worthy church-based projects at St John at Hackney. ◈

Hadham SIBA

Unit 6c, Hadham Industrial Estate, Church End, Little Hadham, Hertfordshire, SG11 2DY
☎ (01279) 771916 ☎ 07770 766376
⊕ hadhambrewery.co.uk

⊗ Hadham began brewing in 2015 with a 10-barrel plant, using its own spring water found on site. Outlets are supplied within a 30-mile radius of the brewery.

Gold (ABV 3.7%)
Oddy (ABV 3.9%)
First (ABV 4%)
Stargazer (ABV 4.5%)

Hadrian Border SIBA

Unit 5, The Preserving Works, Newburn Industrial Estate, Shelley Road, Newburn, NE15 9RT
☎ (0191) 264 9000 ⊕ hadrian-border-brewery.co.uk

Based in Newburn near Newcastle-upon-Tyne using a 40-barrel plant, the brewery can produce up to 200 barrels per week. Beer is delivered directly to the area between Edinburgh, North Yorkshire, Carlisle and the East Coast, and is also available nationally through wholesalers. A three-barrel plant is used for experimental craft brews. One pub is run – the Station East, Gateshead. ‼ ♦ RAIB GF V

Tyneside Blonde (ABV 3.9%)
Refreshing blonde ale with zesty notes and a clean, fruity finish.
Farne Island Pale Ale (ABV 4%)
A copper-coloured bitter with a refreshing malt/hop balance.
Northern Pale (ABV 4.1%)
Secret Kingdom (ABV 4.3%)
Grainger Ale (ABV 4.6%)
Northern IPA (ABV 5.2%)
Ouseburn Porter (ABV 5.2%)
Traditional robust porter, made with chocolate and black malt. Distinct bitter coffee finish.

Hafod

Old Gas Works, Gas Lane, Mold, CH7 1UR
☎ (01352) 750765 ☎ 07901 386638
Office: Gorwel, Hafod Road, Pantglas Gwernaffield, Mold, CH7 5ES ⊕ welshbeer.com

⊛ Hafod began brewing in 2011 on a small scale and relocated to the current premises in 2014 whilst retaining the original kit at the old site for low volumes. A number of one-off special brews are produced on a regular basis. Also on a limited basis, speciality beers using ingredients from the local upland areas are made. ‼ ♦ ◈

Sunrise (ABV 3.8%)
A pale and refreshing golden ale with citrus fruit bitterness evident throughout and a mouthwatering astringent finish.
Moel Famau Ale (ABV 4.1%)
A speciality dark ale brewed using local heather giving a dry, roasty taste with underlying sweet malt flavours.
Landmark (ABV 4.6%)
Copper-coloured and malty with a juicy mouthfeel. Fruit and faint roast flavours also feature in the taste.
Moldbreaker (ABV 4.6%)

Hairy Dog (NEW)

Unit 38, More House Farm, Wivelsfield, West Sussex, RH17 7RE ✉ info@hairydogbrewery.beer

Overlooking the South Downs National Park, the brewery's ethos is to use Sussex ingredients wherever possible and to pursue a policy of sustainability. An on-site taproom is open on Fridays. ◈

Hounded Best Bitter (ABV 4.1%)
Far Fetched Pale Ale (ABV 4.2%)
Bloodhound Red IPA (ABV 5.5%)

Hal's

22a Woodmancote, Dursley, Gloucestershire, GL11 4AF ☎ 07765 890946

Hal's is a one-barrel microbrewery established in Dursley in 2016, occasionally producing a number of small-batch beers for the New Inn, Woodmancote, Dursley and beer festivals. ♦

HHH (ABV 3.6%)
Mick's Mild (ABV 3.8%)
What Sony's Havin (ABV 4.2%)
Gold (ABV 4.4%)
Black Jack (ABV 4.5%)
New Inn Chestnut Bitter (ABV 4.6%)

Hale's

See Grafton

Half Moon SIBA

Forge House, Main Street, Ellerton, East Yorkshire, YO42 4PB
☎ (01757) 288977 ☎ 07741 400508
⊕ halfmoonbrewery.co.uk

Established in 2013 by Tony and Jackie Rogers, the brewery is situated in a former blacksmith's forge with a capacity of 5.5-barrels. Brewing takes place 2-3 times a week. ♦ RAIB GF ◈

Dark Masquerade (ABV 3.6%)
Old Forge Bitter (ABV 3.8%)
F'Hops Sake (ABV 3.9%)

Halfpenny

Crown Inn, High Street, Lechlade, Gloucestershire, GL7 3AE
☎ (01367) 252198 halfpennybrewery.co.uk

Halfpenny was established in 2008 on a four-barrel plant at the Crown at Lechlade, visible in a glazed outbuilding. It has since expanded to a third fermentation vessel. Beers are brewed mainly for the pub and the Swan at Radcot. ‼

Halifax Steam

Conclave, Southedge Works, Brighouse Road, Hipperholme, West Yorkshire, HX3 8EF ☎ 07506 022504 halifax-steam.co.uk

Brewing since 1999, the five-barrel plant supplies only the brewery tap, the Cock o' the North. It is now reputedly the oldest brewery in Calderdale. A range of permanent beers and different rotating beers are brewed, including the only rice beers in the country. Eight-ten Halifax Steam beers are available in the pub at any one time. ♦

Hall & Woodhouse (Badger) IFBB

Bournemouth Road, Blandford St Mary, Blandford Forum, Dorset, DT11 9LS
☎ (01258) 452141 hall-woodhouse.co.uk

Hall & Woodhouse has been brewing in the heart of the Dorset countryside since 1777. Owned and run by the seventh generation of the Woodhouse family, it brews with local spring water filtered through the Cretaceous chalk downs and drawn up 120ft from its wells. A leading, independent UK brewer, its well-known range of Badger ales is award-winning, and has an estate (around 200 pubs) across southern England. Its ales are available exclusively in Hall & Woodhouse public houses. ‼ ♦

Badger Best Bitter (ABV 3.7%)
Well-balanced bitter with malt caramel sweetness and hop fruitiness.
Fursty Ferret (ABV 4.1%)
Easy-drinking best bitter with sweet bitterness that lingers into a dry aftertaste with a hint of orange.
Tanglefoot (ABV 4.7%)
Relatively sweet-tasting and deceptive, given its strength. Pale malt provides caramel overtones and a bittersweet finish.

Halton Turner

Lakey Lane, Hall Green, Birmingham, West Midlands, B28 8QT ☎ 07821 447329

Established in 2018, Halton Turner has a small plant in Hall Green, Birmingham. Brewing a wide range of beers in cask and keykeg, the beers are mainly found in the local area.

Hambleton SIBA

Melmerby Green Road, Melmerby, North Yorkshire, HG4 5NB
☎ (01765) 640108 hambletonbrewery.co.uk

Established in 1991 in a farm shed on the banks of the River Swale, Hambleton now occupies purpose-built premises with capacity for 100 barrels a week. A new storage facility was added in 2020. The core beer range was increased to eight in 2019 and is supplemented by monthly and seasonal specials. Village Brewer, Black Dog and Wharfe Brewery beers are contract brewed. A bottling line handles brands for other brewers. The brewery tap is the King William IV, Ripon. ‼ ♦

Session Pale (ABV 3.6%)
Bootleggers Pale Ale (ABV 3.8%)
Thoroughbred IPA (ABV 4%)
Pink Grapefruit (ABV 4.1%)
Stallion Amber (ABV 4.2%)
A premium bitter, moderately hoppy throughout and richly-balanced in malt and fruit, developing a sound and robust bitterness, with earthy hops drying the aftertaste.
Stud Blonde (ABV 4.3%)
Black Forest (ABV 5%)
Nightmare Porter (ABV 5%)
This impressively flavoured beer satisfies all parts of the palate. Strong roast malts dominate, but hoppiness rears out of this complex blend.

Contract brewed for Black Dog Brewery:
Whitby Abbey Ale (ABV 3.8%)
Schooner (ABV 4.2%)
Rhatas (ABV 4.6%)

Contract brewed for Village Brewer:
White Boar (ABV 3.8%)
Bull (ABV 4%)

Contract brewed for Wharfe Beers:
Verbeia (ABV 3.6%)
Tether Blond (ABV 3.8%)

Hammerton SIBA

Unit 8 & 9 Roman Way Industrial Estate, 149 Roman Way, Barnsbury, London, N7 8XH
☎ (020) 3302 5880 hammertonbrewery.co.uk

Hammerton began brewing in London in 1868 but ceased brewing in the 1950s and was later demolished. In 2014, a member of the Hammerton family resurrected the name and opened a new brewery in Barnsbury. Expanded in 2019 after crowdfunding, the taproom is open more regularly now complementing its nearby bar, the House of Hammerton. RAIB

N1 (ABV 4.1%)
Refreshing pale ale. Honey, caramelised citrus, floral hops, fading in the finish with a spicy hoppy bitterness. Malty, fruity aroma.
N7 (ABV 5.2%)
Peppery, hoppy, pale brown bitter with bitter peely fruit on the palate. Smooth mouthfeel and dry, spicy, bitter, lingering finish.
Pentonville Oyster Stout (ABV 5.3%)
Liquorice and dark fruit on the palate and aroma. Dry, roasty, malty finish and a touch of caramelised fruit.

Hand SIBA

33 Upper St James's Street, Kemptown, Brighton, East Sussex, BN2 1JN ☎ 07508 814541

Founded in 1989, the brewery is the smallest commercially operating tower brewery in the world. Originally operating under the Kemptown Brewery name before being used as a gypsy brewery by Brighton Bier for four years. Now operating as the Hand Brew Co since 2016. Around 10 other outlets are supplied. ‼

Handley's

Willow Tree, Front Street, Barnby in the Willows, Newark, Nottinghamshire, NG24 2SA
willowtreebarnby.co.uk

Handley's began brewing in 2011 on a 0.5-barrel plant installed behind the Willow Tree pub. Beer is mostly sold in the pub, with at least two being on pump at all times, and can occasionally be found at local beer festivals.

Handsome SIBA

Bowstone Bridge Garage, Bowston, Cumbria, LA8 9HD
☎ (0344) 848 0888 🌐 handsomebrew.co.uk

Originally Houston Brewery in Renfrewshire, it was re-established as Handsome in 2016 in the Lake District. It is situated on the River Kent in an old MOT garage, formerly the blacksmith's for James Cropper's paper mills.

Top Knot (ABV 3.7%)
Stranger (ABV 4.2%)
Bar Steward (ABV 4.8%)
Blacksmith (ABV 4.8%)

Contract brewed for Winster Valley Brewery:
Dark Horse (ABV 3.5%)
Hurdler (ABV 3.5%)
Best Bitter (ABV 3.7%)
Lakes Blonde (ABV 3.7%)
An uncomplicated fruity, hoppy bitter.
Old School (ABV 3.9%)
Chaser (ABV 4.1%)

Handyman

461 Smithdown Road, Liverpool, L15 3JL
☎ (0151) 733 3048 🌐 handymansupermarket.co.uk

Handyman Brewery is based within the Handyman Supermarket. For years this was a hardware store but has now been refurbished into the Handyman Pub, which opened in 2017. Its 400-litre brew kit is situated on a mezzanine floor above the bar. ♦

Hanging Bat

c/o Hanging Bat, 133 Lothian Road, Edinburgh, EH3 9AB
☎ (0131) 229 0759 🌐 thehangingbat.com

Brewing began in 2012 from within the Hanging Bat bar using a 50-litre brew kit from the United States.

Hanging Tree

Benleva Hotel, Kilmore Road, Drumnadrochit, IV63 6UH
☎ (01456) 450080

Hanging Tree began brewing in 2017 using a two-barrel brew plant in an old bothy in the grounds of the Benleva Hotel. Named after the 400-year-old chestnut tree growing in the garden, which was used as the hanging tree for the local area. Beers are available in the pub and a few other local outlets.

Hanlons SIBA

Hill Farm, Half Moon Village, Devon, EX5 5AE
☎ (01392) 851160 🌐 hanlonsbrewery.com

Hanlons, one of Devon's largest brewers since 2013, supply a range of award-winning ales nationwide. The purpose-built brewery also has a shop, bar and restaurant. In 2019, it bought Prescott Ales of Cheltenham. Bottled beers are contract brewed for Frank & Otis Brewing Ltd. ‼ ♦

Firefly (ABV 3.7%)
Malty and fruity light bitter. Hints of orange in the taste.
Citra IPA (ABV 4%)
An easy-drinking citrus/floral IPA.
Yellow Hammer (ABV 4.2%)
Zesty fruit aroma, pineapples on taste with a nice sweetness counteracted by bitterness. Even though available all year, it has a summer ale style. Very refreshing.
Brewers Blend (ABV 4.5%)
Port Stout (ABV 4.8%)
Strong, black, speciality ale. Mild coffee and chocolate with fruity port notes. Lots of body.
Stormstay (ABV 5%)
Tawny and full-bodied. Caramel with hints of malt on the nose. Triumvirate of malt, caramel, hops develop into lingering bitterness.

Brewed under the Prescott Ales name:
Hill Climb (ABV 3.8%)
Pit Stop (ABV 4%)
Chequered Flag (ABV 4.2%)
Podium Finish (ABV 4.8%)
Grand Prix (ABV 5%)

Hapax

See Kingstone

Happy Valley

73 Oxford Road, Macclesfield, SK11 8JG
☎ (01625) 618360 ☎ 07758 512080
🌐 happyvalleybrewery.co.uk

Happy Valley was established in 2010 using a 2.5-barrel plant located in Bollington. In 2018 the brewery was sold and relocated to Macclesfield. ♦

Little Mill Town (ABV 3.6%)
Sworn Secret (ABV 3.8%)
Little Rascal (ABV 3.9%)
Lazy Daze (ABV 4.2%)
Hoppiness (ABV 4.3%)
Black Out XO Rum Porter (ABV 4.4%)
Black Magic (ABV 4.6%)

Harbour

Trekillick Farm, Kirland, Bodmin, Cornwall, PL30 5BB
☎ (01208) 832131 ☎ 07870 305063
🌐 harbourbrewing.com

Harbour is an innovative brewery founded on the outskirts of Bodmin in 2011. Brewed using local spring water, the regular beers are established in an increasing number of outlets. A new 30-barrel plant was installed in 2016, and more conditioning tanks in 2017. The brewery produces cask and keg beers. Bottling and canning is done on-site (no RAIB). ♦

Light (ABV 3.7%)
Yellow golden ale with citrus hop aroma. Dominant zesty citrus hops with some pineapple and pear drops. Long hoppy finish.
Daymer Extra Pale (ABV 3.8%)
Blond ale with citrus aroma. Lemon and lime dominate with faint biscuit malt and earthy hop. Bitterness remains but sweetness fades.
Amber (ABV 4%)
Pale brown bitter with a floral hop aroma and malt. Biscuit malt throughout with apple, peach and plum, balanced by hops.
Cornish Bitter (ABV 4%)
Amber session bitter. Marmalade dominates the aroma and flavour with faint biscuit malt and apple and peach fruits. Slightly dry finish.
New Zealand Gold (ABV 4.2%)
Golden Ale with light hop nose. Strong pine needle hop flavour. Bitter, sweet and dry throughout.
Ellensberg (ABV 4.3%)

Amber blond ale with a powerful citrus aroma. Strong grapefruit citrus hop flavour leading to a crisp, longlasting bitter finish.
Session IPA (ABV 4.3%)
India Brown Ale (ABV 4.9%)
Smooth, copper strong bitter. Heavy body and balanced sweet malt and bitter hop flavour, with plums, prunes and some butterscotch.
IPA (ABV 5%)
Amber American India pale with powerful citrus hop aroma and taste. Marmalade, red grapefruit and orange flavours with assertive bitterness.
Panda Eyes (ABV 5%)
Puffin Tears (ABV 5%)
Cascadia (ABV 5.2%)
Light no2 (ABV 5.2%)
Antipodean IPA (ABV 5.5%)
Little Rock IPA (ABV 5.5%)
Porter (ABV 5.5%)
Smooth, creamy, black porter with roast malt aroma. Malty, smoky and sweet followed by a bitter tang. Sweet finish.
Hellstown West Coast IPA (ABV 5.8%)
Harbour Pale (ABV 6%)
Golden ale with powerful citrus hop aroma. Intense citrus hop flavour with marmalade, orange and bitterness. Hoppy, slightly dry finish.

Harbwr Tenby SIBA

Sargeants Lane, St Julian Street, Tenby, SA70 7BU ☎ (01834) 845797 🌐 harbwr.wales

Brewing commenced in 2015 on a five-barrel plant in an outbuilding of the Buccaneer Inn, Tenby. The beers are available in the pub, at the nearby Hope & Anchor and further afield. Information boards explain the building's history and the brewing process. A mezzanine bar area is available for tastings, tapas and tours. ‼♦◆

MV Enterprise (ABV 4%)
North Star (ABV 4.2%)
Caldey Lollipop (ABV 4.5%)
RFA Sir Galahad (ABV 4.6%)

Harby

Bottle & Glass, 5 High Street, Harby, Nottinghamshire, NG23 7EB
☎ (01522) 703438
🌐 wigandmitre-lincoln.blogspot.co.uk

Harby Brewstore is a four-barrel malt extract brewery established in 2015 and located at the Bottle & Glass in Harby. Most output goes to the three pubs in the small Wig & Mitre pub group; the Wig & Mitre, Lincoln, Caunton Beck, Caunton and the Bottle & Glass itself.

Hardys & Hanson

See Greene King

Haresfoot

Unit 1, Symmetry Park, Samian Way, Aston Clinton, Buckinghamshire, HP22 5WJ 🌐 haresfoot.com

Established in Berkhamsted in 2014, the brewery moved to Chesham in 2017 and to its current site in Aston Clinton in 2020. Brewing is concentrated on its core beers, which are produced on a 12-barrel plant. Beers are delivered across the Chiltern area and London.

Sundial Golden Ale (ABV 3.8%)
Lock Keeper's Launch Ale (ABV 3.9%)
New Moon (ABV 4%)
Dragon's Bane (ABV 4.5%)

Harrison's

Unit 1, 108 Carolgate, Retford, Nottinghamshire, DN22 6AS ☎ 07850 228383 🌐 harrisonsbrewery.com

A three-barrel brewery built completely from scratch by the brewer, Christopher Harrison-Hawkes. The first brew was in 2018, and shortly after four beers were available at its own pub, the Brew Shed. It was soon obvious that the pub wasn't large enough so in 2019 the pub moved next door to larger premises. 2019 saw the production of bottle-conditioned beers and 2020 real ale in a can. ‼♦RAIB

Vacant Gesture (ABV 3.8%)
Best Bitter (ABV 4%)
Pale Ale (ABV 4%)
Proof of Concept (ABV 4.3%)
Stout (ABV 4.3%)
American Brown Ale (ABV 4.9%)
Plum Porter (ABV 5.6%)
Porter (ABV 5.6%)

Harrogate SIBA

Unit 7, Hookstone Centre, Hookstone Chase, Harrogate, North Yorkshire, HG2 7HW ☎ 07794 281225 🌐 harrogatebrewery.co.uk

Established in 2013, the brewery also uses the names Spa Town Ales and It's Quicker By Ale on its logo and pumpclips. The brewery now has new owners and a capacity of 10 barrels, and brews several times each week. ◆

Pale (ABV 4.2%)
Cold Bath Gold (ABV 4.4%)
Pinewoods Pale Ale (ABV 4.4%)
Plum Porter (ABV 4.8%)
Vanilla Porter (ABV 4.8%)
Beeching Axe (ABV 5.2%)
Kursaal Stout (ABV 6.7%)

Hartlebury

Station Park, Station Road, Hartlebury, Worcestershire, DY11 7YJ
☎ (01299) 253617 ☎ 07831 570117
✉ hartleburybrewingco@icloud.com

Hartlebury Brewing Co was established in 2019 by David Higgs, the owner of the Tap House pub. It supplies the Tap House and local free trade.

Hooker (ABV 4%)
Crusader (ABV 4.2%)
Off the Rails (ABV 4.2%)
APA (ABV 4.5%)

Hartshorns

Unit 4, Tomlinsons Industrial Estate, Alfreton Road, Derby, DE21 4ED ☎ 07830 367125
🌐 hartshornsbrewery.com

Hartshorns began brewing in 2012 using a six-barrel plant installed by brothers Darren and Lindsey Hartshorn. In 2015 the brewery acquired its first pub, the Little Chester Ale House, Derby.

Barley Pop (ABV 3.8%)
Ignite (ABV 3.9%)
Porter (ABV 4.5%)
Fusion (ABV 4.6%)
Reaper (ABV 4.9%)
Shakademus (ABV 5.4%)

Psychotropic (ABV 5.8%)
Apocalypse (ABV 6.2%)

Harvey's IFBB

Bridge Wharf Brewery, 6 Cliffe High Street, Lewes, East Sussex, BN7 2AH
☎ (01273) 480209 🌐 harveys.org.uk

Established in 1790, this independent family brewery operates from the banks of the River Ouse in Lewes. A major development in 1985 doubled the brewhouse capacity to more than 38,000 barrels a year. There are plans to re-establish small brew lengths of special beers, including replicating old recipes. Harvey's supplies real ale to all its 43 pubs and about 550 free trade outlets in the south east. !! ♦ RAIB

Dark Mild (ABV 3%)
A dark copper-brown colour. Roast malt dominates the aroma and palate leading to a sweet, caramel finish.
IPA (ABV 3.5%)
Sussex Wild Hop (ABV 3.7%)
Sussex Best Bitter (ABV 4%)
Full-bodied brown bitter. A hoppy aroma leads to a good malt and hop balance, and a dry aftertaste.
Old Ale (ABV 4.3%)
Armada Ale (ABV 4.5%)
Hoppy amber best bitter. Well-balanced fruit and hops dominate throughout with a fruity palate.

Harviestoun SIBA

Harviestoun Brewery, Alva Industrial Estate, Alva, FK12 5DQ
☎ (01259) 769100 🌐 harviestoun.com

Harviestoun has grown from one-man brewing in a bucket in the back of a shed in 1983 to a 60-barrel, multi award-winning brewery today. Now based in Alva, Scotland. !! ♦ RAIB

Bitter & Twisted (ABV 3.8%)
Refreshingly hoppy beer with fruit throughout. A bittersweet taste with a long bitter finish. A golden session beer.
Schiehallion (ABV 4.8%)
A Scottish cask lager, brewed using a lager yeast and Hersbrucker hops. A hoppy aroma, with fruit and malt, leads to a malty, bitter taste with floral hoppiness and a bitter finish.

Harwich Town

c/o Unit 1, Upp Hall Farm, Salmons Lane, Coggeshall, Essex, CO6 1RY ☎ 07723 607917
🌐 harwichtown.co.uk

Founded in 2007 with a five-barrel plant in premises next to Harwich Town railway station. In 2018 it moved out of its original home and became a cuckoo brewery, using spare capacity at Red Fox Brewery (qv). The owner/brewer, a former customs officer, names the beers after local characters and landmarks. Local pubs and beer festivals are supplied, with reciprocal trading with other breweries. It organises the Harwich Redoubt Beer Festival in a Napoleonic fort in July each year. ♦ RAIB

EPA Centenary (ABV 3.8%)
SS Brussels (ABV 3.8%)
Ganges (ABV 4%)
Bathside Battery Bitter (ABV 4.2%)
Lighthouse Best Bitter (ABV 4.8%)
Phoenix (ABV 5%)

Hattie Brown's

c/o The Square & Compass, Worth Matravers, Dorset, BH19 3LF
☎ (01929) 439229

Hattie Brown's began brewing in 2014 at the Wessex brewery. In 2015 it moved to its present location. It is owned by the manager of the Square & Compass, Worth Matravers, and partner, Jean, the brewer.

HBA (ABV 3.8%)
Moonlite (ABV 3.8%)
Mustang Sally (ABV 4.3%)
Kirrin Island (ABV 4.5%)
Spangle (ABV 4.6%)
Crow Black (ABV 5.1%)
Dog on the Roof (ABV 6%)

Hawkshead

Beer Hall: Mill Yard, Staveley, Cumbria, LA8 9LR
☎ (01539) 822644

Brewhouse: Moor Lane, Flookburgh, Cumbria, LA11
🌐 hawksheadbrewery.co.uk

Established in 2002, the brewery takes its name from the village it was founded in. It outgrew its original barn and moved to Staveley in 2006 to a purpose-built 20-barrel brewery. Capacity has been increased several times since, a new micro packaging plant was added and the Beer Hall, the brewery tap, developed as a showcase for real ale. In 2018 production of the core range of beers was transferred to a brand new 240-barrel brewery in Flookburgh, with the Stavelely plant continuing to produce small batch beers. Beers are also contract brewed for Sadler's Brewing Co. !! ♦ RAIB

Iti (ABV 3.5%)
A beer packed with grapefruit aroma and taste. Beautifully balanced with a long lasting, hoppy bitter finish.
Windermere Pale (ABV 3.5%)
Crisp and fruity yellow beer with hints of melon and grapefruit and a strong bitter aftertaste.
Bitter (ABV 3.7%)
Well-balanced, thirst-quenching beer with fruit and hops aroma, leading to a lasting bitter finish.
Mosaic Pale (ABV 4%)
Red (ABV 4.2%)
An impressive colour for this richly-flavoured beer; lots of fruitiness and good hop flavour with a lingering aftertaste.
Lakeland Gold (ABV 4.4%)
Dry, refreshing beer with good body and bitterness staying to the end.
Dry Stone Stout (ABV 4.5%)
Black, dry, bitter stout with an astringent, roast finish.
Session IPA (ABV 4.7%)
Prime Porter (ABV 4.9%)
Complex, dark brown beer with plenty of malt, fruit and roast taste. Satisfying full body with a clean finish.
Cumbrian Five Hop (ABV 5%)
A robust, hoppy bitter with citrus hops and fruity middle.
Lakeland Lager (ABV 5%)
NZPA (ABV 6%)
A very hoppy bitter with a sweet, fruity taste and a resounding dry, bitter finish.
IPA (ABV 7%)

Haworth Steam

Rose & Crown, 2 Westgate, Cleckheaton, West Yorkshire, BD19 5ET
☎ (01535) 646059 ☎ 07974 483310
🌐 haworthsteambrewery.co.uk

Established in 2011, the five-barrel brewery is located at the Rose & Crown, Cleckheaton, this being the main outlet for the beers along with the Haworth Steam Bistro, Haworth. Beers are also sold under the Whitechapel brand name.

Hay Rake

Rake Tapas Bar, Blackstone Edge Old Road, Littleborough, OL15 0JX
☎ (01706) 379689 ☎ 07775 792684
hayrakebrewery.info

Mark Wickham, the landlord of the Rake Tapas Restaurant, resurrected the Hay Rake microbrewery in 2013. The Rake brewed its own beer during the reign of Queen Victoria but stopped in 1901. Beers are available in the restaurant, occasionally the nearby White House and at local beer festivals.

Haywood Bad Ram SIBA

Callow Top Holiday Park, Buxton Road, Sandybrook, Ashbourne, Derbyshire, DE6 2AQ
☎ (01335) 344020 ☎ 07974 948427
badrambrewery.co.uk

Established in 2003, the brewery was based in a converted barn but a new brewery and bottling plant became operational in 2012. One pub is owned (on-site) and several other outlets are supplied. !! RAIB

Thoroughbred Bad Ram (ABV 3.8%)
Dr Samuel Johnson (ABV 4.5%)
Callow Top Imperial IPA (ABV 5.2%)

Headcorn Hop

Shenley Road, Headcorn, Ashford, Kent, TN27 9HX
headcornhop.weebly.com

Headcorn Hop is a picobrewery producing small batch beers. Originally brewed in France, the owners now brew both in France and Kent.

Headstocks

See Rufford Abbey

Healey's

Wellington Inn, Main Street, Loppergarth, Cumbria, LA12 0JL
☎ (01229) 582388

Healey's began brewing in the Wellington in 2012 using a custom-made, 2.5-barrel stainless steel plant, which can be viewed through full-length windows in the pub. A range of different beer styles is brewed, available in more than 15 pubs.

Heaney Farmhouse

c/o Boundary Brewing, Portview Trade Centre, Newtownards Road, Belfast, BT4 1HE
heaneyfarmhousebrewing.com

Founded in 2014. Bottled beers are currently brewed at Boundary (qv) in Belfast while its brewhouse project is underway at a farm in Bellaghy, Co Londonderry. No real ale.

Heart of Wales

Stables Yard, Zion Street, Llanwrtyd Wells, LD5 4RD
☎ (01591) 610236 heartofwalesbrewery.co.uk

The brewery was set up with a six-barrel plant in 2006 in old stables at the rear of the Neuadd Arms Hotel. Beers are brewed using water from the brewery's own borehole. Seasonal brews celebrate local events such as the World Bogsnorkelling Championships. Cambrian Heart Ale was commissioned by and is brewed for the Cambrian Mountains Initiative, inspired by the Prince of Wales, which aims to promote and support rural producers and communities in the region. !! ♦ RAIB V

Heathen

Grape & Grain, 51 The Broadway, Haywards Heath, West Sussex, RH16 3AS
☎ (01444) 456217 ☎ 07825 429428
heathenbrewers.co.uk

Located in the basement of the Grape & Grain off-licence and delicatessen, brewing began in 2014 using a full mash, two-barrel plant. Local outlets and beer festivals are supplied. !! ♦ RAIB

ISA (ABV 3.9%)
Black Eye PA (ABV 4.9%)
Stout (ABV 5%)
Pale (ABV 5.3%)
West Coast (ABV 5.4%)
Hoppler Effect (ABV 5.8%)
Mocha (ABV 7%)

Heathton

The Old Gate, Heathton, Shropshire, WV5 7EB

This brewery is planned to be resurrected at the Old Gate pub, but its three beers are produced at present in three different breweries, and served only in the Old Gate. Brewing is currently suspended.

Heavy Water (NEW)

c/o Church Hanbrewery, Unit F2, New Yatt Business Centre, North Leigh, Oxfordshire, OX29 6TJ
☎ (01993) 868998

Office: Williams Stanley & Co, 43-45 Newcombe House, Notting Hill Gate, London, W11 3LQ
heavywaterbrewing.co.uk

Established in 2020, Heavy Water produces a wide range of craft beers in small batches, some being bottle-conditioned. Brewing currently takes place on the Church Hanbrewery (qv) kit and the beers are available at select locations in the Oxford area and at the Cambridge Cheese Company. RAIB

Heidrun

Inn House Brewery, 449 Great Western Road, Glasgow, G12 8HH ✉ hello@valhallasgoat.com

A small batch brewery with beers contract brewed by Drygate Brewery (qv). RAIB

Heineken Royal Trafford

Royal Brewery, 201 Denmark Road, Manchester, M15 6LD

No real ale.

Heist (NEW)

107 Neepsend Lane, Sheffield, South Yorkshire, S3 8AT heistbrewco.com

Established by Dan Hunt and Adam France in 2017 as a craft bar and bottle shop, Heist began brewing operations in Clowne, Derbyshire in 2018. Moving to larger premises in Sheffield in 2020 allowed for greater distribution across the United Kingdom and into Europe. Available in keg and can, with limited cask releases. V◆

Helmsley SIBA

18 Bridge Street, Helmsley, North Yorkshire, YO62 5DX
☎ (01439) 771014 ☎ 07525 434268

⊛Located within the North York Moors National Park, brewing began in 2014. The brewery has a viewing gallery, tasting room and brewery tap. Local pubs are supplied. RAIB ◆

Yorkshire Legend (ABV 3.8%)
Striding the Riding (ABV 4%)
Howardian Gold (ABV 4.2%)
Honey (ABV 4.5%)
H!PA (ABV 5.5%)

Hemlock

37 Main Street, Hemington, Derbyshire, DE74 2RB
☎ 07791 057994 ✉ hembrew@yahoo.com

Established in 2015 on the borders of Derby, Leicester and Nottingham, this two-barrel plant is located in the outbuildings of a 17th century thatched cottage. The brewery originally supplied beers in the immediate area but has now branched out with increasing sales in Derbyshire, Nottinghamshire, Leicestershire and Staffordshire. !! ◆RAIB

Harvest Moon (ABV 4.1%)
Hoptimystic (ABV 4.3%)
Village Idiot (ABV 4.3%)
Call Me Blondie (ABV 4.5%)
Sparky's Dream (ABV 4.5%)
Six Pistols (ABV 6%)

Henry Smith

🍺 Robin Hood, 4 Wakefield Road, Pontefract, West Yorkshire, WF8 4HN ☎ 07547 573378

⊛Set up behind the Robin Hood pub in Pontefract by Dean Smith in 2019 with the help of Revolutions Brewery (where Head Brewer, Paul Windmill, learned to brew). The plant is the former James & Kirkman kit with a few tweaks. One beer is brewed at Revolutions Brewery due to high demand. Small batch specials for Revolutions will be brewed in Pontefract.

Hepworth

Stane Street, North Heath, West Sussex, RH20 1DJ
☎ (01403) 269696 ⊕ hepworthbrewery.co.uk

⊠ Hepworth's was established in 2001. 274 outlets are supplied. Originally situated in Horsham, a new brewery site in North Heath opened in 2016. Its organic status is ratified by the Soil Association. !! 🍺◆RAIB V

Traditional Sussex Bitter (ABV 3.5%)
A fine, clean-tasting amber session beer. A bitter beer with a pleasant fruity and hoppy aroma that leads to a crisp, tangy taste. A long, dry finish.
Dark Horse (ABV 3.8%)
Summer Ale (ABV 3.8%)
Pullman First Class Ale (ABV 4.2%)
A sweet, nutty maltiness and fruitiness are balanced by hops and bitterness in this easy-drinking, pale brown best bitter. A subtle bitter aftertaste.
Prospect Organic (ABV 4.5%)
Classic Old Ale (ABV 4.8%)
Iron Horse (ABV 4.8%)

There's a fruity, toffee aroma to this light brown, full-bodied bitter. A citrus flavour balanced by caramel and malt leads to a clean, dry finish.

Hercules

Unit 5b, Harbour Court, Heron Road, Sydenham, Holywood, Belfast, BT3 9HB
☎ (028) 9036 4516 ✉ niall@herculesbrewery.com

The original Hercules Brewing Company, founded in the 19th century, was one of 13 breweries in Belfast at the time. The company has been re-established to produce small batch brews using old brewing traditions. Its output is all under the Yardsman brand name.

Brewed under the Yardsman brand name:
IPA (ABV 4.3%)
Lager (ABV 4.8%)
Belfast Pale Ale (ABV 5.6%)

Hereford

🍺 88 St Owen Street, Hereford, HR1 2QD
☎ (01432) 342125 ✉ jfkenyon@aol.com

⊛Although there has been a small brewery on this site since 1992, Hereford began life as the Spinning Dog Brewery in 2000, changing its name in 2010. After a period as primarily a brewpub, in 2017 it began to expand its distribution to pubs in Herefordshire and Pembrokeshire. !! ◆RAIB

Heritage SIBA

National Brewery Centre, Horninglow Street, Burton upon Trent, Staffordshire, DE14 1NG
☎ (01283) 777006
⊕ heritagebrewingcompany.co.uk

⊛Heritage Brewing Company (formerly William Worthington's Brewery) was established in 2015 by Planning Solutions Limited, operators of the National Brewery Centre (NBC). They purchased the 25-barrel brewery and nearby bottling plant from the previous owners, Molson Coors. The team has set out to utilise the resources, history and knowledge available at the NBC to breathe new life into heritage beers, including those produced 10-15 years ago by the former Museum Brewing Co. !! 🍺◆RAIB

Victoria Ale (ABV 3.8%)
Charrington Oatmeal Stout (ABV 4%)
Massey's Original Mild (ABV 4%)
Offilers' Best Bitter (ABV 4%)
St. Modwen Golden Ale (ABV 4.2%)
Charrington IPA (ABV 4.5%)
Masterpiece IPA (ABV 5.6%)

Hermitage

Heathwaite, Slanting Hill, Hermitage, Berkshire, RG18 9QG
☎ (01635) 200907 ☎ 07980 019484
⊕ hermitagebrewery.co.uk

⊠ Established in 2013 by semi-retired food science lecturer Richard Marshall. After many years as a keen home brewer, the opportunity arose to go commercial on a very small scale and the 0.5-barrel brewery produces bottle-conditioned, traditional beers and some casks. Volumes vary, but is about 200 bottles per week. A range of seven 'core' beers and four seasonal beers are sold to local shops and festivals and a few local pubs. RAIB

Tom Herrick's

The Stable House, Main Street, Carlton on Trent,, Nottinghamshire, NG23 6NW ☎ 07877 542331
✉ tomherricksbrewery@hotmail.com

Tom Herrick installed his bespoke 2.5-barrel stainless steel brewery at the front of his premises during 2014 and began small scale commercial brewing the following year. The brewery is only operated on a part-time basis with output going to festivals and local pubs.

Bomber Command (ABV 4.2%)

Hesket Newmarket SIBA

Old Crown Barn, Back Green, Hesket Newmarket, Cumbria, CA7 8JG
☎ (01697) 478066 ⊕ hesketbrewery.co.uk

Founded in 1988, and bought by a co-operative in 1999 to preserve a community amenity. Cask beers are generally named after Cumbrian fells. A rebrand in recent years has seen a new look backed up by some modern beer styles and a rejuvenation of some of the more traditional beers. ‼♦

Haystacks (ABV 3.7%)
Light, easy-drinking, thirst-quenching blonde beer; very pleasant for its strength.
Skiddaw (ABV 3.7%)
Red Pike (ABV 3.8%)
Black Sail (ABV 4%)
A sweet stout with roast flavours.
Helvellyn Gold (ABV 4%)
Complex, hoppy and fruity beer with malt presence and refreshing finish.
High Pike (ABV 4.2%)
A traditional style bitter; fruity with a dry finish.
Doris' 90th Birthday Ale (ABV 4.3%)
Scafell Blonde (ABV 4.4%)
A hoppy, sweet, fruity, pale-coloured bitter.
Brim Fell IPA (ABV 4.5%)
Catbells (ABV 5%)
Golden ale with a nice balance of fruity sweetness and bitterness, almost syrupy but with an unexpectedly dry finish.
Smoked Porter (ABV 5.4%)
Old Carrock Strong Ale (ABV 6%)
Reddy brown strong ale, vine-fruity in flavour with slightly astringent finish.
West Coast Red (ABV 6.3%)
Double IPA (ABV 7.4%)

Hetton Law

Hetton Law Farm, Lowick, Berwick upon Tweed, Northumberland, TD15 2UL
☎ (01289) 388558 ☎ 07889 457140
⊕ hettonlawbrewery.co.uk

Brewing began in 2015 using a 2.5-barrel plant. Run by retired dentists Judith and Nicholas Grasse, it uses local spring water and locally grown malt which gives the beers a distinctive character. Due to the size of the brewery availability on draught and in bottles is effectively limited to the local area on both sides of the border. ♦

Hetton Hermit (ABV 3.8%)
Hetton Howler (ABV 4.2%)
Hetton Harlot (ABV 4.8%)
Hare Raiser (ABV 5.2%)

Hexhamshire SIBA

Dipton Mill Road, Hexham, Northumberland, NE46 1YA
☎ (01434) 606577 ⊕ hexhamshire.co.uk

Hexhamshire is Northumberland's oldest brewery and is run by the same family since it was founded in 1993. The Brooker family also run the brewery tap, the Dipton Mill. Outlets are supplied direct and via the SIBA Beerflex scheme.

Devil's Elbow (ABV 3.6%)
Amber brew full of hops and fruit, leading to a bitter finish.
Shire Bitter (ABV 3.8%)
A good balance of hops with fruity overtones, this amber beer makes an easy-drinking session bitter.
Blackhall English Stout (ABV 4%)
Devil's Water (ABV 4.1%)
Copper-coloured best bitter, well-balanced with a slightly fruity, hoppy finish.
Whapweasel (ABV 4.8%)
An interesting smooth, hoppy beer with a fruity flavour. Amber in colour, the bitter finish brings out the fruit and hops.
Old Humbug (ABV 5.5%)

Hidden Lane (NEW)

Argyle Street, Finnieston, Glasgow
☎ (0141) 258 2520 ⊕ hiddenlanebrewery.com

Organic brewery launched in Glasgow in 2018. V

High House Farm SIBA

Matfen, Newcastle upon Tyne, NE20 0RG
☎ (01661) 886192/ 886769
⊕ highhousefarmbrewery.co.uk

The brewery was founded in 2003 by a Brewlab graduate on a working farm, with a visitor centre, brewery shop and function room. This has now expanded to include a restaurant and wedding venue. More than 350 regional outlets are supplied. ‼♦

Auld Hemp (ABV 3.8%)
Tawny-coloured ale with hop, malt and fruit flavours and a good bitter finish.
Lizzie's Dimples (ABV 4%)
Nel's Best (ABV 4.2%)
Golden hoppy ale full of flavour with a clean, bitter finish.
Black Moss (ABV 4.3%)
Matfen Magic (ABV 4.8%)
Well-hopped brown ale with a fruity aroma. Malt and chocolate overtones with a rich, bitter finish.

Highgate

See Davenports

Higson's

See Love Lane

Hilden

Hilden House, Grand Street, Hilden, Lisburn, Co Antrim, BT27 4TY
☎ (028) 9266 0800 ⊕ hildenbrewery.co.uk

Established 1981, Hilden is Ireland's oldest independent brewery. Now in the second generation of family ownership, the beers are widely distributed across the UK. The beers are regularly available in Wetherspoon outlets in Northern Ireland. ‼♦

Nut Brown (ABV 3.8%)
Ale (ABV 4%)
An amber-coloured beer with an aroma of malt, hops and fruit. The balanced taste is slightly slanted towards hops, and hops are also prominent in the full, malty finish.
Barney's Brew (ABV 4.2%)
Irish Stout (ABV 4.3%)
Scullion's Irish Ale (ABV 4.6%)
Twisted Hop (ABV 4.7%)
Halt (ABV 6.1%)

Brewed under the College Brewery brand name:
Headless Dog (ABV 4.3%)

Hill Island

Unit 7, Fowlers Yard, Back Silver Street, Durham, DH1 3RA ☎ 07740 932584
✉ hillisland73@gmail.com

Established in 2002, Hill Island is a literal translation of Dunholme, from which Durham is derived. It is part of Fowler's Yard Craft Workshops on the banks of the River Wear and can be reached by steps down from Silver Street. A pop-up bar operates at the brewery on the first and third Saturday each month, plus other weekends coinciding with Durham events such as the Durham Fire & Ice Festival and the Durham Miner's Gala. !! ♦

Peninsula Pint (ABV 3.7%)
Bitter (ABV 3.9%)
Stout for the Count (ABV 4%)
Neptune's Gold (ABV 4.2%)
Cathedral Ale (ABV 4.3%)
THAIPA (ABV 4.3%)
Griffin's Irish Stout (ABV 4.5%)

Hillside SIBA

Holly Bush Farm, Ross Road, Longhope, Gloucestershire, GL17 0NG
☎ (01452) 830222 hillsidebrewery.com

A six-barrel plant in a reconstructed farm dairy that started in 2011. A 60 metre bore hole produces pure water rich in minerals ideally suited to brewing. The regular beers are supplemented by limited run specials that explore different styles and flavours. The Hop Barn, is now open, which holds monthly events and can be hired privately. !! ♦ RAIB ◆

Over the Hill (ABV 3.5%)
Pinnacle (ABV 3.8%)
Legless Cow (ABV 4.2%)
HCL (ABV 4.3%)
Legend of Hillside (ABV 4.7%)
Summit Ruby Ale (ABV 4.9%)

Hillstown

128 Glebe Road, Randalstown, BT41 3DT
hillstownbrewery.com

Brewing began in 2014 in a converted barn on a farm in Randalstown producing bottle-conditioned beers. ♦ RAIB

Hilltop

Sheffield Road, Conisbrough, South Yorkshire, DN12 2AY
☎ (01709) 868811 ☎ 07947 146746
thehilltophotel.co.uk

Established in 2016, Hilltop Brewery is a 3.5-barrel plant situated in the outbuildings of the Hilltop Hotel in Conisbrough. Beers are available in the hotel and other local outlets. !! ♦ RAIB

Hinks (NEW)

1 Dimon Villas, Hamstreet Road, Ruckinge, Kent, TN26 2NT ☎ 07518 569041
✉ hinkscraftbrewery@gmail.com

A nanobrewery established in 2018. GF

Hitchin

The Outhouse, 16 Thatchers End, Hitchin, Hertfordshire, SG4 0PD
✉ hitchinbrewery@gmail.com

Small brewery using a 100-litre brew kit. Established in 2018 it currently supplies three outlets with bottle-conditioned beers although cask and keg is planned. RAIB

Hiver

56 Stanworth Street, Bermondsey, London, SE1 3NY
☎ (020) 3198 9972 hiverbeers.com

Beers are brewed by Hepworth in Sussex using honey made locally to Bermondsey. The taproom is on the Maltby Street Market side of the Bermondsey Beer Mile and the beers are available in cask, keg and bottle both here and widely around London and the South East. ◆

Hobsons SIBA

Newhouse Farm, Tenbury Road, Cleobury Mortimer, Shropshire, DY14 8RD
☎ (01299) 270837 hobsons-brewery.co.uk

Established in 1993 in a former sawmill, Hobsons relocated to a farm site with more space in 1995. A second brewery, bottling plant and a warehouse have been added along with significant expansion to the first brewery. Beers are supplied within a 50-mile radius. The brewery utilises environmental sustainable technologies where possible. A visitor centre was added in 2014, which also now operates as a brewery tap. !! RAIB ◆

Mild (ABV 3.2%)
A classic mild. Complex layers of taste come from roasted malts that predominate and give lots of flavour.
Twisted Spire (ABV 3.6%)
Best (ABV 3.8%)
A pale brown to amber, medium-bodied beer with strong hop character throughout. It is consequently bitter, but with malt discernible in the taste.
Old Prickly (ABV 4.2%)
Town Crier (ABV 4.5%)

Hogs Back SIBA

Manor Farm, The Street, Tongham, Surrey, GU10 1DE
☎ (01252) 783000 hogsback.co.uk

This traditionally-styled brewery, established in 1992, boasts an extensive range of award-winning ales. The shop sells all the brewery's beers and related merchandise plus over 400 beers and ciders from around the world. In 2014 the brewery planted hops on neighbouring farmland, restoring the ancient Farnham White Bine variety. The brewery is building a new on-site hop kiln to dry its own hops. !! ♦ RAIB

HBB (ABV 3.7%)
Biscuity aroma with some hops and lemon notes. Well-balanced, plenty of hob in the mouth with a long-lasting, dry, bitter aftertaste.
Surrey Nirvana (ABV 4%)
TEA (ABV 4.2%)

A tawny-coloured best bitter with toffee and malt present in the nose. A well-rounded flavour with malt and a fruity sweetness.
Hop Garden Gold (ABV 4.4%)
Full-bodied with an aroma of malt, hops and fruit. Hoppy bitterness grows in an increasingly dry aftertaste with a hint of sweetness.
Rip Snorter (ABV 5%)
Well-balanced, sweet, malty bitter. Red brown in colour, with a moderate bitterness that grows into the aftertaste.

Hogs Head

1 Stanley Street, Sowerby Bridge, West Yorkshire, HX6 2AH
☎ (01422) 836585
hogsheadbrewpub@outlook.com

The Hogs Head Brewery opened in a huge 18th century former malthouse at the end of 2015. The fourteen-barrel brew house, increased from eight-barrels in 2018, is situated at the back of the accompanying bar with the handsome copper and stainless steel brewing vats on display at the back of the building. Almost all the production is sold on the premises with occasional casks being provided to beer festivals. ♦

Holcot Hop-Craft

Chequers Row, Main Street, Holcot, NN6 9SP
roger@gunnett.co.uk

This small brewery started brewing in 2017 and is located in the tiny village of Holcot, Northamptonshire. It is a one-hectolitre brewery, brewing once a week producing 180 pints either in pins or firkins. The beer is usually on tap at the Queens Arms at Orlingbury and is available in other pubs, clubs and beer festivals within a 10 mile radius of the brewery.

Holden's SIBA IFBB

George Street, Woodsetton, Dudley, West Midlands, DY1 4LW
☎ (01902) 880051 holdensbrewery.co.uk

A family brewery spanning four generations, Holden's began life as a brewpub in 1915. Continued expansion means it now has 19 tied pubs in its estate. ‼ ♦

Black Country Mild (ABV 3.7%)
A good, red/brown mild. A refreshing, light blend of roast malt, hops and fruit, dominated by malt throughout.
Black Country Bitter (ABV 3.9%)
A medium-bodied, golden ale. Light, well-balanced bitter with a subtle, dry, hoppy finish.
Golden Glow (ABV 4.4%)
Special (ABV 5.1%)
A sweet, malty, full-bodied amber ale with hops to balance in the taste and in the good, bittersweet finish.

Hollow Stone

See Shipstone's

Hollow Tree (NEW)

3 Glen Road, Whatstandwell, Derbyshire, DE4 5EH
hollowtreebrewing@gmail.com

Brewing began in 2019 in Whatstandwell, Derbyshire. RAIB

Holsworthy

Unit 5, Circuit Business Park, Clawton, Devon, EX22 6RR
☎ (01566) 783678 ☎ 07879 401073
holsworthyales.co.uk

Holsworthy Ales is a 5.5-barrel microbrewery situated in the heart of Devon's Ruby Country. Brewing began commercially in 2011. Its intention is to make its beers taste as clean and natural as possible, so no chemicals or finings are added to the soft Devon water used in many of its ales. ‼ ♦ RAIB V

Mine's a Mild (ABV 3.5%)
Sunshine (ABV 4%)
Smooth golden ale. Hops overwhelm all else. Hints of fruit. Fresh and bitter hoppy aftertaste.
Bang On (ABV 4.2%)
Green Hop (ABV 4.3%)
Muck 'n' Straw (ABV 4.4%)
Hops dominate with hints of malt in aroma and taste. Well-balanced with slight dryness in aftertaste.
Tamar Black (ABV 4.8%)
Dark stout with hints of liquorice and coffee. A complex mix full of malt, roast, fruit, hops and caramel.
Hop on the Run (ABV 5%)
Proper Lager (ABV 5%)
Old Market Monk (ABV 6.1%)

Joseph Holt SIBA IFBB

The Brewery, Empire Street, Cheetham, Manchester, M3 1JD
☎ (0161) 834 3285 joseph-holt.com

Founded in 1849, Joseph Holt is one of the UK's leading independent family breweries. Now in its sixth generation the business operates 127 pubs across Manchester and the North West and supplies more than 20 ales to over 500 outlets nationally.

Mild (ABV 3.2%)
A dark brown/red beer with a fruity, malty nose. Roast, malt, fruit and hops in the taste, with strong bitterness for a mild, and a dry malt and hops finish.
IPA (ABV 3.8%)
Golden bitter with biscuity malt, hops and restrained lemony notes. Dry, bitter finish.
Bitter (ABV 4%)
Pale brown beer with malt and hops in the aroma. Bitter taste with balanced malty flavour. Increased bitter finish.
Two Hoots (ABV 4.2%)

Brewed under the Bootleg Brewery name:
Fools Gold (ABV 3.9%)
Chorlton Pale Ale (ABV 4%)
Urban Fox (ABV 4.2%)
Copper in colour, hoppy aroma, hoppy and bitter throughout, with some biscuity malt in the taste.

Holy Well

4 Barnfield Close, Egerton, BL7 9UP ☎ 07949 179338
holywellbrewing.com

Holy Well Brewing is a nanobrewery specialising in small batch brews celebrating different styles and traditions. The owners have strong links with Halliwell, an ancient township of Bolton whose name derives from the original 'Holy Well'. Most beers are sold bottle-conditioned at local farmers markets, but you may occasionally see them in cask at selected local outlets. The brewers like to meet customers and share their love and knowledge of the beers. RAIB V

THE BREWERIES

Home

See Pheasantry

Hook Norton SIBA IFBB

Brewery Lane, Scotland End, Hook Norton, Oxfordshire, OX15 5NY
☎ (01608) 737210 🌐 hooky.co.uk

⊠ One of the finest examples of a Victorian tower brewery. The oldest independent brewery in Oxfordshire, Hook Norton's been brewing since 1849. The current premises were built in 1900 and still house much of the original machinery, including a 25hp steam engine (occasionally in use). Shire horses make deliveries to local pubs. Remaining family-owned, it combines its brewing heritage with a modern approach. Various parts of the brewery are available for hire. Customers can spend a day brewing their own beer. ‼ ♦ RAIB

Hooky Mild (ABV 2.8%)
A chestnut brown, easy-drinking mild. A complex malt and hop aroma give way to a well-balanced taste, leading to a long, hoppy finish that is unusual for a mild.
Hooky (ABV 3.5%)
A classic golden session bitter. Hoppy and fruity aroma followed by a malt and hops taste and a continuing hoppy finish.
Hooky Gold (ABV 4.1%)
Old Hooky (ABV 4.6%)
A strong bitter, tawny in colour. A well-rounded fruity taste with a balanced bitter finish.

Hop & Stagger SIBA

The Old Cow Shed, Astol Farm, Norton, Shropshire, TF11 9EW
☎ (01952) 730737 ☎ 07487 898151
🌐 hopandstaggerbrewery.co.uk

Hop & Stagger began brewing in 2011 having set up a 2.5-barrel plant at the White Lion Inn in Bridgnorth. In 2015 the brewery relocated to a farm between Bridgnorth and Telford, with all new brewing equipment and an increase in capacity to six barrels. Currently Hop and Stagger produce six permanent beers, with additional seasonal brews. ♦

Shropshire Pale Ale (ABV 3.8%)
Golden Wander (ABV 4.1%)
Beckbury Bitter (ABV 4.2%)
Strategic Blonde (ABV 4.3%)
Bridgnorth Porter (ABV 5%)
Triple Hop IPA (ABV 5%)

Hop Back SIBA

Units 22-24, Batten Road Industrial Estate, Downton, Wiltshire, SP5 3HU
☎ (01725) 510986 🌐 hopback.co.uk

⊠ Founded in 1987, Hop Back owns 10 pubs and distributes nationally. The flagship beer, Summer Lightning, has won numerous CAMRA awards. ‼ ♦ RAIB V

GFB (ABV 3.5%)
A light gold-coloured, refreshing session bitter. The hoppy aroma leads to bitterness initially, lasting through to the finish with some fruit.
Citra (ABV 4%)
Pale yellow almost straw-coloured with lemon and grapefruit on the aroma and taste, rapidly developing a balanced, hoppy aftertaste.
Fuggle Stone (ABV 4%)
Crop Circle (ABV 4.2%)
A pale yellow best bitter with a fragrant hop aroma, complex hop, fruit and citrus flavours and a balanced hoppy, bittersweet aftertaste.
Taiphoon (ABV 4.2%)
A clean-tasting, light, fruity beer with hops and fruit on the aroma, complex hop character and lemongrass notes in the taste, slight sweetness balanced with some astringency in the aftertaste.
Entire Stout (ABV 4.5%)
A smooth, rich, ruby-black stout with strong roast and malt aromas and flavours, with a long bittersweet and malty aftertaste.
Summer Lightning (ABV 5%)
Strong golden ale with a hoppy aroma and slightly astringent bitterness in the taste, balanced with some fruit sweetness in the dry aftertaste.

Hop Fuzz SIBA

Unit 8, Riverside Industrial Estate, West Hythe, Kent, CT21 4NB ☎ 07858 562878 🌐 hopfuzz.co.uk

Hop Fuzz was started by two friends in 2011 and is situated on an industrial estate next to the Royal Military Canal at West Hythe. The brewery tap, Unit Number One, is popular with locals. ♦V

Martello (ABV 3.8%)
Old American Pale Ale (ABV 4%)
Bullion (ABV 5%)

Hop Kettle SIBA

Swindon: Unit 4, Hawksworth Industrial Estate, Newcombe Drive, Swindon, Wiltshire, SN2 1DZ
☎ (01793) 490556

Cricklade: Red Lion, 74 High Street, Cricklade, Wiltshire, SN6 6DD ☎ (01793) 750776
🌐 theredlioncricklade.co.uk

Brewing began in a barn behind the Red Lion Inn, Cricklade, in 2012, using a one-barrel plant. Due to demand a larger four-barrel plant followed, which supplies the pub and is also used for experimental brews. A new 10-barrel plant was installed in an old Royal Mail warehouse in Swindon in 2016. ♦

Ordinary Bitter (ABV 3.8%)
Chameleon (ABV 4%)
Lode Star (ABV 4.3%)
North Wall (ABV 4.3%)
Rising Star (ABV 4.8%)
East Star (ABV 5%)
Red Star (ABV 5.2%)
Evening Star (ABV 5.5%)

Hop Monster

See George's

Hop Shed SIBA

Old Chicken Shed, Stocks Farm, Suckley, Worcestershire, WR6 5EQ
☎ (01886) 884110 ☎ 07484 688026
🌐 hopshed.co.uk

Originally named Unity Brew House, brewing began in 2016 using a 10-barrel plant. It is the only brewery in the UK located on a commercial hop farm. Based in an old chicken shed, the beers are named after breeds of chicken. An on-site bar is open on Fridays and Saturdays.

Wybar (ABV 3.6%)
Sebright Golden Ale (ABV 3.8%)
Pekin (ABV 4%)

Sultan (ABV 4.2%)
Frizzle British IPA (ABV 4.5%)

Hop Studio SIBA

3 Handley Park, Elvington Industrial Estate, York
Road, Elvington, North Yorkshire, YO41 4AR
☎ (01904) 608029 ⊕ thehopstudio.com

⊛Founded in 2012 the Hop Studio brews on a 10-barrel
plant in an industrial unit just outside York. Under new
ownership from 2020, it now brews unique recipes for
every beer. Outlets in Yorkshire are supplied direct and
the rest of the UK via wholesalers. ‼ ➠ ◆ RAIB GF V◆

Hop Stuff

Unit 35.9 Cobalt, White Hart Triangle Estate, White
Hart Avenue, Thamesmead, London, SE28 0GU
☎ (020) 3247 4118 ☎ 07850 086461
⊕ hopstuffbrewery.com

Hop Stuff began brewing in 2013. After crowdfunding
success it moved to a new 65-hectolitre brewhouse in
Thamesmead in 2018. However brewing was suspended
and in 2019 the brewery and brand were transferred to
the ownership of Molson Coors. Brewing restarted later
that year. ◆

Fusilier (ABV 4.3%)
Biscuity malty best bitter with spicy hop notes. Finish is
sweetish, slightly dry with a faint bitterness. Rich,
smooth mouthfeel.
Pale (ABV 4.5%)
Slightly dry, amber bitter with a complex hop character
throughout. Citrus notes in the flavour and finish, which
is bitter.
Renegade IPA (ABV 5.6%)
Smooth dark-gold IPA with grapefruit and spiced hops
aroma and flavour. Warm lingering finish that is bitter
and dry.

Hop Therapy (NEW)

Unit 3, Warkup Barn, Manor Farm, Draycote Cerne,
Wiltshire, SN15 1LD ⊕ hoptherapybrewing.com

⊠ Established in 2020 by CAMRA member Tom Kyte,
Hop Therapy is a 1.5-barrel nanobrewery producing
unfined, hop-forward beers. Beer is available in cask and
keg with some occasionally available from the wood. ‼ V

Hop Vine

⊟ Hop Vine, Liverpool Road North, Burscough,
Lancashire, L40 4BY
☎ (01704) 893799 ☎ 07920 002783
✉ mikejulie6465@gmail.com

⊛Hop Vine began brewing in 2017 using the four-barrel
plant of the defunct Burscough Brewery. It is situated in
old stable buildings in the courtyard to the rear of the
Hop Vine. Beer is usually only supplied to the pub and
the Legh Arms, Mere Brow. ➠◆

Hopburst

80 Grange Road, Darlington, DL1 5NP
☎ (01325) 787912 ☎ 07929 007509

Focussing on small batch ales, commercial brewing
began in 2016.

Hopdaemon SIBA

Unit 1, Parsonage Farm, Seed Road, Newnham, Kent,
ME9 0NA
☎ (01795) 892078 ⊕ hopdaemon.com

Tonie Prins originally started brewing in Tyler Hill near
Canterbury in 2000 and moved to a new site in
Newnham in 2005. The brewery currently supplies more
than 100 outlets. ‼◆RAIB

Golden Braid (ABV 3.7%)
A refreshing golden session bitter with a good blend of
bittering and aroma hops underpinned by pale malt.
Incubus (ABV 4%)
A well-balanced, copper-hued best bitter. Pale malt and
a hint of crystal malt are blended with bitter and slightly
floral hops to give a lingering hoppy finish.
Skrimshander IPA (ABV 4.5%)
Green Daemon (ABV 5%)
Leviathan (ABV 6%)

Hophurst SIBA

Unit 8, Hindley Business Centre, Platt Lane, Hindley,
WN2 3PA
☎ (01942) 522333 ⊕ hophurstbrewery.co.uk

⊛Hophurst Brewery was started in 2014 by Stuart Hurst,
whose passion for producing craft ales combined with 20
years of supporting businesses and re-skilling
unemployed people created a unique social enterprise
brewery that employs people over the age of 50 and
guides them through its training programme. Twisted
Vine Ale House is its award-winning microbar in Ashton-
in Makerfield. ◆

2 Rounds of 6 Before Breakfast (ABV 3.5%)
Mellors (ABV 3.8%)
Light and refreshing beer with fruity, bitter hops and a
bitter finish.
Quench (ABV 3.8%)
Full-bodied, session bitter with lasting hops and dry
finish.
Campfire (ABV 3.9%)
Light-bodied beer with bitter roasted malt.
Cosmati (ABV 4.2%)
Debonair (ABV 4.9%)
Porteresque (ABV 5.5%)
Complex dark beer, with roast and fruit in aroma. Strong
roast flavour with a developing sweet fruitiness. Lasting
roast finish.

Hopper House Brew Farm

Racecourse Road, Sedgefield, TS21 2HL ☎ 07947
874278 ⊕ hopperhousebrewfarm.co.uk

Brewing commenced in 2019 on a one-barrel plant
situated in a working dairy farm on the outskirts of
Sedgefield. There is a taproom in an old milking parlour.
Currently it only has a licence for bank holidays and
occasional weekends but aspires to get a full licence. ◆

Hoppy Family

Harcourt Street, Kettering, Northamptonshire,
NN16 0RS ☎ 07986 019579 ⊕ hfbrewery.com

Microbrewery established in 2017 brewing a range of
bottled-conditioned beers using ingredients such as
blueberries, raspberries and chillies.

Hops & Dots

8 Orchard Road, Linthorpe, Middlesbrough, TS5 5PW
✉ john@hopsanddots.com

The brewery was established in 2019 by a teacher of the
visually impaired and a solicitor. Hops & Dots believe that
craft beer should always be accessible to all, which is
why it promotes braille alongside its beers. ◆RAIB V

Fat Fingers (ABV 5.1%)

Oatie Dotie (ABV 6%)
Sim Specs (ABV 6.4%)
Dimmer Switch (ABV 6.8%)
Graduated Response (ABV 7.1%)
Cognitive Overload (ABV 8.2%)
In the Dark (ABV 8.4%)
Black Out (ABV 8.9%)

Hopscotch

See Crosspool Ale Makers

Hopshackle

Unit F, Bentley Business Park, Blenheim Way, Northfields Industrial Estate, Market Deeping, Lincolnshire, PE6 8LD ☎ 07894 317980
🌐 hopshacklebrewery.co.uk

Hopshackle was established in 2006 using a five-barrel plant. A 10-barrel plant was installed in 2015. More than 40 outlets are supplied direct. !! ♦ RAIB

Simmarillo (ABV 3.8%)
Zen (ABV 3.8%)
American Pale Ale (ABV 4.3%)
Hopnosis (ABV 5.2%)

Hopstar SIBA

Unit 9 Rinus Business Park, Grimshaw Street, Darwen, BB3 2QX ☎ 07933 590159 🌐 hopstarbrewery.co.uk

Hopstar first brewed in 2004 on a 2.5-barrel plant and expanded in 2010 to a new unit with a six-barrel plant. More than 100 outlets are supplied around Lancashire and the Greater Manchester area. The brewery tap is Number 39 in Darwen. !! ♦ RAIB

Chilli (ABV 3.8%)
Dizzy Danny Ale (ABV 3.8%)
Dark Knight (ABV 3.9%)
Off T'Mill (ABV 3.9%)
Smokey Joe's Black Beer (ABV 3.9%)
Darwen Spitfire (ABV 4%)
JC (ABV 4%)
Lancashire Gold (ABV 4%)
Lush (ABV 4%)
Saaz Blonde (ABV 4%)

Horbury

The Brewhouse, Cherry Tree Inn, 19 Church Street, Horbury, West Yorkshire, WF4 6LT ☎ 07970 299292

Following the closure of Bob's Brewing Co, Horbury Ales took over the plant in 2016 and transferred production to the rear of the brewery tap, Cherry Tree Inn. Beers are available locally, regionally and nationally.

Horncastle

Old Nicks Tavern, 8 North Street, Horncastle, Lincolnshire, LN9 5DX
☎ (01507) 526862 🌐 horncastleales.co.uk

Brewing began in 2014 using a 3.75-barrel plant. The brewery is situated in Old Nicks Tavern with beer available in the pub plus other Lincolnshire outlets. It has its own bottling plant and a beer in box scheme is also available for pre-ordering. !!

Hornes SIBA

19b Station Road, Bow Brickhill, Buckinghamshire, MK17 9JU
☎ (01908) 647724 🌐 hornesbrewery.co.uk

A purpose-built, six-barrel brewery established in 2015 and producing a range of beers called Triple Goat after the three goats kept in a paddock at the brewery. A taproom and shop were added in 2018. ♦ GF

Featherstone Amber Ale (ABV 3.6%)
Dark Fox (ABV 3.8%)
Triple Goat Pale Ale (ABV 3.9%)
Ryestone (ABV 4%)
Triple Goat Porter (ABV 4.6%)
Triple Goat IPA (ABV 5%)

Horsforth SIBA

Unit 1a, Station Road, Horsforth, Leeds, West Yorkshire, LS18 5NX ☎ 07854 078330
🌐 horsforthbrewery.co.uk

Brewing began on a part-time basis on a one-barrel plant in 2017 in the owner's garage. In addition to the flagship beer an ever-changing range of specials is produced. The taproom is open on the first Saturday of the month. V

My Horse Came Fourth (ABV 3.5%)
Pale (ABV 4.5%)
Mosaic (ABV 5.1%)
Weize Rose (ABV 5.4%)
Aubretia (ABV 5.5%)
Night Ryder (ABV 5.5%)
Rubis (ABV 6.2%)

Hoskins

See Belvoir

Howard Town SIBA

Hawkshead Mill, Hope Street, Glossop, Derbyshire, SK13 7SS
☎ (01457) 869800 🌐 howardtownbrewery.co.uk

Established in 2005, this award-winning brewery moved to its current location in 2007. In 2019 it moved into the premises next door, increasing the capacity of the brewery from eight-barrel to 15-barrels. Six core beers are brewed for the free trade, along with seasonal beers. An on-site bar caters for members evenings and open days. !! ♦ RAIB

Mill Town Mild (ABV 3.5%)
Longdendale Lights (ABV 3.9%)
Monk's Gold (ABV 4%)
Wren's Nest (ABV 4.2%)
Super Fortress (ABV 4.4%)
Dark Peak (ABV 6%)

Howfen

66 Green Meadows, Westhoughton, BL5 2BN
🌐 howfenbrew.co

Howfen began brewing in 2018 and is situated in the owner's garage. After a year's hiatus it has resumed brewing. It is named after the dialect word for Westhoughton.

Howling Hops

Unit 9a, Queen's Yard, White Post Lane, Hackney Wick, London, E9 5EN
☎ (020) 3583 8262 🌐 howlinghops.co.uk

Brewing began in 2012. Originally brewing at the Cock Tavern in Hackney, a new plant opened in 2015 in Hackney Wick. Beers are now widely available and cover many styles from a standard range to taproom special, hoppy styles being the favourite. RAIB

Howzat (NEW)

▤ Cricketers Arms, Peter Street, St Helens, Merseyside, WA10 2EB
☎ (01744) 758021

A new brewery in the grounds of the Cricketer's Arms – a former CAMRA National Pub of the Year.

Sarah Hughes

▤ Beacon Hotel, 129 Bilston Street, Sedgley, West Midlands, DY3 1JE
☎ (01902) 883381 ⊕ sarahhughesbrewery.co.uk

⊗ Traditional, Black Country, Victorian tower brewery, taken over by Sarah Hughes in 1921. Brewing ceased in the 1950s and recommenced in 1987. The original grist case and rare open-topped copper give a unique character to the brews. The Beacon Hotel is the brewery tap. Famous for its Dark Ruby, the beers can be found far and wide. !! ♦

Pale Amber (ABV 4%)
Sedgley Surprise (ABV 5%)
A bittersweet, medium-bodied, hoppy ale with some malt.
Dark Ruby Mild (ABV 6%)
A dark ruby strong ale with a good balance of fruit and hops, leading to a pleasant, lingering hops and malt finish.

Humber Doucy (NEW) SIBA

St Edmunds Garage, Broad Road, Bacton, Suffolk, IP14 4HP
☎ (01449) 780151 ⊕ humberdoucybrew.co

Humber Doucy started brewing in 2019. Located in Bacton, Suffolk, within the Jeffries of Bacton Subaru dealership, it is a son and father business. The family have a background in grain and malt with connections to Stowmarket-based maltsters Muntons.

King Slayer (ABV 3.6%)
Pale Ale (ABV 4.4%)
American Porter (ABV 5%)

Humpty Dumpty SIBA

Church Road, Reedham, Norfolk, NR13 3TZ
☎ (01493) 701818 ☎ 07843 248865
⊕ humptydumptybrewery.co.uk

⊗ Established in 1998, this 11-barrel, award-winning brewery continues to grow and expand its range of beers, including a new Norfolk Broads Brewing series of occasional one-off brews. !! ⊞ ♦ RAIB

Little Sharpie (ABV 3.8%)
Fruity aroma with malt and hop. Bitter throughout with balanced malt and hop in the background. Crisp, slightly astringent finish.
Branch Line Bitter (ABV 3.9%)
Lemon & Ginger (ABV 4%)
Swallowtail (ABV 4%)
Full-bodied marmalade and biscuit aroma with matching beginning. Grainy texture is enhanced by solid bitter notes flowing onward.
Ale (ABV 4.2%)
A hoppy vanilla fudge edge in both nose and taste. Malt provides balance as a gentle bitterness quickly recedes. Lengthy finish.
Broadland Sunrise (ABV 4.2%)
Red Mill (ABV 4.3%)
Full-bodied, robust and fruity. Coffee, dark fruits and caramel vie for dominance against a malty bitter base. Powerful, rich ending.
Reedcutter (ABV 4.4%)
A sweet, malty beer; golden hued with a gentle malt background. Smooth and full-bodied with a quick, gentle finish.
Cheltenham Flyer (ABV 4.6%)
A full-flavoured golden, earthy bitter with a long, grainy finish. A strong hop bitterness dominates throughout. Little evidence of malt.
EAPA (East Anglian Pale Ale) (ABV 4.6%)
Amber gold with an orange marmalade nose. A bittersweet caramel beginning slowly dries out as malty nuances fade away.

Hungry Bear

10-14 Stonegate Road, Leeds, West Yorkshire, LS6 4HY
☎ (0113) 274 0241
⊕ hungrybearbrewingcompany.com

Hungry Bear began brewing in 2013 in the upstairs rooms of the Hungry Bear restaurant. A wide range of ales are produced in batches of about 70 litres, with a constantly evolving selection available either via the two taps on the draught dispense system, or as bottle-conditioned ale. !! ♦ RAIB

Hunters SIBA

Bulleigh Barton Farm, Ipplepen, Devon, TQ12 5UA
☎ (01803) 873509 ☎ 07540 657115
⊕ thehuntersbrewery.co.uk

⊗ Hunters began brewing in 2008. The award-winning brewery has a 60-barrel brew length and 4,000 gallon fermenting capacity. A bottling, labelling and packing plant means it can turn out 3,000 bottle-conditioned beers per hour; this, coupled with a dedicated conditioning room, is enabling Hunters to bottle for others as well as itself. !! ⊞ ♦ RAIB

Old Charlie (ABV 3.8%)
Crispy Pig (ABV 4%)
Very different ale, a cross between a golden bitter and cider. Aroma very strong apples, tastes of apples. A refreshing drink which would go well on a hot summers day.
Half Bore (ABV 4%)
Light colour and body. Malt dominates from start to finish. Lots of flavour and slightly flowery.
Devon Dreamer (ABV 4.1%)
Amber best bitter with hop aroma and undertones of caramel. Hops in the taste and slight bitterness develops later.
Pheasant Plucker (ABV 4.3%)
Best bitter ale leans slightly towards an old ale style in looks and taste. Slight charcoal sweet taste.
Premium (ABV 4.8%)
A nice traditional strong best bitter. Slight winter fruits on taste with after tones of a bitter pine finish.
Royal Hunt (ABV 5.5%)
An easy-drinking, strong ale. Malt dominates, with rich roast and caramel tones bursting through.
Black Jack (ABV 6%)
A sweet strong stout, very drinkable with a woody caramel taste on the palate.
Full Bore (ABV 6.8%)

Hurly Burly SIBA

Unit 1, Block 4, Inveresk Industrial Estate, Musselburgh, EH21 7UL ☎ 07842 331704

Office: 15 Glenorchy Road, North Berwick
⊕ hurlyburlybrewery.co.uk

THE BREWERIES

Small, family-run brewery. Originally based in the brewer's kitchen, the brewery moved to larger premises in 2019. RAIB

Hurns

See Tomos Watkin (under W)

Hurst SIBA

Highfileds Farm, Hurstpierpoint, West Sussex, BN6 9JT
☎ 07866 438953 🌐 hurstbrewery.co.uk

Hurst was founded in 2012, but reviving a name dating back to 1862.

Husk SIBA

Unit 58a, Railway Arches, North Woolwich Road, West Silvertown, London, E16 2AA
☎ (020) 7474 3827 ☎ 07803 271160
🌐 huskbrewing.com

Brewing in West Silvertown, along from the Royal Docks, since 2015. The first brewery in the area, now has its taproom open every Friday and Saturday. Beers available in cask, keg and RAIB bottles with eye-catching clip and label designs. RAIB ◆

Pale Ale (ABV 5.1%)
Light citrusy, hoppy, bready aroma. Slightly sweet, balanced with lemon peel, spiciness and grapefruit becoming more bitter. Crisp bitter finish.

Hybrid SIBA

Unit 14C Abbotsinch Industrial Estate, Abbotsinch Road, Grangemouth, FK3 9UX
✉ contact@hybridbrewing.com

Hybrid began brewing in 2016 using a 10.5-barrel dual train brewplant, allowing for two different beers to be brewed at a time. Up to 40 outlets are supplied direct, mostly in the Forth Valley. ♦V

Sesh (ABV 3.6%)
Groat (ABV 3.8%)
Apex (ABV 4.1%)
Hindsight (ABV 4.4%)
Citra Storm (ABV 4.5%)
Magic Porridge (ABV 4.7%)
Street Legal (ABV 4.7%)

Hydes SIBA IFBB

The Beer Studio, 30 Kansas Avenue, Salford, M50 2GL
☎ (0161) 226 1317 🌐 hydesbrewery.com

Hydes Brewery has been in the Manchester area since 1863. In 2012 it relocated to Salford's MediaCityUK area. The brewery produces more than forty beers per year, four of which are core brands brewed on a permanent basis. The Kansas Avenue range consists of 12 new beers every year, while the Provenance range offers 12 beers brewed using ingredients sourced from around the world. The Beer Studio range consists of six fruit-based beers. !!♦

1863 (ABV 3.5%)
Lightly-hopped, amber-coloured, session beer with some hops, malt and fruit in the taste and a short, dry finish.
Old Indie (ABV 3.5%)
Dark brown/red in colour, with a fruit and malt nose. Taste includes biscuity malt and green fruits, with a satisfying aftertaste.
Original (ABV 3.8%)
Pale brown beer with a malty nose, malt and an earthy hoppiness in the taste, and a good bitterness through to the finish.
Lowry (ABV 4.7%)
Malt, hops and fruit compete for dominance in this strong beer. Fruit and bitter prominent in finish.

Iâl

Pant Du Road, Eryrys, CH7 4DD ☎ 07956 440402

Office: Bryntirion Cottage, Fford Rhiw Ial, Llanarmon Yn Ial, CH7 4QE 🌐 cwrwial.com

Cwrw Iâl Community Brewery is run as a social enterprise assisted by EU funding with all profits used for local community projects. The 10-barrel plant brews a core range as well as regular specials. It supplies outlets along the North Wales coast and the North West. Jointly with Dovecote it operates the small chain of Hoptomist micropubs.

Pocket Rocket (ABV 4%)
Yellow in colour, with citrus fruit prominent in the aroma and a sharp, hoppy taste.
Kia Kaha! (ABV 4.3%)
A dry, bitter beer, gold in colour with a fruity aroma leading to a good, hoppy taste and finish.
Limestone Cowboy (ABV 4.5%)
A copper-coloured best bitter, malty with faint roast notes and fruit flavours. Hops dominate in the dry, bitter finish.
The Apache Line (ABV 5%)
Pothole Porter (ABV 5.1%)
A rich, fruity porter with a smooth mouthfeel, and good roast notes in aroma and taste.

Iceni

The Walled Garden, Elveden Courtyard, London Road, Elveden, Suffolk, IP24 3TQ
☎ (01842) 878922 ☎ 07949488113

Office: 70 Risbygate St, Bury St Edmunds, IP33 3AZ
✉ icenibrewe@aol.com

The Iceni Brewery is owned by Brendan Moore, who set it up in 1995. In 2020 Iceni Brewery has some changes, with planning permission on the Elveden Estate granted for its garden centre, the current Walled Garden will be changed and a new site on the estate has been promised. In the spring a micropub, the Magic Hammer, opened on the Methwold site. ♦RAIB

Fine Soft Day (ABV 4%)
Golden-hued with toffee notes throughout. A creamy, lightly-hopped backdrop softly sinks into a pleasant sweetness.

Idle

White Hart Inn, Main Street, West Stockwith, DN10 4EY
☎ (01427) 892672 ☎ 07949 137174
✉ theidlebrewery@btinternet.com

The brewery began production in 2007 and is situated in a converted stable at the back of the White Hart Inn, which Brian Cooper, the brewer, now owns. !!♦

Ignition

44a Sydenham Road, Sydenham, London, SE26 5QX
☎ (020) 8852 4100 🌐 ignition.beer

Ignition is a South London brewery, which employs and trains people with learning disabilities to brew beer. Beers are available in key keg and bottled-conditioned.

An on-site taproom was opened in 2018, providing the staff with customer-facing experience. RAIB ✦

Ilkley SIBA

The New Brewery, 40 Ashlands Road, Ilkley, West Yorkshire, LS29 8JT
☎ (01943) 604604 ⊕ ilkleybrewery.co.uk

⊛Ilkley Brewery was founded in 2009 and has expanded rapidly since. Ilkley beers can be found throughout the UK and are now exported into Europe as far as Russia. The brewery is a frequent sponsor of local beer festivals and also holds regular on-site social events and brewery tours. ‼◆RAIB

Mary Jane (ABV 3.5%)
Joshua Jane (ABV 3.7%)
Blonde (ABV 3.9%)
Pale (ABV 4.2%)
Alpha Beta (ABV 4.5%)
Stout Mary (ABV 4.5%)
Lotus IPA (ABV 5.5%)

Imperial

🍺 Arcadia Hall, Cliff Street, Mexborough, South Yorkshire, S64 9HU
☎ (01709) 584000 ☎ 07428 422703
✉ impbrewery@gmail.com

⊛Brewing began in 2010 using a six-barrel tower brewery system located in the basement of the Imperial Club, Mexborough. Beer is available in the club as well as local outlets. ‼◆RAIB

Inadequate

🍺 Holy Inadequate, 67 Etruria Old Road, Stoke-On-Trent, ST1 5PE
☎ (01782) 915170 ☎ 07771 358238
✉ paulcope.cope@gmail.com

⊛This one-barrel plant commenced brewing behind the Holy Inadequate in 2018 and mainly supplies the pub with an ever-changing range of beers (up to four at any one time). Other local pubs are sometimes supplied, along with local beer festivals.

Incredible SIBA

Unit 1, 214/224 Broomhill Road, Brislington, Bristol, BS4 5RG ☎ 07780 977073
⊕ incrediblebrewingcompany.com

⊠ This microbrewery specialises in producing small batches of beer using a 2.5-barrel plant. It was established in 2014 by head brewer Stephen Hall with the aim of promoting experimental beers and traditional recipes. ‼◆RAIB V

Milk Stout (ABV 4.4%)
Pale Ale (ABV 4.4%)
Amber Ale (ABV 5.2%)
Black IPA (ABV 5.6%)
Grapefruit IPA (ABV 5.6%)
Indian Pale Ale (ABV 6.6%)

Indian

119b Baltimore Trading Estate, Baltimore Road, Great Barr, B42 1DD
☎ (0121) 296 9000 ⊕ indianbrewery.com

This six-barrel brewery, established in 2005 as the Tunnel Brewery at the Lord Nelson Inn, relocated to the picturesque stable block at Red House Farm in 2011. In 2015 the owners of Tunnel Brewery went their separate

ways, with Mike Walsh retaining the brewery and renaming it the Indian Brewery. Later that year the Indian Brewery was sold to new owners and relocated to the outskirts of Birmingham. ‼

Indian Summer (ABV 4%)
IPA (ABV 4.9%)
Bombay Honey (ABV 5%)
Peacock (ABV 5%)

Indigenous

Peacock Cottage, Main Street, Chaddleworth, Berkshire, RG20 7EH
☎ (01488) 505060 ⊕ indigenousbrewery.co.uk

⊠ An occasional and informal microbrewer for many years, Kevin Brady established Indigenous in 2014, increasing production using a 2.5-barrel plant. Availability is restricted to local pubs, shops and an increasing number of regional beer festivals. ‼ 🍺◆RAIB

Baldrick (ABV 3.4%)
Forager's Gold (ABV 4%)
Summer Solstice (ABV 4.1%)
BillyNoMates (ABV 4.2%)
Frisky Mare (ABV 4.2%)
Silly Moo (ABV 4.2%)
Monocle (ABV 4.5%)
Nutcracker (ABV 4.5%)
Old Cadger (ABV 4.5%)
Moonstruck (ABV 4.8%)
Dark brown session porter with malt, chocolate and coffee aromas. A full mouthfeel of hops, caramel and fruit with a bitter finish.
Nosey Parker (ABV 5.5%)
Strong ruby mild with malt and toffee notes and aroma. Malt dominates the taste with a balanced malt and hops aftertaste.
AMMO Belle (ABV 5.6%)
Amber IPA with fruit, hops and malt on the nose, followed by some bitterness in the taste. This leads to a malty aftertaste joined by a fruity hoppiness.
Double Warp (ABV 5.8%)
Dark brown strong stout with malt aromas and coffee notes. Roasted, sweet malt flavour finishes with a balanced aftertaste.

Industrial (NEW)

See Silver

Inferno

17 Station Street, Tewkesbury, GL20 5NJ
☎ (01684) 294873 ☎ 07854 949731
✉ cbowley3@yahoo.co.uk

⊠ Inferno began in 2018, after many years of home brewing, using a 2.5-barrel kit which was installed in 2019. Four regular ales and a number of well-received seasonal ales are brewed. The beers are available in local Gloucestershire pubs, clubs and at beer festivals. ◆

Arsonist (ABV 4%)
Tinder Box (ABV 4%)
Golden Embers (ABV 4.2%)
Cinder Stout (ABV 4.8%)

Inishmacsaint

See Fermanagh

Inkspot

Rookery Barn, The Rookery, 40 Streatham Common South, Streatham Common, London, SW16 3BX
☎ (020) 8679 7322 ☎ 07787 832292
⊕ theinkspotbrewery.com

Started in 2012 as Perfect Blend after a bar in Streatham, the brewery changed its name to Inkspot a few years later. Originally cuckoo brewing at various other breweries, brewing began on its own premises in Streatham Common in 2018. Its Art & Craft bottle shops are the best places to find the beers along with irregular openings of the brewery itself.

Inner Bay SIBA

Seacliffe Villa, Hill Street, Inverkeithing, KY11 1AB
⊕ innerbay.co.uk

Brewing began in 2016. Inner Bay is a family-run brewery using traditional ingredients and methods producing bottle-conditioned beers in small batches. RAIB

INNformal

▤ **14 Charnham St, Hungerford, Berkshire, RG17 0ES**
⊕ john-o-gaunt-hungerford.co.uk

⊗ The INNformal brewery was established in 2015 at the Five Bells pub in Wickham. In 2019 the brewery expanded to a four-barrel plant and moved to Hungerford. A selection of the beers can always be found at the John O'Gaunt in Hungerford. ‼◆

Innis & Gunn SIBA

See Inveralmond

Instant Karma

▤ **4 John Street, Clay Cross, Derbyshire, S45 9NQ**
☎ (01246) 250 366 ⊕ instantkarmabrewery.co.uk

Instant Karma began brewing in 2012 using a five-barrel plant with a brew length of 15 barrels per week. The brewery is part of the Rykneld Turnpyke brewpub.

Interbrew UK

Porter Tun House, Capability Green, Luton, Bedfordshire, LU1 3LS
☎ (01582) 391166

Interbrew (Magor): Magor Brewery, Magor, NP26 3DA

Interbrew (Samlesbury): Cuerdale Lane, Samlesbury, PR5 0XD

UK subsidiary of A-B InBev. No real ale.

Intrepid SIBA

Unit 12 Vincent Works, Brough, Bradwell, Derbyshire, S33 9HG
☎ (01433) 621851 ⊕ intrepid.beer

☺Based in the Hope Valley in the Peak District, Intrepid commenced brewing in 2014 using an eight-barrel plant. ‼▭

C'opar (ABV 4.2%)
New World Bitter (ABV 4.2%)
Pale Ale (ABV 4.5%)

Inveralmond

22 Inveralmond Place, Perth, PH1 3TS
☎ (01738) 449448 ⊕ inveralmond-brewery.co.uk

☺Established in 1997, Inveralmond was the first brewery in Perth for more than 30 years. In 2016, Inveralmond became part of the Innis & Gunn family, an independent Scottish craft brewer based in Edinburgh. I&G makes no real ale but the Inveralmond range continues. ‼▭◆

EPA (ABV 3.8%)
Ossian (ABV 4.1%)
Well-balanced best bitter with a dry finish. This full-bodied amber ale is dominated by fruit and hop with a bittersweet character although excessive caramel can distract from this.
Lia Fail (ABV 4.7%)
The Gaelic name means Stone of Destiny. A dark, robust, full-bodied beer with a deep malty taste. Smooth texture and balanced finish.

Iron Pier

Units 6 & 7, May Industrial Estate, May Avenue, Northfleet, Gravesend, Kent, DA11 8RU
⊕ ironpier.beer

⊗ Iron Pier Brewery was established in 2017 using a 15-barrel plant. It takes its name from the oldest iron pier in existence residing on the River Thames at Gravesend. An on-site taproom offers the brewery's beers plus other local brews. ‼V◆

Perry St Pale (ABV 3.7%)
Joined at the Hop Pale Ale (ABV 3.8%)
Bitter (ABV 4%)
Wealdway (ABV 4.5%)
Cast Iron Stout (ABV 4.7%)
Rosherville Red (ABV 4.8%)
Rye IPA (ABV 5.1%)
Porter (ABV 5.3%)

Irving SIBA

Unit G1, Railway Triangle, Walton Road, Portsmouth, Hampshire, PO6 1TQ
☎ (023) 9238 9988 ⊕ irvingbrewers.co.uk

⊗ Established in 2007 by former Gale's brewer Malcolm Irving using a 15-barrel plant. Around 120 outlets are supplied in Hampshire, Sussex and Surrey with beers available further afield through beer swaps with other breweries. Speciality beers may be ordered for festivals. ‼▭◆

Frigate (ABV 3.8%) 🍺
Satisfying session bitter. Hoppy, with a floral aroma and initial sweetness, leading to bitterness and a smooth, slightly dry finish.
Type 42 (ABV 4.2%)
Admiral Stout (ABV 4.3%)
Well-balanced stout, with plenty of fruit and roast, together with pleasant hint of coffee, and a short bitter finish.
Invincible (ABV 4.6%)
Tawny-coloured, strong bitter. Sweet and fruity with underlying maltiness throughout and gradually increasing dryness, contrasting with the sweet finish.
Iron Duke (ABV 5.3%) 🍺

Irwell Works SIBA

Irwell Street, Ramsbottom, BL0 9YQ
☎ (01706) 825019 ⊕ irwellworksbrewery.co.uk

☺Irwell Works has been brewing since 2010 in a building that once housed the Irwell Works steam, tin, copper and iron works. It changed hands in 2018. The brewery operates a six-barrel plant. A taproom on the first floor serves most of the brewery's beers. ‼◆◆

Lightweights & Gentlemen (ABV 3.2%)
Light, refreshing, very pale ale with some fruitiness and a hoppy, bitter finish.
Breadcrumbs (ABV 3.6%)
Tin Plate (ABV 3.6%)
Copper Plate (ABV 3.8%)
Traditional northern bitter. Copper-coloured, with a satisfying blend of malt and hops and good bitterness.
Costa Del Salford (ABV 4.1%)
Steam Plate (ABV 4.3%)
Malty, bitter beer with an increasing bitter finish.
Iron Plate (ABV 4.4%)
Roast malt in the aroma is joined by hops and a toasty bitterness in the taste and finish.
Marshmallow Unicorn (ABV 4.4%)
Sweet stout with a balanced bitter roast and dry bitter finish.
Mad Dogs & Englishmen (ABV 5.5%)

Isaac Poad SIBA

Office: Hay House, Baxby Manor, Husthwaite, North Yorkshire, YO61 4PW
☎ (01423) 358114 ⊕ isaacpoadbrewing.co.uk

☺Established in 2016 by a local grain merchant, which formerly supplied malting barley to local maltsters, the brewery continues despite the subsequent demise of the parent company. Pending construction of its own brew plant, production is actually carried out at another local brewery with the emphasis on using local Yorkshire malt and British hops. ◆

No. 86 Golden Ale (ABV 3.6%)
1863 Best Bitter (ABV 3.8%)
No. 91 Craft Ale (ABV 3.9%)
All Four Yorkshire Red Ale (ABV 4.2%)
No. 84 India Pale Ale (ABV 4.5%)
Piccadilly Porter (ABV 4.8%)

Isca SIBA

Court Farm, Holcombe Village, Dawlish, Devon, EX7 0JT ☎ 07773 444501 ✉ iscaales@yahoo.co.uk

⊠ Established in a disused milking parlour in 2009, Isca has developed a large range of ales. Seasonal and special brews are often available at beer festivals, including outside of the region. ◆RAIB V

Citra (ABV 3.8%)
Dawlish Summer (ABV 3.8%)
Golden Ale (ABV 3.8%)
Dawlish Bitter (ABV 4.2%)
Glorious Devon (ABV 4.4%)
Gold (ABV 4.5%)
Holcombe White (ABV 4.5%)
Dawlish Pale (ABV 5%)
Black IPA (ABV 6%)
Devon Pale (ABV 6.8%)

Isla Vale

17 Westbrook Gardens, Margate, Kent, CT9 5DJ
☎ (01843) 292451 ☎ 07814 192383
⊕ islavalealesmiths.co.uk

⊠ Isla Vale was established in 2014 from a residential address in Westbrook (Margate) and supplies local micropubs. A one-barrel plant is used to brew its core range as well as a specially commissioned beer for the Wheel Alehouse, Birchington. Outlets are supplied locally. ◆

Golding Delicious (ABV 3.8%)
Hopping Mad (ABV 4%)

Two Halves (ABV 4%)
Ninkasi Pale Ale (ABV 4.5%)
Big Red Beer (ABV 4.6%)
Cock-A-Snook (ABV 4.6%)
Natural Blonde (ABV 4.7%)
Befuggled (ABV 5.2%)
IPA (ABV 5.5%)

Island SIBA

Dinglers Farm, Yarmouth Road, Newport, Isle of Wight, PO30 4LZ
☎ (01983) 821731 ⊕ islandbrewery.co.uk

⊠ Island Brewery is the realisation of Tom Minshull's ambition to brew real ales to complement the existing family-owned drinks distribution business. Brewing commenced in 2010 using a 12-barrel brewery. More than 100 outlets are supplied direct. ‼◆

Nipper Bitter (ABV 3.8%)
Wight Gold (ABV 4%)
Yachtsmans Ale (ABV 4.2%)
Wight Diamond (ABV 4.4%)
Wight Knight (ABV 4.5%)
Vectis Venom (ABV 4.8%)
Earls RDA (ABV 5%)

Islay SIBA

The Brewery, Islay House Square, Bridgend, Isle of Islay, PA44 7NZ
☎ (01496) 810014 ⊕ islayales.com

☺The only brewery on an island famous for its malt whiskies, Islay Ales started brewing in 2004 and continues to use a four-barrel plant. Situated in converted farm buildings, including a visitor centre and shop. The brewery tap is the only outlet for the brewery's cask-conditioned beers. ‼☛◆✦

Isle of Avalon SIBA

Little Whitley, Stagman Lane, Ashcott, Somerset, TA7 9BJ
☎ (01458) 210050 ☎ 07809 056855
⊕ avalonwholesaleandbrewing.co.uk

⊠ Brewing began in 2008. Isle of Avalon has a 100-litre plant, brewing very occasionally for one-off events and local supply. Wessex Brewing (qv) are occasionally contracted to brew for the parent company Avalon Wholesale on an 'on demand' basis.

Isle of Harris (NEW)

Croft No. 6, Borrisdale, Isle of Harris, HS5 3UE
☎ 07584 354144 ⊕ isleofharrisbrewery.com

Established in 2020, small batch, limited edition beers are produced in a brewshed overlooking the Sound of Harris. RAIB

Isle of Mull

See Argyll

Isle of Purbeck SIBA

⊟ **Manor Road, Studland, Dorset, BH19 3AU**
☎ (01929) 450227 ⊕ isleofpurbeckbrewery.com

⊠ Founded in 2003, the brewery is situated in the grounds of the Bankes Arms Hotel, overlooking Studland Bay on the Jurassic Coast. A 10-barrel plant is used. The core beers are available locally as well as nationwide via exchange swaps with other microbreweries, and at local beer festivals. ◆RAIB

Purbeck Best Bitter (ABV 3.6%)
A classic, malty best bitter, with rich malt aroma and taste, and smooth, malty, bitter finish.

Force Four (ABV 4%)

Fossil Fuel (ABV 4.1%)
Amber bitter with complex aroma with a hint of pepper. Rich malt dominates the taste, leading to a smooth, dry finish.

Solar Power (ABV 4.3%)
Tawny mid-range ale brewed using Continental hops. Well-balanced flavours combine to provide a strong bitter taste but short, dry finish.

Studland Bay Wrecked (ABV 4.5%)
Deep red ale with slightly sweet aroma reflecting a mixture of caramel, malt and hops that lead to a dry, malty finish.

Purbeck IPA (ABV 4.8%)
Mid-brown beer with hop/malt balance in the flavour and a long, dry aftertaste.

Isle of Sark

La Seigneurie, Sark, GY10 1SF ☎ 07781 439881
✉ sarkbrewing@gmail.com

Nanobrewery established in 2016 using a 2.5-barrel plant, the first brewery to be established in Sark, Channel Islands.

Isle of Skye SIBA

The Pier, Uig, Isle of Skye, IV51 9XP
☎ (01470) 542477 ⊕ skyeale.com

☺The Isle of Skye Brewery was established in 1995. Originally a 10-barrel plant, it was upgraded to 20 barrels in 2004. ‼╦◆

Skyelight (ABV 3.8%)
A slightly hoppy nose leads to a powerful hop and fruit taste, and a sharp finish.

Tarasgeir (ABV 4%)
The peat-roasted barley dominates giving a mellow, peaty, whisky taste.

YP (Young Pretender) (ABV 4%)
A refreshing, amber, hoppy, grapefruit bitter. Some sweetness in the taste but continuing into a lingering, bitter finish.

Skye Red (ABV 4.2%)
A light, fruity nose with a hint of caramel leads to a hoppy, malty, fruity flavour and a dry, bittersweet finish.

Skye Gold (ABV 4.3%)
Porridge oats are used to produce this delicious speciality beer. Nicely balanced. It has a refreshingly soft lemon, bitter flavour, with an oaty background.

Skye Black (ABV 4.5%)
Full-bodied with a malty richness. Malt holds sway but there are plenty of hops and fruit to be discovered in its varied character. A delicious Scottish old ale.

Skye IPA (ABV 4.5%)
Well-balanced with a good malty background and complemented with the flavoursome Sorachi hops.

Blaven (ABV 5%)
A well-balanced, strong, amber bitter with kiwi fruit and caramel in the nose, and a lingering, sharp bitterness.

Skye Blonde (ABV 5.5%)
Citrus hoppy brew, with some caramel sweetness.

Cuillin Beast (ABV 7%)
A winter warmer. Sweet and fruity, and much more drinkable than the strength would suggest. Plenty of caramel throughout, with a variety of fruit on the nose.

It's Quicker by Ale

See Harrogate

Itchen Valley SIBA

Unit D, Prospect Commercial Park, Prospect Road, New Alresford, Hampshire, SO24 9QF
☎ (01962) 735111 ⊕ itchenvalleybrewery.com

⊠ Established in 1997, Itchen Valley moved to new premises in 2006 with a 20-barrel plant. More than 350 pubs are supplied, with wholesalers used for further distribution. ‼╦◆RAIB

Pride of the Valley (ABV 3.8%)

Hampshire Rose (ABV 4.2%)

New Hampshire (ABV 4.3%)

Pure Gold (ABV 4.8%)
Aromatic hoppy, strong bitter. Golden-coloured, with initial maltiness and grapefruit counter-balanced with some sweetness, leading to dry finish.

IVO (NEW) SIBA

10 Church Street, Somersham, Cambridgeshire, PE28 3EG ☎ 07823 400369 ⊕ ivobrewery.co.uk

Established in 2020, IVO Brewery is run by two friends and neighbours, Charlie Abbott and Jason Jones. Every beer is naturally fined and vegan friendly. V

Light on the Chips (ABV 2.5%)

Car Park Cuddle (ABV 3.8%)

No Man (ABV 4.5%)

She Keeps It Nice (ABV 4.5%)

Evening Brown (ABV 5%)

Heavy on the Chips (ABV 6%)

Pidley Cheeks (ABV 6.5%)

Ivybridge (NEW)

The Brewery at The Town Hall, Erme Court, Leonard's Road, Ivybridge, Devon, PL21 0SZ
☎ (01752) 894295 ☎ 07512 961085

Office: 41 Rue St Pierre, Ivybridge, PL21 0HZ
⊕ ivybridgebrewing.co.uk

Established in 2018, Ivybridge is a social enterprise brewery that provides training and employment for people with learning disabilities. It currently produces two bottle-conditioned beers. RAIB

Izaac Walton

See under W

JackRabbit (NEW)

Hops Farm, Hungerdown Lane, Lawford, Essex, CO11 2LX ☎ 07506 596597
⊕ jackrabbitbrewingco.uk

JackRabbit Brewing Co was founded in 2019 by three craft beer lovers. An eight-barrel plant is used to create unfiltered, unfined beers. ╦◆V

Roasted (ABV 3.8%)

College Hop-Out (ABV 4%)

Down the Rabbit Hole (ABV 4.7%)

James Street

See Bath Brewhouse

Jaw SIBA

Unit 9, The Centre Point,, 67b Montrose Avenue, Hilington Industrial Estate, Glasgow, G52 4LA
☎ (0141) 237 5840 🌐 jawbrew.co.uk

An independent, family-run, craft microbrewery from Glasgow. Committed to producing the absolute pinnacle of high quality beer. One of only two breweries in the Renfrewshire branch area. RAIB

Fathom (ABV 4%)
Drop (ABV 4.2%)
Surf (ABV 4.3%)
Drift (ABV 4.6%)
Wave (ABV 4.7%)

Jeffersons

Brew Shed, 84 Verdun Road, Barnes, London, SW13 9AX ☎ 07960 597311
🌐 jeffersonsbrewery.co.uk

Brewing began in 2017 at this nanobrewery in Barnes. Output is mostly cans and keg can be found locally in bars and pubs and at markets and craft beer festivals. There has been the occasional trial with cask for festivals. V

Jennings

Castle Brewery, Cockermouth, Cumbria, CA13 9NE
☎ (01900) 820362 🌐 jenningsbrewery.co.uk

Jennings Brewery was established as a family concern in 1828 in the village of Lorton. The company moved to its present location in 1874. Pure Lakeland water is still used for brewing, drawn from the brewery's own well. All beers were re-branded in 2019 with some beers becoming seasonal, and new beers added to the portfolio. Part of Marston's PLC ‼ ♦

Night Vision (ABV 3.5%)
A malty beer with a good mouthfeel that combines with roast flavour and a hoppy finish.
Atomic Theory (ABV 3.8%)
Cumberland Ale (ABV 4%)
Fruit and caramel in the aroma gives way to a sweet middle, balanced by a gentle bitter finish.

Jesus College

Jesus College, Cambridge, CB5 8BL

In-house brewery for Jesus College at the University of Cambridge. Beers are produced for college use only and are not available to the general public.

John O'Groats

County Road, John O'Groats, KW1 4YR
☎ (01955) 611220 ☎ 07842 401571
✉ johnogroatsbrewery@gmail.com

Brewing began in 2015 with a four-barrel plant. It is housed in the old John O'Groats Fire Station almost opposite its tap, the Seaview Hotel. Tours are not formally offered but if brewing is taking place guests can be shown the process.

Swelkie (ABV 4%)
Slight honey taste in this citrus hoppy brew.
Duncansby (ABV 4.2%)
Deep Groat (ABV 4.8%)
Nearly black brew full of chocolate and coffee with some background roast.

John Smith's

See under S

John Thompson

See under T

Jolly Boys

Unit 16a, Redbrook Business Park, off Wilthorpe Road, Redbrook, South Yorkshire, S75 1JN ☎ 07808 085214 🌐 jollyboysbrewery.co.uk

Jolly Boys started brewing using spare capacity at a local brewery in 2016, prior to brewing on its own plant later the same year. The Jolly Tap, Wakefield, and the Jolly Tap on the Arcade, Barnsley, are owned. ‼♦V◆

Yorkshire Bitter (ABV 3.8%)
Blonde (ABV 4%)
Cascade Blonde (ABV 4%)
La Joll'a Blonde (ABV 4%)
Golden Best (ABV 4.5%)
Yorkshire Pale Ale (ABV 4.8%)
Jolly Collier Porter (ABV 5%)
Jolly IPA (ABV 5.8%)

Jolly Sailor SIBA

Olympia Hotel Tap House, 77 Barlby Road, Selby, North Yorkshire, YO8 5AB
☎ (01757) 707564 ☎ 07923 635755
🌐 jollysailorbrewery.uk

The Jolly Sailor Brewery is an independent family-run microbrewery established in 2013 in the grounds of the Olympia Hotel Tap House in Selby, on the nearby River Ouse and close to the 11th-century abbey. Beers are brewed on a six-barrel plant and available at the brewery's Jolly Sailor Inn, Cawood, and extensively in the free trade. ‼♦V◆

Selby Bitter (ABV 3.8%)
Selby Blonde (ABV 3.8%)
Selby Pale (ABV 3.9%)
Selby Mild (ABV 4%)
Milk Stout (ABV 4.5%)
Dark Nights Porter (ABV 5%)

Joseph Holt

See under H

Joule's SIBA

The Brewery, Great Hales Street, Market Drayton, Shropshire, TF9 1JP
☎ (01630) 654400 🌐 joulesbrewery.co.uk

Re-established in 2010, following a break of 40 years, Joule's is situated in Market Drayton, it has access to pure mineral water drawn from the same aquifer as the original brewery. It runs a collection of 40 Brewery Taphouses across its heartland, Shropshire, Staffordshire and Cheshire. ‼♦

Pure Blonde (ABV 3.8%)
Pale Ale (ABV 4.1%)
Slumbering Monk (ABV 4.5%)

Junction

1 Baildon Road, Baildon, West Yorkshire, BD17 6AB
☎ (01274) 582009 ☎ 07539 923744
✉ andydoug48@gmail.com

THE BREWERIES

Junction is a microbrewery established in 2012 in the cellar of the Junction pub in Baildon, brewing around 300 gallons a week. Beer is sold in the pub and other local outlets. RAIB

Kansas Avenue

See Hydes

Keep

Village Inn, The Cross, Nailsworth, Gloucestershire, GL6 0HH
☎ (01453) 835715 ☎ 07963 200768
✉ paul@dropinpubs.com

After a break of 96 years, brewing returned to Nailsworth in 2004 at the Village Inn. The pub and brewery were sold in 2016 to Paul Sugden and Adam Pavey, who changed the brewery name from Nailsworth to Keep Brewing. Brewing takes place on a six-barrel kit below the bar, with new recipes trialled on a 40-litre pilot plant. ♦RAIB

Keith SIBA

Malcolmburn, Mulben, AB55 6YB
☎ (01542) 488006 🌐 keithbrewery.co.uk

Formerly known as Brewmeister and established in 2012, the brewery was renamed Keith Brewery in 2015. It moved production to Malcolmburn, Mulben, sharing facilities with Spey Valley Brewery (qv). Keith Brewery is part of the Consolidated Craft Breweries Group. ♦RAIB

Herr Keith (ABV 4.5%)
Cloudy white/yellow wheat beer with hints of coriander
Larger Keith (ABV 4.5%)
Pale Keith (ABV 5%)
Grapefruit hoppy bitter.
Stout Keith (ABV 5%)
Sir Keith (ABV 10.1%)

Kelburn SIBA

10 Muriel Lane, Barrhead, G78 1QB
☎ (0141) 881 2138 🌐 kelburnbrewery.com

Kelburn is an award-winning family business established in 2002. ‼♦

Sunriser (ABV 3.4%)
Goldihops (ABV 3.8%)
Pivo Estivo (ABV 3.9%)
Misty Law (ABV 4%)
Red Smiddy (ABV 4.1%)
This bittersweet ale predominantly features an intense citrus hop character that assaults the nose and continues into the flavour, balanced perfectly with fruity malt.
Regnitz (ABV 4.4%)
Dark Moor (ABV 4.5%)
Jaguar (ABV 4.5%)
Cart Noir (ABV 4.8%)
Cart Blanche (ABV 5%)
A golden, full-bodied ale. The assault of fruit and hop camouflages the strength of this easy-drinking ale.

Kelchner SIBA

Unit D, The Sidings, Station Road, Ampthill, Bedfordshire, MK45 2QY ☎ 07508 305754
✉ kelchnerbrewery@gmail.com

Brewing began in 2018 using a six-barrel brew plant. ‼RAIB

Local is Lekker (ABV 3.9%)
Ampthill Gold (ABV 4.1%)
Hat Trick (ABV 4.1%)
IPA (ABV 4.5%)
After Dark (ABV 4.8%)
Ammetelle (ABV 5%)

Kelham Island SIBA

23 Alma Street, Sheffield, South Yorkshire, S3 8SA
☎ (0114) 249 4804
Office: Prospect House, 17 Alma Street, Sheffield, S3 8RY 🌐 kelhambrewery.co.uk

Opened in 1990 behind the Fat Cat pub, the brewery moved to new purpose-built premises in 1999. The old building is used as a visitor centre, and there is a separate brewery shop together with offices and a function room in nearby Prospect House. ‼♦RAIB

Best Bitter (ABV 3.8%)
Pride of Sheffield (ABV 4%)
Easy Rider (ABV 4.3%)
A pale, straw-coloured beer with a sweetish flavour and delicate hints of citrus fruits. A beer with hints of flavour rather than full-bodied.
Riders on the Storm (ABV 4.5%)
Pale Rider (ABV 5.2%)
A full-bodied, straw-coloured, pale ale, with a good fruity aroma and a strong fruit and hop taste. Its well-balanced sweetness and bitterness continue in the finish.

Keltek SIBA

Candela House, Cardrew Way, Redruth, Cornwall, TR15 1SS
☎ (01209) 313620 🌐 keltekbrewery.co.uk

Keltek (meaning Celtic in Cornish) began brewing award-winning ales in 1997, and was founded by Stuart Heath. It started as a 2.5-barrel plant in Stuart's disused stable block on the Roseland Peninsula. Several moves and expansions mean it is now based in Redruth, and can brew more than 250 barrels a week. In 2013 Keltek acquired four pubs in south-west Cornwall (the second brewery in Cornwall to own its estate of pubs). Two more pubs were acquired in 2016. ♦RAIB

Even Keel (ABV 3.4%)
Pale brown session bitter. Refreshing malt and hop taste with apple, plum and pear drops. Gentle dry and bitter finish.
Lance (ABV 4%)
Gold bitter with light fruity aroma. Grassy citrus hops, apples, malt and hints of elderflower and butterscotch. Long, bitter finish.
Magik (ABV 4%)
Copper bitter with smoky malt and hop aroma. Sweet malt is balanced by spicy and marmalade hops with earthy notes.
Kober (ABV 4.2%)
Phoenix (ABV 4.5%)
Golden best bitter. Powerful fruity hops with high bitterness but backed with solid malt which lingers well on the finish.
Wayward Knight (ABV 4.5%)
Lowenek (ABV 4.8%)
Parbaydos (ABV 4.8%)
King (ABV 5.1%)
Copper-coloured, premium bitter with a mix of malt and hop aromas. Biscuit malt balanced by tropical and citrus hops.
Pilot Gig Porter (ABV 5.2%)
Gatekeeper (ABV 5.6%)
Reaper (ABV 6%)
Beheaded (ABV 7.5%)

Tawny, strong old ale with a balanced heavy body. Rich vine fruit accompanied by plum, raisin, apple and sherry flavours.

Kent SIBA

The Long Barn, Birling Place Farm, Stangate Road, Birling, Kent, ME19 5JN
☎ (01634) 780037 🌐 kentbrewery.com

Kent Brewery was founded in 2010 by Toby Simmonds (ex-brewer from Dark Star) and Paul Herbert. Originally brewed at Larkins, a 10-barrel plant has been in operation at the Birling site since 2011. More than 300 outlets are supplied direct, mainly throughout Kent, Sussex and London. ♦RAIB

Session Pale (ABV 3.7%)
Black Gold (ABV 4%)
Pale (ABV 4%)
Cobnut (ABV 4.1%)
KGB (Kent Golding Bitter) (ABV 4.1%)
Single Hop (ABV 4.5%)
Prohibition (ABV 4.8%)
Brewers Reserve (ABV 5%)

Kentish Town

Ingestre Road, Kentish Town, London, NW5 1UF
🌐 kentishtownbrewery.com

The Fleet Lager has been brewed at home in small batches with larger batches brewed at various London breweries. Brewing suspended in 2019 allowing the brewer to take a sabbatical year in Australia, with brewing to start again on his return.

Keppels SIBA

The Workshops, Little Stambridge, Hall Lane, Rochford, Essex, SS4 1EW ☎ 07912 251278
🌐 keppelsbrewery.co.uk

⊗ Keppels was established in 2016. In 2018 it moved to new premises in Stambridge. Further expansion took place in 2019. Pubs throughout Essex are supplied with cask ales. Bottled beers are available to purchase (to raise money for the Vulcan Trust). ‼♦

Crows by the Crouch (ABV 3.8%)
New Beginnings (ABV 3.8%)
Golden Crow (ABV 4%)
Home to Roost (ABV 4.2%)
Tipsy Crow Stout (ABV 5%)
Two Crows (ABV 5.7%)
One of Those Days (ABV 6.8%)

Kernel SIBA

Arch 11, Dockley Road Industrial Estate, Dockley Road, Bermondsey, London, SE16 3SF
☎ (020) 7231 4516 🌐 thekernelbrewery.com

The Kernel was established in 2009 by Evin O'Riordain and moved to larger premises in 2012 to keep up with demand. The brewery produces bottle-conditioned and keg beers, and has won many awards for its wide, ever-changing range. Bottles are available from the brewery as well as a selection of pubs around the country. A new taproom, a few arches along, opened in 2020. RAIB V

Keswick SIBA

The Old Brewery, Brewery Lane, Keswick, Cumbria, CA12 5BY
☎ (01768) 780700 🌐 keswickbrewery.co.uk

Keswick, owned by Sue Jefferson, began brewing in 2006 using a 10-barrel plant on the site of a brewery that closed in 1897. The brewery is set up to be environmentally-friendly using sheeps wool insulation in the vessels and reducing its environmental impact. Outlets include the Fox bar at the brewery, the Dog & Gun, Keswick, and many other pubs across Cumbria. ‼♦

Black Star (ABV 3.5%)
Gold (ABV 3.6%)
Simple, slightly sweet, light ale with some bitterness in the finish.
Bitter (ABV 3.7%)
Gentle bitter with hints of roasted malt and a sweetness which fades.
Thirst Rescue (ABV 3.8%)
Bitter beer with some fruitiness, full-bodied and a lasting bitter finish.
Park Your Thirst (ABV 3.9%)
Thirst Run (ABV 4.2%)
A well-balanced golden beer that maintains its fruitiness from start to finish.
Waimia Pale (ABV 4.2%)
Thirst Quencher (ABV 4.3%)
Light-bodied, fresh, hoppy beer with fruit in the middle and a balancing sweetness.
Pale Ale (ABV 4.4%)
Special Bitter (ABV 4.8%)
Thirst Celebration (ABV 7%)

Kettlesmith SIBA

Unit 16, Treenwood Industrial Estate, Bradford-on-Avon, Wiltshire, BA15 2AU
☎ (01225) 864839 🌐 kettlesmithbrewing.com

⊗ Kettlesmith is an independent microbrewery established in 2016. It brews modern interpretations of a wide variety of beer styles, drawing inspiration from the brewer's background in America and England, as well as love of Belgian beer. ‼♦RAIB V

Streamline (ABV 1.2%)
Outline (ABV 3.8%)
Faultline (ABV 4.1%)
Plotline (ABV 4.4%)
Fogline (ABV 4.7%)
Coastline (ABV 4.9%)
Ridgeline (ABV 5%)
Timeline (ABV 5.4%)
Skyline (ABV 5.6%)

Keystone SIBA

Old Carpenters Workshop, Berwick St Leonard, Wiltshire, SP3 5SN
☎ (01747) 820426 🌐 keystonebrewery.co.uk

⊗ Set up in 2006 with a 10-barrel plant, the brewer aims to be as sustainable and efficient as possible, brewing traditional southern English-style beers using local ingredients whenever possible. The beers are available in the brewery-run Benett Arms, Tisbury. Around 150 other outlets are also supplied. ‼♦

Bedrock (ABV 3.6%)
Copper-coloured bitter, hops and malt in the aroma, followed by fruit and bitterness in the taste. Long, lingering aftertaste.
Large One (ABV 4.2%)
Copper-coloured, malty best bitter. Fruit and bitterness to the fore initially, long fruit and bitter hop flavours to the finish.

THE BREWERIES

Kiln SIBA

Chiddinglye Farm, West Hoathly, RH19 4QS ☎ 07800 556729

Office: 1st Floor, 30 Church Road, Burgess Hill, RH15 9AE ⊕ thekilnbrewery.co.uk

Kiln brewery was set up by two friends in 2014. Following a search for new premises, they have joined forces with Missing Link brewery. Although Kiln's website is focusing on keg and canned beer, they are continuing to produce cask beers, but are no longer sticking with a core range.

King Street SIBA

🍺 Riverside House, Welsh Back, Bristol, BS1 4RR ☎ (0117) 405 8948

Office: City Pub Group Plc. Essel House, 2nd Floor, 29 Foley Street, London, W1W 7TH ⊕ kingstreetbrewhouse.co.uk

⊠ The King Street Brew House is owned by The City Pub Group, which has several pubs and brewpubs around the country. The compact brewery is on the ground floor, with the fermenting vessels and conditioning tanks in the basement. The enthusiastic on-site brewer produces a wide range of beers, from regular favourites, available all year, to one off/seasonal specials. Guest beers are also available. The Group's other pub in Bristol, the Prince Street Social, is also supplied. ‼◆RAIB

King's Cliffe

Unit 10, Kingsmead, Station Road, King's Cliffe, Northamptonshire, PE8 6YH ☎ 07843 288088 ⊕ kcbales.co.uk

⊠ In 2014, exactly 100 years after the last brewery in King's Cliffe ceased brewing, village resident Jeremy O'Neill set up this venture. It currently produces five barrels a week. ‼◆

5C (ABV 3.8%)
A light bitter with balanced taste of malt and hops and a refreshing, bitter finish.
No. 10 (ABV 4%)
Amber beer with a clean malty taste and a long, bitter finish.
66 Degrees (ABV 4.2%)
Amber beer with a floral aroma, a balanced taste of malt and hops, and a long, bitter finish.
B5 (ABV 4.6%)
P51 (ABV 5.1%)

Kings Clipstone

Keepers Bothy, Kings Clipstone, Nottinghamshire, NG21 9BT
☎ (01623) 823589 ☎ 07790 190020
⊕ kingsclipstonebrewery.co.uk

Located close to the heart of Sherwood Forest, Kings Clipstone began brewing in 2012 using a five-barrel plant. The owners, David and Daryl Maguire, produce a range of core beers plus one-off brews and seasonals. Beers are available to freehouses, festivals and wholesale markets. ◆

Palace Pale (ABV 3.6%)
Hop On (ABV 3.8%)
Amazing Gazing (ABV 4%)
Tabaknakas (ABV 4.1%)
Moonbeam (ABV 4.2%)
Sire (ABV 4.2%)
Royal Stag Stout (ABV 4.5%)

Queen Bee (ABV 5.1%)

Kings Head

🍺 Kings Head, 132 High Street, Bildeston, Suffolk, IP7 7ED
☎ (01449) 741434 ⊕ bildestonkingshead.co.uk

⊠ Kings Head has been brewing since 1996 in an old cart lodge at the back of the pub. Under new ownership since 2008, the 2.5-barrel plant brews fortnightly. ‼◆

Kingstone

Tintern, NP16 7NX
☎ (01291) 680111 ⊕ kingstonebrewery.co.uk

Kingstone Brewery is located in the Wye Valley close to Tintern Abbey. Brewing began on a four-barrel plant in 2005. Special brews are marketed under the 'Hapax Brewing Co' label. ‼🍴RAIB

Tewdric's Tipple (ABV 3.8%)
Challenger (ABV 4%)
Gold (ABV 4%)
Llandogo Trow (ABV 4.2%)
Premium Stout (ABV 4.4%)
Classic (ABV 4.5%)
1503 (ABV 4.8%)
Abbey Ale (ABV 5.1%)
Humpty (ABV 5.8%)

Kinver SIBA

Unit 1, Britch Farm, Rocky Wall, Kinver, Staffordshire, DY7 5NW ☎ 07715 842676 ⊕ kinverbrewery.co.uk

☺Established in 2004, Kinver brewery produces a wide range of different beer styles including one-off specials. The brewery relocated in 2012 to a new 10-barrel plant on the edge of Kinver due to increased demand. An ever increasing number of pubs, mainly in the midlands, and beer festivals are supplied with the award-winning ales. ‼◆RAIB

Light Railway (ABV 3.8%)
Straw-coloured, session beer. A fruity and malty start quickly gives way to well-hopped bitterness and lingering hoppy aftertaste.
Cavegirl Bitter (ABV 4%)
Edge (ABV 4.2%)
Amber with a malty aroma. Sweet, fruity start with a hint of citrus marmalade in the spicy-edged malt; lasting hoppy finish that is satisfyingly bitter.
Noble (ABV 4.5%)
Fruity hop aroma. Very fruity start then the grassy hops give a sharp, bitter finish with malt support.
Maybug (ABV 4.8%)
Half Centurion (ABV 5%)
A golden best bitter; malty before the American Chinook hop takes command to give a balanced hoppy finish and provide the great aftertaste.
Black Ram Stout (ABV 5.2%)
Witchfinder General (ABV 5.5%)
Khyber (ABV 5.8%)
Golden, strong bitter with a Centennial hop bite that overwhelms the fleeting malty sweetness and drives through to the long, dry finish.

Kirkby Lonsdale SIBA

Royal Barn, New Road, Kirkby Lonsdale, Cumbria, LA6 2AB
☎ (01524) 272221 ⊕ klbrewery.com

☺Kirkby Lonsdale is a family-run business established in 2009 on a six-barrel plant. In 2016 a further six-barrel plant was installed in its new brewery tap, the Royal Barn, Kirkby Lonsdale. ‼♦⬩

Crafty Mild (ABV 3.6%)
A typical mild with powerful malty aromas and some caramel, which follows through in the taste and finish.
Tiffin Gold (ABV 3.6%)
A full-flavoured, grapefruity, hoppy and bitter beer with a dry finish.
Stanley's Pale Ale (ABV 3.8%)
Hops dominate this sweet and fruity, well-balanced beer.
Ruskins Bitter (ABV 3.9%)
A tawny bitter with a distinctive aroma of fruit and malt. The clean, hoppy flavour is well-balanced with fruity sweetness leading to a sustained bittersweet finish.
Singletrack (ABV 4%)
Crisp, citrus hops predominate in a well-balanced beer with a pleasant, bitter finish.
Pennine Ambler (ABV 4.1%)
Radical Red (ABV 4.2%)
Malty beer with a caramel sweetness that is balanced by a bitter finish.
Monumental Blonde (ABV 4.5%)
Distinctly hoppy, a fruity, sweet, pale-coloured, full-bodied bitter.
Jubilee Stout (ABV 5.5%)
Rich, well-balanced stout with malt. A long aftertaste retains this complexity and is surprisingly refreshing.
Imperial Dragon (ABV 8.2%)

Kirkstall SIBA

100 Kirkstall Road, Leeds, West Yorkshire, LS3 1HJ
☎ (0113) 898 0280 🌐 kirkstallbrewerycompany.com

The brewery was established in 2011 a few yards from the original Kirkstall Brewery beside the Leeds-Liverpool canal. In 2017 it moved to a new state-of-the-art brewery incorporating a 60-barrel plant, malting unit and canning line. Nearby Kirkstall Abbey, which had its own brewhouse, and lost local industries are the inspiration for the beer names. The range can be sampled in the Kirkstall Bridge Inn, the brewery tap, as well as its other pubs, the Cardigan Arms, the Sparrow and in Otley, the Black Horse. ‼♦

Pale Ale (ABV 4%)
Session ale, pale gold in colour. Hoppy bitterness mixes well with the zesty grapefruit flavour.
Three Swords (ABV 4.5%)
Pithy grapefruit flavours characterise this very light-coloured golden ale, plenty of hops from the start, to the lingering finish.
Dissolution IPA (ABV 5%)
Full-flavoured – hops lead the charge with bitter fruit just behind.
Black Band Porter (ABV 5.5%)
Dark, smooth and complex. Expect sumptious fruit cake flavours, hints of malted chocolate, coffee and liquorice, plus occasional smokiness.

Kirrie

Bon Scott Brewery, 8 Bon Scott Place, Kirriemuir, DD8 4LD ☎ 07855 808975 🌐 kirrie-ales.co.nf

Established in 2014, Kirrie Ales is situated in the picturesque town of Kirriemuir, birthplace of J.M Barrie, creator of Peter Pan, and gateway to the Angus Glens. The brewery space measures only 8x9 feet. Brewing is currently suspended. RAIB

Kissingate

Pole Barn, Church Lane Farm Estate, Church Lane, Lower Beeding, West Sussex, RH13 6LU
☎ (01403) 891335
Office: 2 Drury Close, Maidenbower, Crawley
🌐 kissingate.co.uk

Kissingate Brewery was founded in 2010 by husband-and-wife team Gary and Bunny Lucas. Current production capacity is eight barrels. The brewery building is a converted barn set in a wooded valley near the village of Mannings Heath. It has a taproom and minstrels gallery. The brewery is available to hire for private events.
‼♦RAIB V⬩

Storyteller (ABV 3.5%)
Ripple Raspberry Stout (ABV 4%)
Sussex (ABV 4%)
Moon (ABV 4.5%)
Old Tale Porter (ABV 4.5%)
Pernickety Pale (ABV 4.5%)
Mandarina Red (ABV 4.8%)
Chennai (ABV 5%)
Smelter's Stout (ABV 5.1%)
Powder Blue (ABV 5.5%)
Stout Extreme Jamaica (ABV 6%)
Murder of Crows (ABV 10%)

Knight Life

44a-46a Shelbourne Road, Bournemouth, Dorset, BH8 8QY 🌐 knightlifebrewing.com

Established in 2018 brewing on 20-litre Braumeister plant. Keg only beer and off-sales are available direct from the brewery (Monday – Saturday) with some availability in local pubs.

Knockout

Unit 10, Alanbrooke Park, Alexander Road, Belfast, BT6 9HB

Founded in 2009 by Joseph McMullan, Knockout produces a range of bottle-conditioned beers. Each brew is usually in small 900-litre batches. RAIB

Knoydart

St Agathas Chapel & Manse, Knoydart, PH41 4PL
☎ (01687) 462372 🌐 knoydartbrewery.co.uk

Knoydart is one of the most remote breweries on mainland Britain, there are no road links so access is by ferry boat or on foot over mountain passes. Beers are brewed in part of an old chapel using a 60-litre electric brewery and a five-barrel plant with four fermenters.

Krafty Braumeister SIBA

Unit 4a, Eastlands Industrial Estate, Leiston, Suffolk, IP16 4LL ☎ 07508 435893 🌐 kraftybraumeister.co.uk

Krafty Braumeister was established in 2018 and produces historic German beer styles, matured naturally in bottles and kegs.

Krow (NEW)

Penventon Terrace, Redruth, Cornwall, TR15 3AD
✉ contact@krowbrewing.co.uk

New microbrewery established in Redruth. The head brewer has gained experience brewing with several breweries in Cornwall, having initially started out as a home brewer. It is currently making small batch brews, and developing a core range.

Kult

See Plain

THE BREWERIES

LabRat (NEW)

33 Bernham Avenue, Stonehaven, AB39 2WD
☎ 07542 072774

Commercial nanobrewer Peter Mackenzie started brewing in 2019, producing beers based on international styles.

Lacada

7a Victoria Street, Portrush, BT56 8DL
☎ (028) 7082 5684 🌐 lacadabrewery.com

Lacada was established in 2015 and produces its Salamander series alongside three core beers. V

West Bay (ABV 4.6%)
Devil's Washtub (ABV 5.2%)
East the Beast (ABV 6%)

Lacons SIBA

The Courtyard, Main Cross Road, Great Yarmouth, Norfolk, NR30 3NZ
☎ (01493) 850578 🌐 lacons.co.uk

Lacons Brewery has a rich history dating back to 1760, but was closed by Whitbread in the 1960s. It relaunched in 2013 and the Falcon Brewery is now nestled in a courtyard in Great Yarmouth. Beers are available across East Anglia and use the original Lacons yeast. A range of heritage seasonal ales is also produced, based on the brewery's original recipes from the archives. ‼ ♦ RAIB

Charter (ABV 3.7%)
Encore (ABV 3.8%)
Strong citrus and hop notes throughout. A balanced, hoppy, bitter beginning. Full-bodied with a claggy mouthfeel. Strong, bitter finish.
Patriot (ABV 4%)
A powerful hop presence from the nose to the long dry finish. Citrus notes and malt give balance and depth.
Legacy (ABV 4.4%)
Strong grapefruit aroma. Well-balanced mix of malt, citrus and bittersweet hoppiness. Full-bodied with a lemony malt finish.
Audit (ABV 8%)

Lady Luck

Little Angel, 18 Flowergate, Whitby, North Yorkshire, YO21 3BA
☎ (01947) 820475 ☎ 07920 282506

Lady Luck is a 0.5-barrel brewery situated at the back of the Little Angel, Whitby. Brewing began in 2018 and takes place twice a week. Beers, some infused with spirits, are distributed across North Yorkshire as well as at beer festivals. ♦ RAIB

Laine SIBA

Brighton: North Laine Bar & Brewhouse, 27 Gloucester Place, Brighton, East Sussex, BN1 4AA
☎ (01273) 683666

Victoria Park: The People's Park Tavern, 360 Victoria Park Road, South Hackney, London, E9 7BT
🌐 laine.co.uk

Laine launched its first brewery in 2012, in Brighton, using a five-barrel plant based within the North Laine pub. The brewing equipment and process can be viewed from the bar. In 2013 a sister brewery was opened in Acton, London (now closed). Since then two more Laine breweries have been established in London, in Hackney (2014) and Battersea (2015; now closed). The beer range varies in each establishment. ‼

Lakehouse

Lake House, Peachfield Road, Malvern, Worcestershire, WR14 3LE ☎ 07532 440634
🌐 lakehousebrewery.com

Lakehouse was established in 2016 by Dan Frost and Graeme Gordon on a 2.5-barrel plant. Situated below the Malvern Hills, within the grounds of a country house and fishing lake, from which it takes its name. Beers can be found at food and drink festivals, farmers' markets, and in trade outlets. ‼ ♦ RAIB V

Amber Session Ale (ABV 3.9%)
Golden-coloured session beer, aroma of hops and citrus fruits, complex, slightly citrus taste with grassy undertones, followed by a pleasant hoppy finish.
Citrus Pale Ale (ABV 4%)
Pale amber, aroma of hops with hints of apple and grapefruit, pronounced hoppy taste with lemon and orange peel, followed by a lingering citrus then bitter hoppy aftertaste.
Henners Craft Lager (ABV 4.4%)
Cherry Chocolate Porter (ABV 5.5%)
Dark ruby brown, creamy head, aromas of stone fruits with roast malt and chocolate. Taste initially of chocolate and coffee, soft velvety mouthfeel with hints of bitter cherry and a fruity finish with hints of chocolate.

LAMB

Queens Arms, Litton, North Yorkshire, BD23 5QJ
☎ 07900 013245 🌐 lambbrewing.com

The LAMB Brewing Company brews on a 600-litre plant behind the Queen's Arms in Litton, in the heart of the Yorkshire Dales National Park. Independently owned, the beer is served in the pub, as well as a few other outlets in the local area.

X Mild (ABV 3.2%)
X Mild (Dark) (ABV 3.2%)
Bitter (ABV 3.7%)
Pale (ABV 3.9%)

Lancaster SIBA

Lancaster Leisure Park, Wyresdale Road, Lancaster, LA1 3LA
☎ (01524) 848537 🌐 lancasterbrewery.co.uk

Lancaster began brewing in 2005. The brewery moved to new premises in 2010 and installed a larger 60-barrel brewing plant. As well as the regular beers, seasonal beers are brewed under the T'ales from the Brewhouse name. ‼ ♦

Amber (ABV 3.6%)
Amber-coloured. Malt flavours lead to an increasingly astringent bitter finish.
Blonde (ABV 4%)
Well-balanced pale bitter with fruity body and hops lasting well into the finish.
Black (ABV 4.5%)
A satisfying, robust, roast, bitter beer with hints of sweet fruitiness.
Red (ABV 4.8%)
A characterful beer with plenty of fruits, roasts and hops, well-balanced with a lasting finish.

Langdale SIBA

Cross Houses Farm, Docker, Cumbria, LA8 0DE
☎ 07876 838051 🌐 langdalebrewing.co.uk

Langdale Brewing was formed in 2018 by Steve Mitchell formerly of Eden Brewery, and Paul Fry of the Britannia Inn, Elterwater. The brewery USP is producing a range of cask ales using water harvested from a Langdale spring.

Bowfell Bitter (ABV 3.5%)
Elterwater Gold (ABV 3.8%)
Pikes Pale (ABV 3.9%)
Bowfell Blonde (ABV 4.2%)
Bowfell Amber (ABV 4.3%)
Weiss Ghyll (ABV 4.5%)

Langham SIBA

Old Granary, Langham Lane, Lodsworth, West Sussex, GU28 9BU
☎ (01798) 860861 🌐 langhambrewery.co.uk

⊗ Langham Brewery was established in 2006 in an 18th-century granary barn and is set in the heart of West Sussex with fine views of the rolling South Downs. It is owned by Lesley Foulkes and James Berrow who brew and run the business. The brewery is a 10-barrel, steam-heated plant and more than 200 outlets are supplied. !! V

Halfway to Heaven (ABV 3.5%)
Saison (ABV 3.9%)
Hip Hop (ABV 4%)
Sundowner (ABV 4.2%)
Triple XXX (ABV 4.4%)
Best (ABV 4.5%)
Arapaho (ABV 4.9%)
LSD (Langham Special Draught) (ABV 5.2%)
Black Swallow (ABV 6%)

Langton SIBA

Grange Farm, Welham Road, Thorpe Langton, Leicestershire, LE16 7TU
☎ (01858) 540116 ☎ 07840 532826
🌐 langtonbrewery.co.uk

Established in 1999 in outbuildings behind the Bell Inn, East Langton, the brewery relocated in 2005 to a converted barn at Thorpe Langton, where a four-barrel plant was installed. Further expansion in 2010 and 2016 significantly increased capacity. !! ♦ RAIB

Rainbow Bridge (ABV 3.8%)
Caudle Bitter (ABV 3.9%)
Copper-coloured, session bitter that is close to pale ale in style. Flavours are relatively well-balanced throughout with hops slightly to the fore.
Union Wharf (ABV 4%)
Inclined Plane Bitter (ABV 4.2%)
Thomas Lift (ABV 4.4%)
Bullseye (ABV 4.8%)

Larkins SIBA

Larkins Farm, Hampkins Hill Road, Chiddingstone, Kent, TN8 7BB
☎ (01892) 870328

⊗ Larkins brewery was founded by the Dockerty family in Rusthall in Kent in 1986, on the site of the original Royal Tunbridge Wells Brewery. In 1988 the brewery relocated to Larkins Farm in Chiddingstone. All beers include hops grown on the farm itself. The brewery delivers direct to around 40-50 pubs and restaurants within a 20-mile radius. !! ♦

Traditional Ale (ABV 3.4%)
Pale (ABV 4.2%)
Best (ABV 4.4%)
Full-bodied, slightly fruity and unusually bitter for its gravity.

Larrikin (NEW)

Urchin, 15-17 Belfast Street, Hove, West Sussex, BN3 3YS
☎ (01273) 241881 ✉ hello@urchinpub.co.uk

Following two years of homebrewing research, commercial brewing began in 2018 in the Urchin, Hove, a shellfish and craft beer pub. Beer is only available in the pub, mainly in keg, with cask-conditioned beer available infrequently.

Late Night Hype

Unit 17, Andrew Court, South Douglas Street, Clydebank, G81 1PD

Late Night Hype is owned and operated by two friends. Around 25 outlets are supplied direct. There are plans for expansion.

Laverstoke Park

Laverstoke Park, Overton, Hampshire, RG25 3DR

A bottle-conditioned beer is contract brewed for Laverstoke Park by an unnamed brewery. RAIB

Law

Unit 17, Mid Wynd, Dundee, DD1 4JG ☎ 07893 538277 🌐 lawbrewing.co

Law was established in 2016 and is named after Dundee's most distinctive landmark; the volcano-like slopes of the Law.

Lazy Bay

89 Julian Road, Lady Bay, Nottingham, NG2 5AL
☎ 07400 196036 🌐 lazybaybrewery.co.uk

Lazy Bay was established in 2018 by ex-teacher and former homebrewer Brett Phillips using a purpose-built 2.5 barrel plant. All beers are unfined and the higher gravity beers are brewed with Norwegian Kveik yeast. Beers are delivered direct to local pubs and beer festivals. V

Culture Vulture (ABV 4.2%)
El Dorado (ABV 4.5%)
Rebel for Life (ABV 6.5%)
Sy Fy (ABV 7%)
Chikara (ABV 7.5%)
Scene Deleted (ABV 10%)

Lazy Turtle

Meadowbeck, Barnside Lane, Hepworth, Holmfirth, West Yorkshire, HD9 1TN
☎ (01484) 680589 ☎ 07590 532880
🌐 lazyturtlebrewing.com

Founded in 2018 by Dave Bore, a member of the Penistone Homebrew Collective, after he decided to move into commercial brewing. Production is mostly bottled but cask-conditioned beers are occasionally available.

Leadmill

Unit 3 Heanor Small Business Centre, Adams Close, Heanor, Derbyshire, DE75 7SW ☎ 07971 189915
✉ leadmill@fsmail.net

⊗ Set up in Selston in 1999, Leadmill moved to Denby in 2001 and again in 2010 to Heanor. A sister brewery to Bottle Brook (qv), the brewery tap is at the Old Oak, Horsley Woodhouse. ♦

Langley Best (ABV 3.6%)
Mash Tun Bitter (ABV 3.6%)
Old Oak Bitter (ABV 3.7%)
B52 (ABV 5.2%)
Slumdog (ABV 5.9%)

Leatherbritches

Brewery Yard, Tap House, Annwell Lane, Smisby, Derbyshire, LE65 2TA ☎ 07976 279253
leatherbritches.co.uk

The brewery, founded in 1993 in Fenny Bentley, has relocated and expanded over the years, moving to its current address in 2011 where it effectively took over the existing Tap House Brewery (established 2010) but continued to brew the latter's beers. Since 2015, however, Tap House beers have become rebadged Leatherbritches products. !! ♦ RAIB

Lecale (NEW)

5 High Street, Ardglass, County Down, BT30 7TU
☎ 07763 142100 lecalebrewery.com

Based in the historic fishing village of Ardglass on the east coast of County Down, Lecale uses local malts and hops with water from the Mourne Mountains.

Ledbury SIBA

Gazerdine House, Hereford Road, Ledbury, Herefordshire, HR8 2PZ
☎ (01531) 671184 ☎ 07957 428070
ledburyrealales.co.uk

Established in 2012, Ledbury Real Ales uses hops grown in Herefordshire and Worcestershire with other materials sourced locally where possible. The beers are sold mainly within a 15-mile radius of the brewery. !! ♦

Bitter (ABV 3.8%)
Dark (ABV 3.9%)
Gold (ABV 4%)
Pale Ale (ABV 4%)

Leeds SIBA

1 Westland Road, Leeds, West Yorkshire, LS11 5SE
☎ (0113) 244 5866 leedsbrewery.co.uk

Production began in 2007 and Leeds Brewery is now one of the largest in the city. It uses a unique strain of yeast originally taken from a now defunct West Yorkshire brewery. Beer is supplied directly across the region and as far as Nottinghamshire, Lancashire and the North East. It formerly ran an estate of pubs, still trading, across Leeds and York. In 2020 the brewery invested in new state of the art brewing equipment following a move into new premises. ♦

Pale (ABV 3.8%)
Yorkshire Gold (ABV 4%)
Best (ABV 4.3%)
Midnight Bell (ABV 4.8%)

JW Lees IFBB

Greengate Brewery, Middleton Junction, M24 2AX
☎ (0161) 643 2487 jwlees.co.uk

Family-owned since its foundation by John Lees in 1828, the brewery has a tied estate of 150 pubs, mostly in north Manchester, Cheshire, Lancashire and North Wales. The vast majority serve cask beer. The current head brewer is a family member. An in-house microbrewery, Boilerhouse, came on stream in 2018. !!

Dark (ABV 3.5%)
Formerly GB Mild. Dark brown beer with a malt and caramel aroma. Creamy mouthfeel, with malt, caramel and fruit flavours and a malty finish.
Supernova (ABV 3.5%)
Manchester Pale Ale (ABV 3.7%)
Golden beer, moderately-hopped and with gentle bitterness.
Bitter (ABV 4%)
Smooth, copper-coloured beer with caramel malt in aroma and flavour. Dry, bittersweet aftertaste.
Dragon's Fire (ABV 4%)
Boilerhouse Craft Pale (ABV 4.2%)
Game On (ABV 4.2%)
Stout (ABV 4.2%)
Founder's (ABV 4.5%)
Moonraker (ABV 6.5%)
A reddish-brown beer with a strong, malty, fruity aroma. The flavour is rich and sweet, with roast malt, and the finish is fruity yet dry. Available only in a handful of outlets.

Left Bank

Ty Newydd Farm, Llangorse, LD3 7UA ☎ 07815 849523 leftbankbrewery.co.uk

The present brewery location commenced operation in 2019 and occupies the premises of the former Lithic Brewery. The 400-litre (2.5-barrel) plant produces cask, bottled and canned beers.

Left Handed Giant

Unit 3, Wadehurst Industrial Park, St Philips Road, St Philips, Bristol, BS2 0JE lefthandedgiant.com

Originally launched in 2015 as a cuckoo brewery using spare capacity at other local breweries, Left Handed Giant has operated since 2017 using its own 15-barrel plant to brew modern, progressive beers. A second 15-barrel plant was added in 2019 when the Left Handed Giant Brewpub in Bristol city centre was added, doubling its capacity. A small amount of the output goes into cask. !! ♦ RAIB

Legitimate Industries SIBA

10 Weaver Street, Leeds, West Yorkshire, LS4 2AU
legitimateworldwide.com

Founded in 2016, the 30-barrel plant mainly brews keg beer for the company's Red's True Barbecue restaurant chain. However, under new ownership a wider portfolio of non-permanent beers is being produced with canned output substantially increasing too aided through installation of a 200 litre pilot kit. A limited amount of cask beer is sometimes available in the local free-trade.

Leigh on Sea SIBA

35 Progress Road, Leigh-on-Sea, Essex, SS9 5PR
☎ (01702) 817255 leighonseabrewery.co.uk

Established in 2017 to produce vegan-friendly beer, which is unfiltered, unpasteurised and unfined (except for Renown). Initially brewing on a one-barrel kit, it rapidly progressed to a 10-barrel plant. Many of the names of the beers are based on Leigh's maritime heritage. !! V

Legra Pale (ABV 3.8%)
Boys of England (ABV 3.9%)
Brhubarb (ABV 3.9%)
Renown (ABV 4%)
Six Little Ships (ABV 4.2%)
Two Tree Island Red (ABV 4.5%)

Crowstone (ABV 5.5%)
Cockle Row Spit (ABV 5.6%)
SS9 (ABV 9%)

Leighton Buzzard SIBA

Unit 31, Harmill Industrial Estate, Grovebury Road, Leighton Buzzard, Bedfordshire, LU7 4FF
☎ (01525) 839153 ☎ 07538 903753
leightonbuzzardbrewing.co.uk

The first brewery to operate in Leighton Buzzard for more than 100 years. Established in 2014 by Jon d'Este-Hoare, the brewery changed hands in 2019 and is now owned by local CAMRA member Mark Debrick. !! ♦

Captain Cook (ABV 3.8%)
Cuckoo (ABV 3.8%)
Leighton Gold (ABV 3.8%)
Bavarian Dragon (ABV 4.2%)
Vimy Bomber (ABV 4.3%)
Hoptimist (ABV 4.4%)
Restoration Ale (ABV 4.6%)
Black Buzzard (ABV 5.8%)

Leila Cottage

Countryman, Chapel Road, Ingoldmells, Skegness, Lincolnshire, PE25 1ND
☎ (01754) 872268
✉ countryman_inn@btconnect.com

Leila Cottage started brewing in 2007 and now uses a 2.5-barrel plant. The brewery is situated at the Countryman pub – Leila Cottage was the original name of the building before it became a licensed club and more recently a pub. The history of the Countryman and the brewery is on display in the pub. !! RAIB

Leith Hill

c/o Plough Inn, Coldharbour Lane, Coldharbour, Surrey, RH5 6HD
☎ (01306) 711793 ploughinn.com

Leith Hill was established in 1996 at the Plough Inn and was moved to converted storerooms at the rear in 2001, increasing capacity to 2.5 barrels in 2005. New owners took over in 2016. !! RAIB V

Lennox (NEW) SIBA

25 Lime Road, Dumbarton, G82 2RP
☎ (01389) 298642 ☎ 07709 192168

Office: 62 Glencairn Road, Dumbarton, G82 4DW
lennoxbrewery.com

Established in 2018 and brewed on the banks of the River Leven, inspired by the rich local history of the area and the raw ingredients that the local countryside provides. All the beers use as many locally sourced ingredients as possible. Expansion took place in 2020.

Sons Pale Ale (ABV 4%)
Golden Ale (ABV 4.6%)

Lenton Lane SIBA

Unit 5g, The Midway, Lenton Industrial Estate, Nottingham, NG7 2TS
☎ (0333) 003 5008 lentonlane.co.uk

Lenton Lane began brewing in 2014 under the name Frontier, after taking over the brewing plant at the Flower Pot pub in Derby. Lenton Lane changed its name in 2016 and relocated to a purpose-built brewery in Nottingham using a 10-barrel plant. The brewery produces a range of single malt and single hop beers (SM&SH), available throughout the year. ♦ RAIB V

Bluebird (ABV 3.8%)
36 North (ABV 3.9%)
Atlas Stout (ABV 4.2%)
Gold Rush (ABV 4.2%)
Pioneer (ABV 4.3%)
200 Not Out (ABV 6%)

Lerwick SIBA

Staneyhill, North Road, Lerwick, Shetland, ZE1 0QA
☎ 07738 948336 lerwickbrewery.co.uk

Lerwick Brewery was established in 2011 using a 12-barrel plant and sits at the very edge of the North Atlantic. Originally only brewing keg beer, a cask-conditioned range was launched in 2015. ♦ V

Skipper's Ticket (ABV 4%)
Azure (ABV 4.3%)
Refreshing grapefruit/peachy, hoppy, golden bitter.
IPA (ABV 5%)
Grapefruity hoppy bitter with a slight biscuit background
Tushkar (ABV 5.5%)
Good dark brown-coloured, roasted malty stout with chocolate, coffee and liquorice.

Leviathan

Unit 4, 17 Reddicap Trading Estate, Sutton Coldfield, West Midlands, B75 7BU ☎ 07983 256 979
leviathanbrewing.co.uk

Leviathan was established in 2018 by keen homebrewer Chris Hodgetts. Initial production was of keg and bottle-conditioned beers , but there are plans for cask ale as an upgrade of the brewery to a five-barrel plant took place in 2019.

Liberation

Tregar House, Longueville Road, St Saviour, Jersey, JE2 7WF
☎ (01534) 764089 ☎ 07911 744568
liberationgroup.com

The Liberation Brewery (owned by the Liberation Group, which also owns Butcombe Brewery) is located at Longueville, just outside St Helier. Its multi-award-winning flagship beer Liberation Ale can be found in many of the Group's predominantly freehold pubs (43 in Jersey, 26 in Guernsey, three in Alderney and 44 in the UK). Seasonal and one-off beers, often event driven, are produced throughout the year. !! ♦

Ale (ABV 4%)
Herm Island Gold (ABV 4.2%)
IPA (ABV 4.8%)

Lincoln Green SIBA

Unit 5, Enterprise Park, Wigwam Lane, Hucknall, Nottingham, NG15 7SZ
☎ (0115) 963 4233 ☎ 07748 111457
lincolngreenbrewing.co.uk

Anthony Hughes established the Lincoln Green Brewing Company in 2012 using a 10-barrel plant. The brewery takes its name from the colour of dyed woollen cloth associated with the legend of Robin Hood. Locally-sourced ingredients are used to create the beer range, in addition to occasional, seasonal and special edition brews linked to local and national events. A range of craft beers is available in KeyKeg. ♦ RAIB

Marion (ABV 3.8%)

Subtly-hopped golden ale with citrus aroma and a dry, bitter finish.
Archer (ABV 4%)
Citrus golden ale with American hops and a moderately bitter finish.
Hood (ABV 4.2%)
Tawny-coloured ale with balanced hops and bitterness.
Bowman (ABV 4.3%)
Fountain Dale (ABV 4.3%)
Arrow (ABV 4.5%)
Shot Firer (ABV 4.5%)
Tuck (ABV 4.7%)
Full-bodied and rich dark ale with roast and malt flavours throughout.
Gin And Beer It (ABV 5%)
Longbow (ABV 5%)
Quarterstaff (ABV 5%)
Black in colour with roasty aromas and taste, leading to a dry coffee and bitter finish.
Shackler (ABV 5%)
Buttermuch (ABV 5.5%)
Dark brown beer with strong butterscotch caramel taste throughout and a gentle bitter finish.
Sheriff (ABV 5.5%)
Golden, full-bodied IPA, citrus hop taste and bitterness balanced throughout.

Lincolnshire Craft SIBA

Race Lane, Melton Ross, Lincolnshire, DN38 6AA
☎ (01652) 680001 🌐 lincolnshirecraftbeers.com

Lincolnshire Craft Beers is the company formed by Mark Smith who bought the Tom Wood Brewery in 2017. It continues to brew the Tom Wood range of beers on the 60-barrel Melton Ross plant. ♦

Best Bitter (ABV 3.7%)
A good citrus, passion fruit hop dominates the nose and taste, with background malt. A lingering hoppy and bitter finish.
Lincoln Gold (ABV 4%)
Bomber County (ABV 4.8%)
An earthy malt aroma but with a complex underlying mix of coffee, hops, caramel and apple fruit. The beer starts bitter and intensifies to the end.

Linear

Bingham, Nottinghamshire, NG13 8EU 🌐 linear.beer

Small-scale, 50-litre brewery, started production in 2016 and is located at the owner's home. Currently focussing on a series of one-offs in a range of styles (sometimes in collaboration). These are supplied to three local pubs. Limited capacity restricts the supply of cask beers to others, but they have appeared at several local beer festivals in the recent years. A core range of bottle-conditioned beers is also available at several outlets.

Linfit

Sair Inn, 139 Lane Top, Linthwaite, Huddersfield, West Yorkshire, HD7 5SG
☎ (01484) 842370

A 19th-century brewpub that started brewing again in 1982. The beer is only available at the Sair Inn.

Liquid Light

125 Sneinton Boulevard, Nottingham, NG2 4FN
☎ 07530 737842 🌐 liquidlightbrewco.com

The beer range has been named with a strong heavy rock and psychedelic influence, referencing the likes of Frank Zappa and Black Sabbath. It has an emphasis on pale-coloured, hoppy beers and fruit beers. ♦

Lister's SIBA

The Old Dairy, Ford Lane, Ford, West Sussex, BN18 0DF
☎ (01903) 739117 ☎ 07775 853412
🌐 listersbrewery.com

Brewing began in 2012 using a 0.25-barrel kit. The brewery relocated in 2014 and expanded to a five-barrel plant. Lister's donates 5p from every pint and bottle sold to the Battersea Dogs & Cats Home.

Best Bitter (ABV 3.9%)
Golden Ale (ABV 4.1%)
Limehouse Porter (ABV 4.1%)
American Pale Ale (ABV 4.2%)
IPA (ABV 4.3%)
Special (ABV 4.6%)

Litchborough Artisan

Unit 12, Northampton Road, Litchborough, Northamptonshire, NN12 8JB
☎ (01327) 831308
✉ info@litchboroughbrewery.co.uk

Formerly Merrimen Brewery, the name changed along with all the beers in 2019 following the acquisition of Merrimen by Richard Bustin in 2018. The name change reflects the importance of the village of Litchborough, which in 1974 became the home to the first small scale brewing enterprise (now called a microbrewery).

Atomic (ABV 4%)
Monroe (ABV 4%)
DNA (ABV 4.1%)
Nubru (ABV 4.1%)
Infinity (ABV 4.2%)
Liberty (ABV 4.2%)
Black Beauty (ABV 4.5%)
Galaxy (ABV 4.5%)

Lithic

See Cold Black Label

Little Black Dog

Carlton Brewery, Duddings Farm, Carlton, North Yorkshire, DN14 9LU ☎ 07495 026173
🌐 littleblackdogbeer.com

Established in 2015, Little Black Dog is a small batch, family-run brewery. All beer is unfined, unpasteurised and unfiltered. The brewery tap is the Doghouse, Selby. ♦V

Yorkshire Bitter (ABV 3.8%)
Big Red American Amber (ABV 4.5%)
Oatmeal Stout (ABV 4.5%)

Little Creatures

1 Lewis Cubitt Walk, Kings Cross, London, N1C 4DL
☎ (020) 8161 4446 🌐 littlecreatures.co.uk

This US-style brewpub opened in 2019 under Little Creatures of Freemantle, Australia but ultimately Lion of Kirin Group ownership. Usually three or so ever-changing keg house beers are available from tanks behind the bar under the Regents Canal name along with imported Little Creatures beers. Close to the rejuvinated Coal Drops Yard development. Cask is under consideration. ♦

Little Critters SIBA

80 Parkwood Road, Sheffield, South Yorkshire, S3 8AG
☎ (0114) 2763171

Office: Horizon House, 2 Whiting Street, Sheffield, S8 9QR 🌐 littlecrittersbrewery.com

A small batch, family-owned microbrewery, opened in 2016 operating on a 10-barrel brewing plant. Pubs are supplied throughout Yorkshire, the East Midlands and nationally. ♦RAIB

Little Hopper (ABV 3.6%)
Blonde Bear (ABV 4.2%)
Raspberry Blonde (ABV 4.5%)
Sleepy Badger (ABV 4.5%)
White Wolf (ABV 5%)
Coco Nutter (ABV 6%)
Nutty Ambassador (ABV 6%)
Sultanas of Swing (ABV 6%)
C Monster (ABV 6.5%)

Little Dewchurch (NEW)

Plough, Little Dewchurch, Hereford, HR2 6PW
☎ (01432) 840542 🌐 littledewchurchbrewery.co.uk

The Little Dewchurch Brewing Company was established in 2019. The brewery is located in a former store room at the Plough Inn in the village of Little Dewchurch. It is a three-barrel brewery, with five ales to its name. The brewery's ales are available on draft in the Plough Inn. Bottling is also done on the premises.

Little Earth Project

Mill Green, Edwardstone, Suffolk, CO10 5PX
☎ (01787) 211118 🌐 littleearthproject.com

Established as Mill Green Brewery in 2008, becoming Little Earth Project in 2016. The brewery is built on the site of an old stable, behind the White Horse Inn. It has its own borehole for water and was built using local wood, reclaimed bricks, sheep wool and lime plaster. Brewing liquor is heated using bio and solar power and its 3,000-litre storage is constanlty heated by solar panels, topped up by a wood boiler. The brewery continues to create innovative beers and sours in small quantities. Most beers use local ingredients and are aged in old wine barrels for four months to a year or more to develop sour or cider qualities. About half of production is supplied in KeyKeg with the remainder bottled with some available in cask.

Little Eaton

See Black Hole

Little Giant SIBA

Unit 3, Stoke View Business Park, Fishponds, Bristol, BS16 3AE
☎ (0117) 939 2589 🌐 littlegiantbrewery.co.uk

Microbrewery established in the Fishponds area of Bristol in 2017. Its fully programmable, 600-litre brew plant was commissioned in 2018. Its parent company Reyam Ltd manufacture these microbreweries. Six core beers are produced, along with occasional one-off specials !! RAIB

Golden Gosling (ABV 3.6%)
Citrus and pine aroma, bitterness on the palate with grapefruit and pineapple flavours cutting through the resinous hoppiness, bitter, hoppy ending.
Fi (ABV 4.1%)
Full-bodied with malty backbone, caramelised fruit and hints of toffee with balancing hop bitterness before a gentle, bittersweet finish.
Fo (ABV 4.1%)
Hop aroma, light biscuit malt and background bitterness overlaid with soft fruit and crisp hop flavours, dry bitter aftertaste.
Fe (ABV 5%)
Malty nose, spiced fruit cake flavours with hints of caramel cutting across the bitterness and malt, long lasting satisfying finish.
Fum (ABV 5%)
Roasted malt aroma, complex flavours combine rich chocolate and coffee with treacle and dark fruit before a sweet, roasty finish.
Golden Goose (ABV 5.5%)
Powerfully-hopped aroma with zesty and tropical fruit flavours balancing the resinous hop bitterness which continues through the prolonged ending.

Little Goat

70 New Road, Ynysmeurdy, Pontardawe, SA8 4PP
☎ 07590 520457 🌐 littlegoatbrewery.co.uk

Opened in a garden outbuilding by two enthusiastic home brewers, the four-barrel microbrewery was built with equipment from Langton's Brewery in Leicestershire, and commenced trading in 2018. The first ale was sold in bottles only, cask ale was added in 2019. V

Scapegoat (ABV 4.3%)
Golden Goat (ABV 4.4%)
Jumping Jack (ABV 4.9%)
Yankee Doodle Nanny (ABV 6.5%)
Duffel Goat (ABV 7.2%)

Little London

Unit 6b, Ash Park Business Centre, Ash Lane, Little London, Hampshire, RG26 5FL
☎ (01256) 533044 ☎ 07785 225468
🌐 littlelondonbrewery.com

Brewing began in 2015 using a six-barrel plant. Three fermentation vessels ensure a production capability of 60 firkins per week, with capacity for expansion.

Doreen's Dark (ABV 3.2%)
Blacksmith's Gold (ABV 3.5%)
Red Boy (ABV 3.7%)
Hoppy Hilda (ABV 3.8%)
Luvly (ABV 3.9%)
Pryde (ABV 4.2%)
Ash Park Special (ABV 4.9%)

Little Monster

Office: Burton Warren, Burton Park Road, Petworth, West Sussex, GU28 0JS 🌐 littlemonsterbrew.com

Brewing began in 2018. Owner Brenden collaborates with other breweries to produce his beers.

Little Ox SIBA

Unit 6, Wroslyn Road Industrial Estate, Freeland, Oxfordshire, OX29 8HZ
☎ (01993) 881941 ☎ 07730 496525

Office: 25 Castle Road, Wootton, OX20 1EQ
🌐 littleoxbrewery.co.uk

Little Ox began production in 2016 using a 10-barrel plant and expanded to 56 barrels in 2019 following its merger with Oxbrew. Beer is regularly supplied to the

THE BREWERIES

White Horse, Stonesfield, plus other local outlets. Contract bottling is conducted on-site.

Goldilox (ABV 3.9%)
Road Runner (ABV 3.9%)
Oddbod (ABV 4%)
Wipeout (ABV 4.2%)
Ox Blood (ABV 4.3%)
Filthy Rich (ABV 4.5%)
Yabba Dabba Doo (ABV 4.8%)
Dark & Seedy (ABV 5.5%)

Little Valley SIBA

Unit 3, Turkey Lodge Farm, New Road, Cragg Vale, Hebden Bridge, West Yorkshire, HX7 5TT
(01422) 883888 littlevalleybrewery.co.uk

Little Valley began brewing in 2005 on a 10-barrel plant. All beers are organic and vegan, and Radical Roots is licensed by the Fairtrade Foundation. Around 300 outlets are supplied. Several beers are contract brewed for Suma Wholefoods. RAIB V

Withens Pale (ABV 3.9%)
Creamy, light gold-coloured, refreshing ale. Fruity hop aroma, flavoured with hints of lemon and grapefruit. Clean, bitter aftertaste.
Radical Roots (ABV 4%)
Full-bodied speciality ale. Ginger predominates in the aroma and taste. It has a pleasantly powerful, fiery and spicy finish.
Cragg Bitter (ABV 4.2%)
Tawny best bitter with a creamy mouthfeel. Malt and fruit aromas move through to the palate which is followed by a bitter finish.
Dark Vale (ABV 4.5%)
Dark brown speciality beer. Dark roast and fruit blend successfully with flavours of vanilla to create a smooth, mellow porter.
Hebden's Wheat (ABV 4.5%)
A pale yellow, creamy wheat beer with a good balance of bitterness and fruit, a hint of sweetness, but with a lasting, dry finish.
Stoodley Stout (ABV 4.8%)
Dark brown creamy stout with a rich roast aroma and luscious fruity, chocolate, roast flavours. Well-balanced with a clean, bitter finish.
Tod's Blonde (ABV 5%)
Bright yellow-coloured, smooth beer with a citrus hop start, and a dry finish. Fruity, with a hint of spice. Similar in style to a Belgian blonde.
Moor Ale (ABV 5.5%)
Tawny in colour with a full-bodied taste. It has a strong malty nose and palate with hints of heather and peat-smoked malt. Well-balanced with a bitter finish.
Python IPA (ABV 6%)
Amber-coloured creamy beer with a complex bitter fruit palate subtly balanced by a malty sweetness, leading to a strongly lingering bitter after taste.

Littleover

Unit 9 Robinson Industrial Estate, Shaftesbury Street, Derby, DE23 8NL
(01332) 987100 07449 586811
littleoverbrewery.co.uk

Littleover was established in 2015 using a six-barrel plant.

Gold (ABV 3.8%)
8 O'Clock Bus (ABV 3.9%)
King George's Bitter (ABV 4%)
Epiphany Pale Ale (ABV 4.1%)
The Panther Oatmeal Stout (ABV 4.2%)
Dazzler IPA (ABV 4.5%)
Hollow Legs Pale Ale (ABV 5.2%)

Live (NEW)

Unit 2, Reeth Dales Centre, Silver Street, Reeth, North Yorkshire, DL11 6BW livebrewco@gmail.com

Four-barrel microbrewery run by the team behind the 2016 National Pub of the Year, the George & Dragon, Hudswell. It specialises in small-scale one-off brews utilising traditional techniques and locally foraged ingredients, mainly produced for cask with small bottle runs, all naturally conditioned. !! RAIB V

Liverpool Brewing SIBA

39 Brasenose Road, Liverpool, L20 8HL
(0151) 933 9660
liverpoolbrewingcompany.com

Established in 2018, Liverpool Brewing Company purchased the brewing set-up of what was the Liverpool Organic Brewery, including the recipes, names and branding. A 12.5-barrel plant is used with six fermenters. Beers are brewed for Team Toxic. !!

Cascade (ABV 3.8%)
Pale Ale (ABV 4%)
Light, fruity hop aromas, sweet bitter flavours with a light malty finish.
24 Carat Gold (ABV 4.1%)
Beer with intense hoppy aromas, gentle, sweet, fruity bitter flavours and a light hop finish.
Bier Head (ABV 4.1%)
Hoppy malt aromas on this fruity, hoppy, amber bitter with a sweet, mellow malt finish.
Modern Bitter (ABV 4.2%)
Tropical IPA (ABV 4.2%)
Session IPA (ABV 4.3%)
Big Juicy Pale (ABV 4.5%)
Stout (ABV 4.7%)
IPA (ABV 5.7%)

Contract brewed for Team Toxic:
Temple (ABV 3.8%)

Lizard

The Old Nuclear Bunker, Pednavounder, Coverack, Cornwall, TR12 6SE
(01326) 281135 lizardales.co.uk

Launched in 2004 in St Keverne, Lizard Ales is now based at former RAF Treleaver, a massive disused nuclear bunker in the countryside near Coverack on the Lizard Peninsula. Specialising in bottle-conditioned ales, it mainly supplies Asda, but ales can be found as far away as Bristol. !! RAIB

Llangollen SIBA

Abbey Grange Hotel, Horseshoe Pass Road, Llantysilio, LL20 8DD
(01978) 861916 llangollenbrewery.com

Brewing began in 2010 on a 2.5-barrel plant. The brewery was updated and upgraded in 2014 to a 10-barrel plant. !! RAIB

Lleu

Unit A9, Penygroes Industrial Estate, Caernarfon, LL54 6DB 07840 910460/ 07724 902532
bragdylleu.cymru

Brewing began in 2014 using a 1.25-barrel plant. The beer reflects the Welsh folklore tales of the Mabinogi in both name and character. Capacity was upgraded to six barrels in 2016 to meet demand. ‼

Blodeuwedd (ABV 3.6%)
Lleu (ABV 4%)
Gwydion (ABV 4.7%)
Bendigeidfran (ABV 5%)

Llyn

1 Parc Eithyn, Ffordd Dewi Sant, Nefyn, Gwynedd, LL53 6EG
☎ (01758) 721981 ☎ 07792 050134
cwrwllyn.cymru

Brewing began in 2011. In 2016 the brewing moved into a new purpose built 15-barrel brewery that includes a brewery shop, taphouse and a visitor's gallery for tours. ‼

Y Brawd Houdini (ABV 3.5%)
Brenin Enlli (ABV 4%)
A fruity bitter, the initial malty taste leads to a hoppy, bitter aftertaste.
Cwrw Glyndwr (ABV 4%)
A full-bodied, well-balanced amber beer, quite fruity with a good hoppy finish.
Seithenyn (ABV 4.2%)
A fruity golden ale with a tangy citrus taste and a dry, hoppy finish.
Porth Neigwl (ABV 4.5%)

Loch Leven SIBA

The Muirs, Kinross, KY13 8AS
☎ (01577) 864881

Office: Loch Leven, Wymet House, 87 New Row, Dunfermline, KY12 7DZ lochleven.beer

Based opposite the Green Hotel in Kinross, the brewery started production in 2017. Brewing plant and casks have been acquired from the former Loch Leven Brewery in Fife. ‼

Warrior Queen (ABV 3.8%)
Shining Knight (ABV 4%)
Outlaw King (ABV 5%)
King Slayer (ABV 5.2%)

Loch Lomond SIBA

Vale of Leven Industrial Estate, Unit 11, Block 2, Renton, G82 3PD
☎ (01389) 755 698 ☎ 07891 920213
lochlomondbrewery.com

Established in 2011 by Fiona and Euan MacEachern, Loch Lomond was the first brewery to be established in the area. Having reached brewing capacity at its original site, it moved to a new purpose-built 35-hectolitre brewery, which also houses a canning line. ♦RAIB

West Highland Way (ABV 3.7%)
Bonnie & Blonde (ABV 4%)
Southern Summit (ABV 4%)
The Ale of Leven (ABV 4.5%)
Bonnie 'n' Clyde (ABV 4.6%)
Silkie Stout (ABV 5%)
Kessog Dark Ale (ABV 5.2%)
Bravehop Amber IPA (ABV 6%)
Bravehop Dark IPA (ABV 6%)

Loch Ness

See Cairngorm

Lock 81 (NEW)

Unit 21, Wenta Business Centre, Colne Way, Watford, Hertfordshire, WD24 7ND ☎ 07960 634977
lock81brewery.co.uk

Brewing takes place on a one-barrel plant, supplying bottled beers to local bottle shops and off licences.

Loddon SIBA

Dunsden Green Farm, Church Lane, Dunsden, Oxfordshire, RG4 9QD
☎ (0118) 948 1111 loddonbrewery.com

This family-run brewery was established in 2002 in a brick-and-flint barn that was originally a grain store. The custom-built, 17-barrel plant typically produces 120 barrels per week and supplies more than 700 outlets far and wide. An on-site taproom opened in 2018. ‼♦

Hoppit (ABV 3.5%)
Hops dominate the aroma of this drinkable, light-coloured session beer. Malt and hops create a balanced taste and a pleasant bitterness carries through to the aftertaste.
Hullabaloo (ABV 4.2%)
A hint of fruit in the initial taste develops into a balance of hops and malt in this well-rounded, medium-bodied bitter with a bitter aftertaste.
Citra Quad (ABV 4.4%)
Ferryman's Gold (ABV 4.4%)
Golden-coloured with a strong hoppy character throughout, accompanied by fruit in the taste and aftertaste.
Hocus Pocus (ABV 4.6%)
Ruby-coloured old ale with a dark malt, fruit and caramel aroma joined by sweetness in the taste. There is a malty bitterness to finish.
Dragonfly (ABV 5.2%)

Logan Beck

The Barn at Beckfoot Farm, Duddon Bridge, Cumbria, LA20 6EU ☎ 07926 179749
loganbeckbrewing@gmail.com

The Brewery started in 2019 and currently brews using a 0.75-barrel plant. The are tentative plans to expand in future. Beers are only currently available locally.

(Off)Target (ABV 3.3%)
Prime (ABV 3.7%)
Proper (ABV 4.2%)

Loka Polly

See Polly's

Lola Rose

Wanlockhead Inn, Wanlockhead, ML12 6UZ
☎ (01659) 74535 ☎ 07500 663405
lola-rose-brewery.co.uk

Lola Rose is based in the family-run Wanlockhead Inn, situated in the scenic Lowther Hills of the Scottish Lowlands. Local outlets only are supplied at present. RAIB

London Beer Factory SIBA

Unit 4 & 6, 160 Hamilton Road, West Norwood, London, SE27 9SF
☎ (020) 8670 7054 ☎ 07760 290489
thelondonbeerfactory.com

London Beer Factory started brewing in 2014 using a 20-barrel plant on the same estate and at the same time as

Gipsy Hill. The taproom is open at weekends. It also runs the Barrel Project along the Bermondsey Beer Mile, showcasing its range and providing an impressive display of barrels used for aging beer. 360-degree cans are a popular innovation. ◆

Beyond the Pale (ABV 4.2%)
Easy-drinking, unfined pale ale. Malt, tropical fruit and peach aroma and flavour with moderate bitterness. Short, full finish.
Chelsea Blonde (ABV 4.3%)
Grapefruit dominates the flavour and aroma with trace of spiciness and a dry bitterness balanced by a little honey sweetness.
Paxton Pale Ale (ABV 5%)

London Beer Lab SIBA

Arch 283, Belinda Road, Brixton, London, SW9 7DT
☎ (020) 8396 6517

Office: Arch 41, Nursery Road, Brixton, London, SW9 8BP 🌐 londonbeerlab.com

Opened in Brixton in 2013 as a bottle shop and homebrew supplies outlet, also offering brewing workshops and tastings. Commercial brewing began in 2015 for larger batches with the shop focusing on small batch production and collaborations, available downstairs at the 14-line taproom. ◆

Tip Top Citra (ABV 5%)

London Brewing SIBA

Bohemia, 762-764 High Road, North Finchley, London, N12 9QH
☎ (020) 8446 0294 🌐 londonbrewing.com

⊗ London Brewing Co began brewing in 2011 at the Bull in Highgate using a 2.5-barrel plant. In 2014 it acquired its second pub, the Bohemia in North Finchley, at which brewing began in 2015 in a new 6.5-barrel brewhouse, becoming its sole location when the Bull was sold in 2016. Beer is now widely available through pub chains and the free trade. ♦

London Lush (ABV 3.8%)
A pale, hoppy bitter with a good balance of hop and malt and a little fruit. The finish is dry but with some lingering hoppiness.
Beer Street (ABV 4%)
Well-balanced coppery brown-coloured best bitter with the hoppy bitterness underpinned by the caramelised malt character. Fruit is present throughout.
100 Oysters Stout (ABV 4.6%)
Sweet, chocolaty, treacle and soft dark fruit on this smooth stout. Finish is long, dry roast with a little bitterness.
Skyline (ABV 5.3%)
Pale brown beer with a honey sweetness and a some soft fruit notes. Sweetness is balanced by a bitter dryness.
Never Mind the Kent Hops (ABV 5.5%)
A smooth, brown beer with spicy hops on the palate, lingering in the dry, slightly bitter finish. There is a sweet toffee character throughout.

London Fields

365-366 Warburton Street, London Fields, London, E8 3RR
☎ (020) 3960 7820 🌐 londonfieldsbrewery.co.uk

After brewing was suspended in 2014 beers were brewed at Tom Woods. Taken over by Carlsberg UK in 2017, the company was relaunched in 2018 with the main brands brewed at Trumans. The London Fields site itself returned to brewing in 2019 along with a large taproom although some core brands are still brewed at Trumans. ◆

London Road Brew House

67-75 London Road, Southampton, Hampshire, SO15 2AB
☎ (023) 8098 9401 ☎ 07597 147321
🌐 londonroadbrewhouse.com

⊗ Brewing commenced in 2017 in the London Road Brew House using a six-barrel plant. Beer is brewed for the pub, the City Pub Co estate and the trade. ◆

Long Arm

Long Arm, 20-26 Worship Street, Shoreditch, London, EC2A 2DX
☎ (020) 3873 4065 🌐 longarmpub.co.uk

Opening in 2017, this brewpub took over all Long Arm beers when the Ealing Park Tavern kit was suspended. Beers are keg only, served on-site from tanks and in keg. Owned by ETM chain.

Long Man SIBA

Church Farm, Litlington, East Sussex, BN26 5RA
☎ (01323) 871850 ☎ 07976 777992
🌐 longmanbrewery.com

⊗ Long Man began brewing in 2012 using a 20-barrel stainless steel plant. Hops and grain are sourced locally with a view to using homegrown barley, as well as a traditional strain of Sussex yeast. !! ◆

Long Blonde (ABV 3.8%)
Best Bitter (ABV 4%)
Copper Hop (ABV 4.2%)
Old Man (ABV 4.3%)
Sussex Pride (ABV 4.5%)
American Pale Ale (ABV 4.8%)

Longdog SIBA

Unit A1 Moniton Trading Estate, West Ham Lane, Basingstoke, Hampshire, RG22 6NQ
☎ (01256) 324286 ☎ 07579 801982
🌐 longdogbrewery.co.uk

⊗ Established in 2011, the Longdog Brewery is named after a type of Lurcher used for hare coursing – once a popular pastime in the North Hampshire downs.
!! ♦ RAIB

Bunny Chaser (ABV 3.6%)
Golden Poacher (ABV 3.9%)
A fruity nose with plenty of hops, balanced by a malty sweetness in the flavour. The hops build to a faint astringent finish.
Red Runner (ABV 4.2%)
Lamplight Porter (ABV 5%)
Splendid porter, smoky and drier than many, with strong roast flavours giving way to blackberry taste and a slightly vinous finish.

Longhill

Longhill Cottage, Whitstone, Cornwall, EX22 6UG
☎ (01288) 341466

⊗ Longhill began brewing in 2011 using a 0.5-barrel plant, upgraded in 2012 to a four-barrel plant to meet demand. Paul and Sue brew one beer, available in the bar at the rear of the brewery. ◆

Hurricane (ABV 4.8%)

Full-bodied, tawny, premium bitter with earthy malt aroma. Quite bitter with fruit and resinous hop flavours. Refreshing and persistent bitterness.

Loomshed SIBA

Iomairt an Obain, Tarbert, Isle of Harris, HS3 3DS ☎ 07808 098860 🌐 loomshed.scot

Brewing commenced in 2019 on the outskirts of Tarbert. The brewery backs onto the Minch, with views of the Scottish mainland. An eco-friendly approach to brewing extends to the on-site taproom. No real ale. ◈

Loose Cannon SIBA

Unit 6, Suffolk Way, Abingdon, Oxfordshire, OX14 5JX ☎ (01235) 531141 🌐 lcbeers.co.uk

Brewing began in 2010 using a 15-barrel plant, reviving Abingdon's brewing history after the Morland Brewery closed in 2000. Beers can be found in an increasing number of local pubs and within 50 miles of the brewery. Popular brewery evenings take place on the first Tuesday of the month. ‼ ♦ ◈

Gunners Gold (ABV 3.5%)
Abingdon Bridge (ABV 4.1%)
Detonator (ABV 4.4%)
Porter (ABV 5%)
India Pale Ale (ABV 5.4%)

Lord Conrad's

Unit 21, Dry Drayton Industrial Estate, Dry Drayton, Cambridgeshire, CB23 8AT ☎ 07736 739700 🌐 lordconradsbrewery.co.uk

⊗ Lord Conrad's was established in 2007 and moved to Dry Drayton in 2011 using a 2.5-barrel plant. One permanent outlet is supplied, the Black Horse, Dry Drayton, along with other local free houses and beer festivals. The brewery adheres strongly to green principles, using low energy systems, recycled materials and local ingredients. ‼

Zulu Dawn (ABV 3.5%)
Hedgerow Hop (ABV 3.7%)
Her Majes Tea (ABV 3.8%)
Lickety Split (ABV 3.8%)
Tangerine Dream (ABV 3.8%)
Spiffing Wheeze (ABV 3.9%)
Big Bad Wolf (ABV 4%)
Conkerwood (ABV 4%)
Fools Gold (ABV 4%)
Gubbins (ABV 4%)
Lobster Licker (ABV 4.2%)
Slap N'Tickle (ABV 4.3%)
Zulu (ABV 4.5%)
Horny Goat (ABV 4.8%)
Pheasant's Rise (ABV 5%)
Stubble Burner (ABV 5%)

Lord Randalls

Holme View Farm, High Street,, Laxton, Newark, Nottinghamshire, NG22 0NX ☎ 07712 078346 ✉ randallig@aol.com

The five-barrel brewery equipment was purchased in 2018 from the defunct Market Harborough Brewery. Brewing commenced 2020. The proprietors are the Randall family and the head brewer is Dean Penny.

Honey Hole (ABV 3.8%)
Laxton Original (ABV 4%)
Farmers Grundy Stout (ABV 4.6%)

Lord's SIBA

Unit 15, Heath House Mill, Heath House Lane, Golcar, West Yorkshire, HD7 4JW ☎ 07976 974162 🌐 lordsbrewing.com

Established in 2015, Lord's Brewing Co is the brain child of three brothers-in-law, Ben, John and Tim. A picturesque 19th-century mill houses the eight-barrel plant, large tap room and gift/bottle shop. ♦◈

Expedition Blonde (ABV 4%)
Chosen Man (ABV 4.4%)
Malamute (ABV 4.5%)
Silver Spur (ABV 4.6%)
The Bandon Car Porter (ABV 4.8%)
Mount Helix West Coast Pale (ABV 5%)

Lost + Found

12-13 Ship Street, Brighton, East Sussex, BN1 1AD 🌐 lostandfoundbrewery.com

Brewing began in 2016. No real ale.

Lost & Grounded SIBA

91 Whitby Road, Bristol, BS4 4AR ☎ (0117) 332 7690 🌐 lostandgrounded.co.uk

Brewing began in 2016. The brewery has a focus on German and Belgian-style beers. No real ale.

Lost Industry

14a Nutwood Trading Estate, Sheffield, South Yorkshire, S6 1NJ ☎ (0114) 231 6393 ✉ beer@lostindustrybrewing.com

Lost Industry is run by a family of beer enthusiasts and was established in 2015. A wide range of beer styles is brewed with no core range, although favourites may be repeated from time to time. A barrel-aging programme began in 2018. Spare brewing capacity is utilised by Steel City (qv).

Lost Pier (NEW)

c/o 28 Fourth Avenue, Hove, East Sussex, BN3 2PJ 🌐 lostpier.com

Launched in 2017, the three founders transferred more than 50 years of joint experience in the wine industry to brewing. Cuckoo brewing at two local breweries, the beer is unpasteurised, unfiltered and vegan-friendly. The Assemblage series blends beer and wine. V

Loud Shirt SIBA

Unit 5, Bell Tower Industrial Estate, Roedean Road, Brighton, East Sussex, BN2 5RU ☎ (01273) 087077 ☎ 07901 856436 🌐 loudshirtbeer.co.uk

The brewery was set up by two old friends, Martyn and Mike. Established in 2017 using a 10-barrel plant. Regular monthly events are held at the brewery, look out for its psychedelic van at festivals. Around 30 outlets are supplied direct.

Love Lane

62-64 Bridgewater Street, Liverpool, L1 0AY ☎ (0151) 305 1292 🌐 lovelanebrewing.com

Established in 2017 in the Baltic Triangle area of Liverpool, the 30-barrel plant can be seen from the Love

Lane tap pub. Craft beers are produced under this name, cask-conditioned beers are badged as Higson's. ◆

Brewed under the Higson's Brewery name:
Pale (ABV 3.8%)
Amber (ABV 4.1%)
Best Bitter (ABV 4.2%)

LoveBeer SIBA

95 High Street, Milton, Oxfordshire, OX14 4EJ
☎ 07889 455845 ⊕ lovebeerbrewery.com

Established in a garage in 2013, LoveBeer's original 0.5-barrel plant grew to six barrels in 2017. The brewery supplies local pubs including the Plum Pudding, Milton, as well as beer festivals and farm shops. ⬛RAIB

Doctor Roo (ABV 3.7%)
Molly's Malt (ABV 4%)
OG (ABV 4.1%)
Bonnie Hops (ABV 4.6%)

Lovibonds

Friar Park Stables, Badgemore, Henley-on-Thames, Oxfordshire, RG9 4NR
☎ (01491) 576596 ⊕ lovibonds.com

Lovibonds was founded by Jeff Rosenmeier in 2005 and is named after Joseph William Lovibond (inventor of the Tintometer to measure beer colour). Beers are unfiltered and unpasteurised. In 2017, a purpose-built brewery on the outskirts of Henley was established, with a steam-heated mash tun and copper. Beers are available at a number of local outlets.

Lowland

8 Well Street, Lockerbie, DG11 2EY ☎ 07493 716521
⊕ lowlandbrewery.co.uk

⊗ Brewing began in 2018 using a five-barrel plant. Three regular beers are produced with plans to expand the range as the brewery develops. The brewery is located in converted premises in the town centre and supplies direct to pubs in Dumfries & Galloway, Scottish Borders and north Cumbria. ‼◆

Rabbie's Drouth (ABV 3.8%)
Twa Dugs (ABV 4%)
Dryfe Blonde (ABV 5%)

Loxley

⬛ 539 Loxley Road, Sheffield, South Yorkshire, S6 6RR
☎ (0114) 233 4310 ⊕ loxleybrewery.co.uk

Established in 2018, Loxley Brewery uses a five-barrel plant located in the cellar of the Wisewood Inn. Five regular beers complement occasional specials. In 2019, vegan bottle-conditioned beers emerged from a small bottling plant located at the brewery. Beers, both cask and bottled, are becoming increasingly available locally. A second pub, the Raven, opened in nearby Walkley in 2019. Branded merchandise is available. RAIB V

Fearn (ABV 3.8%)
Halliday (ABV 4%)
Revill (ABV 4%)
Lomas (ABV 4.4%)
Gunson (ABV 4.8%)

Lucky 7

Hay On Wye, HR3 5AW
☎ (01497) 822778 ☎ 07815 853353
⊕ lucky7beer.co.uk

This four-barrel brewery produces an extensive range of small-batch craft beers, seasonals and specials. All beers are unfined and suitable for vegans. V

Phoenix Rorter (ABV 4.4%)
SIPA (ABV 4.4%)
Creme Cocoa (ABV 5.7%)

Luddite

⬛ Calder Vale Hotel, Millfield Road, Horbury Junction, West Yorkshire, WF4 5EB
☎ (01924) 277658

Brewing began in 2019 at the Calder Vale pub in Horbury Junction. The pub was shut for five years until being reopened by a group of three former Horbury School friends, Ian Sizer, Tim Murphy and Gary Portman. The six-barrel plant brews, on average, once per week.

Ludlow SIBA

The Railway Shed, Station Drive, Ludlow, Shropshire, SY8 2PQ
☎ (01584) 873291
⊕ theludlowbrewingcompany.co.uk

Established in 2006, the brewery occupies a converted railway sidings shed. Beers are produced using a 20-barrel plant and a recently installed pilot plant for one-off beers. The premises also function as a brewery tap (which now has regularly-changing beer from the pilot plant), visitor centre and event's area. ‼⬛◆

Best (ABV 3.7%)
Blonde (ABV 4%)
Gold (ABV 4.2%)
Black Knight (ABV 4.5%)
Boiling Well (ABV 4.7%)
Stairway (ABV 5%)

Luna

See White Horse

Lydbrook Valley

⬛ Forge Row, Lydbrook, Gloucestershire, GL17 9NP
☎ (01594) 860310 ✉ andy@theforgehammer.co.uk

Brewing commenced in 2018 in the Forge Hammer pub in Lydbrook. Alison and Andrew Jopson use full mash to produce beers for sale in the pub.

Lyme Regis

Mill Lane, Lyme Regis, Dorset, DT7 3PU
☎ (01297) 444354 ⊕ lymeregisbrewery.com

Lyme Regis Brewery (formerly Town Mill Brewery) began brewing in 2010 situated in a part of the Town Mill that previously housed the Lyme Regis electricity generator. Historically also used as a brewer's malthouse, the building now houses their licenced taproom with a one-barrel pilot kit. All cask beers are currently brewed on contract by Gyle 59 Brewery to the original Town Mill Brewery recipes. ⬛RAIB ◆

Lymestone SIBA

The Brewery, Mount Road, Stone, Staffordshire, ST15 8LL
☎ (01785) 817796 ☎ 07891 782652
⊕ lymestonebrewery.co.uk

☺Lymestone commenced brewing in 2008. Based in the old Bents Brewery, it uses a 10-barrel plant. A family-run business, daughter Sarah has joined the brew team as one of the UK's youngest brewsters. The brewery delivers in a 50-mile radius, works with national wholesalers and owns three pubs. ‼ ♦

Stone Cutter (ABV 3.7%)
Hoppy and grassy aroma, clean, sharp and refreshing. A hint of caramel to start then intense bitterness emerges with a good bitter aftertaste and touch of mouthwatering astringency.
Stone Faced (ABV 4%)
Foundation Stone (ABV 4.5%)
An IPA-style beer with pale and crystal malts. Faint biscuit and chewy, juicy fruits burst on to the palate then the spicy hops pepper the taste buds to leave a dry, bitter finish.
Ein Stein (ABV 5%)
Stone the Crows (ABV 5.4%)
A rich, dark beer from chocolate malts. Fruit, roasts and hops abound to leave a deep lingering bitterness from the hop mix.
Abdominal Stoneman (ABV 7%)

Lymm

18 Bridgewater Street, Lymm, Cheshire, WA13 0AB
☎ (0161) 929 0663 lymmbrewing.co.uk

Lymm is a small, family-run brewery, launched in 2013. Located in an old post office, the brewing equipment is downstairs in what used to be the mess rooms with a brewery tap upstairs in what was the sorting office/post office counter. A sister brewery to Dunham Massey (qv), a joint bar opened in 2013, Costello's Bar, Stockton Heath. ♦

Dark (ABV 3.4%)
Bitter (ABV 3.8%)
Bridgewater Blonde (ABV 4%)
Heritage Trail Ale (ABV 4.5%)
IPA (ABV 4.8%)
Dam Strong Ale (ABV 7.2%)

Lytham SIBA

8 Cambells Court, Lord Street, St Annes, FY8 2DF
lythambrewery.co.uk

Lytham is a well-established, family-run brewery that began brewing in 2007. Brewing is currently suspended. ‼♦

McColl's

Unit 4 Randolph Industrial Estate, Evenwood, DL14 9SJ
☎ (01388) 417250 mccollsbrewery.co.uk

Brewing commenced in 2017 using a 20-barrel plant. Outlets are supplied across the north-east and further afield. A brewery tap is open on the last Friday and Saturday of each month.

Petite Blonde (ABV 4.1%)
Lady Marmalade (ABV 4.4%)
North South (ABV 4.6%)
Suma IPA (ABV 5%)

McCracken's (NEW)

Derryall Road, Portadown, BT62 1PL
mccrackensrealale.com

Currently Co Armagh's only real ale brewery, established in 2018. Producing a range of bottle-conditioned beers. RAIB V

McGivern

c/o The Bridge End Inn, 5 Bridge Street, Ruabon, LL14 6DA
☎ (01978) 810881 ☎ 07891 676614
mcgivernales.co.uk

The brewery was established in 2008 and was originally based at the brewer's home in Wrexham but moved in 2011 to the award-winning Bridge End Inn, Ruabon using a 2.5-barrel plant. Production is continuing on an occasional basis. ♦

McMullen SIBA IFBB

26 Old Cross, Hertford, SG14 1RD
☎ (01992) 584911 mcmullens.co.uk

McMullen, Hertfordshire's oldest, independent brewery, was founded in 1827. Its famous brew, AK, is traceable back into the 19th century. The 'Authentic Heritage' tag promotes its core beers. Additional seasonal ales are produced throughout the year, sometimes produced under the Rivertown Brewing name. A microbrewery supplements the main plant. All 125 tied pubs, spread across south-east England, serve cask beer. ‼♦

AK Original Mild (ABV 3.7%)
A pleasant mix of malt and hops leads to a distinctive, dry aftertaste.
Cask Ale (ABV 3.8%)
Country Bitter (ABV 4.3%)
A full-bodied beer with a well-balanced mix of malt, hops and fruit throughout.
IPA (ABV 4.8%)

Mabby

Mabby Brew Pub & Kitchen, Forest Road, Trefforest, CF37 1SY
☎ (01443) 402033

A microbrewery situated in the cellar of the Otley Arms supplying the pub and a few other outlets. The name is derived from a partnership between brewer Matt Otley and his wife Gabby. The beers have no names and each recipe is referred to as a colour, with the colour being reflected on the pumpclip. V

Mad Cat SIBA

Brogdale Farm, Brogdale Road, Faversham, Kent, ME13 8XZ
☎ (01795) 597743 ☎ 07960 263615
madcatbrewery.co.uk

Established in 2012 by Peter Meaney in a refurbished cold store using an eight-barrel plant. Beers are distributed to local pubs. Bottles and polypins are available from the brewery and Peter often attends local markets, festivals and events. ‼♦

Red Ale (ABV 3.9%)
Crispin Ale (ABV 4%)
Golden IPA (ABV 4.2%)
Platinum Blonde (ABV 4.2%)
Emotional Blackmail (ABV 4.5%)
Jet Black Stout (ABV 4.6%)

Mad Dog

Shed 4, Unit 9, Park Farm, Plough Road, Penperlleni, NP4 0AL ☎ 0330 223 2313

Office: Unit 6a, Cwmtillery Industrial Estate, Abertillery, NP13 1LZ maddogbrew.co.uk

THE BREWERIES

Brewing began in 2014. The brewery was taken over in 2020, re-employing the former director as head brewer.

Mad Scientist

c/o The Quakerhouse, 2-3 Mechanics Yard, Darlington, DL3 7QF
☎ (01325) 245052

Brewing commenced in 2017 on a half-barrel plant situated in the cellar of the Quakerhouse.

Mad Squirrel SIBA

Unit 18, Boxted Farm, Berkhamsted Road, Potten End, Hertfordshire, HP1 2SG
☎ (01442) 256970 ⊕ madsquirrelbrew.co.uk

Situated on the outskirts of Hemel Hempstead, brewing began in 2004. Since 2017 it has used a custom brew kit from the US, using water from an on-site borehole at Potten End. The brewery maintains an innovative outlook, introducing many specialised craft beers while maintaining a range of more traditional cask ales and beers. Output is distributed to venues throughout London and the south-east, including to its own chain of Tap & Bottle shops. !! ♦ RAIB

Hopfest (ABV 3.8%)
Mister Squirrel (ABV 4%)
Resolution (ABV 4.2%)
De La Crème (ABV 4.5%)
London Porter (ABV 5%)
Big Sea (ABV 5.5%)

Mad Yank SIBA

Alandale Drive, Northwood Hills, HA5 3UP
⊕ madyank.com

Brewing is done on a small home plant after plans to install a large plant elsewhere fell through (it remains in storage). Mostly bottled output, with keg from time to time, often available at the Beer Asylum in Pinner itself.

Made of Stone

8 Woodford Road, Bramhall, Stockport, SK7 2JJ

Nanobrewery situated at the back of the Mounting Stone micropub in Bramhall. Brewing began in 2018 on a one-barrel plant at the rear of the pub. The brewery specialises in twice monthly, one-off brews and collaborations with local brewers. Beers are usually supplied to the pub and the Chiverton Tap, Cheadle Hulme.

Madrigal

Unit 2, Hele Business Park, Witheridge Place, Hele Bay, Devon, EX34 9RA ☎ 07857 560677
⊕ madrigalbrewery.co.uk

Originally established in Combe Martin in 2014, the brewery relocated to larger premises in Lynmouth and has now relocated again to a new site in Hele Bay, Ilfracombe. Planning permission has been sought for a taproom. !! ♦ RAIB V

Severed Hand (ABV 4%)
Fossil (ABV 4.1%)
Hanged Man (ABV 4.2%)
Veldt (ABV 4.3%)
Wheatear (ABV 4.3%)
Garland (ABV 4.4%)
Surfer Rosa (ABV 4.7%)
Monkey's Fist (ABV 4.8%)
Smooth, dark-coloured old ale with strong fruit and roast from start to lingering, slightly sour finish. Heavy, sweet but satisfying.
Lost & Found (ABV 5%)
North Coast Voodoo (ABV 5.1%)
Burning House (ABV 5.2%)

Magic Dragon SIBA

Plassey Brewery, Eyton, LL13 0SP
☎ (01978) 781675 ⊕ magicdragonbrewing.co.uk

Originally called Plassey, and later New Plassey, another new owner, brewer and personnel took over in 2017. Some beer replicates the old Plassey range but others are new recipes.

Border Bitter (ABV 3.8%)
A well-balanced, session bitter with a fruity aroma, smooth, malty taste, and a satisfying hoppy finish.
Ice Dragon (ABV 3.8%)
Eyton Gold (ABV 4%)
American Dragon (ABV 4.2%)
Obsidian (ABV 4.2%)
Eyton Bitter (ABV 4.5%)

Magic Rock

Units 1-4, Willow Lane, Huddersfield, West Yorkshire, HD1 5EB
☎ (01484) 649823 ⊕ magicrockbrewing.com

Magic Rock began brewing in 2011. The brewery is located about half a mile walk from Huddersfield town centre on an industrial estate. The site also houses a taproom and distribution centre. In 2019 Magic Rock was bought by Lion of Australia, who in turn are owned by Kirin of Japan. ♦ RAIB

Hat Trick (ABV 3.7%)
Ringmaster (ABV 3.9%)
Inhaler (ABV 4.5%)
Rapture (ABV 4.6%)
Common Grounds (ABV 5.4%)
High Wire (ABV 5.5%)
Dark Arts (ABV 6%)

Magic Spells

24 Rigg Approach, Leyton, London, E10 7QN
☎ (020) 3475 1781 ☎ 07740 428952
⊕ magicspellsbrewery.co.uk

Magic Spells is owned and operated by Hare Wines located in its warehouse. The small on-site kit is used for trial brews and events with the main output coming from Firebrand.

Magpie SIBA

Unit 4, Ashling Court, Ashling Street, Nottingham, NG2 3JA ☎ 07419 991310 ⊕ magpiebrewery.com

Launched in 2006 using a six-barrel plant, the brewery upgraded to 17.5-barrels in 2017. Only British hops and malt are used in the core range, with the Wanderlust range taking more worldly influences and ingredients. Shop/Tap opened 2019 at the brewery, please see website for current opening times and events. ♦

Hoppily Ever after (ABV 3.8%)
Golden bitter, gently-hopped with biscuit malt flavours and a bitter finish.
Best (ABV 4.2%)
A malty, traditional, pale brown best bitter, with balancing hops giving a bitter finish.
Cherry Raven (ABV 4.4%)
Raven Stout (ABV 4.4%)

Dark stout with roast coffee aroma and taste leading to a dry, bitter finish.

Thieving Rogue (ABV 4.5%)
A hoppy golden ale with a longlasting, bitter finish.

Jay IPA (ABV 5.2%)

Mains (NEW)

Office: 45a Alderman Road, Glasgow, G13 3YG
✉ mainsbrewco@gmail.com

Mains is a small batch brewery producing farmhouse-inspired beers.

Makemake (NEW)

▌ 39 Osborne Road, Southsea, Hampshire, PO5 3LR
☎ (023) 9273 5939 ● makemake.beer

Makemake Brewing, based in the Greenwich Brewpub in Southsea, have been producing modern craft beers since 2019.

Maldon

Stable Brewery, Silver Street, Maldon, Essex, CM9 4QE
☎ (01621) 851000 ● maldonbrewing.co.uk

⊠ Established in 2002, this family-run brewery is tucked away behind the 14th-century Blue Boar Hotel. The six-barrel plant is at full production serving more than 50 outlets including the brewery's micropub on the High Street. Also produces the Blackwater Brewhouse brand.
☲◆RAIB

Farmer's IPA (ABV 3.6%)
Drop of Nelson's Blood (ABV 3.8%)
Azimuth (ABV 3.9%)
Hotel Porter (ABV 4.1%)
Pucks Folly (ABV 4.2%)
Farmer's Golden Boar (ABV 5%)
Dark Horse (ABV 6.6%)

Mallard

Unit A, Maythorne, Southwell, Nottinghamshire, NG25 0RS ☎ 07811 193930
✉ stevenhussey@tiscali.co.uk

☺Mallard is a 2.25-barrel brewery run by Steve Hussey and Alison Ryan. Beer is available for local outlets in and across the county. ‼◆RAIB

Duck 'n' Dive (ABV 3.7%)
A bitter, pale golden beer, with a dry finish.
Greet Ale (ABV 3.7%)
Golden Duck (ABV 3.9%)
Quacker Jack (ABV 4%)
Feather Light (ABV 4.1%)
A straw-coloured, lager-style beer with a hoppy taste and aroma.
Duckling (ABV 4.2%)
A dry-hopped golden ale. Very bitter; hops dominate in the aroma and aftertaste.
Specduckular (ABV 4.2%)

Mallinsons

Unit 1, Waterhouse Mill, 65-71 Lockwood Road, Huddersfield, West Yorkshire, HD1 3QU
☎ (01484) 654301 ☎ 07850 446571
● drinkmallinsons.co.uk

☺Mallinsons was originally set up in 2008 on a six-barrel plant by CAMRA members Tara Mallinson and Elaine Yendall. The company moved to new premises in 2012 with a 15-barrel plant and specialises in hop-forward

and single hop beers. It has a permanent presence in numerous Huddersfield pubs. ‼☲◆RAIB

Wappy Nick (ABV 3.8%)

Malt SIBA

Collings Hanger Farm, 100 Wycombe Road, Prestwood, Buckinghamshire, HP16 0HW
☎ (01494) 865063 ● maltthebrewery.co.uk

⊠ Family-owned brewery, founded in 2012 using a 10-barrel plant. Based on a dairy farm in the heart of the Chiltern Hills, it has sustainability built into its brewing with spent grains going to feed the pigs on the farm and spent hops being composted. The brewery tasting bar stocks bottled beers that are suitable for vegans alongside local ciders. In-house deliveries are made to trade and direct customers in six surrounding counties. National distribution is through leading distributors and wholesalers. ‼☲◆V✿

Moderation (ABV 3.4%)
Missenden Pale (ABV 3.6%)
Starry Nights (ABV 4%)
Summer Daze (ABV 4%)
Harvest Ale (ABV 4.1%)
Voyager (ABV 5%)

Malt Brewhouse

▌ 166 Town Street, Horsforth, LS18 4AQ
☎ (0113) 467 2001 ● themaltbrewhouse.co.uk

Established in 2019, this microbrewery also supplies the other bars in the pub group, Granvilles, Horsforth, and Parkside Tavern, Leeds.

Malt Coast

Branthill Farm, Wells-next-the-Sea, Norfolk, NR23 1SB ☎ 07881 378900 ● maltcoast.com

Brewing began in 2016. It grows its own barley on the farm. ‼☲

Malvern Hills SIBA

15 West Malvern Road, Malvern, Worcestershire, WR14 4ND
☎ (01684) 560165 ● malvernhillsbrewery.co.uk

⊠ Still in its original (1998) home of an old quarrying dynamite store. Established presence in the Three Counties, Birmingham and the Black Country. Seasonals and specials are directed more by ad-hoc requests from publicans as opposed to a planned brewery timetable. Notable exceptions are the green-hopped beers in September. Plans for a taphouse on-site are progressing. ‼◆

Beacon Gold (ABV 3.7%)
Feelgood (ABV 3.8%)
Bertie's Best (ABV 4.2%)
Malvern Spring (ABV 4.2%)
Priessnitz Plzen (ABV 4.3%)
Straw-coloured, Pilsner-style, cask lager having a mix of soft fruit and citrus. Well-balanced, light in colour, with a resinous, aromatic finish.
Black Pear (ABV 4.4%)
Citrus hoppiness is the main constituent of this golden best bitter that has a long, dry aftertaste.

Manchester

66 North Western Street, Manchester, M12 6DX
☎ (0161) 273 6167 ● manchesterbrewing.co.uk

This eight-barrel brewery commenced production in 2016 and is housed in a railway arch in the Ardwick district of Manchester. Beers are mainly supplied to pubs in Manchester and West Yorkshire.

Factory Pale Ale (ABV 4%)
Some Might Say Session IPA (ABV 4.4%)
Elephant Juice NE Pale (ABV 4.5%)

Manchester Union

96d North Western Street, Manchester, M12 6JL
manchesterunionbrewery.com

Manchester Union is a Central European-style lager brewery co-founded by former Six O'clock brewer Ian Johnson, using a decoction technique in the mash and German lager malts. The beers undergo several weeks conditioning in tanks. Beers are unfiltered and unpasteurised and available across Greater Manchester.

Manning SIBA

Spindle Street, Congleton, Cheshire, CW12 1QN
(01260) 299964 manningbrewers.co.uk

A family-owned and run brewery using only British hops, opened in 2015. It has now joined forces with the established Beartown Brewery (qv), also of Congleton.

Woah Man (ABV 3.8%)
Man Up! (ABV 4%)
Cave-Man (ABV 4.2%)

Mantle SIBA

Unit 16 Pentood Industrial Estate,, Cardigan, SA43 3AG
(01239) 623898 07552 609909
mantlebrewery.com

From start-up in 2013 on a 10-barrel plant, Mantle has become a major player in the West Wales area. Engineer Ian Kimber and his scientist wife Dominique, formerly home brewers, have built a sound reputation for consistent quality. Over 200 outlets are supplied direct with wider distribution via carefully selected wholesalers. ‼ ♦

Rock Steady (ABV 3.8%)
MOHO (ABV 4.3%)
Cwrw Teifi (ABV 4.5%)
Dark Heart (ABV 5.2%)

Manual (NEW)

c/o 36-40 Bellfield Street, Dundee, DD1 5HZ
manualbrewing.co.uk

Launched in 2018, Manual Brewing Co uses spare capacity at 71 Brewing in Dundee.

Many Hands

Dunkeswell Airfield, Dunkeswell, Devon, EX14 4LF
manyhandsbrew.com

Many Hands Brew Co began brewing in 2017, producing small batch bottled beers. Each bottle sold makes a contribution to charity.

Marble SIBA

Unit 7, Boston Court, Salford, M50 2GN
marblebeers.com

Originally based at the Marble Arch pub in 1997, Marble Beers moved to a 15-barrel plant in Salford and opened an on-site taproom. Vegetarian beers are available in both its core and speciality ranges. It supplies its own two pubs and more than 70 other outlets. ‼♦V

Pint (ABV 3.9%)
Fresh hop aroma of grapefruit. Clean citrus hop flavour with pale malt base. Dry bitter aftertaste and lasting hop.
Manchester Bitter (ABV 4.2%)
Peachy hop aroma. Balanced bitter hop and malt taste. Full, fruity palate. Dry, bitter finish.
North South (ABV 4.2%)
Lagonda IPA (ABV 5%)
Golden yellow-coloured beer with a spicy, fruity nose. Fruit, hops and malt in the mouth, with a dry fruitiness continuing into the bitter aftertaste.
Cross Collar (ABV 5.2%)
Alf (ABV 5.4%)
Stout (ABV 5.7%)
Coffee roast aroma and a balanced bittersweet roast taste with smooth, malty mouthfeel. Roast runs to the end with a drying finish.
Earl Grey IPA (ABV 6.8%)
Bold, bitter bergamot flavour. Balanced and lasting hoppy and sweet taste.
Cubbio Damage (ABV 7.2%)

Market Bosworth

Unit 10, Willow Farm Business Centre, Upton, Leicestershire, CV13 0EQ
(01455) 377855 marketbosworthbrewery.co.uk

The brewery was set up by Jon Skinner in 2016 as a natural progression from his homebrew retail business. Rich Brine joined in partnership in 2017 and the kit was doubled in size to two barrels to meet demand. Its two main outlets are the Gate Hangs Well, Carlton, and the Horse & Hockey, Congerstone.

Stout (ABV 4.2%)
Best Bitter (ABV 4.8%)
Porter (ABV 5%)
Pale Ale (ABV 5.2%)

Marko Paulo

Owl & the Pussycat, 106 Northfield Avenue, Northfields, London, W13 9RT
(020) 8810 0880 markopaulo.co.uk

A 1.25-barrel brewpub opened in 2016 in a former bookshop by two ex-teachers. The beer travels about 20 feet from mash tun to glass. Cask-conditioned beers are complemented by a wide range of European-style keg beers. The new Ealing Brewery in Brentford supplements the on-site output. V

Marlpool

5 Breach Road, Marlpool, Heanor, Derbyshire, DE75 7NJ
(01773) 711285 07963 511855
marlpoolbrewing.co.uk

Marlpool was founded in 2010 by brothers Andy and Chris McAuley. The two-barrel brewery is situated behind the Marlpool Ale House. The brewery yard doubles up as a beer garden and the majority of the beer is sold through the Ale House and served unfined. The remainder is sold to reputable outlets. ‼♦RAIB

Marston's

Shobnall Road, Burton upon Trent, Staffordshire, DE14 2BW
(01283) 531131 marstons.co.uk

Brewing in Burton since 1834, the brewery houses the only working Burton Union fermenters, in rooms known as the Cathedral of Brewing. Developed in the 19th century, they are used to cleanse the new style of pale ale yeast. Only Pedigree is fermented in the unions, but the yeast is used in other Marston's beers. A nanobrewery within the visitors centre (DE14) is used for small batch brews. Contract brewing includes Draught Bass brewed for AB Inbev. Part of Marston's PLC
!! ♦ RAIB

EPA (ABV 3.6%)
61 Deep (ABV 3.8%)
Light, golden to amber ale with intense tropical fruit and citrus aromas. Sweet tropical start with hints of spice. Hoppy bitterness overcomes the fruit and leaves a pleasant mouthwatering feel.
Saddle Tank (ABV 3.8%)
Overwhelming sulphurous aroma supports a scattering of hops and fruit with an easy-drinking sweetness. The taste develops from the sweet middle to a satisfyingly hoppy finish.
Pedigree (ABV 4.5%)
Pale brown to amber with a sweet hoppy aroma and hint of sulphur. Malt with a dash of hop flavours give a satisfying tasty finish.
Old Empire (ABV 5.7%)
Sulphur dominates the gentle malt aroma. Malty and sweet to start but developing bitterness with fruit and a touch of sweetness. A balanced aftertaste of hops and fruit leads to a lingering bitterness.

Brewed for A-B InBev:
Draught Bass (ABV 4.4%)
Hints of caramel aroma and taste, lightly-hopped for a short, bitter finish.

Martland Mill

Colmart House, Stephens Way, Warrington Road Industrial Estate, Wigan, WN3 6PH
☎ (01942) 665656 ☎ 07944 814040
martlandmillbrewery.co.uk

Originally established in 2014 then reopened in 2019 under new ownership. The six-barrel brewery sits on the outskirts of Wigan town centre and brews a core range of traditional beers on a weekly basis. ♦

Spinner's Gold (ABV 3.8%)
Lancashire Loom (ABV 4%)
D Day Dodger (ABV 4.1%)
Brown, with subtle malty aroma. Malt dominates throughout, with hop notes. Initial sweetness gives way to a bitter, dry finish.
Wobbly Weaver 4.3% (ABV 4.3%)
Bomber's Blonde (ABV 4.4%)
Arctic Convoy (ABV 4.5%)

MashDown (NEW)

58 Castlewellan Road, Banbridge, BT32 4JF ☎ 07866 580077 mashdownbrewery.com

Formerly brewing took place in collaboration with other breweries, MashDown now has its own nanobrewery.

Mashionistas (NEW)

45 Rochester Road, Coventry, CV5 6AF ☎ 07960 196204 mashionistas.com

Mashionistas, launched in 2018, is an experimental, one-barrel brewery based in a residential garage run by Flo, Jon, and Simon in their spare time. Because only small batches are made, it has the flexibility to brew anything it likes, and since its inception a wide variety of well-received KeyKeg beers has been produced. V

Masquerade

c/o 25 Mina Road, Bristol, BS2 9TA
masqueradebrewing@gmail.com

Tom Hebden and Sam Hipwell of Masquerade Brewing met at university where they laid plans to produce full-on juicy beers, which they started doing in 2017 on a custom-built, one-barrel plant in temporary premises. In 2018 the brewery moved and is now co-located at the Fierce & Noble Brewery (qv) in St Werburgh's.

Matlock Wolds Farm SIBA

South Barn, Cavendish Road, Farm Lane, Matlock, Derbyshire, DE4 3GZ
☎ (01629) 697989 ☎ 07852 263263
woldsfarm.co.uk

Established in 2014, this family-run brewery has expanded several times and now operates on a five-barrel plant in a converted barn on the owner's 17th-century farm. The Pump it Up micropub, Belper, was acquired in 2019. ♦ RAIB V

Simcoe (ABV 3.8%)
High Tor (ABV 4%)
To the Bitter End (ABV 4.2%)
Riber Gold (ABV 4.3%)
100cc (ABV 4.9%)
Classic Porter (ABV 4.9%)

Mauldons SIBA

13 Church Field Road, Sudbury, Suffolk, CO10 2YA
☎ (01787) 311055 mauldons.co.uk

Mauldons started brewing in Sudbury in 1795 and was bought by Greene King in the 1960s. It was re-opened in 1982 and purchased by the Sims family in 2000. A new 30-barrel plant was built and after a hugely successful 19 years the Sims retired and the business was bought by Heathpatch in 2019. A local farming-based company, with other commercial interests, it is hoped that barley and hops from their farms can be used in beer production. More than 200 outlets are supplied together with its three pubs. !! ♦ RAIB

Pale Ale (ABV 3.6%)
Moletrap Bitter (ABV 3.8%)
Plum and toffee on the nose. A good balance of malt, hops and fruit, leading to an increasingly bitter aftertaste.
Silver Adder (ABV 4.2%)
Light, fruity aroma, dry hoppiness and citrus fruit with rich honey in the taste, and a long fruity sweet aftertaste. Refreshing and well-balanced.
225 Anniversary Ale (ABV 4.5%)
Blackberry Porter (ABV 4.8%)
Suffolk Pride (ABV 4.8%)
A full-bodied, copper-coloured beer. A fruity nose leads to a spicy taste, with mild astringency in the aftertaste.
Black Adder (ABV 5.3%)
Malty, roasty aroma leads to a well-balanced, full-bodied beer, malty with roast and dark soft fruit overtones.

Maule SIBA

Rothersthorpe Trading Estate, Northampton, NN4 8JH
maulebrewing.com

Brewing began in 2014 on a self-built plant. Production is mainly unfiltered keg and bottle-conditioned beers, but cask-conditioned ales are occasionally produced for festivals. The beers are available from various local stockists as well as featuring on the London craft beer scene. RAIB

Maxim SIBA

1 Gadwall Road, Rainton Bridge South, Houghton le Spring, DH4 5NL
☎ (0191) 584 8844 🌐 maximbrewery.co.uk

Rising from the ashes of Sunderland brewer Vaux, Maxim was set up with a 20-barrel plant in Houghton-le-Spring in 2007. More than 100 outlets are supplied direct and two pubs are owned. ‼ ♦

Lambtons (ABV 3.8%)
Samson (ABV 4%)
Ward's Best Bitter (ABV 4%)
Swedish Blonde (ABV 4.2%)
Double Maxim (ABV 4.7%)
Raspberry Porter (ABV 5%)
Maximus (ABV 6%)

Mayflower SIBA

2 Woodford Street, Hindley, WN2 4UR ☎ 07703 816183 🌐 mayflowerbrewery.com

Originally established in Standish in 2001, the brewery was mothballed before reopening in late 2018 using a five-barrel plant behind the old police station in Hindley, Wigan. As well as an expanding range of core ales, the brewery specialises in bespoke beers for occasions and events, both national and local, and for venues wishing to personalise or brand their bottled and cask ales.

Pie PA (ABV 3.9%)
Douglas Valley (ABV 4%)
Best Bitter (ABV 4.1%)
Wigan Bier (ABV 4.2%)

Maypole

North Laithes Farm, Wellow Road, Eakring, Nottinghamshire, NG22 0AN ☎ 07971 277598
🌐 maypolebrewery.co.uk

The brewery opened in 1995 in a converted 18th-century farm building. After changing hands in 2001 it was bought by the former head brewer, Rob Neil, in 2005. ♦

Midge (ABV 3.5%)
Little Weed (ABV 3.8%)
Celebration (ABV 4%)
Gate Hopper (ABV 4%)
Hop Fusion (ABV 4.2%)
Major Oak (ABV 4.4%)
Wellow Gold (ABV 4.6%)

Meantime

Lawrence Trading Estate, Blackwall Lane, East Greenwich, London, SE10 0AR
☎ (020) 8293 1111

Head Office: Norman House, 110-114 Norman Road, London, SE10 9EH 🌐 meantimebrewing.com

Founded in 2000, Meantime brews a wide range of continental-style beers. Two pubs are owned. In 2010 the brewery relocated to larger premises in Greenwich. Taken over by SABMiller in 2015 and now owned by Asahi UK. ‼ ♦ RAIB

Meanwood

1 Sandfield View, Leeds, West Yorkshire, LS6 4EU
🌐 themeanwoodbrewery.com

The Meanwood Brewery was started by brothers Baz and Graeme Phillips in 2017 and focuses on brewing beer styles from around the world. The Terminus Tap Room & Bottle Shop opened in 2018. V

Herald (ABV 3.9%)
As Above, So Below (ABV 4.5%)
Black Goddess (ABV 4.9%)
Arecibo Message (ABV 5.7%)

Mechanic

22a Curdworth Street, Bethnal Green, London, E1 5QU
☎ 07410 910810 🌐 mechanicbrewery.co.uk

Brewing began in 2017, with the brewery moving to its current location, using a five-barrel plant, in 2018. Founder, owner and brewster Olga produces a range of beer styles, both classic and modern, available in can, bottle, cask and keg. All are unfiltered and unpasteurised. RAIB V♦

To the Good Times (ABV 3.8%)
Chocolate Jungle (ABV 4.2%)
Snake in the Grass (ABV 4.5%)
Green Diesel (ABV 4.9%)
Man Overboard (ABV 5%)
Downtime (ABV 5.2%)
Opal Fruitshake (ABV 6%)
Feminist Grandpa (ABV 12%)

Melbourn

All Saints Brewery, All Saints Street, Stamford, Lincolnshire, PE9 2PA
☎ (01780) 752186

No real ale. A famous Stamford brewery that opened in 1825 and closed in 1974. It re-opened in 1994 and is owned by Samuel Smith of Tadcaster (qv). ‼

Melwood SIBA

The Kennels, Knowsley Park, Knowsley, Merseyside, L34 4AQ ☎ 07545 265283 🌐 melwoodbeer.co.uk

Melwood began brewing in 2013 using a five-barrel plant in an old dairy. In 2016 the brewery moved to bigger premises in nearby old kennels on the Earl of Derby's Knowsley Estate. In 2019 it rebranded to add a small range of core beers, a series of modern beers, one-off specials and began experimenting with new styles and yeasts. ♦

Lovelight (ABV 3.8%)
Father Ted (ABV 4.2%)
High Time (ABV 4.3%)
Knowsley Blonde (ABV 4.3%)
Moondance (ABV 4.3%)
Stanley Gold (ABV 4.3%)

Merchant City

See Glasgow Beer Works

Merlin SIBA

3 Spring Bank Farm, Congleton Road, Arclid, Cheshire, CW11 2UD
☎ (01477) 500893 ☎ 07812 352590
🌐 merlinbrewing.co.uk

☺Merlin started in 2010 using an eight-barrel plant in a farm unit just outside Sandbach. The family firm of three is gently expanding the brewery. The beers are normally supplied to outlets within a 30-mile radius. The brewery is environmentally-friendly, using power from solar panels and a wind turbine, and spent water soaks away through reed beds on the farm. ‼◆RAIB

Merlin's Gold (ABV 3.8%)
Excalibur (ABV 3.9%)
Spellbound (ABV 4%)
Avalon (ABV 4.1%)
The Wizard (ABV 4.2%)
Castle Black (ABV 4.4%)
Dark Magic (ABV 4.8%)
Dragonslayer (ABV 5.6%)

Merrimen

See Litchborough Artisan

Mersea Island

Rewsalls Lane, East Mersea, Essex, CO5 8SX ☎ 07970 070399 ⊕ merseabrewery.co.uk

⊠ The brewery was established at Mersea Island Vineyard in 2005. It supplies several local pubs on a guest beer basis as well as beer festivals. It holds its own festival of Essex-produced ales over the four-day Easter weekend. ☛RAIB

Mersea Mud (ABV 3.8%)
Yo Boy! (ABV 3.8%)
Gold (ABV 4.4%)
Skippers (ABV 4.8%)
Oyster Stout (ABV 5%) ⌂

Metalhead (NEW)

Unit 16e, Helmsman House, Norham Road North, North Shields, Tyne & Wear, NE29 8RZ ☎ 07923 253890 ⊕ metalhead-brewery.co.uk

☺Metalhead Brewery began life in 2019 following a career change and a love of real ale and music. Beers are available in its micropub, the Lounge, Blyth. Modest expansion of both brewery and range are planned. RAIB

Hammer Best Bitter (ABV 3.8%)
Best Mate (ABV 4.2%)
Axl Gold (ABV 4.8%)

Mighty Medicine

Unit 4, Daniel Street, Whitworth, Lancashire, OL12 8BX ☎ (01706) 558980 ⊕ mightymedicine.com

Established in 2016 this brewery is committed to using the finest ingredients to produce an eclectic range of beers. A tap room is attached to the brewery. ☛

Stunning Blonde (ABV 3.9%)
Greedy Boy (ABV 4%)
Madchester Cream (ABV 4.2%)
Magic Malt (ABV 4.5%)

Mighty Oak

14b West Station Yard, Spital Road, Maldon, Essex, CM9 6TW
☎ (01621) 843713 ⊕ mightyoakbrewing.co.uk

⊠ Mighty Oak was formed in 1996 and has expanded considerably following a move to Maldon in 2001. Current capacity is 8,000 barrels a year following the acquisition of two adjacent buildings and enlarged plant.

Around 450 outlets are supplied. A popular free festive beer tasting day takes place each year in early December. ‼☛◆RAIB

Oscar Wilde (ABV 3.7%)
Roasty dark mild with suggestions of forest fruits and dark chocolate. A sweet taste yields to a more bitter finish.
Captain Bob (ABV 3.8%)
Maldon Gold (ABV 3.8%)
Pale golden ale with a sharp citrus note moderated by honey and biscuity malt.
Jake The Snake (ABV 4%)
Old Man and The Sea (ABV 4.1%)
Gorgeous George (ABV 4.2%)
Kings (ABV 4.2%)

Mikkeller (NEW)

🏠 37-39 Exmouth Market, Clerkenwell, London, EC1R 4QL ⊕ mikkellerbrewpublondon.com

A sister pub to Mikkeller Shoreditch, it opened in early 2020 with brewing beginning mid year.

Mile Tree SIBA

29 Alfric Square, Woodston, Peterborough, Cambridgeshire, PE2 7JP ☎ 07858 930363 ⊕ miletreebrewery.co.uk

⊠ Mile Tree was established in 2012 at the Secret Garden Touring Park in Wisbech, Cambridgeshire and moved to Peterborough in 2018. Beer is brewed on a five-barrel plant. It serves the local area and beer festivals. ◆RAIB

Meadowgold (ABV 3.8%)
Mosaica (ABV 4.2%)
Larksong (ABV 4.5%)
Wildwood (ABV 4.9%)
Porter (ABV 5.2%)
Winter Ale (ABV 6%)

Milestone SIBA

Great North Road, Cromwell, Newark, Nottinghamshire, NG23 6JE
☎ (01636) 822255 ⊕ milestonebrewery.co.uk

☺The brewery was established in 2005. Milestone currently brew on a 12-barrel plant and more than 150 outlets are supplied. ‼☛◆RAIB

Lion Bitter (ABV 3.8%)
Lion's Pride (ABV 3.8%)
Sherwood Pale Ale (ABV 3.9%)
Classic Dark Mild (ABV 4%)
Shine On (ABV 4%)
Azacca Gold (ABV 4.2%)
Loxley Ale (ABV 4.2%)
Black Pearl (ABV 4.3%)
Cromwell Best (ABV 4.4%)
Crusader (ABV 4.4%)
Rich Ruby (ABV 4.5%)
Olde English (ABV 4.9%)
Fletcher's Ale (ABV 5.2%)
Colonial Pale Ale (ABV 5.5%)
Raspberry Wheat Beer (ABV 5.6%)

Milk Street

See Frome

Mill Valley

The Brewhouse, 589 Halifax Road, Hightown, West Yorkshire, WF15 8HQ ☎ 07565 229560 🌐 millvalleybrewery.co.uk

Launched in 2016 on a three-barrel plant in Cleckheaton, the brewery relocated to Liversedge in 2019, taking over the former Partners brewery site together with its 12-barrel plant. More than 40 outlets are supplied as well as numerous beer festivals. Two brewery taps are owned, one at both the old and new brewery sites, which hold regular events. ‼♦V

Luddite Ale (ABV 3.8%)
Panther Ale (ABV 4%)
Yorkshire Bitter (ABV 4%)
Mill Blonde (ABV 4.2%)
Yorkshire Rose (ABV 4.2%)
Black Panther (ABV 4.6%)
Xtra Fudge Stout (ABV 4.6%)

Millis

See Dartford Wobbler

Mills

Jumpers Lane Yard, Berkeley, Gloucestershire, GL13 9BW ☎ 07848 922558 ✉ millsbrewing@gmail.com

Mills was established in Berkeley in 2016 by husband-and-wife team Genevieve and Jonny Mills. Wort is produced in multiple locations, which is then fermented in wooden vessels at its premises in Berkeley using 100% wild yeasts and bacteria from the local surroundings. The Lambic-style beers are mostly available bottle-conditioned. RAIB

Millstone SIBA

Unit 4, Vale Mill, Micklehurst Road, Mossley, Lancashire, OL5 9JL ☎ (01457) 835835 🌐 millstonebrewery.co.uk

Established in 2003 by Nick Boughton and Jon Hunt, the brewery is located in an 18th-century textile mill and uses an eight-barrel plant. More than 30 regular outlets are supplied. ♦

Vale Mill (ABV 3.9%)
Three Shires Bitter (ABV 4%)
Yellow beer with hop and fruit aroma. Fresh citrus fruit, hops and bitterness in the taste and aftertaste.
Tiger Rut (ABV 4%)
Light fruity beer with hop aroma and gentle bitterness.
Stout (ABV 4.5%)
Rising Sunsation (ABV 4.7%)
True Grit (ABV 5%)

Milltown SIBA

The Brewery, The Old Railway Goods Yard, Scar Lane, Milnsbridge, West Yorkshire, HD3 4PE ☎ 07946 589645 🌐 milltownbrewing.co.uk

Milltown began brewing in 2011 using a four-barrel plant. Two pubs are owned, the Dusty Miller at Longwood, which acts as the official brewery tap, and the Traveller's Rest, Meltham. ‼♦RAIB

Spud's (ABV 3.8%)
Weaver's Bitter (ABV 3.8%)
American Pale Ale (ABV 3.9%)
Platinum Blonde (ABV 4%)
Tigers Tail (ABV 4.1%)
Black Jack Porter (ABV 4.5%)

Milton SIBA

Pegasus House, Pembroke Avenue, Waterbeach, Cambridgeshire, CB25 9PY ☎ (01223) 862067 🌐 miltonbrewery.co.uk

The brewery has grown steadily since it was founded in 1999, moving to larger premises in the village of Waterbeach in 2012. It now operates three pubs in Cambridge through a sister company. In 2016 a separate brand, Beach Brewery, was created to market unpasteurised and unfiltered keg beers. ‼V

Minotaur (ABV 3.3%)
A dark ruby mild with liquorice and raisin fruit throughout. Light, dry finish.
Dionysus (ABV 3.6%)
Yellow bitter with good balance of biscuity malt and citrus hop. Some malt and hops linger on the long, dry aftertaste.
Justinian (ABV 3.9%)
Straw-coloured bitter with pink grapefruit hop character and light malt softness. Very dry finish.
Pegasus (ABV 4.1%)
Malty, amber, medium-bodied bitter with faint hops. Bittersweet aftertaste.
Sparta (ABV 4.3%)
A yellow/gold-coloured best bitter with floral hops, kiwi fruit and balancing malt softness, which fades to leave a long, dry finish.
Minerva (ABV 4.6%)
Nero (ABV 5%)
A complex black beer comprising a blend of milk chocolate, raisins and liquorice. Roast malt and fruit completes the experience.
Cyclops (ABV 5.3%)
Marcus Aurelius (ABV 7.5%)
A powerful black brew brimming with raisins and liquorice. Big, balanced finish.

Missing Link

The Old Dairy, Chiddinglye Farm, West Hoathly, West Sussex, RH19 4QS 🌐 missinglinkbrewing.com

Missing Link was established in 2017 by Jeremy Cook using a five-barrel plant. No real ale.

Mission: Creep

See Team Toxic

Mitchell's Hop House

354 Meadowhead, Sheffield, South Yorkshire, S8 7UJ ☎ (0114) 2745587 🌐 mitchellswine.co.uk

Brewing began in 2016 in a converted space at the back of Mitchell's Wine Merchants. Beers are available from the brewery shop and a growing number of local pubs and beer retailers. All production is now bottled.

Mithril

Aldbrough St John, North Yorkshire, DL11 7TL ☎ (01325) 374817 ☎ 07889 167128 🌐 mithrilales.co.uk

Mithril started brewing in 2010 in old stables opposite the brewer's house on a 2.5-barrel plant. Owner/brewer Pete Fenwick, a well-known craft brewer, brews twice a week to supply the local area of Darlington and Richmond. A new beer is brewed every week. ♦

Dere Street (ABV 3.8%)

Flower Power (ABV 3.9%)
A66 (ABV 4%)

Mobberley SIBA

Dairy Farm, Church Lane, Mobberley, Cheshire, WA16 7RA
☎ (01565) 873601 ☎ 07879 771209
🌐 mobberleyfineales.co.uk

⊗ Mobberley began brewing in 2011 in an old milking parlour on a working farm in the heart of the Cheshire countryside. Expansion is planned. ♦

HedgeHopper (ABV 3.8%)
RoadRunner (ABV 3.8%)
Mandalay (ABV 4%)
Maori (ABV 4%)
WhirlyBird (ABV 4%)
Red Vienna (ABV 4.2%)
Legacy (ABV 4.4%)
1924 (ABV 4.5%)
Solstice (ABV 4.5%)
Elysium (ABV 4.7%)
Origin (ABV 4.7%)

Modern Day Monks (MDM) (NEW)

Opus @ Pyramid, Palmyra Square South, Warrington, Cheshire, WA1 1BL ☎ 07837 460923
🌐 mdmbrewery.co.uk

Inspired by the beer they drank travelling the world, Jon and Jim are 'modern day monks' (MDM) creating beers using malt, yeast and hops from around the world.

Californian Lager (ABV 4.1%)
Session Pale Ale (ABV 4.2%)
Stout (ABV 5%)

Modest (NEW)

10a My Lady's Mile, Holywood, BT18 9EG

Small, independent brewery, notably the first in Northern Ireland to produce beer using the Sabro hop.

Moles

See Wickwar

Molson Coors

Molson Coors (Burton): 137 High Street, Burton upon Trent, Staffordshire, DE14 1JZ
☎ (01283) 511000

Molson Coors (Tadcaster): Tower Brewery, Wetherby Road, Tadcaster, DE14 1JZ
🌐 molsoncoorsbrewers.com

Molson Coors is the result of a merger between Molson of Canada and Coors of Colorado, US. Coors established itself in Europe in 2002 by buying part of the former Bass brewing empire, when Interbrew (now AB InBev) was instructed by the British government to divest itself of some of its interests in Bass. Coors owns several cask ale brands. It brews 110,000 barrels of cask beer a year (under licensing arrangements with other brewers) and also provides a further 50,000 barrels of cask beer for other breweries. In 2011 Molson Coors bought Sharp's brewery in Cornwall (qv) in a bid to increase its stake in the cask beer sector. No cask ale is produced in Burton or Tadcaster.

Mona (NEW)

Unit 6, Gaerwen Industrial Estate, Gaerwen, Anglesey, LL60 6HR ☎ 07988 698260

Seven enthusiastic locals got together and set up Mona Brewery, which was launched in 2019. The present offering is one cask beer and a range of four keg beers.

Pabo (ABV 3.8%)

Moncada

37 Humber Road, Dollis Hill, London, NW2 6EN
☎ (020) 8438 6666 🌐 moncadabrewery.co.uk

⊗ Established in 2011, Moncada was originally based in Kensal Town but moved in 2018. The larger premises include a taproom and a larger brew plant. !! ♦ V

Notting Hill Best Bitter (ABV 3.8%)
A fruity, biscuity sweet beer with a gentle lingering bitterness and spicy hops. Aroma is of biscuit and fruit.
Notting Hill Blonde (ABV 4.2%)
Fruity, earthy hoppy nose. Sweet biscuit flavour with citrus notes of tangerine, tart lemon and some tropical fruit. Lingering bitterness.
Notting Hill Pale (ABV 4.5%)
Grapefruit and mandarin dominate the bitterish flavour with some biscuit sweetness. Fruitiness slowly fades in the peppery dry bitterness.
Notting Hill APA (ABV 4.7%)
Dark amber, creamy, strong bitter with earthy hoppy aroma and flavour, balanced by sweet caramelised citrus. Developing spicy bitterness.
Notting Hill Oatmeal Stout (ABV 5%)
Creamy stout with strong, roasty, dark chocolate nose and flavour. A dark plum fruitiness and some malty sweetness provides balance.
Notting Hill Ruby Rye (ABV 5.2%)
Red-brown-coloured, smooth beer. Roast, chocolate fudge and caramel complemented by some hoppy fruitiness and tangy damsons. Dry, roasty, sweet finish.

Mondo

86-92 Stewarts Road, South Lambeth, London, SW8 4UG
☎ (020) 7720 0782 ☎ 07453 312170
🌐 mondobrewingcompany.com

⊗ Mondo began brewing in 2015. An on-site taproom (open Wednesday-Sunday) showcases its wide range of beer styles. A cask collaboration in 2019 renewed enthusiasm for real ale and another cask collaboration appeared in the M&B chain in 2020. !! ♦

Monty's

Unit 1, Castle Works, Hendomen, SY15 6HA
☎ (01686) 668933 🌐 montysbrewery.co.uk

Montgomeryshire's longest operating brewery began in 2009. The brewery owns the Cottage Inn in Montgomery which acts as it's visitor centre, and houses a 250-litre plant producing occasional small runs of experimental beers. ♦ RAIB

Old Jailhouse (ABV 3.9%)
Best Offa (ABV 4%)
MPA (ABV 4%)
Sunshine (ABV 4.2%)
Masquerade (ABV 4.6%)
Mischief (ABV 5%)

THE BREWERIES

Moody Fox

Hilcote Country Club, Hilcote Lane, Hilcote, Derbyshire, DE55 5HR ☎ 07702 253235
✉ moodyfoxbrewery@gmail.com

Established in 2016, Moody Fox is a microbrewery specialising in traditional ales using the finest hops and barley from around the world. One micropub is owned, the Garrison, Mansfield.

Cub (ABV 3.8%)
Pale Tale (ABV 5.4%)

Moody Goose

🏠 King William IV, 114 London Road, Braintree, Essex, CM77 7PU
☎ (01376) 567755 ⊕ moodygoosebrewery.co.uk

A three-barrel brewery, brewing approximately 15 times a year. The beers are currently only available in the King William IV, where the brewery is located, and select beer festivals.

moogBREW

Meads End, Ye Meads, Taplow, SL6 0DH ☎ 07941 241954 ⊕ moogbrew.co.uk

⊠ The brewery was set up in 2016 and moved to new premises in 2019. The majority of the production is keg, with bottle-conditioned beer and a small amount of cask also available. The focus of this tiny brewery is serving the local community and distribution is targeted to within a 10-mile radius. ‼️🍴◆RAIB ✦

Moon Gazer SIBA

Moon Gazer Barn, Harvest Lane, Hindringham, Fakenham, Norfolk, NR21 0PW
☎ (01328) 878495 ⊕ moongazerale.co.uk

⊠ Brewing began in 2012 using a 10-barrel plant. The brewery is owned and run by Rachel and David Holliday. Chalk-filtered water is used from the brewery's own well. ‼️◆

Jumper (ABV 3.9%)
Gentle hop character with supporting sweet malt and bitterness. Caramel swirls in and out as a dry edge develops.
Jigfoot (ABV 4%)
Orange peel and honey nose. Marmalade intro bolstered by well-defined bitterness. Initial sweetness fades into a sharp astringent bitterness.
Nibbler (ABV 4%)
Roasty dark fruit nose flows through into the first taste. Increasing malt and caramel. Smooth, grainy mouthfeel. Short, bitter finish
Bouchart (ABV 4.9%)
Savoury, smoky bacon character throughout. Bittersweet dark chocolate nuances give depth. A smooth and creamy finish with hints of blackcurrant.
White Face (ABV 5%)
Full-bodied with a rich tropical fruit aroma. Oranges the taste, mixing well with a piquant hoppy bitterness.

Moonface (NEW)

13 Moira Street, Loughborough, LE11 1AU
☎ (01509) 700171 ⊕ moonfacebrewery.co.uk

⊠ Moonface Brewery is now up and running in earnest. Two of the beers are on the bar in the tap at any time. The brewery is developing its portfolio. ✦

Moonshine

Hill Farm, Shelford Road, Fulbourn, Cambridgeshire, CB21 5EQ ☎ 07906 066794

Office: 28 Radegund Road, Cambridge, CB1 3RS
⊕ moonshinebrewery.co.uk

⊠ Established in 2004, the brewery produces up to 20 barrels a week. Locally-produced ingredients are used including water from the brewery's own well and barley grown on the farm where the brewery is based. CAMRA beer festivals are supplied throughout the country, with 30 local outlets supplied direct. ◆RAIB

Sundowner (ABV 3.6%)
Trumpington Tipple (ABV 3.6%)
Cambridge Pale Ale (ABV 3.8%)
Shelford Crier (ABV 3.8%)
Spiritual Matter (ABV 3.8%)
Harvest Moon Mild (ABV 3.9%)
Heavenly Matter (ABV 4.1%)
Cambridge Best Bitter (ABV 4.2%)
Nightwatch Porter (ABV 4.5%)
Raspberry Porter (ABV 4.5%)
Black Hole Stout (ABV 5%)
Hot Numbers Coffee Stout (ABV 5.5%)
Chocolate Orange Stout (ABV 6.7%)

Moor SIBA

Days Road, Bristol, BS2 0QS
☎ (0117) 941 4460 ⊕ moorbeer.co.uk

⊠ Starting out in Somerset in 1996, Moor is an established part of the Bristol beer scene. It also exports throughout the UK and around the world. The central Bristol brewery features a brewery tap and a shop, while there is also a Moor London Vaults in Bermondsey, which doubles as a taproom and facility for ageing beers. All beers are unfined and naturally hazy. Moor's canned beers were the first in the UK to be recognised as real ale by CAMRA. ‼️🍴◆RAIB V✦

All-Dayer (ABV 3.5%)
Revival (ABV 3.8%)
Cloudy, orange-coloured beer with some peachy aroma, flavours of slightly resinous hops and a gentle bitterness in the short finish.
Lager (ABV 4%)
Nor'Hop (ABV 4.1%) 🍷
Golden yellow, unfined beer with spicy hops on the nose. Citrus flavours of grapefruit and lemon, short bitter aftertaste.
So'Hop (ABV 4.1%)
Unfined, straw yellow beer with hop-forward nose, hints of tropical fruit within powerful hop flavours, and long bitter finish.
Union Hop (ABV 4.1%)
Raw (ABV 4.3%)
Amber best bitter with a pineapple aroma. Hoppy bitterness on the tongue balanced with malty sweetness leads to a subtle bitter finish.
Amoor (ABV 4.5%)
Roasted malt and coffee aroma, taste adds chocolate and vanilla impressions before a smooth and almost spicy finish.
Claudia (ABV 4.5%)
Dark Alliance (ABV 4.5%)
Illusion (ABV 4.5%)
Black IPA with roast aroma, flavours of rich dark malt overlaid with hoppy bitterness which lingers in the dry aftertaste.
Confidence (ABV 4.6%)
A red ale with a rye beer-like spicy, peppery flavour. A rustic, unpasteurised quality to its taste, with a

sweetness given by hints of stone fruit. Pleasant, short bitter finish.
Ported Amoor (ABV 4.7%)
Radiance (ABV 5%)
Golden ale with floral aromas of citrus fruit and blossom. Grapefruit palate with an initial tanginess, becoming more sweet. The grapefruit is present in the pleasant lingering aftertaste.
Smokey Horyzon (ABV 5%)
A speciality beer made using smoked rye. Hoppy, pale brown, strong ale with plenty of body, balanced by sweetness of unfermented, rich, dry rye malt and very smoky.
Stout (ABV 5%)
A classic black stout. Smoky roast malts and dark fruit aroma with hint of vanilla. Prunes and liquorice notes follow into the taste. Pleasant dark chocolate after taste.
Do It Together (ABV 5.2%)
Pronounced, hoppy tropical fruit aroma. Flavours of sweet mango with a tart hop bitterness which lingers in the prolonged finish.
Pils (ABV 5.2%)
PMA (ABV 5.3%)
Aroma and flavours are both well-balanced with biscuity malt, hops and tropical fruit before a short, bittersweet ending.
Return of the Empire (ABV 5.7%)
B-Moor (ABV 6%)
Aromas of roasted malt and fruit, bitter chocolate and rich dark fruit on the palate with a dry bitter aftertaste.
Hoppiness (ABV 6.5%)
Hop-forward nose with hints of honey. Full-bodied, with tropical fruit flavours and bitterness which increases into the finish.
Old Freddy Walker (ABV 7.3%)
Roasted malt and dark fruit aromas, flavours balance roasted malt with liquorice treacle and blackberry before a slightly dry finish.

Moorhouse's SIBA

The Brewery, Moorhouse Street, Burnley, Lancashire, BB11 5EN
☎ (01282) 422864 🌐 moorhouses.co.uk

Established in 1865 as a soft drinks manufacturer, the brewery started producing cask-conditioned ale in 1978. A new brewhouse and visitor centre opened in 2012. Three pubs are owned. ‼♦

Black Cat (ABV 3.4%)
A dark beer with delicate chocolate and coffee roast flavours and a crisp, bitter finish.
Premier Bitter (ABV 3.7%)
A clean and satisfying bitter aftertaste rounds off this well-balanced hoppy, amber session bitter.
White Witch (ABV 4%)
Delicate citrus aroma. Sweet, fruity taste balanced with gentle bitterness. Increased bitterness in a crisp, citrus finish.
Pride of Pendle (ABV 4.1%)
Well-balanced, amber bitter with a fresh initial hoppiness and a mellow, malt-driven body.
Scaredy Cat (ABV 4.3%)
Blond Witch (ABV 4.5%)
Pronounced sweet taste with gentle pithy bitterness and touch of citrus fruit. Dry finish. Slight fruity hop aroma.
Pendle Witches Brew (ABV 5.1%)
Well-balanced, full-bodied, malty beer with a long, complex finish.

Moot Oak

c/o Red Lion Inn, Matlock Green, Matlock, Derbyshire, DE4 3BT
☎ (01629) 584888 🌐 redlionmatlock.co.uk

Established in 2018, Moot Oak brewery is named after the original name for Matlock, which dates back to the medieval period. Beers are available in the pub and other local outlets.

MòR SIBA

Old Mill, Kellas, DD5 3PD ☎ 07402 900755
🌐 morbeers.co.uk

Established in 2012 and now trading as MòR Beers. Dominic Hughes, an experienced brewer, moved to Scotland from London to take ownership of the brewery in 2018. Dominic is brewing the same core range although with slight changes to the recipes and branding. ‼♦RAIB

Tea Vicar? (ABV 3.8%)
Ish! (ABV 4.2%)
Please! (ABV 4.5%)

Mordue

See Blue

Morland

See Greene King

Morton

Unit 10, Essington Light Industrial Estate, Essington, Wolverhampton, Staffordshire, WV11 2BH ☎ 07988 69647

Office: 96 Brewood Road, Coven, WV9 5EF
🌐 mortonbrewery.co.uk

This family-run brewery was established in 2006 on a three-barrel, purpose-built plant. Beers are supplied locally, further afield by reciprocal arrangements, to various beer festivals and a selection is always available at the brewery's own micropub, Hail to the Ale. ‼♦

Essington Dark Mild (ABV 3.6%)
Essington Bitter (ABV 3.8%)
Merry Mount (ABV 3.8%)
Essington Blonde (ABV 4%)
Essington Ale (ABV 4.2%)
Jelly Roll (ABV 4.2%)
Essington Gold (ABV 4.4%)
Essington Supreme (ABV 4.6%)
Scottish Maiden (ABV 4.6%)
Essington IPA (ABV 4.8%)
Yellow with lots of hop and fruit aromas. A good mouthful of bitterness with hops and fruit jostling for taste. Great, lingering bitter finish.

Morton Collins

Star, Standbridge Lane, Sandal, Wakefield, West Yorkshire, WF2 7DY
☎ (01226) 728746 ☎ 07812 111960

Office: 49 Willow Garth, Durkar, Wakefield, WF4 3BX
✉ ged.morton@aol.com

Set up in 2016 by Ged Morton and Sam Collins using a 100-litre plant in Ged's garage. The brewery produces to demand but can brew every day if required. It took over the lease of the Star, Sandal, in 2016. Several of the beers are named after the nearby Nature Reserve at Wintersett. The brewery kit was upgraded to 200 litres per brew in 2017.

Magna (ABV 4%)

Star Bitter (ABV 4%)
Amber No. 9 (ABV 4.8%)
Stanley's Delight (ABV 4.8%)

Morwell

Morwellham Quay, Morwellham, Devon, PL19 8JL
☎ (01822) 832766 🌐 morwellham.org

Established in 2017 at Victorian tourist attraction, Morwellham Quay, near Tavistock, by brewer George Lister. Using a 100-litre plant, three bottle-conditioned beers are brewed, which are available in the on-site shop and café, the Ship Inn, and a growing number of local outlets. RAIB

Moseley

14 Cleveland Court, St Agnes Road, Moseley, B13 9PR
🌐 moseleybeercompany.co.uk

Moseley Beer Company began brewing in 2016, set up by a family of four brothers. Most production is bottled and available at local events and markets. V

Sightseer Wheat Beer (ABV 4.5%)
Pale Ale (ABV 5%)
Marianna Porter (ABV 8%)
Iron Man Stout (ABV 9%)

Mote & Bailey

Blue Bell Inn, 10 High Street, Annan, DG12 6AG

Brewing began in 2018 in the cellar of the Blue Bell Inn, Annan, using equipment from Andrews Ales. Brewing capacity is one barrel. The range varies and is only available at the pub. ♦

Moulin

2 Baledmund Road, Moulin, Pitlochry, PH16 5EL
☎ (01796) 472196

Office: Moulin Hotel, 11-13 Kirkmicheal Road, Moulin, Pitlochry, PH16 5EH 🌐 moulinhotel.co.uk

The brewery opened in 1995 to celebrate the Moulin Hotel's 300th anniversary. Two pubs are owned and four outlets are supplied. !! RAIB

Mount St Bernard SIBA

Mount St Bernard Abbey, Oaks Road, Charley, Whitwick, Leicestershire, LE67 5UL
☎ (01530) 832298

Monks at this Cistercian abbey launched a beer in 2017, the first monastic beer brewed in England since the Reformation. The beer, Tynt Meadow, is available commercially in selected outlets.

Mountain Hare

Mountain Hare Inn, Brynna Road, Brynnau Gwynion, CF35 6PG
☎ (01656) 860453 🌐 mountainhare.co.uk

Paul Jones, licensee of the Mountain Hare, finally realised his ambition of installing a brewery in his family-owned pub. A 1.5-barrel, custom-built brewing plant was installed in the pub and the beer first went on sale in 2013. Paul plans to increase to a six-barrel plant to keep up with demand. Finings are no longer used so the beers have a slight natural haze and are suitable for vegans. Beer is only available in the pub. V

Mourne Mountains SIBA

Milltown East Industrial Estate, Upper Dromore Road, Warrenpoint, BT34 3PN
☎ (028) 4175 2299
🌐 mournemountainsbrewery.com

Brewing since 2015 with an extensive and varying range of seasonals, specials and one-off brews produced throughout the year – some may appear in cask format. Isinglass finings are used in all cask products, except stouts, and so they are not suitable for vegans. Keg and bottled beers (not bottle-conditioned) are suitable for vegans. ♦V

Mourne Gold (ABV 4%)

Mouselow Farm

3 Mouselow Farm,, Dinting, Glossop, Derbyshire, SK13 7QQ ☎ 07920 048252
✉ glossopowl@btinternet.com

Mouselow Farm began brewing in 2013 using a 2.5-barrel plant housed in a converted barn. Brewing is on a part-time basis. Local free houses, clubs and beer festivals are supplied. ♦

Mouse-low Mild (ABV 3.4%)
Act the Goat (ABV 3.7%)
Orpingtons Buff (ABV 3.9%)

Mr Bees

Unit D, Searsons Farm, Cordys Lane, Trimley, Suffolk, IP11 0UD ☎ 07503 773630 🌐 mrbeesbrewery.co.uk

Mr Bees is based on the beautiful Suffolk Coast. All beers contain honey direct from the brewery's own beehives. All malted barley used comes from Suffolk and only English hops are used. Around 30 local outlets are supplied.

Best Bee-R (ABV 4%)
Beelightful (ABV 4.3%)
Black Bee (ABV 4.5%)

Mr Grundy's SIBA

Georgian House Hotel, 34 Ashbourne Road, Derby, DE22 3AD
☎ (01332) 349806 ☎ 07812 812953
🌐 mrgrundysbrewery.co.uk

Named after a local WW1 veteran who once resided on the site, the brewery opened in 2010 with a made-to-measure 3.5-barrel plant fitted inside a former hotel bedroom. Fermenting capacity allows up to four brews a week. Beers are produced for the two hotels owned by the parent company, GHH Llp, and the free trade. Sales are handled by sister brewery Black Hole (qv). Brewing is currently suspended. ♦

Mr Majolica

Units 7a & 15, Thurrock Enterprise Centre, Maidstone Road, Grays, Essex, RM17 6NF ☎ 07834 539761
🌐 mrmajolica.co.uk

A family-run microbrewery situated in Grays town centre, Mr Majolica began brewing in 2014 on a 2.5-barrel plant. Brewing is currently suspended.

Mr Winter's

8 Keelan Close, Norwich, NR6 6QZ
☎ (01603) 787820 🌐 mrwintersbeers.co.uk

Winter's was established in 2001 by David Winter, who had previous award-winning success as a brewer for both Woodforde's and Chalk Hill breweries. Winter's ales have won many awards, with David now passing his brewing knowledge to his son, Mark, an award-winning brewer in his own right. The brewery rebranded as Mr Winter's in 2020. Some existing beers have been discontinued or renamed, and new brews commenced. ♦

Fusioneer (ABV 3.6%)
Caramel and roast are balanced by a sweet biscuit backdrop. Little loss of flavour as a bittersweet dryness appears.
Twin Parallel IPA (ABV 3.8%)
Evolution APA (ABV 4%)
Clementine on the nose is followed by lemon and grapefruit in the body. Hoppy bitterness develops in a full-bodied finish.
Quantum Gold (ABV 4.1%)
Just a hint of hops in the aroma. The initial taste combines a dry bitterness with a fruity apple buttress. The finish slowly subsides into a long, dry bitterness.
Rorschach (ABV 4.5%)
A dark brown stout that has a smooth mouthfeel with a grainy edge. Roast dominates throughout but is balanced by a mix of malt, a bittersweet fruitiness and an increasingly nutty finish.
Twisted Ladder Pale Ale (ABV 5%)
Citrus Kiss IPA (ABV 6%)

Muckle SIBA

3 Bellister Close, Park Village, Haltwhistle, Northumberland, NE49 0HA ☎ 07711 980086
🌐 mucklebrewing.co.uk

Established in 2016, Muckle Brewing is a tiny brewery in rural Northumberland, close to Hadrian's Wall. Beers are influenced by the local landscape.

Whin Sill Blonde (ABV 3.5%)
Tickle (ABV 4%)
Chuckle (ABV 4.2%)
Moss Stout (ABV 4.3%)
Buster (ABV 4.5%)
Kings Crag (ABV 5.4%)

Muirhouse

Unit 1 Enterprise Court, Manners Avenue, Manners Industrial Estate,, Ilkeston, Derbyshire, DE7 8EW
☎ 07916 590525 🌐 muirhousebrewery.co.uk

Muirhouse was established in 2009 in a domestic garage in Long Eaton. It expanded in 2011 to its present location in Ilkeston and the plant was upgraded in 2016 to 7.5 barrels. ‼♦

Shopping for Hops (ABV 3.9%)
Summit Hoppy (ABV 4%)
Blueberry Porter (ABV 4.1%)
Magnum Mild (ABV 4.5%)
Pirate's Gold (ABV 4.5%)
Hat Trick IPA (ABV 5.2%)

Mumbles SIBA

Unit 14, Worcester Court, Swansea Enterprise Park, Swansea, SA7 9FD
☎ (01792) 792612 ☎ 07757 109938
🌐 mumblesbrewery.co.uk

⊗ Mumbles Brewery was established in 2011 and began brewing in 2013. In 2015, the brewery moved to a new permanent location, with a 10-barrel plant. Director/brewer Rob Turner supplies numerous pubs in South Wales and the Bristol area. ♦V

Hop Kick (ABV 4%)
Mile (ABV 4%)
Malt Bitter (ABV 4.1%)
Murmelt (ABV 4.2%)
Gold (ABV 4.3%)
Beyond the Pale (ABV 4.4%)
Oystermouth Stout (ABV 4.4%)
Lifesaver Strong Bitter (ABV 4.9%)
India Pale Ale (ABV 5.3%)
Albina New World Pale (ABV 5.7%)
Chocolate Vanilla Porter (ABV 6.2%)

Munson's (NEW)

Chequers, The Green, Gazeley, Suffolk, CB8 8RF
☎ (01638) 551511 🌐 munsons.co.uk

Microbrewery at the Chequers in Gazeley, specialising in small-batch hoppy IPAs and Belgian-style beers.

Musket SIBA

Unit 7, Loddington Farm, Loddington Lane, Linton, Kent, ME17 4AG
☎ (01622) 749931 ☎ 07967 127278
🌐 musketbrewery.co.uk

Launched in 2013 with a five-barrel plant, this family-owned brewery is based at Loddington Farm, Linton, in the heart of the Kent countryside. Expanding to a 15-barrel plant with on-site brewery tap, Musket Brewery now supplies more than 300 pubs, micropubs and clubs throughout Kent and Medway. ♦

Trigger (ABV 3.6%)
Fife & Drum (ABV 3.8%)
Matchlock (ABV 3.8%)
Ball Puller (ABV 4%)
Flintlock (ABV 4.2%)
Muzzleloader (ABV 4.5%)

Muswell Hillbilly

24-26 Avenue Mews, Muswell Hill, London, N10 3NP
🌐 muswellhillbillybrewers.co.uk

Originally homebrewers, premises were acquired in Muswell Hill in 2017. Beers are brewed in small batches and named after the local area. Following the successful launch of the taproom in 2018 the brewery moved into a nearby unit in 2020, using the 500-litre brew kit formerly used by Hale, now Exale (qv). ‼

Tetherdown Wheat Saison (ABV 5.1%)
IPA (ABV 5.5%)

Mutineers

London Lane, Bromley, BR1 4HE 🌐 mutineers.beer

Established in 2018, Mutineers brews in small batches using a 100-litre brew kit. Beers can be found locally and at beer festivals.

Filibuster (ABV 3.4%)
Radio Fresh (ABV 3.9%)
You Don't Know Jack (ABV 3.9%)

Myrddins

Church Street, Barmouth, LL42 1EH
☎ (01341) 388060 ✉ myrddins@talktalk.net

Established in 2016 within a café bar in the centre of Barmouth, the brewery relocated a short distance away in 2018.

Nailmaker

Unit 9, Darton Business Park, Barnsley Road, Darton, South Yorkshire, S75 5NH
☎ (01226) 201734 ☎ 07973 824790
nailmakerbrewing.co

Nailmaker is located in an old carpet mill using an eight-barrel plant. Nailmaking was one of the largest occupations in the local area in the early 19th century. The core range is supplemented by a limited edition range (Shuffle) through the year. The brewery has two taphouses in the neighbouring village of Mapplewell, the Talbot Inn and Wentworth Arms. ♦

Auckland (ABV 4%)
Chinook (ABV 4%)
Cascade (ABV 4.2%)
Anvil Porter (ABV 4.4%)
Wentworth (ABV 4.8%)
Clout Stout (ABV 5%)
Chocolate Safari Stout (ABV 5.5%)

NauticAles

Sowell Street, St Peters, Broadstairs, Kent, CT10 2AT
☎ 07552 600919

Office: 347 Margate Road, Ramsgate, CT12 6SG
nauticales@outlook.com

Beers are only available at the brewery's micropub in Ramsgate and at local beer festivals.

Maiden Voyage (ABV 4.4%)

Navigation SIBA

Trent Navigation Inn, 17 Meadow Lane, Nottingham, NG2 3HS
☎ (0115) 986 9877 navigationbrewery.com

Located in Nottingham, just a stone's throw from the iconic Trent bridge, the brewery combines historic Victorian premises, cutting edge technology and a team of brewing experts. !!

Patriot (ABV 3.8%)
Tawny-coloured, malty bitter.
New Dawn Pale (ABV 3.9%)
Golden-coloured ale with initial fruit and hops, and a bitter finish.
Eclipse (ABV 4.1%)
Dark roast stout aroma and aftertaste with bitterness and some sweetness.
Rebel (ABV 4.2%)
Saviour (ABV 5.5%)
Golden in colour with assertive hop aroma and citrus fruit taste throughout, with a balanced bitterness.

Naylor's SIBA

Midland Mills, Station Road, Cross Hills, North Yorkshire, BD20 7DT
☎ (01535) 637451 naylorsbrewery.com

The Naylor brothers started brewing in 2005 at the Old White Bear pub in Cross Hills. The brewery relocated to Midland Mills in 2006 and moved to a larger unit on the same site in 2012. 100 outlets are supplied regularly and about 1,200 on an occasional basis. The on-site bar is open on Friday, Saturday, and Sunday afternoons to early evenings with increased capacity for customers created in 2019. Also operated is the Brewhouse in Yeadon.
!! ♦ ◆

Yorkshire Ale (ABV 3.8%)
Predominantly malty, traditional, mid-brown bitter with subtle fruit and hops in the nose and taste and a growing bitter finish.
Gold (ABV 4%)
Mosaic (ABV 4%)
Velvet (ABV 4%)
Chocolate and roast aromas and flavours predominate in this dark brown mild which has an increasingly roast bitter finish.
Pinnacle Blonde (ABV 4.3%)
Hoppy, fruity aroma followed by grassy hop and tropical fruit flavours. The finish remains hoppy with a bitter, fruity edge.
Black & Tan (ABV 4.4%)
Dark brown best bitter with a roast edge and a hop hit. Liquorice and a malty sweetness lead to a bitter finish
Old Ale (ABV 5.9%)

Neath

Endeavour Close, Port Talbot, SA12 7PT ☎ 07772 468436 neathales.co.uk

Established in 2009, the brewery produces a range of single hop beers. Special beers and one-off monthly brews are also available with some beers being released under the Black Falls brand name. ♦RAIB V

Welsh Amber Ale (ABV 4.5%)
Dewi Sant (ABV 4.8%)

Neatishead

White Horse Inn, The Street, Neatishead, Norfolk, NR12 8AD
☎ (01692) 630828
thewhitehorseinnneatishead.com

Brewing began in 2015 at the White Horse Inn. The brew kit can be viewed through glass from the restaurant. Beer is only available in the White Horse and the owner's other pub, the Lion at Thurne. A range of semi-regular beers is brewed with at least one ever-changing ale.

Neckstamper SIBA

Unit 3, Cromwell Industrial Estate, Staffa Road, Leyton, London, E10 7QZ
☎ (020) 7018 1760 ☎ 07968 150075
neckstamper.com

Neckstamper began brewing in 2016 using a 10-barrel plant. The taproom is now regularly open. ◆

Neepsend

Unit 13, 92 Burton Road, Sheffield, South Yorkshire, S3 8DA
☎ (0114) 2763406 neepsendbrewco.com

Established in 2015 by James Birkett and Gavin Martin, after taking over Little Ale Cart Brewery, and moving to new premises in Sheffield's Valley of Beer. A 10-barrel plant is used, supplying beers locally, including to the company's own pubs, Sheaf View, the Blake Hotel and the Wellington. Despite only having one core beer, the brewery produces an ever-changing range of hop-forward seasonal ales. There is an on-site taproom that opens occasionally. ♦◆

Blonde (ABV 4%)

Nelson SIBA

Unit 2, Building 64, The Historic Dockyard, Chatham, Kent, ME4 4TE

☎ (01634) 832828 🌐 nelsonbrewery.co.uk

Based in Chatham's Historic Dockyard. The brewery supplies award-winning ales direct to more than 330 outlets. Gemstone Ales are brewed on site for its own pub, the Fisherman's Arms, Maidstone, and available to the free trade. !! ♦ RAIB

Admiral IPA (ABV 4%)
Midshipman Dark Mild (ABV 4%)
Trafalgar Bitter (ABV 4.1%)
Powder Monkey (ABV 4.3%)
Friggin' in the Riggin' (ABV 4.5%)
Pursers Pussy Porter (ABV 4.8%)
Nelsons Blood (ABV 6%)

Nene Valley (NVB)

Oundle Wharf, Station Road, Oundle, Northamptonshire, PE8 4DE
☎ (01832) 272776 🌐 nenevalleybrewery.com

Established in 2011, a bespoke 15-barrel plant was installed in former Water Board premises in 2012. Further expansion in 2016 has doubled the floorspace. A brewery tap, Tap & Kitchen, opened on the same site in 2014. !! ♦ RAIB V

Simple Pleasures Ale (ABV 3.6%)
A light, clean and refreshing beer with a pleasing citrus hop aroma and flavour.
Blonde Session Ale (ABV 3.8%)
Dark Horse (ABV 3.8%)
Manhattan Project (ABV 4%)
Bitter (ABV 4.1%)
Floral hop and malt aroma introduces a full, clean biscuit malt taste balanced by bitterness and some fruit, ending with a long malt and bitter finish.
Starless Stout (ABV 4.2%)
Australian Pale (ABV 4.4%)
Release the Chimps (ABV 4.4%)
Egyptian Cream (ABV 4.5%)
Dick's Extraordinary Bitter (ABV 4.6%)
Hop Stash: Simcoe (ABV 5%)
Pulp Fiction (ABV 5.2%)
Big Bang Theory (ABV 5.3%)
Well-balanced pale ale with a huge hop aroma giving way to malty sweetness and a gentle bitter finish.
A Beer Named LEEROY (ABV 5.5%)
Jim Irving Pale (ABV 5.6%)
Supersonic (ABV 6%)
A pale wheat beer brewed with gin and tonic botanicals including lemons, juniper and cardamom.
Bible Black (ABV 6.5%)
An inviting aroma of malt and fruit leads to a rich tasting beer where blackberry dominates but is balanced by malt, hops and some bitterness. The lingering finish is bittersweet, with fruit assertive.
Fenland Farmhouse Saison (ABV 7.2%)
Mid-week Bender (ABV 7.4%)

Neolithic (NEW)

The Hill, Mill End, Bradwell on Sea, Essex, CM0 7HH

Nanobrewery established in 2019 using a one-barrel plant.

Neon Raptor

Unit 14 Avenue A, Sneinton Market, Nottingham, NG1 1DT ☎ 07821 586342
🌐 neonraptorbrewingco.com

Established in 2016 Neon Raptor is a small independent brewery that utilised spare capacity at neighbouring breweries. Production commenced in 2018 in a brand new 10-barrel plant in the Sneinton Market area of Nottingham, which also has a licensed taproom. All beers are unfiltered, unfined and unpasteurised.

Neptune SIBA

Unit 1, Sefton Lane Industrial Estate, Maghull, Merseyside, L31 8BX
☎ (0151) 222 3908 🌐 neptunebrewery.com

Neptune began brewing in 2015 using a six-barrel plant. Beers are unfined and unfiltered. In keeping with the brewery name the majority of beers are named on a water theme deriving from fish, the sea and mythological creatures. V

Ezili (ABV 4%)
Shifting Sands (ABV 4.3%)
Mosaic (ABV 4.5%)
Wooden Ships (ABV 4.7%)
Abyss (ABV 5%)
Rich, roasted, fruity aroma, sweet, fruity, oatmeal stout with dry roast finish.

Nessie

Westoaks, Fort William Road, Fort Augusus, PH32 4BH

Set up in 2017 Nessie Brew is a nanobrewery that markets a range of bottled beers to the tourist trade around Fort Augustus. ♦

Nethergate SIBA

The Brewery, Rodbridge Corner, Suffolk, CO10 9HJ
☎ (01787) 377087 🌐 nethergate.co.uk

Nethergate was formed in 1986 by Dick Burge and Ian Hornsey in Clare, Suffolk, and was one of the original UK microbreweries. Dick Burge remains the Chairman but it is now owned by a group of local beer lovers and moved to its new site at Rodbridge Corner in 2017. The new brewery and visitor centre is only a couple of miles from its original home and produces both traditional recipes and more modern beers. !! ♦ V

Melford Mild (ABV 3.7%)
Venture (ABV 3.7%)
Umbel Ale (ABV 3.8%)
Pleasant, easy-drinking bitter, infused with coriander, which dominates.
Suffolk County Best Bitter (ABV 4%)
Dark bitter with roast grain tones off-setting biscuity malt and powerful hoppy, bitter notes.
Stour Valley Gold (ABV 4.2%)
Old Growler (ABV 5%)
Well-balanced porter in which roast grain is complemented by fruit.
Umbel Magna (ABV 5%)
Old Growler flavoured with coriander. The spice is less dominant than in Umbel Ale, with some of the weight and body of the beer coming through.

New Bristol

20a Wilson Street, Bristol, BS2 9HH ☎ 07837 976871
🌐 newbristolbrewery.co.uk

Having started out in 2013 with his brother Tom, Noel James now brews on a fifteen-barrel plant with wife Maria and assistants. The premises house the Brewery Tap, and the Bristol Brewery School. Year-round beers are supplemented by regularly released brew series based on common but varying themes. All beers are unfined and unfiltered with some oak barrel-aged. !! ♦ RAIB V

Cinder Toffee Stout (ABV 4%)

THE BREWERIES

Caramelised honey and roasted malt aromas, sweet flavours of honeycomb and chocolate, some hop bitterness in the slightly dry finish.

Wonderland IPA (ABV 4.1%)
Tropical fruit aroma and juicy fruit hop burst of pinapple and mango flavours with some bitterness in the short finish.

Joy of Sesh (ABV 4.2%)
Powerfully-hopped, naturally hazy, unfined beer with citrus and tropical fruits on the palate and a long bitter finish.

Super Deluxe Stout (ABV 7%)
Banana and vanilla aromas. The taste and mouthfeel is like vanilla ice cream, but this sweetness contrasts with an assertive bitterness.

New Buildings SIBA

Unit 3, Southways Industrial Estate, Coventry Road, Hinckley, Leicestershire, LE10 0NJ ☎ 07795 954392

Office: 24 Leicester Road, Hinckley, LE10 1LS

Formerly known as Elliswood, the brewery was renamed New Buildings in 2020. Darren and Louise Lavender use a David Porter 5.5-barrel system, and can brew twice a week. Beers are available through Heritage swaps, particularly in Nottinghamshire and Derbyshire, and sometimes at local pubs.

Lighthouse IPA (ABV 4%)
Windmill Best Bitter (ABV 4.1%)
Farmhouse (ABV 4.2%)
Courthouse Porter (ABV 4.5%)
Crookhouse (ABV 4.5%)
Manorhouse (ABV 4.8%)

New Devon (NEW)

Froginwell Vineyard & Cider Barn, Woodbury Salterton, Exeter, EX5 1EP
☎ (01395) 239900 ☎ 07976 981334
newdevonbrewing.co.uk

A collective of brewers and cider makers who have been inspired by the craft beer movement. Initially producing one beer, New Devon Ale, but others will make an appearance during the year. ♦

New Devon Ale (ABV 4.5%)

New Flying Monk

Unit 1, Bradfield Farm, Hullavington, Wiltshire, SN14 6EU
☎ (01666) 838415
thenewflyingmonkbrewery.co.uk

Following a change of ownership and a short closure, the New Flying Monk Brewery commenced brewing in 2020. Now owned by the farm business at which it is located, allowing reduced waste by using brewery by-product as cattle feed. The brewery is named after Elmer, an 11th-century monk at nearby Malmesbury Abbey, who attempted flight from the top of the tower using self-made wings. ♦

Elmers (ABV 3.8%)
A refreshing session beer with floral and citrus aromas, followed by an encouraging bitter finish

Mighty Monk (ABV 4.3%)

New Lion SIBA

Units 2-3, Shinners Bridge, Webbers Way, Dartington, Devon, TQ9 6JY
☎ (01803) 226277 newlionbrewery.co.uk

Community-owned brewery, established in 2013 and named after the Lion Brewery (renowned for Totnes Stout but closed in the 1920s). It is a modern, five-barrel brewhouse, producing a range of core ales, seasonals and dozens of one-off white label beers annually, many in collaboration with local producers and businesses. It runs a popular membership scheme and taproom/bottle shop which also acts as a live venue. !! ♦ RAIB V

Mane Event (ABV 3.8%)

Totnes Stout (ABV 4.4%)
Full-bodied stout with roasted malts and some smoky chocolate and liquorice. Dry bitterness finishes.

Pandit IPA (ABV 4.9%)
In the style of an American IPA. Slightly sweet with a fruity hop taste.

Scorpion (ABV 4.9%)

New River SIBA

Unit 47, Hoddesdon Industrial Centre, Pindar Road, Hoddesdon, Hertfordshire, EN11 0FF
☎ (01992) 446200 newriverbrewery.co.uk

New River commenced brewing in 2015 on a brand new 10-barrel plant. ♦

London Tap (ABV 3.8%)
Twin Spring (ABV 4%)
Riverbed Red (ABV 4.2%)
Blind Poet (ABV 4.5%)
Five Inch Drop (ABV 4.6%)
Isle Of Rye Pale Ale (ABV 5.2%)

New Wharf SIBA

Hyde Farm, Marlow Road, Maidenhead, Berkshire, SL6 6PQ
☎ (01628) 634535 newwharfbrewing.co.uk

A 20-barrel brewery, which was set up in 2017.

Voyage (ABV 5.5%)

Newark

77 William Street, Newark, Nottinghamshire, NG24 1QU ☎ 07804 609917 newarkbrewery.co.uk

Established in 2012 on the site of a former maltings using an eight-barrel plant. The bulk of production is supplied to local pubs.

Best (ABV 3.8%)
NPA (Newark Pale Ale) (ABV 3.8%)
BLH4 (ABV 4%)
Norwegian Blue (ABV 4%)
Pure Gold (ABV 4.5%)
Summer Gold (ABV 4.5%)
Winter Gold (ABV 4.5%)
Phoenix (ABV 4.8%)
5.5 (ABV 5.5%)

Newbarns (NEW)

13 Jane Street, Leith, Edinburgh, EH6 5HE
newbarnsbrewery.com

Newbarns Brewery was established in 2020 after the four founders moved north from London, having worked at Kernel and Siren breweries in the past seven years. The four core beers were contract brewed while installation took place.

Newbridge

Unit 3 Tudor House, Moseley Road, Bilston, West Midlands, WV14 6JD ☎ 07970 456052
🌐 newbridgebrewery.co.uk

First established in 2014, the five-barrel plant incorporates six original Grundy cellar tanks. Occasional specials are brewed to complement the regular beers.

Little Fox (ABV 4.2%)
Solaris (ABV 4.5%)
Indian Empire (ABV 5.1%)

Newby Wyke SIBA

Unit 24, Limesquare Business Park, Alma Park Road, Grantham, Lincolnshire, NG31 9SN
☎ (01476) 565682 🌐 newbywyke.co.uk

The brewery is named after a Hull trawler skippered by brewer Rob March's grandfather. It started life in 1998 as a 2.5-barrel plant in a converted garage then moved to premises behind the Willoughby Arms, Little Bytham. In 2009 it moved back to Grantham. !! ♦

Banquo (ABV 3.8%)
Summer Session Bitter (ABV 3.8%)
Orsino (ABV 4%)
Comet (ABV 4.1%)
Kingston Topaz (ABV 4.2%)
Black Beerd (ABV 4.3%)
Bear Island (ABV 4.6%)
White Squall (ABV 4.8%)
Blonde-hued with a hoppy aroma. Generous amounts of hop are well-supported by a solid malty undercurrent. An increasingly bittersweet tang makes itself known towards the finish.
White Sea (ABV 5.2%)
Chesapeake (ABV 5.5%)

Newcastle

Arch 2, Stepney Bank, Ouseburn, Newcastle upon Tyne, NE1 2NP ☎ 07446 011941
🌐 newcastlebrewingltd.co.uk

Mike and Leo Bell initially founded the brewery in the Quayside Development Centre in Ouseburn before moving to new premises under Byker Bridge. !! RAIB

Newtown

25 Victoria Street, Gosport, Hampshire, PO12 4TX
☎ (023) 9250 4294 🌐 newtownbrewery.co.uk

Brewing commenced in 2016 in this nanobrewery with just a half-barrel plant. Award-winning full mash beers are produced on demand for local pubs and beer festivals. V

Nightjar

2 Richmond House, Caldene Business Park, Mytholmroyd, West Yorkshire, HX7 5QL ☎ 07412 008221 🌐 nightjarbrew.co.uk

Nightjar Brew Co was initially established in 2011, and rebranded in 2018. The 10-barrel brewery is located in an industrial building in Mytholmroyd and supplies around 90 free trade outlets, mainly in Yorkshire and Lancashire. Its extensive beer swaps with other breweries means that its beers can also be found in more distant parts of the country. ♦V

School Night (ABV 3.7%)
Done 'n' Dusted (ABV 3.8%)
Chosen (ABV 3.9%)
Come As You Are (ABV 4%)
Release the Pressure (ABV 4%)
Cut the Mid, Drop the Bass (ABV 4.2%)
I'm Not a Robot (ABV 4.2%)
Lost in Ikea (ABV 4.2%)
Kazoo Hero (ABV 4.3%)
Pith Taker (ABV 4.3%)
Cosmonaut (ABV 4.4%)
Dark, creamy stout with roasted malt dominating the aroma and taste. A liquorice flavour develops in the dry and bitter aftertaste.
Truth or Consequences (ABV 4.4%)
Death By Stereo (ABV 4.5%)
Zed's Dead (ABV 4.5%)
Asking for a Friend (ABV 4.6%)
Batfink (ABV 4.6%)
Big Fish Little Fish (ABV 4.7%)
Moloko Mocha Porter (ABV 4.8%)
Bollywood IPA (ABV 5%)
Not All Heroes Wear Capes (ABV 5.5%)
Supernova (ABV 6.9%)

Nine Standards

See Settle

Nirvana SIBA

Unit T6, Leyton Industrial Village, Argall Avenue, Leyton, London, E10 7QP
☎ (020) 3417 5580 🌐 nirvanabrewer.com

Established in 2017 producing a range of low alcohol beers benefitting from the current trend in NALABs. No real ale.

No Frills Joe

50 Wakefield Road, Greenhithe, Kent, DA9 9JE
☎ 07516 725577

Established in 2015, No Frills Joe is a five-barrel microbrewery. The beer is always unpasteurised, unfiltered, and unfined and therefore may be cloudy. The range is available in a small on-site taproom. RAIB V♦

LaLa Lager (ABV 4.4%)
American Red (ABV 4.5%)
Dreamland IPA (ABV 4.5%)
Wheat (ABV 4.6%)
Joe Solo Pale Ale (ABV 4.9%)

No.18 Yard Brewouse

See Shepherd Neame

Nomadic SIBA

Unit 11, Sheepscar House, 15 Sheepscar Street, Sheepscar, Leeds, West Yorkshire, LS7 1AD ☎ 07868 345228 🌐 nomadicbeers.co.uk

Established in 2017, beers were originally produced using spare capacity at other breweries. Following an expansion in 2018, Nomadic Beers found a new home in Sheepscar installing an eight-barrel kit. All beers produced are vegan-friendly and are distributed across the Yorkshire region. V♦

Pale (ABV 3.8%)
Strider (ABV 4.4%)
Bandit (ABV 4.8%)

Nook SIBA

Riverside, 7b Victoria Square, Holmfirth, West Yorkshire, HD9 2DN
☎ (01484) 682373 northnookbrewhouse.co.uk

The Nook Brewhouse is built on the foundations of a previous brewhouse dating back to 1754, next to the River Ribble. Three brewery taps are supplied, two being restaurants with dishes matched to the beer, plus an on-site pub that rotates the 22 different ales. !! ♦ RAIB

Norfolk Broads

See Humpty Dumpty

Norn Iron

Unit 30, The Cutts, Dunmurry, Belfast, BT17 9HN
✉ nornironbrewcoltd@outlook.com

Brewing began in 2018.

North SIBA

Unit 6, Taverner's Walk Estate, Sheepscar Grove, Leeds, West Yorkshire, LS7 1AH
☎ (0113) 345 3290

Office: Regents Court, 39a Harrogate Road, Leeds, LS7 3PD northbrewing.com

A 15-barrel brewery was established in 2015, originally supplying the North Bar group of bars, in and around Leeds. It has since grown and supplies other outlets. Collaborations with national and international breweries are common. An on-site tap is open on Friday evening and all day Saturday. !! ♦

Session Pale (Action Against Hunger) (ABV 3.8%)

North Cotswold SIBA

Unit 3, Ditchford Farm, Stretton-on-Fosse, Warwickshire, GL56 9RD
☎ (01608) 663947 northcotswoldbrewery.co.uk

North Cotswold started in 1999 as a 2.5-barrel plant, which has since been upgraded to 10-barrel capacity. Beers are also produced under the Shakespeare brand name, available in cask and bottles. ♦ RAIB

Windrush Ale (ABV 3.6%)
Fosseway Flanker (ABV 3.8%)
Jumping Jack Flash (ABV 3.8%)
Moreton Mild (ABV 3.8%)
Cotswold Best (ABV 4%)
Green Man IPA (ABV 4%)
Shagweaver (ABV 4.5%)
Hung, Drawn 'n' Portered (ABV 5%)

North Riding (Brewery)

Unit 6, Barker's Lane, Snainton, North Yorkshire, YO13 9BD
☎ (01723) 864845 northridingbrewery.com

Having outgrown the brewpub in Scarborough, Stuart Neilson established a 10-barrel brewery in East Ayton on the outskirts of Scarborough in 2015. In early 2019 operations moved to a much larger premises in Snainton, enabling further expansion of brewing capacity. Concentrating on hop-forward beers, distribution is throughout the North of England and the Midlands. ♦ RAIB

US Session (ABV 3.8%)
Cascade Pale Ale (ABV 4%)
Mosaic Pale Ale (ABV 4.3%)
Citra Pale Ale (ABV 4.5%)

North Riding (Brewpub)

North Marine Road, Scarborough, North Yorkshire, YO12 7HU
☎ (01723) 370004 northridingbrewpub.com

Brewing commenced in 2011 using a two-barrel plant situated in the cellar of the pub, which is now brewing to capacity with three fermenting vessels. ♦

North Yorkshire SIBA

Unit 7 South Gare Court, Tod Point Road, Warrenby, North Yorkshire, TS10 5BN
☎ (01642) 497298 ✉ sales@nybrewery.co.uk

Founded in Middlesbrough in 1989 the brewery moved to Pinchinthorpe Hall, Guisborough in 1998. In 2017, following the purchase of the brewery, the new owner moved the entire operation to new premises on an industrial estate in Warrenby near Redcar, North Yorkshire. ♦ RAIB

Northern Navigator (ABV 3.6%)
Old Jacks Tipple (ABV 3.8%)
Temptation (ABV 3.8%)
Yorkshire Coble (ABV 3.8%)
Beckwatter (ABV 4%)
Yorkshire Porter (ABV 4.4%)
NYPA (ABV 4.6%)
Flying Herbert (ABV 4.7%)
White Lady (ABV 4.7%)

Northbound

Campsie Industrial Estate, McLean Road, Eglinton, BT47 3XX ☎ 07512 198686
northboundbrewery.com

Established in 2015, Northbound produce a range of bottle-conditioned beers named after their measurement of bitterness (IBUs). ♦ RAIB V

Northdown SIBA

Unit J1C/A, Channel Road, Westwood Industrial Estate, Margate, Kent, CT9 4JS ☎ 07791 441219
northdownbrewery.co.uk

Northdown began brewing in 2018 using a seven-barrel plant. It is run by Jonny and Katie Spanjar and takes its name from their original intention to run out of the Northdown area of Margate. The origins of a Northdown brewery date back to the 1600s. !! ♦ RAIB

Merry Margate (ABV 3.8%)
Pale Ale Mary (ABV 4%)
Reginald Perrin (ABV 4%)
Papworth Victory Best Bitter (ABV 4.2%)
HE-BRU IPA (ABV 4.8%)
Muggy Porter (ABV 5%)

Northern Alchemy

The Old Coal Yard, Elizabeth Street, Byker, Newcastle upon Tyne, NE6 1JS ☎ 07834 386333
wearenorthernalchemy.com

Brewing began in 2014. The brewery was situated in a converted shipping container, known as the Lab, just behind the Cumberland Arms. In 2017 it moved to larger premises in a former coal depot. All beers are unfined and unfiltered. Beers are always available in the Cumberland Arms, and the brewery opens a tap on the last full weekend of the month. V

US Session Pale (ABV 4.1%)

Northern Monk SIBA

Address 1: The Old Flax Store, Marshalls Mill, Holbeck, Leeds, West Yorkshire, LS11 9YJ
☎ (0113) 243 6430

Address 2: Unit 7, Sydenham Road, Holbeck, Leeds, West Yorkshire, LS11 9RU
northernmonkbrewco.com

Northern Monk started using spare capacity at other breweries in 2013. In 2014, it set up a 10-barrel plant at a Grade II-listed mill building and in 2017 expanded into a second, larger site, capable of producing 24,000 hectolitres per week, and installing a canning line. In 2019 it further expanded into the adjacent former Leeds Brewery site. Currently 18 beers are brewed weekly. A taproom is open Tuesday-Sunday at the old Flax Mill. Most production is keg with a small amount of cask beer available. !! GF ◆

Eternal (ABV 4.1%)

Northern Monkey SIBA

Pack Horse, Nelson Square, Bolton, BL1 1JT ☎ 07737 125629 northernmonkeybrew.co.uk

Established in 2016 and based in Bolton town centre, Northern Monkey Brew Co is a six-barrel brewery with an on-site tap bar. It brews a variety of ales, maintaining a traditional edge but with a modern twist. The ales rotate regularly so no core range is available. ♦◆

Northern Whisper

Hill End Mill, Hill End Lane, Cloughfold, Lancashire, BB4 7RN
☎ (01706) 230082
northernwhisperbrewingco.co.uk

Brewing began in 2017.

Blighty (ABV 3.8%)
Oppenchops (ABV 4%)
Yammerhouse (ABV 4.5%)
Beltie (ABV 4.8%)

Norton

Norton Priory, Tudor Road, Manor Park, Runcorn, Cheshire, WA7 1SX
☎ (01928) 716971 ☎ 07767 354674
nortonbrewing.com

Situated within the grounds of Norton Priory, the brewery was created as a social enterprise by Halton Borough Council to provide employment opportunities for people with learning disabilities, autism and other disabilities. It opened in 2011 with a 2.5-barrel plant. Beers in bottles, mini-kegs and casks are for collection from the brewery only.

Noss Beer Works SIBA

Unit 6, Ash Court, Pennant Way, Lee Mill, Devon, PL21 9GE ☎ 07977 479634 nossbeerworks.co.uk

Noss Beer Works, based in Lee Mill, was formed in 2012 using a six-barrel plant. The beers are made from only the finest locally-sourced hops and malts. !! RAIB

Black Rock (ABV 4%)
Church Ledge (ABV 4%)
Bitter dominated by hops and fruit throughout. Hoppy and citrusy, slight caramel balances bitter dryness. Slight kick at the end
Mew Stone (ABV 4.3%)
Ebb Rock (ABV 4.9%)

Nottingham SIBA

Plough Inn, 17 St Peter's Street, Radford, Nottingham, NG7 3EN
☎ (0115) 942 2649 ☎ 07815 073447
nottinghambrewery.co.uk

The former owners of the Bramcote and Castle Rock Breweries re-established the Nottingham Brewery in 2000 in a purpose-built brewhouse behind the Plough Inn. Philip Darby and Niven Balfour set out to revive the brands of the original Nottingham Brewery, closed by Whitbread in the 1950s. Within the LocAle ethos, beers are supplied widely to the local trade including the brewery tap house, the Plough Inn, and its other tied house the Frame Breakers, Ruddington. !!

Rock Ale Bitter Beer (ABV 3.8%)
A pale and bitter, thirst-quenching hoppy beer with a dry finish.
Rock Ale Mild Beer (ABV 3.8%)
A reddish-black malty mild with some refreshing bitterness in the finish.
Trent Bridge Inn Ale (ABV 3.8%)
Legend (ABV 4%)
A fruity and malty pale brown bitter with a touch of sweetness and bitterness.
Extra Pale Ale (ABV 4.2%)
A hoppy and fruity golden ale with a hint of sweetness and a long-lasting bitter finish.
Cock & Hoop (ABV 4.3%)
Dreadnought (ABV 4.5%)
Well-balanced best bitter. Blend of malt and hops give a rounded fruity finish.
Bullion (ABV 4.7%)
A refreshing premium golden ale. Brewed with a single malt variety, it is triple-hopped and exceptionally bitter.
Supreme (ABV 5.2%)
A strong, amber, fruity ale. A touch of malt in the taste is followed by a sweet and slightly hoppy finish.

O'Connor

12 Lime Road, Faughanvale, Greysteel, BT47 3EH
☎ 07748 004065 oconnorbrewing.com

Brewing began in 2013. No real ale.

Oakham SIBA

2 Maxwell Road, Woodston, Peterborough, Cambridgeshire, PE2 7JB
☎ (01733) 370500 oakhamales.com

The brewery started in 1993 in Oakham, Rutland, and moved to Peterborough in 1998. The brewery's main production site is a 75-barrel plant. An additional six-barrel plant is located at its city-centre brewpub, which makes special and one-off brews. Around 350 outlets are supplied and four pubs are owned. !! ♦ RAIB

JHB (ABV 3.8%)
Straw-coloured golden ale dominated by citrus hop character throughout. Long, dry finish.
Inferno (ABV 4%)
The citrus hop character of this straw-coloured brew begins on the nose and builds in intensity on the palate. Clean, dry, citrus finish.
Citra (ABV 4.2%)
Refreshing grapefruit and peach aroma and flavour characterise this golden ale. Bittersweet palate gives way to a long, dry aftertaste.
Scarlet Macaw (ABV 4.4%)
Bishops Farewell (ABV 4.6%)
Powerfully citrus, the hops and fruit on the aroma of this golden/yellow beer become bittersweet on the palate. Zesty citrus aftertaste.

THE BREWERIES

Green Devil (ABV 6%)

Oaks SIBA

Unit 6, Stanney Mill Industrial Estate, Dutton Green, Ellesmere Port, Cheshire, CH2 4SA ☎ 07526 437098
🌐 oaksbrewing.co.uk

Founded as Cheshire Brew Brothers in 2013 and taken into new ownership in 2017. The beers can be found in free and tied trade across north-west England and West Yorkshire. A wide and changing range of additional beers is produced to satisfy customer demand.

Chester Gold (ABV 3.5%)
A fruity, hoppy bitter with a pleasant, sweet finish.
ESB 2020 (ABV 3.8%)
Cheshire Porter (ABV 4%)
Delamere Blonde (ABV 4%)
Stout No. 1 (ABV 4.5%)
NZ Pale (ABV 4.6%)

Oakwood

c/o Northfield Crescent, Wells-next-the-Sea, Norfolk, NR23 1LP ☎ 07512 111211 🌐 oakwoodbrewery.com

Oakwood was established in 2015. After producing beers on a small scale from home, the brewer decided to turn his hobby into a full-time job. Barley is locally-grown by Teddy Maufe at Branthill Farm on the Holkham Estate in Norfolk. Beer is contract brewed elsewhere. RAIB

Oban Bay

See Argyll

Odcombe

Masons Arms,, 41 Lower Odcombe, Odcombe, Somerset, BA22 8TX
☎ (01935) 862591 🌐 masonsarmsodcombe.co.uk

Odcombe opened in 2000, but closed a few years later. It re-opened in 2005 with assistance from Shepherd Neame (qv). Brewing takes place once a week and beers are available only in the Masons Arms. ‼♦RAIB

Oddly

Friern Barnet, London, N11 ☎ 07970 444333
🌐 oddly.beer

Originally founded on an island in the Thames at Hampton, it moved to be one of the three breweries in the Tottenham Brewery location during 2019. The brewery is currently using spare capacity at other breweries while looking for a new site. ‼♦V

Rhia (ABV 4%)
Empathy (ABV 5%)
Fezzik (ABV 7%)

Odin (NEW) SIBA

Glen Mona Loop Road, Maughold, Isle of Man, IM7 1HJ ☎ 07624 266664

Established in 2019 using the 2.5-barrel brewery from Betteridge's of Hampshire. Founder and brewer Rob Storey brews four core beers in cask. RAIB

Manx Mild (ABV 3.4%)
Laksaa Pale (ABV 3.8%)
Asgard Bitter (ABV 4.2%)
Black Claw (ABV 4.5%)

Odyssey

Brockhampton Brewery, Oast House Barn, Bromyard, Herefordshire, WR6 5SH
☎ (01885) 483496 ☎ 07918 553152
🌐 odysseybrewco.com

This six-barrel brewery was bought in 2014 from Brew ON CIC by Alison and Mitchell Evans, who previously owned the Beer in Hand, Hereford. The original building, a restored barn on a National Trust estate, has been retained. A wide range of beers is brewed, predominantly served in keg and can and occasionally bottled for special release.

Off Tempo

See BAD

Offa's Dyke

Chapel Lane, Trefonen, Shropshire, SY10 9DX
☎ (01691) 656889 🌐 offasdykebrewery.com

Established in 2007, the brewery and adjoining pub straddle the old England/Wales border, Offa's Dyke. The Olde Vaults in Oswestry serves as an alternative brewery tap. ‼

Ogwen

5 Rhes Ogwen, Stryd Fawr, Bethesda, LL57 3AY
☎ (01248) 605715 ☎ 07545 684752
🌐 cwrwogwen.cymru

The first brewery in the Ogwen valley for over a century. A local community venture, established in 2016 by a group of shareholders who perform all brewing operations. ‼ RAIB

Cwrw Caradog (ABV 3.9%)
Ryc (ABV 4%)
Tryfan (ABV 4.2%)
Chwalfa (ABV 4.5%)

Okell's SIBA

Kewaigue, Douglas, Isle of Man, IM2 1QG
☎ (01624) 699400 🌐 okells.co.uk

Founded in 1874 by Dr Okell, this is the main brewery on the island and moved in 1994 to a new, purpose-built plant at Kewaigue. All the beers are produced under the Manx Brewers' Act. ‼♦

Okells MPA – Manx Pale Ale (ABV 3.6%)
A golden fruity, session bitter with background sweetness and a rising hoppy finish.
Bitter (ABV 3.7%)
Traditional bitter, malty and fruity aromas at the start, hops and caramel in the middle with the bitterness falling slightly at the end leaving the malts to enhance the finish.
Dr Okell's IPA (ABV 4.5%)
A clean, fruity, sweetish bitter with an alcoholic bite.

Old Cannon

86 Cannon Street, Bury St Edmunds, Suffolk, IP33 1JR
☎ (01284) 768769 🌐 oldcannonbrewery.co.uk

The St Edmunds Head pub opened in 1845 with its own brewery. Brewing ceased in 1917, and Greene King closed the pub in 1995. It re-opened in 1999 as the Old Cannon Brewery complete with a unique state-of-the-art brewery housed in the bar area. A number of pubs also owned by the brewery's owners are supplied. ‼♦

Old Chimneys

Old Chimneys, The Street, Market Weston, Suffolk, IP22 2NX
☎ (01359) 221013 ⊕ oldchimneysbrewery.com

Old Chimneys was established in 1995, moving to a converted farm building in 2001. In 2019 Alan Thompson ceased brewing at Market Weston to concentrate on collaborative brewing projects with other breweries. ‼◆RAIB

Old Dairy SIBA

Tenterden Station Estate, Station Road, Tenterden, Kent, TN30 6HE
☎ (01580) 763867 ⊕ olddairybrewery.com

⊗ Old Dairy was founded in 2009. It relocated from Rolvenden in 2014 to larger premises near the Kent & East Sussex Railway in Tenterden in order to increase capacity. ‼🍺◆RAIB

Red Top (ABV 3.8%)
A sweetish, copper-coloured bitter with hints of caramel and a subtle hop character.
Uber Brew (ABV 3.8%)
Copper Top (ABV 4.1%)
Blue Top (ABV 4.8%)
Rich and full-bodied, this pale brown ale has a long bittersweet finish and a hint of aroma hop.

Old Fountain (NEW)

🍴 Old Fountain, 3 Baldwin Street, Old Street, London, EC1V 9NU
☎ (020) 7253 2970 ⊕ oldfountain.co.uk

Brewing on-site since summer 2016 has been sporadic so call ahead to check availability. Its keg Pilsner is brewed by Bavo Brewery in Belgium.

Old Friends

🍴 Old Friends Inn, 49 Soutergate, Ulverston, Cumbria, LA12 7ES
☎ (01229) 208195 ☎ 07563 521575
⊕ oldfriendsulverston.co.uk

☺Brewing began in 2019 in a room to the rear of the Old Friends pub in Ulverston. Beers are currently only available at the pub.

Old Inn

🍴 Old Inn & Brewpub, Flowerdale Glen, Gairloch, IV21 2BD
☎ (01445) 712006 ⊕ theoldinn.net

Brewing began in 2010 using a 150-litre plant. ◆

Old Kent Road (NEW)

Gordon Road, Peckham, London, SE15 3RB
⊕ oldkentrdbrewery.co.uk

An early user of the UBrew facility from 2016 and taking advantage of the larger commerical kit later on but ultimately a casualty of the closure in 2019. Brewing now continues on a smaller home kit in Peckham.

Old Laxey

🍴 Shore Hotel Brew Pub, Old Laxey Hill, Old Laxey, Isle of Man, IM4 7DA
☎ (01624) 863214 ⊕ shorehotel.im

Beer brewed on the Isle of Man is brewed to a strict Beer Purity Act. Additives are not permitted to extend shelf life, nor are chemicals allowed to assist with head retention. Old Laxey's beer is sold mostly through the adjacent Shore Hotel. ‼

Old Luxters

Old Luxters Vineyard, Dudley Lane, Hambleden, Buckinghamshire, RG9 6JW
☎ (01491) 638330 ⊕ chilternvalley.co.uk

Situated in a 17th-century barn beside the Chiltern Valley Vineyard, Old Luxters is a traditional brewery established in 1990 and awarded a Royal Warrant of Appointment in 2007. The core range is bottle-conditioned beers. ‼🍺◆RAIB

Old Mill SIBA

Mill Street, Snaith, East Yorkshire, DN14 9HU
☎ (01405) 861813 ⊕ oldmillbrewery.co.uk

☺Opened in 1983 in a 200-year-old former malt kiln and corn mill, the brew-length is 60 barrels. The brewery is building a tied estate, now standing at 16 houses. Beers can be found nationwide through wholesalers and around 80 free trade outlets are supplied direct. The RT Brew Co range is produced for HB Clark (qv). ‼◆

Bullion IPA (ABV 3.7%)
Jack's Batch 34 (ABV 3.8%)
Traditional Bitter (ABV 3.8%)
A malty nose is carried through to the initial flavour. Bitterness runs throughout.
Blonde Bombshell (ABV 4%)
La Bolsa Coffee Porter (ABV 4.5%)

Old Moll Spring (NEW)

Old Moll Road, Honley, Huddersfield, HD4 7DN
☎ 07538 211230 ⊕ oldmoll.com

☺Brewery set up in an old silk mill in 2019 by three friends using the 25-barrel brewplant from the former Here Be Monsters Brewery. The beers are brewed using natural spring water from the nearby Old Moll Spring. Cask and bottled beers are produced.

Silk Blonde (ABV 3.9%)
Silk Pils (ABV 4.3%)
Silk IPA (ABV 4.9%)

Old Pie Factory

4 Montague Road, Warwick, CV34 5LW ☎ 07816 413026 ✉ josh@oldpiefactorybrewery.co.uk

☺Brewing began in 2011 using a 5.5-barrel plant and is a joint venture between Underwood Wines, Stratford upon Avon, and the Case is Altered, Five Ways.

Case Bitter (ABV 3.9%)
Pie In The Sky (ABV 4.1%)
Humble Pie (ABV 4.2%)
I.Pie.A. (ABV 4.5%)
American Pie (ABV 5.5%)

Old Sawley SIBA

🍴 The White Lion, 352a Tamworth Road, Sawley, Long Eaton, Derbyshire, NG10 3AT ☎ 07722 311209
⊕ oldsawley.com

⊗ A 10-barrel microbrewery installed at the rear of the White Lion in Sawley. The White Lion stocks a full range of brews and the brewery is supplying Midland beer festivals, local pubs and pubs across the East Midlands. ‼◆

THE BREWERIES

Old School SIBA

Holly Bank Barn, Crag Road, Warton, Lancashire, LA5 9PL
☎ (01524) 740888 ☎ 07515 376700
oldschoolbrewery.co.uk

A 12-barrel brewery, founded in 2012, located in a renovated 400-year-old former school outbuilding overlooking the picturesque village of Warton. Beer is mainly sold to free houses within a 40-mile radius. ‼♦

Hopscotch (ABV 3.7%)
Initially hoppy, astringency builds in this satisfying beer, ending with a bitter finish.
Textbook (ABV 3.9%)
Pale beer with malt and hops in the taste, creamy texture and a dry bitter finish.
Detention (ABV 4.1%)
Light, amber, hoppy bitter with lingering aftertaste.
Headmaster (ABV 4.5%)

Old Spot

Manor Farm, Station Road, Cullingworth, West Yorkshire, BD13 5HN
☎ (01535) 691144 oldspotbrewery.co.uk

Old Spot, named after the owner's sheepdog, started brewing in 2005. The beers are available in several outlets in West Yorkshire. The acting brewery tap is the George, Cullingworth. ♦

Light But Dark (ABV 4%)
OSB (ABV 4%)
Spot Light (ABV 4.2%)
This smooth-drinking golden ale has a slightly fruity, hoppy aroma leading to a well-balanced, fruit/ hop flavour with hints of pineapple and a long, bittersweet finish.
Spot O'Bother (ABV 5.5%)

Old Street

Arch 11, Gales Gardens,, Bethnal Green Road, Bethnal Green, London, E2 0EJ ☎ 07491 990970
oldstreet.beer

Originally situated in the basement of the Queen's Head pub in King's Cross, brewing began in 2013. In 2018 the brewery moved to a railway arch in Bethnal Green with an on-site taproom. No real ale. ◆

Old Tree

Old Tree, Yachtwerks, 28-29 Richmond Place, Brighton, East Sussex, BN2 9NA ☎ 07413 064346
oldtree.house

A co-operative based in Brighton producing a unique range of small-batch, probiotic and celebration drinks. It supplies its own zero-waste Silo restaurant. Brewing and gardening are combined and a production process is used that contributes to land regeneration. RAIB

Old Vicarage

Old Vicarage, Walton, Cumbria, CA8 2DH
☎ (01697) 543002 oldvicaragebrewery.co.uk

A microbrewery, bar and B&B accommodation in North Cumbria. Brewing experience days are offered.

Old Windsor

68 Straight Road, Old Windsor, Windsor, SL4 2RX
owbrewery.com

Run by an enthusiastic home brewer who went commercial in 2016. Brewing takes place in his garage and the beers are sold locally to a couple of regular outlets. Each batch is unique and custom made in small quantities. RAIB

Olde England

See Potbelly

Olde Potting Shed

See TOPS

Olde Swan

Old Swan, 89 Halesowen Road, Netherton, West Midlands, DY2 9PY
☎ (01384) 253075

A famous brewpub best known as Ma Pardoe's after the matriarch who ruled it for years. The pub has been licensed since 1835 and the present brewery and pub were built in 1863. Brewing continued until 1988 and restarted in 2001. More than 30 outlets are supplied. ‼♦

Original (ABV 3.5%)
Straw-coloured, light mild, smooth but tangy, and sweetly refreshing with a faint hoppiness.
Dark Swan (ABV 4.2%)
Smooth, sweet dark mild with late roast malt in the finish.
Entire (ABV 4.4%)
Faintly hoppy, amber, premium bitter with sweetness persistent throughout.
NPA (Netherton Pale Ale) (ABV 4.8%)
Bumble Hole Bitter (ABV 5.2%)
Sweet, smooth, amber ale with hints of astringency in the finish.

Oldershaw

See Zest

On the Edge

Sheffield, South Yorkshire ☎ 07854 983197
ontheedgebrew.com

On the Edge started brewing commercially in 2012 using a 0.5-barrel plant in the brewer's home. Brewing takes place once a week. Three local pubs are supplied as well as beer festivals. There is no regular beer list as new brews are constantly being tried.

One Mile End SIBA

Unit 2, Compass West Estate, 33 West Road, Tottenham, London, N17 0XL
☎ (020) 7998 0610 ☎ 07912 411147

Office: White Hart, 1-3 Mile End Road, Whitechapel, London, E1 4TP onemileend.com

One Mile End took over the former premises of the Redemption Brewery (qv) using a 12.5-barrel plant, brewing up to four times a week. A three-barrel plant is also occasionally in operation at the White Hart in Whitechapel (its original home). Beer is sometimes brewed using the 'Under the Street' brand name. ‼ V◆

Juicy 4pm (ABV 4%)
Smooth, yellow-coloured beer with strong citrus and mango flavours and a little biscuit, becoming more hoppy and bitter on drinking.

Hospital Porter (ABV 5.2%)
Dark brown porter with a smoky, roasty nose. Sweet mocha, roast and nuts on the palate. Dry, dark roast finish.

Opa Hay's

Glencot, Wood Lane, Aldeby, Norfolk, NR34 0DA
☎ (01502) 679144 ☎ 07916 282729
engelfineales.com

Opa Hay's began brewing in 2008. It is a small, family-run brewery, taking its name from the brewer's great grandfather. Only traditional brewing methods are used, with ingredients that are, where possible, sourced locally. ♦ RAIB

Engels Fruity Little Number (ABV 3.6%)
Powerful citrus/grapefruit aroma with malt and hops. Smoky sweetish flavours with fruit notes, and a fruity, hoppy aftertaste.
Engel's Best Bitter (ABV 4%)
Hop Hop Hooray (ABV 4.3%)
Matilda's Revenge (ABV 4.3%)
Samuel Engels Meister Pils (SEMP) (ABV 4.8%)
Liquid Bread (ABV 5.2%)
Bavarian Breakfast Beer (ABV 5.4%)

Ora

Unit 16a, Rosebery Industrial Estate, Rosebery Avenue, Tottenham, London, N17 9SR ☎ 07703 563559 orabeer.com

Originally split between Italy and cuckoo brewing at Ubrew, Ora took over Brewheadz in Tottenham in 2019. A variety of hop-forward beers are brewed complemented with styles incorporating classic Italian ingredients such as lemons, balsamic vinegar and vanilla.

Orbit SIBA

Arches 225 & 228, Fielding Street, Walworth, London, SE17 3HD ☎ 07885 663842 orbitbeers.com

Established in 2014 in a railway arch in Walworth, Orbit produces keg and bottle-conditioned beers. Its core range is supplemented by White Label specials. The design work and beer names relate to the brewer's love of vinyl. RAIB

Origami

75 North Western Street, Manchester, M12 6DY

Office: 83 Ducie Street, Manchester, M1 2JQ
origamibrewingcompany.com

Brewing began in 2016 at Beer Nouveau's Manchester site where Origami has its own brew plant. Most output is bottled, but cask beer is frequently available at the Beer Nouveau beer tap as well as Manchester beer festivals. Unfined, all beer is vegan. V

Fortune Teller (ABV 4%)
1000 Cranes (ABV 5%)
Valley Fold (ABV 5.3%)
Rabbit Ear (ABV 5.5%)
Arctic Fox (ABV 7%)

Orkney SIBA

Orkney Brewery, Quoyloo, Orkney, KW16 3LT
☎ (01667) 404555 ☎ 07721 013227

Office: Sinclair Breweries Ltd, Cawdor, IV12 5XP
orkneybrewery.co.uk

Orkney was established in 1988 in an old village school building. Having incorporated sister brewery Atlas (qv), it moved next door in 2010 to enable an increase in capacity and the completion of an award-winning visitor centre in 2012. !! ♦

Raven (ABV 3.8%)
A well-balanced quaffable bitter. Malty fruitiness and bitter hops last through to the long, dry aftertaste.
Dragonhead (ABV 4%)
A strong, dark roasted malt aroma flows into the taste. The roast malt continues to dominate the aftertaste, and blends with chocolate to develop a strong, dry finish.
Northern Light (ABV 4%)
A well-balanced golden ale with a real smack of fruit and hops in the taste and an increasing bitter aftertaste.
Red MacGregor (ABV 4%)
This tawny red ale has a well-balanced mix of red fruit, malt and hops. Slight sweetness throughout.
Corncrake (ABV 4.1%)
A straw-coloured beer with soft citrus fruits and a floral aroma.
Puffin Ale (ABV 4.5%)
Bittersweet mix of malts and plenty of hops.
Dark Island (ABV 4.6%)
A sweetish roast chocolate malt taste leads to a longlasting roasted, slightly bitter, dry finish. Winning many awards.
Skull Splitter (ABV 8.5%)
An intense velvet malt nose with hints of apple, prune and plum. The hoppy taste is balanced by satiny smooth malt with sweet fruity spicy edges, leading to a long, dry finish with a hint of nut.

Brewed for Atlas Brewery:
Latitude (ABV 3.6%)
This straw-coloured lager has a light citrus taste with a smack of hops and grapefruit in the light bitter finish.
Three Sisters (ABV 4.2%)
Malt, summer fruits and caramel in the nose and blackcurrant in the taste, followed by a short, hoppy, bitter finish.
Wayfarer (ABV 4.4%)
Full of citrus fruits and hops with a bitter finish.
Golden Amber (ABV 4.5%)
Refreshing hops, honey, marmalade and grapefruit to the fore with a dry, hoppy finish.
Blizzard (ABV 4.7%)
Light on malts and hops with ginger and spices coming through.
Nimbus (ABV 5%)
A full-bodied golden beer using some wheat malt and three types of hops. Sweet and fruity at the front, it becomes slightly astringent with lasting fruit and a pleasant, dry finish.

Oscars

Unit 1 Riverside Works, Brunswick Street, Nelson, Lancashire, BB9 0HZ oscarsbrewery.co.uk

Originally based in Preston, the brewery was taken over in 2017 by the Lancashire Beer Co, a pub supplies wholesaler in Nelson. In 2018 the brewery name was changed to Oscars and a new range of beers introduced. Production moved to purpose-built premises in Nelson at the parent company in 2019.

Top Dog (ABV 3.8%)
Dogfather (ABV 3.9%)
Gun Dog (ABV 4%)
Golden Retriever (ABV 4.2%)

Ossett SIBA

Kings Yard, Low Mill Road, Ossett, West Yorkshire, WF5 8ND
☎ (01924) 261333 ● ossett-brewery.co.uk

☺Brewing began in 1998, moving to a new site in 2005. 2017 saw significant investment in brewery improvements and expansion to bring total brewing capacity up to 360-barrels per week. In addition a brand new warehouse and packaging facility was constructed. The on-site taproom is open Friday and Saturday. The brewery owns 26 pubs, three of which are Hop branded bars – larger city centre venues based around a concept of real ale and live music. ‼🍺♦🍂

Yorkshire Brunette (ABV 3.7%)
Yorkshire Blonde (ABV 3.9%)
Silver King (ABV 4.3%)
Excelsius (ABV 5.2%)

Ostlers

🍺 White Horse, Harborne, West Midlands, B17 0HG
☎ (0121) 427 8004 ● whitehorseharborne.com

Started up at the rear of the White Horse pub in Harborne, the brewery was in occasional production for a few years. It now has a 4.5-barrel plant brewing a small range of core beers alongside frequent specials and seasonal beers, many available in KeyKeg as well as cask.

Other Monkey

Three Wise Monkeys, 60 High Street, Colchester, Essex, CO1 1DN
☎ (01206) 543014 ● othermonkeybrewing.com

⊠ Other Monkey is located in the basement of the Three Wise Monkeys pub. The brewery and pub are separately owned but beer is only brewed for the Three Wise Monkeys and two other outlets in Colchester. V🍂

Pale Ale (ABV 4.4%)

Otter SIBA

Mathayes, Luppitt, Honiton, Devon, EX14 4SA
☎ (01404) 891285 ● otterbrewery.com

⊠ A family-run brewery set high up in the Blackdown Hills. Environmental responsibility lies at the heart of its ethos. Otter's eco cellar has been built underground and is naturally chilled. The beers are made from the brewery's own springs and locally-sourced ingredients. ♦🍂

Bitter (ABV 3.6%)
Well-balanced, amber, session bitter with a fruity nose and bitter taste and aftertaste.
Amber (ABV 4%)
Light, refreshing and mellow with hints of citrus hoppiness. Creamy and delicate with hops and fruit.
Bright (ABV 4.3%)
A light and refreshing golden ale with delicate malt, and fruit leading through hops to a lingering bitter aftertaste.
Ale (ABV 4.5%)
Malt dominates from nose to throat. Sweet fruit, toffee and caramel with a dry aftertaste, full of flavour.
Head (ABV 5.8%) 🍷
Smooth strong ale. Caramel malt throughout. Full-bodied with rich, malty fruitiness and a chocolate hint, leaving a bitter aftertaste.

Out of Town (NEW)

84 Telford Road, Lenziemill Industrial Estate, Cumbernauld, G67 2NJ ● outoftown.co

In 2016 three homebrewers, Owen, James and Rich, took the next step and opened their own brewery. The original, self-built plant has since been upgraded piece by piece.

Out There

Unit 4 Foundry Lane Industrial Estate, Newcastle-upon-Tyne, NE6 1LH ☎ 07946 579534
● outtherebrewing.com

Out There was established in 2012 by Steve Pickthall. Branding and beer names are themed around the 1950s space race.

Space is the Place (ABV 3.5%)
Laika (ABV 4.8%)
Celestial Love (ABV 5.1%)

Outgang

🍺 Kinsley Hotel, Wakefield Road, Kinsley, West Yorkshire, WF9 5EH ☎ 07747 694611
✉ thepub@sky.com

☺Originally established in 2011, brewing resumed in 2017 after a period of inoperation. Local outlets are supplied as are outlets further afield due to increased production. ‼♦

Black Gold (ABV 3.5%)
Lamp Room (ABV 3.9%)
Tailgate Ripper (ABV 3.9%)
Pit Bottom (ABV 4%)
Button Man (ABV 4.3%)

Outhouse

c/o Unit 16a, Redbrook Business Park, off Wilthorpe Road, Redbrook, Barnsley, South Yorkshire, S75 1JN
☎ 07572 164446

Office: Henry Morgan House, Industry Road, Carlton, S71 3PQ ● outhousebrewing.co.uk

☺After a 13 year teaching career Andy Jones established Outhouse Brewing in 2018 using spare capacity at Jolly Boys (qv). V

Pristavba (ABV 3.7%)
Garden Shed (ABV 4%)
Bikeshed (ABV 4.5%)

Outlaw

See Rooster's

Outstanding SIBA

Units 1 & 2, Foundry, Ordsall Lane, Ordsall, Manchester, M5 3AN
☎ (0161) 873 8090 ● outstandingbeers.com

Established in 2008, the brewery operates a dual system, brewing on a 15-barrel plant and using a 2.5-barrel plant for special and experimental brews. Originally based in Bury, it moved to Ordsall in 2017. Selected free trade accounts are supplied nationally. ♦

3.9 (ABV 3.9%)
UltraPale (ABV 4.1%)
Straw in colour, with a light citrus aroma. Lemony fruit with hop bitterness to taste and a bitter, astringent finish.

Red (ABV 4.4%)
Blond (ABV 4.5%)
IPA (ABV 5.5%)
Stout (ABV 5.5%)
Imperial IPA (ABV 7.4%)

Ovenstone109 SIBA

Ovenstone Works, Ovenstone, Anstruther, KY10 2RR
☎ (01333) 311394 ⊕ ovenstone109.com

Established in 2018, Ovenstone 109 is a microbrewery in the East Neuk of Fife. The brewer aims to use renewable and sustainable technology in the brewing process.

Overtone SIBA

Unit 19, New Albion Industrial Estate, Halley Street, Yoker, Glasgow, G13 4DJ ⊕ overtonebrewing.com

Established in 2018. No real ale.

Oxhey Village (NEW)

14 Maxwell Rise, Watford, Hertfordshire, WD19 4DX
☎ 07470 422842 ✉ shaun@ruthandshaun.co.uk

A nanobrewery set up by five drinking companions, commercial brewing began in 2019. Currently brewing about once a week, it mainly produces mini-kegs for local clubs but cask beers are available on request for local pubs and beer festivals. Expansion is planned.

OVB Session (ABV 3.4%)
OVB Pale Ale (ABV 3.8%)

Oxted

Oxted, Surrey ☎ 07867 541700
⊕ theoxtedbrewery.co.uk

⊗ Oxted Brewery was established in 2015 using a two-barrel plant and occupies a purpose-built extension at the owner's home. Beers are regularly available in the Crown and Wheatsheaf pubs, Old Oxted, and the Hatch, Redhill. Bottles can be found in local off-licences and farm shops. Occasional events are held locally. RAIB

Hop'dfather (ABV 3.8%)
Amber Ale (ABV 3.9%)
Single Hop (ABV 3.9%)
B.O.B. (Best Oxted Bitter) (ABV 4%)
The Black Perle (ABV 4.4%)
Treehouse IPA (ABV 4.9%)

Padstow SIBA

The Brewery, Unit 4a, Trecerus Industrial Estate, Padstow, Cornwall, PL28 8RW
☎ (01841) 532169 ☎ 07834 924312
⊕ padstowbrewing.co.uk

⊗ Owners Des and Caron Archer established the brewery in 2013, using a 0.5-barrel plant, which has since been upgraded to 10 barrels. Besides the integral brewery shop, a town-centre off-licence shop with tasting room has been established. ‼ ⛟ ♦ RAIB

Pale Ale (ABV 3.6%)
Golden beer with assertive hop aroma. Citrus hops dominate the taste with bitterness and dryness. Hoppy, refreshing and crisp finish.
Local (ABV 4%)
Stowe Away IPA (ABV 4.1%)
Windjammer (ABV 4.3%)
Tawny bitter. Light malty and citrus hop aromas leading to a combination of biscuit malt, pine and resin hops. Lasting bitterness.
Pride (ABV 4.5%)
Balanced, copper beer. Fruity aromas lead to nutty malt complemented by stone and summer fruit. Crisp malt, slightly sweet finish.
IPA (ABV 4.8%)
Refreshing IPA. Fully-hopped on nose and taste with orange bitterness. Sweet finish with citrus hops and faintly dry.
May Day (ABV 5%)
Amber ale with citrus hop aroma. Trace of malt sweetness overwhelmed by strong lemon and stone fruit flavours. Quite bitter.

Palmers SIBA IFBB

Old Brewery, West Bay Road, Bridport, Dorset, DT6 4JA
☎ (01308) 422396 ⊕ palmersbrewery.com

⊗ Palmers is one of Britain's only thatched breweries and dates from 1794. It is situated in Bridport, the heart of the Jurassic Coast in south-west Dorset. The company continues to make substantial investment in its 54 tenanted pubs, all serving cask ale. An additional 400 outlets are supplied within the free trade. ‼ ⛟

Copper Ale (ABV 3.7%)
Beautifully balanced, copper-coloured, light bitter with a hoppy aroma.
IPA (ABV 4.2%)
Hop aroma and bitterness stay in the background in this predominately malty best bitter, with some fruit on the aroma.
Dorset Gold (ABV 4.5%)
More complex than many golden ales thanks to a pleasant banana and mango fruitiness on the aroma that carries on into the taste and aftertaste.
200 (ABV 5%)
This is a big beer with a touch of caramel sweetness adding to a complex hoppy, fruit taste that lasts from the aroma well into the aftertaste.
Tally Ho! (ABV 5.5%)
A complex dark old ale. Roast malts and treacle toffee on the palate lead in to a long, lingering finish with more than a hint of coffee.

Panther

Unit 1, Collers Way, Reepham, Norfolk, NR10 4SW
☎ 07766 558215 ⊕ pantherbrewery.co.uk

⊗ Panther began brewing in 2010 on an industrial estate near the old railway station, formerly the home of Reepham Brewery. ‼ ⛟ ♦ RAIB

Mild Panther (ABV 3.3%)
A smooth, malty character and notes of chocolate, which gives this beer plenty of flavour and aroma.
Ginger Panther (ABV 3.7%)
Refreshingly clean, ginger wheat beer with a distinct fiery kick.
Golden Panther (ABV 3.7%)
Refreshing orange and malt notes flow through this well-balanced, easy-drinking bitter. Hops and a soft bitterness add depth.
Honey Panther (ABV 4%)
A gentle flowing brew with honey and malt throughout. Amber-coloured with a tapering bittersweet finale.
Red Panther (ABV 4.1%)
Full-flavoured brew. Solidly malty in both aroma and taste. Hops, and a residual sweetness, provide balance.
American Pale Ale (ABV 4.4%)
Black Panther (ABV 4.5%)
This dark ale is full-flavoured, smooth and complex. It has a bittersweet balance that leads to a dry finish.
Beast of the East (ABV 5.5%)

Papworth SIBA

24 Earith Business Park, Meadow Drove, Earith, Cambridgeshire, PE28 3QF
☎ (01487) 842442 ☎ 07835 845797
papworthbrewery.com

Brewing began in 2014 in Papworth Everard. The brewery moved to new premises in Earith in 2017 and acquired an 11-barrel plant, significantly increasing its production. The brewery site is licensed for on and off-sales, with a new brewery tap and bottle shop opened in late 2020. !!

Mild Thing (ABV 3.5%)
Mad Jack (ABV 3.8%)
The Whitfield Citrabolt (ABV 3.8%)
Whispering Grass (ABV 3.8%)
Fen Skater (ABV 4%)
Crystal Ship (ABV 4.2%)
Half Nelson (ABV 4.2%)
Red Kite (ABV 4.7%)
Big Sur (ABV 5%)
Robin Goodfellow (ABV 5.4%)
Pass the Porter (ABV 5.5%)
Koura (ABV 5.7%)

Paradigm

4d Green End Farm, 93A Church Lane, Sarratt, Hertfordshire, WD3 6HH
☎ (01923) 291215 paradigmbrewery.com

Founded by two friends, Neil Hodges and Rob Atkinson, Paradigm went into production in 2015. Its five-barrel plant is located in an industrial unit on a farm. One-off beers are also brewed. The brewery and beer names are based on corporate jargon and buzzwords. !! ♦ RAIB

watercress ale (ABV 3.6%)
low hanging fruit (ABV 3.7%)
fyi (ABV 3.8%)
touch point (ABV 3.9%)
juxtaposition (ABV 4%)
heads up (ABV 4.1%)
win-win (ABV 4.2%)
black friday (ABV 6%)

Parish

6 Main Street, Burrough on the Hill, Leicestershire, LE14 2JQ
☎ (01664) 454801 ☎ 07715 369410
bazbrewery@gmail.com

Parish began brewing in 1983 and now operates on a 20-barrel plant, with capacity to brew a further 12 barrels. The brewery is located in a 400-year-old building next to the Stag & Hounds, where its flagship beer, PSB, is permanently available. Other local outlets are also supplied and one-off brews are produced for beer festivals both locally and across surrounding counties. !! RAIB

PSB (ABV 3.9%)

Park Brew

Unit 10, Brechin Business Centre, Brechin, DD9 6DY
☎ 07905 998740 info@parkbrew.com

Established in 2016 by John Leatherbarrow and Andrew Donald. Brewing is currently suspended.

Park Brewery SIBA

Unit 7, Hampden Road, Norbiton, Surrey, KT1 3HG
☎ 07949 574618

Office: 38 St Georges Road, Kingston-upon-Thames, KT2 6DN theparkbrewery.com

The Park Brewery was founded in 2014 in a former greengrocer's premises, using a one-barrel plant, increasing in 2015 to four barrels. Beers are available locally as well as across London and are named after locations in Richmond Park. After a year cuckoo brewing at Reunion, brewing at its new site commenced in 2019. !! ♦ RAIB V

Killcat Pale (ABV 3.7%)
Unfined, golden bitter with grapefruit throughout. Subtle malt and strong hoppy bitter notes in the flavour and short, dry finish.
Gallows Gold (ABV 4.4%)
Tropical fruit, orange and hop notes dominate. Malt is restrained with a gentle biscuit presence and growing bitterness. Well-balanced.
Spankers IPA (ABV 5.5%)
An amber-coloured, hoppy, citrus, dry, golden ale with a similar finish and a touch of dry bitterness.

Parker

Unit 3, Gravel Lane, Banks, Lancashire, PR9 8BY
☎ (01704) 620718 ☎ 07949 797889
theparkerbrewery.co.uk

Parker was established in 2014 using a 25-litre plant, but quickly expanded to a five-barrel plant. In 2018 the brewery opened its own micropub, the Beer Den, Southport. !! RAIB

Centurion Pale Ale (ABV 3.9%)
Barbarian Bitter (ABV 4.1%)
Saxon Red Ale (ABV 4.5%)
Viking Blonde (ABV 4.7%)
Dark Spartan Stout (ABV 5%)
Well-balanced stout with a burnt smoky roast aroma, roast strong on tasting with a little sweetness, ending with mellow flavours and some bitterness to finish.

Parkway (NEW)

Unit 11, Wessex Park, Somerton Business Park, Somerton, TA11 6SB
☎ (01458) 897373 parkwaybrewing.co.uk

Parkway began its journey into brewing in 2018, having purchased the former Glastonbury Ales plant and equipment. Although located in the small market town of Somerton, Parkway is named after a road in North London's Camden Town. The brewery also contract brew under license.

Giggle & Titter (ABV 3.8%)
Mystery Tor (ABV 3.8%)
Full-bodied, golden bitter with floral hop and fruit on the nose and palate, sweetness giving way to bitter hop finish.
Cheeky Monkey (ABV 4%)
Lady of the Lake (ABV 4.2%)
Full-bodied, amber best bitter with hops balanced by fruity malt flavour and a hint of vanilla. Clean, bitter hop aftertaste.
Love Monkey (ABV 4.2%)
Norwegian Blue (ABV 4.2%)
Black As Yer 'At (ABV 4.3%)
Hedge Monkey (ABV 4.6%)
Golden Chalice (ABV 4.8%)
Thriller Cappuccino Porter (ABV 5%)

Partizan

34 Raymouth Road, South Bermondsey, London, SE16 2DB
☎ (020) 8127 5053 🌐 partizanbrewing.co.uk

Partizan began brewing in 2012. Each brew is different, but is based on a variety of international styles.

Pastore (NEW)

Unit 2, Convent Drive, Waterbeach, Cambridgeshire, CB25 9QT 🌐 pastorebrewing.com

Pastore Brewing & Blending specialise in mixed fermentation sour and wild ales. Pastore (Pastor-ray) is Italian for Shepherd and is in honour of the brewer's Italian family. Rustic wild brewing with a modern semi-urban setting, making new age, fresh-fruited weisses as well as barrel-aged old saisons.

Patten (NEW)

The Patten Arms, Park Lane, Winmarleigh, PR3 0JU
☎ (01524) 791484
✉ thepattenarmswinmarleigh@gmail.com

Brewing started in 2019 using a small plant in the cellar of the Patten Arms.

Peak SIBA

Barn Brewery, Chatsworth, Bakewell, Derbyshire, DE45 1EX
☎ (01246) 583737 🌐 peakales.co.uk

Opened in 2005 in former derelict farm buildings on the Chatsworth estate aided by a DEFRA Rural Enterprise Scheme grant and support from trustees of Chatsworth Settlement. Main beer production moved to a new facility at Ashford in the Water in 2014 to increase capacity. A shop and visitor centre opened in 2017 at the original site on the Chatsworth Estate where a pilot brewery for experimental and occasional brews is now operational, with its own gin distillery.

Swift Nick (ABV 3.8%)
Easy-drinking, copper-coloured bitter with balanced malt and hops and a gentle hoppy bitter finish.
Summer Sovereign (ABV 4%)
Bakewell Best Bitter (ABV 4.2%)
Full-bodied, tawny bitter with a hoppy bitterness against a malty background, leading to a hoppy dry aftertaste.
Paxton (ABV 4.4%)
Great Ridge (ABV 4.5%)
Chatsworth Gold (ABV 4.6%)
Speciality beer made with honey, which gives a pleasant sweetness leading to a hop and malt finish.
Black Stag (ABV 4.8%)
IPA (ABV 6%)

Peakstones Rock SIBA

Peakstones Farm, Cheadle Road, Alton, Staffordshire, ST10 4DH ☎ 07891 350908 🌐 peakstonesrock.co.uk

Peakstones Rock was established in 2005 with a five-barrel plant located on a farm in the Peak District National Park. The brewery was expanded to 10-barrel capacity in 2009. It supplies an expanding free trade market in the North Midlands and surrounding areas. RAIB

Nemesis (ABV 3.8%)
Biscuity aroma with some hop background. Sweet start, sweetish body then hops emerge to give a fruity middle. Bitterness develops slowly to a tongue-tingling finish.
Pugin's Gold (ABV 4%)
Chained Oak (ABV 4.2%)
Alton Abbey (ABV 4.5%)
Black Hole (ABV 4.8%)
Grassy aroma with malt background. Hops hit the mouth and intensify. Bitterness lingers with some mouthwatering astringency
Oblivion (ABV 5.5%)

Peerless SIBA

The Brewery, 8 Pool Street, Birkenhead, Merseyside, CH41 3NL
☎ (0151) 647 7688 🌐 peerlessbrewing.co.uk

Peerless began brewing in 2009 and is under the directorship of Steve Briscoe. Beers are sold through festivals, local pubs and the free trade.

Pale (ABV 3.8%)
Deadbeat (ABV 4%)
Triple Blond (ABV 4%)
Lottie Dod (ABV 4.2%)
Skyline (ABV 4.2%)
Langton Spin (ABV 4.4%)
Oatmeal Stout (ABV 5%)
Red Rocks (ABV 5%)
Knee-Buckler IPA (ABV 5.2%)
Full Whack (ABV 6%)
Tectonic (ABV 6.2%)

Penlon

Panteg Farm, New Quay, SA45 9TL
☎ (01545) 560252 🌐 penlonbrewery.co.uk

Established in 2004, Penlon is a six-barrel, farm-based brewery. In 2017 it opened the Granary taproom and pizza bar with stunning views across the Cardigan coastline. The brewery expanded in 2020. RAIB V

Cardi Bay Best Bitter (ABV 4%)
Heather Honey Golden Ale (ABV 4.2%)
Hidden Howler Pale Ale (ABV 4.3%)
RSA Strong Ale (ABV 6.2%)

Pennine SIBA

Well Hall Farm, Well, Bedale, North Yorkshire, DL8 2PX
☎ (01677) 470111 🌐 pennine-brewing.co.uk

Located in the village of Well near Masham, the brewery has been in production on this site since 2013 using an 18-barrel plant complete with lauter tun. Beer is supplied to pubs throughout the north of England as well as to beer festivals and local outdoor events.

Amber Necker (ABV 3.9%)
Hair of the Dog (ABV 3.9%)
Heartland (ABV 3.9%)
Natural Gold (ABV 4.2%)
IPA (ABV 4.4%)

Penton Park

Penton Park, Penton Mewsey, Hampshire, SP11 0RD
☎ (01264) 772400 ☎ 07764 691771
🌐 pentonparkbrewery.com

Started from homebrew equipment, this brewery has now expanded to five barrels and is located in the historic early Georgian kitchen of Penton Park. The room is nearly 300 years old and the brewery draws water from a nearby well.

Hastings (ABV 3.8%)
Colonel Bob (ABV 4%)

THE BREWERIES

Moderately hoppy golden ale with a subtle aroma and bitter aftertaste.

The Duke (ABV 4%)

50 Not Out (ABV 4.5%)
Fruit and malt aroma which combines with a balanced hoppiness in both taste and aftertaste. A well-balanced best bitter.

Pentrich SIBA

Unit B, Asher Lane Business Park, Asher Lane, Pentrich, Derbyshire, DE5 3RB
☎ (01773) 741700
✉ pentrichbrewingco@gmail.com

Two former home brewers began producing beer in their garage in Pentrich, before moving to share the plant of the Landlocked Brewing Co at the Beehive Inn, Ripley in 2014. In 2016 they moved into their own premises using second-hand equipment. In 2019 they purchased a made-to-order 16-barrel plant. Only one regular beer is produced now, preferring to concentrate on special beers. ◆

Brandrith Bitter (ABV 3.8%)

Penzance

▤ Star Inn, Crowlas, Cornwall, TR20 8DX
☎ (01736) 740375 ☎ 07763 956333
⊕ penzancebrewingcompany.co.uk

⊠ Owner Peter Elvin began brewing in 2008 on a self-built, five-barrel plant in the old stable block of the Star Inn. The fermentation capacity has since been expanded, increasing the volume and range of beer produced. Production is now at full capacity of 1,400 barrels a year. Besides the pub, selected outlets and beer festivals are supplied. ‼◆

Mild (ABV 3.6%) ⏛
Creamy, dark brown mild, chocolate and roast aroma. Coffee and chocolate dominate the taste with fruit notes. Bittersweet, balanced finish.

Crowlas Bitter (ABV 3.8%)
Refreshing, copper, session bitter with light malt aroma. Light biscuit maltiness and hops. Lingering finish of malty bitterness with dryness.

Potion No. 9 (ABV 4%)
Refreshing pale ale. Grapefruit and tropical fruit flavours dominate with some pine resin notes, biscuit malt and flashes of bubblegum esters.

Crows-an-Wra (ABV 4.3%)
Straw-coloured golden ale with grassy, hoppy aroma. Bitter hops dominate throughout, balanced by grapefruit and some malt. Long, clean finish.

Brisons Bitter (ABV 4.5%)
Brown best bitter, pleasant malt and hop balance. Biscuit malt accompanies bitter orange fruit with a lasting, bitter, dry finish.

Trink (ABV 5.2%)
Pale golden ale with grapefruit nose. Punchy pine-resin hop flavours with grapefruit, marmalade and peaches. Bittersweet and hoppy finish.

IPA (ABV 6%)
Smooth, golden, genuine IPA with hoppy aroma. Powerful hop bitterness with light malt and tropical fruits, finishing bitter and dry.

Scilly Stout (ABV 7%)
Black, full-bodied, creamy stout with chocolate aroma. Chocolate roast malt with liquorice and plums. Long finish with strong roast malt.

People's

Mill House, Mill Lane, Thorpe-Next-Haddiscoe, Norwich, Norfolk, NR14 6PA
☎ (01508) 548706 ✉ peoplesbrewery@mail.com

⊠ A one-barrel brewery associated with the community-owned Queen's Head pub in Thurlton, which takes most of its draught output. Beers are also available at the Thurlton Community shop.

Northdown Bitter (ABV 3.8%)
Raveningham Bitter (ABV 3.9%)
Thurlton Gold (ABV 4.2%)
Norfolk Cascade (ABV 4.5%)
Northern Brewers (ABV 4.6%)

Perivale

Horsenden Farm, Horsenden Lane North, Perivale, UB6 7PQ ☎ 07850 176177 ⊕ perivale.beer

Established in 2019, the brewery is based at a farm looked after by the Friends of Horsenden Hill. As well as other events, monthly taproom openings are hosted selling beers using hops grown on the farm and other local foraged ingredients. ◆

Phantom (NEW)

Unit 3, Meadow Road, Reading, Berkshire, RG1 8LB

Phantom is a new 12-barrel brewery, situated on the outskirts of Reading town centre. The on-site taproom opened in 2019 and brewing commenced in 2020. It specialises in hop-heavy beers but is beginning to experiment with other styles. Currently only KeyKeg beers are produced. ◆

Pheasantry SIBA

High Brecks Farm, Lincoln Road, East Markham, Nottinghamshire, NG22 0SN
☎ (01777) 872728 ☎ 07948 976749
⊕ pheasantrybrewery.co.uk

☺Pheasantry began brewing in 2012 using a new 10-barrel plant from Canada. Situated in a listed barn on a farm, the brewery incorporates a wedding and events venue, with the brewery visible through glass partitions. It supplies more than 200 pubs and retail outlets in Nottinghamshire, Lincolnshire, Derbyshire and South Yorkshire. A bottling line was installed in 2018 and contract bottling takes place for other breweries. ‼▰

Best Bitter (ABV 3.8%)
Pale Ale (ABV 4%)
Ringneck Amber Ale (ABV 4.1%)
Amber-coloured best bitter, initial malt and caramel leading to a brief bitter, dry finish.
Black Pheasant Dark Ale (ABV 4.2%)
Lincoln Tank Ale (ABV 4.2%)
Dancing Dragonfly (ABV 5%)

Brewed for Home Ales:
Robin Hood Pale Ale (ABV 3.8%)
Maid Marian Blonde (ABV 4.2%)
Little John Proper Ale (ABV 4.8%)

Philsters

Unit 16, Camp Industrial Estate, Rycote Lane, Milton Common, Oxfordshire, OX9 2NP ☎ 07747 827489

Office: Beehive Cottage, Little Haseley, Oxfordshire, OX44 7LH ⊕ philsters.co.uk

⊠ Named after the owner/brewer's nickname, this small brewery, established in 2015 at the brewer's home, expanded with a 4.5-barrel plant into new premises in 2019. It supplies local pubs, including the Plough, Great Haseley and the Bull, Great Milton. ♦V

Glass Blower (ABV 3.6%)
Haseley Gold (ABV 4.1%)
Oxford Red (ABV 4.2%)
Boosh (ABV 4.5%)
Rising (ABV 4.5%)
Darkside (ABV 5.1%)

Phipps SIBA

Albion Brewery, 54 Kingswell Street, Northampton, NN1 1PR
☎ (01604) 946606 ☎ 07717 078402
phipps-nbc.co.uk

Originally founded in Towcester in 1801, Phipps had been brewing in Northampton since 1817 until it was taken over by Watney Mann, and then closed in 1974. The company name and recipes were acquired, and in 2008 the first beer reappeared after 40 years. The Albion Brewery site, once owned by Phipps, was acquired and a new 15-barrel brewing plant was installed in 2014 to enable Phipps beers to be once again brewed in the town. Beer is also brewed under the Gun Dog Ales name. !! ♦ RAIB

Thrupenny Bitter (ABV 3.6%)
Diamond Ale (ABV 3.7%)
Red Star (ABV 3.8%)
Midsummer Meadow (ABV 3.9%)
Cobbler's Ale (ABV 4%)
India Pale Ale (ABV 4.3%)
Ratliffe's Celebrated Stout (ABV 4.3%)
Steam Roller (ABV 4.4%)
Becket's Ale (ABV 4.5%)
Bison Brown (ABV 4.6%)
Black Star (ABV 4.8%)
Last Orders (ABV 4.8%)
Kinky Boots (ABV 4.9%)
Gold Star (ABV 5.2%)

Phoenix SIBA

Green Lane, Heywood, OL10 2EP
☎ (01706) 627009 ✉ tony@phoenixbrewery.co.uk

Established in Ellesmere Port in 1982, Oak Brewery moved to the old Phoenix Brewery in Heywood and adopted the name in 1991. It now supplies more than 400 outlets plus wholesalers. Restoration of the old brewery, built in 1897, is ongoing. ♦

Hopsack (ABV 3.8%)
Navvy (ABV 3.8%)
Amber beer with a citrus fruit and malt nose. Good balance of citrus fruit, malt and hops with bitterness coming through in the aftertaste.
Monkeytown Mild (ABV 3.9%)
Light roast aroma. Mild, creamy, roast flavour with sweet malt and some astringency. Lasting, dry, bitter finish.
Arizona (ABV 4.1%)
Yellow in colour with a fruity and hoppy aroma. A refreshing beer with citrus, hops and good bitterness, and a shortish dry aftertaste.
Spotland Gold (ABV 4.1%)
Pale Moonlight (ABV 4.2%)
Black Bee (ABV 4.5%)
White Monk (ABV 4.5%)
Yellow beer with a citrus fruit aroma, plenty of fruit, hops and bitterness in the taste, and a hoppy, bitter finish.
Thirsty Moon (ABV 4.6%)
Tawny beer with a fresh citrus aroma. Hoppy, fruity and malty with a dry, hoppy finish.
West Coast IPA (ABV 4.6%)
Golden in colour with a hoppy, fruity nose. Strong hoppy and fruity taste and aftertaste with good bitterness throughout.
Double Gold (ABV 5%)
Wobbly Bob (ABV 6%)
A red/brown beer with malty, fruity aroma and creamy mouthfeel. Strongly malty and fruity in flavour, with hops and a hint of herbs. Both sweetness and bitterness are evident throughout.

Brewed for Brunning & Price Pub Co:
Original (ABV 3.8%)

Pictish

Unit 9, Canalside Industrial Estate, Woodbine Street East, Rochdale, OL16 5LB
☎ (01706) 522227 pictish-brewing.co.uk

The brewery was established in 2000 and supplies free trade outlets in the north-west and West Yorkshire. Famed for the consistency and clarity of its brews and its ever-changing single hop series of beers. ♦

Brewers Gold (ABV 3.8%)
Yellow in colour, with a hoppy, fruity nose. Soft maltiness and a strong hop/citrus flavour lead to a dry, bitter finish.
Talisman IPA (ABV 4.2%)
Strong hoppy aroma; hops and fruit in the taste. Some initial sweetness, but with hoppy bitterness throughout.
Alchemists Ale (ABV 4.3%)
Bitter beer with malt aroma.

Piddle SIBA

Unit 24, Enterprise Park, Piddlehinton, Dorchester, Dorset, DT2 7UA
☎ (01305) 849336 ☎ 07730 436343
piddlebrewery.co.uk

Established in 2007, with new owners in 2014. The brewery produces a broad range of beers from its location in the Piddle Valley in Dorset. Some beer names reflect this unusual name. Beers are available in pubs and retail outlets across Dorset and beyond. ♦

Dorset Rogue (ABV 3.9%)
Piddle (ABV 4.1%)
Cocky (ABV 4.3%)
Bent Copper (ABV 4.8%)
Slasher (ABV 5.1%)

Pied Bull

Pied Bull Hotel, 57 Northgate Street, Chester, CH1 2HQ
☎ (01244) 325829 piedbull.co.uk

Pied Bull began brewing in 2011 using a one-barrel plant. Beer is mainly for in-house consumption but local beer festivals are supplied and occasional brewery swaps occur. ♦

Pig & Porter

9 Chapman Way, Tunbridge Wells, Kent, TN2 3EF
☎ (01892) 615071 pigandporter.co.uk

Originally brewing at several microbreweries in Sussex and Kent, brewing has taken place on its own plant in Tunbridge Wells since 2013 using a 10-barrel plant. ♦V

Blackbird (ABV 4%)
Skylarking (ABV 4%)
Slave to the Money (ABV 4.1%)
Stone Free (ABV 4.3%)
All These Vibes (ABV 5.3%)

THE BREWERIES

Pig Beer (NEW)

Hop House, Setley Ridge, Brockenhurst, SO42 7UF
☎ (01590) 607237 ☎ 07747 462139 🌐 pigbeer.com

Pig Beer is an 18-barrel brewery operated by two brothers and their cousin. Currently producing bottled beers only, but expected to produce keykeg beers for local outlets if there is a demand.

Pig Iron

Rowley Village, Rowley Regis, B65 9AT ☎ 07816 018777 🌐 pigironbrewingco.co.uk

Set up in 2015, this three-barrel plant has relocated and is now sited to the rear of the Britannia pub in Rowley village. The brewer, from a former baking family, acquired the kit from Brewmeister in Northern Scotland. The brewery supplies free trade outlets within 15 miles of the brewery and the brewers home, as well as Weavers Real Ale House, Kidderminster. ♦

Blonde (ABV 3.8%)
EPA (ABV 4.2%)
IPA (ABV 4.2%)
Unbeweavable (ABV 4.2%)
APA (ABV 4.5%)

Brewed under the Britt Brewery brand name:
Brew Britannia
Britt Pop (ABV 4.9%)

Pig Pub

Pig In Muck, Manor Road, Claybrooke Magna, Leicestershire, LE17 5AY
☎ (01455) 202859 🌐 piginmuck.com/brewery

Brewing began in 2013 using a two-barrel plant, upgraded to a five-barrel plant built by head brewer Kev Featherstone. ♦ RAIB

Piglove (NEW)

c/o Unit 6, Cross Green Lane, Leeds, West Yorkshire, LS9 8LJ ☎ 07718 630467 🌐 piglovebrewing.com

Small craft brewery that launched in 2020 producing keg and canned beer, inspired by the heritage of British craft brewing (Yorkshire in particular), together with exotic ingredients and flavours from around the world, influenced by its Venezuelan and Spanish co-founders. Brewing is currently taking place using spare capacity at Legitimate Industries (qv) and Quirky Ales (qv). Plans are on hold to establish its own brewery and introduce cask-conditioned ale.

Pilgrim SIBA

11 West Street, Reigate, Surrey, RH2 9BL
☎ (01737) 222651 ☎ 07973 297410 🌐 pilgrim.co.uk

Pilgrim was the first microbrewery in Surrey, set up in 1982 in Woldingham before moving to its current premises in Reigate in 1984. New owners from 2017 are developing new ales to complement the current selection and have enlarged to a 12-barrel brew length, and opened a taproom. Beers are available in around 40 local outlets. !! ♦

Surrey (ABV 3.7%)
Pineapple, grapefruit and spicy aromas. Biscuity maltiness with a hint of vanilla balanced by a hoppy bitterness and refreshing bittersweet finish.
Session IPA (ABV 3.9%)
Progress (ABV 4%)
Well-rounded, tawny-coloured bitter. Predominantly sweet and malty with an underlying fruitiness and hint of toffee, balanced with a subdued bitterness.
Quest (ABV 4.3%)
Saracen (ABV 4.5%)

Pillars SIBA

Unit 2 Ravenswood Industrial Estate, Shernhall Street, Walthamstow, London, E17 9HQ
☎ (020) 8521 5552 🌐 pillarsbrewery.com

Brewing began in 2016 as an exclusively keg lager brewery. As well as the on-site taproom, a bar has been opened near to St James Street station in the Crate development made out of shipping containers.

Pilot Beer

4b Stewartfield, Edinburgh, EH6 5RQ
☎ (0131) 561 4267 🌐 pilotbeer.co.uk

Pilot began brewing in 2013 in an industrial unit in Leith using a five-barrel plant. A recent move to larger premises has allowed for expansion. Beers are unfined and unfiltered. Almost all output is keg or can but cask-conditioned ale is occasionally available. RAIB V

Pilot Brewery

726 Mumbles Road, Mumbles, Swansea, SA3 4EL
☎ 07897 895511 🌐 thepilotbrewery.co.uk

The Pilot Brewery began production on its 2.5-barrel plant in 2013. It is located at the rear of the Pilot Inn on the Mumbles sea front. The output is mainly for the pub but can also be supplied to festivals and other select outlets. The proprietors have also set up BeerRiff brewery (qv). V

Pin-Up SIBA

Unit 3, Block 3, Chalex Industrial Estate, Manor Hall Road, Southwick, West Sussex, BN42 4NH
☎ (01273) 411127 ☎ 07888 836892
🌐 pinupbrewingco.com

Pin-Up began brewing in 2011, initially having its beers contract brewed at an Essex brewery. In 2014 it obtained its own plant and began brewing in Southwick, and expanded from a five-barrel to a 10-barrel plant in 2015. Its first pub, the United Brethren, Chelmsford, opened in 2016. ♦ RAIB

Honey Brown (ABV 4%)
Session IPA (ABV 4.1%)
Summer Pale (ABV 4.1%)
Red Head (ABV 4.2%)
Milk Stout (ABV 4.5%)

Pinnora

Unit 2, rear of Jubilee Parade, Marsh Road, Pinner, HA5 1BB 🌐 pinnorabrewing.com

Moved to a larger facility during 2018 in the centre of Pinner, the origin of its name, beer remains scarce and hard to find due to its small size and output. There are plans to expand into an adjacent unit.

Pipes

183a Kings Road, Cardiff, CF11 9DF ☎ 07776 382244
🌐 pipesbeer.co.uk

Pipes Beer create examples of some of the unique and least known beer styles from around the globe, with no preservatives or additives used in production. The main output is bottled and keg beers although the occasional cask beer is produced.

Pit Top

See Wrytree

Pitchfork

See Epic Beers

Pitfield

See Dominion

Plain SIBA

17c Deverill Trading Estate, Sutton Veny, Wiltshire, BA12 7BZ
☎ (01985) 841481 plainales.co.uk

Plain Ales started production in 2008 on a 2.5-barrel plant in a garage, and expanded to a 10-barrel plant in 2010 to keep up with demand for its award-winning ales. 2018 saw the introduction of its Kult Brewing Co brand to brew edgier beers. !! ♦ V

Sheep Dip (ABV 3.8%)
Innocence (ABV 4%)
Innspiration (ABV 4%)
Inncognito (ABV 4.8%)
India Plain Ale (ABV 5.2%)
Inndulgence (ABV 5.2%)

Plan B

Audley Avenue Enterprise Park, Audley Avenue, Newport, TF10 7DW
☎ (01952) 810091 newbrew.co.uk

Plan B is a family-run brewery set up in 2016 using a 10-barrel plant. Beers are distributed within a 30-mile radius of the brewery and are available from the shop or on-site bar. !! RAIB

New Alchemy (ABV 3.9%)
New Session IPA (ABV 4%)
Newport Pale Ale (ABV 4.4%)
Boscobel Bitter (ABV 4.8%)
Steam Stout (ABV 4.8%)

Platform 5 SIBA

Railway Brewhouse, 197 Queen Street, Newton Abbot, Devon, TQ12 2BS
☎ (01626) 437140 ☎ 07779 000081
platform5brewing.co.uk

Established in 2013 using a six-barrel plant. The Railway Inn is supplied along with Molloys in Teignmouth and Torquay. This family-run brewery is situated in part of an enclosed alley under the disused Platform 5 of Newton Abbot station.

The Coaster (ABV 4%)
The Antelope (ABV 4.3%)
APA (ABV 4.6%)
The Whistleblower (ABV 4.6%)
Complex nose with roast and caramel leading to fruit and sweet hops with bitterness on the tongue. Dry aftertaste.
Western Gold (ABV 4.8%)
Blitzen (ABV 5%)
IPA (ABV 5%)
The Black Crow (ABV 5.2%)
Very smooth, satisfying, oatmeal stout.

Play Brew (NEW) SIBA

8 Cannon Park Way, Middlesbrough, TS1 5JU
☎ (01642) 244769 playbrewco.com

Launched in 2019 by Phil Layton, Play Brew is a brewery, taproom and event space. The 20-hectolitre plant produces unfiltered beers available in keg, cans and occasionally in cask, distributed throughout the north. ♦ V

Plockton

5 Bank Street, Plockton, IV52 8TP
☎ (01599) 544276 ☎ 07823 322043
theplocktonbrewery.com

The brewery started trading in 2007 and expanded to a 2.5-barrel plant in 2009. Bottle-conditioned beers are available and are suitable for vegetarians. !! ♦ RAIB

Yarrowale (ABV 4.2%)
Plockton Bay (ABV 4.6%)
A well-balanced, tawny-coloured best bitter with plenty of hops and malt which give a bittersweet, fruity flavour.
Starboard! (ABV 5.1%)
A fine, fruity golden ale with a light citrus bitterness. Hop and spicy fruit feature in the nose with a smack of grapefruit in the taste. The bitterness holds well into the aftertaste.
Ring Tong (ABV 5.6%)

Plot Five (NEW)

Biggleswade hello@plotfive.co.uk

Small batch microbrewery based in Biggleswade, supplying to the local area and beyond. Home-grown allotment hops demonstrates a commitment to sustainability and environmental impact. Three core beers are available in bottles.

Poachers

439 Newark Road, North Hykeham, Lincolnshire, LN6 9SP
☎ (01522) 807404 ☎ 07954 131972
poachersbrewery.co.uk

The brewery was founded in 2001 in buildings on the former RAF Swinderby site. In 2006 the plant was relocated to outbuildings at the rear of the brewer's home. Regular outlets in Lincolnshire and surrounding counties are supplied direct; outlets further afield, via beer swaps with other breweries. An on-site bar is open to public on a Friday evening and for groups at other times by prior arrangement. !! ♦

Trembling Rabbit Mild (ABV 3.4%)
Shy Talk Bitter (ABV 3.7%)
Rock Ape (ABV 3.8%)
Pride (ABV 4%)
Tedi Boy (ABV 4%)
Bog Trotter (ABV 4.2%)
Lincoln Best (ABV 4.2%)
Billy Boy (ABV 4.4%)
Imp Ale (ABV 4.4%)
Black Crow Stout (ABV 4.5%)
Hykeham Gold (ABV 4.5%)
Monkey Hanger (ABV 4.5%)
Jock's Trap (ABV 5%)
Trout Tickler (ABV 5.5%)

Polarity

5 Abbotts Close, Worthing, West Sussex, BN11 1JB
☎ 07872 105300 polaritybrewing.co.uk

A small brewery established in 2016 by two homebrewing enthusiasts, focusing on small batch cask-conditioned beers. They now work full time as brewer's for other established breweries and come together at weekends to brew Polarity beers.

Rosetta's Comet (ABV 5.4%)

Polly's

Holland Farm, Blackbrook, Mold, CH7 6LU
☎ (01244) 940621 🌐 lokapolly.co.uk

Established in 2016 inside the stable of an old horse called Polly as Black Brook Brewery, it rebranded as Loka Polly in 2018. The brewery rebranded again to Polly's Brew Co in 2019. It concentrates only on keg/ KeyKeg and canned beer widely distributed via wholesalers. The beer range changes constantly.

Pomona Island

Unit 33, Waybridge Enterprise Centre, Daniel Adamson Road, Salford, M50 1DS
☎ (0161) 637 2140 ☎ 07972 445474
🌐 pomonaislandbrew.co.uk

Brewery set up in 2017, close to Salford's Media City. Part owned by the people behind the Gas Lamp in Manchester city centre. Head brewer James Dyer is formerly of Tempest Brew Co (qv). Its brewery tap opened in 2019 at 41 Waybridge Enterprise Centre, available to hire for private functions. V

Pale (ABV 3.8%)
Pungent fruity hop aroma. Sweet, fruity taste with some bitterness. Gentle and balanced. Lasting delicate bitter finish.
Stout (ABV 4.5%)
APA (ABV 5.3%)
Hoppy beer with fruit and moderate bitterness, leading to a rising bitter finish. Brewed with variable hops.

Pope's Yard

Cutter Room, Frogmore Mill, Apsley, Hertfordshire, HP3 9RY
☎ (01442) 767790 🌐 popesyard.co.uk

Pope's Yard began commercial brewing in 2012 using a one-barrel plant. Relocation in 2015 also meant expansion to a five-barrel plant with a one-barrel pilot plant. In 2018 the brewery relocated to Apsley, Hemel Hempstead. RAIB V

Lacerta US (ABV 3.9%)
Luminaire (ABV 3.9%)
Quartermaster (ABV 4.4%)
Club Hammer Stout (ABV 5.5%)

Poppyland

46 West Street, Cromer, Norfolk, NR27 9DS
☎ (01263) 515214 ☎ 07802 160558
🌐 poppylandbrewery.com

Established in 2012 by museum curator and geologist, Martin Warren, as a working retirement project. The two-barrel brewery, which produces unfiltered beers, was bought in 2019 by Dave Cornell. With Martin's help initially, David carried on with a similar style of brewing. Beers are on sale at the brewery and at numerous specialist beer shops across East Anglia. Cask ales available in some Norfolk and Norwich pubs. RAIB V

Shipden Stout (ABV 4.5%)
East Coast IPA (ABV 5.4%)

Portishead (NEW)

Unit 3, The Precinct, Portishead, BS20 6AH
☎ 07526 636167 🌐 theportbar.uk

New brewpub established in Portishead, near Bristol, by Ira and Yav Kostadinchev. The beers were originally brewed in the Netherlands, and were only available in bottles. Twelve beers are now available at the Port Brew Pub, with nine of them brewed on the premises. No real ale.

Portobello SIBA

Unit 6, Mitre Bridge Industrial Estate, Mitre Way, North Kensington, London, W10 6AU
☎ (020) 8969 2269 🌐 portobellobrewing.com

Established in 2012, the beers are widely available around London. ♦

Westway Pale Ale (ABV 4%)
Refreshing yellow beer with tart lemon flavour. Sweet biscuit, soft citrus and earthy hops aroma. Bitter, dry, lingering spicy aftertaste.
Star (ABV 4.3%)
Fruity best bitter with caramel sweetness alongside marmalade and earthy hops. Growing spicy hoppiness and a lingering, dry, bitterish finish.
APA (ABV 5%)
Full-bodied, straw-coloured strong ale. The honey sweetness and soft citrus fruit balanced by a bitter hops. Dry aftertaste.

Posh Boys (NEW)

Riverside House, 8 Lower Southend Road, Wickford, SS11 8BB ☎ 07474 594379 🌐 poshboysbrewery.com

Posh Bloys is a small independent craft brewery in Essex, set up by two friends. Operating on a part-time basis, producing beers in smaller quantities, mainly for the take home market prior to the Taproom opening in 2019. Occasionally festivals can be supplied, but brew-length tends to supply the welcoming bar opposite the post sorting office.

The Blind Butler (ABV 4%)
The Blonde Maid (ABV 4%)
Room No. 6 (ABV 4.1%)
The Bowlers Hat (ABV 4.5%)
The Coachman (ABV 4.5%)
The Night Porter (ABV 4.5%)

Potbelly SIBA

Sydney Street Entrance, Kettering, Northamptonshire, NN16 0JA
☎ (01536) 410818 ☎ 07834 867825
🌐 potbelly-brewery.co.uk

Potbelly started brewing in 2005 on a 10-barrel plant and supplies around 200 outlets. Beers are brewed under the Olde England Ales brand name. ‼ ♦ RAIB V

Piggin' Proud (ABV 3.7%)
Best (ABV 3.8%)
Lager Brau (ABV 3.9%)
A Piggin IPA (ABV 4%)
Hop Trotter (ABV 4.1%)
Piggin' Saint (ABV 4.2%)
Beijing Black (ABV 4.4%)
Pigs Do Fly (ABV 4.4%)
Hedonism (ABV 4.5%)
Black Sun (ABV 5%)
SOAB (ABV 5%)
Crazy Daze (ABV 5.5%)
Saint or Sinner (ABV 6.7%)

Powderkeg SIBA

10 Hogsbrook Units, Woodbury Salterton, Devon, EX5 1PY
☎ (01395) 488181 🌐 powderkegbeer.co.uk

Powderkeg was established in 2015 brewing small batches of beer. It combines international beer styles with new ingredients sourced from around the world. GF V

Idler (ABV 3.9%)
A classic session bitter, crisp, refreshing and malty with a fruity (lemon) hop taste.
Speak Easy Transatlantic Pale Ale (ABV 4.3%)

Poynton

Royal British Legion Club, St George's Road West, Poynton, Cheshire, SK12 1JY ☎ 07771 722403

The Poynton Brewery was established in 2015 by Colin Bavens and Andy King, located at the Poynton Legion Club. Around 20 pubs, clubs and bars are supplied in the Stockport, Altrincham, East Cheshire and Macclesfield areas. ♦

Prescott

See Hanlons

Pressure Drop

Unit 6, Lockwood Industrial Estate, Mill Mead Road, Tottenham Hale, London, N17 9QP
☎ (020) 8801 0616 🌐 pressuredropbrewing.co.uk

Run by three partners who were homebrewers but began commercial brewing in 2013, using a five-barrel plant and a small pilot kit. Moving to Tottenham in 2017, the original location is now a bar called the Experiment, operated with Verdant Brewery (qv). An on-site brewery tap is open at weekends and both bars are the best places to find the usual range plus specials. Beers are mostly sold in KeyKeg, bottles and cans. Cask-conditioned versions are produced occasionally for beer festivals. RAIB ◆

Pretty Decent

Arch 338, Sheridan Road, Forest Gate, London, E7 9EF
☎ (020) 8638 6603 ☎ 07825 381346
🌐 prettydecentbeer.co

Brewing began in 2017 in a railway arch in Forest Gate. Production is mostly keg but cask beer has been made for beer festivals and select local pubs (it intends to make more regularly). Canning regularly, and some bottle-conditioned beers are available. An on-site taproom is open Thursday-Sunday and the beers are available in local bars. A portion of profits is donated to charities such as Pump Aid (a water project in Africa). ♦ RAIB ◆

Priest Town

139 Ribbleton Avenue, Preston, Lancashire, PR2 6YS
🌐 priesttownbrewing.com

Priest Town is a craft microbrewery in Preston, operational since 2017. Originally using a 2.5-barrel plant, it has recently acquired a larger kit and plans to increase production. It has a range of eight bottled beers which are sold at its bottle shop on Preston Market. RAIB

Printworks (NEW)

Windsor Castle Inn, 7 Stourbridge, Lye, Stourbridge, DY9 7BS
☎ (01384) 897809 🌐 printworksbrewery.co.uk

Printworks started full production in 2019 with Emily Sadler at the helm. Based at the Windsor Castle pub, Lye, which is the main outlet for the beers; mostly named after typefaces to reflect a family printing heritage. Core beers and various specials are produced. Equipment is visible through a window in seating area. ‼♦◆

Prior's Well SIBA

Unit 8, Block 22, Farm Way, Old Mill Lane Industrial Estate, Mansfield Woodhouse, Nottinghamshire, NG19 9BQ
☎ (01623) 632393 ☎ 07970 885204
🌐 priorswellbrewery.co.uk

Originally established in a National Trust building on the Clumber Park Estate, but brewing ceased there in 2014. The brewery was subsequently sold and the five-barrel plant modernised and relocated to a new site in Mansfield Woodhouse in 2016 with an on-site bar. ‼

Citra (ABV 3.9%)
Incensed (ABV 4%)
Silver Chalice (ABV 4.2%)
Blade (ABV 4.7%)
Priory Gold (ABV 4.7%)
Prior's Pale (ABV 4.8%)
Resurrected (ABV 4.8%)
Wolfcatcher (ABV 4.8%)
Dirty Habit (ABV 5.8%)

Problem Child

Wayfarer Inn, Alder Lane, Parbold, Lancashire, WN8 7NL
☎ (01257) 464600 ☎ 07588 736926
🌐 problemchildbrewing.co.uk

Problem Child began brewing in 2013 using a five-barrel plant at the Wayfarer Inn, Parbold, where two beers from the range are always available. ‼

Project 88

Beer + Burger, 88 Walm Lane, Willesden Green, London, NW2 4QY
☎ (020) 3019 7575 🌐 beerandburgerstore.com

Established in 2017, Project 88 was a nanobrewery at the Beer + Burger bar in Willesden Green. On-site brewing has ceased and the beers are now contract brewed elsewhere and are available on keg at the Beer + Burger branches and other pubs in the group. No real ale.

Prospect SIBA

Unit 10a, Great George Street, off Wallgate, Wigan, WN3 4DL
☎ (01257) 421329 🌐 prospectbrewery.com

Prospect was founded as a five-barrel plant in 2007 in the Prospect Hill area of Standish, hence the name, relocating to its current town centre premises in 2017. The brewery was sold to a husband and wife partnership in 2019 but continues production and trade largely unchanged. ‼ ♦

Silver Tally (ABV 3.7%)
Pale and light, malty beer with moderate bitterness and fruity hops.
Whatever! (ABV 3.8%)

Yellow beer with a light malt/hop aroma. Some malt in taste, but hop and bitterness dominate. Dry, bitter finish.
Nutty Slack (ABV 3.9%)
Dark brown mild ale with malt and fruit in the aroma. Creamy and chocolaty on the palate, with both malt and fruit in evidence. Malty and moderately bitter finish.
Pioneer (ABV 4%)
Whatever Next! (ABV 4%)
Cascade Blonde (ABV 4.1%)
Smooth beer with fruity hops and a clean citrus aftertaste.
Blinding Light (ABV 4.2%)
Hoppy beer with gentle bitterness.
Gold Rush (ABV 4.5%)
Big John (ABV 4.8%)
Pronounced roast flavour with highlights of blackcurrant and hops. Moderate hoppy bitter aftertaste. Fruit in aroma with malt.

Provenance

See Hydes

Providence

Unit 51 Old Mill Industrial Estate, Bamber Bridge, Lancashire, PR5 6SY ☎ 07811 599147
✉ anne.graham.driver@btinternet.com

Brewing began in 2017 using a 3.25-barrel plant.

Gold Standard (ABV 4.1%)

Pumphouse (NEW)

10d Twydale Business Park, Driffield, East Yorkshire, YO25 6JX ☎ 07811 180195

Launched in 2019, Pumphouse Brewing are a craft brewery producing small batch, one-off beers available in keg and bottle. The constantly-changing range is unfined and unfiltered. V◆

Pumphouse Community

Green Man, Church Lane, Toppesfield, Essex, CO9 4DR
☎ 07421 994518
🌐 pumphousecommunitybrewery.com

Pumphouse was one of the first community-owned breweries in the UK. Established in 2015 it uses a two-barrel plant and specialises in session beers with occasional one-off, experimental brews. Pubs, clubs, special events and festivals are supplied within a 10-mile radius as well as its Green Man tap outlet. ‼ ♦ RAIB ◆

Toppesfield Tap (ABV 3.6%)
St Margaret's Ale (ABV 3.8%)
Pumphouse Gold (ABV 4.2%)
Paula's Pride (ABV 4.5%)

Purity SIBA

The Brewery, Upper Spernal Farm, Spernal Lane, Great Alne, Warwickshire, B49 6JF
☎ (01789) 488007 🌐 puritybrewing.com

Brewing began in 2005 in a purpose-designed plant housed in converted barns. The brewery incorporates an environmentally-friendly, effluent treatment system. It supplies the free trade within a 70-mile radius, plus London postcodes, and delivers to more than 500 outlets. ‼ ♦

Bunny Hop (ABV 3.5%)
Pure Gold (ABV 3.8%)
Mad Goose (ABV 4.2%)
Pure UBU (ABV 4.5%)

Contract brewed for Everards:
Sunchaser (ABV 4%)
Old Original (ABV 5.2%)

Purple Cow

Alexandra Arms, 39 Victoria Street, Kettering, Northamptonshire, NN16 0BU ☎ 07507 398353
🌐 purplecowbrewing.co.uk

Purple Cow started brewing at the Alexanda Arms in Kettering. It is owned by David Burns, who is also the brewer. Plans are afoot to move to a new location with a view to expanding ever so slightly. ♦RAIB

Purple Moose SIBA

Madoc Street, Porthmadog, LL49 9DB
☎ (01766) 515571 🌐 purplemoose.co.uk

A 40-barrel plant housed in a former iron works in the coastal town of Porthmadog. It owns a brewery shop on Porthmadog High St and the 'Australia' pub also in the town. The names of the beers reflect local history and geography. ‼ ♦

Cwrw Eryri/Snowdonia Ale (ABV 3.6%)
Golden, refreshing bitter with citrus fruit hoppiness in aroma and taste. The full mouthfeel leads to a long-lasting, dry, bitter finish.
Cwrw Madog/Madog's Ale (ABV 3.7%)
Full-bodied session bitter. Malty nose and an initial nutty flavour but bitterness dominates. Well-balanced and refreshing with a dry roastiness on the taste and a good, dry finish.
Cwrw Ysgawen/Elderflower Ale (ABV 4%)
A pale and refreshing elderflower beer with a good citrus fruit aroma, bittersweet taste, and a zesty, hoppy, mouthwatering finish.
Cwrw Glaslyn/Glaslyn Ale (ABV 4.2%)
Refreshing, light, malty, amber-coloured ale. Plenty of hop in the aroma and taste. Good smooth mouthfeel leading to a slightly chewy finish.
Ochr Dywyll y Mws/Dark Side of the Moose (ABV 4.6%)
A dark, complex beer quite hoppy and bitter with roast undertones. Malt and fruit flavours also feature in the smooth taste and dry finish.

Q Brew

58 Lower North Road, Carnforth, Lancashire, LA5 9LJ
☎ 07971 073835

Q Brew started brewing in 2019 and is Carnforth's first microbrewery.

Q Brewery

16 The Ringway, Queniborough, Leicestershire, LE7 3DL ☎ 07762 300240 🌐 qbrewery.co.uk

A microbrewery situated in a converted building behind the house of head brewer Tim Lowe. It was established in 2014 and uses a 0.5-barrel brew kit. Beers are brewed on demand.

Ridgemere Bitter (ABV 3.8%)
Q Hop (ABV 4.2%)
Invincibull Stout (ABV 4.4%)
Q IPA (ABV 5%)
1630 (ABV 5.5%)

Quantock SIBA

Westridge Way, Broadgauge Business Park, Bishops Lydeard, Somerset, TA4 3RU
☎ (01823) 433812 🌐 quantockbrewery.co.uk

⊗ Quantock is a family-run brewery that started trading in 2008 on an eight-barrel plant, which has since been expanded. The brewery supplies beer to outlets throughout the South-west, and further afield via wholesalers. The brewery taproom and shop are open six days and three evenings a week. An annual beer festival is held over the last weekend in July. ♦RAIB

Ale (ABV 3.8%)
QPA (ABV 4%)
Sunraker (ABV 4.2%)
Wills Neck (ABV 4.3%)
Stout (ABV 4.5%)
Plastered Pheasant (ABV 4.8%)
Titanium (ABV 5.1%)
Stag (ABV 6%)

Quartz SIBA

Archers, Alrewas Road, Kings Bromley, Staffordshire, DE13 7HW
☎ (01543) 473965 🌐 quartzbrewing.co.uk

Quartz was established in 2005 by Scott and Julia Barnett. Around 50 outlets are supplied direct. !! ♦

Blonde (ABV 3.8%)
Little aroma, gentle hop and background malt. Sweet with unsophisticated sweetshop tastes.
Crystal (ABV 4.2%)
Sweet aroma with some fruit and yeasty Marmite hints. Hoppiness begins but dwindles to a bittersweet finish.
Extra Blonde (ABV 4.4%)
Sweet malty aroma with a touch of fruit. Sweet start, smooth with a hint of hops in the sugary finish.
Heart (ABV 4.6%)
Pale brown with some aroma of fruit and malt. Gentle tastes of fruit and hops eventually appear to leave a bitter finish.
Cracker (ABV 5%)

Queen Inn

28 Kingsgate Road, Winchester, Hampshire, SO23 9PG
☎ (01962) 853898 🌐 thequeeninnwinchester.co.uk

The 2.5-barrel brewery was installed in 2013 during a pub refurbishment. Currently brewing takes place about once or twice a month and almost always just for the pub. In 2020 the brewery will attempt to rationalize its very varied 2019 output.

Quiet

Woodend Barn, Burn O Bennie, Banchory, AB31 5QA
☎ (01330) 826530 🌐 buchananfood.com

Quiet Brewery produces bottle-conditioned beers, supplied to Buchanan's Bistro, Banchory. ♦RAIB

Quirky

Unit 3, Ash Lane, Garforth, Leeds, West Yorkshire, LS25 2HG
☎ (0113) 286 2072 🌐 quirkyales.com

Established in 2015, Quirky Ales brews two or three times a week on its 2.5-barrel plant. Simon Mustill and Richard Scott acquired the brewery in 2019. Its on-site taproom is open every weekend from Thursday evening. Bottled beers are available in the taproom, at delicatessens, and farm shops.

Porter (ABV 3.5%)
Blonde Ale (ABV 3.8%)
Two Islands (ABV 3.8%)
Bitter (ABV 4%)
Ruby (ABV 4%)
1 Hop Wonder (ABV 4.1%)
ITA (ABV 4.8%)
Hip Hop (ABV 5.5%)

Radnorshire

Timberworks, Brookside Farm, Mutton Dingle, New Radnor, LD8 2SU
☎ (01544) 350456 ☎ 07789 909748
🌐 radnorhillsholidaycottages.com

Set up in 2012 in a barn on the grounds of a farm offering holiday cottage accommodation, Radnorshire uses its own spring water. Drinkers staying at the cottages are supplied, as well as a few local pubs. !!

Whimble Gold (ABV 3.8%)
Four Stones (ABV 4%)
Smatcher Tawny (ABV 4.2%)
Water-Break-Its-Neck (ABV 5.7%)

Ralph's Ruin

c/o Royal Oak, Lower Bristol Road, Bath, BA2 3BW
☎ (01225) 481409 🌐 ralphsruin.co.uk

Brewing commenced in 2017 using a two-barrel plant in the old kitchen of the Royal Oak. Beer is only available in the pub.

Ramsbury SIBA

Stockclose Farm, Aldbourne, Wiltshire, SN8 2NN
☎ (01672) 541407 🌐 ramsbury.com/brewery

⊗ The Ramsbury Brewing & Distilling Company started brewing in 2004 using a 10-barrel plant, situated high on the Marlborough Downs in Wiltshire. The brewery uses home-grown barley from the Ramsbury Estate.
Expansion in 2014 saw an upgrade to a 30-barrel plant with a visitor centre and a well to provide the water. A distillery that uses grains grown on the estate became operational in 2015. !! ♦V

Farmer's Best (ABV 3.6%)
Same Again (ABV 3.8%)
Deerstalker (ABV 4%)
RPA (Ramsbury Pale Ale) (ABV 4%)
Flint Knapper (ABV 4.2%)
Gold (ABV 4.5%)
Red Ram (ABV 4.5%)
Chalk Stream (ABV 5%)
Belapur IPA (ABV 5.5%)

Ramsgate (Gadds') SIBA

1 Hornet Close, Pyson's Road Industrial Estate, Broadstairs, Kent, CT10 2YD
☎ (01843) 868453 🌐 ramsgatebrewery.co.uk

Ramsgate was established in 2002 at the back of a Ramsgate seafront pub. In 2006 the brewery moved to its current location, allowing for increased capacity and bottling. A 25-hectolitre brew plant is used. !! ♦

Hoppy Pale (ABV 3.6%)
SheSells SeaShells (ABV 4.7%)

Brewed under the Gadds' Brewery name:
No. 7 Bitter Ale (ABV 3.8%)
Seasider (ABV 4.3%)

THE BREWERIES

No. 5 Best Bitter Ale (ABV 4.4%)
No. 3 Kent Pale Ale (ABV 5%)
Faithful Dogbolter Porter (ABV 5.6%)
Black Pearl (ABV 6.2%)

RAN

Unit 8, Ormonde Street, Fenton, Stoke-on-Trent, Staffordshire, ST4 3NP ☎ 07843 092620
ranales.co.uk

Brewing began in 2014 using a one-barrel kit in the garage to the rear of the owner's house. It relocated in 2015 to larger, purpose-built premises nearby, increasing capacity to 2.5 barrels. Most of the brewery output is supplied to pubs in the Potteries. ♦

Coppa Flya (ABV 4%)
American Pale Ale (ABV 4.5%)
Flya (ABV 4.5%)
Hedge Hopper (ABV 4.5%)
Owd Flya (ABV 5%)
Malt and roast aromas. Liquorice flavours, sweet finish with gentle hops.
Cherry Chilli Stout (ABV 5.3%)
Rum 'n' Raisin Stout (ABV 5.3%)
Chocolate aroma with cocoa. Sweet fruity start with hoppy background which develops to a mouthwatering finish.
Stout (ABV 5.3%)

Randalls

La Piette Brewery, St Georges Esplanade, St Peter Port, Guernsey, GY1 3JG
☎ (01481) 720134 randallsbrewery.com

Randalls has been brewing in Guernsey since 1868. The company was bought out in 2006 and moved into a modern, purpose-built brewery in 2008. 19 pubs are owned and a further 70 outlets are supplied. ‼♦

Range SIBA

Unit N4, Lympne Industrial Estate, Otterpool Lane, Lympne, Kent, CT21 4LR
☎ (01303) 230842 ☎ 07912 207775
rangealesbrewery.co.uk

Range Ales was planned and set up in 2016 by two friends over a few pints in their local. The brewery name comes from associations with the Hythe small arms ranges nearby, which provides the names of the beers. A four-barrel plant is used to supply pubs and clubs in the Hythe and Folkestone areas. ‼

Golden Shot (ABV 3.7%)
C.Q.B (ABV 4%)
Double Tap (ABV 4.1%)
Black 'Ops (ABV 4.8%)

Rat

Rat & Ratchet, 40 Chapel Hill, Huddersfield, West Yorkshire, HD1 3EB
☎ (01484) 542400 ratandratchet@ossett-brewery.co.uk

The Rat & Ratchet was originally established as a brewpub in 1994. Brewing ceased and it was purchased by Ossett Brewery (qv) in 2004. Brewing restarted in 2011 with a capacity of 30 barrels per week. A wide range of occasional brews with rat-themed names supplement the regular beers. ♦

Rat Attack (ABV 3.8%)
White Rat (ABV 4%)
Black Rat (ABV 4.5%)
King Rat (ABV 5%)
Rat Against the Machine (ABV 7%)

Raven Hill

Raven Hill Farm, Kilham, East Yorkshire, YO25 4EG
☎ 07979 674573 hello@ravenhillbrewery.com

Raven Hill Brewery started trading in 2018. Based on a Yorkshire farm near Kilham, it brews four regular beers of varied styles and produces regular seasonal beers in small batch quantities. ♦

Summit (ABV 3.6%)
Trail (ABV 4.2%)
Chasm (ABV 4.8%)
Ridge Way (ABV 5.5%)

RBA

8 Oswestry Close, Oakwood, Derby, DE21 2RT
☎ 07943 367765 rbabrewery@gmail.com

In 2015 two friends, Richard Burton and Colin Fryer, began homebrewing in a shed in a back garden. Five years later they decided to sell commercially and production increased accordingly. The 0.25-barrel plant brews three times a week with occasional brews being bottled.

Reaction (NEW)

47 Erw Goch, Ruthin, LL15 1RS
reactionbrewery@gmail.com

Brewing returned to Ruthin after many years when keen home brewer and CAMRA member Clwyd Roberts made his cask and key keg beers available commercially in 2019. One-off beers are produced on a monthly basis with most of the output going to Mold Alehouse which acts as the brewery tap.

Reality

127 High Road, Chilwell, Beeston, Nottingham, NG9 4AT ☎ 07801 539523
alandenismonaghan@hotmail.com

Since starting in 2010, the brewery has built up a loyal following of pubs locally, while supplying beer festivals across the country, functions and individual customers. ♦

Virtuale Reality (ABV 3.8%)
No Escape (ABV 4.2%)
Bitter Reality (ABV 4.3%)
Stark Reality (ABV 4.5%)
Reality Czech (ABV 4.6%)

Rebel

See Dynamite Valley

Rebellion SIBA

Rebellion Brewery, Bencombe Farm, Marlow Bottom, Buckinghamshire, SL7 3LT
☎ (01628) 476594 rebellionbeer.co.uk

Established in 1993, Rebellion has grown steadily with one site move and several expansion projects. It currently brews approximately 100,000 pints per week, supplying more than 600 local pubs and clubs within a 30-mile radius of Marlow. Its ever-popular membership club now has over 4,500 active members. ‼♦

IPA (ABV 3.7%)

Copper-coloured bitter, sweet and malty, with resinous and red apple flavours. Caramel and fruit decline to leave a dry, bitter and malty finish.
Smuggler (ABV 4.2%)
A red-brown beer, well-bodied and bitter with an uncompromisingly dry, bitter finish.
Touchdown (ABV 4.3%)
Roasted Nuts (ABV 4.6%)

Recoil

See Copper Dragon

Rectory

Streat Hill Farm, Streat Hill, Streat, Hassocks, East Sussex, BN6 8RP
☎ (01273) 890570 ✉ rectoryales@hotmail.com

Rectory was founded in 1995 by the Rev Godfrey Broster to generate funds for the maintenance of his three parish churches. 107 parishioners are shareholders. !! ♦

Rector's Pleasure (ABV 3.7%)
Rector's Light Relief (ABV 4.5%)
The Rector's Revenge (ABV 5%)

Red Cat SIBA

Unit 10, Sun Valley Business Park, Winnall Close, Winchester, Hampshire, SO23 0LB
☎ (01962) 863423 🌐 redcatbrewing.co.uk

Red Cat Brewing Company was established in 2014 using an 11-barrel plant. It supplies Hampshire and bordering counties. A small bar and shop in the brewery sells a range of products. !! V

Art of T (ABV 3.6%)
Easy-drinking, speciality pale ale with a slight fruit aroma. Refreshing, dry astringency and bitterness in the taste and lingering aftertaste.
Prowler Pale (ABV 3.6%)
Pale yellow session bitter with dominant hop flavours and some fruit in the taste and aftertaste.
Scratch (ABV 4%)
Session pale golden bitter, low aroma but well-balanced hop, malt and fruit flavours in the taste and aftertaste.
Mr M's Porter (ABV 4.5%)
A rich, fruity porter, complex flavours with good roast aroma and taste, well-balanced with fruit flavours throughout.
Mosaic Pale (ABV 4.9%)
American pale ale-style beer with a rich floral aroma leading to balanced fruit and hop flavours fading to a hop, fruit and bitter finish.

Red Dragon

Office: Unit 24, Ard Business Park, New Inn, Pontypool, NP4 0SW ☎ 07949 631257
✉ marc@reddragon.beer

Red Dragon beers are usually contract brewed by an unnamed local brewery, however brewing is currently suspended.

Red Fox SIBA

The Chicken Sheds, Upp Hall Farm, Salmons Lane, Coggeshall, Essex, CO6 1RY
☎ (01376) 563123 🌐 redfoxbrewery.co.uk

Red Fox began brewing in 2008 and has continued to expand in line with increasing demand. Brewery experience days are available and contract brewing services are offered. !! ♦ RAIB

Mild (ABV 3.6%)
IPA (ABV 3.7%)
Bitter (ABV 3.8%)
Hunter's Gold (ABV 3.9%)
Best Bitter (ABV 4%)
Coggeshall Gold (ABV 4%)
Surrex Gold (ABV 4.1%)
Black Fox Porter (ABV 4.8%)
Wily Ol' Fox (ABV 5.2%)
Ruby Red Mild (ABV 6.9%)

Red Moon

25 Holder Road, Yardley, Birmingham, West Midlands, B25 8AP ☎ 07825 771388

Office: 39 Kimberley Road, Solihull, B92 8PU
🌐 redmoonbrewery.co.uk

Red Moon Brewery was started in 2015 by two friends. Beer names are inspired by their own life events. The bulk of production is bottled, however some cask beer finds its way into the local free trade. In 2020 the brewery opened its own bar, which is within Ivy's Café and Ale Room.

Back Yard BBQ (ABV 4.5%)
Poisons Pleasure (ABV 4.5%)
Screaming Dwarf (ABV 4.5%)

Red Rock SIBA

Higher Humber Farm, Bishopsteignton, Devon, TQ14 9TD
☎ (01626) 879738 🌐 redrockbrewery.co.uk

Red Rock first started brewing in 2006 using a four-barrel plant and upgraded in 2011 to a 7.5-barrel one. It is based in a converted barn on a working farm using locally sourced malt, fresh hops and the farm's own spring water. It has a bar and can accommodate private functions. !! ♦ RAIB

Lighthouse IPA (ABV 3.9%)
Red Rock (ABV 4.2%)
Break Water (ABV 4.6%)

Red Rose (NEW)

The Old Brewery, Back Square Street, Ramsbottom, BL0 9FZ
☎ (01706) 827582

Office: 2 Hameldon View, Great Harwood, BB6 7BL
🌐 redrosebrewery.co.uk

Brewing began in 2020.

Baxters (ABV 3.9%)
Summit (ABV 4.3%)
Lockdown (ABV 4.7%)
Bridge Hopper (ABV 5.5%)

Red Shoot

Toms Lane, Linwood, Ringwood, Hampshire, BH24 3QT
☎ (01425) 475792 🌐 redshoot.co.uk

The 2.5-barrel brewery was commissioned in 1998 and can be viewed from inside the pub. Production is slightly seasonal, about 2-3 brews a week. Surplus output is sold to a selection of other Wadworth pubs.

Redcastle SIBA

Drummygar Mains, Carmyllie, DD11 2RA

☎ (01241) 860516 ☎ 07967 226357
⊕ redcastlebrewery.co.uk

⊠ Established by local farmer and Clydesdale horse breeder John Anderson, Redcastle started brewing in rural Angus in 2016 in a purpose-built brewery on the family farm. The brewery takes its name from the nearby ruined red castle at Lunan Bay. The beers are named accordingly with a historic theme. In addition to the 10-barrel plant, the brewery also includes a bottling line. V

Headstock (ABV 3.8%)
Crusader (ABV 4%)
Red Lady (ABV 4%)
Nobleman (ABV 4.2%)
Norseman (ABV 4.2%)
Cannonball (ABV 4.5%)
Tower IPA (ABV 4.8%)
Courthill (ABV 5%)
Dark Knight (ABV 5.6%)
Laird (ABV 5.6%)
Monster Hop (ABV 6%)

Redchurch

15-16 Mead Park Industrial Estate, Harlow, Essex, CM20 2SE
☎ (01279) 626895 ☎ 07968 173097
⊕ redchurch.beer

⊠ Redchurch was established in 2011 using an eight-barrel plant in a pair of railway arches at Bethnal Green. Expansion took place in 2016 with most of the production moving to Harlow. Redchurch entered administration in 2019 but was purchased by a new owner who continues to brew in Harlow. No real ale. ➤◆

Redemption SIBA

Unit 16, Compass West Industrial Estate, 33 West Road, Tottenham, London, N17 0XL
☎ (020) 8885 5227 ⊕ redemptionbrewing.co.uk

⊠ Redemption Brewing began brewing in 2010 on a 12-barrel plant. In 2016 it moved into a larger unit with a 30-barrel plant. Most of the beer is supplied in cask to pubs in north and central London and to beer festivals. Successful crowdfunding in 2018 led to an expansion to include keg, cans, bottles, KeyKeg and marketing during 2019. ‼ ➤◆RAIB ⚘

Trinity (ABV 3%)
Refreshing golden beer with strong citrus notes throughout. Bitterness is softened by some sweet malt. Long, dry, astringent, hoppy finish.
Pale Ale (ABV 3.8%)
Well-balanced, amber bitter with peppery hops and citrus throughout. Sweet toffee and fruit fades in the slightly dry, bitter finish.
Rock the Kazbek (ABV 4%)
Golden ale. Citrus fruit with soft malty sweetness in the aroma and flavour balanced by dry bitterness. Bitter marmalade finish.
Hopspur (ABV 4.5%)
Smooth brown best bitter. Sweet coffee roast notes, a little nuttiness with resinous hops on the flavour. Dry, bitter finish.
Urban Dusk (ABV 4.6%)
Full-bodied, brown best bitter. Chocolate and fudge in the aroma and flavour overlaid with citrus. Lingering, dry, bitter finish.
Fellowship Porter (ABV 5.1%)
Sweetish, smooth porter. Liquorice, treacle and caramelised fruit balances the dry, dark roast coffee and chocolate notes in the flavour.

Big Chief (ABV 5.5%)
Smooth ruby-brown bitter. Sweet fudge and caramelised orange notes are balanced by spicy, dry bitterness that lingers. Light coffee character.

Redscar SIBA

🏠 c/o The Cleveland Hotel, 9-11 High Street West, Redcar, North Yorkshire, TS10 1SQ
☎ (01642) 513727 ☎ 07828 855146
⊕ redscar-brewery.co.uk

☺Redscar first brewed in 2008. In 2014 it increased its capacity to a five-barrel plant. The brewery supplies the hotel, local pubs and beer festivals. ‼◆

Redwell SIBA

Under the Arches, Bracondale, Trowse Millgate, Norwich, NR1 2EF
☎ (01603) 624072 ⊕ redwellbrewing.com

⊠ Redwell was started in 2013 by a group of beer lovers, tracing their beery influences from around the world. It is now under new ownership and has recently appointed Belinda Jennings as its head brewer. ‼

RedWillow SIBA

The Lodge, Sutton Garrison, Byrons Lane, Macclesfield, Cheshire, SK11 7JW
☎ (01625) 502315 ⊕ redwillowbrewery.com

☺Established in 2010 by homebrewer Toby McKenzie and his wife Caroline. In 2015 brewing moved to a larger, purpose-built unit on the same site. The award-winning beers are distributed nationwide and are available from the brewery's own RedWillow bars in Macclesfield and Buxton. Experimental brews are branded under the Faithless label. ◆

Effortless (ABV 3.7%)
Headless (ABV 3.9%) 🗐
Nicely-balanced with some malty sweetness. Fruit and hops show in the drinking with hop bitterness lasting to the end.
Feckless (ABV 4.1%)
Well-balanced best bitter, malt and hop in the taste with some fruit and roast flavours.
Weightless (ABV 4.2%)
Well-rounded best bitter with a promise of fruit and hop at the start, full-bodied, bittersweet middle and a quick finish.
Wreckless (ABV 4.8%)
Sleepless (ABV 5.4%)
Breakfast Stout (ABV 5.6%)
Smokeless (ABV 5.7%)
Shameless (ABV 5.9%)
Ageless (ABV 7.2%)
Restless (ABV 8.5%)

Reedley Hallows SIBA

Unit B3, Farrington Close, Farrington Road Industrial Estate, Burnley, Lancashire, BB11 5SH ☎ 07749 414513 ⊕ reedley-hallows-brewery.co.uk

☺Brewing started on this four-barrel plant in 2012. Having moved to larger premises, the brewery now has nine fermenters to cope with demand. ‼

Old Laund Bitter (ABV 3.6%)
Filly Close Blonde (ABV 3.9%)
Chinook (ABV 4%)
Pendleside (ABV 4%)
Gentle malt and hops in the aroma lead to a fruity and peppery bitterness which continues to a dry finish.

Monkholme Premium (ABV 4.2%)
New Laund Dark (ABV 4.4%)
Griffin IPA (ABV 4.5%)
Fruity, hoppy bitter with sweet, fruity flavours and a light bitter finish.
Nook of Pendle (ABV 5%)

Regents Canal

See Little Creatures

Reids Gold

61 Provost Barclay Drive, Stonehaven, AB39 2GE
reidsgold.com

Reids Gold was established in 2018. It is a small-batch microbrewery with an average weekly production of five barrels. No real ale.

Remedy

10-11 Market Place, Stockport, SK1 1EW
☎ (0161) 477 1842
remedybarandbrewhouse.co.uk

Opened in 2016, the three-barrel plant is located in a glazed partition in the main bar of the Remedy Bar & Brewhouse, situated in the historic market place in the heart of the old part of Stockport. Beer is only available in the Remedy Bar.

Republic of Liverpool

See Stamps

Revolutions SIBA

Unit B7, Whitwood Enterprise Park, Speedwell Road, Whitwood, West Yorkshire, WF10 5PX
☎ (01977) 552649 ☎ 07503 007470
revolutionsbrewing.co.uk

Revolutions began brewing in 2010. All beers are musically inspired. The Rewind 33 series of bi-monthly specials references music from 33 years ago. ‼♦V

Candidate US Session Pale (ABV 3.9%)
Clash Porter (ABV 4.5%)
Switch (ABV 4.5%)
Swoon Chocolate Fudge Milk Stout (ABV 4.5%)
Marquee US IPA (ABV 5.4%)
Manifesto Stout (ABV 6%)

Rhymney SIBA

Gilchrist Thomas Industrial Estate, Blaenavon, NP4 9RL
☎ (01495) 790456 ☎ 07831 350635
rhymneybreweryltd.com

In its fifteenth year and going from strength to strength. The full range of beers are available in the 11 tied houses and are widely available in free houses throughout South Wales. Unashamedly traditional in its range of beers, the brewery continues to win a range of CAMRA awards. It is situated in the heart of a Unesco World Heritage Site, close to the National Mining Museum and the Blaenavon Iron Works. ‼♦RAIB

Hobby Horse (ABV 3.8%)
Dark (ABV 4%)
Bevans Bitter (ABV 4.2%)
General Picton (ABV 4.3%)
Bitter (ABV 4.5%)
King's Ale (ABV 4.7%)
Export (ABV 5%)

Richmond SIBA

Station Brewery, Station Yard, Richmond, North Yorkshire, DL10 4LD
☎ (01748) 828266 richmondbrewing.co.uk

Richmond opened in 2008 in the renovated Victorian station complex beside the River Swale. Producion is split 50/50 between cask-conditioned and bottled beers. The former are available in the local area at the Hildyard Arms, Colburn, and the Castle Tavern, Richmond, as well as direct from the brewery. ‼♦RAIB

SwAle (ABV 3.7%)
Gundog Bitter (ABV 3.8%)
Station Ale (ABV 4%)
Greyfriars Stout (ABV 4.2%)
Dale Strider (ABV 4.5%)
Stump Cross Ale (ABV 4.7%)
Richmond Pale Ale (ABV 5%)

Ride SIBA

Unit 1, Bridge Court, 12 Cook Street, Glasgow, G5 8JN
☎ 07463 667097 ✉ Info@ridebrewingco.uk

Ride Brew Co is a social enterprise brewery established in 2017.

Charon (ABV 4.5%)

Ridgeside SIBA

Unit 24, Penraevon 2 Industrial Estate, Meanwood, Leeds, West Yorkshire, LS7 2AW ☎ 07595 380568
ridgesidebrewery.co.uk

Ridgeside began brewing in 2010 using a four-barrel plant. Regular outlets are supplied around Leeds and beers can be found across West and North Yorkshire. Cask beers are unfiltered and unfined. ♦V◆

Plato (ABV 4%)
Objects in Space (ABV 4.8%)
Equator (ABV 5.6%)
Milky Joe (ABV 5.6%)

Ridgeway SIBA

Stane Street, North Heath, Pulborough, West Sussex, RH20 1DJ
☎ (01491) 873474

Office: Ridgeway Brewing Ltd, South Stoke, RG8 0JW
ridgewaybrewery.co.uk

Set up by ex-Brakspear head brewer Peter Scholey, Ridgeway specialises in bottle-conditioned beers, although cask beers are occasionally available at beer festivals and locally. A new brewery has been operational since 2016, located within Hepworth Brewery's new premises near Pulborough, sharing some facilities. RAIB

Rigg & Furrow

Acklington Park Farm, Acklington, Northumberland, NE65 9AA riggandfurrow.com

Brewing commenced in 2017 in a former milking parlour. It is a family-run business celebrating the best of home-grown Northumbrian and British produce creating exciting and innovative beers. A brewery tap is open on selected dates (see website for details). ◆

Lonnen (ABV 3.3%)
Owl Porter (ABV 4%)
Run Hop Run (ABV 4.2%)
Trickster (ABV 4.3%)

THE BREWERIES

Ringwood

Christchurch Road, Ringwood, Hampshire, BH24 3AP
☎ (01425) 471177 🌐 ringwoodbrewery.co.uk

Ringwood was bought in 2007 by Marston's for £19 million. Production has been increased to 50,000 barrels a year. Some 750 outlets are supplied. Ringwood beers are now available in Marston's pubs all over the country. Part of Marston's PLC. !! ♦

Razorback (ABV 3.8%)
A malty session bitter with strong toffee notes in the aroma, leading to a short, bittersweet finish. Malt tends to dominate throughout.
Boondoggle (ABV 4.2%)
Fortyniner (ABV 4.9%)
A caramel, biscuity aroma, with hints of damson, lead to a sweet but well-balanced taste with malt, fruit and hop flavours.
Old Thumper (ABV 5.1%)
A powerful, sweet, copper-coloured beer. A fruity aroma preludes a sweet, malty taste with fruit and caramel and a bittersweet aftertaste.

Rising Sun

Rising Sun, 235 Stockport Road, Mossley, OL5 0RQ
☎ (01457) 238236 🌐 risingsunmossley.co.uk

Brewing since 2016 using a two-barrel plant at the side of the Rising Sun. The beers are only available for sale in the pub. In addition to the regular beer many others of differing styles and strengths are available throughout the year.

Rival

60 Theobald Rd, Cardiff, CF5 1LQ ☎ 07889 596306
✉ info@rivalbrewing.co.uk

Commenced late 2017 with a one-barrel kit in a residential garage. Presently produces kegged beers and occasional bottles.

River Leven

Lab Road, Kinlochleven, PH50 4SG
☎ (01855) 831519 ☎ 07901 873273
🌐 riverlevenales.co.uk

Established in 2011, River Leven Ales is situated among stunning scenery on the West Highland Way in Kinlochleven. Beers are produced using the pure Kinlochleven water with no added sugars or unmalted grain.

Blonde (ABV 4%)
Traditional IPA (ABV 4%)

Riverhead

2 Peel Street, Marsden, Huddersfield, West Yorkshire, HD7 6BR
☎ (01484) 841270 (pub) 🌐 ossett-brewery.co.uk

Riverhead is a brewpub that opened in 1995. Ossett Brewing (qv) purchased the site in 2006 but runs it as a separate brewery. It has since opened the Dining Room on the first floor, which uses Riverhead beers in its dishes. Many different beers are produced on a rotating basis. !! ♦

Riverside

Unit 6, Beeding Court Business Park, Shoreham Road, Upper Beeding, West Sussex, BN44 3TN
☎ (01903) 898030 🌐 riversidebreweryltd.co.uk

Riverside began brewing in 2015 using a five-barrel plant. Beers are available locally. RAIB

Rambling Monarch (ABV 3.6%)
Steyning Stinker (ABV 4%)
Beeding Best Bitter (ABV 4.2%)
Sneaky Steamer (ABV 5.1%)
Tubbers' Tipple (ABV 5.6%)

Rivertown

See McMullen

Riviera

4 Yonder Meadow, Stoke Gabriel, Totnes, Devon, TQ9 6QE ☎ 07857 850110 🌐 rivierabrewing.co.uk

Riviera started brewing commercially in 2015 using a one-barrel plant. ♦

RBC Best (ABV 3.8%)
Riviera Pale Ale / RPA (ABV 3.9%)
Devonian (ABV 4.1%)
Riviera Gold (ABV 4.2%)

Rivington

Home Farm, Horrobin Lane, Rivington, Lancashire, PR6 9HE
☎ (01257) 480403 🌐 rivingtonbrewing.co.uk

Established in 2015 using a three-barrel plant, the brewery moved to its current address in 2020. A number of local outlets are supplied direct from the brewery. Approximately 20 per cent of production is supplied in cask form, but all beers are unpasteurised, unfiltered and unfined. Experimental brews and collaborations are regularly available. ♦ RAIB

Roa Island

Belfast Pier, Roa Island, Cumbria, LA13 0PN
☎ (01229) 825291

Brewing commenced in 2017 in a small room at the back of the Roa Island Boat Club. Beers are brewed once a week in 50-litre quantities and are only available on-site. Following the installtion of solar panels, the beers now have a 'daylight' theme.

Roam SIBA

New Victoria House, Weston Park Road, Plymouth, Devon, PL3 4NU
☎ (01752) 396052 ☎ 07971 411727
🌐 roambrewco.uk

Roam produce small batch beers using a combination of traditional and modern brewing techniques and local ingredients. A six-barrel plant is used. Roam now produce traditional cask, keg and bottle conditioned beers. The brewery relocated to the Peverell area of the city in 2019. !! ♦ RAIB

Tavy Gold (ABV 4%)
Hometown Pale (ABV 4.1%)
A nice, fruity, hopped, American-style pale ale. Fruit aroma, tastes of grapefruit and mango with lasting finish on the palate.
Tavy Best Bitter (ABV 4.3%)
Malt dominates the nose and taste with caramel, roast and hops overpowering a subtle hint of fruit. A complex aftertaste.
Sound Bitter (ABV 4.5%)
A good, drinkable best bitter, full-flavoured on body content.

Tavy IPA (ABV 4.8%)
Gold ale dominated by hops and fruit from start to finish. Slight fruit/straw aroma. Citrus/hoppy dry taste. Dry/bitter finish.
Tavy Porter (ABV 5.2%)
Full-bodied porter. Malt, liquorice, chocolate nose. Slightly bitter fruity taste. Roasted coffee and touch of vanilla in the aftertaste.
Double Take (ABV 7.1%)
An American brown ale with lots of body, swimming in fruity hops. Sweet on taste, complex mix of malty/roast flavours. A beer to saviour.

Robinsons SIBA IFBB

Unicorn Brewery, Lower Hillgate, Stockport, SK1 1JJ
☎ (0161) 612 4061 🌐 robinsonsbrewery.com

The sixth generation of the Robinson family now run the brewery, founded in 1838. Following a significant reduction in the tied estate in recent years, there is now gradual expansion with a couple of individual pubs and one small pub company acquired in 2019. A wide portfolio of beers encompasses a core range, bi-monthly seasonals, occasional 'White Label' brews and one-off additions to the 'Trooper' range brewed with Iron Maiden's Bruce Dickinson. ‼ ♦

Wizard (ABV 3.7%)
Dizzy Blonde (ABV 3.8%)
A light-bodied beer, yellow in colour. It has malt and hops in the taste and a dry, bitter finish.
Cumbria Way (ABV 4.1%)
Pale brown with a malty aroma, this beer has a balance of malt, some hops and a little fruit, with sweetness and bitterness throughout.
Cwrw'r Ddraig Aur (ABV 4.1%)
Unicorn (ABV 4.2%)
Amber beer with a fruity aroma. Malt, hops and fruit in the taste with a bitter, malty finish.
Cascade IPA (ABV 4.8%)
Pale brown beer with malt and fruit on the nose. Full hoppy taste with malt and fruit, leading to a hoppy, bitter finish.
Trooper (ABV 4.8%)
Well-balanced, amber beer with malt and hops in aroma and taste.
Old Tom (ABV 8.5%)
A full-bodied, dark beer with malt, fruit and chocolate on the aroma. A complex range of flavours includes dark chocolate, full maltiness, port and fruits and lead to a long, bittersweet aftertaste.

Contract brewed for Everards Brewery:
Beacon Hill (ABV 3.8%)
Light, refreshing, well-balanced, pale amber bitter in the Burton style.
Tiger (ABV 4.2%)
A mid-brown, well-balanced best bitter crafted for broad appeal, benefiting from a long, bittersweet finish.

Rock & Roll

19 Hall Street, Birmingham, B18 6BS ☎ 07922 554181 ✉ rnrbrewhouse@outlook.com

The Rock & Roll brewery started as Birmingham's only rooftop pub brewery, set up by experienced brewer Mark Shepherd. In 2014 Brewster Lynn Crossland joined and now does all of the brewing. In 2016 the brewery moved and expanded to a six-barrel plant. In 2020 it moved to its current location in the Jewellery Quarter. Specials and experimental beers are regularly available. A brewhouse bar is open at weekends. ‼♦V

Brew Springsteen (ABV 4.2%)
Thirst Aid Kit (ABV 4.2%)
Mash City Rocker (ABV 4.5%)
Voodoo Mild (ABV 5%)

Rock Mill

1b Rock Mill Lane, New Mills, Derbyshire, SK22 3BN
☎ 07971 747050

Office: 81-83 Bridge Street, New Mills, Derbyshire, SK22 4DN ✉ rbpine@Hotmail.co.uk

Rock Mill is a microbrewery established by Ray Barton, a former homebrewer, in 2016. ♦V

Mermaids Pool (ABV 3.5%)
Strange Ways (ABV 3.8%)
Back to the Future (ABV 4%)
Cotton Spinner (ABV 4%)
Toffee Town (ABV 4%)
Orangeytang (ABV 4.3%)
Green Ant Racing Fuel (ABV 5.2%)

Rock Solid

Office: 25 Thornebank, Blackpool, FY3 8QE ☎ 07963 860080 ✉ rocksolidbrewingcompany@gmail.com

This brewery, based at the owner's home, started brewing in 2017 using a one-barrel plant. ♦

Blonde (ABV 3.9%)
Pale, dry bitter with modest hops and dry, hoppy finish.
Amarillo Gold (ABV 4%)
American Pale (ABV 4.5%)

Rock the Boat SIBA

6 Little Crosby Village, Little Crosby, Merseyside, L23 4TS
☎ (0151) 924 7936 ☎ 07727 959356
🌐 rocktheboatbrewery.co.uk

Rock the Boat began brewing in 2015 in a converted 16th-century wheelwright's workshop in the village. Beer names relate to a local theme, often reflecting the brewer's musical tastes and local landmarks. Specials are often brewed for Market Town Taverns pubs in Liverpool. A green hop beer is produced each year. RAIB

Liverpool Light (ABV 3.4%)
Light hoppy aromas on this refreshing straw bitter with a delicate hop flavour and a dry bitter finish.
(Sittin' on) the Dock (ABV 3.5%)
Rich chocolate malt aromas, with caramel roast flavours and light sweetness with a mellow caramel roast finish.
Dazzle (ABV 3.6%)
Bootle Bull (ABV 3.8%)
Mussel Wreck (ABV 3.9%)
A well-balanced, malty, amber bitter, strong malt on tasting with some sweetness and a little fruit. Malty finish and mellow hops
Yellow Submarine Special (ABV 3.9%)
Waterloo Sunset (ABV 4.2%)
Dragon's Teeth Chocolate Stout (ABV 4.3%)
Fab Four Liverpool IPA (ABV 4.4%)

Rocket

The Orchard, Garden Farm, Great Staughton, Cambridgeshire, PE19 5BE
☎ (01733) 390828 ☎ 07747 617527
✉ mikeblakesley@virginmedia.com

Originally using spare capacity at King's Cliffe Brewery (qv), Rocket Ales relocated to its own site in 2017.

Atlas IPA (ABV 5.8%)

Rocket Town

c/o Unit 1, Cleveland Industrial Estate, Darlington, DL1 2PB ☎ 07964 301040
🌐 rockettownbrewing.com

Rocket Town began brewing in 2015 using spare capacity at Schoolhouse Brewery (qv).

Rocket Blonde (ABV 3.6%)
Black India Pale Ale (ABV 3.8%)
Rocket Kolsch (ABV 4%)
Dirty Bumble (ABV 4.2%)
Second Burn (ABV 4.2%)
Maple Dog (ABV 4.4%)
Lift Off (ABV 4.5%)
Rookie (ABV 4.6%)
DPA (ABV 4.8%)

Rockin' Robin SIBA

c/o Old Dairy Brewery, Tenterden Station Estate, Station Road, Tenterden, Kent, TN30 6HE ☎ 07779 986087

Office: 6 Pickering Street, Loose, Kent, ME15 9RS
🌐 rockinrobinbrewery.co.uk

Brewing began in 2011 using a one-barrel plant in a garden shed in Loose. It moved to Boughton Monchelsea in 2014 and in 2019 began cuckoo brewing at Old Dairy (qv). ♦

Rockingham SIBA

Blatherwycke, Northamptonshire, PE8 6YN
☎ (01832) 280722

Office: 25 Wansford Road, Elton, PE8 6RZ
🌐 rockinghamales.co.uk

⊗ Rockingham is a small brewery established in 1997 that operates from a converted farm building near Blatherwycke, Northamptonshire, with a two-barrel plant producing a prolific range of beers. It supplies half a dozen local outlets. ♦

Forest Gold (ABV 3.9%)
Hop Devil (ABV 3.9%)
White Rabbit (ABV 4%)
Saxon Cross (ABV 4.1%)
Fruits of the Forest (ABV 4.3%)
Dark Forest (ABV 5%)

Roebuck SIBA

Roebuck, Tobys Hill, Draycott-in-Clay, Staffordshire, DE6 5BT
☎ (01283) 703411 ☎ 07757 503851
🌐 roebuckdraycott.co.uk

⊜Brewing began brewing in 2017 using a six-barrel plant. Although situated adjacent to the Roebuck pub, the brewery is a separate business. Head brewer Steve Topliss has more than 45 years experience in the industry. The Roebuck and its sister pub, the Hawk & Buckle, Etwall, are supplied. ‼

Blonde (ABV 3.7%)
Hopzester (ABV 4.2%)
Bitter (ABV 4.5%)
Porter (ABV 4.6%)
IPA (ABV 5.2%)

Roman Way (NEW)

Building 79, The Old Depot, Bridge Street, Weedon Bec, Northamptonshire, NN7 4PS ☎ 07950 234991
🌐 romanwaybrewery.co.uk

Roman Way Brewery was established in 2019. Its shop and taproom is usually open to the public on Saturdays. RAIB

IPA Claudius (ABV 4.7%)

Romney Marsh SIBA

Unit 7, Jacks Park, Cinque Ports Road, New Romney, Kent, TN28 8AN
☎ (01797) 362333 ☎ 07796 176011
🌐 romneymarshbrewery.com

⊗ An award-winning, family-run, 12-barrel brewery founded in 2015 by former Come Dine with Me executive producer Matt Calais. Beer is supplied to outlets throughout Kent and East Sussex. ‼ RAIB

Mellow (ABV 3.6%)
Romney Best Bitter (ABV 4%)
Romney Amber Ale (ABV 4.4%)

Rooster's SIBA

Unit H5, Fifth Avenue, Hornbeam Park, Harrogate, North Yorkshire, HG2 8QT
☎ (01423) 865959 🌐 roosters.co.uk

⊜Rooster's Brewing is an independent, family-owned brewery and taproom, based in Harrogate. Weekly production capacity stands at 200 barrels, which includes one-off experimental beers brewed as part of the brewery's Outlaw Project. ♦V

Buckeye (ABV 3.5%)
Highway 51 (ABV 3.7%)
Capability Brown (ABV 4%)
YPA (Yorkshire Pale Ale) (ABV 4.1%)
London Thunder (ABV 4.2%)
Yankee (ABV 4.3%)
A straw-coloured beer with a delicate, fruity aroma leading to a well-balanced taste of malt and hops with a slight evidence of sweetness, followed by a refreshing, fruity/bitter finish.
TwentyFourSeven (ABV 4.7%)
Baby-Faced Assassin (ABV 6.1%)

Rossendale

Griffin Inn, 84 Hud Rake, Haslingden, Lancashire, BB4 5AF
☎ (01706) 214021 🌐 rossendalebrewery.co.uk

⊜The brewery acquired the brew plant previously used by Porter Brewing Co in 2007 and is based in the cellar of the Griffin Inn in Haslingden. The Sportsman in Hyde and many other local outlets are also supplied.

Rother Valley SIBA

Gate Court Farm, Station Road, Northiam, East Sussex, TN31 6QT
☎ (01797) 252922 ☎ 07798 877551
🌐 rothervalleybrewery.co.uk

⊗ Rother Valley Brewey was established in Northiam in 1993, overlooking the Rother Levels and the Kent & East Sussex Railway. Brewing on a 10-barrel plant, around 100 outlets are supplied direct. Established and new hop varieties are sourced locally. ♦

Black Ops (ABV 3.8%)
Smild (ABV 3.8%)
Valley Bitter (ABV 3.8%)
Level Best (ABV 4%)
Full-bodied, tawny, session bitter with a malt and fruit aroma, malty taste and a dry, hoppy finish.
Copper Ale (ABV 4.1%)

Hoppers Ale (ABV 4.4%)
Boadicea (ABV 4.5%)
Blues (ABV 5%)
Exit (ABV 5.7%)

Rothes

77 New Street, Rothes, Aberlour, AB38 7BJ ☎ 07336 233634 ✉ therothesbrewery@sky.com

⊗ Situated in the heart of the Spey Valley, Rothes began producing commercially in 2014. Initially producing only bottle-conditioned beers, cask ales are now also available. RAIB

Blackhall Bitter (ABV 4%)

Rough Brothers (NEW)

Unit 2d, Altnagelvin Industrial Estate, Trench Road, Londonderry, BT47 2ED ☎ 07946 638513

Brewery started with assistance from the Go For It business programme.

Roughacre

Castle Camps, Cambridgeshire, CB21 4TA ☎ (01799) 585956 🌐 roughacre.com

Roughacre Brewery was established in 2018 in Castle Camps. It produces small batch brews in a wide range of styles. Beers are available across South Cambridgeshire, West Suffolk and North Essex. RAIB V

The Saintly One (ABV 1.5%)
Zestival (ABV 3.6%)
Red (ABV 3.8%)
Alliance TPA (ABV 4.2%)
Ashdon Amber (ABV 4.4%)
Nighthawker Coffee Porter (ABV 4.6%)
Three Counties East Anglian Best Bitter (ABV 4.6%)
All Saints Old English Ale (ABV 4.8%)
La Belle Saison (ABV 4.8%)
Abbey Gold (ABV 5.2%)
Mosquito India Pale Ale (ABV 5.2%)
Hurricane (ABV 5.4%)
Saffron Sun (ABV 5.4%)

Round Corner

Melton Mowbray Market, Scalford Road (Gate 2), Melton Mowbray, Leicestershire, LE13 1JY ☎ (01664) 569855

Round Corner was launched after 15 years of planning by city director Combie Cryan and brewer Colin Paige. The state-of-the-art, 20-hectolitre brewery and its taproom can be found in the old sheep shed at the heart of Melton Mowbray Market. Single batch releases began in 2019 and include cask-conditioned ales. Beers are available in several outlets around the East Midlands as well as further afield via Small Beer Ltd.

Roundhill SIBA

Unit 1, Lagonda Court, Cowpen Lane Industrial Estate, Cowpen Bewley, TS23 4JF ☎ 07910 567847

Office: 9 Trevine Gardens, Ingleby Barwick, TS17 5HD ✉ roundhillbrewery@outlook.com

Brewing commenced in 2016 on a five-barrel plant. Along with the core and seasonal beers, collaboration brews are produced with local bars. Brewing is currently suspended. !! ♦ RAIB V

Rowton SIBA

Stone House, Rowton, Telford, Shropshire, TF6 6QX ☎ 07854 885870 🌐 rowtonbrewery.com

Rowton Brewery is family-run and was established in 2008 in a converted Victorian cowshed on a farm. The brewing operation is split over two locations. The original brewery is still in the village of Rowton and uses water from a borehole on the farm. A second brewery has been installed at the Pheasant Pub, Wellington. Combined brew length over the two plants is 10 barrels. ♦

Moonstruck Mild (ABV 3.3%)
Star Light (ABV 3.6%)
Pure Gold (ABV 3.8%)
Bitter (ABV 3.9%)
Meteorite (ABV 4.2%)
Portly Stout (ABV 4.5%)
Area 51 (ABV 5.1%)

Ruddles

See Greene King

Rudgate SIBA

2 Centre Park, Marston Moor Business Park, Tockwith, York, North Yorkshire, YO26 7QF ☎ (01423) 358382 🌐 rudgatebrewery.co.uk

Rudgate Brewery was established in 1992. It is situated in the heart of Yorkshire, in the Vale of York, on the old RAF Marston Moor airfield. The old Roman road of Rudgate runs through the airfield and led the Vikings into Jorvik (York), which is what inspires many of the beer names. ♦

Jorvik Blonde (ABV 3.8%)
Viking (ABV 3.8%)
An initially warming and malty, full-bodied beer, with hops and fruit lingering into the aftertaste.
Battleaxe (ABV 4.2%)
A well-hopped bitter with slightly sweet initial taste and light bitterness. Complex fruit character gives a memorable aftertaste.
Ruby Mild (ABV 4.4%)
Nutty, rich ruby ale, stronger than usual for a mild.
Valkyrie APA (ABV 5%)
York Chocolate Stout (ABV 5%)

Rufford Abbey

Unit 2, Meden Road, Boughton, Nottinghamshire, NG22 9ZD ☎ 07557 049120 ✉ sales@headstocksbrewery.co.uk

Originally known as Headstocks, the brewery was originally established in 2017 to produce Prussia Lager in collaboration with a partner brewery in Kaliningrad on the Lithuania/Poland border. In 2018 cask-conditioned beer was added to the range. !! RAIB

Brakeman Best Bitter (ABV 4%)
Canary Pale Ale (ABV 4%)
White Monk (ABV 4.2%)
Early Rider (ABV 5%)
Warrior (ABV 5.2%)
Rufford Poacher (ABV 1038%)

Runaway

Unit 4, Millgate, Dantzic Street, Manchester, M4 4JW ☎ (0161) 832 2628 ☎ 07505 237078 🌐 therunawaybrewery.com

THE BREWERIES

Runaway is located in a railway arch outside Manchester Victoria station. It began brewing in 2014 producing KeyKeg and bottle-conditioned beers. All core range beers are unfiltered and unpasteurised, with many available locally. ‼◆RAIB

Running Man

26 Greenway, Davis Estate, Chatham, Kent, ME5 9UX

Running Man began brewing in 2018.

Ryedale

Roseberry, Moor Lane, Sinnington, North Yorkshire, YO62 6SE ☎ 07850 510859 ⊕ ryedalebrewing.co.uk

⊛Rydale began brewing in 2013 using a four-barrel plant. In 2016 it relocated to Cross Hills and again in 2019 to Sinnington. Brews only on an occasional basis.

S&P

Homestead, Brewery Lane, Horsford, Norfolk, NR10 3AN ☎ 07884 455425 ⊕ spbrewery.co.uk

⊠ Production commenced in 2013 using a 10-barrel plant constructed upon land once owned by prominent Norfolk brewers Steward & Patteson (1800-1965), hence the name. Locally produced malts are used, as is water from the brewery's own borehole. ‼V

Topaz Blonde (ABV 3.7%)
Blackberry Porter (ABV 4%)
First Light (ABV 4.1%)
Dennis (ABV 4.2%)
Fruit and malt, with some caramel, dominate aroma and taste. Full-bodied throughout, with an increasingly bitter finish.
Darkest Hour (ABV 4.4%)
Smoky, roasty and bitter throughout. Full-bodied. Sweet, malty undertones wane leaving a notable liquorice finish with dark fruit hints.
Gold Rush (ABV 4.4%)
NASHA IPA (ABV 5%) ⏚
Strong banana and grapefruit character throughout. A good balance of malt and hop with a bittersweet background. Rich and filling.

S43 SIBA

Durham Road, Coxhoe, DH6 4HX ☎ (0191) 377 3039 ⊕ sonnet43.com

⊛S43 started brewing in 2012. It owns four outlets. All but one is leased out as a free house. The death at a young age of its founder Mark Hird has precipitated a change in the core range of beers. The brewery will continue to produce specials but now two a month. It has an extensive free trade throughout the land. ◆RAIB

The Mark (ABV 3.9%)
The Doctor (ABV 4%)
The Raven (ABV 4.3%)
The Phoenix (ABV 4.4%)

St Andrews Brewhouse

☰ City Pub Co, 41 St Andrews Street, Norwich, NR2 4TP ☎ (01603) 305995 ☎ 07976 652410 ⊕ standrewsbrewhouse.com

⊠ A city centre brewpub opened in 2015 in the premises formerly occupied by Delaney's Irish Bar. ‼◆

St Andrews Brewing

Unit 7 Bassaguard Business Park, St Andrews, KY16 8AL ☎ (01334) 208586 ⊕ standrewsbrewingcompany.com

Established in 2012 the brewery is a four-barrel plant producing bottle-conditioned, cask and eco-keg beers. In addition to its own five outlets (in St Andrews, Edinburgh and Dundee), beers are supplied to a number of supermarket chains, local retailers and outlets. ‼RAIB

Oatmeal Stout (ABV 4.5%)
Mocha Porter (ABV 6%)
Notorious BIPA (ABV 6%)
Yippie IPA (ABV 6%)

St Annes SIBA

St Annes Church, Shorthill, Lea Cross, Shrewsbury, Shropshire, SY5 8JE ☎ (01743) 860296 ☎ 07505 56951

Office: 38 Hafren Road, Shrewsbury, SY3 8NQ ⊕ shropshirebeers.co.uk

⊠ Brewing began in 2017, this independent brewery is in the quirky location of a restored and occasionally functioning church. Recipes are Scandinavian-influenced but traditional British real ales. A broad range of beers styles is produced. ‼◆

Three Erics (ABV 3.7%)
Golden Dart (ABV 3.8%)
Lea Cross Dark (ABV 3.9%)
Tumbledown Dick (ABV 4.2%)
Round the Wrekin (ABV 4.7%)
Iron & Fire (ABV 7.5%)

St Austell

63 Trevarthian Road, St Austell, Cornwall, PL25 4BY ☎ 0345 241 1122 ⊕ staustellbrewery.co.uk

⊛Founded in 1851, St Austell brewery remains fully independent and family-owned. Cask ale is available in all its pubs, and is widely available nationally. A ten-barrel, small batch plant is used to brew monthly specials, including beers for its annual Celtic beer festival in November. These beers are available in 40 selected outlets, and at Hicks Bar at the Brewery. In 2016 it purchased Bath Ales (qv). ‼☰◆RAIB

Cornish Best Bitter (ABV 3.5%)
Light, refreshing bitter with malt aroma. Gentle biscuit malt and hops flavour with fruity bitterness. Malty, bitter, faintly dry finish.
Trelawny (ABV 3.8%)
Light, tawny bitter with aroma of malt and hops. Resinous hop-bitterness develops into toffee-malt sweetness. Crisp malty, fruity finish.
Nicholson's Pale Ale (ABV 4%)
Copper bitter. Hops dominate the taste with citrus and tropical fruits and malt. Dry bitterness rises in the finish.
Tribute (ABV 4.2%)
Amber bitter with malt and fruity hop aroma. Dominant hop bitterness balanced by sweet malt, ending refreshingly bitter and fruity.
Proper Job (ABV 4.5%)
Smooth premium blond ale with citrus hop aroma. Copious citrus fruits with bitterness, dryness and crisp hop bitter and grapefruit finish.
Hicks (ABV 5%)
Tawny, premium bitter with malt nose. Powerful malt and vine fruit flavour with balancing bitterness. Long malty and floral finish.

Contract brewed for Brunning & Price:
Traditional Bitter (ABV 3.5%)

St Botolphs (NEW)

8 Gladwin Road, Colchester, Essex, CO2 7HS
☎ (01206) 511835 ⊕ stbotolphsbrewery.co.uk

Brewing began in 2014. Its Belgian-style bottled beers can be found in pubs, farm shops, specialist beer shops, markets and food festivals in Essex and Suffolk.

St Ives SIBA

Trewidden Road, St Ives, Cornwall, TR26 2BX
☎ (01736) 793467 ☎ 07702 311595
⊕ stives-brewery.co.uk

⊗ The two-storey brewhouse, with 10-barrel plant, integral visitor centre, gift shop and 60-seater café, was built in 2015. Owner Marco Amura started brewing commercially in 2016, with production steadily increasing since then. Bottled beers are the highest seller, due to strong demand from local restaurants and cafés. The brewery's café, which enjoys a panoramic view of St Ives Bay, is a popular venue. !! ♦ RAIB

Harbourside Light Ale (ABV 3.8%)
A yellow blond ale with citrus hop aroma. Fresh grassy hop, grapefruit and gooseberry flavours with moderate and rising bitterness.
Boilers Golden Ale (ABV 4%)
Gold bitter with fruity, hoppy aroma. Strong, bitter citrus hop flavours balanced by sweet and nutty biscuit malt. Bitter, hoppy finish.
XPA (ABV 4.8%)
Yellow ale with a mixed-peel citrus aroma. Grapefruit and lemon flavours dominate with traces of malt. Crisp, bitter hop finish.
Knill by Mouth (ABV 5%)
Gold beer with citrus hop and malt aroma. Pine, grassy citrus hop and caramel malt flavours with stone fruits and bitterness.
St Ives IPA (ABV 5%)
Yellow beer with grapefruit hop aroma. Very bitter and powerfully-hopped with zesty grapefruit citrus flavours. Dry and faintly sweet.
Brewhouse Belgian Golden Ale (ABV 7.3%)
Smooth, copper barley wine. Oily and alcoholic. Complex flavours of vine and stone fruits, cloves, light malt and rising dry bitterness.

St John at Hackney

See Hackney Church

St Judes

2 Cardigan Street, Ipswich, Suffolk, IP1 3PF
☎ (01473) 413334 ☎ 07879 360879
⊕ stjudestavern.com

⊗ The brewery resumed production in 2015, on a newly installed 10-barrel plant. Run by Frank Walsh and Colleen Seymour, the beers are sold mainly through their Ipswich tavern, but can occasionally be found further afield through a distribution agreement with Nethergate Brewery (qv). A core range of beers is offered, but the emphasis is on a wide range of one-off and special brews.

St Mars of the Desert

90 Stevenson Road, Attercliffe, Sheffield, South Yorkshire, S9 3XG ☎ 07365 222101
⊕ beerofsmod.co.uk

With over 20 years of brewing experience, Dann Paquette, together with partner Martha Holley, relocated from Boston, Massachusetts to the UK and established the brewery in 2018. The brewery is located in an industrial area of Sheffield and consists of two buildings around a courtyard – one containing the brewery, the other the taproom which opens most Fridays and Saturdays, plus selected additional days. ♦

St Mary's

St Mary the Virgin, Elsworthy Road, Primrose Hill, London, NW3 3DJ
☎ (020) 7722 3238 ⊕ stmarysbrewery.co.uk

Based in the church crypt, this nanobrewery produces small-batch bottled beers sold in aid of the church's youth projects. Larger batches are produced elsewhere, the bottle label will honestly show the origin. The first pint was blessed by the Bishop of Edmonton and the names have an ecclesiastical bias.

St Peter's SIBA

St Peter's Hall, St Peter South Elmham, Suffolk, NR35 1NQ
☎ (01986) 782322 ⊕ stpetersbrewery.co.uk

⊗ The brewery, built in 1996, is housed in traditional former agricultural buildings adjacent to moated medieval St Peters Hall, dating from 1280. Brewing makes use of the water from an on-site bore hole combined with locally malted barley. Beer is distributed nationally across the UK and exported to more than 40 countries worldwide. !! ♦

Best Bitter (ABV 3.7%)
A complex, but well-balanced hoppy brew. A gentle hop nose introduces a singular hoppiness with supporting malt notes and underlying bitterness. Other flavours fade to leave a long, dry, hoppy finish.
EPA (ABV 3.8%)
Gatekeeper Golden Ale (ABV 4%)
Amber-coloured, full-bodied, robust ale. A strong hop bouquet leads to a mix of malt and hops combined with a dry, fruity hoppiness. The malt quickly subsides, leaving creamy bitterness.
Organic Best (ABV 4.1%)
A very dry and bitter beer with a growing astringency. Pale brown in colour, it has a gentle hop aroma which makes the definitive bitterness surprising. One for the committed.
Stateside Pale Ale (ABV 4.2%)
Ruby Red (ABV 4.3%)
Organic Ale (ABV 4.5%)
A rich toffee apple aroma and a smooth grainy feel. Malt and caramel initially match the dry hoppy bitterness. As the flavours mature, liqourice dryness develops. Full-bodied.
Plum Porter (ABV 4.6%)
Citrus (ABV 4.7%)
Fudge as well as grapefruit on the nose. A refreshing fruit flavour, with hints of grapefruit peel in the aftertaste.
IPA (ABV 5.5%)
Cream stout (ABV 6.5%)

Sabrina

See Worcester

Saddleworth

Church Inn, Church Lane, Uppermill, Oldham, OL3 6LW
☎ (01457) 820902 ⊕ churchinnsaddleworth.co.uk

Set in an idyllic location near St Chad's Church, Saddleworth started brewing in 1997 in a 120-year-old brewhouse at the Church Inn. Brewery and inn are set above a valley overlooking Saddleworth Moor. Brewing capacity was significantly expanded in 2011 with a new 13-barrel plant. Most of the production is taken by the adjacent inn. ◆

Sadler's

See Hawkshead

Saints Row

Unit 1, Cleveland Industrial Estate, Darlington, DL1 2PB
☎ (01325) 464138 ☎ 07922 617622

Office: 18 Maude Street, Darlington, DL3 7PW
⊕ saintsrowbrewing.com

Formerly known as Hells Kettle, Saints Row commenced brewing in 2017 using equipment at Three Brothers Brewing (qv). In 2019 the brewery moved to its own premises in Darlington. A brewery tap is open at weekends. ◆

Salcombe SIBA

Estuary View, Ledstone, Devon, TQ7 4BL
☎ (01548) 854888 ⊕ salcombebrewery.com

⊠ Salcombe Brewery was purpose built on the site of a decommisioned water reservoir, which utilises the natural ambient temperature of the underground facility for storing ales at perfect conditioning temperature. The brewery has close ties with both the RNLI and the Seahorse Trust. ‼ ▤ ◆ GF V

Devon Amber (ABV 3.8%)
Gold (ABV 4.2%)
Shingle Bay (ABV 4.2%)
Seahorse (ABV 4.4%)
Toffee malt is evident throughout this complex yet subtle mix of everything you would expect from a best bitter.
Lifesaver (ABV 4.8%)
A refreshing ale, deep copper in colour, with a smack of citrus and orange peel and luscious malty flavour. A dry citrus finish with a taste of liquorice.
Island Street Porter (ABV 5.9%)
Porter with a creamy head, aroma of chocolate/coffee and cherries giving a black forest gateau taste. Flavours linger on tongue during aftertaste.

Salopian SIBA

The Old Station Yard, Station Road, Hadnall, Shropshire, SY4 3DD
☎ (01743) 248414 ⊕ salopianbrewery.co.uk

The brewery was established in 1995 in an old dairy on the outskirts of Shrewsbury but moved in 2014 to its new location in an industrial unit in the village of Hadnall, where it now produces more than 150 barrels a week of its multi award-winning ales, for distribution throughout the midlands, and further afield. ‼ ▤ ◆ RAIB

Shropshire Gold (ABV 3.8%)
Oracle (ABV 4%)
Citrus aromas lead to an impressive dry and increasing citrusy taste.
Darwins Origin (ABV 4.3%) ⬚
Pale brown in which hops and fruit are dominant. Hops top the aftertaste with a pleasing lingering bitterness. Well-balanced with a moreish demand.
Hop Twister (ABV 4.5%)
Lemon Dream (ABV 4.5%)

Golden Thread (ABV 5%)
Kashmir (ABV 5.5%)
Automaton (ABV 7%)
Gold with pine forest aromas and peaches! Syrup with a kick. Dry hints and exotic astringency as hops give a dry finish but sweet balance.

Salt

199 Bingley Road, Shipley, West Yorkshire, BD18 4DH
☎ (01274) 533848 ⊕ saltbeerfactory.co.uk

Housed in a Grade II-listed Edwardian tramshed, Salt is a state-of-the-art 200-hectolitre brew plant and one of the Ossett group of independently run breweries. The site includes a taproom and live music space. Two bars, branded as Craft Asylum, are operated. ‼ V◆

Jute (ABV 4.2%)
Alpaca (ABV 6.6%)

Salt Steel (NEW)

Middlesbrough ⊕ saltsteelbrewing.com

Established in 2020 and forged from the industrial landscapes of Teeside and Cheshire, Salt Steel Brewing have been collaborating with other brewers in the North East.

Saltaire SIBA

▤ 103 Dockfield Road, Shipley, West Yorkshire, BD17 7AR
☎ (01274) 594959 ⊕ saltairebrewery.com

Launched in 2006, Saltaire is an award-winning brewery on the banks of the River Aire. A brewery tap and shop are open daily except Monday. A major upgrade took place in 2018, with the installation of a new automated 40-barrel plant. The latest development is a state-of-the-art packaging plant with capacity to bottle up to 100,000 units a week, allowing contract brewing and bottling. More than 600 pubs are supplied across West Yorkshire and the north of England. Beer is exported to more than ten countries. ‼ ▤ ◆ ◆

South Island (ABV 3.5%)
Titus (ABV 3.9%)
Blonde (ABV 4%)
Thirst-quenching and quaffable, this straw-coloured beer is slightly sweet and well-rounded with fruit, malt and hops in the taste and a fruity hoppy finish.
Best (ABV 4.4%)
Amarillo (ABV 4.5%)
Cascade (ABV 4.8%)
Triple Choc (ABV 4.8%)
A creamy, dark brown, roast, chocolate stout with a dry bitter finish and a rich chocolate aroma.

Sambrook's SIBA

Units 1-3, Yelverton Road, Battersea, London, SW11 3QG
☎ (020) 7228 0598 ⊕ sambrooksbrewery.co.uk

⊠ Sambrook's was founded in 2008 and supplies its award-winning ales throughout London. The brewery tap hosts various events, is available for private booking and is open as a pub Thursday-Saturday. Sambrook's brews the Watneys range of beers for Watneys Beer Company (widely available around London). There are plans to move to the old Youngs Brewery site in 2020, bringing with them the private Ram Brewery. ‼ ▤ ◆ RAIB ◆

Wandle Ale (ABV 3.8%)

Touch of dryness balances the rounded, sweetish malt flavour of this fruity, quaffable pale brown bitter. Gentle dry, bitter aftertaste.
Pumphouse Pale Ale (ABV 4.2%)
Refreshing golden beer. Citrus aroma becoming more pronounced on the palate with spicy hops, digestives and hints of vanilla.
APA (ABV 4.5%)
A light-coloured, refreshing, smooth beer with hints of malt and fruit in the flavour.
Junction Ale (ABV 4.5%)
Smooth, full-bodied, tawny bitter with sweet caramelised orange, toffee and spicy hops developing in the gentle, bitter, dryish finish.
Powerhouse Porter (ABV 4.9%)
Dark brown porter with a pleasant roasted malt nose. Coffee, sweet milk chocolate, sultanas, spice with an underlying roasty bitterness.

Sandbanks

Unit 6, 4-6 Abingdon Road, Nuffield Industrial Estate, Poole, Dorset, BH17 0UG
☎ (01202) 671950 🌐 sandbanksbrewery.net

Opened in 2018 on the site of the old Bournemouth Brewery with a new five-barrel plant. The beer is becoming increasingly availably in the local free trade with one-off and special beers from the one-barrel plant available in the taproom.

Sandbanks Bitter (ABV 3.9%)
Session bitter with lingering after taste.
Back in Black (ABV 5%)
Wayward Son IPA (ABV 5%)

Sandstone

Unit 5, Wrexham Enterprise Park, Preston Road, off Ash Road, North Wrexham Industrial Estate, Wrexham, LL13 9JT
☎ (01978) 664805 ☎ 07851 001118
🌐 sandstonebrewery.co.uk

Sandstone Brewery was established as a four-barrel plant in 2008. The brewery was taken over by the current owners in 2013. The beers are available at around 50 outlets in north-west England and north Wales. !!

Sandstone Edge (ABV 3.8%)
A satisfying, session ale, this pale, dry, bitter beer has a full mouthfeel and a lingering hoppy finish that belies its modest strength.
Steam Dragon (ABV 3.9%)
Celtic Pride (ABV 4%)
Onyx Dragon (ABV 4%)
Morillo (ABV 4.2%)
Post Mistress (ABV 4.4%)
A full-bodied, smooth, premium bitter. Ruby-red in colour, with a rich, mellow taste.ôGood combination of malt, hops and fruit in aroma and initial taste leading to a lasting, satisfying finish.
Twisted Dragon (ABV 5.8%)

Sarah Hughes

See under H

Saviour

White Hart Inn, Hamstead Marshall, Berkshire, RG20 0HW
☎ (01488) 657545 ✉ info@saviourwhitehart.co.uk

Brewing began in 2019 on a four-barrel plant in an outbuilding in the grounds of the White Hart pub in Hamstead Marshall. Beers are only available from the pub.

Scarborough SIBA

Unit 21b, Stadium Works, Barry's Lane, Scarborough, North Yorkshire, YO12 4HA
☎ (01723) 367506 🌐 scarboroughbrewery.co.uk

Scarborough is a family-run brewery established in 2010, now using a 10-barrel plant. Beers can be found in the family-owned Valley Bar and Rivelyn Hotel as well as being the sole suppliers to Merchant Bar in Scarborough. ♦

Trident (ABV 3.8%)
Citra (ABV 4.2%)
Sealord (ABV 4.3%)
Stout (ABV 4.6%)
Hello Darkness (ABV 5%)

Scribblers

7 Lime Grove, Stapleford, Nottinghamshire, NG9 7GF
☎ (0115) 875 1759 ☎ 07780 662244
🌐 scribblers-ales.com

Scribbler's was established in 2014 by Richard Nettleton, an author (hence the name) and Roger Frost. The 4.5-barrel plant was constructed by the owners, the fermentation and mash tun converted from old ice cream vessels. Beer names are based on classic book titles.

Ale of Two Cities (ABV 3.8%)
Beerfest at Tiffanys (ABV 3.8%)
Golden-coloured with a citrus fruit aroma and taste, and a dry, bitter finish.
Hoppy Potter & the Goblet of Ale (ABV 4.2%)
Life of IPA (ABV 4.2%)
Mango IPA (ABV 4.2%)
Dark Lord (ABV 4.7%)
Masher In the Rye (ABV 4.8%)
Golden-coloured, delicately-hopped beer, subtle malt, hint of fruit, soft bitterness.
Rubecca (ABV 4.8%)
Dark ruby ale with a mixture of roast malt, raisin, fruit and chocolate, leading to a gentle bitter finish.
One Special Brew Over the Cuckoo's Nest (ABV 5.5%)
Insomnia (ABV 5.9%)
Beyond Reasonable Stout (ABV 6%)
Initial roast malt and coffee giving way to moderate bitterness and a dark fruit finish.

Scruffy Dog

94 Station Road, Sutton-In-Ashfield, Nottinghamshire, NG17 5HF
☎ (01623) 550826 🌐 thescruffydog.co.uk

Microbrewery at the Scruffy Dog pub in Sutton-in-Ashfield.

Seagate (NEW)

Seagate, Lamlash, Isle of Arran, KA27 8JN
☎ (01770) 600110 ☎ 07798 854295
🌐 seagatebrewery.co.uk

In 2020 Stephen Sparshott progressed from homebrewing in his kitchen into commercial brewing in a purpose-built shed. Concentrating on Belgian-style and Scottish ales, four core beers are brewed on his 30-litre and 50-litre kits. ♦RAIB

THE BREWERIES

Serious SIBA

Unit C5, Fieldhouse Industrial Estate, Fieldhouse Road, Rochdale, OL12 0AA ☎ 07840 301797
⊕ shop.seriousbrewing.co.uk

Established in 2015 and run by husband and wife team Ken and Jenny Lynch. The beers are brewed using a six-barrel plant. The focus is on producing high quality beers drawing influences from traditional British ales, US craft beers and artisanal Belgian beers. Many outlets are supplied direct and the beers are available nationwide via wholesalers. A taproom opened at the brewery in 2019. ♦ RAIB V◆

Prime (ABV 4.2%)
Evergreen (ABV 4.5%)
Hoppy aroma. Taste of fruit and bitter hops, with lasting bitterness. Crisp and bitter throughout. Background of sweet malt.
Moonlight (ABV 4.5%)
Redsmith (ABV 4.5%)
Goldrush (ABV 5.6%)

Settle SIBA

Unit 2b, The Sidings, Settle, North Yorkshire, BD24 9RP
☎ (01729) 824936 ⊕ settlebrewery.co.uk

Settle Brewery is located in an industrial unit adjacent to Settle railway station. Brewing started in 2013 using a 12-barrel plant. It supplies more than 40 outlets across Cumbria, the Yorkshire Dales, West Yorkshire and North Lancashire. The beers are also available through wholesalers. ‼◆

Blonde (ABV 3.6%)
Jericho Blonde (ABV 3.6%)
Mainline (ABV 3.8%)
Creamy, traditional Yorkshire Bitter. Good balance of rich malt and bittering hops, giving a pronounced raspberry fruitiness and hints of nuts in both aroma and taste.
Ribblehead Bitter (ABV 3.8%)
Epic IPA (ABV 4.4%)
Ernie's Milk Stout (ABV 4.5%)

Brewed under the Nine Standards brand name:
Golden Ale (ABV 4.1%)
Pale Ale (ABV 4.3%)
Porter (ABV 4.7%)
Roasty porter with coffee and dark fruits. Hints of liquorice and plums in the aroma. The finish is bitter and roasty.

Seven Bro7hers SIBA

Unit 63, Waybridge Enterprise Centre, Daniel Adamson Road, Salford, M50 1DS
☎ (0161) 228 2404 ⊕ sevenbro7hers.com

Brewing began in 2014 using a 10-barrel plant. A new brewhouse and fermentation tanks doubled brewing capacity in 2017, and allowed for the brewing of speciality and one-off beers, plus a brewery tap. The Seven Bro7hers Beerhouse in Ancoats opened in 2016, and a new Beerhouse opened in 2019 in the Middlewood Locks area near Salford Central station. Further outlets are planned in Leeds, Liverpool and at Manchester Airport. ‼

Session (ABV 3.8%)
Fruity hop taste of tropical fruit, well-balanced with bitter and pale malt. Citrus hop aroma. Refreshing bitter finish.

Seven Kings

Wymet House, 87 New Row, Dunfermline, KY12 7DZ

Brewing began in 2019.

Severn SIBA

The Brewery, Tortworth Business Park, Tortworth, Gloucestershire, GL12 8HQ
☎ (01454) 269421 ⊕ s7n.co.uk

⊠ The brewery is owned by Foxstead Ltd, a drinks distribution company. All beers are brewed using a 30-barrel plant, with a five-barrel plant for experimental brews and small batches. ‼ ◆ GF

Copper Ale (ABV 3.8%)
Chocolate Stout (ABV 4.1%)
Double Hopped Pale Ale (ABV 4.2%)
Amarillo Citra APA (ABV 4.3%)
Godiva (ABV 4.3%)
Golden IPA (ABV 4.5%)
Ruby Porter (ABV 4.8%)
Extra Special (ABV 5.2%)

Brewed under the Cotswold Spring brand name:
Mystic (ABV 4.3%)
Waii-iti (ABV 4.3%)

Severn Valley

The Stables, Hollow Ash Lane, Bridgnorth, Shropshire, WV15 6ET ☎ 07402 636482 ⊕ severnvalleyales.co.uk

The trading name of Bridgnorth Brewery Ltd, Severn Valley Ales started brewing in 2019 producing a range of beers in different packaging formats.

SVA (ABV 4%)
Cartway Gold (ABV 4.2%)
Old Mo (ABV 4.8%)

Shadow

44 Whiteley Croft Rise, Otley, West Yorkshire, LS21 3NR ☎ 07792 690536 ⊕ shadowbrewing.co.uk

Established in 2019 by Ian Shutt, one of the founders of the Chevin brewing collective, Shadow consists of a one-barrel plant in Ian's garage.

Shakespeare

See North Cotswold

Shalford SIBA

PO Box 10411, Braintree, Essex, CM7 5WP
☎ (01371) 850925 ☎ 07749 658512
⊕ shalfordbrewery.co.uk

Shalford began brewing in 2007 on a five-barrel plant at Hyde Farm in the Pant Valley in Essex. More than 50 outlets are supplied direct. ◆ RAIB

1319 Mild (ABV 3.7%)
Barnfield Pale Ale (ABV 3.8%)
Pale-coloured but full-flavoured, this is a traditional pale ale. Malt persists throughout, with bitterness becoming more dominant towards the end.
Braintree Market Ale (ABV 4%)
Levelly Gold (ABV 4%)
Stoneley Bitter (ABV 4.2%)
Dark amber, session beer whose vivid hop character is supported by a juicy, malty body. A dry finish makes this beer very drinkable.
Hyde Bitter (ABV 4.7%)
Stronger version of Barnfield, with a similar but more assertive character.
Levelly Black (ABV 4.8%)
Rotten End (ABV 6.5%)

Sharp's

Pityme Business Centre, Rock, Cornwall, PL27 6NU
☎ (01208) 862121 🌐 sharpsbrewery.co.uk

⊗ Sharp's was bought for £20 million by Molson Coors in 2011. The brewery was founded in 1994 and within 15 years had grown from producing 1,500 barrels a year to 60,000. £7.5 million of investment from Molson Coors has brought the capacity up to 200,000 barrels a year. The company owns no pubs and delivers beer to more than 1,200 outlets across the south of England via temperature-controlled depots in Bristol and London. Molson Coors has stressed that it will maintain production in Cornwall. Part of Molson Coors PLC. ♦RAIB

Cornish Coaster (ABV 3.6%)
Refreshing, tawny bitter with malt and tropical fruit nose. Stone fruit and tropical fruit with biscuit malt and caramel notes.
Doom Bar (ABV 4%)
Copper bitter with gentle fruit and hop aroma. Clean, balanced taste of biscuit malt, hops and plum fruit. Bittersweet finish.
Atlantic (ABV 4.2%)
Refreshing amber bitter with citrus hops and caramel aroma. Malt and caramel sweetness balanced by grapefruit hops with resin notes.
Original (ABV 4.4%)
Mid-brown best bitter with pleasant hop and malt aroma. Prune and berry fruits on the palate with smoky malt.
Sea Fury (ABV 5%)
Smooth, auburn, premium bitter with malt and caramel aromas. A combination of berry, stone and dried fruits with spice hints.

Shaws of Grange (NEW)

Palace Buildings, Main Street, Grange-over-Sands, LA11 6AB
☎ (01229) 837955 ☎ 07951 009607
🌐 shawsofgrange.co.uk

This 0.5-barrel brewery began producing beers for sale in 2019. A range of four beers has been developed for sale in cask and by hand bottling.

Bay Walker (ABV 4.2%)
Clock Tower Blonde (ABV 4.2%)
Hampsfell (ABV 4.2%)
Old Pool (ABV 4.2%)

Shed Ales

Broadfields, Pewsey, Wiltshire, SN9 5DT
☎ (01672) 564533 ☎ 07769 812643
🌐 shedales.com

Shed Ales was launched in 2012 operating from a one-barrel plant in a converted garden shed. The brewery currently produces three core ales and several bespoke beers, available at selected local outlets including the brewery-owned Shed Alehouse, a micropub in Pewsey. ♦

Dig It (ABV 3.7%)
Shed Some Light (ABV 3.8%)
Dibber (ABV 4.2%)

Sheffield SIBA

Unit 111, JC Albyn Complex, Burton Road, Sheffield, South Yorkshire, S3 8BT
☎ (0114) 272 7256 🌐 sheffieldbrewery.com

Established in 2006, Sheffield Brewery Company is situated in a former Victorian factory, originally known for making Blanco polish. The 10-barrel plant operates on a gravity-fed tower based system. The brewery has its own on-site tap room. !! ♦

Crucible Best (ABV 3.8%)
Five Rivers (ABV 3.8%)
Blanco Blonde (ABV 4.2%)
Porter (ABV 4.4%)

Shepherd Neame IFBB

17 Court Street, Faversham, Kent, ME13 7AX
☎ (01795) 532206 🌐 shepherdneame.co.uk

⊗ Shepherd Neame traces its history back to at least 1698, making it the oldest continuous brewer in the country. The company has 300 tied houses in the south-east, nearly all selling cask ale. More than 2,000 other outlets are also supplied. The cask beers are made with mostly Kentish hops, and water from the brewery's own artesian well. A microplant within the brewery produces speciality ales for special occasions and product development. A Cask Club offers a new, different cask ale every month. The company also brews cask ales under the Faversham Steam Brewery and No. 18 Yard Brewhouse names. !! ♦RAIB

Master Brew (ABV 3.7%)
A distinctive bitter, mid-brown in colour, with a hoppy aroma. Well-balanced, with a nicely aggressive bitter taste from its hops. It leaves a hoppy/bitter finish, tinged with sweetness.
Whitstable Bay Pale Ale (ABV 3.9%)
Spitfire Gold (ABV 4.1%)
Spitfire (ABV 4.2%)
Bishops Finger (ABV 5%)

Sherfield Village SIBA

Goddards Farm, Goddards Lane, Sherfield on Loddon, Hampshire, RG27 0EL ☎ 07906 060429
🌐 sherfieldvillagebrewery.co.uk

Production started in 2011 in a converted barn on a working dairy farm. Using a five-barrel plant, the brewery supplies local pubs and regional festivals. Extensive use is made of New World hops, particularly those from New Zealand. All beers are unfined. ♦RAIB

Threesome (ABV 3%)
SOLO Southern Gold (ABV 4%)
SOLO Green Bullet (ABV 4.3%)
A strong lemony nose, with hops dominating the taste building to a strong aftertaste with a big astringent hit at the end.
SOLO Single Hop (ABV 4.3%)
Hoppy Harrington (ABV 4.7%)
Pioneer Stout (ABV 5%)

Shilling

92 West George Street, Glasgow, G2 1PJ
☎ (0141) 353 1654 🌐 shillingbrewingcompany.co.uk

Brewing began in 2016.

ShinDigger

Office: 170 Vie Building, 185 Water Street, Manchester, M3 4JU 🌐 shindiggerbrewing.co

Established in 2012, ShinDigger's output is predominantly keg and cans supplied to outlets such as restaurants and music venues around Manchester. Music, beer and food events are run. Beers are contract brewed in Cumbria and Lancaster.

THE BREWERIES

Shiny SIBA

Unit 10, Old Hall Mill Business Centre, Little Eaton, Derbyshire, DE21 5EJ
☎ (01332) 902809

Brewing commenced in 2012 using a six-barrel plant sited in the beer garden of the Furnace Inn, Derby. After initially brewing solely for the pub, 2014 saw an increase in scale and output, with beers distributed across most of the country. A second 12-barrel brew plant was built in 2015 to increase capacity and host a visitor centre, taproom and shop. ♦RAIB V

New World (ABV 3.7%)
Happy People (ABV 4.1%)
Wrench (ABV 4.4%)
4 Wood (ABV 4.5%)
Affinity (ABV 4.6%)
Disco Balls (ABV 5.3%)

Ship Inn

Ship Inn, Newton Square, Low Newton-by-the-Sea, Northumberland, NE66 3EL
☎ (01665) 576262 shipinnnewton.co.uk

Brewing commenced in 2008 on a 2.5-barrel plant. The brewery now produces 7.5 barrels per week. All regular beers are brewed in constant rotation but are only available on the premises. A special beer is brewed for every 100 brews. ♦RAIB

Shipstone's SIBA

Little Star Brewery, Fox & Crown, 33 Church Street, Old Basford, Nottingham, NG6 0GA
☎ (0115) 837 4200 shipstones.com

Set up in 1996 as Fiddlers Ales. In 1999 it became Alcazar Brewery on change of ownership. A full mash brewery with a 10-barrel brew length, it is located behind the Fox & Crown. The brewery changed hands in 2016. The name of the brewery was changed again and a new portfolio of beers was established, but was short lived. It soon reverted back to Alcazar. In late 2016 Shipstone's took over brewing, producing its range of beers that had previously been contract brewed at Belvoir Brewery (qv). Beers are also brewed under the Hollow Stone Brewing Co name. ‼♦

Original (ABV 3.8%)
Pale brown, malty, traditional bitter. Well-balanced in both hops and bitterness without either becoming overpowering.
Nut Brown (ABV 4%)
Gold Star (ABV 4.2%)
Golden in colour with a delicate citrus hop and slight dry, bitter finish.
IPA (ABV 5.5%)

Brewed under the Hollow Stone Brewing Co name:
Oligo Nunk (ABV 4%)
Pale Ale (ABV 4.2%)
Waitomo (ABV 4.5%)
Aruru (ABV 4.7%)

Short Stack

Cock, 315 Mare Street, Hackney, London, E8 1EJ
howlinghops.co.uk

Brewing began in 2018 on kit previously used by Howling Hops and Maregade. Beers brewed by the pub's staff are only available in the pub and its name reflects the limited headroom in the cellar where it is situated.

Shortts SIBA

Shortts Farm, Thorndon, Suffolk, IP23 7LS ☎ 07900 268100 shorttsfarmbrewery.com

An award-winning brewery established in 2012 by Matt Hammond on what has been the family farm for over a century. Ales are produced using carefully selected ingredients to create both traditional and more complex contemporary flavours. The beer names are based around a musical theme and can be found throughout East Anglia. RAIB V

The Cure (ABV 3.6%)
Strummer (ABV 3.8%)
Two Tone (ABV 3.8%)
Blondie (ABV 4%)
Rockabilly (ABV 4.3%)
Skiffle (ABV 4.5%)
Black Volt (ABV 4.8%)
Indie (ABV 4.8%)
Darkside (ABV 5%)

Shotover SIBA

Coopers Yard, Manor Farm Road, Horspath, Oxfordshire, OX33 1SD
☎ (01865) 604620 ☎ 07710 883273
shotoverbrewing.com

A family-owned and run brewery, it began brewing in 2009 and supplies outlets in the Oxford area. ‼♦V

Prospect (ABV 3.7%)
Trinity (ABV 4.2%)
Scholar (ABV 4.5%)
Matilda's Tears (ABV 5%)

Shottle Farm

c/o School House Farm, Lodge Lane, Shottle, DE56 2DS
☎ (01773) 550056 ☎ 07877 723075
shottlefarmbrewery.co.uk

Located in the hills above Belper, the Grade II-listed farm is part of the Chatsworth Estate. Established in 2011 with a 10-barrel plant, beers are now contract brewed elsewhere. Shottle Farm has on on-site bar (limited opening hours), the Bull Shed, which is the only outlet for its beers. ♦RAIB

Shottlecock (ABV 3.6%)
Black Peggy (ABV 3.9%)
Shottle Pale Ale (ABV 4%)
B.O.B (Best of Both) (ABV 4.1%)
Eight Shilling (ABV 4.1%)
Shottle Gold (ABV 4.3%)
Dilks (ABV 5%)

Shugborough

Shugborough Estate, Milford, Staffordshire, ST17 0XB
☎ (01782) 823447 shugborough.org.uk

Brewing in the original brewhouse at Shugborough, home of the Earls of Lichfield, restarted in 1990, but a lack of expertise led to the brewery being a static museum piece until Titanic Brewery of Stoke-on-Trent (qv) began helping in 1996. Brewing is currently suspended. ‼

Signal SIBA

8 Stirling Way, Beddington Farm Road, Beddington, CR0 4XN
☎ (020) 8684 6111 signalbeerco.com

Starting in 2016, Signal Brewery's lager was the staple product in keg and cans. 2018 saw a change and a range of cask ale is now produced. A bar opened in the O2 Arena in North Greenwich during 2019 and this is the best bet for the widest range.

Absolutely Fuggled (ABV 4%)
Yellow-coloured, easy-drinking bitter with earthy hops and orangey fruit on the sweetish nose and biscuit flavour becoming bitter.
Sticky Hoppy Pudding (ABV 4.3%)
A creamy, pale brown beer with a distinct caramel aroma and flavour and with limited hop and fruit taste.
Solo (ABV 4.6%)

Signature SIBA

Unit 15, Uplands Business Park, Blackhorse Lane, Walthamstow, London, E17 5QJ
☎ (020) 7684 4664 ⊕ signaturebrew.co.uk

Signature Brew has been brewing beer inspired by music since 2011. Originally using spare capacity at a number of breweries, a successful crowd funding initiative resulted in it owning its own brewery in Leyton and later expanding into larger premises in Walthamstow by 2019. Special seasonal beers are brewed in collaboration with music artists. ▰◆RAIB◆

Session (ABV 4%)
Refreshing bitter with spicy hop on the nose and palate balanced by a malty sweetness and a lingering bitterness.
Signature Pale (ABV 4.1%)
Golden beer using pale malts with a little wheat. The American hops give the beer its fruity character.
Black Vinyl Stout (ABV 4.2%)
Rich cocoa roasted notes predominate on the palate balanced by some sweetness and American hops giving lightness to the flavour.
Red Wedge (ABV 4.7%)
Reddish brown beer with hoppy fruity aroma. Flavour is dominated by hops with bitterness coming through later. Tangerine fruit notes
Backstage IPA (ABV 5.6%)
Amber, unfined IPA with fruity hops and a bitterness, overlaid with some banana and biscuity malty notes. Lingering, dry finish.

Silhill SIBA

Oak Farm, Hampton Lane, Catherine-de-Barnes, Solihull, West Midlands, B92 0JB
☎ (0845) 519 5101 ☎ 07977 444564
Office: PO Box 15739, Solihull, B93 3FW
⊕ silhillbrewery.co.uk

⊗ Established in 2010, Silhill is a small, independent brewery based in premises just outside Solihull town centre using a 10-barrel plant. Bottling operations commenced in 2015. Beers are available in Solihull, Birmingham and Stratford-upon-Avon as well as in Malmaison restaurants. ‼RAIB

Gold Star (ABV 3.9%)
Blonde Star (ABV 4.1%)
Hop star (ABV 4.2%)
Pure Star (ABV 4.3%)
Super Star (ABV 5.1%)

Silver

Units 3 & 4, Silver House, Adelphi Way, Staveley, Derbyshire, S43 3LJ
☎ (01246) 470074 ☎ 07496 757619
⊕ silverbrewhouse.com

⊗ Born out of the takeover of the RAW brewery in 2018, Silver Brewhouse is a 12-barrel plant which continues to brew under the brand names of Industrial Ales and Funky Hop Donkey but has dropped the RAW brand name while still brewing the same recipe beers but under the Silver Brewhouse banner. V

West Coast Pale Ale (ABV 3.7%)
Baby Ghost (ABV 3.9%)
Independence American IPA (ABV 4.1%)
Grey Ghost IPA (ABV 5.9%)

Brewed under the Industrial Ales brand name:
Brickworks Bitter (ABV 4%)
Stephensons Pale (ABV 4%)
Arkwrights Pale (ABV 4.1%)
Coal Face Stout (ABV 4.5%)

Silver Street SIBA

Britannia Mill, Cobden Street, Bury, BL9 6AW
☎ 07515 651874
⊕ silverstreetbrewingcompany.com

⊛Brewing began in 2014 at the Clarence on Silver Street, Bury. The brewery has since expanded to a 15-barrel plant at Britannia Mill. ‼◆

Session (ABV 3.9%)
Malty beer with bitter hops throughout and balancing sweetness.
Fire Island (ABV 4%)
One (ABV 4%)
Ruby, Ruby, Ruby, Ruby (ABV 4.7%)
Porter (ABV 5%)
Pronounced chocolate roast and raisin in aroma and taste. Moderate bitter caramel finish, with some dark chocolate roast.
Red (ABV 5.5%)
USA IPA (ABV 5.7%)

Silverstone SIBA

Kingshill Farm, Syresham, Northamptonshire, NN13 5TH ☎ 07835 279400
⊕ silverstonebrewery.co.uk

Established in 2008 Silverstone Brewery is a traditional tower brewery located near the celebrated motor racing circuit. The brewery has won multiple awards for it's beers which are supplied in bottles, cask and KeyKeg. ‼◆

Ignition (ABV 3.4%)
Pitstop (ABV 3.9%)
Polestar (ABV 4.1%)
Chequered Flag (ABV 4.3%)
Octane (ABV 4.8%)
Classic IPA (ABV 5.6%)

Simple Things Fermentations (NEW)

The Bakehouse, 6 Hazel Avenue Lane, Glasgow, G44 3LJ
☎ (0141) 237 2202
⊕ simplethingsfermentations.com

Opened in 2019 by Phil Sisson, ex-Heriot-Watt and Harviestoun, the brewery has a 600-litre capacity and currently produces beer in bottle and keg. There are plans to begin producing cask-conditioned beer in the near future. ‼◆RAIB V

Simpsons

⌷ **White Swan, Eardisland, Herefordshire, HR6 9BD**
☎ (01544) 388635 ⊕ thewhiteswaneardisland.com

Tim Simpson acquired the White Swan in 2011 and set up the brewery at the rear of the pub in 2013. All beers are brewed for consumption in the White Swan. ♦

Siren SIBA

Unit 1, Hogwood Lane Industrial Estate, Weller Drive, Finchampstead, Berkshire, RG40 4QZ
☎ (0118) 973 0929 🌐 sirencraftbrew.com

Established in 2013, this is a state-of-the-art, 40-barrel, craft brewery, which produces a range of cask, keg, bottled and canned beers that are distributed throughout Europe. The Siren Tap Yard at the brewery in Finchampstead opened in 2017. Siren have expansion plans funded by a successful crowdfunding project, including rolling out the Tap Yard concept to city centre locations as well as increasing brewing capacity. !! ♦

Yu Lu (ABV 3.6%)
Undercurrent Oatmeal Pale Ale (ABV 4.5%)
Broken Dream Breakfast Stout (ABV 6.5%)

six°north

Reekie House, Aberdeen Road, Laurencekirk, AB30 1AG
☎ (01561) 377047 ☎ 07840 678243
🌐 sixdnorth.co.uk

Established in 2013, the brewery brews beers in the Belgian tradition, using a purpose-built, 470-hectolitre plant. Depending on beer style, the beers are supplied as cask or keg. !! ♦ RAIB

Chopper Stout (ABV 4.1%)
Roasted coffee, malted, with background liquorice.

Six Towns

Wheatsheaf, 234 High Street, Tunstall, Staffordshire, ST6 5TT
☎ (01782) 922628 🌐 sixtownsbrewery.com

Previously known as Sunset Taverns, Six Towns is a small independent brewery at the rear of the Wheatsheaf pub in the Potteries.

Sixpenny SIBA

The Old Dairy, Holwell Farm, Cranborne, Dorset, BH21 5QP
☎ (01725) 762006 🌐 sixpennybrewery.co.uk

Founded in 2007, and after a move in 2016 to renovated Victorian farm buildings near Cranborne, Sixpenny Brewery is now brewing to its 20-barrel plant capacity. This has allowed for the expansion of the brewery bar and shop (the Sixpenny Tap), which is located next door to the brewery in converted stables, in order to meet growing demand. Plans are afoot to increase the amount of bottle beer available year round. !! ♦

6d Best Bitter (ABV 3.8%)
6d Gold (ABV 4%)
6d IPA (ABV 5.2%)

Skinner's SIBA

Riverside, Newham Road, Truro, Cornwall, TR1 2DP
☎ (01872) 271885 🌐 skinnersbrewery.com

Award-winning brewery established in 1997. The brewery moved to bigger premises in 2003, and opened a shop and visitor centre. The 25-barrel plant produces more than 26,000 hectolitres per year. Single batch brews are produced throughout the year, but with limited availability. !! ♦

GTA (ABV 3.8%)
A golden, speciality honey ale. Citrus hop aroma and powerful flavour balanced by bitterness. Lingering bitter finish with some fruitiness.

Sennen (ABV 3.8%)
Blond ale with citrus peel and toffee malt aroma. Fresh fruit and malt taste with resinous citrus hops. Bitter finish.

Betty Stogs (ABV 4%)
Bitter resinous hops balanced by sweet malt flavours. Sweet malt fades into the long bitter finish with rising dryness.

Hops 'n Honey (ABV 4%)
A gold speciality beer containing honey. Balance of light citrus, grassy hops, apple and sweet malt. Pleasant, long, dry finish.

Lushingtons (ABV 4.2%)
Refreshing, smooth, blond ale. Lemon and marmalade citrus hop and malt flavours. Bittersweet, with stone fruits. Long, clean, dry finish.

Cornish Knocker (ABV 4.5%)
Smooth, gold bitter with marmalade hops and malt aroma. Citrus and floral hops blend with biscuit malt with hints of toffee.

Pennycomequick (ABV 4.5%)
Creamy, dark brown, sweet stout with roast grain aroma. Heavy roast coffee, malt, fig and cherry flavours. Roast, dry finish.

Porthleven (ABV 4.8%)
Robust pale blond ale with citrus nose. Assertive citrus hop, bitter and sweet fruity flavours. Bitter, dry, citrus hop finish.

Seven Hop (ABV 5%)
Smooth golden ale. Strong hop aroma and heavy punch of grapefruit citrus hops throughout. Marmalade and stone fruits. Bitter, dry finish.

Slater's SIBA IFBB

St Albans Road, Common Road Industrial Estate, Stafford, ST16 3DR
☎ (01785) 257976 🌐 slatersales.co.uk

The brewery was opened in 1995 and in 2006 moved to new, larger premises. It has won numerous awards from CAMRA and SIBA. The brewery supplies an ever increasing number of outlets throughout the midlands and further afield. !!

Ultra (ABV 3.7%)
Rye IPA (ABV 3.8%)
1 Hop (ABV 4%)
Yellow-hued with a fruit and hop nose. Big malty start leads to citrus hints with mouthwatering edges. Dry finish with tangs of lingering lemon bitterness.

Premium (ABV 4.4%)
Pale brown bitter with malt and caramel aroma. Malt and caramel taste supported by hops and some fruit provide a warming descent and satisfyingly bitter mouthfeel.

Smoked Porter (ABV 4.8%)
Nose full of smoke, bonfire tastes with bacon. Hops break out to a bitter finish; a real treat.

Western (ABV 4.9%)
Haka (ABV 5.2%)
Exotic aromas of tropical fruits lead to a sweet, fruity start with background bitterness. This erupts into a mouthy bitterness with a long finish.

Neon Kiss (ABV 6%)
Strong golden ale with fruit and bitterness. Refreshing and dangerously strong.

Slaughterhouse SIBA

Bridge Street, Warwick, CV34 5PD
☎ (01926) 490986 ☎ 07951 842690
slaughterhousebrewery.com

Production began in 2003 on a four-barrel plant in a former slaughterhouse. Around 30 outlets are supplied. The brewery premises are licensed for off-sales direct to the public. In 2010 Slaughterhouse opened its first pub, the Wild Boar in Warwick, adding a two-barrel plant. ‼

Saddleback Best Bitter (ABV 3.8%)
Extra Stout Snout (ABV 4.4%)
Boar D'eau (ABV 4.5%)
Wild Boar (ABV 5.2%)

SLOPEmeisteR (NEW)

Oak House, Airth Castle Estate, Airth, FK2 8JF
☎ 07895 734867 slopemeister.com

SLOPEmeisteR started brewing in 2018, initially at Hybrid Brewery in Grangemouth, then setting up a nanobrewery in a garage in Airth. Keg beer is supplied to Falkirk Rugby Club with cask-conditioned beer supplied to festivals. Recently purchased brewing equipment from the now closed Kinneil Brewery. V

SlyBeast (NEW) SIBA

Ram Inn, 68 Wandsworth High Street, Wandsworth, London, SW18 4LB
☎ (020) 8871 9752 slybeastbrewing.com

The Ram Inn re-opened in 2019 after years of being closed following the demise of the original Youngs Brewery. Its in-house brewery can be seen in one corner of the pub and the beers are available in the pub on cask and keg and further afield in the Youngs and Ram Co pub chains.

Small Beer (Lincoln)

See Black Hole

Small Beer

70-72 Verney Road, South Bermondsey, London, SE16 3DH
☎ (020) 7096 2353 theoriginalsmallbeer.com

Small Beer Brewery was set up in 2017 as the world's first to specialise exclusively in the production of low strength beers (0.5-2.7% ABV). The on-site taproom closed in 2019. No real ale.

Small Paul's

27 Briar Close, Gillingham, Dorset, SP8 4SS
☎ (01747) 823574 ✉ smallbrewer@btinternet.com

Launched in 2006, this half-barrel brewery is located in the owner's garage. There are usually two brews a month. A small number of local pubs, clubs and beer festivals are supplied direct and beers can be designed and brewed to order. ♦

Small World SIBA

Unit 10, Barncliffe Business Park, Near Bank, Shelley, West Yorkshire, HD8 8LU
☎ (01484) 602805 smallworldbeers.com

The brewery is situated in the former Barncliffe Mill near the picturesque village of Shelley. The beers are brewed on a 20-barrel Moeschle plant using spring water from an on-site bore hole. SALSA + Beer approved. ‼♦

Barncliffe Bitter (ABV 3.7%)
Long Moor Pale (ABV 3.9%)
It's Never One (ABV 4%)
Port Nelson (ABV 4%)
Spike's Gold (ABV 4.4%)
Thunderbridge Stout (ABV 5.2%)
Twin Falls (ABV 5.2%)

Samuel Smith

The Old Brewery, High Street, Tadcaster, North Yorkshire, LS24 9SB
☎ (01937) 832225 samuelsmithsbrewery.co.uk

Fiercely independent, family-owned company. Tradition, quality and value are important, resulting in brewing without any artificial additives. The majority of products are vegetarian and vegan-friendly, with the exception of Old Brewery Bitter and Yorkshire Stingo. All real ale is supplied in traditional wooden casks. RAIB

Old Brewery Bitter (ABV 4%)

John Smith's

The Brewery, Tadcaster, North Yorkshire, LS24 9SA
☎ (01937) 832091 heineken.com

No real ale. The brewery was built in 1879 by a relative of Samuel Smith (qv). John Smith's became part of the Courage group in 1970 before being taken over by S&N and now Heineken UK. John Smith's cask Magnet has been discontinued. John Smith's Bitter in cask form is brewed by Caledonian Brewery (qv) in Edinburgh.

Snaggletooth

c/o Rear of 11 Pole Lane, Darwen, Lancashire, BB3 3LD ☎ 07810 365701
snaggletoothbrewing.com

Snaggletooth was established in 2012 by three beer geeks with a passion for crafting ales. A 2.5-barrel plant is used at the Hopstar Brewery (qv) in Darwen, Lancashire. Beers are available throughout East Lancashire and Manchester. ♦

Allotropic (ABV 3.8%)
BeEr (ABV 3.9%)
I Ain't Afraid of Noh Ghost (ABV 3.9%)
Three Amigos (ABV 3.9%)
Déjà Brewed (ABV 4%)
Rolling Maul (ABV 4.1%)
'Cos I'm a Lobster (ABV 4.2%)
Avonaco (ABV 4.3%)

Snowdon Craft

Quinton Hazell Enterprise Parc, 55 Glan-y-Wern Road, Mochdre, LL28 5BS
☎ (01492) 545143 snowdoncraftbeer.co.uk

Snowdon Craft, formerly Great Orme Brewery, is now located in Mochdre near Llandudno and uses an 18-barrel plant for its latest core range and seasonal beers. It owns or part owns three pubs but supplies many more in the area. ‼♦

Base Camp Session Pale (ABV 3.7%)
Nomad All Night Stout (ABV 3.8%)
Driftwood Dry-Hopped Amber (ABV 4.5%)
Summit Blond IPA (ABV 5.2%)

Snowdonia Parc

Snowdonia Parc Brewpub & Campsite, Waunfawr, Caernarfon, LL55 4AQ
☎ (01286) 650409 snowdonia-park.co.uk

Snowdonia Parc started brewing in 1998 in a two-barrel brewhouse. The brewing is now carried out by the owner, Carmen Pierce. The beer is brewed solely for the Snowdonia Parc pub and campsite.

Snowhill

Snowhill Cottage, Snow Hill Lane, Scorton, Lancashire, PR3 1BA
☎ **(01524) 791352**

⊕Snowhill was established in 2015 by Nigel Stokes following several years of small scale brewing. A one-man operation, Nigel brews 3-4 times per month on a 1.5-barrel plant, to supply pubs in north-west Lancashire and south Cumbria. An environmentally-friendly set-up sees the spent grain feeding local cattle and waste water treated through a small reed bed. ◆

Pale (ABV 3.7%)
Copy Cat (ABV 3.8%)
Target (ABV 3.8%)
Blonded (ABV 3.9%)
Gold (ABV 3.9%)
Best Bitter (ABV 4.2%)
Black Magic IPA (ABV 4.2%)
Porter (ABV 4.8%)
Winter Porter (ABV 4.8%)

Sociable SIBA

6-8 Britannia Road, Worcester, WR1 3BQ ☎ 07957 583984 ⊕ thesociablebeercompany.com

⊕A small craft brewery just outside Worcester city centre, established in 2017. An on-site taproom is open on Fridays. A small range of core beers is brewed, mainly for sale in the local area. ◆

Shindig (ABV 3.6%)
Bash (ABV 4%)
Wingding (ABV 4.2%)

Solvay Society

Unit 8, Aldborough Hall Farm, Aldborough Road North, Aldborough Hatch, Essex, IG2 7TD ⊕ solvaysociety.com

Solvay Society began brewing in 2014 in the cellar of a Walthamstow pub using a small 0.5-hectolitre kit. In 2015 it transferred the equipment to the Hops & Glory pub in North London. In 2016 the brewery moved again, taking over the old equipment from the Ha'penny Brewery in Aldborough Hatch. A taproom in Leytonstone is open at weekends. Production is mostly keg but bottle-conditioned beer is also available. RAIB

Son of Sid

🏠 **Chequers, 71 Main Road, Little Gransden, Cambridgeshire, SG19 3DW**
☎ **(01767) 677348 ⊕ sonofsid.co.uk**

⊠ Son of Sid was established in 2007. The three-barrel plant is situated in a room at the back of the pub and can be viewed from a window in the lounge bar. It is named after the father of the current landlord, who ran the pub for 42 years. His son has carried the business on as a family-run enterprise. Beer is sold in the pub and at local beer festivals. ‼ 🍺 RAIB

Sonnet 43

See S43

Soul

Correspondence: **18 Broomfield Road, Heaton Moor, Stockport, SK4 4ND ☎ 07718 155191**
✉ **bill@soulbrewing.co.uk**

⊠ Brewing commenced in 2017 using spare capacity at Manchester Brewing (qv). Beers are supplied to outlets in Greater Manchester and are inspired by Northern Soul music. A move to its own premises is planned. ‼◆V

All Nighter (ABV 3.8%)
Magic Touch (ABV 4.7%)
Powerfully-hopped beer with sweet, fruity flavour and bitter throughout.
The Snake (ABV 5.8%)
Double-O Soul (ABV 5.9%)

South Causey (NEW)

South Causey Inn, Beamish Burn Road, Stanley, DH9 0LS
☎ **(01207) 235555 ⊕ southcausey.co.uk/rip-gin**

Brewer John Taylor recently moved equipment from the Stables brewery at Beamish Hall Hotel. A selection of beers are only available in the bar and restaurant at South Causey Inn. Bottled beers are available for sale to the public on-site. Bespoke beers can be brewed & personalised for special events held at the establishment. A small still has also been set up at the moment to produce gin but in future different types of spirits may be produced.

South Hams SIBA

Stokeley Barton Farm, Stokenham, Devon, TQ7 2SE
☎ **(01548) 581151 ⊕ southhamsbrewery.co.uk**

⊠ South Hams has been brewing ales for more than 13 years in Start Bay, Devon. A family-run brewery, it supplies more than 350 outlets in Plymouth and South Devon with wholesalers distributing further afield. It is owned and managed by Sam, Mark and Brenda Brooking. ‼ 🍺 ◆RAIB

Devon Pride (ABV 3.8%)
Stumble Bee (ABV 4.2%)
Wild Blonde (ABV 4.4%)
Subtle notes of malt, roast and caramel, dominated by fruity hops. These persist to a refreshing hint of lemon.
Hopnosis (ABV 4.5%)
Eddystone (ABV 4.8%)
Strong, amber-coloured, summery ale. Hoppy, caramel, slightly citrus nose. Dryer taste with light fruit and hops. Dry, yet fruity finish.
Pandemonium (ABV 5%)
A fruity/bready, malty aroma. Tastes of toffee, caramel and blackcurrant. A slight old ale style to this strong beer.

South Lakes

Unit 30, Ulverston Auction Mart, North Lonsdale Road, Ulverston, Cumbria, LA12 0AU ☎ 07795 363523
✉ **aaronpos1@hotmail.com**

South Lakes began brewing on a 1.5-barrel plant in 2016, in a part of the Auction Mart in Ulverston.

4 Cs Extra Pale (ABV 3.8%)
Lucky Dip (ABV 3.8%)
Amacoe (ABV 4%)
Pronounced hoppiness in both the aroma and taste combines with a balancing sweetness and a lasting bitter finish.
Poison Dwarf (ABV 4.1%)
Hoppy and fruity aromas are followed by a full-bodied, lasting bitter finish.

Rakau (ABV 4.4%)
A bitter beer with lots of hops, backed by fruit sweetness and some malt in the background. A well-constructed, ambitious bitter with full mouthfeel and lasting bitter finish.
American Pale Ale (ABV 4.8%)
Ripe (ABV 5.5%)

Southbourne SIBA

41-43 Poole Hill, Bournemouth, Dorset, BH2 5PW ☎ (01202) 421190 ☎ 07845 795464
southbourneales.co.uk

Jennifer Tingay, former technologist and brewer for Ringwood, began brewing in 2013 using spare capacity at Town Mill brewery. The brand quickly became established and a successful crowdfunding campaign allowed her to purchase the lease of a former car showroom on Bournemouth's West Cliff. The tap opened in 2017 and the brewery started production in 2018 using an 80-barrel plant. !! ♦

Paddler (ABV 3.6%)
Easy-drinking bitter with subtle malt flavour and hints of hop bitterness in the aftertaste.
Sunbather (ABV 4%)
Dry, red ale with some caramel sweetness and a lingering nutty aftertaste.
Headlander (ABV 4.2%)
Traditional best bitter with intense malt aroma and sweet flavour. Complex and moorish with hop bitterness in aftertaste.
Beachcomber (ABV 5.7%)
Complex and full-flavoured with sweet aroma. Initial notes of sherry with pepper and bitter aftertaste breaking through.

Southbrew (NEW)

Broyle Mill Farm, Ringmer, East Sussex, BN8 5AR
southbrewcompany.co.uk

Nanobrewery formed by three friends, influenced by both traditional and modern beer styles. No real ale. V

Southey

21 Southey Street, Penge, London, SE20 7JD ☎ 07450 573577 southeybrewing.co.uk

Southey took over the former Late Knights Brewery premises in 2017. An on-site tap opens at weekends and its three other outlets are also supplied in Brockley, Dulwich and Brighton. A range of green hop beers is produced in the autumn in association with Palace Pint, the Crystal Palace-based hop collective. ♦◆

Southport SIBA

Unit 3, Enterprise Business Park, Russell Road, Southport, Merseyside, PR9 7RF ☎ 07748 387652
southportbrewery.co.uk

Southport Brewery was established in 2004 on a five-barrel plant. Outlets are supplied in Southport, north-west England and nationally. ♦

IPA (ABV 3.6%)
Sandgrounder Bitter (ABV 3.8%)
Dark Night (ABV 3.9%)
Golden Sands (ABV 4%)

Southsea

Southsea Castle, Clarence Esplanade, Southsea, Portsmouth, Hampshire, PO5 3PA ☎ 07939 063970
southseabrewing.co.uk

Launched in 2016, Southsea Brewing is located in an old ammunition storage room within the walls of a coastal defence fort built by Henry VIII in 1544. All beers are unfined, unfiltered and unpasteurised, and bottled on-site. !! RAIB

Low Tide (ABV 3.8%)
Casemate IPA (ABV 5.4%)

Southwark SIBA

46 Druid Street, Bermondsey, London, SE1 2EZ
☎ (020) 3302 4190 southwarkbrewing.co.uk

Established in the Bermondsey brewing scene, Southwark Brewing Co opened in 2014. Focusing on cask-conditioned ales and the range of Big Bear craft keg ales. ♦RAIB ◆

Bankside Blonde (ABV 3.8%)
Refreshing golden ale with grapefruit aroma and bittersweet grapefruit flavour, fading in the dry, lingering finish with some peppery hops.
Routemaster Red (ABV 3.8%)
Creamy, red ale with malty, fruity aroma. The dry, slightly hoppy bitter flavour has caramel, peach and red berry notes.
London Pale Ale (ABV 4%)
Easy-drinking, gold-coloured beer with sweet orange, caramelised biscuit on the palate and aroma. Dry, fruity and spicy bitter aftertaste.
Potters' Fields Porter (ABV 4%)
Raisins, prunes caramel, cocoa and bitter chocolate in the flavour fading in the dry roast, bitter aftertaste. Roasty, caramel nose.
Mayflower (ABV 4.2%)
Bermondsey Best (ABV 4.4%)
Balanced best bitter. Nutty and caramelised fruit with a pithy citrus character completed by a toffee sweetness. Spicy, dry finish.
Harvard (ABV 5.5%)
Rich, smooth pale brown strong bitter with honey sweetness throughout. Hops, sweet orange and grapefruit marmalade becoming bitter and dry.

Spa Town

See Harrogate

Spartan

Arch 8, Almond Road, South Bermondsey, London, SE16 3LR spartanbrewery.com

Spartan began brewing at UBrew in 2017, before moving in 2018 to premises vacated by Partizan Brewery, and becoming a part of the Bermondsey Beer Mile. Beer is available in its on-site taproom and an increasing number of other outlets. Cask made a welcome return during 2019. V◆

Fog of War (ABV 2.8%)
Unfined, refreshing golden beer with a hoppy citrus aroma. Flavour is dry, hoppy bitter with orange notes. Dry, bitter finish.
Son of Zeus (ABV 3.6%)
River Styx (ABV 3.7%)
Hoplite (ABV 3.8%)
Phalanx (ABV 5%)
Pole March (ABV 5.5%)

Sperrin

🍺 Lord Nelson Inn, Birmingham Road, Ansley, Warwickshire, CV10 9PQ
☎ (024) 7639 2305 ☎ 07917 772208
⊕ sperrinbrewery.co.uk

Sperrin began brewing in 2012 at the side of the Lord Nelson Inn. The pub always has five of its beers available and two or three at its sister pub, the Blue Boar, Mancetter. Around 25 other outlets are supplied direct. ‼◆RAIB

Ansley Mild (ABV 3.5%)
Head Hunter (ABV 3.8%)
Band of Brothers (ABV 4.2%)
Third Party (ABV 4.8%)
Thick as Thieves (ABV 6.8%)

Spey Valley SIBA

Malcolmburn, Mulben, AB55 6YB ☎ 07780 655199
⊕ speyvalleybrewery.co.uk

Founded in 2007, Spey Valley Brewery merged with Keith Brewery in 2018 and is part of the Consolidated Craft Breweries Group, along with Alechemy Brewing (qv). It brews on a 20-barrel plant on a purpose-built site at Mulben. ‼🍺◆

Sunshine on Keith (ABV 3.5%)
Golden, malt with a light citrus bitter hop.
David's Not So Bitter (ABV 4.4%)
Light brown with a good mix of malts, hops and red fruits.
Stillman's IPA (ABV 4.6%)
Amber hoppy bitter with a whisky background.
1814 Spey Valley Lager (ABV 5%)
Spey Stout (ABV 5.4%)
A good thick, dark, malty stout with a smoky blackcurrant background.

Spitting Feathers SIBA

Common Farm, Waverton, Cheshire, CH3 7QT
☎ (01244) 332052 ☎ 07974 348325
⊕ spittingfeathers.co.uk

☺Spitting Feathers was established in 2005. The brewery is located in a sandstone building set around a cobbled yard. Around 200 local outlets are supplied. Monthly Brewbarn sessions throughout the year include a brewery tour but tickets must be purchased in advance. ‼◆

Session Beer (ABV 3.6%)
Thirstquencher (ABV 3.9%)
Powerful hop aroma leads into the taste. Bitterness and a fruity citrus hop flavour fight for attention. A sharp, clean golden beer with a long, dry, bitter aftertaste.
Brainstorm (ABV 4%)
Special Ale (ABV 4.2%)
Complex, tawny-coloured beer with a sharp, grainy mouthfeel. Malty with good hop coming through in the aroma and taste. Hints of nuttiness and a touch of acidity. Dry, astringent finish.
Old Wavertonian (ABV 4.4%)
Creamy and smooth stout. Full-flavoured with coffee notes in aroma and taste. Roast and nut flavours throughout, leading to a hoppy, bitter finish.
Rush Hour (ABV 4.5%)
Empire IPA (ABV 5.2%)

Spotlight

The Goddards, Goole Road, West Cowick, East Yorkshire, DN14 9DJ ☎ 07713 477069
⊕ spotlightbrewing.co.uk

☺Spotlight is a social enterprise that is passionate about good beer. All beers are brewed, packaged and delivered by people with learning disabilities. The beer names reference medical conditions. A taproom is planned during the currency of this Guide. ‼🍺◆

One More (ABV 3.9%)
Bollingham Bitter (ABV 4.4%)
Spectrum (ABV 4.5%)
Undiagnosed (ABV 5%)
Fragile X (ABV 5.8%)

Springhead SIBA

Robin Hood Site, Main Street, Laneham, Nottinghamshire, DN22 0NA
☎ (01777) 229020 ☎ 07721 892831
⊕ springhead.co.uk

☺ Springhead Fine Ales opened in 1990, expanding and moving to bigger premises three years later to meet increased demand. In 2011 the brewery relocated to its current address. In 2018 the brewery was taken over and now trades as Springhead Ales with new owners. ‼🍺◆V

Outlawed (ABV 3.8%)
Drop o' the Black Stuff (ABV 4%)
Robin Hood (ABV 4%)
Blind Tiger (ABV 4.5%)
Leveller (ABV 4.8%)
Roaring Meg (ABV 5.5%)

Squawk

Unit 4, Tonge Street, Ardwick, Manchester, M12 6LY
☎ 07590 387559 ✉ sales@squawkbrewingco.com

Squawk initially cuckoo-brewed in Huddersfield in 2013, with the first beers from the current Manchester railway-arch site appearing in 2014. In 2019, the brewery expanded with additional fermenters and conditioning tanks. A barrel-ageing programme and a canning line were also introduced. All beers are widely available in the north of England as well as being distributed nationally. RAIB V

Pavo (ABV 3.8%)
Light, hoppy beer with balanced fruity aroma and taste. Dry, bitter finish.
Otis (ABV 3.9%)
Roller (ABV 4%)
Crex (ABV 4.5%)
Fruity and hoppy aroma. Sweet fruit balanced with bitter hops in the flavour, rising to a lasting, dry, bitter finish.
Aix (ABV 4.6%)
Dark, sweet and fruity throughout.
Corvus (ABV 7.4%)
Roast malt aroma and strong, lasting dark chocolate taste with touch of fruit.

Stables

See Big Lamp

Staffordshire

12 Churnet Court, Cheddleton, Staffordshire, ST13 7EF
☎ (01538) 361919 ☎ 07971 808370
⊕ staffordshirebrewery.co.uk

Brewing started in 2002. The brewery was renamed from Leek Brewery in 2013 at which time cask production ceased, being replaced by filtered, pasteurised bottled beers only. A small pilot plant is sometimes used to contract brew for Wicked Hathern (qv) when time permits. ‼

Contract brewed for Wicked Hathern Brewery:
Albion Special (ABV 4%)
Hawthorn Gold (ABV 4.6%)

Stag (Cheshire)

Stag at Walton, Chester Road, Walton, Warrington, Cheshire, WA4 6EG
☎ (01925) 261680 🌐 thestagatwalton.co.uk

Nanobrewery based at the Stag at Walton, near Warrington. Beers are available in the pub and occasionally at local beer festivals.

Stag (Kent)

Little Engeham Farm, Woodchurch, Kent, TN26 3QY
☎ 07539 974068 🌐 stagbrewery.co.uk

Stag began brewing in 2016.

Jane Doe (ABV 4%)
Screeming Sika (ABV 5%)

Staggeringly Good SIBA

Unit 3, St Georges Industrial Estate, Rodney Road, Southsea, Hampshire, PO4 8SS
☎ (023) 9229 7033 🌐 staggeringlygood.com

Brewing began in 2014, originally using spare capacity at other breweries. In 2015 a 10-barrel plant at its own premises came on stream. All beers are real ale but only available in KeyKeg or can, unfined and vegan-friendly. There is an on-site shop and taproom. In 2019 the brewery acquired a large unit to allow for more brewing kit and to expand the taproom and its neighbouring craft beer and music venue, the House of Rapture. ‼ ♦ RAIB V

Stamps

St Mary's Complex, Waverley Street, Bootle, Liverpool, L20 4AP ☎ 07779 000094
🌐 stampsbrewery.co.uk

Brewing began in 2012, producing beers named after famous world postage stamps. The beers can be found regularly in Stamps Bar, Crosby, and the Lock & Quay, Irlam Road, Bootle. Beers are also brewed under the Republic of Liverpool brand name and Stamps beers are sometimes rebadged. ‼

Blond Moment (ABV 3.6%)
Bondi Blond (ABV 3.7%)
Ahtanum (ABV 3.9%)
First Class (ABV 3.9%)
Mail Train (ABV 4.2%)
Swedish Blond (ABV 4.3%)
Inverted Jenny (ABV 4.6%)
Penny Black (ABV 5.5%)

Stancill SIBA

Unit 2, Oakham Drive, off Rutland Road, Sheffield, South Yorkshire, S3 9QX
☎ (0114) 275 2788 ☎ 07809 427716

Stancill began brewing in 2014 and is named after the first head brewer and co-owner. It is situated on the doorstep of the late Stones' Cannon Brewery, taking advantage of the soft Yorkshire water. ‼

Barnsley Bitter (ABV 3.8%)
Blonde (ABV 3.9%)
India (ABV 4%)
No. 7 (ABV 4.3%)
Stainless (ABV 4.3%)
Porter (ABV 4.4%)
Black Gold (ABV 5%)

Stannary

Unit 6, Pixon Trading Centre, Tavistock, Devon, PL19 8DH
☎ (01822) 258130 🌐 stannarybrewing.co.uk

Stannary began operating in 2016 using a 2.5-barrel plant, moving to larger premises with a six-barrel plant in 2018. The brewery tap is open on Friday evenings, showcasing its many unfined and unfiltered craft beers.

Stanway

Stanway House, Stanway, Cheltenham, Gloucestershire, GL54 5PQ
☎ (01386) 584320 🌐 stanwaybrewery.co.uk

Stanway is a small brewery, founded in 1993 with a five-barrel plant, that confines its sales to the Cotswolds area (15 to 20 outlets). The brewery uses wood-fired coppers for all its production. Brewing is currently suspended. ♦

Star Wing SIBA

Unit 6, Hall Farm, Church Road, Redgrave, Suffolk, IP22 1RJ
☎ (01379) 890 586 🌐 starwingbrewery.com

Brewing began in 2017 after converting an old sawmill into a brewery. Half an acre of hops have been planted with plans to grow more. Part of the sawmill has been converted into a taproom, which opened in 2019. Around 75 outlets are supplied direct.

Dawn on the Border (ABV 3.6%)
Gospel Oak (ABV 3.8%)
Spire Light (ABV 4.2%)
Into the Woods (ABV 4.5%)
Red at Night (ABV 4.5%)
Pesky Pilgrim (ABV 4.7%)
Four Acre Arcadia (ABV 5%)
Stain Glass Blue (ABV 5.4%)

Stardust SIBA

Unit 5, Howe Lane Farm Estate, Howe Lane, White Waltham, Berkshire, SL6 3JP
☎ (01628) 947325 🌐 stardustbrewery.co.uk

An independent, family-owned and run brewery, Stardust was established in 2016. Tucked away towards the back of a farm estate, brewing takes place on a six-barrel plant. There is a brewery shop and taproom on-site. ‼ ♦ RAIB

Easy Pale Citra (ABV 3.8%)
English Bitter (ABV 4%)
Optic (ABV 4.2%)
PK3 (ABV 5.6%)

Station 119

See Bruha

THE BREWERIES

Stealth

34 Old Broughton Road, Melksham, Wiltshire, SN12 8BX
☎ (01225) 707111 ☎ 07917 272482
🌐 stealthbrew.co

Known as Kennet & Avon from 2014 to 2018, Stealth has been brewing at its present site since 2015, but may move within the local area during the currency of this guide. Most beers are unfined (except Tiptoe). An associated company runs three microbars. ‼ ♦ RAIB GF V

Covert (ABV 3.9%)
Doublecrosser (ABV 4%)
Tiptoe (ABV 4.2%)
Camouflage (ABV 4.7%)
Solitude (ABV 5.3%)
Full-bodied black beer with aromas of liquorice, roast coffee and chocolate, with a delicate pleasant aftertaste. This barley and oat brewed beer is certified gluten-free.

Steam Machine (NEW)

Unit 14, The IES Centre, Horndale Avenue, Newton Aycliffe, DL5 6DS ☎ 07415 759945
🌐 steammachinebrew.com

Founded by a husband and wife team with a homebrewing background of more than 10 years. Since opening in 2015 production has expanded. Beers are available mainly in keg but KeyKegs are occasionally supplied to beer festivals. ◆

Steam Town SIBA

1 Bishopstoke Road, Eastleigh, Hampshire, SO50 6AD
☎ (023) 8235 9130 🌐 steamtownbrewco.co.uk

⊗ Steam Town is a five-barrel microbrewery with its own craft beer bar and restaurant, established in 2017. Many other local pubs, clubs and micropubs also sell Steam Town's ales, as well as beer festivals and outlets further afield by arrangement. ‼ ♦ RAIB

Stoke (ABV 3.8%)
Barton (ABV 4%)
Reefer (ABV 4.2%)
Steam Stout (ABV 4.5%)
Bishops Gold (ABV 4.6%)
Firebox (ABV 4.6%)
West Coast IPA (ABV 5.4%)

Steamin' Billy

See Belvoir

Steel Brew (NEW)

Melville Building, Royal William Yard, Plymouth, Devon, PL1 3RP ☎ 07976 503844

Office: 22 Aquarius Drive, Sherford, Devon, PL9 8FH
🌐 steelbrew.co

Brewing began in a garage in 2018, producing a range of craft beers on a six-barrel plant. The brewery relocated to the Grade I*-listed Melville Building in 2020. Four core beers and numerous one-off specials are brewed, available in its on-site taproom. ‼ ◆

Steel City

c/o Lost Industry Brewing, 14a Nutwood Trading Estate, Sheffield, South Yorkshire, S6 1NJ
🌐 steelcitybrewing.beer

⊗ Steel City was established in 2009 and operates on a cuckoo basis, brewing once or twice a month. Brewing now takes place at Lost Industry Brewing (qv). Much of the Steel City output is collaborations with other like-minded brewers having a little fun producing interesting and experimental beers. ♦V

Stenroth (NEW)

Edinburgh 🌐 stenrothbrewing.co.uk

Founded by partners Kat Drinnan and Jimmy Mehtala in 2019, this home-based, 60-litre nanobrewery produces four core beers.

Stewart SIBA

26a Dryden Road, Bilston Glen Industrial Estate, Loanhead, EH20 9LZ
☎ (0131) 440 2442 🌐 stewartbrewing.co.uk

Established in 2004 by Steve and Jo Stewart, the brewery moved to a larger, custom-built brewery in 2013 with a brand new 50-hectolitre plant. It produces a wide portfolio of beers including collaborations such as the Natural Selection Brewing partnership with the brewing school at Heriot Watt. The on-site Craft Beer Kitchen is a small 80-litre plant providing a brew-it-yourself facility. ‼ ♦ RAIB V◆

Jack Back (ABV 3.7%)
A pale hoppy beer with strong citrus and tropical fruit aromas. The taste is light, crisp and refreshing.
Pentland IPA (ABV 3.9%)
A delicately-hopped, deep golden-coloured, session ale. The dry bitter taste is well-balanced by sweetness from the malt, and fruit flavours.
80/- (ABV 4.4%)
Superb traditional Scottish heavy. The complex profile is dominated by malt with fruit flavours giving the sweetish character typical of this beer style. Hops provide a gentle balancing bitterness that intensifies in the dry finish.
Radical Road Reverse (ABV 4.6%)
Well-hopped gold/amber ale with hints of biscuit and oodles of tropical fruit (mango) flavour continuing into the aftertaste.
Edinburgh Gold (ABV 4.8%)
A full-bodied, easy-drinking, Continental-style golden ale. Bitterness from the hop character is strong in the finish and complemented in the taste by a little sweetness from malt, and fruit flavours.

Sticklegs

Primrose Farm, Hall Road, Great Bromley, Essex, CO7 7TR ☎ 07971 138038
✉ waterhouse.philip@btinternet.com

⊗ Sticklegs was established in 2008 at the Cross Inn, Great Bromley. The brewery expanded and relocated to Elmstead Market, where it continued to grow. In 2016 it moved to Primrose Farm. The brewery is owned and run by Phil Reeve and his wife Linda, the brewster. Brewing is currently suspended.

Stockport SIBA

Unit 16, The Gate Centre, Bredbury Parkway, Stockport, SK6 2SN
☎ (0161) 637 0306 ☎ 07961 056198
🌐 stockportbrewingcompany.com

A former cuckoo brewery, Stockport Brewing installed its own eight-barrel plant initially under the iconic Stockport Viaduct in 2014. It then moved to a larger, modern facility in the Bredbury Industrial Estate north of

Stockport. The beers are widely available throughout the UK through a trading agreement with other breweries. ‼♦

Pale (ABV 3.9%)
Cascade (ABV 4%)
Centaurus (ABV 4%)
South Island Pale (ABV 4.1%)
Crown Best Bitter (ABV 4.2%)
Ginger Tinge (ABV 4.2%)
Jester (ABV 4.2%)
Stock Porter (ABV 4.8%)
Malty flavour and aroma with some treacle toffee. Coffee and chocolate roast notes and hint of dark fruit.

Stocks

See Welbeck Abbey

Stod Fold

Stod Fold Farm, Hays Lane, Halifax, West Yorkshire, HX2 8UL ☎ 07745 967740 / 07568 487182
🌐 stodfoldbrewing.com

The 10-barrel Stod Fold Brewery is located on the edge of the moors in a renovated farm building. It supplies around 300 free trade outlets each year, mainly in Yorkshire, but occasionally distributes out of the region via nationwide brewing partners on the swaps scheme. Beers can always be sampled at the Stod Fold Brewery Tap at Dean Clough Mills, Halifax.

Gold (ABV 3.8%)
A refreshing golden and fruity session ale with a smooth, hoppy aftertaste.
Best Yorkshire Bitter (ABV 3.9%)
Well-rounded, traditional, tawny-coloured bitter. Lightly-hopped with a lingering malty and bitter aftertaste.
West APA (ABV 4%)
A golden-coloured, session bitter with a fruity and hoppy aroma. Light and refreshing citrus flavours develop in the mouth, leading to a dry, crisp finale.
Yorkshire Blonde (ABV 4.3%)
Smooth-tasting fruity beer with a lingering dry finish. Easy-drinking for its ABV.
Dark Porter (ABV 4.8%)
Easy-drinking, well-balanced, dark brown porter. Smooth and mellow with roast to the fore.

Stonehenge SIBA

The Old Mill, Mill Road, Netheravon, Wiltshire, SP4 9QB
☎ (01980) 670631 🌐 stonehengeales.co.uk

⊗ The brewery was founded in 1984 in what was originally a water-driven mill built in 1914. In 1993 the company was bought by Danish master brewer Stig Andersen and his wife Anna Marie, and now supplies more than 300 outlets. From 2013 a new borehole, accessing the Salisbury Plain aquifer, has been supplying the brewery's water. It is of such pristine quality that the brewery now bottle and sell it under the Stonehenge name. ‼♦

Spire Ale (ABV 3.8%)
A pale golden-coloured, session bitter with an initial bitterness giving way to a well-rounded bitter aftertaste with discernable fruit balance.
Pigswill (ABV 4%)
A tawny-coloured, session bitter with an initial pleasant hop aroma and slight bitterness to the initial taste moving to a well-rounded bitter finish with slight malt and fruit in the finish.
Heel Stone (ABV 4.3%)
A copper-coloured best bitter with some malt and fruit in the aroma continuing into the initial taste along with pleasant hoppiness. Medium-bodied with plenty of flavour in the aftertaste with noticeable malt, fruit and hops.
Great Bustard (ABV 4.8%)
A copper brown-coloured, strong bitter. Complex malt and fruit flavours at first with a long fruit and bitter aftertaste.
Danish Dynamite (ABV 5%)
Golden ale with good hop and fruit aromas. Complex flavours in the initial taste with a beautifully-balanced, full-bodied aftertaste with hops and fruit to the fore.

Stonehouse SIBA

Stonehouse, Weston, Oswestry, Shropshire, SY10 9ES
☎ (01691) 676457 🌐 stonehousebrewery.co.uk

Stonehouse is a family-run brewery and cidery. Established in 2007, operating a 22-barrel plant. It is next to the preserved Cambrian railway line and includes a shop, bar and visitor centre. Direct delivery is within 30 miles of the brewery. ‼

Sunlander (ABV 3.7%)
Station Bitter (ABV 3.9%)
Cambrian Gold (ABV 4.2%)
Kelly Point (ABV 4.4%)
Off the Rails (ABV 4.8%)

Stoney Ford

See Grainstore

Storm SIBA

2 Waterside, Macclesfield, Cheshire, SK11 7HJ
☎ (01625) 431234 🌐 stormbrewing.co.uk

Storm Brewing was founded in 1998. In 2001 it moved to its current location, an old riverside pub building, which until 1937 was called the Mechanics Arms. More than 60 outlets are supplied. ♦RAIB

Beauforts Ale (ABV 3.8%)
Desert Storm (ABV 3.9%)
Bosley Cloud (ABV 4.1%)
Dry, golden bitter with peppery hop notes throughout. Some initial sweetness and a mainly bitter aftertaste. Soft, well-balanced and quaffable.
Ale Force (ABV 4.2%)
Amber, smooth-tasting, complex beer that balances malt, hop and fruit on the taste, leading to a roasty, slightly sweet aftertaste.
Dexter (ABV 4.2%)
Downpour (ABV 4.3%)
PGA (ABV 4.4%)
Light, crisp, lager-style beer with a balance of malt, hops and fruit. Moderately bitter and slight dry aftertaste.
Hurricane Hubert (ABV 4.5%)
Silk of Amnesia (ABV 4.7%)
Smooth, premium, easy-drinking bitter. Fruit and hops dominate throughout. Not too sweet, with a good, lasting finish.
Red Mist (ABV 4.8%)

Stow Fen (NEW)

Flixton Road, Bungay, Suffolk, NR34 1PD ☎ 07775 279181 ✉ stowfenbrewingco@gmail.com

Stow Fen Brewing Co Ltd was established in 2020 by Paul Holland and Philip Gilham. Crisp Maltings supplies the brewery with Norfolk and Suffolk malts and all hops are from the UK.

THE BREWERIES

Gold (ABV 4.2%)
Amber (ABV 4.4%)
Best (ABV 4.6%)

Stowey

Old Cider House, 25 Castle Street, Nether Stowey,
Somerset, TA5 1LN
☎ (01278) 732228 ⊕ stoweybrewery.co.uk

Somerset's smallest brewery was established in 2006,
primarily to supply the owners' guesthouse and to
provide beer to participants at events run from the
accommodation. The small quantities of beer produced
are also supplied to the George, Nether Stowey. !!◆

Strands

▤ Strands Inn, Nether Wasdale, Cumbria, CA20 1ET
☎ (01946) 726237 ⊕ strandshotel.com

⊛Strands Brewery is a ten-barrel plant with a 5,000-litre
fermentation capacity. Six of the beers are available on
the bar of the Strands Inn at all times or in the Screes,
across the road. !!◆RAIB

Strata

c/o Unit 4, Daniel Street, Whitworth, Lancashire,
OL12 8BX ⊕ stratabrewing.co.uk

Brewing began in 2019 using spare capacity at Mighty
Medicine (qv). The name comes from the owner's
background in geology.

Strike (ABV 3.6%)
Thalweg (ABV 4%)
Hoodoo (ABV 4.2%)
Tekapo (ABV 4.5%)
Fram (ABV 4.8%)
Vaalbara (ABV 4.8%)
Drumlin (ABV 5%)

Strathaven SIBA

Craigmill Brewery, Sandford Road, Strathaven,
ML10 6PB
☎ (01357) 520419 ⊕ strathavenales.com

⊛Strathaven Ales is a 10-barrel brewery on the River
Avon close to Strathaven and was converted from the
remains of a 16th-century mill. The range is distributed
throughout Scotland and the north of England. !!➡◆

Craigmill Mild (ABV 3.5%)
Clydesdale (ABV 3.8%)
Duchess Anne (ABV 3.9%)
Avondale (ABV 4%)
Line Out (ABV 4%)
Old Mortality (ABV 4.2%)
Claverhouse (ABV 4.5%)
Teuchter (ABV 5.6%)
500 (ABV 7%)
Usquebae Ale (ABV 7%)

Strathbraan SIBA

Deanshaugh, Amulree, Dunkeld, PH8 0EB
☎ (01350) 725264 ☎ 07747 857908
✉ strathbraan.bry@btinternet.com

Strathbraan began brewing in 2012 using a 10-barrel
plant. RAIB

Due South (ABV 3.8%)
Head East (ABV 4.2%)

Strathcarron

Arinackaig, Strathcarron, IV54 8YN
☎ (01599) 577236 ⊕ strathcarronbrewery.com

⊗ Brewing began in 2016 using a 2.5-barrel plant. Fresh
West Highland water is used from an on-site spring. The
beers are only normally available in cask locally but more
widely bottled. RAIB

Golden Cow (ABV 3.8%)
Black Cow (ABV 4.2%)
Red Cow (ABV 4.2%)
Highland Cow (ABV 5.4%)

Stratton Lane (NEW)

Middle Barn, Burcot Farm, East Stratton, Winchester,
Hampshire, SO21 3DZ ☎ 07990 528790
⊕ strattonlane.com

Having previously run their own businesses, Barnaby and
Bernadette Wheller changed direction and opened their
own brewery and taproom in 2019, taking over the old
MASH brewhouse with its 10-barrel plant. !!➡◆GF❦

First Gold (ABV 3.6%)
Tawny (ABV 3.6%)

Stringers SIBA

Unit 3, Low Mill Business Park, Ulverston, Cumbria,
LA12 9EE
☎ (01229) 581387 ⊕ stringersbeer.co.uk

⊛Stringers is a family-run, small craft brewery. Brewing
started 2008 on a five-barrel plant run on 100%
renewable energy. ◆RAIB

Furness Gold (ABV 3.5%)
A hoppy aroma and a fruity, full-bodied taste of hops,
finishes with a drying bitterness.
Plan B (ABV 3.7%)
An easy-drinking, zingy, pale, thirst-quencher.
No. 2 Stout (ABV 4%)
A robust, drying stout full of roast and hop bitterness.
Yellow Lorry (ABV 4%)
Landlord's Tipple (ABV 4.2%)
Blonde (ABV 4.4%)
The North (ABV 4.9%)
Turbine Porter (ABV 5.1%)
IPA (ABV 5.5%)

Stripey Cat

▤ Tiger Inn, 14-16 Barrack Street, Bridport, Dorset,
DT6 3LY
☎ (01308) 427543 ⊕ tigerinnbridport.co.uk/
the-stripey-cat-craft-brewery

Brewing began in 2017 at the Tiger Inn producing ales
exclusively for the pub.

Stroud SIBA

Kingfisher Business Park, London Road, Thrupp,
Gloucestershire, GL5 2BY
☎ (01453) 887122 ⊕ stroudbrewery.co.uk

⊗ Established in 2006, Stroud Brewery supports the local
ecomomy and does not sell its beers through
supermarkets. The ales are available in 40-50 pubs,
independent retailers and its brewery shop. All beers
have full organic status. !!➡◆RAIB V❦

Tom Long (ABV 3.8%)
OPA (Organic Pale Ale) (ABV 4%)
Big Cat (ABV 4.5%)
Budding (ABV 4.5%)

Stu Brew

Newcastle University, Merz Court, Newcastle upon Tyne, NE1 7RU 🌐 stubrew.com

Stu Brew is Europe's first student-run microbrewery based at Newcastle University. The brewery was set up as part of a research project aimed at reducing waste and costs in all parts of brewing. The university and local pubs are supplied. V

Lab Session (ABV 4.3%)
Exam Room Tears (ABV 5%)
Extended Overdraft (ABV 5.2%)
Into the Black (ABV 5.6%)

Stubborn Mule

Unit 2, Radium House, Bridgewater Road, Altrincham, WA14 1LZ ☎ 07730 515251
🌐 stubbornmulebrewery.com

Brewing began in 2015. Ed Bright, the owner/brewer continues to add new beers to the portfolio and is always searching for interesting ideas to brew. !! ♦ RAIB V

Mandarin Candidate (ABV 3.4%)
Li'l Napoleon (ABV 3.9%)
Absolute Banker (ABV 4.7%)
Donkey Punch (ABV 5.5%)
Pre-Prohibition Cream Ale (ABV 5.5%)
Single Hop IPA (ABV 5.7%)
Chocolate Stout (ABV 5.8%)
WA15 Magnum IPA (ABV 7.2%)

Stumptail

North Street, Great Dunham, Norfolk, PE32 2LR
☎ (01328) 701042 ✉ stumptail@btinternet.com

⊗ Stumptail began commercial homebrewing in 2011 using a 100-litre plant. Bottle-conditioned beers are produced with cask-conditioned versions brewed to order, all to bespoke recipes. Most parts of Norfolk can be supplied. RAIB

Sulwath SIBA

The Brewery, 209 King Street, Castle Douglas, DG7 1DT
☎ (01556) 504525 🌐 sulwathbrewers.co.uk

Sulwath started brewing in 1995. Its award-winning beers are supplied to around 100 outlets and four wholesalers as far away as Devon, and Aberdeen. The brewery has a popular fully licensed tap. !! ♦ RAIB

Cuil Hill (ABV 3.6%)
Distinctively fruity, session ale with malt and hop undertones. The taste is bittersweet with a long-lasting, dry finish.
Tri-ball (ABV 3.9%)
The Grace (ABV 4.3%)
Black Galloway (ABV 4.4%)
Criffel (ABV 4.6%)
Full-bodied beer with a distinctive bitterness. Fruit is to the fore of the taste with hops becoming increasingly dominant in the taste and finish.
Galloway Gold (ABV 5%)
A cask-conditioned lager that will be too sweet for many despite being heavily-hopped.
Knockendoch (ABV 5%)
Dark, copper-coloured, reflecting a roast malt content, with bitterness from Challenger hops.
Solway Mist (ABV 5.5%)

Summershed (NEW)

Brew Cottage, The Bit, Wigginton, HP23 6EQ ☎ 07920 136198 ✉ simon@brewcottage.com

A small brewery established in 2019 producing bottle-conditioned beers in batches of 150 litres. The beers have locally-familiar names and are brewed, bottled and labelled in the brewery which is situated in the brewer's extended garden shed. The beers are available from Wigginton's community shop, the Greyhound in the village and in the Local, a micropub in Markyate, St Albans.

Summerskills SIBA

15 Pomphlett Farm Industrial Estate, Broxton Drive, Billacombe, Plymouth, Devon, PL9 7BG
☎ (01752) 481283 🌐 summerskills.co.uk

⊗ Established in a vineyard in 1983 at Bigbury-on-Sea, Summerskills moved to its present site in 1985. It is the oldest brewery in Plymouth. Wholesalers and pub companies provide national distribution and the beers regularly appear in a selection of local outlets. In recent times the number of beers has increased and the brewer has won many awards. Locally-sourced ingredients are used wherever possible. ♦ RAIB

Start Point (ABV 3.7%)
Westward Ho! (ABV 4.1%)
Malt dominates a light nose. Gentle bitterness introduces its malty-fruit friends. Malt and bitterness remain, with bitterness dominating.
Best Bitter (ABV 4.3%)
A mid-brown beer, with plenty of malt and hops through the aroma, taste and finish. A good session beer.
Tamar (ABV 4.3%)
Bitter hop taste and finish. A mid strength best bitter.
Stout (ABV 4.4%)
Strong coffee aroma, slight sweetness on the taste with coffee/chocolates on tongue. Bitter finish.
Devon Dew (ABV 4.5%)
Pine aroma with a slight grapefruit taste. A refreshing golden ale.
Devon Frost (ABV 4.5%)
A slight nutty roast on the nose and also on taste with grapefruit flavours on the tongue.
Menacing Dennis (ABV 4.5%)
Bolt Head (ABV 4.7%)
Fruit-hop nose has roast-malt hints. Bitter flavours with sweet malt, roast and hoppiness. Lingering bitter finish with background malt and fruit.
Whistle Belly Vengeance (ABV 4.7%)
Full-flavoured, strong red ale. Roast and malt aroma with roasted chestnut taste. Sweetness and bitterness mingle in the aftertaste.
Ninja (ABV 5%)
Plymouth Porter (ABV 5%)
Strong, sweet chocolate aroma, tastes of chocolate and toffee. Aftertaste dies off quickly, a nice, drinkable, sweet Porter.
First Light (ABV 5.5%)
Strong golden ale. Fruity, hoppy aroma. Sweet grapefruit and hops on the palate. Aftertaste continues with fruit and hops.
Indiana's Bones / South Star (ABV 5.6%)
Old ale with good body. Rich malty roasts aroma bursting with strong sweet flavours on the tongue. Slightly dryer finish.

Sunbeam

52 Fernbank Road, Leeds, West Yorkshire, LS13 1BU
☎ 07772 002437 🌐 sunbeamales.co.uk

Sunbeam Ales was established in a house in Leeds in 2009, with commercial brewing beginning in 2011. Since moving, capacity has increased to a two-barrel plant based in a garage. The core range of ales, available in West and North Yorkshire at present, are brewed on rotation up to twice weekly with occasional brews every six weeks or so. ♦

Eclipse (ABV 3.8%)
Blinded By The Light (ABV 4%)
New Dawn (ABV 4.1%)
White Chocolate Pale Mild (ABV 4.2%)
Tropical Rain (ABV 4.3%)
Rain Stops Play (ABV 4.5%)
Nigel's Plum Porter (ABV 4.8%)
Helios (ABV 5.8%)

Sunset Taverns

See Six Towns

Surrey Hills SIBA

Denbies Wine Estate, London Road, Dorking, Surrey, RH5 6AA
☎ (01306) 883603 surreyhills.co.uk

Surrey Hills began brewing in 2005 near Shere, moving to Dorking in 2011. Nearly 95% of production is sold within 15 miles of the brewery. The beers have won several local and national awards. ‼ ♦

Ranmore (ABV 3.8%)
A light, flavoursome, session beer. An earthy, hoppy nose leads into a grapefruit and hoppy taste and a clean, bitter finish.
Shere Drop (ABV 4.2%)
A hoppy ale with some balancing malt. A pleasant citrus aroma and a noticeable fruitiness in the taste, with some sweetness.
Gilt Complex (ABV 4.6%)
Gilt Trip (ABV 4.6%)
Greensand IPA (ABV 4.6%)
A strong-flavoured, easily-drinkable IPA, with intense grapefruit and hops in the aroma and taste and soft, cirtusy finish.
Collusion (ABV 5.2%)

Sussex Small Batch

c/o 23 The Vinery, Poling, West Sussex, BN18 9PY
☎ 07718 22425

Office: 48 Henty Road, Worthing, BN14 7HE
ssbbrewery@outlook.com

Jim Brown started the Sussex Small Batch Brewery in 2018, focusing on producing quality stouts with a difference. Brewing takes place using spare capacity at Goldmark Brewery (qv). V

Tiramisu Stout (ABV 5.5%)
Zucotto Stout (ABV 5.5%)
Smoked Chilli Chocolate Stout (ABV 5.8%)
Vegan Raspberry Wheat Rye (ABV 5.8%)

Suthwyk

See Bowman

Swamp Bog (NEW)

Church Lane, Enborne, RG20 0HB
swampbogbrewery.com

Under the same ownership and sharing the same kit as Two Cocks brewery (qv) this is a new start-up microbrewery based on the edge of Hampshire/ Berkshire, specialising in long-lost craft beer recipes from a time before brewing giants existed. The passion is for taste, not profit, low volume, rather than mass production.

Bottom Biter (ABV 3.6%)
Edge Hopper (ABV 4.2%)
Pixie Pee (ABV 5%)
The Ferryman's Brew (ABV 5%)

Swan SIBA

Unit 17, Brunel Road, Enterprise Park, Leominster, Herefordshire, HR6 0LX
☎ (01568) 617709 ☎ 07377 728822
swanbrewery.co.uk

Swan Brewery was established in 2016 by Jimmy Swan and partner Gill Bullock using a 10-barrel plant in Leominster. A 1.3-barrel plant is used to brew bespoke beers for local pubs.

Blonde (ABV 3.7%)
Ruffled Feathers (ABV 3.8%)
Gold (ABV 4.2%)

Swan on the Green

Swan on the Green, West Peckham, Maidstone, Kent, ME18 5JW
☎ (01622) 812271 swan-on-the-green.co.uk

The brewery was established in 2000 in an old coal shed behind the Swan on the Green pub using a two-barrel plant. ‼♦

Swannay SIBA

Swannay Brewery, Swannay by Evie, Orkney, KW17 2NP
☎ (01856) 721700 swannaybrewery.com

Brewing began in 2006 at the redundant Swannay dairy on Orkney mainland's exposed north-western tip. Two brewing plants are utilised, a five and a twenty barrel. Founder Rob is assisted by son Lewis plus a further small team of passionate beer lovers. ‼ ♦

Orkney Best (ABV 3.6%)
A refreshing, light-bodied, low gravity golden beer bursting with hop, peach and sweet malt flavours. The long, hoppy finish leaves a dry bitterness.
Island Hopping (ABV 3.9%)
Passionfruit hoppiness with some caramel with a lasting, bitter aftertaste.
Dark Munro (ABV 4%)
The nose presents an intense roast hit which is followed by plums and blackcurrant in the mouth. The strong roast malt continues into the aftertaste.
Scapa Special (ABV 4.2%)
A good copy of a typical Lancashire bitter, full of bitterness and background hops, leaving your mouth tingling in the lingering aftertaste.
Sneaky Wee Orkney Stout (ABV 4.2%)
Bags of malt and roast with a mixed fruit berry background. Dry bitter finish.
Pale Ale (ABV 4.7%)
Orkney IPA (ABV 4.8%)
A traditional bitter, with light hop and fruit flavour throughout.
Duke IPA (ABV 5.2%)
Good, refreshing, citrus-fruited IPA with background malt.
Orkney Blast (ABV 6%)

Plenty of alcohol in this warming, strong bitter/barley wine. A mushroom and woody aroma blossoms into a well-balanced smack of malt and hop in the taste.

Swansea SIBA

▤ Joiners Arms, 50 Bishopston Road, Bishopston, Swansea, SA3 3EJ
☎ (01792) 232658

☺Opened in 1996, Swansea was the first commercial brewery in the area for almost 30 years. Beers are regularly available at the Joiners and also the Railway Inn, Killay. ‼◆

T'ales from the Brewhouse

See Lancaster

Taddington

Blackwell Hall, Blackwell, Buxton, Derbyshire, SK17 9TQ
☎ (01298) 85734

Taddington started brewing in 2007, and brews one Czech-style unpasteurised lager in two different strengths. No real ale.

Tally Ho!

▤ 14 Market Street, Hatherleigh, Devon, EX20 3JN
☎ 07730 972980 ⊕ tallyhobrewery.co.uk

⊠ Having stood idle at the rear of the Tally Ho! pub for 14 years, the brewery was resurrected by four brewing enthusiasts in 2015. The current owner and brewer took over in 2018. As well as the pub, several local free houses and other establishments are supplied. ◆

Tamworth

29 Market Street, Tamworth, Staffordshire, B79 7LR
☎ (01827) 319872 ☎ 07712 893353
⊕ tamworthbrewing.co.uk

Owner/brewer George Greenaway brought brewing back to Tamworth town centre after a gap of 70 years. Brewing started in 2017 in a former shop, which dates from Tudor times and also serves as a taproom. In 2020 brewing moved into the adjacent building, which records indicate was a brewhouse in the 1750s. The move allowed production on its five-barrel plant to double. Around 25 outlets are supplied. ‼▀◆⚒

Hopmaster (ABV 4.2%)
Big Game (ABV 4.5%)
Amber-hued with a malty aroma. Generous malt taste with spicy sides. Hints of pepper and lemon lurk under the hop bitterness which emerges with a mouthwatering bite.
Ethelfleda (ABV 4.5%)
Full malt aroma from this golden beer. Sweet and grassy mix to start, developing to a bitter finish.
Hoppy Poppy (ABV 4.6%)
Our Aethel (ABV 4.8%)
Whopper (ABV 6.5%)

Tankleys

Correspondence: 33 Beech Avenue, Sidcup, Kent, DA15 8NH ☎ 07901 333273 ⊕ tankleysbrewery.com

Tankleys is a cuckoo brewery based in south-east London using spare capacity at Beerblefish Brewing (qv) although some small batches are made at home for local micropubs. Its Australian brewer has been brewing for 17

years and produces small batch brews, available occasionally around the local area. V

English Golden Strong Ale (ABV 4.5%)

Tantum (NEW)

Workshop 9, Gate Farm Rural Enterprise Park, Wettenhall Road, Poole, Nantwich, CW5 6AL ☎ 07802 245362 ⊕ tantumbrewing.co.uk

Mike Heaher and Alistair Holt, two real ale enthusiasts, have recently retired from long-term careers and started Tantum Brewing in 2018. After some collaborations with Master Brewers, they set up their own brewery in the heart of the Cheshire countryside in 2019 to supply quality real ale to local outlets.

TAP

Marsden Estate, Rendcomb, Cirencester, Gloucestershire, GL7 7EX ☎ 07931 920988/ 07931 623001 ⊕ tapbrewerygloucestershire.com

⊠ TAP is a microbrewery established near Cirencester in 2015. It prides itself on sourcing materials and services locally, with malt from Warminster, hops from Worcester and the beer labels produced in Cirencester. Twelve local pubs are regularly supplied. ‼◆RAIB

Old Dairy Mild (ABV 3.2%)
Old Dairy Gold (ABV 3.9%)
Old Dairy Bronze (ABV 4.2%)

Tap East SIBA

▤ 7 International Square, The Great Eastern Market, Westfield Stratford City, Montfichet Road, Stratford, London, E20 1EE
☎ (020) 8555 4467 ⊕ tapeast.co.uk

⊠ Tap East is located in Westfield Stratford City Shopping Centre, opposite the main entrance to Stratford International Station. Brewing began in 2011 using a 2.5-barrel plant. One-off and collaborative beers with other breweries are also produced. There are occasional releases of bottle-conditioned beers. Beers are available on-site or at Utobeer cage in Borough Market. ▀◆V

Tap It SIBA

Unit 6, Muira Industrial Estate, William Street, Southampton, Hampshire, SO14 5QH ☎ 07484 649425 ⊕ tapitbrew.co.uk

The first brew by enthusiastic homebrewer Rob Colmer was in 2018. Tap It is an eight-barrel plant producing eight regular beers mainly in KeyKeg and bottles. Occasional cask-conditioned beers are available. There is an on-site brewery tap and a bar in Southampton is planned. ‼▀⚒

Tap Social Movement

27 Curtis Industrial Estate, North Hinksey Lane, Oxford, OX2 0LX
☎ (01865) 236330 ⊕ tapsocialmovement.com

A 1,000-litre brewery in an old warehouse. The three founders have a background in the criminal justice system. Founded in 2016 to give training and opportunities for people serving sentences. A good proportion of the beer is now brewed at the former LAM brewery site in Kenington. Tap room is open Thursday-Sunday. The first pub, the White House is on Abingdon Road, Oxford. Cask beer is available via collaboration brews and on request for beer festivals. Beer is supplied in KeyKegs to local pubs. ▀RAIB⚒

Tapestry SIBA

Unit B, Totterdown Bridge Industrial Estate, Albert Road, St Philips, Bristol, BS2 0XH ☎ 07787 453222 ⊕ tapestrybrewery.com

Previously known as Cocksure, this 10-barrel brewery was established in 2017 and moved from the Severn Vale to Bristol in 2018. Occasional specials and collaboration brews with other breweries complement the core range, most of which have been renamed. ‼◆RAIB V✦

Raconteur Amber Session (ABV 3.9%)
Slight citrus aroma, background sweet biscuit flavours overlaid with pine and citrus hoppiness which fade during the short finish.
Propeller Pale Ale (ABV 4.2%)
Hibiscus + Honey (ABV 4.8%)
Initial hit of hoppy bitterness then the tart flavour of hibiscus combines with honey sweetness which lingers on the palate.
Swingball Session IPA (ABV 4.8%)
Fruity hops on the nose combining on the palate with light malt and tropical fruit hints, lingering dry, bitter ending.
Mango + Orange (ABV 5%)
Definitely not a traditionalist's beer. The aroma, flavours and aftertaste are loaded with mango with an additional citrus orange punch.
Night Ride Cold Brew Stout (ABV 5%)
Roasted malt and coffee aroma and flavours to match with hints of dark fruit before a slightly dry finish.
Topline IPA (ABV 6.5%)

Tapped

⊟ Sheffield: Sheffield Tap, Platform 1b, Sheffield Station, Sheaf Street, Sheffield, South Yorkshire, S1 2BP ☎ (0114) 273 7558

Leeds: 51 Boar Lane, Leeds, LS1 5EL ⊕ tappedbrewco.com

Brewing began in 2013 after the old Edwardian dining rooms were converted into an on-site brewery with a viewing gallery at the Sheffield Tap pub. The beer is supplied via the company's specialist beer wholesale business, Pivovar. A further on-site brewery opened at the Leeds Tap in 2014. V

Ale (ABV 3.5%)
Mojo (ABV 3.6%)
Jericho (ABV 4%)
Sheaf Street Pale (ABV 4.5%)
Station Porter (ABV 5%)

Tapstone

11 Bartlett Park, Millfield, Chard, Somerset, TA20 2BB ☎ (01460) 929156 ☎ 07969 651998 ⊕ tapstone.co.uk

⊠ Founded in 2015, the brewery was custom built around a brewing process that preserves delicate hop oils – making beers with a saturated hop flavour. It is growing Centennial hops about two miles from the brewery. A small on-site taproom recently opened. All beers are unfined and hazy. ‼⊟V✦

Sea Monster (ABV 4.2%)
Soma (ABV 4.6%)
Hop Wire (ABV 4.8%)
Kush Kingdom (ABV 5%)

Tarn Hows

Low Bield, Knipe Fold, Outgate, Cumbria, LA22 0PU ☎ 07852 881105 ⊕ tarnhowsbrewery.com

A microbrewery near Hawkshead specialising in stouts and hoppy pale ales. Oak casks may be used for barrel-aging and occasional seasonal beers. V

Beertrix Porter (ABV 4%)
A well-balanced, fruity beer with some liquorice aromas and a lasting finish of bitterness and roast.
Pale (ABV 4.6%)
Blueberry & Vanilla Oatmeal Stout (ABV 5%)
Easy-drinking dark beer with fruity aromas and sweet fruity taste. The finish lasts well with roast malt flavours coming through.
Guji Coffee Stout (ABV 5.4%)

Tarn51

⊟ Robin Hood, 10 Church Road, Altofts, Normanton, West Yorkshire, WF6 2NJ ☎ (01924) 892911 ✉ realale@tarn51brewing.co.uk

Tarn51 uses a three-barrel plant situated at the Robin Hood in Altofts. Expansion is planned. Five other outlets are supplied.

Tatton SIBA

Unit 7, Longridge Trading Estate, Knutsford, Cheshire, WA16 8PR ☎ (01565) 750747 ☎ 07738 150898 ⊕ tattonbrewery.co.uk

☺Tatton is a family-owned business based in the heart of Cheshire. Brewing commenced in 2010 using a steam-fired, custom-built, 15-barrel brewhouse. It supplies pubs throughout Cheshire and the north-west. ‼⊟◆

Ale (ABV 3.7%)
Blonde (ABV 4%)
Best (ABV 4.2%)
Every Day IPA (ABV 4.5%)
Gold (ABV 4.5%)
Malted Milk Chocolate Stout (ABV 4.6%)
VIPA Pale Ale (ABV 6.3%)

Tavernale

⊟ Bridge Tavern, 7 Akenside Hill, Newcastle upon Tyne, NE1 3UF ☎ (0191) 2321122 ⊕ thebridgetavern.com

A two-barrel plant supplying beers to the Bridge Tavern only. All beers brewed are one-offs. ◆

Taw Valley

Westacott Farm, Westacott Lane, North Tawton, Devon, EX20 2BS ☎ 07900 002299 ⊕ tawvalleybrewery.com

Established in 2017 in a Grade-II listed 17th century thatched barn. Beer is delivered in the brewery dray, a VW camper van. ◆RAIB

Black Ops (ABV 3.9%)
Tawton Session Ale (ABV 4%)
Devon Jester (ABV 4.2%)
Kennard's Steam (ABV 4.3%)

Timothy Taylor SIBA IFBB

Knowle Spring Brewery, Keighley, West Yorkshire, BD21 1AW ☎ (01535) 603139 ⊕ timothy-taylor.co.uk

An independent, family-owned company established in 1858. It has occupied the Knowle Spring site since 1863. Pennine spring water is used to brew its award-winning ales on both the established main plant and a 10-barrel plant introduced in 2017 to develop new beers, including occasional specials. 19 pubs are operated.

Dark Mild (ABV 3.5%)
Malt and caramel dominate throughout in this sweetish beer with background hop and fruit notes.
Golden Best (ABV 3.5%)
Refreshing, amber-coloured, traditional Pennine mild. A delicate fruit hoppy aroma leads to a fruity taste with underlying hops and malt. Fruity finish.
Boltmaker (ABV 4%)
Tawny bitter combining, hops fruit and biscuity malt. Lingering, increasingly bitter aftertaste. Formerly and sometimes still sold as Best Bitter.
Knowle Spring (ABV 4.2%)
Tropical fruitiness on the nose leads to a bitter sweetness that carries through into the finish.
Landlord (ABV 4.3%)
A moreish bitter combining citrus peel aromas, malt and grassy hops with marmalade sweetness and a long, bitter finish.
Landlord Dark (ABV 4.3%)
A black beer with red highlights topped by a coffee-coloured head. Burnt caramel on the nose. Dark fruits with caramel in the taste leading to a light, bitter finish.

Team Toxic

Office: A13/A14 Champions Business Park, Arrow Brook Road, Birkenhead ☎ 07981 535024
✉ sue@theteamtoxic.co.uk

Team Toxic, led by Gazza Prescott and Sue Hayward, produces a range of one-off beers. Those from Gazza appear under the name 'Mission Creep' and those from Sue use the 'Waen' identity. Most of the beers are brewed at Liverpool Brewing Company, with some being brewed in collaboration with other breweries. Beers produced under the Team Toxic brand are a collaboration between Sue and Gazza.

Teignmouth (NEW)

Warehouse 1, Old Quay Street, Teignmouth, TQ14 8ES
teignmouthbrewery.co.uk

The brewery opened in 2019 and is run by the brewer, John Norish and his wife Joanna. Currently a six-barrel brew length, brewing three regular beers (available bottle-conditioned). There are plans for seasonal beers and expansion of the brewing plant as business allows. RAIB

Templer (ABV 4%)
Portside (ABV 4.3%)
Deckhand (ABV 4.5%)

Teignworthy SIBA

The Maltings, Teign Road, Newton Abbot, Devon, TQ12 4AA
☎ (01626) 332066 teignworthybrewery.com

Teignworthy Brewery opened in 1994 within the historic Tucker's Maltings building. The 20-barrel plant produces 50 barrels a week and supplies around 300 outlets in Devon and Somerset. It diversified in 2017 with the addition of the Black Dog gin distillery. !! ♦ RAIB

Neap Tide (ABV 3.8%)
Reel Ale (ABV 4%)
Subtle aromas. The taste is also gentle with malt and fruit dominating the hops. The aftertaste is dry.
Gun Dog (ABV 4.3%)
Easy-drinking, session best bitter. Fruity throughout. Dry aftertaste lingers; sweetness and fruit over malt and caramel, progressing into hoppiness.
Spring Tide (ABV 4.3%)
An excellent, full and well-rounded, mid-brown beer with a dry, bitter taste and aftertaste.
Old Moggie (ABV 4.4%)
Best bitter. Hoppy and bitter with fruity undertones. Complex aftertaste with a balance of malt, hops and fruit.
Beachcomber (ABV 4.5%)
A pale brown beer with a light, refreshing fruit and hop nose, grapefruit taste and a dry, hoppy finish.

Teme Valley SIBA

Talbot, Bromyard Road, Knightwick, Worcestershire, WR6 5PH
☎ (01886) 821235 ☎ 07792 394151
temevalleybrewery.co.uk

Teme Valley was established in 1997 to brew beer for the Talbot, Knightwick. Only hops grown in Herefordshire and Worcestershire are used in brewing. Beers are supplied throughout the West Midlands and Marches. !! ♦ RAIB

T'Other (ABV 3.5%)
This (ABV 3.7%)
That (ABV 4.1%)
Talbot Blonde (ABV 4.4%)
Talbot Porter (ABV 4.4%)
Wotever Next? (ABV 5%)
Roasted malt and toffee aromas lead to a complex taste of stone fruits, dark malt, hops and melon. The finish is at first of slightly smoky malt and fruits fading into lingering, dry hops.

Tempest SIBA

Block 11, Units 1 & 2 Tweedbank Industrial Estate, Tweedbank, TD1 3RS
☎ (01896) 759500 tempestbrewingco.com

Based in a former dairy, Tempest was set up in 2010 by Gavin Meiklejohn, brewer and co-proprietor of the Cobbles Inn in Kelso, which is the brewery tap. In 2015 the brewery moved from Kelso to new premises at Tweedbank. !! ♦ RAIB

Armadillo (ABV 3.8%)
Modern Helles (ABV 4.1%)
Elemental Porter (ABV 5.1%)

Tenby

Unit 15, The Salterns, Tenby, SA70 8EQ
☎ (01834) 218090 ☎ 07410 169447
tenbybrewingco.com

Formerly known as Preseli, Tenby Brewing Co uses a six-barrel plant. Beer is supplied to outlets in Pembrokeshire, neighbouring counties and further afield. Spent grain is fed to animals at a local eco farm and through energy savings the brewery is moving towards becoming carbon neutral. RAIB V

Son of a Beach (ABV 4.2%)
Hang Ten (ABV 4.3%)
Barefoot (ABV 4.7%)
Black Flag Porter (ABV 5.6%)

Tenby Harbour

See Harbwr Tenby

Thame

East Street, Thame, Oxfordshire, OX9 3JS
(01844) 218202
thamebrewery@btinternet.com

This one-barrel brewery was set up in 2009 by Peter Lambert and Oak Taverns in the old stables at the Cross Keys. Beer is produced from time to time for the Cross Keys.

Thames Side SIBA

Bridge Street, Staines-upon-Thames, Surrey, TW18 4TG
(01784) 409887 07749 204242
thamessidebrewery.co.uk

Thames Side was founded in 2015 by CAMRA member Andy Hayward using a four-barrel plant. Originally situated in an old boatyard, it relocated to its current location with an on-site taproom in 2019. A one-barrel pilot brew kit was added in 2020 for experimental brews. Beers are named after birds found on or near the River Thames. !!

Harrier Bitter (ABV 3.4%)
Heron Ale (ABV 3.7%)
White Swan Pale Ale (ABV 4.2%)
Egyptian Goose India Pale Ale (ABV 4.8%)
Wryneck Rye IPA (ABV 5.6%)

Theakston

The Brewery, Masham, North Yorkshire, HG4 4YD
(01765) 680000 theakstons.co.uk

An independent family business, established in 1827 by Robert Theakston. For 19 years from 1984 the brewery was in non-family hands, but following a successful buy back in 2003 the company returned to family control, managed by Simon Theakston and his three brothers (great-great grandsons of the founder). Significant capital investment in the Masham brewery since then has provided additional capacity and flexibility to meet growing demand and variety of beers brewed. !!

Best Bitter (ABV 3.8%)
Black Bull Bitter (ABV 3.9%)
A distinctively hoppy aroma leads to a bitter, hoppy taste with some fruitiness and a short bitter finish.
Lightfoot (ABV 4.1%)
XB (ABV 4.5%)
Old Peculier (ABV 5.6%)
A full-bodied, dark brown, strong ale. Slightly malty but with hints of roast coffee and liquorice. A smooth caramel overlay and a complex fruitiness leads to a bitter chocolate finish.

Thirst Class

Unit 16, Station Road Industrial Estate, Reddish, Stockport, SK5 6ND
(0161) 431 3998 thirstclassale.co.uk

Thirst Class opened in 2014 in the centre of Stockport using a purpose-built two-barrel plant. In 2016 the brewery relocated to larger premises and installed a 10-barrel plant. A collaboration brew is produced each month. RAIB V

Don't Panic (ABV 3.5%)
Kiss My Ace (ABV 4%)
Hoppy Go Lucky (ABV 4.1%)
Mosaic Pale Ale (ABV 4.7%)
Stocky Oatmeal Stout (ABV 4.7%)
Any Porter in a Storm (ABV 4.8%)
Dark roast in aroma and flavour with balanced sweetness and fruit. Dry throughout and lingering sweetness.
Green Bullet Pale Ale (ABV 4.8%)
Hopfordian IPA (ABV 6%)
Elephant Hawk IPA (ABV 6.5%)

John Thompson

Ingleby, Derbyshire, DE73 7HW
(01332) 862469 johnthompsoninn.com

Established by John Thompson in 1977 as an addition to the John Thompson Inn, which he converted from a 15th-century farmhouse in 1968, and is now run by his son Nick. John Thompson Special (formerly JTS XXX) is Derbyshire's longest continuously brewed ale. Brews are exclusively for the John Thompson Inn. !!

Thorley & Sons

30 East Street, Ilkeston, Derbyshire, DE7 5JB 07899 067723 dylan.thorley1@yahoo.co.uk

Thorley & Sons began brewing commercially in 2016 on a 1.5-barrel plant located in an old coach house at the rear of brewer Dylan Thorley's house.

Pale & Interesting (ABV 4.5%)

Thornbridge SIBA

Riverside Business Park, Buxton Road, Bakewell, Derbyshire, DE45 1GS
(01629) 815999 thornbridgebrewery.co.uk

The first Thornbridge craft beers were produced in 2005 using a 10-barrel brewery, housed in the grounds of Thornbridge Hall. The beers have gained considerable success with over 300 consumer and industry awards won. A 30-barrel brewery opened in Bakewell in 2009. The original site continues to develop new, seasonal and speciality beers. 200 outlets are supplied direct. 12 pubs are managed and owned. !! RAIB

Wild Swan (ABV 3.5%)
Extremely pale yet flavoursome and refreshing beer. Plenty of lemony citrus hop flavour, becoming increasingly dry and bitter in the finish and aftertaste.
Brother Rabbit (ABV 4%)
Lord Marples (ABV 4%)
Smooth, traditional, easy-drinking bitter. Caramel, malt and coffee flavours fall away to leave a long, bitter finish.
Ashford (ABV 4.2%)
Kipling (ABV 5.2%)
Golden pale bitter with aromas of grapefruit and passion fruit. Intense fruit flavours continue throughout, leading to a long bitter aftertaste.
Jaipur IPA (ABV 5.9%)
Flavoursome IPA packed with citrus hoppiness that?s nicely counter-balanced by malt and underlying sweetness and robust fruit flavours.
Saint Petersburg Imperial Russian Stout (ABV 7.4%)
Good example of an imperial stout. Smooth and easy to drink with raisins, bitter chocolate and hops throughout, leading to a lingering coffee and chocolate aftertaste.

Three Acre (NEW) SIBA

Dairy Yard, Little Goldsmiths Farm, Beechy Road, Blackboys, East Sussex, TN22 5JG
(01825) 891144 threeacrebrewery.co.uk

Three Acre Brewery was established in 2019 by three lifelong friends, shortly after finishing university. Based in the heart of rural Sussex, it takes the local rich brewing history and combines it with modern ingredients and techniques on its five-barrel plant. ♦V

Session Pale Ale (ABV 3.9%)
English Best Bitter (ABV 4%)
English Golden Ale (ABV 4%)

Three B's

Black Bull, Brokenstone Road, Blackburn, Lancashire, BB3 0LL
☎ (01254) 581381 ☎ 07563 573199
threebsbrewery.co.uk

Robert Bell acquired the Black Bull in 2011 and the brewpub now supplies 50 outlets. !! ♦ RAIB

Bee Thrifty (ABV 3.4%)
Stoker's Slake (ABV 3.6%)
Lightly-roasted coffee flavours are in the aroma and the initial taste. A well-rounded, dark brown mild with dried fruit flavours in the long finish.
Honey Bee (ABV 3.7%)
Bobbin's Bitter (ABV 3.8%)
Bee Blonde (ABV 4%)
Black Bull (ABV 4%)
Tackler's Tipple (ABV 4.3%)
Black Bull Lager (ABV 4.5%)
Doff Cocker (ABV 4.5%)
Pinch Noggin (ABV 4.6%)
Knocker Up (ABV 4.8%)
A smooth, rich, creamy porter. The roast flavour is foremost without dominating and is balanced by fruit and hop notes.
Shuttle Ale (ABV 5.2%)

Three Blind Mice

Unit W10, Black Bank Business Park, Black Bank Road, Little Downham, Cambridgeshire, CB6 2UA
☎ (01353) 864438 ☎ 07912 875825
threeblindmicebrewery.com

Award-winning, seven-barrel brewery, established in 2014. Beer is supplied regularly to the Drayman's Son micropub, Ely, plus other outlets in Ely, Cambridgeshire and further afield. The name comes from the three owners/brewers, who reckoned they didn't have a clue what they were doing when they first started brewing. ♦

Lonely Snake (ABV 3.5%)
Old Brown Mouse (ABV 4.2%)
Juice Rocket (ABV 4.5%)
Milk Worm (ABV 5.3%)

Three Brothers SIBA

Unit 4, Clayton Court, Bowesfield Crescent, Stockton on Tees, TS18 3QX
☎ (01642) 678084 threebrothersbrewing.co.uk

The brewery is the vision of Kit Dodd after brewing for five years with another local brewery. He established it in 2016, together with his brother Dave and brother-in-law Chris. !! ♦ RAIB

The Bitter Ex (ABV 3.7%)
Trilogy (ABV 3.9%)
DDH Pale (ABV 4%)
ThaIPA (ABV 4.1%)
Au (ABV 4.2%)
Session IPA (ABV 4.5%)
S'more Porter (ABV 4.8%)
Feel the Rhythm (ABV 5.3%)
North East IPA (ABV 5.3%)
West Coast IPA (ABV 6.2%)

Three Castles SIBA

Unit 12, Salisbury Road Business Park, Pewsey, Wiltshire, SN9 5PZ
☎ (01672) 564433 ☎ 07725 148671
threecastlesbrewery.co.uk

Three Castles is an independent, family-run brewery established in 2006. It delivers direct to around 80 pubs and independent retailers. Wholesalers and beer festivals are also supplied. !! ♦ RAIB

Chain Mail Pale (ABV 3.8%)
Barbury Castle (ABV 3.9%)
Armour Plated (ABV 4%)
Saxon Archer (ABV 4%)
Heritage (ABV 4.2%)
Uffington Castle (ABV 4.2%)
Vale Ale (ABV 4.3%)
Corn Dolly (ABV 4.7%)

Three Daggers SIBA

Westbury Road, Edington, Westbury, Wiltshire, BA13 4PG
☎ (01380) 830940 threedaggersbrewery.com

Three Daggers Brewery was established in 2013 using a 2.5-barrel brew plant in a farm shop next to a popular roadside pub. Malt is sourced locally from Warminster Maltings and hops from Charles Faram in Herefordshire. Hops are grown on-site for use in seasonal beers. !! ♦ RAIB

Daggers Blonde (ABV 3.6%)
Daggers Ale (ABV 4.1%)
Daggers Edge (ABV 4.7%)

Three Engineers SIBA

The Cow Byers, Winterbourne Medieval Barn, Church Lane, Winterbourne, BS36 1SD
threeengineersbrewery.co.uk

Nanobrewery established near Bristol in 2017. Beers are brewed on demand. After an extended period of cuckoo brewing at other Bristol breweries, Three Engineers moved back to its renovated and enlarged premises at Winterbourne Medieval Barn in 2020.

Three Fiends

Brookfield Farm, 148 Mill Moor Road, Meltham, Holmfirth, West Yorkshire, HD9 5LN ☎ 07810 370430
threefiends.co.uk

The brewery was set up by three friends in 2015 and is based in one of the outbuildings at Brookfield Farm. The original two-barrel kit was upgraded to an eight-barrel plant in 2019. Beers are available around Huddersfield and at CAMRA beer festivals.

Bitter Not Twisted (ABV 3.8%)
Two Face (ABV 4%)
Bad Uncle Barry (ABV 4.2%)
Boomer (ABV 4.3%)
Bandito (ABV 4.5%)
Mok Titi (ABV 4.6%)
Fudge Unit (ABV 4.8%)
Dark Side (ABV 5.3%)
Little Devil (ABV 5.3%)
Mr Badman (ABV 5.3%)
Punch Drunk (ABV 5.5%)
Voodoo (ABV 6%)
Panic Attack Espresso Stout (ABV 6.8%)
Bukowski (ABV 7%)

Three Hills

4 Thrapston Road, Woodford, Northamptonshire, NN14 4HY ☎ 07400 706884 🌐 threehillsbrewing.com

Named after the ancient communal tombs that stand on the outskirts of the village of Woodford, Three Hills is a small batch brewery established in 2016. Initially producing only in bottle, can and KeyKeg, it, now produces a monthly series of varying styles of cask-conditioned ales called the Woodford Experiment.

Three Kings SIBA

14 Prospect Terrace, North Shields, NE30 1DX ☎ 07580 004565 🌐 threekingsbrewery.co.uk

Three Kings started in 2012 using a 2.5-barrel plant, and have steadily upgraded it to its current 25-barrel capacity. Two house beers are brewed for local pubs. As well as the regular beers it typically brews two one-off beers each month. ♦

Shieldsman (ABV 3.8%)
Billy Mill Ale (ABV 4%)
Dark Side of the Toon (ABV 4.1%)
Ring of Fire (ABV 4.5%)
Silver Darling (ABV 5.6%)

Three Legs

Unit 1, Burnt House Farm, Udimore Road, Broad Oak, East Sussex, TN31 6BX ☎ 07939 997622 🌐 thethreelegs.co.uk

⊗ The Three Legs was started in 2014 by two friends who met studying winemaking and viticulture at university. They have grown from a nanobrewery to a 10-barrel plant in a converted farm barn. Regulars and beer-minded visitors find a warm welcome at the thriving brewery tap. Beers can be found in most free-houses and bottle shops across the south east. Beers are ever changing. Majority are modern, hop-forward, unfined, and with bags of flavour. !! RAIB ◈

Three Sisters

See Crafty Little

Three Sods SIBA

Arch 339, Mentmore Terrace, London Fields, London, E8 3PH ☎ 07544 422236 🌐 threesodsbrewery.com

⊗ Originally started in cramped conditions in the basement of the Bethnal Green Working Men's Club, the brewery moved to a railway arch in London Fields in 2020 using the ex-Wild Card six-barrel brew plant. Its range of traditional English style beers is augmented by seasonal specials. ♦◈

BoHo Bitter (ABV 4.1%)
Amber-coloured best bitter. Bready, malty aroma and taste. Sweet taste and aftertaste, with just a hint of hops.
Session (ABV 4.4%)
Citrus zesty nose and flavour where the biscuit sweetness cuts through the bitter hop. Finish is long, bitter and pithy.
Trade Union (ABV 4.5%)
Traditional, smooth, amber best bitter. Malt and fruit are balanced by plenty of bitter hops with a very dry finish.
Mud Puddler Black IPA (ABV 4.9%)
Creamy beer with malty, slightly fruity aroma. Flavour is of dry coffee, fruit, spicy hops and a growing lingering bitterness.
Belgian Bugger (ABV 5%)

Three Tuns SIBA

Salop Street, Bishop's Castle, Shropshire, SY9 5BN ☎ 07973 301099

Office: 16 Market Square, Bishops Castle, SY9 5BW 🌐 threetunsbrewery.co.uk

Brewing on this site started in the 16th century and was licensed in 1642. A small-scale tower brewery from the late 19th century survives. Three Tuns was one of only four pub breweries still running in the 1970s. !! ♦ RAIB

Thurstons

The Courtyard, 102c High Street, Horsell, Surrey, GU21 4ST ☎ (01483) 729555 ☎ 07789 936784 🌐 thurstonsbrewery.co.uk

⊗ Originally based in the Crown, Horsell, Thurstons moved next door in 2014 when the brewery upgraded to a 4.5-barrel plant. The brewery supplies pubs across Surrey. ♦RAIB V

Horsell Best (ABV 3.8%)
Traditional, well-balanced bitter, initially malty with strong caramel flavours throughout and balancing bitterness, becoming drier in the finish.
Horsell Gold (ABV 3.8%)
Light fruit and slightly nutty aroma, lead to some bitterness and malt, which soon fades into a light bitter finish.
Milk Stout (ABV 4.5%)
Smooth, sweet stout with a chocolaty flavour. A sweet, malty flavour with a pleasant sharpness and a slightly dry finish.
Un-American Pale Ale (ABV 4.6%)

Thwaites IFBB

Myerscough Road, Mellor Brook, Lancashire, BB2 7LB ☎ (01254) 686868 🌐 thwaites.co.uk

Founded in 1807, Thwaites brewed in Blackburn until 2018 when it moved to a rural site five miles away in the Ribble Valley. A 20-barrel plant brews exclusively for the company's 240 or so pubs, 11 managed Inns of Character, eight hotels and two lodges. All properties can sell the regular cask beers, plus members of the company's 1807 Cask Club can sell the seasonal ales. Marston's, owner of the Wainwright and Lancaster Bomber brands, continues to sell these beers into Thwaites' outlets. ♦

Mild (ABV 3.3%)
Original (ABV 3.6%)
IPA (ABV 3.8%)
TBC (Thwaites Best Cask) (ABV 3.8%)
Gold (ABV 4.1%)
Amber (ABV 4.4%)

Tigertops

22 Oakes Street, Flanshaw, Wakefield, West Yorkshire, WF2 9LN ☎ (01229) 716238 ☎ 07951 812986 ✉ tigertopsbrewery@hotmail.com

Tigertops was established in 1995 by Stuart Johnson and his wife Lynda who, as well as owning the brewery, ran the Foxfield brewpub in Cumbria (qv). Recently retired, the brewery is run on their behalf by Barry Smith, supplying five regular outlets. ♦

Cass 2CV (ABV 4.6%)

Tiley's

Salutation Inn, Ham, Gloucestershire, GL13 9QH
(01453) 810284 sallyatham.com

This 2.5-barrel microbrewery was established in an outbuilding of the award-winning Salutation Inn in 2015. It concentrates on producing small batches of award-winning beer, predominantly in cask, some in KeyKeg. Most of the brewery's output is sold on-site at the Salutation Inn, and the Butcher's Hook, Thornbury. The rest goes to selected local pubs.

Tilford

Duke of Cambridge, Tilford Road, Farnham, Surrey, GU10 2DD 07710 500967
genesiscraftales@hotmail.com

Tilford Brewery was started in 2017 using a 2.5-barrel plant in an old coaching house on the site of the Duke of Cambridge pub. A shop, tasting room and mini maltings are planned for the upstairs of the building. Beer is supplied to pubs in Surrey and Hampshire. !!

Tillingbourne SIBA

Old Scotland Farm, Staple Lane, Shere, Surrey, GU5 9TE
(01483) 222228 tillybeer.co.uk

Tillingbourne was established in 2011 on a farm site previously used by Surrey Hills Brewery using its old 17-barrel plant. Around 25 local outlets are supplied. !! ♦

The Source (ABV 3.3%)
Light and crisp golden ale with strong grapefruit flavours. Packed full of citra hops and drinking well above its strength.

Black Troll (ABV 3.7%)
A black bitter in which initial roast notes are eventually overpowered by citrus hop through to the finish.

Dormouse (ABV 3.8%)

AONB (ABV 4%)
Golden ale in which citrus hop dominates throughout. Some balancing malt in the aroma and taste, however.

Falls Gold (ABV 4.2%)
Whilst hops dominate, balancing malt is evident throughout. Hints of grapefruit in the aroma and taste lead to a dry finish.

Whakahari (ABV 4.6%)

Hop Troll (ABV 4.8%)
Golden ale with big hop flavours together with peach and apricot. Sweet, fruity taste leads to a floral, bitter finish.

Summit (ABV 6%)

Time & Tide

Statenborough Farm, Felderland Lane, Deal, Kent, CT14 0BX 07739 868256
timeandtidebrewing.co.uk

Time & Tide began by using spare capacity in the now closed Ripple Steam Brewery. It now has its own 20-barrel brewhouse, soon to be extended. A large range of KeyKeg and canned beers is brewed, along with cask-conditioned ales for the Deal Community Hop Farm. ♦RAIB

Bitter (ABV 4%)

Green Hop (ABV 4.8%)

ESB (ABV 5.8%)

Tin Head

Unit 22f, Bradley Fold Trading Estate, Bradley Fold Road, Radcliffe, Bury, BL2 6RT 07980 263766
beer@tinheadbrewery.co.uk

Established in 2017 as a beer canning factory, the site has been expanded and now operates a brewery with a large, dog-friendly taproom. !!

Tindall

Toad Lane, Seething, Norfolk, NR35 2EQ 07703 379116 mike.green4@aol.co.uk

Tindall Ales began brewing in 1998. It was originally based in Ditchingham but moved to its current location in 2001. Mike is passionate about brewing a new generation of cask beer using the finest local ingredients whenever possible and live yeast. !! ♦V

Best Bitter (ABV 3.7%)

Mild (ABV 3.7%)

Liberator (ABV 3.8%)

Alltime (ABV 4%)

Seething Pint (ABV 4.3%)

Tintagel SIBA

Condolden Farm, Tintagel, Cornwall, PL34 0HJ
(01840) 213371 tintagelbrewery.co.uk

Established in 2009 in a redundant milking parlour on the highest farm in Cornwall, using a 7.5-barrel plant. A new purpose-built brewery, shop, restaurant and visitor centre opened in 2017. Around 80 outlets are supplied direct. !! ♦

Castle Gold (ABV 3.8%)
Refreshing gold ale with faint malt aroma. Citrus hop, tropical fruits, sweet malt and distinctly bitter flavours. Hop bitter finish.

Cornwall's Pride (ABV 4%)
Pale brown bitter with malt aroma. Sweet, grainy malt with toffee and summer fruits. Late dried fruit and coffee hints.

Sir Lancelot (ABV 4.2%)

Arthur's Ale (ABV 4.4%)
Pale brown complex beer with balance of sweet toffee, malt and earthy hops. Hints of figs, vine fruits and liquorice.

Pendragon (ABV 4.5%)
Golden beer with citrus hop nose. Refreshing, strong orange citrus and pine hop bitterness. Hints of toffee, honey and malt.

Poldark Ale (ABV 4.5%)
Brown, strong mild with malt aroma. Assertive malty flavour with stone fruits, dates, sweet caramel, smokiness and a citrus edge.

Harbour Special (ABV 4.8%)
Tawny, premium bitter with ripe fruity, malty aroma. Rich nutty malt, stone fruits and esters taste, finishing bitter and malty.

Merlins Muddle (ABV 5.2%)
Auburn, creamy, premium bitter. Malt dominates the taste throughout with spicy hop bitterness and a complex mixture of fruit flavours.

Caliburn (ABV 5.8%)
Dark old ale. Smoky, roast malt and Christmas pudding fruits with rich and complex flavours including treacle and earthy hops.

Tinworks

Unit 20, 1 Trostre Industrial Park, Llanelli, SA14 9UU
07595 841958 tinworksbrewery.co.uk

Brewery commenced operations on a rural farm but relocated and upgraded to a 10-barrel kit in 2019.

Old Castle Pale (ABV 4.6%)
Mashfield Red (ABV 4.7%)
Ashburnham Porter (ABV 5%)
Dafen IPA (ABV 6.3%)

Tiny Rebel

Wern Industrial Estate, Rogerstone, Newport, NP10 9FQ
☎ (01633) 547378 tinyrebel.co.uk

Established in 2012, Tiny Rebel moved to new, bespoke premises in 2017 having outgrown its previous site. Originally using a 12-barrel plant, the brewery now operates a dual-stream 30-barrel plant, and consists of 23 fermentation tanks and four conditioning tanks. It supplies its three tied pubs as well as numerous outlets across the UK. Beers are supplied in cask, keg, bottle and can, all packaging takes place in-house. !! ♦

Dutty (ABV 4.2%)
Cwtch (ABV 4.6%)
Stay Puft (ABV 5.2%)

Tiny Vessel

Unit 505, Platts Eyot, Hampton, TW12 2HF ☎ 07888 730210 tinyvessel.co.uk

Tiny Vessel is a 1.5-barrel brewery established in 2016 on Platts Eyot, an island on the River Thames near Hampton. All beers are unfiltered and unfined, mostly available bottled or in keg, although at least one beer is usually available on cask in the Northumberland Arms, Brentford. RAIB

Dark Matter (ABV 4.5%)
Black porter, malty with chocolate and coffee notes. Malty finish with supporting hops and bitterness. Roasted, dry, bitter finish.

Tipples

Unit 3, The Mill, Wood Green, Salhouse, Norfolk, NR13 6NY
☎ (01603) 721310 tipplesbrewery.com

Tipples was established in 2004 on a six-barrel brew plant. In addition to a full range of cask ales, an extensive range of bottled beers is produced, which can be found in some farmers markets and supermarkets in Norfolk. ♦RAIB

Bowline (ABV 3.8%)
Ginger (ABV 3.8%)
A spicy aroma introduces this yellow-gold brew. Ginger dominates with supporting malty bitterness. Quick, gingernut finish.
Hanged Monk (ABV 3.8%)
Strong roast and malt notes dominate the aroma and taste. A grainy mouthfeel with caramel and a growing vinous finish.
Longshore (ABV 3.8%)
A soft, peachy aroma and creamy mouthfeel. The initial fruity apricot flavour quickly subsides to a long, dry bitterness.
Sundown (ABV 3.9%)
Berries and malt introduce this smooth, creamy bitter. Bitterness gives depth to the fruity malt core as it slowly sweetens.
Aurous (ABV 4%)
Lady Evelyn (ABV 4.1%)
A crisp hoppy aroma. Bitterness and hop throughout. Some malt and sweetness take the edge off a smoky finish.
Sea Lantern (ABV 4.1%)
Redhead (ABV 4.2%)
Malt and hops in both nose and palate. Toffee in the initial taste gives way to an increasing bitterness.
Lazy Summer (ABV 4.3%)
Winter Moon (ABV 4.3%)
Malten Copper (ABV 4.4%)
Topper (ABV 4.5%)
Coffee and dark chocolate to the fore throughout. Just enough malt sweetness and bitterness to provide balance. Strong, big-hearted fiinish.
Brewers Progress (ABV 4.6%)
Solid and malty with strong caramel and vanilla support. Smooth and creamy with depth added by a bitter blackcurrant fruitiness.
Moonrocket (ABV 5%)
A complex golden brew. Malt, hop, bitterness and a fruity sweetness swirl round in an ever-changing kaleidoscope of flavours.
Jack's Revenge (ABV 5.8%)
An explosion of malt, chocolate, roast and plum pudding. Full-bodied with a deep red hue and a strong solid finish.
Indian Hill (ABV 6.5%)
Black Moth (ABV 7.8%)

Tipsy Angel

see 4Ts

Tír Dhá Ghlas

Cullins Yard, 11 Cambridge Road, Dover, Kent, CT17 9BY
☎ (01304) 211666 cullinsyard.co.uk

Brewing began in 2012 using a two-barrel plant. Beers are only available in the bar/restaurant and occasionally at the nearby Royal Cinque Ports Yacht Club.

Tirril SIBA

Red House, Long Marton, Cumbria, CA16 6BN
☎ (01768) 361846 tirrilbrewery.co.uk

Established in 1999, Tirril Brewery has twice outgrown its premises. It delivers to more than 170 outlets, 100 of which regularly stock the beer. One pub is owned. Contract brewing is also carried out for Bitter End Brewery. !! ♦

Original Bitter (ABV 3.8%)
Ullswater Blonde (ABV 3.8%)
Grasmere Gold (ABV 3.9%)
Kirkstone Gold (ABV 3.9%)
Old Faithful (ABV 4%)
Initially bitter, gold-coloured ale with an astringent finish.
1823 (ABV 4.1%)
Academy Ale (ABV 4.2%)
Borrowdale Bitter (ABV 4.2%)
Windermere IPA (ABV 4.3%)
Red Barn Ale (ABV 4.4%)

Titanic SIBA

Callender Place, Burslem, Stoke-on-Trent, Staffordshire, ST6 1JL
☎ (01782) 823447 titanicbrewery.co.uk

One of the earliest microbreweries, founded in 1985. Now owned by two local beer loving brothers, it has grown from a small, seven-barrel brewery, to producing over four million pints per year of its award-winning ales.

With an expanding fleet of tied pubs and café bars, they also supply free trade customers in the Midlands, North West and further afield. Captain Smith, captain of the Titanic was born in Stoke on Trent, hence the name. !! ♦ RAIB

Mild (ABV 3.5%)
Fresh, fruity hop aroma leads to a caramel start then a rush of bitter hoppiness ending with a lingering, dry finish.
Steerage (ABV 3.8%)
Pale yellow bitter. Flavours start with hops and fruit but become zesty and refreshing in this light session beer with a long, dry finish.
Lifeboat (ABV 4%)
Dark brown with fruit, malt and caramel aromas. Sweet start, malty and caramel middle with hoppiness developing into a fruity and dry, lingering finish.
Anchor Bitter (ABV 4.1%)
Amber beer with a spicy hint to the fruity start that says go to the rush of hops for the dry, bitter finish.
Iceberg (ABV 4.1%)
Yellow gold, sparkling, wheat beer with a flowery start leading to a great hop crescendo.
Cherry Dark (ABV 4.4%)
Cappuccino Stout (ABV 4.5%)
Black with a vanilla and strong coffee nose leading to a sweet taste again with strong coffee. Aftertaste is sweet
Chocolate & Vanilla Stout (ABV 4.5%)
Chocoholic paradise with real coffee and vanilla support. Cocoa, sherry and almonds lend depth to this creamy, drinkable 'Heaven in a glass' stout.
Stout (ABV 4.5%)
Roasty, toasty with tobacco, autumn bonfires, chocolate and hints of liquorice; perfectly balanced with a bitter, dry finish reminiscent of real coffee.
White Star (ABV 4.5%)
Hints of cinnamon apple pie are found before the hops take over to give a bitter edge to this well-balanced, refreshing, fruity beer.
Plum Porter (ABV 4.9%)
Dark brown with a powerful fruity aroma. A sweet plum fruitiness gives way to a gentle bitter finish.
Captain Smith's Strong Ale (ABV 5.2%)
Red brown and full-bodied, lots of malt and roast with a hint of honey but a strong, bittersweet finish.

Titsey SIBA

Botley Hill Farmhouse, Limpsfield Road, Titsey, Surrey, CR6 9QH ☎ 07850 914189
titseybrewingco.com

A microbrewery established in 2017 on the Titsey Estate. It recently moved to larger premesis in a former nuclear bunker, still on the Titsey Estate, with a five-barrel plant, purchased through crowdfunding. It supplies two associated pubs, the Botley Hill Farmhouse and the White Bear at Fickleshole, and increasingly to other local outlets. Ales are named after historic owners of the Titsey Estate.

Gresham Hopper (ABV 3.7%)
Leveson Buck (ABV 3.7%)
Gower Wolf (ABV 4%)

To The Moon (NEW) SIBA

3 Woodcote Avenue, Bramhall, Stockport, SK7 3ND
☎ 07795 965053
admin@tothemoonbrewery.com

A nanobrewery capable of producing 6,000 litres per year, but currently operated part time by owner brewer. Concentrating on IPA or pale ale – all distributed in KeyKeg, mainly to microbars and the more adventurous pubs. Specialities produced for development with no guarantee they will be repeated.

Toll End

c/o Waggon & Horses, 131 Toll End Road, Tipton, West Midlands, DY4 0ET ☎ 07903 725574

The four-barrel brewery opened in 2004. With the exception of Phoebe's Ale, named after the brewer's daughter, all brews commemorate local landmarks, events and people. Nearly all of the brewery's output is sold in the Waggon & Horses. !! RAIB

Tollgate SIBA

Unit 1, Southwood House Farm, Staunton Lane, Calke, Derbyshire, LE65 1RG
☎ (01283) 229194 tollgatebrewery.co.uk

This six-barrel brewery was founded in 2005 on the site of the old Brunt & Bucknall Brewery in nearby Woodville, but relocated to new premises on the National Trust's Calke Park estate in 2012. Around 180 outlets are supplied direct, mainly in the north Midlands. The brewery operates three micropubs: Queens Road Tap, Leicester, Tap at No. 76, Ashby-de-la-Zouch, and Town Street Tap, Duffield, and has recently opened a public bar on the premises, the Milking Parlour.
!! ♦ RAIB V

Stand & Deliver (ABV 3.8%)
Hackney Blonde (ABV 3.9%)
Melbourne Bitter (ABV 4%)
California Steam (ABV 4.2%)
Eclipse BIPA (ABV 4.2%)
Pacifica (ABV 4.2%)
Red Storm (ABV 4.2%)
Duffield Amber (ABV 4.4%)
Ashby Pale (ABV 4.5%)
Old Rasputin (ABV 4.5%)
Red Star IPA (ABV 4.5%)
Billy's Best Bitter (ABV 4.6%)
High Street Bitter (ABV 4.7%)
NZ Pilsner (ABV 5.2%)
Spark IPA (ABV 5.6%)

Tolly Cobbold

See Greene King

Tom Herrick's

See under H

Tom's Tap

4-6 Thomas Street, Crewe, Cheshire, CW1 2BD
☎ 07931 573425
tomstapandbrewhouse.wordpress.com

Tom's Tap & Brewhouse consists of three units; brewery equipment in the first, live music and special events in the middle (including meet the brewer events), and a taproom in the third (open to the public Friday and Saturday). Beer is also distributed to four other outlets and local beer festivals. !!

Tombstone

6 George Street, Great Yarmouth, Norfolk, NR30 4HU ☎ 07584 504444
tombstonebrewery.co.uk

Established in 2013, the brewery is run by former homebrewer Paul Hodgson. The original brewery backed

THE BREWERIES

onto the town cemetery, inspiring the name, but it has now relocated to the rear of its brewery tap, the Tombstone Saloon. Around 30 outlets are supplied around Norwich. 🛒♦

Tombstone Ale (ABV 3.7%)
Banana toffee aroma. Piquant, bitter, hoppy beginning softened by a biscuity maltiness. Dry, bitter finish.
Amarillo (ABV 3.8%)
Arizona (ABV 3.9%)
Malt and lemon nose. Initial lemongrass and sweet biscuit beginning quickly fades. Sweet, watery finish enhanced by malt.
Texas Jack (ABV 4%)
Toffee apple and vanilla aroma. Caramel leads the smooth complex mix of flavours. A bittersweet fruitiness continues to the end.
Regulators (ABV 4.1%)
Gunslinger (ABV 4.3%)
Lone Rider (ABV 4.3%)
Stagecoach (ABV 4.4%)
A rich caramel and treacle aroma. Malt, roast and caramel dominate a hoppy bittersweeet foundation. Short, increasingly dry finish.
Cherokee (ABV 4.5%)
Malty nose with plum and cherry. Initial mix of biscuit and roasty bitterness gently changes to a slightly spicy maltiness.
Santa Fe (ABV 5%)
Big Nose Kate (ABV 5.2%)
6 Shooter (ABV 6.6%)
Stage Coach Reserve (ABV 8.5%)

Brewed for Brunning & Price Pub Co:
Blackfoot (ABV 4.8%)

Tomos a Lilford SIBA

Unit 11b, Vale Business Park, Llandow, Cowbridge, CF71 7PF
☎ (01446) 677757 ☎ 07747 858514

Office: 117 Boverton Road, Llantwit Major, CF61 1YA
✉ tomos.lilford@gmail.com

⊗ Tomos a Lilford was launched in 2013 by homebrewers Rolant Tomos, and brothers Rob and James Lilford. The brewery supplies pubs and clubs across the Vale of Glamorgan and further afield. All point of sale material is bilingual. 🛒♦

Cob (ABV 4%)
Annwyl (ABV 5%)
Gaucho (ABV 5%)
O.P.A (ABV 5%)
Rosemary Ale (ABV 5%)
Hay (ABV 5.2%)

Tonbridge SIBA

Unit 19, Branbridges Industrial Estate, East Peckham, Kent, TN12 5HF
☎ (01622) 871239 🌐 tonbridgebrewery.co.uk

⊗ Tonbridge Brewery was launched in 2010 using a four-barrel plant, expanding in 2013 to a 12-barrel plant. It is owned and run jointly by Paul Bournazian and Mark Gardner. Pubs, clubs and shops are supplied throughout Kent and also parts of Surrey, Sussex, Essex and south-east London. ‼

Golden Rule (ABV 3.5%)
Traditional Ale (ABV 3.6%)
Coppernob (ABV 3.8%)
Countryman (ABV 4%)
Rustic (ABV 4%)
Blonde Ambition (ABV 4.2%)
Old Chestnut (ABV 4.4%)
American Pale (ABV 5%)

Toolmakers SIBA

6-8 Botsford Street, Sheffield, South Yorkshire, S3 9PF
☎ 07956 235332 🌐 toolmakersbrewery.com

Toolmakers is a family-run brewery established in 2013 in an old tool-making factory. The regular brews are supplemented by a varying range of different styles and strengths. Beers are brewed on a five-barrel plant. The function room at the brewery also doubles as the brewery taproom. The adjoining Forest pub is owned. ‼◆

Lynch Pin (ABV 4%)
Slide Hammer Stout (ABV 4%)

Tooth & Claw

See Camerons

Top-Notch

Haywards Heath, West Sussex, RH16 1UQ ☎ 07963 829368 🌐 topnotchbrewing.co.uk

This 0.5-barrel brewery is situated in a converted residential outbuilding in Haywards Heath. RAIB

Hop Festival (ABV 3.9%)
Royal Fanfare (ABV 4.6%)

Top Out SIBA

Unit 3, 6b Dryden Road, Loanhead, EH20 9LZ
☎ (0131) 440 0270 ☎ 07742 234970
🌐 topoutbrewery.com

Brewing began in 2013 using a six-barrel plant. Branding has a topographical theme. A core range of eight beers is available plus a changing 'First Ascents' range with an adventurous new style each time. ♦RAIB V

Copperheid (ABV 3.4%)
Refreshing light, gingery beer.
Pale Ale (ABV 3.6%)
Single hop pale ale. Same recipe but different hop each time.
Staple (ABV 4%)
Gold-coloured bitter. Intense hops but with malt coming through. Aroma has a hint of fruit. A lasting, dry finish.
Altbier (ABV 4.5%)
Based on a traditional German-style ale. Malty and fruity but with a certain amount of hop bitterness.
Schmankerl (ABV 4.9%)
Simon Says-on (ABV 5.1%)
Smoked Porter (ABV 5.6%)
The Cone (ABV 6.8%)

Top Rope

Unit 14, Engineer Park, Babbage Road, Sandycroft, CH5 2QD ☎ 07581 483075 🌐 topropebrewing.com

Top Rope commenced brewing on a small scale in Merseyside in 2016 and expanded in 2018, moving to the former Deva Craft brewery in north-east Wales. Output is predominately keg, can and cask, with the beers often named on a wrestling theme. ‼

TOPS (The Olde Potting Shed)

Collingdon Buildings, Collingdon Road, High Spen, NE39 2EQ

TOPS began brewing in 2013 using a five-barrel plant with a small test kit for experimental beers. Pubs are supplied direct within a 30-mile radius of the brewery.

Blondie (ABV 3.8%)

Topsham

The Warehouse, Haven Road, Exeter, Devon, EX2 8GR

The brewery was established in 2018 and moved to its current location at the popular Exeter Quay in 2019, using a 3.5-barrel plant. It features a taproom with an outside drinking area next to the brewery. Beers are also available in the local free trade. ◆

Ten (ABV 3.8%)
Goat Walk (ABV 4.6%)
Mud Monster (ABV 5%)
Ice Works (ABV 6%)

Torrside

New Mills Marina, Hibbert Street, New Mills, Derbyshire, SK22 3JJ
☎ (01663) 745219 ☎ 07539 149175
⊕ torrside.co.uk

☺Established by three friends in 2015, Torrside brews a wide range of beers on a 10-barrel plant, under the tagline Hops, Smoke, Monsters. A changing line-up of largely hop-driven, smoked and strong beers are sold to pubs, bars and bottle shops within a 50-mile radius. All beers are unfined. Brewery tap events usually take place one weekend each month (April-September) and there's a smoked beer festival in early November. ‼🍴RAIB V

Candlewick (ABV 4%)
Euro-Hop (ABV 4.5%)
West of the Sun (ABV 4.5%)
I am Curious Lemon (ABV 4.8%)
Franconia (ABV 5.2%)
I'm Spartacus (ABV 6.8%)

Totnes

🍴 59a High Street, Totnes, Devon, TQ9 5PB
☎ (01803) 849290 ☎ 07974 828971
✉ richard.kidd@idnet.net.uk

☒ Brewing began in 2014 at a family-run pub at the foot of Totnes Castle. The brewery is situated immediately behind the bar. An increase in the portfolio of the brewery has also meant a greater emphasis on keg and KeyKeg output. Beers are available almost exclusively at the pub. All ales are unfined and unfiltered. ◆

Towcester Mill SIBA

The Mill, Chantry Lane, Towcester, Northamptonshire, NN12 6AD
☎ (01327) 437060 ⊕ towcestermillbrewery.co.uk

☒ A five-barrel brewery situated at the Grade-II listed Old Mill in Towcester. There is a brewery tap on-site and a shop off-site at the Bell Plantation Garden Centre in Towcester. ‼🍴◆V◆

Old Mill Bitter (ABV 3.6%)
Crooked Hooker (ABV 3.8%)
Golden/amber in colour with a honeyed fruit aroma, a slightly earthy taste with some fruit and a bitter finish.
Mill Race (ABV 3.9%)
Slightly citrus aroma, followed by a dry citrus taste with hints of grapefruit and a long, bitter aftertaste.
Bell Ringer (ABV 4.4%)
Black Fire (ABV 5.2%)
Roman Road (ABV 5.2%)

Tropical fruit aroma followed by a good balance of malt and hops with pineapple notes and a long, bitter aftertaste.

Tower

Old Water Tower, Walsitch Maltings, Glensyl Way, Burton upon Trent, Staffordshire, DE14 1PZ
☎ (01283) 562888 ☎ 07771 926323
⊕ towerbrewery.co.uk

☺Tower was established in 2001 by John Mills, previously a brewer at Burton Bridge, in a converted, derelict water tower, originally built for Thomas Salt's Brewery in the 1870s. The conversion was given a Burton Civic Society award for the restoration of an industrial building. The premises incorporate a public bar, open Friday evenings only. Tower has 20 regular outlets. ‼🍴◆◆

Salt's Burton Ale (ABV 3.5%)
Bitter (ABV 4.2%)
Gold-coloured with a malty, caramel and hoppy aroma. A full hop and fruit taste with the fruit lingering. A bitter and astringent finish.
Gone for a Burton (ABV 4.6%)
Imperial IPA (ABV 5%)

Townes

🍴 Speedwell Inn, Lowgates, Staveley, Chesterfield, Derbyshire, S43 3TT
☎ (01246) 472252

Townes Brewery, which started in 1994, has been situated in the rear of the Speedwell Inn at Staveley since 1997. After the retirement of brewer Alan Wood in 2013, Lawrie and Nicoleta Evans have continued brewing to the same recipes on the five-barrel plant. Beers are rarely found outside the Speedwell Inn, other than occasional swaps and beer festivals.

Townhouse

Units 1-4, Townhouse Studios, Townhouse Farm, Alsager Road, Audley, Staffordshire, ST7 8JQ ☎ 07976 209437 ✉ j.nixon2@btinternet.com

Townhouse was set up in 2002 with a 2.5-barrel plant. In 2004 the brewery scaled up to five barrels and in 2006 two further fermenting vessels were added. The bulk of its production can be found in the Potteries. ◆

Enigma (ABV 3.5%)
Styrian Pale (ABV 3.5%)
Rye Pale Ale (ABV 3.6%)
Flowerdew (ABV 4%)
Golden with a wonderful floral aroma. Fabulous flavour of flowery hops delivering a crisp hoppy bite and presenting a lingering taste of flowery citrus waves.
Meridian Mild (ABV 4%)
Barney's Stout (ABV 4.5%)
Roast chocolate and toffee nose atop this black stout. Sweet start becoming bitter at the end, with velvety roast throughout.
Armstrong Ale (ABV 4.8%)
Gladstone Strong Ale (ABV 5%)

TQ (NEW)

Unit 6, Kingswood Court, Long Meadow, South Brent, Devon, TQ10 9YS
☎ (01803) 364925 ⊕ tqbeerworks.com

TQ is a small, family-run brewery dedicated to bringing modern craft beer to Torbay and the surrounding area. A core range of five bottle-conditioned beers is available, plus a rolling programme of seasonal one-off brews. ♦RAIB

Track

5 Sheffield Street, Manchester, M1 2ND
☎ (0161) 273 4832 ☎ 07725 692096
trackbrewing.co

Track Brewing Co was established in 2014 and is based in a railway arch underneath Manchester's Piccadilly Railway Station. Since its inception the brewery has expanded considerably in size and now produces a wide variety of beer styles. A taproom opened in nearby Crusader Mill in 2018. !! V

Sonoma (ABV 3.8%)
Prominent fruit hop aroma. Balanced, sweet fruity taste. Moderate bitterness at first with punchy citrus hop after. Unfined.

Tractor Shed SIBA

Tractor Shed, Calva Brow, Workington, Cumbria, CA14 1DB
☎ (01900) 68860 tractor-shed.co.uk

Renamed from Mitchell Krause in 2014 and having previously had its beers brewed under contract, brewing started in an old tractor shed on the family farm in 2013. After initially focusing on bottled and kegged continental-style beers, the first cask-conditioned beer was produced in 2014. The brewery contract brews various beers for Shindigger (qv), mostly for bottle and keg. !! RAIB

Mowdy Pale Ale (ABV 3.9%)
Clocker Stout (ABV 4%)

Traquair House SIBA

Traquair House, Innerleithen, EH44 6PW
☎ (01896) 830323 traquair.co.uk/traquair-house-brewery

The 18th century brewhouse is based in one of the wings of the 1,000-year-old Traquair House, Scotland's oldest inhabited house. All the beers are oak-fermented and 60% of production is exported. !! ♦

Bear Ale (ABV 5%)
Malty aroma and a complex taste of malts, citrus fruit, sweetness and bitterness, all lasting into the aftertaste.

Treboom SIBA

Millstone Yard, Main Street, Shipton-by-Beningbrough, North Yorkshire, YO30 1AA
☎ (01904) 471569 ☎ 07761 608662
treboom.co.uk

Established in 2011 by scientist John Lewis and artist Jane Blackman, this 10-barrel brewery produces a range of core beers alongside monthly seasonal specials using water from its own borehole, whole hops and locally-malted barley. Green hops grown at the brewery are used in the autumn and the award-winning mix of contemporary and traditional beers are distributed throughout Yorkshire. ♦RAIB

Tambourine Man (ABV 3.9%)
Yorkshire Sparkle (ABV 4%)
Kettle Drum (ABV 4.3%)
Orions Belt (ABV 4.5%)
Hop Britannia (ABV 5%)
Myricale (ABV 5%)
Baron Saturday (ABV 5.2%)

Treen's

Unit 3, Viaduct Works, Frog Hill, Ponsanooth, Cornwall, TR3 7JW ☎ 07552 218788

Office: 18 St Michael's Road, Ponsanooth, TR3 7EA
treensbrewery.co.uk

This family-run brewery was founded in 2016, initially using spare capacity at other local breweries. It now has its own premises using a 12-barrel plant. Bottling was introduced in 2018. Expansion is planned. ♦

Essential (ABV 3.8%)
Robustly bitter, gold-amber beer with grassy, peppery hops and light malt flavours. Citrus and stone fruit notes. Long, bitter finish.
Classic (ABV 4.3%)
Brown bitter with malt aroma. Robust malt balanced by spicy hop bitterness. Coffee, molasses with light summer and stone fruits.
Sunbeam (ABV 4.8%)
Smooth gold beer. Refreshing spicy hop and malt flavours with hints of citrus and toffee. Pronounced bitterness. Long, bitter finish.
Resolve (ABV 5.2%)
A dark ruby, strong stout with dark chocolate aroma. Dominant smoky, coffee, bitter chocolate, molasses flavours with malt and stone fruit.

Tremethick

Grampound, Cornwall, TR2 4QY ☎ 07726 427775
tremethick.co.uk

Tremethick began brewing in 2015, and are now well established as a small, village brewery with strong community support. Since a part-time brewer was recruited in 2018, other beers are increasingly being trialled. Brewery open evenings are popular with locals. !! RAIB

Bitter (ABV 3.8%)
Amber bitter with bready malt and citrus hop aroma. Assertive malt is balanced by citrus hops with candied peel fruit.
Pale Ale (ABV 4.3%)
Gold pale ale with faint aroma. Refreshing grapefruit and grassy hops dominate with firm bitterness and apple. Long, bitter, citrus finish.
Dark Ale (ABV 4.6%)
Complex dark brown ale. Nutty malt with kaleidoscope of fruit flavours. Quite sweet with hints of coffee-roast. Faintly bitter and hoppy.
Red IPA (ABV 4.6%)
Auburn bitter with solid hop aroma. Assertive, bitter, citrus hop flavour subordinates malt, treacle and a kaleidoscope of fruit esters.

Tring SIBA

Dunsley Farm, London Road, Tring, Hertfordshire, HP23 6HA
☎ (01442) 890721 tringbrewery.co.uk

Founded in 1992, Tring Brewery moved to its present site in 2010. It brews more than 130 barrels a week, producing an extensive core range of beers augmented by monthly and seasonal specials, most taking their names from local myths and legends. !! ♦RAIB

Side Pocket for a Toad (ABV 3.6%)
Brock Bitter (ABV 3.7%)
Mansion Mild (ABV 3.7%)
Citra Session (ABV 3.9%)
Drop Bar Pale Ale (ABV 4%)
Ridgeway (ABV 4%)
Moongazing (ABV 4.2%)

Pale Four (ABV 4.6%)
Tea Kettle Stout (ABV 4.7%)
Colley's Dog (ABV 5.2%)
Death or Glory (ABV 7.2%)

Triple fff SIBA

Magpie Works, Station Approach, Four Marks, Hampshire, GU34 5HN
☎ (01420) 561422 🌐 triplefff.com

Established in 1997 close to a stop on the Watercress Line, the brewery and all the beers except Alton's Pride are named following a musical theme. The fff refers to fortissimo, meaning louder or stronger. Brewing on a 50-barrel plant since 2006, multiple CAMRA awards have been won. Two pubs are owned: the Railway Arms, Alton, and the Artillery Arms, Southsea. !! ♦RAIB

Alton's Pride (ABV 3.8%)
Full-bodied, session biter. An initially malty flavour fades as citrus notes and hoppiness take over, leading to a lasting hoppy, bitter finish.
Pressed Rat & Warthog (ABV 3.8%)
Toffee aroma with hints of blackcurrant and chocolate lead to a well-balanced flavour with roast, fruit and malt vying with the hoppy bitterness.
Moondance (ABV 4.2%)
An aromatic citrus hop nose, balanced by bitterness and sweetness in the mouth. Bitterness increases in the finish as fruit declines.

Triple Point SIBA

178 Shoreham Street, Sheffield, South Yorkshire, S1 4SQ ☎ 07828 131423 🌐 triplepointbrewing.co.uk

Father and son-operated, modern brewery and bar conversion of what was formerly a carpet showroom. The brewery is clearly visible from the drinking area which operates as the taproom for the brewery. The taproom is open daily. Convenient for Bramall Lane football ground. !!

Gold (ABV 4%)
S.IPA (ABV 4.5%)
Debut (ABV 5.5%)

Triumph

39 Hawthorn Lane, Tile Hill, Coventry, CV4 9LB
☎ 07903 131512 ✉ triumphbrewing@aol.com

Triumph is a nanobrewery offering brew days to the public who want to try homebrewing with professional standard equipment.

True North SIBA

47 Eldon Street, Sheffield, South Yorkshire, S1 4GY
☎ (0114) 272 0569

Office: 127-129 Devonshire Street, Sheffield, S3 7SB
🌐 truenorthbrewco.uk

True North began brewing in 2012 using spare capacity at Welbeck Abbey Brewery (qv). It opened its own plant in Sheffield in 2016. Dean Hollingworth is head brewer, supplying 11 pubs owned by the company plus other independent outlets.

Best Bitter (ABV 3.8%)
Blonde (ABV 4%)
Polaris (ABV 4.3%)

Truman's

New Queens Yard Brewery, Unit 14a, Queens Yard, White Post Lane, Hackney Wick, London, E9 5EN
☎ (020) 8533 3575 🌐 trumansbeer.co.uk

A glorious name in the history of English brewing and a London icon from 1666 to 1989. Reborn in 2013, it has thrived remarkably but in 2020 downsized into the former Crate Brewery in Hackney Wick. A further move to Walthamstow is planned. ♦RAIB

Swift (ABV 3.9%)
Well-balanced, golden bitter with hops and grapefruit on the nose and palate with sweet digestive biscuit throughout. Dryish finish.
Runner (ABV 4%)
Traditional brown best bitter with spicy hoppy aroma and flavour fading in the dry aftertaste. Some marmalade fruity notes.
Lazarus (ABV 4.2%)
Well-balanced, very pale golden ale with peaches and straw aroma, refreshing grassy and citrus flavour, continuing into the short finish.
Zephyr (ABV 4.4%)
Pale brown, smooth beer with a slightly dry-roasted character on palate and bitterish finish. Touch of orange and hops.

Truth Hurts

c/o MSS City Mills, Peel Street, Morley, Leeds, West Yorkshire, LS27 8QL
☎ (0113) 238 0382 ☎ 07950 567341
🌐 truthhurts.co.uk

Established in 2016 as Blue Square Brewery. It produces one-off brews from its four-barrel plant in a split level building that is part of a mill complex.

Tryst

Lorne Road, Larbert, FK5 4AT
☎ (01324) 554000 🌐 trystbrewery.co.uk

The brewery started production in 2003. A large range of beers is available, in cask and bottle. Beers for Clockwork Beer Co are also produced. !! ♦RAIB

Brockville Pale (ABV 3.9%)
Hop Trial (ABV 3.9%)
Carronade Pale Ale (ABV 4.2%)
Drovers 80/- (ABV 4.3%)
Chocolate & Coconut Porter (ABV 4.4%)
Double Chocolate Porter (ABV 4.4%)
Sherpa Porter (ABV 4.4%)
German Hops Pils (ABV 4.5%)
VIP (ABV 4.5%)
RAJ IPA (ABV 5.5%)

Contract brewed for Clockwork Beer Co:
Oregon IPA (ABV 5.5%)

Tudor SIBA

Unit A, Llanhilleth Industrial Estate, Llanhilleth, NP13 2RX
☎ (01495) 214808 ☎ 07498 734896
🌐 tudorbrewery.co.uk

Tudor is family-run and began brewing in 2007 in Abergavenny, before moving in 2012 to Llanilleth. Several local pubs are supplied, in addition to others further afield. There is a bar and function room in the office suite above the brewery, which has occasional live acoustic music. RAIB

Blorenge (ABV 3.8%)
Black Mountain Stout (ABV 4%)
IPA (ABV 4%)
Skirrid (ABV 4.2%)
Sugarloaf (ABV 4.7%)

Winter Cheer (ABV 5%)
Black Rock (ABV 5.6%)

Tunnel SIBA

Correspondence: Red House Farm, Nuneaton Road, Ansley, Nuneaton, Warwickshire, CV10 0QU ☎ 07765 223110 ⊕ tunnelbrewery.co.uk

Beers are brewed at various breweries under the Tunnel and Battlefield Brewery brand names. ◆ RAIB

Percheron (ABV 3.7%)
Late Ott (ABV 4%)
Trade Winds (ABV 4.6%)
Shadow Weaver (ABV 4.7%)
Nelson's Column (ABV 5.2%)
East India Pale Ale (ABV 5.6%)

Brewed under the Battlefield Brewery name:
Let Battle Commence (ABV 4%)
RIchard III (ABV 4%)
Henry Tudor (ABV 5%)

Turning Point

Unit 3, Grimbald Park, Wetherby Road, Knaresborough, North Yorkshire, HG5 8LJ ☎ (01423) 869967 ⊕ turningpointbrewco.com

Two friends, Cameron Brown and Aron McMahon, began brewing in Kirkbymoorside in 2017, before relocating to the former Roosters brewery in Knaresborough in 2019. The expansion into the new brewery means a brew length over 40 hectolitres, with fermenting capacity of 340 hectolitres. All beers are unfined and unfiltered. A partnership with Fossgate Tap in York designates it as the brewery tap. ◆ V ✦

Wavelength (ABV 4.5%)
Lucid Dream (ABV 5%)
Disco King (ABV 5.1%)

Turnstone

20 West Cliff, Whitstable, Kent, CT5 1DN ☎ 07807 262662 ✉ turnstoneales@outlook.com

⊠ Turnstone Ales is a small, home-based brewery set up in 2014. It has a regular stall at the Best of Faversham market (1st and 3rd Saturdays). Beers are supplied to a few local pubs and shops in Whitstable, Tankerton, Faversham and Canterbury. RAIB V

Turpin

Turpins Lodge, Lodge Farm, Tadmarton Heath Road, Hook Norton, Oxfordshire, OX15 5DQ ☎ (01608) 737033 ✉ turpinbrewery@btconnect.com

⊠ Brewing started in 2013, brewing capacity has been extended in 2019. A number of local pubs are supplied regularly, as well as a few pubs further afield in Oxford, Rugby and Birmingham. ◆

Golden Citrus (ABV 4.2%)

Turpin's SIBA

Unit 13b, Sawston Trade Park, London Road, Pampisford, Cambridgeshire, CB22 3EE ☎ (01223) 833883 ⊕ turpinsbrewery.co.uk

⊠ Turpin's is a vibrant, modern brewery based in Pampisford, near Cambridge, established in 2015 and brewing a wide variety of beers. The brewery hosts open days (see Facebook for details). ◆ V ✦

Dragon's Den (ABV 3.9%)
Mozart (ABV 3.9%)
Single Hop Range (ABV 3.9%)
Meditation (ABV 4.3%)
Cambridge Black (ABV 4.6%)
Kupfer (ABV 5%)
NAPA (ABV 5%)
Celebration (ABV 5.5%)

Twice Brewed SIBA

▤ Twice Brewed Inn, Bardon Mill, Hexham, NE47 7AN ☎ (01434) 344534 ⊕ twicebrewedinn.co.uk

Brewing commenced on a five-barrel plant in 2017. Due to the close proximity of Hadrian's Wall, beer names have a Roman theme. Beers are available at the Twice Brewed Inn as well as other outlets.

Best Bitter (ABV 3.8%)
Sycamore Gap (ABV 4.1%)
Ale Caesar (ABV 4.2%)
Steel Rigg (ABV 4.9%)
Vindolanda Excavation IPA (ABV 5.3%)

Twickenham SIBA

Unit 6, 18 Mereway Road, Twickenham, TW2 6RG ☎ (020) 8241 1825 ⊕ twickenham-fine-ales.co.uk

⊠ Established in 2004, Twickenham Fine Ales is London's oldest microbrewery. Operating a 25-barrel plant, it is the first brewery in Twickenham since the 1920s. It opens on match days for the rugby fans going to the nearby stadium. !! ▤ ◆ ✦

Grandstand Bitter (ABV 3.8%)
Sessionable, pale brown beer with peach, citrus, a little caramelised toffee and hop fading in the bitter, slightly dry finish.
Redhead (ABV 4.1%)
A moreish, creamy, chestnut brown best bitter with interesting sweet caramel hints with a mild, short, roasted, bitter finish.
Naked Ladies (ABV 4.4%)
Refreshing, dark golden ale with aromas and flavours of biscuit, stone fruit, pine and citrus. Longlasting, slightly astringent, bitter finish.

Twin Taff

116 High Street, Merthyr Tydfil, CF47 8AP ☎ 07564 187945 ✉ twintaffbrewery@outlook.com

⊕ Twin Taff was established in 2018 by twin brothers Darryl and Daniel Williams. It is Merthyr Tydfil's first town centre microbrewery. Brewing is currently suspended.

Twisted SIBA

Unit 8, Commerce Business Centre, Commerce Close, Westbury, Wiltshire, BA13 4LS ☎ (01373) 864441 ⊕ twisted-brewing.com

⊠ Twisted began brewing in 2014. It is an independent brewery producing traditional ales with a modern twist. ◆

Three And Sixpence (ABV 3.6%)
Rider (ABV 4%)
Pirate (ABV 4.2%)
Urban Legend (ABV 4.3%)
Gaucho (ABV 4.6%)

Twisted Barrel

Unit 11, Fargo Village, Far Gosford Street, Coventry, CV1 5ED

☎ (024) 7610 1701 🌐 twistedbarrelale.co.uk

⊗ Commencing production in a garage in 2013, Twisted Barrel expanded and moved to Fargo Village in 2015 with an on-site bar open at weekends. Continued growth resulted in another move to larger premises on the same site in 2017 and increased opening hours. The brewery hosts a vibrant hombrew club. Beers are distributed throughout the UK and have been exported to mainland Europe and further afield. !! ♦ RAIB V

Gotta Light (ABV 3%)
Beast of a Midlands Mild (ABV 3.5%)
Pixel Juice (ABV 4%)
The Great Went (ABV 4%)
Detroit Sour City (ABV 4.5%)
God's Twisted Sister (ABV 4.5%)
Sine Qua Non (ABV 4.5%)
Vurt (ABV 4.5%)
Naido (ABV 5%)
Kazan (ABV 5.5%)
Lonely Souls (ABV 6.3%)

Twisted Kettle (NEW)

Deadman's Island, Donaghadee, County Down

An independent nanobrewery producing small-batch beers.

Twisted Magnolia (NEW)

Magnolia Belgian Beer Bar & Bistro, 33 Lake Road, Keswick, Cumbria, CA12 5DQ
☎ (01768) 744343 🌐 magnoliabarbistro.co.uk

Brewing began in 2019. This café bar produces a small, interesting range of beers. RAIB

Twisted Oak SIBA

Yeowood Farm, Iwood Lane, Wrington, BS40 5NU
☎ (01934) 310515 🌐 twistedoakbrewery.co.uk

⊗ Twisted Oak began brewing in 2012 using a five-barrel plant, crafting small batches of unique ales. It is situated in a former agricultural building on a working farm in the North Somerset countryside. One pub is owned, the Fallen Tree, Clevedon. Beer is available in several local outlets. ♦ RAIB

Fallen Tree (ABV 3.8%)
Superb, bittersweet, session bitter. Aroma and flavour of hops and ripe fruit. Complex and satisfying, bitter, astringent finish.
Crack Gold (ABV 4%)
Balanced golden ale. Hints of honey on the nose, flavours of malt biscuit and hops, and a short hoppy ending,
Wild Wood (ABV 4%)
Little aroma. Very smooth, with flavours of hops and fruit and a little malt. Minimal aftertaste.
Crack Hops (ABV 4.2%)
Hops on the nose, pale malt with fruity orange and grapefruit hints on the palate leaving a balanced bittersweet aftertaste.
Old Barn (ABV 4.5%)
Fruity red ale. Well-balanced flavour with a very long bitter finish.
Spun Gold (ABV 4.5%)
Classic golden ale with a soft mouthfeel. Spicy notes to the fruity malt aroma and flavour. Hops in the aroma develop into a bitter finish.
Leveret (ABV 4.6%)
Amber best bitter with light citrus aroma. Initial pale malt flavours combine with hoppy bitterness that lingers in the aftertaste
Sheriff Fatman (ABV 5%)
Amber-coloured ale with hops dominant on both the nose and the slightly citrus palate, also in the bitter finish.
Slippery Slope (ABV 5.3%)
Aromas of roast malt and coffee, flavours of black toffee and hints of dark fruits, rather dry and moreish ending.

Twisted Wheel (NEW)

Standish Hall Farm, Beech Walk, off Green Lane, Standish, WN6 0YQ
☎ (01257) 427832 ☎ 07834 216219
🌐 twistedwheelbrewco.co.uk

Twisted Wheel began brewing in 2019 using a 10-barrel brew plant. The brewery name is inspired by the rutted track that leads to the brewery plus the famous Manchester soul club of the same name. Its current range of ales was launched in 2020, all are available unfined in cask, mini-keg and can. The brewery is family owned, sells direct to the public, delivering to WN and M postcodes, and distributes nationally. !! ♦ V

Speed Wobble IPA (ABV 4.7%)
Hoodoo Voodoo IPA (ABV 6.5%)
Soul City New England IPA (ABV 6.5%)
Suede Head Coffee Porter (ABV 6.5%)
Kick Down Double IPA (ABV 8%)

Two by Two

Unit 28, Point Pleasant Industrial Estate, Wallsend, NE28 6HA ☎ 07723 959168

Office: 14 Albany Gardens, Whitley Bay, NE26 2DY
✉ twobytwobrewing@gmail.com

Brewing began in 2014 using a five-barrel plant in Wallsend on Tyneside. At the end of 2018 an additional five-barrel plant was installed, increasing capacity to 10 barrels. RAIB

Session IPA (ABV 4%)
Leap Frog (ABV 4.1%)
Foxtrot Pale (ABV 4.5%)
Snake Eyes Pale (ABV 4.6%)
Dragonfly (ABV 5.5%)
Sitting Duck (ABV 5.7%)
American Pale Ale (ABV 5.8%)
South Paw IPA (ABV 6.2%)

Two Cocks

Church Lane, Enborne, Berkshire, RG20 0HB
☎ (01635) 37777 🌐 twococksbrewery.com

⊗ Under the same ownership and sharing the same kit as Swamp Bog brewery (qv), Two Cocks was established in 2011 after wild hops were found growing in the farm's hedgerows. A 180-feet deep borehole supplies water for the brewery. During the English Civil War, the first Battle of Newbury (1643) was fought on the surrounding land and most of the beer names refer to it in some way.

Diamond Lil' (ABV 3.2%)
1643 Cavalier (ABV 3.8%)
1643 Leveller (ABV 3.8%)
1643 Roundhead (ABV 4.2%)
1643 Puritan (ABV 4.5%)
1643 Viscount (ABV 5.6%)

Two Finches

Finchley Cricket Club, 1 Arden Cottages, 33-45 East End Road, Finchley, London, N3 2TA
☎ (020) 8346 1822 🌐 twofinchesbrewery.co.uk

THE BREWERIES

Brewing began in 2015 on a small kit in the shed beside the clubhouse. The bottled beers are available at the bar (open to the public). No real ale. Brewing is currently suspended.

Two Rivers SIBA

2 Sluice Bank, Denver, Norfolk, PE38 0EQ
☎ (01366) 858365 ☎ 07518 099868
denverbrewery.co.uk

Two Rivers was established in 2012 by John Nash. Bottled-conditioned ale has been available since the establishment of the brewery and cask ales have been produced since 2013. John has taken over the historic Denver Windmill and Blackstone Bar to become a successful brewery tap. !! ♦ RAIB

Miners Mild (ABV 3.1%)
Hares Hopping (ABV 4.1%)
Kiwi Kick (ABV 4.1%)
Denver Diamond (ABV 4.4%)
Porters Pride (ABV 5%)
Norfolk Stoat (ABV 5.8%)

Two Thirsty Men

The Brewery, Grantown on Spey, PH26 3EL
☎ (01479) 872246 twothirstymen.com

Brewing began in 2016 in a garage at the back of a café bar.

Spey IPA (ABV 3.5%)
Malt and hops with a slight citric taste and a dry finish.
No74 (ABV 4.5%)
Malty, red fruited, bittersweet brew.

Two Towers SIBA

29 Shadwell Street, Birmingham, B4 6HB
☎ (0121) 439 3738 ☎ 07795 247059
twotowersbrewery.co.uk

Established in 2010, the 10-barrel brewery is located behind its taphouse, the Gunmakers Arms, and is visible from the beer garden. !! ♦ RAIB V

Baskerville Bitter (ABV 3.8%)
Hockley Gold (ABV 4.1%)
Complete Muppetry (ABV 4.3%)
Chamberlain Pale Ale (ABV 4.5%)
Peaky Blinders Mild (ABV 4.5%)
Jewellery Porter (ABV 5%)

Two Towns Down (NEW)

c/o 36-40 Bellfield Street, Dundee, DD1 5HZ
twotownsdown.com

Two Towns Down is a brewing project founded in 2019 by Sandy McKelvie, formerly of Hanging Bat, Fallen and Black Isle breweries. Spare capacity is used at 71 Brewing (qv).

Two Tribes

Unit 4, Tileyard Studios, Tileyard Road, Barnesbury, London, N7 9AH twotribes.co.uk

Brewing started in the old King's Brewery in Horsham in 2015. The London brewery was set up in 2018 north of King's Cross. Brewing was then moved. Beers are brewed both on-site and using third parties. The name is based on the idea of collaboration. Beers are sold in the Tap Room, around London, Horsham and Leeds. Don't be surprised to find music; it allows students from the nearby college to put on events.

Twt Lol SIBA

Unit B27, Trefforest Industrial Estate, Pontypridd, CF37 5YB ☎ 07966 467295 twtlol.com

Established in 2015 using a 10-barrel plant, the brewery has a capacity of 80 firkins a week, with the potential to expand to 160. All of its branding is produced in both Welsh and English. The brewery is now open on the first weekend of each month. Check website and social media for details. !! ♦

Bwgan Brain / Scarecrow (ABV 3.5%)
Buwch Goch Gota / Little Red Cow (ABV 3.7%)
Glog (ABV 4%)
Twti Ffrwti (ABV 4%)
Cwrw'r Afr Serchog / Horny Goat Ale (ABV 4.2%)
Cymryd y Pyst (ABV 4.4%)
Lol! (ABV 4.4%)
Glo in the Dark (ABV 4.5%)
Blwbri (ABV 4.6%)
Pewin Ynfytyn / Crazy Peacock (ABV 4.8%)
Pyncio Pioden IPA / Pretty Fly For A Magpie (ABV 5%)
Dreigiau'r Diafol / Diablo Dragons (ABV 5.5%)

Tydd Steam SIBA

Manor Barn, Kirkgate, Tydd Saint Giles, Cambridgeshire, PE13 5NE
☎ (01945) 871020 ☎ 07932 726552
tyddsteam.co.uk

Established in 2007 in a converted agricultural barn, the brewery is named after two farm steam engines. A 15-barrel plant was installed in 2011. Around 70 outlets are supplied direct. !! ♦ RAIB

Barn Ale (ABV 3.9%)
A golden bitter that has good biscuity malt aroma and flavour, balanced by spicy hops. Long, dry, fairly astringent finish.
Scoundrel (ABV 4%)
A dry, pale amber bitter with a gentle malty and hoppy aroma, plenty of hop bitterness with fruity hints in the taste and a persistent dry aftertaste.
Piston Bob (ABV 4.6%)
Malt and faint hops on the aroma progress through to a malty flavour complemented by a balance of hops and fruit. A long, dry finish.

Tyne Bank SIBA

375 Walker Road, Newcastle upon Tyne, NE6 2AB
☎ (0191) 265 2828 tynebankbrewery.co.uk

Brewing began in 2011. It moved and expanded in 2016, with an on-site event space and taproom offering a wide range of events. As well as its core range, many ever-changing beers are available. !! ♦ V

Castle Gold (ABV 3.8%)
Summer Breeze (ABV 3.9%)
West Coast IPA (ABV 4%)
Monument Bitter (ABV 4.1%)
Northern Porter (ABV 4.5%)
Silver Dollar (ABV 4.9%)
Helix (ABV 5%)
Cherry Stout (ABV 5.2%)

Tyton (NEW)

54 Bradshaw's Lane, Ainsdale, PR8 3LQ ☎ 07487 598787 tytonbrewing@gmail.com

Brewing began in 2018. V

Uffa

🏴 White Lion Inn, Lower Street, Lower Ufford, Suffolk, IP13 6DW
☎ (01394) 460770 🌐 uffabrewery.co.uk

Uffa began brewing in 2011 using a 2.5-barrel plant. It is situated next to the White Lion pub in a converted coach house. ♦

Uley

The Old Brewery, 31 The Street, Uley, Gloucestershire, GL11 5TB
☎ (01453) 860120 🌐 uleybrewery.com

🚫 Brewing at Uley began in 1833 as Price's brewery. After a long gap, the premises were restored and Uley Brewery opened in 1985. Now operating a 10-barrel plant, it uses its own spring water. Uley delivers to 40-50 outlets in the Cotswolds area. 🏴♦

Pale Ale (ABV 3.8%)
Bitter (ABV 4%)
A copper-coloured beer with hops and fruit in the aroma and a malty, fruity taste, underscored by a hoppy bitterness. The finish is dry, with a balance of hops and malt.
Old Ric (ABV 4.5%)
A full-flavoured, hoppy bitter with some fruitiness and a smooth, balanced finish. Distinctively copper-coloured, this is the house beer for the Old Spot Inn, Dursley.
Taverner (ABV 4.5%)
Old Spot Prize Strong Ale (ABV 5%)
A ruby ale with an initial strong malty sweetness that develops into a smooth dry malty finish. A beer that is deceptively easy to drink.
Pig's Ear Strong Beer (ABV 5%)
A golden pale ale with an initial refreshing taste with a hint of fruitiness that develops into a light malty finish. A smooth quaffable strong ale.

Ulverston

Lightburn Road, Ulverston, Cumbria, LA12 0AU
☎ (01229) 586870 ☎ 07840 192022
🌐 ulverstonbrewingcompany.co.uk

⊛ The brewery occupies the octagonal bullring of the old livestock market. There is a bar that overlooks the brew-plant, which opens by prior arrangement and during some local festivals. Some beers have a Laurel and Hardy theme: Stan Laurel was born in Ulverston. ‼🏴♦

Flying Elephants (ABV 3.7%)
Clean, refreshing, yellow bitter, sweet and fruity with a dry citrus finish.
Celebration Ale (ABV 3.9%)
Yellow, fruity bitter with hints of tangerine and a notably sustained, dry finish.
Harvest Moon (ABV 3.9%)
A well-balanced, pale, hoppy bitter.
Laughing Gravy (ABV 4%) 📋
Smooth and grainy brown bitter with a good mix of flavours.
Lonesome Pine (ABV 4.2%)
A fresh and fruity pale gold beer. Honeyed, lemony and resiny with an increasingly bitter finish.
Fra Diavolo (ABV 4.3%)

UnBarred

19-23 Elder Place, Brighton, East Sussex, BN1 4GF
☎ 07850 070471 🌐 unbarredbrewery.com

🚫 UnBarred has upscaled from a purpose-built brewery in the owner's garden via cuckoo brewing at Missing Link Brewery (qv) to, in 2019, its own bespoke brewery and taproom in Brighton. It has a core range of beers, almost exclusively in can and keg, but also brews small batches and occasional casks for festivals and a small number of local pubs. The Modern Pale series of 5.5% cask beers was launched in 2020. ‼🏴 RAIB V◆

Under the Street

See One Mile End

Unity SIBA

23-27 Princes Street, Northam, Southampton, SO14 5RP
☎ (023) 8178 2627 🌐 unitybrewingco.com

Founded in 2016, Unity Brewing Co produces beers influenced by Belgian and North East American styles, using traditional techniques and modern ingredients. Output is mainly keg or cans with occasional special releases in cask. In 2019 it expanded and moved into a brand new, crowd-funded, 12-barrel brewery with a modern taproom on site. 🏴◆

Unsworth's Yard SIBA

4 Unsworth's Yard, Ford Road, Cartmel, Cumbria, LA11 6PG ☎ 07810 461313 🌐 unsworthsyard.co.uk

⊛ Unsworth's Yard opened in 2011, brewing on a five-barrel plant. The brewery produces beers named after historic figures and legends associated with the Cartmel area. Beers are available in Cartmel pubs and other local outlets as well as the brewery's tap bar. ‼🏴

Peninsula Best (ABV 3.8%)
Crusader Gold (ABV 4.1%)
Eel River IPA (ABV 4.3%)
Sir Edgar Harrington's Last Wolf (ABV 4.5%)
Well-balanced, rich, fruity, tawny ale with gentle bitterness.
The Flookburgh Cockler (ABV 5.5%)

Untapped

Unit 6, Little Castle Farm Business Park, Raglan, NP15 2BX
☎ (01291) 690074 🌐 untappedbrew.com

Established in 2009, 2013 saw Untapped move to its current premises. It has recently rebranded its range of filtered beers, Except Triple S, are all Vegan-friendy. ‼🏴♦ RAIB

Border Bitter (ABV 3.8%)
Sundown (ABV 4%)
Monnow (ABV 4.2%)
Whoosh (ABV 4.2%)
UPA (ABV 4.5%)
Triple S (ABV 4.9%)
Crystal (ABV 6%) 📋

Up Front

Office: 45 Springfield Gardens, Glasgow, G31 4HP
☎ 07526 088973 🌐 upfrontbrewing.com

Founded in 2015 by former homebrewer Jake Griffin, Up Front is a gypsy brewery primarily using spare capacity at Overtone Brewing Co (qv), plus that at other local breweries. Predominantly producing canned beers and speciality bottles, cask-conditioned beers are available on rare occasions.

Upham

See Crafty Brewing

Uprising

See Windsor & Eton

Urban Alchemy (NEW)

New Barnet, EN5 1LJ ☎ 07894 452263
🌐 urban-alchemy-brewing.co.uk

⊗ Urban Alchemy started brewing commercially in 2019 and was established by a group of friends with years of brewing experience between them. A bespoke three-barrel plant is used. Beers are supplied to local pubs and beer festivals. RAIB V

Fat Labrador (ABV 5.2%)
Crumbling Ghost (ABV 5.4%)

Urban Chicken

Ilkeston, Derbyshire, DE7 5EH ☎ 07976 913395
🌐 urbanchickenale.co.uk

One-barrel brewery producing small batches of beer for local pubs, restaurants, bottle shops and beer festivals. Registered as a commercial brewery in 2016. Cask and bottle, unfined.

Spinning Bird Kick (ABV 3.8%)
Urban Gold (ABV 4.5%)
Pit Pony (ABV 4.9%)
Insane in the Henbrain (ABV 5.9%)
Mildly Urban (ABV 6%)

Urban Island SIBA

Unit 28, Limberline Industrial Estate, Limberline Spur, Portsmouth, Hampshire, PO3 5DZ
☎ (023) 9266 8726 🌐 urbanislandbrewing.uk

⊗ Urban Island began production in 2015 on a bespoke five-barrel, purpose-built plant. Due to demand, the brew length has increased to 10 barrels. The range is distributed throughout Hampshire and the South East and is expanding further afield. !! ⛿ V ◆

Urban Pale (ABV 3.8%)
Mosaic (ABV 4%)
Ammo (ABV 4.5%)
DSB (Dolly's Special Beer) (ABV 4.6%)
Porter 28 (ABV 5%)
High & Dry (ABV 5.5%)
Urban Graffiti (ABV 6%)

Utopian SIBA

Unit 4 Clannaborough Business Units, Bow, Crediton, EX17 6DA
☎ (01392) 769765 🌐 utopianbrewing.com

Utopian began brewing in 2019 producing craft lagers. No real ale.

Uttoxeter SIBA

26b Carter Street, Uttoxeter, Staffordshire, ST14 8EU
☎ 07734 392321 🌐 uttoxeterbrewingcompany.com

A nanobrewery set up in 2016, exploiting the famous Burton upon Trent hard water.

Bunting's Blonde (ABV 3.7%)
Dark Horse Mild (ABV 3.7%)
Ground Breaker (ABV 4%)
? (Question Mark) (ABV 4.5%)
Admiral Lord Gardner (ABV 4.5%)
Chinook (ABV 4.5%)
Dr Johnson's Contrafibularity (ABV 4.5%)
Earthmover (ABV 4.5%)
Final Furlong (ABV 4.5%)
Sargeant's Special Ale (ABV 4.6%)
Earthmover Gold (ABV 4.7%)
Full Gallop (ABV 4.7%)
Paddock Porter (ABV 4.8%)
Uxonian (ABV 4.9%)
American IPA (ABV 5.2%)
Yogi Beer (ABV 6.1%)

Vaguely (NEW)

15 Lune Way, Bingham, Nottinghamshire, NG13 8YX
☎ 07969 137248 🌐 vaguelybrewing.co.uk

⊗ Vaguely Brewing launched as a commercial nanobrewery in 2019 following four years of homebrewing and recipe development. It produces vaguely traditional beers that are naturally conditioned, unfiltered and unfined. There are plans to increase the range and brewing capacity over the next year. RAIB V

Bitter (ABV 4.2%)
Hazy (ABV 4.5%)
Porter (ABV 4.7%)
Pale Ale (ABV 6%)

Vale SIBA

Tramway Business Park, Ludgershall Road, Brill, Buckinghamshire, HP18 9TY
☎ (01844) 239237 🌐 valebrewery.co.uk

⊗ Established in 1995 and initially based in Haddenham, Vale moved to Brill in 2007. In 2010 it expanded to a 20-barrel brew plant. Five pubs are owned, including the Hop Pole, where sister brewery the Aylesbury Brewhouse operated from 2011 to 2019. !! ⛿ ◆ RAIB

Brill Gold (ABV 3.5%)
Best IPA (ABV 3.7%)
This pale amber beer starts with a slight fruit aroma. This leads to a clean, bitter taste where hops and fruit dominate. The finish is long and bitter with a slight hop note.
Black Swan Mild (ABV 3.9%)
Wychert Ale (ABV 3.9%)
VPA (Vale Pale Ale) (ABV 4.2%)
Red Kite (ABV 4.3%)
Black Beauty Porter (ABV 4.4%)
A very dark ale, the initial aroma is malty. Roast malt dominates initially and is followed by a rich fruitiness, with some sweetness. The finish is increasingly hoppy and dry.
Gravitas (ABV 4.8%)

Vault City (NEW)

c/o 36-40 Bellfield Street, Dundee, DD1 5HZ
🌐 vaultcity.co.uk

Launched as a kitchen brewery in Edinburgh in 2018, Vault City Brewing relocated to share facilities at 71 Brewing in Dundee in 2019. Making fruit-forward, modern sour beers, the monthly Farm to Fermenter series utilises local fruits. Available in bottles.

Verdant

Unit 30, Parkengue, Kernick Road, Penryn, Cornwall, TR10 9EP
☎ (01326) 619117 ☎ 07970 503574
🌐 verdantbrewing.co

Brewery established by keen homebrewers in 2014. It moved to new premises in 2020 with the aid of crowdfunding, upgrading from a 10-barrel to a new 20-barrel plant. No real ale. ‼

Veterans (NEW) SIBA

Unit 0, Dundyvan Enterprise Park, Dundyvan Way, Coatbridge, ML5 4AQ
☎ (01236) 425281

South East: 35 Carden Hill, Brighton, East Sussex, ☎ (BN1 8AA) 🌐 veteransbrewing.co.uk

Established on Armistice Day 2014, Veterans Brewing is owned and run by, and supporting veterans. Initially based only in Scotland, a second depot was launched in Brighton in 2018, with its beers contract brewed at Franklins (qv).

.303 (ABV 4.1%)
Tracer (ABV 4.2%)

Vibrant Forest

The Purlieu Centre, Units 3-6, Hardley Industrial Estate, Hardley, Hampshire, SO45 3NQ
☎ (023) 8200 2200 ☎ 07921 753109
🌐 vibrantforest.co.uk

⊗ Vibrant Forest Brewery started brewing commercially in 2011, as a one-barrel plant, this gradually increased to 10 barrels over the next five years at Lymington. It relocated to a four unit brewery at Hardley and increased in size to a 12-barrel plant. ‼ ♦ V

Summerlands (ABV 3.5%)
PUPA (ABV 4.5%)
Farmhouse (ABV 5%)
Single Hop Pale Ale (ABV 5%)
Kick-Start (ABV 5.7%)
Metropolis (ABV 6%)
Kaleidoscope (ABV 6.5%)
Umbral Abyss (ABV 8.8%)

Victoria Inn

Roch, SA62 6AW
☎ (01437) 710426 ☎ 07814 684975
🌐 thevictoriainnroch.com

⊗ A small brewery on the site of the Victoria Inn, which also offers B&B. ‼ V

Village Brewer

See Hambleton

Village Brewer: Brew 22

Number Twenty 2, 22 Coniscliffe Road, Darlington, DL3 7RG
☎ (01325) 354590 🌐 villagebrewer.co.uk

☺ One-barrel microbrewery, established in 2013, which has been brewing on a regular basis since 2015. The plant is also used to produce the malt wash for the distilling of gin and vodka on-site. The beer strength and style varies from brew to brew and complement the Village Brewer beers produced by Hambleton Ales (qv) since 1995.

Villages

21-22 Resolution Way, Deptford, London, SE8 4NT
☎ (020) 3489 1143 🌐 villagesbrewery.com

Established in 2016 by brothers Archie and Louis Village. Production of real ale started at the end of 2019 and is available in the on-site taproom and increasingly further afield.

Vine (NEW)

Vine, 27-29 High Street, Tarring, West Sussex, BN14 7NN
☎ (01903) 201121 ✉ thevinepub@hotmail.com

⊗ Brewery established in 2018 in the barn at the rear of the Vine pub. Beer is brewed monthly and sold exclusively at the pub. ♦

Vine Inn

Vine Inn & Brewery, Sheep Fair, Rugeley, Staffordshire, WS15 2AT
☎ (01889) 574443 ✉ oli@thevinebrewery.com

⊗ The Vine Brewery is based in Rugeley, within the Vine Inn public house, parts of which date back to the sixteenth century. The brewery's beers can be found in a number of pubs in the Cannock Chase area.

Vittles

Hull Trinity Market, Trinity House Lane, Hull, East Yorkshire, HU1 2JH ☎ 07598 098632
🌐 vittlesandcompany.co.uk

Vittles & Co started brewing in 2018 at the Trinity Market, Hull. The site can produce just 50 litres at a time. The brewery name comes from the fact that the owner loves to pair beer and food, hence the old name for food, vittles.

Vocation SIBA

Unit 8, Craggs Country Business Park, New Road, Cragg Vale, Hebden Bridge, West Yorkshire, HX7 5TT
☎ (01422) 410810 🌐 vocationbrewery.com

☺ Vocation began brewing in 2015 on a bespoke 20-barrel plant. The brewery is located high above Hebden Bridge. In 2017 it opened its first bar in Hebden Bridge called Vocation & Co and a second one, Assembly Underground, Leeds, in 2018. Brewing capacity trebled to 45 barrels in 2018 due to increased demand. ♦ V

Bread & Butter (ABV 3.9%)
A feast of floral hops with citrus aroma and taste. Robust bitter aftertaste.
Heart & Soul (ABV 4.5%)
A golden ale with a strong citrus aroma. Hops dominate taste and aftertaste.
Pride & Joy (ABV 5.3%)
Flavoursome IPA packed with citrus hoppiness. A hint of sweetness gives way to a mellow aftertaste.
Life & Death (ABV 6.5%)

VOG

Unit 8a, Atlantic Trading Estate, Barry, CF63 3RF
☎ (01446) 730757 🌐 vogbrewery.co.uk

☺ Created in 2005, the founders handed over the reins to a new team in 2015 who rebranded the brewery and refreshed the beer range. VOG's beers can be found frequently in a number of South Wales pubs, as well as occasionally throughout the country thanks to the brewery's beer swaps. The brewery has recently opened two taphouse outlets and has six associated gastropubs. ♦ RAIB

Paradigm Shift (ABV 4.2%)
South Island (ABV 4.2%)

THE BREWERIES

Dark Matter (ABV 4.4%)
Speak Easy IPA (ABV 4.6%)
Lady Liberty (ABV 4.8%)

Volden SIBA

77 Malham Road, Forest Hill, London, SE23 1AH
volden.co.uk

Volden produce beer for the Antic pub group with branches throughout London. Originally taking over the Clarence & Fredericks brewery in Croydon in 2015, a new brewery was installed in Forest Hill in 2020. ♦V

Session Ale (ABV 3.8%)
Amber bitter with caramel malt and orange aroma. Fruit, hops and sweetish malty biscuit fading to a bitter, dryish finish.
Pale Ale (ABV 4.6%)
Gold-coloured beer with floral hop flavour with slight hint of fresh orange peel and biscuit, becoming more bitter on drinking.

Wadworth SIBA IFBB

Northgate Brewery, Devizes, Wiltshire, SN10 1JW
(01380) 723361 wadworth.co.uk

Established in 1875 by Henry Alfred Wadworth, this impressive family-owned brewery has a modern brewhouse and a microbrewery, which enables it to create unique small batch beers. Its traditional horse-drawn drays deliver beer daily around Devizes. Wadworth has more than 200 pubs in the south-west of England. !! ♦ RAIB

Henry's IPA (ABV 3.6%)
Horizon (ABV 4%)
6X (ABV 4.1%)
Copper-coloured ale with a malty and fruity nose, and some balancing hop character. The flavour is similar, with some bitterness and a lingering malty, but bitter finish.
Bishops Tipple (ABV 5%)
Swordfish (ABV 5%)

Waen

See Team Toxic

Wagtail

New Barn Farm, Wilby Warrens, Old Buckenham, Norfolk, NR17 1PF
(01953) 887133 wagtailbrewery.com

Wagtail Brewery went into full-time production in 2006. All beers are only available bottle-conditioned. This is a chemical-free brewery. No chemicals are on-site and all cleaning is done with hot water and 'elbow grease'. RAIB

Walled City

70 Ebrington Square, Londonderry, BT47 6FA
(028) 7134 3336 walledcitybrewery.com

Restaurant-based brewery established in 2015. No real ale.

Izaac Walton

Whitehouse Farm, Cold Norton, Staffordshire, ST15 0NS
(01785) 760780

Brewing began in 2017.

Last Cast (ABV 4%)
Last Drop (ABV 4%)
Amber Nymph (ABV 4.5%)

Wander Beyond

98 North Western Street, Manchester, M12 6HR
(0161) 661 3676
sales@wanderbeyondbrewing.com

Wander Beyond launched in 2017 in a railway arch under Piccadilly Station. The range of beer available can vary. V

Peak (ABV 3.8%)
Northern Night (ABV 4.1%)
Great Rift (ABV 6%)
Finders Keepers (ABV 6.2%)

Wanderlust

See Magpie

Wantsum SIBA

Kent Barn, St Nicholas Court Farm, Court Road, St Nicholas at Wade, Kent, CT7 0PT
(01227) 910135 wantsumbrewery.co.uk

Wantsum Brewery, established by James Sandy in 2009, takes its name from the nearby Wantsum Channel. Previously located in Hersden near Canterbury, the brewery relocated to a farm site in 2017. It has an extensive range of beers, named after pivotal events in Kent's history. Outlets are supplied throughout the south of England. An on-site taproom showcases the beers. !! ♦ RAIB

More's Head (ABV 3.5%)
1381 (ABV 3.8%)
Black Prince (ABV 3.9%)
Imperium (ABV 4%)
Montgomery (ABV 4%)
Fortitude (ABV 4.2%)
One Hop (ABV 4.2%)
Dynamo (ABV 4.3%)
Turbulent Priest (ABV 4.4%)
Yellow Tail (ABV 4.5%)
Black Pig (ABV 4.8%)
Hengist (ABV 5%)
Red Raddle (ABV 5%)
Golgotha (ABV 5.5%)
Ravening Wolf (ABV 5.9%)

Ward & Houldsworth (NEW)

Office: 62 Drakehouse Lane West, Beighton, South Yorkshire, S20 1FX 07912 028880 ifinfused.com

Former Kelham Island brewer Paul Ward together with Darren Houldsworth established the company in 2019. Beers are contract brewed at Pheasantry (qv) and distributed from storage in Sheffield.

Warwickshire SIBA

Bakehouse Brewery, Queen Street, Cubbington, Leamington Spa, Warwickshire, CV32 7NA
(01926) 450747 warwickshirebeer.co.uk

A six-barrel brewery in a former village bakery which has been in operation since 1998. Bottled beers are available from local farm shops, garden centres, wine specialists and supermarkets, as well as from the brewery direct and its four pubs. More unusual craft beers are available under the Bakehouse Brewery brand name. ♦ RAIB

SPA (Spa Pale Ale) (ABV 3.8%)
Darling Buds (ABV 4%)
Duck Soup (ABV 4.2%)
Lady Godiva (ABV 4.2%)

Yer Bard (ABV 4.3%)

Brewed under the Bakehouse Brewery name:
Liquid Bread (ABV 4.5%)

Wash House

See Allanwater

Wasted Degrees (NEW)

Unit 11, Sawmill Yard, Blair Atholl, PH18 5TL
🌐 wasteddegrees.com

Leaving the degrees and day jobs behind, Wasted Degrees began small-batch brewing commercially in 2017 before expanding to a 1000-litre brewhouse in Blair Atholl in 2019. A barrel-ageing programme was established in 2018. ‼ ◆

Watermill

See Windermere

Tomos Watkin SIBA

Unit 3, Alberto Road, Century Park, Valley Way, Swansea Enterprise Park, Swansea, SA6 8RP
☎ (01792) 797280 🌐 tomoswatkin.com

Brewing began in 1995, originally in Llandeilo behind the Castle Hotel. The brewery moved to Swansea in 2000 and was taken over by Hurns Mineral Water Company in 2002. More than 60% of production is bottled beer (not bottle-conditioned). ‼ ⚑ ◆

Delilah (ABV 4%)
Swansea Jack (ABV 4%)
OSB (Old Style Bitter) (ABV 4.5%)
Amber-coloured with an inviting aroma of hops and malt. Full bodied; hops, fruit, malt and bitterness combine to give a balanced flavour continuing into the finish.
IPA (ABV 4.8%)

Watling Street

Unit 6, Triumph Trading Estate, Tariff Road, Tottenham, London, N17 0EB ☎ 07713 841936
🌐 watlingstreetbeer.com

Starting in Aldenham in 2015 and latterly North Watford in 2017, Watling Street moved to be one of the three breweries making up the Tottenham Brewery site during 2019. The cask beers are available during its irregular opening days, often when nearby Spurs play at home or during major sports tournaments. ⚑ ◆

Uncle Damn (ABV 3.7%)
Sir Newton (ABV 3.8%)
Queen Boudicca (ABV 4.2%)
Miss Shelley (ABV 4.3%)
Salted Caramel Stout (ABV 4.4%)
Mr Ripper (ABV 4.6%)
Wat Tyler (ABV 4.8%)

Watneys

See Sambrook's

Watson's

Old Heath, Colchester, Essex, CO1 2HD ☎ 07804 641267 🌐 watsonsbrewery.co.uk

Small batch, home brewery set up in 2016 using a 100-litre brew plant. Local pubs, festivals and bottle shops are supplied with one-off beers.

Watts Brewing?

Magnet Freehouse, 51 Wellington Road North, Stockport, SK4 1HJ
☎ (0161) 429 6287 🌐 themagnetfreehouse.co.uk

Brewing began in 2014 on the premises of the Magnet freehouse. No regular beers. Speciality beers are brewed to suit the season, and are mostly sold in the pub. ◆

Waveney

Queen's Head, Station Road, Earsham, Norfolk, NR35 2TS
☎ (01986) 892623 ✉ lyndahamps@aol.com

Established at the Queen's Head in 2004, the five-barrel brewery produces three beers, regularly available at the pub along with other free trade outlets. ◆

Way Outback

144 Seabourne Road, Southbourne, Bournemouth, Dorset, BH5 2HZ 🌐 thewayoutback.co.uk

Started in 2017 and born in a shed, Way Outback is based in Southbourne. It is run by owner and head brewer Richard Brown (with help from his four-legged assistant Arthur), and specialises in beers using high quality ingredients with provenance. ◆

Take Me to Valhalla (ABV 4%)
Hopposites Attract (ABV 5.6%)

Weal SIBA

Unit 6, Newpark Business Park, London Road, Chesterton, Staffordshire, ST5 7HT
☎ (01782) 565635 ☎ 07980 606966
🌐 wealales.co.uk

Formed in 2014 by husband-and-wife team Paul and Andrea Wealleans, Weal Ales is a multiple SIBA award-winning microbrewery. Having expanded to a six-barrel plant in 2015, it distributes its range of cask and bottled beers to events and independents both locally and nationally. Its taphouse, Wellers, opened in Newcastle under Lyme in 2016. ⚑ RAIB V

This is the Modern Weal (ABV 3.8%)
Wagon Weal (ABV 4.1%)
Weald Wood (ABV 4.1%)
Wealy Hopper (ABV 4.2%)
Weller Weal (ABV 4.6%)
Noir (ABV 4.8%)
Centwealial Milk Stout (ABV 4.9%)
Ginger Weal (ABV 5.5%)
Lemon & Ginger Weal (ABV 5.5%)

Weard'ALE

Hare & Hounds, 24 Front Street, Westgate, DL13 1RX
☎ (01388) 517212

Brewing commenced in the Hare & Hounds in 2010. The beers are mainly sold on the premises but some have found their way to nearby beer festivals and other local pubs.

Weatheroak

Unit 7, Victoria Works, Birmingham Road, Studley, Warwickshire, B80 7AP
☎ (01527) 854 433 ☎ 07798 773894

Office: Weatheroak Tap House, 21a High Street, Studley, B80 7HN 🌐 weatheroakbrewery.co.uk

The brewery was set up in 1997 at Weatheroak Hill. It is now in a spacious factory unit in Studley. Around 20 outlets are supplied. Off sales are available for all beers at the Tap House on High Street, Studley. 18 and 36 pint polypins are available with notice. !! ♦

Bees Knees (ABV 3.7%)
This straw-coloured, quaffing ale has lots of hoppy notes on the tongue and nose, and a fleetingly sweet aftertaste.
Ale (ABV 4.1%)
The aroma is dominated by hops in this golden-coloured brew. Hops also feature in the mouth and there is a rapidly fading dry aftertaste.
The Dark Side (ABV 4.3%)
Victoria Works (ABV 4.3%)
Keystone Hops (ABV 5%)
A golden yellow beer that is surprisingly easy to quaff given the strength. Fruity hops are the dominant flavour without the commonly associated astringency.

Weatheroak Hill

Coach & Horses, Weatheroak Hill, Worcestershire, B48 7EA
☎ (01564) 823386 ☎ 07496 289924
✉ weatheroakhillbrewery@gmail.com

Established in 2008, Weatheroak Hill Brewery has been supplying the Coach & Horses with quality beers brewed on-site for over a decade, travelling a mere 50 meters from grain to glass. The free trade and CAMRA festivals are also supplied. !! ♦

IPA (Icknield Pale Ale) (ABV 3.8%)
Impossible IPA (ABV 4.1%)
Cofton Common (ABV 4.9%)

Websters

73 Bridgnorth Road, Wollaston, West Midlands, DY8 3PZ
☎ (01384) 440315 ✉ info@grahams-place.co.uk

Microbrewery set up to the side of Graham's Place in 2014. Currently brewing with malt extract, full mash beers are planned. All beers are sold though the pub including some one-off specials.

Weetwood SIBA

The Brewery, Common Lane, Kelsall, Cheshire, CW6 0PY
☎ (01829) 752377 weetwoodales.co.uk

Weetwood Ales were founded in a barn back in 1992 but now operate out of a modern 30-barrel plant close to Kelsall. The broad range of beers is available across the north-west and North Wales. Besides regular brewery tours and an on-site shop, a distillery (an enterprise totally complementary to the brewery) produces a range of spirits including gin and vodka, with plans for a single malt release in 2022. !!

Southern Cross (ABV 3.6%)
Best Bitter (ABV 3.8%)
Pale brown beer with an assertive bitterness and a lingering, dry finish. Despite initial sweetness, peppery hops dominate throughout.
Mad Hatter (ABV 3.9%)
A typical red beer, malty aromas lead to a fruity sweet middle backed up with a bitter finish.
Cheshire Cat (ABV 4%)
Pale, dry bitter with a spritzy lemon zest and a grape aroma. Hoppy aroma leads through to the initial taste before fruitiness takes over. Smooth, creamy mouthfeel and a short, dry finish.

Eastgate (ABV 4.2%)
Well-balanced and refreshing clean amber beer. Citrus fruit flavours predominate in the taste and there is a short, dry aftertaste.
Oregon Pale (ABV 4.3%)
Old Dog (ABV 4.5%)
Robust, well-balanced, amber beer with a slightly fruity aroma. Rich malt and fruit flavours are balanced by bitterness. Some sweetness and a hint of sulphur on nose and taste.

Weighbridge

See BrightBeer

Weird Beard SIBA

Unit 5, Boston Business Park, Trumpers Way, Hanwell, London, W7 2QA
☎ (020) 3645 2711 weirdbeardbrewco.com

Brewing began in 2013 on an industrial estate in Hanwell. The plant has expanded a few times, including into the adjacent unit. Bottle-conditioned beers are mostly produced, but the range is also widely available in keg and cask. RAIB V

Dark Hopfler (ABV 2.5%)
Black Perle (ABV 3.8%)
Coffee milk stout with roast notes throughout this full-favoured, sweetish black beer with some red fruits. Bitterish, dry finish.
Little Things That Kill (ABV 3.9%)
Hoppy, fruity golden ale which varies in flavour as the hops that are used can alter.
Hops Maiden England (ABV 4.5%)
Mariana Trench (ABV 5.3%)
Passionfruit and citrus are noticeable throughout this malty, sweet, golden beer. Bitterness builds and lingers overlaid by dryness.
Decadence Stout (ABV 5.5%)
Orange with some black treacle sweetness balances the dry chocolate and coffee character that lingers pleasantly with the bitterness developing.
K*ntish Town Beard (ABV 5.5%)
Fade to Black (ABV 6.5%)
Balanced black IPA with some fruitiness. The beer contains crystal rye and chocolate malt, which gives roast coffee notes throughout.
Five O'Clock Shadow (ABV 7%)
Golden ale with an apple nose and palate. Sweet biscuit and resinous spicy hops dominating. Dry sweet aftertaste fading to spicy

Weird Sisters

24 Timworth Heath Cottages, Great Barton, Suffolk, IP31 2QH ☎ 07827 923923

A nanobrewery established by a father and three daughters (the weird sisters) in 2018. The brewery has one core beer and mainly produces seasonal beers to mark the eight seasonal festivals of the wheel of the year. Beers can be found at festivals, morris dancing events and in specialist beer shops. RAIB V

Slaphead (ABV 6.7%)

Welbeck Abbey SIBA

Brewery Yard, Welbeck, Nottinghamshire, S80 3LT
☎ (01909) 512539 ☎ 07921 066274
welbeckabbeybrewery.co.uk

Welbeck Abbey opened in 2011. The microbrewery is housed in a listed barn at the centre of the traditional landed Welbeck estate. General manager Claire Monk trained at the Kelham Island Brewery after studying microbiology at Sheffield University. The brewery produces the Foraged & Found range of beers and contract brews for Stocks Brewing Co. ‼

Henrietta (ABV 3.6%)
Red Feather (ABV 3.9%)
Kaiser (ABV 4.1%)
St Leger Gold (ABV 4.1%)
Harley (ABV 4.3%)
Portland Black (ABV 4.5%)
Black ale with a roast malt aroma and taste throughout, and a well-balanced bitterness.
Cavendish (ABV 5%)
Golden in colour with a smooth, hoppy and malt mouthfeel and a lingering hoppy, bitter finish.
Old Horizontal (ABV 5.3%)

Weldon

Bencroft Grange, Bedford Road, Rushden, Northamptonshire, NN10 0SE
☎ (01536) 601016
Office: 12 Chapel Road, Weldon, Northamptonshire, NN17 3HP 🌐 weldonbrewery.co.uk

Weldon originally started brewing in 2014 on a two-barrel plant at the Shoulder of Mutton, after which the brewery was originally named. In 2016 the premises and 3.5-barrel kit of the former Copper Kettle brewery in Rushden were purchased and became the main production facility, with the brewery being renamed Weldon. The original plant at the Shoulder of Mutton has been retained and is used for small runs and test batches. ♦V

Diab-Lo (ABV 3.7%)
Essanell (ABV 3.8%)
Dragline (ABV 3.9%)
Stahlstadt (ABV 4%)
Galvy Stout (ABV 4.2%)
Windmill (ABV 4.2%)
Mad Max (ABV 4.4%)
Paradisium (ABV 4.4%)
Roman Mosaics (ABV 4.6%)

Welland

Cradge Bank, Spalding, Lincolnshire, PE11 3AN
☎ (07732) 033702 ✉ info@wellandbrewery.co.uk

Welland Brewery commenced in 2018 and was set up by Tom Bradshaw and Dave Jackson, assisted by the owner and brewer of nearby Austendyke Ales, Charlie Rawlings. A brewery taphouse is planned.

Shipshape Blonde (ABV 3.7%)
Sneaky St.oat (ABV 3.9%)
Fen Tiger (ABV 4%)
Flatland Bitter (ABV 4%)
Pale RyeNo (ABV 4.1%)
YFM (ABV 4.2%)
Jack Rawlshaw (ABV 4.4%)
Black Cow (ABV 4.7%)
Rusty Giraffe (ABV 5%)

Weltons SIBA

1 Mulberry Trading Estate, Foundry Lane, Horsham, West Sussex, RH13 5PX
☎ (01403) 242901/ 251873 🌐 weltonsbeer.co.uk

⊗ Ray Welton moved the brewery into a factory unit in 2003. More than 70 different beers are brewed every year. Pubs throughout the south-east and London are supplied. ‼♦RAIB

Pride 'n' Joy (ABV 2.8%)
A light brown bitter with a slight malty and hoppy aroma. Fruity with a pleasant hoppiness and some sweetness in the flavour, leading to a short, malty finish.
Horsham Pale (ABV 3.7%)
Sussex Pride (ABV 4%)
Old Cocky (ABV 4.3%)
American Graffiti (ABV 4.5%)
Horsham Old (ABV 4.6%)
Roast and toffee flavours predominate with some bitterness in this traditional old ale. Bittersweet with plenty of caramel and roast in a rather short finish.
Old Harry (ABV 5.2%)
Churchillian Stout (ABV 6.6%)

Wensleydale SIBA

Unit 4, Badger Court, Leyburn, North Yorkshire, DL8 5BF
☎ (01969) 622463 ☎ 07765 596666
🌐 wensleydalebrewery.co.uk

☺Wensleydale was set up in 2003 and has since moved to larger premises in Leyburn utilising a 10-barrel plant. Around 200 outlets are supplied direct in Yorkshire and Co Durham. ‼🛒♦

Falconer (ABV 3.9%)
Semer Water (ABV 4.1%)
Gamekeeper (ABV 4.3%)
Black Dub (ABV 4.4%)
High Fives (ABV 5.7%)

Weobley

Jules Restaurant, Portland Street, Weobley, Herefordshire, HR4 8SB
☎ (01544) 318206 🌐 theweobleybrewing.co

Commercial brewing began in 2019 at this nanobrewery, which is part of Jules restaurant in the village of Weobley and is run by chef and head brewer Tom Evans. Four beers are regularly brewed along with two occasional beers, available from the brewery, restaurant and other local outlets and pubs. ♦RAIB

Goldfinger Golden Ale (ABV 4.2%)
Magnus Pale Ale (ABV 4.6%)
Mr Magpie's Bitter (ABV 4.8%)
Mr Magpie's Stout (ABV 5.8%)

Wessex

Rye Hill Farm, Longbridge Deverill, BA12 7DE
☎ (01985) 844532 ✉ wessexbrewery@gmail.com

⊗ This four-barrel brewery, hidden away on a farm industrial complex in the West Wiltshire Area of Outstanding Natural Beauty, was established in 2001. The brewery sources its malt from the nearby Warminster Maltings. Around 2010 two new fermenters were installed. A handful of regular outlets are supplied, with wider availability via selected wholesalers. The brewery is able to brew beer for other concerns when capacity permits. Beers are occasionally brewed for Isle of Avalon (qv). ♦

Stourton Pale Ale (ABV 3.5%)
Mild (ABV 3.9%)
Kilmington Best (ABV 4.2%)
Deverill's Advocate (ABV 4.5%)
Maltings Gold (ABV 4.5%)
Warminster Warrior (ABV 4.5%)
Golden Apostle (ABV 4.8%)
Old Ale (ABV 4.8%)
Beast of Zeals (ABV 6.6%)

Festive Ferret (ABV 7%)
Russian Stoat (ABV 9%)

WEST

Binnie Place, Glasgow Green, Glasgow, G40 1AW
(0141) 550 0135 westbeer.com

Brewery producing artisan lagers and ales in strict accordance with the German Purity Law of 1516, which also has an on-site beerhall, restaurant and events venue. All beers are unpasteurised.

West Berkshire SIBA

The Old Dairy, Yattendon, Berkshire, RG18 0XT
(01635) 767090 wbbrew.com

West Berkshire was established in 1995. In 2018, following investment from new shareholders, capacity was increased tenfold to 50,000 hectolitres. The state-of-the-art brewery is located in a former dairy building and since opening, has expanded to take over the whole building, covering 68,000 sq ft. The site also includes a shop, taproom and kitchen. Beers are available throughout the south of England.

Mister Chubb's (ABV 3.4%)
A drinkable, balanced, session bitter. A malty caramel note dominates aroma and taste and is accompanied by a nutty, bittersweetness and a hoppy aftertaste.
Maggs' Mild (ABV 3.5%)
Silky, full-bodied, dark mild with a creamy head. Roast malt aroma is joined in the taste by caramel, sweetness and mild, fruity hoppiness. Aftertaste of roast malt with balancing bitterness.
Good Old Boy (ABV 4%)
Tawny bitter with malty aroma, then a balanced flavour with hops and fruit, leading to a long, dry, bitter aftertaste.
Gold Star (ABV 4.1%)
Maharaja IPA (ABV 5.1%)

West by Three

See Freetime

West Coast

See Conwy

West Coast Rock

1877 The Brew Room, 137-139 Church Street, Blackpool, FY1 3NX
(01253) 319165 thebrewroom1887.co.uk

Historic Blackpool pub, which reopened as a specialist beer outlet in 2017 and first brewed in 2018 using a six-barrel plant. Many of the beers have a Blackpool Football Club theme, the club being founded in the pub in 1887.

West End

68-70 Braunstone Gate, Leicester, LE3 5LG
07875 745302 thewestendbrewery.co.uk

The West End Brewery is Leicester city centre's original brewpub, which opened in 2016 using a 2.5-barrel plant. Total capacity doubled to five barrels in 2019. Beers are available in the pub and occasionally in other local outlets. RAIB

Westerham SIBA

Beggars Lane, Westerham, Kent, TN16 1QP
(01732) 864427 westerhambrewery.co.uk

Founded in 2004, Westerham moved in 2017 to a new purpose-built brewery. It also houses a taproom, shop and tasting room for the Squerryes Estate Winery. Greensand aquifer water from a borehole below the brewery, and use of the original heritage yeasts from the former Black Eagle Brewery, maintain a link to the Kent style of the past. More than 500 outlets are supplied in Kent, Surrey, Sussex and London. RAIB

Grasshopper Kentish Bitter (ABV 3.8%)
Summer Perle (ABV 3.8%)
Spirit of Kent (ABV 4%)
British Bulldog (ABV 4.1%)
1965 – Special Bitter Ale (ABV 4.8%)
Audit Ale (ABV 6.2%)

Westmorland

Kendal, Cumbria 07554 562662

Office: Mint Street, Kendal, LA9 6DS
westmorlandbrewery@gmail.com

Westmorland began brewing in 2016 using a one-barrel plant.

Wetherby

Beer Station, York Road Estate, York Road, Wetherby, LS22 7SU
(01937) 584637 07725 850654
wetherbybrewco.com

Wetherby Brew Co was established in 2017 and is located a short walk from the town centre. It is independently owned and operated and brews on a 1.25-barrel plant. The brewery incorporates an on-site taproom and bottle shop. Regular events are held and half day brewing experiences are offered.

Wharfe

See Hambleton

Wharfedale

Back Barn, 16 Church Street, Ilkley, West Yorkshire, LS29 9DS
(01943) 609587 wharfedalebrewery.com

Wharfedale began brewing in 2012 using spare capacity at Five Towns brewery in Wakefield. Brewing moved to Ilkley in 2013 using a 2.5-barrel plant located at the rear of the Flying Duck pub, creating Wharfedale's first brewpub.

Whim SIBA

Whim Farm, Hartington, Derbyshire, SK17 0AX
(01298) 84991 whimales.co.uk

Whim opened in 1993 in outbuildings at Whim Farm. The beers are available in 50-70 outlets and the brewery's tied house, Wilkes Head, Leek.

Marynka (ABV 3.3%)
Arbor Light (ABV 3.6%)
Hartington Bitter (ABV 4%)
Earl Grey Bitter (ABV 4.2%)
Hartington IPA (ABV 4.5%)
Flower Power (ABV 5.3%)

Whitacre

Dog Inn, Dog Lane, Nether Whitacre, Warwickshire, B46 2DU

☎ (01675) 481318 ☎ 07977 393833
🌐 thedoginnwhitacre.co.uk

Established in 2017 by licencees Gary and Joanne Webb to supply the adjacent Dog Inn. The nine-gallon brewery is situated in an outbuilding. All the beer names are dog themed as the owners are dog lovers with two Shih Tzus, Ted and Chicco. ◆

Whitby SIBA

East Cliff, Whitby, North Yorkshire, YO22 4JR ☎ 07516 116377 🌐 whitby-brewery.com

Whitby Brewery was established in 2012 under the Conquest name by a local team who built the brewery from scratch. It expanded in 2016 to a new site in the shadow of Whitby Abbey, with a 20-barrel capacity. Music events are hosted occasionally at weekends. Beers are distributed across Yorkshire and the North East. !! ♦ RAIB V◆

Abbey Blonde (ABV 3.8%)
Whaler (ABV 4%)
Saltwick Nab (ABV 4.2%)
Smugglers Gold (ABV 4.2%)
Jet Black (ABV 4.5%)
IPA (ABV 5.2%)
Black Death (ABV 6.6%)

White Hart

White Hart Hotel & Restaurant, 15 High Street, Halstead, Essex, CO9 2AP
☎ (01787) 475657 🌐 whitehartbrewery.co.uk

Brewing began in 2017 in old stables at the back of the White Hart. Both the brewery and pub are owned by father and son, Charles and Hugo Townsend. Beers are available in the pub and at local beer festivals.

White Hart Tap

White Hart Tap, 4 Keyfield Terrace, St Albans, Hertfordshire, AL1 1QJ
☎ (01727) 860974 🌐 whiteharttap.co.uk

Brewing began in 2015. Beers are only available in the pub. Brewing is currently suspended.

White Horse SIBA

3 Ware Road, White Horse Business Park, Stanford in the Vale, Oxfordshire, SN7 8NY
☎ (01367) 718700 🌐 whitehorsebrewery.co.uk

White Horse was founded in 2004. In 2018 a new management team took over the running of the brewery. The brewery has major outlets in Oxfordshire, as well as supplying other outlets nationally. In addition to its regular beers, a range of seasonal monthly beers is brewed as well as a number of one-off beers brewed under the Luna brand name. ♦

WHB (White Horse Bitter) (ABV 3.7%)
Black Beauty (ABV 3.9%)
Stable Genius (ABV 4%)
Village Idiot (ABV 4.1%)
Dark Blue Oxford University Ale (ABV 4.3%)
Wayland Smithy (ABV 4.4%)

White Rabbit

Unit 15a, Weston Industrial Estate, Honeybourne, Worcestershire, WR11 7GB ☎ 07713 952807
✉ **whiterabbit@aol.co.uk**

Housed in a refurbished nissan hut on an industrial estate in Honeybourne, and incorporating the former Cannon Royall brewery, White Rabbit started brewing in 2018. The 15-barrel plant produces beers for its own pub, the Red Lion in Evesham, as well as the local free trade. ♦ RAIB

Brown Bess (ABV 3.5%)
Aunt Lucy (ABV 3.7%)
Not Red Baron (ABV 4%)
Opal (ABV 4%)
Elwood's Dark (ABV 4.1%)
Dark brown porter, small creamy head, coffee and chocolate aromas continue with smoky stone fruit flavours finishing with a slightly sweet, then peaty, slightly bitter finish.
Stouty McStout (ABV 4.2%)
Jammers Ale (ABV 4.3%)
Rhubarb (ABV 4.3%)
Old Ale (ABV 4.6%)

Brewed under the Cannon Royall brand name:
Black Betty (ABV 3.5%)
Black Coffee (ABV 3.7%)
Fruiterers Mild (ABV 3.7%)
Fruity aroma with a hint of damsons, slightly sweet, fruity taste balanced with roasted malt. Fruity finish with smoky malt undertones.
Hunny Bear (ABV 3.8%)
King's Shilling (ABV 3.8%)
Light Beer (ABV 3.8%)
Amber session bitter, malty aroma with hints of toffee, initial hoppiness revealing a biscuit malt base, a slight grassiness and a lingering bitter finish.
Pioneer (ABV 3.8%)
Arrowhead Bitter (ABV 3.9%)
Well-balanced, fruity aroma with hints of banana, fruit and hops with mango and peach on the palate, followed by a long, sweet, hoppy finish.
Muzzle Loader (ABV 4.2%)
Flavoursome, full-bodied, amber best bitter. A fruity nose with hints of butterscotch and apple continues into the taste, with a long bitter finish.
Arrowhead Extra (ABV 4.3%)
Foxy Lady (ABV 4.3%)
Light-bodied, amber bitter, sweetshop aroma, moderate sweet malt taste with faint hops and a short bitter finish.
Love is Ale You Need (ABV 4.3%)
Paddington (ABV 4.3%)
Silver Fox (ABV 4.3%)
Teddy Bear (ABV 4.3%)
Jeff's Old Ale (ABV 4.6%)
Full-flavoured, fruity, copper ale with hints of plum, banana and molasses, balanced sweetness and hops leading to a fruity, lightly-hopped finish.
Son of Bertie (ABV 5%)
Bertie's Stout (ABV 6.7%)

White Rock SIBA

Units 6 & 7, Dysons Complex, Southside, St Sampsons, Guernsey, GY2 4QJ
☎ (01481) 249920 ☎ 07911 760302
🌐 whiterockbrewery.gg

White Rock began brewing in 2013 in a modern industrial unit and supplies the limited free trade on the island as well as a small number of tied houses. !! ♦

Pushang (ABV 3.8%)
Wonky Donkey (ABV 4.7%)
Lost Tourist (ABV 5.3%)

White Rose

Premises R/O, 7 Doncaster Road, Mexborough, South Yorkshire, S64 0HL
☎ (0114) 2466334

Office: 119 Chapel Road, Burncross, Chapeltown, Sheffield, S35 1QL
✉ whiterose.brewery@btinternet.com

☺Established in 2007 by Gary Sheriff, former head brewer at Wentworth Brewery. Formerly sharing premises with Little Ale Cart, White Rose then brewed in Mexborough, sharing premises with Imperial Brewery (qv). In 2018 it moved to its own premises using a new seven-barrel plant. ‼◆

Original Blonde (ABV 4%)
Stairlift to Heaven (ABV 4.2%)
Raven (ABV 4.9%)

Whitechapel

See Haworth Steam

Whitefaced

c/o 24 Ashfield Close, Penistone, South Yorkshire, S36 6EY ☎ 07894 532456

Established in 2017 producing bottled and keg beers, the brewery moved into cask production in 2019, winning CAMRA awards the same year. Owner/brewer David Hampshaw operates from his residence on a recently upgraded two-barrel kit, and is now able to offer cans. The brewery is named after the highly-prized, local, whitefaced woodland sheep. ◆RAIB

Whitewater

Lakeside Brae, Clarkhill Road, Castlewellan, Northern Ireland, BT31 9RH
☎ (028) 4377 8900 ⊕ whitewaterbrewery.com

Established in 1996, Whitewater is now the biggest brewery in Northern Ireland. ‼◆

Copperhead (ABV 3.7%)
Belfast Black (ABV 4.2%)
Belfast Ale (ABV 4.5%)
Maggie's Leap IPA (ABV 4.7%)
Clotworthy Dobbin (ABV 5%)

Whitley Bay

🍺 The Brewery, 2-4 South Parade, Whitley Bay, **NE26 2RG ☎ 07392 823480**
✉ whitleybaybrewingcompany@gmail.com

☺Brewing commenced in 2016 on a five-barrel plant and relocated to larger premises, a new brewery tap, in the centre of Whitley Bay in 2018. Around 40 local outlets are supplied. V

Slow Joe (ABV 3.9%)
Warrior (ABV 3.9%)
Spanish City Blonde (ABV 4.2%)
Dark Knight (ABV 4.3%)
Ghost Ships (ABV 4.3%)
Equinox (ABV 5%)
55 Degrees North (ABV 5.5%)

Whitstable SIBA

Little Telpits Farm, Woodcock Lane, Grafty Green, Kent, ME17 2AY
☎ (01622) 851007 ⊕ whitstablebrewery.co.uk

Whitstable Brewery was founded in 2003. It currently provides all the beer for the Whitstable Oyster Company's three restaurants, its hotel and a brewery tap, as well as supplying pubs all over Kent, London and Surrey. ◆

Native Bitter (ABV 3.7%)
A classic, copper-coloured, Kentish, session bitter with hoppy aroma and a long, dry, bitter hop finish.
Renaissance Ruby Mild (ABV 3.7%)
East India Pale Ale (ABV 4.1%)
A well-hopped, golden IPA with good grapefruit aroma hop character and lingering bitter finish.
Oyster Stout (ABV 4.5%)
Pearl of Kent (ABV 4.5%)
Winkle Picker (ABV 4.5%)
Kentish Reserve (ABV 5%)

Why Not

27 Redfern Road, Thorpe St Andrew, Norwich, Norfolk, NR7 9RB
☎ (01603) 300786 ⊕ thewhynotbrewery.co.uk

Why Not began brewing in 2005 on a 1.5-barrel plant located to the rear of the house of proprietor Colin Emms. In 2006 the brewery was extensively upgraded, doubling in capacity. In 2011 the brewery was moved to a new location in Thorpe St Andrew. RAIB

Wally's Revenge (ABV 4%)
An overtly bitter beer with a hoppy background. The bitterness holds on to the end as an increasing astringent dryness develops.
Roundhead Porter (ABV 4.5%)
Cavalier Red (ABV 4.7%)
Explosive fruity nose belies the gentleness of the taste. The summer fruit aroma dominates this red-gold brew. A sweet, fruity start disappears under a quick, bitter ending.
Norfolk Honey Ale (ABV 5%)
Chocolate Nutter (ABV 5.5%)

Whyte Bar

Exeter, Devon ⊕ whytebarbrew.com

Whyte Bar (pronouced White Bear) began brewing in 2018 using spare capacity at other breweries. No real ale.

Wibblers SIBA

Goldsands Road, Southminster, Essex, CM0 7JW
☎ (01621) 772044 ⊕ wibblers.com

⊗ Wibblers was established in 2007 and expanded to a 20-barrel plant in 2009. In 2016 the brewery moved to new premises in Southminster with a taproom. In 2018 the taproom was expanded four fold, along with capacity. Craft beers and ciders are now produced, as well as seasonal specials. Wibblers supply numerous outlets throughout East Anglia, London and Kent in addition to exporting to mainland Europe. ‼🍺◆RAIB V✿

Dengie IPA (ABV 3.6%)
Apprentice (ABV 3.9%)
Dengie Dark (ABV 4%)
Dengie Gold (ABV 4%)
Hop Black (ABV 4%)
Crafty Stoat (ABV 5.3%)

Wicked Hathern

See Staffordshire

Wickham House (NEW)

Church Lane, Conisholme, Lincolnshire, LN11 7LX
☎ 07817 467303 ✉ bearplumb64@gmail.com

Wickham House was formed in 2018 as a small artisan brewery concentrating on traditional ales produced in small batches. RAIB

Blonde Jester (ABV 4%)
Kings Island Bitter (ABV 4%)

Wickwar SIBA

Old Brewery, Station Road, Wickwar, Gloucestershire, GL12 8NB
☎ (01454) 292000 wickwarbrewing.co.uk

Wickwar was established as a 10-barrel brewery in 1990. In 2004 it expanded to 50 barrels. Moles Brewery and pubs were acquired in 2017, bringing its pub estate up to 20. This has now been rationalised to 16. 350 outlets are supplied on a regular basis and the beers are available nationally through most distributors and SIBA. ‼ ♦

BOB (ABV 4%)
Amber-coloured, this has a distinctive blend of hop, malt and apple/pear citrus fruits. The slightly sweet taste turns into a fine, dry bitterness, with a similar malty-lasting finish.
Cotswold Way (ABV 4.2%)
Amber-coloured, it has a pleasant aroma of pale malt, hop and fruit. Good dry bitterness in the taste with some sweetness. Similar though less sweet in the finish, with good hop content.
Falling Star (ABV 4.2%)
Stand-Up IPA (ABV 4.6%)
Station Porter (ABV 6.1%)

Brewed under the Moles brand name:
Gold (ABV 3.8%)
Golden, hoppy beer with subtle citrus fruit aroma and flavour derived from the Brewers Gold hops, with a malty background.
Best (ABV 4%)
An amber-coloured bitter, clean, dry and malty with some bitterness, and delicate floral hop flavour.
Elmo's (ABV 4.4%)
Medium-bodied bitter with subtle fruit aroma and flavours, leading to a long bitter finish.

Wigan Brewhouse

The Old Brewery, Brewery Yard, off Wallgate, Wigan, WN1 1JU
☎ (01942) 234976 ☎ 07764 936410
wiganbrewhouse.co.uk

Wigan Brewhouse commenced brewing in 2018 after local businessman Martin Blythe leased the now-defunct AllGates Brewery premises, including the acquisition of beers formerly brewed by AllGates. Beers are also brewed to its own recipes, developed by head brewer Jonathan Provost with Martin's input. ‼♦

Pretoria (ABV 3.6%)
California (ABV 3.9%)
A pale yellow beer with a restrained hoppy and fruity aroma. It is clean and fresh tasting, with hops and fruit in the mouth and a bitter, hoppy finish.
Casino (ABV 3.9%)
Junction (ABV 3.9%)
Dry Bones (ABV 4%)
Slider (ABV 4%)
Tempo (ABV 4.1%)
Blue Sky Tea (ABV 4.2%)
Kicker IPA (ABV 4.2%)
All-Nighter (ABV 4.3%)
Station Road Stout (ABV 4.5%)
Dark brown beer with a malty, fruity aroma. Creamy and malty in taste, with blackberry fruits and a satisfying aftertaste.

Wild Barn (NEW)

The Old Barn, Annat, PH33 7NA ☎ 07387 268193

Office: 14 Torr an Eas, Glenfinnan, PH37 4LS
✉ delvauxsimon6@hotmail.com

Launched in 2019 and rebranded in 2020, Wild Barn is a nanobrewery owned and operated by Simon Delvaux and Freja MacDougall, a Belgian and a Highlander. Beers with a strong nod to Simon's Belgian heritage are produced on a 500-litre kit. ‼♦RAIB V

Wild Beer SIBA

Lower Westcombe Farm, Evercreech, Somerset, BA4 6ER
☎ (01749) 838742 ☎ 07968 721841
wildbeerco.com

Brewing began in 2012 using a 24-hectolitre plant. Set on a Somerset farm, the brewery shares premises with Westcombe Dairy in an adjacent building. A wide range of beers is produced, including sour beers using alternative fermentation methods and unusual yeasts, alongside barrel-aging and a blending programme. Seasonal wild ingredients are also foraged. Two pub restaurants are owned. ♦RAIB

Bibble (ABV 4.2%)

Wild Boar

Wild Boar, Crook Road, Bowness-on-Windermere, Cumbria, LA23 3NF
☎ (0845) 850 4604 englishlakes.co.uk

Brewing began in 2013 at the Wild Boar, a large, traditional Lakeland luxury hotel. The hotel is part of the English Lakes Hotels group and supplies beers to hotels within the group. ♦

Wild Card SIBA

Unit 2, Lockwood Way, Blackhorse Road, Walthamstow, London, E17 5RB
☎ (020) 8935 5560 wildcardbrewery.co.uk

Wild Card began brewing in 2013, initially using spare capacity at several breweries in and around London. After brewing at its Ravenswood site, production moved to Lockwood in 2018 along with increasing the capacity of the brewery. Both sites remain popular taprooms at the weekend.

Pale Amrarillo (ABV 3.4%)
Jack of Clubs (ABV 4.5%)
Complex, ruby-brown best bitter with malty nose. Flavour has hints of chocolate, citrus and malt and a slightly bitter finish.
King of Hearts (ABV 4.5%)
Easy-drinking beer with a lager character in the lemony flavour, which is sweet and biscuity. Clean, dry finish.
Ace of Spades (ABV 4.7%)
Black porter with fruity nose overlaid with a little roast. Liquorice, caramelised fruit and roasted malt flavour. Lingering dryness.
Queen of Diamonds (ABV 5%)
Smooth golden ale with strong citrus aroma and flavour alongside biscuit notes. The finish is dry with a little bitterness.

Wild Horse SIBA

Unit 4, Cae Bach Builder Street, Llandudno, LL30 1DR
☎ (01492) 868292 wildhorsebrewing.co.uk

Small brewery concentrating on supplying KeyKeg, bottled and canned beers to local bars and off-licences.

All products are unfiltered and unpasteurised. Occasional one-off casks are produced ♦◈

Wild Weather SIBA

Unit 19, Easter Park, Benyon Road, Aldermaston, Berkshire, RG7 2PQ
☎ (0118) 970 1837 ⊕ wildweatherales.com

⊗ Established in 2012, this is a 15-barrel plant brewing a vast array of beer styles, distributed throughout the UK. Many of the beers are one-off collaborations. The Weather Station pub/taproom, Reading, opened in 2019. ‼ ♦ V

King Street Pale (ABV 4.2%)
Shepherd's Warning (ABV 5.6%)

Wildcraft

Forager's Rest, Coltishall Road, Buxton, Norfolk, NR10 5JD
☎ (01603) 278054 ☎ 07584 308850
⊕ wildcraftbrewery.co.uk

⊗ Wildcraft was set up in 2016 and uses as much foraged and locally sourced ingredients as possible to produce its beers. ‼

Wild Eye P.A. (ABV 3.8%)
Wild Norfolk (ABV 4.2%)
Strong, cut grass and citrus hop aroma. Full-bodied with lemon, sweet biscuit and a dry bitterness. Increasingly astringent finish.
Wild Bill Hiccup (ABV 4.5%)
Wild Summer (ABV 4.5%)
Wild Ride (ABV 5%)
Wild Stallion Stout (ABV 5%)

Wilde Child

Unit 5 Armley Road, Leeds, West Yorkshire, LS12 2DR
☎ 07908 419028 ⊕ wildechildbrewing.co.uk

Established as one of the smallest breweries in Leeds in 2016, Keir McAllister-Wilde took his operation from a one-barrel plant in a garage to a 10-barrel operation in a 2,000 sq ft unit within two years. There are a large number of different ales in Wilde Child's portfolio, all are unfined. As well as distributing nationwide, pallets are being sent to Holland, Spain and Finland. ◈

Opaque Reality (ABV 5.9%)

Wilderness

Unit 54, Mochdre Industrial Estate, Newtown, SY16 4LE
☎ (01686) 449020 ⊕ wildernessbrew.co.uk

Wilderness began brewing in 2018 using a custom-made, five-barrel plant. The brewery focuses on seasonal, barrel-aged and mixed fermentation beers. Belgian and farmhouse-style beers make up the majority of the range. V

Motueka Grisette (ABV 3.8%)
Southern Pale (ABV 4.3%)
Keller Weiss (ABV 5.1%)
Equinox Saison (ABV 5.2%)
Mandarina Pale (ABV 5.9%)

Williams Bros SIBA

New Alloa Brewery, Kelliebank, Alloa, FK10 1NT
☎ (01259) 725511 ⊕ Williamsbrosbrew.com

A brotherhood of brewers, creating unique beers. Bruce and Scott Williams started brewing Heather Ale in 1988. A range of indigenous, historic ales have been added since. Hundreds of cask ale outlets are supplied worldwide. ‼♦

Fraoch Heather Ale (ABV 4.1%)
Unique taste of heather flowers is noticeable. A fine floral aroma and spicy taste give character to this drinkable speciality beer.
Birds & Bees (ABV 4.3%)
March of the Penquins (ABV 4.9%)
Joker IPA (ABV 5%)
Seven Giraffes (ABV 5.1%)

Willy's

17 High Cliff Road, Cleethorpes, Lincolnshire, DN35 8RQ
☎ (01472) 602145

The brewery opened in 1989 to provide beer mainly for its in-house pub in Cleethorpes, although some beer is sold in the free trade. It has a five-barrel plant with maximum capacity of 15 barrels a week. The brewery can be viewed at any time from pub or street. ‼♦

Wily Fox SIBA

1 Kellet Close, Wigan, WN5 0LP
☎ (01942) 215525 ⊕ wilyfoxbrewery.co.uk

A bespoke 20-barrel brewery, set up in 2016. Head brewer Dave Goodwin previously worked for Thwaites and Samuel Smith. ‼

Blonde Vixen (ABV 3.8%)
Light-bodied, fruity beer.
Prohibition APA (ABV 3.9%)
Hoppy beer with citrus character throughout.
Crafty Fox (ABV 4%)
Well-balanced bitter and malty sweetness, with fruity hops. Creamy mouthfeel, and bitter finish.
The Fox Hat (ABV 4.2%)
Fruity aroma. Citrus hop taste and bitter hoppy aftertaste.
Karma Citra (ABV 4.3%)
Citrus fruit in aroma and taste with balanced bitterness, and a dry finish.
Dark Flagon (ABV 4.4%)

Wimbledon SIBA

8 College Fields, Prince George's Road, Colliers Wood, London, SW19 2PT
☎ (020) 3674 9786 ⊕ wimbledonbrewery.com

⊗ Set up by Mark Gordon after a 23 year career in the City, Wimbledon began production in 2015 with former Young's and Fuller's brewer Derek Prentice at the helm of a brand new 30-barrel plant. The brewery expanded in 2017 with two new 60-barrel fermenters and further expanded in 2018 with an additional 60-barrel fermenter. ‼ ♦ RAIB ◈

Common Pale Ale (ABV 3.7%)
Well-balanced, easy-drinking, gold-coloured bitter with mandarin and hoppy aroma and flavour overlaying a biscuit sweetness. Lingering dry bitterness.
Copper Leaf Ale (ABV 4%)
Caramelised toffee, roast, raisins and citrus is complemented by a growing dry spicy bitterness. Aroma has a touch of marmalade.
SW19 (ABV 4%)
Easy-drinking, pale ale with honeyed citrus and a gentle hopping flavour, becoming peppery in the subtle dry finish.
Quartermaine IPA (ABV 5.8%)

Well-balanced amber beer with an underlying sweetness complementing citrus, fruit cake and spicy hops in aroma and dry, bitter finish.

Wincle SIBA

Tolls Farm Barn, Dane Bridge, Wincle, Cheshire, SK11 0QE
☎ (01260) 227777 ⏺ winclebeer.co.uk

☺Wincle Beer Co was set up in 2008 on a working farm close to its present location. It now has a 15-barrel plant in Wincle, adjacent to the River Dane just inside Cheshire and within the Peak District National Park. The beers are brewed using water from its own borehole. A brewery shop and sampling room is housed in a converted stable next to the brewery. An annual beer festival is held at the end of June. ‼️🍺◆🍴

Waller (ABV 3.8%)
Rambler (ABV 4%)
Sir Philip (ABV 4.2%)
Wibbly Wallaby (ABV 4.4%)
Burke's Special (ABV 5%)

Windermere SIBA

🏠 **Watermill Inn, Ings, Cumbria, LA8 9PY**
☎ (01539) 821309 ☎ 07831 873300
⏺ lakelandpub.co.uk

☺Originally known as Watermill, the brewery was established in 2006 in a purpose-built extension to the inn. The beers have a doggy theme – dogs are allowed in the main bar. Windermere Brewing was originally a separate brand but all beers are now brewed under the name. ‼️◆

Windmill Hill SIBA

Unit 1, Eastfield Farm, Deppers Bridge, CV47 2SU
☎ (01926) 355450 ⏺ whbrewery.co.uk

Windmill Hill is an independent microbrewery using a one-barrel plant brewing small batch beers. Around 30 outlets are supplied direct.

Table Beer (ABV 2.9%)
Amber Post (ABV 4.2%)
The Chesterton (ABV 4.2%)
Grindstone (ABV 4.5%)

Windsor & Eton SIBA

Unit 1, Vansittart Estate, Duke Street, Windsor, Berkshire, SL4 1SE
☎ (01753) 854075 ⏺ webrew.co.uk

⊠ Four friends, including two fully-qualified brewers, set up the brewery in 2010. Their brewing experience goes back to the original Courage Brewery. In 2018 it was granted a Royal Warrant as Brewer to Her Majesty the Queen. The purpose-built plant is 18 barrels, which supplies around 300 outlets in London and the Thames Valley area. Beers are also produced under the Uprising brand name. ‼️🍺◆RAIB🍴

Knight of the Garter (ABV 3.8%)
Golden ale with a citrusy hop aroma, joined by some sweetness in the taste, followed by bitterness in the finish.
Windsor Knot (ABV 4%)
Guardsman (ABV 4.2%)
Eton Boatman (ABV 4.3%)
Golden ale with tropical fruit and citrus hop aroma, continuing into the taste with some sweetness and subtle bitter finish.
Father Thames (ABV 4.8%)

Conqueror (ABV 5%)
A black IPA. Malty and hoppy with berry notes. A full, rounded, slightly dry finish.

Windswept SIBA

Unit B, 13 Coulardbank Industrial Estate, Lossiemouth, IV31 6NG
☎ (01343) 814310 ⏺ windsweptbrewing.co.uk

Windswept Brewing Co was established in 2012 and is situated near the gates of RAF Lossiemouth. It is run by two former Tornado pilots who are CAMRA members. The brewery has developed to include a bar, shop and regular tours. Bottle-conditioned, seasonal and barrel-aged beers are produced. ‼️🍺◆RAIB V🍴

Blonde (ABV 4%)
Smooth, golden, citrus hoppy brew with hints of peach. Slight malty background.
APA (ABV 5%)
Good mix of malts and grapefruit hop throughout. Tangy finish.
Weizen (ABV 5.2%) 🍾
Cloudy wheat beer full of bananas and pear drops with a hint of spices.
Wolf (ABV 6%) 🍾
Dark, strong-tasting, slightly sweet, roasted malty brew with chocolate and a vanilla coffee background.

Windy

🏠 **Volunteer Inn, New Road, Seavington St Michael, Somerset, TA19 0QE**
☎ (01460) 240126 ⏺ thevolly.co.uk

The brewery was established at the Volunteer Inn in 2011 using a four-barrel plant. The name stems from the time when alterations were carried out to the back of the pub and the workmen suffered extremes of varying weather conditions. All beers are named with a weather theme. ‼️◆

Wingtip (NEW)

The Grain Shed, Ford Lane, Ashurst, West Sussex, BN44 3AT
☎ (0333) 224 4888 ⏺ wingtipbrewing.com

⊠ Established in 2015, Wingtip is influenced by the history of Shoreham Airport and its founders experience of aviation and travel. Beers are available in pubs and bars around Sussex and London.

Autopilot (ABV 3.9%)

Winster Valley

See Handsome

Winter's

See Mr Winter's (under M)

Winton (NEW)

Implement Road, West Barns, EH42 1UN
⏺ wintonbrewery.com

After a spell brewing at Top Out (qv), Winton moved to a site adjacent to Thistly Cross Cider and are producing a range of distinctive beers, mainly in cask and can. In 2020 it took over the Station Yard micropub, Dunbar.

Wintrip

7 Copenhagen Street, Worcester, WR1 2HB ☎ 07964 196194 🌐 wintripbrew.co

Wintrip began brewing in 2014 as Three Shires Brewery on a hand-built plant in Worcester before moving to new premises and subsequent name change. Local outlets are supplied.

Butchers Beastly Best (ABV 4%)
Salt Mine Stout (ABV 4.6%)

Wiper and True SIBA

2-8 York Street, St Werburghs, Bristol, BS2 9XT ☎ (0117) 941 2501 🌐 wiperandtrue.com

Originally launched in 2012 by Michael Wiper as a gypsy brewery, Wiper and True has operated since 2015 using its own 20-barrel plant. Producing an ever-changing range of seasonals along with four core beers, a proportion of its output goes into casks. The beers are available locally in Bristol/Bath, nationally and internationally. ‼ ♦ V

Wishbone

2a Worth Bridge Industrial Estate, Chesham Street, Keighley, West Yorkshire, BD21 4NS ☎ (01535) 600412 ☎ 07867 419445 🌐 wishbonebrewery.co.uk

Established in 2015 and run by a husband and wife team with many years previous experience in the brewing industry, beers are brewed on a modern, 10-barrel plant. V

Blonde (ABV 3.6%)
A hoppy golden ale with with a strong citrus character. A bitter, hoppy and slightly astringent finish.
Drover (ABV 3.9%)
Volk (ABV 3.9%)
Flux (ABV 4.1%)
Tiller Pin (ABV 4.2%)
Abyss (ABV 4.3%)
Caramel and coffee bean aroma in a stout of chocolate and liquorice, leading into a malty finish.
Gumption (ABV 4.5%)
Well-balanced, amber-coloured best bitter. Look for hints of dried fruit, biscuit and nuts, underpinned by dry hoppiness, leading to a bitter finish.

Witham

c/o The Chicken Sheds, Upp Hall Farm, Salmons Lane, Coggeshall, Essex, CO6 1RY ☎ (01376) 563123 ☎ 07824 698235 ✉ glennackerman15@gmail.com

Brewing started in 2012, using a 0.5-barrel plant at the Woolpack Inn, Witham. In 2015 it began using spare capacity at the Red Fox Brewery. The beer continues to be available at the Woolpack, Witham.

Scruffy (ABV 3.9%)
Gold (ABV 4.1%)
No Name (ABV 4.3%)

Withnell's SIBA

Artisan House, 101 Anderton Street, Chorley, Lancashire, PR7 2AY ☎ (01257) 460535 ☎ 07787 567471 🌐 withnells.co.uk

Withnell's was established in 2016 using a five-barrel plant. Beers are supplied direct to pubs within a 20-mile radius of the brewery.

Invincibles Ale (ABV 3.7%)
Blonde Summit (ABV 4%)
Hoppy Fettler (ABV 4.3%)
Push Iron (ABV 4.5%)
Pike Stone IPA (ABV 5.5%)

Wobbly

Unit 22c, Beech Business Park, Tillington Road, Hereford, HR4 9QJ ☎ (01432) 355496 🌐 wobblybrewing.co

Wobbly began brewing in 2013, as an offshoot of AJP Process Pipework, in a small business park in Hereford, and is closely linked with its sister canning company Wecan Solutions. The brewery has a tap house open Thursday, Friday and Saturday evenings. Contract brewing, canning and the brewing of its six core cask-conditioned ales remain the main lines of business. A new canning line has been installed, greatly increasing capacity. ‼ ♦ RAIB

Wabbit (ABV 4%)
Gold (ABV 4.2%)
American Amber Ale (ABV 4.5%)
Crow (ABV 4.5%)
Welder (ABV 4.8%)
India Pale Ale No. 3 (ABV 6%)

Wold Top SIBA

Hunmanby Grange, Wold Newton, Driffield, East Yorkshire, YO25 3HS ☎ (01723) 892222 🌐 woldtopbrewery.co.uk

An integral part of Hunmanby Grange Farm, Wold Top brewed its first ale in 2003. It uses home and Wolds-grown malting barley and chalk-filtered water from the farm's own borehole. Now brewing on a 40-barrel plant, the range includes special edition cask and bottled beers plus three gluten-free beers. The brewery installed a bottling line in 2007 and contract bottles for other breweries. ‼ ♦ GF

Bitter (ABV 3.7%)
Anglers Reward (ABV 4%)
Wolds Way (ABV 4%)
Headland Red (ABV 4.3%)
Against The Grain (ABV 4.5%)
Wold Gold (ABV 4.8%)

Wolf SIBA

Decoy Farm, Old Norwich Road, Besthorpe, Attleborough, Norfolk, NR17 2LA ☎ (01953) 457775 🌐 wolfbrewery.com

The brewery was founded in 1995 on a 20-barrel plant, which was upgraded to a 25-barrel plant in 2006. It moved to its current site in 2013. More than 300 outlets are supplied. ♦

Edith Cavell (ABV 3.7%)
Hoppy, peppery nose flows into taste. Malt, caramel and bitterness give depth and complexity. Crisp finish with a hoppy edge.
Golden Jackal (ABV 3.7%)
Gentle orange citrus aroma. A balanced mix of malt and hop with a crisp bitter tang. Burgeoning bitter swansong.
Wolf in Sheep's Clothing (ABV 3.7%)
Strong fruity nose with roast. A strong caramel beginning with a bitter roast counterpoint. Gently tapering finish. Increasing raspberry sweetness.
Lavender Honey (ABV 3.8%)
Malty caramel aroma leads into a bittersweet beginning with background honey notes A long, drying finish.

Battle of Britain (ABV 3.9%)
Wolf Ale (ABV 3.9%)
Copper-coloured with a smooth mix of biscuit and hop. A growing grainy bitterness gives contrast to the long finale.
Lupus Lupus (ABV 4.2%)
Hops, with a citrus edge, dominate both aroma and taste. A biscuity background disappears quickly in a short, sharp finish.
Sirius Dog Star (ABV 4.4%)
Rich tapestry of malt, roast and caramel with interwoven hop hints. Sweetness and bitterness provide a light but growing undercurrent,
Sly Wolf (ABV 4.4%)
Straw Dog (ABV 4.5%)
Delicately-flavoured with a fruity character. A redcurrant aroma gives way to marmalade and hops. A strong increasingly bitter finale.
Mad Wolf (ABV 4.7%)
Granny Wouldn't Like It (ABV 4.8%)
Complex, with a malty bouquet. Increasing bitterness is softened by malt as a gentle, fruity sweetness adds depth.
Woild Moild (ABV 4.8%)
Heavy and complex with malt, vine fruit, bitterness and roast notes vying for dominance. Increasingly dry finish.

Contract brewed for City of Cambridge Brewery:
Boathouse (ABV 3.7%)
Hobson's Choice (ABV 4.2%)
Atom Splitter (ABV 4.5%)
Parkers Piece (ABV 5%)

Wood SIBA

Craven Arms, Wistanstow, Craven Arms, Shropshire, SY7 8DG
☎ (01588) 672523 🌐 woodbrewery.co.uk

The brewery opened in 1980 in buildings next to the Plough Inn, the brewery's only tied house. Steady growth over the years included the acquisition of the Sam Powell Brewery in 1991. The brewery was sold to drinks firm Yarrawaddie in 2018 and continues to operate, supplying around 200 outlets. ‼♦

Parish Bitter (ABV 3.8%)
A blend of malt and hops with a bitter aftertaste. Pale brown in colour.
Shropshire Lass (ABV 4%)
Beauty (ABV 4.2%)
Shropshire Lad (ABV 4.5%)

Tom Wood

See Lincolnshire Craft

Woodcote Manor

Kidderminster Road, Dodford, Worcestershire, B61 9DY
☎ (01527) 558141 ☎ 07779 166174
🌐 woodcotemanor.com

⊗ Opened in 2015 in former dairy outbuildings attached to the brewer's house. The one-barrel plant can produce 20 firkins a week. It is run by a keen homebrewer who turned his hobby into a business, using locally sourced ingredients including own grown hops. The regular beers are distributed to a number of local pubs. ♦RAIB V

SSS (ABV 3.8%)
Half Cut (ABV 4.2%)
Single Hop (ABV 4.4%)
Well-balanced, golden bitter, light hop aromas with subtle melon, the initial sweetness is followed by a hint of ginger with hops predominating. Long and smooth hoppy finish.
Weavers Exclusive (ABV 4.4%)
IPA (ABV 4.6%)
Golden, well-balanced and hoppy, grapefruit aromas are followed by a pronounced hop and slightly spicy taste, with a lingering, bitter finish.
Oatmeal Stout (ABV 4.9%)
Dark in colour, roasted malt, chocolate and coffee tones are evident in the aroma and flavour, leading to a satisfying, slightly bitter finish.
Cap'n Will's Rum & Raisin Stout (ABV 6%)

Woodford Experiment

See Three Hills

Woodforde's SIBA

Broadland Brewery, Woodbastwick, Norfolk, NR13 6SW
☎ (01603) 720353 🌐 woodfordes.co.uk

⊗ Founded in 1981 by two members of the Homebrewers' Society, Woodforde's is named after Parson Woodforde, the 18th century Norfolk diarist with a penchant for real ale. In 1989 the brewery moved to its current home at Woodbastwick. It has its own boreholes and brews using locally-grown Maris Otter. Investment in 2001 and 2008 more than doubled the production capacity. Brewery tap, the Fur & Feather, is located next door, and more than 600 outlets are supplied on a regular basis. ‼🛒♦RAIB

Wherry (ABV 3.8%)
Malty aroma infused with summer fruits. Smooth and creamy with a huge biscuit base and peachy elements. Hoppy bittersweet ending.
Reedlighter (ABV 4%)
A hop, lemon and biscuit nose. Well-balanced with citrus and hop softened by a biscuity background. Short lemony ending.
Bure Gold (ABV 4.3%)
Singularly citrus throughout with a succinct hop garland. Sweet biscuit floats in the background over a bitter footing.
Nelson's (ABV 4.5%)
Malt aroma with hop. Initially malt and caramel float over a slightly hoppy sweetish character. Tapering biscuity finish with caramel.
Volt (ABV 4.5%)
Nog (ABV 4.6%)
Echoes of Pontefract cake dominate. A plummy sweetness is aided by a dry bitterness and a hint of caramel.

Woodman's

Unit 1, Viaduct Works, Frog Lane, Ponsanooth, Cornwall, TR3 7JW ☎ 07941 069890
🌐 woodmanswildale.co.uk

Wild food forager, Stuart Woodman, started brewing in 2016. He brews a core range of speciality beers, plus seasonal and special brews, with most featuring fruits and herbs. Having sold the brewery to Louis Simpson, Stuart remains as head brewer, and is trialling a number of new beers in consultation with Louis and other members of the team. A new set of regular beers will result, alongside the continuing and diverse seasonal and short-term brews. ‼♦RAIB V

WooHa SIBA

Upper Hempriggs Farm, Kinloss, Moray, IV36 2UB

☎ (01667) 459929 ☎ 07811 260732
🌐 woohabrewing.com

Wooha opened in 2015 using a 10-barrel plant. It specialises in producing bottle-conditioned ales. Cask-conditioned beers are brewed on demand for beer festivals. Pubs and retail outlets are supplied locally, in Nairn, and across Scotland. In 2017 the brewery moved to larger premises. RAIB

IPA (ABV 6.2%)
Malty background but with a strong peachy hop character in this pale brown IPA.

Woolybutt

31 Alexandra Road, Hull, East Yorkshire, HU5 2NS
☎ 07966 511242 🌐 woolybuttbrewshed.co.uk

Woolybutt Brew Shed is a two-barrel brewery. Rob Sutherland moved to commercial brewing after years of homebrewing experience.

English Pale Ale (ABV 4.4%)

Worcester

Arch 49, Cherry Tree Walk, Worcester, WR1 3AU
☎ 07906 432049 🌐 worcesterbrewingco.co.uk

A small brewery in the heart of Worcester and home to Sabrina Ales. A range of beers is brewed in rotation using traditional British hops, named with a loose association to the English Civil War.

Holy Ground (ABV 4.2%)
Powick Porter (ABV 4.5%)
1651 (ABV 5.1%)
Sabrina's Dark Ruby Ale (ABV 5.5%)

Working Hand

Three Horseshoes, Pit House Lane, Leamside, DH4 6QQ
☎ (0191) 584 2394 ☎ 07703 337556
🌐 threehorseshoesleamside.co.uk

Brewing began in 2012 using a 2.5-barrel plant. Beers are available at the Three Horseshoes as well as the four other pubs in the group. The brewery was renamed the Working Hand Brewery in 2016 when Matthew Booth took over the brewing. In 2018 it upgraded to a seven-barrel plant.

World's End

Crown Inn, 60 Wilcot Road, Pewsey, Wiltshire, SN9 5EL
☎ (01672) 562653 🌐 thecrowninnpewsey.com

World's End Ales was established in 2009 on a one-barrel plant at the rear of the Crown Inn, Pewsey. World's End is the 18th-century name for the area in which the brewery is located. ‼♦

Worsthorne SIBA

Unit 11, Siberia Mill, Holgate Street, Briercliffe, Lancashire, BB10 2HQ
☎ (01282) 422588 ☎ 07815 708289
🌐 worsthornebrewingcompany.co.uk

Worsthorne began brewing in 2011 using a 5.5-barrel plant. The brewery moved to larger premises behind the original building in 2014. An expansion to a 10-barrel plant was carried out in 2016, including a licensed visitor centre. More than 150 outlets are supplied. ‼♦

Gold (ABV 3.6%)
Packhorse (ABV 3.7%)
Palamino (ABV 3.9%)
Some Like It Blonde (ABV 3.9%)
Chestnut Mare (ABV 4%)
Great White (ABV 4.2%)
Red Man (ABV 4.2%)
Old Trout (ABV 4.5%)
Blackthorne Stout (ABV 4.9%)
Colliers Clog (ABV 5.5%)

Worthington's

See Heritage

Wrexham Lager

42 St Georges Crescent, Wrexham, LL13 8DB
☎ (01978) 266222 🌐 wrexhamlager.co.uk

Lager was first brewed in Wrexham in 1882 and returned to the town in 2011 following the closure in 2000 of the original Wrexham Lager brewery. This new, German-built, 50 hectolitre brewery produces keg and bottled lagers but no cask beers are produced.

Wriggle Valley SIBA

Unit 4 The Sidings, Station Road, Stalbridge, Dorset, DT10 2RQ
☎ (01963) 363343 ☎ 07952 198777
🌐 wrigglevalleybrewery.co.uk

Wriggle Valley began brewing in 2014 based in a converted garage at the owner's house but relocated in 2017 to an industrial unit using a three-barrel plant. Beers are mainly supplied within a 15-mile radius of the brewery. A taproom was opened at the brewery in 2019. ♦RAIB V

Dorset Nomad (ABV 3.8%)
Golden Bear (ABV 4%)
Golden ale with fruit notes in the aroma and taste leading to a dry, slightly astringent finish.
Ryme Rambler (ABV 4%)
Lightly-hopped best bitter with some elements of malt, caramel and fruit in the taste with malt and fruit coming to the fore in the aftertaste.
Dorset Pilgrim (ABV 4.2%)
A traditional best bitter with some malt and fruit in the aroma developing hop and bitterness in the taste, with a more bitter, balanced finish.
Copper Hoppa (ABV 4.5%)
Light malt and hop aroma with a relatively sweet taste predominated by fruit and caramel, which linger in a pleasant aftertaste along with slight bitterness coming forward.
Valley Gold (ABV 4.5%)
Golden ale with some fruit and hop in the aroma with bitterness and astringency developing with a light citrus note in the taste and through to a bitter aftertaste.
Five Buzzards (ABV 4.7%)

Wriggly Monkey

B.131 Motor Transport Yard, Bicester Heritage Centre, Bicester, Oxfordshire, OX26 5HA
☎ (01869) 246599 ☎ 07590 749062
🌐 wrigglymonkeybrewery.com

Established in 2018 on a 1.25-barrel kit, the brewery and its taproom are based in an old motor transport workshop at an automotive centre on the old RAF Bicester site. It is named after the compartment of a chain-drive mechanism of the Fraser Nash car. ‼

Super Sports (ABV 3.2%)

Gullwing Lager (ABV 4%)
Full Tilt (ABV 4.2%)
Charabanc (ABV 5.3%)
Ambassador (ABV 5.5%)

Wrong Side of the Tracks (NEW)

South Park Crescent, Catford, London, SE6 1JW
☎ 07917 106079 🌐 wrongsideofthetracks.beer

A small scale home brewer selling bottled beers commercially to local bottle shops as listed on its website.

Wrytree

Unit 1, Wrytree Park, Greenhead, Northumberland, CA8 7JA

Brewing commenced in 2015 as Pit Top Brewery. The name changed to Wrytree in 2019.

Gold (ABV 3.9%)
Copper (ABV 4%)

Wychwood

Eagle Maltings, The Crofts, Witney, Oxfordshire, OX28 4DP
☎ (01993) 890800 🌐 wychwood.co.uk

Wychwood brewery is located in the Cotswold market town of Witney. The brewers take inspiration from the myths and legends associated with the ancient medieval Wychwood forest. Part of Marston's PLC. ‼ ♦ RAIB

Hobgoblin Gold (ABV 4.2%)
Hobgoblin Ruby (ABV 4.5%)

Wye Valley SIBA IFBB

Stoke Lacy, Herefordshire, HR7 4HG
☎ (01885) 490505 ☎ 07970 597937
🌐 wyevalleybrewery.co.uk

Founded in 1985 in the back of a village pub, this award-winning brewery is now producing around 250,000 pints per week and delivers direct to more than 1,200 pubs, including eight of its own. Its products are also available through selected wholesale and retail stockists.
‼ ♦ RAIB

Bitter (ABV 3.7%)
A beer whose aroma gives little hint of the bitter hoppiness that follows right through to the aftertaste.
The Hopfather (ABV 3.9%)
HPA (ABV 4%)
A pale, hoppy, malty brew with a hint of sweetness before a dry finish.
Golden Ale (ABV 4.2%)
Butty Bach (ABV 4.5%)
Wholesome Stout (ABV 4.6%)
A smooth and satisfying stout with a bitter edge to its roast flavours. The finish combines roast grain and malt.

Wylam

Palace of Arts, Exhibition Park, Newcastle upon Tyne, NE2 4PZ
☎ (0191) 650 0651 🌐 wylambrewery.co.uk

Wylam commenced brewing in 2000 on a 4.5-barrel plant. Originally brewing in Heddon-on-the-Wall in Northumberland, the brewery moved to Newcastle upon Tyne in 2016 with a new 30-barrel brew kit with an on-site brewery tap. ‼ ♦

Galatia (ABV 3.9%)
Gold Tankard (ABV 4%)
Fresh, clean flavour, full of hops. This golden ale has a hint of citrus in the finish.
Collingwood (ABV 4.1%)
Swipe Right (ABV 4.7%)
Puffing Billy (ABV 5.5%)
Jakehead IPA (ABV 6.3%)

Wylde Sky

Unit 8a, The Grip, Hadstock Road, Linton, Cambridgeshire, CB21 4XN
☎ (01223) 778350 🌐 wyldeskybrewing.com

Established in 2018, the brewery has a purpose-built, 10-barrel plant brewing small batches of innovative beers in a range of styles from around the world. All beers are unfined, unfiltered and unpasteurised. A number of outlets are supplied in the area and an on-site taproom is open on Fridays and Saturdays. V

Wyre Piddle

See Ambridge

XT SIBA

Notley Farm, Chearsley Road, Long Crendon, Buckinghamshire, HP18 9ER
☎ (01844) 208310 🌐 xtbrewing.com

XT started brewing in 2011 using an 18-barrel plant. It supplies direct to pubs across southern England and the Midlands. The brewery taproom and shop sell draught and bottled beers to drink in or take out. A range of limited edition, but ever-changing, one-off brews is produced under the Animal Brewing Co name.
‼ ♦ RAIB

Four (ABV 3.8%)
Hop Kitty (ABV 3.9%)
Nineteen (ABV 4.2%)
One (ABV 4.2%)
Three (ABV 4.2%)
Eight (ABV 4.5%)
Fifteen (ABV 4.5%)
Seventeen (ABV 4.5%)
Thirteen (ABV 4.5%)
Lion London Porter (ABV 4.6%)
Squid Ink (ABV 5.5%)

Xtreme

Unit 21-22, Alfric Square, Maxwell Road, Woodston, Peterborough, Cambridgeshire, PE2 7JP ☎ 07825 680932 🌐 xtremeales.com

The Hunt brothers took over Xtreme Ales in 2020. The core range of ales is retained, along with some of the popular seasonals, but a number of new brews have also been added. Bumbling Brewery beers are also brewed for the Bumble Inn micropub, Peterborough. ‼ ♦

BeXt Bitter (ABV 3.9%)
Route 701 (ABV 4%)
SmoXey Mild (ABV 4%)
Xplorer Pale Ale (ABV 4.1%)
Pigeon Ale (ABV 4.3%)
Triple Hop (ABV 4.5%)
Chocolate Stout (ABV 5%)
Triple Hop Xtra IPA (ABV 5%)
Vogon Poetry (ABV 5%)
Evil Pigeon (ABV 5.5%)
LoXdown IPA (ABV 5.6%)
Xplosive Rhubarb Porter (ABV 6%)

THE BREWERIES

XYLO (NEW)

Unit 1, 2-14 High Street, Margate, Kent, CT9 1AT
☎ (01843) 229403 ⊕ xylobrew.com

Neil Wright and Ben Atkins set up the XYLO brewery and pub in 2019 using a four-barrel brew plant built in the cellar. ‼ ◈

Yard of Ale

Surtees Arms, Chilton Lane, Ferryhill, DL17 0DH
☎ (01740) 655724 ☎ 07540 733513
⊕ thesurteesarms.co.uk

Established in 2008, the 2.5-barrel microbrewery supplies ales to its brewery tap, the Surtees Arms, beer festivals and to a growing number of pubs. ‼ ♦ RAIB

Reach for the Yard (ABV 3.8%)
One Foot in the Yard (ABV 4.5%)

Yardsman

See Hercules

Yates'

Unit 4c, Langbridge Business Centre, Newchurch, Isle of Wight, PO36 0NP
☎ (01983) 867878 ⊕ yates-brewery.co.uk

Brewing started in 2000 on a five-barrel plant at the Inn at St Lawrence. In 2009 it moved to Newchurch and upgraded to a 10-barrel plant. In 2015 the brewery was moved on to the same site as the wholesale unit at Newchurch. ‼ ♦

Golden Bitter (ABV 4%)
Islander (ABV 4%)
Beachcomber (ABV 4.3%)
Holy Joe (ABV 4.9%)
Dark Side of the Wight (ABV 5%)
Yule Be Sorry (ABV 7.2%)

Yelland Manor

Lower Yelland Farm, Yelland, Barnstaple, Devon, EX31 3EN ☎ 07770 267592
✉ yellandmanor@gmail.com

Located on the Taw Estuary and close to the Tarka Trail, this five-barrel plant in a converted milking parlour was established in 2013. It supplies a small number of local pubs and hotels, although the majority of sales are now made from the premises, either as takeaways or for consumption as part of a 'brewery experience'. Small functions are also catered for, together with regular steak, and fish n' chip evenings. ♦

The Tarka Special (ABV 4.1%)
Standard (ABV 4.2%)

Yeovil SIBA

Unit 5, Bofors Park, Artillery Road, Lufton Trading Estate, Yeovil, Somerset, BA22 8YH
☎ (01935) 414888 ⊕ yeovilales.com

Yeovil Ales was established in 2006 using an 18-barrel plant. More than 300 pubs are supplied in the South West. ‼ ♦ V

Hopkandi (ABV 3.8%)
Star Gazer (ABV 4%)
Easy-drinking, tawny-coloured, standard bitter. Malt and toffee in the aroma lead to a predominantly sweet flavour. Short, bitter finish.
Summerset (ABV 4.1%)
Lynx Wildcat (ABV 4.3%)
Stout Hearted (ABV 4.3%)
Ruby (ABV 4.5%)
POSH IPA (ABV 5.4%)

Yetman's

Bayfield Farm Barns, Bayfield Brecks Farm, Bayfield, Norfolk, NR25 7DZ ☎ 07774 809016 ⊕ yetmans.net

A 2.5-barrel plant built by Moss Brew was installed in restored medieval barns near Holt in 2005. The brewery supplies local free trade outlets. RAIB

Red (ABV 3.8%)
A plummy malt carapace with a balanced hop and caramel undercoat. Full-bodied and long-lasting. Bittersweet notes slowly intercede.
Amber (ABV 4.2%)
Orange (ABV 4.2%)
Stout (ABV 4.2%)
Green (ABV 4.8%)

York

c/o Black Sheep Brewing, Wellgarth, Masham, North Yorkshire, HG4 4EN ⊕ york-brewery.co.uk

York started production in 1996 and was bought out of administration by Black Sheep Brewery (qv) in 2018. Four pubs are owned in York and Leeds. Brewing of all York Brewery beers is temporarily taking place at Black Sheep until new premises can be found. ‼ ♦

Guzzler (ABV 3.6%)
Refreshing, golden ale with dominant hop and fruit flavours developing throughout.
Yorkshire Terrier (ABV 4.2%)
Refreshing and distinctive amber/gold brew where fruit and hops dominate the aroma and taste. Hoppy bitterness remains assertive in the aftertaste.
Centurion's Ghost Ale (ABV 5.4%)
Dark ruby in colour, full-tasting with mellow roast malt character balanced by light bitterness and autumn fruit flavours that linger into the aftertaste.

Yorkshire Brewhouse

Matrich House, Goulton Street, Hull, East Yorkshire, HU3 4DD
☎ (01482) 755199 ⊕ yorkshirebrewhouse.com

Founded in 2017 by friends Jon Constable and Simon Cooke as a weekend family venture, the brewery has expanded from a 200-litre per week operation to a 1,000-litre one, supplying cask and bottled ales to East Yorkshire pubs and outlets. Most of the beers are given names that mirror Yorkshire dialect or have a local connection. RAIB V

1904 (ABV 3.8%)
Reet (ABV 3.8%)
EYPA (ABV 3.9%)
Tenfoot (ABV 3.9%)
Ey Up (ABV 4%)
Faithful (ABV 4.5%)
Flippin Eck (ABV 4.6%)
Red Robin (ABV 4.6%)

Yorkshire Coast (NEW)

105 Hilderthorpe Road, Bridlington, East Yorkshire, YO15 3ET ⊕ yorkshire-coast-brewery.com

Established in the basement of the Funny Onion pub in 2019, Yorkshire Coast Brew Co was launched commercially in 2020. With 30 years experience of brewing, head brewer Steve Golden brews small batches of traditional ales. ‼

Yorkshire Dales

Abbey Works, Askrigg, North Yorkshire, DL8 4LP
☎ (01969) 622027 ☎ 07818 035592
yorkshiredalesbrewery.com

Situated in the heart of the Yorkshire Dales, brewing started in a converted milking parlour in 2005. In 2016 the brewery moved to larger premises. More than 150 pubs are supplied throughout the north of England. A tap and bottle shop opened at the brewery in 2017. ‼♦RAIB

Butter Tubs (ABV 3.7%)
Askrigg Bitter (ABV 3.8%)
Bainbridge Blonde (ABV 3.8%)
Buckden Pike (ABV 3.9%)
Nappa Scar (ABV 4%)
Muker Silver (ABV 4.1%)
Askrigg Ale (ABV 4.3%)
Garsdale Smokebox (ABV 5.6%)

Yorkshire Heart SIBA

The Vineyard, Pool Lane, Nun Monkton, North Yorkshire, YO26 8EL
☎ (01423) 330716 ☎ 07838 030067
yorkshireheart.com

Yorkshire Heart has been brewing since 2011 and is situated near to York adjacent to the Yorkshire Heart vineyard and winery run by the same family. The brewery uses a five-barrel plant. ‼♦

Hearty Bitter (ABV 3.7%)
Rhubarbeer (ABV 3.7%)
Blonde (ABV 3.9%)
Silverheart IPA (ABV 4%)
Blackheart Stout (ABV 4.8%)
Platinum EPA (ABV 5%)
Ghost Porter (ABV 5.4%)

Young's

See Eagle

Zapato

Unit 1a, Holme Mills, West Slaithwaite Road, Marsden, Huddersfield, West Yorkshire, HD7 6LS
☎ (01484) 841201 ☎ 07788 513432
zapatobrewery.co.uk

Small company, established in 2016, that nomadic brewed in the Leeds and Manchester areas prior to establishing a permanent home in Marsden. It produces innovative beers based in traditional European styles. Collaboration brews are a staple part of its output. V

Zepto

Graig Fawr Lodge, Blackbrook Road, Caerphilly, CF83 1NF ☎ 07951 505524 zeptobrew.co.uk

Established in 2016, Zepto is a 100-litre brewery set up by CAMRA member Chris Sweet. Although production is mainly bottled, cask-conditioned beers are occasionally brewed. Beers can be obtained via Wales Ales online shop.

Zerodegrees SIBA

Blackheath: 29-31 Montpelier Vale, Blackheath, London, SE3 0TJ

Bristol: 53 Colston Street, Bristol, BS1 5BA

Cardiff: 27 Westgate Street, Cardiff, CF10 1DD

Reading: 9 Bridge Street, Reading, RG1 2LR
zerodegrees.co.uk

Brewing started in 2000 in Blackheath, London, and now four brewpubs are owned, each incorporating a state-of-the-art, computer-controlled, German plant producing unfiltered and unfined ales and lagers. All beers use natural ingredients, are suitable for vegetarians, and are served from tanks using air pressure (not CO2). ♦V

Zest SIBA

Heath Lane, Barkston Heath, Grantham, Lincolnshire, NG32 2DE
☎ (01476) 572135 zest-brewery.com

In 2020 Zest Brewery took over from Oldershaw Brewery, which had been brewing since 1997. Owned and run by brewster Kathy Britton, Zest produces a core range of beers in both traditional and contemporary styles, as well as seasonal ales. Bespoke bottled and cask beers can be created to order and a mobile bar service is also available. ‼♦

Heavenly Blonde (ABV 3.8%)
Newton's Drop (ABV 4.1%)
Balanced malt and hops but with a strong bitter, lingering taste in this mid-brown beer.
Blond Bombshell (ABV 4.3%)
Mosaic Blonde (ABV 4.3%)
Atomic IPA (ABV 4.5%)
Blonde Volupta (ABV 5%)

Zoo (NEW) SIBA

Excal House, Capel Hendre Industrial Estate, Ammanford, SA18 3SJ ☎ 07889 592614
zoo-brew.com

Zoo Brew was established in 2019 using equipment from the former Castlegate brewery. As part of the purchase it inherited the recipe for the popular Merlin's Own. Beer is mainly supplied direct to local pubs.

Amman Eagle (ABV 4.4%)
Towy Tiger (ABV 5%)
Merlin's Own (ABV 5.2%)

Zulu Alpha SIBA

51b Symondscliffe Way, Caldicot, NP26 5PW ☎ 07578 196275 / 07899 794294
info@zulualphabrewing.co.uk

Brewing since 2018, Zulu Alpha Brewing consists of a seven-barrel brewhouse with four fermenters. Open days are held at the brewery, which has a licensed bar. One of the ales is a regular at the Cellar, Caldicot. ♦

New Horizon (ABV 4%)
Voyager (ABV 4.8%)
Evolution (ABV 5.2%)

Zymurgorium

Unit 19, Irlam Business Centre, Soapstone Way, Irlam, M44 6RA zymurgorium.com

The UK's first craft meadery and Manchester's first distillery. In combination with the brewery it was established in Irlam in 2013. Most of its output is in bottled form.

THE BREWERIES

Closed breweries

The following breweries have closed or gone out of business since the 2020 Guide was published:

22 Bake & Brew, Torphins, Aberdeen & Grampian
Abstract Jungle, Langley Mill, Derbyshire
Alphabeta, Aldgate, Greater London
Amber, Ripley, Derbyshire
Applecross, Applecross, Highlands & Western Isles
Ash Valley, Green Tye, Hertfordshire
Axholme, Crowle, Lincolnshire
Axton, Prestatyn, North-East Wales
Aylesbury, Aylesbury, Buckinghamshire
Baa, Chepstow, Gwent
Bale, Liddaton, Devon
Barrahooley Craft, Ballymena, Northern Ireland
Beer Monkey, Skipton, North Yorkshire
Beer Refinery, Chester, Cheshire
Beer Story, Insch, Aberdeen & Grampian
Belrose, NW3: Belsize Park, Greater London
Betteridge's, Hurstbourne Tarrant, Hampshire
Black Rock, Falmouth, Cornwall
Blackhill, Chester-le-Street, County Durham
Bloomfield, Blackpool, Lancashire
Blue Bell Brewhouse, Warings Green, Warwickshire
Bluestone, Whitworth, Lancashire
Borough Arms, Crewe, Cheshire
Brewheadz, N17: Haringey, Greater London
Brick House, Patcham, East Sussex
Bridlington, Bridlington, East Yorkshire
Brigstock, Brigstock, Northamptonshire
Britman, Burton, Cheshire
Brockenhurst, Brockenhurst, Hampshire
Brodie's, Greater London
Broken Bridge, Upper Swanmore, Hampshire
Brotherhood, Westbury, Wiltshire
Buccanneer, Sutton Weaver, Cheshire
Buffy's, Wicklewood, Norfolk
Bullen, Ledbury, Herefordshire
Campbells, Peebles, Edinburgh & the Lothians
Cap House, Batley, West Yorkshire
Cheeky Imp, Skellingthorpe, Lincolnshire
Coastal, Redruth, Cornwall
Concertina, Mexborough, South Yorkshire
Cosmic, Bristol, Gloucestershire & Bristol
Crate, E9: Hackney Wick, Greater London
Custom Head, Lichfield, West Midlands
Dancing Cows, Lymington, Hampshire
Darkplace, Colyton, Devon
Darkwave, Preston, Lancashire
Deben Peninsular, Rendlesham, Suffolk
Dogbreath, Kinver, Staffordshire
Doghouse, Darwen, Lancashire
East Yorkshire, Woodmansey, East Yorkshire
Edinbrew, Livingston, Edinburgh & the Lothians
Emsworth Brewery, Emsworth, Hampshire
Evolution, Shrewsbury, Shropshire
Eyes, Leeds, West Yorkshire
Faultline, Dorking, Surrey
Fisher's, High Wycombe, Buckinghamshire
Forager's, St Albans, Hertfordshire
Fox Meadow, Braintree, Essex
Golcar, Golcar, West Yorkshire
Great Heck, Great Heck, North Yorkshire
Greenfield, Greenfield, Greater Manchester
Gun Dog, Woodford Halse, Northamptonshire
Hale, N15: Tottenham Hale, Greater London
Hammerpot, Poling, West Sussex
Hart Family, Wellingborough, Northamptonshire
Hart of Stebbing, Stebbing, Essex
Hawk Wing, Lesbury, Northumberland
Heavy Industry, Henllan, North-East Wales
Helm Bar, Appleby, Cumbria
High Peak, Chapel-en-le-Frith, Derbyshire
High Weald, East Grinstead, West Sussex
Hillfire, Aylesbury, Buckinghamshire
Holler, Brighton, East Sussex
Hooded Ram, Douglas, Isle of Man
Hopjacker, Dronfield, Derbyshire
Horner Bros, Lancaster, Lancashire
House, N22: Wood Green, Greater London
Hubsters, Bamber Bridge, Lancashire
Jollyboat, Bideford, Devon
Kew, SW14: East Sheen, Greater London
Kinneil, Bo'ness, Loch Lomond
Kitchen, SW15: Putney, Greater London
Knops, Dirleton, Edinburgh & the Lothians
Korruptd, Penistone, South Yorkshire
Laig Bay, Glamisdale: Isle of Eigg, Highlands & Western Isles
Laine, SW11: Battersea, Greater London
Lincolnshire, Langworth, Lincolnshire
Lonesome, SW15: Streatham, Greater London
Long Arm Brewing, W5: Ealing, Greater London
Maregade, E9: Homerton, Greater London
Marts, Stoke on Trent, Staffordshire
Middle Earth, Derby, Derbyshire
Mix, Hemel Hempstead, Hertfordshire
Moonchild, Petrockstow, Devon
Moonstone, Burnley, Lancashire
Nant, Llanrwst, North-West Wales
Nobby's, Thrapston, Northamptonshire
Old Cross, Hertford, Hertfordshire
Old Vault, Thorne, South Yorkshire
Old Worthy, Broughton, Borders
Oxbrew, Freeland, Oxfordshire
Partridge, Chipping, Lancashire
Penistone, Penistone, South Yorkshire
Pershore, Pershore, Worcestershire
Portpatrick, Portpatrick, Dumfries & Galloway
Potton, Potton, Bedfordshire
Punchline, Wolverhampton, West Midlands

Closed breweries (continued)

Redhouse, Newcastle upon Tyne, Tyne & Wear
Red Star, Formby, Merseyside
Regather, Sheffield, South Yorkshire
Reunion, Feltham, Greater London
Rockhopper, Luton, Bedfordshire
Rowditch, Derby, Derbyshire
Saeburh, Tendring, Essex
Saffron, Henham, Essex
Sandiway, Sandiway, Cheshire
Sawbridgeworth, Sawbridgeworth, Hertfordshire
Seal Bay, Cardigan, West Wales
Shardlow, Cavendish Bridge, Leicestershire
Sheelin, Bellanaleck, Northern Ireland
Silks, Sible Hedingham, Essex
Skippool Creek, Thornton Cleveleys, Lancashire
Speyside, Forres, Aberdeen & Grampian
Sprey Point, Teignmouth, Devon
Stansfield, Stansfield, Suffolk
Station Works, Newry, Northern Ireland
StoatCraft, Aberdeen, Aberdeen & Grampian
Stockton, Stockton on Tees, County Durham
Summer Wine, Honley, West Yorkshire
Sunset, St Columb Major, Cornwall
Taylor Illingworth, Middlesbrough, North Yorkshire
Taylors, Attleborough, Norfolk
Test, Broughton, Hampshire
Three Peaks, Settle, North Yorkshire
Three Valleys, Todmorden, West Yorkshire
Totally Brewed, Nottingham, Nottinghamshire
Trinity, Gisleham, Suffolk
Tweed, Denton, Greater Manchester
Two Drifters, Exeter, Devon
Two Tone, Shebbear, Devon
Ubrew, SE16: Bermondsey, Greater London
Vadum, Wath-upon-Dearne, South Yorkshire
Valhalla, Unst: Shetland, Northern Isles
Vendetta, Southend on Sea, Essex
Willy's Brew, Stone, Buckinghamshire
Wizard, Ilfracombe, Devon
George Wright, Rainford, Merseyside
Yaarbrew, Hickling, Norfolk
Yorkshire, Hull, East Yorkshire

Future breweries

The following new breweries have been notified to the Guide and will start to produce beer during 2020/2021. In a few cases they were in production during the summer of 2020 but were too late for a full listing:

Alicehead, Ashover, Derbyshire
BB18, Earby, Lancashire
Beer Station, Formby, Merseyside
Billy Ruffian's, Plymouth, Devon
Brewhouse & Kitchen, Worthing, West Sussex
Dog's Grandad, Greater London
Edwards & Sons, Dronfield, Derbyshire
Gravity, Dronfield, Derbyshire
Isle of Eigg, Galmisdale: Isle of Eigg, Highlands & Western Isles
Jawbone, Strawberry Hill, Greater London
Jiddlers Tipple, N8: Haringey, Greater London
Lines, Usk, Gwent
Morgan Brewmasters, Derbyshire
Old Prentonian, Louth, Lincolnshire
On the Level, Wrantage, Somerset
One More Than Two Brew, South Shields, Tyne & Wear
Rusty Garage, Swindon, Wiltshire
Shed Brewery, Horsham, West Sussex
Tower, Bodmin, Cornwall
Uppingham, Uppingham, Rutland
Wantage, Wantage, Oxfordshire
Wells & Co, Bedford, Bedfordshire

Breweries for sale

The following breweries are reported as being for sale:

Bullmastiff, Cardiff, Glamorgan
Burton Old Cottage, Burton, Staffordshire
Bute, Rothesay: Isle of Bute, Argyll & the Isles
Double Top, Worksop, Nottinghamshire
Nutbrook, West Hallam, Derbyshire
Salamander, Bradford, West Yorkshire
Shropshire Brewer, Longden Common, Shropshire
Violet Cottage, Gwaelod y Garth, Glamorgan
Well Drawn, Caerphilly, Glamorgan

View from Whitby Brewery, Whitby, North Yorkshire

Indexes & Further Information

Places index

C

PLACES INDEX

PLACES INDEX

T

PLACES INDEX

Beers index

These beers refer to those in bold type in the breweries section (beers in regular production) and so therefore do not include seasonal, special or occasional beers that may be mentioned elsewhere in the text.

C

D

F

G

H

I

J

M

N

O

P

Q

R

S

T

U

BEERS INDEX

X

Y

Readers' recommendations

Suggestions for pubs to be included or excluded

All pubs are regularly surveyed by local branches of the Campaign for Real Ale to ensure they meet the standards required by the *Good Beer Guide*. If you would like to comment on a pub already featured, or on any you think should be featured, please fill in the form below (or a copy of it), and send it to the address indicated. Alternatively, email **gbgeditor@camra.org.uk**. Your views will be passed on to the branch concerned. Please mark your envelope/email with the county where the pub is, which will help us to direct your comments efficiently.

Pub name:

Address:

Reason for recommendation/criticism:

Pub name:

Address:

Reason for recommendation/criticism:

Pub name:

Address:

Reason for recommendation/criticism:

Your name and address:

Please send to: [Name of county] Section, Good Beer Guide,
230 Hatfield Road, St Albans, Hertfordshire AL1 4LW

Readers' recommendations

Suggestions for pubs to be included or excluded

All pubs are regularly surveyed by local branches of the Campaign for Real Ale to ensure they meet the standards required by the *Good Beer Guide*. If you would like to comment on a pub already featured, or on any you think should be featured, please fill in the form below (or a copy of it), and send it to the address indicated. Alternatively, email **gbgeditor@camra.org.uk**. Your views will be passed on to the branch concerned. Please mark your envelope/email with the county where the pub is, which will help us to direct your comments efficiently.

Pub name:

Address:

Reason for recommendation/criticism:

Pub name:

Address:

Reason for recommendation/criticism:

Pub name:

Address:

Reason for recommendation/criticism:

Your name and address:

Please send to: [Name of county] Section, Good Beer Guide,
230 Hatfield Road, St Albans, Hertfordshire AL1 4LW

AWARD-WINNING PUBS

The Pub of the Year competition is judged by CAMRA members. Each of the CAMRA branches votes for its favourite pub: criteria include the quality and choice of real ale, atmosphere, customer service and value. The pubs listed below are the current winners of the title; look out for the 🏆 next to the entries in the Guide.

ENGLAND

Bedfordshire
Devonshire Arms, Bedford
Engineers Arms, Henlow
Black Lion, Leighton Buzzard

Berkshire
John o'Gaunt, Hungerford
Bell, Waltham St Lawrence
Corner House, Windsor
Ship Inn, Wokingham

Buckinghamshire
King's Head, Aylesbury
Mitre, Buckingham

Cambridgeshire
Live & Let Live, Cambridge
Green Man, Colne
Prince Albert, Ely
Frothblowers, Peterborough

Cheshire
Bhurtpore, Aston
Beartown Tap, Congleton
Malt Disley, Disley
Lion, Moulton
Norton Arms, Runcorn

Cornwall
White Hart, Chilsworthy

Cumbria
Fell Bar, Penrith

Derbyshire
White Hart, Bargate
Neptune Beer Emporium, Chesterfield
Smithfield Alehouse, Derby
Barley Mow, Kirk Ireton
Newsroom, Matlock
Royal Oak, Ockbrook

Devon
Globe Inn, Beaford
Horse & Groom, Bittaford
Queen's Arms, Brixham
Bicton Inn, Exmouth

Dorset
Ship Inn, Shaftesbury
King's Arms, Thornford
Horse & Groom, Wareham

Durham
Grey Horse, Consett
Quakerhouse, Darlington
Victoria Inn, Durham
Surtees Arms, Ferryhill Station
Lucifers, Stockton-on-Tees

Essex
Railway Tavern, Brightlingsea
Orange Tree, Chelmsford
White Hart, Grays
Queen Victoria, Maldon
Woodbine Inn, Waltham Abbey
Mile and a Third, Westcliff-on-Sea
Fleur de Lys, Widdington
Black Buoy, Wivenhoe

Gloucestershire & Bristol
Snuffy Jack's, Bristol: Fishponds
Kemble Brewery, Cheltenham
Eight Bells, Chipping Campden
Pelican Inn, Gloucester
King's Arms, Newent

Hampshire
Steel Tank Alehouse, Chandler's Ford
Queen's Hotel, Gosport
Golden Pheasant, Lower Farringdon
Wonston Arms, Wonston

Hertfordshire
Lordship Arms, Benington
Monk's Inn, Hemel Hempstead
Land of Liberty, Peace & Plenty, Heronsgate
Old Cross Tavern, Hertford

Isle of Wight
Newport Ale House, Newport

Devonshire Arms, Bedford (p21)

Fell Bar, Penrith (p79)

Bicton Inn, Exmouth (p102)

Kent
Haywain, Bramling
Larkins' Alehouse, Cranbrook
Past & Present Ale House, Gillingham
Old House, Ightham Common
Admiral's Arms, Queenborough
This Ancient Boro', Tenterden
Nelson Arms, Tonbridge
Berry, Walmer
Bake & Alehouse, Westgate-on-Sea

Greater London
Robin Hood & Little John, Bexleyheath
Star & Garter, Bromley
Hope, Carshalton
Gidea Park Micropub, Gidea Park
Willoughby Arms, Kingston
Northcote Arms, E11: Leytonstone
Little Green Dragon, N21: Winchmore Hill
Antwerp Arms, N17: Tottenham
Dog & Bell, SE8: Deptford
Railway, SW16: Streatham
Harp, WC2: Charing Cross
Dodo Micropub, W7: Hanwell

Greater Manchester
Old Packet Horse, Altrincham
Twisted Vine Ale House, Ashton in Makerfield
Northern Monkey, Bolton
Grocers, Cadishead
Bobbin, Leigh
Marble Arch Inn, Manchester
Flying Horse Hotel, Rochdale
Magnet, Stockport

Lancashire
Craft House Beer Café, Lytham
Little Bare, Morecambe
Tap Room No. 12, Ormskirk
Swan with Two Necks, Pendleton
Guild Ale House, Preston

Leicestershire
Geese & Fountain, Croxton Kerrial
Stamford Arms, Groby
Pestle & Mortar, Hinckley
Blue Boar, Leicester
Moonface Brewery & Tap, Loughborough
Stilton Cheese, Somerby

Lincolnshire
Sweyn Forkbeard, Gainsborough
Pooley's, Messingham
Green Man, Ropsley

Merseyside
Lion Tavern, Liverpool: City Centre
Magazine Hotel, New Brighton
Turks Head, St Helens
Guest House, Southport

Norfolk
Tombstone Saloon, Great Yarmouth
Hop In, North Walsham
Kings Arms, Shouldham

Northumberland
Dipton Mill Inn, Hexham

Nottinghamshire
Royal Oak, Car Colston
Mallard, Worksop

Oxfordshire
Bird in Hand, Henley-on-Thames
Red Lion, Horley
Royal Blenheim, Oxford
Royal Oak, Wantage

Rutland
Railway, Ketton

Shropshire
Clive & Coffyne, Market Drayton
Prince of Wales, Shrewsbury
Pheasant Inn, Telford: Wellington

Somerset
Royal Oak, Bath
Crossways Inn, West Huntspill

Hope, Carshalton (p276)

Crossways Inn, West Huntspill (p375)

Waterworks, Rye (p413)

Marine, South Shields (p427)

Staffordshire
Devonshire Arms, Burton upon Trent
Black Lion, Cheddleton
George & the Dragon, Gnosall
Andy's Ale House, Great Wyrley
Hopinn, Newcastle-under-Lyme
Tamworth Tap, Tamworth

Suffolk
Oakes Barn, Bury St Edmunds
Stanford Arms, Lowestoft
Star Wing Tap Room, Redgrave
Walnut, Stowmarket

Surrey
Happy Man, Englefield Green
Running Horse, Leatherhead
Surrey Oaks, Newdigate
Alfred Free House, Upper Hale

East Sussex
Hare & Hounds, Framfield
Waterworks, Rye

West Sussex
Anchor Tap, Horsham
Inglenook, Pagham
Duke of Wellington, Shoreham-by-Sea
Fox & Finch Alehouse, Worthing

Tyne & Wear
Marine, South Shields
Dog & Rabbit, Whitley Bay

Warwickshire
Lord Hop, Nuneaton
Seven Stars, Rugby
Old Post Office, Warwick

West Midlands
Broomfield Tavern, Coventry: Spon End
Queen's Head, Stourbridge
Black Country Arms, Walsall
Bird in Hand, Wordsley
Lych Gate Tavern, Wolverhampton

Wiltshire
Prince of Wales, Chippenham
Five Bells, Royal Wootton Bassett
Deacons, Salisbury

Worcestershire
Cross Inn, Finstall
Black Star, Stourport-on-Severn

East Yorkshire
Hugh Fitz-Baldric, Cottingham
Butchers Dog, Driffield
Whalebone, Hull

North Yorkshire
Disappearing Chin, Harrogate
George & Dragon, Hudswell
Infant Hercules, Middlesbrough
Sun Inn, Pickering
North Riding Brew Pub, Scarborough
Slip Inn, York

South Yorkshire
Old No. 7, Barnsley
Hilltop, Conisbrough
Hallcross, Doncaster
Jack Hawley at the Grange, Hatfield
Kelham Island Tavern, Sheffield: Kelham Island
Wath Tap, Wath upon Dearne

West Yorkshire
Record Café, Bradford
Market Tavern, Brighouse
West Riding Refreshment Rooms, Dewsbury
Cricketers Arms, Horbury
King's Head, Huddersfield
Brown Cow, Keighley
Cardigan Arms, Leeds: Burley
Salt Cellar, Saltaire

WALES

Glamorgan
Cross inn, Cwmfelin
Gwaelod y Garth Inn, Gwaelod Y Garth

Prince of Wales, Chippenham (p452)

Salt Cellar, Saltaire (p515)

Sign above the door at Royal Oak Inn, Fishguard (p557)

Steam Packet Inn, Isle of Whithorn (p579)

White Hart Inn, Llantwit Major
Queen's Hotel, Swansea
Star Inn, Wick

Gwent
Queen's Head, Chepstow
Goose & Cuckoo,
Upper Llanover

Mid-Wales
New inn, Bwlch
Arvon Ale House,
Llandrindod Wells

North-East Wales
Bridge End Inn, Ruabon

North-West Wales
Black Boy Inn, Caernarfon
Bay Hop, Colwyn Bay
Eagles Inn (Tafarn Yr Eryrod),
Llanuwchllyn

West Wales
Rhos Yr Hafod Inn,
Cross Inn (Llanon)
Royal Oak Inn, Fishguard
Mansel Arms, Porthyrhyd

SCOTLAND

Aberdeen & Grampian
Queen Vic, Aberdeen

Borders
Craw Inn, Auchencrow

Dumfries & Galloway
Blue Bell Inn, Annan
Steam Packet Inn,
Isle of Whithorn

Edinburgh & the Lothians
Dreadnought,
Edinburgh: North
Volunteer Arms (Staggs),
Musselburgh

Greater Glasgow & Clyde Valley
State Bar, Glasgow
Fox & Hounds, Houston

Highlands & Western Isles
Bandstand, Nairn

Kingdom of Fife
Hillend Tavern, Hillend

Tayside
Ericht Alehouse, Blairgowrie

NORTHERN IRELAND

Northern Ireland
Northern Lights, Belfast

CHANNEL ISLANDS

Guernsey
Golden Lion, St Peter Port

Craw Inn, Auchencrow (p575)